Atlas of Polymer and Plastics Analysis

HUMMEL/SCHOLL

Atlas of Polymer and Plastics Analysis

Second, completely revised edition

Vol. 1 Polymers: Structures and Spectra

By Prof. Dr. Dieter O. Hummel, Cologne

Vol. 2 Plastics, Fibres, Rubbers, Resins

Spectra and Methods of Identification

By Prof. Dr. Dieter O. Hummel, Cologne

Vol. 3 Additives and Processing Aids

Spectra and Methods of Identification

By Dr. Friedrich Scholl, Stuttgart

Carl Hanser Verlag
Munich · Vienna
Verlag Chemie
Weinheim · Deerfield Beach, Florida · Basel
Verlag Chemie International
Deerfield Beach, Florida · Weinheim · Basel

HUMMEL/SCHOLL

Atlas of Polymer and Plastics Analysis

Second, completely revised edition

Vol. 3
Additives and Processing Aids

Spectra and Methods of Identification

By Dr. Friedrich Scholl, Stuttgart

Carl Hanser Verlag
Munich · Vienna
Verlag Chemie
Weinheim · Deerfield Beach, Florida · Basel
Verlag Chemie International
Deerfield Beach, Florida · Weinheim · Basel

Dr. Friedrich Scholl
Robert Bosch GmbH
Johannes-Auwärter-Straße 7
D-7050 Waiblingen

2nd reprint, 1990, of 2nd edition 1983

Copy Editor: Dr. Hans F. Ebel

Production Manager: Dipl.-Ing. (FH) Hans Jörg Maier

This book contains 47 pictures, 109 tables and 1350 spectra.

CIP-Kurztitelaufnahme der Deutschen Bibliothek

Atlas of polymer and plastics analysis /
Hummel ; Scholl. – Munich ; Vienna : Hanser ;
Weinheim ; Deerfield Beach, Florida ; Basel : Verlag Chemie ;
Deerfield Beach, Florida ; Weinheim ; Basel : Verlag Chemie Internat.
   Dt. Ausg. u.d.T.: Atlas der Polymer- und
   Kunststoffanalyse

NE: Hummel, Dieter O. [Mitverf.]

Vol. 3. Additives and processing aids :
spectra and methods of identification / by
Friedrich Scholl. – 2. completely rev. ed.
– 1981.
   ISBN 3-446-12592-2 (Hanser)
   ISBN 3-527-25803-5 (Verl. Chemie)
   ISBN 0-89573-014-6 (Verl. Chemie Internat.)

NE: Scholl, Friedrich [Mitverf.]

Compositor and Printer: Schwetzinger Verlagsdruckerei, D-6830 Schwetzingen
Bookbinder: Klambt-Druck GmbH, D-6720 Speyer
Printed in the Federal Republic of Germany

Introduction to the Second Edition

In the ten years that have passed since the first edition of this "Atlas" appeared, plastics have found further uses and have played even more important roles in the development of almost all industrial sectors. The increase of the production and processing capacities for plastics was greater than average industrial growth.

The development of better, more economic or new products through material-oriented construction, the use of custom-made plastics and their appropriate processing will continue. A pre-requisite for this is a profound knowledge of the properties and characteristics of polymers and of thermoplastic and thermosetting materials, elastomers, lacquers, emulsions, adhesives, casting resins and other systems produced from them.

Parallel to the growth of technical importance, interest in the analysis of plastics has increased. The wide usage of plastics, the almost unlimited possibilities of combining plastics and additives as well as the problems that arise in connection with industrial hygiene and environmental protection have enlarged the tasks of the analyst. His requirements have been met by improved methods and apparatus. Today, infrared spectroscopy, chromatography and mass spectroscopy, either by themselves or combined, are the most efficient tools for plastics analysis, provided that well-arranged data collections are available.

It has been confirmed in many conversations with users of the first edition of this "Atlas" that the classification of additives and processing aids by their functions, and the concentrated tabular presentation of analytical data are optimal. This format has therefore been carried over into the new edition.

Many of the additives and processing aids included in the first edition have retained their importance. Their infrared spectra are therefore reprinted in this edition. The spectra registered with newer apparatus (Perkin-Elmer 283, Model 1977) have been reduced in size so that spectra measured with different instruments are congruent in the wave-length range from 400 to 2000 cm^{-1}. Tables containing new chromatographic and mass spectroscopic data were added. Changes of trade names were taken into account in a few cases only. Normally, substances appear under the trade names that they had when they were supplied. Since chemical compositions are listed whenever possible, trade names are of secondary importance for the user of this work.

I am grateful to many colleagues for their suggestions and for reprints of relevant articles. I thank Robert Bosch GmbH, Stuttgart, for the permission to publish spectra and data that were compiled in the analytical laboratory of the Central Research Group of this company. Special thanks go to Hannelore Fuchs who assisted me in collecting and selecting the compounds and, together with other coworkers, carried out much of the spectroscopic work. Thanks are also due to my wife and to my son Bernd who helped in proof-reading and with the compilation of the indexes.

I hope that the "Atlas of Polymer and Plastics Analysis" will continue to play its role in assisting the analyst in his day-to-day work. Every user is invited to inform me of errors that may have occurred, to draw my attention to new results or developments and to suggest improvements.

Stuttgart, in Summer 1981   F. K. Scholl

Preface to the First Edition

This second volume of the "Atlas of Plastics Analysis" was completed later than the publishers and the author originally intended, with the result that three years have elapsed since the appearance of Volume I "High Polymers and Resins". Perhaps the impatience of those who have been awaiting the appearance of this volume will be appeased by the fact that it covers recent publications and information that has come to light during this time.

Since the basic principles of the most important analytical methods were discussed in Volume I, a few additional sections on recent progress and new applications have been sufficient here. Insofar as these are concerned with high polymers, they are grouped in one section of the list of references.

IR spectroscopy is at present the most important method for the identification of additives and processing aids. The greater part of this volume is therefore occupied by comparison spectra, which are essential for IR spectroscopic work. However, chromatographic methods and mass spectroscopy are also very useful for the analysis of low molecular weight substances, and form an excellent complement to optical spectroscopy. There is no doubt, therefore, that all these methods will find increasing use in the analysis of plastics. We have had very good results from the combination of several methods in our laboratory, and various tables therefore include the available chromatographic and mass-spectroscopic data for additives. Though there are still many gaps and it has not been possible to check all the values taken from the literature, the usefulness of these data should outweigh the few errors that may have crept in. As far as we found errors after printing they are mentioned in notes following the registers.

Unlike Volume I, where the high polymers are classified on a chemical basis, the additives and processing aids are grouped according to their use, and only within these groups are they arranged according to their chemical structure. Since some additives have several functions, occasional overlapping has been unavoidable.

Tabular summaries, which also serve as an index to the spectra, are useful in our experience, since they allow a quick survey of the substances used in industry and of their analytical data in a minimum of space. It would have been even better if the preferred combinations of processing aids, additives, and polymers had been indicated, but this was impossible in the space available. However, references have been made to literature from which this information can be found, and some of which also contains tables showing the trade names under which various chemically definite additives are marketed.

Corresponding to the title "Atlas of Plastics Analysis" we have tried to give a comprehensive picture. However, we have had to admit that despite the demonstrable use of some additives, little or nothing has so far been published about their analysis. Owing to shortage of time, we have been unable to give some of these "Blank areas" more than a preliminary, not always entirely satisfactory examination. This may be excusable in an atlas appearing for the first time; it will be up to later "cartographers" to fill in the gaps and to correct any errors.

A fundamental problem that always arises in the analysis of industrial products is that the analyst often has to use comparison methods for the analysis and to construct calibration curves with the aid of technically pure substances. He frequently has to use the manufacturer's data on the chemical structure and purity. For obvious reasons, no purity data are given in many cases. This means that the information obtained for certain additives, such as the spectra, may be influenced by impurities or by deliberately introduced additives that are not mentioned by the manufacturer, and they may therefore not be entirely identical with those of the chemically uniform principal components.

In the case of the present collection, this means that the chemical composition given in most cases for an additive or processing aid refers to the principal component, and that the product in question may contain other components in smaller quantities. This is confirmed for some products by the chromatographic methods.

I should like to thank numerous assistants, colleagues, and superiors for their support in the preparation of this book. I am particularly grateful to Robert Bosch GmbH, Stuttgart, for kind permission to publish the data obtained in the analytical laboratory of the Central Research Department. Hannelore Fuchs gave untiring support in the collection and selection of the material. She carried out the IR spectroscopic work together with Sigrid Sparn, Elfriede Wituschek, and other assistants. The thin layer and gas-chromatographic studies were carried out mainly by Jana Drazil and Bert Peters, the mass-spectroscopic measurements by Renate Land, the UV-spectroscopic and gel-chromatographic studies and the molecular weight determinations by Rolf Gladen and Waltraud Morsy, and the X-ray measurements by Renate Solf. Bernhard Blaich, Friedbert Meier, and other colleagues supported these assistants and myself. Leonhard Heckl (Siegle & Co.) provided us with the classification of the organic pigments and numerous pigment samples. Hannelore Fuchs, Jana Drazil, Bert Peters, Rolf Gladen, and my wife helped with the proofreading. To all those, as well as to many coworkers who have not been mentioned by name, I am sincerely grateful for their assistance. I should also like to thank numerous companies who supplied sample and informations.

Summer 1972

F. K. Scholl

Contents

Contents

Contents of the Spectral Part

List of Abbreviations

CC	coupling component		sp. gr.	specific gravity
CC	column chromatography		t-	tertiary
CI	Colour Index		TCD	thermal conductivity detector
dec.	decomposition		TLC	thin layer chromatography
dec. no.	decimal number		UV	ultraviolet
FID	flame ionization detector		XFA	X-ray fluorescence analysis
FIR	far infrared			
g	gram			
GC	gas chromatography			

Abbreviations for Vibration Modes

ν	stretching
δ	bending
γ	out-of-plane deformation
t	twisting 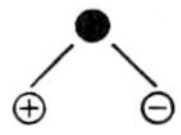
r	rocking
τ	torsion (about a single bond)
w	wagging

Abbreviations for Band Intensities

vs	very strong
s	strong
m	medium
w	weak
vw	very weak

Symbols in Band Assignment Diagrams

white or cross-hatched: wider range in which bands are expected

black: range in which the band maxima are usually observed

The heights of the columns indicate the band intensities.
Example: Broad band with two maxima

Main list (left column, continued)

GPC	gel permeation chromatography
h	hour
HC	hydrocarbon
HPLC	high performance liquid chromatography
hR_f	relative migration distance with respect to the solvent front = 100 (in TLC)
IR	infrared
l	liter
m-	meta-
M	molecular weight
m/e	mass/charge (in MS)
min	minute
ml	milliliter
m.p.	melting point
MS	mass spectrometry
MU	mass unit
n	refractive index
N	normality (in solutions)
NIR	near infrared
NMR	nuclear magnetic resonance
o-	ortho-
p-	para-
PC	paper chromatography
PVC	polyvinyl chloride
R	residue on evaporation
R_f	relative migration distance
RI	retention index after KOVATS (in GC)
S	solvent
s	second
sec-	secondary
sh	shoulder
Sp.	spectrum

Alphabetical List of the Manufacturers or Suppliers of Materials Mentioned in this Book

Abbreviation	Name
Advance	Ciba-Geigy Marienberg GmbH Postfach 209 6140 Bensheim (FRG)
Alcolac	Alcolac Chem. Corp. 3440 Fairfield Road Baltimore, Maryland 21226 (USA)
Allied Chem.	Allied Chem. Corp. Plastics Div. P.O. Box 365 Morristown, N. J. (USA)
Am. Resin	American Resin & Chemical Corp. P.O. Box 4505, Wichita Falls, Texas 76308 (USA)
Amoco	Amoco Chem. Corp. Chicago 80, Ill. 60680 (USA)
An. Chem. L.	Analytical Chemical Laboratories 22 West Madison Street Chicago 2, Illinois (USA)
Anorgana	Anorgana GmbH 8261 Gendorf (FRG)
Antara Chem.	Antara Chemicals Div. of General Aniline & Film Corp. New York 14, N. Y. (USA)
Argus	Argus Chemical Corp. 633 Court St. Brooklyn, N. Y. 11231 (USA)
Armour	Armour Industrial Chemicals Co. Chicago 6, Ill. (USA)
Axel	Axel Plastics Research Lab. Inc. P.O. Box 855 Woodside, N. Y. 11377 (USA)
Bacillol	Bacillolfabrik Dr Bode & Co. Melanchthonstraße 27 2000 Hamburg 54 Stellingen (FRG)
Baker	Baker Castor Oil Co. 40 Ave. A , Bayonne, N. J. (USA)
BASF	Badische Anilin- und Soda- Fabrik AG. 6700 Ludwigshafen/Rhein (FRG)
Bärlocher	Chem. Werke München O. Bärlocher GmbH Riesstr. 16 8000 München 50 (FRG)
Bayer	Farbenfabriken Bayer AG 5090 Leverkusen (FRG)
Baird	Baird Chem. Ind. Inc. 185 Madison Avenue New York, N. Y. 10016 (USA)
Boehringer	C. H. Boehringer Sohn 6507 Ingelheim/Rhein (FRG)

Abbreviation	Name
Briggs	Briggs & Townsend Ltd. Commercial St., Knott Mill Manchester (UK)
Carbide	Union Carbide Corp. 270 Park Ave. New York, N. Y. 10017 (USA)
Cassella	Cassella Farbwerke Mainkur AG Hanauer Landstraße 526 6000 Frankfurt/M.-Fechenheim (FRG)
Catalin	Catalin Corp. of America New York 16, N. Y. (USA)
CFK	Chemische Fabrik Kalk GmbH Postfach 910210 5000 Köln 91 (FRG)
Celanese	Celanese Polymer Specialities Co. P.O. Box 506 Charlotte, N. C. 28230 (USA)
Chemical Development Corp.	Chemical Development Corp. Endicott Str. Danvers, Mass. 01923 (USA)
Ciba	Ciba AG Basel (Schweiz)
Cyanamid	Cyanamid International Wayne, N. J. (USA) Cyanamid GmbH 8190 Wolfratshausen (FRG)
DAP	Deutsche Advance Production GmbH, see Ciba-Geigy Marienberg 6140 Bensheim (FRG)
Deecy	Deecy Prod. Div. Reichold Chem. Inc. 120 Potter St. Cambridge 42, Mass. (USA)
Dehydag	Deutsche Hydrierwerke GmbH. Postfach 2340 4000 Düsseldorf 1 (FRG)
Dow	Dow Chemical Co. P.O. Box 1767 Midland, Mich. 48640 (USA)
Diamond	Diamond Alkali Company Union Commerce Building Cleveland, Ohio 44115 (USA)
Drew	Drew, Div. Pacific Vegetable Oil Corp. 416 Division St. Boonton, N. Y. 07005 (USA)
Du Pont	E. I. Du Pont de Nemours & Co., Inc., 1007 Market St. Wilmington, Del. 19898 (USA) Du Pont de Nemours Deutschland GmbH. Bismarckstraße 95 4000 Düsseldorf (FRG)
Dynamit	Dynamit Nobel AG 5210 Troisdorf/Köln (FRG)

By moving and merging of companies many addresses have changed throughout the last years. These were regarded as far as it became known to us but we cannot guarantee for the listed addresses.

Alphabetical List of the Manufacturers or Suppliers of Materials

Abbreviation	Name	Abbreviation	Name
East Coast	East Coast Chemicals Comp. Cedar Grove, N. J. (USA)	Hercules	Hercules Inc. 910 Market St. Wilmington, Del. 19899 (USA)
Eastman	Eastman Chem. Prod. Inc., P.O. Box 431 Kingsport, Tenn. 37662 (USA)	Heyden	Heyden Newport Chem. Corp. New York 17, N. Y. (USA)
EGA	EGA-Chemie 7924 Steinheim/Heidenheim (FRG)	Hoechst	Farbwerke Hoechst AG. 6230 Frankfurt/M.-Höchst (FRG)
Emery	Emery Ind. Inc., Carew Tower Cincinnati, Ohio (USA)	Howards	Howards & Sons Ltd. Cornwall, Ont. (Canada)
Ethyl	Ethyl Corp. 451 Florida St. Baton Rouge, La. 70801 (USA)	Hooker	Hooker Chem. & Plastics Corp. 1024 Iroquois St. Niagara Falls, N. Y. 14302 (USA)
Esso	Esso AG 2000 Hamburg 36 (FRG)	Hüls	Chem. Werke Hüls AG. 4370 Marl (FRG)
Ferro	Ferro Chemical Corp. 7050 Krick Road Bedford, Ohio 44146 (USA) Ferro GmbH Herderstr. 30 4010 Hilden (FRG)	Imhausen	Imhausen Werke GmbH. 5810 Witten/Ruhr (FRG)
		ICI	Imperial. Chem. Industries Millbank, London S. W. 1 (UK)
Fine Org.	Fine Organics Inc. 205 Main St. Lodi New Jersey, N. J. 07644 (USA)	Interstab C	Interstab Chemie GmbH. 5160 Düren (FRG)
		Isochem	Isochem Resins Co. Cook St. Lincoln, R. I., 02865 (USA)
Fluka	Fluka AG Buchs (Schweiz)	Jäger	Ernst Jäger, Fabrik chem. Rohstoffe 4000 Düsseldorf-Reisholz (FRG)
FMC	FMC Corp., Chem. Div. 633 Third Avenue New York 17, N. Y. (USA)	Jefferson	Jefferson Chem. Co., Inc. Houston 1, Texas (USA)
Fuchs	Rudolf Fuchs KG. Mineralölwerk 6800 Mannheim (FRG)	Kautschuk	Kautschuk GmbH. Reuterweg 14 6000 Frankfurt/Main (FRG)
GAF	General Aniline & Film Co. 140 W. 51 St. New York, N. Y. 10020 (USA)	Kessler	Kessler Chem. Div. Armour Ind. Chem. Co. Philadelphia 35, Pa. (USA)
Geigy	J. R. Geigy AG. Basel 21 (Schweiz)	Kettlitz	Kettlitz Chemie GmbH. 8070 Ingolstadt (FRG)
Gen. Mills	General Mills Chemicals Inc. 4620 W 77th St. Minneapolis, Minn 55435 (USA)	Kleen Chem.	Kleen Chem. Mfg. Co. 2511 N. Sheffield Ave., Chicago, Ill. 60614 (USA)
Glyco	Glyco Chemicals Inc. 417 5th Avenue New York, N. Y. 10016 (USA)	M & T	Metal & Thermit Chemicals Inc. Woodbridge Ave. Rahway, N. J. 07065 (USA)
Goldschmidt	Th. Goldschmidt AG. Chem. Fabrik 4300 Essen (FRG)	Merck	E. Merck AG. 6100 Darmstadt (FRG)
Goodyear	Goodyear Tire & Rubber Co. 1144 E. Market St. Akron 16, Ohio 06830 (USA)	Merix	Merix Chem. Comp. 2234 East 75th Street Chicago, Ill. 60649 (USA)
Hall	C. P. Hall Co. 73rd St. & Central Ave. Chicago, Ill. 60638 (USA)	Metall AG	Metallgesellschaft AG. 6000 Frankfurt/Main 1 (FRG)
Harchem.	Wallace & Tiernan Div. Pennwalt Corp. 25 Main St. Belleville, N. J. 07109 (USA)	Miles	Miles Chem. Comp. Clifton, N. J. (USA)
		Minnesota	Minnesota Mining & Manufacturing Co. St. Paul, Minn. (USA)
Hatco	Grace W. R. & Co. Hatco Chem. Div. King George Post Road Fords, New Jersey, N. J. 08863 (USA)	Monsanto	Monsanto Chem. Co. 800 N. Lindbergh Blvd. St. Louis, Mo. 63166 (USA)
		Montrose	Montrose Chem. Div. Baldwin-Montrose Chem. Co., Inc. 100 Lister Ave. Newark 5, N. J. (USA)

Abbreviation	Name	Abbreviation	Name
Naftone	Naftone Inc. 425 Park Avenue New York, N. Y. 10022 (USA)	Schuchardt	Dr. Theodor Schuchardt GmbH & Co.,Chemische Fabrik 8000 München 80 (FRG)
National Lead	National Lead Co. New York 6, N. Y. (USA)	Schülke u. Mayr	Schülke u. Mayr 2000 Hamburg (FRG)
Naugatuck	Naugatuck Chem. Div. of United States Rubber Co. Naugatuck, Conn. (USA)	Shell	Deutsche Shell AG Alsterufer 4/5 2000 Hamburg (FRG)
Nopco	Nopco Chem. Co. 60 Park Avenue Newark 1, N. J. (USA)	Siegle	G. Siegle & Co., GmbH. 7000 Stuttgart-Feuerbach (FRG)
Noury	Noury van der Lande N. V. Deventer (Netherlands)	Simco	Simco Comp. Inc. 920 Walnut Street Landsdale, Pennsylvania 19446 (USA)
Oel Chemie	Oel Chemie AG. Hausen bei Brugg (Schweiz)	Stauffer	Stauffer Chem. Co. Westport, Conn. 06880 (USA)
Onopex	Ohio Apex Inc. Div. Food Machinery & Chem. Corp. Nitro, W. Va. (USA)	Oe. Stickstoffwerke	Oesterreichische Stickstoffwerke Linz (Austria)
Oxydo	Oxydo Ges. f. chem. Prod. Industriestraße 10 4240 Emmerich/Rhein (FRG)	SKW	SKW Trostberg AG Postfach 1150 8223 Trostberg (FRG)
Pennsalt	Pennsalt Chemicals Corp. Philadelphia 2, Pa. (USA)	Sun Chem	Sun Chem. Corp. 185 Sixth Ave. Paterson, N. J. 07524 (USA)
Pfizer	Pfizer, Chas & Co. Inc. Chem. Div. Plastics & Plasticizers Dept. 235 E 42nd St. New York, N. Y. 10017 (USA) Inc., Spec. Chemicals Depr. 2110 High Point Road Greensboro, N. C. 27403 (USA)	Swift	Swift Chemical Co. 1211 W 22nd St. Oak Brook, Ill. 60521 (USA)
		Tennessee	Tennessee Prod. & Chem. Corp. 2611 West End Avenue Nashville 5, Tenn. (USA)
Pure Chem.	Pure Chemicals Ltd. Stockpit Road Kirkby Industrial Estate Liverpool (UK)	Union Carbide	Union Carbide Corp. 270 Park Ave. New York, N. Y. 10017 (USA)
Raschig	Dr. F. Raschig GmbH 6700 Ludwigshafen/Rhein (FRG)	Unilever	Unilever-Emery N. V. Gouda (Netherlands)
Reichhold	Reichhold Chemie AG Iversstraße 57 2000 Hamburg-Wandsbek (FRG)	UOP	Universal Oil Products Norplex Div. La Crosse, Wisc. 54601 (USA)
Riedel	Riedel de Haen AG. 3016 Seelze (FRG)	Vanderbilt	Vanderbilt R. T. Co. 30 Winfield St. E. Norwalk, Conn. 06855
Rhein-C	Rhein-Chemie, Rheinau GmbH 6800 Mannheim (FRG)	VCC	Velsicol Chemical Co. 341 E. Ohio St. Chicago, Ill. 60611 (USA)
Rhône	Société des Usines Chimiques Rhône-Poulenc, Paris 8e (France)	Wacker	Wacker Chemie GmbH. Postfach 8000 München 22 (FRG)
Rohm & Haas	Rohm & Haas Comp. Independence Mall W. Philadelphia, Pa. 19105 (USA)	Ward	Ward, Blantlinson & Co., Ltd. Wembley, Middlesex (UK)
Scado	Scado-GmbH Postfach 1580 4470 Meppen (FRG)	Witten	Chem. Werke Witten GmbH. 5810 Witten/Ruhr (FRG)
Schering	Schering AG Müllerstraße 170/172 1000 Berlin 65 (FRG)	Wyandotte	Wyandotte Chem. Corp. 1609 Biddle Ave. Wyandotte, Michigan 48192 (USA)
Scholven	Scholven Chemie AG. Dontener Straße 227 4660 Gelsenkirchen-Buer (FRG)		

1 Methods of Analysing Plastics Additives and Auxiliaries

1.1 Introduction

The properties of high polymers are greatly modified and improved by additives. Generally speaking, it is only the incorporation of additives which makes polymers useful plastics materials, elastomers, surface coating compositions, adhesives and many other synthetic materials whose uses, physical and chemical properties as well as the properties and price of products made from them are matched to market demands. New fields of application for synthetic products have made new technical and quality demands, whilst growing knowledge on the medical and ecological side have influenced the application potentials.

There are many thousands of organic and inorganic substances, marketed under a variety of trade names, which may be used as additives for polymers. The patent literature on plastics additives is extremely extensive, although only a small proportion of the substances described has been found of practical use.

The amounts of additives in polymer materials vary considerably. Whilst unfilled, unplasticised thermoplastics normally contain only about 1% or less, this can rise to considerably more than 50% in the case of highly filled, polymer bound compounds.

To characterise a plastics material it is often not enough to merely identify the polymer. It is usually necessary to also know the type of additive and the amount used. In many cases, the base polymer will be known and only the additives will be of interest because the material exhibits certain processing or performance characteristics, or because the additives may provide information on origin, or because the question of toxicity has to be investigated.

The following procedure has given good results for the analysis of plastics additives:

1. The first step is to find out what base polymer is contained in the material under test. Experience or specialised literature on plastics additives [1–12] will then indicate with which group of additives the polymer in question is usually modified for specific types of application.

2. In most cases it will be necessary to separate the additive from the polymer, usually by physical methods. Suitable techniques must be selected. In certain cases it may be possible to directly identify the additives, e. g. UV absorbers or phenolic antioxidants in polyolefin film by means of direct UV spectroscopy of the film, or by a combination of separation and analysis, as, for example, in the case of mass spectrometric determination of volatile constituents in plastics.

3. After separation, which may consist of several stages, the main constituents of the additives should be identified, e. g. on the basis of an infra-red spectrum, so that the most suitable method of separating the various additives can be chosen.
   During subsequent separation/identification cycles, which can sometimes be repeated several times, using different separating and analytical techniques, the individual constituents are qualitatively analysed.

4. If necessary, the mixture which has now been qualitatively identified is subjected to quantitative analysis to determine the amounts of additive present.

The above remarks show that the analysis of plastics additives can be a long and complex task. The less precise the analytical problem and the less knowledge there is about the probable or possible additives, the more difficult will be the analytical process. Another factor is that even chemically specific plastics additives are technical products which generally are of only technical purity. They therefore contain certain impurities originating from their source of origin or the manufacturing process.

Finally, a large number of additives are secondary products of naturally occurring multi-component mixtures such as mineral oils or natural fatty acids etc. which are difficult – or even impossible – to separate into their component parts.

The last problem to be mentioned briefly is the changes which occur in additives, especially processing aids, during plastics manufacture and processing. Reactive additives will form more or less specific secondary products, from whose presence one must deduce the nature of the original compound. Here, close collaboration between analysts and plastics, paint and rubber technologists is important for the correct interpretation of analytical results.

Regarding the first of the steps mentioned above, only a few hints can be given in this book. However, there is an extensive literature in which the applications of many additives are shown [1—12; further information in the appropriate sections].

Nevertheless, a certain gap will always exist between newly developed plastics formulations and the state of progress reflected in the literature.

No schemes or separation sequences corresponding to the conventional cation analysis can be given for the subsequent steps, i. e. the separation and identification, simply because the number of possible combinations is too great and there are several analytical methods that are applied in various laboratories, depending on their availability, in various orders and in various combinations. The following discussion can therefore only show the possibilities offered by the various methods for separation and identification and the data that characterize the various additives and processing aids in the individual methods.

In sections 1.2—1.13, therefore, the methods and their uses are briefly outlined, but no details of principles and equipment are given.

In sections 2—11, additives and processing aids are grouped and tabulated according to their use. The data obtainable by the various methods of analysis are also given largely in the form of tables.

The most valuable single method is IR spectroscopy, since measurements can be carried out on practically all classes of substances in any state of aggregation with small samples. The collection of data for this method therefore occupies more space than for any other.

There is no doubt, however, that the best solution of complex analytical problems is achieved in most cases by a combination of several methods, and the analysis of additives in plastics is no exception.

Unfortunately, the collections of data for other methods are less comprehensive at present, and a number of gaps will therefore be found in this book.

1.2 Separation of Additives

1.2.1 Extraction and Reprecipitation

The separation of additives in practice is based mainly on differences in solubility, the methods used being extraction and fractional precipitation.

KUPFER [38], WHEELER [44], and other authors [13—20, 25] have collected data on the separation of additives, from which some of the examples in Table 1.1 are taken.

The extraction is usually carried out in reflux extractors (Soxhlet principle, etc., for recent review see [40]) at the boiling point of the solvent used. Higher temperatures increase the solubility, the dissolution rate, and the diffusion of the low molecular weight additives from the insoluble or swollen polymers. As far as possible, the latter should be used in a finely divided state or as a thin layer for the extraction. Lump formation can be largely avoided by the

Table 1.1: **Extraction of additives from plastics (examples)**

Plastic		Extraction system	Additives extracted
Polyethylene		Hexane	Phenolic antioxidants
		Chloroform	Phenolic antioxidants
		Ether	Phenolic antioxidants
Polyethylene	Successive extraction with	Benzene	Waxes
		Methanol	Emulsifiers, antistatics
		Chloroform	Montan waxes
		Water	Cellulose derivatives, polyvinyl alcohol
Polyvinyl chloride		Methanol	Diphenylthiourea, 2-phenylindole, dicyanodiamide
		Ether	Plasticizers, stabilizers
Polyvinyl chloride	Successive extraction with	Hexane	Plasticizers, lubricants
		Chloroform	Antioxidants, UV absorbers
		Acetone	Stabilizers
Polyvinyl chloride	Successive extraction with	Ether (8 h)	Plasticizers, antioxidants, stabilizers
		Methanol/carbon tetrachloride 1 : 2 (16 h)	Polymeric plasticizers
Polyvinyl chloride	Successive extraction with	Carbon tetrachloride	Plasticizers and stabilizers
		Ether	
		Benzene	(different components in various
		Methylene chloride	fractions)
Polyformaldehyde	Successive extraction with	Chloroform	Phenolic antioxidants
		Methanol	Dicyanodiamide
		Hydrolysis with hydrochloric acid	Ternary copolyamide
Rubber		Water	Antioxidants (partial)
		Methanol (95%)	p-Phenylenediamine derivative
		Ethanol + HCl	Amine und phenol antioxidants
		Acetone	Antioxidants, sulfur, mineral oil, fatty acids
		Ether	Phenyl salicylate, resorcinal benzoate
Cellulose esters		Ether	Plasticizers
Polyvinyl acetate dispersions		Pentane/ether	Plasticizers

addition of a granular inert material, such as washed quartz sand.

Solutions or dispersions of plastics may be mixed with a fine-grain filler to improve the extractability when the composition is dried as a thin layer.

It is advantageous to spread the solution or paste on aluminum foil to dry, and then to cut it up with the support and use it in this form for the extraction. Foils allow efficient extraction when wound into a roll with a strip of thin wire gauze.

A number of polymers and extraction solvents are listed in Table 1.1. Preliminary separation is possible in some cases by the use of different solvents in succession during the extraction. However, since the additives present are not usually known, separations by extraction cannot generally be used. It is sometimes impossible to prevent oligomers of the plastic from dissolving at the same time and being carried into the extract. These must then be taken into account in the chemical or chromatographic separation that usually follows. The complete extraction of polymer plasticizers is generally very difficult, since the diffusion of these large molecules from the plastic is very slow.

After the extraction, the solvent is evaporated, and the residue is then subjected to further chemical, spectroscopic, or chromatographic investigation or separation. If solvents that are transparent to UV light are used for the extraction, conclusions concerning the presence of additives containing aromatic structures (phthalates, antioxidants, etc.) can often be reached quickly from the UV spectra of the extracts.

Various procedures are used for the separation of additives by fractional precipitation or reprecipitation. One possibility is to stir the solution of the plastic slowly into at least 10 times its volume of a solvent that acts as a precipitant for the polymer in solution but is miscible in all proportions with the first solvent. The precipitated polymer is repeatedly washed with the precipitating solvent or else reprecipitated. In another method, a non-solvent is added slowly with stirring to a solution of the plastic until the first sign of turbidity due to precipitating polymer is observed. A large proportion of the solvent is then removed on a waterbath or by evaporation under vacuum, whereupon most of the polymer precipitates. In this case, the solvent and the non-solvent must be miscible in all proportions, and the solvent must boil at a lower temperature than the non-solvent. Dissolution and precipitation with a single solvent is possible only if the plastic dissolves at high temperatures and separates out again on cooling, while the additives remain in solution. This is so e.g. in the case of polyolefins and aromatic solvents.

For dispersions of plastics, the polymeric components can be separated by modification of the solvent phase, and the emulsion can be broken by addition of acids or oppositely charged surface active agents or by freezing. Some examples of reprecipitation and fractional precipitation are given in Table 1.2. Further solvents for many polymers can be found in vol. 2 and published literature [13–26].

Reference should be made here to the separation of fillers on the basis of differences in density, as described e.g. by VERES [20]. After separation from the dissolved polymer or lacquer, the fillers are repeatedly washed and centrifuged to remove adhering binder. While still moist with solvent, the residue is then made into a paste with a few drops of linseed oil, and tetrabromoethane (sp. gr. = 2.97) is slowly added with continuous stirring. On centrifugation (approx. 5000 rpm, 1 h), the heavy fillers having specific gravities greater than 3 (lead compounds, TiO_2, corundum) are separated by sedimentation from the lighter silicates and chalks. The particles at the top edge of the centrifuge tube are wiped back into the liquid and then decanted. The lighter components can be obtained by dilution of the tetrabromoethane with methanol and centrifugation.

1.2.2 Separation by Distillation and Sublimation

Additives that are sufficiently stable to heat can be separated from polymers and in some cases even fractionated by di-

stillation under vacuum or in a current of protective gas. Various methods can be used for this purpose.

A short-path vacuum distillation or sublimation can be carried out in the apparatus shown in Figure 1.2. Fractional distillation or sublimation is possible by heating in stages and replacement of the cold finger.

The use of temperature gradient furnaces has been described by various authors [41]. The principle is shown in Figure 1.3.

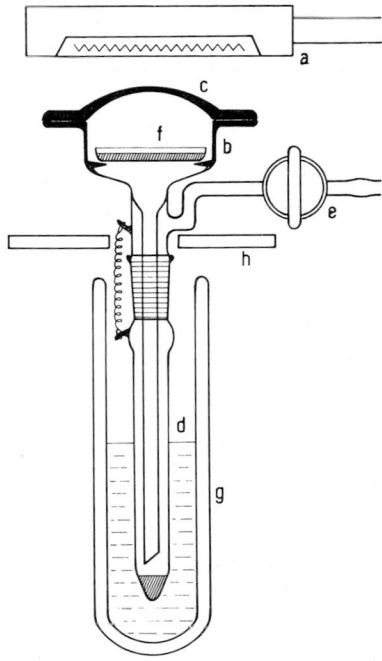

Fig. 1.1: Vacuum distillation apparatus for small quantities of lacquer
a) IR heater
b) Distillation compartment
c) Cover with ground glass joint
d) Receiver
e) Tap
f) Aluminum boat for lacquer sample
g) Dewar flask containing refrigerant
h) Radiation shield (asbestos sheet or the like)

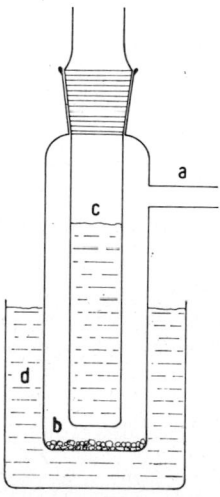

Fig. 1.2: Apparatus for vacuum distillation or sublimation of additives from plastics
a) Distillation vessel with vacuum connection
b) Finely chopped plastic
c) Cold finger cooled with water or refrigerant
d) Heating bath with bath liquid

Table 1.2: Removal of additives by precipitation (examples)

Plastic	Solvent	Precipitant
Polyethylene	Benzene (boiling)	
	p-Xylene (100 °C)	Cooling
	Tetrahydronaphthalene (120 °C)	Cooling
Polypropylene	As polyethylene	
Polystyrene	Benzene, toluene	Methanol
	Tetrahydrofuran	Methanol
	Methylene chloride	Methanol
Polyvinyl chloride	Tetrahydrofuran	Methanol
Polyacrylates	Acetone	Water
Polyamides	Formic acid	Methanol
Polyoxymethylene	Dimethylformamide (140 °C)	
Polycarbonate	Cyclohexanone	Methanol

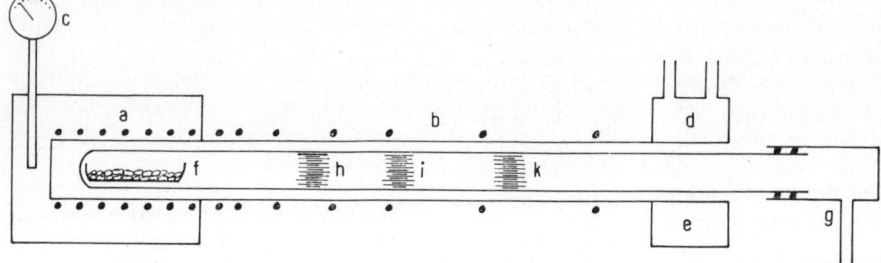

Fig. 1.3: Diagram of a temperature gradient furnace for the thermal separation of additives from plastics
 a) Heating block
 b) Metal tube with stepped auxiliary heating (300—500 mm long)
 c) Temperature gauge or temperature regulator
 d) Cooling block (water-cooled)
 e) Glass tube (inside diameter approx. 6—12 mm)
 f) Boat containing finely chopped plastic
 g) Sealing cap with vacuum connection
 h, i, k) Condensation zones of various substances

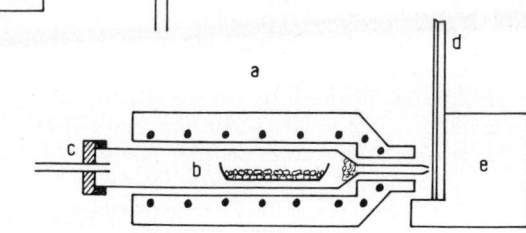

Fig. 1.4: Apparatus for evaporation of volatile components and condensation on thin layer plates
 a) Furnace block
 b) Evaporation tube with sample boat
 c) Sealing cap with carrier gas inlet
 d) Thin layer plate
 e) Holder and heat sink

After the distillation (0.5—3 h), the tube is cooled and cut up; the various zones are scraped out or washed out and qualitatively identified.

With a block temperature of 200 °C at 1 mm/Hg, the C_2—C_6 alcohol esters of aliphatic dicarboxylic acids up to sebacic acid and of phthalic acid as well as the trialkyl and triphenyl phosphates can be removed from PVC in 15—30 min. In a good furnace, boiling point differences of 5—10 °C still give separate zones. Useful results were obtained with furnace temperatures of up to 300 °C for higher-boiling plasticizers and polymeric plasticizers [41].

Temperatures of 200 and 270 °C have been used for the separation of additives from rubber mixes. For fourteen rubber mixes containing different plasticizers (plasticizer content 10 % in each case), the application of this method at 270 °C and 1 mmHg, with a separation time of 60 min, gave quantities of distillate roughly corresponding to the acetone extracts of the same rubber samples. Sufficiently volatile accelerators and antioxidants were later identified separately in part with the aid of IR micro techniques.

Another possible application of distillative separation at normal pressure with or without carrier gas consists in the direct condensation of the volatile components on a thin layer plate as the starting spot, with subsequent separation and identification by thin layer chromatography (Fig. 1.4). STAHL [42] described a commercially obtainable apparatus by means of which the thin layer plate is moved continuously or in steps and the volatile components are condensed on the plate as a strip or as several spots, so that various fractions are present at the start of the chromatogram, and these are separated in a single operation.

Direct evaporation of volatile components in analytical apparatus, particularly gas chromatographs and mass spectrometers, is also possible, and is described in Sections 1.5 and 1.8.

1.3 Thin Layer Chromatography
1.3.1 Applications
Thin layer chromatography (TLC) has developed very rapidly since 1960, and as in many other fields, it has also become practically indispensable in the analysis of plastics, for the separation and identification both of chemical and thermal degradation products of polymers and of low molecular weight additives and processing aids of all kinds. TLC

has almost entirely replaced paper chromatography because of the wide possibilities offered by the use of different types of layers, solvents, and development methods, as well as by the use of very corrosive reagents, and many of its applications have become possible for the first time through this method. From the extensive literature, we can refer only a small part [45–60], and the reader's attention is drawn in particular to the book by E. STAHL [48] in which various sections deal with experimental techniques and applications to additives in plastics.

A number of progress reports [56–59] contain reviews of the more recent literature. KNAPPE [60] has reported on the possible uses of TLC in the lacquer field, and KREINER and WARNER [61] on the investigation of rubber additives. Reference will be made to other publications in the discussion of the various classes of substances. Thin-layer chromatography of plastics additives is dealt with extensively in the books by CROMPTON [16] and other authors [21–24, 240].

The significance of various experimental influences on the separation efficiency and flow paths, the characterisation of layers and solvents, as well as the relationships between thin layer chromatography (TLC) systems and chemical structure of the substances to be separated, has been clearly summarised by GEISS [47] in a monograph.

1.3.2. Documentation of TLC Data

The distance travelled by a substance in a TLC separation is expressed as the R_f value (distance from the start to the spot divided by the distance from the start to the solvent front) or as 100 times this value. The values obtained in the latter case are between 0 and 100. Since the R_f values are strongly dependent on external conditions, it is particularly important to keep these as constant as possible. Nevertheless, the R_f values should be regarded only as a guide, and should preferably be checked by simultaneous chromatography of reference substances on the same plate.

Various methods are available and have been described for fixing the developed layers [68—70]. Since preserved original layers are usually inconvenient to handle and the life of the colors is limited, we usually trace interesting chromatograms on transparent paper in their original size on a preprinted form, on which all the important data are simultaneously noted (Fig. 1.5). Spots that are visible in UV light are outlined on the plate with a broken line and transfered to the paper in this way. The spots obtained with spray reagent are outlined with a continuous line, and an abbreviation for the color is given.

The same form is used when the chromatogram is photographed. The principal data and the picture of the original chromatogram are then recorded on a negative whose sides are related approximately as 2 : 3.

Finally, mention should also be made of presentation as a line diagram, which we have used e. g. for the technical antistatics. In this case, the spot is represented by a line, whose length corresponds to the extension of the spot in the direction of migration. The symbols correspond to those in the traced chromatogram.

1.3.3 Transfer Methods

After the TLC separation, further investigation of the individual spots by chemical, spectroscopic, or chromatographic methods is often desired. This usually requires the isolation of the substances from the thin layer material and their conversion into a solution or an analysis system. The spot is scraped off or sucked off, and is then eluted with a sufficiently polar solvent (e. g. in a microcolumn). Traces of

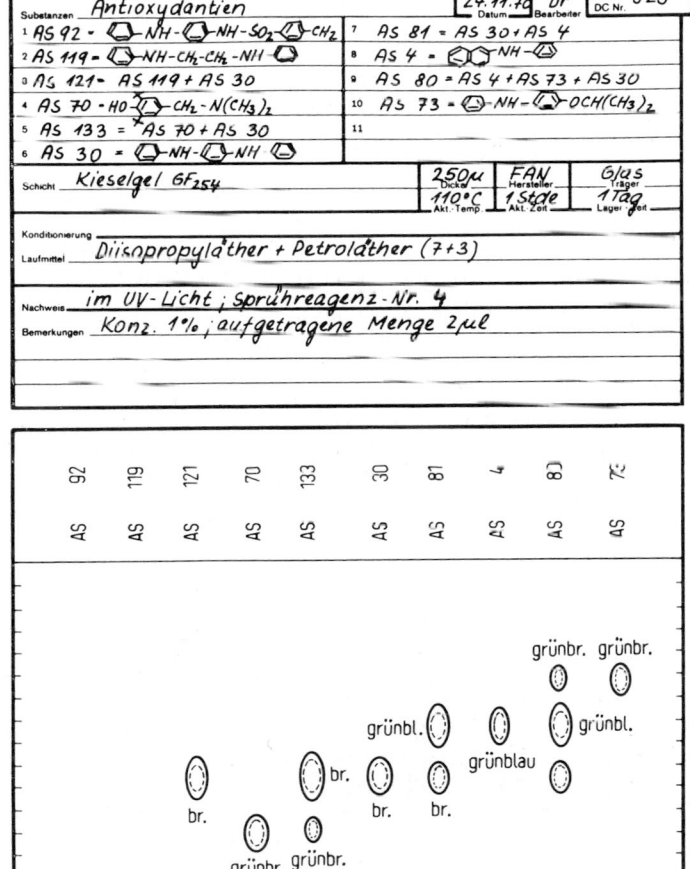

Fig. 1.5: Form for documenting TLC data (example)

layer material are removed by filtration or centrifugation, and further investigations are carried out on the solution or on the residue obtained on evaporation of the solvent. In this method, unfortunately, traces of colloidally divided layer material (silica gel, alumina, cellulose) usually remain with the substance and interfere in particular with examination by IR spectroscopy.

"Chromatography" on a porous potassium bromide wedge has proved to be a very elegant method for the preparation of micro quantities of up to a few μg for IR spectroscopy [63, 66, 157]. The spot of substance scraped from a TLC plate, the spot cut from a paper chromatogram, or a comparable sample is introduced into a glass tube with a flat base (inside diameter approx. 10—12 mm, height 30—35 mm). A porous KBr molding in the form of a wedge (25 mm high, 7 mm wide at the bottom, 2 mm thick; "Wick-Stick", produced by Harshaw) is placed on the sample. A glass or metal ring prevents the wedge from coming in contact with the side wall. The tube is closed by a centrally drilled cap (drilling diameter approx. 3 mm). Approximately 0.5 ml of a suitable solvent (methanol, CCl_4, benzene) is added to the sample. The KBr wedge sucks up the solution, and the solvent evaporates at the tip of the wedge, with the result that the dissolved substances concentrates here. Depending on the boiling point of the solvent and the ambient temperature, the solvent evaporates in 1—5 h; this step may be repeated if necessary.

The KBr wedge is dried for a short time, and the tip is then broken off, crushed, and compressed to form a KBr microdisc. Interfering traces of layer material are eliminated in this way. The danger of contamination is also greatly reduced by the simplicity of the procedure. In some comparative experiments with 15 μg each of insecticides that had been separated by thin layer chromatography, 70—80 % of the quantity of substance used for the TLC was converted into the KBr disc [157]. However, even considerably smaller quantities of substance can be identified.

1.3.4 High Performance Thin-layer Chromatography

Efforts to further improve the separation efficiency of thin-layer chromatography have been increasingly successful since the mid-seventies and have resulted in high performance thin-layer chromatography (HPTLC) [67, 68, 69]. For this purpose, very fine particle size sorbents, reduced and accurately matched measuring out of samples and definite solvent feed were particularly important.

Some of the typical differences between TLC and HPTLC are apparent from the following table:

	Ammount of sample [µl]	Separating distance [mm]	Separating time [min]
Conventional TLC	0.2 — 5	100 — 120	25 — 40
HPTLC with linear development	0.05 — 0.5	40 — 50	5 — 10
HPTLC with circular development	0.05 — 0.3	20 — 25	1 — 5

The absolute detection limits for HPTLC are lower by more than a power of ten than for normal TLC, although the volume of the sample used for the separation must be rather smaller. The time gained, and the greater sharpness of separation represent an important advantage for routine analysis. With specially designed separating chambers and sample metering valves (wet metering), results can be achieved which can be utilised for chosing separating column and solvent in HPLC separation.

Besides various types of instruments for HPTLC [53], coated plates and films [70] are also available for this technique.

1.4 Liquid Column Chromatography

1.4.1 High Performance Liquid Chromatography (HPLC)

The classic technique of column chromatography has, in recent years, made great progress in the shape of high performance liquid chromatography (HPLC) and is being increasingly used. The high separating efficiency of short, packed columns (preferably 20–50 cm long and 2–4 mm inside diameter) with fine particle absorption agents, efficient pumps and detectors (UV absorption, refractive index measurement) enables the eluated substances to be quickly and automatically separated and recorded.

The elution time depends on the substance concerned and the signal intensity provides quantitative information. As in thin-layer chromatography, separation is governed by adsorption or distribution processes, depending on the type of stationary phase, the latter in the case of reverse phase chromatography.

Sorption agents, usually silica gel, are of fine particle size, with a narrow particle size distribution (5–10 μm). Their specific surface area is between 200 and 500 m²/g, the pore size of 10 nm is fairly even. The tightly packed columns produce separating efficiencies of several hundred theoretical plates per cm length.

The polarity of the substances to the separated, the stationary phase and the solvent can be matched with each other in such a way that separation can be effected quickly. Throughflow rates are generally between 0.5 and 5 ml/min.

Gradient elution particulary, i.e. the continual change of solvent composition in the direction of increasing polarity, here offers many possibilities.

When examining mixtures which are totally or partly unknown, it is advisable to first carry out a qualitative thin-layer chromatography to obtain information for the carrying out of HPLC.

The HPLC separation of phthalate plasticizers (Fig. 1.6) and vulcanising aids (Fig. 1.7) are examples for the use of this technique in analysing plastics additives. Further information on HPLC may be found under the various groups of substances.

1.4.2 Gel Chromatography

In the chromatography of dissolved substances on porous gels, usually in a column, the separation is essentially based on differences in molecular size. The first substances can emerge from the column when the volume of liquid that has emerged (elution volume) corresponds to the volume of solution in the intestices between the gel particles. If no interaction occurs with the surface of the gel, the last substances are eluted at latest when the elution volume corresponds to the volume of liquid between and in the gel particles. Substances with high molecular weights migrate more rapidly, since they penetrate less into the pores than smaller molecules. Molecules whose size exceeds the exclusion mole-

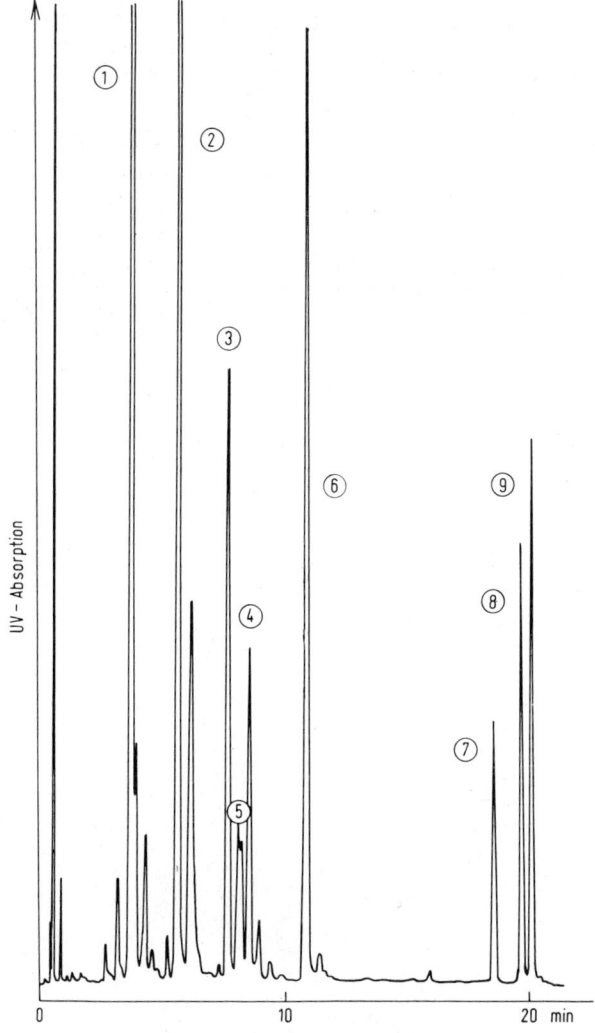

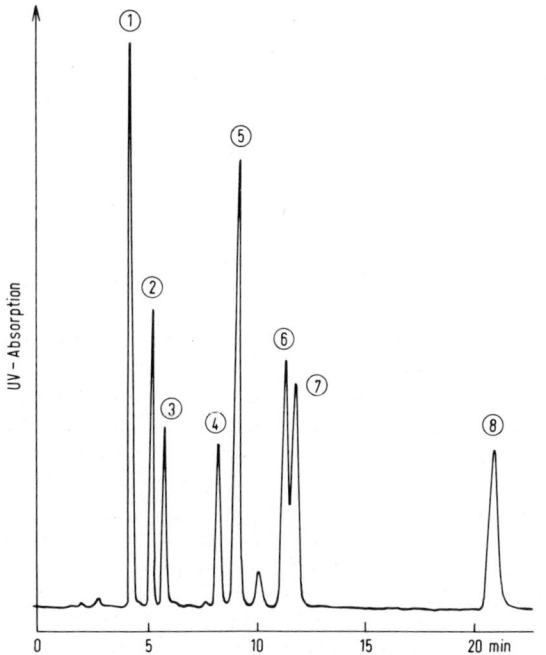

Fig. 1.6: HPLC separation of phthalate plasticizers
  Column: 2 × ODS-SiL-X-1 (reversed phase) 25 × 0.46 cm
  Eluent: H₂O + acetonitrile, 60 + 40, in 80 min to 0 + 100 with convex gradient
  Temp.: 75 °C; flow rate 2 ml/min; pressure: 500 bar
  Detector: UV, 260 nm (LC 55 Perkin-Elmer)
  Chromatograph: Model 601 (Perkin-Elmer)
  Peak Identification: 1 Dimethyl-, 2 Diethyl-, 3 Diallyl-, 4 Biphenyl-, 5 Dibutyl-, 6 Diamyl-, 7 Dicyclohexyl-, 8 Dioctyl-phthalate

Fig. 1.7: HPLC separation of plastic additives after Stoveken [84]
  Column: Silica gel HC-ODS/SiL-X, 25 × 0.26 cm
  Eluent: Acetonitrile + H₂O, 50 + 50, in 25 min to 100 + 0 with linear gradient
  Detector: LC 50, 200 nm (Perkin-Elmer)
  Temp.: 80 °C
  Peak Identification: 1 BHT, 2 Oleamide, 3 Topanol CA, 4 UV 531, 5 Stearamide, 6 Erucamide, 7 Dilaurylthiopropionate, 8 Irganox 1010, 9 Irganox 1076. 1, 3, 7, 8, 9: Antioxidants; 4: UV-Inhibitor

cular weight of the gel, i. e. which are too large to penetrate into the pores, cannot be separated from one another. This simplified picture can be treated quantitatively if diffusion processes, adsorption phenomena, the flow rate, and the column and gel geometry are taken into account.

Various types of polymers, silica gel, porous glasses, etc. can be used as gels, so that choice of solvent is practically unlimited.

A large volume of literature exists on gel chromatography, only a few of the more recent reviews being mentioned here [85—96, 101]. Various manufacturers now offer equipment in which the composition of the eluate is continuously determined and recorded in the form of chromatograms with the aid of differential refractometers, UV photometers, or calorimetric detectors.

1.4.3 Applications

The main application of gel chromatography is in the investigation of the molecular weight distribution of polymers. However, gels and glasses with narrow pores also allow good separations in the molecular weight range of monomeric and oligomeric substances, and have been used with very good results for the separation of monomers from one another [93–98, 100–103]. Some examples of applications are shown in figures 1.8–1.10. Further examples of separations will be discussed in the sections on the analysis of plasticizers, antioxidants, and antistatics.

The use of HPLC and gel chromatography in the analysis of plastics should increase in the years to come, since they offer many further possibilities as a separation method and for quantitative determinations.

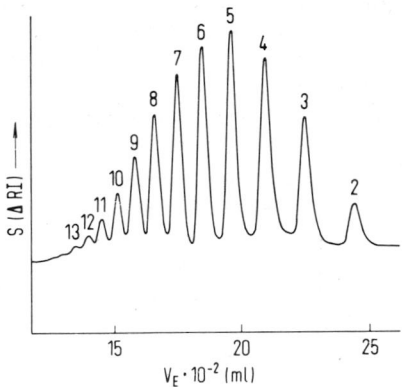

Fig. 1.8: Separation of oligostyrenes $C_4H_9(CH_2CH\ C_6H_5)_nH$ by gel chromatography. The numbers by the bands indicate the degree of polymerization m. Column: 5 x 200 cm, eluent: THF, polystyrene gel (2 % of divinylbenzene), $d_n = 74\ \mu m$, $M_n = 583$.
S = pen deflection (differential refractometer) [101]

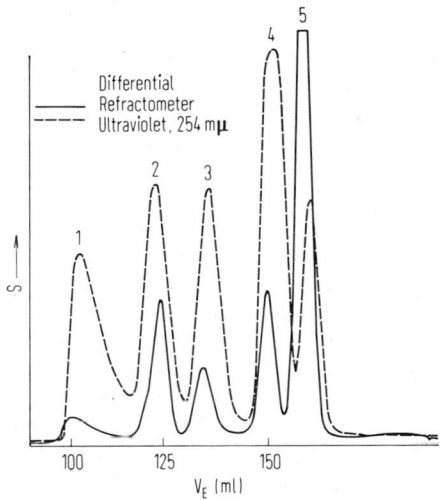

Fig. 1.10: Separation of additives (synthetic mixture) by gel chromatography
Column: 0.7 x 600 cm, eluent: THF, 1 ml/min. 23 °C
Poragel 60 Å [102]
1. Irganox 1010
2. Topanol CA + dilauryl thiodipropianate
3. Antioxidant AM-101
4. UV stabilizer UV 531 + DOPI
5. t-Butylcresol

1.5 Gas Chromatography

1.5.1 Applications

Gas chromatography (GC) has become indispensable for the analysis of volatilizable additives, processing aids, and chemical and thermal degradation products. The range of applications has been greatly extended by stationary phases with higher thermal stability, better column preparation, and more sensitive and in some cases even specific detectors. In combination with mass spectroscopy, it is probably the most valuable method of separation and analysis available at present. GC can be used directly for the investigation of solvents, monomeric plasticizers, and a number of antioxidants, stabilizers, and other additives, as well as indirectly for processing aids with very low vapor pressures. The reader is referred to a number of reviews, particularly on the application of gas chromatography to systems containing solvents [119–119b].

The present position in gas chromatography has been described at length in various books [103–111] and reviews [113–116]. The articles appearing in some 500 journals are being continuously collected in a documentation system [114].

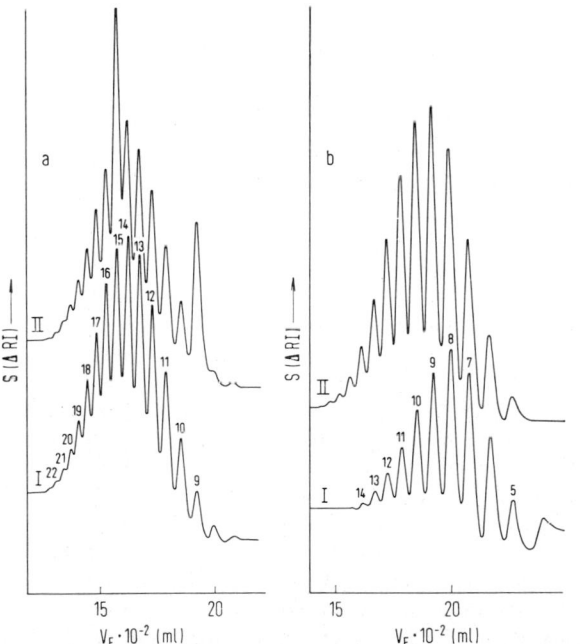

Fig. 1.9: Separation of oligoethylene oxides by gel chromatography. For experimental data see Fig. 1.6

a: $M_n \approx 300$ (curve I); $M_n \approx 430$ (curve II)

b: $M_n \approx 1000$ (curve I); $M_n \approx 1000$, with addition of degrees polymerization 15 and 27 (curve II) [101]

Collections of retention data are extremely valuable for the identification of substances separated by gas chromatography. The use of the retention index (RI) after Kovats, in which the retention time is referred to the n-alkanes separated under the same conditions, the RI of the latter being taken as 100 times the number of C atoms in the molecule, has gained wide acceptance and is used in tables [103, 115]. Optimum use of retention indices (possibly determined in different columns) and their differences, together with the use of chemical information or prior technological knowledge, in many cases yields very reliable information about the nature of the substances.

However, additional identification during or after the gas-chromatographic separation by means of reaction columns, substance-specific detectors, chemical reactions of the emerging substances, or coupling with another analytical instrument, e. g. a mass spectrometer, is often simpler, and is sometimes the only method possible [107, 117, 117a, 197, 600–602]. Numerous methods have been described for the collection of individual GC peaks for further investigation [103—107, 121—123]. Further information is provided in Sections 1.6 and 1.8.

In the analysis of plastics, it is often desirable to introduce the volatilizable components such as residual monomer, technical impurities and plasticizers into the gas chromatograph without previous separation from the plastic. Some notes on this procedure are given below.

1.5.2 Direct Introduction of Volatilizable Components into Gas Chromatographs

The main problem here is the instantaneous introduction of the volatilizable substances into the separating column. The following possibilities are available. A thin layer of the sample is applied to a surface that can be heated rapidly, where it is heated for only 10—20 s sufficiently for the volatile components to evaporate without allowing appreciable thermal degradation of the polymer. In a method described by ZULAICA and GUIOCHON for the identification of plasticizers [271], a sample weighing approximately 5 mg is placed in a thin-walled glass tube and heated electrically from outside the tube with a coil of wire. Satisfactory quantitative results have not been obtained by this method,

Much more suitable methods are those in which the evaporation of volatile components is carried out in a closed but a qualitative identification of the C_2—C_8 phthalates and adipates and of tributyl phosphate was possible.

Much more suitable methods are those in which the evaporation of volatile components is carried out in a closed ampule with no restriction as to time; the ampule is then broken in a heated apparatus and the vapor is swept into the gas chromatograph by the stream of carrier gas. WANDEL, TENGLER and OSTROMOW [240] have described such an arrangement, in which the evaporation and the breakage of the ampule are carried out in a unit that is connected to the gas chromatograph.

The GC data given for the various substance groups were determined mainly using packed columns, since these instruments can now be used in many laboratories. Another consideration is that packed columns can be subjected to much greater loads and that the catching of individual fractions is thereby made easier. Much better separation results are, however, achieved with capillary columns [103, 109, 109a] which, however, must normally be coupled with a mass spectrometer for identification purposes, but which are exceptionally efficient in this combination. Silica cappillaries especially which have an almost inert, metal ion-free surface, facilitate, with high boiling stationary phases, the separation of strongly polar substances such as free carboxylic acids or amines without derivatisation. They thus extend the possible uses of gas chromatography.

A method that is similar in principle is head space analysis [112–112b], in which the ampule is sealed with a silicone rubber cap, and after equilibrium has been reached between the solid and the gas phase, the gas or part of the gas is instantaneously introduced into the gas chromatograph through an injection system. This technique is being used successfully for the determination of solvent residues, contaminants and monomers in polymers.

A further variant of the ampule technique that should be mentioned involves the condensation of the volatile components in the colder part of an ampule, which is then sealed off, reheated, and broken in the stream of carrier gas (Fig. 1.11).

1.6 IR Spectroscopy

1.6.1 Applications, Collections of Spectra

IR spectroscopy is the most effective method for the analysis of plastics and the identification of additives and processing aids, since it requires only small quantities of substance (in favorable cases around or less than 1 μg of a component) and allows the identification of solid, liquid, and gaseous substances.

The fundamental principles of the method and the possible applications of various spectral regions are discussed at length in Volume 2, where band assignment charts are reproduced. The present state of IR spectroscopy is presented in the recent literature [130–146] and progress reports [145]. The assignment charts [135, 140, 146] and collections of spectra [147–150] are particularly useful for analytical work.

The possibilities offered by the far infrared (FIR) complete that of the standard range of 4000–400 cm^{-1}. SAUNDERS et al. [151] showed for 89 esters of saturated, branched and unbranched C_1–C_7 alcohols with linear aliphatic carboxylic acids from formic acid to palmitic acid that additional information or qualitative identification, which is specific for alkyl groups, can be obtained from the bands in the spectral region between 500 and 100 cm^{-1}. An assignment chart for saturated aliphatic esters was constructed. BENTLEY et al. [136] have published assignment tables for the region between 700 and 300 cm^{-1}.

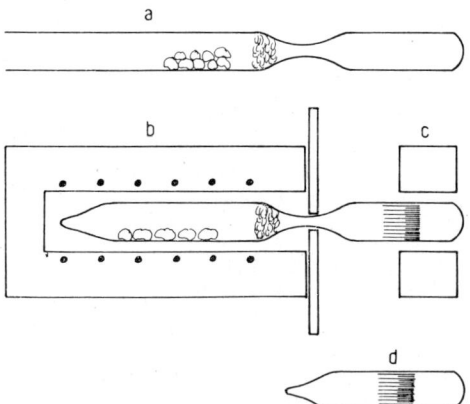

Fig. 1.11: Transfer of volatile components into an ampule for analysis by gas chromatography
a) Ampule with sample and plug of quartz wool
b) Furnace with evacuated and sealed ampule and cooler c
c) Sealed ampule with condensed volatile components

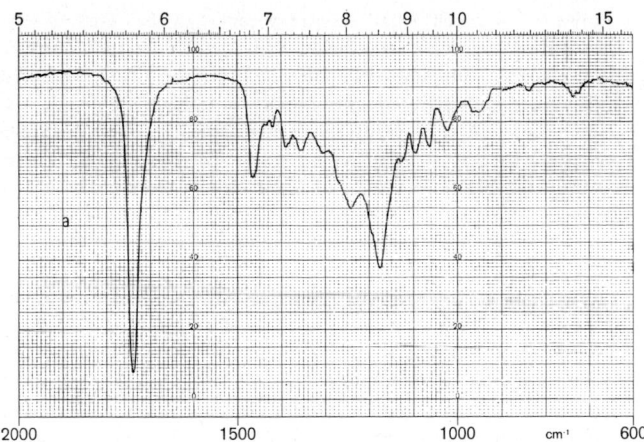

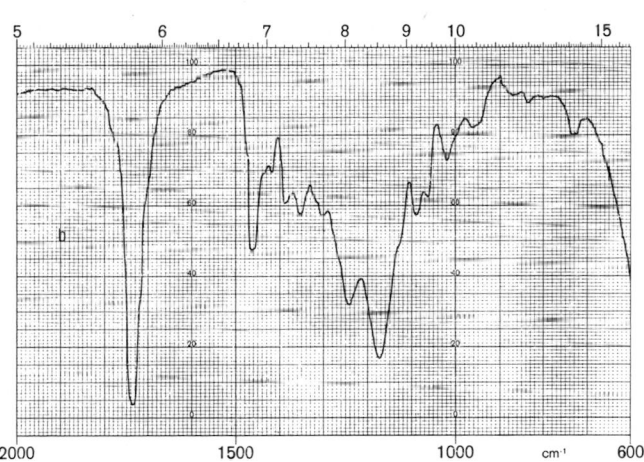

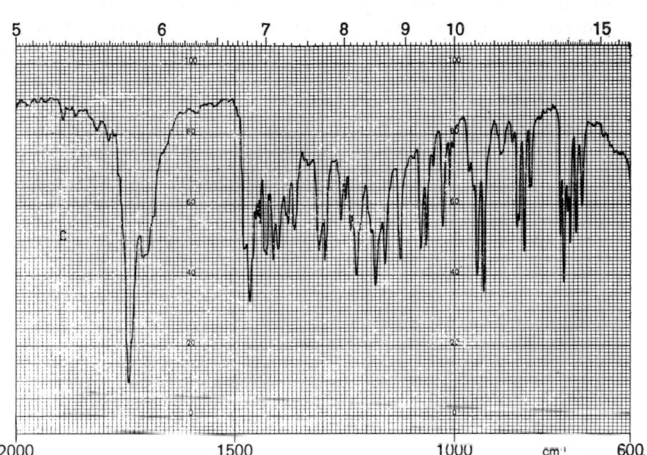

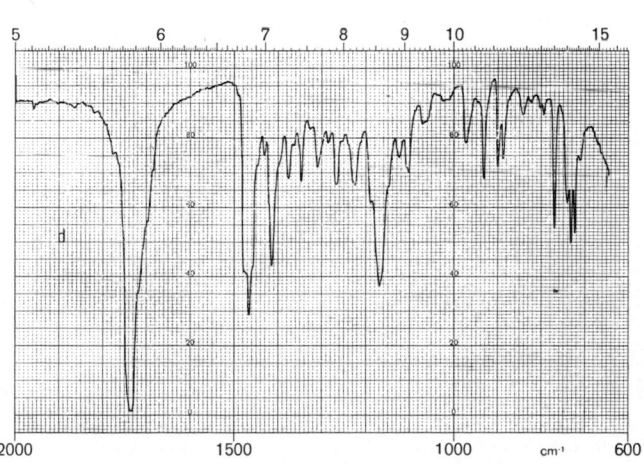

The principles and applications of ATR (attenuated total reflection) spectroscopy, which is useful for surfaces, polymers, and small quantities of substance, are described in recent publications [126—128].

An elegant method of improving the contact between the sample material and the ATR crystal has been described by HIRSCHFELD [129]. In this method, the finely divided sample material, e. g. fibers or powder, is first pressed into the surface of a silver chloride disc about 0.5 mm thick, and the disc is then applied to the ATR crystal with light pressure. This avoids damage to the crystal, since the silver chloride is very soft. HIRSCHFELD showed the improvement of the spectra that can be achieved in this way for cotton fibers.

Within homologous series, the IR spectra sometimes show only slight differences from member to member. The spectra of substances that are liquid at room temperature usually exhibit much more pronounced differences when recorded at low temperatures with the substances in the solid state. CASPARY [153] demonstrated this interesting possibility for n-hexyl bromide and n-heptyl bromide, the corresponding chlorides, n-butylamine and n-hexylamine, n-ethylbenzene and n-butylbenzene, and the di-n-butyl esters of sebacic and azelaic acids. The spectra of the solid samples at temperatures about 30—50 °C below the melting point show much more significant differences in the region of the deformation vibrations than the spectra of liquid samples. A similar picture was found for aldehydes and ketones. This is illustrated in Figure 1.12 for plasticizers. HERMANN and HARVEY [154] have published a detailed report of spectroscopy at low temperatures.

1.6.2 IR Spectroscopy of Small Quantities of Substances

In the case of additives isolated from plastics, only small quantities are usually available for identification. The preparation methods and the detection limits of the various procedures therefore deserve special attention.

KROHMER and KEMMNER [157] have carried out comparative investigations on phenacetin, as a result of which they give the following values for the minimum quantities required for identification by various techniques:

KBr dis 0.5 mm diameter, microilluminator and extension of ordinate scale	0.1	μg
0.5 mm diameter, microilluminator	0.2	μg
0.5 mm diameter,	0.5	μg
1.5 mm diameter,	2	μg
3 mm diameter,	10	μg
CH_3Cl solution in micro liquid cell	8	μg
Micro reflection (mirror diameter 2 mm)	10	μg
Multiple ATR	15	μg

The methods used are described in detail in the article. Various publications deal with the micro KBr technique [80—84, 155], the micro reflection technique on small metal mirrors [155—157], and the micro ATR technique [158, 159]. The methods mentioned above are only of limited applicability to liquids, particularly if the boiling point is around or significantly below 100 °C. For the identification of liquids that have been separated by gas chromatography, however, there is great interest in methods that allow the use of small quantities and in which the collection of the sample and the subsequent spectroscopic investigation can

Fig. 1.12: IR spectra of dibutyl azelate (a, c) and dibutyl sebacate (b, d) at room temperature in the liquid state (a, b, and at — 60 °C in the solid state (c, d)

be carried out without appreciable losses. Collection in cold traps, sometimes together with solvent vapor introduced at the outlet from the gas chromatograph, and condensation on cooled KBr or on a thermoelectrically cooled ATR crystal [174] are the main possibilities described [160—174], apart from spectroscopy in the vapor form, which is discussed in Section 1.6.3. However, the attainable detection limits for liquids are mostly around or only slightly less than 100 μg. The state of microphotometry in the IR is discussed in a review by BEYERMANN [175].

The above mentioned detection limits can be reduced by more than a power of ten by using computer aided IR spectroscopy. The disturbance level can be reduced, and the signal: noise ratio improved by determining the same spectrum several times [179, 179a].

1.6.3 IR Spectra of Vapors

IR spectra of vapors have gained in interest through the separation possibilities offered by gas chromatography, since a direct combination of a gas chromatograph with an IR spectrometer allows the rapid identification of individual substances.

WELTI [177] described the heatable gas cells suggested for this purpose, in which a favorable ratio of light path to volume is particularly important if the quantities of substance required are to be kept as small as possible [179]. For coupling with a gas chromatograph, moreover, continuous operation and rapid recording during the elution of the GC peak are necessary. At the same time, there must be no serious loss of resolving power and sensitivity in comparison with conventional IR spectrometers.

The data listed by WELTI [177] for various systems show that these requirements are satisfied only by IR interference spectrometers [180] and expensive special instruments [181], which still require the use of at least 0.1 mg of substance. Quantities as low as 0.01 to 0.1 μg are sufficient for mass-spectroscopic identification, and this method is therefore also used in combination with capillary columns.

However, conventional spectrometers can be used if the gas-chromatographic separation and the IR spectroscopy are carried out independently of one another. The separated substances are collected individually in cold traps or adsorption tubes and then transferred into IR cells. The advantage of spectroscopy in the vapor phase is that the losses on evaporation into an evacuated gas cell, particularly in the case of substances with boiling points below 150 °C, are much lower than in the manipulation of liquid samples. WELTI also reviewed this method. Another method is "interrupted elution" [177, 179], in which one peak of a chromatogram is adsorbed at a time in a short, cooled gas chromatography column, separated from the GC gas stream, and eluted into a gas cell, after heating, by a weak stream of carrier gas in the reverse direction. An automatic GC system for this technique has been described. Under favorable conditions, useful spectra can be obtained with 0.05 mg of substance.

Spectra of low-boiling substances (b. p. lower than about 150 °C) are given in the various commercial collections of spectra (ASTM, Sadtler, API, DMS, etc.). WELTI [177] reproduces IR spectra of 306 substances with boiling points of up to about 260 °C in the vapor form in the region between 4000 and 625 cm^{-1}, and at the end of his book, in tabular form, he gives about 2000 gas spectra from commercial collections, arranged according to molecular formula (21 pages). He discusses [176] spectra of primary and secondary alcohols (C_1—C_8), primary, secondary, and aromatic amines, carboxylic acids, aliphatic esters, amides, and phenols, and presents assignment charts in tabular form. Comparisons with the spectra of liquid samples show considerable frequency shifts, particularly for substances with hydrogen bonds. The spectra are similar to those in very dilute solution, where the influence of hydrogen bonding is again absent. This means that the spectra become simpler and their information content for qualitative identification is less.

Spectra of members of homologous series usually resemble those of other members more than those of liquid or solid samples of the same substance.

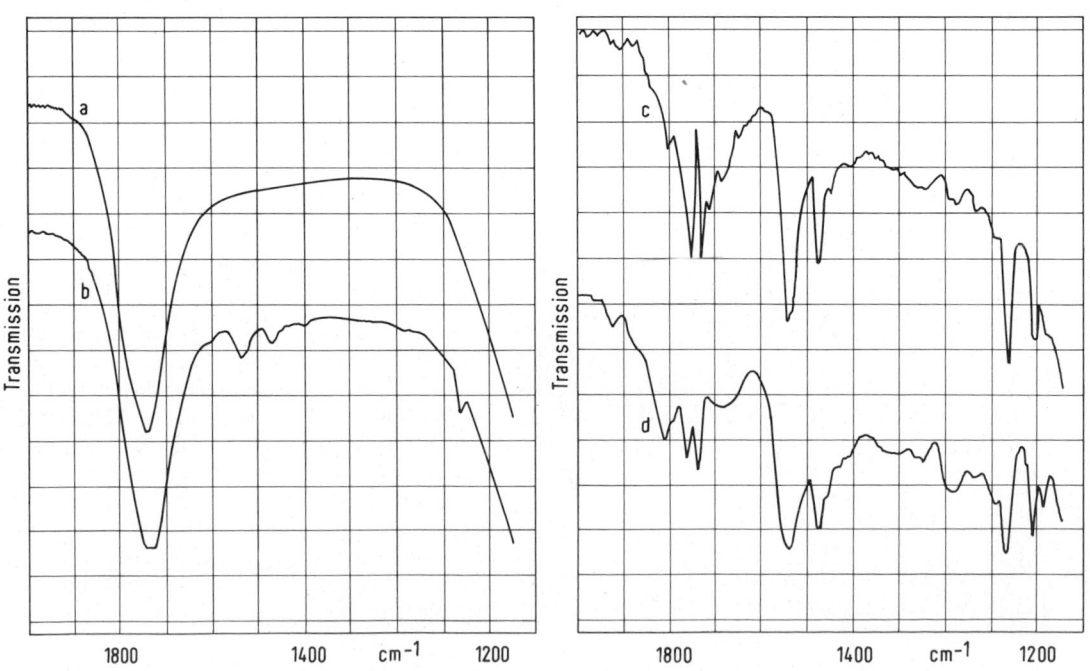

Fig. 1.13: Computer aided IR-spectroscopy of an aquous emulsion [179]. a) IR Spectrum of water (cap. film), b) Latex emulsion (cap. film), c) computer difference spectrum of b–a after smoothing and ordinate expansion, d) IR spectrum of latex film after evaporation of latex emulsion

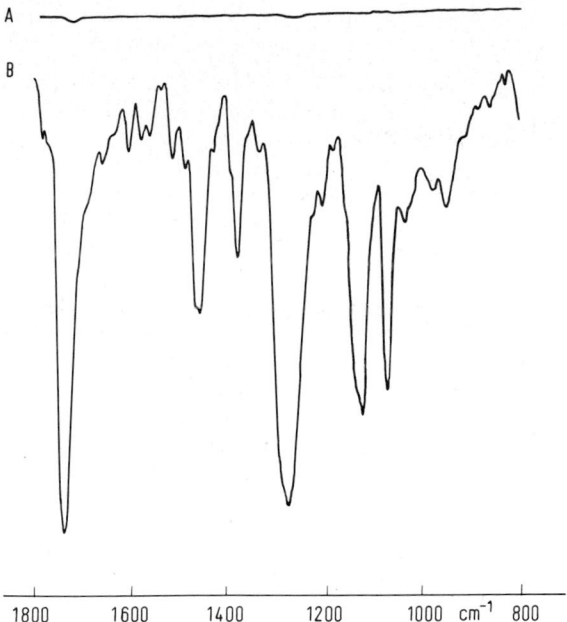

Fig. 1.14: Computer aided IR spectroscopy of micro samples [179a]
a) Original spectrum of an evaporation residue consisting of about 5 µg plasticizer on a 25 mm KBr disk; T > 99,25%,
b) Computer spectrum after the following operations: 1. Transforming transmission to absorption; 2. 200 × amplified; 3. Transforming back to transmission; 4. smoothing

1.6.4 Computer Aided IR Spectroscopy

Various more recent models of IR spectrometers enable the measured results to be produced digitally for further processing with computers. An important condition for an appropriate spectrometer-computer combination is very good reproducibility of the spectra. Thanks to the mini-computers which have been available since the late seventies, it has become possible to greatly improve the efficiency of IR spectroscopy even without the use of complex computer equipment.

The following possibilities are of special interest:

1. Differential spectroscopy to determine small amounts of substance added to the main component. The spectrum of the pure matrix, obtained separately or already available, is subtracted from the spectrum of the analytical sample. The differential spectrum which is often weak in intensity, can be made clearer so that it can be compared with other spectra, by means of ordinate stretching and smoothing.
2. Signal-noise improvement through mathematical smoothing processes after one or more determinations on the same sample (signal averaging). In the last named method, the signal-noise ratio improves about proportionally to the root of the number of runs, with a corresponding improvement in detection sensitivity.
3. Transformation of transmission into absorption, which is useful for quantitative determinations as well as for spectrum addition or subtraction.
4. Ordinate and abscissa extension as well as spreading out in wide ranges. In this way it is possible to draw – or project on to a

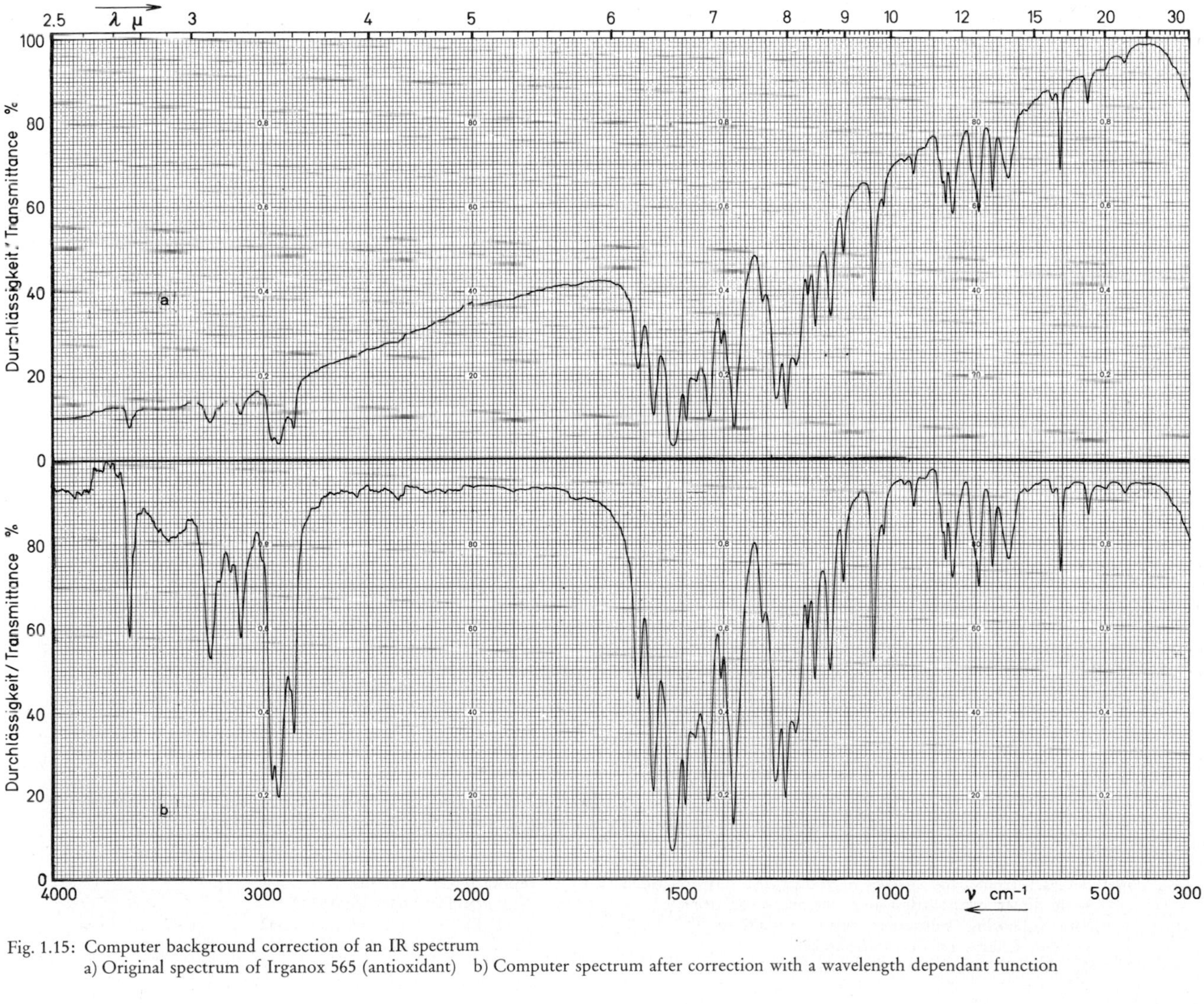

Fig. 1.15: Computer background correction of an IR spectrum
a) Original spectrum of Irganox 565 (antioxidant)   b) Computer spectrum after correction with a wavelength dependant function

screen – the spectra in the same size as available reference spectra from the published literature or collections.

5. Addition and subtraction of spectra from data files. In this way, spectra of mixtures of various substances can be obtained mathematically for comparative purposes as well as for semi-quantitative analyses.

6. Correction of scattered light and strong substrate absorption through subtraction of part of the spectrum, this occurring in dependence of the wave number according to specific functions.

Figs. 1.13–1.15 shows a number of examples of the use of computer-aided IR spectroscopy. They illustrate the usefulness of the method in the identification of small amounts of additives in a spec-

troscopically dominating matrix and the determination of small amounts of substance where the normal "untreated" IR spectrum no longer provides any information [179, 179a].

1.7 UV Spectroscopy

1.7.1 Applications

UV spectroscopy is not as extensively used as IR spectroscopy for the qualitative analysis of additives in plastics, since only unsaturated and aromatic systems absorb in the easily accessible region of about 210—390 μm, and since the sample must generally be in the form of a solution or a

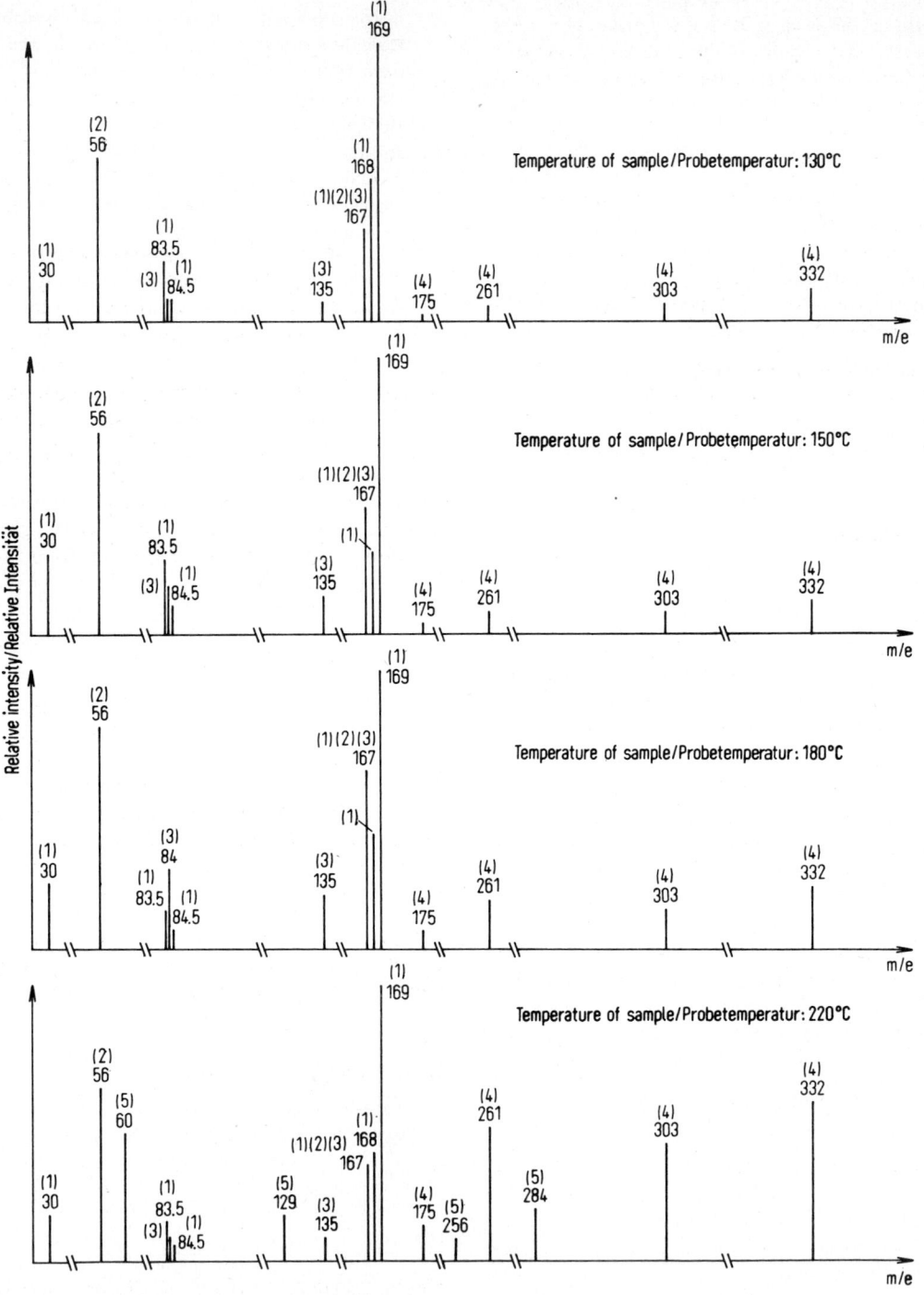

Fig. 1.16: Sections from mass spectra of rubber additives recorded with direct evaporation into the mass spectrometer.
The following substances were present in the rubber sample: Characteristic mass numbers
  1. Vulkalent A   38, 83.5, 84.5, 167, 168, 169
  2. Vulkacit CZ   57, 167
  3. Vulkacit DM   64, 135, 167
  4. UOP 88   175, 261, 303, 332
  5. Stearic acid   60, 129, 256, 284

very thin film. However, if this specificity is used for the detection of aromatic structures, a number of group-characteristic data are obtainable by UV spectroscopy. The high molar extinction coefficient, which is in the region of 10^3—10^5 for phthalates, phenols, aromatic amines, and similar additives, allows the sensitive detection of such substances.

UV spectroscopy is particularly useful in quantitative determinations of aromatic substances.

For further information, the reader is referred to specialized textbooks [182—188]. A survey of analytical methods is presented by R. G. White [189]. The determinations are outlined in 1630 short reports Fikhtengol'ts et al. [190] have published a collection of the UV spectra of elastomers and rubber chemicals, in which about 140 spectra are reproduced. A large volume of material from the field of chemistry as a whole is contained in various other collections of spectra and data [191—194].

1.7.2 UV Spectra of Additives

The UV spectra of a small selection of additives for plastics are reproduced after the IR spectra. The commercial products indicated were used for the spectra, which may therefore differ slightly from those of pure substances. The use of the UV spectra in analysis is discussed in connection with the classes of substances in question.

All the spectra reproduced in this book were recorded with a Perkin-Elmer UV spectrometer 137 and 330. The wavelength calibration was carried out at regular intervals with benzene vapor. Solvents, concentrations, and light paths are indicated for the spectra.

1.8 Mass Spectroscopy

1.8.1 Applications

Mass spectroscopy has gained new impetus in recent years, particularly in conjunction with efficient separation methods such as gas chromatography. This is due mainly to the great sensitivity (10^{-10} g of substance or less is sufficient in favorable cases) and the high recording rate (approx. 1 s per spectrum) of the method. The analysis of small quantities of multicomponent mixtures by direct coupling of a gas chromatograph with a mass spectrometer has been impressively demonstrated [117, 117a, 197]. In the analysis of plastics, this combination is particularly interesting for the identification of thermal or chemical degradation products of polymers after gas-chromatographic separation and of solvents and other processing aids and additives, again after gas-chromatographic separation. However, the possibility of direct evaporation of volatilizable additives from plastics and rubber in fractions into the mass spectrometer offers a very elegant and efficient method for the qualitative investigation of volatile components from plastics (Fig. 1.16).

There is a large volume of recent literature [195–200] on mass spectroscopy.

In recent years, new ionisation techniques have been introduced to mass spectroscopy with which lower fragmentation of the molecules is achieved, so that the identification – especially of high molecular weight substances in natural products, as well as oligomers and polymers – has been made easier.

In field desorption mass spectroscopy (FDMS, Beckey 1969) the sample is placed on to a specially prepared ion emitter (tungsten wire with "carbon surface") whence it is vapourised and ionised [201, 201a, b].

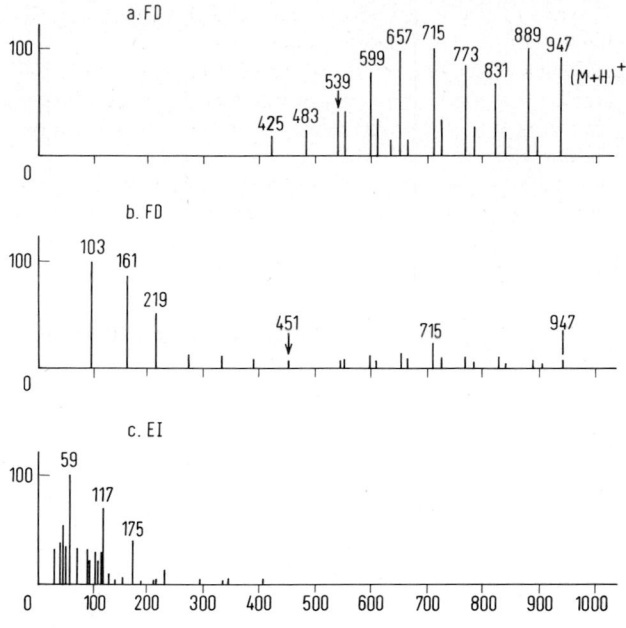

Fig. 1.17: Field desorption mass spectrum of polypropylene glycol (average molecular weight 790) after [201b]
a) FD-MS with low emitter current
b) FD-MS with higher emitter current
c) Electron impact mass spectrum

As an example, Fig. 1.17 shows FD and electron impact ionisation spectra (EI) for a polypropylene glycol with a molecular weight of 790 (average 14 monomer units). This shows positive molecule ions of the various oligomers in the FD spectrum with low emitter flow. As the emitter flow increases, fragments occur increasingly. The ion frequency decreases considerably in the EI spectrum at mass numbers above 200, and there are hardly any determination possibilities. In "chemical ionisation" (CI), too, more molecule ions and fewer fragments are produced than in EI, using an ion source at pressures of around 1 mbar through ion molecule reactions and using a gas such as methane or i-butane.

Fig. 1.18 shows some examples of EI and CI mass spectra for di-2-amyl phthalate [202a], which show that in the case of CI with the "soft reagent" i butane, few fragments are produced, whereas with CI using methane, there is also a marked quasi-molecule peak in the spectrum. There are also signals with higher mass number (M + 29, M + 41) through fragment accumulation, as well as fragments similar to those encountered in EI. There is no molecule peak in the latter instance.

CI-MS can also be carried out in direct coupling with gas chromatography. By using EI and CI spectra, identification of the separated substances is made easier.

1.8.2 Collections of Spectra

No systematic collections of mass spectra are published for additives and processing aids for plastics, but data for numerous pure substances are contained in tables [202—205], some of which are being continuously updated. Where MS data from our laboratory are given in the following sections, they are the results of measurements with a Hitachi/Perkin-Elmer RMU 6-E single focusing mass spectrometer. The ionization voltage was 70 eV, and the temperature of the ion source was 150—200 °C. The spectra, which were recorded photoelectrically, were normalized, after correction for the background, with a value of 100 or 1000 for the relative intensity of the strongest peak.

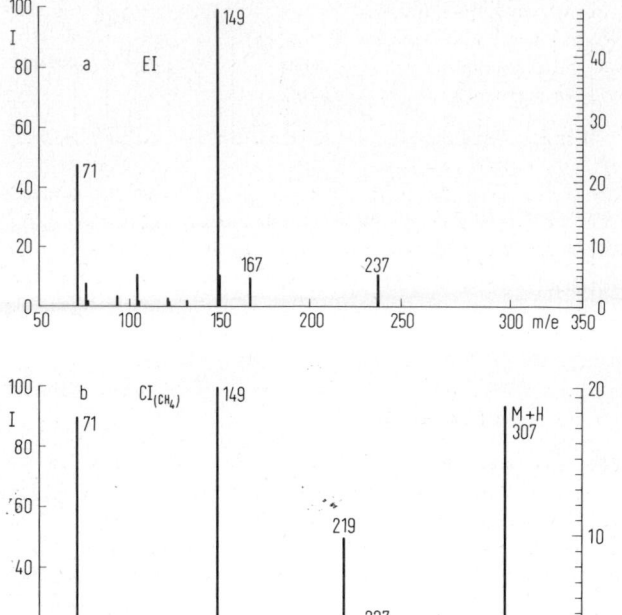

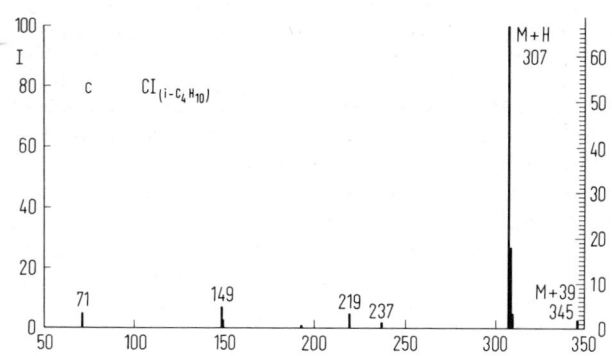

In recording the spectra, care was taken to ensure that the sample introduced into the inlet was completely vaporized into the all-glass storage system, which was heated at 150—250 °C, and only then passed into the spectrometer. Incorrect results due to more volatile impurities were largely avoided in this way.

1.9 Emission Spectral Analysis

For the simultaneous determination of numerous elements, particularly in samples whose compositions are unknown, emission spectral analysis is still the most efficient in terms of cost, the number of elements that can be detected, and the possibilities of detection. The qualitative and semi-quantatitive analysis in particular of metallic elements in plastics and additives is almost exclusively carried out by this method in our laboratory. These results are very valuable for the identification of fillers, pigments, stabilizers, and catalyst residues. In many cases, it ist unnecessary to ash the samples of plastics. These can usually be applied to the surface or introduced into a hore hole of a carbon electrode. The detection limits for many elements are in the ppm range. A few references to literature on this standard method should be sufficient [206—210].

1.10 X-Ray Fluorescence Analysis

In X-ray fluorescence analysis (XFA), solid or liquid samples are stimulated with X-rays to cause them to emit X-ray fluorescence radiation. The emitted radiation is resolved into its spectrum by means of an analyzer crystal, and the intensity of the X-rays characteristic of each element is measured. The intensity is a measure of the quantity of the element in question.

X-ray fluorescence analysis is very suitable for the fast quantitative determination of additives in plastics that contain elements having atomic numbers higher than 12 (Mg), since direct measurements on samples of plastics are possible in many cases, with no need for chemical disintegration. Si, S, P, Cl, and Br in the various polymers and additives can be quantitatively determined as well as the metallic elements in fillers, pigments, stabilizers and other additives.

The fundamental principles and the possible applications are described in the literature [211—217].

Fig. 1.18: Mass spectra of diamyl phthalate [202a] with
  a) Electron impact ionisation EI (70 eV)
  b) Chemical ionisation with methane $CI_{(CH_4)}$
  c) Chemical ionisation with i-butane $CI_{(i-C_4H_{10})}$

Fig. 1.19: X-ray diffraction diagram of a filler
  Original recorded curve and line diagram
  (Cu-Kα radiation)
  • $BaSO_4$, | ZnS

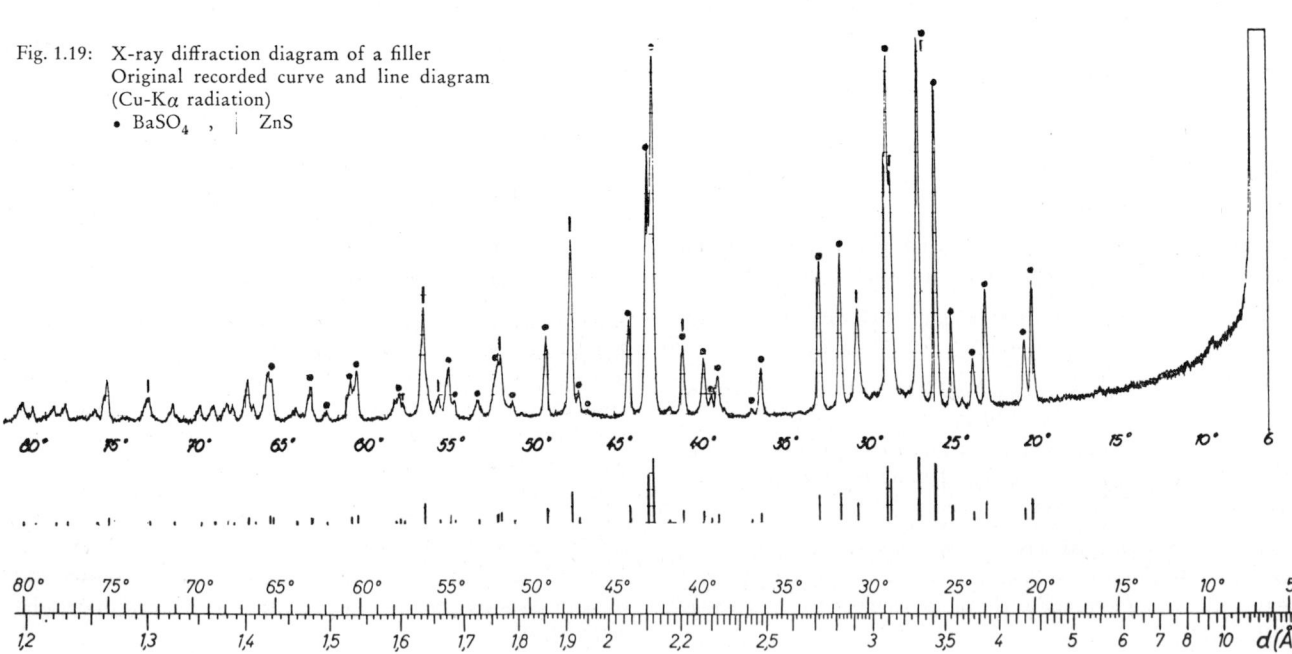

1.11. X-Ray Diffraction Analysis

1.11.1. Applications

X-ray diffraction analysis is a very useful method, even in the analysis of plastics, for the identification of crystalline phases. This is true in particular of inorganic fillers and pigments, where the knowledge of the elementary composition is often not enough to characterize the substance. Since the organic matrix has practically no effect on the investigation, fillers and pigments can usually be identified without first being separated from the plastic. A flat area of approximately 1—2 cm² is generally sufficient for this purpose. Some references to recent literature on the method [218—221] and to the collections of data [222—224], which are very useful for the identification of spectra, should be sufficient here.

1.11.2 Diffraction Diagrams

X-ray diffraction diagrams of finely divided substances (powder diagrams) are nowadays largely recorded with counter tube diffractometers, the results being diagrams similar to that shown in Figure 1.12. The reflections recorded are usually tabulated as a function of the interplanar distance. For comparisons within limited groups of substances, however, the picture is generally clearer if the recorded diffraction diagram is presented in the form of a line spectrum.

The line diagrams reproduced for the inorganic fillers and pigments were drawn from diffraction diagrams recorded in our laboratory for powder samples with Cu-Kα radiation and with a Siemens crystalloflex IV X-ray diffractometer.

1.12 Other Instrumental Methods

Nuclear magnetic resonance (NMR) spectroscopy is an excellent method for the structural analysis, particularly for the conformation and sequence analysis, of soluble polymers. Numerous publications in recent years have dealt with the application of this method to the quantitative analysis of copolymers. NMR spectroscopy is also suitable in principle for the analysis of additives in plastics. However, since considerably more material is required than in the other spectroscopic methods, and the cost is also higher, there have been few reports so far on this application. This situation will probably change with the introduction of cheap instruments for routine analysis, since the most reliable information on the structure of an organic substance, particularly if there is little material available for comparison, is provided by a combination of the various spectroscopic methods. The reader is referred to a number of books and reviews on NMR spectroscopy [225].

Polarography [226] has frequently been used for the quantitative determination of unsaturated monomers, of antioxidants, and of accelerators.

Fluorimetric methods [227] have also been suggested for the quantitative determination of some antioxidants and polycyclic hydrocarbons in additives.

Differential thermal analysis and thermogravimetric analysis [228] can help with the characterization and identification of some fillers.

Molecular weight determinations are very useful when they can be carried out with small quantities of material. A drop diluted solution is sufficient for vapor pressure osmometry [229]. As in ebullioscopic studies, use is made of the depression of the vapor pressure in a solution. A drop of solution hangs from a thermistor in saturated solvent vapor at a constant temperature. A drop of pure solvent hangs on a second thermistor in the same atmosphere.

Whereas equilibrium prevails on the surface of the drop of solvent, condensation of the solvent vapor occurs on the surface of the drop of solution, and the temperature rises as a result of the heat of condensation. Solvent vapor continues to condense until the temperature rise is such that the vapor pressure of the solution is equal to that of the solvent in the vapor space. The molecular weight can be calculated from the temperature difference between the solution and the solvent and the concentration of the solution. Equilibrium is generally reached within a few minutes in the measurements.

We have used this method with very good results for the determination of the molecular weights of various additives in plastics, and particularly of polymeric plasticizers. The method is also useful in conjunction with chromatographic separation methods for characterizing the various fractions.

1.13 Surface Analytical Methods

Since the early sixties, various methods have been developed for the determination of topography, morphology and elementary composition of small surface areas. There has, in recent years, been growing interest in the use of these techniques for examining plastics surfaces.

In scanning electron microscopy (SEM), a picture of the surface, with great depth of field and a resolution of up to 100–120 Å, is obtained through determination of the back-scattered electrons of an electron beam scanning across the specimen. If the X-rays produced in the specimen by the electron beam are also determined with an energy dispersive analyser, it is possible to determine the presence and distribution of elements with atomic numbers greater than 11 (Na) in a surface layer with a thickness of about 10,000–20,000 Å.

The electron probe microanalyser (EPM) differs from the scanning electron microscope by a sharply focussed electron beam and a crystal X-ray spectrometer. With this it is possible to achieve a much greater detection sensitivity (about 0.1%) and lighter elements such as B, C, O, F and Li can be determined.

In the scanning auger microanalyser (SAM) an electron beam, about 3 μm in diameter, is used to excite Auger electron transitions in a surface layer 5–25 Å thick, the elements in this layer being identified with the help of the electron energy spectrum. Using an ion source incorporated in the instrument, it is also possible to wear away the surface by bombarding it with ions (ionic etching). Gradually, by alternately using auger electron spectroscopy and wearing away the surface, a surface profile of the element distribution in a surface layer from a few 100 to a few 1000 Å thick, can be obtained.

Similar results are obtained with the ESCA (electron spectroscopy for chemical analysis) technique, in which the surface is excited by means of soft X-rays (K line of Mg or Al), whose energy spectrum again is typical for the excited elements and their frequency. Here, too, depths of between 5 and 20 Å are reached, from which the photoelectrons can issue [229c].

Fig. 1.19 shows schematically which surface layers contribute in the different processes towards the measuring signal and how the resolving power is influenced thereby.

There are numerous instruments on the market today with which several of the above described techniques – which, incidentally, are

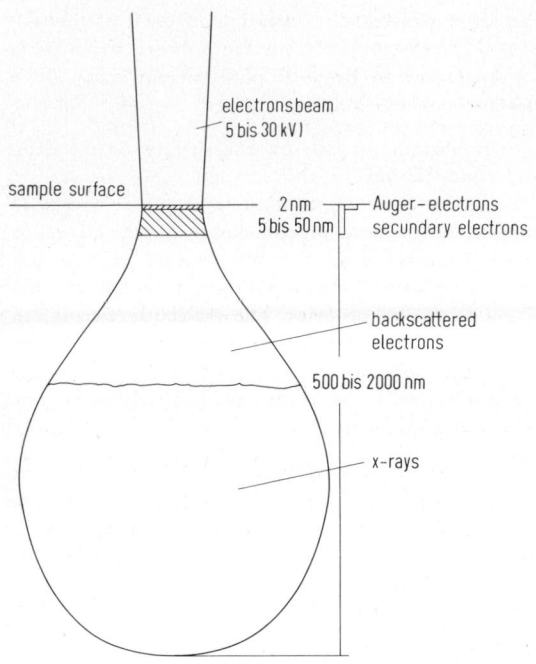

electrons beam
5 bis 30 kV)

sample surface

2 nm ── Auger-electrons
5 bis 50 nm ── secundary electrons

backscattered
electrons

500 bis 2000 nm

x-rays

Fig. 1.20: Electron back scattering and secondary emission from different parts of solid surface excitated by an electron beam

Finally, we must mention secondary ion mass spectroscopy (SIMS), in which the secondary ions produced on a surface through ion bombardment (e. g. with Ar ions) and worn away are analysed with a mass spectrometer. This provides information about the substances on the surface of the test specimen, which are responsible for the secondary ions.

Monolayers of solid surfaces may be examined by ion scattering spectroscopy (ISS), with whose help the type and amount of surface elements can be determined. A mono-energetic beam of ions of an inert gas such as ^{3}He or ^{20}Ne is focussed on to the surface to be examined. If these primary ions are of low energy (50–5000 eV) there will be elastic back-scattering from the atoms of the sample surface. For an elastic collision between two bodies one obtaines a relationship between the energy of the back-scattered ions, the mass of the surface atom and the scattering angle. All elements except hydrogen can be determined in this way, the limits of detection in certain cases being below 0.5%.

Surfaces can be worn away by ionic etching, using energy rich ions such as argon ions, the new surface then being examined by means of ISS. If He-ions are used, the wear on the surface is very slight, so that little or no changes occur.

ISS has given good results in the examination of metals, semi-conductor surfaces, fracture points in different materials, as well as in the investigation of organic and biological materials. The technique may also be used to analyse interface and surface problems in plastics.

all carried in a high vacuum – can usually be carried out.
By combining several methods of surface analysis, many problems – especially in metallurgy – have been solved. In the case of plastics for example, it is now possible to investigate uneven dispersion of fillers and additives, surface deposits and blemishes, as well as local changes in the micro-range.

2 Plasticizers

2.1 Survey and Classification

Extensive use is made of plasticizers for modifying the physical and technological properties of plastics. These are

Table 2.1: Classification of plasticizers and IR spectra numbers

	IR spectra No.		IR spectra No.
1. Esters of aromatic carboxylic acids	5000–5056	4. Epoxy plasticizers	5198–5206
1.1 Esters of phthalic acid	5000–5033	5. Glycols and ethers	5207–5251
1.2 Polyesters containing phthalic acid	5034–5039	5.1 Ethylene and polyethylene glycols	5207–5214
1.3 Esters of isophthalic acid	5040–5042	5.2 Polypropylene glycols	5215–5220
1.4 Esters of benzoic acid	5043–5049	5.3 Other diols and triols	5221–5228
1.5 Esters of trimellitic acid	5050–5056	5.4 Glycol ethers	5229–5243
2. Esters of aliphatic dicarboxylic and tricarboxylic acids	5057–5119	5.5 Other ethers	5244–5251
		6. Esters of phosphorus acids	5252–5275
2.1 Esters of C_4 dicarboxylic acids	5057–5063	6.1 Phosphates	5252–5268
2.2 Esters of adipic acid	5064–5081	6.2 Thiophosphates	5269–5271
2.3 Esters of azelaic acid	5082–5087	6.3 Phosphonates	5272–5275
2.4 Esters of sebacic acid	5088–5096	7. Sulfonic acid derivatives	5276–5283
2.5 Esters of tartaric and citric acids	5097–5106	7.1 Sulfonamides	5276–5282
2.6 Polyesters of aliphatic dicarboxylic acids	5107–5119	7.2 Esters of sulfonic acids	5283
3. Esters of aliphatic monocarboxylic acids	5120–5197	8. Hydrocarbons	5284–5307
3.1 Esters of C_2—C_4 carboxylic acids	5120–5135	8.1 Paraffinic and naphthenic mineral oils	5284–5291
3.2 Esters of C_5—C_{10} carboxylic acids	5136–5144	8.2 Aromatic oils	5292–5298
3.3 Esters of lauric, myristic, and palmitic acids	5145–5154	8.3 Halogenated paraffinic hydrocarbons	5299–5301
3.4 Esters of oleic acid	5155–5168	8.4 Halogenated aromatic hydrocarbons	5302–5307
3.5 Esters of stearic acid	5169–5184	9. Other plasticizers	5308–5312
3.6 Esters of ricinoleic acid	5185–5194		
3.7 Other esters	5195–5197		

usually low molecular weight liquid or solid, inert organic substances with low vapor pressures, though increasing use is being made of high molecular weight polyesters. Some plasticizers dissolve polymers, but solvent or swelling action is not necessary for the formation of a homogeneous system in plasticized polymers.

A considerable volume of literature exists on the properties, behavior, and action of plasticizers [1, 2, 230–239]. In particular, very many data are contained in the book by THINIUS [230]. Many organic substances have been suggested as plasticizers, and about 300–400 of these have found practical use. They are mostly esters of aliphatic and aromatic monocarboxylic and dicarboxylic acids and of phosporus acids; together with mineral oils, which are used mainly for elastomers, these compounds also account for the greater part of the volume of plasticizers used.

Table 2.1 is a list of plasticizers arranged on chemical principles. Occasional overlapping is unavoidable in this type of classification, but the scheme has proved useful for analytical purposes.

Tables 2.2—2.10 contain the individual substances of the various groups of plasticizers, together with data that are of interest in analysis.

The analysis of plasticizers is dealt with in numerous publications, the most comprehensive of which is probably the book by WANDEL, TENGLER and OSTROMOW [240]. This book also contains many detailed procedures in particular for chromatography, which extend far beyond the scope of the present book. In addition to 46 IR spectra (2—25 μm), many thin layer and gas chromatograms are reproduced. HUMMEL [13] and HASLAM and WILLIS [16] have also published numerous data on the chemical and IR-spectroscopic identification of plasticizers (70 and 44 spectra respectively, 2—15 μm).

2.2 Physical Data and Chemical Detection of Plasticizers

The use of chemical detection reactions for the identification of plasticizers is generally useful only as an identity check or for a rough assignment of a plasticizer to a specific group. The detection of hetero elements and functional groups is described in detail in vol. 2 of this Atlas. The reactions mentioned there can be used for the identification of the groups of plasticizers listed in Table 2.1.

Physical data for plasticizers, such as the spezific gravity (sp. gr.), the refractive index (n), the vapor pressure or boiling point, the molecular weight (M), and the viscosity (V) can be determined in cases where a sufficiently large quantity of a homogeneous plasticizer is available, and can be used together with chemical information as a means of identification. Tables of these data are published annually [3], and numerous data can also be obtained from monographs [26, 230—232].

SEYMOUR [313] is the source of the diagram reproduced in Figure 2.1, from which an indication of the plasticizer group can be obtained if the refractive index and the specific gravity are known. Physical methods have proved particularly useful for the characterization of mineral oils, which are extensively used as plasticizers for rubbers, and which are complex mixtures. Paraffinic, naphthenic, and aromatic compounds or structures in hydrocarbons with mixed structures differ in specific gravity, refractive index, viscosity, and other physical properties, and a definite dependence

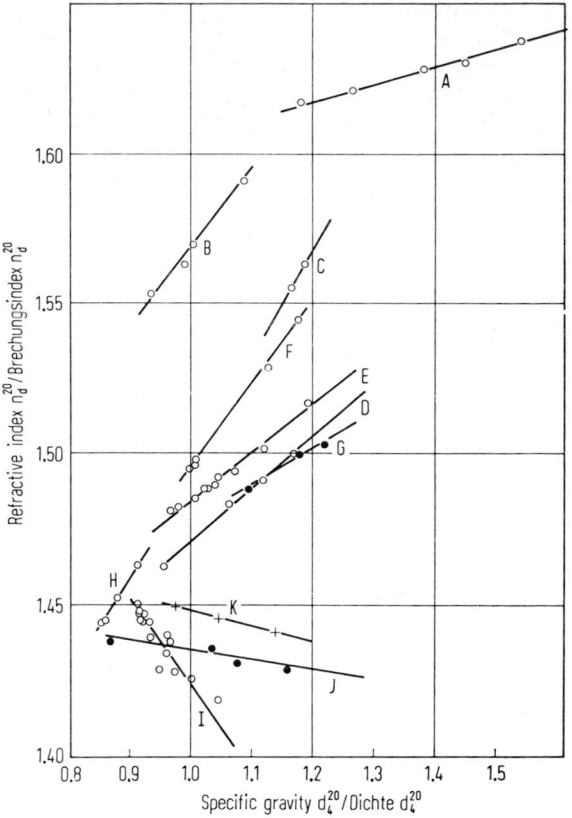

Fig. 2.1: Specific gravities and refractive indices of various groups of plasticizers (after *R. B. Seymour*)
 A) Chlorinated biphenyl
 B) Mineral oil extenders
 C) Triaryl phosphates
 D) Dialkoxyalkyl phthalates
 E) Alkyl phthalates
 F) Alkyl benzoates
 G) Phthalyl alkyl glycolates
 H) Alkyl stearates, alkyl oleates
 I) Alkyl succinates, alkyl adipates, alkyl sebacates
 J) Triesters of glycerol
 K) Alkyl tartrates, alkyl citrates

on the molecular weight is found within homologous series. With the aid of these data, it is possible to classify mineral oils or to carry out a structural group analysis in which the proportions of paraffinic, naphthenic, and aromatic carbon (C_P, C_N, C_A) are calculated.

The refractive index / specific gravity / molecular weight method, the refractive index / specific gravity / viscosity method, the viscosity / specific gravity constant (VGC) method and other similar methods have therefore attained great practical importance.

A review of the methods of structural analysis is presented by BERTHOLD, RÖSNER, and WILDE [304].

The VGC has proved useful in the rubber industry. It is calculated as follows:

$$VGC = \frac{d_{60} - 0.24 - 0.022 \log (v_{210} - 35.5)}{0.755} \qquad (1)$$

where d_{60} = specific gravity at 60 °F (15.5 °C) based on water at the same temperature

v_{210} = the viscosity of the oil in Saybolt seconds at 210 °F (99 °C).

The base value (German „Basiswert") after GRÜNWALD is also used. This value is found from the equation

$$B = d_4^{15} + 0.1 (0.3 - W_{50}) \qquad (2)$$

17

Table 2.2: Plasticizers,
1.1 Phthalates; IR spectra No.,
TLC data, GC data

Dec. No.	IR sp. No.	Composition	Trade name
1.1.1	5000	Dimethyl phthalate	Palatinol M
1.1.2	5001	Diethyl phthalate	
1.1.3	5002	Dipropyl phthalate	
1.1.4	5003	Dibutyl phthalate	Palatinol C
1.1.5	5004	Diisobutyl phthalate	
1.1.6	5005	Diamyl phthalate	
1.1.7	5006	Butyl cyclohexyl phthalate	Elastex 50 B
1.1.8	5007	Butyl benzyl phthalate	Santicizer 160
1.1.9	5008	Isobutyl methylcyclohexyl phthalate	
1.1.10	5009	Dicyclohexyl phthalate	Unimoll 66
1.1.11	5010	Di-n-hexyl phthalate	
1.1.12	5011	Di-(1,3-dimethylbutyl) phthalate	Plastoflex 520
1.1.13	5012	Butyl octyl phthalate	Santicizer 165
1.1.14	5013	Butyl isooctyl phthalate	Plasticizer 84
1.1.15	5014	Di(methylcyclohexyl) phthalate	Howflex SP
1.1.16	5015	Butyl decyl phthalate	
1.1.17	5017	Dicapryl phthalate	
1.1.18	5018	Di-(2-ethylhexyl) phthalate	Weichmacher IW 100
1.1.19	5016	Diisooctyl phthalate	Howflex 1001
1.1.20	5019	Isooctyl alkyl phthalate	Reomol DIOP

S3	S5	S7	S9	S10	S11	S12	S13	Dec. no.	SE-30 220°	SE-30 200°	SE-30 250°	SE-52 200°	SE-52 220°	SE-52 250°	SE-52 280°	PNGS 220°	U III 190°	U III 230°	LAC 190°	LAC 230°
38	5	21	43	19	11	20	27	1.1.1	1457			1495	1495	~1470		1870	0,73		0,80	
	8	34	58	28	17	27	32	1.1.2	1587	0,031	0,069	1625	1610	~1630		1975	1,00*		1,00*	
52	19	59	76	45				1.1.3	1760			1790	1800	1820		2128				
						22		1.1.4	1926	0,111	0,190	1972	1972	2012		2294	3,11	0,40	2,95	1,00*
								1.1.5				1885	1905							
								1.1.6	—			2075	2117							
								1.1.7						2010						
														2270						
														2555						
53	9	39	65	48				1.1.8	2037		0,585	2363		2390				2,52		
	14	48	70																	
	18	57	75																	
								1.1.9						1905						
														2265						
53								1.1.10	2442	1,000	1,000			2540						
57								1.1.11	2272		0,550					2627				
					33	43	59	1.1.12				2085		2100						
					28			1.1.13		0,380	0,432	1980		2020				2,96		7,50
					35									2300						
					24			1.1.14				1875		1900						
					34							2445		2475						
48	23	64	78	64				1.1.15						2610						
														2640						
								1.1.16						2020				1,60		1,30
														2600						
								1.1.17						2565						
58	42	72	83	76	35	48	59	1.1.18		1,000*	1,000*			2555						
					33	45	59	1.1.19						1990						
														2265						
														2608						
								1.1.20						2545	2555					
														2600	2620					
														2660	2672					

TLC data: See table 2.12   GC data: See table 2.13   *Standard

Table 2.2 (continued)

Dec. No.	IR sp. No.	Composition	Trade name
1.1.21	5020	Dinonyl phthalate	
1.1.22	5021	Diisononyl phthalate	IW 150
1.1.23	5022	Diisodecyl phthalate	Reomol DIDP
1.1.24	5023	Diisotridecyl phthalate	Reomol DTDP
1.1.25	5024	Phthalates of mixed alcohols	Palatinol HSH
1.1.26	5025	Phthalates of mixed higher alcohols	Mollan M 20
1.1.27	5026	Alkylaryl-modif. phthalates	Santicizer 213
1.1.28	5027	Alkylaryl-modified phthalates	Santicizer 214
1.1.29	5028	Diallyl phthalate	
1.1.30	5029	Dimethoxyethyl phthalate	Palatinol O
1.1.31	5030	Diethoxyethyl phthalate	
1.1.32	5031	Dibutoxyethyl phthalate	Palatinol K
1.1.33	5032	Methyl ethoxyethyl phthalate	Santicizer M-17
1.1.34	5033	Butyl butoxyethyl phthalate	Santicizer B-16

TLC data (silica gel layer)								Dec. No.	SE-30			SE-52				PNGS	U III		LAC	
S3	S5	S7	S9	S10	S11	S12	S12		220°	200°	250°	200°	220°	250°	280°	220°	190°	230°	190°	230°
60								1.1.21			1,87			2685	2705					
														2765	2770					
														2820	2825					
56	37	71	82	69				1.1.22						2670			2,96		4,78	
57	40	71	83	71				1.1.23			2,67			2600						
														2925						
								1.1.24			>3			~3400	2670					
															3000					
															3330					
					31	44	55	1.1.25						2090						
														2165						
														2210						
														2247						
														2280						
					30	43	58	1.1.26						2000						
														2415						
														2560						
														2675						
														2735						
														2800						
					18	31	47	1.1.27						1675						
					62	62	71							2427						
					34	47	60	1.1.28						1675						
					62	62	72							2900						
														3030						
								1.1.29						1790						
10	0	3	9	0				1.1.30	1956	0,131	0,204			2080			1,00*		3,50	
								1.1.31						2160						
								1.1.32	2420		0,802			2505						
								1.1.33		0,085	0,142			1955						
														2350						
								1.1.34		0,411	0,510									

TLC data: See table 2.12   GC data: See table 2.13   * Standard

Table 2.3: Plasticizers, 1.2. Polyesters of phthalic acid, 1.4. Benzoates, 1.5. Trimellitates, 2.1. Fumarates; IR spectra No., GC data

GC data columns for 1.3 Isophthalates under **SE 52** (200°, 250°); for 2.1 Fumarates under **SE-30** (220°, 200°, 250°) and **PNGS** (220°).

Dec. No.	IR sp. No.	Composition	Trade name	220°	200°	250°	220°
1.2. Polyesters of phthalic acid							
1.2.1	5034	Polyesters of phthalic acid	Hercoflex 900				
1.2.2	5035	Polyesters of phthalic acid	Santicizer 462				
1.2.3	5036	Polyesters of phthalic acid	Staflex KA				
1.2.4	5037	Polyesters of phthalic acid	Plastolein 9722				
1.2.5	5038	Polyesters of phthalic acid	Plastolein 9730				
1.2.6	5039	Polyesters of phthalic acid	Plastolein 9765				
1.3. Isophthalates							
1.3.1	5040	Dimethyl isophthalate			1565	1590	
1.3.2	5041	Di-(2-ethylhexyl) isophthalate	Flexol 380			2685	
1.3.3	5042	Diisooctyl isophthalate	RS 190			2570	
						2660	
						2715	
						2767	
1.4. Benzoates							
1.4.1	5043	Ethylene glycol dibenzoate	Hallco 870				
1.4.2	5044	Diethylene glycol dibenzoate	Benzoflex 2-45				
1.4.3	5045	Triethylene glycol dibenzoate	Benzoflex T-150				
1.4.4	5046	Dipropylene glycol dibenzoate	Benzoflex 9-88				
1.4.5	5047	Polyethylene glycol(200) dibenzoate	Benzoflex P 200				
1.4.6	5048	Polyethylene glycol (600) dibenzoate	Benzoflex P-600				
1.4.7	5049	2-Ethylhexyl p-hydroxybenzoate	Weichmacher 13				
1.5. Trimellitates							
1.5.1	5050	Tri-(2-ethylhexyl) trimellitate	Rucoflex 26 TM				
1.5.2	5051	Triisooctyl trimellitate	Rucoflex TM				
1.5.3	5052	Tri-(n-octyl, n-decyl) trimellitate	Rucoflex NTM				
1.5.4	5053	Tri-(n-octyl, n-decyl) trimellitate	Weichmacher ODTM				
1.5.5	5054	Diisooctyl decyl trimellitate	Staflex DIODTM				
1.5.6	5055	Tri(i-octyl, i-decyl) trimellitate	Rucoflex ODTM				
1.5.7	5056	Triisodecyl trimellitate	Morflex 530				
2.1. Fumarates, maleates, succinates							
2.1.1	5057	Dibutylfumarat	Rucoflex DBF				
2.1.2	5058	Di(2-ethylhexyl)fumarat	Rucoflex DOF				
2.1.3	5059	Diisooctylfumarat	Pfizer DIOF				
2.1.4	5060	Dibutylmaleat	Staflex DBM				
2.1.5	5061	Dioctylmaleat	Staflex DOM				
2.1.6	5062	Diäthylsuccinat			0,235	0,312	
2.1.7	5063	Dibutylsuccinat		1149			1394
				1560			1791

GC data: See table 2.13

Table 2.4 see p. 24
Table 2.5 see p. 23
Table 2.6 see p. 30

Table 2.7: Plasticizers, 4. Epoxy plasticizers

Dec. No.	IR sp. No.	Composition	Trade name
4.1	5198	Alkyl epoxystearate	Celluflex 23
4.2	5199	Esters of epoxidized fatty acids	Monoplex S 71
4.3	5200	2-Ethylhexyl epoxytallate	Flexol EP 8
4.4	5201	Esters of epoxidized fatty acids	Flexol GPE
4.5	5202	Triglycerides of epoxidized fatty acids	Paraplex G 61
4.6	5203	Esters of epoxidized fatty acids	Epoxy-Weichmacher LSO
4.7	5204	Epoxidized soybean oil	Epoxol 7-4
4.8	5205	Triglycerides of epoxidized fatty acids	Epoxol 9-5
4.9	5206	Epoxytetrahydrophthalate	Flexol PEP

Table 2.5: Plasticizers, 2.5. Tartrates, citrates, 2.6. Polyesters of adipic and sebacic acids, 3.1. Acetates, propionates, butyrates, 3.2. Esters of C_5–C_{10} carboxylic acids

Dec. No.	IR sp. No.	Composition	Trade name	TLC data (silica gel) S 3	S 7	GC data SE - 30 200°	250°	U III 220°	LAC 230°
2.5.		**Tartrates, citrates**							
2.5.1	5097	Diethyl tartrate							
2.5.2	5098	Dibutyl tartrate							
2.5.3	5099	Triethyl citrate	Citroflex 2	15	7	0,038	0,070	1,00*	1,00* / 1,00*
2.5.4	5100	Triethyl acetylcitrate	Citroflex A-2	19	21	0,053	0,103	1,00	1,00 / 1,00
2.5.5	5101	Tri-n-butyl citrate	Citroflex 4	20	20	0,290	0,380	1,56	5,28 / 3,57
2.5.6	5102	Tri-n-butyl acetylcitrate	Citroflex A-4	32	42	0,365	0,423	1,49	5,28 / 3,29
2.5.7	5103	Tricyclohexyl citrate	Citroflex 6 R						
2.5.8	5104	Tri-2-ethylhexyl citrate							
2.5.9	5105	Tri-2-ethylhexyl acetylcitrate	Citroflex A-8	52	84	> 3		>2,29	23,80
2.5.10	5106	Tri-(n-octyh, n-decyl) acetylcitrate	Citroflex A-810						
2.6.		**Polyesters of adipic and sebacic acid**							
2.6.1	5107	Polyester of adipic acid	Plastolein 9715						
2.6.2	5108	Polyester of adipic acid	Plastolein 9720						
2.6.3	5109	Ethylene glycol polyadipate							
2.6.4	5110	Polyester of adipic acid	Diolpate PPA						
2.6.5	5111	Polyester of adipic acid	Diolpate 214						
2.6.6	5112	Adipic acid butylenglycol polyester	Weichmacher ABG						
2.6.7	5113	Polyester of adipic acid	Ultramoll I						
2.6.8	5114	Polyester of adipic acid	Ultramoll II						
2.6.9	5115	Polyester of adipic acid	Ultramoll III						
2.6.10	5116	Polyester of adipic acid	Hartflex 330						
2.6.11	5117	Polyester of adipic acid	Plasticizer NP 10						
2.6.12	5118	Polyester of sebacic acid	Scadoplast RS 20						
2.6.13	5119	Polyester of sebacic acid	Scadoplast RS 150						
						LAC P 2000 170°	160°		
3.1.		**Acetates, propionates, butyrates**							
3.1.1	5120	Glycerol monoacetate	Acetin			1,00*	1,00*		
3.1.2	5121	Glycerol diacetate	Diacetin			1,65	1,21		
3.1.3	5122	Glycerol triacetate	Triacetin	18		1,96	1,43		
3.1.4	5123	Glycerol triethylene glycol acetate ether	Weichmacher 90						
3.1.5	5124	Triethylene glycol monoacetate	Weichmacher GNM						
3.1.6	5125	Triethylene glycol diacetate	Weichmacher GN						
3.1.7	5126	Hexanetriol triacetate	Triacetin H						
3.1.8	5127	Ethylene glycol dipropionate							
3.1.9	5128	Diethylene glycol dipropionate							
3.1.10	5129	Triethylene glycol dipropionate							
3.1.11	5130	Glycerol tripropionate	Tripropionin						
3.1.12	5131	Ethylene glycoldibutyrate							
3.1.13	5132	Glycerol tributyrate	Tri-n-butyrin						
3.1.14	5133	2,2,4-Trimethyl-1,3-zentanediol monoisobutyrate	TMPDMI						
3.1.15	5134	2,2,4-Trimethyl-1,3-pentanediol diisobutyrate	Texanol Isobutyrate						
3.1.16	5135	Sucrose diacetate hexaisobutyrate	Saib 100						
						SE - 30 250°			
3.2.		**Esters of C_5—C_{10} carboxylic acids**							
3.2.1	5136	Triethylene glycol di-2-ethylbutyrate	Flexol 3 GH						
3.2.2	5137	Butanediol dicaprylate	Rucoflex BD 8						
3.2.3	5138	Triethylene glycol dicarprylate	Rucoflex TG 8						
3.2.4	5139	Triethylene glycol di-2-ethylhexoate	Flexol 3 GO			0,833			
3.2.5	5140	Polyethylene glycol di-2-ethylhexoate	Flexol 4 GO						
3.2.6	5141	2-Butoxyethyl pelargonate	Hallco 3425						
3.2.7	5142	Butanediol dipelargonate	Rucoflex BD-9						
3.2.8	5143	Diethylene glycol dipelargonate	Plastolein 9055 DPG						
3.2.9	5144	Triethylene glycol dipelargonate	Plastolein 9404 TGP						

* Standard   TCL data: See table 4.12   GC data: See table 2.13

Table 2.4: Plasticizers,
2.2. Adipates, 2.3. Azelates,
2.4. Sebacates; IR spectra No.,
TLC data, GC data

Dec. no.	IR sp. no.	Composition	Trade name
2.2.	Adipates		
2.2.1	5064	Dimethyl adipate	
2.2.2	5065	Diethyl adipate	
2.2.3	5066	Dibutyl adipate	
2.2.4	5067	Diisobutyl adipate	
2.2.5	5068	Di-n-hexyl adipate	
2.2.6	5069	Di-n-octyl adipate	
2.2.7	5070	Di-2-ethylhexyl adipate	Plastomoll DOA
2.2.8	5071	Diisooctyl adipate	Adipol A
2.2.9	5072	Diisononyl adipate	Plastomoll NA
2.2.10	5073	Octyl decyl adipate	Hercoflex 290
2.2.11	5074	Didecyl adipate	
2.2.12	5075	Butyl benzyl adipate	Adimoll BB
2.2.13	5076	Octyl benzyl adipate	Adimoll BO
2.2.14	5077	Di(methoxyethyl) adipate	
2.2.15	5078	Di(ethoxyethyl) adipate	
2.2.16	5079	Di(butoxyethyl) adipate	Adipol BCA
2.2.17	5080	2,2,4-Trimethyl-1,3-pentanediol monoadipate	TMPDM-Adipate
2.2.18	5081	Tetrahydrofurfuryl adipate	
2.3.	Azelates		
2.3.1	5082	Dibutyl azelate	
2.3.2	5083	Dicyclohexyl azelate	Morflex X-1114
2.3.3	5084	Di-n-hexyl azelate	Plastolein 9051
2.3.4	5085	Di-2-ethylbutyl azelate	Plastolein 9050
2.3.5	5086	Di-2-ethylhexyl azelate	Flexol Z-88
2.3.6	5087	Esters of azelaic acid	Plastolein 9078 LT
2.4.	Sebacates		
2.4.1	5088	Dimethyl sebacate	
2.4.2	5089	Diethyl sebacate	Reomol DES
2.4.3	5090	Diisobutyl sebacate	
2.4.4	5091	Dibutyl sebacate	
2.4.5	5092	Di-(2-ethylhexyl) sebacate	Reomol DOS
2.4.6	5093	Diisooctyl sebacate	Reomol DIOS
2.4.7	5094	Mixture of C_8-alcohol sebacates	Reomol D 79 S
2.4.8	5095	Fatty alcohol sebacate	Sebacinsäureester B 172
2.4.9	5096	Dibenzyl sebacate	Harflex 90

TLC data: See table 2.12   GC data: See table 2.13

S 3	S 5	S 6	Dec. no.	SE-30 220°	SE-30 200°	SE-30 250°	SE-30 140 to 350°	SE-52 200°	SE-52 250°	SE-52 280°	PNGS 220°	U III 210°	U III 240°	LAC 220°	LAC 230°
			2.2.1	1234	0,026	0,058		1220	1243		1530				
			2.2.2	1368				1362	1300		1626				
		48	2.2.3		0,046	0,083		1750	1790			1,00*	0,16	0,19	
			2.2.4		0,021	0,055		1669	1700						
			2.2.5	2140							2381				
49			2.2.6	2567				2410	2400						
50		68	2.2.7			0,660			2395			6,35	1,00*	1,00*	
			2.2.8						2350						
									2425						
									2475						
		68	2.2.9						2505				1,15	1,31	
									2585				1,35		
									2630				1,72		
			2.2.10						2460						
									2600						
									2770						
			2.2.11												
		23	2.2.12						2935						
		45						1765	1800						
								2155	2165						
									2600						
50		23	2.2.13						2390						
		45							2480						
		69							2590						
									2630						
			2.2.14					1800	1830						
			2.2.15					1648	1680						
								1915	1945						
			2.2.16					2290	2300						
			2.2.17												
			2.2.18						2475						
			2.3.1		0,180	0,250							0,41	0,47	
	38		2.3.2												
			2.3.3			0,802							1,43	1,39	
	47		2.3.4										1,00*	1,00*	
	51		2.3.5			1,62							2,56	2,34	
	60		2.3.6												
23		27	2.4.1	1646			0,84	1654	1660		1928		0,75		1,00
23		32	2.4.2	1804			1,00*	1790	1775		2031		1,00*		1,00*
			2.4.3		0,265	0,354		2090	2090						
35		58	2.4.4	2169			1,39	2178	2170		2392		3,33		3,29
47		75	2.4.5				2,06		2850				18,83		17,28
									2690						
									2740						
			2.4.6						2730						
									2795						
			2.4.7						2320						
									2525						
									2740						
			2.4.8												
41		41	2.4.9						3090	3030					

* Standard

where $d_4{}^{15}$ = the specific gravity of the oil at 15 °C

W_{50} = the double logarithm of the viscosity at 50 °C in centistokes + 0.8, i. e.

W_{50} = log log $(V_{50} + 0.8)$.

The VGC and the base value are related by the equation

$$B = 0.727 \; VDK + 0.3 \qquad (3)$$

The plasticizers prepared from naturally occurring mineral oil mixtures are divided on the basis of these values into the following groups:

Type of hydrocarbon	Range of viscosity/ specific gravity constants	Range of base values
Paraffinic	0.791—0.820	0.874—0.895
Relatively naphthenic	0.821—0.850	0.896—0.915
Naphthenic	0.851—0.900	0.916—0.955
Relatively aromatic	0.901—0.950	0.956—0.990
Aromatic	0.951—1.000	0.991—1.025
Highly aromatic	1.001—1.050	1.026—1.065
Extremely aromatic	above 1.050	above 1.065

Details on the use of the method can be seen from a number of publications [306, 314].

Another very important physical parameter is the molecular weight, a knowledge of which is useful in the case of homogeneous substances, and also particularly in the case of plasticizer mixtures such as are present in polymeric plasticizers and mineral oils. In our work, vapor pressure osmometry has proved very useful for the determination of molecular weights [229]; only a few mg of material are required for the determination. The molecular weights given in the legends to the spectra of polymeric plasticizers were determined in this way. (Vapor pressure osmometer manufactured by Knauer, Berlin; solvent: benzene).

2.3 Thin Layer, Column, and Gel Chromatography of Plasticizers

The thin layer chromatography of plasticizers [18, 20, 240, 242—264] is carried out almost exclusively on silica gel layers, the main solvent systems used being those listed in Table 2.12. R_f values are given in the plasticizer tables. Detailed procedures, chromatograms, and tables can be found in the book by WANDEL et al. [240].

Whereas mineral oils and chloroparaffins have high R_f values, polymeric plasticizers remain in the vicinity of the starting spot under these conditions. The R_f values of the esters increase with the number of C atoms in the alcohol. The larger the polar part of the molecule (ester group, alkoxy group), the lower is the R_f value. Esters of higher alcohols ($> C_7$) generally cannot be separated. Esters of linear and branched alcohols having the same number of C atoms also have equal R_f values.

According to HAGEN [18, 261], esters of aliphatic dicarboxylic acids can be separated on alumina layers impregnated with urea. With urea saturated methanol as the solvent, linear esters remain at the starting spot as a result of the formation of inclusion compounds, whereas the branched esters migrate.

Table 2.8: Plasticizers; Ethylene glycols, 5.2. Propylene glycols, 5.3. Other polyols, 5.4. Glycol ethers, 5.5. Other ethers

Dec. no.	IR sp. no.	Composition
5.1.	Ethylene glycols	
5.1.1	5207	Diethylene glycol
5.1.2	5208	Triethylene glycol
5.1.3	5209	Tetraethylene glycol
5.1.4	5210	Polyethylene glycol
5.1.5	5211	Polyethylene glycol
5.1.6	5212	Polyethylene glycol
5.1.7	5213	Polyethylene glycol
5.1.8	5214	Polyethylene glycol
5.2.	Propylene glycols	
5.2.1	5215	Polypropylene glycol
5.2.2	5216	Polypropylene glycol
5.2.3	5217	Polypropylene glycol
5.2.4	5218	Polyethylene oxide propylene glycol
5.2.5	5219	Polyethylene oxide propylene glycol
5.2.6	5220	Glycol ethylene oxide
5.3.	Other polyols	
5.3.1	5221	1,4-Butanediol
5.3.2	5222	1,2,6-Hexanetriol
5.3.3	5223	Glycerol tripolyoxypropylene ether
5.3.4	5224	Glycerol tripolyoxypropylene ether
5.3.5	5225	Glycerol tripolyoxypropylene ether
5.3.6	5226	Polytriol
5.3.7	5227	Polytriol
5.3.8	5228	Glycerol tripolyoxypropylene ether
5.4.	Glycol ethers	
5.4.1	5229	Ethylene glycol mono-n-hexyl ether
5.4.2	5230	Ethylene glycol monophenyl ether
5.4.3	5231	Ethylene glycol dimethyl ether
5.4.4	5232	Ethylene glycol di-n-butyl ether
5.4.5	5233	Diethylene glycol monomethyl ether
5.4.6	5234	Diethylene glycol monoethyl ether
5.4.7	5235	Glycerol trihydroxyethyl ether
5.4.8	5236	Polymethylene glycol momethyl ether
5.4.9	5237	Polyglycol monomethyl ether
5.4.10	5238	Polyglycol monobutyl ether
5.4.11	5239	Polyglycol ester
5.4.12	5240	Modified polyglycol ether
5.4.13	5241	Ethylenediaminetetrapolyoxypropylene polyethylene glycol
5.4.14	5242	Ethylenediaminetetrapolyoxypropylene polyethylene glycol
5.4.15	5243	Ethylenediaminetetrapolyoxypropylene polyethylene glycol
5.5.	Other ethers	
5.5.1	5244	Ether thioether
5.5.2	5245	Dibutoxyethoxyethyl formal
5.5.3	5246	Diphenoxyethyl formal
5.5.4	5247	Dichlorophenyl isodecyl ether
5.5.5	5248	Dibenzyl ether
5.5.6	5249	Bis[p-(1,1,3,3-tetramethylbutyl)phenyl] ether
5.5.7	5250	Tetrachlorodibutoxybenzene
5.5.8	5251	Aromatic polyethers

TLC data: See table 2.12   GC data: See table 2.13

Trade name	TLC data (silica gel)						GC data P 2000
	S 14	S 15	S 17	S 1	S 2	S 4	130 °
Diglykol		25 ... 40					4,18
Triglykol		13 ... 36					17,8
Diol 4 P		21 ... 32					
Polyglykol 300		11 ... 35					
Polyglykol 600		9 ... 46	17 ... 58				
Polyglykol 1500		6 ... 32	0 ... 29				
Polyglykol 4000		4 ... 26	0 ... 9				
Polyglykol 20 000		0 ... 29	0 ... 8				
Pluracol P 410		54 ... 73					
Pluracol P 1310		63 ... 82					
Polyglykol P 4000	57 ... 86	78 ... 98					
Pluronic L 44		28 ... 65					
Pluronic L 62		34 ... 78					
Pluronic L 61		43 ... 84					
Diol 14 B	13	85					3,72
		21	66				
Pluracol TP 340		30 ... 45					
Pluracol TP 740	34 ... 50	61 ... 83					
Pluracol TP 1540	47 ... 72	66 ... 87					
Pluracol TP 4040		34 ... 61					
Niox Triol LF 70 N 17		48, 70, 88					
Triol G 700		64					
		50, 63					
	74	73					
		52					
		56					
Methyldiglykol		10 ... 43	24 ... 53				
Äthyldiglykol		45 ... 62, 75					
Weichmacher 9		19, 34, 54, 74					
Methylpolyglykol							
Äthylpolyglykol							
Butylpolyglykol		18, 54, 77					
Nopco 1225-L		14, 34 ... 57, 80					
Antistat. Weichmacher KA		0 ... 18	0 ....19, 28, 59				
Tetronic 701	1 ... 34	30 ... 81					
Tetronic 901	2 ... 37	37 ... 87					
Tetronic 904		9 ... 65					
Plastikator 85	45 ... 90	73 ... 93				85	
Reomol BCF							
Desavin							
Mollan DCD					27,35		
Plastoflex DBE							
Plastiflex 1099							
Jäganol CB					46,60		
Plastikator FH							

Epoxidized alkyl esters of fatty acids can be separated on silica gel G with benzene + methylene chloride (2 + 1) [20]. A deactivated silica gel G layer obtained by storage for 3 days in a desiccator at a relative humidity of 92 % (over CaCl₂ solution, sp. gr. 1.08) is suitable for the epoxidized fatty oils (triglycerides). With methanol saturated with water as the solvent, groups of spots with R_f values of 0—80 are obtained [20].

The spots can be detected by examination in UV light (layers with a fluorescence indicator) or exposure to iodine vapor. By treatment with antimony pentachloride (Table 2.11, No. 21) yellow-brown, brown, and brown-black spots being formed with monomeric and polymeric plasticizers. Spraying with alcoholic Rhodamine B solution (Table 2.11, No. 25), possibly with examination in UV light, is of universal application [258].

Phthalates and adipates can be recognized by the formation of yellow and yellow-red spots on spraying with resorcinol and sulfuric acid (Table 2.11, No. 24). Other aliphatic dicarboxylic esters do not give this reaction, nor do polyesters of adipic acid. Spraying with ammonium molybdate/hydrazine (Table 2.11, No. 26) can be used for the detection of esters of phosphorus acids, which give white and yellow-brown spots.

Polyethylene glycols having molecular weights in the range 200—6000 can be separated on silica gel G with chloroform/methanol/water (6 + 50 + 24) [48, 265]. Good results have also been obtained with a 1 : 99 mixture of pyridine and water [248a]. For polyethylene glycol stearates, a two-dimensional separation with n-butanol/ethanol/ammonia solution (25%) (70 + 15 + 25) in the first direction and chloroform/methanol/water (30 + 50 + 24) in the second direction is recommended. BÜRGER [247] has used thin layer chromatography for the determination of the molecular weight distribution and the degree of oxyethylation of polyethylene oxide compounds and polyethylene glycols.

Methyl ethyl ketone saturated with water is used as the solvent for oxyethylated fatty acids, fatty alcohols, and alkylphenols. Compounds with low degrees of oxyethylation have highest R_f values, while polyglycols remain at the starting spot.

Separate spots are obtained for substances with 1—10 and in some cases up to 15 ethylene oxide units. Fatty acid, fatty alcohol, and alkylphenol derivatives having the same degree of oxyethylation have the same R_f value.

Polyglycols can be separated by the same method if they are first converted into esters by reaction with 3,5-dinitrobenzoyl chloride [248].

For oxyethylated fatty amines, methyl ethyl ketone is shaken with 2.5 % aqueous ammonia solution and then separated from the aqueous phase for use as the solvent.

DRAGENDORFF reagent (Table 2.11, No. 2) can be used as a spray reagent for polyglycols and polyglycol derivatives.

The greater separation efficiency of HPLC compared with TLC is an advantage in the analysis of plasticisers, especially for higher homologous esters [252, 254, 255]. Fig. 1.7 shows the curve for the separation of phthalates.

GROSS and STRAUSS [254] have examined the separation possibilities of aromatic and aliphatic dicarboxylic acid esters as well as phosphoric acid esters, the best results being obtained with reverse phases (silica gel whose surface had been modified with octadecyl

Table 2.9: Plasticizers; 6.1. Phosphates, 6.2. Thiophosphates, 6.3. Phosphites, Phosphonates, 7.1. Sulfonamides, 7.2. Sulfonates

Dec. no.	IR sp. no.	Composition
6.1.		**Phosphates**
6.1.1	5252	Trialkyl phosphate
6.1.2	5253	Triethyl phosphate
6.1.3	5254	Tributyl phosphate
6.1.4	5255	Triisobutyl phosphate
6.1.5	5256	Tri-2-ethylhexyl phosphate
6.1.6	5257	Tributoxyethyl phosphate
6.1.7	5258	Chloroalkyl aryl phosphate
6.1.8	5259	Tri-2-chloroethyl phosphate
6.1.9	5260	Triphenyl phosphate
6.1.10	5261	Octyl diphenyl phosphate
6.1.11	5262	Cresyl diphenyl phosphate
6.1.12	5263	Xylyl diphenyl phosphate
6.1.13	5264	Diphenyl mono-o-biphenyl phosphate
6.1.14	5265	Tricresyl phosphate
6.1.15	5266	Tricresyl phosphate
6.1.16	5267	Trixylyl phosphate
6.1.17	5268	Trixylyl phosphate
6.2.		**Thiophosphates**
6.2.1	5269	Triethyl thiophosphate
6.2.2	5270	Tributyl thiophosphate
6.2.3	5271	Triisooctyl thiophosphate
6.3.		**Phosphites, phosphonates**
6.3.1	5272	Tri-(2-chloroethyl) phosphite
6.3.2	5273	Diethyl ethylphosphonate
6.3.3	5274	Dibutyl butylphosphonate
6.3.4	5275	Di-(2-ethylhexyl) 2-ethylhexylphosphonate
7.1.		**Sulfonamides**
7.1.1	5276	N-Methylbenzenesulfonamide
7.1.2	5277	N-Butylbenzenesulfonamide
7.1.3	5278	Mixture of o- and p-toluenesulfonamides
7.1.4	5279	N-Ethyl-p-toluenesulfonamide
7.1.5	5280	Mixture of o- and p-N-ethyltoluenesulfonamides
7.1.6	5281	N-Cyclohexyl-p-toluenesulfonamide
7.1.7	5282	Sulfonamide plasticizer
7.2.		**Sulfonates**
7.2.1	5283	Phenol and cresol pentadecanesulfonates

Trade name	TLC data (silica gel)						GC data							
	S 1	S 2	S 3	S 4	S 8	S 16	Dec. no.	S-30 220°	S-30 250°	SE 52 200°	SE 52 250°	PNGS 220°	U III 230°	LAC 230°
Vircol 189							6.1.1							
						94	6.1.2	1108		1115		1375		
			13		15	93	6.1.3	1663		1654		1873	0,13	0,12
							6.1.4			1513				
			32		51		6.1.5		0,820		2465		1,00*	1,00*
KP 140							6.1.6				2435			
Celluflex FR-2							6.1.7				2398			
Cetamoll Q			9		0		6.1.8	1799		1780	1820		1,00	1,82
Disflamoll TP			41		45	61	6.1.9		0,680	2410	2480		5,46	10,00
Santicizer 141			38				6.1.10				2470			
Disflamoll DBK			54		48		6.1.11		0,660		2480		several	
											2570		peaks	
Disflamoll XDP			62		43		6.1.12				2465			
					51						2540			
					60						2570			
											2610			
											2690			
											2720			
Plasticizer 5			59		58		6.1.13				3020			
Celluflex 179 A							6.1.14		>3		2910			
							6.1.15		>3		2750			
TXP							6.1.16				2920			
											2960			
							6.1.17				2960			
											3000			
		11		76		80	6.2.1							
	6	13		76			6.2.2							
	8	20		86			6.2.3							
		35												
							6.3.1							
							6.3.2							
							6.3.3							
							6.3.4							
Dellatol MMA				23			7.1.1							
Plastomoll BMB		38		47			7.1.2							
Santicizer 9				8			7.1.3		>3					
Santicizer 3				32			7.1.4							
Santicizer 8				9			7.1.5							
				35										
				66										
Santicizer 1-H				49			7.1.6							
Weichmacher TS				3			7.1.7							
				57										
				69										
Mesamoll							7.2.1							

TLC data: See table 2.12   GC data: See table 2.13

Table 2.6: Plasticizers; 3.3. Laurates, myristates, palmitates, 3.4. Oleates, 3.5. Stearates, 3.6. Ricinoleates, 3.7. Other esters

Dec. no.	IR sp. no.	Composition	Trade name	TLC data S 3	GC data (SE-30) 200°	250°
3.3.		**Laurates, myristates, palmitates**				
3.3.1	5145	1,2-Propylene glycol monolaurate	Nopco 1325 L			
3.3.2	5146	Glycerol monolaurate	Nopco 2225 L			
3.3.3	5147	Diethylene glycol monolaurate	Nopalcol 1-L			
3.3.4	5148	Isopropyl myristate				
3.3.5	5149	Methyl palmitate				
3.3.6	5150	Ethyl palmitate				
3.3.7	5151	Isopropyl palmitate				
3.3.8	5152	n-Butyl palmitate				
3.3.9	5153	Isobutyl palmitate				
3.3.10	5154	Tetrahydrofurfuryl palmitate				
3.4.		**Oleates**				
3.4.1	5155	Methyl oleate	Nopco 2060			
3.4.2	5156	Ethyl oleate				
3.4.3	5157	n-Propyl oleate				
3.4.4	5158	Isopropyl oleate				
3.4.5	5159	n-Butyl oleate	Butyloleat 554			
3.4.6	5160	Isobutyl oleate				
3.4.7	5161	2-Ethylhexyl oleate				
3.4.8	5162	Methoxyethyl oleate	Kapsol			
3.4.9	5163	Butoxyethyl oleate				
3.4.10	5164	1,2-Propylene glycol monooleate				
3.4.11	5165	Glycerol monooleate				
3.4.12	5166	Diethylene glycol monooleate				
3.4.13	5167	Tetrahydrofurfuryloleate	Plastolein 9250			
3.4.14	5168	Pentaerythritol esters of fatty acids	Hercoflex 600			
3.5.		**Stearates**				
3.5.1	5169	Methyl stearate				
3.5.2	5170	Ethyl stearate				
3.5.3	5171	n-Butyl stearate			0,265	0,354
3.5.4	5172	n-Hexyl stearate				
3.5.5	5173	Cyclohexyl stearate				
3.5.6	5174	2-Ethylhexyl stearate				
3.5.7	5175	Methoxyethyl stearate				
3.5.8	5176	Butoxyethyl stearate	KP 23			
3.5.9	5177	Ethylene glycol distearate				
3.5.10	5178	1,2-Propylene glycol monostearate				
3.5.11	5179	Glycerol monostearate	Glyceryl CPH 53-N			
3.5.12	5180	Diethylene glycol distearate	Nopalcol 1-S			
3.5.13	5181	Polyethylene glycol(400) monostearate				
3.5.14	5182	Polyethylene glycol(400) distearate				
3.5.15	5183	Butyl acetoxystearate	Paricin 6			
3.5.16	5184	Glycerol triacetoxystearate	Paricin 8			
3.6.		**Ricinoleates**				
3.6.1	5185	Methyl ricinoleate	Nopco 1060 C			
3.6.2	5186	Butyl ricinoleate	Flexricin P-3			
3.6.3	5187	Ethylene glycol monoricinoleate	Flexricin 15			
3.6.4	5188	1,2-Propylene glycol monoricinoleate	Flexricin 9			
3.6.5	5189	Glycerol monoricinoleate	Flexricin 13			
3.6.6	5190	Methoxyethyl ricinoleate				
3.6.7	5191	Methyl acetylricinoleate	Flexricin P 4	33		
3.6.8	5192	Butyl acetylricinoleate	Flexricin P 6	40		1,25
3.6.9	5193	Methoxyethyl acetylricinoleate	KP 120			
3.6.10	5194	Glycerol triacetylricinoleate	Flexricin P-8			
3.7.		**Other esters**				
3.7.1	5195	Ethyl lactate	Lactonal			
3.7.2	5196	Dibutyl thiodibutyrate				
3.7.3	5197	Dichlorobutanediol bisbutylcarbonate	Plastomoll WH			

TLC data: See table 2.12   GC data: See table 2.13

Table 2.10: Plasticizers; 8.1. Paraffinic and naphthenic oils, 8.2. Aromatic oils, 8.3. Chlorinated paraffins, 8.4. Chlorinated aromatic hydrocarbons, 9. Plasticizers containing nitrogen

Dec. No.	IR sp. No.	Composition	Trade name	TLC data (silica gel)			
				S 1	S 2	S 4	S 15
8.1. Paraffinic and naphthenic oils							
8.1.1	5284	Paraffin oil	Weißöl 505				
8.1.2	5285	Paraffinic mineral oil	Esso Tellura 38				
8.1.3	5286	Naphthenic mineral oil	Ingraplast XU				
8.1.4	5287	Naphthenic mineral oil	Ingraplast L				
8.1.5	5288	Naphthenic mineral oil	Ingraplast S				
8.1.6	5289	Naphthenic mineral oil	Sundex 790				
8.1.7	5290	Naphthenic mineral oil	Naftolen ZD	21, 67			
8.1.8	5291	Naphthenic mineral oil	Esso NUSO 90N				
8.2. Aromatic oils							
8.2.1	5292	Aromatic mineral oil	Kettlitz Weichmacher				
8.2.2	5293	Aromatic mineral oil	Kettlitz NS				
8.2.3	5294	Aromatic mineral oil	Kettlitz PM				
8.2.4	5295	Polyaromat. hydrocarbon oil	Panaflex BN 1	21, 36			
8.2.5	5296	Hydrogenated terphenyl	HB 40	12, 18, 26			
8.2.6	5297	Benzylnaphthalene	Vulkazol B	5, 11, 19			
8.2.7	5298	Poly-α-methylstyrene	Amoco AmS 10	20, 27			
8.3. Chloroparaffins							
8.3.1	5299	Chlorinated paraffinic hydrocarbons	Tetrachloralkan				
8.3.2	5300	Chlorinated paraffinic hydrocarbons	Chlorowax 40	0—15	9—57	83	
8.3.3	5301	Chlorinated paraffinic hydrocarbons	Arubren CP	20	41—60	84	
8.4. Chlorinated aromatic hydrocarbons							
8.4.1	5302	Chlorinated diphenyl	Clophen A 30	35, 41			
8.4.2	5303	Chlorinated diphenyl	Clophen A 40				
8.4.3	5304	Chlorinated diphenyl	Clophen A 50				
8.4.4	5305	Chlorinated diphenyl	Clophen A 60				
8.4.5	5306	Chlorinated aromatic hydrocarbon	Clophen T 64				
8.4.6	5307	Chlorinated diphenyl	Aroclor 1221				
9. Plasticizers containing nitrogen							
9.1	5308	Fatty acid nitrile	Aneel OD		4—13	77	
9.2	5309	Diester amide	Flexol 8 N 8				
9.3	5310	N,N,N',N'-Tetrakis-(2-hydroxypropyl) ethylene diamine	Quadrol				0—13
9.4	5311	N,N'-Diethyl-N,N'-diphenylurea	Mollit I		36		
9.5	5312	Dimethylthianthrene	Sintol T	22			

TLC data: See table 2.12

groups). Their results, supplemented by some figures obtained by STOVEKEN [255] are summarised in table 2.12.

HPLC and TLC make it possible to partly separate the isomers in polychlorinated biphenyls and naphthalenes. The best separation results are achieved with TLC with reverse phases (kieselguhr impregnated with paraffin oil, solvent acetonitrile/methanol/acetone/water in a proportion of 20:20:9:1). Silica gel and n-hexane are mostly used for HPLC. BRINKMAN and coworkers [267 a–d] have given numerous analytical data.

Intensive studies were carried out by SCHÖLLNER et al. [263, 264] on the gel and thin layer chromatography of linear and branched polyester oligomers. In TLC separation of oligomers of the type M-(S-G)$_x$-S-M [esterification products of a monohydric alcohol M (octadecyl alcohol), a dicarboxylic acid S (adipic acid), and a glycol G (ethylene glycol)] on silica gel G with ether/formic acid (200 + 3)], the members with $_x$ = 0—7 were separated. This was also possible by gel chromatography. Reference is made in the articles mentioned to the influence of other alcohols and acids and the significance of functional end groups (—COOH and —OH).

Suggestions for gel chromatographic separations of plasticizers are also to be found in other articles [268—270].

Examples of gel-chromatographic investigations on plasticizers are shown in Figures 2.2 and 2.3. The separating columns used for these investigations were not optimized, and considerably better separations are possible if required.

2.4 Gas-Chromatographic Analysis of Plasticizers

Good thermal stability coupled with adequate vapor pressures in the temperature range between 200—300 °C allows the direct gas-chromatographic analysis of the most important monomeric plasticizers on heat-resistant stationary phases such as silicone oils, silicone rubber, and various polyesters.

ZULAICA and GUIOCHON [272] have investigated the separation of the principal C$_1$—C$_8$ esters of aliphatic dicarboxylic acids, of phthalic acid, and of phosphoric acid on silicone grease SE 30 and on neopentyl glycol polysebacate, and determined the retention indices and the group increments. The results

Table 2.11: Spray reagents for the thin layer chromatography of plastics additives

No.	Name (Application)	Composition	Notes on application
1	Iodine/sulfuric acid (polyglycol derivatives)	1:1 mixture of 0.1 N iodine solution and 10 % sulfuric acid	
2	Dragendorff reagent (polyglycol derivatives)	a: 1.7 g of basic bismuth nitrate is dissolved in 20 ml of acetic acid. After addition of 80 ml of water, a solution of 40 g of potassium iodide in 100 ml of water, and 200 ml of glacial acetic acid, the solution is diluted to 1000 ml with b: Barium chloride solution (20 % in water).	Mix a and b 2:1 before spraying
3	Cobalt(II) thiocyanate (amines)	3 g ammonium thiocyanate and 1 g of cobalt(II) chloride are dissolved in 20 ml of water.	The colors fade after about 2 h, but can be restored by spraying with water or by introduction of the plate into an atmosphere saturated with water vapor.
4	2,6-Dibromoquinonechlorimide (Gibbs reagent for phenols)	Freshly prepared 2,6-dibromoquinon-echlorimide solution (0.4 % in methanol).	Treatment after spraying: Spray with sodium carbonate solution (10 % in water) or place in a chamber containing ammonia solution (25 %)
5	2,6-Dichloroquinonechlorimide (phenols, amines)	1 % solution of 2,6-dichloroquinonechlor-imide in isopropanol or 0.1 % solution in methanol.	
6	α,α'-Dipyridyl/iron(III) chloride (phenols)	a: Iron(III) chloride solution, (0.5 % in ethanol (store in the dark). b: α,α'-Dipyridyl solution, (0.5 % in ethanol)	Mix a and b 1:1 before spraying
7	Iron(III) chloride (phenols)	Approx. 3 % iron(III) chloride in 0.5 N hydrochloric acid	
8	Silver nitrate (phenols)	1 ml of silver nitrate solution (saturated aqueous) is added with stirring to 20 ml of acetone, and water is then added dropwise until the silver nitrate that precipitates just redissolves.	
9	$CuSO_4 \cdot 5 H_2O$	1 % aqueous copper sulfate solution	
10	$Bi(NO_3)_3 \cdot 5 H_2O$	5 % bismuth nitrate solution in 0.5 N nitric acid.	
11	Ninhydrin	5 % ninhydrin solution in ethanol (10 % acetic acid and 0.5 % cadmium acetate)	
12	Phosphomolybdic acid (phenols)	Phosphomolybdic acid, 3.5 %	
13	Chromotropic acid (compounds that release formaldehyde)	a: 1,8-Dihydroxynaphthalene-3,6-disul-fonic acid, sodium salt b: 5 volumes of sulfuric acid (conc.) are added to 3 volumes of water and cooled to room temperature.	Mix a and b 1:5 before spraying. Subsequent tratment: 30 min at 105 °C
14	Sodium hypochlorite	5 % solution of sodium hypochlorite in water	

Table 2.11 (continued)

No.	Name (Application)	Composition	Notes on application
15	Benzoyl peroxide	4 % solution of benzoyl peroxide in benzene.	
16	Sodium nitroprusside (SH- and -S-S- compounds)	a: 1.5 g of sodium nitroprusside is dissolved in 5 ml of 2 N hydrochloric acid. After the addition of 95 ml of methanol and 10 ml of ammonia solution (25 %) the solution is filtered.	SH compounds visible as red spots.
		b: A solution of 2 g of sodium cyanide in 5 ml of water is made up to 100 ml with methanol.	On subsequent spraying with b, compounds with S-S bridges appear as red spots on a yellow ground. Take precautions during spraying with sodium cyanide. Very toxic.
17	Sodium nitroprusside (-S-S- bridges)	a: 5 g of sodium cyanide and 5 g of sodium carbonate are dissolved in aqueous ethanol (25 %) in a 100 ml graduated flask and made up to the mark.	Spray with a, allow to dry in air, and then spray with b. Take precautions during spraying with sodium cyanide. Very toxic.
		b: 2 g of sodium nitroprusside are dissolved in 100 ml of ethanol (75 %).	
18	8-Hydroxyquinoline/hypo-bromite (guanidine derivatives)	a: 8-Hydroxyquinoline solution (0.1 % in acetone)	Spray with a, dry, then spray with b.
		b: 0.2 ml of bromine is dissolved in 100 ml of 0.5 N sodium hydroxide solution.	
19	Iodine azide (sulfides)	A solution of 3 g of sodium azide in 100 ml of 0.1 N iodine solution is freshly prepared. Iodine azide is explosive in the dry state.	
20	Iodine azide/starch (sulfides)	a: A solution of 1 g of sodium azide in 100 ml of 0.005 N iodine solution is freshly prepared.	Spray with a, then with b.
		b: Starch solution (1 % in water).	
21	Antimony pentachloride (universal)	2 volumes of antimony(V) chloride are mixed with 8 volumes of carbon tetrachloride or chloroform. Prepare freshly.	Subsequent treatment: Heat at 120 °C until the spots appear.
22	Iodine vapor (universal)	Solid iodine.	Allow iodine vapor to act on the plate in a closed vessel. Then air in a fume cupboard.
23	Nitrazol CF extra (amines, phenols)	0.5 % solution of 4-nitrobenzene-diazonium fluoroborate in 5 % acetic acid.	
24	Resorcine/sulfuric acid	a: 10 g resorcinol and 0.5 g of ZnCl$_2$ in 50 ml of ethanol.	Spray with a, heat for 10 min at 100 °C, then spray with b and heat for 20 min at 120 °C.
		b: 4 N sulfuric acid.	
25	Rhodamine B	0.5 % Rhodamine B in ethanol.	Observation in UV light
26	Molybdate/hydrazine	a: 3 g of ammonium molybdate, 20 ml of 40 % perchloric acid, and 5 ml of conc. hydrochloric acid in 200 ml of water.	Spray with a, heat for 10 min at 100 °C, then spray with b and keep at 110 °C for 20 min (phosphates give light spots on a blue ground).
		b: 5 g of hydrazine sulfate in 100 ml of water.	

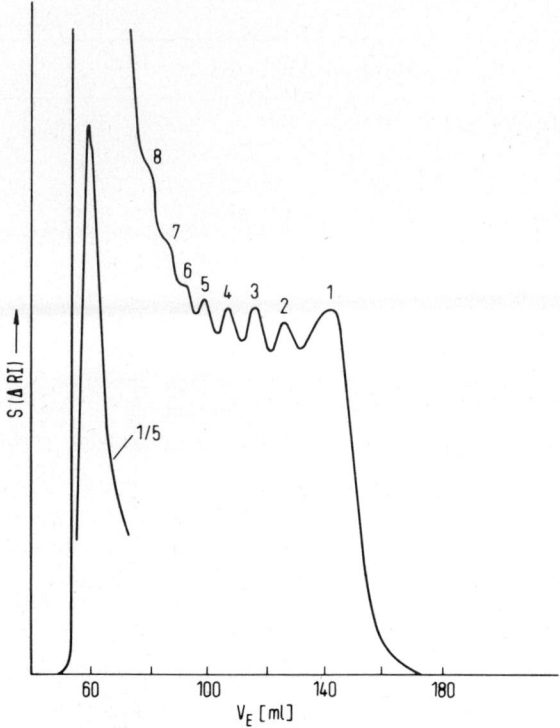

Fig. 2.2: Fractionation of a polymeric plasticizer
(1W 615, polypropylene glycol adipate) by gel chromatography
Column: 2.0 x 55 xm,   eluent: dimethylformamide
Polyvinyl acetate gel Merckogel OR 500
Detector: flow refractometer, sample size: 20 mg
The numbers at the peaks show the degree of polymerization n corresponding to the formula

$$HO—(CH_2)_2—[OOC—(CH_2)_4—COO(CH_2)_3O]_nH$$

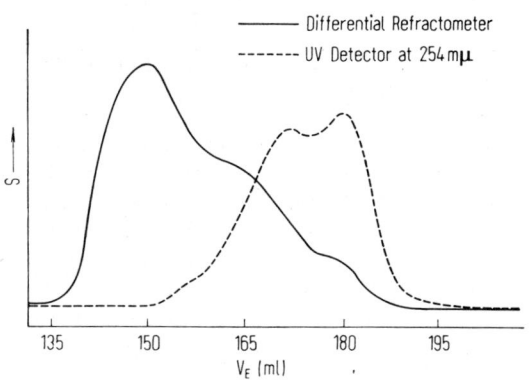

Fig. 2.3: Fractionation of mineral oil by gel chromatography [102]
Column: 0.7 x 630 cm,   eluent: THF, 1 ml/min
Poragel A-1, 60 Å,   sample size: 20 μl

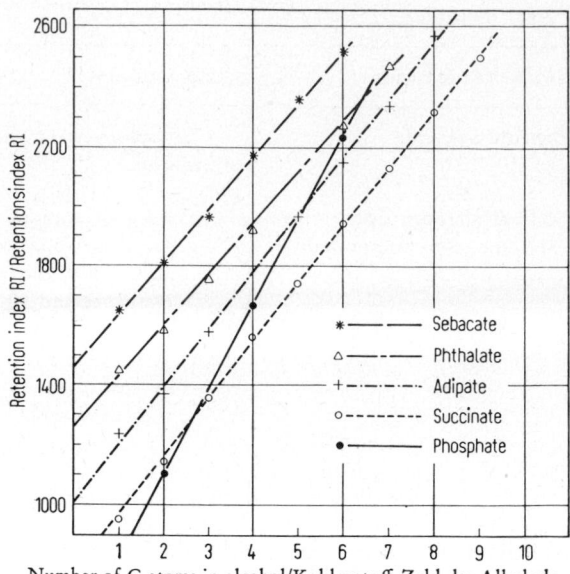

Fig. 2.4: Retention indices of the n-alkyl esters of dicarboxylic acids and of phosphoric acid on an apolar column (silicone grease SE 30) at 150—220 °C after *Zulaica* and *Guiochon* [272]

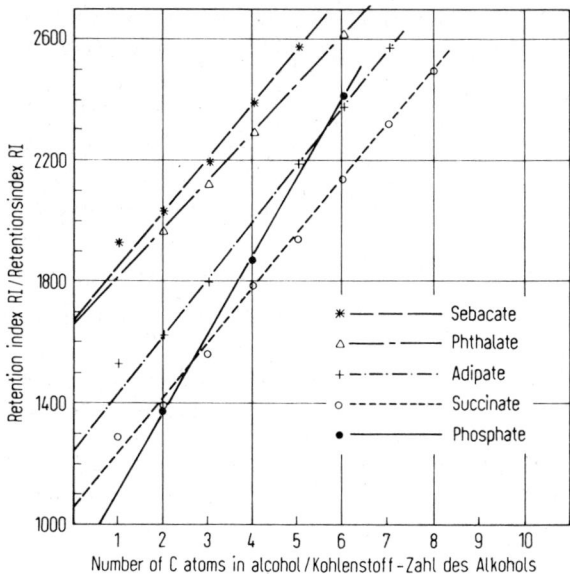

Fig. 2.5: Retention indices of the n-alkyl esters of dicarboxylic acids acids and of phosphoric acid on a polar column (neopentyl glycol polysebacate) at 150—220 °C after *Zulaica* and *Guiochon* [272]

are presented in the form of graphs in Figures 2.4 and 2.5. The values found for the increments are:

Stat. phase	Group			
	—COO—	—CH$_2$—	—C$_6$H$_5$	OPO$_3$
SE 30	290	100	655	560
Polyester	400	100	790	770

When these values were used to calculate the retention index from the formula of a plasticizer, the deviations from the experimental values were mostly less than 1 % for the esters of dicarboxyl acids and phosphoric acid with n-alcohols from propyl alcohol upward.

Numerous data for separations on various stationary phases, mainly polyesters, have been collected by WANDEL, TENGLER and OSTROMOW [240] and published together with chromatograms and detailed information on the experimental procedure. Separations of esters of dicarboxylic acids, phthalates, and phosphates on silicone rubber SE 30 are described by various authors [20, 273—275]. C$_2$—C$_8$ esters of fatty acids, epoxidized alkyl esters of fatty acids, mixtures of higher alkylaromatic and arylaromatic compounds, and alkylsulfonates of phenol and cresols (Mesamoll) were also separated on SE 30 (temperature-programmed, 200—380 °C); typical chromatograms of such plasticizers, most of which are chemically non-uniform, have been published by VERES [20].

Table 2.12:
Solvents for the TLC of
plasticizers on silica gel

Short designation	Solvent	Mixture ratio (vol)	Ref.
S 1	Cyclohexane		–
S 2	Carbon tetrachloride		–
S 3	Methylene chloride		240, 243, 252, 254
S 4	Chloroform		–
S 5	Petroleum ether (40–60) + diisopropyl ether	90 + 10	240, 251, 253
S 6	Petroleum ether (40–60) + diisopropyl ether	80 + 20	240, 252, 253
S 7	Petroleum ether (40–60) + diisopropyl ether	70 + 30	240, 251, 252
S 8	Petroleum ether (40–60) + diisopropyl ether	50 + 50	240, 254
S 9	Petroleum ether (40–60) + diisopropyl ether	30 + 70	251
S 10	Hexane + dibutyl ether	20 + 80	242, 251
S 11	Isooctane + ethyl acetate	90 + 10	242
S 12	Isooctane + ethyl acetate	80 + 20	–
S 13	Benzene + ethyl acetate	95 + 5	242
S 14	Chloroform + methanol	95 + 5	–
S 15	Chloroform + methanol	90 + 10	–
S 16	Hexane + benzene + methanol	50 + 25 + 25	246
S 17	Acetone + methanol	10 + 90	–

(entries for which no references are given refer to our own work)

Retention data for plasticizers on various stationary phases are given in Tables 2.2—2.10; the experimental conditions are shown in Table 2.13.

In our GC investigations on plasticizers, particularly the esters of dicarboxylic acids with mixed higher alcohols, phosphoric acid esters of phenols, and epoxidized fatty acid esters, we found a 2 m packed separating column with 2.5 % silicone rubber SE 52 as the stationary phase to be effective, particularly with temperature-programmed operation (200—280 °C, heating rate 5 °C/min). Figure 2.6 shows some chromatograms of plasticizers that were obtained in this way. The chromatograms in Figure 2.7 were recorded isothermally at various temperatures. A comparison of the temperature-programmed and isothermal procedures is possible for Palatinol HSH (1.1.25), since both figures contain chromatograms of this compound (2.6a and 2.7a and b).

Depending on their preparation, commercial dicarboxylic esters of mixed alcohols, such as benzyl butyl phthalate (1.1.8) contain varying quantities of the diesters of each two alcohols, i. e. dibenzyl and dibutyl phthalates in the above examples, as well as the mixed ester. This cannot be seen in the IR spectrum, whereas different peaks are recorded in the gas chromatogram.

Much information has been published, in connection with ecological studies, on the gas chromatography of polychlorinated biphenyls (PCB) and other higher chlorinated compounds which are used as plasticizers. Some of the publications are listed in the bibliography [275 a–c]. GC data were determined on a whole range of isomers, these being tabulated in the papers mentioned.

2.5 Thin Layer and Gas Chromatography of Plasticizer Degradation Products

Ester plasticizers can be converted into the alkali metal salts of the acids and the free alcohols by hydrolysis, into the methyl esters of the carboxylic acids and the free alcohols by transesterification with methanol, and into the methyl esters and the acetates of the alcohols by reaction with methyl acetate. These reaction products can then be separated, identified, and quantitatively determined by thin layer or gas chromatography [240, 286].

The usual procedures are as follows.

Hydrolysis: About 50 to 300 mg of plasticizer are refluxed for 3 hours with 5—10 ml of ethanolic potassium hydroxide solution.

After cooling, part of the solution is shaken with cation exchange resin in the H form until the solution is neutral to remove the potassium ions. This solution then can be used for the thin layer chromatography of the monocarboxylic and dicarboxylic acids. TLC data for dicarboxylic acids are given in table 2.12b [77]. Mono and dicarboxylic acids can also determined separately and quantitatively by HPLC using an ion exchange column [282a].

If the hydrolysis is carried out at normal pressure, it is advisable to use a solution of potassium hydroxide in ethyl glycol because of the higher boiling point. After dilution with water, the alcohols are extracted with ether and analyzed by gas chromatography after concentration of the ether solution.

Table 2.12a: HPLC-data of plasticizers [254, 255], retention time in min.

	Silica gel			reversed phase				
	L 1	L 2	L 3	L 4	L 5	L 6	L 7	L 8
Phthalates								
Dimethyl phthalate	21,5	13,5			1,3			4,6
Diethyl phthalate	15	9,1			1,4			5,3
Di-n-butyl phthalate	7,6	4,2			2,0			9,2
Dicylohexyl phthalate	7,4	3,9			2,9			11,9
Di-n-octyl phthalate	4,5	2,8			9,2			20,8
Di-(2-ethylhexyl) phthalate	3,3	2,4			7,4			
Di-i-nonyl phthalate	4,0	2,6			9,5			
Di-i-decyl phthalate	3,4	2,3			15,0	6,5		
Di-i-tridecyl phthalate	2,85	2,0				15,0		
Butylbenzyl phthalate	10	5,4			2,0			
Diamyl phthalate								11,5
Diallyl phthalate								5,9
Adipates								
Dibutyl adipate	9,5		3,2		2,1			
Dihexyl adipate					3,9			
Di-(2-ethylhexyl) adipate	4,7		2,0		7,6			
Dioctyl adipate	4,6		1,9		7,7			
Dinonyl adipate	5,1		2,2		8,8			
Butylbenzyl adipate			4,0 (3,3/5,3/9,6)		2,0			
Dibenzyl adipate	16,1		5,2		2,0			
Sebacates								
Diethyl sebacate	10,4	3,5			2,1			
Dibutyl sebacate	5,9	2,3			3,6			
Phosphates								
Tri-(chlorethyl) phosphate					1,3			
Tri-(2-ethylhexyl) phosphate					13,1			
Di(phenyl)-2-ethylhexyl phosphate			9,1	6,3 (2,5)				
Triphenyl phosphate			8,9 (4,1)	2,5 (1,4)				
Cresyldiphenyl phosphate			8,0 (6,6/7,4/9,0)	3,1 (2,0/4,0/5,1)				
Tricresyl phosphate			6,6	5,1 (3,2/4,0)				
Other								
Acetyltributyl citrate	20,2	4,6			2,3			
C$_6$...C$_{10}$-trimellitate	4,4						5,9 (2,9/3,9/4,6/7,6/10,5)	
C$_8$...C$_{10}$-trimellitate	4,4/4,6/5,0/5,6/6,4/7,4						7,5 (5,9/10,2/13,9)	
Phenylalkyl sulfonate	1,3 (2,5/3,1) (< 1)						2,4 (1,7/< 1)	

Column: L 1–L 3: Nucleosil 50–5, 20 × 0,4 cm
L 4–L 7: Nucleosil 10–C 18, 25 × 0,4 cm
L 8: 2 X ODS–SIL–X 1, 25 × 0,45 cm [255]

Flow rate: L 1, L 2, L 4–L 8: 2 ml/min L 3: 1,6 ml/min

Eluent:
L 1: Heptane + diisopropyl ether 90 + 10   L 4: Methanol + water + butanol 82 + 18 + 1
L 2: Heptane + diisopropyl ether 80 + 20   L 5: Methanol + water + butanol 90 + 10 + 1
L 3: Heptane + diisopropyl ether 75 + 25   L 6: Methanol + water + butanol 95 + 5 + 1
L 8: Water + acetonitrile 60 + 40, in 80 min. changed to L 7: Methanol 0 + 100 [255]

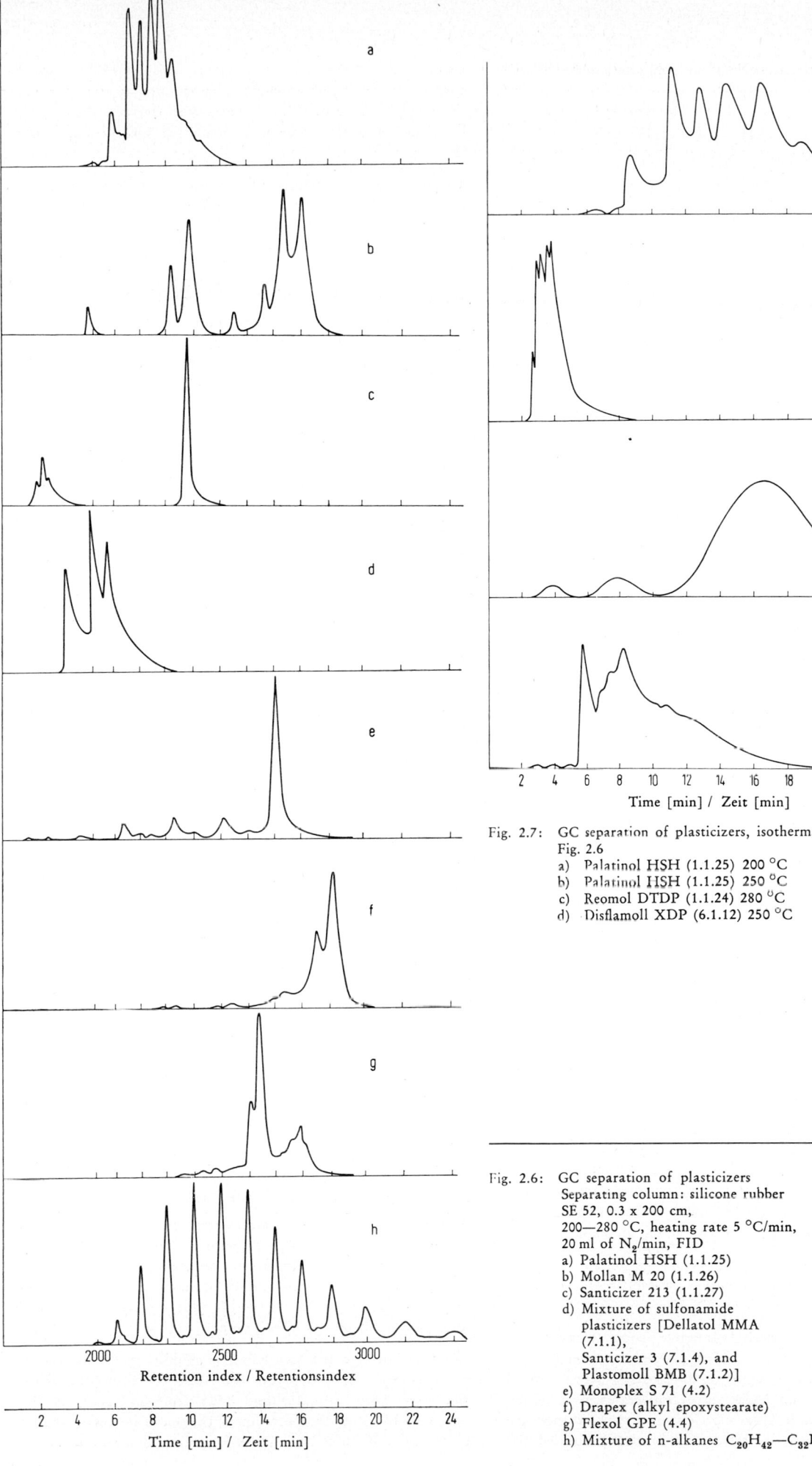

Retention index / Retentionsindex

Time [min] / Zeit [min]

Time [min] / Zeit [min]

Fig. 2.7: GC separation of plasticizers, isothermal, otherwise as for Fig. 2.6
a) Palatinol HSH (1.1.25) 200 °C
b) Palatinol HSH (1.1.25) 250 °C
c) Reomol DTDP (1.1.24) 280 °C
d) Disflamoll XDP (6.1.12) 250 °C

Fig. 2.6: GC separation of plasticizers
Separating column: silicone rubber
SE 52, 0.3 x 200 cm,
200—280 °C, heating rate 5 °C/min,
20 ml of N_2/min, FID
a) Palatinol HSH (1.1.25)
b) Mollan M 20 (1.1.26)
c) Santicizer 213 (1.1.27)
d) Mixture of sulfonamide plasticizers [Dellatol MMA (7.1.1),
Santicizer 3 (7.1.4), and Plastomoll BMB (7.1.2)]
e) Monoplex S 71 (4.2)
f) Drapex (alkyl epoxystearate)
g) Flexol GPE (4.4)
h) Mixture of n-alkanes $C_{20}H_{42}$—$C_{32}H_{66}$

Table 2.12b: TLC of dicarboxylic acids from plasticizers (Knappe)

Acid	I	II	III	IV	V	VI
			hR$_F$-values			
Oxalic acid	4	9	14	10	17	11
Malonic acid	16	23	21	27	52	39
Citric acid	3	4	4	17	10	
Succinic acid	44	31	28	40	67	56
Tartaric acid	4	4		4	28	15
Adipic acid	49	51	43	57	75	73
Pimelic acid	54	61	55	72	76	79
Suberic acid	62	82	67	84	79	83
Acelaic acid	67	91	82	95	80	86
Sebacic acid	72	96	92	98	82	88
Phthalic acid	51	30	24	39	41	36
Isophthalic acid	75	64	57	71	46	59
Pyromellitic acid	0	2	6	2	0	0
Trimellitic acid	41	13	12	14	9	13

Layers
IV, V, VI   Polyamide Woelm DC
Mobile phase IV: Diisopropyl ether + petrol ether + CCl$_4$ + HCOOH + H$_2$O (50 + 20 + 20 + 8 + 1)
Mobile phase V: Acetonitrile + ethyl acetate + HCOOH (90 + 10 + 10)
Mobile phase VI: Butyl formate + ethyl acetate + HCOOH (90 + 10 + 10)

The alcohols can be analyzed by thin layer chromatography in the form of the nitrobenzoates.

Transesterification with Methanol: About 50 to 300 mg of plasticizer are placed in a small ampule (volume about 5 ml), and 1—2 ml of dry methanol containing about 3 wt. % of toluenesulfonic acid as catalyst is added. The ampule is sealed and heated in a protective metal tube for about 3 h at 130 °C.

After cooling with dry ice, the ampule is opened. The solution of alcohols and methyl esters of the acids can be used directly for GC.

Similar methods can be used for transesterification with methanol/BF$_3$.

Aryl esters of phosphorus acids can also be hydrolyzed with methanol/p-toluenesulfonic acid in a pressure tube in preparation for GC, but since the esters of phosphorus acids are difficult to hydrolyze, higher temperatures are required (180 °C, about 3 h). If the hydrolysis is carried out with alkali, it is advisable to remove the alkali metal salts before the GC separation.

Information on the separation of phenols can be obtained from Table 2.17.

Interesterification with Methyl Acetate: About 20 to 100 mg of plasticizer are placed in a pressure-resistant ampule (volume about 5 ml), 1.5 to 2 ml of dry methyl acetate (dried and stored over 4 Å molecular sieve) and about 30 to 50 mg of 25 % sodium methoxide solution in dry methanol are added, and the ampule is sealed. The ampule is heated for

1 h at 175 °C in a protective metal tube (possibly a small autoclave); during this process the pressure in the tube can rise to about 25 atm. After cooling with dry ice, the ampule is opened and the solution is used for GC directly after filtration.

The thin layer chromatography of ester degradation products has been dealt with and reviewed very systematically by KNAPPE et al. [60].

Gas chromatography is more elegant than thin layer chromatography for the investigation of the degradation products, since the determination of alcohols and acids is possible in one temperature-programmed analysis. The "interesterification" method described by RAWLINSON and DEELEY [286] is particularly elegant, though the diols and triols occur together as monoacetates and diacetates. Retention data are given in Table 2.14 for methyl esters and acetates of the acids and alcohols commonly found in esters and polyesters [286]. Columns with ethylene glycol polysuccinate as the stationary phase are suitable for the complete separation of methyl esters of fatty acids and of dicarboxylic acids in the same mixture. Saturated and unsaturated fatty acids having the same number of C atoms are separated on this phase [291].

ASHES and HAKEN [285a] have tabulated the GC data for esters of C$_1$ to C$_6$ monocarboxylic acids with C$_1$ to C$_6$ mono-alcohols for 15 stationary phases, and discussed structure parameters.

Some further data on the GC of methyl esters are listed in Table 2.15.

Information on the separation of alcohols is given in Table 2.16. This table also contains the data reported by ESPOSITO and SWANN [285], who converted the alcohols obtained from polyesters on aminolysis with n-butylamine into acetates by reaction with acetic anhydride and separated them by gas chromatography.

Finally, reference should be made to the identification of polyglycol units after degradation with hydrobromic acid in glacial acetic acid. The molar ratio of ethylene glycol and propylene glycol can be determined by gas chromatography of the bromides formed [287].

SULLY et al. [292] described a GC method for the determination of impurities that are detectable in plasticizers by their odor.

FISCHER et al. [290] described experiments on the identification of plasticizers in PVC and elastomers by pyrolysis gas chromatography. Though this is possible in principle, the direct GC separation of the plasticizers or of their chemical degradation products is probably preferable in general to pyrolysis GC, in which the degradation depends on numerous experimental conditions.

2.6 IR Spectroscopy of Plasticizers

The identification of plasticizers was one of the first applications of IR spectroscopy to additives in plastics, and has been the subject of numerous reviews [13, 16, 240, 293]. A collection of spectra of about 900 commercial plasticizers (a considerable number of which, however, are chemically identical) has been compiled [294].

Examination of a few key bands provides a rapid indication of the plasticizer group. For all esters of carboxylic acids, the ester band $\nu_{C=O}$ around 1725 cm^{-1} (5.8 μm) is the strongest band in the spectrum. If this band is absent, strong bands around 1000 cm^{-1} (10 μm) point to esters of phos-

Table 2.13: Separating conditions for the GC of plasticizers

GC conditions (short designation)		Stationary phase	Column * material / length m diameter mm	Temp. °C	Carrier gas/flow rate ml/min	Reference substance	Ref.
SE-30	220	Silicone rubber GE SE 30 (0.5 % on glass beads)	Cu/2(3)/4	220		Alkanes	272
	200	Silicone rubber GE SE 30 (5 % on Chromosorb W)	Cu/1,5/3,2	200	N$_2$/58	Di-(2-ethylhexyl) phthalate	275
	250	dto.	Cu/1,5/3,2	250	N$_2$/58	Di-(2-ethylhexyl) phthalate	275
	140—350	dto.	St/1,2/4	140—350 15°/min	He/100	Diethyl sebacate (2.4) Triethyl citrate (2.5)	240
SE-52	200	Silicone rubber SE 52 (2.5 % on Chromosorb G)	St/2/2,7	200	N$_2$/26	Alkanes	
	220	dto.	St/2/2,7	220	N$_2$/26	Alkanes	
	250	dto.	St/2/2,7	250	N$_2$/26	Alkanes	
	280	dto.	St/2/2,7	280	N$_2$/26	Alkanes	
PNGS	220	Neopentyl glycol polysebacate (0.5 % on glass beads)	Cu/2(3)/4	220		Alkanes	272
U III	160	Polyadipate „Ultramoll III" (15 % on silica gel)	Gl/1/4	160	He/244	Dimethyl phthalate	249
	190	dto.	Gl/1/4	190	He/150	Diethyl phthalate	
	210	dto.	Gl/1/4	210	He/160	Dibutyl adipate	
	220	dto.	Gl/1/4	220	He/208	Triethyl citrate	
	230	dto.	Gl/0,5/4	230	He/190	Tri-(2-ethylhexyl) phosphate	
	230	dto.	Gl/1/4	230	He/170	Dimethoxyethyl phthalate	
	240	dto.	Gl/1/4	240	He/200	Di-(2-ethylhexyl adipate (2.2) Di-(2-ethylbutyl) azelate (2.3) Diethyl sebacate (2.4)	
	100—200	dto.	St/1/4	100—200 4°/min	He/115	Methyl laurate	
LAC	160	Diethylene glycol penta-erythritol polyadipate "Resoflex LAC-2 R-446" (10 % on silica gel)	Gl/1/4	160	He/160	Dimethyl azelate	240
	170	dto.	Gl/2/4	170	He/ 90	Glycerol monoacetate	
	190	dto.	Cu/0,5/4	190	He/ 75	Diethyl phthalate	
	220	dto.	Gl/1/4	220	He/160	Di-(2-ethylhexyl) adipate (2.2) Di-(2-ethylbutyl) azelate (2.3)	
	230	dto.	Gl/0,5/4	230	He/116	Diethyl sebacate (2.4) Triethyl citrate (2.5)	
	230	dto.	St/0,5/3	230	He/ 52	Di(2-ethylhexyl) phthalate	
	230	dto.	Cu/0,5/4	230	He/120	Dibutyl phthalate	
P 2000	130	Polyglycol P 200 (20 % on silica gel)	Gl/0,3/4	130	He/160	Ethylene glycol and 2,3-butanediol	240
	160	dto.	Gl/2/4	160	He/116	Glycerol monoacetate	

phorus acids, a group of strong broad bands around 1100 cm^{-1} (9 μm) indicate polyglycol ethers, a spectrum with few bands and having the strongest bands at 2950 cm^{-1} (3.4 μm) and 1470 cm^{-1} (6.8 μm) indicates aliphatic hydrocarbons, and strong bands at 830 to 710 cm^{-1} (12—14 μm) point to aromatic or chlorinated aromatic hydrocarbons.

The characteristic bands for various groups of plasticizers are shown in Figure 2.8. In the case of the esters, the bands due to different alcohol structures are not shown.

In the following discussion of the individual groups of plasticizers, no special mention is made of the ester bands in the case of the esters.

Esters of phthalic acid have a very characteristic spectrum, with a double band at 1580 and 1600 cm^{-1} (6.3 μm), strong bands at 1280 cm^{-1} (7.8 μm), 1120 cm^{-1} (8.9 μm), 1070 cm^{-1} (9.4 μm), 740 cm^{-1} (13.4 μm), and 700 cm^{-1} (14.2 μm), and a weak band at about 650 cm^{-1} (15.4 μm).

Table 2.14: GC retention data for monomethyl and dimethyl esters and for diol and triol acetates after Rawlinson and Deeley [286] (all relative retention times are based on dimethyl phthalate = 1.00)

Column Temperature Heating rate	8 % Polyester 70°—200° C 4° C/min.	8 % Polyester 100°—200° C 3° C/min.	25 % Apiezon L 100°—260° C 4° C/min.
Methyl pelargonate	0.34	0.26	0.64
Propylene glycol diacetate	0.37		0.25
Propylene glycol monoacetate	0.40		0.13
Ethylene glycol diacetate	0.40	0.30	0.22
Dimethyl fumarate	0.41		0.31
Ethylene glycol monoacetate	0.43	0.33	0.11
Dimethyl succinate	0.45		0.28
Methyl benzoate	0.46	0.37	0.52
1,3-Butanediol diacetate	0.49		0.39
Dimethyl maleate	0.52		0.26
1,3-Butanediol monoacetate	0.53		0.25
Methyl laurate	0.62	0.53	1.13
1,4-Butanediol diacetate	0.62		0.54
Dipropylene glycol monoacetate	0.64		0.48
1,4-Butanediol monoacetate	0.65		
Dimethyl adipate	0.66		0.60
Dipropylene glycol diacetate	0.70		0.68
Diethylene glycol monoacetate	0.73		0.41
Methyl p-tert-butylbenzoate	0.76		1.09
Diethylene glycol diacetate	0.77		0.63
Glycerol triacetate	0.87	0.82	0.66
Dimethyl azelate	0.89		1.09
Glycerol diacetate	0.96	0.94	0.56
Dimethyl sebacate	0.96		1.23
Trimethylolelethane triacetate	0.97		0.91
Dimethyl isophthalate	1.00	1.00	1.15
Dimethyl terephthalate	1.00		1.15
Trimethylolpropane triacetate	1.04		1.04
Trimethylolpropane diacetate	1.16		
Dimethyloltricyclodecane monoacetate	1.62		1.71
Dimethyloltricyclodecane diacetate	1.73		1.75
Trimethylolpropane allyl ether/ acetates	0.77		1.05
	0.91		n. b.
	0.94		n. b.
	1.28		n. b.
Methyl esters of trimellitic acid	> 3		1.43
	> 3		1.53
Dimethyl chlorendate	> 3		1.91
Dimethyl tetrachlorophthalate	> 3		2.12
Methyl myristate		0.72	1.40
Methyl palmitate		0.91	1.64
Methyl stearate		1.09	1.99
Methyl oleate		1.13	1.90
Methyl linoleate		1.21	1.90
Methyl linolenate		1.30	1.90
Pentaerythritol tetraacetate		> 3	1.23
Pentaerythritol triacetate		> 3	1.21
Methyl ricinoleate (acetate derivative)		> 3	2.36
Methyl esters of resin acids	1.5—3.5		2.5—4.0

n. b.: not observed

Table 2.15: GC data of fatty acid methyl esters and dicarboxylic acid methyl esters

Stationary phase	Apiezon L	Apiezon M	Silicone DC 200	Butanediol succinate			DEGA		U III		EGS		Carbowax 20 M	
Concentration	25			15	3	3	(Cap.)	(Cap.)		15	15	15		
Column length	2			2	2	2	50	50		1	2	2		
Temperature	100–260	200	213	190	70–200	100–200	180	170–190	100–200	160	187	175	139	213
Heating rate	4			4	4	3		0,5	4					
Ref.	[286]	[115]	[115]	[285]		[286]	[240]		[240]				[115]	[115]
Methyl laurate	1,13	0,18		0,33	0,53	0,62	0,43		0,57	0,23	0,39	1905	5,18	
Methyl myristate	1,40	0,42		0,56	0,72		0,65		0,82	0,56	0,59	2085		
Methyl palmitate	1,64	1,00	1926	1,00	0,91		1,00	1,00	1,05	1,33	1,00	2253		
Methyl stearate	1,99	2,31	2126	1,81	1,09		1,53	1,97	1,29	3,24	1,77	2428		
Methyl oleate	1,90	2,02		2,02	1,13		1,65	2,13	1,29	3,24	2,12	2460		
Methyl linolate	1,90	1,97		2,36	1,21			2,53	1,33	3,78	2,69	2526		
Methyl linolenate	1,90	2,25		2,98	1,30			3,18	1,38	4,74	3,66	2598		
Methyl ricinoleate									1,62	8,39	>13			
Methyl acetylricinoleate	2,36				>3									
Dimethyl succinate	0,28			0,45								1905	2,13	
Dimethyl adipate	0,60		1209	0,66					0,52	0,20		2124	5,18	1830
Dimethyl azelate	1,09		1508	0,89					0,90	0,76				2118
Dimethyl sebacate	1,23		1620	0,96	1,00				1,02	1,18		2450		2230
Dimethyl phthalate	1,00		1436	1,00	1,00				1,00	1,00		2565		2287
Dimethyl isophthalate	1,15		1503	1,00	1,00							2540		2287

Cap: Capillary column
DEGA: Diethylene glycol polyadipate
U III: Plasticizer Ultramoll III (polyadipate)
EGS: Ethylene glycol polysuccinate

Table 2.16: GC data for diols and diol acetates

Stationary phase	Apiezon L	Apiezon L	Apiezon M	Silicone DC 200	Silicone SE 52	BDS	DEGA	Diethylene glycol succinate	Diethylene glycol succinate	Carbowax 1540	Carbowax 20 M	Carbowax 20 M	Carbowax 20 M
Concentration	20,0	25	20,0		19,9	8	24,5	24,3	24,3	20,6	21,9		10
Column length		2				2							1,8
Temperature	160	100–260	160	213	160	70–200	140	120	140	120	160	213	50–225
Heating rate		4				4							79
Ref.	[115a]	[286]	[115a]	[115]	[115a]	[286]	[115a]	[115a]	[115a]	[115a]	[115a]	[115]	[285]
Ethylene glycol	659		673	626	769		1698	1957	2003	1673	1588	1597	
Propylene glycol	781		794	772	893		1860		2147	1840	1731	1744	
2,3-Butanediol	747		758		827		1619	1847	1885		1500		
1,2-Butanediol	756		766		836		1656	1889	1921		1525		
1,3-Butanediol	809		820		896		1758	1982	2031		1633		
1,4-Butanediol	821		836	889	919		1837	2060	2107		1692		
1,6-Hexanediol	900		915		1013						1861	1877	
Diethylene glycol	1093		1105	1121	1211		2084		2262		1917	2100	
Glycerol	927		938		1054						2315		
Ethylene glycol monoacetate		0,11				0,43							
Propylene glycol monoacetate		0,13				0,40							
1,3-Butanediol monoacetate		0,25				0,53							
1,4-Butanediol monoacetate						0,65							
1,6-Hexanediol monoacetate													
Diethylene glycol monoacetate		0,41				0,73							
Ethylene glycol diacetate	895	0,22	905		1005	0,40	1681	1933	1950	1551	1542		0,71
Propylene glycol diacetate		0,25				0,37							0,68
1,3-Butanediol diacetate		0,39				0,49							
1,4-Butanediol diacetate		0,54				0,62							
Diethylene glycol diacetate		0,63		1379		0,77							1,16
Hexanediol diacetate													
Glycerol diacetate		0,56				0,96							
Glycerol triacetate		0,66				0,87							1,24

BDS: Butanediolpolysuccinate   DEGA: Diethylene glycol polyesteradipate

Table 2.17: GC data for phenols, cresols, and xylenols

Stationary phase	Apiezon L			Apiezon M	Silicone DC 200	DEGS	TXP	TMCP	TXP+ TMCP 1 + 2	Y	Carbowax 20 M
Concentration		20—30%				25 %	gep. Kap.	gep. Kap.	gep. Kap.	15 %	
Column length		not given				1,2 m	5 m	5 m	5 m	2 m	
Temperature (°C)	135	155	183	170	177	160	120	140	115		177
Ref.	[115]	[115]	[115]	[115]	[115]	[115]	[289]	[289]	[289]	165	[115]
Phenol	1,00	1,00	1,00	1,00	943	1,00	1560	1290	1382	1266	2000
o-Cresol	1,87	1,60	1,95	1,67	1031	1,00	1589	1344	1422	1318,5	2000
m-Cresol	2,10	1,89	1,90	1,80	1048	1,29	1649	1386	1473	1362	2073
p-Cresol	2,06	1,93	2,10	1,79	1048	1,29	1638	1376	1463	1358,5	2073
2.3-Xylenol	4,12	3,49	4,20	3,38	1167	1,49	1714	1461	1546	1445	2125
2.4-Xylenol	3,50	2,93	3,60	2,93	1127	1,22	1667	1423	1504	1408,5	2073
2.5-Xylenol	3,48	2,96	3,50	2,92		1,18	1673	1430	1510	1408	
2.6-Xylenol	3,18	2,52	2,90		1102	0,83	1534	1334	1406	1382	1900
3.4-Xylenol	4,42	3,93	4,50	3,50	1170	1,96	1757	1503	1588	1480	2200
3.5-Xylenol	3,88	3,38	3,80	2,97		1,63	1735	1479	1567	1454	

DEGS: diethylene glycol polysuccinate
 TXP: trixylyl phosphate
TMXP: di-(3,3,5-trimethylcyclohexyl) phthalate
   Y: trimethylol tripelargonate

gep. Kap.: packed capillary column

Columns 1—4 and 6: relative retention times
Other columns: retention indices

The various alkyl groups give distinct differences in the shape and intensity of the CH stretching bands at 2850 to 3000 cm^{-1} (3.5—3.65 μm) and the deformation bands at 1300 to 1500 cm^{-1} (7.6—6.7 μm). The size of the alkyl groups can be estimated from the intensity ratios of these bands and those of the aromatic skeleton or of ester group. The more highly branched the alkyl group the stronger is the group of bands around 1370 cm^{-1} (7.3 μm) in relation to the bands around 1450 cm^{-1} (6.9 μm).

The phthalates of the C$_8$—C$_{13}$ alcohols (1.1.19—1.1.26) are mostly based on isomer mixtures of the alcohols in question, which differ in their IR spectra according to the degree of branching. However, specific assignment to individual alcohols is impossible.

For the alkylaryl-modified phthalates (1.1.27 and 28), the intensity of the band around 700 cm^{-1} (14.3 μm) is higher than for the alkyl phthalates.

The alkoxyalkyl phthalates (1.1.30—1.1.32) exhibit distinct broadening of the band at 1120 cm^{-1} (8.9 μm), and in the case of the glycolates (1.1.33—1.1.34), an additional band appears at 1210 cm^{-1} (8.3 μm).

The various polyesters of phthalic acid (1.2.1—1.2.6) have different contents of phthalic acid, in some cases together with other dicarboxylic acids, as is shown by the intensity ratios of the phthalate double band at about 1600 cm^{-1} (6.3 μm) to the other bands in the spectrum. However, since this double band is clearly recognizable in the spectra reproduced, the polyesters in question have been included in the group of polyesters of phthalic acid. For example, the polyesters 1.2.4.—1.2.6 (Plastolein 9722, 9730, and 9765) contain mainly azelaic acid, the end groups being fatty acids, which have been detected together with phthalic acid on hydrolysis and esterification.

The esters of isophthalic acid show very strong bands at about 730 cm^{-1} (13.7 μm) and 1230 cm^{-1} (8.1 μm).

The glycol dibenzoates (1.4.1—1.4.6) are characterized by strong, sharp bands around 720 cm^{-1} (14 μm) and around 1280 cm^{-1} (7.8 μm) and by the group of bands at 1000—1200 cm^{-1} (10—8.35 μm).

In 2-ethylhexyl p-hydroxybenzoate (1.4.7.), the additional hydroxyl group leads to a marked change in the spectrum in relation to that of the benzoates.

The esters of trimellitic acid (1.5.1—1.5.7) also have an aromatic double band (which is, however, weak) at 1570 and 1610 cm^{-1} (6.4 and 6.2 μm). The structure of the bands around 1240 cm^{-1} (8.1 μm), 1110 cm^{-1} (9 μm), and 750 cm^{-1} (13.3 μm) differs clearly from that of other esters of aromatic carboxylic acids. The difference in the compositions of the C$_8$—C$_{10}$ alcohols leads only to insignificant shifts in the spectra, so that hydrolysis and separate analysis of the alcohols is necessary for the identification of the alcohols.

In the IR spectra of the esters of aliphatic dicarboxylic acids, the various acids can be distinguished by differences in position, intensity, and shape in the region of the ν_{CO} bands at 1300—1150 cm^{-1} (7.7—8.7 μm), almost irrespective of the nature of the alkyl groups. The following combinations of bands are characteristic (in cm^{-1} and μm):

Fumarates: 1290 (7.75) s, 1260 (7.95) s, 1220 (8.2) m, 1175 (8.5) s, 1155 (8.7) s

Maleates: 1290 (7.75) s, 1255 (7.97) s, 1205 (8.3) s, 1160 (8.6) s.

The group of bands is not as well resolved as in the case of the fumarates.

43

The stretching vibration $\nu_{C=C}$ at 1640 cm^{-1} (6.1 μm) is narrower and somewhat weaker for the fumarates than for the maleates.

Succinates: 1260 (7.95) m, 1240 (8.07) m, 1210 (8.26) s, 1160 (8.6) s

Adipates: 1310 (7.6) m, 1280 (7.8) m, 1240 (8.07) s, 1170 (8.55) s, 1140 (8.77) s,

Azelates: 1310 (7.64) w, 1240 (8.07) s, 1170 (8.55) s, 1135 (8.8) m sh, 1090 (9.18) w.

Sebacates: 1240 (8.07) s, 1170 (8.55) s, 1130 (8.85) m, 1100 (9.1) w.

The bands on the short wavelength side of the group of bands at 1310 cm^{-1} (7.6 μm) and 1280 cm^{-1} (7.8 μm) are more distinct for the adipates than for the sebacates. The band at 1140 cm^{-1} (8.07 μm) is stronger than for the sebacates and azelates. For the latter, it is usually detectable only as a very weak shoulder, and it may thus allow a distinction between sebacate and azelate (e. g. spectra 5086 and 5092).

Benzyl alkyl or dibenzyl esters of dicarboxylic acids give changes in the appearance of the ν_{CO} band group due to overlapping of bands as well as the characteristic bands of the benzyl group at 1500 cm^{-1} (6.67 μm) m, 750 and 735 cm^{-1} (13.3 and 13.6 μm) s, and the very sharp band at 700 cm^{-1} (14.3 μm) s.

This is even more pronounced for the alkoxyalkyl esters (2.2.14 to 2.2.16, spectra 5077–5079).

Tartrates and citrates (2.5), in addition to the broad band $\nu_{OHassoc.})$ with the maximum around 3400—3500 cm^1 (2.85 to 2.95 μm), also have a typical band picture around 1300—1150 cm^{-1} (7.7—8.7 μm), which changes as expected for the acetylcitrates.

Polyesters of adipic and sebacic acids (2.6) cannot always be definitely distinguished by means of the criteria mentioned for the monomers, since the spectrum is influenced by the diols used and by the monoalcohols or carboxylic acids incorporated as end groups. However, the identification of unknown polyesters should be possible on the basis of the spectra reproduced for this group (5107–5119), which have been selected from a large number of spectra of polymeric plasticizers. To obtain more precise information regarding the structural units and the molecular weight distribution, additional procedures are necessary.

The acetates, propionates, and butyrates of glycerol, glycols, and glycol ethers (3.1) are characterized by a broad, strong band around 1240 cm^{-1} (8.07 μm) for the acetates, and 1175 cm^{-1} (8.5 μm) for the propionates and butyrates. The monoesters with diols or glycerol give the broad band of associated OH groups at about 3400 cm^{-1} (2.9 μm); however, this band is sometimes also found for products that are formally completely esterified according to the manufacturers' data.

The other bands in the ν_{CO} and δ_{CH} vibration regions allow a good differentiation of the various acid-polyol compounds.

This is only of limited validity for group 3.2, i. e. the esters of C$_5$—C$_{10}$ carboxylic acids. The group of bands at 1170 and 1140 cm^{-1} (8.55 and 8.77 μm) may be helpful in the identification.

Esters of fatty acids (3.3) are indicated by the weak band at 720 cm^{-1} (13.9 μm) that occurs with more than four paraffinic CH$_2$ groups, the intensity of which increases with increasing chain length, and the pair of bands at about 1240 cm^{-1} (8.07 μm) m and 1170 cm^{-1} (8.55 μm) s.

For the alkoxyalkyl esters of oleic and stearic acids (spectra 5162, 5163, 5175, and 5176), a characteristic band is found at 1130 cm^{-1} (8.85 μm); for the polyethylene glycol stearates (spectra 5181 and 5182), the position of this band is shifted slightly, and its intensity is greater than that of the ester band.

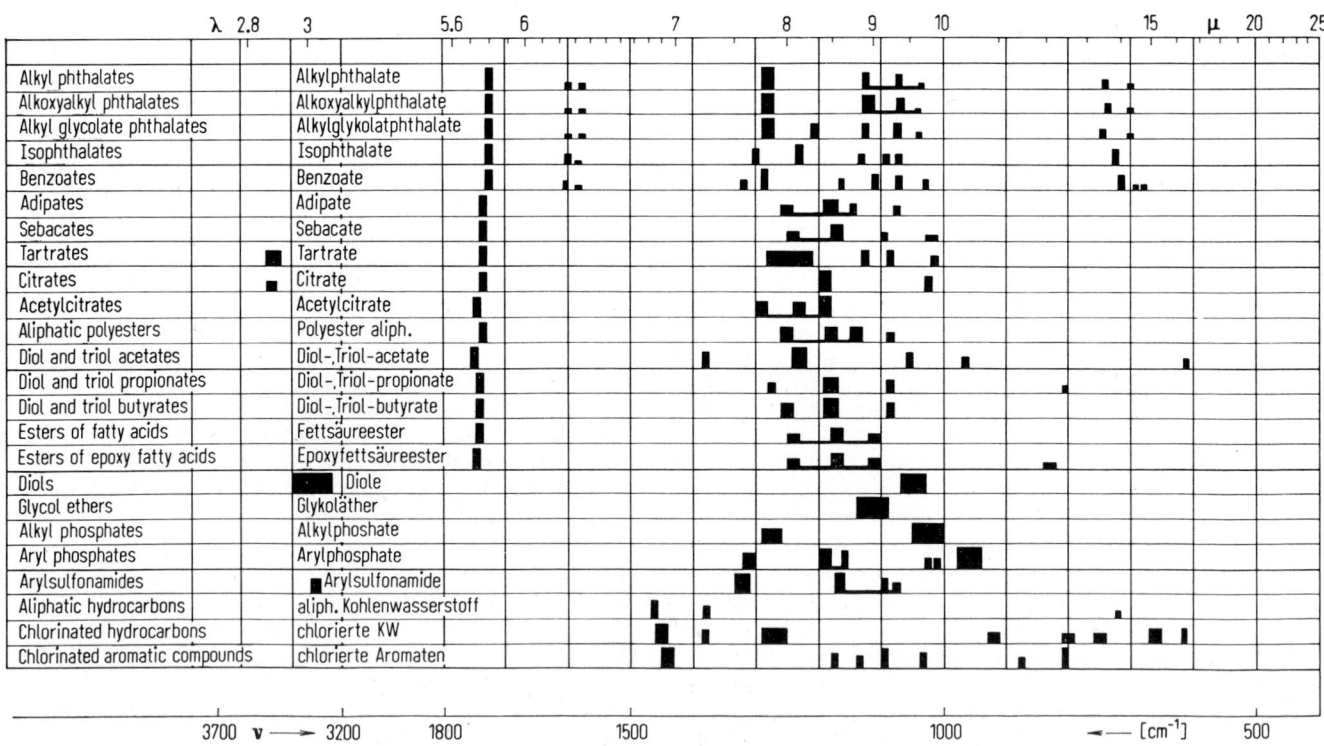

Fig. 2.8: IR band chart for plasticizers

The esters of unsaturated fatty acids (oleic acid, ricinoleic acid) give weak bands at 3000 cm⁻¹ (3.33 μm) and 1650 cm⁻¹ (6.06 μm), which are due to the double bond.

The OH band at about 3400 cm⁻¹ (2.94 μm) in the spectra of the ricinoleates is also present in a similar form in those of the diethylene and polyethylene glycol stearates (cf. spectra 5186 and 5180). In such cases, the double bond bands mentioned above are useful for differentiation. The band at about 1240 cm⁻¹ (8.07 μm) is very strong in the case of acetylated ricinoleic esters (3.6.7—3.6.10).

Since technical esters of fatty acids usually are mixtures of different fatty acids, transesterification and subsequent gas-chromatographic analysis of the methyl esters of the fatty acids is advisable for reliable identification. This method is nowadays widely used and well developed for the analysis of natural fats.

The spectra of Dibutyl dithiobutyrate (5196) and Plastomoll WH (5197) are reproduced as examples of esters containing sulfur and clorine.

The spectra of epoxidized fatty acid esters (4.1—4.8) differ from those of esters of fatty acids only in having weak bands at about 845 and 825 cm⁻¹ (11.85 and 12.15 μm), the latter usually being somewhat stronger.

The spectra of the polyethylene glycols follow easily from those of diethylene and triethylene glycols (spectra 5207 and 5208). The relative intensities of the ν_{OH} band at 3380 cm⁻¹ (2.98 μm) and of the ν_{C-OH} band at 1060 cm⁻¹ (9.45 μm) decrease with decreasing relative frequency of the end groups. The ether band at about 1110 cm⁻¹ (9.0 μm) becomes the strongest band in the spectrum of the polyglycols. In the high molecular weight polyglycols (5.1.7 and 5.1.8), the OH band has almost entirely disappeared, and the spectra recorded for solid samples exhibit very sharp bands split into the rotational branches (see Section 1.6).

The polypropylene glycols (2.2) can be distinguished from the polyethylene glycols by the CH₃ bands at 2970 cm⁻¹ (3.37 μm) and 1380 cm⁻¹ (7.25 μm). For copolymers of ethylene and propylene glycols, it is possible to estimate the ratio of the two monomers from the ratio of these bands to CH₂ bands, e. g. at 1350 cm⁻¹ (7.4 μm).

The glycerol tripolyoxypropylene ethers (5.3.3 5.3.5) can be distinguished from the polypropylene glycols only by a weak band at 790 cm⁻¹ (12.65 μm) and a difference in intensity around 1280 cm⁻¹ (7.8 μm). These differences decrease with increasing molecular weight, and can no longer be detected with the usual light paths at molecular weights above 1500.

Ethylenediamine tetrasubstituted with polyoxypropylene polyethylene glycol (5.4.13—5.4.15 "Tetronic") cannot be distinguished spectroscopically, and the spectra agree with those of the mixed polyglycols (5.2.4—5.2.6).

The various low molecular weight glycol monoethers and diethers (5.4.1—5.4.6) can be distinguished fairly readily. The ester bands sometimes observed around 1725 cm⁻¹ (5.8 μm) point to impurities. This is also true of some polyglycol monoethers (5.4.8—5.4.10), but these can be distinguished by the bands between 1500 and 1200 cm⁻¹ (6.7—8.3 μm).

The spectrum of the polyglycol ester listed under 5.4.11 largely corresponds to that of polyethylene glycol (400) monostearate (MW 700), but the low intensity of the band

at 720 cm⁻¹ (13.9 μm) suggests that a shorter-chain fatty acid has been used for esterification.

Of the ethers listed in group 5.5.1, Plastikator 85 (ether thioether, spectrum no. 5244) and Reomol BCF (spectrum no. 5245) exhibit spectral characteristics similar to those of the glycol ethers discussed above, whereas the aromatic ethers and polyethers (5.5.3—5.5.8) and ethylene glycol monophenyl ether (5.4.2) give spectra with large numbers of bands, some of which can be assigned to specific structures, such as the phenoxy group (spectra 5230 and 5246 or the benzyl group (spectrum no. 5248).

The trialkyl phosphates (6.1.1—6.1.8) give strong bands at 1150—970 cm⁻¹ (8.7—10.3 μm), with a maximum at 1040—1010 cm⁻¹ (9.6—9.9 μm), which are assigned to the vibrations of the group P—O—R, while the strong band at 1260—1280 cm⁻¹ (7.81—7.93 μm) is assigned to $\nu_{P=O}$. Ohada[296] pointed out that an interpretation of the bands at 860—800 cm⁻¹ (11.6—12.5 μm) as ν_{P-O} offers a ready explanation for the very weak bands around 1890—1770 cm⁻¹ (5.3—5.65 μm) as a combination of ν_{C-O} at 1100 cm⁻¹ to 980 cm⁻¹ (9.1—10.2 μm) and ν_{P-O}. The various alkyl groups in the trialkyl phosphates give well differentiated spectra. Alkyl phosphates containing chlorine also give the strong ν_{C-Cl}-band at 700—670 cm⁻¹ (14.3—14.9 μm), as can be seen from a comparison of the spectra of triethyl phosphate and tri-2-chloroethyl phosphate (spectra 5553 and 5559).

The aryl phosphates (6.1.9—6.1.17) all have strong bands at about 1590 cm⁻¹ (6.3 μm), 1500 cm⁻¹ (6.67 μm), 1300 cm⁻¹ (7.7 μm), 1190—1140 cm⁻¹ (8.4—8.8 μm), 1030—1010 cm⁻¹ (9.7—9.9 μm) and 960 cm⁻¹ (10.4 μ). The positions and intensities of the bands in the region between 840 and 400 cm⁻¹ (12—25 μm) differ with the degree of substitution of the aryl residues. This is naturally also observed in the ν_{CH} combination band region between 2000 and 1700 cm⁻¹ (5.0—5.9 μm) in the spectra recorded with longer light paths.

An indication of the relative number of methyl groups is provided by the intensity of the weak band at 1380 cm⁻¹ (7.25 μm), which is entirely absent in the case of pure triphenyl phosphate (spectrum no. 5260), whereas it is very pronounced in the case of trixylyl phosphate (spectra 5267 and 5268). Two spectra of tricresyl phosphate and two of trixylyl phosphate (spectra 5265 5268) illustrate the differences resulting from differences in the isomer compositions of the starting phenol mixtures. Owing to the toxicity of o-cresyl phosphates, this isomer is not generally present in technical plasticizers. Pure tri-o-cresyl phosphate gives a strong band at 758 cm⁻¹ (13.2 μm). This is observed at most as a very weak band in the two spectra reproduced.

The alkyl thiophosphates (6.2.1 6.2.3) give bands almost identical with those of the corresponding phosphate in the region around 1070—970 cm⁻¹ (9.3—10.3 μm), but they also have a weak band at around 1250 cm⁻¹ (8.0 μm). This is clearly discernible in the case of the tributyl compounds (spectra 5254 and 5271).

The spectra of the dialkyl alkylphosphonates (6.3.2—6.3.4) are also similar to those of the trialkyl phosphates, but contain additional bands at 910 cm⁻¹ (11.0 μm) and 810—790 cm⁻¹ (12.35—12.65 μm).

The sulfonamide plasticizers exhibit characteristic bands around 3300 cm⁻¹ (3.03 μm), 1600 cm⁻¹ (6.25 μm), 1320 cm⁻¹ (7.6 μm), and 1150 cm⁻¹ (8.7 μm). In addition to the band

Table 2.18: Mass spectra of plasticizers; phthalates and isophthalates

Dec. No.	Composition	Molecular formula	Molecular weight	Strongest mass number	Mass number m/e / Relative intensities (strongest peak = 1000)								
1.1.	**Phthalate**													
1.1.1	Dimethyl phthalate	$C_{10}H_{10}O_4$	222	149	77/241	76/50	50/150	15/147	194/144	164/118	92/114	135/87	104/84
1.1.2	Diethyl phthalate	$C_{12}H_{14}O_4$ *	250	149	177/260	65/162	160/147	150/125	144/119	118/105	104/104	77/67	93/84
1.1.3	Dipropyl phthalate	$C_{14}H_{18}O_4$	278	149	41/123	27/43	111/150	113/96	209/191	94/76	91/104	67/77	58/39
1.1.4	Dibutyl phthalate	$C_{16}H_{22}O_4$	278	149	29/210	41/150	150/106	56/84	57/82	82/80	223/205	76/59	104/57
1.1.5	Diisobutyl phthalate	$C_{16}H_{22}O_4$	306	149	57/264	165/155	144/223	116/29	29/84	104/83	80/56	76/65	39/48
1.1.6	Diamyl phthalate	$C_{18}H_{24}O_4$	304	149	43/289	41/172	277/29	70/145	41/139	237/129	150/107	167/84	55/77
1.1.7	Butyl cyclohexyl phthalate	$C_{19}H_{20}O_4$	312	91	41/419	29/329	227/76	55/224	104/209	27/195	39/152	50/116	150/94
1.1.8	Butyl benzyl phthalate	$C_{19}H_{26}O_4$	318	149	149/861	107/329	385/521	65/319	41/274	92/170	39/155	76/139	104/138
1.1.9	Isobutyl methylcyclohexyl phthalate	$C_{20}H_{26}O_4$	330	149	41/328	55/268	57/264	29/162	104/223	136/170	150/112	76/108	97/92
1.1.10	Dicyclohexyl phthalate	$C_{20}H_{30}O_4$	334	149	167/411	55/355	41/280	150/150	83/67	103/98	248/54	54/70	29/65
1.1.13	Butyl acetyl phthalate	$C_{22}H_{30}O_4$	358	149	57/360	41/238	238/154	223/134	104/117	150/113	43/97	167/93	76/77
1.1.15	Di(methylcyclohexyl) phthalat	$C_{24}H_{38}O_4$	390	149	167/752	55/621	482/97	269/41	150/81	254/167	263/165	29/108	76/103
1.1.17	Dicapryl phthalate	$C_{24}H_{38}O_4$	390	112	167/511	43/289	283/57	41/248	279/230	71/168	150/167	29/150	55/147
1.1.18	Di-(2-ethylhexyl) phthalate	$C_{26}H_{42}O_4$	418	57	167/559	149/516	149/494	70/261	57/418	113/401	71/365	83/347	55/338
1.1.21	Dinonyl phthalate	$C_{26}H_{42}O_4$	418	149	149/867	71/545	403/291	390/331	318/331	55/318	69/272	70/174	29/161

Table 2.18 (continued)

Dec. No.	Composition	Molecular formula	Molecular weight	Strongest mass number	Mass number / Relative intensities (strongest peak = 1000)								
1.1.22	Diisononyl phthalate	$C_{10}H_{10}O_4$	194	163	293	57	71	69	70	55	127	41	43
					889	796	747	656	649	582	578	560	513
1.1.23	Diisodecyl phthalate	$C_{28}H_{46}O_4$	446	149	57	167	43	71	307	55	85	41	69
					435	422	9	356	268	262	260	252	237
1.1.25	Phthalates of mixed alcohols	(Palatinol HSH)		149	43	57	85	167	41	56	55	99	29
					564	555	524	452	391	362	295	281	260
1.1.26	Phthalates of mixed higher alcohols	(Mollan H 20)		149	223	57	71	293	41	43	55	69	150
					650	630	600	540	506	498	490	480	420
1.1.27	Alkylaryl-modif. phthalates	(Santicizer 213)*		149	91	206	132	65	123	104	150	105	29
					833	786	417	405	405	381	357	345	286
1.1.28	Alkylaryl modif. phthalates	(Santicizer 214)		119	105	91	133	120	118	57	246	41	106
					894	851	809	702	596	577	575	560	532
1.1.29	Diallyl phthalate	$C_{14}H_{14}O_4$	246	149	189	104	76	41	132	50	188	65	42
					373	270	267	257	236	171	135	130	103
1.1.30	Di(methoxyethyl) phthalate	$C_{14}H_{18}O_6$	282	59	58	29	31	45	15	149	104	76	43
					741	167	130	118	112	86	64	63	61
1.1.31	Di(ethoxyethyl) phthalate	$C_{16}H_{22}O_6$	310	45	72	73	29	31	44	43	59	149	27
					999	963	486	449	436	293	234	226	194
1.1.32	Di(butoxyethyl) phthalate	$C_{20}H_{30}O_6$	366	149	57	56	45	85	29	101	100	41	104
					872	753	567	430	424	384	334	290	208
1.3.	Isophthalates												
1.3.1	Dimethyl isophthalate	$C_{10}H_{10}O_4$	194	163	194	135	76	50	15	44	103	75	77
					118	105	75	65	60	54	47	46	46
1.3.2	Di-(2-ethylhexyl) isophthalate	$C_{24}H_{38}O_4$	390	112	167	149	70	261	57	113	71	83	55
					559	516	494	487	418	401	365	347	338
1.3.3	Diisooctyl isophthalate	$C_{24}H_{38}O_4$	390	57	43	112	41	55	84	69	70	71	149
					833	780	770	710	690	661	576	534	400

* E. M. Emery "Mass Spectra of Aromatic Esters" Analytical Chemistry 32 (1960) 1945

Table 2.19: Mass spectra of plasticizers: adipates and sebacates

Dec. No.	Composition	Molecular formula	Molecular weight	Strongest Mass number	Mass numbers m/e Relative intensities (strongest peak = 1000)								
2.2.	Adipate/Adipates												
2.2.1	Dimethyl adipate	$C_8H_{14}O_4$	174	55	59	15	114	41	43	27	101	74	29
					800	594	581	541	406	387	380	361	336
2.2.2	Diethyl adipate	$C_{10}H_{18}O_4$	202	29	55	129	111	128	27	88	73	101	60
					764	733	680	676	644	591	573	569	542
2.2.4	Diisobutyl adipate	$C_{14}H_{26}O_4$	258	57	129	185	56	55	41	29	111	101	100
					942	881	616	594	551	503	476	324	263
2.2.7	Di-2-ethylhexyl adipate	$C_{22}H_{42}O_4$	370	129	57	43	41	55	70	71	112	29	147
					794	698	627	618	606	524	524	444	253
2.2.8	Diisooctyl adipate	$C_{22}H_{42}O_4$	370	129	57	55	43	71	241	41	112	69	84
					866	714	680	676	619	557	402	381	361
2.2.9	Diisononyl adipate	$C_{24}H_{46}O_4$	398	57	71	129	55	43	41	69	255	83	70
					625	602	468	430	358	307	301	236	228
2.2.12	Butyl benzyl adipate	$C_{17}H_{24}O_4$	292	91	129	111	101	55	65	92	235	107	83
					815	250	194	156	122	111	107	100	89
2.2.13	Octyl benzyl adipate	$C_{21}H_{32}O_4$	348	91	129	112	57	55	43	71	41	70	111
					852.	433	408	308	247	241	232	232	200
2.2.17	2,2,4-Trimethyl-1,3-pentanediol monoadipate	$C_{14}H_{26}O_5$	274	71	43	56	89	41	83	57	55	98	73
					799	724	536	250	195	182	179	179	177
2.4.	Sebacates/Sebacate												
2.4.1	Dimethyl sebacate	$C_{12}H_{22}O_4$	230	55	74	41	98	15	43	59	125	84	157
					913	717	565	554	532	478	456	446	391
2.4.2	Diethyl sebacate	$C_{14}H_{26}O_4$	258	29	55	41	213	69	97	88	171	125	98
					930	625	424	389	388	360	347	340	334
2.4.3	Diisobutyl sebacate	$C_{18}H_{34}O_4$	314	57	41	29	56	185	55	241	43	27	98
					709	678	519	418	386	373	260	196	177
2.4.4	Dibutyl sebacate	$C_{18}H_{34}O_4$	314	29	41	56	55	57	241	185	43	98	69
					975	757	609	589	535	420	333	280	263
2.4.5	Di-(2-ethylhexyl) sebacate	$C_{26}H_{50}O_4$	426	57	41	43	149	55	64	29	56	65	185
					557	547	509	380	367	349	301	297	286
2.4.6	Diisooctyl sebacate	$C_{26}H_{50}O_4$	426	57	71	43	41	55	67	56	70	69	84
					541	530	391	367	313	302	299	294	272
2.4.7	Mixture of C_8 alcohol sebacates	Reomol D 79 S		57	43	185	149	41	55	56	98	69	29
					699	695	688	622	534	426	379	**323**	296
2.4.8	Fatty alcohol sebacate	B 172 (Dehydag)		77	43	57	41	51	29	55	44	30	27
					799	723	584	577	516	470	470	400	331
2.4.9	Dibenzyl sebacate	$C_{24}H_{30}O_4$	382	92	91	76	107	65	74	51	39	93	63
					917	342	275	267	258	208	183	158	92

Table 2.20: Mass spectra of plasticizers: phosphates, thiophosphates, phosphites, and phosphonates

Dec. no.	Composition	Molecular formula	Molecular weight	Strongest mass number	Mass numbers m/e — Relative intensities (strongest peak = 1000)								
6.1	Phosphates												
6.1.2	Triethyl phosphate	$C_6H_{15}O_4P$	182	99	155	127	81	109	82	29	27	125	45
					915	575	563	414	316	287	230	230	161
6.1.3	Tributyl phosphate	$C_{12}H_{27}O_4P$	266	99	41	155	211	29	57	55	56	27	39
					342	268	232	195	183	110	110	98	98
6.1.4	Triisobutyl phosphate	$C_{12}H_{27}O_4P$	266	99	41	57	43	29	27	39	155	112	55
					628	426	409	409	287	213	166	139	135
6.1.5	Tri-(2-ethylhexyl) phosphate	$C_{24}H_{51}O_4P$	434	99	113	57	71	43	55	41	211	69	112
					228	227	148	133	125	122	108	86	77
6.1.6	Tributoxyethyl phosphate	$C_{18}H_{39}O_7P$	398	57	45	56	29	41	85	100	125	101	27
					906	814	671	620	585	357	336	296	271
6.1.7	Chloralkyl aryl phosphate	(Celluflex FR-2)		75	99	77	39	49	41	191	155	193	321
6.1.8	Tri-(2-chloroethyl) phosphate	$C_6H_{12}O_4Cl_3P$			398	394	338	278	252	230	149	149	145
			286	63	249	27	251	65	143	99	205	125	233
6.1.9	Triphenyl phosphate	$C_{18}H_{15}O_4P$			974	797	635	621	500	446	311	257	243
			326	326	325	77	65	170	51	39	94	233	215
6.1.10	Octyl diphenyl phosphate	$C_{20}H_{27}O_4P$			678	547	424	269	267	250	224	212	177
			362	251	94	250	41	77	43	65	55	249	252
6.1.11	Cresyl diphenyl phosphate	$C_{19}H_{17}O_4P$			328	282	234	207	172	152	135	134	134
			340	77	94	65	39	326	66	51	325	340	107
6.1.12	Xylyl diphenyl phosphate	$C_{20}H_{19}O_4P$			975	900	720	536	494	437	337	262	226
			354	77	65	326	325	51	39	94	165	170	354
6.1.15	Tricresyl phosphate	$C_{21}H_{21}O_4P$			610	605	378	327	288	259	244	217	206
			368	77	91	65	368	165	79	354	39	107	78
6.1.16	Trixylyl phosphate	$C_{24}H_{27}O_4P$			678	666	428	392	369	336	334	334	310
			410	410	77	193	91	105	396	179	79	209	104
					987	768	725	620	536	535	527	527	511
6.2.	Thiophosphates												
6.2.1	Triethyl thiophosphate	$C_6H_{15}O_3PS$	198	121	198	93	65	97	29	109	115	27	45
					975	774	679	600	556	478	417	357	348
6.2.2	Tributyl thiophosphate	$C_{12}H_{27}O_3PS$	282	227	171	115	129	57	41	29	55	99	56
					958	938	688	650	556	542	502	396	388
6.2.3	Triisooctyl thiophosphate	$C_{24}H_{51}O_3PS$	450	339	115	227	113	129	71	57	97	69	43
					827	808	769	692	673	664	654	577	556
6.3.	Phosphites, phosphonates												
6.3.1	Tri-(2-chloroethyl) phosphite	$C_6H_{12}O_3Cl_3P$	270	233	235	189	191	207	65	145	209	27	127
					929	857	776	755	665	571	571	520	510
6.3.2	Diethyl ethylphosphonate	$C_6H_{15}O_3P$	166	111	93	139	31	29	65	27	45	138	166
					708	583	500	463	446	367	350	321	300
6.3.3	Dibutyl butylphosphonate	$C_{12}H_{27}O_3P$	250	139	195	97	153	57	41	121	29	55	83
					999	830	830	626	594	540	536	504	368
6.3.4	Di-(2-ethylhexyl) 2-ethylhexyl-phosphonate	$C_{24}H_{51}O_3P$	418	195	97	57	307	43	55	41	209	71	69
					752	526	500	454	446	426	413	380	352

around 3300 cm⁻¹ (3.03 μm) as in the case of the amides with secondary NH groups, mixtures of toluenesulfonamides (spectrum no. 5278) with primary amino groups give further bands in the NH stretching region at 3390 cm⁻¹ (2.95 μm) and 3250 cm⁻¹ (3.08 μm) and at 1560 cm⁻¹ (6.41 μm). The stretching vibrations of the O=S=O grouping, which occur around 1320 cm⁻¹ (7.6 μm) and 1150 cm⁻¹ (8.7 μm), are situated at 1360 cm⁻¹ (7.35 μm) and 1150 cm⁻¹ (8.8 μm) for Mesamoll, which is given as an example of a sulfonate plasticizer. Since the sulfonates do not give amine bands, they are easy to distinguish from the sulfonamides.

The hydrocarbons used as plasticizers are mineral oil fractions or synthetic products obtained by various methods. The average molecular weights of these complex mixtures, which are extensively used as rubber plasticizers, are preferably in the range between 250 and 400.

Pure paraffin oils and waxes, with a thickness of around 50 μm, give spectra containing few bands, as do polyethylene wax and polyethylene (vol. 1, spectra 2, 3). In the case of solid paraffins, the band at 720 cm⁻¹ (13.9 μm) is split. The presence of aromatic structures in mineral oils is shown by bands around 1600 cm⁻¹ (6.25 μm) and in the region between 1050 and 650 cm⁻¹ (9.5–15.5 μm). IR-spectroscopic methods have been suggested for the structural group analysis of such mixtures, and these will be described below.

Investigations by Brandes [300] and by Luther and Oelert [301—303] and other authors have shown that relations exist between the values found for aromatic and paraffinic carbon by the refractive index/specific gravity/molecular weight method (Section 2.2) and the intensities of certain key bands in the IR spectrum. On this basis, methods have been devised for the determination of the percentages of aromatic and paraffinic carbon (C_A and C_P) in a mineral oil by IR spectroscopy.

From measurements on a large number of oils, Brandes [300] derived the relations

$$C_A = 9.8\,E_{1610} + 1.2 \tag{1}$$

and

$$C_P = 6.6\;E_{720} + 29.9 \tag{2}$$

where E_{720} and E_{1610} are the maximum extinctions of the bands at 1610 cm⁻¹ and 720 cm⁻¹, as determined by a baseline method, for a light path of 1 mm.

In an other article, Luther and Oelert [303] show that the equation

$$C_A = 10.9\,E_{1610} - 2.44 \tag{3}$$

gives even less scatter than equation (1) in comparison with the values obtained by the refractive index/specific gravity/ molecular weight method for a large number of oils. A method has been described for the determination of C_P, in which less scatter is found for the values of C_P with the integral absorption B_{910} in the region between 910 cm⁻¹ and 650 cm⁻¹, the aromatic component being taken into account.

The equation is

$$C_P = 0.0255\,(141 + B_{910} - 2730 \cdot E_{1610}) \tag{4}$$

where the aromatic component is represented by the term $2730 \cdot E_{1610}$.

Figure 2.9 shows how the integral and maximum absorptions are measured. To obtain the baseline forming the boundary

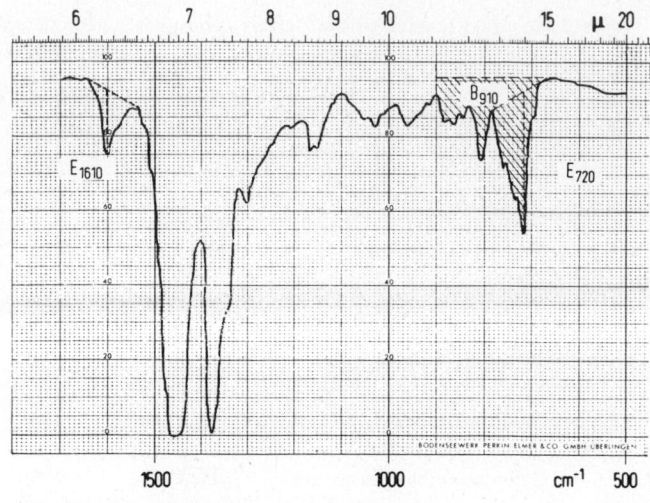

Fig. 2.9: IR spectrum of a mineral oil (portion)
The extinction values E_{1610} and E_{720} required for the structural analysis are measured between the dotted baselines and the band maxima, and the integral absorption B_{910} is calculated from the area of the shaded part.

for the determination of B_{910}, a spectrum is recorded with the same cell filled with a substance that does not absorb. The methods for the structural group analysis of mineral oils have been described in detail by Berthold et al. [304]. The same author also described an IR-spectroscopic method for the determination of the average content of methyl groups in hydrocarbon waxes by measurement of E_{1385} [305]. The various aromatic oils (8.2) are examples chosen from a large number of commercial products, whose spectra are characterized by different intensities of the C—C and C—H bands due to different frequencies of the various structures. For the assignment of individual bands, the reader is referred to the assignment diagrams reproduced in Vol. I, pp. 50—52. The spectra of the chloroparaffins (8.3) have few bands. In addition to the CH vibrations of the paraffins, they give a number of strong C—Cl stretching bands in the region between 800 and 600 cm⁻¹ (12.5 and 16.66 μm) and a broad band at 1280 cm⁻¹ (7.8 μm). The increasing degree of chlorination can be seen from the decrease in the relative intensity of the CH bands. The spectra of chlorinated biphenyls and polyphenyls (8.4) contain only weak CH bands. However, the various types of substitution in these mixtures lead to characteristic spectra with large numbers of bands (spectra 2302—2307), with groups of bands at 1500—1300 cm⁻¹ (6.66—7.69 μm), 1200—1000 cm⁻¹ (8.33—10.0 μm), and 900—500 cm⁻¹ (11.1—20 μm). The principal components are 1,2,4-trisubstituted and p- and o-disubstituted aromatic compounds. The increasing degree of chlorination is accompanied by a decrease in the intensity of the sharp band at about 1004 cm⁻¹ (9.96 μm) and an increase in the intensity of the band at 1172 cm⁻¹ (8.53 μm).

2.7 UV Spectroscopy of Plasticizers

Esters of arylcarboxylic acids, aryl phosphates, alkylphenol derivatives, aromatic hydrocarbons, and chlorinated aromatic compounds absorb in the UV, and can be identified as groups on the basis of the UV spectra.
Maxima or pronounced shoulders are observed at roughly the following wavelengths (nm):

Dialkyl phthalates: 215, 274, 280
Dialkyl isophthalates: 215, 274, 281, 288

Dialkyl mellitates: 217—225, 272, 279
Triaryl phosphates: 255—275 (several maxima, depending on the aryl residues)
Benzenesulfonamides: 210, 250, 253, 257, 263, 270
Aryl alkylsulfonates: 250—265 (depending on the aryl group
Aromatic mineral oils: 233, 260
Chlorinated diphenyls: 243

The differences in the shapes and intensities of the bands allow a distinction between the groups mentioned. However, further differentiation of the phthalates is practically impossible, since various alkyl groups cause only small differences in the extinction coefficients.

For the phenyl, cresyl, and xylyl phosphates, the spectrum varies with the substitution of the aromatic residues.

The UV spectra 1—12 present only a small selection of plasticizer spectra, but include representatives of the most important groups.

2.8 Mass Spectroscopy of Plasticizers

Nearly all monomeric plasticizers have sufficiently high vapor pressures for mass-spectroscopic analysis, and can be readily identified by their mass spectra. However, no general treatment of this topic exists at present.

The mass spectra of aromatic esters, particularly esters of phthalic acid, are reported in a number of articles [309—311]. The mass-spectroscopic data collections [203—205] contain data on a number of compounds used as plasticizers, and compounds and groups of compounds that are of interest as plasticizers are also mentioned in recent monographs on mass spectroscopy [195—200].

In Tables 2.18—2.20, we have listed the 10 strongest signals in the mass spectra of phthalates, isophthalates, adipates, sebacates, and esters of various phosphorus acids, with their mass numbers (m/e) and relative intensities. With a few exceptions, these data are the results of our own measurements by the method described in Section 1.8.2.

A detailed discussion of the spectra is impossible here, though a number of points can be mentioned.

In the spectra of nearly all dialkyl phthalates, the strongest peak occurs at a mass number of 149, which corresponds to the ion of protonated phthalic anhydride. Another characteristic fragment is the ion $m/e = (M - R + 2)^+$, where M is the molecular weight, resulting from the removal of an alkyl group R and recombination with two hydrogen atoms. This fragment occurs at $m/e = 223$ for dibutyl phthalate, and at $m/e = 279$ for dioctyl phthalate. The alkyl groups are recognizable from the masses R and R — 1, as well as from other fragments. The alkoxyalkyl phthalates give strong peaks at $m/e = (R_1OR_2 - 1)^+$ and $(R_1OR_2 - 2)^+$. If R_1 and R_2 are methyl or ethyl groups, these peaks occur at $m/e = 73$ and 72, 59 and 58, and 45 and 44. The molecule peak is usually very weak for dialkyl phthalates, and is not generally discernible for alkyl chains having more than five carbon atoms.

It is interesting in this connection to mention an article by Tou [312], who investigated dialkyl phthalates and isophthalates by field ion mass spectroscopy, and, as a result of the much smaller amount of fragmentation in comparison with excitation by electron bombardment, obtained strong molecule peaks.

The molecule peak is of medium intensity only for dimethyl phthalate and dimethyl isophthalate.

Isophthalates also give a strong peak at $m/e = 149$. The ion having the mass $m/e = (M - OR)^+$ is usually much stronger for the isophthalates than for the phthalates.

In the mass spectra of the adipates and sebacates, the fragment $m/e = 129$ or $m/e = 185$ corresponding to a protonated anhydride is usually strong. The peaks also include $m/e = (M - OR)^+$.

The trialkyl phosphates and trialkyl thiophosphates are characterized by fragments of the type $(M - R + 2)^+$, $(M - 2R + 3)^+$, and $(M - 3R + 4)^+$. For the triaryl phosphates, these fragments can also be designated $(H_2PO_4R_2)^+$, $(H_3PO_4R)^+$, and $(H_4PO_4)^+$, the last having $m/e = 99$. The analogous ion $(H_4PO_3S)^+$ for triaryl thiophosphates occurs at $m/e = 115$. The molecule peak is very strong for the triaryl phosphates, and the typical fragments of the phenyl, cresyl, and xylyl residues ($m/e = 77, 91, 105$) are also present, as well as fragments of the type $(H_2PO_2)^+$ at $m/e = 65$ and many others.

Field ion mass spectroscopy and mass spectroscopy with chemical ionisation, described in section 1.9, produce spectra with large fragments and often also molecule peaks, especially with oligomeric plasticisers, which greatly helps identification.

These MS techniques are, however, very much dependent on experimental conditions and on the type of equipment used, so that data obtained from different sources can often be used only as a guide.

3 Inorganic Fillers and Pigments

3.1 Survey and Classification

Inorganic fillers are extensively used to reduce the cost of filled plastics (extenders), but in many cases they are also incorporated as reinforcing fillers to achieve a specific improvement in the technical properties. Numerous naturally occurring silicates, silicas, and oxides ranging from rock powder to high grades of absbestos are used, as well as calcium carbonate, barium sulfate, a number of synthetic oxides, and other inorganic compounds. They are mostly light-colored or white substances, whose action is due in some cases to purely mechanical effects, but in other to physico-chemical or chemical interaction between the surface of the filler particles and the macromolecules. Carbon blacks are particularly important as reinforcing fillers, and have a decisive effect on the properties of elastomers. Further information on the use and action of fillers can be found in the literature [320—322].

The boundary between fillers and pigments is not easy to draw, particularly in the case of white substances, which can have both functions. White fillers extenders are also of coloristic importance in particular in paints. We have therefore used the classification shown in Tables 3.1—3.3 for a number of substances investigated by us, the fillers (Group 1) being grouped on chemical principles and the pigments (Groups 2—7) according to color.

For the production, properties, and use of inorganic pigments, the reader is referred to the literature [1, 323—326].

3.2 Chemical Analysis of Inorganic Fillers and Pigments

Inorganic fillers and pigments can be identified chemically by the well-known methods of qualitative inorganic analysis.

Table 3.1: Classification of inorganic fillers and pigments and their IR spectra numbers

	IR spectra No.
1. Fillers	5400–5437
1.1 Silica	5400–5404
1.2 Clay minerals, micas	5405–5416
1.3 Asbestos	5417–5423
1.4 Other silicates	5424–5429
1.5 Carbonates	5430–5432
1.6 Sulfates	5433–5435
1.7 Oxides	5436–5437
Inorganic pigments	
2. White pigments	5438–5448
2.1 Oxides	5438–5442
2.2 Sulfates, carbonates	5443–5446
2.3 Others	5447–5448
3. Yellow and orange pigments	5449–5459
3.1 Chromates	5449–5456
3.2 Antimonates	5457–5459
4. Brown and red pigments	5460–5475
4.1 Iron oxide pigments	5460–5468
4.2 Lead compounds	5469–5475
5. Green pigments	5476–5478
5.1 Chromium oxide pigments	5476–5477
5.2 Cobalt pigments	5478
6. Blue pigments	5479–5483
6.1 Various	5479, 5480
6.2 Manganese pigments	5481, 5482
7. Black pigments	5483, 5484

Table 3.2: Inorganic fillers

Dec. no.	IR sp. no.	Trade name
1.1.	**Silica**	
1.1.1	5400	Powdered quartz
1.1.2	5401	Kieselgur
1.1.3	5402	Ultrasil VN 3
1.1.4	5403	Hoesch KS 207
1.1.5	5404	China Clay 501
1.2.	**Clay minerals, micas**	
1.2.1	5405	McNamee Clay
1.2.2	5406	China Clay 565
1.2.3	5407	Kaolin
1.2.4	5408	Glimmerspat
1.2.5	5409	Siliceous chalk
1.2.6	5410	Mica glimmer
1.2.7	5411	Sericite
1.2.8	5412	Lepidolite
1.2.9	5413	Ground shale
1.2.10	5414	Porphyry
1.2.11	5415	Phonolite
1.2.12	5416	Nepheline
1.3.	**Asbestos**	
1.3.1	5417	Cassiar asbestos
1.3.2	5418	Rhod. chrysotile
1.3.3	5419	S. African chrysotile
1.3.4	5420	Micro hornblende asbestos
1.3.5	5421	Italian anthophyllite asbestos
1.3.6	5422	Blue asbestos
1.3.7	5423	Portug. anthophyllite asbestos
1.4.	**Other silicates**	
1.4.1	5424	Mistron Vapor
1.4.2	5425	Talc
1.4.3	5426	Serpentine
1.4.4	5427	Calsil
1.4.5	5428	Fireclay
1.4.6	5429	Sintered glass
1.5.	**Carbonates**	
1.5.1	5430	Calcite
1.5.2	5431	Chalk Omya BSH
1.5.3	5432	Dolomite
1.6.	**Sulfates**	
1.6.1	5433	Barite
1.6.2	5434	Calcium sulfate
1.6.3	5435	Gypsum
1.7.	**Oxides**	
1.7.1	5436	Corundum
1.7.2	5437	Barium ferrite

HEZEL [332] has described a systematic sequence for the qualitative analysis of inorganic pigments. KAPPELMEIER [330] has also given detailed descriptions, and there is consequently no need for further discussion here.

In addition to wet chemical methods, emission spectral analysis is used for the detection of elements, particularly in very small samples. We have found this method very useful for the identification of pigments in combination with IR spectroscopy and X-ray diffraction analysis.

Inorganic pigments in plastics and on painted surfaces can also be detected very rapidly in some cases and without previous isolation by X-ray fluorescence analysis, particularly in tests for specific pigments, on the basis of the elementary composition [333].

Many methods have been described for the isolation of carbon black from vulcanized products and polyolefins filled with carbon black; these methods are mainly based on pyrolysis in a stream of inert gas or on wet chemical digestion [335—339]. Comparative experiments with other methods on various vulcanizates have been reported by KURZMANN et al. [338], who use pyrolysis in a stream of N_2 for practical work. The pyrolytic recovery of carbon blacks and their characterization by surface area measurements, particle size determinations, and oil absorption have also been reported in further publications [335–340].

FISCHER [341] has described a spectrophotometric method for the determination of polycyclic hydrocarbons in carbon blacks by extraction, column or thin layer chromatography, and UV absorption or fluorescence measurement [341].

Composition: name, ideal formula	Analytical data
Quartz, SiO_2	
SiO_2 (amorphous)	
SiO_2 (amorphous)	
SiO_2 (amorphous)	
SiO_2 + silicates	
Kaolinit, $Al_4[(OH)_8/Si_4O_{10}]$	53 % SiO_2, 44 % Al_2O_3
Kaolinite + quartz, $Al_4[(OH)_8/Si_4O_{10}]$ + SiO_2	
Kaolinite + quartz, $Al_4[(OH)_8/Si_4O_{10}]$ + SiO_2	63 % SiO_2, 19,5 % Al_2O_3; 3,5 % K_2O, 1 % TiO_2, 0,4 % Fe_3O_2
Clay minerals + quartz	62,6 % SiO_2, 23 % Al_2O_3, 10,1 % K_2O, 0,4 % MgO
Quartz + clay minerals	86 % SiO_2, 6,9 % Al_2O_3, 0,5 % CaO, 0,3 % Na_2O
Mica, $KAl_2[(OH, F)_2 / AlSi_3O_{10}]$	
Sericite, a variety of muscovite	72,5 % SiO_2, 20 % Al_2O_3, 4,5 % K_2O, 1,3 % Fe_2O_3, 1 % MgO
Lepidolite, $K(Li, Al)_3[(F, OH)_2 / AlSi_3O_{10}]$	51 % SiO_2, 28 % Al_2O_3, 9 % K_2O, 4 % Li_2O, 7,2 % F
Shale	
Eruptive rock	75 % SiO_2, 13 % Al_2O_3, 8 % K_2O, 2,5 % Fe_2O_3
Eruptive rock	62,3 % SiO_2, 29,4 % Al_2O_3, 8,2 % K_2O + Na_2O, 2,4 Fe_2O_3; 2,1 % CaO
$(Na, K) Al / SiO_4$	60,7 % SiO_2, 23,3 % Al_2O_3, 9,8 % Na_2O, 4,6 % K_2O; 0,7 % CaO
Asbestos, $Mg_6[(OH)_8 / Si_4O_{10}]$	
Asbestos, $Mg_6[(OH)_8 / Si_4O_{10}]$	
Asbestos, $Mg_6[(OH)_8 / Si_4O_{10}]$	
Asbestos	42 % SiO_2, 24 % MgO, 10 % Al_2O_3, 8 % FeO, 6 % CaO, 2 % Fe_2O_3
Asbestos, $(Mg, Fe)_7[OH / Si_4O_{11}]_2$	
$Ca_2(Mg, Fe)_5[OH / Si_4O_{11}]_2$	
Asbestos, $(Mg, Fe)_7[OH / Si_4O_{11}]_2$	
$Mg_3[(OH)_2 / Si_4O_{10}]$	51,3 % SiO_2, 29,6 % MgO, 9,6 % Al_2O_3, 1,5 % Fe_2O_3
$Mg_6[(OH)_0 / Si_4O_{10}]$	36 % SiO_2, 23 % MgO, 13 % Fe_2O_3, 12 % Al_2O_3, 5 % CaO, 1 % TiO
$CaSiO_3$	
$Al_2O_3 \cdot 2 SiO_2$	
Silicate glass	64 % SiO_2, 15 % BaO, 7 % Na_2O, 6 % K_2O, 4 % Al_2O_3, 1 % Li_2O
$CaCO_3$	99 % $CaCO_3$; 0,4 % Fe_2O_3, 0,3 % SiO_2, 0,2 % $MgCO_3$
$CaCO_3$	
Dolomite, $MgCa(CO_3)_2$	
Barite, $BaSO_4$	
$CaSO_4$	
$CaSO_4 \cdot 2 H_2O$	
Al_2O_3	
$BaO \cdot 6 Fe_2O_3$	

3.3 IR Spectroscopy of Inorganic Fillers and Pigments

The use of IR spectroscopy for the analytical identification and characterization of inorganic substances is becoming increasingly important, since the molecule-specific information together with the analysis of the elements allows a much better characterization than the elementary composition alone.

From the considerable number of publications on the IR spectroscopy of minerals and inorganic compounds, the reader is referred to a few reviews and monographs [342, 343], some of which also contain assignment diagrams. A

Table 3.3: Inorganic pigments

Dec. No.	IR sp. No.	CI Name	CI No.	Trade name	Composition
2.1.	Oxides				
2.1.1	5438	W 6	77891	Titanium dioxide RN 56	Rutil, TiO_2
2.1.2	5439	W 6	77891	Special white	Anatas, TiO_2
2.1.3	5440	W 4	77947	Zinc white	Zinc oxide, ZnO
2.1.4	5441			Magnesium oxide	MgO
2.1.5	5442	W 11	77052	Antimony white	Antimony oxide Sb_2O_3
2.2.	Sulfates, carbonates				
2.2.1	5443	W 21	77120	Blanc fixe F	Barium sulfate, $BaSO_4$
2.2.2	5444	W 5	77115	Zinc white green seal GS	Lithopone, $BaSO_4 + ZnS$
2.2.3	5445			Basic lead sulfate	$(PbO)_n \cdot PbSO_4$
2.2.4	5446	W 1	77597	White lead	Basic Lead carbonate, $2\,PbCO_3 \cdot Pb(OH)_2$
2.3.	Others				
2.3.1	5447			Lead silicate	Basic Lead silicate, $2\,PbSiO_3 \cdot Pb(OH)_2$
2.3.2	5448			Zinc phosphate ZNP	$Zn_3(PO_4)_2 \cdot 4\,H_2O$
3.1.	Chromates				
3.1.1	5449			Chrome yellow 7520	Lead chromate, Lead chromate sulfate
3.1.2	5450	Y 34	77603	Chrome yellow 51	Lead chromate sulfate
3.1.3	5451	Y 34	77603	Chrome yellow 48	Lead chromate sulfate
3.1.4	5452	Y 36	77955	Zinc yellow 3682 N	Potassium zinc chromate containing Pb
3.1.5	5453	Y 36	77955	Zinc yellow 760 B	Zinc tetroxychromate containing Pb
3.1.6	5454	Y 31	77103	Barium chromate 840 SV	$BaCrO_4$
3.1.7	5455	Y 32	77839	Strontium chromate A	$SrCrO_4$
3.1.8	5456			Calcium chromate S II 1472	$CaCrO_4$
3.2.	Antimonates				
3.2.1	5457	Y 41	77588	Naples yellow	Lead antimonate, $Pb_3(SbO_4)_2$
3.2.2	5458	Y 53	77788	Nickel titanium yellow R 4	Antimony nickel titanium oxide
3.2.3	5459			Mineral fast yellow 1893	Lead titanium antimonate
4.1.	Iron oxides pigments				
4.1.1	5460			α-Iron oxide	Iron(III) oxide, α-Fe_2O_3
4.1.2	5461			γ-Iron oxide	Iron(III) oxide, γ-Fe_2O_3
4.1.3	5462			Iron oxide WM S II 2132	Iron oxide
4.1.4	5463	R 101	77491	Iron oxide red AFK/M	Iron oxide
4.1.5	5464			Iron oxide WM S II 2396	Iron oxide
4.1.6	5465	BR 6	77491	Iron oxide brown FDK/F	Iron(II, III) oxide $+ SiO_2$
4.1.7	5466			Oxide fast brown K 65	Iron(III) oxide, Fe_2O_3
4.1.8	5467	Y 42	77492	Iron oxide yellow	Hydrated iron oxide $Fe_2O_3 \cdot H_2O$
4.1.9	5468			Chrome iron brown 1	Chromium iron oxide
4.2.	Lead compounds				
4.2.1	5469	R 105	77578	Red Lead	Lead (II, IV) oxide, Pb_3O_4
4.2.2	5470			Lead molybdate VM S II 1098	$PbMoO_4$
4.2.3	5471	R 104	77605	Molybdate red DL	Lead chromate molybdate sulfate
4.2.4	5472	R 104	77605	Molybdate red VM	Lead chromate molybdate sulfate
4.2.5	5473			Chrome red 1	Basic lead chromate
4.2.6	5474	OR 21	77601	Chrome orange 58	Basic Lead chromate
5.1.	Chromium oxide pigments				
5.1.1	5475	GR 17	77288	Chrome oxide green RN	Chrome oxide, Cr_2O_3
5.1.2	5476	GR 18	77289	Hydrated chrome oxide green LN	Chrome oxide hydrate, $Cr_2O_3 \cdot H_2O$
5.2.	Cobalt pigments				
5.2.1	5477	GR 14	77346	Cobalt green 771	Cobalt aluminate, $CoO \cdot Al_2O_3$

Table 3.3 (continued)

Dec. No.	IR sp. No.	CI Name	No.	Trade name	Composition
6.1.	Various				
6.1.1	5478	BL 28	77346	Cobalt blue 767	Cobalt aluminate, $CoO \cdot Al_2O_3$
6.1.2	5479	BL 29	77007	Ultramarine blue 130	Sulfur containing Na-Al-silicate
6.1.3	5480	BL 27	77510	Prussian blue R 28543	Ferri-ferrocyanide, $Fe_4[Fe(CN)_6]_3$
6.2.	Manganese pigments				
6.2.1	5481	BL 33	77112	Manganese blue M	Barium manganate sulfate
6.2.2	5482	V 16	77742	Manganese violet Y	Manganese ammonium pyrophosphate, $(NH_4)_2Mn_2(P_2O_7)_2$
7.	Black pigments				
7.1.	5483	BLA	1177499	Oxide black 30 V	Iron(II, III) oxide, Fe_3O_4
7.2.	5484	BLA	977266	Bone black	Carbon + $Ca_3(PO_4)_2$

collection with 473 spectra of minerals (4000—400 cm⁻¹) in card form has been published by MOENKE [345]. This is particularly useful for the identification of naturally occurring fillers. HARKINS et al. [346] presented the spectra of 21 inorganic pigments in the range between 5000 and 650 cm⁻¹ (2 to 15 μm) to show the possibilities of IR analysis for the identification of pigments. These can be considerably improved by extending the spectral range to 400 or 200 cm⁻¹ (25 or 50 μm), since many oxides and sulfides give no fundamental vibration bands in the range down to 650 cm⁻¹ (15 μm). AFREMOW and VANDENBERG [347] have demonstrated clearly the value of IR spectroscopy with the spectra of 78 fillers and pigments in the range between 1500 and 200 cm⁻¹ (6.7—50 μm).

The spectra of fillers and pigments are generally recorded by the KBr disc technique. If the spectra in the region below 400 cm⁻¹ (above 25 μm) are of interest, cesium iodide can be used as the disc material. AFREMOW [347] uses a "triple compression technique", in which the pelletizer is packed with about 300 mg of well ground powder mixture and evacuated for about 2 min; the contents of the pelletizer are then compressed under vacuum for 2 min at about 1500 kg/cm², the pressure is removed, and after about 30 s, is re-applied for about 2 min. The removal and re-application of the pressure is repeated once more. The scattering of radiation by the pellets can be greatly reduced in this way.

The concentration of the sample in the pellet is generally 0.1—1 wt. %, preferably about 0.5 %.

Embedding in liquid paraffin can be useful in the case of silicates containing OH, hydrated oxides, and basic salts if one desires to avoid interaction with the embedding material and to obtain trouble-free detection of the OH bands around 3700 to 3400 cm⁻¹ (2.7—2.95 μm). Discs may also be made by pelletizing with polyethylene powder. Finally, the very finely ground powder may be sprinkled on a thin film of polyethylene and covered with a second film, the two films then being welded by the action of heat under pressure.

The spectra of fillers and pigments, which contain few bands in comparison with the spectra of organic substances, have their strongest bands mainly in the region between 1500 and 200 cm⁻¹ (6.7—50 μm). These are mainly stretching and deformation vibrations of X—O bonds, where X (C, S, Si, heavy metals) is usually surrounded tetrahedrally or octahedrally with oxygen. The spectra and their assignments will not be discussed here, since special literature on this topic exists [342—345]. However, a number of useful hints will be given for identification with the aid of IR spectra. Compounds containing water of crystallization have a broad band around 3400 cm⁻¹ (2.94 μm). Very sharp bands due to free monomeric OH groups are observed between 3700 and 3600 cm⁻¹ (2.7—2.8 μm) for various chain and layer silicates containing OH. These bands are useful for distin-

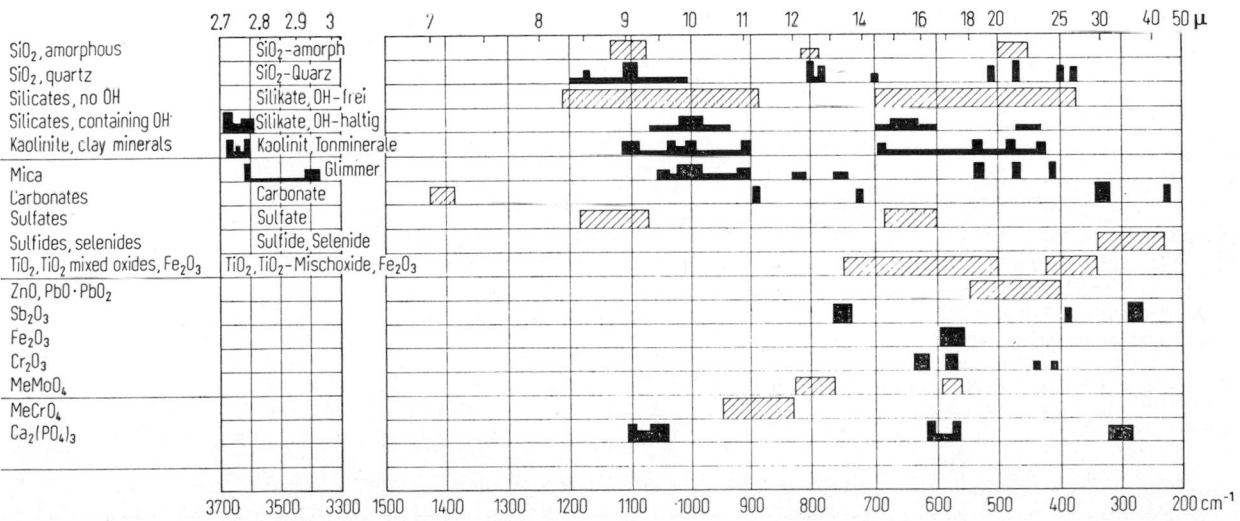

Fig. 3.1: Band chart for inorganic fillers and pigments

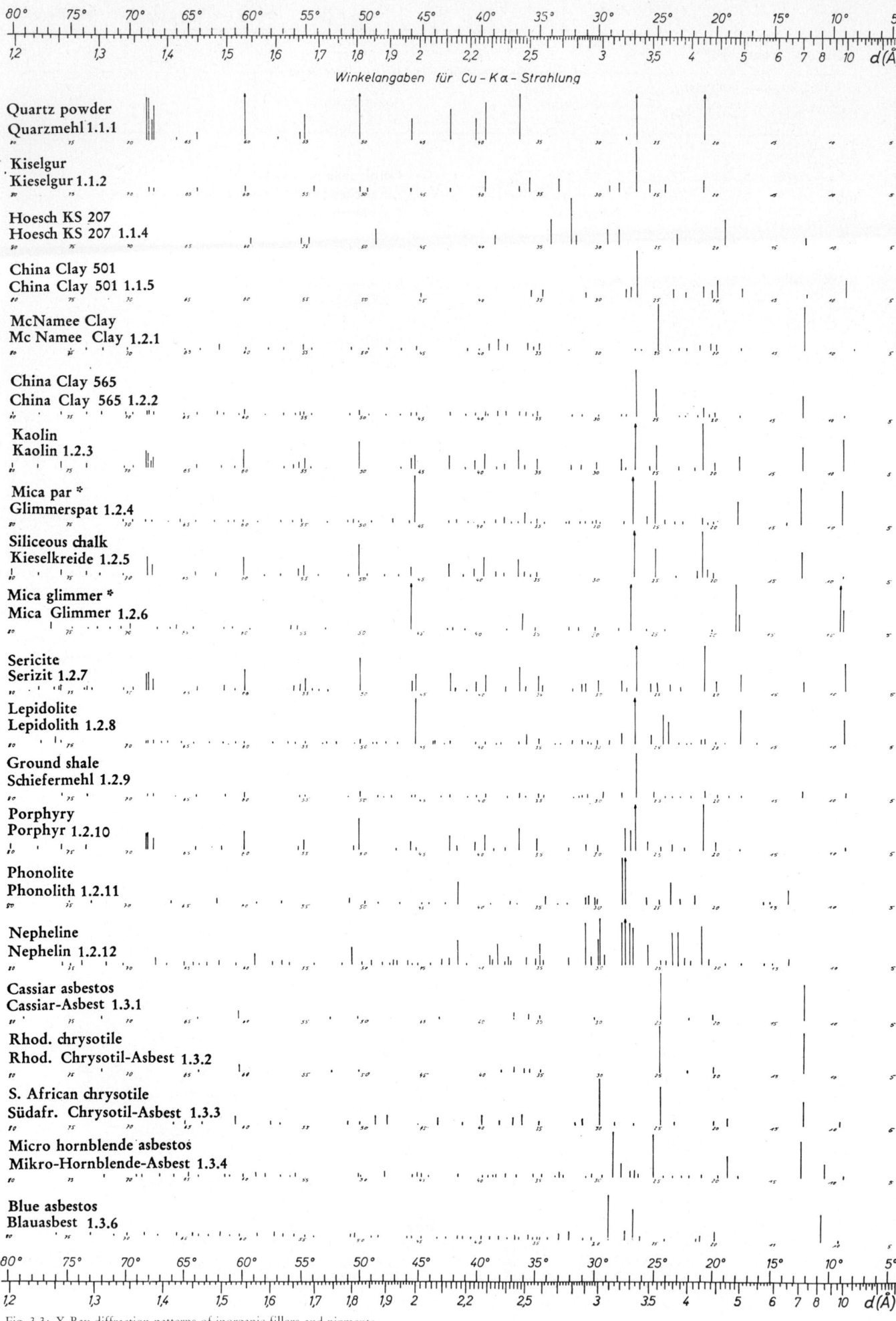

Fig. 3.3: X-Ray diffraction patterns of inorganic fillers and pigments

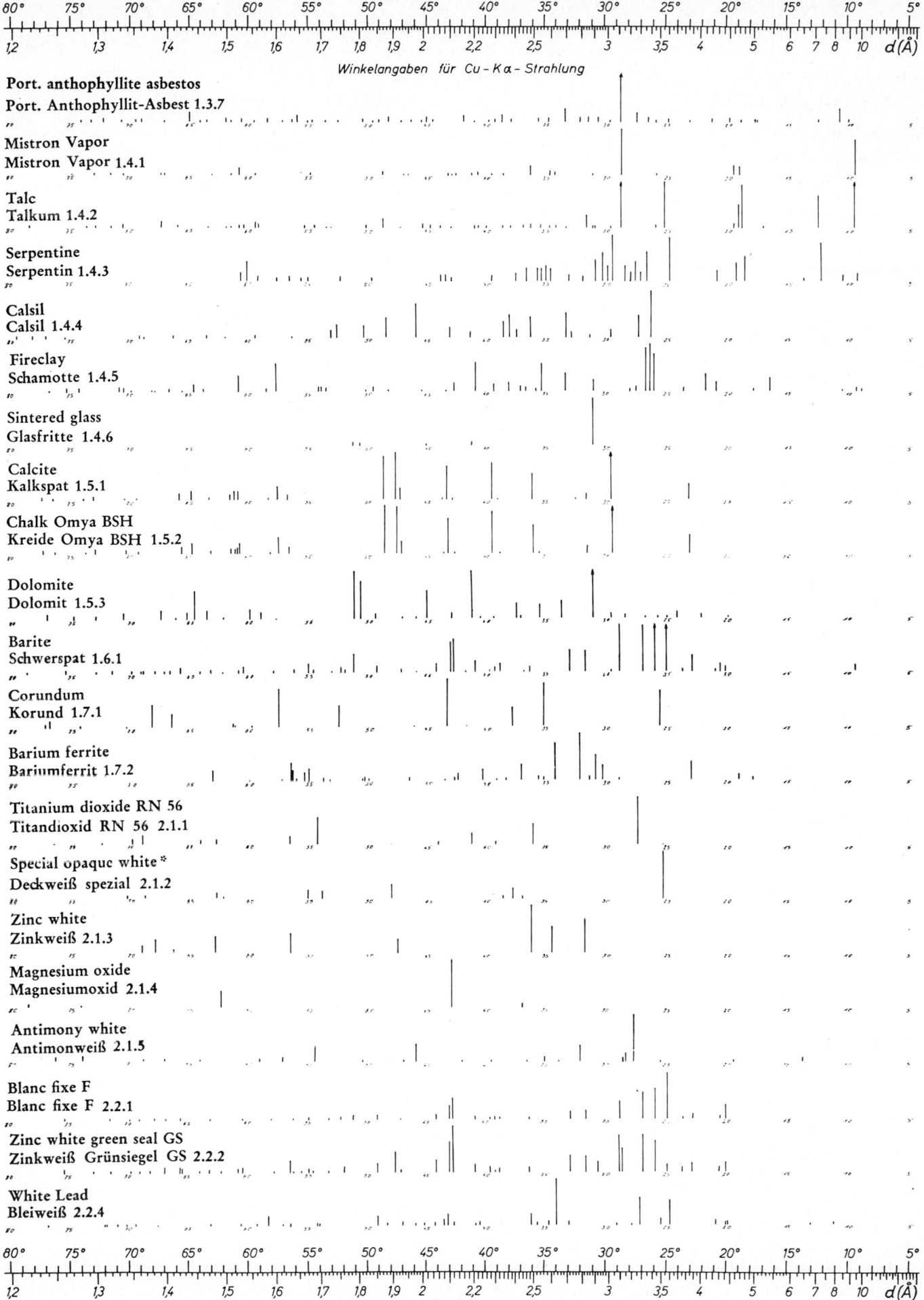

Port. anthophyllite asbestos
Port. Anthophyllit-Asbest 1.3.7

Mistron Vapor
Mistron Vapor 1.4.1

Talc
Talkum 1.4.2

Serpentine
Serpentin 1.4.3

Calsil
Calsil 1.4.4

Fireclay
Schamotte 1.4.5

Sintered glass
Glasfritte 1.4.6

Calcite
Kalkspat 1.5.1

Chalk Omya BSH
Kreide Omya BSH 1.5.2

Dolomite
Dolomit 1.5.3

Barite
Schwerspat 1.6.1

Corundum
Korund 1.7.1

Barium ferrite
Bariumferrit 1.7.2

Titanium dioxide RN 56
Titandioxid RN 56 2.1.1

Special opaque white*
Deckweiß spezial 2.1.2

Zinc white
Zinkweiß 2.1.3

Magnesium oxide
Magnesiumoxid 2.1.4

Antimony white
Antimonweiß 2.1.5

Blanc fixe F
Blanc fixe F 2.2.1

Zinc white green seal GS
Zinkweiß Grünsiegel GS 2.2.2

White Lead
Bleiweiß 2.2.4

80° 75° 70° 65° 60° 55° 50° 45° 40° 35° 30° 25° 20° 15° 10° 5°

1,2 1,3 1,4 1,5 1,6 1,7 1,8 1,9 2 2,2 2,5 3 3,5 4 5 6 7 8 10 d(Å)

Angles for Cu-Kα radiation / Winkelangaben für Cu-Kα-Strahlung

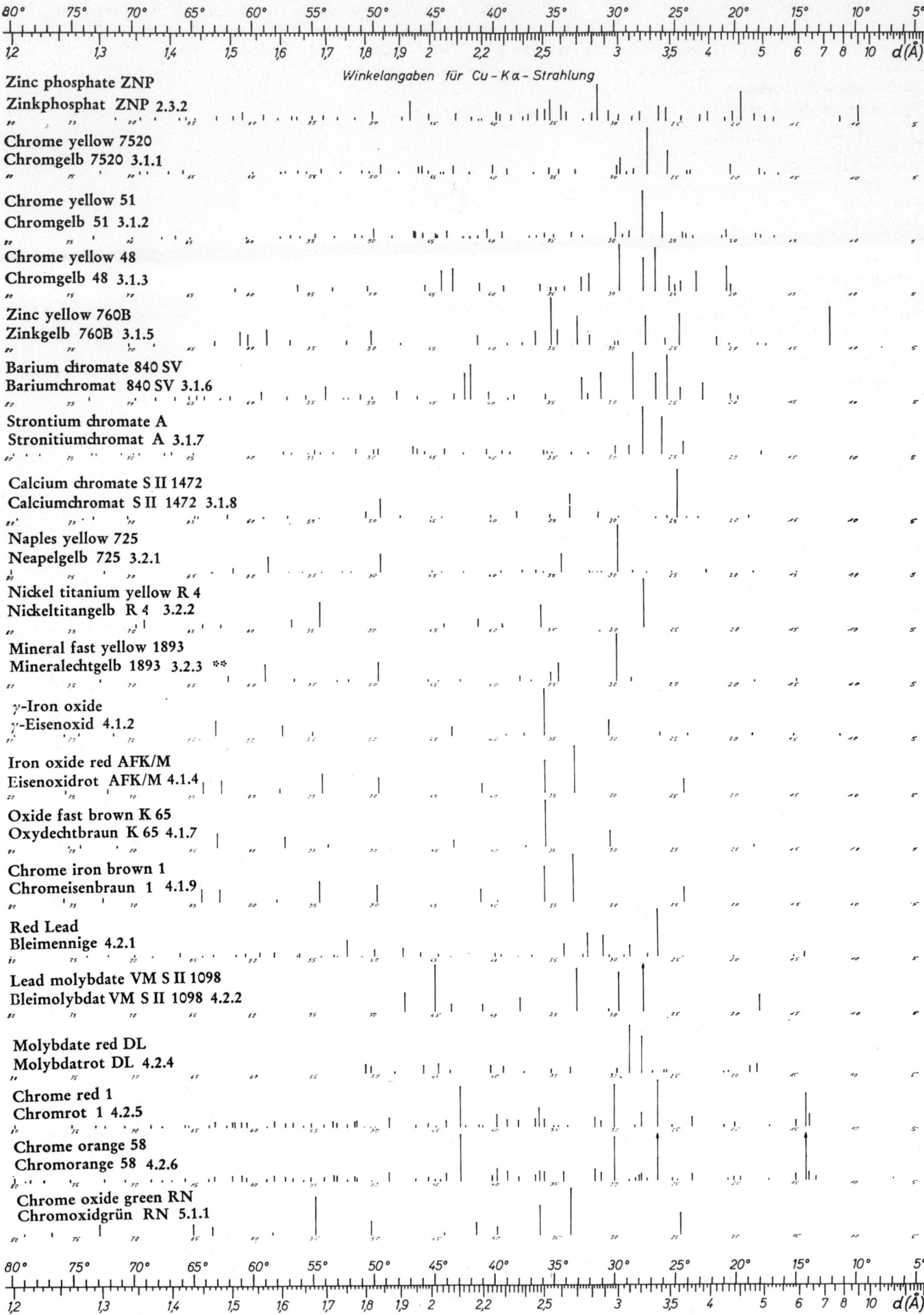

Zinc phosphate ZNP
Zinkphosphat ZNP 2.3.2

Chrome yellow 7520
Chromgelb 7520 3.1.1

Chrome yellow 51
Chromgelb 51 3.1.2

Chrome yellow 48
Chromgelb 48 3.1.3

Zinc yellow 760B
Zinkgelb 760B 3.1.5

Barium chromate 840 SV
Bariumchromat 840 SV 3.1.6

Strontium chromate A
Stronitiumchromat A 3.1.7

Calcium chromate S II 1472
Calciumchromat S II 1472 3.1.8

Naples yellow 725
Neapelgelb 725 3.2.1

Nickel titanium yellow R 4
Nickeltitangelb R 4 3.2.2

Mineral fast yellow 1893
Mineralechtgelb 1893 3.2.3 **

γ-Iron oxide
γ-Eisenoxid 4.1.2

Iron oxide red AFK/M
Eisenoxidrot AFK/M 4.1.4

Oxide fast brown K 65
Oxydechtbraun K 65 4.1.7

Chrome iron brown 1
Chromeisenbraun 1 4.1.9

Red Lead
Bleimennige 4.2.1

Lead molybdate VM S II 1098
Bleimolybdat VM S II 1098 4.2.2

Molybdate red DL
Molybdatrot DL 4.2.4

Chrome red 1
Chromrot 1 4.2.5

Chrome orange 58
Chromorange 58 4.2.6

Chrome oxide green RN
Chromoxidgrün RN 5.1.1

Angles for Cu-Kα radiation / Winkelangaben für Cu-Kα-Strahlung

58

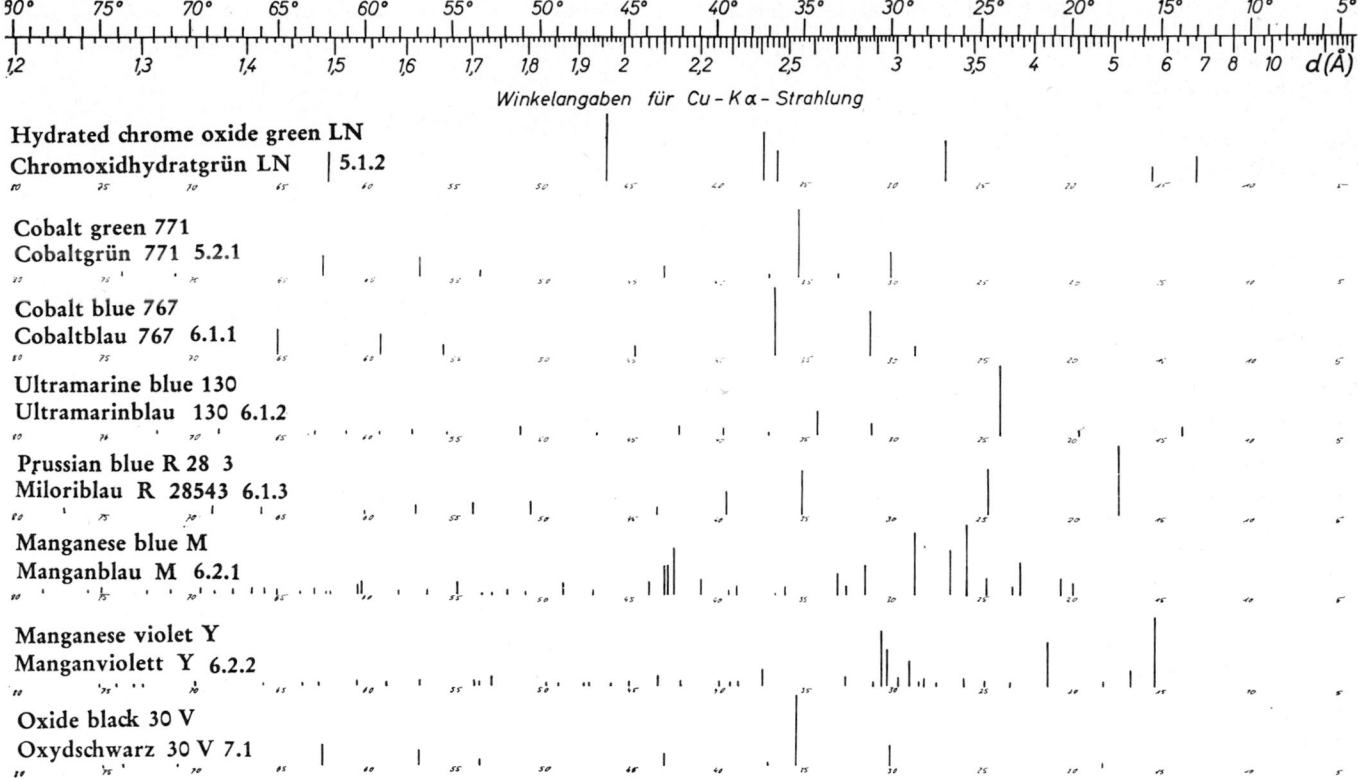

guishing various silicates. The strong, narrow C=N stretching band of the complex cyanides at 2088 cm⁻¹ (4.79 μm) is particularly characteristic.

Figure 3.1 shows the characteristic band regions and individual bands for a number of inorganic fillers and pigments.

The influence of the crystallinity on the spectra can be demonstrated for various forms of silicon dioxide (spectra 5400–5403). The characteristically split bands obtained for quartz appear only as broad, unresolved bands, in some cases of low intensity, for the amorphous silicas.

In the layer silicates (clay minerals, mica), the absorption maximum of the antisymmetric Si—O stretching vibration is displaced in relation to that of SiO₂, and is situated around 1000 cm⁻¹ (10 μm), while for the chain silicates, which include the various types of asbestos, the maximum occurs at 960 cm⁻¹ (10.4 μm).

The silicate glasses and fireclay flour containing vitreous phase (spectra 5428, 5429) exhibit even stronger broadening of the bands than the amorphous silicas.

The alkaline earth metal carbonates and sulfates are easily recognizable from their characteristic spectra, which contain a broad principal band and a number of very sharp bands of various intensities. The carbonation of basic sulfates and silicates can also be detected in the spectra by the appearance of carbonate bands.

The oxides and mixed oxides of Ti, Fe, Ni, Sb, Cr, Pb, and other heavy metals have broad bands below 750 cm⁻¹ (above 13.3 μm), but mixed oxides containing SiO₂ also have a band at 1100 cm⁻¹ (9.1 μm), depending on the SiO₂ content. Chromates and molybdates have the strongest bands at 950—800 cm⁻¹ (10.5—12.5 μm).

A large number of yellow, yellow-brown, brown, red, and red-violet pigments contain iron oxide hydrates and iron

oxides as the main components. RIEDERER [348] has investigated 24 natural and synthetic iron oxide pigments and presented a detailed discussion of the IR spectra in the region between 5000 and 650 cm⁻¹ (2 15 μm). The natural yellow earth pigments (ochers) mostly contain considerable quantities of clay minerals and quartz as well as yellow iron oxide hydrate, so that their spectra can be interpreted as resulting from the superposition of the spectra of iron yellow (spectrum no. 5467) with those of clay minerals or clay minerals containing quartz (spectra 5400—5403) However, the characteristic bands of hydrated iron oxide at 900 cm⁻¹ (11.1 μm), 795 cm⁻¹ (12.55 μm), and 600 cm⁻¹ (16.7 μm) are mostly quite distinct. The carbonates that are sometimes also present in natural iron oxide pigments can be recognized by a broad band at 1420 cm⁻¹ (7.0 μm). A similar situation is found for the red earth pigments, but the band around 3400 cm⁻¹ (2.95 μm) due to the water of hydration is absent. Here again, the spectra can vary with the content of clay minerals.

In the spectra of the burnt earth pigments, the intensity of the OH band decreases more or less strongly, depending on the burning temperature. At temperatures up to about 300 °C, the band around 3400 cm⁻¹ (2.95 μm) disappears, while at temperatures above 600 °C, kaolinite and other layer silicates also lose water, so that the bands in the region between 3700 and 3600 cm⁻¹ (2.7—2.77 μm) also disappear.

The synthetic iron oxide pigments do not contain clay minerals, but other additives or diluents such as calcium carbonate and calcium sulfate may be present, depending on the production process. In addition to the absorption of the brown and red iron oxide pigments in the region between 650 and 450 cm⁻¹ (15.2—22 μm), there is often also a weak or medium strong, broad band with a maximum around 1100 cm⁻¹ (9.1 μm), which is indicative of the presence of SiO₂.

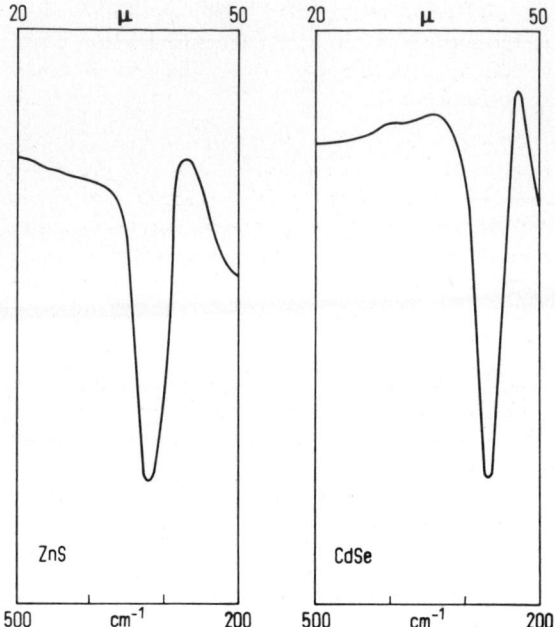

Fig. 3.2: IR spectra of zinc sulfide and cadmium selenide

Zinc sulfide absorbs around 322 cm⁻¹ (31 μm), and calcium sulfide and selenide at 270 cm⁻¹ (37 μm). They cannot therefore be detected in the spectra of pigments containing these compounds (e. g. lithopone, cadmium lithopone) in the spectral region above 400 cm⁻¹ (below 25 μm). Figure 3.2 shows the absorption of these compounds in the region between 500 and 200 cm⁻¹ (20—50 μm).

Carbon blacks and other carbon pigments exhibit a differentiated IR spectrum only if they contain appreciable quantities of foreign components or functional groups. The former is true e. g. in bone black, of which 90—95 % is calcium phosphate, so that the spectrum (spectrum no. 5484) is identical with that of pure calcium phosphate.

3.4 X-Ray Diffraction Analysis of Inorganic Fillers and Pigments

X-ray diffraction analysis, which has been in use for some time for the determination of structures of crystalline substances, is a very elegant aid to the identification of fillers and pigments, since it is frequently unnecessary to separate these from the organic binder (lacquer, plastic, or rubber).

X-ray diffraction data for many of the inorganic substances used as fillers and pigments can be found in the literature and in data collections [221—224]. Data on silicate minerals are also given by JASMUND [322], and the application of X-ray diffraction analysis to pigments is described by KÖNIG [323, 349].

If recording counter-tube diffractometers are used to record the X-ray diffraction diagrams, the fastest method for the evaluation of the latter is by the use of comparison diagrams.

Figure 3.3 (p. 56—59) shows X-ray diagrams in line form for some of the substances listed in Tables 3.2 and 3.3. When enlarged to the scale of the original diagram, these have proved to be a useful evaluation aid.

Before the X-ray diffraction analysis, we usually determine the elements present in the sample by a semiquantitative emission spectral analysis. This simplifies the evaluation

of the X-ray diffraction analysis, and also provides additional information in the case of amorphous fillers.

4 Organic Pigments
4.1 Survey and Classification

Organic pigments are necessary in order to obtain the wide range of colors currently demanded in paints, coating materials, and plastics. The number of organic pigments that are of industrial interest, excluding soluble dyes for transparent colors, is probably about 300—400, i. e. twice the number of inorganic pigments in current use. A large volume of special literature exists on their preparation, properties, and applications [1, 2, 323, 350—363].

The organic pigments can be grouped in various ways [357, 364—366]. Following proposals by HECKL [366], we have taken the classification shown in Table 4.1 as a basis for our analytical investigations. In naming the individual pigments in the subsequent tables and in the spectra, we have largely avoided trade names and trivial names, and have used the Colour Index names and numbers [357].

Many of the organic pigments are azo pigments (groups 1—3), which contain one or more chromophoric — N = N groups, and which are important yellow and red pigments.

They are prepared by diazotization of aniline, its homologs (toluidine, xylidine), and their nitration and halogenation products, followed by coupling with a naphthol, an acetoacetarylamide or a pyrazolone. The subdivision of the monoazo and disazo pigments was therefore based on the coupling component (abbreviation CC) used. An example of the preparation of a monoazo pigment (Pigment Yellow 5) is given in the following reaction scheme:

NO₂—NH₂ $\xrightarrow[0\,°C]{NaNO_2 + HCl}$ NO₂—N=N-Cl + CH₂CONH— $\overset{|}{COCH_3}$

Diazotization

2-Nitroaniline   Diazo-2-nitroaniline   Acetoacetic anilide

→ NO₂—N=N-CHCONH— $\overset{|}{COCH_3}$

Pigment Yellow

In the legends to the spectra, the composition is shown by the arylamine and the coupling component used. For the above example, therefore, the composition is 2-nitroaniline → acetoacetanilide. The arrow symbolizes the diazotization before coupling.

Important monoazo pigments used in our investigations are listed in Tables 4.2, 4.3, and 4.4.

If the aniline derivatives or the coupling components or both contain carboxyl groups — COOH or sulfo groups — SO₃H, the water-solubility is greatly increased. Such azo dyes can be used as pigments in the form of sparingly soluble barium, calcium, copper, manganese, and in some cases even sodium salts precipitated from aqueous solution (group 2, see Tables 4.5 and 4.6).

When arylamines with two diazotizable amino groups, such as derivatives of benzidine $H_2N \cdot C_6H_4 \cdot C_6H_4 \cdot NH_2$, are used for the preparation of azo dyes, yellow and orange-red diazo dyes are obtained on diazotization and coupling with acetoacetarylamides and orange-red and red diazo dyes with pyrazolones, many of these compounds being suitable for use as pigments owing to their low solubility (group 3, Table 4.7). Blue indigo pigments and red thioindigo pigments (group 4, Table 4.8) are obtainable in various hues by chlorination, bromination, and methylation.

The anthraquinone pigments and the pigments with condensed rings include red, violet, and blue as well as some yellow and orange-red pigments.

Derivatives of anthraquinone are commonly used as the Al lakes (violet) and in substituted and condensed forms as yellow to violet pigments (groups 5.1 and 5.2, Table 4.9).

Naphthoylenebenzimidazoles and the similarly constructed perylenes are used as orange-red and red pigments (groups 5.3 and 5.4, Table 4.10).

Quinacridones and dioxazines (groups 5.5 and 5.6, Table 4.10) are red and violet pigments. In the case of the linear trans-quinacridone (Pigment Violet 19), it is surprising that this relatively simple organic substance is so sparingly soluble and can assume a wide range of hues between red (γ-crystal form) and violet (β form) [392]. Hydrogen bonds between the molecules play an important part in this behavior.

Blue and green phthalocyanine pigments (group 6, Table 4.11) have attained great practical importance because of their pure, brilliant hues, their great intensity of color, and their very good color fastness (high chemical and thermal stability). Here again, the color depends on the crystal form. Copper phthalocyanine (Pigment Blue 15), which is the most commonly used blue pigment at present, is available in the α form, the β form, or mixtures of these two modifications [391]. Small quantities of phthalocyanines are added to many commercial pigments to modify the color.

Group 7 of our classification contains blue, violet, and green lakes of basic, water-soluble triphenylmethane dyes (7.1), red lakes of basic xanthene dyes (7.2, Table 4.12), blue lakes of acid triphenylmethane dyes (7.3), and yellow and red xanthene pigments (7.4, Table 4.13). Of the pigments of groups 7.1—7.3 laked with heteropolyacids, we have confined our investigations almost entirely to the phosphotungstomolybdic acid lakes (abbreviated to PWMo acid lakes).

An example of a diphenylmethane pigment (7.6) is auramine O, which is also laked with PWMo acid.

Green nitroso pigments (7.6) based on the iron complexes of 1-nitroso-2-naphthol and its 6-sulfonic acid are still of industrial interest, as are some yellow nitro pigments (7.7) the first example of which was picric acid, which is no longer of any importance as a pigment.

Finally, an example of a thiazole pigment is Pigment Yellow 18, the PWMo acid lake of thioflavine (7.8), and an example of an azine pigment is Pigment Black 1 (aniline black).

4.2 Separation of Organic Pigments

Separation of the Pigments from Additives and Binders: Organic pigments can be separated from aqueous pastes and dispersions by addition of watermiscible solvents followed by centrifugation of the pigment. A precipitant that has been suggested is a hot acetone/water mixture (1:1), to which a few drops of hydrochloric acid are added to facilitate flocculation [369].

They can also be separated from pastes containing plasticizers or binders by dilution with large quantities of suitable solvents, e. g. hydrocarbons or acetone, followed by centrifugation of the pigment.

Lakes, uncured resin mixes, and printing inks are also diluted with solvent (e. g. ether) and the pigments are flocculated and centrifuged off. If traces of binder also remain undissolved, further separation must be attempted with other solvents or solvent mixtures in an effort to dissolve either the binder or the pigment. The identification of the binder is of great importance to the choice of suitable solvents.

In the case of dry paints or plastics, one must either extract the pigment, chloroform (for azo dyes, fat dyes) or glacial acetic acid (for laked pigments) frequently being suitable, or dissolve the binder and separate the pigment. This must usually be followed by chromatography for further separation. Pigments can sometimes be isolated from dried paint films by hydrolytic degradation of the binder.

Separation of Pigments from One Another: The pigments used in practice, particularly in finished products, are frequently mixtures, and can be identified only after separation. Solubility differences in cold and hot solvents can be used for this purpose (the sparingly soluble phthalocyanines can be separated particularly readily in this way). Some pigments can be sublimed. Monoazo pigments can usually be separated in this manner from diazo pigments. The microscopic examination of crystal form and size sometimes gives an indication that mixtures are present. The most elegant method of testing for uniformity is undoubtedly thin layer chromatography, since this simultaneously provides information that can be used for identification, and several components can be separated from one another in a single operation. The quantities that can be isolated from chromatograms are often sufficient for IR-spectroscopic analysis.

Both in the separation from binders and other additives and in the separation of pigments from one another, repeated checking of the separation, e. g. by IR spectroscopy, is useful

4.3 Thermal and Optical Methods for the Investigation of Organic Pigments

Melting and Sublimation Points: The melting and sublimation points of some organic pigments are occasionally used together with microscopic examination of the sublimates for identification purposes [370]. The publications mentioned also contain numerical data for some azo and anthraquinone pigments. Laked pigments cannot be identified in this way.

More reliable information is certainly obtainable from thermal data obtained by thermogravimetric analysis and by differential thermal analysis, but no systematic studies by these methods on large numbers of pigments have been reported so far.

Microscopic Investigation of the Crystal Form: The pigment crystals deposited on a slide by sublimation can be used for identification. Since the shape and size of the crystals depend on the sublimation conditions (temperature, time, distance to the slide, etc.), it is necessary to use accurately defined conditions. KUTZELNIGG [370] described an apparatus and reproduced photographs of 16 pigments. STOCK [373] also reproduced photomicrographs of sublimed pigment crystals and of pigment crystals obtained from organic and aqueous solutions. VESCE [372] used the crystals obtained from concentrated sulfuric acid (34 photographs) for identification.

Absorption and Reflection Spectra in the Visible Region: Absorption and reflection spectra in the visible region are widely used for the characterization of dyes and pigments and for the measurement of color fastness. VESCE [372, 377] and SALTZMANN [379] reproduced spectra of numerous organic pigments, and data can also be found in collections of tables and in books [374, 377, 380, 381].

Since the bands are usually broad and not very well differentiated, the spectra in the visible region are of analytical interest only for a few classes of pigments.

The fluorescence stimulated by UV light can be a valuable aid to identification in some cases. However, since numerous factors can considerably affect the fluorescence, particularly in the solid state, only the positive fluorescence can be used as a reliable indication.

4.4 Solubility and Chemical Behavior of Organic Pigments

The solubility in various organic and inorganic solvents, the behavior on reduction, the dyeing behavior, and the determination of metals and hetero elements allow the identification of the pigment group in most cases, and even of the pigment present in some cases. SCHWEPPE [419] has described the preferred methods for this purpose, which are partly based on the work of GREEN [416], and has published data on the behavior of numerous individual pigments. However, since pigments with similar constitutions usually differ very little in their reactions, SCHWEPPE pointed out the possibilities of IR spectroscopy.

The chemical tests described below are based on the data reported by SCHWEPPE [376]. An attempt has been made in Table 4.14 to summarize the behavior of the pigments in the various tests. For details, particularly concerning color reactions, the reader must refer to the original publications [375, 376].

Determination of Inorganic Elements: Conclusions regarding the nature of the pigments can be drawn from the presence of various metals, which can be determined by chemical analysis of the ash, by emission spectral analysis of the ash or of the pigment, or by X-ray fluorescence analysis of the pigment (non-destructive) (Table 4.15). However, it must be remembered that metal compounds of various types may be present in technical products through the production process (e. g. salts that cause hardness in water) or through other additives (drying agents in lakes), so that one should not deduce too much from the presence in particular of traces.

Solubility: 10—50 mg of the pigment are heated for a few minutes in turn with about 10 ml each of water, ethyl alcohol, concentrated ammonia, and alcohol + ammonia (1 : 1) in a test tube. The supernatant solution is decanted, filtered, and concentrated, possibly with addition of water, so that one finally obtains an aqueous solution or the dyes precipitated from it. A separate sample is heated with glacial acetic acid.

The various extracts contain mainly the following dyes:

Water and ammonia:	Direct dyes
Alcohol and glacial acetic acid:	Basic dyes, many ether-soluble pigments (organic pigments with no sulfo group), alcohol-soluble dyes
Ammonia and ammonia-alcohol:	Acid dyes (also acid laked dyes)
Glacial acetic acid:	Azo pigments, alizarin dyes, indigo and some vat dyes
Residue:	Phthalocyanines, quinacridones, dioxazines, vat dyes.

Nearly all pigments dissolve in concentrated sulfuric acid, very often with no change in color. Color changes occur on addition of potassium iodate (1 g per 150 ml of conc. sulfuric acid). Anthraquinone derivatives exhibit typical color changes in borosulfuric acid (1 g of boric acid per 10 ml of conc. sulfuric acid).

Other suitable solvents are ether, chloroform, dimethylformamide, and N-methylpyrrolidone (for phthalocyanines).

Color Reactions: Further distinctions are possible within individual groups of pigments with the aid of color reactions. These reactions involve the use of the above-mentioned sulfuric acid mixtures, as well as sulfuric acid/nitric acid mixtures, nitric acid, sodium hydroxide solution, and other reagents.

The color reactions are best carried out by spotting on pigment solution that has been poured on filter paper or on dyed absorbent cotton. Reference must be made here to the original literature [368, 375, 376]. Characteristic color changes are often observed, particularly in the case of azo pigments, when a sample is heated with ethanol and approximately 10 % of 1 N sodium hydroxide solution. If the solution is poured on filter paper, it forms a strongly colored jagged edge surrounded by a less strongly colored or colorless edge zone.

Dyeing Properties: If water-soluble dyes are still present after concentration of the aqueous, alcoholic, ammoniacal, or acetic acid extracts of the pigments, it is possible to establish, by dyeing tests on wool and on unmordanted and mordanted cottons, whether an acid, a substantive, or a basic dye is present. For this test, a strand of wool and a cotton thread mordanted with tannin and tartar emetic are placed in part of the solution, and 1—2 drops of dilute acetic acid are added. The solution is boiled for about 1 minute. If the cotton thread is dyed while little or no dyeing of the wool has occurred, a basic dye is present. If the wool and the cotton are equally strongly dyed, acid and basic dyes are distinguished as follows. The dye solution is heated with sodium hydroxide solution, and the color base formed in the case of basic dyes is extracted with ether. Dilute acetic acid is added to the separated ether layer. If the lower acetic acid layer is colored, a basic dye is present.

Table 4.1: Classification of organic pigments and their IR spectra numbers

	IR spectra No.
1. Monoazo pigments	5500–5574
1.1 CC Acetoacetarylamides	5500–5514
1.2 CC β-Hydroxynaphtharylamides	5515–5556
1.3 CC β-Naphthol	5557–5564
1.4 CC Phenylmethylpyrazolone	5565–5567
1.5 CC Benzimidazolone	5568–5574
2. Monoazo Lakes	5575–5619
2.1 With COOH groups	5575–5577
2.2 With SO_3H groups	5589–5601
2.3 With COOH and SO_3H groups	5602–5617
2.4 Chelates	5618, 5619
3. Disazo pigments	5620–5640
3.1 CC Acetoacetarylamides	5620–5634
3.2 CC Pyrazolones	5635–5641
3.3 CC β-Naphthols	5642, 5643
3.4 Other Disazo pigments	5644–5653
4. Indigo pigments	5654–5664
4.1 Indigo and its derivatives	5654–5657
4.2 Thioindigo derivatives	5658–5664
5. Pigments with condensed rings	5665–5707
5.1 Simple anthraquinones	5665–5677
5.2 Condensed anthaquinones	5678–5690
5.3 Naphthoylenebenzimidazoles	5691, 5692
5.4 Perylenes	5693–5701
5.5 Quinacridones	5702–5707
5.6 Dioxazines	5706
6. Phthalocyanine pigments	5708–5716
6.1 Cu phthalocyanines	5710–5712
6.2 Halogenated Cu phthalocyanines	5713, 5714
6.3 Metal-free phthalocyanines	5715, 5716
7. Miscellaneous pigments	5717–5746
7.1 Lakes of basic triphenylmethanes	5717–5722
7.2 Lakes of basic xanthenes	5723–5726
7.3 Lakes of acidic triphenylmethanes	5727–5734
7.4 Xanthenes with acidic groups	5735–5738
7.5 Diphenylmethanes	5739
7.6 Nitroso pigments	5740, 5741
7.7 Nitro pigments	5742–5744
7.8 Thiazole pigments	5745
7.9 Azine pigments	5746

If the acetic acid layer is not colored, an acid dye is present. If the wool is dyed, an acid or a substantive dye may be present. To decide which, a piece of unmordanted cotton and 2—3 drops of sodium sulfate solution are introduced into the dye solution, which is then boiled for about 1 minute. The cotton is washed, and is then boiled for a short time with water. If the cotton remains colored, a substantive dye is present.

Vat dyes are recognized by dyeing unmordanted cotton from a solution of 1 N sodium hydroxide solution with addition of sodium dithionite. The dye solution is left on the water bath for a few minutes, and after cooling, the cotton is thoroughly washed with water. If the original color of the pigment returns, the dye is a vat dye.

Behavior Toward Reducing Agents: Tin(II) chloride solution in hydrochloric acid, alkaline sodium dithionite solution, or zinc dust and ammonia can be used as reducing agents. Conclusions regarding the nature of the pigments or dyes can be drawn from the behavior of a small sample of pigment on reduction in the cold and with heating in the presence of water, alcohol, or dimethylformamide, a spatula tip of zinc dust, and a few drops of ammonia.

Azo dyes usually undergo irreversible cleavage even in the cold, and colorless or yellow products may be formed. Azo pigments containing 2-hydroxy-3-naphtharylamides are not reduced by zinc dust and ammonia.

Simple anthraquinone derivatives with and without sulfo groups vat when treated with zinc dust and ammonia at room temperature, i.e. the solution changes color, and on standing in air, the original color reappears at the surface. Vatting is no longer observed if the reduction is carried out with heating.

Azine, oxazine, and thiazine dyes also vat when the reduction solution is warmed. The original color reappears if they are poured on filter paper.

Triphenylmethane and xanthene dyes are reduced to colorless leuco compounds. On addition of mild oxidizing agents such as iron(III) chloride or hydrogen peroxide, the original color is restored.

Vat dyes remain unchanged on reduction with zinc dust and ammonia. When heated with sodium hydroxide solution and sodium dithionite, on the other hand, they pass into solution with a change in color, but are reoxidized to the original dye in air. Azo pigments containing 2-hydroxy-3-naphtharylamides are irreversibly decolorized with sodium hydroxide/sodium dithionite.

Chemical Degradation of Azo Pigments and Identification of the Degradation Products: The chemical degradation of azo pigments by reduction with tin/hydrochloric acid, zinc/acetic acid, zinc/ammonia, or sodium dithionite leads to cleavage of the diazo group to form amines (nitro groups are also reduced to amino groups), and in the case of acetoacetarylamide pigments, selfcondensation of the intermediate amino ketone leads to the formation of 2,5-dimethyl-3,6-dihydropyrazine-3,6-dicarboxarylamides. The latter can be cleaved at the amide linkage by refluxing with hydrobromic acid [390], the corresponding aromatic amines being formed. The amines are obtained directly if the cleavage is carried out by dry distillation with a 4-fold excess of calcium oxide [368, 369].

IR spectroscopy [369], thin layer chromatography [388, 389], gas chromatography, and mass spectroscopy can be used for

Table 4.2: Monoazo pigments with acetoacetarylamides as coupling components (organic pigments, group 1.1)

Formula

$$
\underset{5}{\overset{3}{\underset{6}{\overset{2}{\bigcirc}}}}\!\!-N=N-\overset{\overset{OH}{|}}{\underset{CONH}{C}}\!\!-CH_3 \quad \underset{6'}{\overset{2'}{\underset{5'}{\overset{3'}{\bigcirc}}}}\!\!{}_{4'}
$$

Pigment data — Formula — R_f values (silica gel GF; solvent: chloroform + xylene, 3 + 1)

Dec. No.	Sp. No.	CI Name	CI No.	2	3	4	5	6	2'	3'	4'	5'	6'	R_f values
1.1.1	5500	Y 1	11680	NO_2		CH_3								75 ge, L
1.1.2	5501	Y 5	11660	NO_2										75 ge, L/43 Fwe
1.1.3	5502	Y 6	11670	NO_2		Cl								78 ge, L
1.1.4	5503	Y 3	11710	NO_2		Cl			Cl					81 ge, L
1.1.5	5504	Y 2	11730	NO_2		Cl			CH_3	CH_3				79 ge, L
1.1.6	5505	Y 98	11727	NO_2		Cl			CH_3	Cl				81 ge, L/15 Fwe
1.1.7	5506	OR 1	11725	OCH_3		NO_2			CH_3					68 ge, L
1.1.8	5507	Y 74	11741	OCH_3		NO_2			OCH_3					70 ge, L
1.1.9	5508	Y 65	11740	NO_2		OCH_3			OCH_3					64 ge, L
1.1.10	5509	Y 25		CH_3		Cl			— benzo —					84 ge, L
1.1.11	5510	Y 82		NO_2		Cl			Cl			CH_3		86 ge, L
1.1.12	5511	Y 97	11767	OCH_3		R_1	OCH_3		OCH_3	Cl	OCH_3			23 ge, L
1.1.13	5512	Y 73	11738	NO_2		Cl			OCH_3					
1.1.14	5513	Y 74	11741	OCH_3		NO_2								
1.1.15	5514	Y 49	11765	CH_3		Cl					Cl	OCH_3		

$R_1 = - SO_2NH\!\!-\!\!\bigcirc$

be = beige	ro = red	F = fluorescence (366 nm)	
bl = blue	rs = pink	F_1 = fluorescence (254 nm)	
br = brown	vi = violet	L = quenching of fluorescence of silica gel GF, (254 nm)	
ge = yellow	we = white		
gr = green	h = light		
or = orange	d = dark		

the subsequent identification of the amines. The reactions are discussed and examples are given to illustrate the details of the procedure in the publications indicated. GEMOZOVA and GASPARIC [388, 389] have published comprehensive tables of R_f values for the thin layer and paper chromatography of aromatic amines.

For identification by IR spectroscopy, it is necessary to use collections of spectra [147—150].

Examples of reductive and thermal cleavage are given in the following reaction schemes.

Reduction:

$$H_3C\!-\!\bigcirc\!\overset{NO_2\ \ HO}{-N=N-}\!\bigcirc\!\bigcirc \longrightarrow H_3C\!-\!\bigcirc\!\overset{NH_2}{-NH_2} + H_2N\!-\!\bigcirc\!\bigcirc\overset{HO}{}$$

Pigment Red 3 (1.3.4) — 4-Methyl-1,2-phenylene diamine — 1-Amino-2-naphthol

Destillation:

$$
\begin{array}{c}
Cl \quad COCH_3 \\
\bigcirc\!\!-N=NCHCO\!-\!NH\!-\!\bigcirc \\
\bigcirc\!\!-N=NCHCO\!-\!NH\!-\!\bigcirc \\
Cl \quad COCH_3
\end{array}
\longrightarrow
\begin{array}{c}
Cl \\
\bigcirc\!\!-NH_2 \\
\bigcirc\!\!-NH_2 \\
Cl
\end{array}
+ H_2N\!-\!\bigcirc
$$

Pigment Yellow 12 (3.1.1) — 3,3'-Dichloro-benzidine — Aniline

4.5 Thin Layer Chromatography of Organic Pigments

Reviews on the thin layer chromatography of organic dyes have been published by RETTIE and HAYNES [383] and by SCHWEPPE [48, 382] and THOMSON [382a]. Only small parts of these reviews are devoted to organic pigments. BAIER [390] reports on the TLC of organic pigments – especially using silica gel layers – and discusses relationships between structure and R_f values. Information on the pigments present can also be obtained from the soluble portions of certain pigments which are normally insoluble.

A number of the procedures suggested for various classes of dyes and pigments are listed in Table 4.16.

Most monoazo, disazo, and indigo pigments can be applied to the layer as solutions in chloroform. Depending on the solvent system, limited solubility may restrict the quantities of substance that can be chromatographed without tailing.

The precipitated or laked acid and basic dyes must be cleaved and brought into solution by treatment with glacial acetic

acid or weak hydrochloric acid/ethanol, possibly with heating. The dyes can then be separated by thin layer chromatography.

Thin layer chromatography is practically out of the question for the phthalocyanines (6), the condensed anthraquinones (5.2), the naphthoylenebenzimidazoles (5.3), and the perylene pigments (5.4), owing to very low solubility. Only one publication [369] mentions the possibility of separating phthalocyanine blue from phthalocyanine green and dioxazine violet with 1-methylnaphthaline as the solvent, but this is of little practical interest, since these pigments are

Tabelle 4.3: Monoazo pigments with β-hydroxynaphtharylamides as coupling components (group 1.2)

Structural formula header (silica gel GF; solvent: chloroform + xylene, 3 + 1), ring positions 2, 3, 4, 5, 6 (diazo ring) and 2', 3', 4', 5', 6' (anilide ring).

Dec. No.	Sp. No.	CI-Name	CI-No.	2	3	4	5	6	2'	3'	4'	5'	6'	R_f values
1.2.1	5515	R 21	12300	Cl										
1.2.2	5516	OR 24	12305		Cl									
1.2.3	5517	OR 4		Cl					OCH_3					68 orro, L
1.2.4	5518	R 2	12310	Cl			Cl							68 orro, L/50 F we, F_1 we
1.2.5	5519	R 5	12490	OCH_3			R_2		OCH_3	OCH_3	Cl			47 F we, F_1 we/34 ro, L
1.2.6	5520	R 7	12420	CH_3	Cl				CH_3	Cl				76 ro, L/47 F we, F_1 we
1.2.7	5521	R 8	12335	CH_3			NO_2			Cl				71 ro, L/45 F we, F_1 we
1.2.8	5522	R 9	12460	Cl			Cl		OCH_3					54 orro, L
1.2.9	5523	R 10	12440	Cl			Cl				CH_3			65 orro, L/53 F we, F_1 we
1.2.10	5524	R 11	12430	CH_3			Cl		CH_3		Cl			80 ro, L/49 F we, F_1 we
1.2.11	5525	R 12	12385	CH_3		NO_2			CH_3					66 ro, L/55 F we, F_1 we
1.2.12	5526	R 16	12500	OCH_3		NO_2	– benzo –							69 ro, L/61 ro, L/53 F we, F_1 we
1.2.13	5527	R 17	12390	CH_3			NO_2		CH_3					59 orro, L/50 F we, F_1 we
1.2.14	5528	R 18	12350	NO_2	CH_3					NO_2				62 F we, F_1 we/51 ro, L
1.2.15	5532			NO_2	CH_3				CH_3		Cl			65 ro, L/49 F we, F_1 we
1.2.16	5529	R 13	12395	NO_2	CH_3				CH_3					
1.2.17	5530	R 14	12380	NO_2	Cl				CH_3					
1.2.18	5531	R 162	12431	CH_3			NO_2		CH_3		Cl			
1.2.19	5533	R 22	12315	CH_3			NO_2							59 orro, L/49 F we, F_1 we
1.2.20	5534	R 23	12355	OCH_3			NO_2			NO_2				0 orro
1.2.21	5535	R 30	12330	CH_3			R_3				Cl			42 ro, L
1.2.22	5536	R 31	12360	OCH_3			R_1			NO_2				28 ro, L
1.2.23	5537	R 32	12320	OCH_3			R_1				Cl			73 F we, F_1 we/56 F we, F_1 we/31 ro, L
1.2.24	5538	R 95		OCH_3		R_5		CH_3						54 ro, F we, L
1.2.25	5539	R 96		CH_3		Cl								81 ro, L/55 F we, F_1 we
1.2.26	5540	R 112	12370	Cl		Cl	Cl							69 orro, L
1.2.27	5541	R 98					formula unknown							53 F we, F_1 we/49 rovi, L
1.2.28	5542	R 136		NO_2	NO_2				OC_2H_5					68 F we, F_1 we/0 ro, L
1.2.29	5543	BL 23		OC_2H_5	R_1	OC_2H_5			CH_3					50 vi, L
1.2.30	5544	BR 1	12480	Cl			Cl		OCH_3		OCH_3			38 orro, L/51 F we, F_1 we
1.2.31	5545	R 146	12485	OCH_3	R_1				OCH_3		Cl	OCH_3		61 F we, F_1 we/23 ro, L
1.2.32	5546	R 147		OCH_3			R_1		CH_3		Cl			50 F we, F_1 we/32 ro, L
1.2.33	5547	R 148		Cl	Cl				CH_3					70 ro, L/52 F we, F_1 we
1.2.34	5548	R 150					formula unknown							0 ro, F we, F_1 we
1.2.35	5549	R 163	12455	OCH_3			R_4		CH_3	CH_3				59 F we, F_1 we/41 ro, L
1.2.36	5550	Heliofil violet BV 150		OCH_3		R_1	CH_3				Cl			79 ro, L/51 F we, F_1 we
1.2.37	5553	R 170	12475			$CONH_2$			OC_2H_5					
1.2.38	5554	R 187	12486	OCH_3	R_6				OCH_3		OCH_3	Cl		
1.2.39	5555	OR 38	12367	Cl		$CONH_2$				R_7				
1.2.40	5556	R 171	12512	OCH_3		NO_2				$-R_{10}-$				
1.2.41	5557	R 185	12516	CH_3	R_9	OCH_3								
1.2.42	5558	R 188	12467	R_8			R_{11}		OCH_3	$-R_{10}-$				

R_1 = $-CO \cdot NH-$〈phenyl〉

R_2 = $-SO_2N(C_2H_5)_2$

R_3 = $-CONH-$〈phenyl with CH_3, CH_3 substituents〉

R_4 = $-SO_2-CH_2-$〈phenyl〉

R_5 = $-SO_2 \cdot O-$〈phenyl〉$-NO_2$

R_6 = $-CONH-$〈phenyl〉$-CONH_2$

R_7 = $-NHCOCH_3$

R_8 = $-COOCH_3$

R_9 = $-SO_2-NHCH_3$

R_{10} = $-NH-CO-NH-$

R_{11} = $-CONH-$〈phenyl with Cl, Cl substituents〉

Table 4.4:
Monoazo pigments with β-naphthol (group 1.3), phenylmethylpyrazolone (group 1.4) and benzimidazole (group 1.5) as coupling components

	Pigment data			Formula					R_f values (silica gel GF; solvent: chloroform + xylene, 3 + 1)
Dec. No.	Sp. No.	CI-Name	CI-No.	2	3	4	5	6	

Dec. No.	Sp. No.	CI-Name	CI-No.	2	3	4	5	6	R_f
1.3.1	5551	OR 2	12060	NO_2					56 orro, L / 21 L / 3 L
1.3.2	5552	R 1	12070			NO_2			67 orro, L / 22 L / 2 L
1.3.3	5559	OR 5	12075	NO_2		NO_2			66 orro, L / 2 L
1.3.4	5560	R 3	12120	NO_2		CH_3			62 ro, L
1.3.5	5561	R 4	12085	Cl		NO_2			77 or, L
1.3.6	5562	R 40	12170			2-Naphthyl			88, L / 76-82 rovi, L
1.3.7	5565	R 6	12090	NO_2		Cl			
1.3.8	5566	R 93	12152	OCH_3			Cl		

Dec. No.	Sp. No.	CI-Name	CI-No.	2	3	4	5	6	R_f
1.4.1	5563	Y 10	12710	Cl		Cl			85 ge, L
1.4.2	5564	Y 60	12705	Cl					86 ge, L
1.4.3	5567	OR 6	12730	NO_2	CH_3				

Dec. No.	Sp. No.	CI-Name	CI-No.	2	3	4	5	6
1.5.1	5569	Y 120	11783	$-COOCH_3$	$-COOCH_3$			
1.5.2	5570	OR 36	11780	NO_2	Cl			

Dec. No.	Sp. No.	CI-Name	CI-No.	2	3	4	5	6
1.5.3	5571	BR 25	12510	Cl		Cl		
1.5.4	5672	R 175	12519	$COOCH_3$				
1.5.5	5573	R 176	12515	OCH_3		R_1		
1.5.6	5574	V 32	12517	OCH_3		R_9	OCH_3	

$R_1 = -CONH-\phi$ $R_9 = -SO_2-NHCH_3$

Table 4.5: Monoazo pigments with COOH and SO₃ groups (groups 2.1 and 2.2)

Dec. No.	Sp. No. (CI)	CI Name	CI No.	Me	2	3	4	5	3'	6'	R_f values (silica gel GF; solvent: n-butanol + acetic acid + water, 4 + 1 + 5)	R_f values (silica gel GF; solvent: chloroform + acetic acid 9 + 1)
2.1.1	R 55 5575	15820		Mn	$COO^\ominus$		Cl		$COO^\ominus$		80 bror, L/73 bror, L	68 bebr, L/51 ro, L
2.1.2	R 55 5576	15820		Cu	$COO^\ominus$		Cl		$COO^\ominus$		89 be, L/75, L/30, L	86 L/75 colour, L/63, 57, 57, 5-12, 3-5 L
2.1.3	R 64 5678	15800		Ba					$COO^\ominus$			
2.2.1	OR 19 5579	15990		Ba	Cl					$SO_3^\ominus$	83 bror, L/57 bror, L	95 or br, L
2.2.2	OR 18 5577	15970		Ca						$SO_3^\ominus$	72 F bl/67 brro, L	80 F, bl/71 F, bl
2.2.3	R 49 5581	15630		Na	SO_3^-	– benzo –					83 orro, L/69 brro, L	93 ro, L
2.2.4	R 49 5582	15630		Ba	SO_3^-	– benzo –					82, L/63 bror, L/54 brro, L	87, L/75, L/71, L
2.2.5	R 51 5583	15580		Ba		CH_3	SO_2				84 be, L/70 bror, L	95 be, L/91 ro, L/77, 69 bero, L/3-5 L
2.2.6	R 53 5584	15585		Na	$SO_3^\ominus$		Cl	CH_3			71 bror, L	91 ge, L
2.2.7	R 53 5585	15585		Ba	$SO_3^\ominus$		Cl	CH_3				0
2.2.8	G 62 5587			Ba	R_5				Pyrazolone*		–	0
2.2.9	G 61 5588			Ba	R_6				Pyrazolone*		–	96 ge, L
2.2.10	R 94 5592			Ba	OC_6H_5			Cl		$SO_3^\ominus$	31 robr, L	0
2.2.11	R 120 5593	15603		Ba		Cl	Cl	$i\text{-}C_3$		$SO_3^\ominus$	21 robr, L	0
2.2.12	R 117 5594	15603		Ba	$SO_3^\ominus$		Cl	C_2H_5			85, L/69 robr, L	0
2.2.13	OR 26 5595	15602		Ba	$SO_3^\ominus$		Cl	C_2H_5			86, L/70 robr, L	82 F, bl
2.2.14	R 133 5596			Ba	$SO_3^\ominus$	$SO_3^\ominus$			R_3		86-91 ge, Fbe, L/76-85 br, Fbe, L/28-34, 23 rs, L	92 ro, Fbe, L/88 ge, Fbe, L/82 ro, Fbl, L/74, L
2.2.15	R 134 5597			Ca	$SO_3^\ominus$	$SO_3^\ominus$			R_4		81-95 ge, F bebr, L/52 rs, L/40 rs, L	94 be, L/88 be, Fbr, L/82 be, Fbe, L
2.2.16	R 151 5598			Ba	$SO_3^\ominus$		Cl		R_7		75 Fbl/31 rs, L/28 rs, L	0
2.2.17	OR 7 5599	15530		Na	$SO_3^\ominus$		Cl	Cl				
2.2.18	OR 46	15602		Na	$SO_3^\ominus$		Cl	C_2H_5				
2.2.19	R 69 5601	15595		Na	$SO_3^\ominus$		CH_3	Cl				

Dec. No.	Sp. No. (CI)	CI Name	CI No.	Me	2	3	4	3'	5'	R	R_f (n-butanol 4 + 1 + 5)	R_f (chloroform 9 + 1)
2.2.20	R 54 5586	14830		Ca	– benzo –				$SO_3^\ominus$	R_1	94 gebr, L/24 vi, L	98 ge be, L/93, L/82, L/74, L
2.2.21	V 8 5589	18005		Ba	– benzo –				$SO_3^\ominus$	R_1	95 gebr, L/41, 32 rovi, L	78 ge, L
2.2.22	R 66 5590	18000		Na			CH_3		$SO_3^\ominus$	R_2	39 rovi, L	96, L/77 L
2.2.23	R 67 5591	19025		Ba	OCH_3				$SO_3^\ominus$			

* Sulfonated phenylmethylpyrazolone instead of the naphthoyl group

$R_1 = -NHCO-C_6H_5$

$R_2: -NHCO-C_6H_3Cl_2$ (dichlorophenyl)

$i\text{-}C_3: -CH(CH_3)_2$

$R_3: -CONH-$ (aryl bearing OCH_3, OCH_3, Cl)

$R_4: -CONH-$ (naphthyl)

$R_5 = -CONH-$ (o-tolyl, H_3C-)

$R_6: -CONH-C_6H_5$

$R_7: -CONH-C_6H_4-SO_3^\ominus$

Table 4.6: Monoazo Lakes (group 2.3) and chelates of monoazo dyes (group 2.4)

Formula (naphthol–azo structure with positions OH, 3', 4', 1', 5', 8', 6', 7', N=N, and benzene ring positions 2, 3, 4, 5, 6)

Dec. No.	Sp. No.	CI Name	CI No.	Me	2	3	4	5	3'	6'	R_f values (silica gel GF; solvent: n-butanol + acetic acid + water 4 + 1 + 5)	R_f values (silica gel GF; solvent: chloroform + acetic acid 9 + 1)
2.3.1	5602	R 48	15865	Na	$SO_3^{\ominus}$		CH_3	Cl	$COO^{\ominus}$		84 F bl, L/76 F we, L/62 ro, L/54 or, L	92 F bl/79 F be, L
2.3.2	5603	R 48	15865	Ba	$SO_3^{\ominus}$		CH_3	Cl	$COO^{\ominus}$		85 F bl, L/63 ro, L	91 F bl
2.3.3	5604	R 48	15865	Mn	$SO_3^{\ominus}$		CH_3	Cl	$COO^{\ominus}$		84 F bl, L/63 ro, L	86 F bl
2.3.4	5605	R 52	15860	Ca	$SO_3^{\ominus}$		Cl	CH_3	$COO^{\ominus}$		83 F bl, L/67 ro, L	88 F bl, L
2.3.5	5606	R 56	15870	Ba	OCH_3		$SO_3^{\ominus}$	CH_3	$COO^{\ominus}$		84 F bl, L/76 ro, L	92 F bl/8 L F bl, L
2.3.6	5607	R 57	15850	Na	$SO_3^{\ominus}$		CH_3		$COO^{\ominus}$		82 F bl, L/76 F we, L/58 ro, L	89 F bl/77 F be, L
2.3.7	5608	R 57	15850	Ca	$SO_3^{\ominus}$		CH_3		$COO^{\ominus}$		83 F bl, L/67 ro, L	89 F bl, L
2.3.8	5609	R 68	15525	Ca	$SO_3^{\ominus}$		Cl	$COO^{\ominus}$			—	—
2.3.9	5610	R 58	15825	Na	$SO_3^{\ominus}$		Cl	1)$SO_3^{\ominus}$	$COO^{\ominus}$		84 F bl/78 F be/73 F bl	66 F bl
2.3.10	5611	R 58	15825	Ca	$SO_3^{\ominus}$		Cl	1)$SO_3^{\ominus}$	$COO^{\ominus}$		85 F bl, L	90, L
2.3.11	5612	R 58	15825	Mn	$SO_3^{\ominus}$		Cl	1)$SO_3^{\ominus}$	$COO^{\ominus}$		89 F bl/82 F be/64 ro	94 F bl
2.3.12	5613	R 63	15880	Na	$SO_3^{\ominus}$	– benzo –			$COO^{\ominus}$		86 F bl/80 F be/70 ro, L	94 F bl/79 F be, L/2—4 L
2.3.13	5614	R 63	15880	Ca	$SO_3^{\ominus}$	– benzo –			$COO^{\ominus}$		85 F bl, L/74 ro, L/74 F ro br, L	93 L/85 F bl, L/78 L/68 L/53 L/21 L
2.3.14	5615	R 63	15880	Mn	$SO_3^{\ominus}$	– benzo –			$COO^{\ominus}$		87 F bl, L/72 ro, L	94 L/86 F bl, L/80 L/54 L/22 L
2.3.15	5616	R 60	16105	Ba	$COO^{\ominus}$				$SO_3^{\ominus}$	$SO_3^{\ominus}$	91 F bl/38, L/20 ro br, L	0
2.3.16	5617		19120	Ba	$SO_3^{\ominus}$				R_1		36 ge, L	0
2.3.17	5580	R 115	15851	Mn			CH_3	$SO_3^{\ominus}$	$COO^{\ominus}$		79 ge, L	90 ge, F_1 gr
2.4.1	5618	GR 10	12775	Ni			Cl	$SO_3^{\ominus}$				
2.4.2	5619	BR 2	12071	Cu			NO_2				81 or br, L	99 or br, L/78 F bl/70 L/25—31 L

R_1 = (chelate structure: HO–pyrazolone–N=N–benzene ring with COO–Ba and SO_3)

R_2 = (quinoline structure: OH, N, O)

R_1 and R_2 instead of naphthoyl group

2.4.1 and 2.4.2 are Ni and Cu chelates, respectively, of the azo dyes.
Explanation of the TLC data abbreviations see table 4.2

Table 4.7: Disazo pigments with acetoacetarylamides (group 3.1), pyrazolones (group 3.2) and 2-naphtholes (group 3.3) as coupling components

Structure (group 3.1): $CH_3-C(OH)=...-N=N-$ [biphenyl core] $-N=N-C(OH)=...-CH_3$ with NHCO / CONH linkages; ring positions 2,3,5,6 (left coupler 5',6',4',3',2') and 2',3',4',5',6' (right coupler).

R$_f$ values (silica gel GF; solvent: chloroform + xylene, 3 + 1)

Dec. No.	Sp. No.	CI Name	CI No.	2	3	5	6	2'	3'	4'	5'	6'	R$_f$ values
3.1.1	5620	Y 12	21090		Cl								85 ge, L/17 F we, L
3.1.2	5621	Y 14	21095		Cl			CH$_3$					0
3.1.3	5622	Y 13	21000		Cl			CH$_3$	CH$_3$				0
3.1.4	5623	Y 17	21105		Cl			OCH$_3$					0
3.1.5	5624	Y 83			Cl			OCH$_3$		Cl	OCH$_3$		0
3.1.6	5625	Y 81		Cl		Cl		CH$_3$	CH$_3$				0
3.1.7	5626	Y 15	21220	Cl		OCH$_3$		CH$_3$	CH$_3$				84 ge, L/24 F we, L
3.1.8	5629	OR 14	21165		OCH$_3$			CH$_3$	CH$_3$				0
3.1.9	5630	Y 81	21127		Cl	Cl		CH$_3$	CH$_3$				90 ge, L
3.1.10	5632	OR 15	21130		CH$_3$								
3.1.11	5633	OR 16	21160		OCH$_3$								
3.1.12	5634	Y 55	21096		Cl						CH$_3$		
3.1.13	5641	Y 113	21126		Cl	Cl	CH$_3$		Cl				

Structure (middle): $H_3C-C(OH)=C-CONH-$ [dimethylbiphenyl core with CH$_3$, CH$_3$] $-NHCO-C=C(OH)-CH_3$; azo couplers with ring positions 2,3,4,5,6.

Dec. No.	Sp. No.	CI Name	CI No.	2	3	4	5	6	R$_f$ values
3.1.14	5627	Y 16	20040	Cl		Cl			0
3.1.15	5628	Y 77	20045	CH$_3$			Cl		90 L/24 L/17 ge, L

Structure (group 3.2): $R_1-C-C-N=N-$ [biphenyl core] $-N=N-C-C-R_1$ with pyrazolone rings (C-OH, N, N) and 4'-phenyl; ring positions 3, 4', R$_1$.

Dec. No.	Sp. No.	CI Name	CI No.	3	4'	R$_1$	R$_f$ values
3.2.1	5631	OR 13	21110	Cl		CH$_3$	83 be, L
3.2.2	5635	R 37	21205	OCH$_3$		CH$_3$	44 ge/15 L
3.2.3	5636	R 38	21120	Cl		COOC$_2$H$_5$	42–47 ro, L
3.2.4	5637	R 128	21200	OCH$_3$	CH$_3$	CH$_3$	76 ge/60 ro br, L/22 L
3.2.5	5638	OR 34	21115	Cl	CH$_3$	C$_6$H$_5$	
3.2.6	5639	R 41	21200	Cl	CH$_3$	4-MePh	
3.2.7	5640	R 37	21205	OCH$_3$	CH$_3$	4-MePh	

Explanation of the TLC data abbreviations see table 4.2

$4\text{-MePh} = $ [4-methylphenyl] $-CH_3$

Table 4.7 (continued)

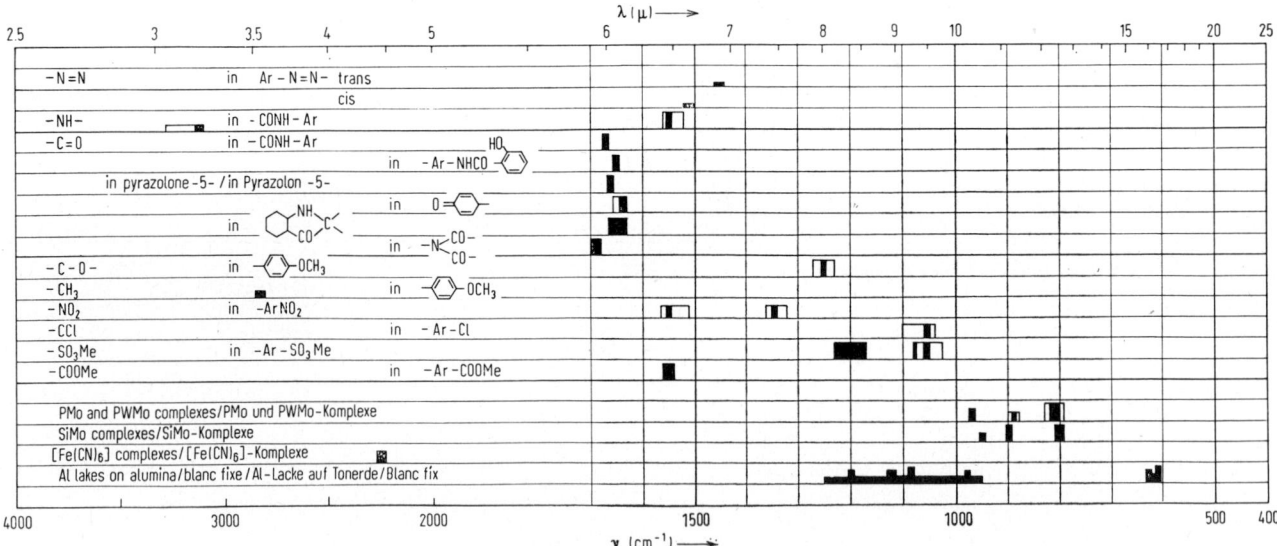

Dec. No.	Sp. No.	CI Name	CI No.	2	3	3'	6'
3.3.1	5642	BL 25	21180	OCH_3	$CONHC_6H_5$		
3.3.2	5643	R 62	23925	CH_3		$SO_3Ba_{0,5}$	$SO_3Ba_{0,5}$
3.4.1	5644	Y 93					
3.4.2	5645	Y 94					
3.4.3	5646	Y 95					
3.4.4	5647	OR 31	CI-No and formula not published				
3.4.5	5648	Y 127					
3.4.6	5649	Y 129					
3.4.7	5650	Y 151					
3.4.8	5651	R 166					
3.4.9	5652	R 220					
3.4.10	5653	R 221					

Explanation of the TLC data abbreviations see table 4.2

easily recognized in the presence of one another by spectroscopy.

The thin layer chromatographic behavior of some groups of pigments investigated by us is indicated in Tables 4.2—4.6.

Since thin layer chromatography has largely replaced paper chromatography for separating organic dyes in recent years, the latter will not be discussed here. HPLC has recently found increased interest because it enables certain separations to be carried out quickly and with automatic and quantitative determination. Details have been given by Papa [382b].

4.6 IR Spectroscopy of Organic Pigments

IR spectroscopy is very well suited to the identification of organic pigments with the aid of comparison spectra, since differences in substituents and substitution types cause changes in the spectra, which contain many bands, and some of the functional groups in the usually aromatic systems can be identified on the basis of characteristic bands.

However, considerable difficulty is involved in a complete band assignment, since the positions and intensities of the bands may be strongly influenced by coupling and resonance phenomena. In most cases, therefore, only a few bands are assigned, and the general picture of the spectrum is used for identification.

McClure et al. [369] have pointed out the possibilities of IR spectroscopy on the basis of 96 spectra of organic pigments in the region between 5000 and 650 cm^{-1} (2—15 μm), and have given examples to show that the pigment group and functional groups can be recognized even for pigments Figure 4.1 shows the positions of the bands of some functional groups present in organic pigments and characteristic

Fig. 4.1: Band positions for functional groups in organic pigments

Table 4.8: Indigo pigments (groups 4.1 and 4.2)

Pigment data				Formula	R_f values (silica gel GF; solvent: benzene + chloroform, 4 + 1)
Dec. No.	Sp. No.	CI-Name	CI-No.		

Indigo pigments

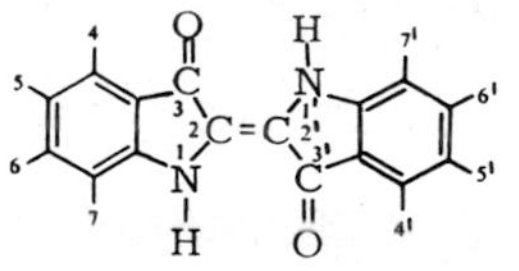

4,4' 5,5' 6,6' 7.7'

Dec. No.	Sp. No.	CI-Name	CI-No.	4,4'	5,5'	6,6'	7,7'	R_f
4.1.1	5656	Vat Bl 1	73000					0
4.1.2	5657	Vat Bl 2	73045	Cl	Br			69 bl, L / 33 bl, L
4.1.3	5654	Bl 63	73015	SO₃Na				

Thioindigo pigments

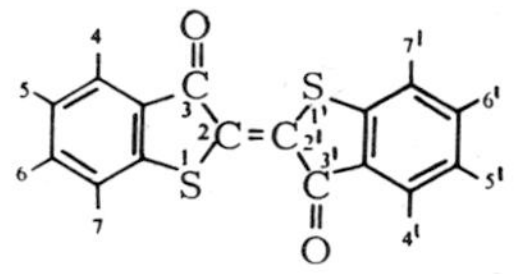

4,4' 5,5' 6,6' 7,7'

Dec. No.	Sp. No.	CI-Name	CI-No.	4,4'	5,5'	6,6'	7,7'	R_f
4.2.1	5658	R 87	73310			Cl		79 L
4.2.2	5659	R 88	73312	Cl		Cl		80 L
4.2.3	5660	R 198	73390	Cl		CH₃		79 L
4.2.4	5661	V 36	73385		Cl	CH₃		80 L
4.2.5	5662	R 181	73360	CH₃		Cl		73 ge, L
4.2.6	5655	R 86	73375	CH₃		Br		
4.2.7	5663	Vat R 2	73365	CH₃		Cl	Cl	78 L / 53 L 24 rovi, L
4.2.8	5664	V 38	73395	CH₃	Cl		CH₃	78 L / 63 L

Explanation of the TLC data abbreviations see table 4.2

Table 4.9: Pigments with concensed rings; simple anthraquinones (group 5.1) and condensed anthraquinones (group 5.2)

Formula

Dec. No.	Sp. No.	CI-Name	CI-No.	1	2	3	4	5	6
5.1.1	5665	R 83	58000	OH	OH				Al-lake
5.1.2	5666	V 6	58060	OH			OH	$SO_3^{\ominus}$	Al-lake
5.1.3	5668	V 5	58055	OH	$SO_3^{\ominus}$		OH		Na-salt
5.1.3	5669		58055 : 1						Al-salt
5.1.4	5670	V 7	58065	OH	$SO_3^{\ominus}$		OH	$SO_2^{\ominus}$	Na-salt
5.1.4	5671		58065 : 1						Al-salt
5.1.5	5672	V 20	58225	OH	R_3	SO_3H	OH		
5.1.6	5667		60515	R_1					
5.1.7	5673	Y 23	60520	R_2					
5.1.8	5674	R 85	63350	R_1			OH	R_3	
5.1.9	5675		68420	R_4					
5.1.10	5676	R 177	65300	NH_2			R_5		
5.1.11	5677		68420	R_4					

$R_3 =$ —O—⟨⟩—SO_3

$R_2 =$ —NHCO—⟨OH⟩

$R_1 =$ —NHCO—⟨⟩

$R_5 =$

$R_4 =$ NH—CO—

Composition (for formulas see IR spectra)

Dec. No.	Sp. No.	CI-Name	CI-No.	Composition
5.2.1	5678	Y 24	70600	Flavanthrone
5.2.2	5679	BL 60	69800	Indanthrone
5.2.3	5690	BL 22	69810	(3-)Chloroindanthrone
5.2.4	5689	BL 64	69825	3,3'-Dichloroindanthrone
5.2.5	5688	OR 40	59700	Pyranthrone
5.2.6	5680	R 216	59710	4,8,8'-Tribromopyranthrone
5.2.7	5681	R 168	59300	2,7-Dibromoanthanthrone
5.2.8	5682	VAT R 35	68000	3,8,16-Trioxo-3,8,9,16-tetrahydronaphtha-leno [2,3-c]benz[k]acridine
5.2.9	5683	VAT R 20	67000	Oxazoleanthranquinone pigment
5.2.10	5684	VAT R 13	70320	N,N'-Diethyldipyrazoleanthronyl
5.2.11	5685	VAT V 1	60010	Dichloroisoviolanthrone
5.2.12	5686	VAT V 9	60005	Bromoisoviolanthrone
5.2.13	5687	VAT GR 1	59825	12,12'-Dimethoxyviolanthrone

Table 4.10: Pigments with condensed rings, various groups (5.3–5.6)

Dec. No.	IR-Sp. No.	CI Name	CI-No.	Composition
	Naphthoylenebenzimidazoles			
5.3.1	5691	OR 43	71105	Dibenzimidazolo [1,2-e; 1',2'-m] 4,9-diaza-3,8-pyrenequinone
5.3.2	5692	R 194	71100	Dibenzimidazolo [1,2-e; 2',1-l] 4,9-diaza-3,8-pyrenequinone
	Perylenes			Formula:
5.4.1	5693	BR 26	71129	R = H
5.4.2	5694	R 190	71140	R = 4-methoxyphenyl
5.4.3	5695	R 179	71130	R = CH_3
5.4.4	5696	R 126		R = ?
5.4.5	5697	R 149		R = 3,5-dimethylphenyl
5.4.6	5701	R 179	71130	R = CH_3
5.4.7	5698	R 123	71445	R = 4-ethoxyphenyl
5.4.8	5699	R 178	71155	R = 4-phenylazophenyl
5.4.9	5700	R 189	71135	R = 4-chlorophenyl
	Quinacridones			Formula: γ-Form β-Form
5.5.1	5702	V 19	46500	R = H
5.5.1	5703	V 19	46500	R = H
5.5.2	5704	R 122	46500	R = CH_3
5.5.3	5705	V 19	46500	R = H
5.5.4	5707	R 209	73905	R – Cl
	Dioxazine			Formula:
5.6.1	5706	V 23	51319	

Table 4.11: Phthalocyanine pigments (group 6)

Dec. No.	Sp. No.	CI Name	CI No.	Composition (for formulas see IR spectra)
	Cu phthalocyanines			
6.1.1	5710	BL 15	74160	Cu phthalocyanine, α form
6.1.2	5711	BL 15	74160	Cu phthalocyanine, β form
6.1.3	5712	BL 15	74160	Cu phthalocyanine
	Cu halophthalocyanines			
6.2.1	5713	GR 7	74260	Cu hexadecachlorophthalocyanine
6.2.2	5714	GR 38		Cu halophthalocyanine
6.2.3	5708	GR 36	74265	Cu hexabromodecachlorophthalocyanine
	Metal-free phthalocyanines			
6.3.1	5715	BL 16	74100	Phthalocyanine
6.3.2	5716	(Heliogen green 5 G)		Halophthalocyanine

Table 4.12: Lakes of basic triphenylmethanes (7.1) and basic xanthenes (7.2)

Dec. no.	Sp. no.	CI Name	CI No.	3	4	3'	4'	2"	3"	4"	X	Notes
7.1.1	5717	BL 1	42595		NEt$_2$		NEt	- benzo -		NHEt	Cl	PW-Mo-complex
7.1.2	5718	V 3	42535		NHCH$_3$ o. N(CH$_3$)$_2$		NHCH$_3$ o. N(CH$_3$)$_2$			NHCH$_3$ o. N(CH$_3$)$_2$	Cl	PW-Mo-complex
7.1.3	5719	BL 9	42025		N(CH$_3$)$_2$		N(CH$_3$)$_2$	Cl			Cl	PW-Mo-complex
7.1.4	5720	BL 3	42140	CH$_3$	NHEt	CH$_3$	NHEt	Cl			Cl	PW-Mo-complex
7.1.5	5721	GR 1	42 040		NEt$_2$		NEt$_2$				HSO$_4$	PW-Mo-complex
7.1.6	5722	GR 2	42040 + 49005		NEt$_2$		NEt$_2$				HSO$_4$	PW-Mo-complex mixture with 7.8.1

Dec. no.	Sp. no.	CI Name	CI No.	2	7	9	X	Notes
7.2.1	5723	R 81	45 160	NEt$_2$	NHEt	COOEt	Cl	PW-Mo-complex
7.2.2	5724	R 82	45150 + 41000	NHEt	NHEt	COOH	Cl	PW-Mo-complex mixture with 7.5.1
7.2.3	5725	V 1	45170	NEt$_2$	NEt$_2$	COOH	Cl	PW-Mo-complex
7.2.4	5726	V 2	45175	NEt$_2$	NEt$_2$	COOEt	Cl	PW-Mo-complex

PW-Mo-complex = Phosphotungstomolybdate complex

R_f values (silica gel GF; solvent: n-butanol + ethanol + water + glacial acetic acid, 9 + 1 + 1 + 0.1)	R_f values (silica gel GF; solvent: n-butanol + glacial acetic acid + water, 5 + 1 + 2)	R_f values (silica gel GF; solvent: chloroform + ethanol, 8 + 2)
65 bl, L	84 dbl, L	83 bl, L/44 bl, L
65 vi, L/59 vi, L/54 vi, L	79 vi, L	71 vi, L/47 vi, L
65 h bl, L/49 h bl, L/37 h bl, L	85 hbl, L / 56 L	68 bl gr, L/47 bl gr, L
53 bl gr, L	81 blgr, L	68 bl gr, L/48 bl gr, L
63 bl gr, L	79 blgr, L	86 bl gr, L/47 bl gr, L
52 bl gr, L	79 blgr, L / 71 ge, L / 60 ge, I	87 bl gr, L/49 bl gr, L/32 ge, L
50 rs, F ge gr, F_1 ge	74 rs, Fgegr, F_1 ge	53 rs/44 be/53, 44, 33, 25, 12 F ge gr, F_1 ge
54 rs, F ge gr, F_1 ge	73 rs, Fgegr, F_1 ge	58 rs/48 be/58, 48, 37, 28, 12 F ge gr, F_1 ge
45 rs ro, F or, F_1 or	73 rs, For, F_1 or	71, 53, 38, 18 rs, F or, F_1 or/25, 10 F ge gr,
55 rs ro, F or, F_1 or	74 rs, For, F_1 or	F_1 ge 78, 50, 37 rs, F or, F_1 or/44 be, F ge gr, F_1 ge/28, 21 F ge gr, F_1 ge

Explanation of the TLC data abbreviations see table 4.2

Table 4.13: Lakes of acidic triphenylmethane dyes (group 7.3) and acidic xanthene dyes

Pigment data

$$R^1R^2N\text{---}C_6H_4\text{---}\overset{\oplus}{C}\text{---}C_6H_4\text{---}NR^3R^4 \quad (\text{with positions } 2,3,4 \text{ on central ring})$$

Dec. No.	Sp. No.	CI Name	CI No.	R^1	R^2	R^3	R^4	2	3	4	Me
7.3.1	5727	BL 24	42090	Et	$-CH_2-C_6H_4-SO_3^\ominus$	Et	$-CH_2-C_6H_4-SO_3^\ominus$ $SO_3^\ominus$				Ba
7.3.2	5728		42095	Et	$-CH_2-C_6H_5$	Et	$-CH_2-C_6H_5$			$SO_3^\ominus$	Al
7.3.3	5729	BL 19	42750 A		$-C_6H_4-SO_3^\ominus$		$-C_6H_5$	CH_3	NH_2		—
7.3.4	5730		42750		$-C_6H_4-SO_3^\ominus$		$-C_6H_5$	CH_3	NH_2		Al
7.3.5	5731	BL 93	42780		$-C_6H_4-SO_3^\ominus$		$-C_6H_4-SO_3^\ominus$			$-NH-C_6H_4-SO_3^\ominus$	Al
7.3.6	5732	BL 18	42770 A		$-C_6H_4-SO_3^\ominus$		$-C_6H_4-SO_3^\ominus$			$-NH-C_6H_5$	—
7.3.7	5733	BL 56	42800		$-C_6H_3(CH_3)-SO_3^\ominus$		$-C_6H_4-CH_3$			$-NH-C_6H_4-CH_3$	—
7.3.8	5734	BL 57	42795		$H_3C-C_6H_3-SO_3^\ominus$		$H_3C-C_6H_4$			$-NH-C_6H_5$	—

Xanthene structure (positions 1, 2, 3, 6, 7, 8, 9)

Dec. No.	Sp. No.	CI Name	CI No.	1	2	3	6	7	8	9	Me	
7.4.1	5735	Acid Y 73	45350		$O^\ominus$			$O^\ominus$		$COO^\ominus$	Na	
7.4.2	5736	Acid Y 73	45350		OH			OH		$COO^\ominus$	—	betaine
7.4.3	5737	R 90	45380	Br	$O^\ominus$	Br	Br	$O^\ominus$	Br	$COO^\ominus$	Pb	
7.4.4	5738	R 90	45380	Br	$O^\ominus$	Br	Br	$O^\ominus$	Br	$COO^\ominus$	Na	

76

	Rf values (silica gel GF; solvent: n-butanol + acetic acid + water, 4 + 1 + 5)	Rf values (silica gel GF; solvent: chloroform + acetic acid, 9 + 1)
	25 hbl, L/15 blgr., L	O bl, L
(on alumina)	23, 19, 17 gr, L	O blgr, L
betaine	86 bl, L/80 vi, L/71 bl, L/52 vi, L/37 bl, L	93, 7 ge, L/3—5 bl, L/1—3 blgr, L
	91 hbl, L/82 blvi, L/68, 46, 32, 16, hbl, L	4—6 hbl, L/2—4 vi, L
	81 blvi, L/69, 47, 33, 16 hbl, L	2—5 vi, L
free acid		93 ge, L/5—7 vi, L/3—5 bl, L/2—3 vi, L
betaine	91 bl, L/85 vi, L/78 bl, L	9 ge/3—6 bl, L/1—3 vi, L
betaine	87 bl, L/81 vi, L/77 rs, L/72 bl, L	7 ge/2—6 blvi, L/0—2 vi, L
	85 ge, Fgegr, F₁gegr	15—20 ge, Fge, F, ge
	83 ge, Fgegr, F₁gegr	13—18 ge, Fge, F₁ge
	86, 81 ro, F bebr, F₁or/74 rs, F bebr, F₁or	95 rsvi, L/88 rsro, Fbr, F₁vi/73—79 rsor Fbr, F₁br 64, 42, 36 be, Fbe/12 ge, Fgegr, F₁ge
	86, 81 ro, F bebr, F₁or/74 rs, F bebr, F₁or	87 rsro, Fbe, F₁vi/78—80 hrs, Fbe, F₁br/ 73—77 or, Fbr, F₁br/63 be, Fbe, L/38, 14 Fbe

Explanation of the TLC data abbreviations see table 4.2

Table 4.14: Solubility and chemical and dyeing behavior of organic pigments

Organic pigments	Solubility and solution colors							Behavior on reduction	Dyeing behavior	
	Glacial acetic acid	Alcohol + NaOH	H_2SO_4	H_2SO_4 + KJO_3	Ether	Dimethyl-for-mamide	Chloro-form		Wool	Cotton
1. Monoazo pigments	l	l					l	red.		
1.1 CC Acetoacetarylamides	l	ro	ge	rovi						
1.2 CC β-Hydroxynaphtharylamides	l	ro, Z	vi							
1.3 CC β-Naphthol	l	ro	vi		l					
1.4 CC Phenylmethylpyrazolone	l	or	or	blgr	l					
1.5 CC Benzimidazolone										
2. Monoazo lakes	l							red.		
2.1 With COOH groups			or ge							
2.2 With SO_3H groups				fu					f	
2.3 With COOH and SO_3H groups			ro	fu					f	
2.4 Chelate			or bl							
3. Disazo pigments	l						l	red.		
3.1 Acetoacetarylamides			roor, fu	rovi, br						
3.2 C Pyrazolones		Z	rovi							
4. Indigo pigments	l					l	l	k		
4.1 Indigo and derivatives			gegr				l			
4.2 Thioindigo derivatives			ro, gr							ro

4.6 IR Spectroscopy of Organic Pigments

Table 4.14 (continued)

Organic pigments	Solubility and solution colors							Behavior on reduction	Dyeing behavior	
	Glacial acetic acid	Alcohol + NaOH	H₂SO₄	H₂SO₄ + KJO₃	Ether	Dimethyl-for-mamide	Chloro-form		Wool	Cotton
5. Anthraquinone pigments; pigments with condensed rings						l				
5.1 Simple anthraquinones							l	k (k)		
5.2 Condensed anthraquinones							l	k (k)		
5.3 Naphthoylenebenzimidazoles										
5.4 Perylenes			l				l			
5.5 Quinacridones			rovi			or, ro				
5.6 Dioxazines			l			l				
6. Phthalocyanine pigments			cr, ol, br							
6.1 Cu phthalocyanines			rovi							
6.2 Halogenated Cu-Phthalocyanines			rotr							
6.3 Metalfree Phthalocyanines			grtr							
7. Other pigments										
7.1 Phosphotungstomolybdic acid lakes of triphenylmethanes			l				l	k (o)		f
7.2 Phosphotungstomolybdic acid lakes of xanthenes			ge							f

79

Table 4.14 (continued)

Organic pigments	Solubility and solution colors						Behavior on reduction	Dyeing behavior Wool Cotton
	Glacial acetic acid	Alcohol + NaOH	H$_2$SO$_4$	H$_2$SO$_4$ + KJO$_3$	Ether	Dimethyl-formamide		
7.3 Lakes of triphenylmethanes with acidic groups			ge			l	k (o)	
7.4 Xanthenes with acidic groups							k (o)	
7.5 Diphenylmethanes			l			l	k (o)	
7.6 Nitro pigments		gr	robr					
7.7 Nitro pigments							red.	
7.8 Thiazole pigments								
7.9 Azine pigments							k (w)	

l = soluble
f = dyes
Z = decomposition

bl = blue
br = brown
fu = mauve
ge = yellow
gr = green

ol = olive
or = orange
ro = red
rs = pink
vi = violet

k = vats
k (k) = vats in the cold
k (w) = vats in the cold after hot reduction
k (o) = vats with addition of oxidizing agent
red. = is reduced or decomposed

Data of solubility and reduction given in the line of the main group are relevant for the total group.

Pigments of group 1. and 3. are sparingly soluble in H$_2$O, alcohol, aqueous and alcoholic NH$_4$OH.

Pigments of group 7.2, 7.3 and 7.5 are partially soluble in alcohol.

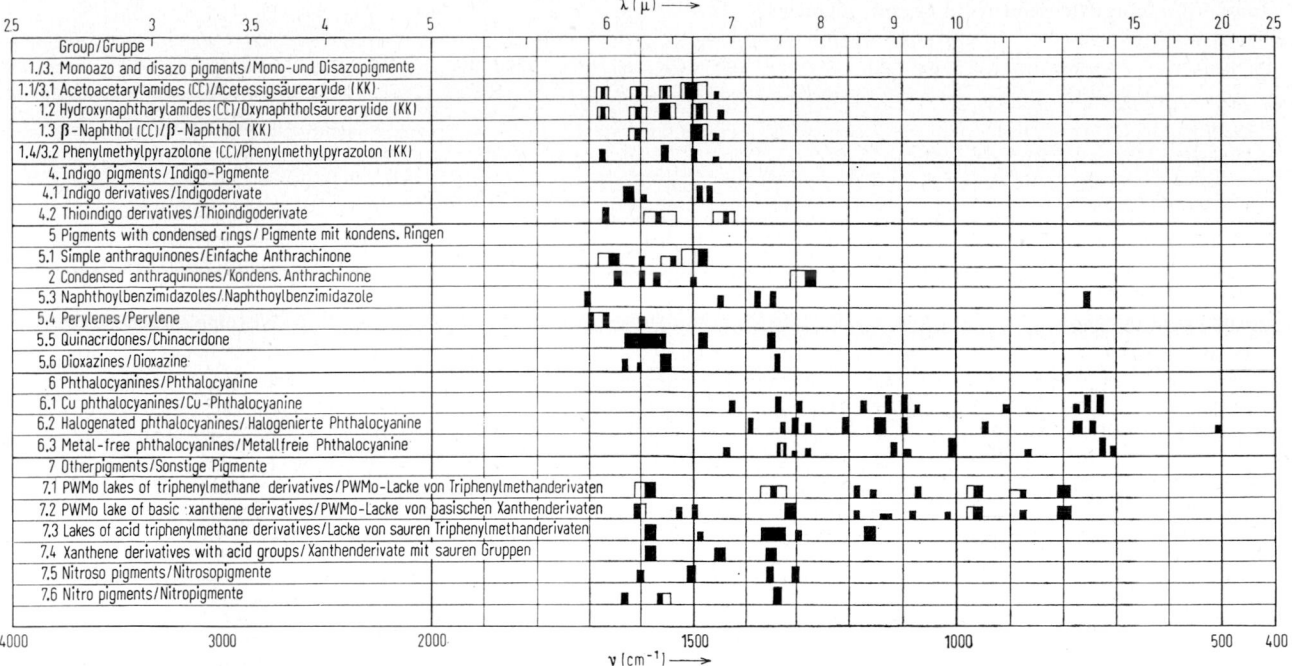

Fig. 4.2: Characteristic bands for various groups of organic pigments

band combinations for various types of pigments. These can be used to narrow the range of possibilities in preparation for identification with the aid of comparison spectra.

whose comparison spectra are not available. By subsequent chemical degradation and spectroscopic identification of the degradation products, analysis of the pigment is possible within a few hours. Spectral reference material for the identification of the degradation products is to be found in commercial collections [147—150].

A few words on the effects of crystallinity and crystal form and of inorganic laking components on the spectra seem appropriate.

IR spectra of organic pigments are also included in a series of SADTLER spectra of technical products [395].

Pigment Violet 19 (5.5.1), which is also known as linear trans-quinacridone, occurs in various crystal forms (α, β, γ, δ), of which the β form in particular is used as a brilliant violet pigment, though the γ form is also used as a light-fast and solvent-fast red pigment with a tendency toward violet.

The spectra of these crystal forms (spectra 5702, 5703) differ characteristically in the X—H stretching region of 3260—2960 cm^{-1} (3.07—3.38 μm), with band splitting in the γ form, and in differences in the relative band intensities, particularly in the longer-wave region between 900 and 450 cm^{-1} (11—22 μm).

On this basis, Pigment Red 122 (5.5.2, spectrum no. 5704) should also be in the β form, while Permanent Red E 5 B (5.5.3, spectrum no. 5705) should be mainly in the γ form. Pigment Blue 15, copper phthalocyanine (6.1.1), also occurs in various crystalline modifications, of which the α form is more reddish, while the β form is somewhat greenish. The two forms, which are easily distinguishable by X-ray studies, also differ in their IR spectra (spectra 5711, 5712).

The bands at 1269 cm^{-1} (7.89 μm), 868 cm^{-1} (11.63 μm), and 775 cm^{-1} (12.9 μm) are weaker for the β form than for the α form, or are even completely absent, whereas the band at 785 cm^{-1} (12.73 μm) becomes more intense in the β form. The changes in the pair of bands at 785 and 775 cm^{-1} can be used for the quantitative determination of the two forms when both are present.

Intensity changes due to differences in crystallinity and in crystal form are also found in the IR spectra of other pigments.

The IR spectra of the lakes (groups 7.1 and 7.2), which are prepared by precipitation of basic dyes with complex inorganic acids, show a superposition of the spectra of the inorganic and organic components. Preference is nowadays given to pigments based on phosphotungstomolybdic acid lakes, which are obtained by acidification of solutions of the dyes and sodium phosphate, tungstate, and molybdate.

PWMo acid lakes are characterized by medium-strong and strong bands around 965 cm^{-1} (10.37 μm) s, 880 cm^{-1} (11.4 μm) m, and 800 cm^{-1} (12.5 μm) vs.

A weak or medium-strong OH band is also found at 3450 cm^{-1} (2.9 μm).

The silicomolybdates, whose spectra are not given here, also give three characteristic bands at about 950, 905, and 800 cm^{-1}, the intensities of the bands at about 905 and 800 cm^{-1} being roughly equal. The ferrocyanide complexes of basic dyes have no bands in this region, but are easily recognizable by a strong C $\equiv$ N band at about 2100 cm^{-1} (4.8 μm). The bands due to the dye molecule are practically unaffected by the laking component.

In addition to the heteroacid complexes, other substrates such as alumina or barium sulfate are sometimes also coprecipitated. In the spectrum of Pigment Violet 1 (spectrum no. 5725), hydrated aluminum oxide is recognizable by the broad bands at about 1100 cm^{-1} (9.1 μm) and 570 cm^{-1}

Table 4.15: Inorganic elements in organic pigments

Pigments	Ca	Ba	Al	Mn	Fe	Cr	Co	Ni	Cu	Pb	W	Mo	P	Si	Notes
Azo lakes	+														Laked with Ca
(e. g. 2.2)		+													Laked with Ba
Azo lakes	+														Laked with Ca
(e. g. 1.1, 2.3)				+											Laked with Mn
									+						Laked with Cu
In complexes of								+							Ni complexes
azo dyes (e. g. 2.4)									+						Cu complexes
Alizarin lakes			+												Al-lake
(e. g. 5.1)	+		+												As Al-Ca complex
			+										+		Laked with Al phosphate
Lakes of sulfonated anthraquinone derivatives			+												Alumina lakes
Phthalocyanines (6.)									+						
Lakes of basic											+	+	+		Laked with phosphotungstomolybdic acid
triphenylmethane,											+		+		Laked with phosphotungstic acid
diphenylmethane and												+	+		Laked with phosphomolybdic acid
xanthene dyes					+							+		+	silicomolybdic acid
(7.1, 7.2, 7.5)					+				+						Laked with copper ferrocyanide
Nitroso pigments (7.6)					+										Fe complexes
Lakes of nitro pigments (7.7)	+														Ca lake
Aniline black					+										Depends on starting
						+									materials and production
									+						method
Cobalt complex dyes							+								Co may also originate
Chromium complex dyes						+									of siccatives
Eosinlack (7.4)										+					Pb may also originate of siccatives

Table 4.16: Thin layer chromatography of organic pigments or of dyes from pigments

Group No.	Group of pigments or dyes	Solvent	Layer	Solvent system for chromatography (vol. parts)	Ref.
1.	Monoazo pigments	Chloroform	Silica gel G	Chloroform-xylene (3 + 1)	369
				Chloroform-toluene-benzene (1 + 1 + 1)	48
3.	Disazo pigments			Hexane-benzene-pyridine (65 + 20 + 15)	369
4.	Indigo pigments	Chloroform	Silica gel	Benzene-chloroform (4 + 1)	382
2.	Acid dyes of Monoazo salts	Glacial acetic acid extract	Silica gel G	n-Butanol-acetic acetic-water (40 + 10 + 50)	382
				n-Butanol-ethanol-water-acetic acid (60 + 20 + 20 + 0.5)	382
5.1	Anthraquinone Lakes	Alcohol-NaOH		Benzene-propionic acid (4 + 1)	382
7.3	Triphenylmethane complexes			Benzene-chloroform-propionic acid (2 + 2 + 1)	369
7.4	Xanthenes		Silica gel + 25% soda	Chloroform-acetic acid (9 + 1)	48
			Cellulose	Butyl acetate-pyridine-water (30 + 45 + 25)	369
				Methanol-water-hydrochloric acid (75 + 75 + 1)	369
	Basic dyes of	Glacial acetic acid extract	Silica gel G		
7.1	Triphenylmethane complexes			Chloroform-methanol (9 + 1 and 8 + 2)	382, 387
7.2	Xanthene complexes	Ethanol + some HCl		Butanol-acetic acid-water (4 + 1 + 4)	382
7.5	Diphenylmethane complexes			n-Butanol-ethanol-water-acetic acid (90 + 30 + 10 + 1.5)	369
				n-Butanol-ethanol-water-ammonia (90 + 30 + 10 + 1.5)	369
			Alumina	Ethanol-water (5 + 2)	384
	Solvent dyes (fat-soluble dyes)	Benzene, carbon tetrachloride, chloroform	Silica gel	Benzene	48, 382
				Chloroform	
				Mixtures of benzene and/or chloroform with diethyl ether, acetone, ethyl acetate, methanol, acetic acid	

(17.5 μm) and the strong broad OH band at 3450 cm⁻¹ (2.9 μm).

These bands are also found in the spectra of other Al lakes on alumina (e. g. spectra 2514 and 2515).

If the dye is precipitated on alumina and barium sulfate (the latter may also be present from the manufacturing process), the characteristic bands of barium sulfate (spectrum no. 2358) at 1187, 1120, and 1075 cm⁻¹ (8.4, 8.9, and 9.3 μm) s, 637 and 608 cm⁻¹ (15.7 and 16.4 μm) m, and the very narrow, weak band at 981 cm⁻¹ (10.2 μm) are also present (e. g. spectrum no. 2562).

5 UV Stabilizers and Fluorescent Whitening Agents

5.1 Survey and Classification of UV Stabilizers

The amount of UV contained in sunlight in the wave length range of 290–400 nm is about 6% of the total solar radiation energy. The photon energy corresponding to this wave length range is 419–293 kJ/mol and is therefore greater than the linkage energy of certain typical linkages found in polymers. This leads in many polymers to photochemical reactions, which result in changes in the optical and mechanical properties. Examples of polymers that are particularly sensitive are polyvinyl chloride, polyolefins, cellulose esters, polystyrene, and polyamides, which exhibit deterioration after a short time in weathering tests. Although most polymers have little or no inherent absorption above 290 nm, radiation consisting of longer waves can exert a degrading effect because the contaminants present in engineering plastics can, like catalyst residues or oxidation products, absorb in the UV range and lead to photochemical reactions.

Different kinds of stabilisers have different effects. The protection given by UV absorbers is essentially based on the absorption of harmful UV rays and the conversion into heat energy without damaging the substrate. Compounds suitable for this purpose must have high inherent absorption and be light resistant so as not to be used up too quickly. Such compounds include hydroxybenzophenones (I), hydroxylphenylbenzotriazols (II) and esters of cinnamic acid (III). Resorcinol monobenzoate (IV), which is also used as a light stabiliser, shows but little UV absorption but is easily converted into 2,4-dihydroxybenzophenone, in which form it is more effective.

The effect of UV stabilisers, however, goes beyond the pure "light filtration effect". In this connection, various energy transfer mechanisms are discussed. Stabilisers known as quenchers, e. g. nickel complexes are intended to take over the energy absorbed by chromophores in the polymer and effectively dissipate it. This characteristic is exhibited by various nickel phenolate complexes (V) and nickel dithiocarbamate complexes (VI) which, however, also exhibit considerable inherent UV absorption.

Substances which decompose hydroperoxides, which can be effective already in small amounts, are meant to destroy the hydroperoxides formed during photo-oxidative degradation and thereby suppress chain reactions. Also suitable are dialkyldithiocarbamates (VI), dialkyldithiophosphates (VII) and thiobisphenolates (V).

(II)

X = H, Cl
R₁ = CH₃·····C₈H₁₇, verzw. Alkyl
R₂ = H, verzw. Alkyl

(III)

R₁ = H, OCH₃
X = H, CH₃, C₆H₅
Y, Z = CN, COOR

(V)

(VI)

(VII)

(VIII)

(IX)

(X)

$\llcorner$ = –C(CH₃)₃   < = <CH₃ / CH₃

(I)

R = H, CH₃·····C₁₂H₂₅

The stabilising effect of radical interceptors is based on the interception of radicals formed intermediately through degradation by light. Alkyl, alkoxy and hydroxyl radicals have a greater reactivity and a longer life than radicals formed through thermo-oxidative degradation and are not fixed sufficiently by antioxidants. Good results have, however, been achieved with nickel thiophenolate complexes (V), with nickel-bis(3,5-di-tert. butyl-4-hydroxybenzyl)butyl phosphate (VIII), as well as with benzoic acid (IX) and benzophenone derivatives (I) having the structure illustrated. A new group of sterically hindered amines such as bis-2,2,6,6-tetramethyl-4-piperidyl sebacate (X), is also very effective. The radical intercepting effect is probably due to photochemically produced nitroxide radicals.

Light stabilisers for polymers must be compatible with the polymer matrix, resistant to extraction by water, colour-less and non-toxic. Various publications deal with the structure, use and mode of action of UV stabilizers, which are mostly combined in quantities of 0.1–1% with other pigments [1, 2, 4–6, 400–406].
UV stabilizers are listed in Table 5.1 based on their chemical structure.

Table 5.1: Classification of UV stabilizers and fluorescent whitening agents and their IR spectra numbers

	IR spectra No.
UV stabilizers	
1. Benzophenones	2581—2594
2. Salicylates	2595—2604
3. Cyanoacrylates	2605—2607
4. Benzotriazoles	2608—2612
5. Others	2613—2618
fluorescent whitening agents	2619—2625

Most inorganic pigments and carbon black also absorb UV radiation, and so reduce photochemical degradation.

The benzophenones are mainly derivatives of 2-hydroxy-benzophenone and of 2,2'-dihydroxybenzophenone. The absorption limit can be displaced to higher wavelengths by varying the substitution. Aliphatic substituents increase the compatibility with polyolefins.

The salicylates and benzoates are inferior to other UV stabilizers in their UV absorption, but are still used at present because of their good compatibility and their favorable price. Cinnamic acid derivatives contain no free OH groups, and are therefore useful in some formulations in which reaction with other additives must be avoided.

The benzotriazoles absorb up to the limit of the visible range, and are very stable. They are extensively used in polyester resins, since they are compatible with the curing agents used for these resins.

5.2 Chemical Detection of UV Stabilizers

Though UV stabilizers are fairly extensively used, there are very few published data on their chemical identification. This is undoubtedly partly because certain functional groups (phenolic OH, alkoxy, carboxylic ester) are present in several classes of substances, and the chemical detection reactions

are therefore not very specific. Conversion into derivatives and determination of the melting point (e. g. hydrazones and phenylhydrazones of the benzophenones) generally involve too much work, and are sometimes impossible in any case because of lack of material.

Since reliable conclusions can be drawn by the use of chromatographic and spectroscopic methods, the lack of chemical detection reactions is not very serious.

5.3 Thin Layer Chromatography of UV Stabilizers

KNAPPE et al. [407] described the separation of eight benzophenone derivatives, two esters of salicylic acid, and 2,4-dibenzoylresorcinol by chromatography on thin layers impregnated with triethylene glycol polyadipate. The solvent system used for this separation was xylene + formic acid (98 + 2). It was possible to influence the R_f values by varying the nature of the support layer. Silica gel G and kieselgur were therefore used as the support for the separation of critical pairs, the salicylates in particular differing in their behavior on this support.

The separated substances were detected by fluorescence at 365 nm (benzophenones yellow and yellow-brown, salicylates blue-violet) or by coupling with Fast Red Salt AL, which gave red spots.

UHDE and ZYDEK [408] found that a separation is possible even on normal silica gel G layers with cyclohexane + ethyl acetate (80 + 20). The spots became visible in UV light or on spraying with a 2% aqueous solution of Fast Red Salt AL and heating to 100 °C.

The hR_f values found by the above authors are listed together with our own data in Table 5.1. In our experiments, the identification was carried out mainly in UV light.

SIMPSON and CURREL [411] have separated UV absorber on silica gel GF$_{254}$ (Merck) with chloroform and hexane (2:1). Their hR_f values were lower than ours (table 5.2, hR_f values with L$_1$), due to the lower polarity of the solvent. To show up the substance, the gel was sprayed with 2,6-dichloro-p-benzoquinone 4 chlorimine solution (0.2% in ethanol) after examination in UV light, followed by drying for a few minutes with a hair drier. Further spots are identified with iodine.

The gel chromatography of light stabilisers has been extensively investigated by ROTSCHOVA et al. [411a] with benzophenones, benzotriazoles and salicylates on polystyrene-gel columns, with tetrahydrofurane as eluent. The separating efficiency is only moderate, however, and of little use for technical additive mixtures.

5.4 IR Spectroscopy of UV Stabilizers

The IR spectra of benzophenone and its derivatives are interesting, since the C=O band is strongly displaced from the positions for aliphatic (approx. 1715 cm^{-1}) and aromatic ketones (around 1690 cm^{-1}). This band is situated at 1656 cm^{-1} (6.04 μm) for benzophenone, at about 1630—1620 cm^{-1} (6.14—6.17 μm) for the 2-hydroxybenzophenones, and at 1610 cm^{-1} (6.21 μm) for some 2,2'-dihydroxybenzophenones. This displacement is accompanied by an increase in intensity, so that the C=O band becomes the strongest in the spectrum. The OH band, on the other hand, becomes weaker, and considerable displacement and broadening are observed in some cases.

All the benzophenone derivatives give a strong pair of bands, which are situated at 1318 and 1274 cm^{-1} (7.6 and 7.85 μm) for benzophenone (spectrum no. 5800), and at 1350—1340

Table 5.2: UV stabilizers, structure, spectra number and TLC data

Dec. no.	IR sp. no.	UV sp. no.	Trade name	Structure					hR$_f$ values		
				R^2	R^4	R^5	R$^{2'}$	R$^{4'}$	Silica gel GF$_{254}$	Silica gel G	
1.			Benzophenones	R^2	R^4	R^5	R$^{2'}$	R$^{4'}$	L$_1$	L$_2$	L$_3$
1.1	5800	19	Benzophenon						63		
1.2	5801	20	Advastab 45	—OH	CH$_3$O-				57	80	56
1.3	5802		Cyasorb UV 531	—OH	C$_8$H$_{17}$-				72		83
1.4	5803		Eastman DOBP	—OH	C$_{12}$H$_{25}$-				74		
1.5	5804		Permasorb MA 78—4000	—OH	R^4 = (2-hydroxy-3-methacryloxy)propoxy- 4, (28)						
1.6	5805		Uvistat 2211	—OH	CH$_3$O-			CH$_3$-	60	81	
1.7	5806	21	Cyasorb UV 207	—OH	CH$_3$O-		—COOH		0		
1.8	5807		Cyasorb UV 284	—OH	CH$_3$O-	-SO$_3$H			0		
1.9	5808	22	Eastman DHBP	—OH	-OH				42	5	21
1.10	5809		Advastab 47	—OH	CH$_3$O-		—OH		48	65	44
1.11	5810	23	Cyasorb UV 314	—OH	C$_8$H$_{17}$O-		—OH		64		
1.12	5811		Uvinul D 49	—OH	CH$_3$O-		—OH	CH$_3$O-	43	70	
1.13	5812		Uvinul DS 49	—OH	CH$_3$O-	-SO$_3$Na	—OH	CH$_3$O-	0		
1.14	5813	24	Uvinul D 50	—OH	-OH		—OH	—OH	11	0	

2.			Salicylates, benzoates	R			
2.1	5814	25	Salicylic acid	H-			(0-22)
2.2	5815		Sunkem SRS	Sr$_{1/2}$			0-7
2.3	5816	26	Sunkem MS	CH$_3$-			65
2.4	5817		Sunkem DDS	C$_{12}$H$_{25}$-			82
2.5	5818	27	Salol	C$_6$H$_5$-			73	83
2.6	5819		Light Absorber TBS	4-tert.Butylphenyl			81	80
2.7	5820		Eastman OPS	4-Octylphenyl			80
2.8	5821	28	Sunkem CPS	Carboxyphenyl-			0-22
2.9	5822		Eastman RMB	Resorcinol monobenzoate			43
2.10	5823	29	Permyl B 100	Resorcinol monobenzoate and 2,4-dihydroxy-benzophenone			41

and 1265—1250 cm^{-1} (about 7.45 and 7.95 μm) for the substituted benzophenones. The spectra, which contain numerous bands, show the characteristics of the various substitution types. In the almost identical spectra of the 2-hydroxyalkoxybenzophenones (1.3 and 1.4, spectra 5802 and 5803), conclusions can be drawn regarding the lengths of the alkyl groups from the different relative intensities of the CH$_2$ bands.

Spectrum no. 5801 shows the influence of crystallinity, which can lead to band splitting.

In the esters of salicylic acid, the C=O band of the ester group is also displaced in relation to the position for aliphatic esters, and occurs at about 1690—1670 cm^{-1} (5.92—5.99 μm). The OH band, as in the benzophenones, again shows strong displacements as a result of interaction with the neighbouring substituents. The spectra of the solid preparations contain various vibrational modes of isolated and associated OH groups at the same time, with the result that several bands are found in the OH stretching region.

Aromatic cyanoacrylic acid derivatives (group 3) can be identified by the CN band at 2215 cm^{-1} (4.52 μm) in the IR

Table 5.2 (continued)

Dec. Nr.	IR sp. No.	UV sp. No.	Trade name	Structure			hR$_f$ values

				R^1	R^2	R^3	Silica gel GF$_{254}$ L$_1$
3.			Cinnamic acid derivatives				
3.1	5824	30	Absorber UV 318	CH$_3$–	CH$_3$–	CH$_3$O–	34
3.2	5825		Uvinal N 35	C$_2$H$_5$–	C$_6$H$_5$–	H–	55
3.3	5826	31	Unival N 539	C$_8$H$_{17}$–	C$_6$H$_5$–	H–	70

				R^5	R$^{2'}$	R$^{3'}$	R$^{5'}$	
4.			Benzotriazoles					
4.1	5827	32	Tinuvin P		–OH		CH$_3$–	65
4.2	5828	33	Tinuvin 320		–OH	t-C$_4$H$_9$–	t-C$_4$H$_9$–	71
4.3	5829		Tinuvin 327	–Cl	–OH	t-C$_4$H$_9$–	t-C$_4$H$_9$–	74
4.4	5830	34	Tinuvin 326	–Cl	–OH	t-C$_4$H$_9$–	CH$_3$–	73
4.5	5831	35	Uvitex OB		Benzotriazole derivative			71
4.6	5338		Tinuvin 328		–OH	t-C$_5$H$_{11}$–	t-C$_5$H$_{11}$–	
4.7	5839		Cyasorb UV 5411		–OH		C$_8$H$_{17}$	

				Structure	hR$_f$ values
5.			Others		
5.1	5832	36	Eastman Inhibitor DPQ	2,5-Diphenyl-benzoquinone	47–67
5.2	5833		Cyasorb UV 1084	[2,2′-Thiobis-(4-tert-octylphenolato)]-n-butylamine-Ni(II)	90
5.3	5840		Ferro AM 105	Thiophenyl-Ni-complex	
5.4	5841		Irgastab 2002	3,5-Di-t.butyl-4-hydroxybenzyl-monoethyl-phosphonate-Ni complex	
5.5	5834		Stabilizer Cu-386	Organic nickel compound	75
5.6	5842		Tinuvin 120	Steric hindered amine	
5.7	5843		Tinuvin 144	Steric hindered amine	
5.8	5844		Tinuvin 770	Steric hindered amine	
5.9	5835		Stabilizer UV 1261	Aromatic ester	
5.10	5836		Stabilizer UV 928	Organic P,S compound	54
5.11	5837		Eastman HPT	Hexamethylphosphoric triamide	

L$_1$ = Diisopropyl ether + petroleum ether (7 + 3), identif. in UV light, our experiments
L$_2$ = m-Xylene + formic acid (98 + 2), identif. in UV light, after *E. Knappe* et al.: Z. analyt. Chemie 197 (1963) 364
L$_3$ = Cyclohexane + ethyl acetate (80 + 20), identif. in UV light, after *W. J. Uhde*: Z. analyt. Chemie 239 (1968) 25

spectrum. The various members of this group exhibit characteristic differences.

A characteristic feature of the triazole derivatives is a sharp, medium-strong band at about 1560 cm^{-1} (6.41 μm), which can be assigned to the C=N stretching vibration. In conjugated systems with C=C and C=N bonds, however, the assignment in the region of the stretching vibrations is uncertain because of the interaction.

The UV stabilizers from other classes of compounds and those having unknown compositions (group 5) can be identified from the numerous bands in the spectra with the aid of comparison spectra.

5.5 UV Spectroscopy of UV Stabilizers

UV spectra 19—36 (spectrum section) were selected as examples of spectra of various groups of UV stabilizers, and each represents a series of very similar spectra.

In the case of the benzophenones, the UV spectrum is determined by the position of the OH groups. The transition from 2-hydroxybenzophenones (spectra 20 and 21) to the 2,4- (spectrum no. 22) and the 2,2′-dihydroxybenzophenones, and finally to 2,2′4,4′-tetrahydroxybenzophenone is accompanied by changes in band position and intensity, which are even more pronounced in alkaline methanol solution.

In the spectra of the salicylates (spectra 25—28), the absorption maxima occur at higher wavelengths for the phenyl esters than for the free acid and the methyl ester.

The benzotriazoles (spectra 32—35) are distinguished from the UV stabilizers mentioned so far by the two maxima at about 300 and 340 nm.

Further data on UV spectra of benzophenones may be found in the articles by ARVENTIEV et al. [413], HRDLOVIC et al. [414] and LIND [2].

UV stabilizers in clear films or in solutions of thermoplastics can be determined by UV spectroscopy. THINIUS [7] referred to the determination of benzophenones at 330 nm in 1 % solutions of PVC in tetrahydrofuran. Plasticizers, stabilizers, and phenolic antioxidants do not interfere.

5.6 Fluorescent Whitening Agents (FWA)

Fluorescent whitening agents are mainly colorless, fluorescent substances, which have been in widespread use for a long time in the production and subsequent treatment of paper and textiles, but have only recently attracted interest for the brightening of plastics.

The water soluble fluorescent whitening agents (FWA) for textiles and paper are primarily derivatives of cumarin (I) and 4,4'-diaminostilbenedisulphonic acid (II). Of the cumarin derivatives, it is the 3,7-disubstituted compounds especially which have achieved practical importance as FWA for synthetic fibres. One row has been phenyl-substituted in the 3-position and contains, in the 7-position, triazin (III), diazol (IV), benzotriazol (V) or naphthotriazol (VI) groups, whilst the other shows diazol (VII) or triazol (VIII, IX) groups also in the 3-position.

As far as stilbene compounds are concerned, it is the derivatives of bis-(triazinylamino)-stilbene-disulphonic acid (X) which are of importance, some of which (XI) - (XXII) are listed according to information supplied by GOLD [1].

To brighten polymers, one also uses bisbenzoxazoles (XXIII-XXV), bis-(styryl)-biphenyls (XXVI) and naphthalimide derivatives (XXVII, XXVIII).

Detailed information about the preparation and uses of FWA is given by GOLD [1, 418], BERGER [2] and others [417–421].

3,7-disubstituted coumarin derivatives		Application for
(I)	R⁷ · · · R³	
(III)		
(IV)		Plast
(V)		PE-F
(VI)		PE-F
(VII)		PE-F
(VIII)		Plast PE-F
(IX)		PE-F PAN-F

Bis(triazinylamino)-stilbene-disulfonic acid derivatives		Application for
(X)	R¹ · · · R²	
(XI)	$-N(CH_2CH_2OH)_2$ · $-Cl$	Pap, PA-F
(XII)	$-N(CH_2CH_2OH)_2$ · $-NH_2$	Pap, Bw
(XIII)	$-NH-\bigcirc$ · $-NH_2$	Pap, Bw
(XIV)	$-NH-\bigcirc$ · $-NHCH_3$	Bw-Det
(XV)	$-NH-\bigcirc$ · $-N(CH_2CH_2OH)_2$	PA-F, Bw-Det
(XVI)	$-NH-\bigcirc$ · $-N\bigcirc O$	Bw-Det
(XVII)	$-NH-\bigcirc$ · $-NH-\bigcirc$	Bw, PA-F-Det
(XVIII)	$-NH-\bigcirc$ · $-OCH_3$	PA-F, Bw, Pap
(XIX)	$-NH-\bigcirc-SO_3H$ · $-N(CH_3)CH_2CH_2OH$	Pap, Bw
(XX)	$-NH-\bigcirc-SO_3H$ · $-N(CH_2CH_2OH)_2$	Pap, Bw
(XXI)	$-NH-\bigcirc-SO_3H$ · $-N(CH_2CHOHCH_3)_2$	Pap, Bw
(XXII)	$-NH-\bigcirc$ (SO₃H, SO₃H) · $-N(C_2H_5)_2$	Pap, Bw

Benzoaxazole derivatives, others		Application for
(XXIII)		PE
(XXIV)		PE, PAN
(XXV)		PAN
(XXVI)		
(XXVII)		(For XXVI and XXVIII) R = CH₃ R = OC₄H₉
(XXVIII)		

Abbreviations

PA = Polyamide, PE = Polyester, PAN = Polyacrylonitrile
Bw = cotton, Pap = paper
F = fibers, Det = from detergents

The purpose of adding FWA to polymers – as in the case of textiles and paper – is to lighten the often slightly yellowish colour of the polymer, especially where this is to be used for making very white articles from film and coated fabrics (packaging, clothing). They also, however, increase the sparkle of pigmented materials, making their colour appear more intense. This effect is usually achieved with 0.01–0.05% of FWA, only special applications requiring more than 0.1%.

The FWA normally used when laundering fabrics are mostly contained in the washing powder in amounts of around 0.5%. They usually consist of three components: a white toner resistant to bleach, for cotton, and a brightener for nylon and polyester fibres. The composition can be characterised by thin layer chromatography, and is typical for the washing powder (THEIDEL, in [1].

The spectral position, intensity, and edge steepness of the fluorescence emission are of vital importance to the whiteness of an optical brightener. Their action is based on the transformatin of UV radiation into visible light (violet or blue). This explains why UV absorbers have an adverse effect on the action of FWA. The physical action and the chemical structure of FWA are discussed in the literature [1, 2, 416–421].

Since manufacturers in most cases do not give details of the chemical compositions of their FWA, we have determined spectroscopic and thin layer chromatographic data for the products listed in Table 5.3 and of some pure substances as typical representatives of important groups.

5.7 Thin Layer Chromatography of Fluorescent Whitening Agents

To isolate the FWA from paper and fabric samples, 50–500 mg of the material are refluxed with about 50 ml of solvent and allowed to stand for about 1 hour until cool. A 7 : 3 mixture of ethylene glycol monomethyl ether + ammonia (sp. gr. = 0.91) has been found to universally applicable [424]. After concentration of the solvent, a spot sample on filter paper in UV light shows whether the concentration is sufficiently high for the subsequent separation by thin layer chromatography.

The FWA are extracted from plastics with acetone or isolated by reprecipitation (in the case of polyacrylonitrile fibers, for example, by dissolution in dimethylformamide and precipitation with acetone). The concentrated acetone extract may be subjected to preliminary separation by column chromatography, the FWA zone being followed by observation with a UV lamp. Other acetone-soluble additives can also be separated by dissolving them in acetone-water-ammonia mixtures, followed by evaporation of the solvent.

The thin layer chromatography of FWA is mainly carried out on silica gel layers [422–425], though polyamide layers [424, 424a] and aluminum oxide layers [422] have also been suggested. THEIDEL and SCHMITZ [424, 424a] carried out paper chromatographic and thin layer chromatographic separations on 16 chemically defined, homogeneous optical brighteners, and were able to show that these can be distinguished by use of several chromatograms. In the case of FWA of the stilbene and oxazolyl types, the cis and trans isomers can be separated, so that two spots appear. The rapidly migrating cis form should exhibit no fluorescence. However, THEIDEL was able to show that the cis form in the adsorbed state is converted by light into the trans form. Knowledge of the R_f values of both isomers is of analytical value. Both forms are present if the FWA extract is exposed for a short time to daylight or to a xenon lamp before the chromatography. The chromatography should be carried out in the absence of light, since interconversion of the two forms during the separation otherwise leads to strip formation.

Table 5.3: Fluorescent whitening agents

IR Sp. No.	UV Sp. No	Name	DC data Layer polyamide hR$_F$-value	
			L$_1$	L$_2$
5850	55	4,4′-Bis (4-phenyl-1,2,3-triazol-2-yl)stilbene-2,2′-disulfonic acid, Na salt		
5851	56	3-Phenyl-7-(4-methyl-5-phenyl 1,2,3-triazol-2-yl)-coumarin		
5852	57	1-(4-Amidosulfonylphenyl)-3-(4-chlorophenyl)-2-pyrazoline		
5853	58	4,4′-Bis [(4-anilino-6-bis (2-hydroxyethyl) amino-1,3,5-triazin-2-yl)amino]stilbene-2,2′-disulfonic acid, Na salt		
5854		Uvitex OB		
5855		Uvitex 551		
5856	13	Blankophor Kum	0, (0–13)	1
5857	14	Blankophor K 2002	16	18
5858		Blankophor DCB	10	21
5859	15	Hoe T 1/283	0	0
5860	16	Tinopal PCR C	0	1
5861	17	Tinopal Bop	(0), 43–84	2, (2–30)
5862	18	Tinopal Up	37–67, 70, 76	1, (1–49)

L$_1$ = methanol + water + ammonia (10 + 1 + 4)
L$_2$ = methanol + 6 N hydrochloric acid (10 + 2) } Identif. in UV light, our experiments
( ) = faint spots

Table 5.4: DC data of fluorescent whitening agents according to THEIDEL [424, 424 a]

No.	Formula	Name		B	E	C	F	D

General structure: R¹–triazine–NH–[stilbene, NaO₃S / SO₃Na, CH=CH]–NH–triazine–R¹ (R, R on triazines)

Name column header: **Na salt of 4,4'-bis[(4-R-6-R'-1,3,5-triazin-2-yl)-amino]stilbene-2,2'-disulfonic acid** — hR$_F$-values in columns B E C F D

No.	Formula	Name	isomer	B	E	C	F	D
1	R = –NH–C₆H₅; R¹ = –OCH₃	4,4'-bis[(4-anilino-6-methoxy-1,3,5-triazin-2-yl)-amino]stilbene-2,2'-disulfonic acid	trans	18		3		68
			cis	89		56		55
2	R = –NH–C₆H₅; R¹ = –N(CH₂–CH₂–OH)₂	4,4'-bis{[4-anilino-6-(2-hydroxyethyl)amino-1,3,5-triazin-2-yl]-amino}stilbene-2,2'-disulfonic acid	trans	12		0		35
			cis	53		25		45
3	R = –NH–C₆H₅; R¹ = –N(CH₂–CH₂–OH)₂	4,4'-bis{[4-anilino-6-bis(2-hydroxyethyl)amino-1,3,5-triazin-2-yl]-amino}stilbene-2,2'-disulfonic acid	trans	11		3		35
			cis	51		33		45
4	R = –NH–C₆H₅; R' = –N(CH₃)(CH₂CH₂OH)	4,4'-bis{[4-anilino-6-(N-methyl-2-hydroxyethyl)amino-1,3,5-triazin-2-yl]-amino}stilbene-2,2'-disulfonic acid	trans	4		0		36
			cis	45		26		48
5	R = –NH–C₆H₅; R¹ = –NH–C₆H₅	4,4'-bis[(4,6-dianilino-1,3,5-triazin-2-yl)amino]stilbene-2,2'-disulfonic acid	trans	0		0		76
			cis	36		9		58
6	R = –NH–C₆H₅; R¹ = –N(morpholino)	4,4'-bis[(4-anilino-6-morpholino-1,3,5-triazin-2-yl)amino]stilbene-2,2'-disulfonic acid	trans	6				72
			cis	84		42		55
7	R = –NH–C₆H₄–SO₃Na; R¹ = –N(CH₂–CH₂–OH)₂	4,4'-bis{[4-(3-sulfoanilino)-6-bis(2-hydroxyethyl)-amino-1,3,5-triazin-2-yl]amino}stilbene-2,2'-disulfonic acid	trans	76		02		27
			cis	95		21		14
8	R = –NH–C₆H₄–SO₃Na; R¹ = –N(CH₂–CH₂–OH)₂	4,4'-bis{[4-(4-sulfoanilino)-6-bis(2-hydroxyethyl)-amino-1,3,5-triazin-2-yl]amino}stilbene-2,2'-disulfonic acid	trans	65		02		18
			cis	96		18		9

Other stilbene disulfonic acid derivatives

No.	Formula	Name	isomer	B	E	C	F	D
9	(4-phenyl-1,2,3-triazol-2-yl)₂ stilbene with NaO₃S / SO₃Na	4,4'-bis(4-phenyl-1,2,3-triazol-2-yl)stilbene-2,2'-disulfonic acid	trans	48		0		72
			cis	85		11		58
10	CH=CH–C₆H₄–C₆H₄–CH=CH with SO₃Na / NaO₃S	4,4'-bis(2-sulfostyryl)biphenyl	trans	78		5		59
			cis	95		15		59
11	bis(5-methylbenzoxazol-2-yl)ethylene (H₃C–, CH₃–)	1,2-bis(5-methylbenzoxazol-2-yl)ethylene	trans		35		54	
			cis		17		93	
12	CH=CH–C₆H₄–CH=CH (CN, NC)	1,4-bis(2-cyanostyryl)benzene	trans		65		32	
			cis		65		88	
13	phenyl-triazolyl-coumarin (H₃C–)	3-phenyl-7-(4-methyl-5-phenyl-1,2,3-triazol-2-yl)-coumarin			62		27	

Table 5.4 (continued)

No.	Formula	Name	hR$_F$-value			
			B	E	F	G
14		3-phenyl-7-(2H-naphtho[1,2-d]triazol-2-yl-)-coumarin		67	9	
15		2,5-bis(benzoxazol-2-yl)thiophene		39	41	
16		N-methyl-4-methoxynaphthalimide		32	80	
17		1-(4-amidosulfonylphenyl)-3-(4-chlorophenyl)-2-pyrazoline		4	58	
18		2,4-dimethoxy-6-(1-pyrenyl)-1,3,5-triazine		50	42	
19		3-(4-methyl-1,2,4-triaz-4-olio-1-yl)-7-(4-methyl-5-ethyl-1,2,3-triazol-2-yl)coumarin methylsufate	84			41
20		N-(1,2,3,5-tetramethylpyrazolio-4-yl)-4-methoxy-naphthalimide methylsulfate	84			23
21		1,2-bis[5-methyl-6-(pyridinio-1-yl-methyl)benzoxazol-2-yl]-ethylene dichloride	87			4
22		1⟨4-{N-[3-(N,N,N-trimethyl-ammonio)propyl]amidosulfonyl} phenyl⟩-3-(4-chlorophenyl)-2-pyrazoline methylsulfate	9			58
23		1-⟨4-{2-[1-methyl-2-(N,N-dimethylammonio)ethoxy]ethyl-sulfonyl} phenyl⟩-3-(4-chlorophenyl)-2-pyrazoline hydrochloride	46			58

Systems for DC of fluorescent whitening agents after Theidel (424 a)

No.	Layer	Mobile phase
B	Polyamid 6,6 (Macherey & Nagel)	methanol + water + ammonia (d = 0,91), 10 + 1 + 4
C	PA 6,6, wie B	methanol + 6 n HCl, 10 + 2
D	Silica gel G (according to Stahl)	n-hexanol + pyridine + ethylacetate + ammonia (d = 0,91) + ethanol, 5 + 5 + 5 + 5 + 3
E	Silica gel G as D	toluene + chloroform, 4 + 6
F	PA 6,6 as B	methanol + 6 n HCl + chloroform, 70 + 14 + 10
G	Silica gel G as D	water + acetic acid + n-butanol + methanol + 6 n HCl, 10 + 15 + 70 + 10 + 10

Table 5.5: TLC data for commercial fluorescent whitening agents, after WANDEL and TENGLER [422]

Trade name	hR_F-values	
	I	II
Blankophor ACF	21*)	38
	37	70
	63	79*)
Blankophor DCB	5*)	12
	24	27*)
Blankophor DRC	44*)	6
	53	26
	62	64
	69	89*)
Uvitex ALN	5*)	5*)
	9*)	13*)
	37	53
Tinopal AN	0*)	0*)
	43	16
	55	90

*) Spots due to the principal components
Layer: Silica gel G; Solvent I: Methylenchloride, II: Aceton + petroleum ether, 3 + 7

WERTHMANN and BOROWSKI [423] have managed to separate various derivatives of bis(triazinylamino)-stilbenedisulphonic acid by TLC on silica gel G, the solvent being a mixture of n-amyl alcohol, ethanol, pyridine and water in a ration of 14 : 5 : 12 : 11. In this way, a large proportion of 33 commercial products, used mainly for paper but unfortunately not listed in the above publication, can be differentiated.

Cis-trans transformation, too, was examined in greater detail and the two isomers chromatographed, when it was found that the trans-isomer migrated more quickly.

Table 5.6. HPLC separation of fluorescent whitening agents (stilben sulfonic acid derivates) after KIRKPATRICK [425 a]
Column: Siliga gel "Partisil 10" (Whatman) 25 cm × 0,46 cm, 25°
Mobile phase: Benzene + p-dioxane + methanol + ammonium hydroxide (30%), (32 + 50 + 8 + 8); 0,4 ml/min

No.	Formula as (No. of table 5.4)	Ret. time (min)
I		2,7
II	6	3,2
III		8,4
IV	4	13,0
V		10,6
VI	3	15,0
VII	10	28,7

V as II, but R' = –NHCH₃

By separating FWA from other inorganic substances with methanol, followed by recrystallising several times, samples were obtained of which IR spectra were produced. These show typical bands, especially at 1220 and 1180 cm⁻¹ (sulphonate), at 1080 cm⁻¹ (amine) and at 800 cm⁻¹ (triazine ring).

Tables 5.4 and 5.5 contain thin layer chromatographic data for a series of FWA.

The column chromatographic separation of FWA of the type stilbene sulphonates and disulphonates, as well as bis-(styrylsulphonate)-biphenyls on silica gel columns (25 cm long) and aluminium oxide columns, has been described by KIRKPATRICK [425a]. The best results were obtained with silica gel columns, using a 32 : 50 : 8 : 8 mixture of benzene, p-dioxane, methanol and 30% ammonia. In this way it proved possible to separate seven of the brighteners most widely used in the USA, and identify them with the UV detector.

The quantitative determination of FWA through direct photometric measurements carried out on thin layer chromatograms on silica gel layers (absorption determination in reflexion) in amounts of 0.5–5 μg is possible, according to THEIDEL [424a] with an error of 5–10%, provided that every trace of residual solvent has been driven off by heating in a stream of nitrogen (2 hours at 150 °C).

6 Antioxidants

6.1 Survey and Classification

Antioxidants prevent or retard the oxidation of organic substances by acting at various points in the course of the oxidation and intercepting free-radical intermediates (free-radical interceptors, inhibitors) or decomposing (peroxide intermediates decomposers). A number of antioxidants that are particularly effective against the attack of ozone on polymers are known as antiozonants.

The following scheme shows the principal reactions in the oxidation of hydrocarbon polymers and the action of antioxidants (AH).

Chain Oxidation in Hydrocarbon Polymers

Initiation by heat or light

$$RH \xrightarrow{\hspace{2cm}} R^{\cdot} + H^{\cdot}$$

$$RH + O_2 \xrightarrow{\hspace{1.5cm}} R^{\cdot} + {}^{\cdot}OOH$$

$$ROOH \xrightarrow{\hspace{2cm}} RO^{\cdot} + {}^{\cdot}OH$$

$$\left.\begin{array}{l} ROOH + M^{++} \longrightarrow RO^{\cdot} + M^{+++} + OH^{-} \\[1em] ROOH + M^{++} \longrightarrow ROO^{\cdot} + M^{++} + OH^{+} \end{array}\right\} \begin{array}{l}\text{Decomposition}\\\text{of peroxides}\\\text{induced by}\\\text{metal ions}\end{array}$$

Propagation

$$\begin{array}{l} ROO^{\cdot} + RH \longrightarrow RO^{\cdot} \\ R^{\cdot} + O_2 \longrightarrow ROOH + R^{\cdot} \\ RO^{\cdot} + RH \longrightarrow ROH + R^{\cdot} \\ OH^{\cdot} + RH \longrightarrow H_2O + R^{\cdot} \end{array} \left.\right\}\begin{array}{l}\text{Chain}\\\text{branching}\end{array}$$

Termination by recombination

$$\left.\begin{array}{l} R^{\cdot} + R^{\cdot} \longrightarrow \\ ROO^{\cdot} + R^{\cdot} \longrightarrow \\ ROO^{\cdot} + ROO^{\cdot} \longrightarrow \\ RO^{\cdot} + R^{\cdot} \longrightarrow \end{array}\right\} \begin{array}{l}\text{Stable}\\\text{reaction}\\\text{products}\end{array} \left.\right\}\text{Crosslinking}$$

Inhibition by antioxidants

$$\left.\begin{array}{l} ROO^{\cdot} + AH \longrightarrow ROOH + A^{\cdot} \\[1em] RO^{\cdot} + AH \longrightarrow ROH + A^{\cdot} \\[1em] OH^{\cdot} + AH \longrightarrow H_2O + A^{\cdot} \end{array}\right\} \begin{array}{l}\text{Interception of}\\\text{free radicals by}\\\text{antioxidants}\\\text{and formation}\\\text{of a stable}\\\text{antioxidant}\\\text{radical}\end{array}$$

$$ROOH + PD \longrightarrow \begin{array}{l}\text{Stable}\\\text{reaction}\\\text{products}\end{array} \quad \begin{array}{l}\text{Decomposition}\\\text{of peroxide by}\\\text{antioxidant}\\\text{with formation}\\\text{of stable}\\\text{products}\end{array}$$

The principal initiation reactions are cleavage of the molecule by the action of light or heat and reaction with oxygen or ozone. The hydroperoxides formed in the first phase react in various ways, this reaction sometimes being accelerated by heavy metal ions.

Numerous phenols and aromatic amines are used as radical acceptors; the interception of free radicals takes place with hydrogen transfer. The primary anti-oxidants producing this chain rupture are, in the main, sterically hindered phenols or secondary aromatic amines. Because of the tendency of most effective amines to discolour because of the formation of coloured reaction products, amines are used mainly in dark coloured elastomer blends and less so in thermoplastics.

Peroxide-decomposing agents are mainly sulfur and phosphorus compounds in which the hetero atoms are present in a low valency stage. These compounds are oxidized by peroxides. Of these secondary antioxidants, the phosphites, phosphonites, thioethers as well as zinc dibutyldithiocarbamate are of considerable practical importance.

N,Ń-Dialkyl-p-phenylenediamines, substituted ureas, aminophenol ethers, and saturated and unsaturated fatty acids have been found to be useful as antiozonants.

Metal deactivating agents, also sometimes referred to as copper inhibitors because special importance is attached to the copper-

Table 6.1: Classification of antioxidants and their IR spectra numbers

	IR spectra No.
1. Phenols	2626—2673
1.1 Monophenols	2626—2633
1.2 Dihydroxybenzenes and tri-hydroxybenzenes	2634—2635
1.3 Bisphenols	2636—2647
1.4 Thiobisphenols	2648—2652
1.5 Phenol ethers	2653—2655
1.6 Aminophenol	2656—2659
1.7 Phenol condensation products	2660—2661
1.8 Other phenols	2662—2673
2. Amines	2675—2707
2.1 Naphthylamines	2674—2676
2.2 Diphenylamines	2677—2682
2.3 Phenylenediamines	2683—2692
2.4 Alkyldiphenylamines	2693—2694
2.5 Other amines and mixtures of amines	2695—2700
2.6 Amine condensation products	2701—2707
3. Other compounds containing N	2708—2717
3.1 Quinolines	2708—2711
3.2 Mercaptobenzimidazoles	2712—2713
3.3 Derivatives of urea and of carbodiimide	2714—2717
4. Various	2718—2724

catalysed oxidation of polyolefins in cables, are likewise of technical importance. Catalytic amounts of heavy metals greatly accelerate the decomposition of hydroperoxides formed during the thermo-oxidative degradation of polyolefins, thereby accelerating oxidative degradation considerably. The normally occurring induction period of oxidation is much reduced or eliminated completely thereby.

Antioxidants based on sterically hindered phenols or aromatic diamines can delay this effect only inadequately. It is therefore often necessary to also incorporate metal deactivators.

Metal deactivators must be readily soluble or dispersible in the polymer and should be compatible with it so that there is no exudation. They should have minimum volatility during processing and use and should have good resistance to extraction. Finally, they should not discolour, nor react with other additives and they should be harmless in use (MÜLLER [2]).

Of the many different substances suggested in the patent literature, the following compounds have achieved practical importance: hydrazones and bishydrazones, acyl derivatives of aminotriazoles and compounds based on sterically hindered phenols. e. g. di-tert.-butylphenol with metal complexing groups. Phosphoric acid esters are also used. Examples of metal deactivators are the compounds indicated under 1.1.9 (spectrum No. 5922) and 4.11 (spectrum No. 6013).

We have classified the antioxidants on a chemical basis in Tables 6.1–6.4.

Comprehensive published lists of antioxidants are to be found in various places [1–4, 9, 10, 427]. The tables published by KURZE [1] and the comprehensive review by VOIGT [4] are particularly clear. Considerable literature exists on the oxidation of organic polymers and the action of antioxidants [1–6, 400–404, 426, 427].

Table 6.2: Antioxidants, 1.1. Monophenols, 1.2. Dihydroxybenzenes, 1.3. Bisphenols, 1.4. Thiobisphenols

Dec. no.	IR sp. no.	UV sp. no.	Trade name	Structure				A	B	C	H	I	K
1.1			Monophenols	R¹	R²	R⁴	R⁶						
1.1.1	5900			-OH	-CH$_3$	-C(CH$_3$)$_3$	-H	57					
1.1.2	5901			-OH	-C(CH$_3$)$_3$	-CH$_3$	-H	69					
1.1.3	5902		Topanol A	-OH	-C(CH$_3$)$_3$	-CH$_3$	-CH$_3$	70					
1.1.4	5903		Nonox WSO	-OH	n-C$_9$H$_{17}$-	-CH$_3$	-CH$_3$	68				18	53
1.1.5	5904	37	ASM KB	-OH	-C(CH$_3$)$_3$	-CH$_3$	-C(CH$_3$)$_3$	76	67	78	74	—	68
1.1.6	5905		Inhibitor DOPC	-OH	-C$_{18}$H$_{37}$	-CH$_3$	-C$_{18}$H$_{37}$	80					
1.1.7	5906		Irganox 1076	-OH	-C(CH$_3$)$_3$	-(CH$_2$)$_2$COOC$_{18}$H$_{37}$	-C(CH$_3$)$_3$	76					
1.1.8	5921		Irganox 1222	-OH	-C(CH$_3$)$_3$	-PO(OC$_2$H$_5$)$_2$	-C(CH$_3$)$_3$						
1.1.9	5922		Irganox 1425	-OH	-C(CH$_3$)$_3$	-PO$_2$OC$_2$H$_5$Ca$_{0,5}$	-C(CH$_3$)$_3$						

Dec. no.	IR sp. no.	UV sp. no.	Trade name	Structure	A B C H I K
1.2.				Dihydroxybenzenes and trihydroxybenzenes	
1.2.1	5908			tert. Butylprocatechol	62,40
1.2.2	5909		Inhibitor THBP	2,4,5-Trihydroxybutyrophenone	
1.2.3	6006		Santovar A	2,5-Di-t-amylhydroquinone	87

Dec. no.	IR sp. no.	UV sp. no.	Trade name	R²,R²′ R³, R³′	R⁴,R⁴′	R⁵, R⁵′	X	A	B	C	H	I	K
1.3.			Bisphenols										
1.3.1	5910	38	ASM DOD		-OH			26	0	20			
1.3.2	5911		Antioxydant 712	-C(CH$_3$)$_3$	-OH	-C(CH$_3$)$_3$		72		74			
1.3.3	5912		Bisphenol A		-OH		>C(CH$_3$)$_2$	26					
1.3.4	5913	39	Antioxydant 720	-C(CH$_3$)$_3$	-OH	-CH$_3$	-CH$_2$-	61		41			
1.3.5	5914		Antioxydant 702	-C(CH$_3$)$_3$	-OH	-C(CH$_3$)$_3$	-CH$_2$-	74		76			
1.3.6	5915	40	CAO 5	-OH -C(CH$_3$)$_3$		-CH$_3$	-CH$_2$-	69		62	—		54
1.3.7	5916		Antioxydant 425	-OH -C(CH$_3$)$_3$		-C$_2$H$_5$	-CH$_2$-	70		59	49		70
1.3.8	5917		ASM ZKF	-OH Cyclohexyl-		-CH$_3$	-CH$_2$-	70	24	73			
1.3.9	5918		Nonox WSP	-OH α-Methyl cyclohexyl-		-CH$_3$	-CH$_2$-	70		62			
1.3.10	5919		Santowhite Powder	-CH$_3$ -C(CH$_3$)$_3$	-OH		> CHC$_3$H$_7$	61		19			
1.3.11	5923		Irganox 259	-C(CH$_3$)$_3$	-OH	-C(CH$_3$)$_3$	X¹						
1.3.12	5924		Irganox 1098	-C(CH$_3$)$_3$	-OH	-C(CH$_3$)$_3$	X²						

X¹ = -OOC(CH$_2$)$_6$COO⁻   X² = -(CH$_2$)$_2$CONH(CH$_2$)$_6$NHCO(CH$_2$)$_2$-
TLC data: See table 6.6

6.2 Chemical Detection of Antioxidants

A number of color reactions are known as tests for phenolic or amine antioxidants; these tests are carried out with solutions of the antioxidants in acetone or alcohol. Extracts from polymers containing large quantities of plasticizers or other additives are first carefully concentrated and treated with acetone/methanol 1:1 or with alkaline methanol to dissolve phenols. Amines are dissolved with methanol containing hydrochloric acid.

Phenolic antioxidants in methanol solution give a yellow or yellowishred color when heated with an equal quantity of Millon's reagent. The reagent is prepared by dissolving 10 g of mercury in 10 g of fuming nitric acid (sp. gr. = 1.4) and adding 20 ml of demineralised water after cooling. On coupling with diazo compounds in alkaline solution at room temperature, phenols that are capable of coupling give colored compounds. A few drops of a 1 % solution of 4-nitrobenzenediazonium fluoroborate (Nitrazol CF extra) in methanol or of a 0.1 % solution of diazobenzenesulfonic acid in 0.05 N NaOH are added to the alkaline solution of the phenol [440]. Since phenols substituted in the o or p position cannot be detected, the two detection reactions complement each other. Secondary aromatic amines also couple with the diazo com-

MS data															
m/e	I	m/e	I	m/e	I	m/e	I	m/e	I	m/e	I	m/e	I	m/e	I
163	100	135	39	178	32	91	14	41	13	121	11	77	10	39	9
205	100	220	34	57	17	206	16	145	8	41	8	81	7	105	6
43	100	57	99	55	98	41	91	69	72	83	63	71	57	97	56
153	100	137	32	196	32	213	31	214	28	77	12	154	9	69	7
221	100	250	27	222	17	43	15	71	9	41	9	192	8	29	8
186	100	170	38	57	18	43	16	55	16	187	14	157	11	41	10
410	100	57	35	411	31	396	14	190	10	41	7	176	5	162	5
213	100	228	56	119	49	91	33	214	30	39	27	65	25	99	22
340	100	325	92	177	35	283	34	127	28	341	27	326	24	161	19
424	100	409	55	57	41	425	33	219	24	410	18	197	17	368	15
177	100	161	75	164	66	340	53	149	44	57	37	121	30	41	24
191	100	368	82	178	71	175	59	163	35	311	24	369	21	57	23
204	100	217	97	121	93	120	91	55	69	135	49	148	43	161	42
339	100	340	27	57	15	149	12	382	11	203	10	41	9	176	8

pounds mentioned above in neutral and acidic media at room temperature to form red, blue, or violet solutions. A freshly prepared 0.1 % solution of diazobenzenesulfonic acid (diazotized sulfanilic acid) in 25 % acetic acid or a freshly prepared 1 % solution of 4-nitrobenzenediazonium fluoroborate in methanol, to which a few drops of concentrated hydrochloric acid are added, is used as the reagent.

Various other color reactions for individual compounds are given in the literature [13, 14, 16, 21, 26, 42, 44, 61, 120, 440, 441].

An example is the reaction of chloroform solutions of substituted phenylenediamines with $FeCl_3$. Antioxidants 4010 Na (2.3.5) and 4010 (2.3.8) give a deep blue color, while DNP (2.3.10) gives a green color.

The aryl-substituted phenylenediamines (2.3.5—2.3.10) react with benzoyl peroxide (4 % in benzene) to give yellow and orange-yellow colors, which change to red-violet or blue in some cases on addition of $SnCl_2$.

Some of the color reactions mentioned can be used for quantitative determinations. HASLAM et al. [21] gave detailed descriptions of methods for the quantitative determination of Nonox WSP (1.3.9), 4,4′-thiobis-(3-methyl-6-t-butylphenol) (1.4.1), butylated 4-methoxyphenol (1.5.3), DPPD (2.3.9), and DNP (2.3.10). Other methods are described elsewhere [440, 441].

The use of color reactions for the identification of individual antioxidants is only of limited value in the analysis of ex-

Table 6.2 (continued)

Dec. No.	IR sp. No.	UV sp. No.	Trade name	Structure	hR$_f$ values on silica gel A B C H I K
1.3.11	5920		Antioxydant CA	1,1,3-Tris(2'-methyl-4'-hydroxy-5-tert.butylphenyl)butane	53
1.3.12	5927		Ionox 330	1,3,5-Trimethyl-2,4,6-tris(3',5'-ditertbutyl-4-hydroxybenzyl)benzolene	74
1.3.13	5907		Irganox 1010	Pentaerythritol ester of β(3,5-ditert-butyl-4-hydroxyphenyl)-propionic acid	69
1.3.14	5925		Hostanox O 3	Succinic acid-di[bis-(3t.butyl-4-hydroxyphenyl)-2-propyl]-ester	
1.3.15	5926		Cyanox 1790	Isocyanuric acid-tri[(4-t.butyl-3-hydroxy-2,6-dimethyl)-benzyl]-ester	

$$R^{4'}\underset{R^{5'}}{\overset{R^{3'}\quad R^{2'}}{\bigcirc}}-S-\overset{R^{2}\quad R^{3}}{\underset{R^{5}}{\bigcirc}}R^{4}$$

Dec. No.	IR sp. No.	UV sp. No.	Trade name	$R^2,R^{2'}$	$R^3, R^{3'}$	$R^4,R^{4'}$	$R^5, R^{5'}$	A	B C H I K
1.4.			Thiobisphenols						
1.4.1	5928		Stabilisator BS	-OH			-C(CH$_3$)$_3$	52	
1.4.2	5929	41	Santowhite Crystals	-CH$_3$		-OH	-C(CH$_3$)$_3$	59	28 13,(30) 24 (47)
1.4.3	5930	42	CAO 4	-OH	-C(CH$_3$)$_3$		-CH$_3$	75	72
1.4.4	5931		Santowhite L	-C$_5$H$_{11}$		-OH	-C$_5$H$_{11}$	76	64
1.4.5	5932		Antioxydant 736		-C(CH$_3$)$_3$	-OH	-CH$_3$	56	45
1.4.6	5933		Irganox 1035*		-C(CH$_3$)$_3$	-OH	-C(CH$_3$)$_3$		

* instead of S-bridge a thioester-bridge -(CH$_2$)$_2$OCO(CH$_2$)$_2$S(CH$_2$)$_2$COO(CH$_2$)$_2$-

tracted additives, owing to the possible presence of other interfering substances. In conjunction with thin layer chromatography, however, color reactions provide more reliable information, and are successfully used together with the R$_f$ value for identification.

POSPISIL and ROTSCHOVA [430] have given a tabular bibliography of the colour reactions suggested for qualitative and quantitative determinations. CROMPTON [16] has assembled various reactions.

6.3 Thin Layer and Column Chromatography of Antioxidants

Extensive work has been carried out in recent years on the thin layer chromatography of antioxidants [44, 48, 61, 120, 440, 441], and this method has now replaced paper chromatography in many laboratories in the plastics and rubber industries. Paper chromatography had been intensively studied by ZIJP [452] with acetylated paper, and had later been described [13, 27, 440, 441] and modified [453, 455] by various authors.

Thin layer chromatography is usually carried out on silica gel layers, though separations on polyamide layers have also been suggested.

Tables 6.2—6.5 present thin layer chromatographic data for antioxidants according to OSTROMOW and HOFMANN [440,

441], KREINER and WARNER [61], and our own investigations. In every case, the separation was carried out on silica gel G (sometimes with a fluorescence indicator) with saturation of the chamber. The solvent systems and detection reagents used are listed in Table 6.6.

For complicated mixtures of antioxidants, several TLC separations with various solvents or two-dimensional thin layer chromatography may be useful. KREINER and WARNER [61] showed that 17 amine antioxidants can be separated if benzene + acetone + concentrated ammonia solution (100 + 5 + 0.1) is used for flow direction 1 and cyclohexane + acetone + concentrated ammonia solution (100 + 5 + 0.1) for direction 2. VAN DER NEUT and MAAGDENBURG [439] proposed a method in which 4 different solvent systems are used in succession, the nature of the systems and the order in which they are used being decided on the basis of the results of the previous separation. The separation of antioxidants by column chromatography on silica gel [21, 119] and on aluminum oxide [457] will be mentioned only briefly here. These separations are often used before spectrophotometric determinations, and are particularly useful in conjunction with UV detectors for the continuous monitoring of the eluate.

Antioxidants can also be separated by gel chromatography if their molecular weights differ sufficiently. This is illustrated

						MS data									
m/e	I	m/e	I	m/e	I	m/e	I	m/e	I	m/e	I	m/e	I	m/e	I
91	100	92	85	65	15	39	15	63	9	51	9	93	6	90	6
57	100	219	31	163	12	41	12	203	12	387	11	157	6	220	6
135	100	167	64	330	60	315	47	150	37	107	31	259	31	182	20
358	100	149	72	181	72	196	38	164	27	359	23	343	20	121	20
164	100	149	53	358	42	57	24	136	20	41	19	146	17	150	16
237	100	266	36	223	35	275	28	239	16	205	16	238	15	167	13
358	100	359	25	136	13	343	12	195	10	164	7	150	6	179	6

in Figure 1.9 and in the chromatogram reproduced here (Fig. 6.1).

PROTIVOVA et al. [455] have examined antioxidants and accelerators using GPC (polystyrene gel, tetrahydrofuran) and tabulated the figures for amines, phenols and accelerators. By combining GPC with TLC and colour tests, the methods can be used in rubber analysis.

HPLC has recently been very successfully used to separate and identify antioxidants [84, 458–458d]. Fig. 1.7 shows an example of the separation of different antioxidants and other additives. Table 6.6a has been compiled from a paper by GROSS and STRAUSS [458] and gives retention data for different phenolic and amine antioxidants in HPLC on silica gel. The UV absorption maxima for the various components have also been indicated.

6.4 Gas Chromatography of Antioxidants

The gas-chromatographic analysis of 2,6-di-t-butyl-p-cresol and other phenolic antioxidants was described in 1958 [459] and later modified [16, 21, 44, 456, 459–462], and was even extended to the determination of bisphenols and aromatic amines [460–462]. At temperatures of 150–300 °C, the strongly polar antioxidants can be effectively separated on silicone oil, silicone rubber, and Apiezon grease columns with a coating of 2.5–10% of stationary phase. It was possible to show [120–460] that even 1,3,5-trimethyl-2,4,6-tris-(3,5-di-t-butyl-4-hydroxybenzyl)benzene, with a molecular weight of 775 (Ionox 330, dec. no. 1.3.12) is eluted from a silicone rubber column at temperatures of around

280 °C in about 10 minutes with a retention index of above 4000. WHEELER [44] has surveyed operating conditions for gas chromatographic separations of antioxidants on the basis of publications that appeared between 1962 and 1966. GAETA et al. [462] achieved the gas-chromatographic detection of 95—100% of the antioxidants (0.2% of 2,6-di-t-butyl-p-cresol, 1.25% of N-phenyl-2-naphthylamine, 1.1% of N-heptyl-N'-phenyl-p-phenylenediamine, and 0.5% of Agerite Superlite) added to oil-extended polybutadiene and styrene-butadiene rubber after extraction of 10 g of rubber with ethanol (165 ml, 16 h). The ethanol extract was concentrated to about 10 ml and made up to 50 ml with acetone or carbon tetrachloride. This solution was used for the gas chromatography. Since most of the mineral oil extender extracted with the antioxidants was eluted before the latter, no appreciable interference occurred. However, this will not always be so. An electron capture detector (ECD) which is much less sensitive to hydrocarbons than to antioxidants, can be useful for distinguishing hydrocarbons in chromatograms.

The separation and subsequent gas chromatographic analysis of p-phenylenediamine and dihydroquinoline antioxidants from SBR elastomers have been examined by THORBURN, BURNS et al. [462a]. 80–90% of the antioxidants contained in the compound were extracted by shaking 5 g of the broken-up sample with two lots of 25 ml acetonitrile, each lot being shaken for 45 minutes. After concentration to 10 ml, cooling to − 20 °C and decanting, most of the plasticiser was separated from the antioxidant solution. The best

Table 6.3: Antioxidants, 1.5. Phenol ethers, 1.6. Aminophenols, 1.7. Phenol condensation products, 1.8. Other phenols

Dec. no.	IR sp. no.	UV sp. no.	Trade name	Structure	hR_f values on silica gel G A	B	C
1.5.			Phenol ethers				
1.5.1	5936		Agerite Alba	4-Benzoxyphenol	47		
1.5.2	5937		Tenox BHA	2-t-Butyl- and 3-t-butyl-4-methoxyphenol	61		
1.5.3	5938		Antioxydant 762	2,6-Di-t-butyl-α-methoxy-p-cresol			
1.6.			Aminophenols				
1.6.1	5939	43	Antioxydant 703	2,6-Di-t-butyl-α-dimethylamino-p-cresol	3		
1.6.2	5940		Suconox 12	N-Lauroyl-4-aminophenol	6		
1.6.3	5941		Suconox 18	N-Stearoyl-4-aminophenol	5		
1.6.4	5942		Nonox CNS	Phenolic compound containing N	28, 72		
1.7.			Phenol condensation products				
1.7.1	5943	44	Nonox EX	Phenol condensation product	(45, 51, 57)		
1.7.2	5944		Nonox EXN	Phenol condensation product	(44, 51, 66)		
1.8.			Other phenols				
1.8.1	5945		Nonox T	Mixture of phenols	49, 71, 87		
1.8.2	5946		Wingstay T	Alkylated phenol	72, 78		
1.8.3	5947		Stabilite White	Polyalkylphenol	62, 82, 88		
1.8.4	5948		Nonox HO	Mixture of phenols	56, 68, 75		
1.8.5	5949	45	Agerite Superlite	Alkylated polyphenol	61, 69, 75		
1.8.6	5950		Zalba Spezial	Phenolic compound	(64), 74		
1.8.7	5951		Wingstay L	Phenol condensation product	75		
1.8.8	5952		Nonox WSL	Cyclohexylated phenols	(43, 58, 76), 70		
1.8.9	5953	46	Styphen 1	Styrenated phenol	68, 79		
1.8.10	5954		ASM TSP	Alkylated and aralkylated phenols	57, 65, 77	3, 13, 36	51, 55, 67
1.8.11	5955		ASM KSM	Mixture of aralkylated phenols	57, 69, 75	11, 35	48, 69
1.8.12	5956		ASM RR 10N	Mixture of alkylated phenols	(21, 54, 67), 61		

TLC data: See table 6.6

Dec. no.	m/e	I	m/e	I	m/e	I	m/e	I	m/e	I	m/e	I	m/e	I	m/e	I
1.5.1	91	100	65	12	200	11	92	8	39	7	27	3	51	3	53	3
1.5.2	165	100	180	59	137	42	166	11	41	10	77	10	91	9	39	8
1.5.3	235	100	57	82	219	66	197	40	250	40	41	33	45	24	161	20
1.6.1	161	100	44	90	203	69	218	56	45	45	175	41	41	37	163	38
1.6.4	150	100	287	54	302	33	105	21	122	17	65	15	91	15	118	13
1.7.1	122	100	149	90	107	85	135	64	121	59	39	56	77	52	91	46
1.7.2	135	100	122	82	256	54	255	40	91	19	149	15	150	14	136	13
1.8.1	177	100	57	71	287	69	191	55	163	47	175	40	41	35	189	35
1.8.2	247	100	191	75	303	61	57	60	41	20	248	18	304	14	29	11
1.8.4	205	100	163	48	57	33	219	30	220	25	41	19	206	15	178	10
1.8.6	267	100	282	82	57	39	268	20	336	17	283	17	41	16	321	13
1.8.7	283	100	298	84	205	81	91	79	57	79	41	66	121	63	161	63
1.8.8	135	100	218	97	149	42	175	37	162	33	203	33	203	22	219	16
1.8.9	285	100	300	57	105	30	286	24	209	20	197	17	301	15	136	12
1.8.10	211	100	226	43	105	39	159	31	43	27	91	25	41	23	212	21
1.8.11	315	100	301	89	316	87	197	65	211	62	105	52	330	47	212	35
1.8.12	133	100	176	80	107	79	199	56	120	51	258	41	55	28	41	28

Table 6.4: Antioxidants, 2.1. Naphthylamines, 2.2 Diphenylamines, 2.3. Phenylenediamines, 2.4. Diarylethylenediamines, 2.5. Other amines, 2.6. Amine condensation products

Dec. no.	IR no.	UV sp. sp.	Trade name	Structure
2.1.			Naphthylamines	
2.1.1	5957	47	ASM PAN	N-Phenyl-1-naphthylamine
2.1.2	5958	48	Nonox D	N-Phenyl-2-naphthylamine
2.1.3	5959		Agerite Resin	Aldol-1-naphthylamine
2.2.			Diphenylamines	
2.2.1	5960		Nonox OD	Octylated diphenylamine
2.2.2	5961		Octamine	Octylated diphenylamine
2.2.3	5962		Agerite Stalite	Monooctyl- + dioctyldiphenylamine
2.2.4	5963		Agerite Iso	4-Isopropoxydiphenylamine
2.2.5	5964		ASM DDA	Diphenylamine derivative
2.2.6	5965		Aranox	4-(p-Toluenesulfonamido)diphenylamine
2.2.7	5934		Permanax	4,4'-Dicumyldiphenylamine

$$R^2\text{-NH}-\langle\text{C}_6\text{H}_4\rangle-\text{NH-}R^1$$

Dec. no.	IR no.	UV sp. sp.	Trade name	R^1	R^2
2.3.			Phenylenediamines		
2.3.1	5966		Tenamene 2	$-CH(CH_3)C_2H_5$	$-CH(CH_3)C_2H_5$
2.3.2	5967		Santoflex 77	$-CH(CH_3)(CH_2)_2CH(CH_3)_2$	$-CH(CH_3)(CH_2)_2CH(CH_3)_2$
2.3.3	5968	49	UOP 288	$-CH(CH_3)C_6H_{13}$	$-CH(CH_3)C_6H_{13}$
2.3.4	5969		Santoflex 17	$-CH(C_2H_5)CH_2CH(CH_3)C_2H_5$	$-CH(C_2H_5)CH_2CH(CH_3)C_2H_5$
2.3.5	5970		ASM 4010 NA	$-CH(CH_3)_2$	Phenyl-
2.3.6	5971		Santoflex 13 Flakes	$-CH(CH_3)CH_2CH(CH_3)_2$	Phenyl-
2.3.7	5972		UOP 688	$-C_8H_{17}$	Phenyl-
2.3.8	5973	50	ASM 4010	Cyclohexyl-	Phenyl-
2.3.9	5974		Nonox DPPD	Phenyl-	Phenyl-
2.3.10	5975	51	ASM DNP	2-Naphthyl-	2-Naphthyl-

Dec. no.	IR no.	UV sp. sp.	Trade name	Structure
2.4.			Diarylethylenediamines	
2.4.1	5976		Stabilite	N,N'-Diphenylethylenediamine
2.4.2	5977		Stabilite Alba	N,N'-2-Methylphenyl ethylenediamine
2.5.			Other amines and mixtures of amines	
2.5.1	5978		Tonox	4,4'-Diaminodiphenylmethane
2.5.2	5979		Stabilisator I	2-Phenylindole
2.5.3	5980		Wingstay 100	Mixture of diaryl-p-phenylenediamines
2.5.4	5981		Agerite HP	Mixture of PBN + DPPD (2 + 1)
2.5.5	5982		Santoflex 75	Mixture of DPPD + Santoflex DD (3 + 1)
2.5.6	5983		Nonox HFN	Mixture of aromatic amines
2.6.			Amine condensation products	
2.6.1	5984		Permanex 47	Diphenylamine-acetone condensation product
2.6.2	5985		Santoflex DPA	Diphenylamine-acetone condensation product
2.6.3	5986		Nonox B	Amine-ketone condensation product
2.6.4	5987		Betanox Special	PBN-Acetone condensation product
2.6.5	5988		Antox	Butyraldehyde-aniline condensation product
2.6.6	5989		Nonox NS	Phenol-aldehyde-amine condensation product
2.6.7	5990		Flexamine G	Mixture with diarylamine-ketone condensation product

TLC data: See table 6.6

	hR_f values on silica gel G					MS data															
A	D	E	F	G	m/e	J	m/e	J	m/e	J	m/e	J	m/e	J	m/e	J	m/e	J	m/e	J	
64	61	60	72		219	100	218	40	217	38	220	31	108.5	26	115	24	216	18	109.5	15
61	53	44	67		219	100	218	34	217	28	220	20	108.5	13	115	12	109.5	7	216	7
35, 64	0—21	0	10, 21, 33, 44, 60																	
76					210	100	322	68	57	22	393	19	211	18	281	18	323	17	169	13
61, 76			76, 79	34, 46	322	100	210	64	57	34	393	29	323	29	250	18	41	12	211	11
65—79			71, 74, 78	21, 30, 37, 48																
65			64		185	100	227	38	184	29	186	14	77	8	228	6	51	6	39	5
68	60, 70	52, 79			258	100	273	92	180	33	259	21	274	20	165	16	77	12	166	9
18			18		44	100	45	67	91	62	43	52	92	32	41	30	39	21	184	20
14—33			15		191	100	220	44	81	20	107	16	192	13	205	13	163	7	161	7
40			21																	
16—37			21		100	332	247	90	333	26	81	26	248	17	107	14	43	11	161	11
(25), 73			47																	
43	25	8	31		211	100	226	80	183	35	212	18	105,5	14	227	14	167	12	169	11
61																				
(28), 65			47		211	100	296	64	212	17	183	16	297	15	184	15	105.5	14	281	9
28—45	31	10	37		266	100	183	27	223	25	184	20	267	20	130	18	111.5	12	41	11
57, 64			42		260	100	169	23	261	22	167	19	183	15	168	13	77	11	130	9
0—48	0, 25	0,6	46																	
33, 63			39																	
44, 82			47																	
4			4																	
65, (73)					193	100	96,5	17	191	17	165	17	89	10	90	10	192	8	83.5	7
42, 58, (68)			51, 55, 59		185	100	183	75	169	66	274	47	51	43	77	40	167	39	168	39
(33, 59), 70																				
(38), 61, (82)																				
(38), 63, (70)					219	100	260	34	218	31	108,5	29	217	26	167	25	51	24	77	18
(60), 75					194	100	169	64	196	55	168	32	211	24	115	23	51	20	83.5	19
(17, 31), 77																				
61—72					169	100	194	88	168	45	167	28	51	23	21	83,5	77	18	196	18
59 (0—70)			58, 62																	
59, 73			28, 42, 68		93	100	160	71	171	64	170	30	184	26	158	24	66	21	199	20
20, 25, 34					84	100	85	52	28	45	56	43	57	37	29	36	30	31	44	31
58, 76																				

Table 6.5: Antioxidants, 3.1. Quinolines, 3.2. Mercaptobenzimidazoles, 3.3. Urea derivatives, 4. Various

Dec. no.	IR sp. no.	UV sp. no.	Trade name	Structure	hR_f values on silica gel G		
					A	C	F
3.1.			Quinolines				
3.1.1	5991		Santoflex AW	6-Ethoxi-2,2,4-trimethyl-1,2-dihydroquinoline	(29, 59, 67), 73		44
3.1.2	5992		Santoflex DD	6-Dodecyl-2,2,4-trimethyl-1,2-dihydroquinoline	(49, 59, 82) 74		40, 67
3.1.3	5993		Flectol H	Polymeric 2,2,4-trimethyl-1,2-dihydroquinoline	1–47, 51		
3.1.4	5994	52	Agerite Resin D	Polymeric 2,2,4-trimethyl-1,2-dihydroquinoline	(27, 37, 66)		26, 34, 45, 54
3.2			Mercaptobenzimidazoles				
3.2.1	5995	53	ASM MB	2-Mercaptobenzimidazoles	0–16	27	
3.2.2	5996		ASM ZMB	Zn-2-mercaptobenzimidazole	0–10		
3.3.			Derivatives of urea and of carbodiimide				
3.3.1	5997		Stabilisator VH	Monophenylurea	0		
3.3.2	5998	54	Stabilisator C	N,N'-Diphenylthiourea	0–22		
3.3.3	5999		Stabaxol	Bis-(2,6-diisopropylphenyl)carbodiimide			
3.3.4	6000		ASM PCD	Polycarbodiimide	77–94		
3.3.5	6008		NBC	Ni-dibutyldithiocarbamate			
4.			Various				
4.1.	6001		Irganox 858	2-n-Octylthio-4,6-di-(4'-hydroxy-3',5'-di-t-butylphenoxy)-1,3,5-triazine	71		
4.2.	6009		Irganox 565	2,4-Bis(n-octylthio)-6-(4-hydroxy-3,5-di-t.butylanilino)-1,3,5-triazin			
4.3.	6002		Mark 328	Phenol condens. product + dialkyl thiodipropionate	52		
4.4	6003		KA 2009	Benzocyclobutane derivative	11, 33		
4.5.	6004		KA 9019	Cyclobutane derivative	(13, 57), 84		
4.6.	6005		Tenox PG	Propyl gallate	11		
4.7.	6010		Vulcanox AFC	Benzofurane derivative			
4.8.	6011		Vulcanox AFD	not published			
4.9.	6012		Vulcanox AFS	not published			
4.10.	6007		Polygard	Tri(nonylphenyl)phosphite	(63), 92		
4.11.	6013		Irganox MD 1024	N,N'-Bis[3-(3',5'-di-t.butyl-4'-hydroxyphenyl)propionyl]hydrazin			

I = intensity

						MS data							
m/e	I	m/e	I	m/e	I	m/e	I	m/e	I	m/e	I	m/e	J	m/e	I
202	100	174	37	145	15	203	15	217	13	173	12	144	7	175	4
150	100	65	11	151	11	75	11	122	10	118	10	167	9	63	9
135	100	93	89	77	58	66	26	51	23	65	16	39	11	136	10
347	100	361	93	162	53	188	47	43	37	41	35	149	35	360	33
91	100	92	13	79	11	65	10	109	9	200	8	39	7	77	5
153	100	170	79	31	47	212	39	76	27	41	23	43	20	125	16

Table 6.6: Solvents and spray reagents for the TLC of antioxidants
(explanation of tables 6.2–6.5)

	Solvent	Spray reagent (no. in Table 2.11)	Ref.
A	Diisopropyl ether + petroleum ether (7 + 3)	Identif. in UV light	our experiments
B	n-Hexane + benzene (1 + 2)	2,6-Dichloroquinonechlorimide (5)	
C	n-Hexane + benzene + methanol (15 + 29 + 6)	2,6-Dichloroquinonechlorimide (5)	
D	n-Hexane + chloroform (1 vol. % ethanol) + diethyl ether (3 + 1 + 1)	Nitrazol CF extra (23)	61
E	n-Pentane + diethyl ether (10 + 1)	Nitrazol CF extra (23)	
F	Benzene + acetone + conc. NH₄OH (100 + 5 + 0.1)	Benzoyl peroxide (15)	
G	Cyclohexane + benzene + acetone (100 + 10 + 1)	Benzoyl peroxide (15)	
H	Benzene	2,6-Dichloroquinonechlorimide (5)	440, 441
I	n-Hexane + benzene (8 + 1)	2,6-Dichloroquinonechlorimide (5)	

Table 6.6a: HPLC data of antioxidants (D. Gross, K. Strauss [458])

Dec. No.	Substance	UV-Abs. Max. nm	Retention time in min				
			I	II	III	IV	V
1.1.5	2,6-Di-t.butyl-4-hydroxytoluene	276	2,35	2,75	2,5	2,9	6,6
1.3.1	4,4'-Dihydroxydiphenyl	261	4,85	11,15		18,8	1,2
1.3.3	2,2'-Bis-(4-hydroxy-phenyl)-propane	279	4,35	11,3		19,8	1,45
1.3.6	Bis-[(2-hydroxy-3-t.butyl-5-methyl)-phenyl]-methane						
1.3.8	Bis-[(2-hydroxy-3-cyclohexyl-5-methyl)-phenyl]-methane	284	2,30	2,55			30,4
1.3.12	1,3,5-Trimethyl-2,4,6-tris-(3,5-di-t.butyl-4-hydroxy-benzyl)-benzene	277	2,10	2,3	2,3	2,4	32
	2-t.butyl-4-methoxyphenol	290	2,85	6,35	12,3		1,95
1.4.2	4,4-Thio-bis(3-methyl-6-t.butylphenol)	247	2,95	7,8	11,5	5,6	4,95
2.1.1	N-Phenyl-1-naphthylamine	253	2,50	2,5	3,5	3,6	3,45
2.1.2	N-Phenyl-2-naphthylamine	310	2,75	2,1	4,1	4,0	3,55
2.3.2	N,N'-Di-(1,4-dimethylpentyl)-p-phenylendiamine	290	3,25	4,2		7,6	4,30
2.3.6	N-(1,3-Dimethyl-butyl)-N'-phenyl-p-phenylene diamine	257	2,70	5,3			24,0
3.2.1	2-Mercaptobenzimidazole	303	3,0	7,0			1,2
7.2.2 (accelerator)	2-Mercaptobenzothiazole	325	3,15	6,3			1,35

Explanations table 6.6a

I–IV: Column Kieselgel Si 60 (Merck) size 10 μm, 30 cm × 4 mm
UV-Detector (Perkin-Elmer LC 55)

Mobile phase I: Heptane + isopropanol (87,5 + 12,5), 2 ml/min
II: Heptane + isopropanol, 2 ml/min every 2 min from 98 + 2 to 90 + 10 in 6 steps

III: Heptane + dichloromethane + isopropanol, 2 ml/min every 2 min from 25 + 75 + 1 to 30 + 70 + 1 in 8 steps
IV: Heptane + diisopropylether + isopropanol, 2 ml/min every 2 min from 75 + 25 to 25 + 60 + 2 in 8 steps

V: Column Nucleosil 10-C 18 (Machery + Nagel), C 18 modified silica gel 25 cm × 4 mm
Mobile phase methanol + H₂O + butanol, 82 + 18 + 1, 2 ml/min

Table 6.7: GC data for various antioxidants on silicone rubber SE-52
(2 m steel column, inside diameter 2.7 mm, 2.5% SE-52 on Chromosorb G, 22 ml of N_2/min)

Dec. no.	Trade name	Retention index	
		200° C	250° C
1.1.2	2-t. Butyl-p-kresol	1374	1395
1.1.5	ASM KB	1545	1575
1.3.1	ASM DOD	2088	2152
1.3.3	Bisphenol A	2193	2245
1.3.4	Antioxidant 720		2562
1.3.5	Antioxidant 702		2678
1.4.5	Antioxidant 730		2758
2.1.1	ASM PAN	2175	2236
2.1.2	Nonox D		2316
2.1.3	Agerite Resin		1987
2.2.1	Nonox OD		2978
2.2.2	Octamine		2980
2.3.1	Tenamene 2	1807	1823
2.3.2	Santoflex 77	2258	2277
2.3.3	UOP 288		2546
2.3.4	Santoflex 17		2377
2.3.5	ASM 4010 NA	2138	2165
2.3.7	UOP 688		2628
2.3.8	ASM 4010		2638
2.3.9	Nonox DPPD		2614

Table 6.8: UV difference spectra of some phenolic antioxidants in methanol and in 1 N alkaline methanol
(measuring beam: alkaline solution, reference beam: neutral solution. 2, 3, 5, 6 after WEXLER [469], 1, 4 our measurements)

No.	Dec. No.		Absorption maxima					Absorption minimum
			λ_1 nm	$E_1 \frac{1}{g \cdot cm}$	λ_2 nm	$E_2 \frac{1}{g \cdot cm}$	E_1/E_2	λ_{min} nm
1	1.1.5	2,6-Di-t-butyl 4 methylphenol	253	8	306	5	1,6	283
2	1.3.5	4,4'-Methylenebis-(2,6-di-t-butyl)-phenol	256	54	297	8	6,7	283
3	1.3.6	2,2'-Methylenebis-(4-methyl-6-t-butyl)-phenol	250	20	306	22	0,9	278
4	1.3.12	1,3,5-Trimethyl-2,4,6-tris-(3,5-di-t-butyl-4-hydroxybenzyl)benzene	255	10	303	6	1,6	281
5	1.4.2	4,4'-Thiobis-(3-methyl-6-t-butyl)-phenol	269	52	295	26	2,0	242
6	1.4.5	4,4'-Thiobis-(2-methyl-6-t-butyl)-phenol	272	44	297	9	4,9	247
7	1.6.1	2,6'-Di-t-butyl-4-(α-dimethyl-aminomethyl)phenol	258	41	300	17	2,4	330

Table 6.9: UV spectra of phenolic antioxidants in neutral and in alcoholic ethanol before and after oxidation with nickel peroxide [471]

Dec. no.		Absorption maxima (λ_{max})				
		Ethanol solution	Alkaline ethanol solution (0.5 N)	Ethanol solution after oxidation	Alkaline ethanol solution after oxidation (0.1 N)	Increase in E_{max} in ethanol solution due to oxidation (factor)
		mμ	mμ	mμ	mμ	
1.1.5	2,6-Di-t-butyl-4-methylphenol	277	303 274 257	340 286	Bands disappear	×8
1.3.5	4,4'-Methylenbis(2,6-di-t.butyl)-phenol	277	303 255	428	578	×30
1.3.12	1,3,5-Trimethyl-2,4,6-tris-(3,5-di-t.butyl-4-hydroxybenzyl)benzene	277	303 274	336 304	336 304	×8

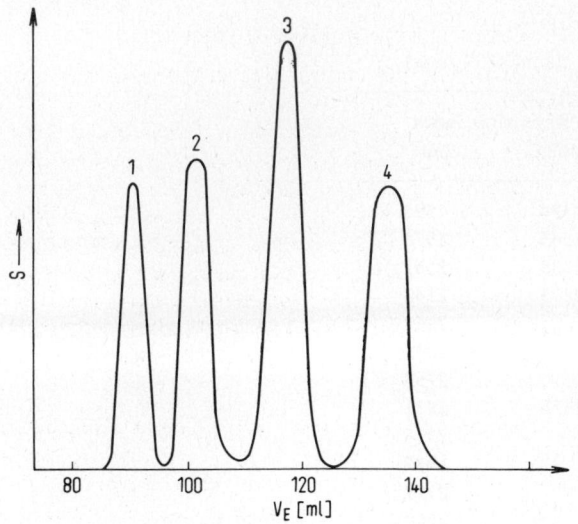

Fig. 6.1: Separation of phenolic antioxidants by gel chromatography
Column: 20 x 550 mm, polyvinyl acetate gel Merckogel OR 20 000
Solvent: dimethylformamide 0.35 ml/min
Detector: UV detector, 254 nm
Quantity of substance: 6 mg each
1. Antioxidant Irganox 1010, pentaerythritol ester of β-(3,5-di-t-butyl-4-hydroxyphenyl)propionic acid, NW 1177.4
2. Antioxydant Ionox 330, 1,3,5-trimethyl-2,4,6-tris-(3,5-di-t-butyl-4-hydroxybenzyl)-benzene, MW 775
3. Antioxidant ZKF, 2,2'-methylene-bis-(4-methyl-6-cyclohexylphenol), MW 392
4. Phenol, MW 94

GC separations were achieved with 3% silicone rubber on Chromosorb as the stationary phase.

The gas chromatography of metal dithiocarbamates has been described by several authors, $C_1 - C_4$ alkyldithiocarbamates of Ni, Zn, Cd, Pb and Hg were separated on silicone rubber (3% SE 30 on Chromosorb) as the stationary phase [462d, e and f].

A number of GC data found by us for antioxidants are given in Table 6.7. Figure 6.2 shows a chromatogram of antioxidants.

6.5 IR Spectroscopy of Antioxidants

The spectra of phenolic antioxidants, which contain numerous bands, show the characteristics of substituted aro-

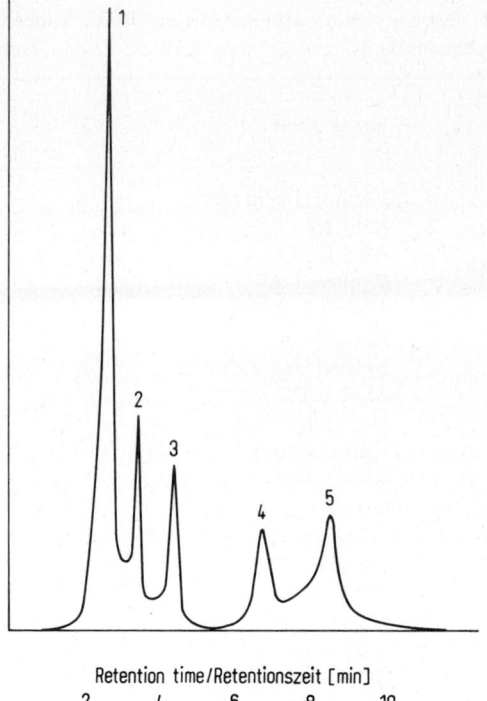

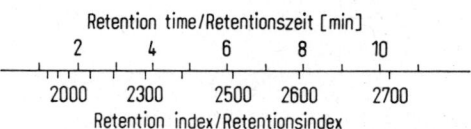

Fig. 6.2: Separation of amine antioxidants by gas chromatography
Column: silicone rubber SE 52; 0.3 x 200 cm;
250 °C; 22 ml of N_2/min; FID
1. Antioxidant 4010 Na (Table 6.4; 2.3.5)
2. Santoflex 77 (2.3.2)
3. Santoflex 17 (2.3.4)
4. UOP 288 2.3.3)
5. Antioxidant 4010 (2.3.8)

matic compounds, certain substituents such as the t-butyl group, and the phenolic OH group.

For the identification of the substitution type, the reader is referred to the tables and diagrams in Vol. 2 and to the literature [146].

The differences in the spectra of various phenols in the region between 3700 and 3300 cm⁻¹ (2.7–3.15 μm) are due to free associated OH groups, whose stretching vibrations may be displaced with increasing association from 3650 cm⁻¹

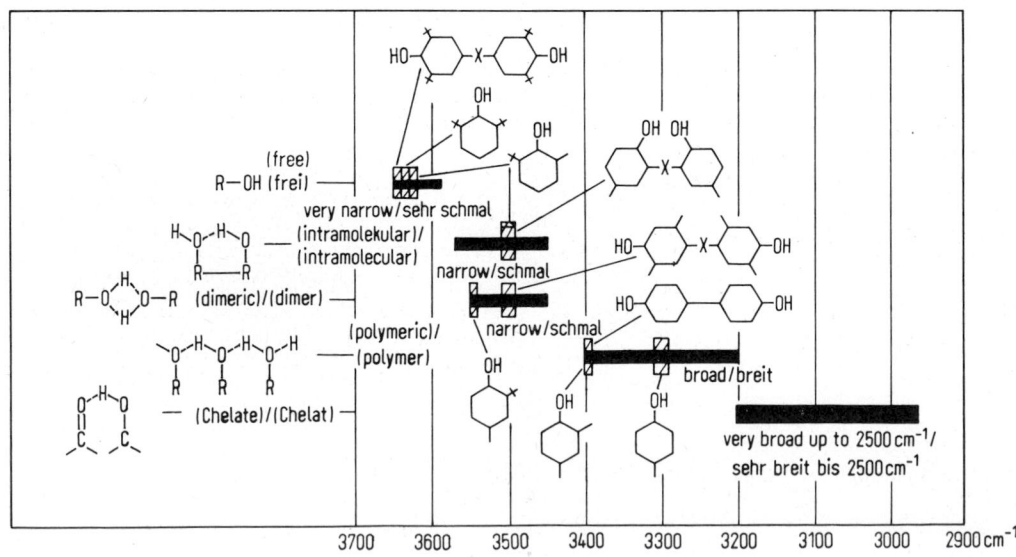

Fig. 6.3: Positions of the OH band of phenolic structures in antioxidants

(2.74 μm) for the free OH group to about 2500 cm⁻¹ (4 μm) on chelation.

The observed ranges for various structures are shown in Figure 6.3. In addition to the ranges generally observed for OH groups (black strips), a number of band positions found for phenolic antioxidants (shaded) are also given together with the corresponding structures. A characteristic feature are the changes in the bands in the OH stretching range from vibrations of associated OH groups to those of dimeric and isolated OH groups in the following series, where the various states being capable of occurring together in various proportions, depending on the external conditions. Similar changes are found for the 4,4'-bisphenols (spectra 5910 and 5911) and for the 4,4'-methylenebisphenols and 4,4'-thiobisphenols (e. g. spectra 5912–5914, 5919 and 5929, 5931, 5932).

The 2,2'-methylenebisphenols and 2,2'-thiobisphenols give free and dimeric OH bands or only free OH bands, depending on the 6,6 substitution next to the OH group and the nature of the 4,4'-substituents (e. g. spectra 5915–5918).

The CO stretching vibration of the phenols occurs around 1205–1150 cm⁻¹ (8.3–8.7 μm) and is generally a medium-strong or strong, somewhat broadened band, which is situated at the long-wave end of the region mentioned with 2,6-di-t-butyl substitution.

The amine antioxidants nearly all give the NH stretching band of secondary amines at 3400–3380 cm⁻¹ (2.95 μm). This band is generally narrower for the diarylamines than for the arylalkylamines. If a molecule contains both structures, the bands often exhibit distinct broadening at the base. However, this is also found if OH groups are present.

The very strong or strong band observed for all aromatic amines at about 1320–1300 cm⁻¹ (7.55–7.7 μm) is attributed to the C—N stretching vibration.

The bands that occur around 1600 cm⁻¹ (6.25 μm), 1500 cm⁻¹ (6.7 μm), and 1000–500 cm⁻¹ (10–20 μm), corresponding to the aromatic structures and substitution types, will not be discussed further. However, they provide a quick aid to identification, e. g. the typical bands around 810 cm⁻¹ (12.3 μm) for 1,4-substituted phenylenediamines and the bands of the monosubstituted aromatic compounds around 740 and 690 cm⁻¹ (13.5 and 14.5 μm) for phenylamine groups. The differences in ν_{CH} found for different aliphatic substituents, which are easily recognizable, provide an indication of the relative content of aliphatic structures.

Of the other antioxidants containing nitrogen in group 3, the 2,2,4-trimethyl-1,2-dihydroquinoline derivatives have similar spectra, but can be easily distinguished from one another. For 2-mercaptobenzimidazole (spectrum no. 2712), the band maximum is situated at about 3150 cm⁻¹ (3.2 μm) because of association of the NH vibrations, further bands occuring on the flank of the principal band down to 2460 cm⁻¹ (4.1 μ).

Monophenylurea and N,N'-diphenylthiourea (spectra 5997 and 5998) also have characteristic spectra, and are therefore easy to identify.

6.6 UV Spectroscopy of Antioxidants

The identification and quantitative determination of antioxidants with the aid of UV spectra has been described in a number of publications [190, 466–471]. This seems an obvious method to use, since phenols and aromatic amines have high extinction coefficients in the UV and are therefore easy to detect in the presence of aliphatic additives. Some antioxidants in clear polyolefin films can be detected directly by UV spectroscopy without first being extracted. However, distinctions are usually possible only between phenols and amines of different substitution types, since different aliphatic substituents have practically no effect on the UV spectrum if the substitution type remains the same, and cannot therefore be recognized.

Phenols of different substitution types can be distinguished even better if in addition to the UV spectrum in neutral alcoholic solution, one also considers the bathochromic shift of 20—30 nm in alkaline solution for the maximum that occurs at 260—290 nm in neutral solution. Phenols with free OH groups are largely in the form of the phenoxide ion even in 0.1 N alkali solution, whereas sterically hindered phenols, e. g. with the OH group situated between two tert-butyl groups, exhibit changes in the spectrum only at higher alkalinities (1 N). This difference can be used for analytical purposes if the alkalinity is increased step by step.

Wexler [469] and other workers before him recorded differences between neutral and alkaline solutions directly as a difference spectrum, which they used for the identification of the type of phenol. The procedure is simple, the alkaline methanol solution being placed in the measuring beam of a twin-beam instrument, and a neutral methanolic solution having the same concentration in the reference beam. Small differences between the two spectra and between different substances are clearly recognizable in this way. Wexler published difference spectra obtained in this way for a series of 2,6-dialkylphenols and various bisphenols. Figure 6.4a shows difference spectra of two sterically hindered phenols, Figure 6.4b shows the influence of the alkalinity on the difference spectrum of 2,6-di-t-butyl-4-methylphenol.

Table 6.8 shows the band positions and extinction coefficients of some difference spectra. The intensity ratio of the two maxima provides analytically useful information.

It should be noted that the phenols are sensitive to oxidation, so that solutions exhibit a gradual change in their spectra on prolonged standing, and even absorb in the visible region.

The result is a change in the band position and absorption. This is illustrated in Figure 6.5 by difference spectra of 2,6-di-t-butyl-4-methylphenol.

For phenols having the same OH group configuration, such as 2,6-di-t-butyl-4-methylphenol (1.1.5), the corresponding 4,4'-methylenebis-(2,6-di-t-butylphenol) (1.3.5), and Ionox 330 (1.3.12), differences are small even in the Wexler method, particularly in the band position. Ruddle and Wilson [471] showed that oxidation of such phenols to quinones with solid nickel peroxide in ethanol solution (5 min at room temperature) yields different reaction products, some of which

(IR sp. No.)   (2626)   (2627)   (2628)   (2630)

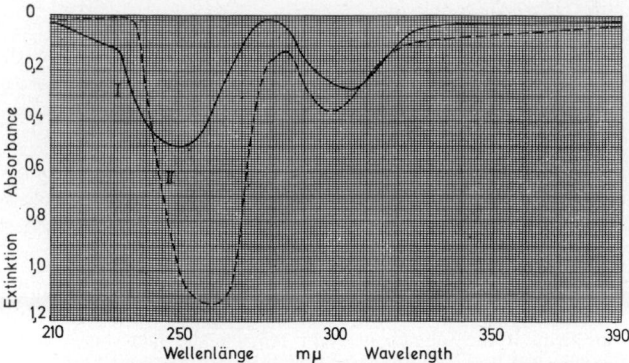

Fig. 6.4a: UV difference spectra of phenolic antioxidants in neutral and in 1 N alkaline methanol solutions
    I. Antioxidant KB (2,6-di-t butyl-4-methylphenol) 0.5 mg/ml, light path 1 mm
    II. Antioxidant 702 [4,4'-methylenebis(2,6-di-t-butyl-phenol)] 0.3 mg/ml, light path 1 mm

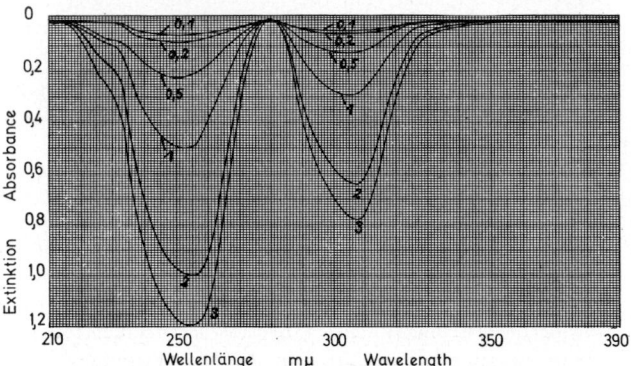

Fig. 6.4b: UV difference spectra of Antioxidant KB (2,6-di-t-butyl-4-methylphenol) in neutral and alkaline methanol solutions. Measuring beam: alkaline solution; reference beam: neutral solution. The numbers (0,1 ... 3) indicate the normality of the methanolic KOH solution

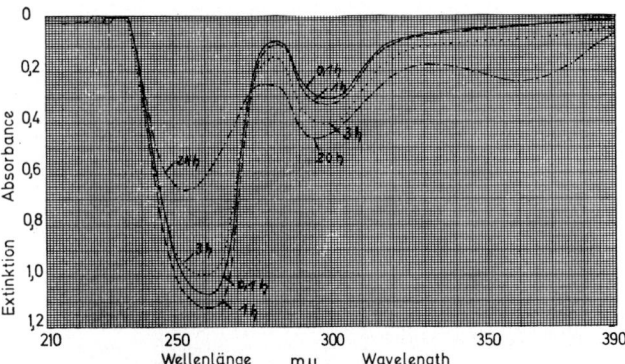

Fig. 6.5: UV difference spectra of Antioxidant 702 [4,4'-methy-lenebis-(2.6-di-t-butylphenol)] in neutral and in 1 N alkaline methanol solution after various times
  0.1 h: freshly prepared solution
    1 h: after 1 hour
    3 h: after 3 hours
  20 h: after 20 hours

are colored, and whose spectra in alcoholic and alkaline alcoholic solutions show more pronounced differences, corresponding to the values in Table 6.9.

The phenylnaphthylamines and phenylenediamines (UV spectra 48—51) with several aromatic groups in the molecule and with different linkages of the groups have characteristic UV spectra which may be suitable for identification.

The aromatic amines show no change on addition of alkali, but change slowly on prolonged standing as a result of the gradual oxidation that occurs in light. CORISH [468] demonstrated the identification of N-phenyl-2-naphthylamine (PBN) in cyclohexane extracts of rubber in the presence of other additives.

The UV spectra of cyclohexane/ethanol solutions of the ether extracts from commercial grades of polyethylene mostly show absorption maxima of phenolic antioxidants at 275—285 nm [467].

Spectra of other commercial products are included in the collection published by FIKTENGOLTS et al. [190]. The spectra reproduced in the present book are confined to typical examples from a few groups, since the spectra of other members of the groups are very similar.

6.7 Mass Spectroscopy of Antioxidants

Since most antioxidants have sufficiently high vapor pressures for mass spectroscopy, this provides a very elegant identification method. The reviews on mass spectroscopy [195—202] contain information on the spectra of phenols, amines, and other classes of substances that are used as antioxidants. HAYES and ALTENAU [472] described the use of mass spectroscopy for the analysis of vulcanizates, and showed that antioxidants can be easily detected in the presence of various extender oils by mass spectroscopy.

Tables 6.2—6.4 contain the 8 strongest mass numbers (m/e) found in our laboratory for commercial antioxidants. The measuring conditions used were indicated in Section 1.8.

Most phenols and bisphenols give a strong molecule peak, as do the phenylnaphthylamines, the phenylenediamines, and 2-phenylindole. However, the molecule peak is also clearly recognizable for nearly all other antioxidants, so that the mass spectra offer very good possibilities for identification.

6.8 Other Methods for the Analysis of Antioxidants

In addition to the methods mentioned so far, various colorimetric and electrochemical methods are used for the quantitative determination of antioxidants. HASLAM and WILLIS [21] as well as CROMPTON [16] give detailed procedures for the colorimetric determination of phenol and amine antioxidants. Other methods have been described for p-phenylenediamine derivatives [473, 474]. Polarographic methods for the determination of phenols allow quantitative determination in the μg range [474]. Volumetric determination is possible by bromination of the phenols [456]. Further recent work is described in reviews [18, 44, 120].

7 PVC Stabilizers

7.1 Survey and Classification

Owing to the pronounced thermal and photochemical instability of vinyl chloride polymers, particularly effective stabilization is necessary for the processing and use of these plastics. The elimination of hydrogen chloride and subsequent reactions (formation of double bonds and discoloration) are specific for polymers containing chlorine, and it is therefore sometimes necessary to use stabilizers that are not used in other plastics.

An extensive literature exists on the degradation processes in PVC and the stabilization of PVC. Only a few reviews will be cited here [2, 4—6, 475—479]. The processing and mode of action PVC stabilizers are also described in numerous manufacturers' brochures.

A large number of substances and mixtures have been suggested for the stabilization of PVC, which is generally supplied unstabilized by the manufacturer; the stabilizing systems vary according to the starting material, processing, and field of application. Synergistic effects are often observed on combination of different stabilizers, i. e. the stabilizing action of the mixture is better than one would expect from summation of the individual effects. Many of the PVC stabilisers on the market today therefore consist of blends.

According to THINIUS [6], e. g. on the basis of the patent literature, combinations of epoxidized soybean or castor oil, one or more metal soaps of Ca, Ba, Zn, Cd, or Pb, and an alkyl or aryl phosphite are often used as stabilizer systems for PVC. However, the manufacturers usually give only limited information, if any, on the composition of stabilizers, e. g. only the cations present in the stabilizer being indicated. VOIGT [4] dealt in great detail with the stabilization of PVC, and divided the stabilizers into lead compounds, metal soaps, organotin compounds, organic compounds containing nitrogen, and auxiliary stabilizers, among which he included epoxy compounds and complexing agents (phosphites, polyols, dicyanodiamide, melamine, etc.). In an impressive inventory (28 pages), he lists more than 500 PVC stabilizers arranged according to their trade names, and where possible he provides information on the chemical composition, physical data, and fields of application. Similar, less comprehensive lists appear annually [3].

In a recently published resumé, ANDREAS [2] exhaustively discusses the chemical and applicational effects of different stabiliser groups. Compounds suitable as heat stabilisers are those which suppress or delay dehydrochlorination reactions through eliminating initiating points and, furthermore, chemically bonding the hydrogen chloride liberated. Examples are tin stabilisers and metal carboxylates.
Of the organo-thin stabilisers (formulae I–IV) it is the ones containing sulphur (III, IV) which are the most effective heat stabilisers. They can be used as general purpose stabilisers since they are suitabel for the various PVC resins, copolymers as well as polyblends, and also facilitate the production of very transparent materials.

The heat stabilising effect of tin compounds is achieved through the mercapto, sulphide or carboxyl group. The alkyl and ester-alkyl groups attached to the tin atom are of importance for the processing characteristics. Stabilising reactions produce, in stages, the appropriate alkyl tin chlorides.

Mono and di-organotin mercaptides are also often combined because syngergistic effects can be achieved in this way.

Calcium carboxylates give good initial effects but poor long-term stability, whereas barium compounds (alkyl-carboxylates, sometimes with phenolates) cause the opposite effect, so that the combination of the two produces the best results.

The metal chlorides formed from metal carboxylates in stabilising reactions also, however, exert a destabilising effect, so that co-stabilisers are usually necessary to deactivate these chlorides or the metal ions. In the case of barium/cadmium stabilisers, this is achieved with polyols. In zinc stabilisers, the negative effect of the zinc chloride produced can be reduced by means of polyols, epoxidised fatty acid esters and phosphides. Although calcium and zinc carboxylates, primarily of fatty acids, show a similar interaction to barium/cadmium stabilisers, their stabilising effect is much less marked. Unlike barium/cadmium and lead stabilisers they are, however, non-toxic so that they are used for many applications.
Whilst barium/zinc combinations are meant to further reduce the use of cadmium and lead compounds, they do not achieve the same effect.

Table 7.1: PVC stabilizers

	IR spectrum no.
1. Inorganic stabilizers	6050–6061
1.1 Silicates	6050–6053
1.2 Sulfates	6054–6056
1.3 Phosphites, phosphates	6057–6059
1.4 Carbonates, hydrated oxides	6060–6061
2. Metal carboxylate stabilizers	6062–6132
2.1 Metal salts of fatty acids	6062–6077
2.2 Metal salts of other carboxylic acids	6078–6080
2.3 Ester-free metal complex stabilizers	6081–6091
2.4 Metal complex stabilizers containing esters	6092–6095
2.5 Phosphorus compound/metal compound stabilizers	6096–6103
2.6 Phosphorus containing ester/metal soap stabilizers	6104–6114
2.7 Sulfur-free tin stabilizers	6115–6123
2.8 Tin stabilizers containing sulfur	6124–6130
2.9 Other metal salt stabilizers	6131, 6132
3. Epoxy compounds	6133–6145
3.1 Epoxy resins	6133, 6134
3.2 Ester of epoxy fatty acids	6135–6139
3.3 Epoxy compound/metal soap stabilizers	6140–6145
4. Phosphorus compounds	6146–6161
4.1 Aryl and alkyl phosphites	6146–6152
4.2 Mixture containing phosphites	6153–6156
4.3 Other phosphorus stabilizers	6157–6161
5. Other stabilizers	6162–6168
5.1 Esters of fatty thioacids	6162, 6163
5.2 Esters of aminocrotonic acid	6164–6166
5.3 Other complexing agents	6167, 6168

I R^1 Sn $O-CO-R^2$ / $O-CO-R^2$
$R^1 = -nC_4H_9$, $-nC_8H_{17}$

II R^1 Sn $O-CO-CH$ / $O-CO-CH$
$R^2 = -Alkyl$, $-CH=CH-COOR$

III R^3 Sn $S-R^4$ / $S-R^4$
$R^3 = -CH_3$, $-nC_4H_9$, $-nC_8H_{17}$, CH_2CH_2COOR

IV R^3-Sn $S-R^4$ / $S-R^4$ / $S-R^4$
$R^4 = -CH_2COOR$, $-CH_2CH_2COOR$, $-R$
$R = -Alkyl$

V $CH_3-C=CH-COOR^5$ / NH_2
$R^5 = -Alkyl$ $(C_6 \cdots\cdots C_{15})$

VI $\left[CH_3-C=CH-COO \atop NH_2 \right]_2 R^6$
$R^6 = -(CH_2)_4-$, $-(CH_2)_2-S-(CH_2)_2-$

VII   (indole structure with R^5)

Pb (II) compounds have long been very successfully used as stabilisers. The lead chloride formed as reaction product does not have a destabilising effect and the reaction products also have very little effect on the electrical properties and conductivity, so that these compounds can be used for cable insulation and other electrical insulating materials.

Certain weakly basic nitrogen compounds have achieved a degree of importance as non-metallic PVC stabilizers. These include βaminocrotonates of types V and VI, as well as 2-phenylindol derivatives (VII), phenylurea and diphenylthiourea.

Co-stabilisers suitable for use in combination with barium/cadmium and barium/zinc stabilisers are phosphites $P(OR_3)$, R representing the same or different alkyl and aryl radicals. Epoxidised soybean oil as well as epoxidised esters of oleic acid from sunflower oil, linseed and castor oil are used as co-stabilisers because they reduce the negative effect of Zn and Cd ions and bind hydrogen chloride. This effect is also ascribed to epoxy resins.

Polyvalent alcohols such as pentaerythritol, dipentaerythritol, trimethylolpropane and sorbitol, as well as polyglycol ethers, deactivate Cd and Zn ions through complex formation.

For analytical purposes, we have used the classification indicated in Table 7.1 and in the case of technical stabilizer blends which are not chemically well defined, we have relied mainly on features of the IR spectra. The substances listed in Tables 7.2–7.8 have been selected from a larger number of commercial products on the basis of the spectra; an effort was made to include the most important chemi-

Table 7.2: PVC stabilizers; 1. Inorganic stabilizers

Dec. No.	IR sp. No.	Trade name	Principal components								Others
			Pb	Ba	SiO_2	$[SiO_4]^{4-}$	$[CO_3]^{2-}$	$[SO_4]^{2-}$	$[PO_3]^{3-}$	$[PO_4]^{3-}$	
1.1.1	6050	Plumbosil C	+		+	+					
1.1.2	6051	Barosil		+		+	+				
1.1.3	6052	Lectro 60	+		+						Chloride complex
1.1.4	6053	Tribase E	+		+			+			basic
1.2.1	6054	Tribase	+					+			basic
1.2.2	6055	Stabilisator V 220	+					+			basic, additives
1.2.3	6056	Hoesch Pb Sn 104	+					+			basic
1.3.1	6057	Dutch Boy Dyphos	+						+		basic
1.3.2	6058	Hoesch Pb Lev 238	+						+		additives
1.3.3	6059	Nicostab DP 12	+							+	
1.4.1	6060	Hoesch Pb Carb 310	+				+				basic
1.4.2	6061	Stabilisator MOH									hydrated manganese oxide

Table 7.3: PVC stabilizers, 2.1. Metal salts of fatty acids, 2.2. Metal salts of other carboxylic acids

Dec. No.	IR sp. No.	Trade name	Salts of fatty acids	Principal components					Others
				Ba	Cd	Ca	Zn	Pb	
2.1.1	6062	Stavinor 60	+						Li
2.1.2	6063	Stavinor 30	+			+			
2.1.3	6064	Stavinor 40	+		+				
2.1.4	6065	Dutch Boy Barinac	+		+				
2.1.5	6066	Nycostab SCD	+		−	+			
2.1.6	6067	Stabilisator Pb 28f	+					+	
2.1.7	6068	Dutch Boy DS 207	+					+	basic
2.1.8	6069	Sicostab D 13	+					+	
2.1.9	6070	Advastab BC 12	+		+	+			
2.1.10	6071	Advastab BC 123	+		+	+			
2.1.11	6072	Nuostab V 131	+		+	+			
2.1.12	6073	Nycostab H 112	+		+	+			
2.1.13	6074	Nuostab V 1072	+			+	+		
2.1.14	6075	Ferro 1701	+		+		+		
2.1.15	6076	Nuostab G 1004			+		+		
2.1.16	6077	Hoesch CMZ 3120	+			+	+		Mg
2.2.1	6078	Hoesch Pb 3153						+	Phthalate
2.2.2	6079	Dutch Boy Normasal						+	Salicylate
2.2.3	6080	Thermolite 124				+			Ethyl acetoacetate

Table 7.4: PVC stabilizers; 2.3. Ester-free metal complex stabilizers 2.4. Metal complex stabilizers containing esters
2.5. Phosphorus compound/metal compound stabilizers

Dec. no.	IR sp. no.	Trade name	Fatty acid salts	Principal components					Aryl, alkyl P compound	Esters	Additives	Others
				Ba	Cd	Ca	Zn	Pb				
2.3.1	6081	Hoesch Pb Lev 141	+					+				Sulfate
2.3.2	6082	Hoesch Pb Ca 3106	+			+		+	+			Phosphite basic
2.3.3	6083	Advastab CZ 111				+	+					
2.3.4	6084	Stabilisator ZBM-A				+	+					
2.3.5	6085	Stabilisator ZBM-B				+	+					
2.3.6	6086	Stabilisator ZBM-C				+	+					
2.3.7	6087	Stabilisator PV 31						+				
2.3.8	6088	Advastab BC 13	+	+	+	+						
2.3.9	6089	Nuostab V 1284	+	+	+	+						
2.3.10	6090	Advastab BC 26		+	+							
2.3.11	6091	Ferro 768				+	+					Mg
2.4.1	6092	Stavinor 250	+					+		+		
2.4.2	6093	Estabex Z 20	+					+		+		
2.4.3	6094	Advastab C 86			+	+			+	+		
2.4.4	6095	Ferro 1976		+		+	+		+	+		Si, Na, Mg
2.5.1	6096	812 A Stabilisant	+		+				+			
2.5.2	6097	Nuostab V 134		+	+				+			
2.5.3	6098	Nuostab V 1008		+	+				+			
2.5.4	6099	Nuostab V 1204		+	+				+			
2.5.5	6100	Advastab BC 206		+	+				+			
2.5.6	6101	Nuostab V 1300		+	+		+		+			
2.5.7	6102	Nuostab V 983				+	+		+			Mg
2.5.8	6103	Stabilisator BCN 7		+	+		+		+			

Table 7.5: PVC stabilizers, 2.6. Ester containing phosphorus/metal soap stabilizers

Dec. no.	IR sp. no.	Trade name	Fatty acid salts	Principal components				Phen-oxide	P	Esters	Others
				Ba	Cd	Ca	Zn				
2.6.1	6104	Advastab C 77	+	+		+		+	+	+	
2.6.2	6105	Stabilisator BCN 6	+		+	+	+		+	+	Mg
2.6.3	6106	Advastab BC 105	+	+	+	+	+	+	+	+	Na
2.6.4	6107	Advastab BC 100	+	+	+	+		+	+	+	
2.6.5	6108	Stabilisator BW 21	+	+	+	+	+	+	+	+	
2.6.6	6109	Stabilisator BCO II A	+	+	+	+		+	+	+	
2.6.7	6110	Stabilisator B CR D	+	+	+	+	+	+	+	+	
2.6.8	6111	Hoesch BCdZ 3270	+	+	+	+	+	+	+	+	
2.6.9	6112	Nuostab V 152	+				+	+	+	+	
2.6.10	6113	Advastab C 89	+		+			+	+	+	
2.6.11	6114	Ferro 203	+		+			+	+		

cally definite substances and representatives of stabilizers whose compositions are not precisely known.

Since some PVC co-stabilizers are also used in other plastics as antioxidants or plasticizers or with some other function, these may be listed in this book under some other heading (amines, urea derivatives, polyols).

The best stabilization is usually achieved by combination of pigments, antioxidants, and UV absorbers with PVC stabilizers proper. In the complete analysis of PVC additives, therefore, it is frequently also necessary to identify these additives.

Various examples for PVC formulations according to ANDREAS [2] show in what amounts stabilisers and other additives are used. The figures are given in parts per 100 parts of PVC.

For transparent sheets for outdoor use:

Sulphur-contianing butyl tin stabiliser	2 − 2.5
Fatty alcohols	0.5 − 0.8
Fatty acid esters	0.5 − 0.8
Polyethylene wax	0.1 − 0.2
UV absorber (benztriazole type)	0.3 − 0.5
Flow acid	1 − 2.

Table 7.6: PVC stabilizers, 2.7. Sulfur-free tin stabilizers 2.8. Sulfur containing tin stabilizers 2.9. Other metal salt stabilizers

Dec. no.	IR sp. no.	Trade name	Principal component
2.7.1	6115	Advastab DBTL	Dibutyltin dilaurate
2.7.2	6116	Advastab DBTM	Dibutyltin maleate
2.7.3	6117	Estabex EN	Modified dibutyltin maleate
2.7.4	6118	Estabex U 18	Dioctyltin maleate
2.7.5	6119	Advastab 5216	Dialkyltin maleate
2.7.6	6120	Stanclere 80	Di-n-octyltin compound
2.7.7	6121	Meister Z 16	Modified dialkyltin maleate
2.7.8	6122	Advastab 52	Modified dialkyltin maleate
2.7.9	6123	Thermolite 17	Bis(dibutyltin monolaurate) maleate
2.8.1	6124	Thermolite 31	Dibutyltin mercaptoester
2.8.2	6125	Advastab 15 M	Dibutyltin mercaptoester
2.8.3	6126	Advastab 15 MS	Dialkyltin mercapotoester
2.8.4	6127	Advastab 17 M	Dibutyltin diisooctyl thioglycolate
2.8.5	6128	Stanclere 186	Dibutyltin mercaptide
2.8.6	6129	Stanclere 386	Di-n-octyltin mercaptide
2.8.7	6130	Thermolite 20	Dibutyltin dilauroylmercaptide
2.9.1	6131	Mark M	Mixture of Ba-octylphenolate, Cd-2-ethylhexanoate and triphenyl phosphite
2.9.2	6132	Nuostab V 1082	Ca-Mg stabilizer

Table 7.7: PVC stabilizers: 3. Epoxy compounds, 4. Phosphorus compounds

Dec. no.	IR sp. no.	Trade name	Principal component
3.1.1	6133	Stabilisator CWM 34	Epoxy resin
3.1.2	6134	Estabex 3001	Epoxy resin
3.2.1	6135	Advaplast 42	Epoxidized butyl oleate
3.2.2	6136	Stabilisator LSA	Alkyl epoxystearate
3.2.3	6137	Drapex 4.4	Octyl epoxystearate
3.2.4	6138	Estabex 2375	Alkyl epoxystearate
3.2.5	6139	Stabilisator LSO	Alkyl esters of epoxidized fatty acids
3.3.1	6140	Stabilisator ZBM-X	Esters of epoxy fatty acids, zinc soaps
3.3.2	6141	Stabilisator ZBM-O	Esters of epoxy fatty acids, zinc calcium soaps
3.3.3	6142	Ferro 763-X	Esters of epoxy fatty acids, zinc calcium soaps
3.3.4	6143	Advastab CZ 11	Esters of epoxy fatty acids, zinc calcium soaps
3.3.5	6144	Estabex 3009	Epoxy resin, phthalate (2 + 1)
3.3.6	6145	Ferro 900	Epoxy resin, plasticizer
4.1.1	6146	Triphenylphosphit	Triphenyl phosphite
4.1.2	6147	Phosclere T 268	Diphenyl isooctyl phosphite
4.1.3	6148	Phosclere T 26	Diphenyl isodecyl phosphite
4.1.4	6149	Phosclere T 210	Diisodecyl phenyl phosphite
4.1.5	6150	Mark 329	Tri(nonylphenyl) phosphite
4.1.6	6151	Phosclere T 310	Triisodecyl phosphite
4.1.7	6152	Phosclere T 312	Tridodecyl phosphite
4.2.1	6153	Phosclere C 55	Trimethoxycarbowax 550, phosphite ester
4.2.2	6154	Advastab CH 20	Triphenyl phosphite, ester of epoxy fatty acid
4.2.3	6155	Advastab C 114	Aryl phosphite, phthalate
4.2.4	6156	Hoesch KB 3019	Aryl phosphite, ester, additives
4.3.1	6157	Phosclere X 10	3,9-Diisodecyloxy-2,4,8,10-tetraoxa-diphosphaspiro[5,5]undecane
4.3.2	6158	Stabilisator SZN	Na-Ba-Ca polyalkyl triphosphate
4.3.3	6159	Ferro 541 A	Na-Ba polylalkyl polyphosphate
4.3.4	6160	Provinite B	
4.3.5	6161	Clarite B	

Table 7.8:	Dec. no.	IR sp. no.	Trade name	Principal component
PVC stabilizers,				
5.1 Esters of fatty thioacids,				
5.2 Esters of aminocrotonic acid,	5.1.1	6162	Advastab PS 801	Lauryl thiodipropionate
	5.1.2	6163	Advastab 802	Stearyl thiodipropionate
5.3. Other complexing agents	5.2.1	6164	Advastab G 1	Esters of aminocrotonic acid with 1,4-butylene glycol and fatty alcohols (C_{16}–C_{18})
	5.2.2	6165	Advastab A 76	Esters of thioaminocrotonic acid
	5.2.3	6166	Advastab A 80	Thiodiethylene glycol-bis-β-aminocrotonate + Cd-Zn stearate
	5.3.1	6167	Hoesch KB 3017	Organic complexing agent
	5.3.2	6168	Hoesch KB 3055	Organic complexing agent

Crystal clear packaging film:
Di-n-octyl tin mercaptide	1 – 1.5
Glycerine esters	0.5 – 1
Montanic acid esters	0.1 – 0.4

Drinking water pipes:
Di-n-octyl tin mercaptide or methyl tin stabiliser	0.3 – 0.5
Calcium stearate	0.6 – 1
Paraffin wax	0.6 – 0.8
Polyethylene wax	0.1 – 0.2

White profiles for outdoor use:
Ba-Cd stabilisers, powdered	2.5 – 3
Phosphites	0.5 – 0.7
Epoxidised soybean oil	1 – 1.5
12-hydroxystearic acid	0.4 – 0.6
Wax esters	0.4 – 0.6
Antioxidant	0.1 – 0.2
Titanium dioxide	2 – 4
Chalk	0 – 10
Impact strength modifier (ethylene vinyl acetate copolymer or similar)	6 – 12

Leathercloth:
Ba-Zn stabilisers	1.5 – 2
Epoxidised soybean oil	3 – 5
UV absorber	0.2 – 0.3
Plasticiser	40 – 60

Electrical insulating compounds:
Tribasic lead sulphate	2 – 4
Neutral lead stearate	0.5 – 1.5
Stearic acid	0 – 0.2
Chalk	20 – 40
Plasticiser	30 – 60

FREY [478] gives the following additives as a typical example for unplasticized PVC or for blends of PVC with chlorinated polyethylene:

2 —3 wt.% of Ba-Cd stabilizer
0.5—1 wt.% of organic phosphite
1 —2 wt.% of epoxy compounds
0.2—0.3 wt.% of UV absorber
lubricant as required.

7.2 Chemical Detection of PVC Stabilizers

To detect stabilizers containing metals, tests are carried out for tin, lead, zinc, cadmium, calcium, and barium on the ash, the solution obtained on digestion with peroxide, or the extract. In the case of PVC containing fillers, however, it should be noted that calcium and barium, and less frequently the other elements, may have come from the filler or pigment. However, some inorganic fillers and pigments also have stabilizing properties.

The presence of stabilizers containing sulfur, phosphorus, and nitrogen can also be established by detection of these elements.

The reaction of about 1—2 ml of a very dilute solution in acetone with a few drops of a freshly prepared 2.5 % solution of p-dimethylaminobenzaldehyde in 50 % sulfuric acid can be used as a test for epoxidized fatty acid esters and fatty oils. Development of a pink color after a few minutes indicates a positive result [482]. In the case of extracts, it is necessary to separate other stabilizers (phenylindole and phenolic antioxidants) by thin layer chromatography with chloroform; the epoxy compounds remain at the starting line, and are scraped off and eluted with acetone.

7.3 Thin Layer Chromatography of PVC Stabilizers

Thin layer chromatography has been used by various workers [451, 480—488], particularly for the separation and identification of tin stabilizers.

TÜRLER [483] separated dialkyltin salts on silica gel with butanol + acetic acid and sprayed the chromatograms with dithizon solution (10 mg in 100 ml of chloroform), whereupon the dialkyltin compounds gave orangered spots, while the trialkyltin compounds that were present as impurities gave yellow spots.

NEUBERT [448] described the separation of organotin stabilizers on silica gel G with isopropyl ether + 15 % of glacial acetic acid. The compounds containing Sn are detected after UV irradiation for 30 min by means of 0.5 % pyrocatechol violet solution, and substances containing sulfur by means of phosphomolybdic acid. The compounds of the series $(n\text{-}C_4H_9)_xSnCl_y$ with x = 2—4, as well as $(n\text{-}C_8H_{17})_2SnCl_2$ and $(i\text{-}C_8H_{17})_2SnCl_2$ could be satisfactorily separated. Dialkyltin compounds with different acid residues exhibit identical behavior; this points to a reaction with the solvent system to form the diacetate. Organotin carboxylates of the type $(n\text{-}C_4H_9)_2Sn(OOCR)_2$ can be separated from the mercaptides $(n\text{-}C_4H_9)_2Sn(SRCOOR)_2$ and distinguished with the aid of the spray reagents mentioned. With solvents of lower polarity (e. g. chloroform), di-n-octyltin maleate and di-n-octyltin thioglycolate remain at the starting spot [480].

HUBER and WIMMER [482] achieved a good separation of dialkytin compounds with the solvent system tetrahydrofuran + benzene + glacial acetic acid (90 + 10 + 1.6). After drying for a short time at 100—110 °C, the chromatogram is thinly sprayed with fresh pyrocatechol violet solution (50 mg in 10 ml of ethanol), whereupon Sn compounds turn blue.

113

Table 7.9: TLC data for PVC stabilizers on silica gel G with hexane + chloroform (1 + 1) as the solvent: 2.3 Ester-free metal complex stabilizers, 2.4 Metal complex stabilizers containing esters, 2.5 Phosphorus compound/metal compound stabilizers, 2.6 Ester containing phosphorus/metal soap

Dec. no.	Trade name	hR$_f$ values	Dec. no.	Trade name	hR$_f$ values
2.3.1	Hoesch Pb Lev 141	7	2.5.1	812 A Stabilisant	4, 20, 79
2.3.2	Hoesch Pb Ca 3106	—	2.5.2	Nuostab V 134	0, 17, 25, 33, 44, 56, 74, 81
2.3.3	Advastab CZ 111	—	2.5.3	Nuostab V 1008	0, 7, 16, 32, 43, 55, 74, 83
2.3.4	Stabilisator ZBM-A	—	2.5.4	Nuostab V 1204	0, 9, 15, 67, 74, 82
2.3.5	Stabilisator ZBM-B	—	2.5.5	Advastab BC 206	0, 8, 16, 57
2.3.6	Stabilisator ZBM-C	—	2.5.6	Nuostab V 1300	0, 8, 14, 30, 42, 65, 72, 79, 84
2.3.7	Stabilisator PV 31	0, 5, 11, 25, 36, 68, 79	2.5.7	Nuostab V 983	0, 7, 66
2.3.8	Advastab BC 13	79	2.5.8	Stabilisator BCN 7	0, 9, 33, 42, 51, 73, 81
2.3.9	Nuostab V 1284	0	2.6.1	Advastab C 77	0, 9, 20, 51, 59, 66, 72
2.3.10	Advastab BC 26	0	2.6.2	Stabilisator BCN 6	7, 47, 62, 76, 83, 88
2.3.11	Ferro 768	0	2.6.3	Advastab BC 105	8, 17, 57, 62
2.4.1	Stavinor 250	25	2.6.4	Advastab BC 100	0, 8, 13, 65, 77
2.4.2	Estabex Z 20	23	2.6.5	Stabilisator BW 21	0, 10, 31, 56, 68, 76
2.4.3	Advastab C 86	10, 50	2.6.6	Stabilisator BCO II A	0, 10, 18, 36, 44, 53, 69, 78
2.4.4	Ferro 1976	0	2.6.7	Stabilisator B CR D	0, 11, 39, 47, 58, 72, 81
			2.6.8	Hosech BCdZ 3270	0, 9, 21, 36, 49, 80, 89
			2.6.9	Nuostab V 152	8, 60, 71, 79
			2.6.10	Advastab C 89	10, 25, 70

The hR$_f$ values for dibutyltin derivatives are around 30, and those for dioctyltin derivatives are around 50, dialkyltin mercaptides giving an additional spot at about 90, which is due to the liberated mercapto group. Less polar solvent systems are more suitable for the separation of lubricants and various types of stabilizers. VAN DER HEIDE [480] uses chloroform and various detection reagents (see Table 10.4), and HUBER and WIMMER [482] also use chloroform, as well as petroleum ether + diethyl ether + glacial acetic acid (80 + 20 + 1).

Tables 7.9 and 7.10 contain TLC data for PVC stabilizers and stabilizer mixtures with various solvent systems.

Table 7.11 contains TLC data for other substances that can be used for the stabilization of PVC.

7.4 Gas Chromatography of PVC Stabilizers

Among the PVC stabilizers, the alkyl esters of expoxidized fatty acids [20], the phosphites, and the volatile stabilizers containing nitrogen can be determined directly by gas chromatography. The acids of the metal soaps can be identified and separated by gas chromatography after conversion into the methyl esters. The fatty acid distribution in epoxidized triglycerides can also be determined via the methyl esters. Further information is obtainable from Sections 2.4 and 2.5. According to NEUBERT and WIRTH [484a], it is possible to subject mono, di, tri and tetra-alkyl tin compounds to gas chromatographic analysis after conversion of the partly alkylated compounds into tetra-alkylated ones with n-alkyl magnesium bromide whose alkyl group does not form part of the original tin compound (mostly

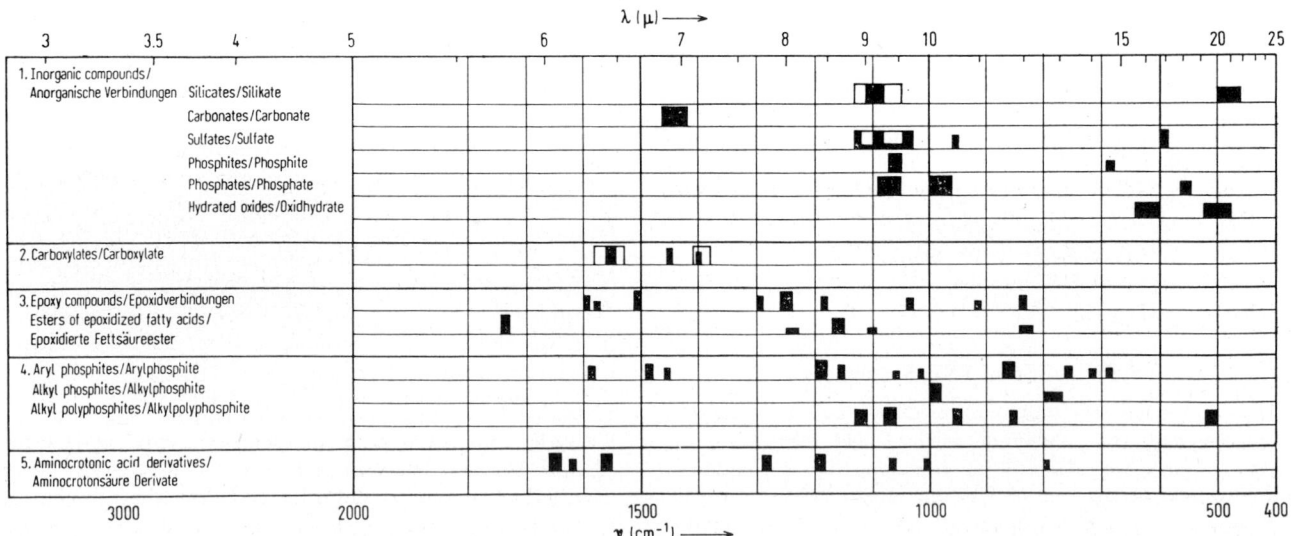

Fig. 7.1: Band positions of some PVC stabilizers

Table 7.10: TLC data for PVC stabilizers on silica gel G with various solvents
(detection: UV light, iodine vapor, spraying with ammonium molybdate/perchloric acid)
2.7. Sulfur-free tin stabilizers,
2.8. Tin stabilizers containing sulfur,
2.9. Other metal salt stabilizers,
3. Epoxy compounds
4. Phosphorus compounds,
5.2. Esters of aminocrotonic acid

| Dec. no. | Trade name | hR_f values with solvents | | | | |
		Hexane + chloroform (1 + 1)	Methylene chloride	Diisopropyl ether + petroleum ether (1 + 1)	Chloroform [480]	Tetrahydrofuran + benzene + glac. acetic acid (90 + 10 + 1.6)
2.7.2	Advastab DBTM					31
2.7.4	Estabex U 18				80—85	
2.8.5	Stanclere 186					31, 90
2.8.6	Stanclere 386					50, 90
2.9.1	Mark M	8, 16, 36, 47, 77, 84	34, 46, 69, 79, 91			
3.1.1	Stabilisator CWM 34	1, 12	43	0, 7		
3.2.1	Advaplast 42	42	48	69		
3.2.2	Stabilisator LSA					
3.2.3	Drapex 4,4	11, 41, 72	31, 51	1, 30, 69		
3.2.4	Estabex 2375	17, 46, 75	27, 52	1, 32, 73		
3.3.4	Advastab CZ 11	12, 26, 37, 72				
4.1.2	Phosclere T 268	8, 15, 72, 77	13, 32, 89	7, 46, 72, 79		
4.1.3	Phosclere T 26	8, 17, 72, 79	18, 33, 89	11, 47, 73, 80		
4.1.4	Phosclere T 210	8, 18, 71, 78	19, 34, 91	12, 48, 74, 81		
4.1.5	Mark 329	8, 15, 33, 45, 57, 69, 84	32, 64, 75, 83, 93	55, 75, 86		
4.1.6	Phosclere T 310	14, 70, 77	28, 38, 89	13, 75, 88		
4.1.7	Phosclere T 312	7, 17, 78, 83	22, 35, 93	11, 47, 90		
4.2.1	Phosclere C 55	1, 11, 71	2, 34	2, 30, 69		
4.2.2	Advastab CH 20	9, 15, 21, 70	35, 90			
4.2.3	Advastab C 114	10, 20, 34, 53, 70	34, 58, 74			
4.2.4	Hoesch KB 3019	10, 16, 20, 37, 45, 69, 77	36, 46, 54, 76, 91			
4.3.4	Provinite B	0, 12, 31, 37, 48, 77				
4.3.5	Clarite B	0, 9, 34, 45, 77				
5.2.1	Advastab G 1				14, 57, 77	0

Table 7.11: TLC of organo tin derivatives (SIMPSON and CURREL [411]). Layer: silica gel G, solvent: butanol + acetic acid (97 + 3).

	hR_F-value
Butyl tintrichloride	0
Dimethyl tindichloride	4
Diphenyl tindichloride	21,76
Hexabutyl tin	26,96
Dibutyl tindilaurate	29
Dioctyl tindilaurate	46
Tributyl tinlaurate	82
Dibutyl tin bis(2-ethylhexylthioglycolate)	33

ethyl magnesium bromide). Silicones (OV 17) are suitable as stationary phase for the temperature-programmed separation (100 – 300 °C, 5 – 10 °C/min). FIGGE et al [484c] have confirmed, with radiocarbon marked test compounds, that the ethylation of n-octyl tin thioglycol esters takes place quantitatively and that this method appears to be suitable also for other tin stabilisers.

7.5 IR Spectroscopy of PVC Stabilizers

There are only a few publications at present [13, 20] on the identification of PVC stabilizers by IR spectroscopy. This is undoubtedly largely due to the fact that relatively little is known in most cases about the composition of the substances or mixtures offered as stabilizers. These gaps become particularly noticeable in the compilation of collections of spectra. Practically the only solution available at present, therefore, is that proposed by us, i. e. classification of the substances according to important features of the IR spectrum and according to manufacturers' data.

The remarks in Section 3.3 regarding the IR spectroscopy of inorganic fillers and pigments are largely valid for the inorganic stabilizers of group 1.

The strongest bands in the spectra of the aliphatic metal soaps (see Fig. 7.1) are the CH stretching vibrations at 2960–2840 cm^{-1} (3.38–3.52 μm) and the groups of bands between 1600 and 1400 cm^{-1} (6.25–7.15 μm). In the carboxylates, the two oxygen atoms are equivalent, and this leads to a strong, sometimes split asymmetric stretching vibration in the region of 1600–1500 cm^{-1} (6.25–6.67 μm) and the weaker symmetrical stretching vibration at 1480–1400 cm^{-1} (6.75 to 7.15 μm).

In the case of the metal salts of fatty acids, the shape and position of the bands depend on the cation. The following typical band positions are observed (cm^{-1} and μm):

Na soaps: 1630—1610 (6.1—6.2) w, m — 1560 (6.41) s — 1425 (7.02) w
Li soaps: 1580 (6.33) s — 1558 (6.42) m — 1405 (7.12)
Ca soaps: 1575 (6.35) s — 1538 (6.5) s — 1420 (7.05) w, m
Ba soaps: 1515 (6.6) s — 1410 (7.1) m
Zn soaps: 1540 (6.5) s — 1400 (7.14) m
Cd soaps: 1535 (6.52) s — 1405 (7.1) m
Pb soaps: 1535 (6.2) s, m — 1508 (6.63) s — 1412 (7.07) m

The soaps prepared from unbranched fatty acids give the characteristic CH$_2$ rocking vibration of the -(CH$_2$)$_5$- chains at 720 cm^{-1} (13.9 μm). They are mostly mixtures of C$_{12}$—C$_{18}$ fatty acids, e. g. stearates usually having appreciable contents of palmitates. The same is true of the other soaps. Gas chromatography of the methyl esters is a very suitable method for the accurate analysis of the fatty acid composition.

The spectra of free fatty acids are reproduced in Vol. 2.

The soaps of highly branched synthetic carboxylic acids do not give the band at 720 cm^{-1} (13.9 μm). The bands of the CH$_3$ group are also stronger.

The lead salts of phthalic and salicylic acids (2.2.1 and 2.2.2) have a characteristic group of bands at 870—650 cm^{-1} (11.5 to 15.4 μm), and are thus readily distinguishable from salts of fatty acids.

An example of a metal complex of an oxo compound is calcium ethylacetoacetate (2.2.3), which may be regarded as a chelate with two molecules of ethylacetoacetic acid. The spectrum, which contains numerous bands, is characterized by the displacement of the carboxylate bands, which usually occur at much longer wavelengths for Ca soaps.

Groups 2.3—2.6 contain a series of commercial stabilizers, for which the information obtained from the manufacturers' data, our own preliminary investigations, and the IR spectra are given in Tables 7.4 and 7.5.

The sulfur-free dibutyltin laurates and maleates (2.7) also give the characteristic bands of the carboxylates. These bands are situated at 1602 and 1564 cm^{-1} (6.25 and 6.4 μm) in the case of dibutyltin laurate, while the maleates give a weak band at about 1640 cm^{-1} (6.1 μm), which is sometimes recognizable only as a shoulder, and a strong band at about 1575 cm^{-1} (6.35 μm).

The weak to medium-strong, sharp double band at about 870—860 cm^{-1} (11.5—11.65 μm) is characteristic of the

maleates. Some of the commercial products listed also contain esters and even traces of free acid.

The epoxy resins based on bisphenol A (3.1) that are offered for the stabilization of PVC are spectroscopically largely identical with the high molecular weight varnish resins, and the reader is therefore referred to Vol. I, p. 173 (spectra 1029—1032) for a discussion of the spectra.

The esters of epoxidized fatty acids (3.2) are in some cases almost identical spectroscopically with the epoxy compounds listed among the plasticizers (spectra 6198—6205). The alkyl epoxystearates can be distinguished from the epoxidized triglycerides by the intensity of the band at about 1100 cm^{-1} (9.1 μm), which is of roughly the same intensity as the band at about 1240 cm^{-1} (8.06 μm) in the case of the triglycerides.

The stabilizers 3.3.1—3.3.4 are mixtures of epoxidized triglycerides and soaps. The epoxy compounds can be separated from the soaps with acetone or petroleum ether.

The epoxidized fatty acid alkyl esters and triglycerides are usually not uniform, since various fatty acids and in many cases various alkyl isomers are present. Moreover, the epoxidation may be incomplete and different in degree. Such epoxy compounds therefore usually give several spots or peaks in XLC and GC [20].

Epoxy resins mixed with esters of phthalic acid can also be used as PVC stabilizers (3.3.5 and 3.3.6). The phthalic ester is superimposed by the epoxy resin in the spectrum, but is easily recognizable by the bands at 1280, 1115, 1070, and 735 cm^{-1} (7.8, 8.97, 9.35, and 13.6 μm).

Aryl phosphites and alkyl aryl phosphites (4.1) show strong bands with maxima at about 1180 cm^{-1} (8.47 μm) and 850 cm^{-1} (11.76 μm), with the addition of a broad strong band at 990 cm^{-1} (10.1 μm) on introduction of alkyl groups. The first two bands mentioned are assigned to P-O-aryl structures, the band at the shorter wavelength being attributed to the O-phenyl stretching vibration and that at the longer wavelength to the P-O stretching vibration [130a]. The bands that occur at 1600—1450 cm^{-1} (6.25—6.9 μm) and about 770 and 685 cm^{-1} (13.0 and 14.6 μm) in the case of triphenyl phosphate are also found for the phenyl phosphites, sometimes with small changes in intensity. As is shown by the thin layer chromatograms, the aryl alkyl phosphates contain various esters in an equilibrium mixture that depends on their manufacture.

The stabilizers of group 4.2 are mixtures containing phosphites, whose spectra show the presence of additives, i. e. trimethoxycarbowax in 4.2. 1, an ester of an epoxidized fatty acid in 4.2.2, a phthalic ester in 4.2.3, and phthalic esters and polyglycol derivatives in 4.2.4.

Medium-strong bands due to the grouping —S—CH$_2$— are expected to occur in the range 1440—1410 cm^{-1} (6.94—7.04 μm) and 1260—1220 cm^{-1} (7.9—8.2 μm). The lauryl and stearyl thiodipropionates (spectra 2837 and 2838) differ in their band structures in these regions from those usually found for esters of fatty acids, and can be distinguished (even from the very similar esters of difatty acids with ether linkages) by means of these differences.

The esters of aminocrotonic acid (5.2) give very similar spectra (spectra 2839—2841), which resemble those of aromatic compounds. The two sharp, strong bands of primary amines at 3470—3320 cm^{-1} (2.88—3.01 μm) and the groups of bands at 1670—1550 cm^{-1} (6.0—6.46 μm), which are due to the structure of a carboxyl group with a β-conjugated NH_2 group to it, are characteristic. The spectrum also contains the strong deformation bands fo the alkene group. No detailed data are available on the composition of the complexing agents containing ester groups and aromatic groups (group 5.3), which are included as example of complex stabilizers.

7.6 Other Methods for the Analysis of PVC Stabilizers

X-ray fluorescence analysis can be used for the direct detection of metal stabilizers and of stabilizers containing phosphorus. If the plastic is in the form of a film or sheet about 20 mm in diameter, chemical pretreatment is usually unnecessary.

Increasing use has recently been made of atomic absorption spectroscopy for quantitative determinations in extracts and ashes. Tin can also be detected with high sensitivity in extracts by polarography.

Various photometric methods for the determination of stabilizers containing nitrogen have been described by O. KORN and G. WOGGON [494a, b].

Diphenylurea reacts with dichlorodiphenylmethane (1 ml of 10% solution in chloroform + 3 ml of chloroform + 1 ml of 50% sulfuric acid) to give a violet solution, which gives a linear calibration curve at a wavelength of 530 nm for 20—250 μg of diphenylurea after standing in the dark for 48 hours [494a]. Monophenylurea does not interfere.

Diphenylthiourea also gives this reaction, but the sensitivity is considerably lower. Since diphenylthiourea is largely decomposed during processing and is present only in traces in the final product, no serious interference is to be expected from this source.

With a similar procedure, 2-phenylindole gives a brown red color, which is measured after 20 hours at 470 nm [494b].

Organic phosphites such as triphenyl phosphite can be determined volumetrically with t-butyl peroxide, both being dissolved in octane. Excess peroxide is determined by photometric back-titration with potassium iodide [7].

Alkyl aryl phosphites and aryl phosphites can also be determined by UV spectrometry. In the presence of other aromatic compounds, the phosphites may be hydrolyzed first, the resulting phenols then being determined on the basis of the displacement of the phenoxide ion.

8 Antistatics, Biostabilizers, Flame Retardants

8.1 Survey and Classification of Antistatics

The function of antistatics is to prevent or reduce the build-up of electrostatic charges on plastics. This can be achieved by reducing the electric resistance of the plastic or at least of its surface, since faster leakage of the charge is then possible. Charge build-up is usually insignificant on plastics filled with graphite, carbon black, or metal, but not on unfilled polymers or polymers with organic and inorganic fillers. A particularly noticeable consequence of static electricity is the deposition of dust on polycarbonate, polystyrene, and polymethacrylates. Various data on the susceptibility of plastics to charge build-up (also in the form of a "triboelectric series") are to be found in the literature [2, 495, 496, 498, 500].

The action of antistatic additives is usually based on the formation of a continuous, thin, polar, hydrophilic film on the surface of articles made of plastics. They may be applied by dipping or by spraying the finished articles with solutions of antistatics, or the film may be formed by the addition of "internal" antistatics to the plastic if the diffusion of the antistatics out of the plastic leads to the formation of a surface layer.

The substances used as antistatics are polar and in some cases weakly hygroscopic, and are identical with or closely related to the wetting agents in current industrial use. Besides allowing the charge to leak away from the surface, they should prevent charge build-up due to friction, i. e. they should act as lubricants. However, this function is of no importance if the charge build-up occurs in strong electric fields (e. g. in television receivers).

The patent literature contains numerous suggestions for antistatic agents. RIETHMAYER [498] has dealt with these in a comprehensive survey, with special reference to PVC additives. BALBACH [500] deals with the internal and external antistatic agents used for polyolefins and discusses their mode of action, likewise FINCK [2].

Mainly used are cationic, anionic and non-ionic surface active substances. Of the first group, quaternary ammonium salts are the most important. In addition to a long chain modified fatty alcohol, fatty acid amide or fatty acid ester radical, short chain alkyl and alkylol groups as well as ring systems (pyridine, imidazoline) are attached to the quaternary nitrogen atom. The anion is usually chloride, nitrate, methoxysulphate or phosphate. Cationic antistatics are used mainly for polar polymers.

Anionic compounds include alkyl sulphonates, alkyl phosphates and carboxylates which are used in the form of alkali or alkaline earth salts. The main representatives of this group are sodium alkyl sulphonates which are used for PVC and styrene polymers.

Non-ionic surface active compounds include modified fatty acid esters, fatty acid ethanolamides, mono and diglycerides, ethoxylated fatty amides and polyethylene glycol esters and ethers. Because of their low polarity these compounds are suitable as internal antistatic agents for polyolefins. To achieve maximum compatibility, the structure of the antistatic agent i. e. chain length, hydroxyl and polyether groups, must be matched to polymer characteristics such as molecular weight and crystallinity.

Normal concentrations for internal antistatic agents are around 0.1% for LDPE, 0.2–0.3% for HDPE, 0.5% for PP, 0.5–1.5% for PVC and 1.5–4% for PS and PS copolymers.

When selecting an antistatic agent, a possible reaction with other additives, as well as the processing temperature should be taken into account, bearing in mind that not all antistatics are thermally stable. Information on the properties, processing, and action of antistatics is obtainable from the literature [2, 496—499] and from manufacturers' literature, though the latter and even tables of commercial products [3] provide practically no information on the composition of the antistatics. Data on the structure and properties and on the analysis of wetting agents are to be found in various monographs [501, 502].

We have recorded the IR spectra of the evaporation residues and carried out thin layer chromatographic separations for more than 100 antistatics of the American and German markets (1969/70), for which the manufacturers gave little or no information about composition. On the basis of this work, 45 products were selected, corresponding to the groups listed in Table 8.1. Tables 8.2—8.4 show the spectrum numbers and the thin layer chromatographic data in line form.

Table 8.1: Antistatic agents

Dec. no.	Composition	IR spectra no.
1.	Nitrogen compounds	6200–6215
1.1	Quaternary ammonium compounds	6200–6209
1.2	Alkylolamines, amides	6210–6215
2.	Glycol derivatives	6216–6220
2.1	Polyglycol ethers	6216
2.2	Polyglycol ethers with esters	6217–
2.3	Polyglycol ethers and oxyethylated alkylphenols with additives	6218–6220
3.	Mixtures containing esters of fatty acids	6221, 6222
4.	Anionic mixtures	6223–6227

Individual components were not isolated and investigated separately.

Substances similar to or identical with those used as anti-statics are also suitable for use as antifogging agents. The purpose of these agents is to prevent condensation in the form of droplets in closed, clear film packs, in order to ensure an unhindered view of the contents. This can be achieved if the surface tension of the condensing moisture can be reduced to cause the moisture to spread out on the surface of the film and form a continuous film of water. This is made possible by the addition of surface active agents that form a thin hydrophilic film on the surface [534].

Substances that can be used as antifogging agents for food packs include monoesters of glycols in the molecular weight range around 200—300, polyglycol esters of fatty acids (molecular weight about 600—900), sorbitol esters of fatty acids, and ethoxylated alkylphenols.

Some of the glycol derivatives mentioned were listed under plasticizers (Section 2), where data on the analysis of these compounds may be found.

8.2 Chemical Detection of Antistatics

The detection reactions described for wetting agents [501, 502] can also be used for the identification of antistatics. This is particularly simple with an aqueous or alcoholic solution obtained by washing a large area of the plastic.

If antistatics are extracted with other additives, it is preferable or necessary to separate them from the latter.

The TLC separation described by CORNILLE [503, 504] and the detection reactions for the principal groups of antistatics will be described below. Single antistatics can be identified by combination of the various reactions corresponding to Table 8.5.

Where mixtures are present, as is often the case in practice, separation of the antistatics by thin layer chromatography

(Section 8.3) is necessary in order to obtain useful information.

The following procedure is suggested for the identification of antistatics in polyolefins. After thorough extraction of about 50 g of film with isopropanol, the extract is concentrated to about 1 ml and applied as a line to a silica gel G thin layer plate.

Antioxidants and other additives are separated with chloroform. The antistatics remain in the region of the starting

Table 8.2: Antistatics; 1.1. Quaternary ammonia compounds, 1.2. Amines and amides

Dec. no.	IR sp. no.	Trade name	hR_f	Thin layer chromatogramm, silica gel GF₂₅₄ Methanol + acetone (9 + 1)
1.1		Quaternary ammonium compounds		
1.1.1	6200	Stat-Eze 100		
1.1.2	6201	Barquat CO-50		
1.1.3	6202	Catanac SP		
1.1.4	6203	AR-9		
1.1.5	6204	Catanac SN		
1.1.6	6205	Arc-Ease		
1.1.7	6206	Anstac M		
1.1.8	6207	Sun-Stat BTC		
1.1.9	6208	Cetol		
1.1.10	6209	Barquat CME		
1.2		Amines and amides		
1.2.1	6210	Antistatic Agent C-2		
1.2.2	6211	Antistatic Agent 273 E		
1.2.3	6212	Antistat 61		
1.2.4	6213	Hallco Antistat C-1015		
1.2.5	6214	Hallcomid M-12		
1.2.6	6215	Warcobase A		

══════ Visible after spraying with iodine-sulfuric acid   ·········· Visible in UV light

Table 8.3: Antistatics; 2. Polyglycol ethers, 3., 4. Mixtures

Dec. no.	IR sp. no.	Trade name	Thin layer chromatogram, silica gel GF$_{254}$ Chloroform + methanol (9 + 1)
2.1		Polyglycol ethers	
2.1.1	6216	Hatcol 1606	
2.2		Polyglycol ethers + ester	
2.2.1	6217	Drewplast 095	
2.3		Poly glycol ethers, oxyethylated alkylphenols	
2.3.1	6218	Merix Wipe	
2.3.2	6219	Merix Rins	
2.3.3	6220	On the Ball	
3.		Mixtures containing fatty acids	
3.1	6221	Drewplast 017	
3.2	6222	Drewplast 050	
4.		Anionic mixtures	
4.1	6223	Antistatic DCZ	
4.2	6224	Spac	
4.3	6225	Gafstat AS-610	
4.4	6226	Gafstat AE-610	
4.5	6227	Repuls	

════════ Visible after spraying with *Dragendorff* reagent   ·················· Visible in UV light

line (R_f = 0—20). Their presence is checked at the edge of the plate by spraying with iodine. Antioxidants such as sterically hindered phenols have R_f values around 40, while the values for paraffins are 80—90. The zone in the region of R_f = 0—20 is scraped off and extracted with isopropanol, and the extract is again concentrated to about 1 ml. The following chemical tests are then carried out with drops of this extract.

Test for aromatic compounds

Reagent: 0.2 ml of CH_2O (37 %) in 10 ml of conc. H_2SO_4. A drop of extract is allowed to evaporate on a spot plate, and a drop of reagent solution is added to the residue. A brown-red color indicates the presence of aromatic compounds.

Test for -OCH$_2$-CH$_2$O-groups

Reagents: 1 part of 20 % aqueous morpholine is mixed with 1 part of 5 % aqueous sodium nitroprusside. Anhydrous $ZnCl_2$.

5 drops of the extract are allowed to evaporate to dryness in a micro test tube, and 100 mg of $ZnCl_2$ are added. The mouth of the test tube is covered with filter paper that has been moistened with a drop of reagent solution. The test tube is heated on a sand bath for five to ten minutes at 250 °C. Blue coloration of the reagent indicates the presence of -OCH$_2$CH$_2$O-groups.

Detection limit for antistatics based on polyoxyethylene compounds: 2 mg or approximately 0.05 % in the film.

Table 8.4: Identification of antistatics with chemical group detection reactions

No.	Component	Detection of aromatic compounds	sulfate	phosphate	oxyethylene	amine
1	N,N-Bis(hydroxyethyl)-alkylamine	−	−	−	+	+
2	Oxyethylated fatty alcohols	−	−	−	+	−
3	Oxyethylated amines	−	−	−	+	+
4	Oxyethylated fatty acids	−	−	−	+	−
5	Oxyethylated alkylphenols	+	−	−	+	−
6	Sulfate esters of oxyethylated alkylphenols	+	+	−	+	−
7	Phosphate esters of oxyethylated alkylphenols	+	−	+	+	−
8	Alkyl arylsulfonates	+	−	−	−	−
9	Alkyl sulfate	−	+	−	−	−
10	Quaternary ammonium compounds	−	−	−	−	+
11	Alkylpyridinium chlorides	−	−	−	−	+

Table 8.5: Thin layer chromatographic separation of nonionic surfactants on acidic silica gel after KÖNIG [510]
(layer: silica gel GF prepared with 0.1 N oxalic acid; solvent: chloroform + methanol, 9 + 1)

| | hR$_f$ values | Staining with | |
		Dragendorff reagent	BaCl$_2$ and I$_2$ solutions
Ethoxylated amino alcohols	0...10	orange	brown
Ethoxylated fatty acids	20...30	orange	rust brown
Free polyglycols	30...40	orange	dark brown
Fatty acid alkanolamides	about 40	yellow	brownish
Fatty alcohol polyglycol ethers	50...70	orange	yellow
Alkylphenol polyglycol ethers	50...70	brownish	yellow
Ethoxylated fatty acid alkanolamides	about 60	orange	brownish yellow
Ethoxylated fatty acid partial esters	60...90	orange	yellow
Fatty acid partial esters	70...90	yellow	yellow

Detection limit for antistatics based on polyoxyethylene-alkylphenol compounds: 0.05 mg or 0.005 % in a film.

Test for sulfates and phosphates

Reagents: 0.2 % aqueous Congo red solution, H$_2$O$_2$ (30 %) previously neutralized to Congo red solution, Na$_2$S$_2$O$_3$ A. R. 5 drops of the extract are allowed to evaporate in a micro test tube, and 100 mg of Na$_2$S$_2$O$_3$ are added. The mouth of the test tube is covered with filter paper that has previously been soaked with the Congo red solution and moistened before the test with a drop of H$_2$O$_2$. The test tube is heated in a glycerol bath for 5 minutes at 180 °C. Blue coloration of the indicator paper indicates the presence of phosphates or sulfates. Detection limit for antistatics based on alkyl sulfate: 2 mg or about 0.05 % in the film.

Test for amines

Reagent: 2 % 2,4-dinitrochlorobenzene in ether.

2 drops of the extract are allowed to dry on a spot plate, and 1 drop of reagent is added. The spot plate is heatet for 1 h at 100 °C. A yellow ring indicates the presence of amines. Detection limit for antistatics containing amino groups: 0.1 mg or approximately 0.005 % in the film.

Detection of sulfates and phosphates

Reagents: a) Sulfate: Saturated KMnO$_4$ solution, 1 N oxalic acid, 0.5 N BaCl$_2$

b) Phosphates: 5 g of (NH$_4$)$_2$MoO$_4$ are dissolved in 100 ml of 10 % aqueous potassium bitartrate solution and diluted with 35 ml of HNO$_3$ (sp. gr. 1.2).
0.05 g of benzidine is dissolved in 10 ml of glacial acetic acid and made up to 100 ml with water.

A few drops of extract are evaporated to dryness with 2 drops of 0.5 N NaOH and ashed, and the residue is dissolved in 3 drops of 1 N HCl. One part of the solution is investigated for sulfates, and the other part for phosphates.

a) Sulfates: Reagent paper is prepared by soaking filter paper in the BaCl$_2$ solution and allowing it to dry. 1 drop of test solution is mixed on a spot plate with 1 drop of KMnO$_4$, and a drop of the mixture is applied to the reagent paper, which is now heated for about 8 minutes at 80 °C.

The reagent paper is then washed in distilled water and immersed in the oxalic acid solution. A spot indicates the presence of sulfates.

Note: Substances, particularly sulfonates, that form sulfates on ashing with NaOH also give a positive test.

b) Phosphates: 1 drop of the test solution and 1 drop of the molybdate solution are applied to a piece of filter paper, which is then heated for about 30 s at 100 °C. After addition of 1 drop of benzidine solution, the filter paper is held over NH$_3$ vapor.

A blue color points to the presence of phosphates. The detection limit of these tests for a number of sulfates and phosphates investigated is 0.1 mg or approximately 0.01 % in the film.

Detection of sulfonates

Reagents: Solution of 0.08 g of FeCl$_3$ and 0.10 g of K$_3$(Fe[CN]$_6$) in 100 ml of H$_2$O. Solution of 5 g of sodium formate and 6 g of NaOH in 100 ml of H$_2$O. SO$_2$free sulfuric acid 1/1 (or phosphoric acid 1/1).

A drop of extract is evaporated to dryness in a test tube with a drop of sodium formate and ashed. After cooling, 3 drops of phosphoric acid 1/1 are added, and the test tube is covered with a glass finger on which a drop of ferric ferricyanide solution is suspended. Blue coloration of this drop when the test tube is heated indicates the presence of sulfonates.

Detection limit for alkylarylsulfonates: 0.1 mg or about 0.01 % in the film.

8.3 Thin Layer Chromatography of Antistatics

Only a few preliminary experiments on the TLC of antistatics have been reported [504, 505], but some of the information obtained in the analysis of surfactants is applicable.

Nonionic surfactants, which are mostly polyglycols and their derivatives, have been systematically studied by KÖNIG [510], who thus extended the work of BÜRGER et al. [274]. On silica gel G with butanol + water (1 + 1), BÜRGER achieved a separation of the ethoxylated compounds according to the degree of ethoxylation, the separation being practically uninfluenced by the hydrophobic parts of the molecule such as fatty acid, fatty alcohol, and alkylphenol groups. The

R_f values decrease with increasing degree of ethoxylation. Highly ethoxylated compounds and polyglycols remain at the starting spot. An analogous separation on silica gel columns has been described by WICKBOLD [508].

After examining various systems, KÖNIG finally achieved a separation according to groups of compounds, in which the degree of ethoxylation has little influence, with the aid of "acidic" silica gel layers. The hR_f values and color reactions observed are listed in Table 8.6.

However, subsequent IR spectroscopic examination of the separated substances is useful for a reliable identification. UV absorption can be used for the recognition of ethoxylated alkylphenols.

The thin layer chromatographic separation of antistatics from other additives with chloroform (Section 8.2) was also confirmed by HELMSTEDT et al. [505]. When carbon tetrachloride + chloroform (4 + 1) or chloroform + ether (1 + 1) was used, the antistatics again remained predominantly in the lower half of the plate, while plasticizers, antioxidants, and many stabilizers had R_f values of 50—80.

A separation on silica gel G with isopropanol + water (3 + 1) is recommended, with the use of reference substances, for the TLC of antistatics containing amino groups. The amines give yellow spots when the chromatogram is sprayed with 2 % ethereal 2,4-dinitrochlorobenzene solution and heated for 1 h at 100 °C [503].

In our preliminary TLC investigations on commercially obtainable antistatics, we used methanol + acetone (9 + 1) as the solvent for the strongly polar quaternary ammonium compounds, the amines, and the amides, and chloroform + methanol (9 + 1) for the less polar antistatics.

The results of our TLC separations are presented in Tables 8.2—8.4 as line diagrams.

The thick and thin dotted lines show the lengthwise extension of the spots that are visible in UV light.

Thick and thin continuous lines represent spots that become

visible on spraying. Iodine/sulfuric acid (see Table 2.11, no. 1) was used as the spray reagent for the strongly polar antistatics containing nitrogen of group 1, and DRAGGENDORFF reagent (see Table 2.11, no. 2) for the remaining groups.

The gas chromatographic analysis of polyethoxylated, non-ionic surface active substances has been described in various publications. Thus, it has been found possible to separate polyoxyethylene-p-tert.-nonylphenyl ethers having the general formula $RO(CH_2$-

$CH_2O)_nH$ up to $n = 15$, using temperature-programmed silicone rubber columns. The quantitative results of the degree of ethoxylation distribution were in good agreement, up to $n = 10$, with the TLC results using silica gel G with water saturated methyl ethyl ketone as solvent [513b].

8.4 IR Spectroscopy of Antistatics

A comprehensive collection of the IR spectra of surface active substances is to be found in the book "Analyse der Tenside" (Analysis of Surfactants) by HUMMEL [502], which also contains assignment diagrams for these substances. With the aid of this collection, it is possible to identify antistatics on the basis of their IR spectra.

The commercially obtainable antistatics for which IR spectra are given here were selected from about 90 products, some of which had been found to be practically identical on the basis of their spectra. The main components of the various products are usually recognizable in the spectrum. However, since the products are very often mixtures, separation and concentration of the less concentrated compounds is necessary for the determination of all the components.

Band positions are given in Figure 8.1 for the structures observed in antistatics. Only a few observations on IR-spectroscopic identification will therefore be given below. For a more detailed description, the reader is referred to the book by HUMMEL [502].

The antistatics of Group 1.1, according to the IR spectra, contain quaternary ammonium compounds as the main components, the most important of these being dodecyltrimethylammonium, palmityltrimethylammonium, and stearyltrimethylammonium chlorides. The IR spectra of these substances, in addition to the characteristics of long-chain alkyl residues, contain bands at about 908 and 965 cm^{-1} (10.38 and 11.0 μm); in the spectra of crystalline samples, these bands, like the CH$_2$ chain vibration at about 720 cm^{-1} (13.9 μm), exhibit splitting. This splitting is found in the case of Stat-Eze 100 (spectrum number 6200), whereas the greasy residue obtained on evaporation of Barquat CO-50 (spectrum number 6201) gives the bands without splitting. Some compounds of this type retain water very tenaciously, and this leads to broad bands at 3400, 2100, and 1640 cm^{-1} (2.9, 4.75, and 6.1 μm). The tendency to retain water even on drying under vacuum is particularly noticeable with the short-chain alkyltrimethylammonium chlorides.

In the case of dialkyldimethylammonium compounds, the bands at 908 and 965 cm^{-1} are fairly weak. Quaternary ammonium nitrates (spectra 6203 and 6204) are recognizable by the strong bands of the NO$_3$ group at 1383 cm^{-1} (7.22 μm).

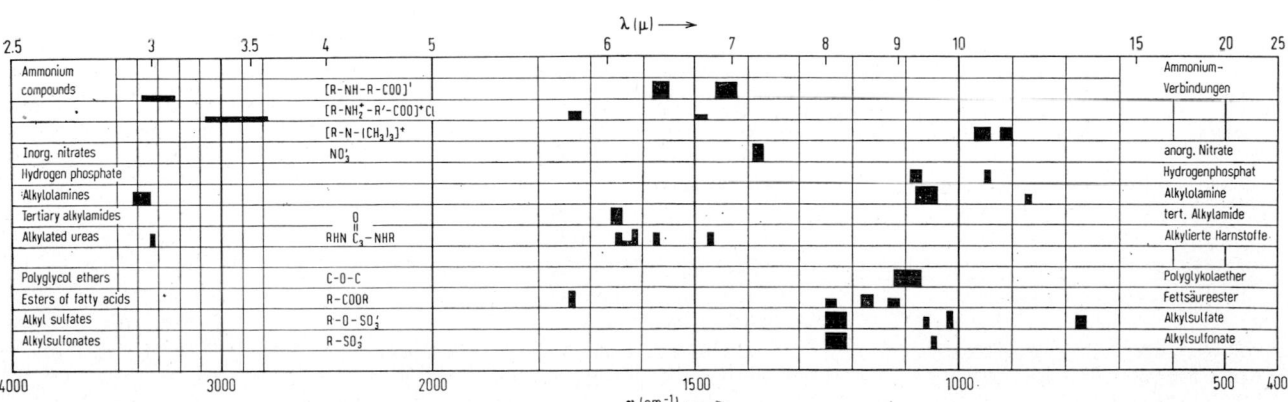

Fig. 8.1: Band positions for functional groups in antistatics

The two stearylamidopropyldimethyl-β-hydroxyethylammonium derivatives Catanac SP and SN (spectra 6202 and 620 differ in their anions and in the bands due to the anions (hydrogen phosphate 1082 and 947 cm^{-1}, nitrate 1383 cm^{-1}). The spectrum of Anstac' M (spectrum number 6206) largely corresponds to that of the alkylpyridinium salts with a C$_{12}$ to C$_{16}$ alkyl group.

Substitution of the alkyl group or of a methyl group by benzyl groups leads to spectra containing more bands (spectra 6207 and 6208).

The main component of Baquat CME is N-cetyl-N-ethylmorpholinium ethyl sulfate, the spectrum of which is dominated by bands of the ethyl sulfate ion at 1240, 1220, 1020, 915, and 764 cm^{-1} (8.06, 8.2, 9.8, 10.9, and 13.1 μm). The medium-strong band at 1125 cm^{-1} (8.9 μm) is due to the C-O-C vibration of aliphatic ethers.

Antistatics with alkyldiethanolamines as the main components give spectra like those of e. g. Antistatic Agent C-2 (spectrum number 6210) and other substances of this group. The bands of primary OH groups around 3380 cm^{-1} (2.95 μm) and 1070 and 1045 cm^{-1} (9.35 and 9.55 μm), that of the ethylene group around 875 cm^{-1} (11.45 μm), and those of long-chain alkyl groups are characteristic. The hydrochlorides of these compounds (e. g. Antistat 61, spectrum number 6212 exhibit a number of changes, of which the change in the band around 1060 cm^{-1} (9.45 μm) in particular is typical.

Hallcomid M-12 (spectrum number 6215) is an example of a tertiary alkylamide, and Warcobase A (spectrum number 2859) is an example of a mixture of monostearylurea and distearylurea.

The spectra of the antistatics of group 2 all contain the strong, broad C-O-C stretching vibration of the polyglycol derivatives around 1110 cm^{-1} (9 μm). For further information on the spectra of polyglycols, see Section 2.6.

Partly esterified polyglycols (spectra 6217) also give the ester band at 1736 cm^{-1} (5.76 μm).

A number of antistatics with alkylaryl polyglycol derivatives as the principal components are included in group 2.3 (spectra 6218–6220).

Of the various fatty acid exters of group 3, Drewplast 017 (spectrum number 6221 contains mainly glycerol monostearate and Drewplast 050 (spectrum number 6222 and glycerol monooleate.

As examples of other antistatic mixtures suitable for industrial use, group 4 includes a number of products that contain sulfonates, glycol derivatives, and other components. As is shown by the thin layer chromatograms reproduced in Table 8.4, these are mixtures of several components.

8.5 Biostabilizers

Numerous additives having pesticidal and fungicidal activities have been proposed for the protection of organic materials against microbial attack and for the prevention of the transfer of germs by plastics, paints, and rubber [515–520]. One of the oldest examples is the addition of organometallic compounds to paints for ships' bottoms and other underwater coating compositions. Some of the accelerators and antioxidants used in the production of rubber exhibit pesticidal properties [515], but special additive mixtures are also commonly used, particularly in porous rubber articles. Halogenated compounds are preferentially used for thermoplastics.

An important feature of all additives of this kind is a long-lasting action on the surface. This can be achieved if the active additives are maintained by diffusion as a protective film.

Table 8.7 shows a number of biostabilizers which are offered for use in plastics and whose IR spectra were available to us.

The tin and lead compounds are used mainly for paints and PVC. The analytical methods described in the literature, of

Table 8.6: Biostabilizers

Dec. No.	IR sp. No.	Trade name	Composition
1	6250	Irgarol Bl 540	Tributyltin oxide
2	6251	Irgarol Bl 543	Modified tributyltin oxide
3	6252	Tributyllead acetate	Tributyllead acetate
4	6253	Triphenyllead chloride	Triphenyllead chloride
5	6254	Irgarol Bl 547	Triphenyllead acetate
6	6255	Triphenyllead thiophenolate	Triphenyllead thiophenolate
7	6256	Pentachlorophenol	Pentachlorophenol
8	6257	Hexachlorophene	2,2'-Methylene bis(3,4,6-chlorophenol)
9	6258	Preventol CMK	3-Methyl-4-chlorophenol
10	6259	Preventol K 1	Mixture containing pentachlorophenol
11	6260	VP 1250	Halogenated methylol fatty acid nitrile
12	6261	Preventol GD	2,2'-Dihydroxy-5,5'-dichlordiphenylmethane
13	6262	Preventol A 2	Dithiocarbaminate
14	6263	Preventol A 3	N-(Fluorodichloromethylthio)-phthalimide
15	6264	Preventol A 4	N-Dimethyl-N'-phenyl-N'-(fluorodichloromethylthio)-sulfamide
16	6265	Microcheck 12	N-(trichloromethylthio)-4-cylohexene-1,2-dicarboximide
17	6266	Microcheck 11	2 n-octyl-4-isothiazolin-3-one in phthalic ester
18	6267	Estabex ABF	10,10'-Oxy-bis-phenoxarsine in epoxidized soybean oil

which only a few examples need be mentioned [521—525], are mostly based on the colorimetric determination of the metal.

UV spectroscopic methods have been described for the determination of pentachlorophenol and its laurate [526]; these involve the evaluation of bands around 312 and 214 μm. A thin layer chromatographic method has been proposed for the detection of pentachlorophenol in latex [527]. Pentachlorophenol can also be readily identified by mass spectroscopy because of its characteristic mass spectrum (chlorine isotope frequency distribution).

A comprehensive survey of the chromatographic analysis of fungicides, covering published literature up to 1974, has been given by SHERMA, TLC and GC data for organo-mercury compounds, dithiocarbamates, chlorine-containing compounds and other fungicides being divided into groups and the methods being discussed in relation to the important individual substances. Very many of the substances used as biocides for polymers are also used for pesticides and these have been dealt with in a paper by SHERMA. The greatly increased importance of residue analysis, as well as the interest shown in the distribution of technical products in the environment, have resulted in a large number of publications in a wide range of technical journals, dealing with the identification of halogen and phosphorus compounds as well as organo-metallic substances.

Some of the groups of substances used as biocides and flame retardants in polymers have also been covered in these papers.

8.6. Flame Retardants

Flame-retarding additives can influence the combustibility of polymers in various ways; they can change the nature and quantity of combustible volatile pyrolysis products, the additive may form incombustible gaseous products that displace oxygen and exert a thermally insulating action, it may favor the formation of an insulating layer of carbon on the surface, it may exert a cooling action by endothermic reactions in the flame zone, or it may terminate chain reactions in the combustion process.

Organic and inorganic compounds containing large numbers of hetero atoms (Cl, Br, P, B, N) are used as flame retardants.

The best known is antimony trioxide, Sb_2O_3, which is usually combined with additives containing chlorine. The synergistic action is attributed to the formation of antimony oxide chloride. Other inorganic additives are aluminium hydroxide, boric acid, sodium and zinc borates, barium metaborate, ammonium phosphate and dicyanodiamide.

Organic halogen compounds may be incorporated as additives or built into the polymer in the form of polymerizable monomers. The

Table 8.7: Flame retardants

Dec. No.	IR-Sp. No.	Composition	Trade name	Br-content
1.		Brominated compounds		
1.1	6275	Hexabromocyclododecane	BROMKAL 73–6 CD	73–74%
1.2	6276	Pentabromotoluene	BROMKAL 81–5 T	81–82%
1.3	6277	2,2'-Bis[4-(2,3-dibromopropoxy)-3,5-dibromophenyl]propane	BROMKAL 66–8	65–67%
1.4	6278	Pentabromodiphenyl ether	BROMKAL 70–5 DE	67 71%
1.5	6279	Octabromodiphenyl ether	BROMKAL 79–8 DE	79–81%
1.6	6280	Nonabromodiphenyl ether	BROMKAL 80–9 DE	81–82,5%
1.7	6281	Decabromodiphenyl ether	BROMKAL 82–0 DE	82–83%
1.8	6282	Bromine containing compounds	BROMKAL F 441	12% (3,6% P)
1.9	6283	Bromine containing compounds	BROMKAL N 1040	40%
1.10	6284	Polybromophenylenoxide	FIREMASTER 935	
2.		N-containing compounds		
2.1	6285	Guanyl urea		
2.2	6286	Guanyl urea phosphate		
2.3	6287	Sec. guanidine phosphate		
2.4	6288	Guanidine carbonate		
2.5	6289	Guanidine silicate		
2.6	6290	Melamine borate		
2.7	6291	Melamine phosphate		
2.8	6292	Melamine pyrophosphate		
2.9	6293	Dicyandiamide formaldehyde condensation product with phosphate	Flame retardant SKW-VP 130 SP	
2.10	6294	Dicyandiamide resin	Flame retardant	
3.		Other compounds		
3.1	6295	Aluminum hydroxide		
3.2	6296	Poly-di(2-chloroethyl)-ethylphosphonate	Phosgard C 22 R	
4.	5299-5301	Chlorinated paraffins	group 8.3 plasticizers	
5.	5302-5307	Chlorinated diphenyls	group 8.4 plasticizers	
6.	5252-5268	Phosphate esters	group 6.1 plasticizers	
7.	5272-5275	Phosphite-, phosphonate esters	group 6.3 plasticizers	

former situation is found with chlorinated plasticizers (chloroparaffins, chlorinated diphenyls and polyphenyls) and a number of brominated alkylaryl and aryl derivatives containing 60–85% of Br. The reactive flame retardent additives tetrachlorophthalic anhydride, tetrabromophthalic anhydride, and chlorendic anhydride are used mainly for flame-resistant polyester and epoxy resins. Brominated castor oil (containing up to 30% Br) and other brominated, unsaturated vegetable oils are of interest as reactive components for rigid polyurethane foams.

The organic esters of phosphoric acid that are used as plasticizers also have a flame retardant action, particularly when they contain halogenated alkyl groups, as in the case of tri-(2-chloroethyl) phosphate or polymeric 2-chloroethyl ethylphosphonate. For polymers which must not contain any of the above mentioned flame retardants for toxicological reasons, the use of compounds with a high nitrogen content, e. g. melamine, guanyl and guanidine phosphate, silicate, carbonate or borate is suggested. These compounds may also be used in thermosetting materials.

The amount of flame retardant incorporated in polymers can be up to 25%, depending on the degree of flame retardance required. The usual amount is between 10 and 20% and is composed of mixtures of a number of substances.

JENKNER [2] quotes the following examples for imparting flame resistance to polyethylene: 5% octabromodiphenyl + 1.6% chlorparaffin 70 + 3.5% antimony trioxide, for polypropylene: 3.5% bis (dibromopropyl ether of tetrabromobisphenol A with 2% antimony trioxide, and for polystyrene: 15% octabromodiphenyl + 5% antimony trioxide.

Numerous modifications of the flame retardants mentioned are described in patents. Further information about the uses and effects is obtainable from the literature [1–3 and 528–533].

The qualitative analysis of antimony, phosphorus compounds and halogenated additives indicates the presence of flame retardants. Bromine compounds, organic phosphates and phosphonates can be separated by extraction or precipitation. An example is the analytical procedure described by SCHINDLBAUER and DOKUZOVIC [533] for the identification and quantitative determination of flame retardants in polystyrene, which is based on the precipitation of the polystyrene dissolved in benzene, using methanol, followed by TLC of the dissolved organic flame retardant and elementary analysis of Sb, P and Br. The TLC data determined by these authors for various flame retardants have been summarised in Table 8.9. For reliable qualitative identification, IR spectroscopy of the substances isolated from the TLC separations is recommended.

Table 8.8 lists a number of commercial flame retardants and their IR spectra. The bromine compounds are mostly mixtures with varying degrees of bromination and different isomers, the named compound constituting the principal component of the mixture.

The IR spectra, as well as analytical data (TLC, GC, MS) of chlorinated paraffins, chlorinated diphenyls, phosphates, phospites and phosphonates are given under plasticisers (section 2). IR spectra of phosphites are also shown under PVC stabilisers.

The identification of organic flame retardants is possible, in certain instances, direct from the mass spectra of the halogen compounds vaporising from the polymer at high temperatures.

9 Accelerators, Curing Agents and Activators

9.1 Survey and Classification of Vulcanisation Accelerators

The vulcanization of rubber-sulfur mixes can be speeded up or carried out at lower temperatures by the addition of small quantities of vulcanization accelerators, and an improvement in the mechanical properties and aging resistance is generally achieved at the same time. The accelerating action of inorganic substances such as magnesium oxide, calcium hydrate, litharge, and antimony sulfides is far exceeded by the action of organic accelerators. However, to develop their full activity, these accelerators require the addition of a metal oxide. The best results are usually obtained with zinc oxide.

Depending on their activity, accelerators are classified in the rubber industry as ultra-accelerators and strong, medium-strong and weak accelerators.

The ultra-accelerators include the metal salts and amine derivatives of dithiocarbamic acids, xanthates, and thiuram monosulfides, disulfides, and tetrasulfides.

Strong accelerators ("semi-ultra-accelerators") include 2-mercaptobenzothiazole, its disulfide, benzothiazole sulfenamides, condensation products of aldehydes with aromatic bases, and polyethylenepolyamines.

Examples of medium-strong accelerators are guanidines and guanidine derivatives, biguanides, tricrotonylidenetetramine, and similar amines. Weak accelerators include aliphatic amines, hexamethylenetetramine, thiocarbanilide, anhydroformaldehyde-p-toluidine, and some inorganic oxides and sulfides.

The medium-strong and weak accelerators are used as the sole accelerator only on occasion in order to obtain special effects. However, they are fairly extensively used for the activation of other accelerators, e. g. from the thiazole group. The system rubber-sulfur-accelerator-zinc oxide is additionally activated by the addition of fatty acids or zinc salts of fatty acids, aliphatic monoamines and diamines, monoethanolamine, diethanolamine, triethanolamine, dibutyl aminooleate, 1,3-diphenylguanidine phthalate, and other amines.

Monographs on vulcanization aids and lists of commercial products have been published [1, 8—12]. The identification

Table 8.8: TLC data of flame retardants [533]

| Flame retardant | Layer: silica gel HF 254 (type 60, Merck) hRf-values with solvent | | | | | |
	A	B	C	D	E	F
Diphenylcresyl phosphate	0	29	61	51		68
Tris(2,3-dibromopropyl)-phosphate	4	0	10	49	26	39
Dibromopropyldian	40	13	60	79	81	85
Pentabromophenylallyl ether	58	47	69	76	79	84
Tribromophenylallyl ether	68	51	73	75	78	83

Solvents

A n-heptane + acetone (10 + 1)
B n-heptane + benzene (5 + 1)
C n-heptane + ethylacetate (10 + 3)
D benzene + ethylether (3 + 1)
E benzene + ethylacetate (95 + 5)
F carbontetrachloride + ethylether (1 + 1)

Table 9.1: Classification of accelerators and their IR spectra numbers

Accelerator	IR-Sp. No.
1. Amino compounds	6300–6307
1.1 Aldehyde-ammonia condensation products	6300, 6301, 6369
1.2 Aliphatic amines and their condensation products	6302, 6303
1.3 Aniline and toluidine condensation products	6304–6307
2. Aromatic nitroso compounds	6308–6310
3. Thioureas	6311–6314, 6370
4. Guanidine derivatives	6315–6321
5. Dithiocarbamates	6322–6341
6. Thiurames	6342–6345
7. Heterocyclic compounds	6346–6363
7.1 Imidazolines and piperidine derivatives	6346, 6347
7.2 Benzothiazole derivatives	6348–6363
8. Others	6364–6368

of accelerators in vulcanized material is complicated by the fact that chemical reactions take place with the sulfur, the zinc oxide, and other additives during vulcanization, so that the vulcanized products contain little or none of the compounds originally used. Some reaction products are volatile, and are no longer present in the extract. A number of reactions are mentioned below on the basis of a series of investigations on the changes in accelerators, which are summarized elsewhere [8, 13, 535].

Guanidines are converted in part into the arylamines and ammonia.

Ammonium dithiocarbamate derivatives react with zinc oxide to form zinc dithiocarbamates.

The thiuram disulfides react with zinc oxide, again with formation of zinc dithiocarbamates.

2-Mercaptobenzothiazole and 2,2'-dithiobisbenzothiazole exist in an equilibrium with each other that is established during vulcanization, irrespective of the starting material. In mixes containing ZnO, zinc 2-mercaptobenzothiazole is formed.

2-Benzothiazolesulfenamides decompose mainly into 2-mercaptobenzothiazole and amines.

Whether the reactions mentioned proceed to completion depends on the vulcanization conditions and on the formulation of the mix. Traces of the original accelerator can be extracted from some materials together with reaction products.

To avoid excessive dependence on knowledge of the vulcanization conditions, which is not usually available to the analyst, methods have been suggested in which the accelerators are identified on the basis of the reaction products formed by acid hydrolysis. The hydrolysis may be carried out either by direct extraction of the rubber sample with hydrochloric acid/ethanol or by treatment of the acetone extract with acid. Further information is given in Sections 9.2 and 9.3.

9.2 Chemical Detection of Accelerators

Various methods have been suggested for the chemical identification of accelerators [13, 440, 441, 535]; these methods allow the identification of groups of accelerators or of individual accelerators before processing and vulcanization, and to a limited extent in extracts from vulcanized material.

An initial group separation is possible by treatment of the dry substance or of the concentrated extract with dilute acid or alkali. Amine condensation products, amines, anilides, guanidines, and other basic compounds dissolve in dilute acid. Aqueous ammonia or methanolic sodium hydroxide dissolve the acidic accelerators, which include the dithiocarbamates, mercaptobenzothiazoles, and xanthates.

For the examination of the pure antioxidants, usually an approx. 1—5 % solution in chloroform is used, which can also be obtained from the concentrated extract.

The following detection methods, which have been described in detail by HOFMANN and OSTROMOW [441], are used.

Hexamethylenetetramine: An aqueous solution reacts with alcoholic iodine solution to form a green-yellow, crystalline precipitate, which is insoluble in iodine, and which may turn red with an excess of iodine.

Condensation products liberating formaldehyde: A few drops of aqueous solution and a spatulatip of the sodium salt of chromotropic acid are introduced into 2—3 ml of 70 % sulfuric acid. A violet color appears when the mixture is heated for a few minutes at 60—70 °C.

Guanidine derivatives: A few ml of chloroform solution are shaken vigorously with 2—3 ml of water and a few drops of a 6 % hypochlorite solution. Diarylguanidines give a brown color in the chloroform layer, while the aqueous phase remains colorless. When o-tolybiguanide is present, the chloroform remains colorless and the aqueous layer becomes yellow.

Dithiocarbamates: Addition of a 1 % solution of copper oleate in chloroform to a chloroform solution of a dithiocarbamate gives a dark brown precipitate or color due to Cu dithiocarbamate. Thiuram derivatives are converted into dithiocarbamates on vulcanization or on reduction with 2-mercaptobenzothiazole, and these compounds then also give this reaction.

Thiuram derivatives: Addition of copper oleate solution to the chloroform solution gives a yellow-green color, which changes to brown-red or dark brown on addition of 2-mercaptobenzothiazole solution.

2-Mercaptobenzothiazole (MBT): Copper oleate solution turns the chloroform solution yellow. On addition of a few drops of fresh tetramethylthiuram disulfide solution in chloroform, the chloroform layer turns brown.

On addition of a few drops of a solution of bismuth nitrate in strong nitric acid to an alkaline alcoholic MTB solution, a yellow precipitate is formed. Zinc 2-mercaptobenzothiazole, dibenzothiazyl disulfides, and benzothiazole-sulfenamides also form MBT on vulcanization, and the MBT can be detected in the extract from vulcanized samples.

BROCK and LOUTH [535] have suggested a method for the analysis of accelerators from vucanized material, in which total cleavage of the dithiocarbamates, thiurams, benzothiazoles, and thiazolesulfenamides with simultaneous extraction of the degradation products is achieved by extraction with ethanol + N hydrochloric acid (1 + 1).

In this method, which is also described in detail by Hummel [13], about 20 g of finely comminuted vulcanizate are refluxed for 2 h with passage of air through the flask by means of a gas inlet tube; the air is then passed through a wash bottle containing 50 ml of 10 % CuSO₄ solution, followed by a second wash bottle containing 0.2 N alcoholic sodium hydroxide solution. Any hydrogen sulfide and carbon disulfide formed are absorbed in the two wash bottles.

The hydrochloric acid solution is filtered and made alkaline with 25 % sodium hydroxide solution, and the volatile amines together with most of the alcohol are distilled into a receiver containing 0.5 N HCl. The dithiocarbamates, the thiuram derivatives, and the benzothiazolesulfenamides give the corresponding alkylamines and diamines, including piperidine; on evaporation of the distillate, these products are obtained as the hydrochlorides and identified by chemical or preferably by chromatographic or spectroscopic methods. Benzothiazole derivatives, including the sulfonamides, form MBT, which remains in the alkaline solution.

The degradation of thiuram sulfides and dithiocarbamates yields carbon disulfide, which can be detected in the second wash bottle. For this test about 10 ml of the absorption solution are weakly acidified with glacial acetic acid, and 5 ml of 1 % CuSO₄ solution are added. A yellow-green precipitate, which changes into pure yellow copper xanthate on addition of a few drops of concentrated nitric acid, shows the presence of carbon disulfide.

The alkaline distillation residue is first extracted with chloroform to remove nonvolatile basic (e. g. guanidines, antioxidants) and neutral components. After acidification of the aqueous solution, acidic components (thiazoles) are extracted, again with chloroform, and examined further.

9.3 Thin Layer Chromatography of Accelerators

The procedures described by Kreiner and Warner [61, 545], Hofmann and Ostromow [440, 441], and other authors for the thin layer chromatography of accelerators have largely replaced the paper-chromatographic methods, which were elaborated in great detail at an early date [13, 26, 452–454]. The reader is therefore referred to the literature for the latter methods.

The thin layer chromatography of accelerators is carried out mainly on silica gel G layers with solvents of medium to strong polarity. Tables 9.2 and 9.3 give R_f values from our own TLC separations and from the literature [78, 440, 441]. The solvents and detection reagents used are listed in Table 9.4. The colors obtained with the spray reagents listed are as follows.

Thiurams and dithiocarbamates give red and brown-red spots with Ninhydrin (Table 2.11, no. 11). Copper dimethyldithiocarbamate, however, gives a yellow-green spot. Dithiocarbamates give light brown spots with copper sulfate (no. 9) which change to a green-yellow/brown color.

Bismuth nitrate gives yellow-brown spots for 2-mercaptobenzothiazole, its zinc salt, and benzothiazyl disulfide, and yellow to yellow-brown spots for 2-benzothiazolesulfenamides. These compounds give orange-red, brown-red, and dark red colors with 2,6-dichloroquinonechlorimide.

Nearly all compounds give brown spots with iodine azide (no. 19) and iodine/sulfuric acid (no. 1).

The amine hydrochlorides obtained by extraction with hydrochloric acid/ethanol or by treatment of the acetone extract with hydrochloric acid can also be separated by thin layer chromatography on silica gel G. Table 9.5 shows the TLC

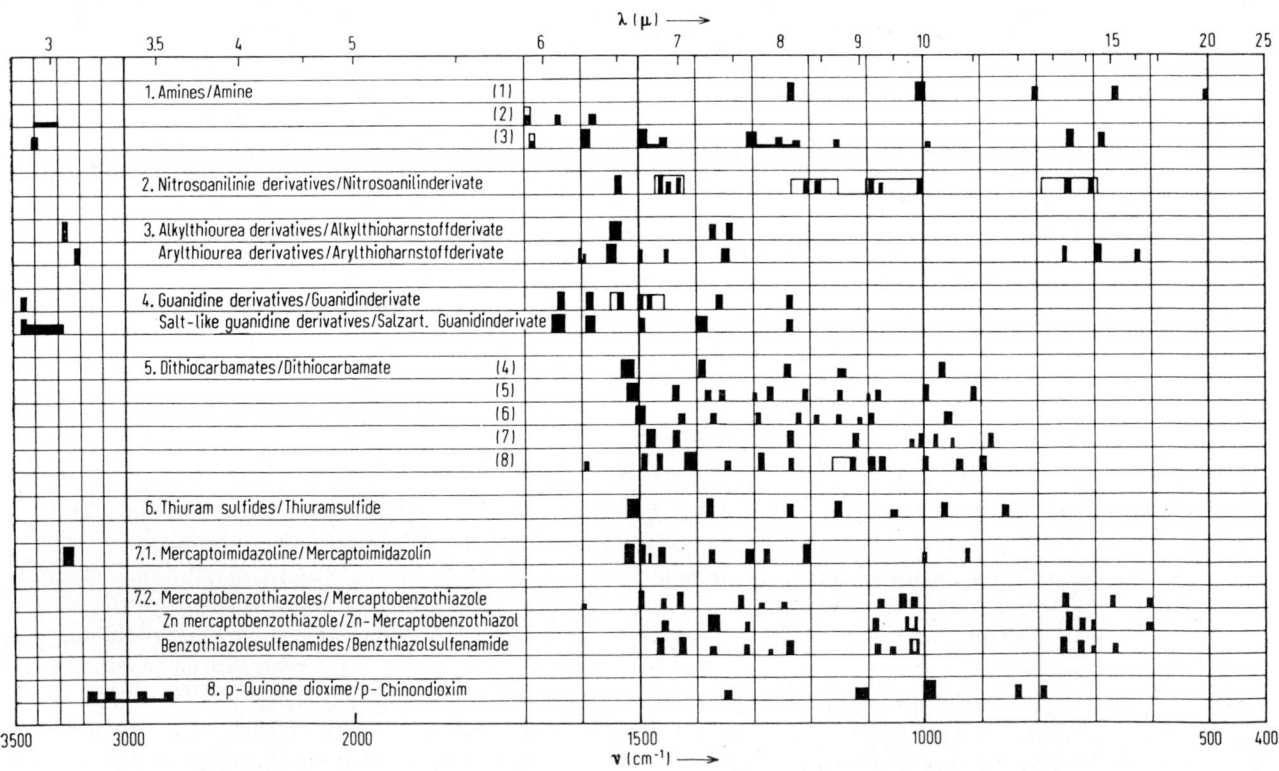

(1) Hexamethylenetetramine/Hexamethylentetramin
(2) Aldehyde-alkylamine cond. products/Aldehyd-Alkylamin-Kond.-Produkte
(3) Aldehyde-arylamine cond. products/Aldehyd-Arylamin-Kond.-Produkte
(4) methyl/Methyl-
(5) ethyl/Ethyl-
(6) butyl/Butyl-
(7) pentamethylene/Pentamethylen-
(8) alkylaryl/Alkylaryl-

Fig. 9.1: Band positions for accelerators

Table 9.2: Accelerators, 1. Amino compounds, 2. Aromatic nitroso compounds, 3. Thioureas, 4. Guanidine derivatives

Dec. No.	IR Sp. No.	Trade name	Structure	hRf values on silica gel G or GF254						
				L4	L5	L7	L9	L11	L12	L13
1.1.			Aldehyde-ammona condensation products							
1.1.1	6300	Vulkacit H 30	Hexamethylenetetramine		10	0				0
1.1.2	6301	Vulkacit CT-N	Tricrotonylidenetetramine		10	2, 88				0, 80
1.1.3	6369	Vulcafor EFA	CH2O/NH3-ethylchloride-cond. prod.							
1.2.			Aliphatic amines and their condensation products							
1.2.1	6302	Vulkacit HX	Cyclohexylethylamine	26–44				0–9	0	0
1.2.2	6303	Accelerator 833	Cond. prod. of butyraldehyde and monobutyl-amine		2,60					49, 81
1.3.			Condensation products of aniline and of toluidine							
1.3.1	6304	A 32	Cond. prod. of butyraldehyde and aniline		41, 89					57, 80
1.3.2	6305	Vulkacit 576	Cond. prod. of α-ethyl-β-propylacrolein and aniline		80, 89					57, 81
1.3.3	6306	Vulkacit FP	Anhydroformaldehyde-p-toluidine		45–57					27
1.3.4	6307	A-100	Cond. prod. of acetaldehyde, butyraldehyde and arom. amine							36, 58, 76
2.			Aromatic nitroso compounds							
2.1	6308	Accelerator 1	p-Nitrosodimethylaniline		49, 55					39–55
2.2	6309	Elastopar	1,4-Nitroso-N-methylaniline		9, 64					58
2.3	6310	Vulkalent A	N-Nitrosodiphenylamine		72					50
3.			Thioureas							
3.1	6311	Thiate E	Trimethylthiourea							7
3.2	6312	Pennzone E	N,N'-Diethylthiourea							8
3.3	6313	Pennzone B	N,N'-Dibutylthiourea							22, 43
3.4	6314	A-1	N,N'-Diphenylthiourea							28–44
3.5	6370	Vulcafor 322	Modif. thiourea							
4.			Guanidine derivatives							
4.1	6315	Vulkacit D	N,N'-Diphenylguanidine	53	50			3, 18	0–10	
4.2	6316	Guantal	Diphenylguanidinephthalate							
4.3	6317	DOTG	N-Phenyl-N'-o tolylguanidine							
4.4	6318	Vulkacit DOTG	N,N'-Di-o-tolylguanidine	57	53			3, 36	3, 29	
4.5	6319	Permalux	Di-o-tolylguanidin salt of dipyrocatechol borate		52, 75				0, 70	0, 41
4.6.	6320	Accelerator 49	Mixed diarylguanidine	25	23		0, 2	0		
4.7.	6321	Vulkacit 1000	α-o-Tolylbiguanide							

Solvents L4–L13, see Table 9.4

data for some amine hydrochlorides and the colors observed on spraying with Ninhydrin [61].

TLC data and detection reactions for aliphatic amines are summarised in Table 9.6, according to PRANDL [546], whilst Table 9.6a contains details of operating conditions and reagents.

HIGGINS and McSWEENY [545a] treat a finely cut-up, 1 g sample of vulcanised rubber for 30 minutes at 80°C with 1 ml of a 10% solution of sodium bicarbonate and 1 ml of a 1% solution of 4-chloro-7-nitrobenzo-2,1,3-oxadiazol (NBD for short) in methyl ethyl ketone. After cooling they shake the mixture with 2 ml toluene. The organic phase is concentrated by evaporation in a stream of nitrogen, taken up with a little chloroform and chromatographed on silica gel GF254 with petroleum ether (b.pt. 40–60°C) toluene + ethyl acetate (4 + 1) and petroleum ether (b.pt. 60–80°C) + triethylamine (3 + 1) as solvent. Accelerators in the benzothiazolsulphenamide series were detected in this manner through their appropriate amine-NBD derivatives. The NBD derivatives obtained from the corresponding pure amines were used as reference substances.

Table 9.7 contains some data on the gaschromatographic analysis of amines that may be formed as degradation products of accelerators. The separation of rubber additives by column chromatography is becoming increasingly attractive through the use of efficient detectors. An example is the separation of amine antioxidants and 2-mercaptobenzothiazole on alumina [454], where plasticizers and extenders of low polarity are first eluted with benzene, and the antioxidants followed by the accelerator are then eluted with ethanol. Separations of this kind can also be carried out successfully on silica gel G columns.

Even more suitable is HPLC [446]. GROSS and STRAUSS [548b] have shown that 95–100% of the accelerator can be recovered from unvulcanised compounds after extraction with methanol and methylene chloride, followed by HPLC separation. Table 9.8 lists the columns, solvents and retention times [459a].

It was not possible to extract any accelerator residues from vulcanised systems, or at least only very small residual amounts. The amines formed as reaction products can likewise be separated by means of HPLC after extraction. The retention data of some amines are likewise listed in Table 9.8.

9.4 IR Spectroscopy of Accelerators

The identification of accelerators in vulcanized products described by MANN [463] in 1948 was one of the first applications of IR spectroscopy to analytical problems in industry. Since then, the IR-spectroscopic determination of accelerators has been reported in various further publications [13, 241, 464], and a collection of spectra of rubber chemicals [544] has been published.

Hexamethylenetetramine (spectrum number 6300) has a characteristic spectrum due to the high symmetry of the molecule, with very strong bands at 1231 cm^{-1} (8.12 μm) and 1000 cm^{-1} (10 μm), as well as further strong, narrow bands between 1450 and 500 cm^{-1} (6.9—20 μm).

N-Ethylcyclohexylamine (spectrum number 6302) has the typical spectrum of a secondary aliphatic amine, with a strong band at 1036 cm^{-1} (9.65 μm) due to the C-N stretching vibration.

The aldehyde-amine condensation products (spectra 6301 and 6303–6307) in some cases still contain traces of free C=O groups, which give a band at 1690—1680 cm^{-1} (5.92—5.95 μm). In the case of the aniline condensation products, the bands around 740 and 690 cm^{-1} (13.5 and 14.5 μm), which are typical of monosubstituted aromatic compounds, are very pronounced. Various products of this type have very similar spectra.

The spectra of the three nitroso accelerators (spectra 6308–6316) are largely determined by the aryl group and its substitution. The bands in the region between 1500 and 1400 cm^{-1} (6.67—7.15 μm) are partly due to the N=O vibrations in nitroso and nitrosamine compounds.

The thiourea derivatives (spectra 6311–6314) all give the strong bands at 3280—3200 cm^{-1} (3.05–3.12 μm) and 1560 to 1540 cm^{-1} (6.41—6.5 μm).

The arylguanidines (spectra 6315–6321) give a characteristic group of bands for the stretching vibrations of free and associated NH groups in the region between 3480 and 3000 cm^{-1} (2.87–3.35 μm), this group being bounded at about 3450 cm^{-1} (2.9 μm) by the narrow band due to the free NH group. Further strong bands between 1640 and 1450 cm^{-1} (6.1—6.9 μm) and the bands of monosubstituted and o-disubstituted aromatic compounds characterize the spectra of these groups.

The dimethyldithiocarbamates (spectra 6322–6326) of various cations have very similar spectra, with 5 typical bands, which also appear with a similar shape and intensity and with small changes in position in the spectra of the tetramethylthiuram sulfides (spectra 6342 and 6343).

The spectra of the diethyldithiocarbamates (spectra 6327–6329) contain many more bands, and are recognizable by

Table 9.3: Accelerators, 5. Dithiocarbamates, 6. Thiurams, 7. Heterocyclic compounds, 8. Others

Dec. no.	IR sp. no.	Trade name
5.		Dithiocarbamates
5.1	6322	Vulkacit L
5.2	6323	Cumate
5.3	6324	Ledate
5.4	6325	Bismate
5.5	6326	Methyl Selenac
5.6	6327	Vulkacit LDA
5.7	6328	Ethyl Cadmate
5.8	6329	Ethyl Selenac
5.9	6330	Ethyl Tellurac
5.10	6331	Vulkacit LDB
5.11	6332	R. Z. 100
5.12	6333	Vulkacit ZP
5.13	6334	Vulkacit P
5.14	6335	Vulkacit Pextra N
5.15	6336	Vulkacit WL
5.16	6337	Vulkacit 774
5.17	6338	Vulkacit DB 1
5.18	6339	Setsit-5
5.19	6340	Setsit-9
5.20	6341	Setsit-1
6.		Thiurams
6.1	6342	Vulkacit Thiuram MS
6.2	6343	Vulkacit Thiuram
6.3	6344	Vulkacit J
6.4	6345	Tetrone A
7.1		Imidazolines and piperidine derivatives
7.1.1	6346	NA-22
7.1.2	6347	R-2 Crystals
7.2		Benzothiazole derivatives
7.2.1	6348	El-Sixty
7.2.2	6349	Vulkacit Mercapto
7.2.3	6350	Vulkacit MDA/C
7.2.4	6351	Vulkacit MT/C
7.2.5	6352	Vulkacit ZM
7.2.6	6353	Vulkacit AZ
7.2.7	6354	Santocure NS
7.2.8	6355	Vulkacit CZ
7.2.9	6357	Vulkacit FZ
7.2.10	6358	Vulkacit MOZ
7.2.11	6359	Santocure 26
7.2.12	6360	Nobs No. 1
7.2.13	6361	Vulkacit DZ
7.2.14	6362	Vulkacit DM
7.2.15	6363	Vulkacit F
8.		Others
8.1	6364	Vulkanisiermittel CGO
8.2	6365	CDO 50
8.3	6366	Rhenocure TP
8.4	6367	Rhenocure AT
8.5	6368	Rhenocure ZAT

Solvents L$_1$...L$_{13}$ see Table 9.4

Structure	hR$_f$ values on silica gel G or GF$_{254}$											
	L$_1$	L$_2$	L$_3$	L$_5$	L$_6$	L$_7$	L$_8$	L$_9$	L$_{10}$	L$_{11}$	L$_{12}$	L$_{13}$
Zn dimethyldithiocarbamate	22	21	57		49					61	0—62	57
Cu dimethyldithiocrabamate					63							59
Pb dimethyldithiocarbamate					54							35, 43
Bi dimethylthiocarbamate					32							35, 43
Se dimethyldithiocarbamate					51, 56							36, 50
Zn diethyldithiocarbamate	50	41	66		64			91	44	65	26—73	67
Cd diethyldithiocarbamate												52, 63
Se diethyldithiocarbamate					47							55, 67
Te diethyldithiocarbamate					48, 60							55, 71
Zn dibutyldithiocarbamate	78	64	75		77					75	80	79
N,N'-Dimethylcyclohexylammonium dibutyldithiocarbamate												82
Zn pentamethylenedithiocarbamate												
Piperidine pentamethylenedithiocarbamate	0, 46	0, 32	0, 68		54					64	46—73	73
Zn ethylphenyldithiocarbamate	60	49	73						42	0, 65	72	0, 60, 71
Na cyclohexylethyldithiocarbamate										70	36—79	74
Cyclohexylethylammonium cyclohexyl-ethyldithiocarbamate										78	77	39, 75
											79	81
Zn ethylcyclohexyldithiocarbamate + cyclohexylethylamine									0, 41		22—80	35, 73
Dithiocarbamates												19, 40
Dithiocarbamate												
Dithiocarbamate												
Tetramethylthiuram monosulfide					27	50	9					41
Tetramethylthiuram disulfide					41	54	14	87	4, 9			45
N,N'-Dimethyl-N,N'-diphenylthiuram disulfide												73
Dipentamethylenethiuram tetrasulfide					61, 56							75, 82
2-Mercaptoimidazoline	0	18	9	57				57	0			4
Reac. product of methylenepiperidine and CS$_2$												5—16
Dibenzothiazyldimethylthiourea												5, 27, 37
2-Mercaptobenzothiazole	40	0	65		25	31	49	82, 93	5	66	77	4, 17
2-Mercaptobenzothiazole + Zn diethyldithiocarbamate								80, 90	6, 42	67	76	20, 55
2-Mercaptobenzothiazole + tetramethyl-thiuram disulfide					30, 54		50	80, 88	5, 9			19, 45
Zn 2-mercaptobenzothiazole											78	5, 20, 30
N,N'-Diethyl-2-benzothiazolesulfenamide						63	62					32
N-tert-Butyl-2-benzothiazolesulfenamide					45							5, 32
N-Cyclohexyl-2-benzothiazolesulfenamide					48				9, 27			49
Mixture of N-cyclohexyl-2-benzothiazolesulfen-amide with basic accelerators									9, 27			0, 51
N-Oxydiethylene-2-benzothiazolesulfenamide					24	35, 58	32					4, 26, 54
N-Oxydiisopropylene-2-benzothiazolesulfenamide					23, 31							24, 35
N-Oxydiethylene-2-benzothiazolesulfenamide + di-2-benzothiazyl disulfide												19, 46
N,N-Dicyclohexyl-2-benzothiazolesulfenamide									40			30, 68
Di-2-benzothiazyl disulfide					30, 58	53						0, 39
Mixture of di-2-benzothiazyl disulfide with basic accelerators					58	53						0, 44
p-Quinone dioxime				68					0	69		2
p-Quinone dioxime + approx. 50 % kaolin									0	69		
Zn salt of dithiophosphate ester												
Amin salt of dialkyldithiophosphate ester												
Metal amin dithiophosphate complex												

Table 9.4: Solvents and spray reagents for the TLC of accelerators (explanation of Tables 9.2 and 9.3)

	Solvent	Spray reagent (no. in Table 2.11)		Ref.
L₁	n-Hexane + diethyl ether + methylene chloride + acetic acid (100 + 50 + 30 + 2)	CuSO₄ · 5 H₂O	(9)	
L₂	Carbon tetrachloride + ethyl acetate + n-hexane (28 + 3 + 6)	2,6-Dichloroquinonechlorimide	(5)	[580]
L₃	Ethyl acetate + carbon tetrachloride (1–1)	Bi(NO₃)₃ · 5 H₂O	(10)	
L₄	Benzene + methanol + acetic acid (7 + 3 + 1)	Natrium hypochlorite	(14)	
L₅	Benzene + methanol + acetic acid (7 + 3 + 1)	8-Hydroxyquinoline hypobromite Iodine sulfuric acid	(18) (1)	
L₆	Benzene + ethyl acetate + acetone (100 + 5 + 1)	Ninhydrin Bi(NO₃)₃ · 5 H₂O	(11) (10)	[61]
L₇	Methylene chloride	Dragendorff reagent Chromotropic acid	(2) (13)	
L₈	Diisopropyl ether + petroleum ether (7 + 3)	Iodine/sulfuric acid	(1)	
L₉	Chloroform + methanol (9 + 1)	Sodium nitroprusside Iodine azide	(16) (19)	our experiments
L₁₀	n-Hexane + methylene chloride (1 + 1)	Iodine azide	(19)	
L₁₁	Ethyl acetate	Iodine azide	(19)	
L₁₂	n-Butanol saturated with water	Iodine azide	(19)	
L₁₃	Chloroform	Iodine/sulfuric acid	(1)	

the typical groups of bands between 1500 and 770 cm⁻¹ (6.7—13 μm). The various cations influence the bands around 1000 cm⁻¹ (10 μm), which are attributed to the S=C—N group.

The spectra of the selenium dithiocarbamates contain a medium-strong C=O band, which is presumably due to impurities resulting from the preparation.

The associated OH band found for some dithiocarbamates is presumably due to incompletely reacted hydrated oxides. Dipentamethylenethiuram tetrasulfide (spectrum no. 6345) has a spectrum similar to that of zinc pentamethylenedithiocarbamate (spectrum no. 6333).

2-Mercaptobenzothiazole (spectrum no. 6349) is easily recognizable, even in mixtures with other accelerators (spectra 6350 and 6351), by a characteristic band structure in the CH stretching region and in the region of 750–500 cm⁻¹ (13.3–20 μm), as well as by other bands.

The spectrum of the zinc salt of 2-mercaptobenzothiazole spectrum no. 6452) is entirely different from that of 2-mercaptobenzothiazole, owing to the loss of resonance (no mesomeric structures between -NH and -SH groups are now possible). Only the bands around 748 cm⁻¹ (13.4 μm) and 1240 cm⁻¹ (8.07 μm) remain in their original position. The structure of the CH stretching vibration is also greatly simplified.

The N-alkyl-2-benzothiazolesulfenamides (spectra 6353–6364) and di-2-benzothiazyl disulfide (spectra 6362 and 6363) are characterized by the strong bands around 1460 and 1430 cm⁻¹, 1020 and 1010 cm⁻¹, and 747 and 720 cm⁻¹ (6.85 and 7 μm, 9.8 and 9.9 μm, 13.3 and 13.9 μm).

9.5 Curing Agents and Activators for Epoxy Resins and Polyurethanes

Many different compounds can be used for curing epoxy resins, some of which cause catalytic polymerisation of the epoxides whilst

Table 9.5: TLC data for amine hydrochlorides

Layer: silica gel G; solvent: n-butanol + water + formic acid (5 + 1 + 1); spray reagent: Ninhydrin

	hR$_f$	Color
Dimethylamine	16	red
Diethylamine	25	red
Diisopropylamine	35	yellow-brown
Di-n-butylamine	52	red-brown
tert-Butylamine	38	light yellow
Cyclohexylamine	42	orange-brown
Aniline	48	red-violet
Piperidine	23	purple-red
Morpholine	18	red-violet
2,6-Dimethylmorpholine	29	dark brown

Table 9.6: GC data of amines

Amine	Stat. phase Temp. (°C) Temp.-progr. (°C/min)	Relative retention times				
		P 223 75—220 4	P 223 + KOH 160	P 223 + KOH 130	C 103 200—250 15	PEG 100—250 10
Methylamine					0,49	5,40
Ethylamine		6,0		2,2	0,62	5,59
		10,4			1,00	6,65
Isopropylamine		7,7			0,78	5,15
Butylamine		16,4			1,54	9,23
Isobutylamine		14,2				6,94
sec-Butylamine		13,1			1,27	6,12
Pentylamine					2,30	13,00
Isopentylamine		20,7			2,11	9.98
Hexylamine					3,21	18,87
Cyclohexylamine			3,4			
Methylcyclohexylamine			5,5			
Diethylamine		11,5		4,2		
Dipropylamine		22,2				
Diisopropylamine		15,5				
Dibutylamine		34,1				
Diisobutylamine		27,8				
Di-sec-butylamine		26,8				
Cyclohexylisopropylamine			6,1			
n-Pentyl-(2-methylbutyl)amine		46,9				
Piperidine			2,0			
Morpholine			2,7			
Triethylamine		17,0		7,5		
Tripropylamine		31,0				
Tributylamine		53,3			240° C	
Aniline			9,7		2,7	
N-Methylaniline					3,6	
N-Ethylaniline					4,3	
N-Butylaniline					6,3	
N-Dimethylaniline			13,2			
Pyridine			2,3			

P 223:   Pennwalt 223 (alkyl aryl polyglycol ether) on Gas-Chrom R (80–100 mesh), Cu column 3 m long, 4 mm in diameter (after Appl. Sci. Lab. Gas Chrom Newsletter 1969, no. 3, p. 2)

P 223 + KOH: 27% Pennwalt 223 + 4% KOH on Gas-Chrom R, glass column 2 m long, 4 mm in diameter (after Appl. Sci. Lab. Gas Chrom Newsletter 1970, no. 2, p. 1)

C 103:   Chromosorb 103 (porous organic polymer), glass colun 1.2 mm long, 4 mm in diameter (after Chromosorb Bulletin FF 181, Johns Maniville)

PEG: Glass capillary column, 30 m × 0,25 mm, coated with polyethyleneglycol 20 M; temp: 1 min 100°C, then 10°/min to 250°C; amines converted to Schiff bases by reaction with 2-thiophen aldehyde (after Hoshika)

Table 9.6 a: Data for TLC of aliphatic amines (see Table 9.6)

Layer: Silica gel G					
Mobile phase: chloroform	+	methanol	+	ammonia (17% in H$_2$O)	
I	82,5	+	15,5	+	2
II	70	+	26	+	4
III	40	+	40	+	20
IV	25	+	50	+	25
V			35	+	65

Layer: Paraffine oil impregnated Kieselguhr		
Mobile phase: aceton	+	ammonia (17% in H$_2$O)
VI	55	+	45
VII	70	+	30

Detection reagents

A   1% ninhydrin in ethanol + acetic acid (95 + 5)
B   1% KMnO$_4$ in H$_2$O + 1% K$_2$S$_2$O$_7$ in H$_2$O (50 + 50)
C   25% I$_2$ in methanol
D   5% Na$_2$Fe(CN)$_5$NO · 2 H$_2$O in acetaldehyde solution + 2% NaCO$_3$-solution (50 + 50)
E   1% 2,5-dimethoxytetrahydrofuran in buffered H$_2$O (pH 6,6). After spraying the layer is heated for 5 min to 110 °C and then sprayed with 1% solution of p-dimethylaminobenzaldehyde in 3% HCl.

Reagent A is applicable on all layers, the other ones only on Kieselguhr layers.

others are chemically incorporated into the polymer molecule during curing and decisively influence resin properties.

Major importance has been achieved by polycarboxylic acid anhydrides, the most important of which are listed in Table 9.8. They are usually incorporated in resin formulations in amounts of at least 30% w/w. Curing can be greatly speeded up by adding small amounts (0.5–2%) of accelerator, preferably tertiary amines such as tributylamine, benzyldimethylamine as well as piperidine.

The second major group of epoxy resin hardeners are the polyamines. Here, primary aliphatic polyamines, modified aliphatic amines (alkoxylated amines, amine adducts), cyclic aliphatic amines, tertiary aliphatic amines and their salts, as well as aromatic amines are used.

Modified aliphatic polyamines are frequently reaction products of diamines and glycidyl ethers, which lead to compounds of type I. By reacting alkyl diamines with ethylene oxide, ethoxylated amines of types II and III are produced.

Like acid anhydrides, aromatic polyamines produce resins with better heat distortion characteristics than aliphatic amines, but cure more quickly than anhydride systems. Typical examples include 4,4'-methylenedianiline, m-phenylenediamine and 4,4'-diaminodiphenylsulphone.

Polyaminoamides are condensed from di- and trimerised vegetable oils, unsaturated fatty acids and alkyl or aryl polyamines, and cure with epoxides through their primary and secondary amino groups. Finally, reactive thinners such as butylglycidyl ether and, to a lesser degree, phenyl and cresylglycidyl ethers are of importance in the production of epoxy resins, because they make the high viscosity resins easier to handle.

Polysulphides of type IV are used as reactive plasticisers. These likewise react with epoxides, although they require an amine hardener to effect complete cure to form stiff, impact resistant polymers.

I
$$R^2-CH_2-\overset{\displaystyle OH}{\overset{\displaystyle |}{CH}}-CH_2-NH-R^1-NH_2$$

R^1 = Alkylrest des Diamins
R^2 = Alkylrest des Glycidylethers

II $HOCH_2-CH_2-NH-R^1-NH_2$

III $HOCH_2-CH_2-NH-R^1-NH-CH_2-CH_2OH$

R^1 = Alkyl

IV $HS-(R-O-CH_2-O-R-S-S)_n-R-O-CH_2-O-R-SH$

R = $-CH_2-CH_2-$

Tertiary amines with different structures are mainly used as activators for the preparation of polyurethanes through polyaddition of diisocyanates and polyethers or polyester polyols. They include trialkylamines, preferably with C$_2$ – C$_5$ alkyl radicals, as well as mixed alkyl arylamines, tertiary ether amines, substituted pyridines, morpholin derivatives, pyrolidones and esters of alkylol dialkylamines with dicarboxylic acids. Catalysts with reactive hydroxyl, amino or carboxyl groups react with isocyanate groups and are built into the polymer molecule. This is especially useful for odourless polyurethanes.

Organo-tin compounds such as dibutyl tin dilaurate, dibutyl tin diacetate and dioctyl tin oxide, as well as tin (II) salts of long chain fatty acids such as hexoates, naphthenates, palmitates and stearates are of importance for highly reactive systems.

Tin compounds can be intensified with tertiary amines through synergistic action.

Alkali compounds, too, such as alkali phenolates, acetates, naphthenates and other easily hydrolysed alkali salts of organic acids act as accelerators. Alkali and alkaline earth hydroxides and carbonates have also been mentioned in the literature.

Hardeners in cured epoxy resins based on bisphenol A have been identified by STAHL und BRÜDERLE [43a, 541] by means of thermofractography (TFG) and temperature programmed hydrolysis with an alkali melt, followed by TLC of the volatile constituents deposited on silica gel layers (TAS method according to STAHL [42, 43]. In thermofractography, 3–5 mg of the sample are heated in a stream of nitrogen from 100–450 °C at the rate of 8° per minute. In the alkali melt method, 5–8 mg of sample are covered with ten times the amount of alkali melt mixture (3 g KOH + 0.09 g sodium acetate, fused and broken up) in a nickel combustion boat and heated to 450 °C at the rate of 4 °C per minute.

In the case of anhydride-cured resins, the alkali melt was cooled and then mixed with o-phosporic acid until the mixture showed an acid reaction, the liberated acids and anhydrides likewise being transferred to TLC plates by means of thermofractography, and then separated.

The TLC data of the reaction products and their appearance in dependence of the TFG temperature are listed in Table 9.10a–9.10d for epoxy resins cured by different methods. Papers by STAHL and BRÜDERLE contain examples of the two-dimensional chromatograms obtained by this method, as well as details about method of operation and comparative samples.

Table 9.7: TLC of aliphatic amines and detection behaviour [547]
(for TLC data see 9.6a, detection: + positive reaction, + – faint reaction, – negative reaction)

No.	Empirical formula	Name	E I hR$_F$	E II hR$_F$	E III hR$_F$	E IV hR$_F$	E V hR$_F$	A	B	C	D	E
1	CH$_5$N	Methylamine	3.5	6				+	+–	–	+–	+
2	C$_2$H$_5$NO$_2$	Glycine	0	2	36	47	80	+	+	+	+	+
3	C$_2$H$_7$N	Ethylamine	7	16				+	+–	–	+–	+
4	C$_2$H$_7$N	Dimethylamine	4	7	11	12		+–	+	+	+	–
5	C$_2$H$_7$NO	Ethanolamine	4	10	37	44	58	+	+	+	+	+
6	C$_2$H$_8$N$_2$	Ethylenediamine	2	4	15	20	40	+	+	+	+	+
7	C$_3$H$_9$N	Propylamine	16	35				+	+–	+	+	+
8	C$_3$H$_9$N	Isopropylamine	17.5	36	73			+–	+	+	+–	+
9	C$_3$H$_9$N	Trimethylamine		43				–	+–			–
10	C$_3$H$_9$NO	Propanolamine	4	8	28	31	50	+	+	+	–	+
11	C$_3$H$_{10}$N$_2$	Propylenediamine	3	10	35	40	55	+	+	+	+	+
12	C$_4$H$_9$NO	Morpholine	4.3	71	86			+–	+	+	+	–
13	C$_4$H$_{10}$N$_2$	Piperazine	3	5	23	25	40	+	+	+	+	–
14	C$_4$H$_{11}$N	Butylamine	22	48				+	+	+	+	+
15	C$_4$H$_{11}$N	Isobutylamine	31	58	84			+	+	+	+	+
16	C$_4$H$_{11}$N	Diethylamine	16	32	57	41		+–	+–	+	–	–
17	C$_4$H$_{11}$NO	3-Methoxypropylamine	18	43	63			+	+	+	+	+
18	C$_4$H$_{11}$NO	Ethylethanolamine	11	23	54			+	+	+	+	–
19	C$_4$H$_{11}$NO$_2$	Diethanolamine	5	16	50			+–	+	–	+	+–
20	C$_4$H$_{13}$N$_3$	Diethylenetriamine	0	0	7	8.5	30	+	+	+	–	+
21	C$_5$H$_{13}$N	Pentylamine	29	55				+	+	+	+	+
22	C$_5$H$_{13}$N	Isoamylamine	30	56	84			+	+	+	+	+
23	C$_5$H$_{13}$N	2-Methylbutylamine	36	68	85			+	+	+	+	+
24	C$_6$H$_{13}$N	Cyclohexylamine	33	63	85					+	+	+	+
25	C$_6$H$_{13}$NO	N-Ethylmorpholine	95	100								
26	C$_6$H$_{15}$N	3-Amino-2,2′-dimethylbutane	51	90				–	+	+	+	+–
27	C$_6$H$_{15}$N	2-Amino-3-methylpentane	47	78	88			–	+	+	+	+–
28	C$_6$H$_{15}$N	2-Amino-4-methylpentane	42	73	82			–	+	+	+	+ +
29	C$_6$H$_{15}$N	Di-n-propylamine	51	80	91			+–	+	+	+	–
30	C$_6$H$_{15}$N	Diisopropylamine	33	66	90			–	–	+	–	–
31	C$_6$H$_{15}$N	Triethylamine		75				+–	+			–
32	C$_6$H$_{15}$NO$_2$	Ethyldiethanolamine	30	52	84			+	+	+	–	–
33	C$_6$H$_{15}$NO$_3$	Triethanolamine	18	36	75			–	+	+	–	–
34	C$_7$H$_{17}$NO$_2$	Propyldiethanolamine	52	69	92			+–	+	+	–	–
35	C$_8$H$_{19}$N	2-Ethylhexylamine	54	88				+	+	+	+	+
36	C$_8$H$_{19}$N	Di-n-butylamine	63	95				+	+	+	+	+–
37	C$_8$H$_{19}$N	Diisobutylamine	85	99				+	+	+	+	+–
38	C$_8$H$_{19}$N	tert.-Octylamine	52	87				–		–		
39	C$_8$H$_{23}$N$_5$	Tetraethylenepentamine			0	3.0	20	+	+	+	–	+
40	C$_9$H$_{20}$N$_2$	N-(3-Aminopropyl)cyclohexylamine	5	18	61			+	+	+	+	+
41	C$_9$H$_{21}$NO$_3$	Triisopropanolamine	52	85				–	+	+	–	–
42	C$_{16}$H$_{35}$N	Di-2-ethylhexylamine	100					+	+	+	+	–
43	C$_{10}$H$_{23}$NO	2-Ethylhexylethanolamine	65	93				+	+	+	+	+–

No.	Empirical formula	Name	E I hR$_F$	E II hR$_F$	E VI hR$_F$	E VII hR$_F$	A	B	C	D	E
44	C$_6$H$_{15}$N	Hexylamine	34	65	70	86	+	+	+	+	+
45	C$_7$H$_{17}$N	Heptylamine	36	70	56	82	+	+	+	+	+
46	C$_8$H$_{19}$N	Octylamine	37.5	74	49	78	+	+	+	+	+
47	C$_9$H$_{21}$N	Nonylamine	39	77	36	74	+	+	+	+	+
48	C$_{10}$H$_{23}$N	Decylamine	40.5	78	27	70	+	+	+	+	+
49	C$_{11}$H$_{25}$N	Undecylamine	42	79	19	65	+	+	+	+	+
50	C$_{12}$H$_{27}$N	Dodecylamine	44	79	10	58	+	+	+	+	+
51	C$_{13}$H$_{29}$N	Tridecylamine	47	80	6.5	50	+	+	+	+	+
52	C$_{14}$H$_{31}$N	Tetradecylamine	50	82	4.5	43	+	+	+	+	+
53	C$_{15}$H$_{33}$N	Pentadecylamine	52	83	3.2	38	+	+	+	+	+
54	C$_{16}$H$_{35}$N	Hexadecylamine	55	85	2.5	30	+	+	+	+	+
55	C$_{17}$H$_{37}$N	Heptadecylamine	58	85	2.0	24	+	+	+	+	+
56	C$_{18}$H$_{39}$N	Stearylamine	60	85	1.5	18	+	+	+	+	+

Table 9.8: HPLC data of accelerators and amines (after GROSS, STRAUSS)

Substance	retention time min		UV-Absorpt. Maxim. nm
	I	II	
Mercapto accelerators			
2-Mercaptobenzthiazole	3,2	1,2	325
2-Mercaptobenzimidazole	3,2	2,1	304, 244
2-Mercaptothiazoline	3,0	2,5	241
2-Mercaptoimidazoline	2,75	12	257, 241
Guanidines			
O-Tolylbiguanidine	3,3		235
Diphenylguanidine	3,9		257
Di-o-tolylguanidine	4,1		251
Triphenylguanidine	10,6		259
Thiurams		III	
Tetramethylthiuram monosulfide	3,8	9,8	
Tetramethylthiuramdisulfide	4,7	6,2	
Dimethyl-diphenylthiuramdisulfide	22,5	1,6	
Tetraethylthiuramdisulfide	12,9	1,8	
Dithiocarbamates			
Zn-N-ethylphenyldithiocarbamate	3,2	1,45	
Zn-N-diethyldithiocarbamate	3,3	1,7	
Zn-N-dimethyldithiocarbamate	3,0	3,3	
Zn-N-pentamethylenedithiocarbamate	3,5	1,8	
Amines			
Dimethylamine	3,3		
Diethylamine	3,3		
Dipropylamine	3,6		
Dibutylamine	4,7		
2-Ethylhexylamine	7,0		
Cyclohexylamine	3,8		
Dicyclohexylamine	5,5		
N-Ethylhexylamine	4,0		
Piperidine	3,8		
Urotropin	2,9		
Aniline	3,6		
N-Methylaniline	5,0		
N-Ethylaniline	6,2		

I   Column: C_{16} modified Silicagel "Lichrosorb RP 18–5", 25 cm × 4 mm
            Mobile phase: Methanol + H_2O + $(NH_4)_2CO_3$, 70 + 30 + 2 flow rate 1 ml/min
II, III   Column: Silica gel "Nucleosil 50–5", 20 cm + 4 mm
II   Mobile phase: Diisopropyl ether + methanol, 50 + 50
III   Mobile phase: Diisopropyl ether

Information about the identification of isocyanates and polyethers and polyesters in polyurethanes are given in vol. 2.

TLC and GC techniques, as described for use with plasticisers and antioxidants, are suitable for the diamines produced through hydrolysis from diisocyanates.

Activators based on tertiary amines can, after extaction, likewise be separated by TLC, HPLC and, in part, by GC and identified.

The IR spectra of activators and amine hardeners are well suited for identification, particularly in the case of aromatic amines.

Table 9.9a: Curing Agents and Activators, Anhydrides and Acid-Derivatives

Dec. No.	IR-Sp. No.	Substance	M	MS-Data upper line mass number lower line intensity (most intensive mass nos. = 100)							
1		Anhydrides									
1.1		Aromatic carboxylic anhydrides									
1.1.1	6400	Phthalic anhydride	148	104	76	148	50	52	77	149	51
					85	47	40	14	8	6	3
1.1.2	6401	Tetrahydrophthalic anhydride	152	79	124	80	39	77	78	27	51
					48	42	14	13	8	8	8
1.1.3	6402	Tetrachlorophthalic anhydride	286	242	212	214	240	286	107	142	244
					70	63	62	61	57	54	53
1.1.4	6415	Hexahydrophthalic anhydride	154	67	54	82	44	41	79	27	39
					98	97	83	76	65	63	52
1.1.5	6403	Methyltetrahydrophthalic anhydride	166	79	93	94	39	77	91	80	118
					81	82	79	74	65	49	47
1.1.6	6404	Methylhexahydrophthalic anhydride	168	81	96	54	55	39	44	67	82
					89	85	44	38	38	30	29
1.1.7	6405	Endomethylene tetrachlorophthalic anhydride	369	43	57	71	41	56	26	70	54
					88	88	87	84	72	71	66
1.1.8	6406	Endomethylenemethyl tetrahydrophthalic anhydride (Methyl Nadic Anhydrid)	196	79	26	80	77	54	39	78	51
					98	94	93	93	91	76	45
1.1.9	6407	Trimellitic acid anhydride	192	148	75	120	104	50	102	103	76
					55	53	45	44	33	33	31
1.1.10	6408	Pyromellitic acid anhydride	218	174	74	102	37	73	51	175	101
					81	79	60	35	21	17	14
1.2		Aliphatic carboxylic anhydrides									
1.2.1	6409	Dodecenyl succinic acid anhydride	268	43	41	57	69	97	55	83	109
					99	92	90	90	89	85	83
1.2.2	6410	1,2,3,4-Cyclopentane tetracarboxylic anhydride	210								
1.2.3	6417	Polyazelaic acid anhydride									
1 3		Carboxylic acids									
1.3.1	6411	Decane dicarboxylic acid									
1.3.2	6412	Diphenyl ether dicarboxylic acid									
1.4		Carboxylic acid salts									
1.4.1	6413	Dibutyl tin dilaurate									
1.4.2	6415	Tin dioctoate									
1.4.3	6414	Adipic acid hydrazide									

Table 9.9b: Curing Agents and Activators, amines and alkylamines

Dec. No.	IR-Sp. No.	Substance	M	MS-Data upper line mass number lower line intensity (most intensive mass no. = 100)							
2		Aliphatic amines									
2.1											
2.1.1	6420	Diethylamine	73								
2.1.2	6421	Triethylamine	101	86	58	30	101	44	42	29	100
				100	24	24	20	10	9	9	7
2.1.3	6418	N,N-Dimethylisopropylamine	87								
2.1.4	6419	N,N-Dimethylisobutylamine	101								
2.1.5	6422	Trimethylcyclohexylamine	141								
2.1.6	6423	Ethylenediamine	60	30	28	43	42	18	60	27	59
				100	9	6	4	4	3	3	3
2.1.7	6424	Diethylenetriamine	103	44	73	30	19	28	27	56	42
				100	59	34	18	15	15	15	11
2.1.8	6425	Triethylenetriamine	146								
2.1.9	6426	Trimethylhexamethylenediamine	158								
2.1:10	6427	Hexamethylenetriethylenetetramine	173								
2.1.11	6428	N-Bis(2,2'-dimethylaminoethyl)-methylamine	173								
2.1.12	6429	N,N,N',N'-Tetramethylethylenediamine	116								
2.1.13	6430	N,N,N',N'-Tetramethyl-1,3-butandiamine	144								
2.1.14	6431	Isophorondiamine	170								
2.1.15	6432	Dicyanodiamide	84								
2.1.16	6433	Dicyanodiamidine	103								
2.2		Alkylolamines									
2.2.1	6434	Ethanolamine	61	30	18	28	42	17	31	15	61
				100	30	15	7	6	6	5	5
2.2.2	6435	Diethanolamine	105	74	56	30	36	45	38	28	42
				100	53	48	43	16	13	11	8
2.2.3	6436	Triethanolamine	149	118	56	45	42	44	43	41	5
				100	69	60	56	27	25	14	8
2.2.4	6437	Propanolamine	75								
2.2.5	6438	Isopropanolamine	75	18	30	17	28	44	58	42	15
				100	24	23	13	9	8	6	6
2.2.6	6439	4-Aminobutanol-2	89								
2.2.7	6440	Triisopropanolamine	191								
2.2.8	6441	N,N-Dimethylethanolamine	89	58	42	30	44	28	15	43	89
				100	26	22	20	17	10	10	8
2.2.9	6442	N,N-Diisopropylethanolamine	145								
2.2.10	6443	N,N-Dimethylisopropanolamine	103								
2.2.11	6444	N-Methyldiethanolamine	119	44	88	45	42	28	43	27	2
				100	89	39	36	25	14	13	1
2.2.12	6445	N-Aminoethylethanolamine	104								
2.2.13	6446	1,3-Diaminopropanol-2	90								
2.2.14	6447	N',N'-Dimethylaminoethyl-N-methylethanolamine	146								
2.2.15	6448	N,N,N',N'-tetra(2-hydroxypropyl)-ethylenediamine	292								

Table 9.9b (continued)

Dec. No.	IR-Sp. No.	Substance	M	MS-Data upper line mass number lower line intensity (most intensive mass no. = 100)							
2.3		Aromatic amines									
2.3.1	6457	Dimethylbenzylamine	135	58	135	91	134	136	42	65	44
				100	83	59	44	39	18	14	11
2.3.2	6449	N-Benzylisopropylamine	164								
2.3.3	6450	Dimethylaminomethylphenol									
2.3.4	6451	N-Phenylethylenediamine	108								
2.3.5	6452	1,3-Phenylenediamine	108								
2.3.6	6453	2,4,6-Tri(dimethylaminomethyl)phenol	237								
2.3.7	6454	4,4'-Diaminodiphenylmethane	198								
2.3.8	6455	3,3'-Dichloro-4,4'-diaminodiphenylmethane	267								
2.3.9	6456	3,3'-Dichlorobenzidine	253								
2.3.10	6459	4,4'-Diaminodiphenylsulfone	248								
2.3.11	6458	1,3-Phenylenediamine + Cumoldiamine									
2.4.1	6460	2-Tolylbiguanide									
2.4.2	6461	Xylylbiguanide									
2.4.3	6462	Methoxymethylbenzoguanamine									
2.4.4	6463	Benzimidazolylguanidine									
3.1	6464	Triethylenediamine									
3.2	6465	Dimethylaminopyridine									
3.3	6466	1-Methylimidazole									
3.4	6467	2-Methylimidazole	82	28	82	54	81	42	41	27	40
					97	95	85	83	80	50	48
3.5	6468	2-Phenylimidazoline									
3.6	6469	2-Phenyl-5-methylimidazoline									
3.7	6470	1-Methyl-4-(dimethylamino-)piperazine									
3.8	6475	1,4-Dimethyl-diethylpiperazine									
3.9	6471	1,4-Bis(2-hydroxypropyl-)piperazine									
3.10	6472	Morpholine	87	29	57	28	56	30	87	42	27
					84	80	59	47	45	27	20
3.11	6473	N-Methylmorpholine									
3.12	6476	N-Ethylmorpholine									
3.13	6477	N-Cocomorpholine									
3.14	6474	1,4-(2,2'-bisoxalino)benzene									

Table 9.9c: Curing Agents and Activators; Polyamines and others Compounds

Dec. No.	IR-Sp. No.	Substance	Dec. No.	IR-Sp. No.	Substance
4.		Polyamines	5.		Others
4.1	6478	Aliphatic polyamine (Härter HY 951)	5.1	6484	Aliphatic ketimine
4.2	6479	Aliphatic Polyamine (Härter HY 956)	5.2	6487	Adduct TMA/Sebazic acid (Härter XB 2731)
4.3	6480	Polyamide (Härter HY 843)	5.3	6488	Adduct-Phenylimidazoline/Pyromellitic acid
4.4	6481	Cycloaliphatic polyamine (Härter HY 2954)	5.4	6489	Adduct TCSDA
4.5	6482	Aminopolyoxypropylene (Stacast 1264)	5.5	6485	Adduct Boron trifluorid/Ethylamine (Curing agent 1040)
4.6	6483	Polyaminoimidazoline (Härter GMI 350)			
			5.6	6486	Isophoronediisocyanate/Caprolactam (Härter B 1065)

Table 9.10 a: TLC-conditions for dicarbonic anhydrides and dicarbonic acids and TFG-quantities of hardened epoxy resins (thermolysis T and acidic desintegration after alkaline fusion SA, other abbreviations see table 9.10 d)

Decomposition product		Layers, Solvents, hRf-Values		Detection			TFG-Start of Zones [°C] with hardener							
							MSA		PSA		HPA		MHPA	
		I	II	FL	R3	R4	T	SA	T	SA	T	SA	T	SA
Maleic acid	MS	8–13	8–10	+	+	+	100	200	–	–	–	–	–	–
Maleic anhydrid	MSA	65–70	18–20	+	+	+	140	150	–	–	–	–	–	–
Fumaric acid	FS	48–50	33–35	+	+	+	135	150	–	–	–	–	–	–
Phthalic acid	PS	20–24	14–17	+	+	+	–	–	150	100	–	–	–	–
Phthalic anhydrid	PSA	65–70	73–76	–	+	+	–	–	280	130	–	–	–	–
Hexahydrophthalic acid	HPS	33–37	35–38	–	+	+	–	–	–	–	300	125	–	–
Hexahydrophthalic anhydrid	HPA	70–75	78–80	–	+	+	–	–	–	–	380	150	–	–
Methylhexahydrophthalic acid	MHPS	35–40	46–49	–	+	+	–	–	–	–	–	–	265	120
Methylhexahydrophthalic anhydrid	MHPA	70–75	83–85	–	+	+	–	–	–	–	–	–	330	200

I   Silica gel GF254–HF254 (1 + 1); chloroform-ethyl acetate-formic (49 + 49 + 2), 1 × 10 cm, CS.
II Kieselguhr G 25% with polyethylenglycole 1000 impregnated (with fluorescence indicator), diisopropylether-formic acid-water-polyethylenglycole 1000 (90 + 7 + 3 + 2) upper phase, 1 × 15 cm, CS.
R 3: + yellow spots on blue ground   R 4: + dark brown spots on light ground

Table 9.10 b: TLC-conditions for aromatic and cycloaliphatic amines and TFG-quantities of hardened epoxy resins (thermolysis T and alkaline fusion A)

Decomposition product		Layers, solvents, hRf-Values			Detection			TFG-Start of zones [°] with hardener							
								DDM		DDS		m-PDA		MBCA	
		I	II	III	FL	Rl	F	T	A	T	A	T	A	T	A
Aniline		55–60	55–60	50–55	(+)	wr	gegn	350	225	240	200	–	200	–	–
2-Toluidine		–	–	60–65	+	–	hgn	–	–	–	–	–	–	–	–
4-Toluidine		52–57	–	–	+	li	gn	355	–	–	–	–	–	–	–
4,4'-Diaminodiphenylmethane	DDM	28–32	25–30	34–38	+	wr	orbr	350	225	–	225	–	–	–	–
4,4'-Diaminodiphenylsulfone	DDS	6–11	7–12	20–23	+	dro	tu	–	–	200	200	–	–	–	–
m-Phenylenediamine	m-PDA	15–20	14–19	25–30	+	–	grbr	–	–	–	–	120	125	–	–
4,4'-Methylen-bis-(2-methylcyclohexylamine)	MBCA	0–5	–	–	–	vi	grgn	–	–	–	–	–	–	280	230

I   Silica gel HF254–GF254 (1 + 1), toluene-acetone-ammonia 25% (80 + 20 + 1), 1 × 10 cm, CS.
II Silica gel HF254, toluene-acetone (85 + 15), 1 × 10 cm, CS.
III Silica gel HF254, benzene-chloroform-methanol (60 + 30 + 10), 1 × 10 cm, CS.

Table 9.10 d: TLC-conditions of decomposition products of dicyanodiamide-hardened epoxy resins (thermolysis *T* and alkaline fusion *A*)

Decomposition product	Layers, solvents, hRf-Values		Detection		TFG – start of zones [°C]	
	I	II	R 1	R 2	T	A
Cyanoamide	80–85	90–93	–	ge, vi Rd	150	50
Dicyanodiamide	50–60	73–78	robr	ge, vi Rd	65, 160, 310	50
Melamine	15–20	35–40	–	ge, vi Rd	175	225
Dicyanodiamidine	3– 6	30–35	–	ge, vi Rd	–	225

I   Silica gel HF_{254}–GF_{254} (1 + 1), pyridine-benzene-acetonitrile-water (25 + 40 + 30 + 3), 1 × 10 cm, NS.
II Silica gel HF_{254}–GF_{254} (1 + 1), acetonitrile-petroleum ether-carbon tetrachloride-tetrahydrofurane-water-formic acid (65 + 8 + 8 + 8 + 8 + 3), 1 × 10 cm, NS.

F = Fluorescence at 366 nm with fluorescamine reagent
FL = Fluorescence quenching at 254 nm on silica gel HF_{254} layers

R 1   Ninhydrine reagent
R 2   Chlorine-toluidine reagent
R 3   Bromo cresol-green reagent
R 4   Glucose-aniline reagent (Schweppe)

Colour abbreviation
bl blue   h   light
br brown   d   dark
ge yellow
gn green   Rd edge
gr gray
li purple
ro red
wr burgundy
tu turquoise
vi violet

Table 9.10 c: TLC-conditions for polyalkylenpolyamines and TFG-quantities of hardened epoxy resins after alkaline fusion.

Decomposition product		Layers, solvents, hRf-values		Evaluation			TFG-Start of zones [°C] with hardener			
		I	II	F	R₁	T₂	DETA	TETA	PEHA	MBCA
Ethylenediamine	EDA	53 57	36–40	tu	robr	ge	200	230	235	–
Diethylenetriamine	DETA	35–40	36–43	tu	robr	ge	220	235	265	–
Triethylenetetramine	TETA	28–33	25–31	tu	robr	ge	–	240	265	–
Pentaethylenhexamine	PEHA	10–20	5–20	tu	robr	ge	–	–	265	–
Piperazine		30–35	5–10	dvi	dro	gevi	–	230	225	–
4,4′-Methylene-bis (2-methylcyclohexylamine)	MBCA	85–90	84–88 90 94	grgn	vi		–	–	–	230

I   Silica gel HF_{254}–GF_{254} (1 + 1), ethanol-ammonia 25% (33 + 66), 1 × 10 cm, CS.
II Silica gel HF_{254}, acetone-ammonia 25% (85 + 15), 1 × 10 cm, CS.

10. Processing Aids

10.1. Survey and Classification

Various aids are used for the production and processing of polymers, and many of these remain in the polymer unchanged or in a chemically modified form.

These aids include inorganic or organometallic catalysts in hydrocarbon polymers, emulsifiers in PVC, hardeners in thermosets, vulcanization aids in rubber, blowing agents, lubricants, adhesion promoters, antiskinning agents, solvents, mold lubricants, and other additives. Some of these substances also have a positive influence on the properties of the processed plastic, but their main function is as processing aids.

The analysis of polymerization catalysts is not discussed here. Accelerators, hardeners and solvents are discussed in separate sections. Some further processing aids are described below under the headings indicated in Table 10.1. Some analytical possibilities are also pointed out.

Table 10.1: Processing aids

	IR spectra No.
1. Lubricants	6500–6504
2. Blowing agents	6505–6521
3. Adhesion promoters	6522–6529
4. Peptizers	6530–6532
5. Antiskinning agents	6533–6535
6. Other processing aids	6536–6538

10.2 Lubricants

Lubricants are used to improve the processability of thermoplastics, and they also reduce friction on walls and within the material by external and internal lubrication. They prevent the plastic from adhering to hot metal objects. The substances used must have limited compatibility with the polymers, so that on the one hand they can form boundary layers, while on the other they do not form greasy or tacky coatings.

The nature and action of lubricants is discussed in the literature [1–3, 550–552]. The lubricants, which are mainly added to PVC and the polyolefins in quantities of 0.2 to 1.5 %, mostly belong to the following classes of substances:

Hydrocarbons
  Mineral oils, paraffins, polyethylene wax
Fatty alcohols
  Long-chain alcohols such as stearyl alcohol
Fatty acids
  Stearic acid, hydroxystearic acid, and other long-chain fatty acids
Fatty acid esters
  Ethyl palmitate, butyl stearate, monoglycerides, diglycerides, and triglycerides of fatty acids, ester waxes of C_{28}—C_{32} fatty acids (montanic acids), natural glycerides, epoxidized oils, natural ester waxes, and partly hydrolyzed ester waxes
Fatty acid amides
  C_{12}—C_{16} acid amides, e. g. distearoylamine
Metal soaps
  Alkaline earth and heavy metal salts of fatty acids and hydroxylated fatty acids.

Table 10.2. Processing aids, IR-spectra of lubricants

Material	IR-Sp. No.
Paraffin wax	6500
Mineral oils	5284–5294
Polyethylene	2–4
Polytetrafluoroethylene	238
Stearic acid	6501
Zn-stearate	6503
Ca-stearate	6063, 6504
Other stearates	6064, 6066–6068
Montanester wax (partially saponified)	6502
Polyglycoles	451–453, 5210–5220
Siloxanes	1720, 1737

(IR-spectra no. below 2000 see Vol. 1)

Some of these substances are also used in higher concentrations as plasticizers. Typical plasticizers, such as the phthalic acid esters of long-chain alcohols, also act as lubricants. Metal soaps (Ca, Zn, Pb stearates, etc.) act as stabilizers in PVC, and usually also give an adequate lubricant action. Small quantities of polyethylene waxes and also Ca stearate are often used for polyolefins. Long-chain fatty alcohols are used e. g. for polystyrene.

The detection reactions for functional groups and degradation products and those given for plasticizers listed in Volume 2 can be used for the chemical identification of lubricants. The metals in soaps are detected by conventional methods.

Thin layer chromatographic methods are suitable for the isolation of lubricants in extracts, which usually also contain other additives. The values given in Table 10.3 were collected from literature data on the determination of lubricants in PVC [480, 482]. Phosphomolybdic acid (20 % alcoholic solution) can be used for the detection of the spots. After spraying, the plates are heated at 130—140 °C for about 20 min [482]. Van der Heide [480] uses various spray reagents and identifies the substances present on the basis of the colors (see Table 10.4).

Iodine vapor and iodine solution (0.5 % in ethanol) can also be used for the detection of the spots, but give no color differentiation. Reference should be made to a publication by Hagen [554], which describes separations on silica gel and alumina with solvents having various polarities for paraffins, stearic acid, fatty alcohols, alkyl stearates, and oligomeric allyl stearate, in which each of the groups named was separated as fully as possible from the others.

IR spectroscopic identification of lubricants is more reliable than chemical identification. The reference spectra required are obtainable in various places in Volumes 1–3, and are listed in Table 10.2.

10.3 Blowing Agents

Porous rubber and plastics are produced with the aid of blowing agents, which cause pore formation either by vaporization (this is so in the case of low-boiling hydrocarbons, such as pentane and chlorofluorohydrocarbons) or by chemical decomposition at high temperatures with the evolution of gases.

Table 10.3: TLC of lubricants

Layer + Solvents Lit.	silica gel G petroleum ether diethylether acetic acid (80 + 20 + 1) [482]	silica gel G chloroforme [480]
Paraffin oil	90	90...95
Fatty acid esters	83	
Dioctyl phthalate	58	
Glycerol monoesters, techn. grade	0, 6, 51	
Glycerol monostearate	0	
Wax esters	0...40	20...25
Fatty alcohols	0, 14	0
Stearic acid	19	0
Fatty acid amides		0...5
Epoxid. fatty acid esters	0	0, 15, 25

Table 10.4: TLC data for lubricants and stabilizers after VAN DER HEIDE [480]

	hR$_f$ value	2,6-Dichloro-quinone-chlorimide	Diazotized nitro-aniline	Ultra-phor	Rhod-amine B	Pyocatechol violet	Dithizon
\multicolumn{8}{l}{Color spots with various detection reagents}
Lubricants							
Paraffin oil	90...95	–	–	dk	light pink	–	–
Montan wax	20...25	–	–	l	–	–	–
Lauryl alcohol	30...40	gray	white	dk	light pink	yellow-white	–
Stearic acid	0	white	–	l	dark pink	yellow-white	greenish
Fatty acid amide	0...5	white	white	dk	l	yellow-white	–
Bisstearoylethylenediamine	0	–	–	dk	dark pink	yellow	greenish
Epoxidized soybean oil	15, 25	–	–	dk	–	–	pink
Epoxidized zinc oleate	0, 17	–	–	dk	–	–	–
Stabilizers							
Diphenylthiourea	65...70	brown	yellow	dk	l	–	–
α-Phenylindole	80...85	blue-violet	red-brown	dk	dk	blue-green	yellow-green
Esters of aminocrotonic	12...17	brown	light yellow	–	l	–	–
acid	55...80	–	–	dk	–	–	–
	75...80	–	–	dk	–	–	–
Di-n-octyltin dioctyl-	0	–	–	–	dk	blue	red
thioglycolate	80...85	–	–	dk	dk	greenish	gray
Di-n-octyltin maleate	0	–	–	dk	dk	blue	red
	80...85	–	–	–	dk	greenish	gray

l = light; dk = dark; – no spot observed

The low-boiling blowing agents are used mainly for foamed plastics, particularly polyurethane foams. In the case of the insulating foams produced with chlorofluorohydrocarbons, it is advantageous to retain the blowing agent in the pores to make use of its lower thermal conductivity in comparison with that of air.

Gas-chromatographic methods are the most suitable for the analysis of volatile blowing agents [558]. This is also true of the analysis of pore gases, in which a foam sample is crushed in the carrier gas stream of a gas chromatograph, and the gas liberated is analyzed. Gas samples can also be taken directly from the foamed material by means of hypodermic syringes. Gas chromatograms of pore gases are shown in Figure 10.2 [559].

The inorganic blowing agent that release gases (sodium and ammonium carbonates and dicarbonates, sodium nitrite/ammonium chloride mixtures, ammonium carbamate) have been largely replaced by organic blowing agents based on azo compounds and hydrazine derivatives, semicarbazides, tetrazols and benzoxazine derivatives, because of the greater processing reliability of the latter.

By far the most widely used is azodicarbonamide and its preparations which can contain plasticisers, other blowing agents as well as activators (kickers) to influence the decomposition temperature and speed. Azodicarbonamide decomposes at 205–215 °C to about 30% w/w of nitrogen, CO and CO_2 and residues consisting mainly of urazol and cyanuric acid, the latter partly sublimating during processing. The formation of cyanuric acid, which forms deposits on moulds and machine parts, can be slightly reduced by means of zinc oxide.

Azo-bis-isobutyronitrile finds little use because of the formation of the toxic tetramethyl succinic acid nitrile as decomposition product. The aromatic disulphohydrazides decompose with the formation of

nitrogen and water and form polymeric disulphides and thisulphonates. The reaction products formed by various other blowing agents are listed in Table 10.5.

N,N'-Dinitrosopentamethylenetetramine is generally used as a mixture with inert fillers; it decomposes at temperatures above 130 °C into nitrogen, formaldehyde, and traces of methylenediamine.

MIKSCH and PRÖLSS [557] have investigated the chemical and paperchromatographic identification of rubber blowing agents, and have reported some detection methods.

Diazoaminobenzene can be recognized by a light red color in 20 % hydrochloric acid. This color is also observed on extraction of green and vulcanized mixes with 20 % hydrochloric acid.

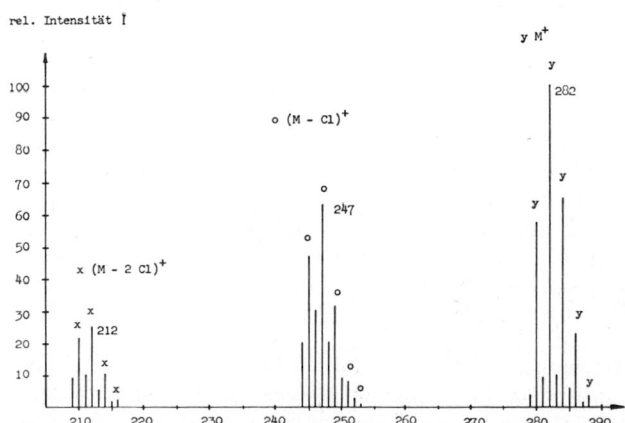

rel. Intensität I

Fig. 10.1: Part from the mass spectrum of pentachlorothiophenol C$_6$Cl$_5$SH. The Cl isotope distribution is as follows:

m/e	280	282	284	286	288
^{35}Cl	5	4	3	2	1
^{37}Cl	0	1	2	3	4

Table 10.5: Processing aids – blowing agents and their decomposition products

Dec. Nr.	IR-Sp. Nr.	Trade name	Composition	Decomposition temperature	reaction products (main compounds) gaseous	solid residue
2.1	6505	Porofor ADC/M	Azodicarbonamide	205–215	N_2, CO, CO_2	urazole, cyanuric acid
2.2	6506	Porofor N	Azobisisobutyronitrile		N_2	
2.3	6507	Vulcacel BN 94	N,N'-Dinitrosopenta-methylene tetramine		N_2	
2.4	6508	Porofor DNO/F	N,N'-Dinitrosopenta-methylene tetramine, 20% inact. additives		N_2, H_2O	
2.5	6513	Porofor BSH	Benzene sulfonylhydrazide		N_2, H_2O	
2.6	6509	Porofor B 13	Benzene 1,3-sulfonylhydrazide		N_2, H_2O	
2.7	6510	Porofor D 33	Diphenylsulfone-3,3'-disulfohydrazide	155	N_2, H_2O	polymeric sulfides and thiosulfonates
2.8	6511	Porofor S 44	Based on sulfohydrazide		N_2, H_2O	
2.9	6512	Porofor TR	Morpholyl thiotriazol			

Decomposition products

2.10	6514	Cyanuric acid
2.11	6515	Decomp. product of azodicarbonamide (200°)
2.12	6516	Decomp. product of azobisisobutyronitrile (200°)
2.13	6517	Decomp. product of N,N'-dinitrosopentamethylene tetraamine (200°)
2.14	6518	Decomp. product of benzene sulfonylhydrazide (200°)
2.15	6519	Decomp. product of benzene-1,3-disulfonylhydrazide (200°)
2.16	6520	Decomp. product of diphenylsulfone-1,3-disulfonylhydrazide (160°)
2.17	6521	Decomp. product of morpholyl thiotriazole (120°)

N,N'-Dinitrosopentamethylenetetramine forms formaldehyde on treatment with dilute sulfuric acid, even in green and vulcanized mixes, and the formaldehyde can be detected with chromotropic acid (see Section 9.2).

Benzenesulfonohydrazide and benzenedisulfonohydrazide can be detected with phosphomolybdic acid (blue color) after chromatographic separation from other substances extracted from green mixes. Benzenesulfonohydrazide can also be detected in the acetone extract from vulcanized mixes on the basis of its reaction products. These are converted into thiophenol by treatment wih 1.5 % potassium amalgam in methanol solution, and the thiophenol is then separated chromatographically and identified with chloranil by the formation of a very stable, intense ochre color. Benzenedisulfono-hydrazide cannot be detected in the vulcanized product on the basis of definite reaction products.

The most reliable method for the identification of unprocessed blowing agents and of blowing agents extracted from green mixes is by their IR spectra. They exhibit characteristic differences, which will not be discussed in detail here. We merely mention the significant key bands of the nitriles around 2240 cm^{-1} (4.47 μm) and the amine bands at 3400–3000 cm^{-1} (2.95–3.35 μm) as immediately recognizable group characteristics.

The residues left after the decomposition of blowing agents can be extracted together with other additives and auxiliaries, and give an indication of the type of blowing agent used. The IR spectra of the residues may be used for this purpose and some of these are shown in Sp. Nos. 6515–6521.

The residues were obtained by heating 100 mg of blowing agent in a glass beaker to the appropriate temperature.

10.4 Adhesion Promoters

The most important compounds used as adhesion promoters between inorganic fibers or fillers and polymers are silanes having the structure $(MeO)_3$-Si-R and $(EtO)_3$-Si-R, where MeO and EtO are methoxyl and ethoxyl groups respectively, and in some cases other alkoxy and alkoxyalkyl ether structures, while R are mainly vinyl groups, vinyl derivatives, or γ-substituted propyl groups Some of the common functional groups are listed below:

Vinyl	-CH=CH$_2$
3-Chloropropyl	-CH$_2$CH$_2$CH$_2$Cl
3-Mercaptopropyl	-CH$_2$CH$_2$CH$_2$SH
3-Aminopropyl	-CH$_2$CH$_2$CH$_2$NH$_2$

N-(2-Aminoethyl)-

-3-aminopropyl $-(CH_2)_3NH(CH_2)_2NH_2$

3-Methacryloxypropyl $-(CH_2)_3OC\text{-}C\text{=}CH_2$
                          $O\text{-}CH_3$

3-Glycidoxypropyl $-(CH_2)_3O\text{-}CH_2CH\text{-}CH_2$
                                 O

2-(3,4-Epoxycyclohexyl)ethyl $-CH_2CH_2$

On hydrolysis, an organophilic film bonded by oxygen bridges is formed on inorganic surfaces, the functional groups of this film being capable in part of participating in the polymerization of the binder or plastic. Adhesion promoters of this kind may be added to the low molecular weight system before mixing with the filler and curing. The other method is to treat the filler separately, with subsequent further processing of the silylated inorganic material. A special line of development is represented by the silyl peroxides, of which

vinyltris-(t-butylperoxy)silane is of special interest. These compounds also allow adhesion promotion between different organic materials, since the reaction is initiated thermally instead of by hydrolysis.

Further information about the effect of silane primers on glass fibres and other inorganic fillers is to be found in the literature [1–3, 564–569]. A comprehensive report has been given by ROSEN [569], this also including the results of chromatographic and spectroscopic methods in the silanisation of fillers.

The chemical analysis of primers on glass fibres has been described by WIEDEMANN et al. [572], based on earlier work carried out by other authors. Its qualitative analysis scheme is based on spot reactions and colour reactions in solution, with which the functional groups of the silanes used, as well as the type of size, can be identified. The analytical procedure described by these authors is shown in a slightly modified form in Table 10.7.

With the aid of IR spectroscopy, it is possible to detect the surface treatment on fillers or glass fibers and in some

Table 10.6: Chemical identification of primers on glasscloth according to Wiedemann et al. [572].
The tests should be carried out in the order indicated. If there is a positive reaction, the colour indicated is produced. The result can be confirmed by complementary tests (a). In the case of a negative result, the next test is carried out (S = spot reaction on pieces of fabric measuring about 5×5 cm).

Test No.	Type	Reagent	Colour	Nature of fibre or fabric coating
1	S	ninhydrin	violet	aminosilane 1a: colouring with Chrome Green GW: violet: primary amino group grey: primary and secondary amino groups
2	S	iodine/potassium iodide	dark blue to violet orange-yellow	starch-oil size paraffin emulsion size 2a: colouring with bromocresol green: blue colouration
3		diphenylcarbazide	violet	methacrylic acid-chromium complex
4	S	Rhodamine B	red	methacrylic silane or vinyl silane 4a: sample with $KMnO_4$ solution: discolouration
5		sodium thiosulphate + bromothymol blue	blue	epoxysilane (also aminosilane)

	Reagent	Composition, test details
1	ninhydrin	1% aqueous solution (store cold), heat 5–10 min at 90–100 °C in drying oven after spot test.
2	iodine/potassium iodide	0.1 g iodine and 1.5 g KI in 100 ml water. Rinse briefly after spot test and dry.
3	diphenylcarbacide	1 g diphenylcarbazide in 100 ml acetone. 20 g of fabric, separated into fibres, are mixed with 100 ml 10% NaOH, 125 ml water and 2 g sodium peroxide and boiled for 10 minutes. The hot extract is poured off, acidified with dilute sulphuric acid, 1 ml diphenylcarbazide solution added and stirred.
4	Rhodamine B	0.1 g Rhodamine B in 100 ml ethanol. After spotting wash with warm water and air dry.
5	Sodium thiosulphate/bromothymol blue	mixsaturated solution in ethanol : water 1 : 1. Dissolve 40 mg bromothymol blue in 100 ml ethanol and add dilute NaOH until the solution is still just orange yellow before the end point is reached. 25–30 g of the fabric, separated into fibres, are briefly washed with very dilute formic acid and then thoroughly rinsed several times with distilled water. The rinsed sample is then boiled for 10 minutes with 100 ml water, and the hot aqueous extract concentrated to about 1 ml on the waterbath. A few drops are now placed on a circular filter paper (medium pore size), followed by a few drops of sodium thiosulphate solution. The filter paper is then heated for 10 minutes to 60–80 °C in a drying cabinet and then sprayed with bromothymol blue solution.
1a	Chrome Green GW	3% aqueous solution. Fabric sample, about 5×5 cm is dyed in the chrome green solution for 15 min at 100 °C. The sample is then rinsed, and washed in soap solution (2 g soap/1000 ml water) at 40 °C, followed by a further rinse.
2a	Bromocresol green	0.04 g bromocresol green dissolved in 100 ml water at 60 °C. 5×5 cm fabric sample is then moved about in this solution for 30 seconds and then immediately washed in running cold water and air dried.
4a	$KMnO_4$ solution	0.2 g $KMnO_4$ dissolved in 100 ml water. About 20 g fabric, separated into fibres, are then boiled for 10 minutes in 150 ml water. The aqueous extract is then made slightly alkaline with a dilute sodium bicarbonate solution and the $KMnO_4$ added dropwise.

cases to determine the nature of the functional groups on the surface. However, only limited information can be deduced regarding the original adhesion promoter.

The situation changes when samples of adhesion promoters are available, since chemical reactions can then be used for their identification. However, identification by IR spectroscopy is more elegant and more reliable, the spectra of the various silanes differing sufficiently from one another.

Out of the many silanes described in the literature [2, 564–570], a few of the products that are commercially obtainable at present have been selected and their spectra reproduced (spectra 6522–6529). All the spectra contain the strong Si-O band ($\nu_{asym.}$) at about 1090 cm^{-1} (9.2 μm) and the weaker sym. Si-O stretching vibration at about 850–750 cm^{-1} (11.8–13.3 μm). The spectra are characterized by further bands due to the functional groups.

In addition to the organosilicon compounds, numerous other substances have been suggested as adhesion promotors for specific applications. Some examples are given below.

Polyesters containing hydroxyl groups and diisocyanates or triisocyanates are used as adhesion promoters to improve the bonding of textile fibers and PVC mixes. The bonding of rubber to fabrics can be greatly improved by additives containing resorcinol, substances that liberate formaldehyde, and active silica [571, 572]. The addition of cobalt salts has been found effective for the vulcanization of natural rubber and butadiene-styrene elastomers on zinc-plated metal surfaces. This is true in particular of the naphthenates and 2-ethylhexanoates, which are also used to accelerate the drying of paints based on drying oils. The IR spectra, which are not reproduced here, are similar to those of the other metal soaps of branched and cyclic aliphatic fatty acids.

Cobalt naphthenate gives 2 broad strong bands with maxima at 1580 and 1425 cm^{-1} (6.33 and 7.02 μm) and weak bands at 1320 cm^{-1} (7.57 μm), 970 cm^{-1} (10.3 μm), and 730 cm^{-1} (13.7 μm).

2-Ethylhexanoate also has strong bands in roughly the same positions, but weaker or medium-strong bands are also present at 1320 cm^{-1} (7.57 μm), 1110 cm^{-1} (9.9 μm) and about 800 cm^{-1} (12.5 μm).

10.5 Peptizers and other Rubber Auxiliaries

To incorporate additives into raw rubber, it is necessary to masticate the tough material. The mastication is carried out by mechanical working at high temperatures, and leads to plasticization through partial oxidative degradation of the macromolecules. Whereas this can be achieved without addi-

tional chemical aids or with only small quantities (0.1—0.5 %) in the case of natural rubber, synthetic rubbers usually require the addition of larger quantities of masticating aids (1—3 %). Some of the compounds commonly used as accelerators, such as 2-mercaptobenzothiazole, are suitable for this purpose.

Other aromatic compounds containing sulfur, such as 2-thionaphthol, xylylmercaptans and their zinc salts, o,o'-dibenzamidodiphenyl disulfide, and the zinc salt of o-benzamidothiophenol, have been offered as peptizers. Chlorinated thiophenols, such as pentachlorothiophenol and its zinc salt, have a much stronger action than unsubstituted thiophenols, and are therefore frequently used.

A number of reactions for the chemical identification of peptizers have been described by MIKSCH and PRÖLSS [557].

Di-o-benzamidophenyl disulfide (Pepton 22) can be reduced to thiophenol with potassium amalgam or magnesium in methanol or with lithium aluminum hydride in ether, and can then be detected with chloranil. This is also possible in the acetone extract from vulcanized products. However, it should be noted that other aromatic compounds containing sulfur are also converted into thiophenol during the reduction.

The zinc salt of pentachlorothiophenol (Renacit IV) is smoothly reduced with potassium amalgam to thiophenol, which gives a brown-violet color with chloranil. The detection is also possible in the acetone extract. However, only small quantities can be extracted from vulcanized products containing ZnO.

During the reduction of Renacit V, MIKSCH and PRÖLSS observed decomposition and darkening, which they attributed to the activators that were present in addition to pentachlorothiophenol. No chemical or chromatographic detection was possible in the extract from vulcanized mixes.

Pentachlorothiophenol (Sadtler spectrum no. 20 250) and its zinc salt spectrum no. 6531) have almost identical spectra with few bands ,both having three strong bands at 1333, 1307, and 684 cm^{-1} (7.5, 7.65, and 14.6 μm). One of the weak bands, the S-H stretching vibration at 2590 cm^{-1} (3.86 μm) is characteristic of pentachlorothiophenol.

In addition to pentachlorothiophenol, Renacit V (spectrum no. 6530) contains a considerable quantity of hydroquinone and some dibutyl phthalate. Hydroquinone can be removed with water. The residue gives the spectrum of pentachlorothiophenol with weak bands due to the phthalic ester. Pentachlorothiophenol can be very satisfactorily identified by mass spectroscopy, both by itself and in vucanized mixes. The

Table 10.7: Silane adhesion promoters

Dec. no.	IR sp. No.	Trade name	Composition
3.			
3.1	6522	Silicon Finish GF 81	1,3,5-Trimethyl-1,3,5-tris-(2,3-epoxypropoxypropyl)-trisiloxane
3.2	6523	Silicon Finish VP 1428	Trimethoxy-(3-chlorpropyl)silane
3.3	6524	Silicon Finish GF 91	Trimethoxy-[3(2'-aminoethylamino)propyl]silane
3.4	6525	Silicon Finish GF 90	Methyldi-(2'-aminoethoxy)-[3-(2''-aminoethoxy)propyl]silane
3.5	6526	Silicon Finish VP 1451	Trimethoxy-[3-(di-2'-hydroxyethylamino)propyl]silane
3.6	6527	Silicon Finish GF 56	Triethoxyvinylsilane
3.7	6528	Silicon Finish GF 66	Trialkoxy-[3-(methacryloyloxy)propyl]silane
3.8	6529	Silicon Finish GF 62	Vinyltriacetoxysilane

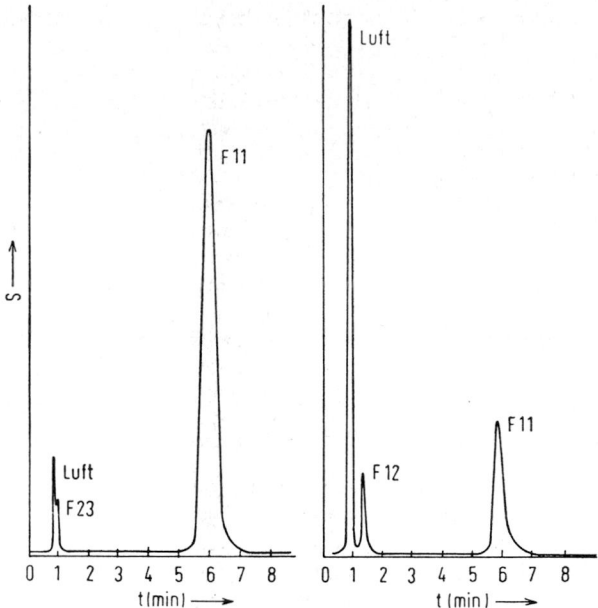

Fig. 10.2: Gas-chromatographic analysis of the pore gas of poly-
urethane foam from refrigerators.
Sample A and B from different sources. Samples taken
two years after manufacture of the foam.
Separation conditions: 20 °C, 58 ml of He/min, thermal
conductivity detector
Separating column: 2 m long, inside diameter 4 mm
Stat. phase: 15 % ethylene glycol polysebacate with n-
hexyl endgroups on kieselgur
F11: $CFCl_3$
F12: CF_2Cl_2
F23: CHF_3

combinations of peaks in the region of mass numbers M^+
and $(M-1)^+$ at 280—288 MU, with a maximum at 282 MU,
and $(M-Cl)^+$, $(M-Cl-1)^+$, $(M-2Cl)^+$, and $(M-2Cl-1)^+$, with
maxima at 247 and 212 MU, correspond to the isomer
distributions typical of 5, 4, and 3 Cl atoms (Fig. 10.2). However, it should be noted that the $(X-1)^+$ peaks have superimposed on them the ^{13}C isotope fragments of the X^+
fragments that are nominally 2 mass units lower. Thus the
signal at 283 MU is somewhat stronger than that at 281 MU,
since the former is due not only to 284-1 but also to the
^{13}C isotope of 282 MU.

10.6 Antiskinning Agents

Inhibitors of various kinds are added to paints to prevent
skin formation as a result of oxidation during storage. These
inhibitors include hydroquinone, pyrocatechol, guaiacol and
other phenols, benzoic acid, dipentene, glycols, o-dichloro-
benzene, and amines. Growing interest has been shown in ket-
oximes and aldoximes [560, 561].

A function similar to that of the antiskinning agents is
served by the inhibitors added to unsaturated polyester resins
to prevent premature gelling during storage. Suitable agents
again include hydroquinone, as well as some hydroquinone
derivatives, such as the monomethyl ether, mono-t-butyl-
hydroquinone, and 2,5-di-t-butylhydroquinone, and also p-
benzoquinone, 2,5-diphenylbenzoquinone, and toluquinone,
which are preferably added in quantities of 0.01—0.1 %
[562]. Inhibitors of this type are also commonly used in
other polymerizable systems (e. g. cyanoacrylate adhesives).

Finally, reference should be made to the addition of hydroquinone to peptizers, again to provide protection against
oxidative polymerization.

No systematic studies have been carried out on the identification of antiskinning agents and inhibitors in paints and
resins. However, the phenol derivatives can be identified in
the same way as the phenolic antioxidants by thin layer and
gas chromatography and by IR, UV, and mass spectroscopy.
Of the additives mentioned, IR spectra are given for hydroquinone (spectrum no. 6533), methyl ethyl ketoxime (spectrum
no. 6534), butyraldoxime (spectrum no. 6535), and o-dichlo-
robenzene (spectrum no. 6626) IR spectra of other
inhibitors are to be found in the commercial collections.
Examples are the following spectra of the Sadtler collection:
(P = prism spectrum, G = grating spectrum)

Pyrocatechol P 268, guaiacol G 8013, 2,5-di-t-butylhydro-
quinone G 15071, p-benzoquinone G 21019, 2,5-diphenyl-p-
benzoquinone P 8194, p-toluquinone G 18529, benzoic acid
G 162.

11 Solvents

11.1 Survey and Classification

Organic solvents are extensively used in the production,
processing, and application of plastics. However, the analysis of the solvent is of interest not only in connection with
the technical properties of the solvents and of the solvent-
polymer systems, but also in relation to the assessment of
the toxicity of solvent residues in the polymer.

Various criteria are commonly used for the classification of
solvents, e. g. the field of applications, the physical properties (particularly the boiling range), and chemical structure.

Table 11.1: Classification of solvents and their IR spectrum
numbers

	IR spectrum no.
1. Hydrocarbons	6600–6628
1.1 Aliphatic hydrocarbons	6600–6605
1.2 Aromatic hydrocarbons	6606–6617
1.3 Halogenated hydrocarbons	6618–6628
2. Alcohols	6629–6668
2.1 Monoalcohols	6629–6647
2.2 Dialcohols and trialcohols	6648–6655
2.3 Ester alcohols, keto alcohols, halogenated alcohols	6656–6659
2.4 Ether alcohols	6660 6668
3. Esters	6669–6683
3.1 Simple esters	6669–6679
3.2 Ether esters	6680–6683
4. Ketones	6684–6693
4.1 Simple ketones	6694–6692
4.2 Ether ketones	6693
5. Ethers	6694–6697
6. Solvents containing S and N	6698–6706
6.1 Solvents containing sulfur	6698–6700
6.2 Solvents containing nitrogen	6701–6706
7. Mixtures	6707–6708

Table 11.2: Solvents, spectrum numbers, and GC data; 1.1. Aliphatic hydrocarbons, 1.2. Aromatic hydrocarbons, 1.3. Chlorinated hydrocarbons

Dec. no.	IR sp. no.	Solvent	Apiezon grease L		Silicone oil DC 200	DC 401	OV-17	Emulphor O	DEGS	Di(ethylhexyl) sebacate	Polyglycol 1500	Carbowax 1540	Silicone oil DC 200		
		Column / Temp. / Ref.	130° A	150° B	150° A	150° B	150° D	130° A	150° B	100° A	150° A	80° E	50° C	100° C	150° C
1.		**Hydrocarbons**													
1.1.		**Aliphatic hydrocarbons**													
1.1.1	6600	n-Pentane	500	500	500	500	500	500	500	500	500	500	500	500	500
1.1.2	6601	n-Octane	800	800	800	800	800	800	800	800	800	800	800	800	800
1.1.3	6602	Isooctane (2.2.4-trimethylpentane)	694		689			693		690	659		692	698	
1.1.4	6603	Cyclohexane	700		655			734		675	750		662	678	
1.1.5	6604	Methylcyclohexane	760		726			788		739	794		723	738	751
1.1.6	6605	Decalin, trans	1125					1165						1063	1093
		Decalin, cis						1219						1102	1137
1.2.		**Aromatic hydrocarbons**													
1.2.1	6606	Benzene	691	704	683	658	800	862	1138	717	909		656	667	673
1.2.2	6607	Toluene	798	811	753	769	903	963	1234	820	997		759	770	782
1.2.3	6608	o-Xylene	930	946	849	895		1090	1389	944	1092		881	894	911
1.2.4	6609	m-Xylene	904	922	827	874	1006	1056	1330	921	1059		861	870	883
1.2.5	6610	p-Xylene	904	922	831	874		1051	1330	921	1056		860	871	883
1.2.6	6611	Ethylbenzene	893		822			1053		907	1051		851	862	877
1.2.7	6612	Mesitylene													979
1.2.8	6613	Pseudocumene												992	1007
1.2.9	6614	Cumene	947	957	915	950		1104	1360	962				923	938
1.2.10	6615	p-Cymene	1051					1199						1021	1034
1.2.11	6616	Hydrindene												1033	1056
1.2.12	6617	Tetralin												1150	1181
1.3.		**Chlorinated hydrocarbons**													
1.3.1	6618	Methylene chloride	511	585	535	600	717	784	990	603	732		526	525	
1.3.2	6619	Chloroform	622	625	609	630	761	879	1060	702	944		609	611	
1.3.3	6620	Carbon tetrachloride	691	665	683	675	640	806	1145	695	859		659	672	
1.3.4	6621	1,2-Dichloroethane			631					728	1006		636	641	
1.3.5	6622	1,1,1-Trichloroethane											643	642	
1.3.6	6623	Trichloroethylene		860	713	810			1195	750	939		693	700	698
1.3.7	6624	Tetrachloroethylene		940	794	920			1708	844	976		802	816	832
1.3.8	6625	Chlorobenzene	885	895	809	880		1099	1445	913	1109		835	848	865
1.3.9	6626	o-Dichlorobenzene	1076	1072	960	1010		1126	1720		1288			1055	
1.3.10	6627	p-Dichlorobenzene						1288						1007	1029
1.3.11	6628	1,2,2-Trifluoro-1,1,2-trichloroethane											538	525	

Ref. see p. 150

Table 11.3: Solvents; IR-spectra numbers and GC-data of alcohols

Dec. no.	IR sp. no.	Solvent	Apiezon grease L 130° A	Apiezon grease L 150° B	Silicone oil DC 200 150° A	Silicone oil DC 401 150° B	OV-17 150° D	Emulphor O 130° A	DEGS 150° B	Di(ethylhexyl) sebacate 100° A	Polyglycol 1500 150° A	Carbowax 1540 80° E	Silicon oil DC 200 50° C	Silicon oil DC 200 100° C	Silicon oil DC 200 150° C
2.		Alcohols													
2.1.		Simple alcohols													
2.1.1	6629	Methanol	292	272	343	370		716	1070		891	907			
2.1.2	6630	Ethanol	372	374	411	462		761	1073		903	940			
2.1.3	6631	n-Propanol	499	468 (f)	535	535	640	865	1185	551	986	1040			
2.1.4	6632	Isopropanol	428	501 (f)	494	456		766	1058	664	894	932			
2.1.5	6633	n-Butanol	612	613	645	650	746	973	1277	596	1036	1144			
2.1.6	6634	Isobutanol	575	608		580		929	1220	770		1090			
2.1.7	6635	sec-Butanol	553		601			871		702	946				
2.1.8	6636	tert-Butanol	472		527					628	862	904			
2.1.9	6637	n-Amyl alcohol	721	700	739	715	854	1087	1380	872	1125				
2.1.10	6638	2-Pentanol										1120			
2.1.11	6639	2-Methylbutan-2-ol	587 (100 °C)		629					736	950		634	632	
2.1.12	6640	n-Hexanol	323		838		964	1191			1188				
2.1.13	6641	2-Hexanol													
2.1.14	6642	3-Hexanol											802	868	793
2.1.15	6643	n-Octanol	1026	1003	1007		1173	1397	1623		1328			1064	1025
2.1.16	6644	2-Ethylhexanol												1023	
2.1.17	6645	Cyclohexanol	880		863			1242		948	1203				
2.1.18	6646	3,3,5-Trimethylcyclohexanol													
2.1.19	6647	Benzyl alcohol	1010					1572							1068
2.2.		Dialcohols and trialcohols													
2.2.1	6648	Glycol			626*)						1441		615		
2.2.2	6649	1,3-Propanediol			772*)						1559				
2.2.3	6650	1,2-Propanediol			772*)						1558				
2.2.4	6651	1,4-Butanediol			889*)										
2.2.5	6652	1,3-Butanediol													
2.2.6	6653	Diethylene glycol													1014

*) at 213 °C

Table 11.3 (continued)

Dec. no.	IR sp. no.	Solvent	Column Temp. Ref./Lit.	Apiezon grease L 130° A	150° B	Silicone oil DC 200 150° A	DC 401 150° B	OV-17 150° D	Emul-phor O 130° A	DEGS 150° B	Di(ethyl-hexyl) sebacate 100° A	Poly-glycol 1500 150° A	Carbo-wax 1540 E 80°	Silicon oil DC 200 50° C	100° C	150° C
2.2.7	6654	Glyceron				970										
2.2.8	6655	Trimethylpropane														
2.3.		Ester alcohols, keto alcohols, Halogenated alcohols														881
2.3.1	6656	Ethylene glycol monoacetate														
2.3.2	6657	Butyl glycolate														
2.3.3	6658	Diacetone, alcohol														
2.3.4	6659	2-Chloroethanol						820							792	
2.4.		Ether alcohols														
2.4.1	6660	Ethylene glycol monomethyl ether[1]		626		646				1427						
2.4.2	6661	Ethylene glycol monoethyl ether[2]		702	703	702				1440	802	1129				
2.4.3	6662	Ethylene glycol monoisopropyl ether												767	781	
2.4.4	6663	Ethylene glycol monobutyl ether[12]		888		908				1625						
2.4.5	6664	Diethylene glycol monomethyl ether[3]		904		908				1930					976,5	
2.4.6	6665	Diethylene glycol monoethyl ether[4]														
2.4.7	6666	Diethylene glycol monobutyl ether[5]		1154		1174				2110						
2.4.8	6667	Tetrahydrofurfuryl alcohol														
2.4.9	6668	4-Methyl-4 methoxy-pentanole-2														

1) Methyl Cellosolve   2) Cellosolve   3) Methyl Carbitol   4) Carbitol   5) Butyl Carbitol   12) Butyl Cellosolve

Ref. see p. 150

Table 11.4: Solvents, IR spectra no. and GC data; 3. Esters, 4. Ketones, 5. Ethers, 6. Solvents with N and S

Dec. no.	IR sp. no.	Solvent	Apiezon grease L 130° A	Apiezon grease L 150° B	Silicone oil DC 200 150° A	Silicone oil DC 401 150° B	OV-17 150° D	Emulphor O 130° A	DEGS 150° B	Di(ethylhexyl) sebacate 100° A	Polyglycol 1500 150° A	Carbowax 1540 80° E	Silicon oil DC 200 50° C	Silicon oil DC 200 100° C	Silicon oil DC 200 150° C
3.		**Esters**													
3.1.		**Simples esters**													
3.1.1	6669	Methylacetate	468		509			717		555	832	828		513	
3.1.2	6670	Ethylacetate	547	540	603	554		779	1065	637	878	886	598	592	
3.1.3	6671	n-Propylacetate	648	640	675	660		874	1065	733	934		698	693	
3.1.4	6672	n-Butylacetate	755	752	772	769		981	1276	836	1004	1076		794	
3.1.5	6673	i-Butylacetate	713	710	738	734		921	1235	788	961	1013	759	754	
3.1.6	6674	sec-Butylacetate	692					895					745		
3.1.7	6675	tert-Butylacetate	636					820					670		
3.1.8	6676	i-Amylacetate													860
3.1.9	6677	Cyclohexanol acetate						1028						1024	
3.1.10	6678	Diethyl carbonate											766		754
3.1.11	6679	Butyrolactone		876		894			1627						909
3.2.		**Ether ester**													
3.2.1	6680	Ethylene glycol mono-methyl ether acetate[6]		757		773			1520				817	806	801
3.2.2	6681	Ethylene glycol mono-ethyl ether acetate[7]		822	900	852			1695					874	870
3.2.3	6682	3-Methoxybutyl acetate[8]													951
3.2.4	6683	Diethylene glycol mono-ethyl ether acetate[10]		1094		1147			2012					1150	1154
4.		**Ketones**													
4.1.		**Simple ketones**													
4.1.1	6684	Acetone	450	472	489	466		705	1053	553	855	823	467		
4.1.2	6685	Methyl ethyl ketone	550	553	582	560		794	1127	648	911	906	582		
4.1.3	6686	Diethyl ketone	631		667			884		739	963		680	680	
4.1.4	6687	Methyl isobutyl ketone	706	692		714		923	1217	790			725	728	

6) Methyl Cellosolve Acetate   7) Cellosolve Acetate   8) Butoxyl   10) Carbitol Acetate

Ref. see p. 150

Table 11.4 (continued)

Dec. no.	IR sp. no.	Solvent	Apiezon grease L 130° A	Apiezon grease L 150° B	Silicone oil DC 200 150° A	Silicone oil DC 401 150° B	OV-17 150° D	Emulphor O 130° A	DEGS 150° B	Di(ethylhexyl) sebacate 100° A	Polyglycol 150° A	Carbowax 1540 80° E	Silicone oil DC 200 50° C	Silicone oil DC 200 100° C	Silicone oil DC 200 150° C
4.1.5	6688	Diisobutyl ketone		945				1108	1430					959	964
4.1.6	6689	Cyclohexanone	886	898	853	894		1171	1757	987	1230				
4.1.7	6690	3,3,5-Trimethylcyclohexanone		1124										1052	1070
4.1.8	6691	Isophorone				1121			2110						1131
4.1.9	6692	Acetophenone	1067					1445						1028	1051
4.2.		Ether ketones													
4.2.1	6693	Diacetone alcohol methyl ether [11]		880		910			1530					500	901
5.		Ethers													
5.1.	6694	Diethyl ether	484		504			578		511	642		895	494	
5.2.	6695	Diisopropyl ether	568		600			630		605	685		598	595	
5.3.	6696	Tetrahydrofuran	631	650		630		800	1070	755		873	624	630	
5.4.	6697	Dioxan			670						1025	1066	693	698	
6.		Solvents containing S and N													
6.1.		Solvents containing S													
6.1.1	6698	Dimethyl sulfoxide													
6.1.2	6699	Sulfolan													
6.1.3	6700	Carbon disulfide		825	849	840			2000						
6.2.		Solvents containing N													
6.2.1	6701	Nitromethane	487					967							
6.2.2	6702	Nitrobenzene	1088					1499	1270		1450		546	549	
6.2.3	6703	Acetonitrile	447	560	500			853		585	976	1011		471	
6.2.4	6704	Morpholine												824	837
6.2.5	6705	Dimethylformamide							1795		1261		ca. 800	794	776
6.2.6	6706	Dimethylacetamide	745		790								ca. 800	892	878
7.		Solvent mixtures													
7.1.	6707														
7.2.	6708														

Ref./Lit.: A: ASTM Gas Chromatographic Data Compilation, (Philadelphia 1967)
Selected data, some values are averages.
B: D. G. Anderson, J. Paint Technol. **40** (1968), 549 . . . 557.
C: Own data
D: R. Hatch, J. Gas Chromatog. **6** (1968), 611
E: J. N. Caroff, Y. Bohurel, J. Veron, J. Gas Chromatog. **4** (1966), 234.

11) Pentoxone

The only classification that is of interest for analytical purposes is that based on chemical aspects. We have carried out such a classification, as shown in Table 11.1.

The further subdivision is shown in Tables 11.2 to 11.4, which also give the IR spectrum numbers and the GC data of solvents.

The properties and applications of the various solvents are discussed in detail in the special literature [230, 231, 581—587]. The book by RIDDICK and BUNGER [587], in particular, contains numerous data and references to literature in which further information e. g. on the spectra of the solvent in question can be found. Some of the books mentioned earlier also contain tables showing the solubilities of various polymers in solvents (see Vol. 2). Other important properties that affect their use, such as evaporation rate and mixing properties, are also discussed.

There are a number of earlier monographs [588—591] on solvent analysis, which deal mainly with the determination of physical data (density, refractive index, vapor pressure, boiling behavior, evaporation number, viscosity, etc.) and with chemical group reactions (hydrolysis value, acetylation value, bromine value, sulfonation value, etc.). A series of chemical detection reactions (color reactions, melting points of derivatives) are also described.

The physical methods of investigation are largely standardized (DIN, ASTM, etc.), as is the determination of chemical group characteristics.

The importance of qualitative detection reactions has been greatly diminished by the more reliable spectroscopic and chromatographic methods. They are therefore discussed only briefly below. The purity tests for solvents laid down in various standards and specifications (e. g. DAB) are not discussed.

11.2 Chemical Detection of Solvents

Clues as to the nature of a solvent or the principal components of a solvent mixture are obtainable from odor, water-solubility, density, refractive index, and boiling behavior. Some numerical values are given in Table 11.5.
Before any chemical detection reactions are carried out, it is advisable to separate water-soluble components by extrac-

tion and examine the water-soluble and the water-insoluble components separately.

Chemical reactions for the detection of alcohols, glycols, and ketones are described in Volume 2. Reference should also be made to the reaction of alcohols with vanillin/sulfuric acid (0.5 g of vanillin in 100 ml of concentrated sulfuric acid). 3—4 drops of the solvent sample are added to 2 ml of this solution, and water is then added dropwise (caution). The following colors are observed:

	Color	
	after addition of the alcohol	after dropwise addition of water
Methyl alcohol	yellow	gradually turns green
Ethyl alcohol	yellow-green, blue-green	gradually fades
n-Propyl alcohol	yellow	yellow-red, purple-red
Isopropyl alcohol	yellow	blue-violet
Butyl alcohol	yellow	yellow-red, red
Isobutyl alcohol	yellow-red	red-violet
t-Butyl alcohol	orange-red	deep red, violet
Isoamyl alcohol	yellow-red	red-violet
Amyl alcohol	orange-red	purple-red

Aromatic hydrocarbons give color reactions with antimony pentachloride in carbon tetrachloride. Antimony pentachloride (approx. 30 % solution in CCl_4) is added dropwise to an approx. 5—10 % solution of the aromatic compound in carbon tetrachloride.

The following colors are observed:

	initially	later
Pure benzene	yellow, yellow-red	yellow-green, possibly light colored precipitate
Technical benzene	yellow, green	dark precipitate
Toluene	light red	red precipitate
Xylene	red	deep red precipitate
Mesitylene	yellow, deep red	deep red precipitate
Naphthalene	yellow-brown, violet	deep lilac precipitate

Table 11.5: Chemical reactions for the detection of gas-chromatographically separated substances with various functional groups, after MERRIT [601]

Class of substances	Reagent	Color for positive reaction	Detection limit (μg)	Checked for
Unsaturated aliphatic compounds	$HCHO + H_2SO_4$	wine red	40	$C_2...C_8$
Aromatic compounds	$HCHO + H_2SO_4$	wine red	20	$C_6...C_{10}$
Alkyl halides	$AgNO_3$ + alcohol	white, ppt.	20	$C_1...C_5$
Alcohols	$K_2Cr_2O_7 + HNO_3$	gray-blue	20	$C_1...C_8$
	Cerium nitrate soln.	yellow, yellow-red	100	$C_1...C_8$
Aldehydes	2,4-DNP	yellow, ppt.	20	$C_1...C_6$
	Schiff reagent	pink	50	$C_1...C_6$
Ketones	2,4-DNP	yellow, ppt.	20	$C_1...C_5$ (methyl ketones)
Esters	Fe hydroxamate	red	40	$C_3...C_8$ (acetates)
Amines	Hinsberg reagent	orange	100	$C_1...C_4$
	$Na[Fe(CN)_5NO]$	red	50	$C_1...C_4$
		blue		diethyl and diamyl
Nitriles	Fe hydroxamate P	red	40	$C_2...C_5$

Mixture of aromatic compounds		
from benzine	brown	dark brown precipitate
Styrene	brown precipitate	

When methyl ketones are mixed with a drop of 5 % sodium nitroprusside solution and a drop of 30 % sodium hydroxide solution, they give a pale color, which becomes stronger on addition of 1—2 drops of glacial acetic acid.
The following colors appear:

Acetone	pink
Methyl ethyl ketone	pink
Methylheptanone	brown-violet
Acetylacetone	purple-red
Acetophenone	blue

When aqueous solutions of methyl ketones are heated (water bath) with a drop of o-nitrobenzaldehyde solution in 2N sodium hydroxide solution and the cooled solution then extracted with chloroform, a blue color is found in the chloroform layer. Red colors may also appear in the presence of alcohol.

Esters are identified by hydrolysis followed by identification of the carboxylic acids.

Chlorinated hydrocarbons, when present in large quantities, increase the density of a solvent. Various color reactions have been described by WEBER [232, 588]. Heating with a 2 % solution of α-naphthol in cyclohexanol gives a yellow-brown color; when the cooled solution is mixed with an equal quantity of 85 % sulfuric acid, the color changes to blue if chloroform or carbon tetrachloride is present, and to green-blue if methylene chloride, trichloroethylene, or tetrachloroethylene is present.

For the determination of olefinic and aromatic hydrocarbons by extraction with sulfuric acid of various concentrations and for the calculation of the olefins and aromatic hydrocarbons from the bromine number and the sulfonation number, the reader must be referred to the literature [231, 319].

11.3 Gas Chromatography of Solvents

Gas chromatography is the most elegant method available at present for the analysis of solvent mixtures. Though the method is widely used, there are practically no general publications on solvent analysis. The GC literature [103—115] contains numerous references to the separation of substances and mixtures of substances that are used as solvents. Examples of some special applications in the paint and plastics fields can be found in further publications [116—118, 592—597].
Tables 11.2—11.4 contain retention data from the literature and from our own measurements. The scatter ranges of the retention indices are probably about ± 10 units, though greater deviations are possible in some cases. In one collection of data for solvents, scatter ranges of up to ± 30 IR units are given [595].

Since the retention index on one stationary phase does not allow the conclusive identification of the particular component in the case of an unknown mixture, but would usually be equally applicable to a number of substances, the behavior on two or more stationary phases with different polarities is frequently used for identification. The assignment is much easier if information is available about the composition (odor, IR spectrum), in which case the assignment is often possible from a single chromatogram.

Simple preliminary separations by distillation or by extraction of the water-soluble components and separate GC analysis of the water-soluble and of the insoluble components also facilitate the qualitative assignment (see Fig. 11.1). The high sensitivity of the flame ionization detector for solvents and its insensitivity to water allows the direct analysis of an aqueous extract of a solvent with 10–100 times as much water. The direct identification of individual components of gas-chromatographically separated solvents by combination of the gas chromatograph with a mass spectrometer is the simplest and most reliable identification method (see Section 1.8). The IR spectroscopic identification of solvent vapors after GC separation has also been described (see section 1.6). It is also possible to collect GC fractions on activated charcoal, followed by IR analysis and desorption [608].

Explanatory notes to table 11.5

	ppt. = precipitate
$HCHO + H_2SO_4$:	1 drop of 37 % formaldehyde solution + 10 drops of conc. H_2SO_4
$AgNO_3$ + alcohol:	2 % alcoholic $AgNO_3$ solution
$K_2Cr_2O_7 + HNO_3$:	1 drop of 1 % $K_2Cr_2O_7$ solution + 10 drops of 7.5 N HNO_3
Cerium nitrate:	1 drop of 1 % cerium nitrate solution + 10 drops of 7.5 N HNO_3
2,4-DNP:	Dissolve 0.2 g of 2,4-dinitrophenylhydrazine in 1.5 ml of H_2SO_4, add solution to 15 ml of ethanol, and make up to 50 ml with water.
Schiff reagent:	0.5 g of fuchsin + 9 g of sodium bisulfite in 500 ml of H_2O + 10 ml of HCl
Fe hydroxamate:	10 drops of 1 N $NH_2OH \cdot HCl$ in methanol + 3—5 drops of 2 N alcoholic KOH until a blue color appears. After passage of sample, add 5—7 drops of 2 N HCl to decolorize the solution. Then add 1—2 drops of 10 % FeCl solution. Red color indicates positive reaction
Fe hydroxamate P:	10 drops of N $NH_2OH \cdot HCl$ in propylene glycol + 2 drops of 2 N KOH in propylene glycol. After passage of sample, heat to boiling, cool, and add 1—2 drops of 10 % $FeCl_3$ solution to the clear, colorless solution. Red color indicates positive reaction
Hinsberg reagent:	5 drops of pyridine + 1 drop of 5 % NaOH. After passage of effluent add 1—2 drops of benzenesulfonyl chloride. Yellow for primary and secondary and pink and red for tertiary aliphatic amines
$Na[Fe(CN)_5NO]$:	10 drops of H_2O + 2 drops of acetone + 1 drop of 1 % sodium nitroprusside solution. Primary amines give red color. After addition of 1—2 drops of acetaldehyde solution, secondary amines give blue color. If acetone is added, the blue color is obtained directly.

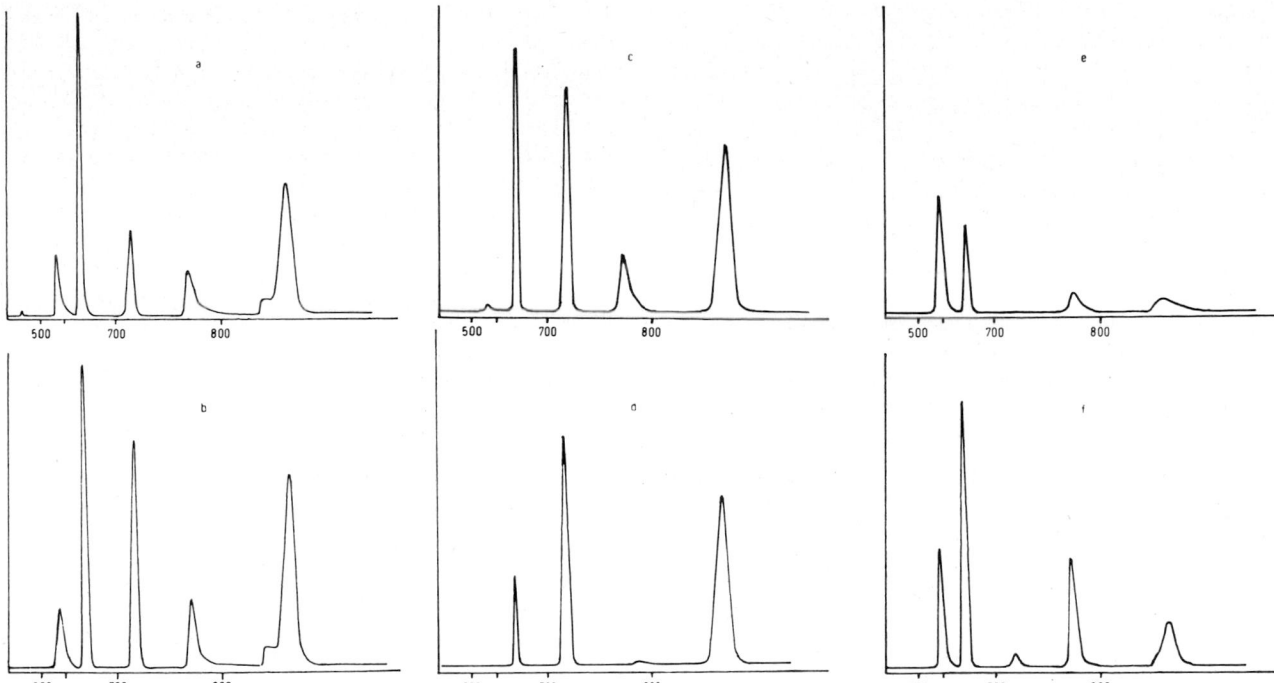

Fig. 11.1: GC analysis of a solvent mixture

Column: Sebacic acid polyester, 2 m, 100 °C.
Thermal conductivity detector (TCD) and flame ionisation detector (FID)

The solvent was extracted with same volume of water (I) and a second sample with the 10 fold volume of water (II). The organic and aqueous layers were separately chromatographed.

a: Original solvent mixture (TCD)
b: Original solvent mixture (FID)
c: Organic layer after I (FID)
d: Organic layer after II (FID)
e: Aqueous layer after I (FID)
f: Aqueous layer after II (FID)

The different signals of TCD and FID in GC of the original mixture the behavior in separation by extraction (water solubility) and the retention indices (RI) indicate the following assignment.

Peak 1 (RI 570): Ethanol
2 (RI 640): Ethylacetate
3 (RI 722): Benzene
4 (RI 770): Butanol
5 (RI 820): Ethylene glycol monoethyl ether
6 (RI 840): Butylacetate

The chemical detection of gas-chromatographically separated components containing functional groups has been described by WALSH and MERRIT [600, 601]. The mixture of carrier gas and unknown substance emerging from the gas chromatograph is led into tubes containing a few drops of reagent solution. Color reactions show the presence of certain functional groups. If the gas stream is divided into several secondary streams and simultaneously passed through tubes containing different reagents and arranged in parallel, it can
be tested simultaneously for several functional groups. The reactions tested by the authors mentioned are listed in Table 11.5.

The detection limits can be improved if the reactants are diluted as little as possible. This can be achieved e. g. by applying the reagent to a support material such as silica gel. This procedure is used in the gas detection tubes commonly used for the detection of gases and vapors [599], detection limits in the μg range being obtained. Such tubes can also be used for the identification of individual components.

An elegant method for identification with the aid of chemical detection reactions was proposed by CASU and CAVALLOTI [602]. These authors transported a thin layer plate impregnated with reagent directly along the gas outlet of the gas chromatograph at a constant rate, and on elution of a reactive component, they obtained a spot. In this method, if the recording chart speed and the transport speed of the plate are equal, direct assignment of the gas chromatogram and the position of the reaction spot is possible. If two different detection reagents are arranged immediately next to each other in strips and the GC outlet directed at the separation line, two specific detections can be carried out simultaneously. This method can be used even if the color reaction does not occur immediately but requires subsequent chemical or thermal treatment. In such cases the techniques commonly used in thin layer chromatography can be applied.

Various authors have described the direct introduction of paint samples into gas chromatographs. The solvent is evaporated in a preliminary heated column, while the binder and the pigments remain behind as residue. A number of equipment manufacturers offer accessories for this purpose. We have carried out various investigations by this method, and found that it presents practical advantages only in special cases, since the separating efficiency usually suffers (the evaporation is not as fast as when the pure solvent is used), interference occasionally arises from decomposition products of the binder, and additional work is involved in cleaning syringes and the preliminary column. Since the separation of the solvent from the binder is desirable in any case for other investigations, such as IR spectroscopy, we find it preferable to investigate the solvent after separation by distillation. If direct introduction of the paint is chosen to save time, it is advisable to dilute the sample with a large quantity of a solvent that does not interfere with the separation.

Aqueous paint systems, which usually have only a low solid content (5—20 %), have recently attracted interest. The solvent contains 60—98 % of water, to which mainly glycol ethers and lower alcohols are added as solubilizing agents. The water-insensitive flame ionization detector is very well suited for the GC analysis of mixtures with such high water contents [597].

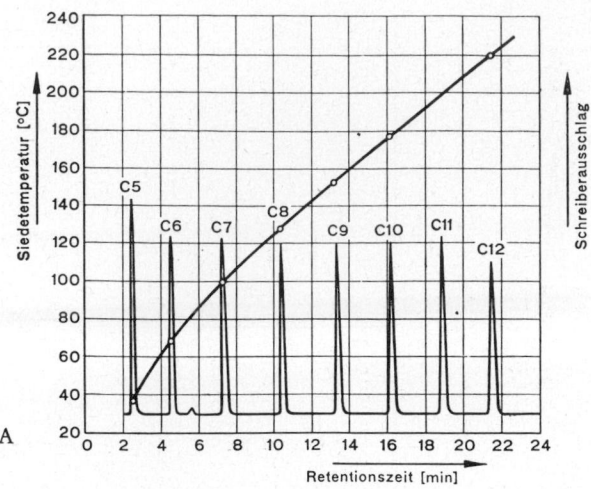

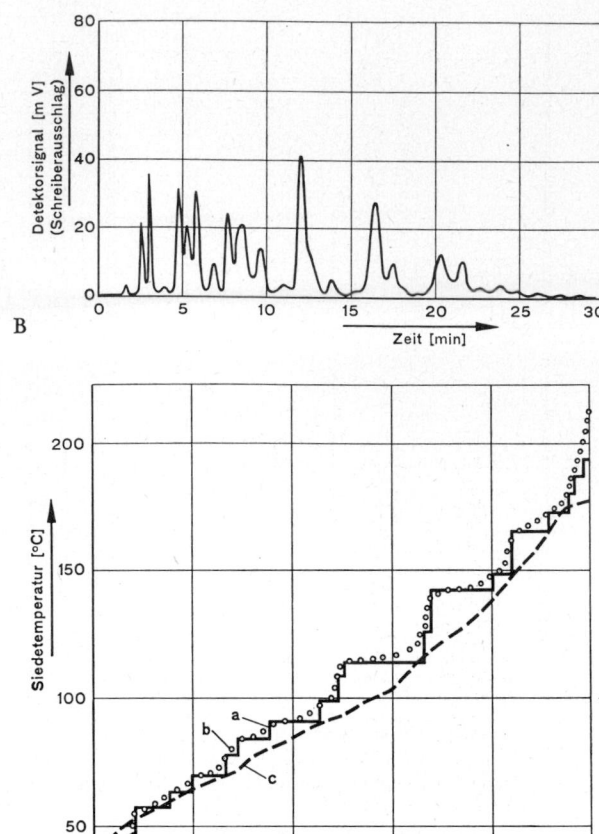

Fig. 11.2: Gas-chromatographic boiling analysis

A: Calibration chromatogram for C_5—C_{12} n-paraffins with the corresponding boiling point — retention time curve (GC column: silicone oil on kieselgur, 2 m long, inside diameter 5 mm, start temp. 50 °C, final temp. 200 °C, heating rate 5 °C/min, carrier gas N_2, 60 ml/min, FID)
Ordinate: left Boiling point [°C]   right: Pen deflection
Abscissa Retention time [min]

B: Chromatogram of a gasoline (GC data as above)
Ordinate: Detector signal [mV] (pen deflection)
Abscissa: Time [min]

C: Boiling curves (a, b, obtained from the chromatogram in comparison with the boiling curve (c) obtained by single-stage standard distillation
a: Stepped curve from the peak areas
b: From the area integrals obtained at 10s intervals
Ordinate: Boiling point [°C]
Abscissa: Fraction distilled over [wt.%]

Brief mention should be made of the gas-chromatographic boiling analysis of solvents, particularly of hydrocarbon mixtures [603, 604]. In this method, use is made of the fact that gas-chromatographic separation on apolar liquid phases takes place to a first approximation according to the boiling point of the substance in question. An almost linear relation exists between the boiling point and the retention index for hydrocarbons. It is thus possible to obtain information from a chromatogram about the boiling points of the individual components and to construct a boiling curve for the mixture. Depending on the evaluation method used, this would correspond to a simple boiling curve or to the boiling curve obtained on a high-efficiency distillation column (see Fig. 11.2).

11.4 IR Spectroscopy of Solvents

The IR spectroscopic identification of solvents and simple solvent mixtures can usually be carried out rapidly for components present in concentrations of more than 10 %, since the predominantly used lower members of the various homologous series still exhibit characteristic differences in their IR spectra. Complicated mixtures may be separated into several fractions by distillation or by extraction of the water-soluble components. The differences in the spectra of the various fractions in comparison with the spectrum of the starting mixture enables one to recognize the bands due to the individual components, even though complete separation has not been achieved.

There is no need to discuss the spectra of solvents individually, since the bands can be assigned with the aid of correlation tables in Vol. 2

or in the literature [131, 135, 136, 140, 141, 146]. Rapid evaluation of a solvent spectrum is possible with aid of the strong bands of groups of solvents and of individual solvents shown in Figure 11.3 in the form of a line diagram.

IR spectra of other alcohols that are sometimes used as solvents are reproduced in the spectral part of Vol. 2. The commercial collections of spectra [147–150] also contain spectra of nearly all substances that are likely to be used as solvents. The reader is referred to lists of solvent spectra in the near infrared region [605, 606].

Quantitative determinations of the components of simple solvent mixtures were formerly much-quoted examples of the application of IR spectroscopy [130, 140]. One example is the description by HOFFMANN [607] of the analysis of harmful solvents in technical mixtures by IR spectroscopy. The chlorinated hydrocarbons and the C_6—C_6 aromatic compounds have 1—3 characteristic narrow absorption bands each in the region of 850 to 650 cm⁻¹ (11.7—15.4 µm), which can be used for identification and quantitative determination. In some combinations of chlorinated hydrocarbons and aromatic compounds, however, these bands overlap, with the result that preliminary separation by distillation is necessary (e. g. carbon tetrachloride 775 cm⁻¹, m-xylene 768 cm⁻¹, p-xylene 794 cm⁻¹).

When the mixture contains large quantities of esters or ketones, the band maximum for the aromatic compounds is displaced to higher wavelengths and the bands become broader. The broadening can be as much as + 2 to + 10 cm⁻¹ in ethyl acetate or acetone [607]. This effect can be eliminated

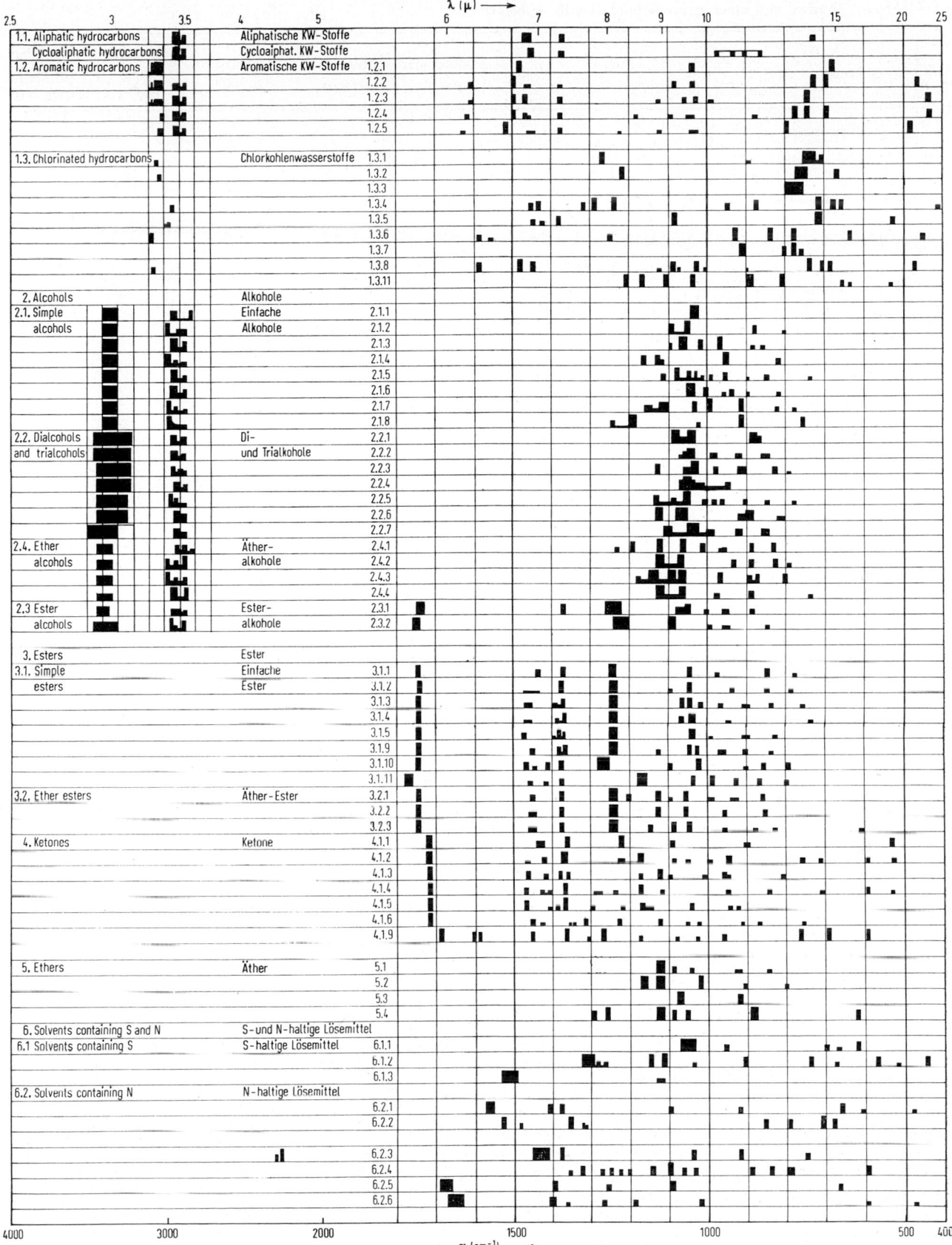

Fig. 11.3: IR band chart of solvents
        (Dec. No. according to table 11.2—11.4)

Table 11.6: Physical and mass spectroscopic data for solvents

Dec. no.	Solvent	Molecular formula	Molecular weight	Density $d20°/4°$	Refractive index n_D^{20}	Solubility in H_2O (wt. %)
1.	Hydrocarbons					
1.1.	Aliphatic hydrocarbons					
1.1.1.	n-Pentane	C_5H_{12}	72,2	0,631	1,3575	
1.1.2.	n-Octane	C_8H_{18}	114,2	0,707	1,3974	0,001
1.1.3.	Isooctane (2.2.4-trimethylpentane)	C_8H_{18}	114,2	0,696	1,3915	
1.1.4.	Cyclohexane	C_6H_{12}	84,2	0,778	1,4264	0,005
1.1.5.	Methylcyclohexane	C_7H_{14}	98,2	0,774	1,4231	
1.1.6.	Decalin, trans	$C_{10}H_{18}$	138,3	0,8699	1,4695	
1.2.	Aromatic hydrocarbons					
1.2.1.	Benzene	C_6H_6	78,1	0,879	1,5007	0,07
1.2.2.	Toluene	C_7H_8	92,1	0,872	1,4998	0,05
1.2.3.	o-Xylene	C_8H_{10}	106,2	0,881	1,5050	0,02
1.2.4.	m-Xylene	C_8H_{10}	106,2	0,866	1,4972	0,02
1.2.5.	p-Xylene	C_8H_{10}	106,2	0,861	1,495	0,02
1.2.6.	Ethylbenzene	C_8H_{10}	106,2	0,876	1,496	0,02
1.2.7.	Mesitylene	C_9H_{12}	120,2	0,865	1,4994	
1.2.8.	Pseudocumene	C_9H_{12}	120,2	0,876	1,5064	
1.2.9.	Cumene	C_9H_{12}	120,2	0,862	1,4920	
1.2.10.	p-Cymene	$C_{10}H_{14}$	134,2	0,857	1,4909	
1.2.11.	Hydrindene	C_9H_{10}	118,2	0,964	1,5385	
1.2.12.	Tetralin	$C_{10}H_{12}$	132,2	0,973	1,5461	
1.3.	Chlorinated hydrocarbons					
1.3.1.	Methylene chloride	CH_2Cl_2	84,9	1,326	1,4244	2,0
1.3.2.	Chloroform	$CHCl_3$	119,4	1,483	1,4467	0,8
1.3.3.	Carbon tetrachloride	CCl_4	153,8	1,595	1,4631	0,08
1.3.4.	1,2-Dichloroethane	$C_2H_4Cl_2$	99,0	1,253	1,4451	0,8
1.3.5.	1,1,1-Trichloroethane	$C_2H_3Cl_3$	133,4	1,325	1,4376	0,01
1.3.6.	Trichloroethylene	C_2HCl_3	131,4	1,468	1,4771	0,1
1.3.7.	Tetrachloroethylene	C_2Cl_4	165,9	1,623	1,5055	0,04
1.3.8.	Chlorobenzene	C_6H_5Cl	112,6	1,106	1,5248	0,05

Dec. no.	Mass numbers m/e and relative intensities (Upper line: mass number, lower line: relative intensity for the corresponding mass number, based on a value of 100 for the strongest peak)								
1.1.1.	43	42	41	27	29	39	57	72	28	15
		58	40	35	24	14	12	9	7	5
1.1.2.	43	41	29	57	85	27	56	42	39	70
		38	35	34	30	29	18	16	14	12
1.1.3.	57	56	41	43	29	27	39	99	15	58
		32	27	23	15	12	9	5	5	4
1.1.4.	56	84	41	55	27	42	39	69	28	43
		75	65	35	30	30	29	22	14	14
1.1.5.	83	55	41	98	42	27	39	56	69	7C
		83	59	44	36	33	31	31	23	22
1.1.6.	44	138	67	41	68	96	82	81	95	55
		89	84	78	71	69	66	59	53	51
1.2.1.	78	52	51	50	77	39	79	76	38	74
		19	19	16	14	14	6	6	6	5
1.2.2.	91	92	39	65	63	51	93	50	62	38
		73	15	11	9	8	6	6	5	4
1.2.3.	91	106	105	39	51	77	27	65	78	92
		60	24	16	15	13	10	8	8	8
1.2.4.	91	106	105	39	51	77	27	78	65	52
		65	29	18	15	14	10	8	8	8
1.2.5.	91	106	105	39	77	51	27	78	79	65
		67	30	15	15	14	10	8	8	8
1.2.6.	91	106	51	39	65	77	92	78	27	50
		30	13	10	9	8	8	8	7	6
1.2.7.	05	120	119	39	77	27	51	91	106	79
		67	16	15	13	10	10	9	9	6
1.2.8.	05	120	119	39	77	27	51	91	106	41
		59	16	14	12	10	10	9	9	6
1.2.9.	05	120	77	51	106	79	28	91	103	39
		26	13	10	10	10	9	8	7	6
1.2.10.	19	134	91	39	120	41	27	77	117	65
		24	16	10	10	8	7	7	7	6
1.2.11.	17	118	115	91	39	58	57	63	116	51
		75	27	17	17	13	11	10	9	9
1.2.12.	104	132	91	131	117	115	65	128	105	51
		72	56	17	17	13	10	10	10	9
1.3.1.	49	84	86	51	47	35	48	88	41	37
		58	36	30	18	12	9	6	5	4
1.3.2.	84	86	47	49	35	88	37	51	82	119
		63	35	26	20	10	8	5	2	2
1.3.3.	117	119	121	82	84	47	35	49	123	37
		97	32	19	13	13	6	4	4	2
1.3.4.	62	27	49	64	26	63	98	51	61	100
		91	40	32	31	19	14	13	12	9
1.3.5.	97	99	61	117	119	63	101	62	60	35
		65	50	19	19	17	10	8	7	7
1.3.6.	83	97	61	85	99	26	27	63	35	96
		100	73	64	63	47	38	29	26	22
1.3.7.	166	164	129	131	168	47	94	35	96	133
		79	69	66	48	42	40	35	26	21
1.3.8.	112	77	114	51	50	38	113	75	74	56
		48	32	16	14	9	7	6	6	5

Table 11.6 (continued)

Dec. no.	Solvent	Molecular formula	Molecular weight	Density $^{d}20°/4°$	Refractive index n_D^{20}	Solubility in H_2O (wt. %)
1.3.9.	o-Dichlorobenzene	$C_6H_4Cl_2$	147,0	1,304	1,5515	0,01
1.3.10.	p-Dichlorobenzene	$C_6H_4Cl_2$	147,0	1,231*	1,5267*	
1.3.11.	1,2,2-Trifluoro-1,1,2-trichloroethane	$C_2F_3Cl_3$	187,4	$1,5635^{25}$	$1,3557^{25}$	
2.	Alcohols					
2.1.	Simple alcohols					
2.1.1.	Methanol	CH_4O	32,0	0,792	1,3287	∞
2.1.2.	Ethanol	C_2H_6O	46,1	0,789	1,3605	∞
2.1.3.	n-Propanol	C_3H_8O	60,1	0,804	1,3854	∞
2.1.4.	Isopropanol	C_3H_8O	60,1	0,785	1,3771	∞
2.1.5.	n-Butanol	C_4H_{10}	74,1	0,810	1,3993	7,8
2.1.6.	Isobutanol	C_4H_{10}	74,1	0,803	1,3962	8,5
2.1.7.	sec-Butanol	C_4H_{10}	74,1	0,806	1,3971	12,5
2.1.8.	tert-Butanol	C_4H_{10}	74,1	$0,780^{25}$	1,3838	∞
2.1.9.	n-Amyl alcohol	$C_5H_{12}O$	88,2	$0,8110^{25}$	1,4101	
2.1.10.	2-Pentanol	$C_5H_{12}O$	88,2	0,8103	1,4053	4,2
2.1.11.	2-Methylbutan-2-ol	$C_5H_{12}O$	88,2	$0,8048^{25}$	1,4052	
2.1.12.	n-Hexanol	$C_6H_{14}O$	102,2	0,819	1,4191	0,58
2.1.13.	2-Hexanol	$C_6H_{14}O$	102,2	$0,8104^{25}$	$1,4126^{25}$	
2.1.14.	3-Hexanol	$C_6H_{14}O$	102,2	0,8183		
2.1.15.	n-Octanol	$C_8H_{18}O$	130,2	0,825	1,4304	0,03
2.1.16.	2-Ethylhexanol	$C_8H_{18}O$	130,2	0,833	1,4328	0,1
2.1.17.	Cyclohexanol	$C_6H_{12}O$	100,2	$0,942^{30}$	$1,4629^{30}$	3,6
2.1.18.	3,3,5-Trimethylcyclo-hexanol	$C_9H_{18}O$	142,1	$0,9006^{16}$	$1,4550^{16}$	
2.1.19.	Benzyl alcohol	C_7H_8O	108,1	1,0419	1,5396	4,0
2.2.	Dialcohols and trialcohols					
2.2.1.	Glycol	$C_2H_6O_2$	62,1	1,111	1,4318	∞
2.2.2.	1,3-Propanediol	$C_3H_8O_2$	76,1	1,0529	1,4389	∞

* at 70 °C

Dec. no.	Mass numbers m/e and relative intensities (Upper line: mass number, lower line: relative intensity for the corresponding mass number, based on a value of 100 for the strongest peak)								
1.3.9.	146	148	111	75	113	74	50	150	73	147
		64	38	23	12	12	11	10	9	7
1.3.10.	146	148	111	75	74	50	113	73	150	147
		64	35	22	14	12	11	11	10	7
1.3.11.	101	151	103	85	153	31	66	116	87	47
		62	56	41	39	29	17	16	13	13
2.1.1.	31	32	29	28	30	33	27			
		72	42	9	8	1	1			
2.1.2.	31	45	27	29	46	26	43	28	30	42
		34	24	23	17	8	8	7	6	3
2.1.3.	31	27	29	59	42	60	28	41	26	39
		17	16	9	7	6	6	6	5	5
2.1.4.	45	43	27	29	41	31	39	42	59	44
		17	16	10	7	6	6	4	4	3
2.1.5.	56	41	31	43	27	42	44	29	28	39
		70	69	65	34	32	30	25	21	17
2.1.6.	43	31	42	41	33	27	29	39	74	28
		67	57	56	51	44	24	21	9	7
2.1.7.	45	59	41	43	31	29	27	44	56	28
		22	18	18	15	10	10	9	6	5
2.1.8.	59	31	41	43	15	29	57	27	28	39
		28	18	12	10	10	9	7	7	6
2.1.9.	42	31	29	41	55	70	43	57	39	28
		69	66	60	59	37	29	22	18	15
2.1.10.	45	43	55	27	29	44	31	41	73	39
		17	16	13	9	8	6	6	6	5
2.1.11.	59	73	43	31	55	27	29	41	45	39
		52	38	34	33	22	19	18	11	10
2.1.12.	56	43	55	41	31	27	42	29	69	28
		87	63	61	59	54	53	51	25	13
2.1.13.	45	43	27	41	29	69	44	28	42	31
		22	20	17	16	13	8	6	5	5
2.1.14.	59	55	31	27	43	73	29	47	57	28
		77	61	51	51	42	40	33	15	11
2.1.15.	41	56	43	55	29	31	27	42	70	69
		86	82	81	71	69	63	59	55	49
2.1.16.	57	41	43	29	27	55	31	56	70	83
		44	42	37	30	25	21	20	17	15
2.1.17.	57	67	82	41	39	54	29	44	43	55
		68	53	45	45	34	30	25	23	19
2.1.18.	109	83	41	57	55	43	71	56	85	124
		59	54	37	36	35	33	29	29	27
2.1.19.	79	108	107	77	51	39	50	27	29	91
		79	62	58	39	24	23	18	18	18
2.2.2.	31	33	15	29	43	27	19	30	44	41
		29	18	17	7	6	3	3	3	2
2.2.1.	28	58	31	57	29	27	45	43	19	41
		93	76	70	40	26	24	23	18	7

Table 11.6 (continued)

Dec. no.	Solvent	Molecular formula	Molecular weight	Density $^d20°/4°$	Refractive index n_D^{20}	Solubility in H_2O (wt. %)
2.2.3.	1,2-Propanediol	$C_3H_8O_2$	76,1	1,0361	1,4324	∞
2.2.4.	1,4-Butanediol	$C_4H_{10}O_2$	90,1	1,0171	1,4467	∞
2.2.5.	1,3-Butanediol	$C_4H_{10}O_2$	90,1	1,0053	1,4418	∞
2.2.6.	Diethylene glycol	$C_4H_{10}O_3$	106,0	1,118	1,4475	∞
2.2.7.	Glycerol	$C_3H_8O_3$	92,1	1,261	1,4744	∞
2.2.8.	Trimethylolpropane	$C_6H_{14}O_3$	134,2			
2.3.	Ester alcoholes, keto alcoholes, halogenated alcoholes					
2.3.1.	Ethylene glycol monoacetat	$C_4H_8O_3$	104,1	1,11	1,4209	∞
2.3.2.	Butyl glycolate	$C_6H_{12}O_3$	132,2	1,022	1,4255	7,5
2.3.3.	Diacetone alcohol	$C_6H_{12}O_2$	116,2	0,938	1,4241	∞
2.3.4.	2-Chloroethanol	C_2H_5OCl	80,5	1,200	1,4420	∞
2.4.	Ether alcohols					
2.4.1.	Ethylene glycol monomethyl ether	$C_3H_8O_2$	76,0	0,965	1,4028	∞
2.4.2.	Ethylene glycol monoethyl ether	$C_4H_{10}O_2$	90,0	0,930	1,4079	∞
2.4.3.	Ethylene glycol monoisopropyl ether	$C_5H_{12}O_2$	104,1	0,930	1,4095	∞
2.4.4.	Ethylene glycol monobutyl ether	$C_6H_{14}O_2$	118,1	0,903	1,4196	∞
2.4.5.	Diethylene glycol monomethyl ether	$C_5H_{12}O_3$	120,1	1,034	1,4263	∞
2.4.6.	Diethylene glycol monoethyl ether	$C_6H_{14}O_3$	134,1	0,990	1,427	∞
2.4.7.	Diethylene glycol monobutyl ether	$C_8H_{18}O_3$	162,1	0,954	1,432	∞
2.4.8.	Tetrahydrofurfuryl alcohol	$C_5H_{10}O_2$	102,1	1,054	1,4517	∞
2.4.9.	4-Methyl-4-methoxy-2-pentanol	$C_7H_{16}O_2$	132,1			
3.	Esters					
3.1.	Simple esters					
3.1.1	Methyl acetate	$C_3H_6O_2$	74,1	0,927	1,3593	24
3.1.2.	Ethyl acetate	$C_4H_8O_2$	88,1	0,901	1,3725	7,9
3.1.3.	n-Propyl acetate	$C_5H_{10}O_2$	102,1	0,888	1,3847	2,3
3.1.4.	n-Butyl acetate	$C_6H_{12}O_2$	116,2	0,882	1,3951	1,0
3.1.5.	Isobutyl acetate	$C_6H_{12}O_2$	116,2	0,870	1,391	0,7

Dec. no.	Mass numbers m/e and relative intensities (Upper line: mass number, lower line: relative intensity for the corresponding mass number, based on a value of 100 for the strongest peak)								
2.2.3.	45	43	31	27	29	44	19	61	15	18
		14	12	9	8	7	5	5	4	3
2.2.4.	42	31	44	41	43	29	71	27	57	28
		74	66	41	29	25	24	23	18	13
2.2.5.	43	45	28	29	31	57	72	44	19	27
		99	49	36	34	27	27	24	23	23
2.2.6.	45	75	31	27	29	43	28	44	76	19
		18	14	13	11	10	9	9	9	9
2.2.7.	61	43	31	44	29	18	27	42	60	45
		90	57	54	38	32	12	11	10	10
2.2.8.	57	29	41	31	86	55	43	45		
		59	46	41	38	38	37	29		
2.3.1.	43	59	31	72	44	29	45	27	87	88
		73	70	66	49	44	26	21	20	18
2.3.2.	31	57	29	41	56	43	42	27	44	61
		96	95	89	78	38	34	30	24	21
2.3.3.	43	59	58	101	15	31	41	27	29	39
		34	20	10	10	8	7	5	5	5
2.3.4.	31	27	43	29	15	44	49	51	80	26
		8	6	6	6	4	3	3	3	2
2.4.1.	45	29	31	43	27	76	47	28		
		36	26	10	8	6	6	5		
2.4.2.	31	29	59	27	45	15	72	43		
		51	50	27	26	14	14	14		
2.4.3.	43	45	73	89	41	27	31	59		
		76	37	32	25	16	16	14		
2.4.4.	57	29	41	45	31	39	87	43		
		71	61	51	31	19	17	15		
2.4.5.	45	29	59	31	44	58	43	89		
		48	41	36	25	21	17	9		
2.4.6.	45	59	72	73	60	31	75	44		
		55	36	21	13	13	11	8		
2.4.7.	57	85	58	43	41	29	142	39		
		85	36	35	32	18	11	10		
2.4.8.	71	43	41	27	29	31	42	39	18	44
		79	44	41	36	31	22	22	12	12
2.4.9.	73	56	43	41	45	57	29	55	39	85
		26	26	22	21	17	12	10	9	7
3.1.1.	43	74	29	42	59	31	44	28		
		15	11	10	6	3	3	2		
3.1.2.	43	61	45	29	70	88	27	28	42	73
		16	16	13	10	7	6	6	5	5
3.1.3.	43	61	31	27	42	73	29	41	39	59
		19	18	15	11	9	9	9	5	5
3.1.4.	43	56	41	27	29	73	61	28	39	55
		34	17	16	15	11	10	7	6	6
3.1.5.	43	56	15	73	41	27	29	39	62	42
		23	15	15	13	11	10	8	7	4

Table 11.6 (continued)

Dec. no.	Solvent	Molecular formula	Molecular weight	Density $^d20°/4°$	Refractive index n_D^{20}	Solubility in H_2O (wt. %)
3.1.6.	sec-Butyl acetate	$C_6H_{12}O_2$	116,2	0,8701	1,3877	
3.1.7.	tert-Butyl acetate	$C_6H_{12}O_2$	116,2	0,8817	1,3840	
3.1.8.	Isoamyl acetate	$C_7H_{14}O_2$	130,1	0,8670	1,4003	0,25
3.1.9.	Cyclohexanol acetate	$C_8H_{14}O_2$	142,1	0,97	1,4420	
3.1.10.	Diethyl carbonate	$C_5H_{10}O_3$	118,1	0,9752	1,3845	
3.1.11.	Butyrolactone	$C_4H_6O_2$	86,1	1,128	1,436	∞
3.2.	Ether esters					
3.2.1.	Ethylene glycol monomethyl ether acetate	$C_5H_{10}O_3$	118,1	1,005	1,4019	∞
3.2.2.	Ethylene glycol monoethyl ether acetate	$C_6H_{12}O_3$	132,1	0,975	1,4058	22
3.2.3.	3-Methoxybutyl acetate	$C_7H_{14}O_3$	146,2	0,953	1,4091	3
3.2.4.	Diethylene glycol monoethyl ether acetate	$C_8H_{16}O_4$	176,1	1,009	1,4213	∞
4.	Ketones					
4.1.	Simple ketones					
4.1.1.	Acetone	C_3H_6O	58,1	0,791	1,3591	∞
4.1.2.	Methyl ethyl ketone	C_4H_8O	72,1	0,805	1,3788	26
4.1.3.	Diethyl ketone	$C_5H_{10}O$	86,1	0,8159	1,3905	
4.1.4.	Methyl isobutyl ketone	$C_6H_{12}O$	100,2	0,801	1,3958	2,8
4.1.5.	Diisobutyl ketone	$C_9H_{18}O$	142,2	0,8053	$1,4111^{25}$	
4.1.6.	Cyclohexanone	$C_6H_{10}O$	98,1	0,948	1,4500	2,3
4.1.7.	3,3,5-Trimethylcyclo-hexanone	$C_9H_{16}O$	140,1			
4.1.8.	Isophorone	$C_9H_{14}O$	138,2	0,923	1,4781	1,2
4.1.9.	Acetophenone	C_8H_8O	120,2	1,0281	$1,5363^{15}$	
4.2.	Ether ketones					
4.2.1.	Diacetone alcohol methyl ether	$C_7H_{14}O_2$	130,1			
5.	Ethers					
5.1.	Diethyl ether	$C_4H_{10}O$	74,1	0,714	1,3526	6,9

Dec. no.	Mass numbers m/e and relative intensities (Upper line: mass number, lower line: relative intensity for the corresponding mass number, based on a value of 100 for the strongest peak)								
3.1.6.	43	56	87	15	29	41	27	57	39	73
		16	16	14	13	12	11	8	5	4
3.1.7.	43	57	41	59	56	15	29	39	101	27
		48	34	31	27	27	22	13	12	12
3.1.8.	43	70	55	15	41	27	42	29	39	73
		36	27	17	15	15	12	12	10	8
3.1.9.	43	82	67	57	54	55	41	83	81	61
		93	57	20	19	17	15	11	10	9
3.1.10.	44	62	45	31	27	18	29	74	43	46
		97	70	33	22	22	22	17	12	9
3.1.11.	28	42	28	29	27	41	56	86	26	39
		74	49	35	34	34	23	18	16	11
3.2.1.	45	43	58	29	44	15	31	42	27	73
		99	95	50	48	47	34	23	21	18
3.2.2.	43	31	59	29	72	15	44	45	73	27
		20	15	15	13	12	12	9	6	6
3.2.3.	43	59	55	44	71	45	61	42	88	29
		88	78	76	69	62	55	53	33	53
3.2.4.	43	87	45	31	59	73	72	29	44	15
		57	33	20	18	18	17	17	10	9
4.1.1.	43	58	15	27	42	14	26	29	33	41
		33	31	8	7	6	5	4	3	2
4.1.2.	43	29	72	27	57	42	26	28	44	
		25	17	16	6	5	5	3		
4.1.3.	57	29	27	86	28	26	43	42	58	56
		100	37	17	11	9	4	4	4	4
4.1.4.	43	58	57	41	29	85	100	39	27	42
		32	18	18	12	11	9	8	8	5
4.1.5.	57	85	41	43	58	28	26	39	42	14
		82	46	39	33	30	30	22	12	11
4.1.6.	55	42	41	27	98	39	69	70	28	43
		85	34	33	31	27	26	20	14	13
4.1.7.	83	41	55	56	69	39	27	29	43	140
		77	67	61	60	33	32	28	26	19
4.1.8.	82	39	138	27	41	54	53	29		
		28	17	17	13	13	9	7		
4.1.9.	105	77	51	120	43	50	78	106	39	74
		86	41	33	21	20	9	8	8	6
4.2.1.	43	73	41	29	115	56	27	39	15	55
		63	12	9	8	8	7	7	7	7
5.1.	31	59	29	45	27	43	41	28	73	15
		53	41	39	17	7	6	5	4	3

Table 11.6 (continued)

Dec. no.	Solvent	Molecular formula	Molecular weight	Density $d20°/4°$	Refractive index n_D^{20}	Solubility in H_2O (wt. %)
5.2.	Diisopropyl ether	$C_6H_{14}O$	102,2	0,724	1,3681	0,9
5.3.	Tetrahydrofuran	C_4H_8O	72,1	0,888	1,4073	∞
5.4.	Dioxan	$C_4H_8O_2$	88,1	1,034	1,4221	∞
6.	Solvents containing S and N					
6.1.	Solvents containing sulfur					
6.1.1.	Dimethyl sulfoxide	C_2H_6OS	78,1	1,101	1,4783	∞
6.1.2.	Sulfolan	$C_4H_8O_2S$	120,1			
6.1.3.	Carbon disulfide	CS_2	76,1	1,26	1,635	0,2
6.2.	Solvents containing nitrogen					
6.2.1.	Nitromethane	CH_3O_2N	61,0	1,139	1,3819	9,5
6.2.2.	Nitrobenzene	$C_6H_5O_2N$	123,1	1,203	1,5521	0,2
6.2.3.	Acetonitrile	C_2H_3N	41,0	0,783	1,3442	∞
6.2.4.	Morpholine	C_4H_9ON	87,1	1,001	1,4540	∞
6.2.5.	Dimethylformamide	C_3H_7ON	73,1	0,949	1,430	∞
6.2.6.	Dimethylacetamide	C_4H_9ON	87,0	0,9434	1,4371	

by dilution of the solvent with cyclohexane or some other optically empty, apolar substance.

11.5 UV and Mass Spectroscopy of Solvents

The presence of aromatic compounds in solvents can be recognized immediately from the UV spectrum. In the case of solvents containing acetone, which also absorbs in the UV, the acetone must be separated in order to allow a reliable identification of the aromatic compounds in the water-insoluble fraction. Semiquantitative and quantitative methods are known for the determination of the total content of aromatic hydrocarbons or of individual components by UV spectroscopy [608—610]. The UV spectra of the aromatic hydrocarbons that occur in solvents can be found in various collections [191—194].

Mass spectroscopy in conjunction with gas chromatography has become almost the ideal identification method (see Section 1.8). In Table 11.6, together with physical data, we have given the ten strongest signals in the mass spectra of the solvent components listed.

Dec. no.	Mass numbers m/e and relative intensities (Upper line: mass number, lower line: relative intensity for the corresponding mass number, based on a value of 100 for the strongest peak)								
5.2.	45	43	87	27	41	59	39	29	42	31
		52	18	15	15	10	9	4	4	4
5.3.	42	41	27	72	71	39	43	29	40	15
		52	33	29	27	25	22	22	13	10
5.4.	28	29	88	58	31	15	30	43	26	57
		37	31	24	17	17	13	11	9	6
6.1.1.	63	78	15	45	29	61	46	31	48	47
		68	40	35	16	13	12	11	10	10
6.1.2.	41	56	55	28	27	120	39	29	57	26
		75	65	58	34	29	22	21	10	10
6.1.3.	76	32	44	78	77	64	34	46		
		22	18	9	3	1	1	1		
6.2.1.	30	61	15	46	14	29	27	28	45	16
		54	52	36	8	8	7	6	6	6
6.2.2.	77	51	123	50	30	65	39	93	74	38
		59	42	25	16	13	10	9	7	7
6.2.3.	41	40	39	38	28	14	42	26		
		50	17	5	5	5	3	1		
6.2.4.	57	29	87	28	30	56	86	31	27	15
		99	69	69	38	33	28	28	12	7
6.2.5.	44	73	42	28	15	30	29	18	43	14
		86	47	40	39	31	23	16	11	8
6.2.6.	44	43	15	87	42	45	30	72	28	14
		48	38	32	23	18	12	12	9	7

Bibliography

1 Methods for the Analysis of Additives and Processing Aids for Plastics

General Literature

Additives and Processing Aids for Plastics

[1] E. Bartholomé, E. Biekert, H. Hellmann, H. Ley, M. Weigert, E. Weise (Eds.), Ullmanns Encyclopädie der technischen Chemie, 4. ed., Verlag Chemie, Weinheim-New York, 1972 f.

In the following the volume numbers of this encyclopedia (italic) appear before the dates (in brackets), and the page numbers are shown after the dates.

W. Kurze, Antioxidantien *8* (1974) 19;

W. Noll, Asbest *8* (1974) 67;

K. Hunger, P. Mischke, W. Rieper, Azofarbstoffe *8* (1974) 244;

H. Batzer, Epoxidverbindungen *10* (1979) 63;

H. Hartmann, Fettsäuren *12* (1976) 525;

E. Sturm, Fungizide *12* (1976) 1;

W. Barendrecht, L. J. Lees, Natürliche Harze *12* (1976) 525;

W. Barendrecht, G. Collin et al., Synthetische Harze *12* (1976) 539;

K. Eisenmann, K. Zenner, Isocyanate *13* (1977) 347;

W. Hofmann, Kautschuk *13* (1977) 581;

R. Casper, J. Witte, G. Kuth, Synthetischer Kautschuk *13* (1977) 595;

M. Abele, K. D. Albrecht, U. Eholzer, H. Fries, G. P. Languer, W. Hofmann, Kautschuk-Chemikalien und Zuschlagstoffe *13* (1977) 637;

J. Voigt, Zusätze von Kunststoffen *15* (1978) 253;

J. Spille, Färbung von Kunststoffen *15* (1978) 275;

K. F. Elgert, Kunststoff-Analyse *15* (1978) 371;

U. Biethan et al., Lacke *15* (1978) 589;

H. G. Völz, F. Hund, Anorganische Pigmente *18* (1979) 545;

E. Lang, C. Thiene, G. Jülich, H. Hentschel, H. Ferch, D. Klose, W. Tufar, Füllstoffe *18* (1979) 647;

K. Hunger, H. Herbst, Organische Pigmente *18* (1979) 661;

H. Gold, H. Theidel, Optische Aufheller und Fluoreszenzfarbstoffe *17* (1979) 459;

K. Stober, A. Kleemann, Organische Peroxide und Persäuren *17* (1979) 661.

[1a] W. Foerst (Ed.), Ullmanns Encyklopädie der technischen Chemie, 3. ed., Urban & Schwarzenberg, München-Berlin.

W. Kling, H. Frotscher, Antistatica *17* (1967) 45;

F. Linhardt, F. Oschatz et al., Weichmacher *18* (1967) 540.

[2] R. Gächter, H. Müller (Ed.), Taschenbuch der Kunststoff-Additive, Carl Hanser Ed., München-Wien 1979.

K. Schwarzenbach, Antioxidantien, p. 1;

H. Müller, Metalldesaktivatoren, p. 69;

H. Lind, Lichtschutzmittel für thermoplastische Kunststoffe, p. 91;

H. Andreas, PVC-Stabilisatoren, p. 145;

A. L. Berg, Organische Peroxide als Vernetzer, p. 201;

W. Brotz, Gleitmittel und verwandte Hilfsstoffe für Thermoplaste, p. 229;

K.-D. Böhme, Hochpolymere PVC-Verarbeitungshilfsmittel, p. 275;

G. Menzel, Hochpolymere Additive zur Verbesserung der Schlagzähigkeit von Thermoplasten, p. 295;

W. Bosshard, H.-P. Schlumpf, Füllstoffe und Verstärkungsmittel, p. 319;

H. Jenkner, Brandschutzausrüstung für Thermoplaste, p. 387;

H. Finck, Antistatika, p. 417;

K. Berger, Optische Aufheller, p. 437;

J. Lorenz, Biostabilisatoren, p. 453;

K. Müller, H. Hurnik, Chemische Treibmittel, p. 479;

W. Sommer, Weichmacher, p. 493;

R. Leimgruber, Gewerbe- und Lebensmittelhygienische Aspekte von Kunststoff-Additiven, p. 549;

[3] J. L. O'Toole, G. M. Kline (Eds.), Modern Plastics Encyclopedia, McGrawn-Hill, New York, annual.

[4] J. Voigt, Die Stabilisierung der Kunststoffe gegen Licht und Wärme, Springer, Berlin-Heidelberg-New York 1966.

[5] M. B. Neiman, Aging and Stabilization of Polymers, Consultants Bureau – Plenum Press, New York 1965.

[6] K. Thinius, Stabilisierung und Alterung von Plastwerkstoffen, Vol. I Stabilisierung und Stabilisatoren von Plastwerkstoffen, Verlag Chemie, Weinheim 1969.

[7] K. B. Piotrovskii, K. Yu. Salnis, Auxiliary Substances for Polymeric Materials, Rubber and Plastics Research Association of Great Britain, June 1967.

[8] L. Mascia, The Role of Additives in Plastics, Edward Arnold Publ., London 1974.

[9] W. Hofmann, Vulkanisation und Vulkanisationshilfsmittel, Berliner Union GmbH, Stuttgart 1967.

[10] J. V. Del Gatto, Rubber World, Materials and Compounding Ingredients for Rubber, 5. ed., Bill Publ., New York 1968.

[10a] Rubber Red Book, Rubber Age, New York 1968.

[11] H. Mark, N. G. Gaylord, N. M. Bikales, Encyclopedia of Polymer Science and Technology Vol. 1–16, Interscience, New York 1964–1972.

[12] J. Brandrup, E. H. Immergut, Polymer Handbook, 2. ed., Wiley & Sons, New York 1975.

Reports on Analysis of Plastics

[13] D. Hummel, Kunststoff-, Lack- und Gummianalyse, Carl Hanser, München 1958.

[14] G. M. Kline (Ed.), Analytical Chemistry of Polymers.
Part I: Analysis of Monomers and Polymer Materials
Part II: Molecular Structure and Chemical Groups
Part III: Identification Procedures and Chemical Analysis
Interscience, New York-London 1962.

[15] H. Knittel (Ed.), Deutsches Jahrbuch der plastischen Massen (9. Ser.), F. Scholl, Chemisch-analytische Untersuchung von Kunststoffen, p. 229, Wilh. Pansegrau Verlag, Berlin 1965.

[16] T. C. Crompton, Chemical Analysis of Additives in Plastics, 2. ed., Pergamon Press, Oxford-New York 1977.

[17] R. Houwink (Ed.), Chemie und Technologie der Kunststoffe, Vol. III, G. Bandel, W. Kupfer, Die chem. Prüfung der Kunststoffe, p. 212, Akademische Verlagsgesellschaft, Leipzig 1963.

[18] E. Schröder, E. Hagen, Ausgewählte Methoden der Plasthilfsstoffanalytik, Plaste-Kaut. *15* (1968) 625.

[19] H. Fassy, P. Lalet, Analyse von Mischungen des Polyvinylchlorid, Plast. Mod. Elastomeres *21* (1969) 131.

[20] L. Veres, Die Analytik des Weich-PVC, Kunststoffe *59* (1969) 241.

[21] J. Haslam, H. A. Willis, D. C. M. Squirrel, Identification and Analysis of Plastics, 2. ed., Iliffe Books, London 1977.

[22] E. Schröder, J. Franz, E. Hagen, Ausgewählte Methoden zur Plastanalytik, Akademie-Verlag, Berlin 1976.

Bibliography

[23] J. Urbanski, W. Czerwinski (Eds.), Handbook of Analysis of Synthetic Polymers and Plastics, Wiley, New York 1977.

[24] M. Hoffmann, H. Krämer, R. Kuhn, Polymeranalytik, 2 Vols., Thieme Taschenlehrbuch der organischen Chemie B. Spezielle Gebiete 5. Thieme, Stuttgart 1977.

[25] B. K. Tidd, Chemical analysis of rubber vulcanisates, Plast. Rubber, Mater. Appl. 2 (1977) 100.

[26] A. Krause, A. Lange, Kunststoff-Bestimmungsmöglichkeiten: Eine Anleitung zur einfachen qualitativen und quantitativen chemischen Analyse, Vol. 3, Carl Hanser, München 1979.

[27] W. C. Wake, The Analysis of Rubber and Rubber-like Polymers, 2. ed., Wiley Interscience, New York 1969.

[28] G. C. Ives, J. A. Mead, M. M. Riley, Handbook of Plastics Test Methods, Iliffe Books, London 1971.

Reviews on Analysis of Plastics

[29] J. Mitchell, J. Chiu, Analysis of high polymers, Anal. Chem. 41 (1969) 248 R, 45 (1973) 5, 279 R, 47 (1975) 5, 289 R.

[30] J. G. Cobler, C. D. Chow, Analysis of high polymers, Anal. Chem. 51 (1979) 5, 287 R.

[31] C. W. Wadelin, G. S. Trick, Review of analytical applications: Rubber, Anal. Chem. 39 (1967) 239 R, 41 (1969) 299 R, 43334 R.

[32] C. W. Wadelin, M. C. Morris, Rubber, Anal. Chem. 45 (1973) 5, 333 R, 47 (1975) 5, 327 R, 49 (1977) 5, 133 R, 51 (1979) 5, 303 R.

[33] M. H. Swann, M. L. Adams, G. G. Esposito, Analytical chemistry reviews: Coatings, Anal. Chem. 39 (1967 42 R, 41 (1969) 35 R.

[34] G. H. Esposito, M. L. Adams, Applications review: Coatings, Anal. Chem. 47 (1975) 5, 39 R.

[35] R. A. Sweeney, C. W. Gehrke, P. A. Rexroad, Coatings, Anal. Chem. 51 (1979) 5, 80 R.

1.2 Separation of Additives

[36] K. E. Kress, Semimicro rapid reflux method for solvent extraction of rubber products, Rubber World (1956) 709.

[37] M. W. Robertson, R. M. Rowley, The separation of plasticizers from polyvinyl chloride compositions, Brit. Plastics (1960) 26.

[38] W. Kupfer, Kunststoff-Analyse, Z. Anal. Chem. 192 (1963) 219.

[39] J. H. van der Neut, Toegankelijkheid van macromoleculaire materialen voor analyse, Plastica 18 (1965) 307.

[40] D. Martin, Extrahieren von festen und flüssigen Stoffen im Laboratorium, GIT-Fachz. Lab. 14 (1970).

[41] P. Svoboda, Abtrennung der Zusätze aus polymeren Werkstoffen in Öfen mit Temperaturgefälle für die Erfordernisse der IR-Spektroskopie, Plaste-Kautsch. 17 (1970) 560.

[42] E. Stahl, TAS – ein Thermomikro-Abtrenn- und Applikationsverfahren, gekoppelt mit der Dünnschichtchromatographie, J. Chromatogr. 37 (1968) 99.

[43] Company publication, TAS-Ofen und TASOMAT, Fa. Desaga, Heidelberg 1978.

[43a] E. Stahl, V. Brüderle, Polymer Analysis by Thermofractography in H. J. Cantow et al. (Eds.) Advances in Polymer Science, Vol. 30, Springer, Berlin-Heidelberg 1979.

[44] D. A. Wheeler, Determination of antioxidants in polymeric material, Talanta 15 (1968) 1315.

1.3 Thin Layer Chromatography

[45] E. Heftmann, Chromatography, 2. ed., Reinhold Publ., New York 1967.

[46] D. R. Browning (Ed.), Chromatography, McGraw Hill, London 1969.

[47] K. Randerath, Dünnschicht-Chromatographie, 2. ed., Verlag Chemie, Weinheim 1965.

[48] E. Stahl (Ed.), Dünnschicht-Chromatographie, 2. ed., Springer, Berlin-Heidelberg-New York 1967.
R. Kaiser, Kopplung Gas-Dünnschicht-Chromatographie, p. 114;
H. Schweppe, Synthetische Farbstoffe, p. 583,
J. W. Copius-Peereboom, Nahrungsmittel und deren Hilfsstoffe, p. 601;
H. J. Petrowitz, Organische Synthetica, p. 626,
K. G. Krebs et al., Sprühreagentien, p. 813.

[49] F. Geiss, Die Parameter der Dünnschicht-Chromatographie, F. Vieweg & Sohn, Braunschweig 1972.

[50] J. C. Touchstone (Ed.), Quantitative Thin Layer Chromatography, Wiley-Interscience, New York 1973.

[51] J. Kirchner, Thin Layer Chromatography, 2. ed., Wiley-Interscience, New York 1978.

[52] H. Inagaki, Thin Layer Chromatography in: Tung, L. H., Fractionation of Synthetic Polymers. Principles and Practices, Dekker, New York 1977.

[53] CAMAG, Dünnschicht-Chromatographie, Company publication TL-8-D, 1978.

[54] H. P. Kaufmann, Fortschritte auf dem Gebiet der Lipoid-Analyse, Dünnschicht-Chromatographie Part 1, 2 and 3, Fette, Seifen, Anstrichm. 72 (1970) 811, 902, 993.

[55] R. Amos, Thin-Layer Chromatography in the heavy organic industry, Talanta, 20 (1973) 1231.

[56] B. J. Haywood, Thin Layer Chromatography an Annotated Bibliography 1964–1968, Ann Arbor Sci. Publ., Ann Arbor 1968.

[57] D. Jänchen, Thin-Layer Chromatography, Cumulative Bibliography I 1965–67 and II 1967–1969, CAMAG, Muttenz 1967, 1969.

[58] H. J. Issag, E. W. Barr, Recent developments in thin layer chromatography, Anal. Chem. 49 (1977) 83 A.

[59] G. Zweig, J. Sherma, Paper and thin-layer chromatography, Anal. Chem. 50 (1978) 5, 51 R, 52 (1980) 5, 276 R.

[60] E. Knappe, Die Dünnschicht-Chromatographie als Hilfsmittel bei der Untersuchung und Identifizierung von Lackmaterialien, Farbe + Lack 75 (1969) 36.

[61] J. G. Kreiner, W. C. Warner, The identification of rubber compounding ingredients using thin-layer chromatography, J. Chromatogr. 44 (1969) 315.

[62] E. Stahl, Gradient- und Transfer-Techniken in der Chromatographie, Z. Anal. Chem. 221 (1966) 3.

[63] H. A. Szymanski (Ed.), Progress in Infrared Spectroscopy, Vol. 3, Plenum Press, New York 1967.

[64] D. D. Rice, A direct transfer technique for preparing micropellets from thin-layer chromatograms for infrared identification, Anal. Chem. 39 (1867) 1906.

[65] K. Beyermann, E. Röder, Kombination von Dünnschicht-Chromatographie und infrarot-spektroskopischer Bestimmung von Mikromengen, gezeigt am Beispiel der Analyse von oralen Antikonzipientien, Z. Anal. Chem. 230 (1967) 347.

[66] H. R. Garner, H. Packer, New techniques for the preparation of KBr pellets from microsamples, Appl. Spectrosc. 22 (1968) 122.

[67] W. J. de Klein, Infrared spectra of compounds separated by thin layer chromatography using a potassium bromide micropellet technique, Anal. Chem. 41 (1969) 667.

[68] A. Zlatkis, R. E. Kaiser, HPTLC – High Performance Thin Layer Chromatography, J. Chromatogr. Lib. Vol. 9, Elsevier, Amsterdam 1977.

[69] A. Sidhu, J.-J. Martens, Typenunterscheidung basisgleicher Polymere mittels Dünnschicht-Chromatographie, Kunststoffe 65 (1976) 10, 699.

[70] HPTLC-Platten der Firmen Merck, Camag.

1.4 Liquid Column Chromatography

[71] L. R. Snyder, Principles of Adsorption Chromatography, Marcel Dekker, New York 1968.

[72] S. G. Perry, R. Amos, P. I. Brewer, Practical Liquid Chromatography, Plenum Press, New York 1972.

[73] L. R. Snyder, J. J. Kirkland, Introduction to Modern Liquid-Chromatography, Interscience, New York 1974.

[74] R. Amos, S. G. Perry, Liquid chromatography columns or thin layers? J. Chromatogr. 83 (1973) 245.

[75] Z. Deyl, K. Macek, J. Janak (Ed.), Liquid Columns Chromatography – a Survey of Modern Techniques and Applications, Elsevier, Amsterdam-Oxford-New York 1975.

[75a] Z. Deyl, K. Macek, J. Janak, Liquid Column Chromatography, J. Chromatography Library, Vol. 3, Elsevier, New York 1977.

[76] N. A. Parris, A Practical Manual on High Performance Liquid Chromatographic Methods, Instrumental Liquid Chromatography, Elsevier, Amsterdam-Oxford-New York 1976.

[77] N. A. Parris, Instrumental liquid chromatography, J. Chromatography Library, Vol. 5, Elsevier, Amsterdam-New York 1978.

[78] C. F. Simpson, Practical High Performance Liquid Chromatography, Heyden & Son, London 1976.

[79] H. Engelhardt, Hochdruck-Flüssigkeits-Chromatographie, Springer, Berlin/Heidelberg/New York 1975.

[79a] H. Engelhardt, High Performance Liquid Chromatography: Chemical Laboratory Practice, Springer, Berlin 1979.

[80] P. M. Rajcsanyi, E. Rajcsanyi, High Speed Liquid, Chromatography, Marcel Dekker, New York-Basel 1976.

[81] R. P. W. Scott, Contemporary Liquid Chromatography in A. Weissberger (Ed.), Techniques of Chemistry, Vol. XI, John Wiley, New York/London-Sidney/Toronto 1976.

[82] J. Cazes, (Ed.), Liquid Chromatography of Polymers and related Materials, Marcel Dekker, New York-Basel 1977.

[83] J. Cazes, G. Fallcik, Application of liquid chromatography to the solution of polymer problems, Polym. News 3 (1977) 295.

[83a] G. J. Fallcik, P. C. Talarico, R. R. McGough, Separation and analysis of polymer additives and components by liquid chromatography, SPE Techn. Pap. 22 (1976) 574.

[83b] R. Clément, La chromatographie en phase liquide, moyen moderne de recherche et d'analyse dans le domaine des peintures, FATIPEC Congr. 1976, 172.

[84] J. J. Stoveken, Effect of temperature on the analysis of polymer additives, Perkin-Elmer Liquid Chromatography, Technical Note 58, 1977.

[85] J. F. Johnson, R. S. Porter, M. J. R. Cantow, Gel permeation chromatography with organic solvents, Rev. Macromol. Chem. 1 (1966) 393.

[86] M. J. Cantow, Polymer Fractionation, Academic Press, New York-London 1967.

[87] H. Determann, Gelchromatographie, Springer, Berlin-Heidelberg-New York 1967.

[88] W. Heitz, W. Kern, Principles of gel chromatography and possibilities for its development, Angew. Makromol. Chem. 1 (1967) 150.

[89] J. F. Johnson, R. S. Porter (Ed.), Analytical Gel Permeation Chromatography, Polymer Symposia No. 21, J. Wiley, New York 1968.

[90] L. Fischer, Introduction to Gel Chromatography, North-Holland, Amsterdam-London 1969.

[91] J. C. Gidding, R. A. Keller (Ed.), Advances in Chromatography, Vol. 7: K. H. Altgeld, Theory and mechanism of gel permeation chromatography, Vol. 8: H. Determann, Principles of gel chromatography, Marcel Dekker, New York 1969.

[92] H. Determann, Gelchromatographie, eine Methode zur Stofftrennung aufgrund von Molekulargewichtsunterschieden, Chimia 23 (1969) 94.

[93] R. M. Mate, H. S. Lundstrom, Simultaneous measurements of oil content and molecular weight distribution of oil-extended elastomers by gel permeation chromatography, J. Polym. Sci. Part C 8 (1965) 233.

[94] D. G. Lesnini, Die Trennung von Alkydharzen durch Gelchromatographie, J. Paint Technol. 38 (1966) 498.

[95] D. F. Zinkel, L. C. Zank, Separation of resin from fatty acid methyl esters by gel-permeation chromatography, Anal. Chem. 40 (1968) 1144.

[96] W. Heitz, B. Bömer, H. Ullner, Gelchromatographie, 7. Commun.: Die Auflösung bei Trennung von Oligomeren, Makromol. Chemie 121 (1969) 102.

[97] H. Heitz, Gelchromatographie, Angew. Chemie 89 (1970) 675, Angew. Chem., Int. Ed. Engl. 9 (1970) 689.

[98] L. Mandik, Applications of GPC in the paint industry, Prog. Org. Coatings 5 (1977) 131.

[99] V. F. Gaylor, H. L. James, Gel permeation chromatography, Anal. Chem. 50 (1978) 5, 29 R.

[100] R. L. Bartosiewicz, The use of gel permeation chromatography as an analytical tool in the coating industry, J. Paint Technol. 39 (1967) 28.

[101] K. J. Bombaugh, W. A. Dark, R. F. Levangie, Application of gel chromatography to small molecules, Z. Anal. Chem. 236 (1968) 28.

[102] K. A. Boni, F. A. Sliemers, Jr, Gel permeation chromatography and the characterization of polymers, Batelle Techn. Rev. 17 (1968) 2.

[102a] D. Kranz, Methodik und Ergebnisse der Gelchromatographie, Kolloid Z. 227 (1968) 11.

1.5 Gas Chromatography

[103] R. Kaiser, Chromatographie in der Gasphase, 3. ed., Bibliographisches Institut, Mannheim 1975.

[104] E. Leibnitz, H. G. Struppe, Handbuch der Gaschromatographie, Verlag Chemie, Weinheim 1967.

[105] V. G. Berezkin, Analytical Reaction Gas Chromatography, Plenum Press, New York 1968.

[106] O. E. Schupp, Gas Chromatography, Wiley-Interscience, New York 1968.

[107] L. S. Ettre (Ed.), Ancillary Techniques of Gas Chromatography, Wiley-Interscience, New York 1969.

[108] R. L. Grob (Ed.), Modern Practice of Gas Chromatography, Wiley, New York 1977.

[109] L. S. Ettre, Gaschromatographie mit Kapillarsäulen, Eine Einführung, Vieweg & Sohn, Braunschweig 1975.

[109a] W. Jennings, Gas Chromatography with Glass Capillary Columns, Academic Press, New York 1978.

[110] V. G. Berezkin, V. R. Alishoyev, I. B. Nemirovskaya, Gas Chromatography of Polymers, Elsevier, Amsterdam 1977.

[111] K. H. Altgelt, T. H. Gouw, (Ed.), Chromatography in Petroleum Analysis, Marcel Dekker, New York-Basel 1979.

[112] H. Hachenberg, Industrial GC-Trace-Analysis, Heyden & Son, London-New York 1973.

[112a] H. Hachenberg, New examples for the application of GC head space analysis, Bodenseewerk Perkin-Elmer, Angewandte Chromatographie No. 25 E (1976).

Bibliography

[112b] H. Hachenberg, A. P. Schmidt, Gas Chromatographic Head Space Analysis, Heyden & Son, London-New York-Rheine 1977.

[113] C. E. H. Knapman, Gas Chromatographic Abstracts 1958–1968, Butterworths Scientific Publications, London 1960–1963 and 1964–1968, The Institute of Petroleum London.

[114] S. T. Preston, Gas Chromatographic Abstracts Cards and GC Abstracts Service, Preston Techn. Abstracts Co, Evanston, serial since 1958.

[115] O. E. Schupp et al. (Eds.), Gas Chromatographic Data Compilation, American Society for Testing Materials, Philadelphia 1967.

[115a] W. O. McReynolds, Gas Chromatographic Retention Data, Preston Technical Abstracts Co, Evanston, Ill. 1966.

[116] S. P. Cram, R. S. Juvet, Gas Chromatography (Review), Anal. Chem. 48 (1976) 5, 41 R.

[116a] S. P. Cram, T. H. Risby, Gas Chromatography, Anal. Chem. 50 (1978) 5, 213 R.

[117] B. J. Gudzinowicz, M. J. Gudzinowicz, H. F. Martin, Fundamentals of Integrated GC-MS, Marcel Dekker, New York-Basel 1977.

[117a] A. B. Littlewood, The coupling of gas chromatography with methods of identification: I. Mass spectrometry, Chromatographia 1 (1968) 37.

[118] K. Blau, G. King, Handbook of Derivatives for Chromatography, Heyden, London 1977.

[119] F. Scholl, Die Gaschromatographie und ihre Anwendung auf dem Anstrichmittelgebiet, Deut. Farben Z. 16 (1962) 146.

[119a] J. K. Haken, Gas chromatography – its application and potential in the analysis of coating materials, J. Oil Colour Chem. Ass. 49 (1966) 993.

[119b] J. K. Haken, Gas chromatography of coating materials, Dekker, New York 1975.

[119c] T. Helmen, Einsatzmöglichkeiten von IR-Spektroskopie und Gaschromatographie in der Lackindustrie, beleuchtet durch einige ausgewählte Beispiele, Farbe + Lack 80 (1974) 5, 715.

[120] T. R. Crompton, Identification of additives in polyolefines and polystyrenes, Eur. Polym. J. 4 (1968) 473.

[121] I. A. Fowlis, D. Welti, The collection of fractions separated by gasliquid chromatography, Analyst 92 (1967) 639.

[122] K. Witte, O. Dissinger, Eine neue Methode zum Auffangen gas-chromatographischer Mikrofraktionen, Z. Anal. Chem. 236 (1968) 119.

[123] W. H. King, R. T. O'Connor, Sampling aerosol GLC peaks for spectroscopy, J. Amer. Oil Chem. Soc. 45 (1968) 599.

1.6 IR-Spectroscopy

[124] R. W. B. Pearse, A. G. Gaydon, The Identification of Molecular Spectra, Chapman and Hall, London, 3. ed. 1965.

[125] D. H. Williams, I. Fleming, Spektroskopische Methoden in der organischen Chemie, Georg Thieme, Stuttgart 1968.

[126] N. J. Harrick, Internal Reflectance Spectrometry, Interscience-Wiley, New York 1967.

[127] W. Wendlandt, Modern Aspects of Reflectance Spectroscopy, Plenum Press, New York 1968.

[128] K. Kortüm, Reflexionsspektroskopie, Springer, Berlin-Heidelberg-New York 1969.

[129] P. Hirschfeld, Solution for the sample contact problem in ATR, Appl. Spectrosc. 21 (1967) 335.

[130] A. L. Smith, R. L. Kiley, Infrared quantitative analytical data index, Appl. Spectrosc. 18 (1964) 2.

[131] N. B. Colthup, L. H. Daly, S. E. Wiberly, Introduction to Infrared and Raman Spectroscopy, 2. ed., Academic Press, New York 1975.

[131a] C. N. R. Rao, Chemical Applications of Infrared Spectroscopy, Academic Press, New York-London 1963.

[132] L. H. Little, Infrared Spectra of Adsorbed Species, Academic Press, London-New York 1966.

[133] M. L. Hair, Infrared Spectroscopy in Surface Chemistry, Marcel Dekker, New York 1967.

[134] D. H. Martin, Spectroscopic Techniques for Infrared, North Holland, Amsterdam 1967.

[135] L. J. Bellamy, Advances in Infrared Group Frequencies, Barnes & Noble, New York 1968.

[135a] H. J. Hediger, Infrarotspektroskopie – Grundlagen, Anwendungen, Interpretation, Akademische Verlagsgesellschaft, Frankfurt am Main 1971.

[136] F. F. Bentley, L. D. Smithson, A. L. Rozek, Infrared Spectra and Characteristic Frequencies 700–300 cm^{-1}, Interscience, New York 1968.

[137] L. May (Ed.), Spectroscopic Tricks, Plenum Press, New York 1968.

[138] G. Kemmner, IR-Spektroskopie, Franckh'sche Verlagsbuchhandlung, Stuttgart 1969.

[138a] J. H. van der Maas, Basic Infrared Spectroscopy, Heyden & Son, London 1969.

[139] A. D. Cross, R. A. Jones, An Introduction to Practical Infra-Red Spectroscopy, 3. ed., Butterworths, London 1969.

[140] W. Brügel, Einführung in die Ultrarot-Spektroskopie, 4. ed., D. Steinkopff, Darmstadt 1969.

[141] H. A. Szymanski, R. E. Erickson, Infrared Band Handbook, 2. ed., 2. Vol., Plenum Press, New York 1970.

[141a] N. L. Alpert, W. E. Keiser, H. A. Szymanski, IR-Theory and Practice of Infrared Spectroscopy, 2. ed., Plenum Press, New York 1970.

[142] B. Schrader, W. Meier, (Eds.), Raman/IR-Atlas, Verlag Chemie, Weinheim.

[142a] H. Volkmann (Ed.), Handbuch der Infrarot-Spektroskopie, Verlag Chemie, Weinheim 1972.

[142b] H. Günzler, H. Böck, IR-Spektroskopie, Verlag Chemie, Weinheim 1975.

[143] IR-Spectroscopy Committee of Chicago Soc. for Paint Technology, Infrared Spectroscopy, Its Use in Coatings Industry, Fed. Soc. Paint Technology, Philadelphia 1969.

[143a] IR-Spectroscopy Committee of the Chicago Soc. for Coatings Technology, An Infrared Spectroscopy Atlas for the Coatings Industry, Fed. of Soc. for Coatings Technology, Philadelphia 1980.

[144] K. Nakamoto, Infrared Spectra of Inorganic and Coordination Compounds, Wiley Interscience, New York 1970.

[145] R. O. Crisler, Analytical chemistry review: Infrared spectroscopy, Anal. Chem. 43 (1970) 388 R.

[146] R. G. J. Miller, H. A. Willis, IRSCOT, Infrared Structural Correlation Tables and Data Cards, Heyden & Son, London 1964–1971.

[146a] Infrared Correlation Charts in Handbook of Chemistry and Physics, 61. ed., F 249, CRC-Press 1980/81.

[147] The ASTM Index to 92 000 IR Spectra, Vol. 1: Molecular Formula List; Vol. 2: Serial Number List; Vol. 3: Alphabetical List; American Society for Testing and Materials, Philadelphia, Pa.

[148] R. Mecke, F. Langenbucher, Infrared Spectra of Selected Chemical Compounds, Heyden & Son, London 1966.

[149] Dokumentation Molekülspektroskopie, Verlag Chemie, Weinheim, Butterworths, London.

[150] The Sadtler Standard Spectra, Sadtler Research Laboratories, Inc., Philadelphia.

[151] J. E. Saunders, F. F. Bentley, J. E. Katon, Low frequency infrared spectra of aliphatic mono-carboxylic acids, Appl. Spectrosc. 22 286.

J. E. Saunders, J. H. Lucier, F. F. Bentley, Far infrared spectra of saturated aliphatic esters, Appl. Spectrosc. *22* (1968) 697.

[152] R. J. Jakobsen, J. W. Brasch, Y. Mikawa, Past results and future prespects of the far-infrared studies of hydrogen bonding, Appl. Spectrosc. *22* (1968) 641.

[153] R. Caspary, Infrared spectroscopy at low temperature for the improved resolution of spectra, Appl. Spectrosc. *22* (1968), Spectrochim. Acta *21* (1965) 763.
R. Caspary, Alterations in the infrared spectrum (2 to 15 µ) of some ketones at the transition liquid-solid in the low temperature range, Appl. Spectrosc. *22* (1968) 689.

[154] T. S. Hermann, S. R. Harvey, Infrared spectroscopy at subambient temperatures, I–IV, Appl. Spectrosc. *23* (1969) 435, 451, 561, 473.

[155] W. Grimm, Zur UR-spektroskopischen Untersuchung kleiner Mengen fester Substanzen ohne Mikropreßeinrichtung, Chem. Techn. *17* (1965) 167.
W. J. de Klein, Infrared-spectroscopic identification of compounds separated by gas-liquid chromatography, using a potassium bromide micropellet technique, Z. Anal. Chem. *246* (1969) 294.

[156] H. J. Sloane, T. Johns, W. F. Ulrich, W. J. Cadman, Infrared examination of micro samples. Application of a specular reflectance system, Appl. Spectrosc. *19* (1965) 130.
K. Beyermann, Ein einfaches Verfahren zur infrarot-spektroskopischen Untersuchung von Mikrogramm-Mengen, Z. Anal. Chem. *226* (1967) 16.

[157] P. Krohmer, G. Kemmner, Methoden und Nachweisgrenzen bei der IR-spektroskopischen Untersuchung von Mikromengen, Z. Anal. Chem. *243* (1968) 80.
P. Krohmer, R. Duelli, Anwendungsmöglichkeiten eines neuen Mikroreflexionszusatzes, Perkin-Elmer-Tips, UR 39, 1968.

[158] T. S. Hermann, Identification of trace amounts of organophosphorus pesticides by frustrated multiple internal reflectance spectroscopy, Appl. Spectrosc. *19* (1965) 10.

[159] A. C. Gilby, J. Cassels, P. A. Wilks, Internal reflectance spectroscopy, III. Micro Sampling, Appl. Spectrosc. *24* (1970) 539.

[159a] J. D. Frazee, Internal reflection spectroscopy: application to organic coatings and plastic sheeting, J. Oil Colour Chem. Ass. *57* (1974) 9, 300.

[159b] K. Reichert, Zur chemischen Analytik von Druckbeschichtungen, Farbe + Lack *80* (1974) 920.

[160] G. L. K. Huntct, Modified infrared salt plate for liquid microliter samples without beam condenser, Appl. Spectrosc. *18* (1964) 159.

[161] B. H. Blake, D. S. Erley, F. L. Beman, Sampling technique for obtaining infrared spectra of gas chromatographic fractions, Appl. Spectrosc. *18* (1964) 114.

[162] K. H. Kubeczka, Einfache Anordnung zum Auffangen kleinster, gaschromatographisch getrennter Substanzmengen für die IR-Spektroskopie, Naturwissenschaften *52* (1965) 429.

[163] H. Feuerberg, M. Manjock, H. Weigel, Schnelle Identifizierung gaschromatographisch getrennter Substanzen mit Hilfe eines handelsüblichen Infrarot-Spektralphotometers, Z. Anal. Chem. *219* (1966) 241.

[164] S. Behrendt, H. Richtering, Infrared microspectrometry of capillary gas chromatography effluents and of gasphase free radicals, J. Chromatogr. *24* (1966) 1.

[165] G. D. Price, E. C. Sunas, J. F. Williams, Microcell for obtaining normal contrast infrared solution spectra at the five microgram levels, Anal. Chem. *39* (1967) 138.

[166] M. K. Snavely, J. G. Grasselli, Simple techniques for trapping fractions from gas chromatographs for infrared spectroscopy, Perkin-Elmer Instrum. News Sci. Ind. *17* (1966) 6.

[167] K. Beyermann, Zur Kombination von Gas-Chromatographie und Infrarot-Mikroanalyse, Z. Anal. Chem. *230* (1967) 414.

[168] R. F. Kendall, Method for rapid transfer of GLC fractions into infrared cavity, Appl. Spectrosc. *21* (1967) 31.

[169] H. Copier, J. H. van der Maas, Micro infrared spectrometry of gas chromatographic fractions, Spectrochim. Acta *23* A (1967) 2699.

[170] M. S. D. Low, S. K. Freeman, Measurement of IR spectra of gas-liquid chromatography fractions using multiple-scan interference spectroscopy, Anal. Chem. *39* (1967) 194.

[171] B. Littlewood, The coupling of gas chromatography with methods of identification. III. Infrared spectroscopy, Chromatographia *1* (1968) 223.

[172] A. S. Curry, D. F. Read, C. Brown, R. W. Jenkins, Micro infrared spectroscopy of gas chromatographic fractions, J. Chromatogr. *38* (1968) 200.

[173] W. J. de Klein, Infrared-spectroscopic identification of compounds separated by gas-liquid chromatography, using a potassium bromide micropellet technique, Z. Anal. Chem. *246* (1969) 294.

[174] G. Leukroth, Analyse von Klebstoffen durch Kombination von Gaschromatographie und IR-Spektroskopie mit Hilfe eines GC-IR-Analysators, Adhäsion *12* (1970) 457.

[175] K. Beyermann, Grundlagen und Arbeitstechnik der Mikrophotometrie, 3. Commun., Mikrophotometrische Methoden im infraroten Spektralbereich, Fortschr. Chem. Forsch. *11* (1969) 484.

[176] D. Welti, R. Stephany, Some comments on the infrared spectra of vapors, Appl. Spectrosc. *22* (1968) 678.

[177] D. Welti, Infrared Vapour Spectra, Heyden & Son, London 1970.

[177a] Digital IR Spectra of 2300 Vapor-Phase Compounds of interest to EPA, K. H. Shafer, Environmental and health Chem., Battelle Columbus Labs, Columbus, Ohio 45 200.

[178] A. B. Littlewood (Ed.), Gas Chromatography, 1966, Inst. of Petroleum, London 1967.

[179] R. W. Hannah, IR spectra of latex emulsions by computer subtraction, Perkin-Elmer Infrared Bulletin 56 (1977).

[179a] J. P. Coates, Applications of the Model 580 (issue 1, 2, 3, 4), Perkin-Elmer, 1978.

[179b] G. Peitscher, Rechnerunterstützte IR-Spektroskopie in der industriellen Analytik, Chem.-Anl.-Verfahren *7* (1979) 86.

[180] Wilks Model 41 Vapor Phase GC-IR-Attachment, Wilks Scientific Co, Norwalk.

[180a] IR-Interference-spectrometers, e.g. Block-Model 200, Block FTS-14 Block Engineering Inc., Distr. Dunn Analytical Instruments, Silver Spring, Maryland, USA.

[180b] Fourier Transform Infrared Spectroscopy in Combination with Chromatography, J. Chromatogr. Sci. *17* (1979) No. 8.

[181] Fast-IR-Spectrometer Warner and Swasey Model 501, The Warner and Swasey Co, 32–16 Downing Street, Flushing, NY.

1.7 UV Spectroscopy

[182] M. Pestemer, Anleitung zum Messen von Absorptionsspektren im Ultraviolett und Sichtbaren, G. Thieme, Stuttgart 1964.

[183] H. H. Jaffe, M. Orchin, Theory and Applications of Ultraviolet Spectroscopy, John Wiley, New York 1962.

[184] C. N. R. Rao, UV and Visible Spectroscopy, 2. ed., Butterworths, London 1967.

[184a] A. D. Baker, C. R. Brundle (Eds.), Electron. Spectroscopy: Theory, Techniques, Applications, 3. Vol., Academic Press, London 1978.

Bibliography

[185] W. Foerst (Ed.), Ullmanns Encyklopädie der technischen Chemie, Vol. II/1, V. Zanker: Spektroskopie im Sichtbaren und Ultraviolett, Urban & Schwarzenberg, München – Berlin 1961.

[186] R. F. Barrow, D. A. Long, J. Sheridan (Ed.), Molecular Spectroscopy – A Review of the Literature published in 1977 and 1978.

[186a] J. P. Phillips (Ed.), Organic Electronical Spectral Data, (since 1946), New York, Vol. 15 in 1979.

[187] E. I. Stearns, Practice of Absorption Spectrophotometry, Wiley, New York 1969.

[188] M. Pestemer, Correlation Tables for the Structural Determination of Organic Compounds, Verlag Chemie, Weinheim 1975.

[189] R. G. White, Handbook of Ultraviolet Methods, Plenum Press, New York 1965.

[190] V. S. Fikhtengol'ts, R. V. Zolotareva, Yu. L'vov, S. V. Lebedev, Ultraviolet Spectra of Elastomers and Rubber Chemicals (engl. translation), PP Data Division, 1966.

[191] J. P. Phillips, R. E. Lyle, P. R. Jones, Organic Electronic Spectra Data, Vol. I–V (Vol. V 1960–61), Interscience, New York 1969.

[192] Sadtler Standard Spectra, Ultraviolet, Sadtler Res. Lab., Philadelphia.

[193] L. Lang, Absorption Spectra in the Ultraviolet and Visible Region, Vol. I–XI, Akademiai Kiado, Budapest 1960–1968.

[194] DMS, UV-Atlas organischer Verbindungen Vol. I–V, Butterworths, London, Verlag Chemie, Weinheim 1966–1971.

1.8 Mass Spectroscopy

[195] G. Spiteller, Massenspektrometrische Strukturanalyse organischer Verbindungen, Verlag Chemie, Weinheim 1966.

[196] M. Spitteler, G. Spitteler, Massenspektren von Lösemitteln, Verunreinigungen, Säulenbelegmaterialien und einfachen aliphatischen Verbindungen, Springer, Wien 1973.

[197] H. Kienitz (Ed.), Massenspektrometrie, Verlag Chemie, Weinheim 1968.

[198] J. H. Beynon, R. A. Saunders, A. E. Williams, The Mass Spectra of Organic Molecules, Elsevier, New York 1968.

[199] F. A. White, Mass Spectrometry in Science and Technology, Wiley, New York 1968.

[200] W. Benz, Massenspektrometrie organischer Verbindungen, Akademische Verlagsgesellschaft, Frankfurt 1969.

[201] H. D. Beckey, Principles of Field Ionisation and Field Desorption Mass Spectrometry, Pergamon Press, New York 1977.

[201a] K. H. Maurer, U. Rapp, Field Desorption – a powerful technique in mass spectrometry, Varian MAT Application Note No. 14, 1973.

[201b] P. P. Lattimer, K. R. Welch, J. B. Pausch, U. Rapp, Field Desorption Mass Spectra of Polymers and Polymer Chemicals, Varian MAT Application Note No. 27, 1978.

[201c] T. Matsuo, H. Matsuda, I. Katakuse, Use of field desorption mass spectra of polystyrene and polypropylene glycol as mass references up to mass 10000, Anal. Chem. 51 (1979) 1329.

[202] E. C. Horning, M. G. Horning, D. I. Caroll, I. Dzidic R. N. Stillwell, Chemical Ionisation Mass Spectrometry in Gas Chromatography, in E. Costa, B. Holmstedt (Eds.), Mass Spectrometry in Neurobiology, Raven Press, New York 1973.

[202a] D. H. Hunnemann, The electron impact and chemical ionisation mass spectra of diester plasticizers, Varian MAT application Note No. 19, 1978.

[203] A. Cornu, R. Massot, Compilation of Mass Spectral Data, Heyden & Son, London 1966.

[204] ASTM (Ed.), Index of Mass Spectral Data, American Society for Testing and Materials, Philadelphia 1969.

[205] E. Stenhagen, S. Abrahamsson, F. W. McLafferty (Eds.), Atlas of Mass Spectral Data, Wiley, New York 1969.

[205a] Archives of Mass Spectral Data, Wiley, New York (Journal, started 1969).

[205b] MSDC, Eight Peak Index of Mass Spectra Data, 2. ed., Mass Spectrometry Data Center, Aldermaston UK 1974.

1.9 Emission Spectral Analysis

[206] H. Scheller, Einführung in die Angewandte Spektrochemische Analyse, VEB Verlag Technik, Berlin 1953.

[207] W. Seith, K. Ruthardt, W. Rollwagen, Chemische Spektralanalyse, 5. ed., Springer, Berlin 1958.

[208] ASTM, Methods for Emission Spectrochemical Analysis, 5. ed., American Society for Testing Materials, Philadelphia 1968.

[209] L. H. Ahrens, S. R. Taylor, Spectrochemical Analysis, 2. ed., Pergamon Press, London–Paris 1961.

[210] R. Mannkopff, G. Friede, Grundlagen und Methoden der chemischen Emissionsspektralanalyse, Verlag Chemie, Weinheim 1975.

1.10 X-Ray Fluorescence Analysis

[211] R. Jenkins, J. L. de Vries, Practical X-Ray Spectrometry, Springer, New York 1967.

[212] R. O. Müller, Spektrochemische Analysen mit Röntgenfluorenszenz, Oldenbourg, München 1967.

[213] L. S. Birks, X-Ray Spectrochemical Analysis, 2. ed., Wiley-Interscience, New York 1969.

[214] E. P. Bertin, Principles and Practice of X-Ray Spectrometric Analysis, Plenum Press, New York 1970.

[215] R. Wollast, A. Toussaint, Utilisation de la spectroscopie de fluorescence des Rayons X dans l'etude des revetements protecteurs, VIII Fatipec Congress, 1966.

[216] G. M. Kline, X-ray analysis of metallic trace elements in polymers, Mod. Plast. 45 (1968) 157.

[217] J. D. McGinness, R. W. Scott, X-ray emission analysis of paints by thin film method, Anal. Chem. 41 (1969) 1858.

1.11 X-Ray Diffraction Analysis

[218] H. S. Peiser, H. P. Rooksby, A. J. C. Wilson, X-Ray Diffraction by Polycrystalline Materials, Institute of Physics, London 1955.

[219] H. Neff, Grundlagen und Anwendung der Röntgen-Feinstruktur-Analyse, Oldenbourg, München 1962.

[220] A. Guinier, X-Ray Diffraction in Crystals, Imperfect Crystals and Amorphous Bodies, Freeman and Co, San Francisco-London 1963.

[221] L. I. Mirkin, Handbook of X-Ray Analysis of Polycristalline Materials, Consultants Bureau, New York 1964.

[222] J. D. H. Donnay, H. M. Ondik (Eds.), Crystal Data Determinative Tables, US Dept. of Commerce, NBS and JCPDS, 1972.

[223] K. Lonsdale (Ed.), International Tables for X-Ray Crystallography;
Vol. I   Symmetry Groups 1965;
Vol. II Mathematical Tables 1959;
Vol. III Physical and Chemical Tables 1962;
The Kynoch Press, Birmingham 1959–1965.

[224] Joint Committee on Powder Diffraction Standards (JCPDS), Powder Diffraction File, Swarthmore, Pennsylvania.

1.12 Other Instrumental Methods

[225] Nuclear Magnetic Resonance Spectroscopy – Principles and Applications in Organic Chemistry, Academic Press, New York 1969.

[225a] H. Günther, NMR-Spektroskopie, Thieme, Stuttgart 1973.

[225b] L. M. Jackman, S. Sternhell, Applications of Nuclear Magnetic Resonance Spectroscopy in Organic Chemistry, 2. ed., Pergamon Press, New York 1969.

[225c] Th. Clerc, E. Pretsch, Kernresonanzspektroskopie, Akademische Verlagsgesellschaft, Frankfurt 1970.

[225d] I. Ya. Slonim, A. N. Lyubimov, The NMR of Polymers, Plenum Press, New York 1970.

[226] D. C. Johnson, W. R. Heineman, P. T. Kissinger, Analytical Electrochemistry, Anal. Chem. 52 (1980) 5, R 131.

[227] M. D. Lumb, Luminescence Spectroscopy, Academic Press, London 1978.

[227a] E. L. Wehry, Molecular fluorescence, phosphorescence and chemiluminescence spectrometry, Anal. Chem. 52 (1980) 5, 75 R.

[228] D. Schultze, Differentialthermoanalyse, VEB Verlag der Wissenschaften, Berlin 1969.

[228a] M. I. Pope, M. D. Judd, Differential Thermal Analysis, Heyden, London 1977.

[229] A. H. Wachter, W. Simon, Molecular weight determination of polystyrene standards by vapor pressure osmometry, Anal. Chem. 41 (1969) 91.

[229a] Apparatus descriptions of following companies:
Hewlett-Packard, Böblingen;
Bodenseewerk Perkin-Elmer, Überlingen;
Knauer, Berlin.

[229b] T. P. Schreiber, Coordinated surface analysis, Intern. Lab. May/June 1979, 171.

[229c] R. Holm, L. Morbitzer, S. Storp, Anwendungsmöglichkeiten von ESCA im Polymerbereich, Kunststoffe 67 (177) 11.

[229d] E. N. Haeussler, Ion Scattering Spectroscopy (ISS) Chem. Produktion 5 (1978) 33.

2 Plasticizers

2.1 Survey and Classification

[230] K. Thinius, Chemie, Physik und Technologie der Weichmacher, VEB Verlag Technik, Berlin 1960.

[231] F. Fritz, Die wichtigsten Lösungs- und Weichmachungsmittel, VEB Verlag Technik, Berlin 1957.

[232] H. Gnamm, W. Sommer, Die Lösungs- und Weichmachungsmittel, 7. ed., Wissenschaftliche Verlagsgesellschaft, Stuttgart 1958.

[233] W. M. Münzinger, Weichmachungsmittel für Kunststoffe und Lacke, Konradin Verlag, Stuttgart 1959.

[234] P. Bruins, Plasticizer Technology, Reinhold Publ., New York 1965.

[235] B. Parkyn, F. Lamb, B. V. Clifton, Polyesters Vol. II. Unsaturated Polyesters and Polyester Plasticizers, American Elsevier, New York.

[236] I. Mellan, Plasticizer Evaluation and Performance 1967, Noyes Development Corp.

[237] A. L. Baseman, Plasticizers 67, Plast. Technol. 13 (1967) 37.

[238] A. O. Focsaneanu, Primäre und sekundäre Weichmacher in der Kunststoffindustrie, Seifen-Öle-Fette-Wachse 96 (1970) 895.

[239] E. J. Wickson, P. O. Miller, Plasticizers, Mod. Plast. Encycl. 1970/71, 390.

2.3 Thin Layer, Column, and Gel Chromatography of Plasticizers

[240] M. Wandel, H. Tengler, H. Ostromow, Die Analyse von Weichmachern, Springer, Berlin–Heidelberg–New York 1967.

[241] A. Fiorenza, G. Bonomi, Identification of antioxidants, accelerators and plasticizers in rubber compounds by column chromatography and ultraviolet and infrared spectrophotometry, Rubber Chem. Technol. 41 (1968) 630.

[242] J. W. Copius-Peereboom, Über die Identifizierung von Weichmachern mit Hilfe der Dünnschichtchromatographie, J. Chromatogr. 4 (1960) 323.

[243] D. Braun, Dünnschichtchromatographische Analyse von Weichmachern, Kunststoffe 52 (1962) 2.

[244] D. Braun, Qualitative Analyse von Weichmachern mittels Dünnschichtchromatographie, Chimia 19 (1965) 77.

[245] D. Braun, Chromatographische Verfahren zur Analyse von Weichmachern, Gummi Asbest Kunstst. 18 (1965) 686

[246] R. Klement, A. Wild, Dünnschichtchromatographie von Phosphorsäureestern, Z. Anal. Chem. 195 (1963) 180.

[247] K. Bürger, Dünnschichtchromatographische Methode zur Bestimmung der Molgewichtsverteilung und des Oxethylierungsgrades von Polyethylenoxidverbindungen, Z. Anal. Chem. 196 (1963) 259.

[248] K. Bürger, Die Dünnschichtchromatographische Kennzeichnung von Polyethylenglykolen, Z. Anal. Chem. 224 (1966) 421.

[249] F. Nagy, Zur Trennung und Identifizierung einzelner Kunststoff-Weichmacher mit Hilfe der Dünnschichtchromatographie, Z. Lebensm. Unters. Forsch. 126 (1965) 282.

[250] A. Hilt, W. Funke, Charakterisierung von Polyestern durch chromatographische Methoden, Deut. Farben Z. 20 (1966) 567.

[251] M. Wandel, H. Tengler, Chromatographische Verfahren zur Identifizierung von Weichmachern. Analyse von Phthalsäureestern, Kunststoffe 55 (1965) 655.

[251a] M. Wandel, H. Tengler, Chromatographische Verfahren zur Identifizierung von Weichmachern. Analyse von Citronensäure- und Sebacinsäureestern, Kunstst. Rundsch. 12 (1965) 559.

[251b] M. Wandel, H. Tengler, Chromatographische Verfahren zur Identifizierung von Weichmachern. Analyse von Adipin- und Azelainsäureestern, Plastverarbeiter 16 (1965) 251, 559, 607, 711.

[252] C. Persiani, P. Cukor, Liquid chromatographic method for the determination of phthalate esters, J. Chromatogr. 109 (1975) 413.

[252a] S. Mori, Identification and determination of phthalate esters in river water by HPCL, J. Chromatogr. 129 (1976) 53.

[252b] A. Otsuki, Reversed phase chromatography of phthalate esters from aqueous solutions, J. Chromatogr. 133 (1977) 402.

[253] J. G. Kreiner, The identification of epoxy plasticizers using TLC, J. Chromatogr. 75 (1973) 271.

[254] D. Gross, K. Strauss, Hochdruck-Flüssigkeitschromatographie – eine Analysenmethode für Weichmacher-Gemische, Kunststoffe 67 (1977) 426.

[255] J. K. Stoveken, Rapid analysis of phthalate plasticizers, Perkin-Elmer, Liquid Chromatography 62 (Report).

[256] Anfärbreagenzien für die Dünnschicht- und Papierchromatographie, E. Merck, Darmstadt 1970, TLC Visualization Reagents and Chromatographic Solvents Eastman Kodak Co, No. J. J. 5, Rochester 1969.

[257] W. Diemair, K. Pfeilsticker jr., Bestimmung des Übergangs fremder Stoffe von Kunststoffgegenständen auf Lebensmittel, Z. Anal. Chem. 212 (1965) 53.

Bibliography

[258] J. H. Rau, H. Haase, Dünnschichtchromatographische Trennung und infrarotspektroskopische Identifizierung von Weichmacher-Mischungen aus beschichteten Geweben, Melliand Textilber. *46* (1965) 1317.

[259] H. Haase, Trennung und Identifizierung von Kunststoff-Weichmachern. Part I. Isolierung von Weichmachern und deren gaschromatographische Trennung und Bestimmung, Kaut. Gummi Kunstst. *20* (1967) 501.

[260] H. Haase, Trennung und Identifizierung von Kunststoff-Weichmachern. Part II. Dünnschichtchromatographische Trennung und infrarotspektroskopische Bestimmung, Kaut. Gummi Kunstst. *21* (1968) 9.

[261] E. Hagen, Über neue Möglichkeiten zur Identifizierung und Abtrennung isomerer aliphatischer Weichmacher über Harnstoffeinschlußverbindungen, Plaste Kaut. *15* (1968) 557.

[262] R. Schöllner, J. Hellwig, Trennung von ölmodifizierten Polyesteroligomeren durch Säulen-, Dünnschicht- und Gelpermeationschromatographie, Fette, Seifen, Anstrichm. *70* (1968) 770.

[263] R. Schöllner, P. Löhnert, Die Trennung von linearen Polyesteroligomeren durch Dünnschichtchromatographie, Harnstoffeinschluß und Craigverteilung, Plaste Kaut. *15* (1968) 436.

[264] R. Schöllner, Die Inhaltsstoffe der Polyester des Systems Triol/Monool-Dicarbonsäure, Plaste Kaut. *15* (1968) 216.

[265] K. Thoma, R. Rombach, E. Ullmann, Dünnschichtchromatographischer Nachweis und Identifizierung grenzflächenaktiver Ester und Ether von Polyethylenglykolen, Sci. Pharm. *32* (1964) 216, Arch. Pharm. *298* (1965) 19.

[266] H. Steuerle, W. Pfab, Bestimmung von Weichmachern in Milchschläuchen aus weichgemachtem PVC, Deut. Lebensm. Rundsch. *65* (1969) 113.

[267] W. Fischer, G. Leukroth, Trennung und Nachweis von PVC-Weichmachern mit Hilfe physikalisch-chemischer Analysenverfahren, Plastverarbeiter *20* (1969) 107.

[267a] U. Brinkman, A. de Kok, G. de Vries, H. Reymer, HPLC and TLC of polychlorinated biphenyls, J. Chrom. *128* (1976) 101.

[267b] U. Brinkman, A. de Kok, H. Reymer, G. de Vries, Analysis of polychlorinated naphthalenes by HPLC and TLC, J. Chrom. *129* (1976) 193.

[267c] U. Brinkman, J. Seetz, H. Reymer, High-speed liquid chromatography of polychlorinated biphenyls and related compounds, J. Chrom. *116* (1976) 353.

[267d] U. Brinkman, A. de Kok, HPLC analysis of the heptachloronaphthalenes present in Halowax 1051, J. Chrom. *129* (1976) 451.

[268] E. Schröder, W. Mische, Auftrennung von Weichmachern unterschiedlichen Molekulargewichts durch Gelpermeationschromatographie an lipophilen Dextrangelen, Plaste Kaut. *15* (1968) 258.

[268a] R. A. Proseus, Rapid monitoring of variations in lubricating oils by gel permeation chromatography J. Chrom. *97* (1974) 201.

[269] R. W. R. Baker, Gel filtration of phthalate esters, J. Chromatogr. *154* (1978) 3.

[270] D. F. Zinkel, L. C. Zank, Trennung der Harzsäuremethylester von den Fettsäuremethylestern durch Gel-Permeations-Chromatographie, Anal. Chem. *40* (1968) 1144.

[270a] T. Kato, S. Kido, H. Watanabe, M. Yamamoto, T. Hashimoto, High resolution and high speed gel permeation chromatography on oligomers and plasticizers, J. App. Polym. Sci. *19* (1975) 629.

[270b] S. C. Ammundson, Determination of di (2-ethylhexyl)-phthalate, mono (2-ethylhexyl)phthalate and phthalic acid by high pressure liquid chromatography, J. Chromatogr. Sci. *16* (1978) 170.

2.4 Gas-Chromatographic Analysis of Plasticizers

[271] J. Zulaica, G. Guiochon, Fast qualitative and quantitative microanalysis of plasticiziers in plastics by gas liquid chromatography, Anal. Chem. *35* (1963) 1724.

[272] J. Zulaica, G. Guichon, Analisis de plastificantes por cromatografia en fase gaseosa, Rev. Plast. Mod. *79* (1963) 13.

[273] G. Esposito, Identification and determination of plasticizers in laquers by programmed-temperature gas chromatography, Report No. AD 403572, Office Techn. Service, US Department of Commerce, Washington DC 1964.

[273a] A. Krishen, Programmed temperature GC for identification of ester plasticizers, Anal. Chem. *43* (1971) 1130.

[274] J. H. Rau, G. Balbach, H. Haase, Die gaschromatographische Trennung und Bestimmung von Weichmachern in beschichteten Geweben, Melliand Textilber. *45* (1964) 539.

[274a] M. Gillio-Tos, A. Vimercati, Gaschromatographische Identifizierung von Weichmachern in Kunststoffen, Kunststoffe *56* (1966) 409.

[275] E. Knappe, N. Miessner, Die Gaschromatographie der Polyalkohole als aussagefähiges Instrument bei der Untersuchung von Lackharzen und Lackfilmen, FATIPEC Congr. (1976) 316.

[275a] D. Sissons, D. Welti, Structural identification of polychlorinated biphenyls in commercial mixtures by GLC, NMR and MS, J. Chrom. *60* (1971) 15.

[275b] J. Krupcik, P. A. Leclercq, A. Simova, P. Suchanek, M. Collak, J. Hrivnak, Possibilities and limitations of capillary GC and MS in the analysis of polychlorinated biphenyls, J. Chrom. *119* (1976) 271.

[275c] P. W. Albro, J. K. Hasemann, T. A. Clemmer, B. J. Corbett, Identification of the polychlorinated biphenyls in a mixture by GC, J. Chrom. *136* (1977) 147.

[276] J. Pollerberg, Die Gas-Chromatographie von Ethylenoxid-Addukten, Fette, Seifen, Anstrichm. *69* (1967) 179.

[277] J. Törnquist, Quantitative Analysis of polyethylene glycols by gas chromatography after silylation, Acta Chem. Scand. *21* (1967) 2095.

[278] M. K. Withers, Gas-Chromatographie von Polyethern. 1. Commun. Polyethylenglykole, J. Gas Chromatogr. *6* (1968) 242.

[279] J. P. Fletcher, H. E. Persinger, Molecular weight distribution of liquid polyethylene glycols: Determination by gas chromatography, J. Polymer. Sci. Part A-1, *6* (1968) 1025.

[280] C. Calzolari, E. Favretto, Gas-chromatographische Bestimmung der Molekulargewichtsverteilung von Polyethylenglykol-Produkten, J. Chromatogr. *39* (1969) 318.

2.5 Thin Layer and Gas Chromatography of Plasticizer Degradation Products

[281] E. Bancher, H. Scherz, Dicarbon- und Hydroxycarbonsäuren, Mikrochim. Acta (1964) 1159.

[281a] M. Richards, Separation of mono- and dicarboxylic acids by liquid chromatography, J. Chromatogr. *115* (1975) 259.

[282] D. Braun, G. Vorendohre, Über den dünnschichtchromatographischen Nachweis von phenolischen Komponenten in Weichmachern, Z. Anal. Chem. *207* (1965) 26.

[283] W. Diemair, K. Pfeilsticker, Zur Analytik der Weichmacher in Kunststoffen. Dünnschicht-chromatographische Trennung der Alkohole aus monomeren Esterweichmachern, Z. Anal. Chem. *234* (1968) 418.

[284] R. E. Sinclair et al., A durable high-temperature GC column, J. Chromatogr. Sci. 9 (1971) 126.

[285] G. G. Esposito, M. H. Swann, Identification of polyhydric alcolhols in synthetic resins by programmed temperature gas chromatography, Anal. Chem. 33 (1961) 1854.

[285a] J. R. Ashes, J. K. Haken, Gas Chromatography of homologous esters, J. Chromatogr. 101 (1974) 103.

[285b] G. Castello, G. D'Amato, S. Munari, Correlations between the physical properties and structure of alcohols and their gas chromatographic behaviour on polar and non polar stationary phases, J. Chromatogr. 131 (1977) 41, 150 (1978) 319.

[285c] R. V. Golovnya, V. P. Uralets, T. E. Kuzmenko, Characterization of fatty acid methyl esters by gas chromatography on siloxane liquid phases, J. Chromatogr. 121 (1976) 118, (1978) D 29, Table 1113.

[285d] B. J. Allen, G. M. Elsea, K. P. Keller, H. D. Kinder, Quantitative hydrolysis-gas chromatographic methods for the determination of selected acids and glycols in polyesters, Anal. Chem. 49 (1977) 741.

[285e] M. Mattson, G. Petersson, Reference GLC data for the analysis of phenolic components as trimethylsilyl derivatives, J. Chromatogr. Sci. 15 (1977) 546.

[286] J. Rawlinson, E. L. Deeley, The analysis of polymeric esters by interesterification and gas liquid chromatography, J. Oil Colour Chem. Ass. 50 (1967) 373.

[287] J. B. Stead, A. H. Hindley, Eine modifizierte Analysenmethode für Oxyethylen-Oxypropylen-Copolymere durch chemische Spaltung und Gas-Chromatographie, J. Chromatogr. 42 (1969) 470.

[288] M. Wandel, H. Tengler, Gaschromatographische Methoden zur Bestimmung von Weichmacheranteilen aus Kunstfolien, die in darin verpackte Lebensmittel diffundieren, Deut. Lebensm. Rundsch. 59 (1963) 326.

[289] C. Landault, G. Guiochon, Fast analysis of phenol, methylphenols and polymethylphenols by gas chromatography using packed capillary columns, Anal. Chem. 39 (1967) 713.

[290] W. Fischer, L. Jaehn, Analytische Untersuchungen von Weichmachern in PVC-Materialien durch Pyrolyse-Gaschromatographie, Plastverarbeiter 17 (1966) 117.

[290a] W. Fischer, H. Meuser, Analytische Bestimmung von Weichmachermaterialien in Vulkanisaten durch Pyrolyse Gaschromatographie, Gummi Asbest Kunstst. 20 (1967) 17.

[291] A. Kuksis, Progress in the analysis of lipids IX u. X Gas chromatography, Part 1 and 2, Fette, Seifen, Anstrichm. 73 (1971) 130, 332.

[292] B. D. Sully, J. F. Janes et al., Residual odour in plasticizers measurement of volatile components by a modified GLC technique, J. Appl. Chem. 16 (1966) 333.

2.6 IR Spectroscopy of Plasticizers

[293] M. Meise, H. Ostromow, Infrarotspektroskopische Identifizierung von Weichmachern in Extrakten aus Kunststoffen, Kunststoffe 54 (1964) 213.

[294] Sadtler Spectra of Commercial Compounds; Plasticizers, Sadtler Res. Lab., Philadelphia.

[295] K. Ohwada, Infrared-absorption studies on some organic phosphates, Appl. Spectrosc. 21 (1967) 332.

[296] K. Ohwada, Infrared spectra of organic phosphates in the combination region of the C-O and P-O vibrations, Appl. Spectrosc. 22 (1968) 209.

[297] J. E. Saunders, F. F. Bentley, J. E. Katon, Low frequency infrared spectra of aliphatic mono-carboxylic acids, Appl. Spectrosc. 22 (1968) 286.

[298] W. R. Feairhiller, J. E. Katon, Infrared spectra-structure correlation of conjugated unsaturated mono-carboxylic acids in the 750–250 cm^{-1} region, Appl. Spectrosc. 22 (1968) 488.

[299] H. Schmidt, UV- und NIR-Absorptionsspektroskopie für die Analyse von Aromatengemischen, Erdöl Kohle 21 (1968) 334.

[300] G. Brandes, Die Strukturgruppen von Erdölfraktionen. Die Strukturgruppenanalyse mit Hilfe der IR-Spektroskopie, Brennst. Chem. 37 (1956) 263, 700.

[301] H. Luther, H. H. Oelert, Zur molekülspektroskopischen Gruppenanalyse gesättigter Kohlenwasserstoffe, Angew. Chem. 69 (1957) 262.

[302] H. Luther, H. H. Oelert, Zur molekülspektroskopischen Gruppenanalyse gesättigter Kohlenwasserstoffe, Z. Anal. Chem. 183 (1961) 161.

[303] H. Luther, H. H. Oelert, Neue Ergebnisse der Strukturgruppenanalyse von Mineralölen durch Infrarot- und Kernresonanzspektroskopie, Erdöl Kohle 24 (1971) 216.

[304] P. H. Berthold, H. Rösner, G. Wilde, Strukturgruppenanalyse, Vol. 2, VEB Dt. Verlag für Grundstoffindustrie 1967/68.

[305] P. H. Berthold, IR-spektrometrische Bestimmung des mittleren Methylgruppengehaltes in Kohlenwasserstoffwachsen, Chem. Techn. 20 (1968) 103.

[306] W. Fischer, G. Leukroth, Qualitative Bestimmung von Mineralölweichmachern in Vulkanisaten mit Hilfe moderner physikalischer Analysenmethoden, Gummi Asbest Kunstst. 20 (1967) 1266.

[307] S. Kägler, Neue Mineralölanalyse, Spektroskopie und Chromatographie in Grundlagen, Geräten und Anwendung, Alfred Hüthig, Heidelberg 1969.

[308] H. H. Oelert, Entwicklung einer auf IR-, NMR-Spektroskopie und Elementaranalyse beruhenden Strukturgruppenanalyse höhersiedender Kohlenwasserstoffgemische und Mineralölanteile, Z. Anal. Chem. 257 (1971) 177.

2.8 Mass Spectroscopy of Plasticizers

[309] C. Djerassi, C. Fenselau, MS von Dialkylphthalaten, J. Amer. Chem. Soc. 87 (1965) 5756.

[310] F. W. McLafferty, R. S. Gohlke, Mass spectrometric analysis, aromatic acids and esters, Anal. Chem. 31 (1959) 2076.

[311] E. H. Emry, Mass spectra of aromatic esters, Anal. Chem. 32 (1960) 1495.

[312] J. T. Tou, Field ionisation mass spectra of dialkyl phthalates, Anal. Chem. 42 (1970) 1381.

Other Methods for the Analysis of Plasticizers

[313] R. B. Seymour, The identification of plasticizers, Plast. World 1961 (Sept.) 58.

[314] H. A. Munderloh, Mineralöl-Weichmacher und Extender-Öle für die Kautschuk-Industrie, Kaut. Gummi 12 (1959) WT 246.

[315] M. E. Traxton, Determination of maleic, fumaric and phthalic acids in polyester resins and plasticizers, Chem. Ind. (London) 39 (1966) 1613.

[316] H. Woggon, U. Köhler, Zur Prüfung von Bedarfsgegenständen aus Kunststoffen. Polarographische Bestimmung von Di-(2-ethylhexyl)-phthalat und Untersuchung der Migrationstendenz, Kunststoffe 57 (1967) 583.

[317] G. Lehmann, G. Wilhelm, Colorimetrische Bestimmung von Phthalsäureestern neben anderen Carbonsäureestern nach der Hydroxamatmethode, Z. Anal. Chem. 238 (1968) 415.

[318] Ja. G. Urman, T. S. Chramova et al., Untersuchung von Polyester-Weichmachern mit Hilfe der paramagnetischen Kernspin-Resonanz. Bestimmung der Struktur und des Molekulargewichts, Vysokomol. Soedin. A 12 (1970) 160.

[319] C. Zerbe (Ed.), Mineralöle und verwandte Produkte, 2. ed., Springer, Berlin–Heidelberg–New York 1969.

Bibliography

3 Inorganic Fillers and Pigments

3.1 Survey and Classification

[320] R. B. Seymour, Fillers for polymers, Mod. Plast. 1970/71, 334.

[321] J. Hansmann, Füllstoffe, Arten und Wirkung, Adhäsion *10* (1970) 360.

[322] K. Jasmund, Die silikatischen Tonminerale, 2. ed., Verlag Chemie, Weinheim 1955.

[323] H. Kittel (Ed.), Pigmente, Wissenschaftliche Verlagsgesellschaft, Stuttgart 1960.

[324] D. Patterson, Pigments, An Introduction to their Physical Chemistry, p. 215, Elsevier, Amsterdam 1967.

[325] F. Hund, Anorganische Pigmente durch iso-, homöo- und heterotype Mischphasenbildung, Farbe + Lack *73* (1967) 111.

[326] W. G. Miller, Background to PVC filler selection, Brit. Plast. *42* (1969) 99.

[327] E. Herrmann, Anorganische Buntpigmente zum Einfärben von Kunststoffen, Plastverarbeiter *21* (1970) 529.

[328] J. Behre, Kolloidwissenschaftliche Betrachtungen bei der Entwicklung von Kautschukmischungen, Gummi Asbest Kunstst. *20* (1967) 13.

[329] F. Schweizer, B. Mühlethaler, Einige grüne und blaue Kupferpigmente, Herstellung und Identifikation, Farbe + Lack *74* (1968) 1159.

3.2 Chemical Analysis of Inorganic Fillers and Pigments

[330] C. P. A. Kappelmeier (Ed.), Chemical Analysis of Resin-Based Coating Materials, Interscience Publ., New York-London 1959.

[331] C. E. Moore, N.P.I.R.I. standard test methods for pigment identification, Paint Manufacture (1957) **377**.

[332] E. Hezel, Systematische qualitative Analyse von anorganischen Pigmentgemischen, Farbe + Lack *69* (1963) 361, 828 and *71* (1965) 293.

[333] K. Heinonen, Semiquantitative analysis of paint pigments by X-ray fluorescence, Kem. Teollisuus 23 (1966).

[334] R. Svrdklik, I. Prazak, Papierchromatographie zur qualitativen Analyse anorganischer Pigmente und Füllstoffe in Anstrichmitteln, Chem. Prum. *18* (1968) 503.

[335] M. H. Swann, D. G. Lund et. al., Determination of carbon black in high gloss enamels and lacquers, J. Paint Technol. *39* (1968) 191.

[336] H. M. Cole, D. F. Walker, Die Rückgewinnung von Rußen aus Vulkanisaten und ihre Identifizierung, Gummi, Asbest, Kunstst. *22* (1969) 1332.

[337] H. M. Cole, D. F. Walker, Recuperation et identification des noirs de carbone contenus dans des vulcanisats, Rev. Gen. Caout. Plast. *47* (1970) 751.

[338] P. Kurzmann, A. Tieste et. al., Vergleich pyrolytischer und naßchemischer Verfahren zur quantitativen Bestimmung von Ruß in Vulkanisaten und Kunststoffen, Kaut. Gummi Kunstst. *23* (1970) 322.

[339] T. G. Lamond,, C. R. Cillingham, The identification of carbon blacks in vulcanisates, Rubber J. *152* (1970) 65.

[340] A. I. Medalia, E. R. Eaton, Neue analytische Prüfmethoden für Ruß und ihre Beziehung zu Vulkanisat-Eigenschaften, Kaut. Gummi Kunstst. *20* (1967) 61.

[341] R. Fischer, Spektrophotometrisches Verfahren zur raschen Beurteilung von Rußen auf ihren Gehalt an polycyclischen, aromatischen Kohlenwasserstoffen, Z. Anal. Chem. *249* (1970) 110.

3.3 IR Spectroscopy of Inorganic Fillers and Pigments

[342] F. A. Miller, C. H. Wilkins, Infrared Spectra and Characteristic Frequencies of Inorganic Ions, Anal. Chem. *24* (1952) 1253.

[342a] F. A. Miller, G. L. Carlson, F. F. Bentley, W. H. Jones, Infrared spectra of inorganic ions in the caesium bromide region, Spectrochim. Acta *16* (1960) 135.

[342b] S. R. Yoganarasimhan. C. Rao, Correlation chart for group frequencies in inorganic substances for the infrared region 4000–300 cm^{-1}, Chemist Analyst *51* (1962) 21.

[342c] C. Karr, J. J. Kovach, Far-Infrared Spectroscopy of Minerals and Inorganics, Appl. Spectrosc. *23* (1969) 219.

[343] K. E. Lawson, Infrared Analysis of Inorganic Substances, Reinhold Publ. Corp., New York 1961.

[343a] K. Nakamoto, Infrared Spectra of Inorganic and Coordination Compounds, Wiley, New York 1963.

[343b] H. Siebert, Anwendungen der Schwingungsspektroskopie in der anorganischen Chemie, Springer, Berlin-Heidelberg-Wien 1966.

[344] H. Moenke, Spektralanalyse von Mineralien und Gesteinen, Akad. Verlagsgesellschaft Geest & Portig, Leipzig 1962.

[345] H. Moenke, Mineralspektren II. Die Ultrarotabsorption der häufigsten und wirtschaftlich wichtigsten Halogenid-, Oxid-, Hydroxid-, Nitrat-, Carbonat-, Borat-, Sulfat-, Chromat-, Molybdat-, Phosphat-, Arsenat-, Vanadat- und Silikatmineralien im Spektralbereich 400–4000 cm^{-1}, Akademie-Verlag, Berlin 1962.

[346] R. T. Harkins, J. T. Harris, O. D. Shreve, Identification of pigments in paint products by infrared spectroscopy, Anal. Chem. *31* (1959) 541.

[347] L. C. Afremow, J. T. Vandenberg, High resolution spectra of inorganic pigments and extenders in the mid infrared region from 1500 cm^{-1} to 200 cm^{-1}, J. Paint Technol. *38* (1966) 169.

[348] J. Riederer, Infrarotspektrographische Untersuchung der gelben und roten Eisenoxidpigmente, Deut. Farben Z. *23* (1969) 569.

3.4 X-Ray Diffraction Analysis of Inorganic Fillers and Pigments

[349] R. König, Anorganische Pigmente und Röntgenstrahlen, F. Enke, Stuttgart 1956.

4 Organic Pigments

4.1 Survey and Classification

[350] L. S. Pratt, The Chemistry and Physics of Organic Pigments, Wiley, New York-London 1947.

[351] H. E. Fierz-David, L. Blangey, Grundlegende Operationen der Farbenchemie, Springer, Wien 1952.

[351a] P. Rys, H. Zollinger, Leitfaden der Farbstoffchemie, 2. ed., Verlag Chemie, Weinheim 1975.

[352] J. St. Remington, W. Francis, Pigments, their Manufacture, Properties and Use, Hill Ltd., London 1954.

[353] H. A. Lubs (Ed.), Chemistry of Synthetic Dyes and Pigments, Reinhold, New York 1955.

[354] A. W. C. Harrison, The Manufacture of Lakes and Precipitated Pigments, 2. ed., London 1957.

[355] H. R. Schweizer, Künstliche organische Farbstoffe und ihre Zwischenprodukte, Springer, Berlin 1964.

[356] K. Venkataram (Ed.), The Chemistry of Organic Dyes, Academic Press, New York 1971.

[356a] H. Kittel, Lehrbuch der Lacke und Beschichtungen, W. A. Colomb, Berlin 1974.

[356b] T. C. Patton (Ed.), Pigment Handbook, 3. Vol., J. Wiley-& Sons, New York, London 1973.

[356c] D. Patterson, Pigments, Elsevier, Amsterdam 1967.

[357] Soc. of Dyers and Colourists and Am. Assoc. of Textile Chemists and Colorists (Ed.), Colour Index, 3. ed. Bradford 1971, 1. Revision 1975.

[358] H. Gaertner, Modern chemistry of organic pigments, J. Oil Colour Chem. Ass. 46 (1963) 13.

[359] E. Herrmann, Kunststoffeinfärbung, Zechner & Hüthig, Speyer 1976.

[359a] J. Koerner, Lösliche Farbstoffe in der Kunststoff-Industrie, Kunstst. Rundsch. 16 (1969) 613.

[360] G. Kaufmann, Das Verhalten organischer Pigmente in Polymeren, Angew. Makromol. Chem. 10 (1970) 83.

[361] O. Lückert, Probleme im Lacklabor, Pigmente und Farbstoffe, Farbe + Lack 80 (1974) 1038.

[361a] M. and O. Lückert, Pigment + Füllstoff-Tabellen, O. Lükkert, Laatzen 1977.

[362] W. Kaiser, Die organischen Pigmente in der Druckfarbenindustrie, Farbe + Lack 76 (1970) 237.

[363] H. Herbst, K. Hunger, Azopigmente – Eigenschaften, Anforderungen und Entwicklungstendenzen, Progr. in Organic Coatings 6 (1978) 211.

[364] V. C. Vesce, L. W. Ryan, Classification System of Pigments in J. J. Mattiello (Ed.), Protective and Decorative Coatings, Vol. II, Wiley, New York 1947.

[365] W. W. Spencer, A classification of pigment colors, Amer. Paint J. (1966) 77.

[366] L. Heckl, Zusammenstellung organ. Pigmente, (personal communications 1966/68).

4.2 – 4.4 Separation and Chemical Analysis of Organic Pigments

[367] J. Barker, Identification of Pigments, J. Oil Colour Chem. Assoc. 25 (1942) 240.

[368] K. G. Hargreaves, The analysis of organic pigments, J. Oil Colour Chem. Soc. 382 (1952) 139.

[369] A. McClure, J. Thomson, J. Tannahill, The Identification of Pigments, JOCCA 51 (1968) 580.

[370] A. Kutzelnigg, Identification of Organic Pigments in Coating Materials in C. P. A. Kappelmeier, Chemical Analysis of Resin Based Coating Materials, Interscience, New York 1959.

[371] H. E. Weisberg, A. D. Smith, Systematic Identification of Organic Pigments, Reichhold Chemicals Inc., 1941.

[372] V. C. Vesce, The Microscopic Identification of Azo Dyes and Organic Pigments in J. J. Matiello (Ed.), Protective and Decorative coating, Vol. II, 126, Vol. V, 345, Wiley, New York 1947.

[373] E. Stock, Analyse der Körperfarben, Wissenschaftliche Verlagsgesellschaft, Stuttgart 1953.

[374] J. Formanek, P. Knop, Untersuchung und Nachweis organischer Farbstoffe auf spektrochemischem Wege, 2. ed., Berlin 1927.

[375] A. Green, Analysis of Dyestuffs, London 1920.

[375a] A. Green in Vol. 5, 1389, Berl-Lunge, Chemisch-technische Untersuchungsmethoden, 8. ed., Springer, Berlin 1934.

[376] H. Schweppe, Qualitative Analyse von organischen Pigmenten, FATIPEC Congr. 1962, 162.

[377] V. C. Vesce, Vivid Light Fast Organic Pigments, Off. Dig. 377 (1956) 1.

[378] D. A. Derret-Smith, J. Gray, The Identification of Vat Dyes on Cellulosic Materials, Pergamon Press, Oxford 1967.

[379] M. Saltzmann, A. M. Keay, Colorant identification, J. Paint Technol. 39 (1967) 360.

[380] Landolt-Börnstein (A. Encken, Ed.), Zahlenwerte und Funktionen aus Physik, Chemie, Astronomie, Geophysik, Technik, 6. ed. M. Pestemer, G. Scheibe, A. Schöntag, D. Bruck, Lichtabsorption von Lösungen im Ultraviolett und Sichtbaren, I. Vol., 3. Part (1951) 78, Springer, Berlin-Göttingen-Heidelberg.

[381] K. Venkatamaran (Ed.), The Analytical Chemistry of Synthetic Dyes, Wiley, New York 1977.

4.5 Thin Layer Chromatography of Organic Pigments

[382] K. Schweppe, Thin Layer Chromatography, in [381], 25.

[382a] J. Thomson, Identification of Organic Pigments on Substrates other than Textile Fibers, in [381], 431.

[382b] L. J. Papa, High-Pressure Liquid Chromatography, in [381], 93.

[382c] H. Schweppe, Identification of Dyes on Textile Fibers, in [381], 389.

[383] G. H. Rettie, G. G. Haynes, Thin layer chromatographie and its application to dyes, J. Soc. Dyers Colour. 80 (1964) 629.

[384] S. Logar, J. Perkavec, M. Perpar, Papier- und Dünnschichtchromatographie der basischen Farbstoffe für Polyacrylnitrilfasern, Mikrochim. Acta 3 (1967) 496.

[385] Gallotti, Identificazione cromatografica di coloranti sintetici smontati da fibre tessili, Tinctoria 62 (1965) 367.

[386] A. Lörinc, O. K. Dobozy, F. Peter, Chromatography of azo dyes capable of forming H-bonds, Text. Res. J. 37 (1967) 60.

[387] K. C. Walker, M. Beroza, J. Ass. Offic. Agr. Chem. 46 (1963) 250.

[388] I. Gemzova, J. Gasparic, Dünnschichtchromatographie primärer aromatischer Amine an Aluminiumoxid, Collect. Czech. Chem. Commun. 31 (1966) 2525.

[388a] I. Gemzova, J. Gasparic, Identifizierung und Konstitutionsanalyse von Dispersionsazofarbstoffen, Collect. Czech. Chem. Commun. 31 (1967) 2740.

[389] A. Bassl, H. J. Heckemann, E. Baumann, Zur Identifizierung und Konstitutionsermittlung von Acetessigarylidpigmenten, Plaste Kaut. 14 (1967) 696.

[390] E. Baier, Über die Dünnschicht-Chromatographie organischer Pigmente, Farbe + Lack 80 (1974) 614.

4.6 IR Spectroscopy of Organic Pigments

[391] F. M. Smith, J. D. Easton, Phthalocyanine pigments – their form and performance, J. Oil Colour Chem. Ass. 49 (1966) 614.

[392] S. S. Labana, L. L. Labana, Quinacridones, Chem. Rev. 67 (1967) 1.

[393] G. Lincke, Strukturelle Betrachtungen zur Kristallisation der Chinacridone, Farbe + Lack 76 (1970) 764.

[394] A. Pugin, Influence de la constitution sur la nuance et les propriétés des pigments dioxaziniques, FATIPEC Congr. 1962, 147.

[395] Sadtler Commercial Spectra, Dyes, Pigments and Stains, Sadtler Res. Lab., Philadelphia.

[396] M. Pestemer, Über die Infrarotabsorptionsspektren von Polymethinfarbstoffen, Chimia 15 (1961) 31.

[397] B. K. Manukian, H. Lichti, Chimia 24 (1970) 1.

[398] F. Valero, Double Liaison 165 (1969) 55.

[399] K. Hoffmann, Die quantitative Erfassung von Farbstoffen auf Geweben mittels Röntgenfluoreszenz, Melliand Textilber. 50 (1969) 210.

5 UV Stabilizers and Fluorescent Whitening Agents

5.1 Survey and Classification of UV Stabilizers

[400] W. L. Hawkins, Polymer Stabilization, Wiley, New York 1972.

[401] R. Ranby, J. F. Rabek, Photodegradation, Photooxidation and Photostabilization of Polymers, Wiley Interscience, London 1975.

[402] G. Geuskens (Ed.), Degradation and Stabilization of Polymers, Applied Science Publ., London 1975.

[403] H. H. G. Jellinek (Ed.), Aspects of Degradation and Stabilization of Polymers, Elsevier, New York 1978.

[404] B. Dolezel, Die Beständigkeit von Kunststoffen und Gummi, Carl Hanser, München 1978.

[405] C. Savides, P. V. Susi, Ultraviolet stabilizers, Mod. Plast. (1970/71) 410.

[406] M. Kamal (Ed.), Weatherability of Plastic Materials, Interscience Publ., New York 1969.

5.3 Thin Layer Chromatography of UV Stabilizers

[407] E. Knappe, D. Peteri, I. Rohdenwald, Imprägnierung chromatographischer Dünnschichten mit Polyestern: Trennung und Identifizierung substituierter 2-Hydroxybenzophenone und anderer UV-Absorber, Z. Anal. Chem. 197 (1963) 364.

[408] W. J. Uhde, G. Zydek, Dünnschicht-Chromatographie von substituierten 2-Hydroxybenzophenonen, Z. Anal. Chem. 239 (1968) 25.

[408a] L. Durisinova, D. Bellus, Dünnschicht-Chromatographie von 2-Hydroxybenzophenonen, J. Chromatogr. 32 (1968) 584.

[409] H. Woggon, D. Jehle, Beitrag zur Prüfung von Bedarfsgegenständen aus Plasten. Zum Nachweis von Antioxidantien und UV-Absorbern in Plasten. Z. Lebensm. Unters. Forsch. 136 (1968) 77.

[410] R. S. Dobies, TLC method for determining UV absorbers in paraffin wax, J. Chromatogr. 35 (1968) 370.

[411] D. Simpson, B. R. Currel, Analyst. 56 (1971) 515.

[411a] J. Rotschová-Protivová, J. Pospišil, J. Holčik, J. Durmis, Antioxidants and stabilizers, LVI: Behaviour of light stabilizers and model compounds in gel chromatography, J. Chrom. 106 (1975) 343.

5.5 UV Spectroscopy of UV Stabilizers

[412] H. J. Heller, Lichtstabilisatoren für Kunststoffe, Battelle Information Frankfurt 9 (1970) 76.

[413] B. Arventiev, L. Singurel et al., Ultra-violet absorption spectra of some 2-hydroxy-6-methylbenzophenones and their behaviour with regard to polyvinylchloride, Eur. Polym. J. Suppl. (1969) 505.

[414] P. Hrdlovic, D. Bellus, M. Lazar, UV-Spektren von 2-Hydroxybenzophenonen mit versch. Substit. in 4 und 5 Positionen, Collect. Czech. Chem. Commun. 33 (1968) 59.

[415] L. I. Zjuzina, S. Ja. Chajkin et al., Spektroskopische Bestimmung von Stabilisatoren gegen Licht und Wärme in Polyolefinen, Plast. Massy 7 (1970) 66.

5.6 Fluorescent Whitening Agents

[416] F. Coulston, F. Korte (Eds.), Environmental Quality and Safety Suppl. Vol. IV, R. Anliker, G. Müller, Guest (Eds.), Fluorescent Whitening Agents, Georg Thieme, Stuttgart.

[417] A. Wagner, Optische Aufheller; Über ihre Physik, Chemie und Anwendungstechnik, Naturwissenschaften 55 (1968) 533.

[418] E. Preininger, Die optische Aufhellung von Polyvinylchlorid, Plastverarbeiter 20 (1969) 845.

[419] E. Preininger, Fluorescent whitening agents for PVC, Mod. Plast (1970) 126.

[420] K. Eschle, E. Preininger, Die optische Aufhellung von Styrol-Polymeren, Plastverarbeiter 21 (1970) 145.

[421] K. Eschle, Die optische Aufhellung von Polyolefinen und einigen weiteren thermoplastischen Kunststoffen, Plastverarbeiter 21 (1970) 629.

5.7 Thin Layer Chromatography of Fluorescent Whitening Agents

[422] M. Wandel, H. Tengler, Deutscher Färberkalender 1965, p. 71, Franz Edler, München 1965.

[423] B. Werthmann, R. Borowski, Erfahrungen bei der Identifizierung optischer Aufheller für Papiere, Papier 28 (1974) 235.

[424] H. Theidel, G. Schmitz, Zur chromatographischen Analyse optischer Aufheller, J. Chromatogr. 27 (1967) 413.

[424a] H. Theidel, Qualitative TLC of Fluorescent Whitening Agents in [416], 94.

[425] K. Figge, Trennung und Identifizierung optischer Aufheller durch ein- und zweidimensionale Dünnschicht-Chromatographie, Fette, Seifen, Anstrichm. 70 (1968) 680.

[425a] D. Kirkpatrick, Separation of optical brighteners by liquid-solid chromatography, J. Chrom. 121 (1976) 153, 139 (1977) 168.

[425b] G. R. Weiß, Säulenchromatographische Trennung fluoreszierender optischer Aufheller, Tenside, Deterg. 12 (1975) 43.

6 Antioxidants

6.1 Survey and Classification

[426] W. O. Lundberg, Antioxidation and Antioxidants, Vol. 1 and 2, Interscience Publ., New York 1961/62.

[427] G. Scott, Atmospheric Oxidation and Antioxidants, Elsevier, Amsterdam 1965.

[428] W. W. Tobin, Antioxidants, Mod. Plast. Encycl. (1970/71) 314.

[429] H.-R. Linhardt, Die Wirkungsweise von Lichtschutzwachsen, Kaut. Gummi Kunstst. 21 (1968) 558.

[429a] G. Matscholl, Charakterisierung von Ozonschutzwachsen, Kaut. Gummi Kunstst. 23 (1970) 267.

[430] J. Pospišil et Mme J. Rotschová, Identification et dosage des stabilisants de polymeres, Rev. Gen. Caout. Plast. 94 (1977) 587, 73.

6.2 Chemical Detection of Antioxidants

[431] S. S. Juskevicjute, Ju. A. Sljapnikov, Bestimmung von Antioxidantien in Polyolefinen – Isolierung durch Destillation im Vakuum, Kunststoffe, Moskau 12 (1966) 62.

[432] R. H. Campbell, E. J. Young, Determination of antidegradants, Rubber Age 100 (1968) 71.

[433] E. J. Latos, A. K. Sparks, Auswaschen von p-Phenylendiamin-Antiozonantien aus Vulkanisaten durch Wasser, Kaut. Gummi Kunstst. 23 (1970) 417.

[434] E. Schröder, E. Hagen, M. Helmstedt, Identifizierung und quantitative Bestimmung von Antioxidantien und Thermostabilisatoren in Formaldehydpolymerisaten, Plaste Kaut. 14 (1967) 560.

6.3 Thin Layer Chromatography of Antioxidants

[435] D. F. Slonaker, D. C. Sievers, Identification of trace quantities of antioxidants in polyethylene, Anal. Chem. 36 (1964) 1130.

[436] R. F. van der Heide, The Safety of Plastics Food Packaging Material, Utrecht 1964.

[437] R. F. van der Heide et al., Het aantonen van anti-oxidanten in kunststoffen, Chem. Weekbl. *61* (1965) 440.

[438] R. F. van der Heide, Reagentien zum Nachweis von Anti-oxydantien (AO) auf Kieselgel-Dünnschicht-Chromato-grammen, J. Chromatogr. *24* (1966) 239.

[439] J. H. van der Neut, A. C. Maagdenberg, Qualitative analysis of antioxidants by thin layer chromatography, Plastics *31* (1966) 66.

[440] H. Ostromow, W. Hofmann, Chemische Analyse von Kaut-schukmischungen und -vulkanisaten (6. Part). Nachweis und Bestimmung von Alterungsschutzmitteln und Stabilisatoren, Bayer-Mittlg. für die Gummiind. *39* (1966) 65.

[441] W. Hofmann, H. Ostromow, Analytische Untersuchungsbe-funde des Ausschusses Gummi des Bundesgesundheitsamtes über Kautschuk, Kautschuk-Chemikalien und Vulkanisate im Rahmen des Lebensmittelgesetzes, Kaut. Gummi Kunstst. *21* (1968), 244, 318, 322, 368, 432, 481, 560, 620, 693 und *22* (1969) 14.

[442] J. Jentzsch, R. Martin, Beiträge zur Gummianalytik II. Über die Anwendung der Dünnschichtchromatographie für den Nachweis von Antioxidantien, Plaste Kaut. *13* (1966) 464.

[443] A. N. Crabtee, A. E. J. McGill, Die dünnschicht-chromato-graphische Trennung von 17 phenolischen Verbindungen, Mikrochim. Acta (1967) 85.

[444] J. Davidek, G. Janicek et al., Chromatographische Trennung von Antioxidantien mit Hilfe der Dünnschichtchromatogra-phie, Lebensmittelunters. *131* (1966/67) 345.

[445] D. T. Miles, Antioxidant analysis incorporation a TLC sepa-ration procedure, Analyst *99* (1974) 364.

[446] A. B. Sullivan, G. H. Kuhls, R. H. Campbell, Determination of additives with HPLC and TLC, Rubber Age *108* (1976) 3, 41.

[447] L. H. Ruddle, J. R. Wilson, Determination of phenolic antioxidants in polymers, Analyst *94* (1969) 105.

[448] A. Gömöryova, Verteilung und Identifizierung von Inhibito-ren mittels Dunnschichtchromatographie, Plaste Kaut. *7* (1970) 203.

[449] W. Schneider, Dünnschicht-chromatographische Trennung und Identifizierung von Antioxidantien, Seifen-Öle-Fette-Wachse *96* (1970) 559.

[450] S. N. Chakravarty, R. Ketter, Dünnschichtchromatographi-sche Identifizierung von phenolischen Alterungsschutzmit-teln, Kaut. Gummi Kunstst. *23* (1970) 93.

[451] O. Korn, H. Woggon, Beitrag zur Prüfung von Bedarfsge-genständen aus Plasten. Nachweis von PVC-Stabilisatoren mittels der Dünnschichtchromatographie, Nahrung *8* (1964) 351, *11* (1967) 278.

[452] J. W. H. Zijp, Rec. Trav. Chim. *75* (1956) 1053, 1060, 1083, 1129, *77* (1958) 129, Kaut. Gummi *10* (1957) 14.

[453] R. Miksch, L. Proelss, Kaut. Gummi *11* (1958) 91, 133.

[454] H. Auler, Die Analyse von Antioxidantien und Beschleuni-gern in Kautschukmischungen und Vulkanisaten, Gummi, Asbest Kunstst. *14* (1961) 1024, 1081.

[454a] H. Auler, The analysis of antioxidants and accelerators in rubber compounds and vulcanisates, Rubber Chem. Technol. *37* (1964) 950.

[455] J. Protivová, J. Pospišil, J. Holčik, Antioxidants and stabili-zers, XLVIII: Analysis of the components of stabilization and vulcanization mixtures for rubbers by gel permeation and thin-layer chromatography methods, J. Chrom. *92* (1974) 361.

[455a] J. Protivová, J. Pospišil, Antioxidants and stabilizers XLVII: Behaviour of amine antioxidants and antiozonants and model compounds in gel permeation chromatography, J. Chrom. *88* (1974) 99.

[456] E. Schröder, G. Rudolph, Nachweis und Bestimmung phe-nolischer Antioxidantien in Polyethylen, Plaste Kaut. *10* (1963) 22.

[457] R. H. Campbell, R. W. Wise, Determination of some mixed phenolic antioxidants in polyethylene, J. Chromatogr. *12* (1963) 178.

[458] D. Gross, K. Strauss, Analyse von Alterungsschutzmitteln in Elastomeren durch Hochdruck-Flüssigkeits-Chromatogra-phie, Kaut. Gummi, *29* (1976) 741.

[458a] D. Gross, K. Strauss, Analyse von Vulkanisationsbeschleu-nigern durch Hochleistungs-Flüssigkeitschromatographie, Kaut. Gummi *30* (1977) 811.

[458b] D. Gross, K. Strauss, Hochleistungs-Flüssigkeitschromato-graphie in der Gummi-Analyse, Katuschuk, Gummi, Kunst-stoffe *32* (1979) 18.

[458c] A. M. Wims, S. J. Swarin, Determination of antioxidants in polypropylene by liquid chromatography, J. Appl. Polym. Sci. *19* (1975) 5, 1234.

[458d] G. J. Fallcik, P. C. Talarico, R. R. McGough, Separation and analysis of polymer additives and components by liquid chromatography, SPE Tech. Pap. *22* (1976) 574.

[458e] M. Dengreville, High Pressure liquid chromatographic determination of additives in low density polyethylene, Ana-lysis *5* (1977) 195.

[458f] J. E. Schabron, L. E. Fenska, Determination of BHT, Irga-nox 1076 and Irganox 1010 antioxidant additives in polyethy-lene by HPLC, Anal. Chem., *52* (1980) 1411.

6.4 Gas Chromatography of Antioxidants

[459] C. Heft, D. Bochmann, Gaschromatographische Bestim-mung von Antioxidantien im Synthesekautschuk, Plaste Kaut. *11* (1964) 624.

[460] H. S. Knight, H. Siegel, Analysis of a high-molecularweight phenolic inhibitor, Anal. Chem. *38* (1966) 1221.

[461] R. E. Long. G. Christian, Determination of trace quantities of 2,6-Di-tert-butyl-4-methyl phenol in polyethylene using electron capture gas chromatography, Anal. Chem. *39* (1967) 1493.

[462] L. J. Gaeta, E. W. Schlueter, A. G. Altenau, Antioxidant analysis using a chromatographic detector, Rubber Age (March 1969) 48.

[462a] H. L. Styskin, Y. A. Gurvich, Gas chromatography of phe-nolic antioxidants, J. Chrom. *77* (1973) 11.

[462b] S. Dilli, K. Robards, Comparative gas chromatographic behaviour and detection limits of 2,6-ditert.-butyl-4-methyl-phenol, 3-tert.-butyl-4-hydroxyanisole (BHA), and the tri-fluoroacetate of BHA, J. Chrom. *133* (1977) 363.

[462c] D. Thorburn Burns, D. F. Covey, E. W. Johnson, Identifi-cation and determination of certain n, n'-disubstituted p-phe-nylenediamine antiozonants in cured styrene-butadiene ela-stomers, J. Chrom. *103* (1975) 247.

[462d] J. Masaryk, J. Krupčik, J. Garaj, M. Košik, Gas chromato-graphic separation of dithiocarbamates of some metals, J. Chrom. *115* (1975) 256.

[462e] J. Krupčik, J. Garaj, Š. Holotik, D. Oktovec, M. Košik, Gas chromatographic separation of some dialkyldithiocarba-mates of nickel (II), J. Chrom. *112* (1975) 189.

[462f] M. Ahmad, A. Aziz, Gas chromatography of metal di-ethyldithiocarbamates with electron-capture detection, J. Chrom. *152* (1978) 542.

6.5 IR Spectroscopy of Antioxidants

[463] J. Mann, Identification of accelerators and antioxidants in vulcanisates by infrared sprectroscopy, Trans. Inst. Rubber Ind. *27* (1951) 232.

[464] A. Fiorenza, G. Bonomi, R. Piacentini, Spectrophotometry and chromatography for identification of antioxidants and accelerators in rubber mixtures, Rubber Chem. Technol. *36* (1963) 1119.

[465] M. Okamoto, O. Ishizuka, Quantitative Analyse von Stabilisatoren in handelsüblichem Polypropylen, welche in CCl_4 leicht löslich sind, J. Chem. Soc. Jap. *71* (1968) 1848.

6.6 UV Spectroscopy of Antioxidants

[466] H. L. Spell, R. D. Eddy, Determination of additives in polyethylene by absorption spectroscopy, Anal. Chem. *32* (1960) 1811.

[467] V. Cieleszky, F. Nagy, Nachweis von Antioxidantien in verschiedenen Polyethylensorten, Z. Lebensm. Unters. Forsch. *114* (1961) 13.

[468] P. J. Corish, Rapid characterization of antioxidant in cured blackloaded rubbers from ultraviolet spectra of extracts of sections, J. Appl. Polym. Sci. *7* (1963) 727.

[469] A. S. Wexler, Determination of phenolic substances by ultraviolet difference spectrometry, Anal. Chem. *35* (1963) 1936.

[470] J. Soucek, J. Vasatkova, I. Cadersky, Die Identifizierung und Bestimmung phenolischer Antioxidantien und UV-Absorber in Polypropylen durch differentiale Ultraviolett-Spektrophotometrie, Chem. Prum. *16* (1966) 348.

[471] L. H. Ruddle, J. R. Wilson, An ultraviolet sprectrophotometric method for the characterization of some phenolic stabilizers in extracts of polymer composition, Analyst *94* (1969) 105.

6.7 Mass Spectroscopy of Antioxidants

[472] M. W. Hayes, A. G. Altenau, Mass spectrometry, Rubber Age *102* (1970) 59.

6.8 Other Methods for the Analysis of Antioxidants

[473] C. L. Hilton, Spectrophotometric determination of Flexzone 3 C and other p-phenylenediamine derivatives, Anal. Chem. *32* (1960) 1555.

[473a] V. Kapisinska, V. Kosljar, Bestimmung eines kleinen N-Isopropyl-N'-Phenyl-p-Phenylendiamingehaltes in Gummierzeugnissen, Plast. Hmoty Kauc. *6* (1969) 359.

[474] U. Köhler, H. Woggon, Polarographische Bestimmung von 4,4'-Thio-bis (6-tert.-butyl-m-kresol), Plaste Kaut. *15* (1968) 630.

[474a] J. Pospíšil, J. Rotschová, Identification et dosage des stabilisants de polymeres, Rev. Gen. Caout. Plast. *54* (1977) 567, 72.

[474b] W. Becker, Measurement of naphthylamines in rubber antioxidants, Rubber Age *107* (1975) 3, 53.

7 PVC Stabilizers

7.1 Survey and Classification

[475] F. Chevassus, R. De Brontelles, The Stabilization of Polyvinyl Chloride, Edward Arnold, London 1963.

[476] L. I. Nass (Ed.), Encyclopedia of PVC, Marcel Dekker, New York 1976.

[477] H. Schlegel, PVC und seine Stabilisierung, Kunstst. Plast. *1* (1964) 1.

[478] H. H. Frey, Licht- und Wetterbeständigkeit von schlagfestem PVC, Kunststoffe *52* (1962) 667.

[479] K. Figge, W. Findeiß, Untersuchungen zum Mechanismus der PVC-Stabilisierung mit Organozinn-Verbindungen, Angew. Makromol. Chem. *47* (1975) 141.

7.2–7.5 Analysis of PVC Stabilizers

[480] R. F. van der Heide, Dünnschichtchromatographische Analyse organischer Stabilisatoren in Hart-PVC, Z. Lebensm. Unters. Forsch. *124* (1964) 198.

[481] E. Hagen, Beiträge zur analytischen Chemie der Plaste XXXIII, Zur Analytik des PVC-Stabilisators Diphenylthioharnstoff, Plaste Kaut. *14* (1967) 158.

[482] H. Huber, J. Wimmer, Dünnschichtchromatographische Bestimmung von Gleitmittel- und Stabilisator-Zusätzen in PVC-Mischungen, Kunststoffe *58* (1968) 786.

[483] M. Türler, Über den Nachweis und die Identifizierung von Organozinnstabilisatoren in Polyvinylchlorid, Mitt. Geb. Lebensmittelunters. Hyg. *52* (1961) 123.

[484] G. Neubert, Zur Analytik von Organozinnstabilisatoren, Z. Anal. Chem. *203* (1964) 265.

[484a] G. Neubert, H. O. Wirth, Zur Analytik von Organozinnstabilisatoren, Z. Anal. Chem. *273* (1975) 19.

[484b] G. Neubert, H. Andreas, Zur Analytik von Organozinnverbindungen, Z. Anal. Chem. *280* (1976), 31.

[484c] K. Figge, J. Koch, H. Luba, Beitrag zur GC-Analyse von Organozinnstabilisatoren für PVC, J. Chrom. *131* (1977) 317.

[485] R. F. van der Heide, Identifizierung von schwefelhaltigen Organozinnstabilisatoren durch Dünnschichtchromatographie, Z. Lebensm. Unters. Forsch. *124* (1964) 348.

[486] E. Helberg, Beitrag zur Analytik von Organozinnstabilisatoren, Deut. Lebensm. Rundsch. *62* (1966) 178.

[487] D. Braun, T.-Th. Heimes, Zur Dünnschicht-Chromatographie von zinnorganischen Verbindungen, Z. Anal. Chem. *239* (1968) 6.

[488] K. Freitag, R. Bock, Analyse von Gemischen aus Tri-, Di- und Monophenylzinnverbindungen und anorg. Zinn (IV), Z. Anal. Chem. *270* (1974) 337.

[488a] A. Vastagh, Schnellverfahren zum Nachweis von Trimethylzinnchlorid neben analogen Methylzinnchloriden durch Dünnschicht-Chromatographie, Z. Anal. Chem. *279* (1976), 366.

[488b] W. D. Bieber, J. Koch, K. Figge, Zur Analytik von Methylzinnstabilisatoren, Plaste Kaut. *23* (1976) 355.

[488c] B. Herold, K. H. Droege, Bestimmung von Trimethylzinnverbindungen in Dimethylzinn-di-(thioglykolsäureisooctylester), Z. Anal. Chem. *289* (1978) 285.

[489] E. Schröder, E. Hagen, Zur Analytik stickstoffhaltiger PVC-Stabilisatoren und ihrer Zersetzungsprodukte, Plaste Kaut. *14* (1967) 814.

[490] V. Kapisinska, Quantitative Bestimmung der zinnorganischen Stabilisatoren, Chem. Prum. *20* (1970) 487.

[491] P. Ochsenbein, Zur Analytik von Organozinnstabilisatoren, Kunststoffe *58* (1968) 366.

[492] W. Groebel, Zur Bestimmung von N,N'-Diphenylthioharnstoff in Polyvinylchlorid, Lebensmittelunters. *129* (1965) 26.

[493] R. Sawyer, Bestimmung von Dialkylzinnstabilisatoren in wäßriger Extraktion von PVC und anderen Plastiken, Analyst *92* (1967) 569.

[494] H.-J. Seidlitz, Zur Analytik der Organozinnverbindungen, Diss. d. Fak. f. Stoffwirtsch. d. TH. f. Chemie, Leuna-Merseburg, 8. Juli 1966.

[494a] O. Korn, Beitrag zur Prüfung von Bedarfsgegenständen aus Plasten. Photometrische Bestimmung von Diphenylharnstoff neben Monophenylharnstoff mit Dichlordiphenylmethan, Nahrung *8* (1964) 188.

[494b] O. Korn, H. Woggon, Photometrische Bestimmung von 2-Phenylindol, Nahrung 9 (1965) 42.

8 Antistatics, Biocides, Flame Retardants

8.1 Survey and Classification of Antistatics

[495] L. B. Loeb, Static Electrification, Springer, Berlin-Heidelberg 1958.

[496] R. Reichherzer, Astatische Kunststoffe, Kunstst. Plast. 15 (1968) 79.

[497] W. Pohl, Antistatika, ihre Einarbeitung und ihre Wirkungsweise in Thermoplasten, Verpack. Rundsch. 21 (1970) 11.

[498] S. Riethmayer, Antistatika, Gummi, Asbest, Kunststoffe 26 (1973) 76, 182, 298, 419, 506.

[499] A. M. Schwartz, J. W. Perry, Surface Active Agents, Interscience, New York-London 1959.

[500] G. Balbach, Antistatica für Polyolefine, Kunststoffe 67 (1977) 154.

8.2 Chemical Detection of Antistatics

[501] M. J. Rosen, H. A. Goldsmith, Systematic Analysis of Surface Active Agents, Interscience, New York-London 1960.

[502] D. O. Hummel, Analyse der Tenside, Hanser, München 1962.

[503] G. Cornille, Analyse von Antistatica in Kunststoff-Folien, Plastica 1 (1967) 16.

[504] G. Cornille, Analyse von antistatischen Mitteln in Kunststoff-Folien, Plast. Mod. Elastomeres 19 (1967) 105.

8.3 Thin Layer Chromatography of Antistatics

[505] M. Helmstedt, E. Schröder, Beiträge zur analytischen Chemie der Plaste XLIV. Versuche zur Analytik von Antistatika in Plastformstoffen, Plaste Kaut. 15 (1968) 405.

[506] G. Löser, Auftrennung tensioaktiver Gemische durch Dünnschichtchromatographie, Seife-Öle-Fette-Wachse 91 (1965) 728.

[506a] K. Bey, Die dünnschichtchromatographische Analyse auf dem Gebiet der Tenside, Fette, Seifen, Anstrichm. 67 (1965) 217.

[507] K. Thoma, R. Rombach, E. Ullmann, Nachweis und Identifizierung grenzflächenaktiver Ester und Ether von Polyethylenglykolen, Arch. Pharm. Weinheim 298 (1965) 298.

[508] R. Wickbold, Die chromatographische Zerlegung der Ethylenoxid-Addukte in ihre Homologen und deren quantitative Bestimmung, Fette, Seifen, Anstrichm. 70 (1968) 688.

[509] W. Gerhardt, R. Holzbauer, Dünnschicht-Chromatographie zur qualitativen Kennzeichnung und Reinheitsprüfung von definierten Polyethylenglykolen, Chromatographie 2 (1969) 468.

[510] H. König, Trennung nichtionogener Tenside mittels Dünnschicht-Chromatographie, Z. Anal. Chem. 251 (1970) 167.

[510a] H. König, Die Analyse amphoterer Tenside, Z. Anal. Chem. 251 (1970) 359.

[511] W. A. Mameniskis, Determination of poly(oxypropylene diol) present in poly(oxypropylene triol) by thinlayer chromatography, J. Appl. Polym. Sci. 14 (1970) 1189.

[512] R. Brüschweiler, Analyse nichtionogener Emulgatoren mittels HPLC, Mit. Geb. Lebensmittelunters. Hyg. 68 (1977) 46.

[513] D. G. H. Daniels, Die Gaschromatographie langkettiger α,ω-Diole, J. Chromatogr. 21 (1966) 305.

[513a] J. T. Davies, B. H. Denham, Gas-chromatographische Bestimmung antistatischer Additive in Polyethylen, Analyst 93 (1968) 336.

[513b] B. Stancher, L. Favretto, Analysis of polyoxyethylene non ionic surfactants by coupling gas-liquid and thin layer chromatography, J. Chrom. 111 (1975) 459.

[514] D. L. Wolfe, Multiple internal reflection spectroscopy of an antistatic agent on the surface of polyethylene, SPE (28th Ann. Techn. Conf.) Tech. Pap. 16 (March 1970) 721.

[514a] B. Hänsel, C. Otto, Zum direkten Nachweis von Neutraltensiden in Polyamid 6 mittels der Methode der geschwächten Totalreflexion, Faserforsch. Textiltechn. 28 (1977) 2, 81.

8.5 Analysis of Biostabilisers

[515] W. Hofmann, Antimikrobiell ausgerüstete Gummiartikel, Kaut. Gummi 15 (1962) 501.

[516] M. Giesen, Metallorganische Verbindungen als Biocide für Anstrichstoffe, VIII, FATIPEC Congr. 1966, 185.

[517] –, Über den Zusatz fungistatischer Stoffe zu Anstrichmitteln, Fette, Seifen, Anstrichm. 70 (1968) 106.

[518] K.-H. Wallhäußer, W. Fink, Konservierung von Dispersionen und Dispersionsfarben gegen mikrobiellen Verderb, Farbe + Lack 76 (1970) 471.

[519] T. Wexler, D. Cornilescu et al., Noi agenti fungistatici si comportarea lor in amestecurile de PVC, Mater. Plast. 7 (1970) 305.

[520] H. B. Hopfenberg, J. J. Tulis, Advances in antibacterial plastics, Mod. Plast (1970) 110.

[521] E. Hofmann, A. Saracz, Bestimmung von Phenylquecksilber-Verbindungen in Fungiciden und Anstrichstoffen, Z. Anal. Chem. 214 (1965) 428.

[522] E. Hofmann, A. Saracz, B. Bursztyn, Analysis for fungicides in paint - Part IV. Determination of copper 8-hydroxyquinolinate, Z. Anal. Chem. 215 (1966) 101.

[523] L. Chromy, K. Uhacz, Antifouling paints based on organotin compounds Part. I. Colorimetric determination of microgram amounts of organotin compounds in aqueous solutions, J. Oil Colour Chem. Ass. 51 (1968) 494.

[524] L. Chromy, W. Mlodzianowska et al., Antifouling paints based on organotin compounds Part II: Spectrographic determination of microgram amounts of bis-(tri-n-butyltin) oxide in aqueous solutions, J. Oil Colour Chem. Ass. 53 (1970) 121.

[525] E. Rogers, E. Lawley, The determination of pentachlorophenyl laurate in textile and paper materials, J. Text. Inst. 60 (1969) 347.

[526] A. Basch, B. Hirschman, The determination of pentachlorophenol and pentachlorophenol laurate, Text. Res. J. 40 (1970) 670.

[527] J. R. Davies, S. T. Thuraisingham, Nachweis und Bestimmung von Pentachlorphenol in Naturkautschuk-Latex durch Dünnschicht-Chromatographie, J. Chromatogr. 35 (1968) 43.

8.6 Analysis of Flame Retardants

[528] J. W. Lyons, The Chemistry and Uses of Fire Retardants, Wiley-Interscience, New York-London-Sidney-Toronto 1970.

[529] H. Vogel, Flammfestmachen von Kunststoffen, Hüthig, Heidelberg 1966.

[530] C. J. Hilado, Flammability Handbook for Plastics, Technomic, Stanford, Conn. 1969.

[531] J. Troitzsch, Die Wirkungsweise von Flammschutzmitteln in Kunststoffen, Kunststoffe 69 (1979) 557.

[531a] U. Kerschner, Bromhaltige Flammschutzmittel zur Brandschutzausrüstung von Kunststoffen, Kunststoffjournal 1/79, 6.

Bibliography

[532] W. C. Kuryla, A. J. Papa (Eds.), Flame Retardancy of Polymeric Materials, Vol. 1–3, 1973, Vol. 4, 1978, Marcel Dekker, New York.

[532a] M. Levin, S. M. Atlas, E. M. Pearce (Eds.), Flame-Retardant Polymeric Materials, 2. Vol., Plenum Press, New York 1975, 1978.

[533] H. Schindlbauer, L. Dokuzovic, Nachweis und Bestimmung von Flammschutzmitteln in Polystyrol. Z. Anal. Chem. 276 (1975) 285.

[534] W. F. Bernholz, G. Roberts, What makes a good PVC antifogging agent, Plast. Technol. 15 (1969) 48.

9 Accelerators

[535] M. J. Brock, G. D. Louth, Identification of accelerators and antioxidants in compounded rubber products, Anal. Chem. 27 (1955) 1575.

[536] T. Yuasa, K. Kamiya, Identifizierung von Antioxidantien und Beschleunigern in vulkanisiertem Gummi, Jap. Anal. 13 (1964) 966.

[537] A. Popov, V. Gadeva, Zum Nachweis papierchromatographisch getrennter Vulkanisationsbeschleuniger, J. Chromatogr. 16 (1964) 256.

[537a] I. L. Gotti, R. Piancentini, Identificazione di acceleranti, agenti vulcanizzanti e ritardanti acidi nelle mescolanze di gomma vulcanizzata, Mater. Plast. Elastomeri (1975) 7, 500.

[538] W. Hofmann, H. Hostromow, Analytische Untersuchungsbefunde des Ausschusses Gummi des Bundesgesundheitsamtes über Kautschuk, Kautschuk-Chemikalien und Vulkanisate im Rahmen des Lebensmittelgesetzes II, Kaut. Gummi Kunstst. 21 (1968) 318.

[539] V. Kapisinska, V. Kosljar, Die Chromatographie von Beschleunigern, Alterungsschutzmitteln und Stabilisatoren auf kleinen Plättchen, Plast. Hmoty Kauc. 6 (1969) 338.

[540] P.-L. Hu, W. Scheele, Über die quantitative Analyse von Kautschuk-Hilfsstoffen, Kaut. Gummi Kunstst. 18 (1965) 290, 784.

[541] E. Stahl, V. Brüderle, Thermofraktographie zur Schnellanalyse von Kunststoffen. 4. Comm.: Identifizierung der Basiskomponenten von Epoxidharzen, Angew. Makromol. Chem. 68 (1978) 87, 5. Comm.: Identifizierung der Härter von Epoxidharzen, Progr. Colloid Polymer Sci. 66 (1979) 417.

[542] W.-J. Uhde, Dünnschichtchromatographische Bestimmung tertiärer Amine in ungesättigtem Polyesterharz, Plaste Kaut. 13 (1966) 722.

[543] J. Pasciak, Polarographische Untersuchung und Bestimmung von Natriumdimethyldithiocarbamat in Butadien-Styrol-Kautschuklatex, Chem. Anal. 13 (1968) 263.

[544] S. K. Bhatnagar, Rubber News, 8 (1969) 28.

[545] J. G. Kreiner, Thin layer chromatographic identification of rubber compound ingredients, Rubber Chem. Technol. 44 (1971) 381.

[546] G. M. Higgins, G. P. McSweeney, The analysis of rubber vulcanisates – identification of amine residues from sulfenamide accelerators by thin layer chromatography, Rubber Chem. Technol. 47 (1974) 5, 1206.

[547] C. Prandi, Thin layer chromatography of aliphatic amines, J. Chrom. 155 (1978) 149.

[548] P. Schneider, Kaut. Gummi 6 (1952) 21 WT.

[549] M. Pike, F. Watson, J. Polym. Sci. 9 (1952) 229.

10 Processing Aids

10.2 Lubricants

[550] G. Pfahler, T. Riedel, Gleitmittel, Kunststoffe 66 (1976) 10.

[551] G. J. Veersen, Zur Wirkungsweise von Gleitmitteln beim Verarbeiten von PVC, Kunststoffe 59 (1969) 180.

[552] A. Riethmayer, PVC-Gleitmittel, Fette, Seifen, Wachse 98 (1972) 193, 227, 322, 399.

[553] H. P. Kaufmanns, B. Das, Dünnschichtchromatographie auf dem Fettgebiet IX: Die Analyse der Esterwachse, Fette, Seifen, Anstrichm. 65 (1963) 398.

[554] E. Hagen, Beiträge zur analytischen Chemie der Plaste XLIII – Versuche zur dünnschichtchromatographischen Analyse von Gleitmitteln in Plastformstoffen aus Polyvinylchloridharz, Plaste Kaut. 15 (1970) 25.

[555] W. Dietsche, Dünnschicht-Chromatographie von Kohlenwasserstoff-Wachsen an harnstoffbeschichteten Platten, Fetten, Seifen, Anstrichm. 72 (1970) 778.

10.3 Blowing Agents

[556] H. Piechota, H. Röhr, Integralschaumstoffe, Carl Hanser, München-Wien 1975.

[557] R. Miksch, L. Prölss, Nachweis von Bläh- und Plastiziermitteln in Gummi-Mischungen, Gummi Asbest 13 (1960) 250.

[558] H-G. Mosle, W. Wolf, W. Bode, Gaschromatographische Bestimmung von n-Pentan in treibmittelhaltigem Polystyrol, Kunststoffe 56 (1966) 760.

[559] F. Scholl, unpublished results, 1961/62.

[560] Bayer-Handbuch für die Gummi-Industrie, Bayer Leverkusen 1975.

[561] Celogen Blowing Agents, Bulletin ASP – 3917, Uniroyal Inc., Naugatuck, Conn.

[562] Blowing Agents and Aktivators, Dupont de Neurours, Elastomers Laboratory, Wilmington.

[563] H. Hurnik, Treibmittel für Schaumkunststoffe, Kunststoffe 66 (1976) 698.

10.4 Adhesion Promoters

[564] E. P. Plueddemann, H. A. Clark, L. E. Nelson, K. R. Hoffmann, New silan coupling agents for reinforced plastics, Mod. Plast. 39 (1962, Aug.) 135.

[565] S. Sterman, J. G. Marsden, Silane coupling agents as integral blends, in resin-filler systems, Mod. Plast 40 (1963, July) 125.

[566] E. P. Plueddemann, Silane coupling agents in reinforced plastics, Appl. Polym. Symp. 14 (1970) 95.

[566a] E. P. Plueddemann, Fillers and Reinforcement for Plastics, in Advances in Chem. Series, No. 134, Chapt. 9, 86 a, Am. Chem. Soc. 1974.

[567] J. G. Marsden, Silicone coupling agents and primers for thermosets, thermoplasts, and elastomers, Appl. Polym. Symp. 14 (1970) 107.

[568] Dow Corning Corp., Silane Coupling Agents, 1970.

[568a] H. Marwitz, Silan-Haftvermittler, Adhäsion 4 (1970) 122.

[569] M. R. Rosen, From treating solution to filler surface and beyond, J. Coatings Techn. 50 (1978) No. 644, 70.

[570] P. E. Cassidy, B. J. Yager, Coupling agents as adhesive promoters, J. Macromol. Sci. D. 1 (1971) 1.

[571] H. Fredenhagen, Haftvermittelnde Zusätze zu Gummi- und PVC-Mischungen für die Textil- und Metallbindung, Gummi, Asbest, Kunstst. 21 (1968) 1041.

[571a] J. D. Harris, C. D. Ashurst, Direct bonding rubber and PVC to textiles and metals, Polymer Age 1 (1970) 148.

[572] G. Wiedemann, B. Wustmann, H. Frenzel, S. Keusch, Zur chemischen Analytik von Haftmitteln bei Glasseidenerzeug-

nissen für Verbundwerkstoffe, Faserforschg. und Textil-techn. *29* (1978) 681.

[573] H. Ishida, L. J. Koenig, FTIR-spectroscopy study of the silane coupling agent / porous silica interface, J. Colloid Interface Sci. *64* (1978) 567.

10.6 Antiskinning Agents

[574] H. Hadert, Prooxygene und Antioxygene, Farbe + Lack *56* (1950) 349.

[574a] H. Hadert, Rezeptbuch für die Lackindustrie.

[574b] L. P. Foster, S. B. Miller, Inhibitors for unsaturated polyesters, Mod. Plast *44* (1967, March) 163.

[574c] D. T. Gabris, Anti-Hautbildungsmittel für Polyamid-Harze, Adhäsion (1970) 142.

Other Processing Aids

[575] W. G. Strunk, Rheological control agent for polyester resins, Mod. Plast. *45* (1967) 166.

[576] H. Seyffert, Modifizierte Polysiloxane als Stabilisatoren für die Polyurethan-Verschäumung, Gummi, Asbest, Kunstst. *23* (1970) 953.

[576a] E. G. Schwarz, Silicone surfactants for urethane foams: Mechanism, performance and applications, Appl. Polym. Symp. *14* (1970) 71.

[576b] E. Schröder, M. Helmstedt, H. Jehring, Beiträge zur analytischen Chemie der Plaste XXIII, Bestimmung von Alkylsulfonaten in Emulsions-PVC, Plaste Kaut. *12* (1965) 666.

[577] M. H. Akstinat, Organische Korrosions-Inhibitoren in Farben und Lacken, Farbe + Lack *76* (1970) 988.

[578] J. Kaupp, W. Straßberger, Über Amidwachse, Vom Wachs, Vol. II, 790, Farbwerke Hoechst 1971.

[579] H. Domininghaus, Zusatzstoffe für Kunststoffe, Zechner & Hüthig, Speyer 1978.

11 Solvents

11.1 Survey and Classification

[580] J. Mellan, Industrial Solvents, 2. ed., Reinhold Publ., New York 1950.

[581] I. Mellan, Industrial Solvents Handbook 2. ed. Noyes Data Corp., Park Ridge, USA 1977.

[582] L. Scheflan, B. Jacobs, The Handbook of Solvents, New York 1953.

[583] A. K. Doolittle, The Technology of Solvents and Plasticizers, New York-London 1954.

[584] T. Durrans, Solvents, 8. ed., Chapman & Hall, London 1971.

[585] C. Marsden, S. Mann, Solvent, Guide, 2. ed., Cleaver-Hume Press, London 1963.

[586] Lösungsmittel HOECHST, 4. ed., Farbwerke Hoechst AG, Frankfurt 1966.

[587] J. A. Riddick, W. B. Bunger, Organic Solvents, Physical Properties and Methods for Purification, Wiley-Interscience, New York 1970.

[588] H. Weber, Praktische Lösungsmittelanalyse, Leipzig 1936.

[589] H. Persiel, Analyse von Lösungsmittelgemischen in Houben-Weyl, Methoden der organischen Chemie, Vol. II, Stuttgart 1953.

[589a] F. W. Kerckow, Analyse technischer Lösungsmittel und ihrer Gemische, Z. Angew. Chem. *66* (1954) 27.

[590] B. Jacobs, L. Scheflan, Chemical Analysis of Industrial Solvents, New York 1953.

[591] K. Thinius, Anleitung zur Analyse der Lösungsmittel, J. A. Barth, Leipzig 1957.

11.3 Gas Chromatography of Solvents

[592] R. R. Scott, Gaschromatographische Bestimmung von Lösungsmittelresten in gegossenen Filmen, Chem. Ind. (1964) 2130.

[593] G. G. Esposito, M. H. Swann, Determination of aromatic content of hydrocarbon paint solvents by gas chromatography, J. Paint Technol. *38* (1966) 377.

[594] R. J. Klepser, The direct determination of chemical solvents in coating materials by means of gas chromatography, J. Paint Technol. *39* (1967) 663.

[595] D. G. Anderson, The use of kovats retention indices and response factors for the qualitative and quantitative analysis of coatings solvents, J. Paint, Technol. *40* (1968) 549.

[596] R. Fischbach, Bestimmung von Lösungsmittelresten in Zellglasbeschichtungen, Kunststoffe *60* (1970) 194.

[596a] A. P. Jaecklin, M. Buri, Beitrag zur Bestimmung von Restlösungsmitteln in Farb- und Lackfilmen Verpack. Rundsch., Tech. wiss. Beil. *28* (1977) 19.

[597] J. Flack, Gaschromatographische Bestimmung von Lösungsvermittlern in wäßrigen Anstrichstoffsystemen, Plaste Kaut. *18* (1971) 132.

[598] J. Benes, Gaschromatographie von Lösungsmitteln, Chem. Prum. *17* (1967) 261.

[598a] P. Bartl, A. Schaaff, X. H. Funke, Analyse von Lacklösemitteln mit Hilfe der Kapillar-Gaschromatographie, Farbe + Lack *84* (1978) 148.

[598b] M. F. Dante, Analysis of solvent blends using modified liquid chromatography separations and subsequent gas-liquid chromatography, J. Paint Technol. *47* (1975) 606, 49.

[599] Gasspürröhrchen und Indikatorröhrchen verschiedener Hersteller z. B. Drägerwerk, Lübeck; Auer, Berlin.

[600] J. T. Walsh, C. Merrit, Qualitative functional group analysis of gas chromatographic effluents, Anal. Chem. *32* (1960) 1378.

[601] C. Merrit, Chemical identification of gas chromatographic fractions in [107], p. 325.

[602] B. Casu, L. Cavalloti, A simple device for qualitative functional group analysis of gas chromatographic effluents, Anal. Chem. *34* (1962) 1514.

[603] J. D'Ans, E. Lax, Taschenbuch für Chemiker und Physiker, Vol. II, Springer, Berlin–Göttingen–Heidelberg 1964.

[604] C. D. Hodgmann (Ed.), Handbook of Physics and Chemistry, The Chemical Rubber Publ. Co., Cleveland (annual).

11.4 IR Spectroscopy of Solvents

[605] A. Visapää, The near-infrared spectra of common solvents, Kem. Teollisuus *22* (1965) 487.

[606] NIR-Spektren von Lösemitteln, Beckman Company publication.

[607] E. G. Hoffmann, Analyse gesundheitsschädlicher Lösemittel in technischen Gemischen, Z. Anal. Chem. *164* (1958) 182.

[608] D. Goldfarb, C. W. Brown, Collection of GC-fractions on activated charcoal and identification by IR-spectroscopy, Appl. Spectrosc. *33* (1979) 126.

Weichmacher

Plasticizers

Weichmacher
1. Aromat. Carbonsäureester
1.1. Phthalsäureester

Plasticizers
1. Aromatic Carboxylic Acid Esters
1.1. Phthalic Acid Esters

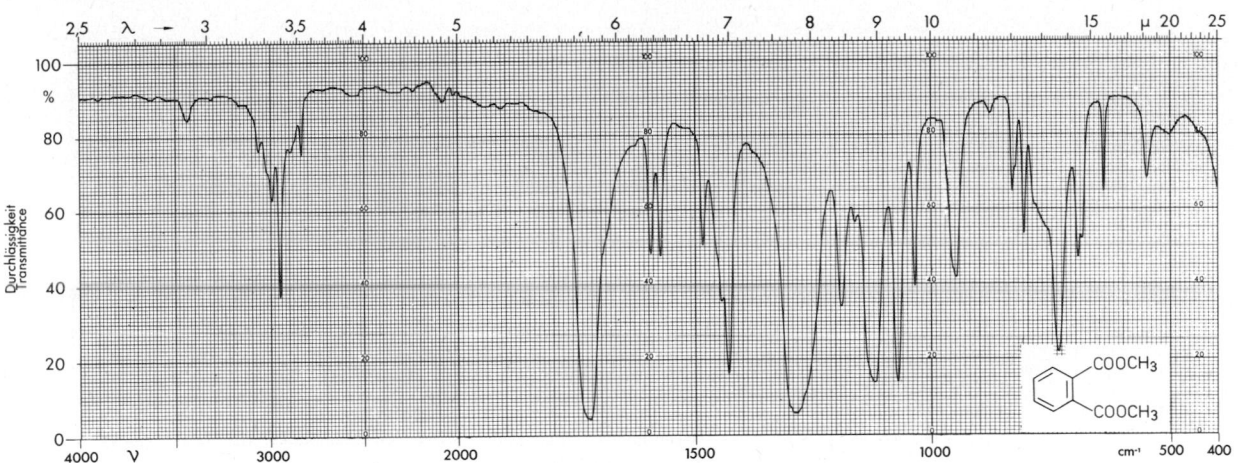

Verbindung:	Dimethylphthalat			Compound:	Dimethyl phthalate			5000
Formel:	$C_{10}H_{10}O_4$	M.:	194,2	Formula:	$C_{10}H_{10}O_4$	M. w.:	194,2	
Handelsname:	Palatinol M	Herst.:	BASF	Tradename:	Palatinol M	Manuf.:	BASF	
Präparation:	Kapill. Film	Dez. Nr.:	1.1.1	Preparation:	Capill. Film	Dec. No.:	1.1.1	

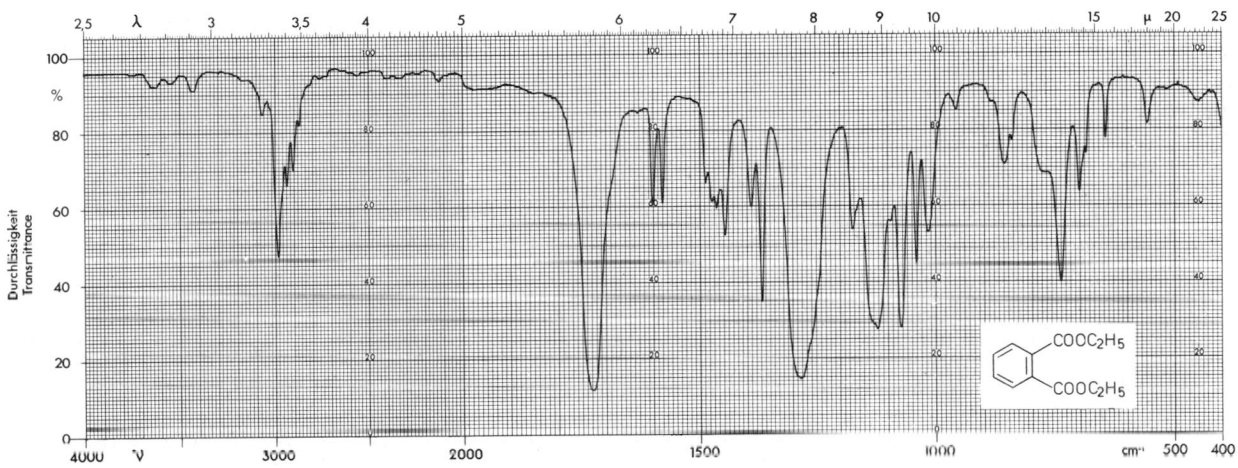

Verbindung:	Diethylphthalat			Compound:	Diethyl phthalate			5001
Formel:	$C_{12}H_{14}O_4$	M.:	222,2	Formula:	$C_{12}H_{14}O_4$	M. w.:	222,2	
Handelsname:		Herst.:	Merck	Tradename:		Manuf.:	Merck	
Präparation:	Kapill. Film	Dez. Nr.:	1.1.2	Preparation:	Capill. Film	Dec. No:.	1.1.2	

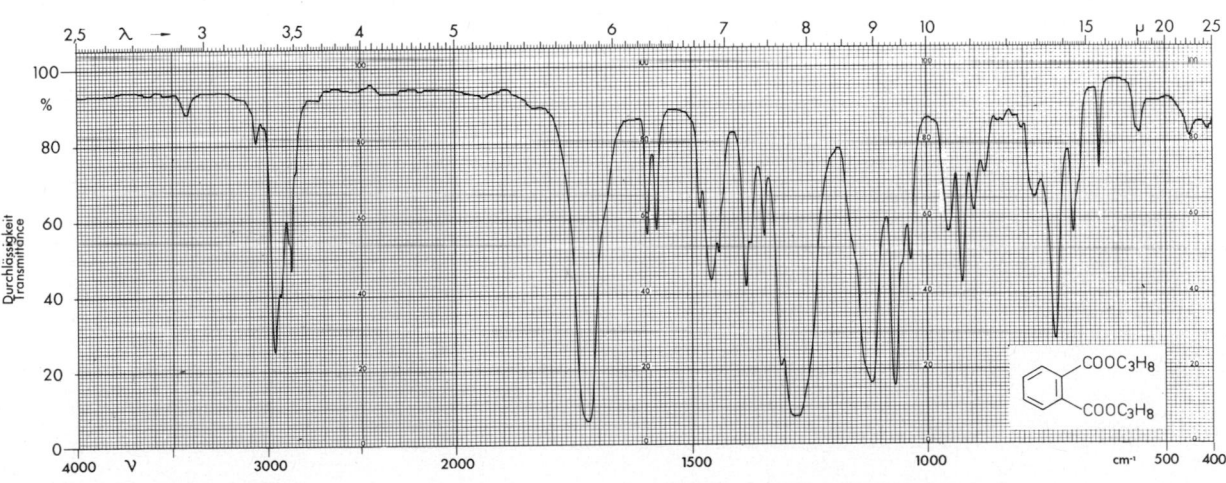

Verbindung:	Dipropylphthalat			Compound:	Dipropyl phthalate			5002
Formel:	$C_{14}H_{18}O_4$	M.:	250,3	Formula:	$C_{14}H_{18}O_4$	M. w.:	250,3	
Handelsname:		Herst.:	Eastman	Tradename:		Manuf.:	Eastman	
Präparation:	Kapill. Film	Dez. Nr.:	1.1.3	Preparation:	Capill. Film	Dec. No.:	1.1.3	

Weichmacher
1. Aromat. Carbonsäureester
1.1. Phthalsäureester

Plasticizers
1. Aromatic Carboxylic Acid Esters
1.1. Phthalic Acid Esters

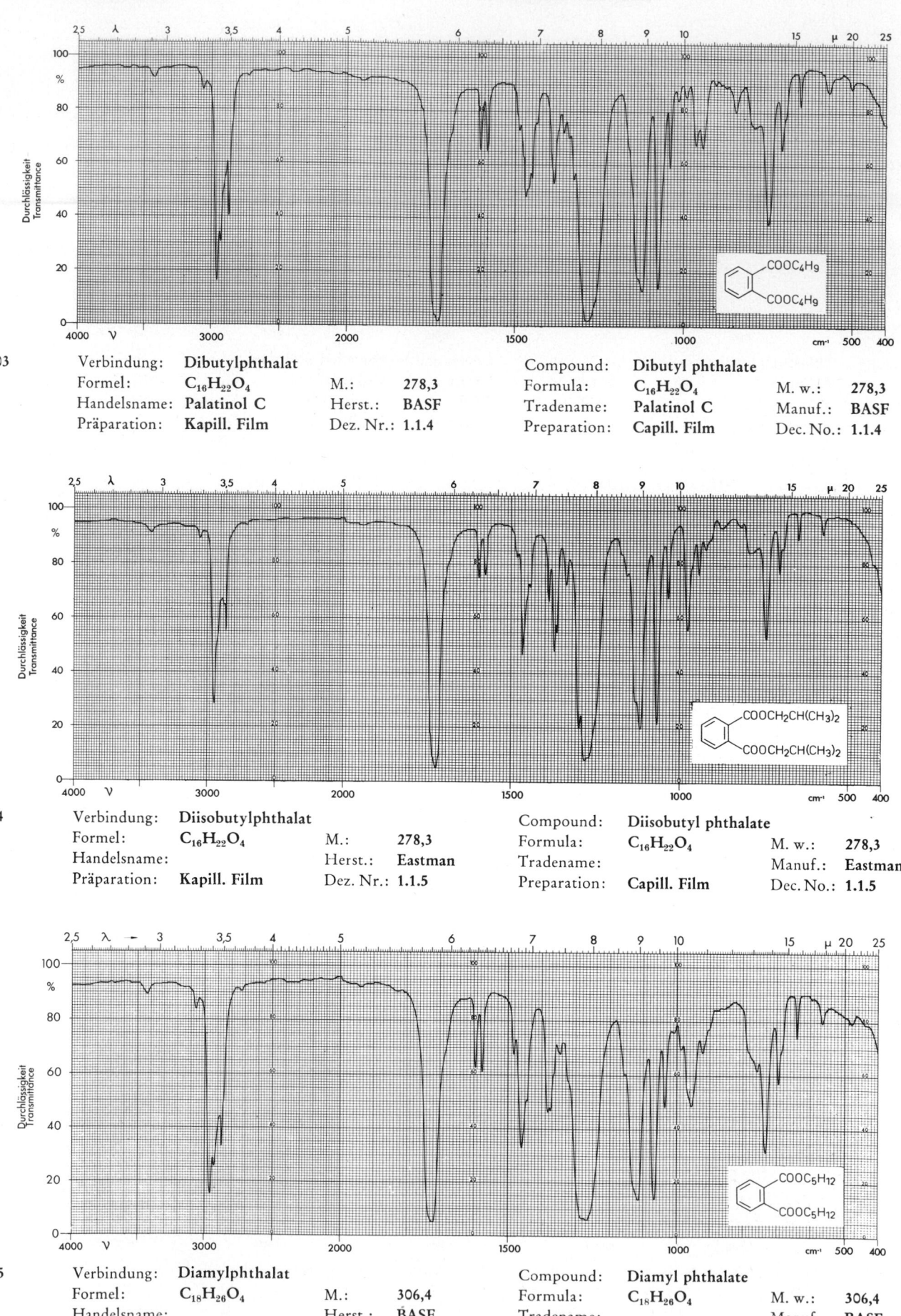

5003

Verbindung:	Dibutylphthalat			Compound:	Dibutyl phthalate		
Formel:	$C_{16}H_{22}O_4$	M.:	278,3	Formula:	$C_{16}H_{22}O_4$	M. w.:	278,3
Handelsname:	Palatinol C	Herst.:	BASF	Tradename:	Palatinol C	Manuf.:	BASF
Präparation:	Kapill. Film	Dez. Nr.:	1.1.4	Preparation:	Capill. Film	Dec. No.:	1.1.4

5004

Verbindung:	Diisobutylphthalat			Compound:	Diisobutyl phthalate		
Formel:	$C_{16}H_{22}O_4$	M.:	278,3	Formula:	$C_{16}H_{22}O_4$	M. w.:	278,3
Handelsname:		Herst.:	Eastman	Tradename:		Manuf.:	Eastman
Präparation:	Kapill. Film	Dez. Nr.:	1.1.5	Preparation:	Capill. Film	Dec. No.:	1.1.5

5005

Verbindung:	Diamylphthalat			Compound:	Diamyl phthalate		
Formel:	$C_{18}H_{26}O_4$	M.:	306,4	Formula:	$C_{18}H_{26}O_4$	M. w.:	306,4
Handelsname:		Herst.:	BASF	Tradename:		Manuf.:	BASF
Präparation:	Kapill. Film	Dez. Nr.:	1.1.6	Preparation:	Capill. Film	Dec. No.:	1.1.6

Weichmacher
1. Aromat. Carbonsäureester
1.1. Phthalsäureester

Plasticizers
1. Aromatic Carboxylic Acid Esters
1.1. Phthalic Acid Esters

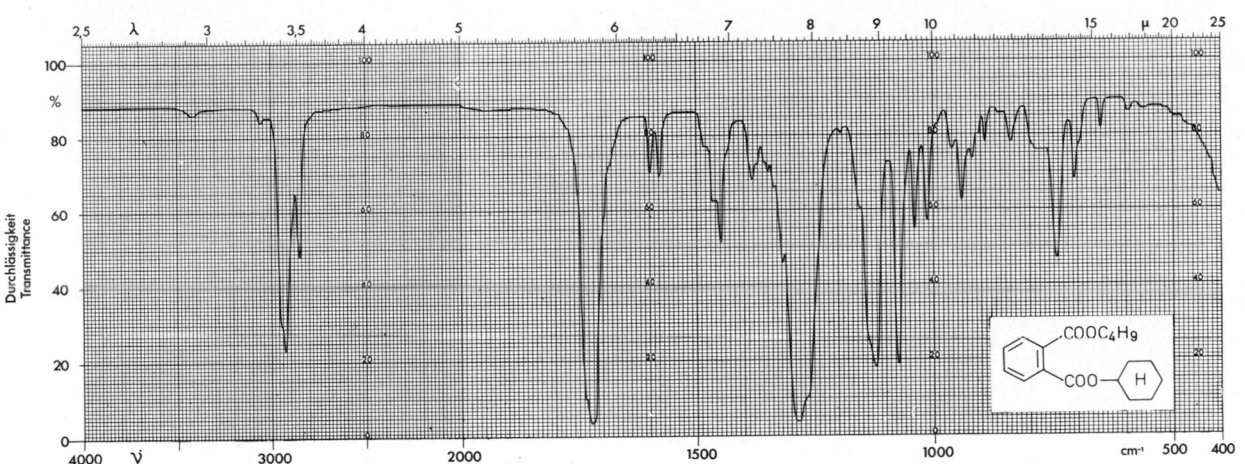

Verbindung:	Butylcyclohexylphthalat			Compound:	Butyl cyclohexyl phthalate		5006
Formel:	$C_{18}H_{24}O_4$	M.:	304,4	Formula:	$C_{18}H_{24}O_4$	M. w.: 304,4	
Handelsname:	Elastex 50 B	Herst.:	Allied Chem.	Tradename:	Elastex 50 B	Manuf.: Allied Chem.	
Präparation:	Kapill. Film	Dez. Nr.:	1.1.7	Preparation:	Capill. Film	Dec. No.: 1.1.7	

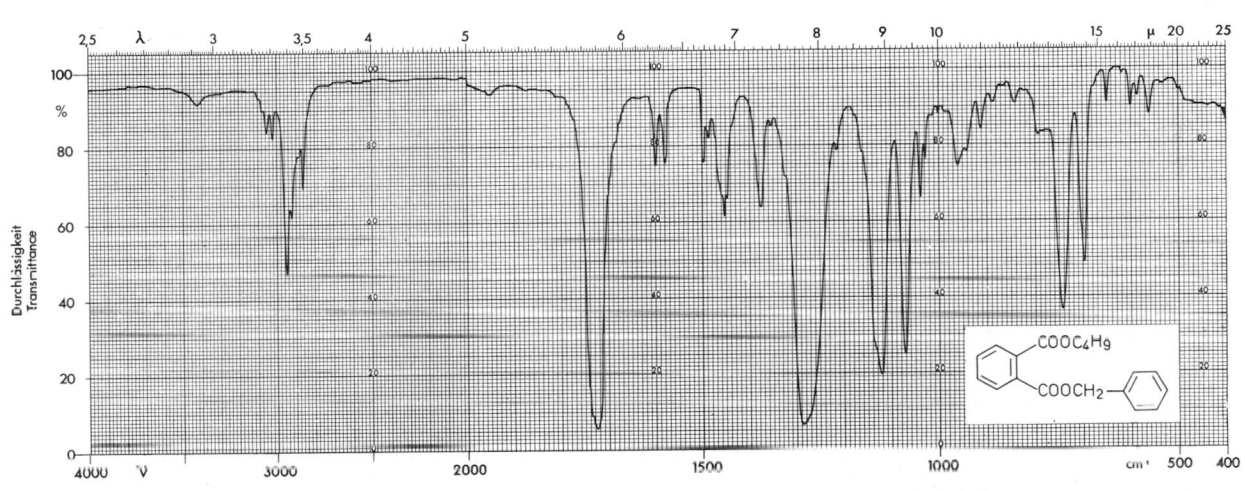

Verbindung:	Butylbenzylphthalat			Compound:	Butyl benzyl phthalate		5007
Formel:	$C_{19}H_{20}O_4$	M.:	312,4	Formula:	$C_{19}H_{20}O_4$	M. w.: 312,4	
Handelsname:	Santicizer 160	Herst.:	Monsanto	Tradename:	Santicizer 160	Manuf.: Monsanto	
Präparation:	Kapill. Film	Dez. Nr.:	1.1.8	Preparation:	Capill. Film	Dec. No.: 1.1.8	

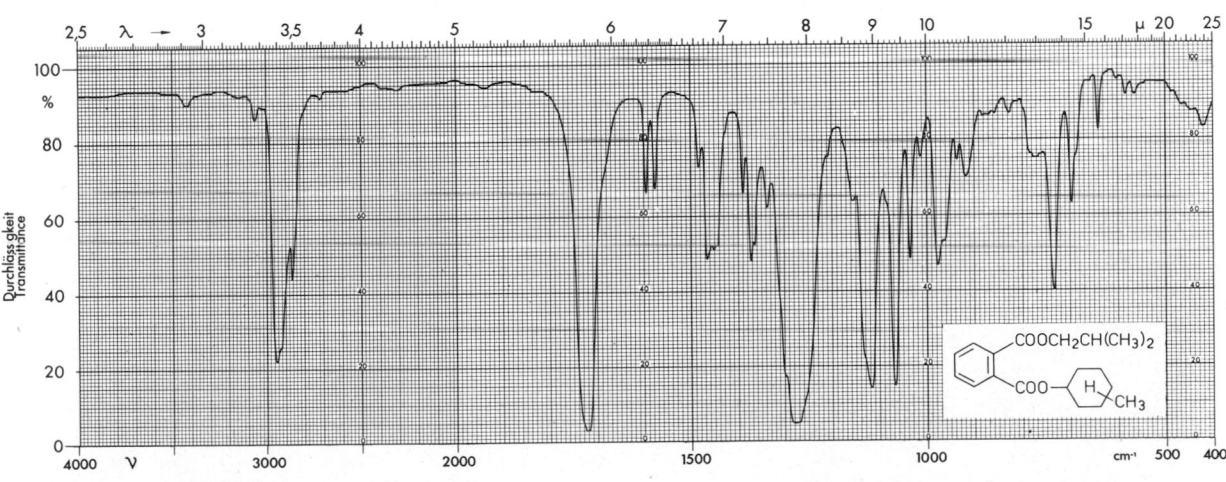

Verbindung:	Isobutylmethylcyclohexylphthalat			Compound:	Isobutyl methylcyclohexyl phthalate		5008
Formel:	$C_{19}H_{26}O_4$	M.:	318,4	Formula:	$C_{19}H_{26}O_4$	M. w.: 318,4	
Handelsname:		Herst.:	Howards	Tradename:		Manuf.: Howards	
Präparation:	Kapill. Film	Dez. Nr.:	1.1.9	Preparation:	Capill. Film	Dec. No.: 1.1.9	

Weichmacher
1. Aromat. Carbonsäureester
1.1. Phthalsäureester

Plasticizers
1. Aromatic Carboxylic Acid Esters
1.1. Phthalic Acid Esters

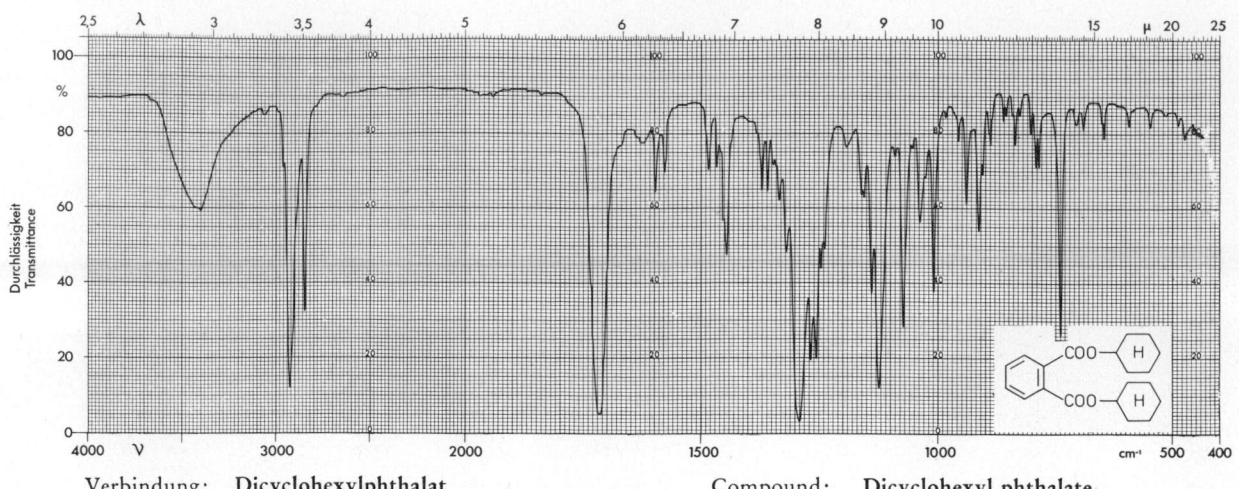

5009

Verbindung:	**Dicyclohexylphthalat**			Compound:	**Dicyclohexyl phthalate**	
Formel:	$C_{20}H_{26}O_4$	M.:	**330,4**	Formula:	$C_{20}H_{26}O_4$	M. w.: **330,4**
Handelsname:	**Unimoll 66**	Herst.:	**Bayer**	Tradename:	**Unimoll 66**	Manuf.: **Bayer**
Präparation:	**Kapill. Film**	Dez. Nr.:	**1.1.10**	Preparation:	**Capill. Film**	Dec. No.: **1.1.10**

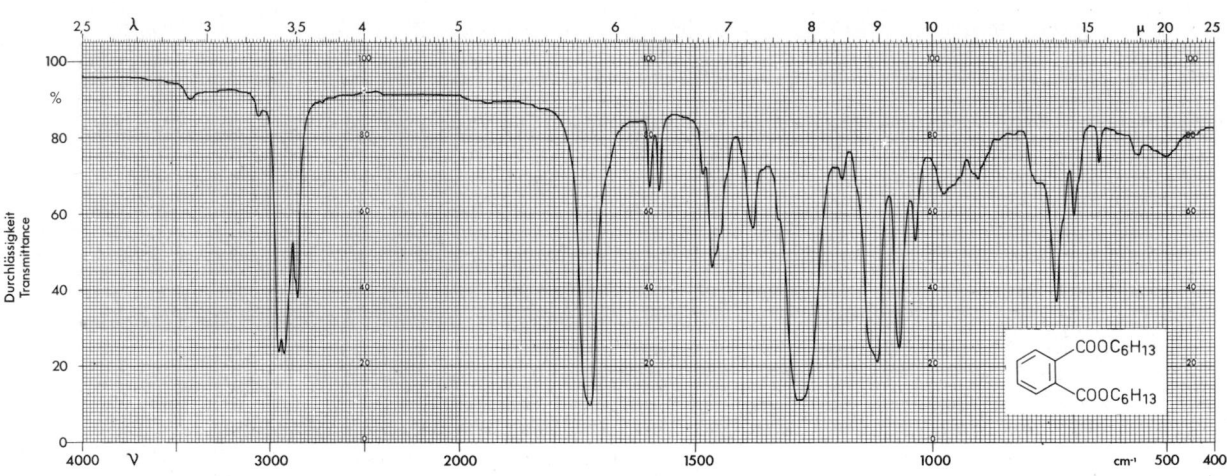

5010

Verbindung:	**Di-n-hexylphthalat**			Compound:	**Di-n-hexyl phthalate**	
Formel:	$C_{20}H_{30}O_4$	M.:	**334,5**	Formula:	$C_{20}H_{30}O_4$	M. w.: **334,5**
Handelsname:		Herst.:	**Bosch**	Tradename:		Manuf.: **Bosch**
Präparation:	**Kapill. Film**	Dez. Nr.:	**1.1.11**	Preparation:	**Capill. Film**	Dec. No.: **1.1.11**

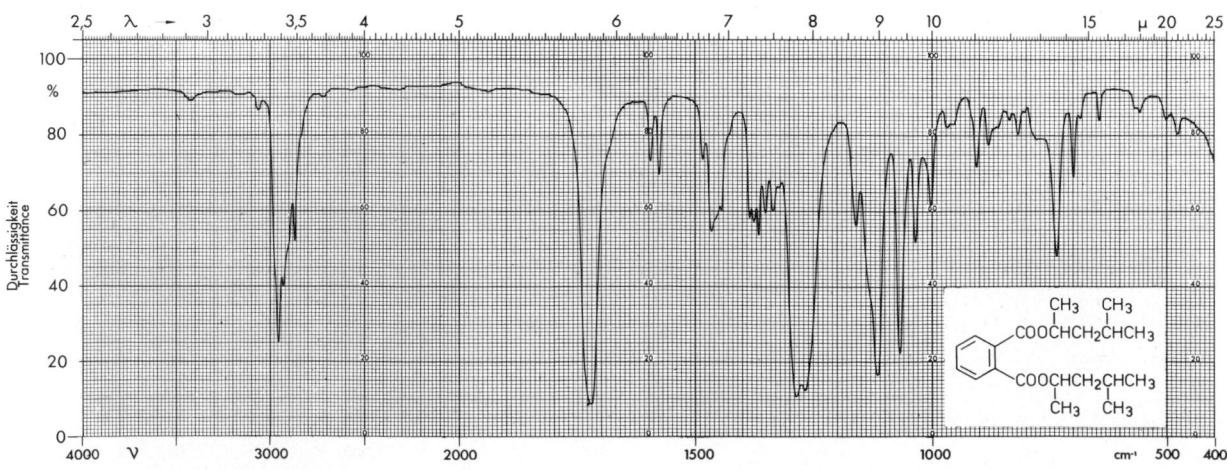

5011

Verbindung:	**Di-(1,3-dimethylbutyl)-phthalat**			Compound:	**Di-(1,3-dimethyl butyl) phthalate**	
Formel:	$C_{20}H_{30}O_4$	M.:	**334,5**	Formula:	$C_{20}H_{30}O_4$	M. w.: **334,5**
Handelsname:	**Plastoflex 520**	Herst.:	**Advance**	Tradename:	**Plastoflex 520**	Manuf.: **Advance**
Präparation:	**Kapill. Film**	Dez. Nr.:	**1.1.12**	Preparation:	**Capill. Film**	Dec. No.: **1.1.12**

Weichmacher
1. Aromat. Carbonsäureester
1.1. Phthalsäureester

Plasticizers
1. Aromatic Carboxylic Acid Esters
1.1. Phthalic Acid Esters

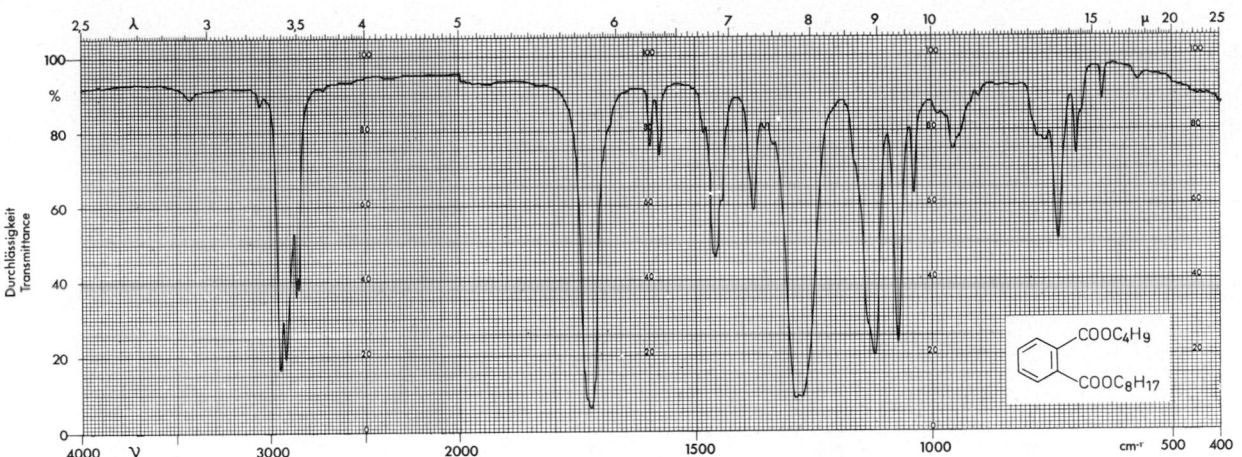

Verbindung:	**Butyloctylphthalat**			Compound:	**Butyl octyl phthalate**			**5012**
Formel:	$C_{20}H_{30}O_4$	M.:	**334,5**	Formula:	$C_{20}H_{30}O_4$	M. w.:	**334,5**	
Handelsname:	**Santicizer 165**	Herst.:	**Monsanto**	Tradename:	**Santicizer 165**	Manuf.:	**Monsanto**	
Präparation:	**Kapill. Film**	Dez. Nr.:	**1.1.13**	Preparation:	**Capill. Film**	Dec. No:.	**1.1.13**	

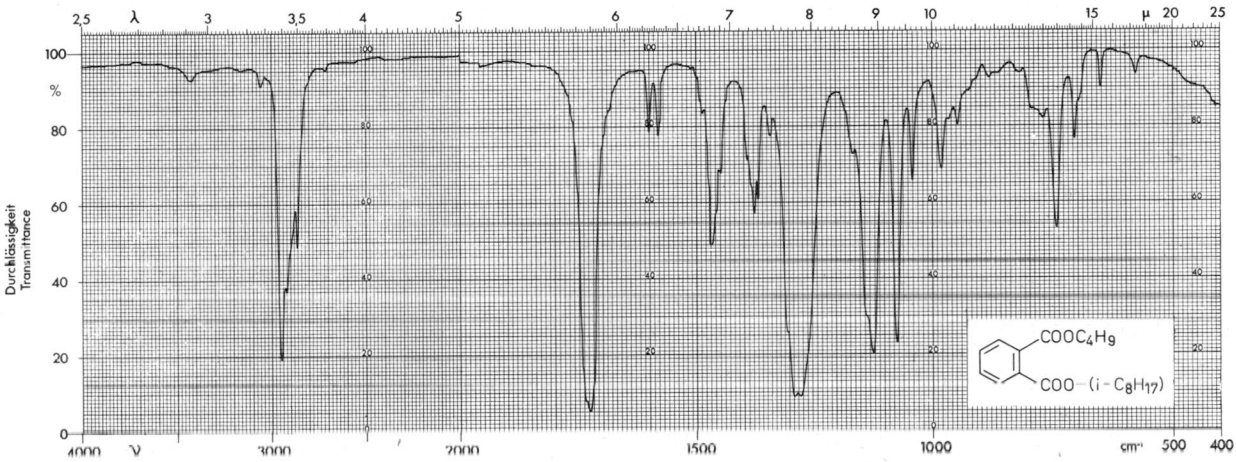

Verbindung:	**Butylisooctylphthalat**			Compound:	**Butyl isooctyl phthalate**			**5013**
Formel:	$C_{20}H_{30}O_4$	M.:	**334,5**	Formula:	$C_{20}H_{30}O_4$	M. w.:	**334,5**	
Handelsname:	**Plasticizer 84**	Herst.:	**Eastman**	Tradename:	**Plasticizer 84**	Manuf.:	**Eastman**	
Präparation:	**Kapill. Film**	Dez. Nr.:	**1.1.14**	Preparation:	**Capill. Film**	Dec. No:.	**1.1.14**	

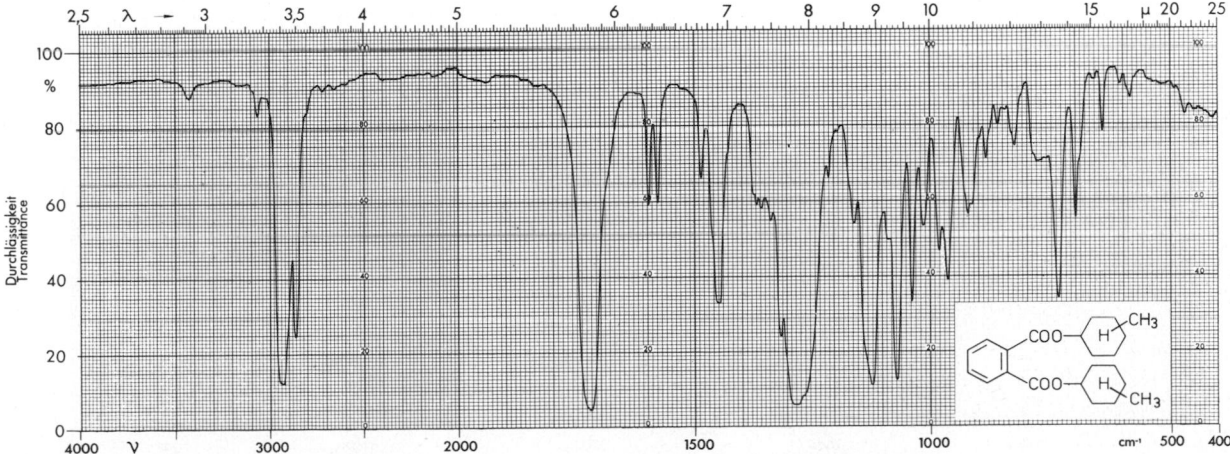

Verbindung:	**Di-(methylcyclohexyl)phthalat**			Compound:	**Di-(methylcyclohexyl) phthalate**			**5014**
Formel:	$C_{22}H_{30}O_4$	M.:	**358,5**	Formula:	$C_{22}H_{30}O_4$	M. w.:	**358,5**	
Handelsname:	**Howflex SP**	Herst.:	**Howards**	Tradename:	**Howflex SP**	Manuf.:	**Howards**	
Präparation:	**Kapill. Film**	Dez. Nr.:	**1.1.15**	Preparation:	**Capill. Film**	Dec. No:.	**1.1.15**	

Weichmacher
1. Aromat. Carbonsäureester
1.1. Phthalsäureester

Plasticizers
1. Aromatic Carboxylic Acid Esters
1.1. Phthalic Acid Esters

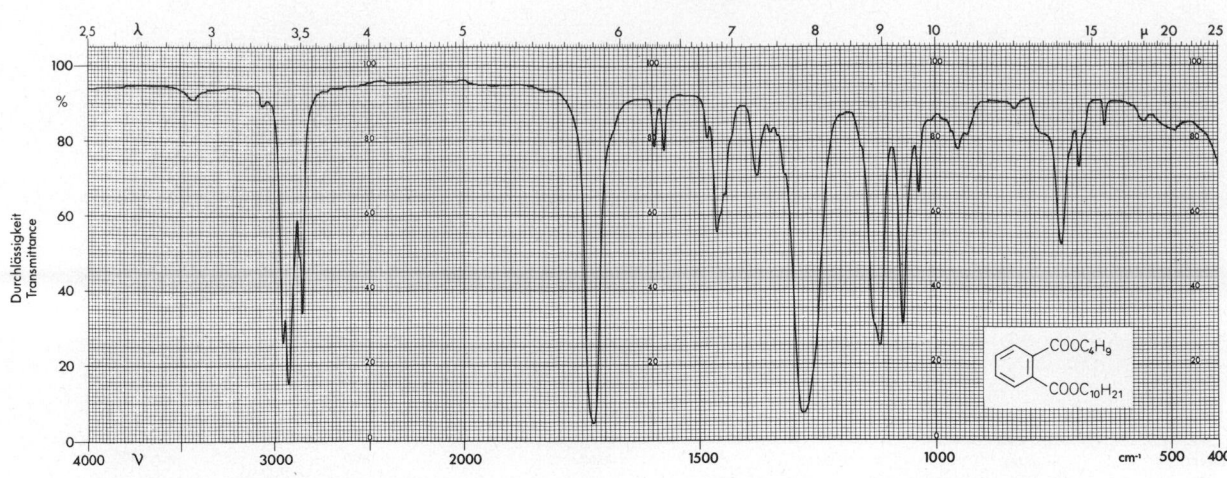

5015   Verbindung: **Butyldecylphthalat**   Compound: **Butyl decyl phthalate**

Formel:	$C_{22}H_{34}O_4$	M.:	**362,5**	Formula:	$C_{22}H_{34}O_4$	M. w.: **362,5**
Handelsname:		Herst.:	**Bosch**	Tradename:		Manuf.: **Bosch**
Präparation:	**Kapill. Film**	Dez. Nr.:	**1.1.16**	Preparation:	**Capill. Film**	Dec. No:. **1.1.16**

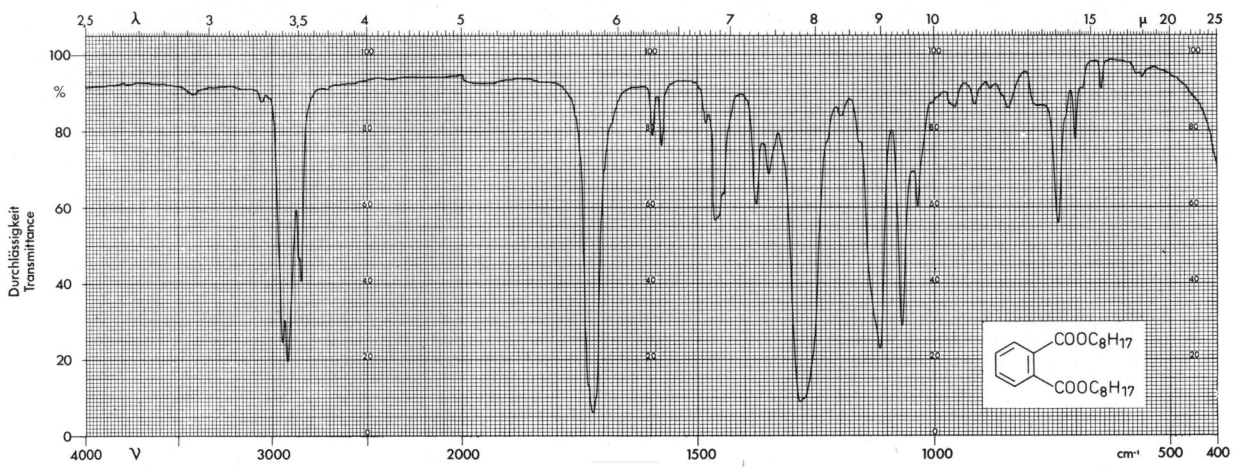

5016   Verbindung: **Dicaprylphthalat**   Compound: **Dicapryl phthalate**

Formel:	$C_{24}H_{38}O_4$	M.:	**390,6**	Formula:	$C_{24}H_{38}O_4$	M. w.: **390,6**
Handelsname:		Herst.:	**Harchem**	Tradename:		Manuf.: **Harchem**
Präparation:	**Kapill. Film**	Dez. Nr.:	**1.1.17**	Preparation:	**Capill. Film**	Dec. No:. **1.1.17**

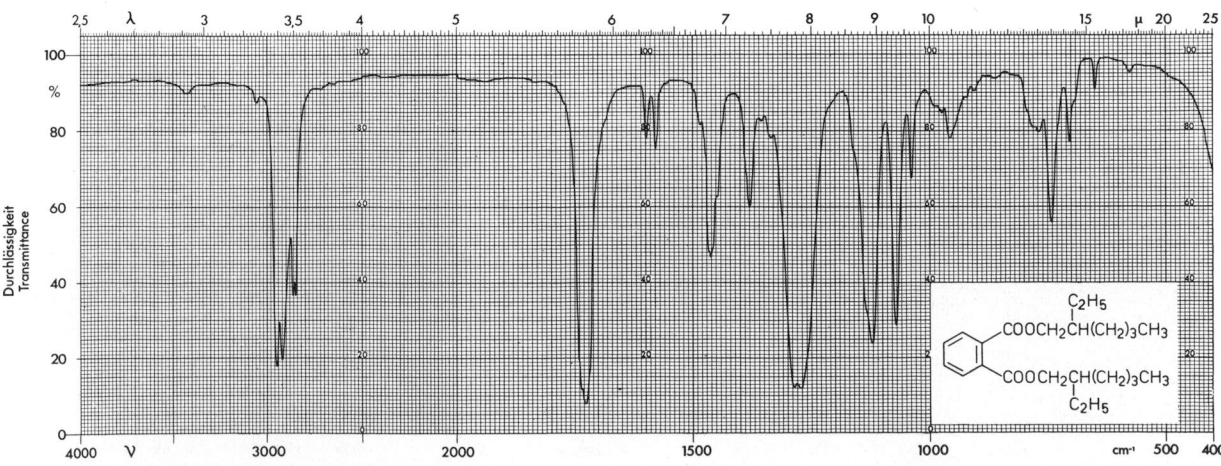

5017   Verbindung: **Di-(2-ethylhexyl)phthalat**   Compound: **Di-(2-ethyl hexyl) phthalate**

Formel:	$C_{24}H_{38}O_4$	M.:	**390,6**	Formula:	$C_{24}H_{38}O_4$	M. w.: **390,6**
Handelsname:	**Weichmacher IW 100**	Herst.:	**Imhausen**	Tradename:	**Weichmacher IW 100**	Manuf.: **Imhausen**
Präparation:	**Kapill. Film**	Dez. Nr.:	**1.1.18**	Preparation:	**Capill. Film**	Dec. No:. **1.1.18**

Weichmacher
1. Aromat. Carbonsäureester
1.1. Phthalsäureester

Plasticizers
1. Aromatic Carboxylic Acid Esters
1.1. Phthalic Acid Esters

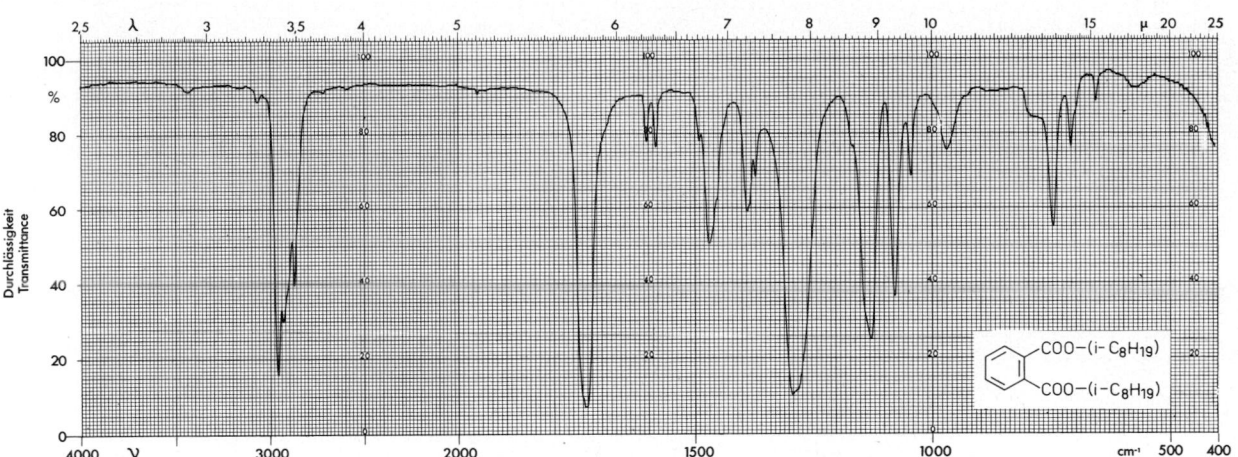

Verbindung:	Diisooctylphthalat			Compound:	Diisooctyl phthalate			5018
Formel:	$C_{24}H_{38}O_4$	M.:	390,6	Formula:	$C_{24}H_{38}O_4$	M. w.:	390,6	
Handelsname:	Reomol DIOP	Herst.:	Geigy	Tradename:	Reomol DIOP	Manuf.:	Geigy	
Präparation:	Kapill. Film	Dez. Nr.:	1.1.19	Preparation:	Capill. Film	Dec. No:.	1.1.19	

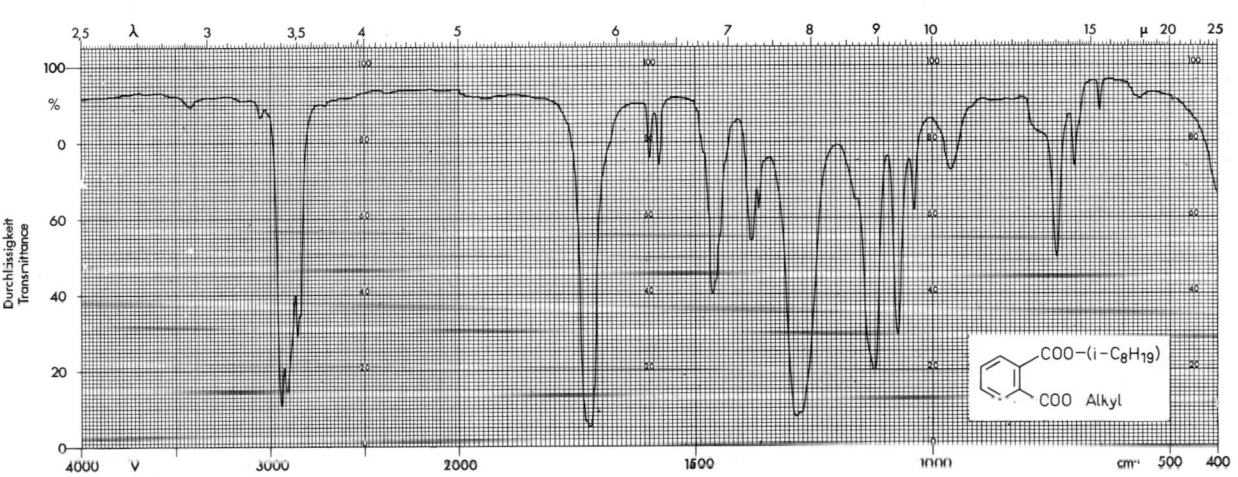

Verbindung:	Isooctylalkylphthalat			Compound:	Isooctyl alkyl phthalate			5019
Formel:		M.:	~ 400	Formula:		M. w.:	~ 400	
Handelsname:	Howflex 1001	Herst.:	Howards	Tradename:	Howflex 1001	Manuf.:	Howards	
Präparation:	Kapill. Film	Dez. Nr.:	1.1.20	Preparation:	Capill. Film	Dec. No:.	1.1.20	

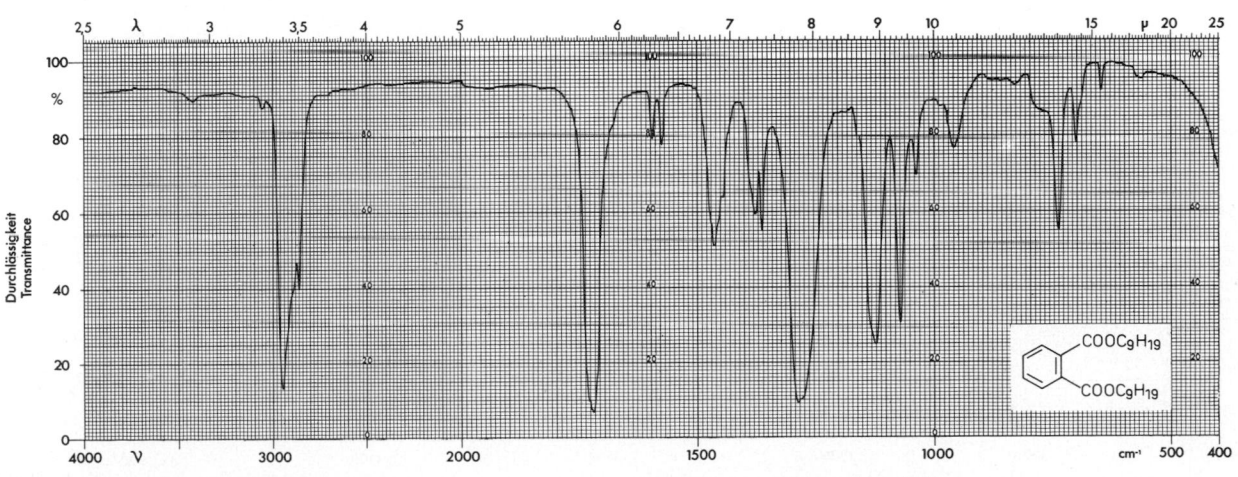

Verbindung:	Dinonylphthalat			Compound:	Dinonyl phthalate			5020
Formel:	$C_{26}H_{42}O_4$	M.:	418,6	Formula:	$C_{26}H_{42}O_4$	M. w.:	418,6	
Handelsname:		Herst.:	Heyden	Tradename:		Manuf.:	Heyden	
Präparation:	Kapill. Film	Dez. Nr.:	1.1.21	Preparation:	Capill. Film	Dec. No.:	1.1.21	

Weichmacher
1. Aromat. Carbonsäureester
1.1. Phthalsäureester

Plasticizers
1. Aromatic Carboxylic Acid Esters
1.1. Phthalic Acid Esters

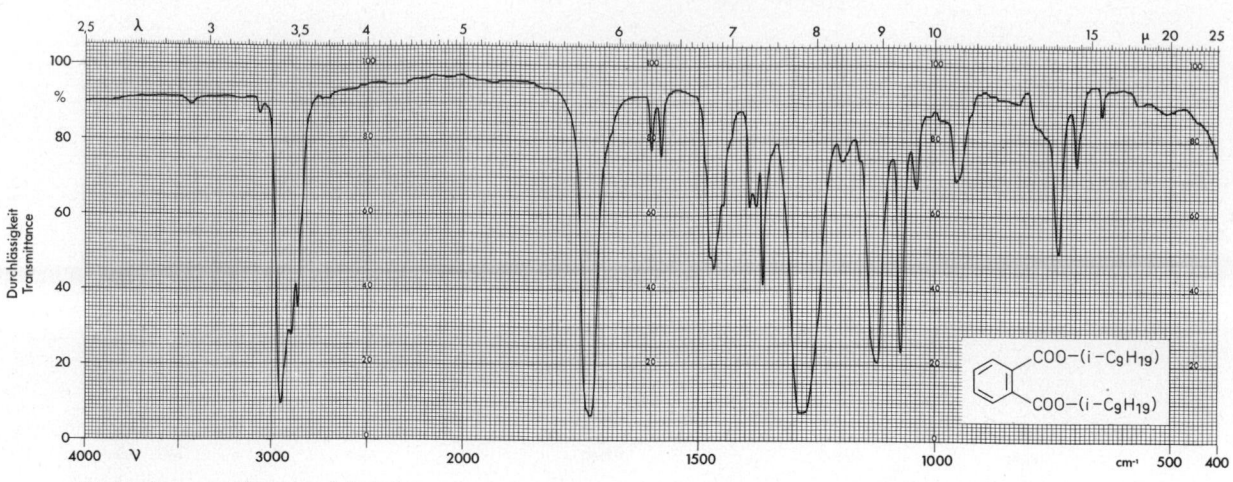

5021

Verbindung:	Diisononylphthalat		Compound:	Diisononyl phthalate	
Formel:	$C_{26}H_{42}O_4$	M.: 418,6	Formula:	$C_{26}H_{42}O_4$	M. w.: 418,6
Handelsname:	IW 150	Herst.: Witten	Tradename:	IW 150	Manuf.: Witten
Präparation:	Kapill. Film	Dez. Nr.: 1.1.22	Preparation:	Capill. Film	Dec. No.: 1.1.22

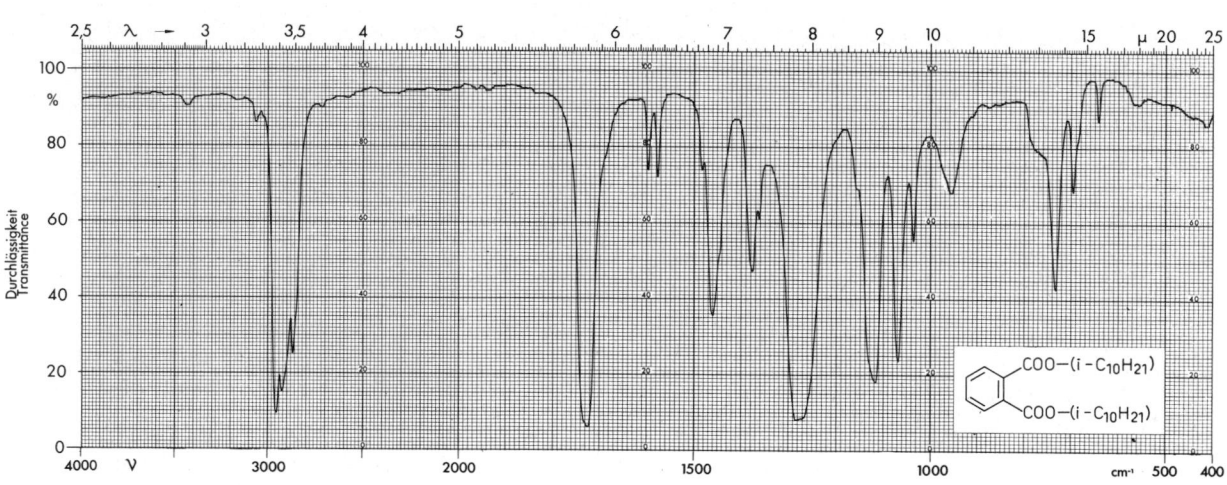

5022

Verbindung:	Diisodecylphthalat		Compound:	Diisodecyl phthalate	
Formel:	$C_{28}H_{46}O_4$	M.: 446,7	Formula:	$C_{28}H_{46}O_4$	M. w.: 446,7
Handelsname:	Reomol DIDP	Herst.: Geigy	Tradename:	Reomol DIDP	Manuf.: Geigy
Präparation:	Kapill. Film	Dez. Nr.: 1.1.23	Preparation:	Capill. Film	Dec. No.: 1.1.23

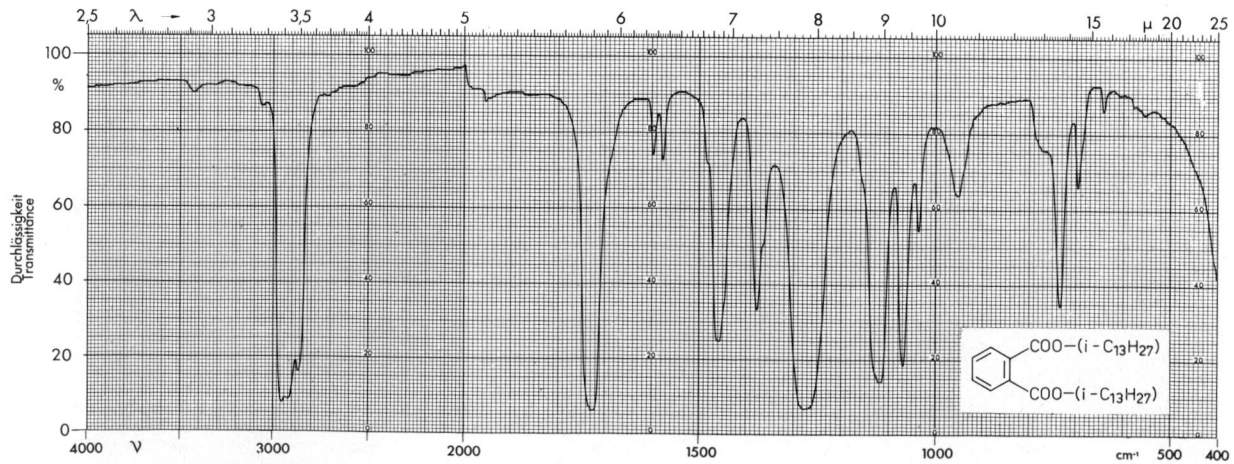

5023

Verbindung:	Ditridecylphthalat		Compound:	Ditridecyl phthalate	
Formel:	$C_{34}H_{58}O_4$	M.: 530,8	Formula:	$C_{34}H_{58}O_4$	M. w.: 530,8
Handelsname:	Reomol DTDP	Herst.: Geigy	Tradename:	Reomol DTDP	Manuf.: Geigy
Präparation:	Kapill. Film	Dez. Nr.: 1.1.24	Preparation:	Capill. Film	Dec. No.: 1.1.24

Weichmacher
1. Aromat. Carbonsäureester
1.1. Phthalsäureester

Plasticizers
1. Aromatic Carboxylic Acid Esters
1.1. Phthalic Acid Esters

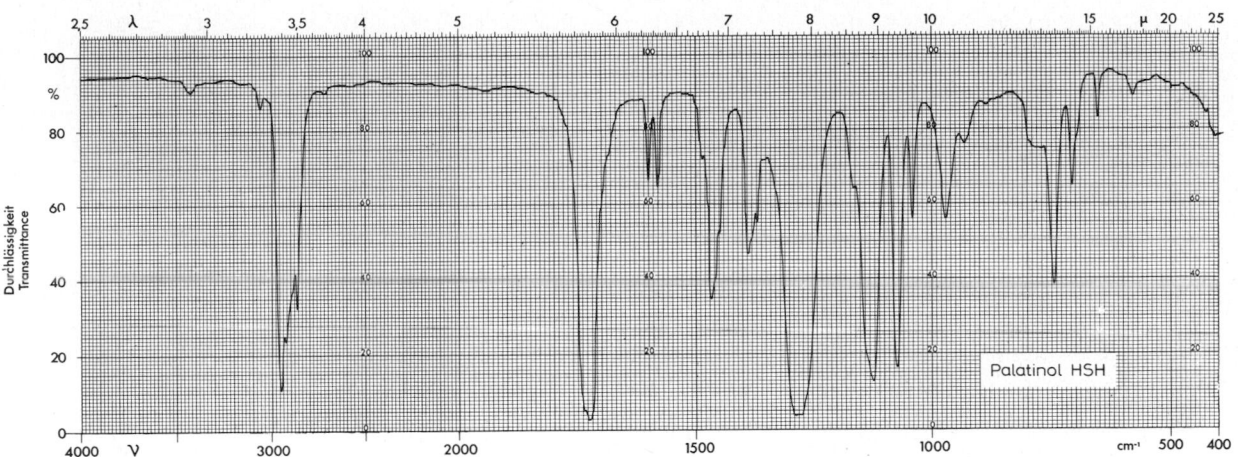

Palatinol HSH

Verbindung:	Phthalester gemischter Alkohole			Compound:	Mixed alcohol phthalate		5024
Formel:		M.:	~ 350	Formula:		M. w.: ~ 350	
Handelsname:	Palatinol HSH	Herst.:	BASF	Tradename:	Palatinol HSH	Manuf.: BASF	
Präparation:	Kapill. Film	Dez. Nr.:	1.1.25	Preparation:	Capill. Film	Dec. No.: 1.1.25	

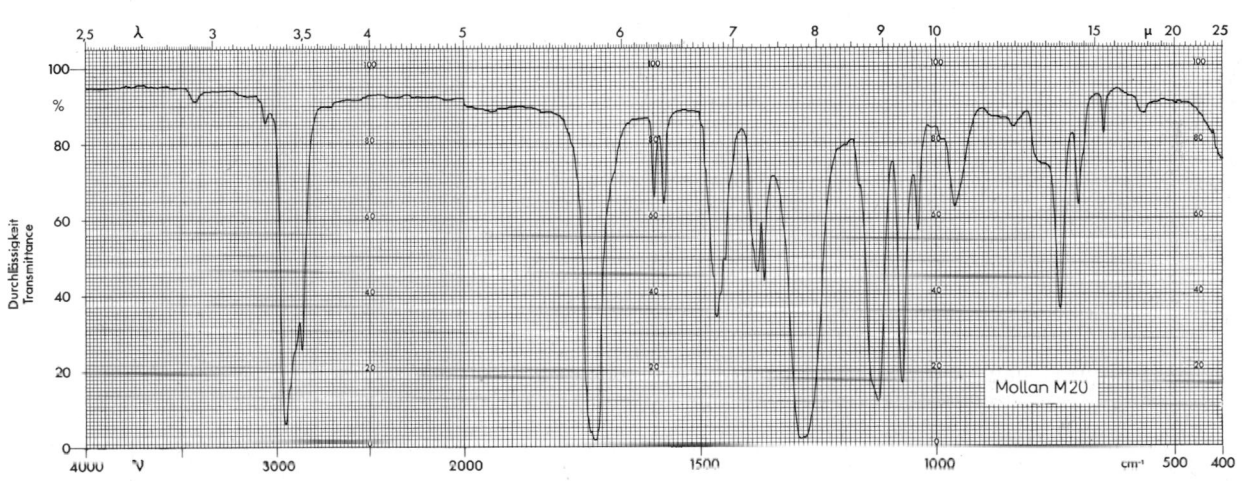

Mollan M 20

Verbindung:	Phthalester gemischter Alkohole			Compound:	Mixed alcohol phthalate		5025
Formel:		M.:	~ 370	Formula:		M. w.: ~ 370	
Handelsname:	Mollan M 20	Herst.:	Oe-Stick	Tradename:	Mollan M 20	Manuf.: Oe-Stick	
Präparation:	Kapill. Film	Dez. Nr.:	1.1.26	Preparation:	Capill. Film	Dec. No:. 1.1.26	

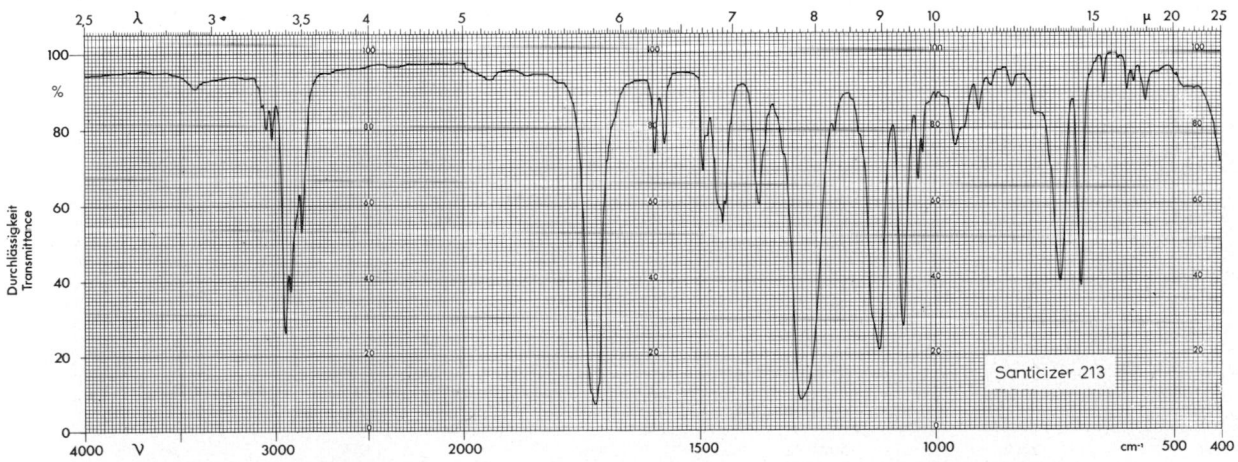

Santicizer 213

Verbindung:	Alkylaryl modif. Phthalate			Compound:	Alkylaryl modified phthalates		5026
Formel:		M.:	~ 350	Formula:		M. w.: ~ 350	
Handelsname:	Santicizer 213	Herst.:	Monsanto	Tradename:	Santicizer 213	Manuf.: Monsanto	
Präparation:	Kapill. Film	Dez. Nr.:	1.1.27	Preparation:	Capill. Film	Dec. No:. 1.1.27	

Weichmacher
1. Aromat. Carbonsäureester
1.1. Phthalsäureester

Plasticizers
1. Aromatic Carboxylic Acid Esters
1.1. Phthalic Acid Esters

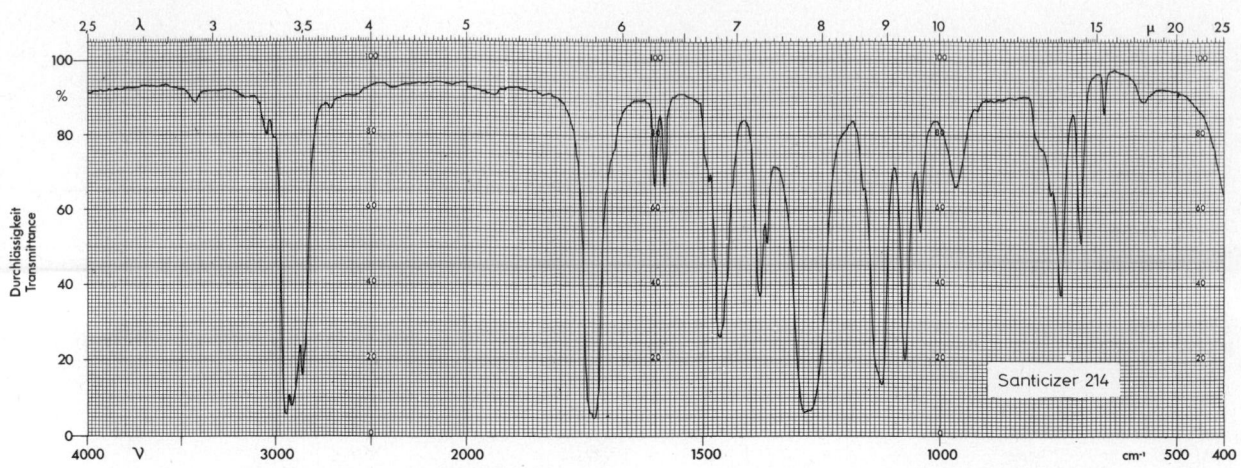

5027

Verbindung:	**Alkylaryl modifiz. Phthalate**			Compound:	**Alkylaryl modified phthalate**		
Formel:		M.:	**~ 420**	Formula:		M. w.:	**~ 420**
Handelsname:	**Santicizer 214**	Herst.:	**Monsanto**	Tradename:	**Santicizer 214**	Manuf.:	**Monsanto**
Präparation:	**Kapill. Film**	Dez. Nr.:	**1.1.28**	Preparation:	**Capill. Film**	Dec. No.:	**1.1.28**

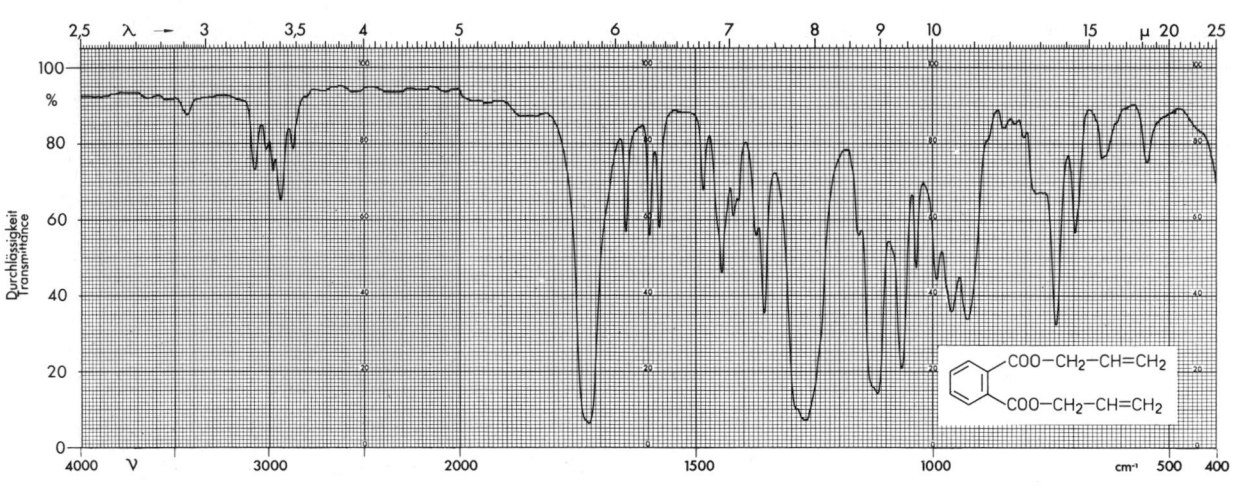

5028

Verbindung:	**Diallylphthalat**			Compound:	**Diallyl phthalate**		
Formel:	$C_{14}H_{14}O_4$	M.:	**246,3**	Formula:	$C_{14}H_{14}O_4$	M. w.:	**246,3**
Handelsname:		Herst.:	**Hüls**	Tradename:		Manuf.:	**Hüls**
Präparation:	**Kapill. Film**	Dez. Nr.:	**1.1.29**	Preparation:	**Capill. Film**	Dec. No:.	**1.1.29**

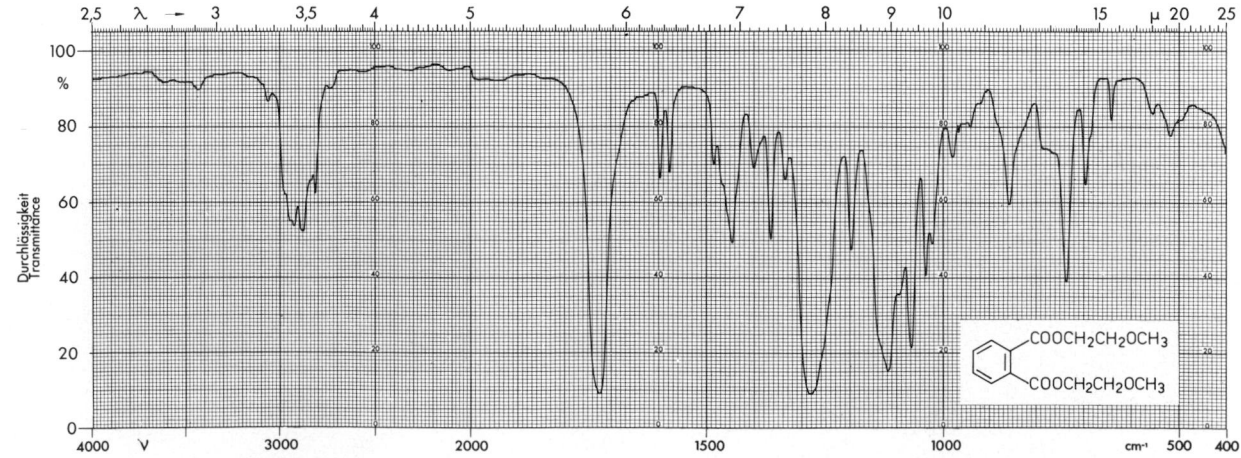

5029

Verbindung:	**Dimethylglykolphthalat**			Compound:	**Dimethoxyethyl phthalate**		
Formel:	$C_{14}H_{18}O_6$	M.:	**282,3**	Formula:	$C_{14}H_{18}O_6$	M. w.:	**282,3**
Handelsname:	**Palatinol O**	Herst.:	**BASF**	Tradename:	**Palatinol O**	Manuf.:	**BASF**
Präparation:	**Kapill. Film**	Dez. Nr.:	**1.1.30**	Preparation:	**Capill. Film**	Dec. No:.	**1.1.30**

Weichmacher
1. Aromat. Carbonsäureester
1.1. Phthalsäureester

Plasticizers
1. Aromatic Carboxylic Acid Esters
1.1. Phthalic Acid Esters

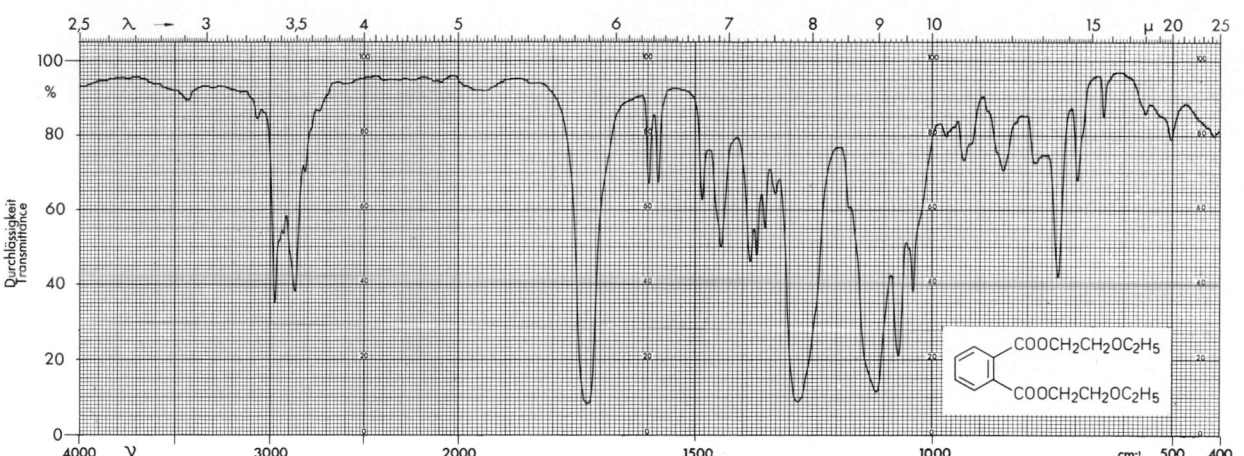

Verbindung:	Diethylglykolphthalat			Compound:	Diethoxyethyl phthalate			5030
Formel:	$C_{16}H_{22}O_6$	M.:	310,4	Formula:	$C_{16}H_{22}O_6$	M. w.:	310,4	
Handelsname:		Herst.:	Eastman	Tradename:		Manuf.:	Eastman	
Präparation:	Kapill. Film	Dez. Nr.:	1.1.31	Preparation:	Capill. Film	Dec. No:.	1.1.31	

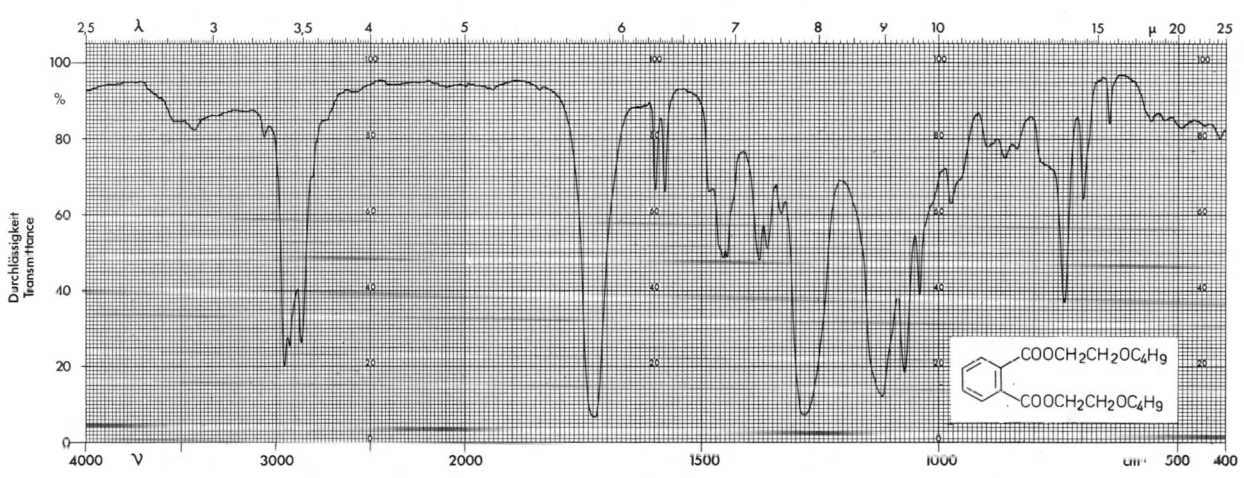

Verbindung:	Dibutoxyethylphthalat			Compound:	Dibutoxyethyl phthalate			5031
Formel:	$C_{20}H_{30}O_6$	M.:	366,5	Formula:	$C_{20}H_{30}O_6$	M. w.:	366,5	
Handelsname:	Palatinol K	Herst.:	BASF	Tradename:	Palatinol K	Manuf.:	BASF	
Präparation:	Kapill. Film	Dez. Nr.:	1.1.32	Preparation:	Capill. Film	Dec. No:.	1.1.32	

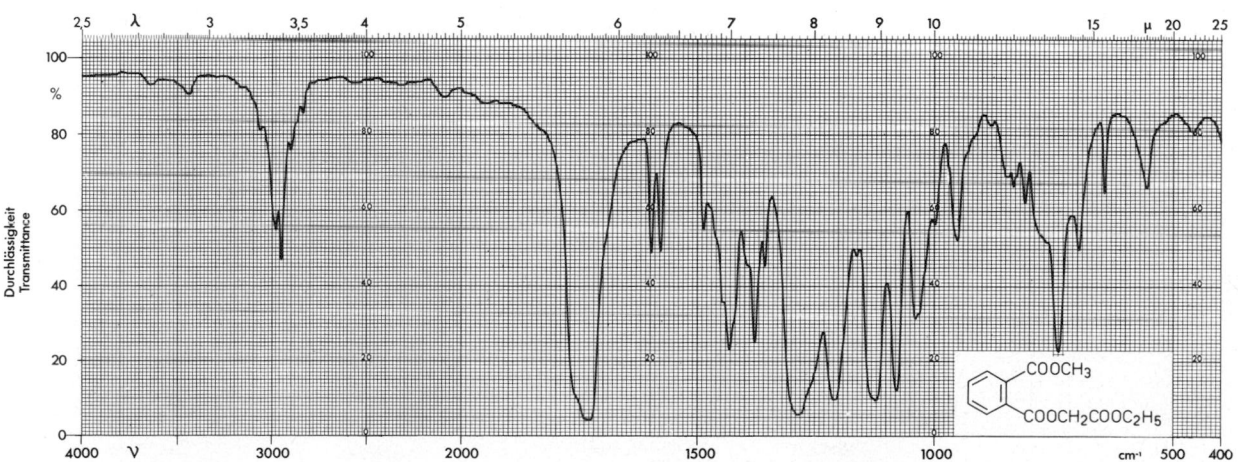

Verbindung:	Methyl-ethylglycolat-phthalat			Compound:	Methyl-ethylglycolate-phthalate			5032
Formel:	$C_{13}H_{14}O_6$	M.:	266,3	Formula:	$C_{13}H_{14}O_6$	M. w.:	266,3	
Handelsname:	Santicizer M-17	Herst.:	Monsanto	Tradename:	Santicizer M-17	Manuf.:	Monsanto	
Präparation:	Kapill. Film	Dez. Nr.:	1.1.33	Preparation:	Capill. Film	Dec. No.:	1.1.33	

Weichmacher
1. Aromat. Carbonsäureester
1.2. Phthalsäurehaltige Polyester

Plasticizers
1. Aromatic Carboxylic Acid Esters
1.2. Phthalic Acid Polyesters

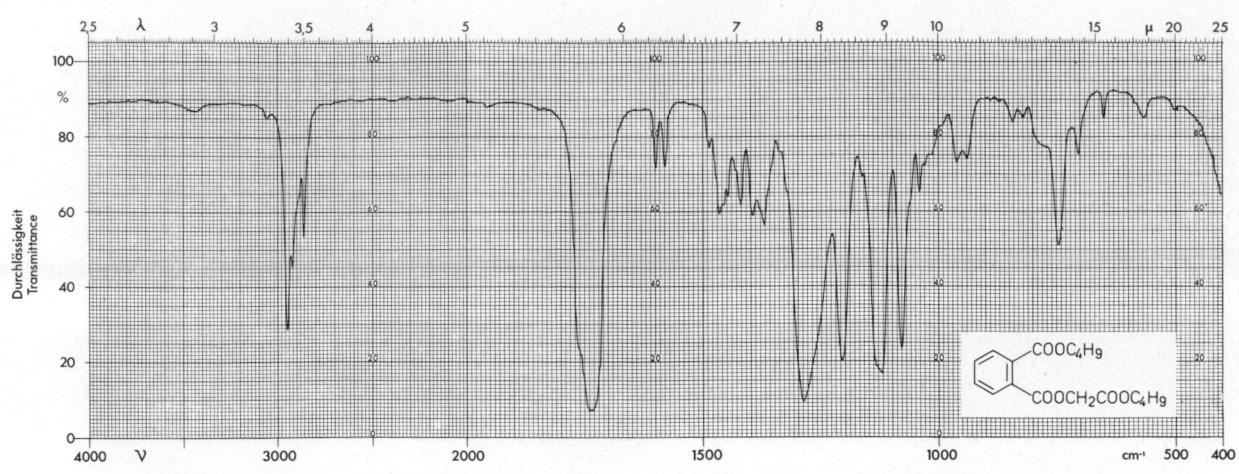

5033   Verbindung: **Butyl-butylglykolat-phthalat**   Compound: **Butyl-butylglycolate-phthalate**

Formel:	$C_{18}H_{24}O_6$	M.:	336,4	
Handelsname:	Santicizer B-16	Herst.:	Monsanto	
Präparation:	Kapill. Film	Dez. Nr.:	1.1.34	

Formula:	$C_{18}H_{24}O_6$	M. w.:	336,4	
Tradename:	Santicizer B-16	Manuf.:	Monsanto	
Preparation:	Capill. Film	Dec. No:.	1.1.34	

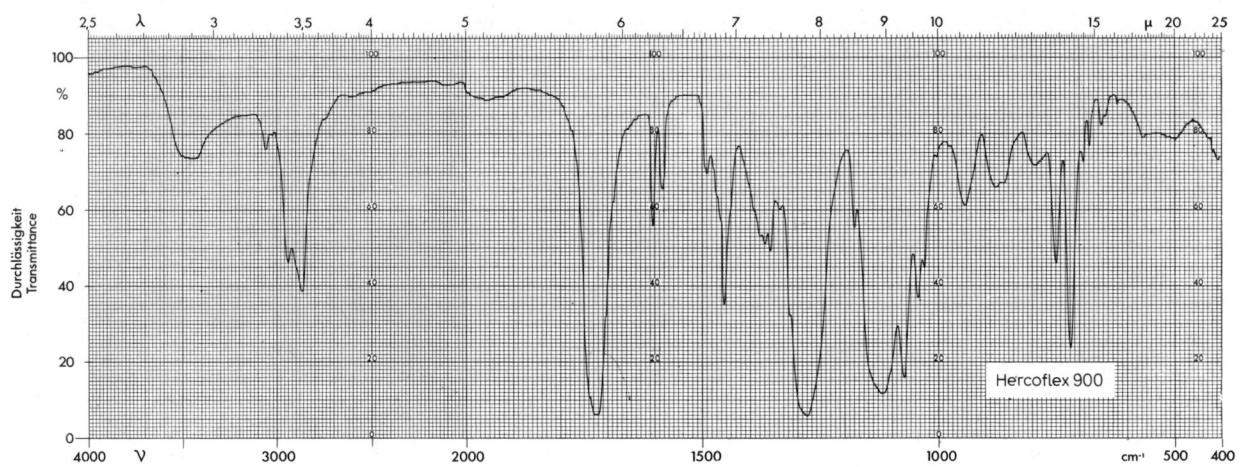

Hercoflex 900

5034   Verbindung: **Phthalsäurepolyester**   Compound: **Phthalic acid polyester**

Formel:		M.:	~ 570	
Präparation:	Hercoflex 900	Herst.:	Hercules	
Handelsname:	Kapill. Film	Dez. Nr.:	1.2.1	

Formula:		M. w.:	~ 570	
Tradename:	Hercoflex 900	Manuf.:	Hercules	
Preparation:	Capill. Film	Dec. No:.	1.2.1	

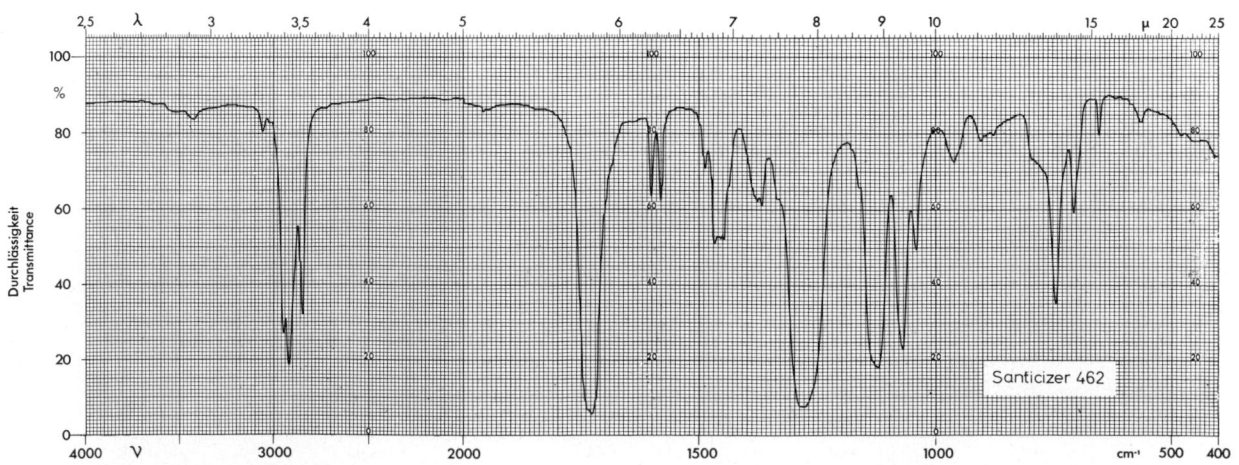

Santicizer 462

5035   Verbindung: **Phthalsäurepolyester**   Compound: **Phthalic acid polyester**

Formel:		M.:	~ 640	
Handelsname:	Santicizer 462	Herst.:	Monsanto	
Präparation:	Kapill. Film	Dez. Nr.:	1.2.2	

Formula:		M. w.:	~ 640	
Tradename:	Santicizer 462	Manuf.:	Monsanto	
Preparation:	Capill. Film	Dec. No:.	1.2.2	

Weichmacher
1. Aromat. Carbonsäureester
1.2. Phthalsäurehaltige Polyester

Plasticizers
1. Aromatic Carboxylic Acid Esters
1.2. Phthalic Acid Polyesters

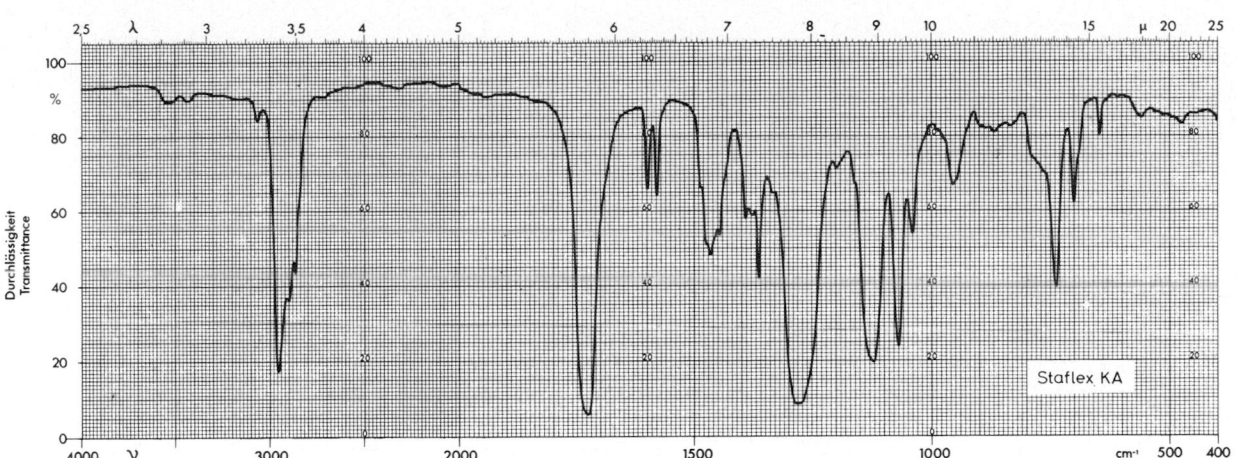

Verbindung:	Phthalsäurepolyester			Compound:	Phthalic acid polyester			5036
Formel:		M.:	~ 530	Formula:		M. w.:	~ 530	
Handelsname:	Staflex KA	Herst.:	Reichhold	Tradename:	Staflex KA	Manuf.:	Reichhold	
Präparation:	Kapill. Film	Dez. Nr.:	1.2.3	Preparation:	Capill. Film	Dec. No.:	1.2.3	

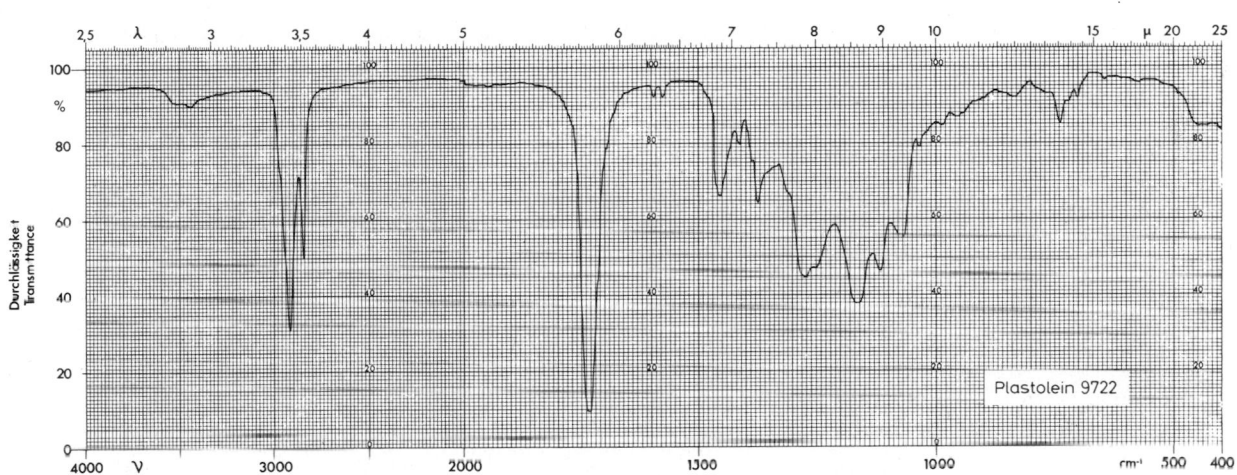

Verbindung:	Phthalsäurepolyester			Compound:	Phthalic acid polyester			5037
Formel:		M.:	~ 1000	Formula:		M. w.:	~ 1000	
Handelsname:	Plastolein 9722	Herst.:	Emery	Tradename:	Plastolein 9722	Manuf.:	Emery	
Präparation:	Kapill. Film	Dez. Nr.:	1.2.4	Preparation:	Capill. Film	Dec. No.:	1.2.4	

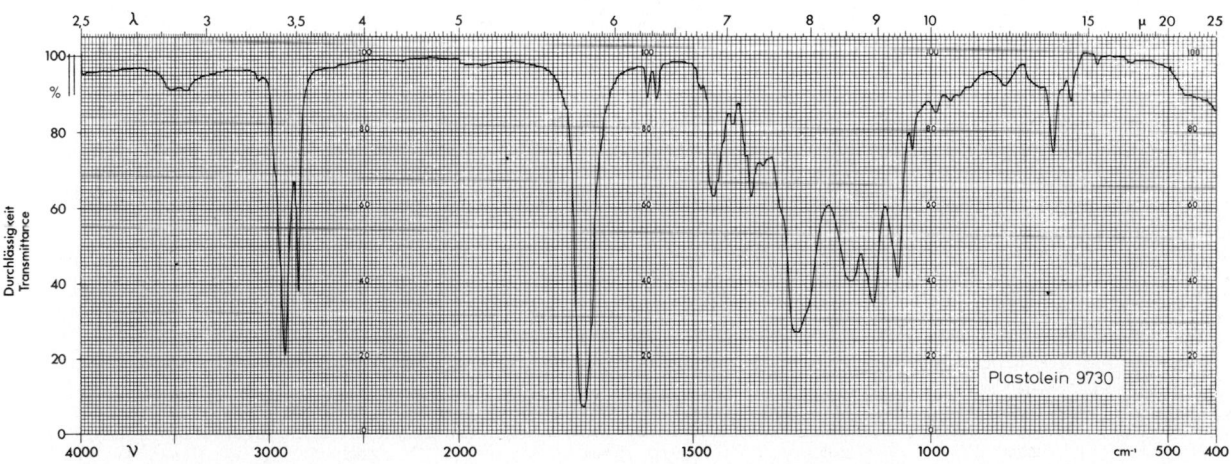

Verbindung:	Phthalsäurepolyester			Compound:	Phthalic acid polyester			5038
Formel:		M.:	~ 1100	Formula:		M. w.:	~ 1100	
Handelsname:	Plastolein 9730	Dez. Nr.:	Emery	Tradename:	Plastolein 9730	Manuf.:	Emery	
Präparation:	Kapill. Film	Herst.:	1.2.5	Preparation:	Capill. Film	Dec. No.:	1.2.5	

Weichmacher
1. Aromat. Carbonsäureester
1.3. Isophthalsäureester

Plasticizers
1. Aromatic Carboxylic Acid Esters
1.3. Isophthalic Acid Esters

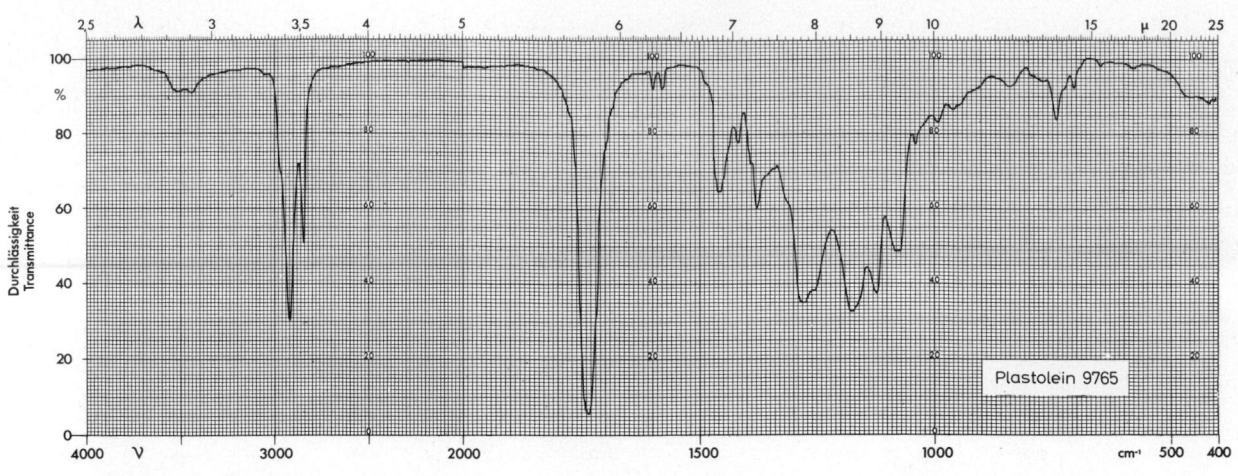

5039

Verbindung:	**Phthalsäurepolyester**			Compound:	**Phthalic acid polyester**		
Formel:		M.:	**~ 1650**	Formula:		M. w.:	**~ 1650**
Handelsname:	**Plastolein 9765**	Herst.:	**Emery**	Tradename:	**Plastolein 9765**	Manuf.:	**Emery**
Präparation:	**Kapill. Film**	Dez. Nr.:	**1.2.6**	Preparation:	**Capill. Film**	Dec. No.:	**1.2.6**

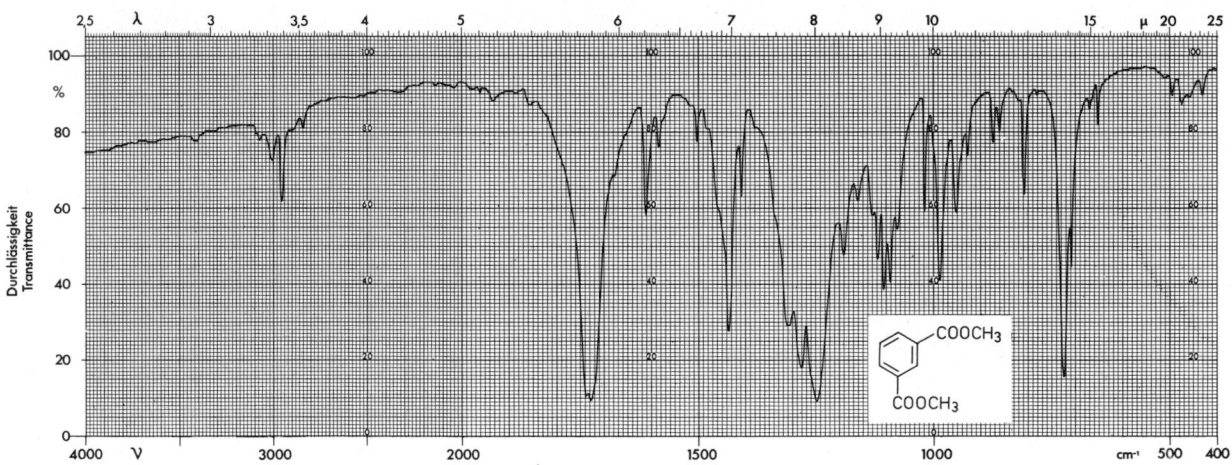

5040

Verbindung:	**Dimethylisophthalat**			Compound:	**Dimethyl isophthalate**		
Formel:	$C_{10}H_{10}O_4$	M.:	**194,2**	Formula:	$C_{10}H_{10}O_4$	M. w.:	**194,2**
Handelsname:		Herst.:	**Montrose Ch.**	Tradename:		Manuf.:	**Montrose Ch.**
Präparation:	**Kapill. Film**	Dez. Nr.:	**1.3.1**	Preparation:	**Capill. Film**	Dec. No.:	**1.3.1**

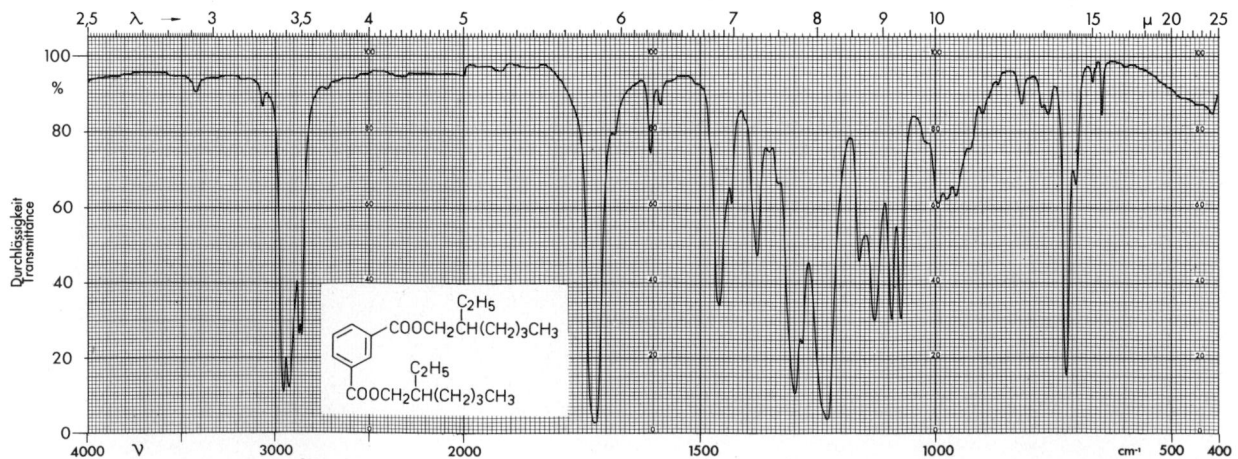

5041

Verbindung:	**Di-(2-ethylhexyl)isophthalat**			Compound:	**Di-(2-ethylhexyl) isophthalate**		
Formel:	$C_{24}H_{38}O_4$	M.:	**390,6**	Formula:	$C_{24}H_{38}O_4$	M. w.:	**390,6**
Handelsname:	**Flexol 380**	Herst.:	**Union Carb.**	Tradename:	**Flexol 380**	Manuf.:	**Union Carb.**
Präparation:	**Kapill. Film**	Dez. Nr.:	**1.3.2**	Preparation:	**Capill. Film**	Dec. No.:	**1.3.2**

Weichmacher
1. Aromat. Carbonsäureester
1.4. Benzoesäureester

Plasticizers
1. Aromatic Carboxylic Acid Esters
1.4. Benzoic Acid Esters

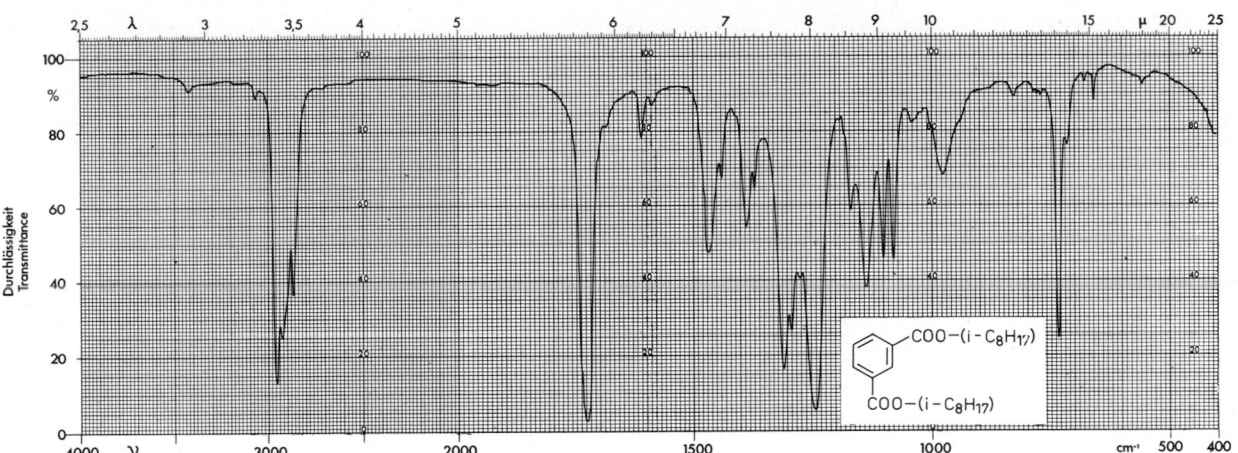

Verbindung:	Diisooctylisophthalat			Compound:	Diisooctyl isophthalate			5042
Formel:	$C_{24}H_{38}O_4$	M.:	390,6	Formula:	$C_{24}H_{38}O_4$	M. w.:	390,6	
Handelsname:	RS 190	Herst.:	Reichhold	Tradename:	RS 190	Manuf.:	Reichhold	
Präparation:	Kapill. Film	Dez. Nr.:	1.3.3	Preparation:	Capill. Film	Dec. No.:	1.3.3	

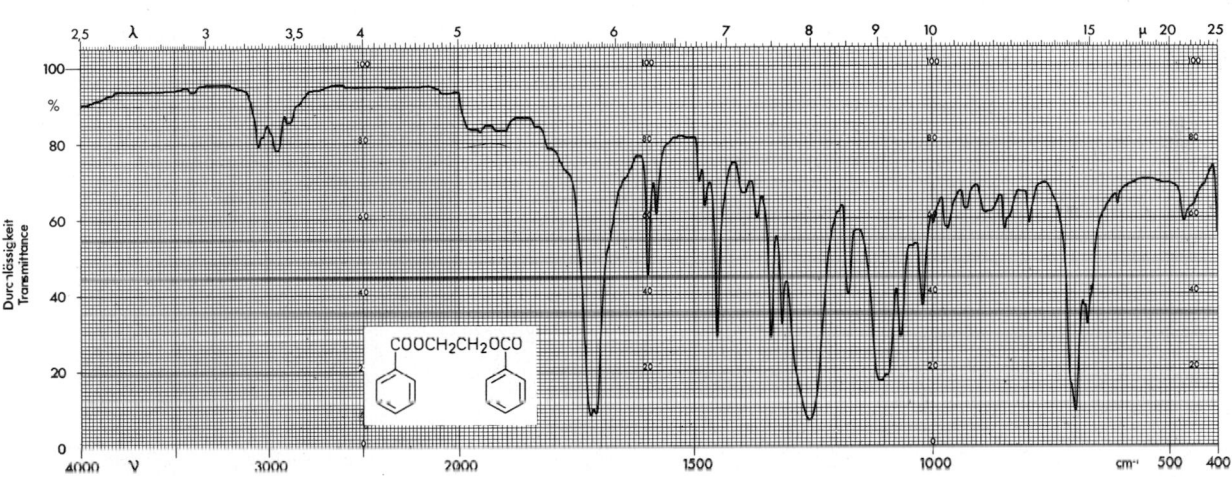

Verbindung:	Ethylenglykoldibenzoat			Compound:	Ethyleneglycol dibenzoate			5043
Formel:	$C_{16}H_{14}O_4$	M.:	270,3	Formula:	$C_{16}H_{14}O_4$	M. w.:	270,3	
Handelsname:	Hallco 870	Herst.:	Hall	Tradename:	Hallco 870	Manuf.:	Hall	
Präparation:	KBr (10/1000)	Dez. Nr.:	1.4.1	Preparation:	KBr (10/1000)	Dec. No.:	1.4.1	

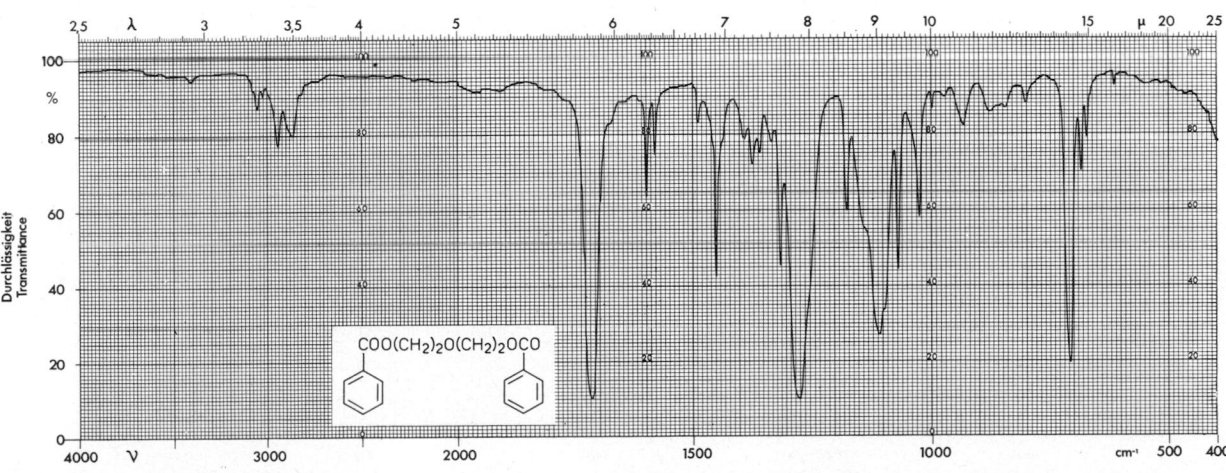

Verbindung:	Diethylenglykoldibenzoat			Compound:	Diethyleneglycol dibenzoate			5044
Formel:	$C_{18}H_{18}O_5$	M.:	314,3	Formula:	$C_{18}H_{18}O_5$	M. w.:	314,3	
Handelsname:	Benzoflex 2-45	Herst.:	Tennessee	Tradename:	Benzoflex 2-45	Manuf.:	Tennessee	
Präparation:	Kapill. Film	Dez. Nr.:	1.4.2	Preparation:	Capill. Film	Dec. No.:	1.4.2	

Weichmacher
1. Aromat. Carbonsäureester
1.4. Benzoesäureester

Plasticizers
1. Aromatic Carboxylic Acid Esters
1.4. Benzoic Acid Esters

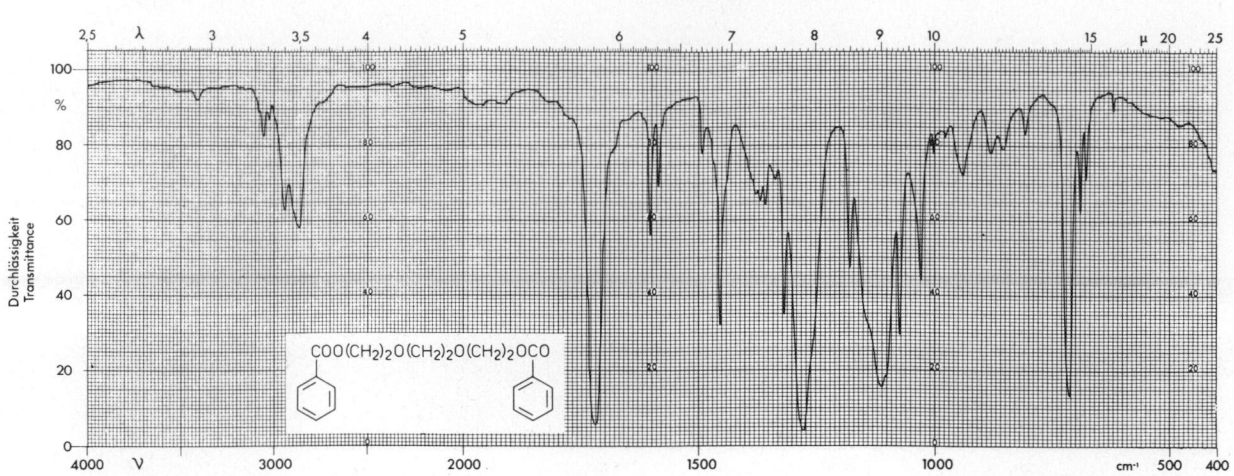

5045

Verbindung:	**Triethylenglykoldibenzoat**			Compound:	**Triethyleneglycol dibenzoate**	
Formel:	**C$_{20}$H$_{22}$O$_6$**	M.:	**358,4**	Formula:	**C$_{20}$H$_{22}$O$_6$**	M. w.: **358,4**
Handelsname:	**Benzoflex T-150**	Herst.:	**Tennessee**	Tradename:	**Benzoflex T-150**	Manuf.: **Tennessee**
Präparation:	**Kapill. Film**	Dez. Nr.:	**1.4.3**	Preparation:	**Capill. Film**	Dec. No.: **1.4.3**

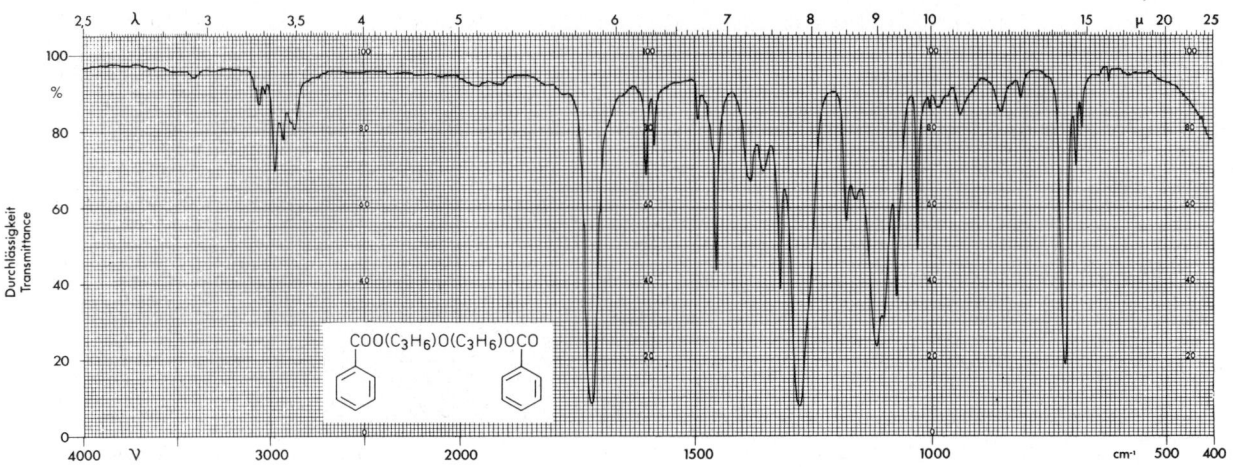

5046

Verbindung	**Dipropylenglykoldibenzoat**			Compound:	**Dipropyleneglycol dibenzoate**	
Formel:	**C$_{20}$H$_{22}$O$_5$**	M.:	**342,4**	Formula:	**C$_{20}$H$_{22}$O$_5$**	M. w.: **342,4**
Handelsname:	**Benzoflex 9-88**	Herst.:	**Tennessee**	Tradename:	**Benzoflex 9-88**	Manuf.: **Tennessee**
Präparation:	**Kapill. Film**	Dez. Nr.:	**1.4.4**	Preparation:	**Capill. Film**	Dec. No:. **1.4.4**

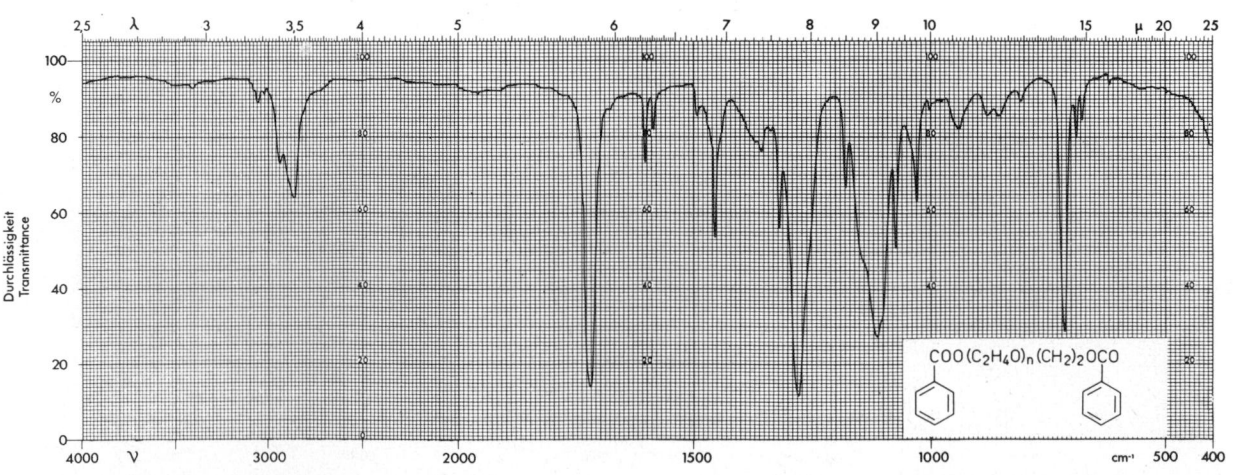

5047

Verbindung:	**Polyethylenglykol(200)-dibenzoat**			Compound:	**Polyethyleneglycol(200) dibenzoate**	
Formel:		M.:	**∼ 450**	Formula:		M. w.: **∼ 450**
Handelsname:	**Benzoflex P 200**	Herst.:	**Tennessee**	Tradename:	**Benzoflex P 200**	Manuf.: **Tennessee**
Präparation:	**Kapill. Film**	Dez. Nr.:	**1.4.5**	Preparation:	**Capill. Film**	Dec. No:. **1.4.5**

Weichmacher
1. Aromat. Carbonsäureester
1.5. Trimellitsäureester

Plasticizers
1. Aromatic Carboxylic Acid Esters
1.5. Trimellite Acid Esters

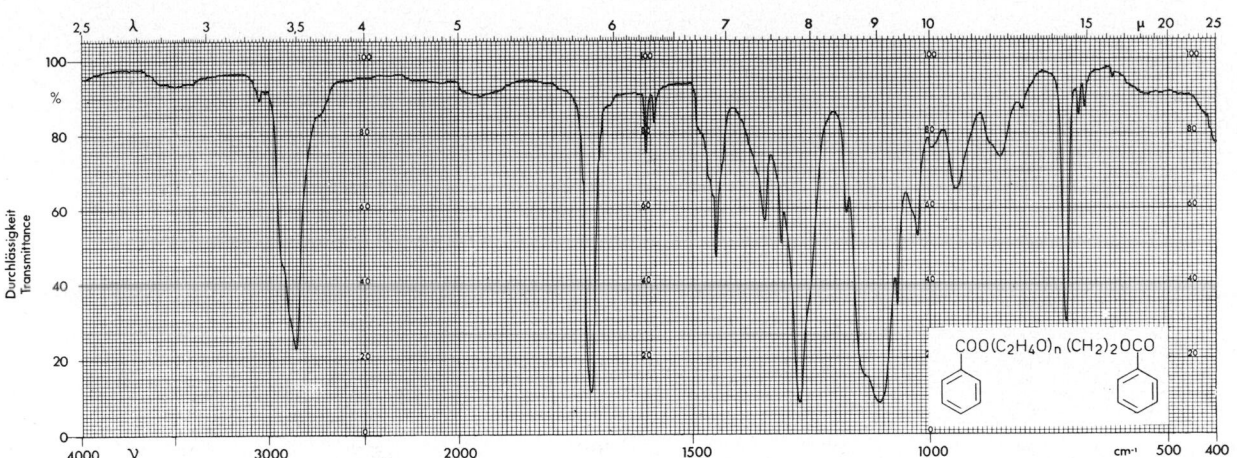

Verbindung:	Polyethylenglykol(600)-dibenzoat			Compound:	Polyethyleneglycol(600) dibenzoate			5048
Formel:		M.:	~ 800	Formula:		M. w.:	~ 800	
Handelsname:	Benzoflex P 600	Herst.:	Tennessee	Tradename:	Benzoflex P 600	Manuf.:	Tennessee	
Präparation:	Kapill. Film	Dez. Nr.:	1.4.6	Preparation:	Capill. Film	Dec. No:.	1.4.6	

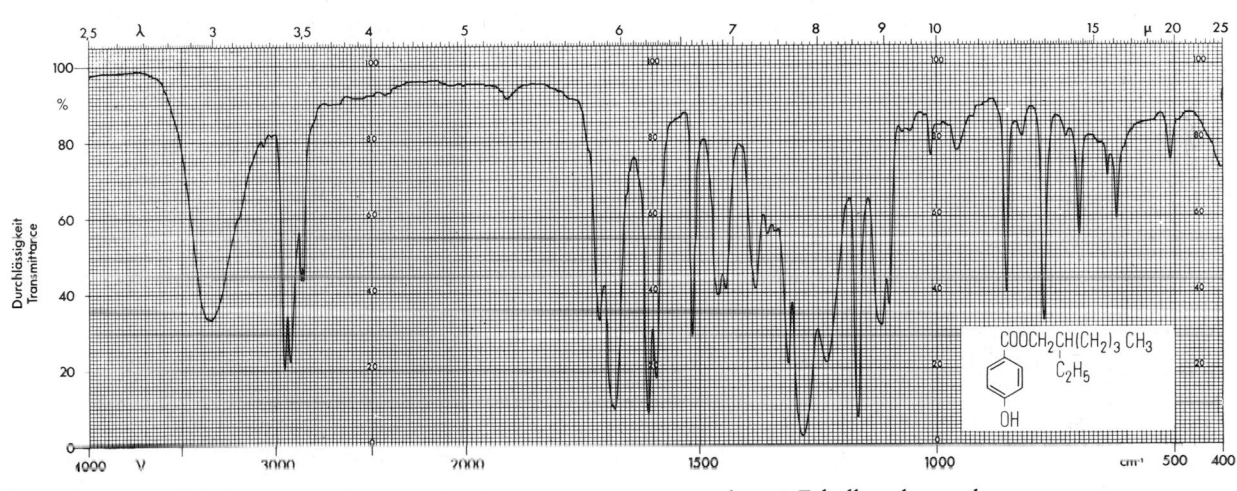

Verbindung:	2-Ethylhexyl-p-oxybenzoat			Compound:	2-Ethylhexyl-p-oxybenzoate			5049
Formel:	$C_{15}H_{22}O_3$	M.:	250,3	Formula:	$C_{15}H_{22}O_3$	M. w.:	250,3	
Handelsname:	Weichmacher 13	Herst.:	BASF	Tradename:	Weichmacher 13	Manuf.:	BASF	
Präparation:	Kapill. Film	Dez. Nr.:	1.4.7	Preparation:	Capill. Film	Dec. No:.	1.4.7	

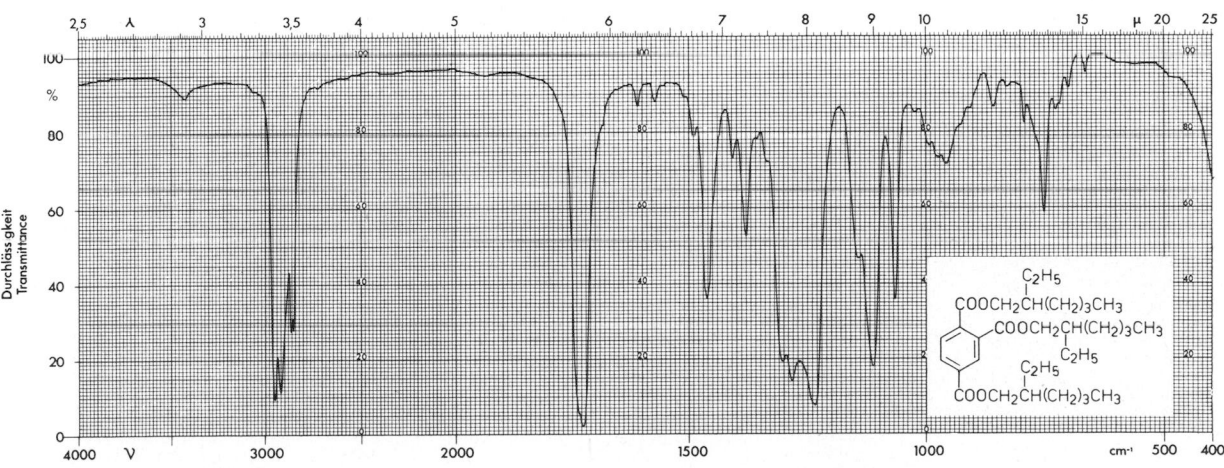

Verbindung:	Tri-(2-ethylhexyl)-mellitat			Compound:	Tri-(2-ethylhexyl) mellitate			5050
Formel:	$C_{33}H_{54}O_6$	M.:	546,8	Formula:	$C_{33}H_{54}O_6$	M. w.:	546,8	
Handelsname:	Rucoflex 26 TM	Herst.:	Hooker	Tradename:	Rucoflex 26 TM	Manuf.:	Hooker	
Präparation:	Kapill. Film	Dez. Nr.:	1.5.1	Preparation:	Capill. Film	Dec. No:.	1.5.1	

Weichmacher
1. Aromat. Carbonsäureester
1.5. Trimellitsäureester

Plasticizers
1. Aromatic Carboxylic Acid Esters
1.5. Trimellite Acid Esters

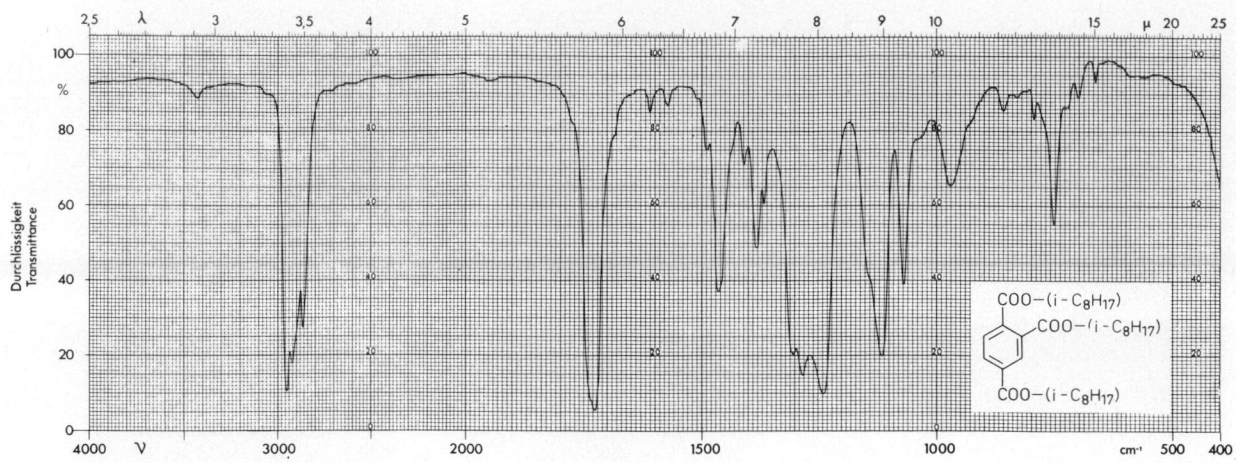

5051

Verbindung:	Triisooctyl-trimellitat			Compound:	Triisooctyl trimellitate		
Formel:	$C_{33}H_{54}O_6$	M.:	546,8	Formula:	$C_{33}H_{54}O_6$	M. w.:	546,8
Handelsname:	Rucoflex TM	Herst.:	Hooker	Tradename:	Rucoflex TM	Manuf.:	Hooker
Präparation:	Kapill. Film	Dez. Nr.:	1.5.2	Preparation:	Capill. Film	Dec. No:.	1.5.2

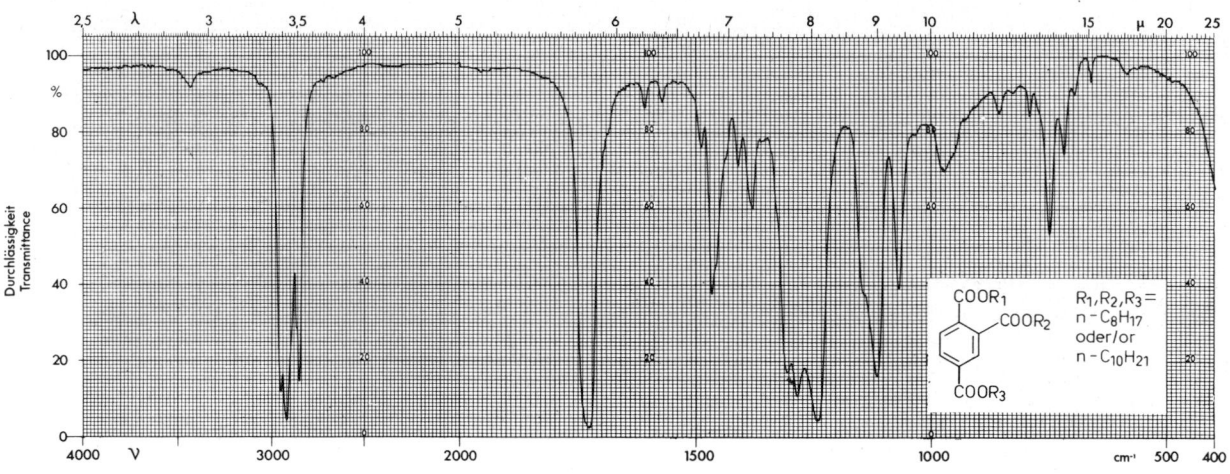

5052

Verbindung:	Tri-(n-octyl,n-decyl)-trimellitat			Compound:	Tri-(n-octyl,n-decyl) trimellitate		
Formel:		M.:	~ 550	Formula:		M. w.:	~ 550
Handelsname:	Rucoflex NTM	Herst.:	Hooker	Tradename:	Rucoflex NTM	Manuf.:	Hooker
Präparation:	Kapill. Film	Dez. Nr.:	1.5.3	Preparation:	Capill. Film	Dec. No:.	1.5.3

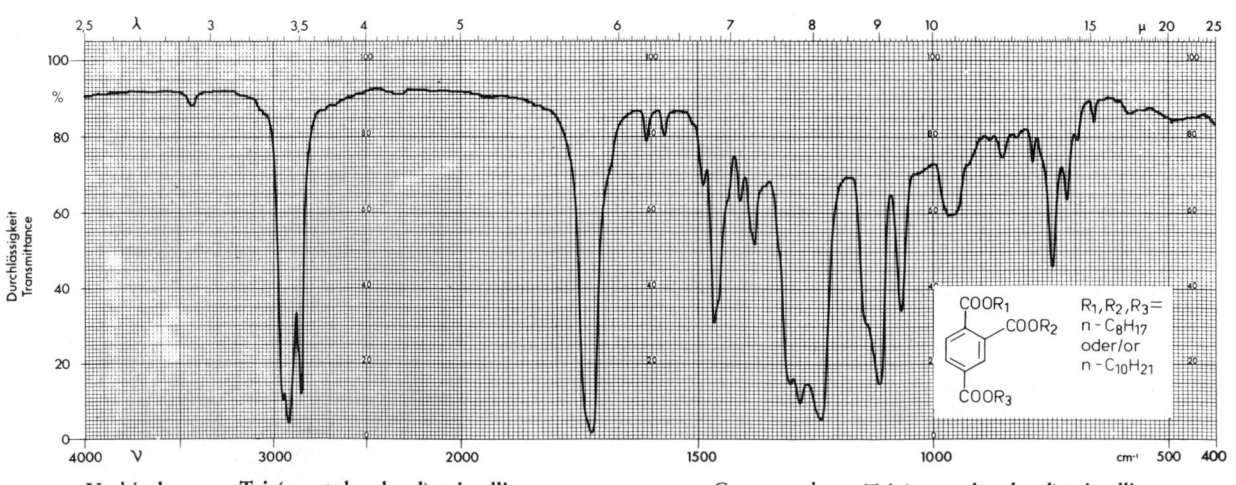

5053

Verbindung:	Tri-(n-octyl,n-decyl)-trimellitat			Compound:	Tri-(n-octyl,n-decyl) trimellitate		
Formel:		M.:	~ 540	Formula:		M. w.:	~ 540
Handelsname:	Weichmacher ODTM	Herst.:	Ölchemie	Tradename:	Weichmacher ODTM	Manuf.:	Ölchemie
Präparation:	Kapill. Film	Dez. Nr.:	1.5.4	Preparation:	Capill. Film	Dec. No.:	1.5.4

Weichmacher
1. Aromat. Carbonsäureester
1.5. Trimellitsäureester

Plasticizers
1. Aromatic Carboxylic Acid Esters
1.5. Trimellite Acid Esters

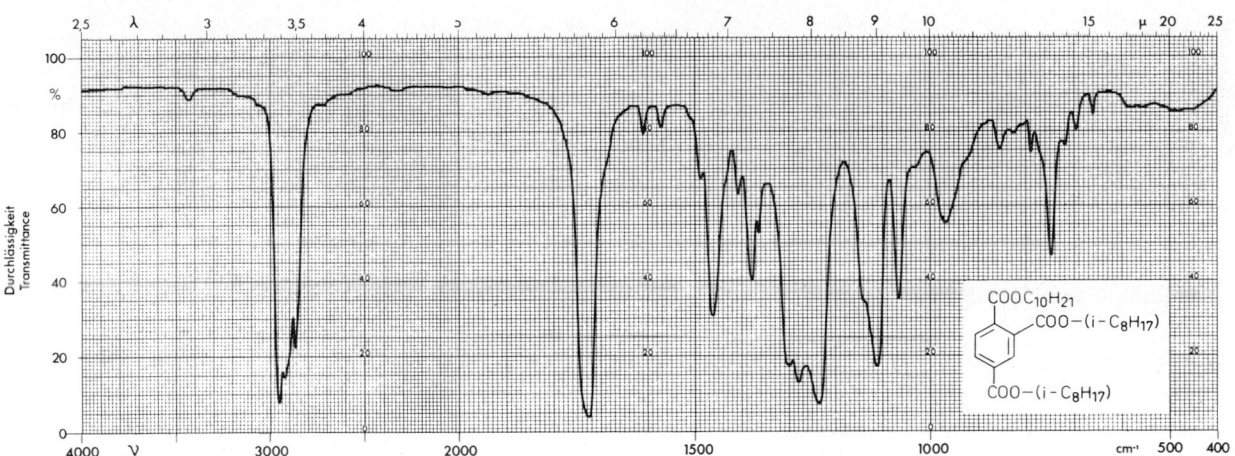

Verbindung:	Diisooctyl-decyl-trimellitat			Compound:	Diisooctyl decyl trimellitate			5054
Formel:	$C_{35}H_{59}O_{6}$	M.:	574,9	Formula:	$C_{35}H_{59}O_{6}$	M. w.:	574,9	
Handelsname:	Staflex DIODTM	Herst.:	Reichhold	Tradename:	Staflex DIODTM	Manuf.:	Reichhold	
Präparation:	Kapill. Film	Dez. Nr.:	1.5.5	Preparation:	Capill. Film	Dec. No.:	1.5.5	

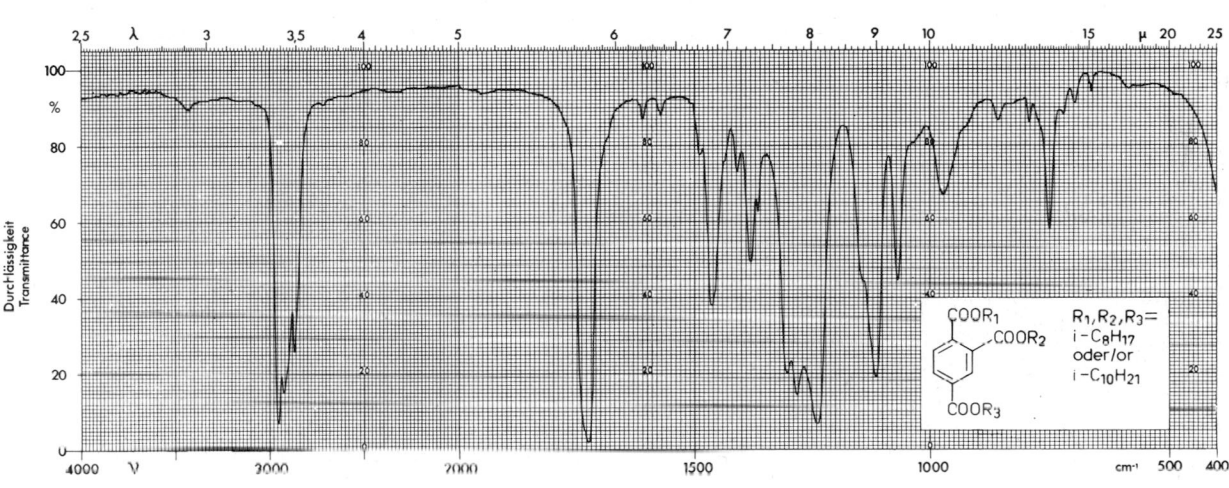

Verbindung:	Tri-(i-octyl,i-decyl)-trimellitat			Compound:	Tri-(i-octyl,i-decyl) trimellitate			5055
Formel:		M.:	~ 600	Formula:		M. w.:	~ 600	
Handelsname:	Rucoflex ODTM	Herst.:	Hooker	Tradename:	Rucoflex ODTM	Manuf.:	Hooker	
Präparation:	Kapill. Film	Dez. Nr.:	1.5.6	Preparation:	Capill. Film	Dec. No.:	1.5.6	

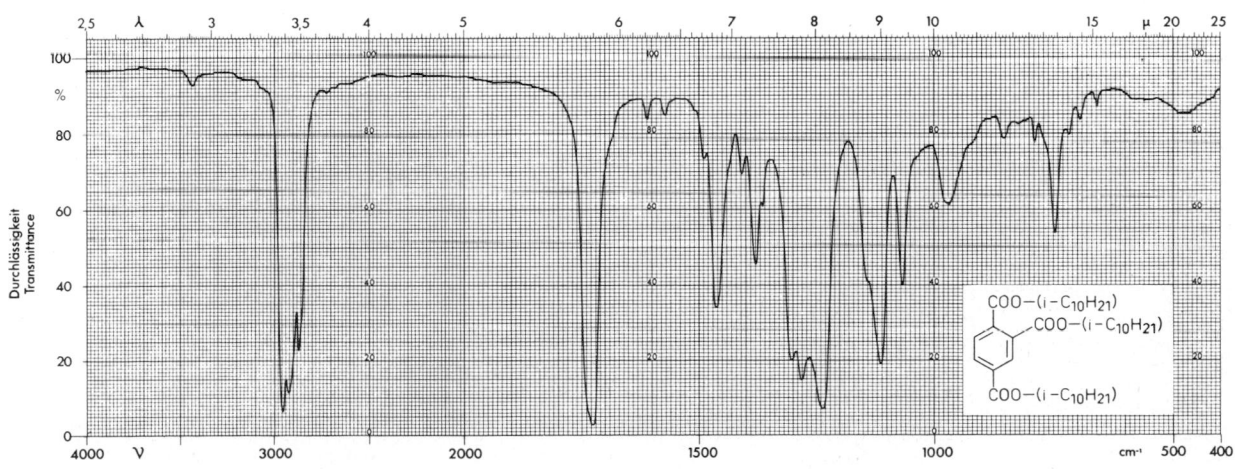

Verbindung:	Triisodecyl-trimellitat			Compound:	Triisodecyl trimellitate			5056
Formel:	$C_{39}H_{66}O_{6}$	M.:	631	Formula:	$C_{39}H_{66}O_{6}$	M. w.:	631	
Handelsname:	Morflex 530	Herst.:	Pfizer	Tradename:	Morflex 530	Manuf.:	Pfizer	
Präparation:	Kapill. Film	Dez. Nr.:	1.5.7	Preparation:	Capill. Film	Dec. No.:	1.5.7	

Weichmacher
2. Aliphatische Di- und Tricarbonsäureester
2.1. C₄-Dicarbonsäureester

Plasticizers
2. Aliphatic Di- and Tricarboxylic Acid Esters
2.1. C₄-Dicarboxylic Acid Esters

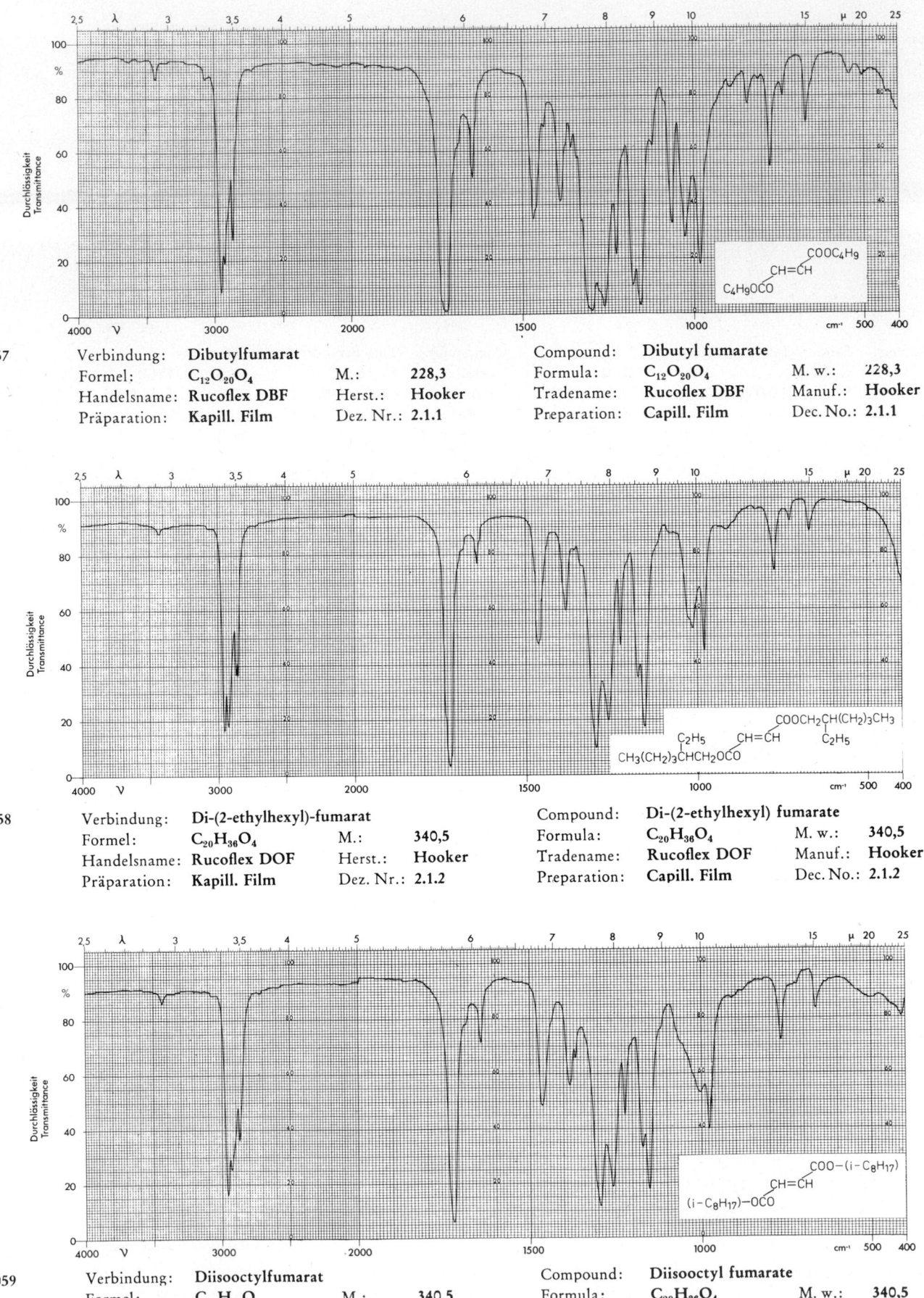

5057

Verbindung:	**Dibutylfumarat**			Compound:	**Dibutyl fumarate**	
Formel:	$C_{12}O_{20}O_4$	M.:	**228,3**	Formula:	$C_{12}O_{20}O_4$	M. w.: **228,3**
Handelsname:	**Rucoflex DBF**	Herst.:	**Hooker**	Tradename:	**Rucoflex DBF**	Manuf.: **Hooker**
Präparation:	**Kapill. Film**	Dez. Nr.:	**2.1.1**	Preparation:	**Capill. Film**	Dec. No.: **2.1.1**

5058

Verbindung:	**Di-(2-ethylhexyl)-fumarat**			Compound:	**Di-(2-ethylhexyl) fumarate**	
Formel:	$C_{20}H_{36}O_4$	M.:	**340,5**	Formula:	$C_{20}H_{36}O_4$	M. w.: **340,5**
Handelsname:	**Rucoflex DOF**	Herst.:	**Hooker**	Tradename:	**Rucoflex DOF**	Manuf.: **Hooker**
Präparation:	**Kapill. Film**	Dez. Nr.:	**2.1.2**	Preparation:	**Capill. Film**	Dec. No.: **2.1.2**

5059

Verbindung:	**Diisooctylfumarat**			Compound:	**Diisooctyl fumarate**	
Formel:	$C_{20}H_{36}O_4$	M.:	**340,5**	Formula:	$C_{20}H_{36}O_4$	M. w.: **340,5**
Handelsname:	**Pfizer DIOF**	Herst.:	**Pfizer**	Tradename:	**Pfizer DIOF**	Manuf.: **Pfizer**
Präparation:	**Kapill. Film**	Dez. Nr.:	**2.1.3**	Preparation:	**Capill. Film**	Dec. No.: **2.1.3**

Weichmacher
2. Aliphatische Di- und Tricarbonsäureester
2.1. C₄-Dicarbonsäureester

Plasticizers
2. Aliphatic Di- and Tricarboxylic Acid Esters
2.1. C₄-Dicarboxylic Acid Esters

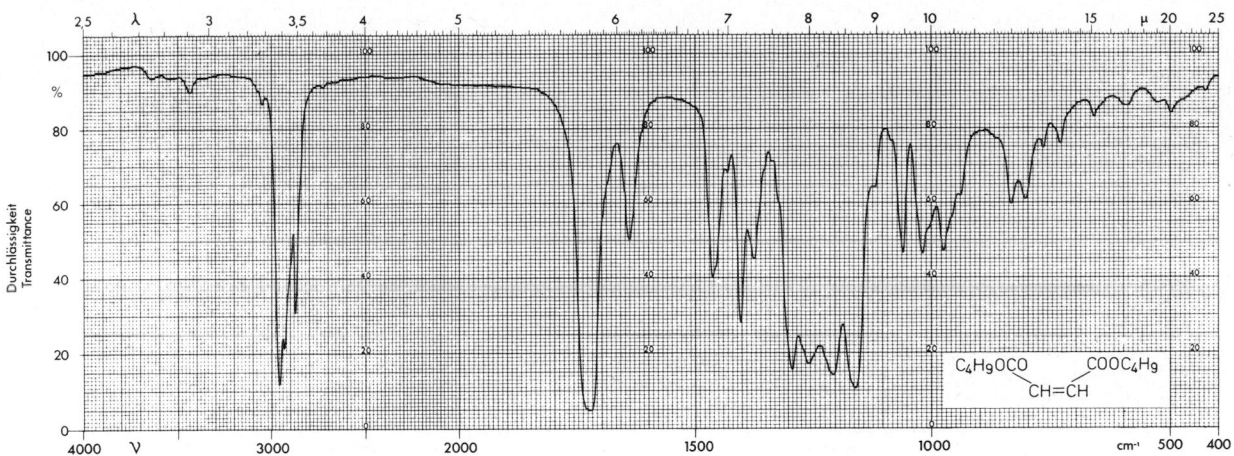

Verbindung:	Dibutylmaleat			Compound:	Dibutyl maleate			5060
Formel:	$C_{12}H_{20}O_4$	M.:	228,3	Formula:	$C_{12}H_{20}O_4$	M. w.:	228,3	
Handelsname:	Staflex DBM	Herst.:	Reichhold	Tradename:	Staflex DBM	Manuf.:	Reichhold	
Präparation:	Kapill. Film	Dez. Nr.:	2.1.4	Preparation:	Capill. Film	Dec. No.:	2.1.4	

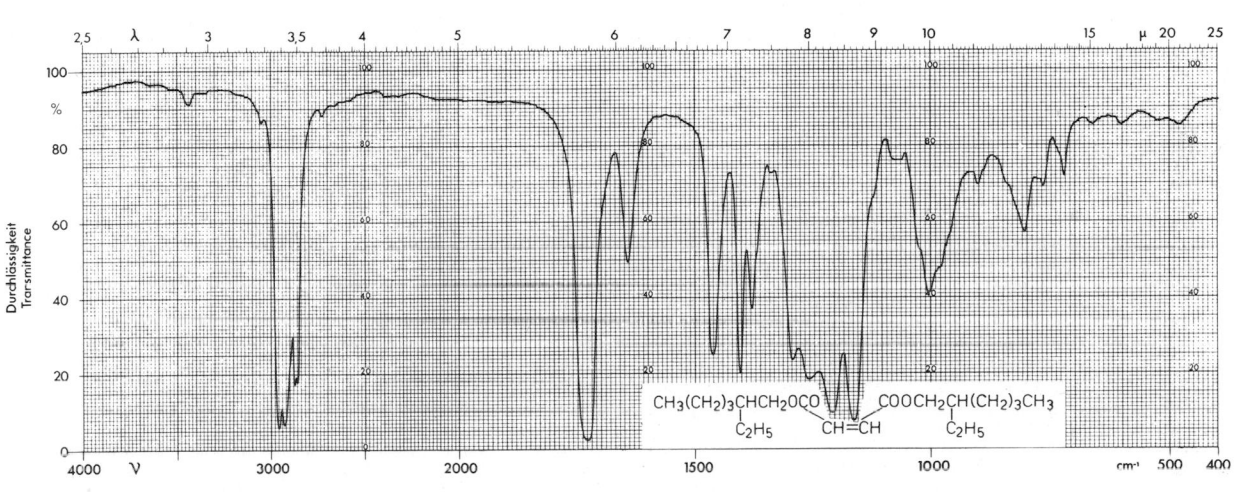

Verbindung:	Dioctylmaleat			Compound:	Dioctyl maleate			5061
Formel:	$C_{20}H_{36}O_4$	M.:	340,5	Formula:	$C_{20}H_{36}O_4$	M. w.:	340,5	
Handelsname:	Staflex DOM	Herst.:	Reichhold	Tradename:	Staflex DOM	Manuf.:	Reichhold	
Präparation:	Kapill. Film	Dez. Nr.:	2.1.5	Preparation:	Capill. Film	Dec. No.:	2.1.5	

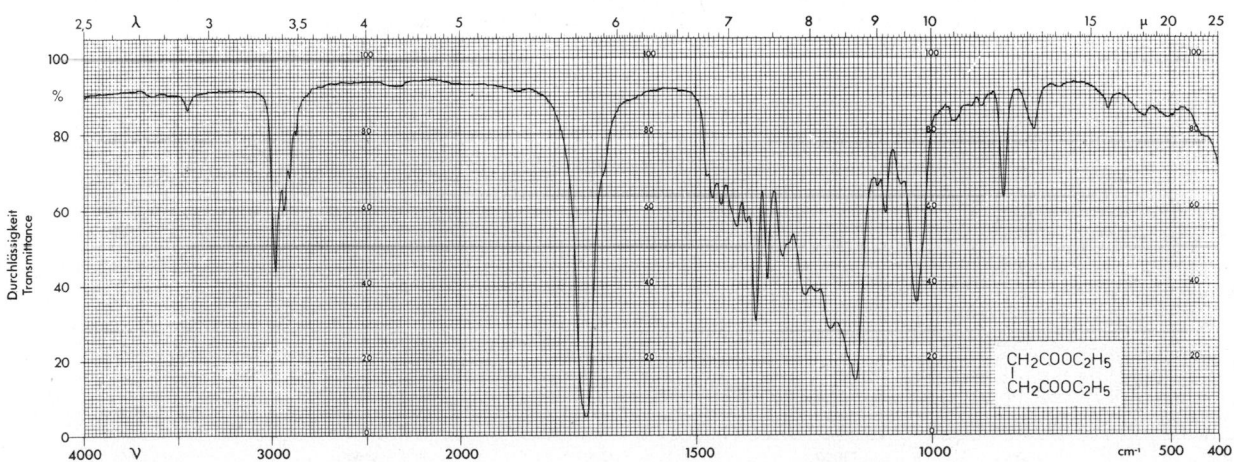

Verbindung:	Diethylbernsteinsäureester			Compound:	Diethyl succinate			5062
Formel:	$C_8H_{14}O_4$	M.:	174,2	Formula:	$C_8H_{14}O_4$	M. w.:	174,2	
Handelsname:		Herst.:	Eastman	Tradename:		Manuf.:	Eastman	
Präparation:	Kapill. Film	Dez. Nr.:	2.1.6	Preparation:	Capill. Film	Dec. No.:	2.1.6	

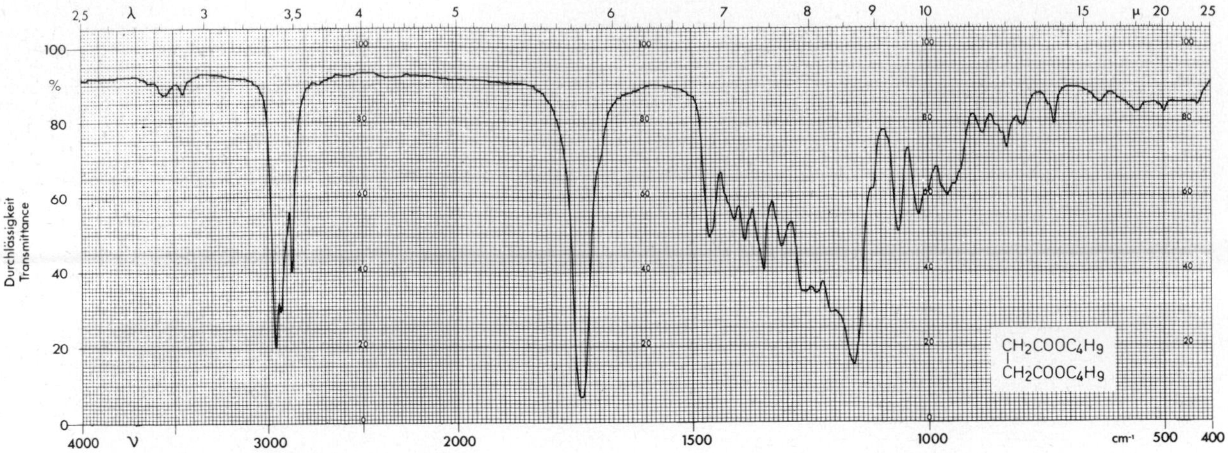

Weichmacher
2. Aliphatische Di- und Tricarbonsäureester
2.2. Adipinsäureester

Plasticizers
2. Aliphatic Di- and Tricarboxylic Acid Esters
2.2. Adipic Acid Esters

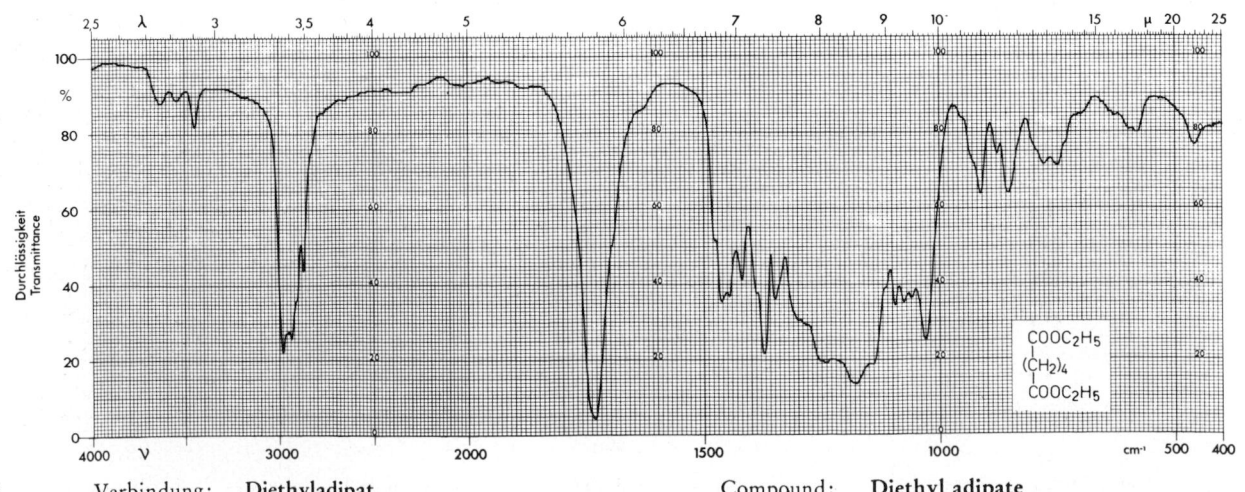

5063

Verbindung:	Dibutylbernsteinsäureester		Compound:	Dibutyl succinate	
Formel:	$C_{12}H_{22}O_4$	M.: 230,3	Formula:	$C_{12}H_{22}O_4$	M. w.: 230,3
Handelsname:		Herst.: Bosch	Tradename:		Manuf.: Bosch
Präparation:	Kapill. Film	Dez. Nr.: 2.1.7	Preparation:	Capill. Film	Dec. No.: 2.1.7

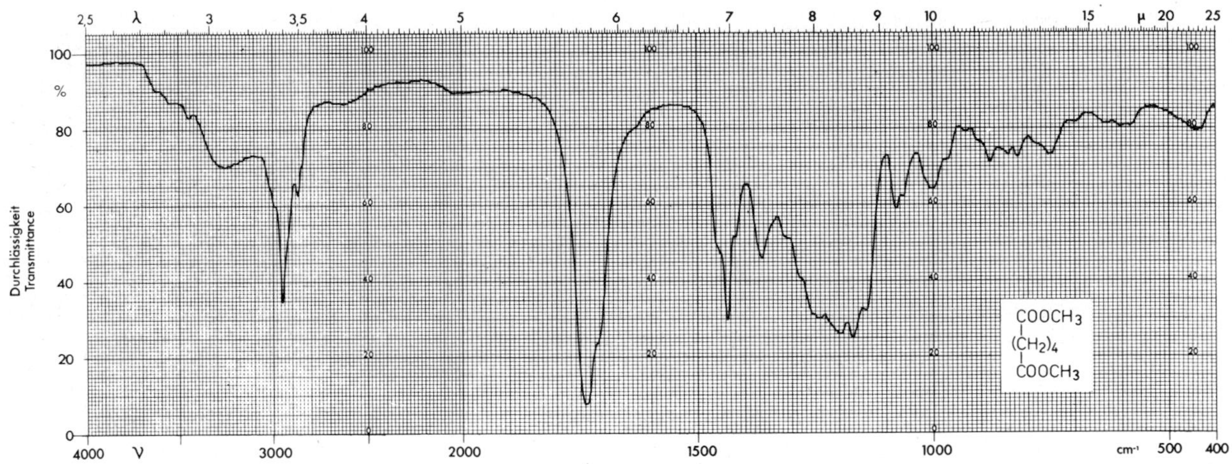

5064

Verbindung:	Dimethyladipat		Compound:	Dimethyl adipate	
Formel:	$C_8H_{14}O_4$	M.: 174,2	Formula:	$C_8H_{14}O_4$	M. w.: 174,2
Handelsname:		Herst.: BASF	Tradename:		Manuf.: BASF
Präparation:	Kapill. Film	Dez. Nr.: 2.2.1	Preparation:	Capill. Film	Dec. No.: 2.2.1

5065

Verbindung:	Diethyladipat		Compound:	Diethyl adipate	
Formel:	$C_{10}H_{18}O_4$	M.: 202,3	Formula:	$C_{10}H_{18}O_4$	M. w.: 202,3
Handelsname:		Herst.: BASF	Tradename:		Manuf.: BASF
Präparation:	Kapill. Film	Dez. Nr.: 2.2.2	Preparation:	Capill. Film	Dec. No.: 2.2.2

Weichmacher
2. Aliphatische Di- und Tricarbonsäureester
2.2. Adipinsäureester

Plasticizers
2. Aliphatic Di- and Tricarboxylic Acid Esters
2.2. Adipic Acid Esters

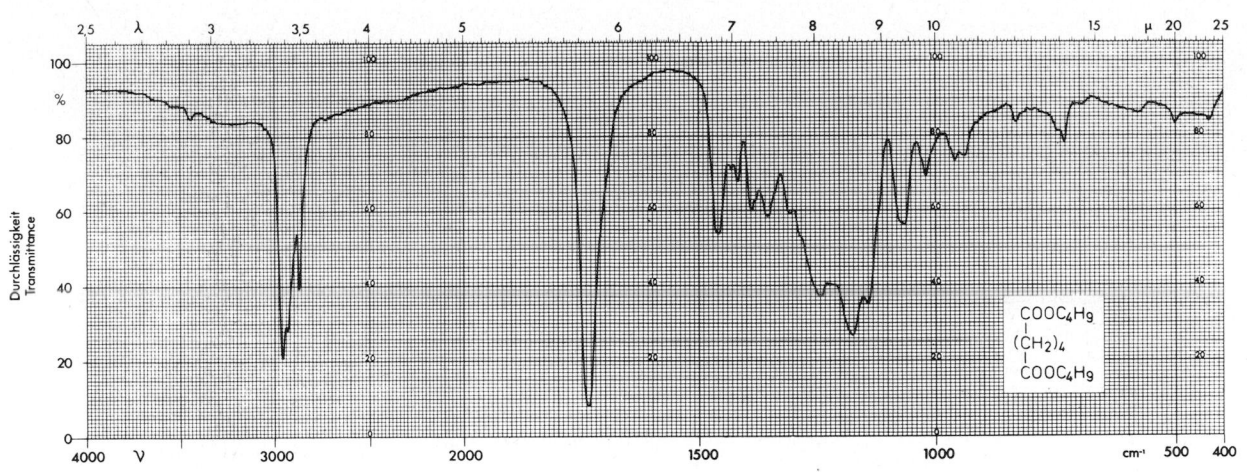

Verbindung:	**Dibutyladipat**			Compound:	**Dibutyl adipate**			5066
Formel:	$C_{14}H_{26}O_4$	M.:	**258,4**	Formula:	$C_{14}H_{26}O_4$	M. w.:	**258,4**	
Handelsname:		Herst.:	**BASF**	Tradename:		Manuf.:	**BASF**	
Präparation:	**Kapill. Film**	Dez. Nr.:	**2.2.3**	Preparation:	**Capill. Film**	Dec. No.:	**2.2.3**	

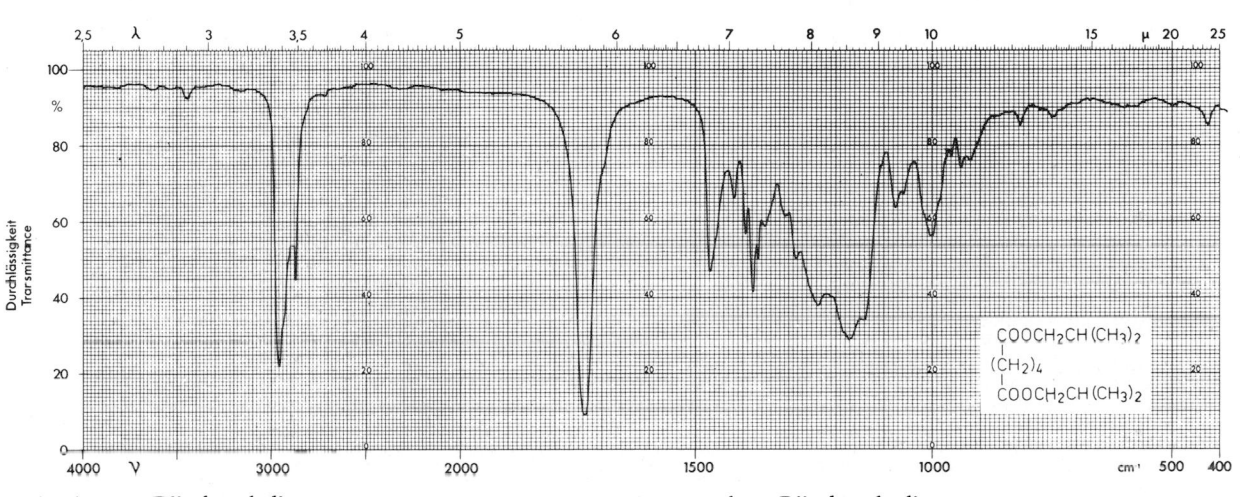

Verbindung:	**Diisobutyladipat**			Compound:	**Diisobutyl adipate**			5067
Formel:	$C_{14}H_{26}O_4$	M.:	**258,4**	Formula:	$C_{14}H_{26}O_4$	M. w.:	**258,4**	
Handelsname:		Herst.:	**BASF**	Tradename:		Manuf.:	**BASF**	
Präparation:	**Kapill. Film**	Dez. Nr.:	**2.2.4**	Preparation:	**Capill. Film**	Dec. No.:	**2.2.4**	

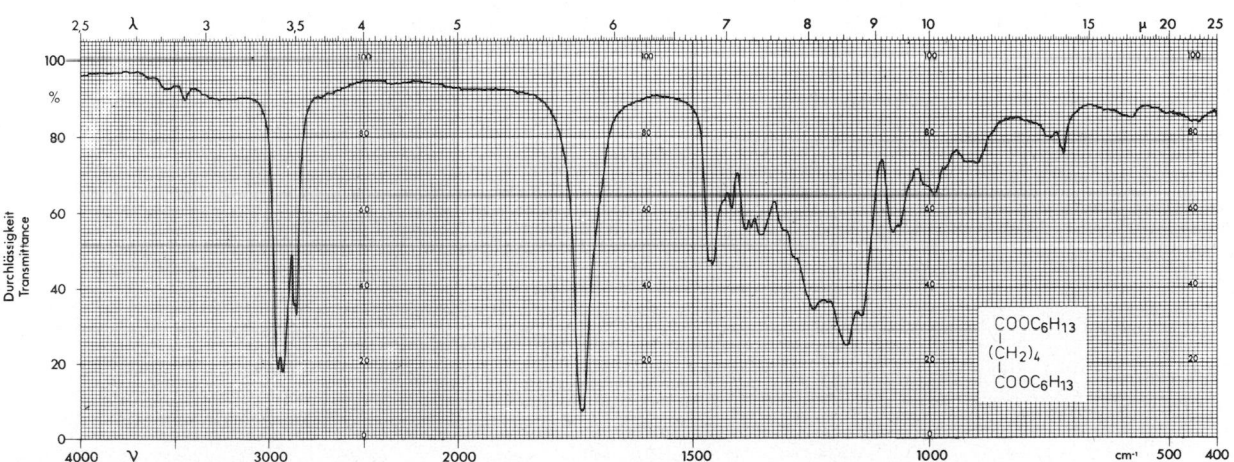

Verbindung:	**Di-n-hexyladipat**			Compound:	**Di-n-hexyl adipate**			5068
Formel:	$C_{18}H_{34}O_4$	M.:	**314,5**	Formula:	$C_{18}H_{34}O_4$	M. w.:	**314,5**	
Handelsname:		Herst.:	**BASF**	Tradename:		Manuf.:	**BASF**	
Präparation:	**Kapill. Film**	Dez. Nr.:	**2.2.5**	Preparation:	**Capill. Film**	Dec. No.:	**2.2.5**	

Weichmacher
2. Aliphatische Di- und Tricarbonsäureester
2.2. Adipinsäureester

Plasticizers
2. Aliphatic Di- and Tricarboxylic Acid Esters
2.2. Adipic Acid Esters

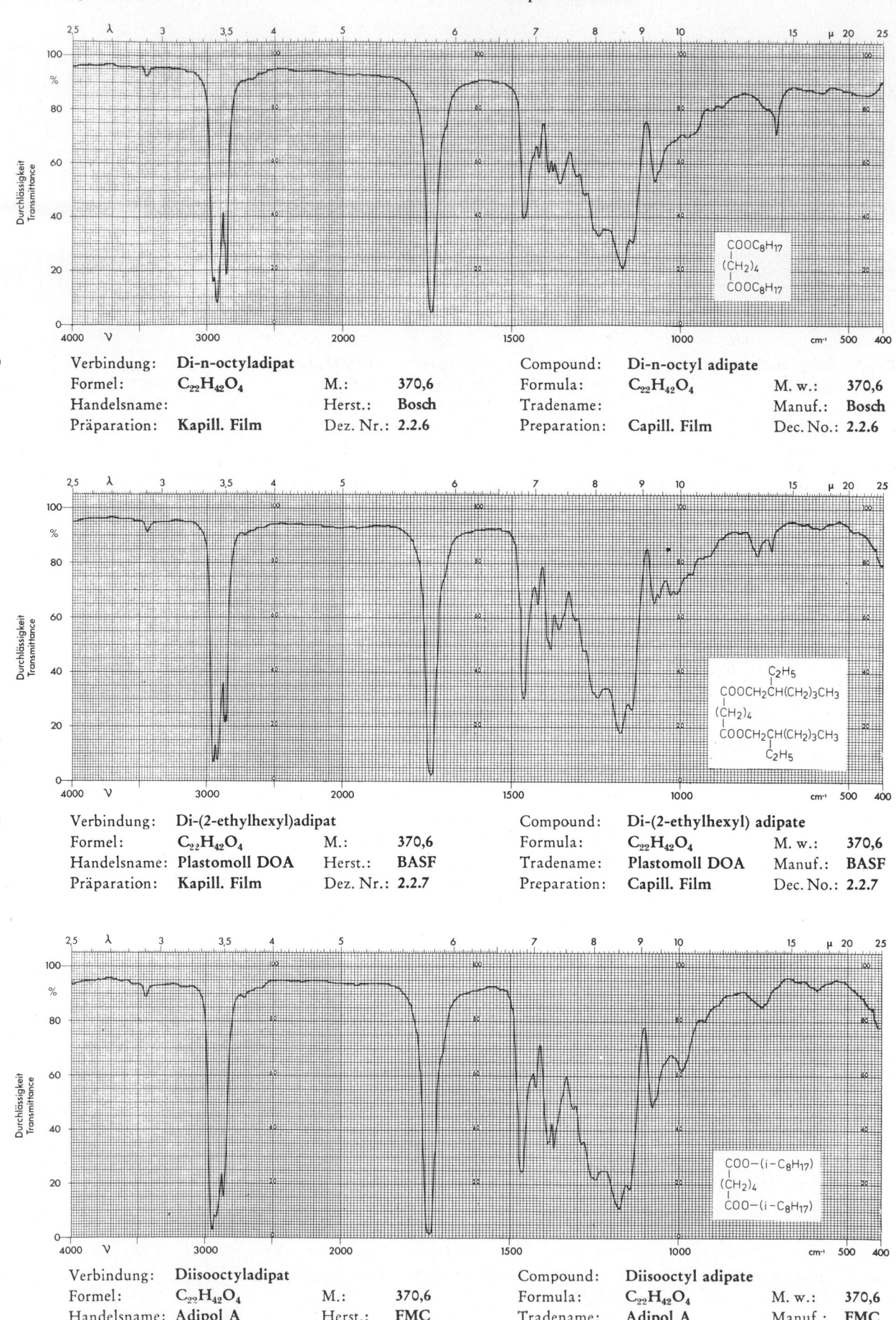

5069

Verbindung:	**Di-n-octyladipat**			Compound:	**Di-n-octyl adipate**	
Formel:	$C_{22}H_{42}O_4$	M.:	**370,6**	Formula:	$C_{22}H_{42}O_4$	M. w.: **370,6**
Handelsname:		Herst.:	**Bosch**	Tradename:		Manuf.: **Bosch**
Präparation:	**Kapill. Film**	Dez. Nr.:	**2.2.6**	Preparation:	**Capill. Film**	Dec. No.: **2.2.6**

5070

Verbindung:	**Di-(2-ethylhexyl)adipat**			Compound:	**Di-(2-ethylhexyl) adipate**	
Formel:	$C_{22}H_{42}O_4$	M.:	**370,6**	Formula:	$C_{22}H_{42}O_4$	M. w.: **370,6**
Handelsname:	**Plastomoll DOA**	Herst.:	**BASF**	Tradename:	**Plastomoll DOA**	Manuf.: **BASF**
Präparation:	**Kapill. Film**	Dez. Nr.:	**2.2.7**	Preparation:	**Capill. Film**	Dec. No.: **2.2.7**

5071

Verbindung:	**Diisooctyladipat**			Compound:	**Diisooctyl adipate**	
Formel:	$C_{22}H_{42}O_4$	M.:	**370,6**	Formula:	$C_{22}H_{42}O_4$	M. w.: **370,6**
Handelsname:	**Adipol A**	Herst.:	**FMC**	Tradename:	**Adipol A**	Manuf.: **FMC**
Präparation:	**Kapill. Film**	Dez. Nr.:	**2.2.8**	Preparation:	**Capill. Film**	Dec. No.: **2.2.8**

Weichmacher
2. Aliphatische Di- und Tricarbonsäureester
2.2. Adipinsäureester

Plasticizers
2. Aliphatic Di- and Tricarboxylic Acid Esters
2.2. Adipic Acid Esters

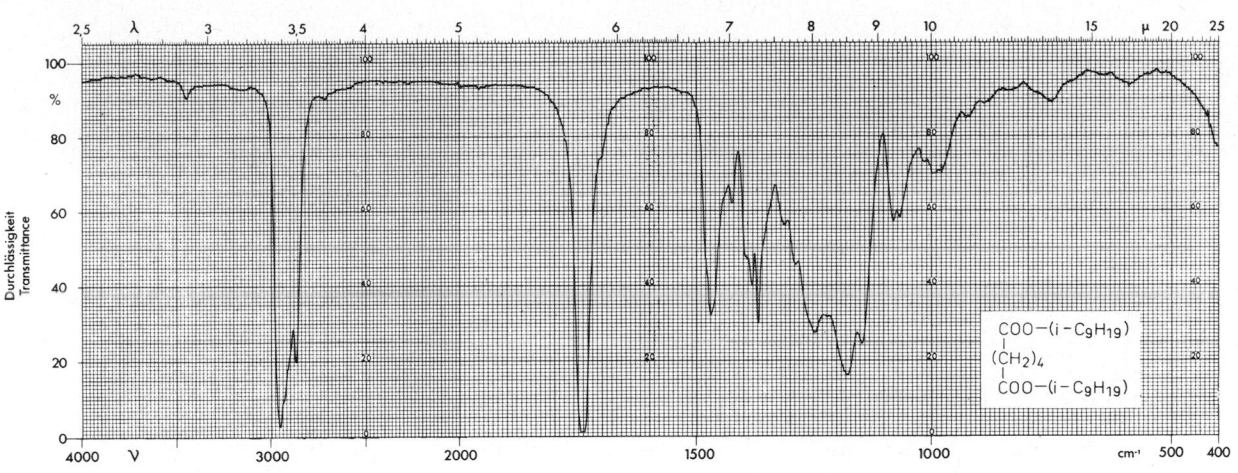

Verbindung:	Diisononyladipat			Compound:	Diisononyl adipate		5072
Formel:	$C_{24}H_{46}O_4$	M.:	398,7	Formula:	$C_{24}H_{46}O_4$	M. w.: 398,7	
Handelsname:	Plastomoll NA	Herst.:	BASF	Tradename:	Plastomoll NA	Manuf.: BASF	
Präparation:	Kapill. Film	Dez. Nr.:	2.2.9	Preparation:	Capill. Film	Dec. No.: 2.2.9	

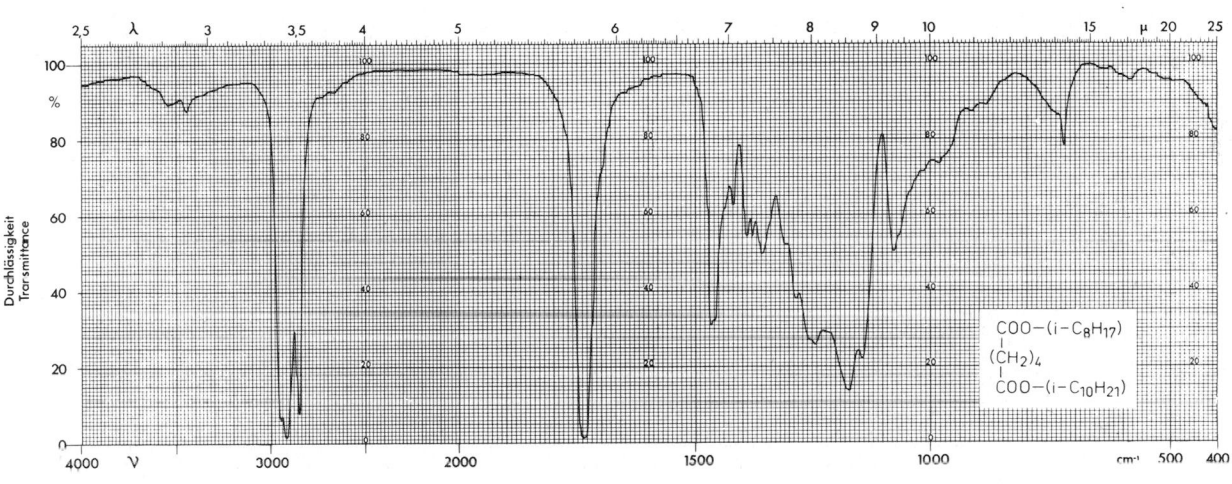

Verbindung:	Octyldecyladipat			Compound:	Octyl decyl adipate		5073
Formel:	$C_{24}H_{46}O_4$	M.:	398,7	Formula:	$C_{24}H_{46}O_4$	M. w.: 398,7	
Handelsname:	Hercoflex 290	Herst.:	Hercules	Tradename:	Hercoflex 290	Manuf.: Hercules	
Präparation:	Kapill. Film	Dez. Nr.:	2.2.10	Preparation:	Capill. Film	Dec. No.: 2.2.10	

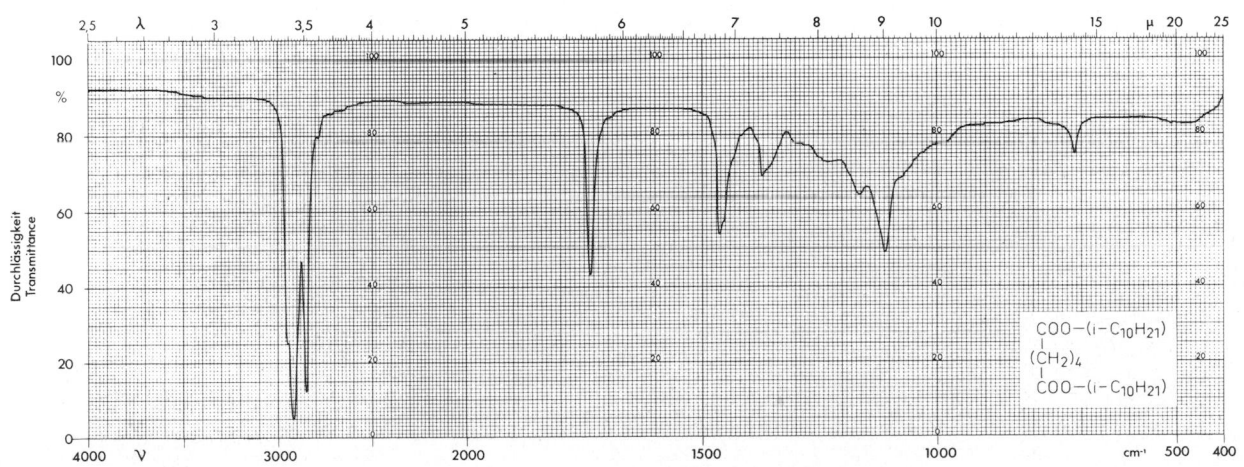

Verbindung:	Didecyladipat			Compound:	Didecyl adipate		5074
Formel:	$C_{26}H_{50}O_4$	M.:	426,8	Formula:	$C_{26}H_{50}O_4$	M. w.: 426,8	
Handelsname:		Herst.:	Bosch	Tradename:		Manuf.: Bosch	
Präparation:	Capill. Film	Dez. Nr.:	2.2.11	Preparation:	Kapill. Film	Dec. No.: 2.2.11	

Weichmacher
2. Aliphatische Di- und Tricarbonsäureester
2.2. Adipinsäureester

Plasticizers
2. Aliphatic Di- and Tricarboxylic Acid Esters
2.2. Adipic Acid Esters

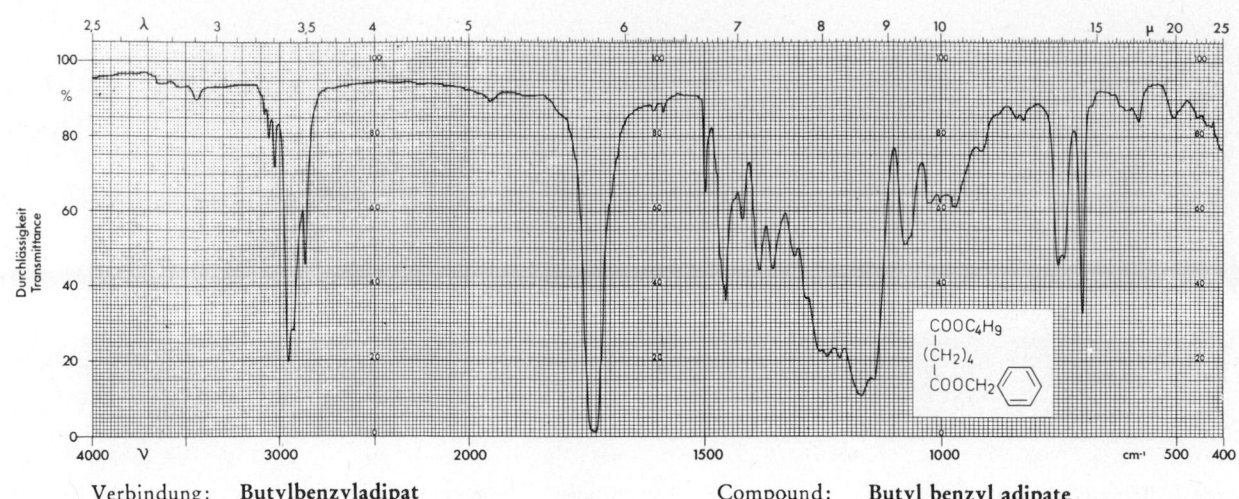

5075

Verbindung:	Butylbenzyladipat			Compound:	Butyl benzyl adipate		
Formel:	$C_{17}H_{24}O_4$	M.:	292,4	Formula:	$C_{17}H_{24}O_4$	M. w.:	292,4
Handelsname:	Adimoll BB	Herst.:	Bayer	Tradename:	Adimoll BB	Manuf.:	Bayer
Präparation:	Kapill. Film	Dez. Nr.:	2.2.12	Preparation:	Capill. Film	Dec. No.:	2.2.12

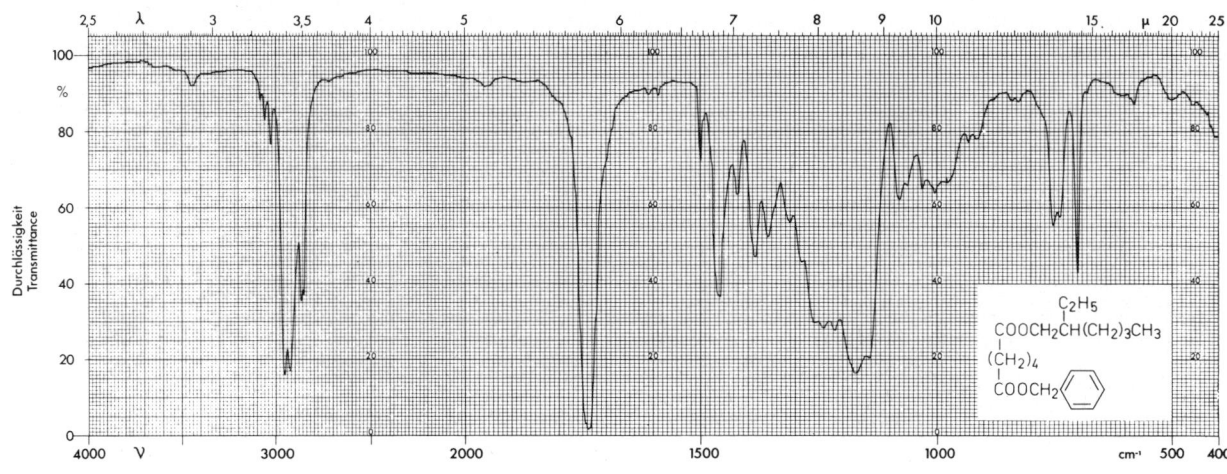

5076

Verbindung:	Octylbenzyladipat			Compound:	Octyl benzyl adipate		
Formel:	$C_{21}H_{32}O_4$	M.:	348,5	Formula:	$C_{21}H_{32}O_4$	M. w.:	348,5
Handelsname:	Adimoll BO	Herst.:	Bayer	Tradename:	Adimoll BO	Manuf.:	Bayer
Präparation:	Capill. Film	Dez. Nr.:	2.2.13	Preparation:	Kapill. Film	Dec. No.:	2.2.13

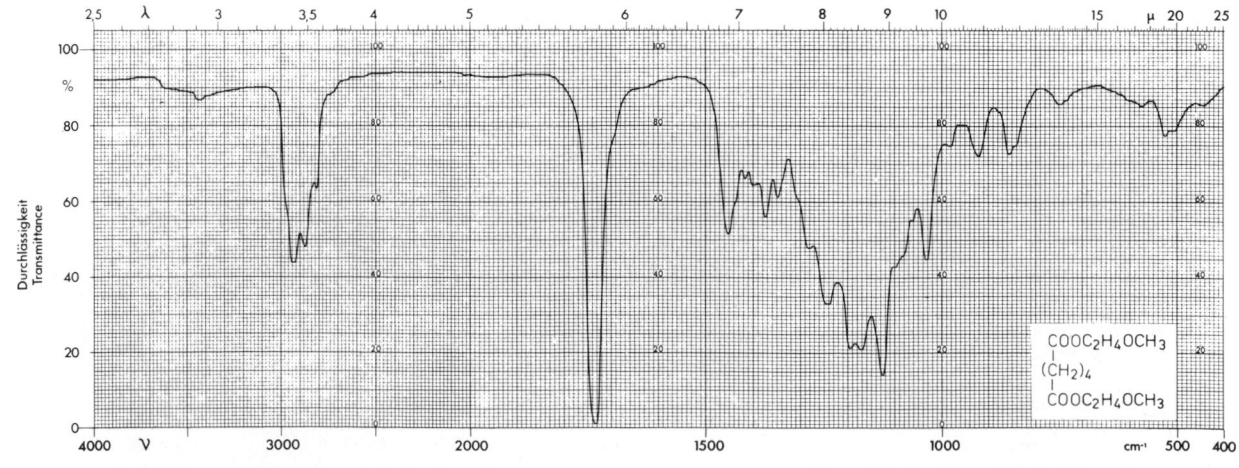

5077

Verbindung:	Di-(methoxyethyl)adipat			Compound:	Di-(methoxyethyl) adipate		
Formel:	$C_{12}H_{22}O_6$	M.:	262,3	Formula:	$C_{12}H_{22}O_6$	M. w.:	262,3
Handelsname:		Herst.:	Bosch	Tradename:		Manuf.:	Bosch
Präparation:	Kapill. Film	Dez. Nr.:	2.2.14	Preparation:	Capill. Film	Dec. No.:	2.2.14

Weichmacher
2. Aliphatische Di- und Tricarbonsäureester
2.2. Adipinsäureester

Plasticizers
2. Aliphatic Di- and Tricarboxylic Acid Esters
2.2. Adipic Acid Esters

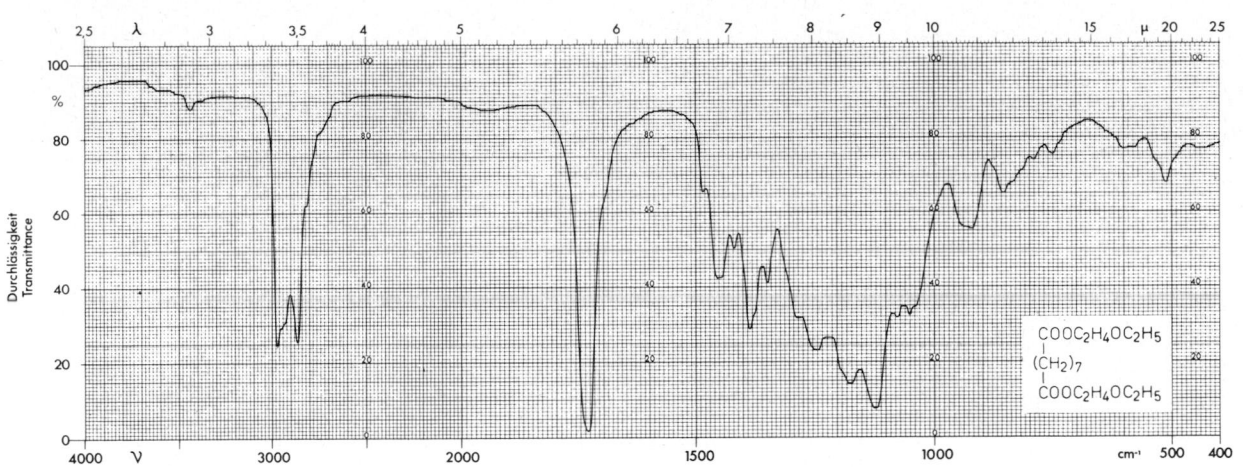

Verbindung:	Di-(ethoxyethyl)adipat			Compound:	Di-(ethoxy ethyl) adipate			5078
Formel:	$C_{14}H_{26}O_6$	M.:	290,4	Formula:	$C_{14}H_{26}O_6$	M. w.:	290,4	
Handelsname:		Herst.:	Bosch	Tradename:		Manuf.:	Bosch	
Präparation:	Kapill. Film	Dez. Nr.:	2.2.15	Preparation:	Capill. Film	Dec. No.:	2.2.15	

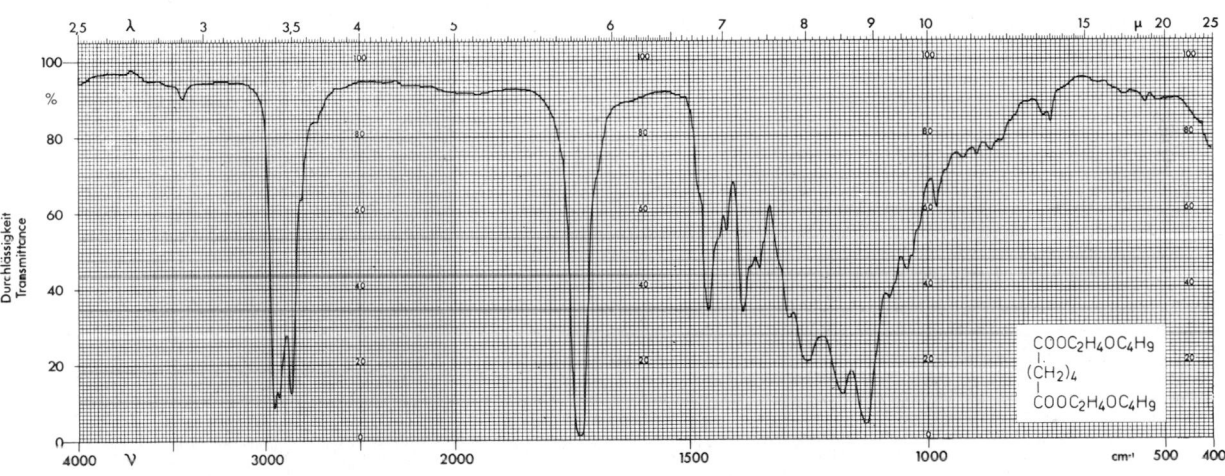

Verbindung:	Di-(butoxyethyl)adipat			Compound:	Di-(butoxyethyl) adipate			5079
Formel:	$C_{18}H_{34}O_6$	M.:	346,5	Formula:	$C_{18}H_{34}O_6$	M. w.:	346,5	
Handelsname:	Adipol BCA	Herst.:	FMC	Tradename:	Adipol BCA	Manuf.:	FMC	
Präparation:	Kapill. Film	Dez. Nr.:	2.2.16	Preparation:	Capill. Film	Dec. No.:	2.2.16	

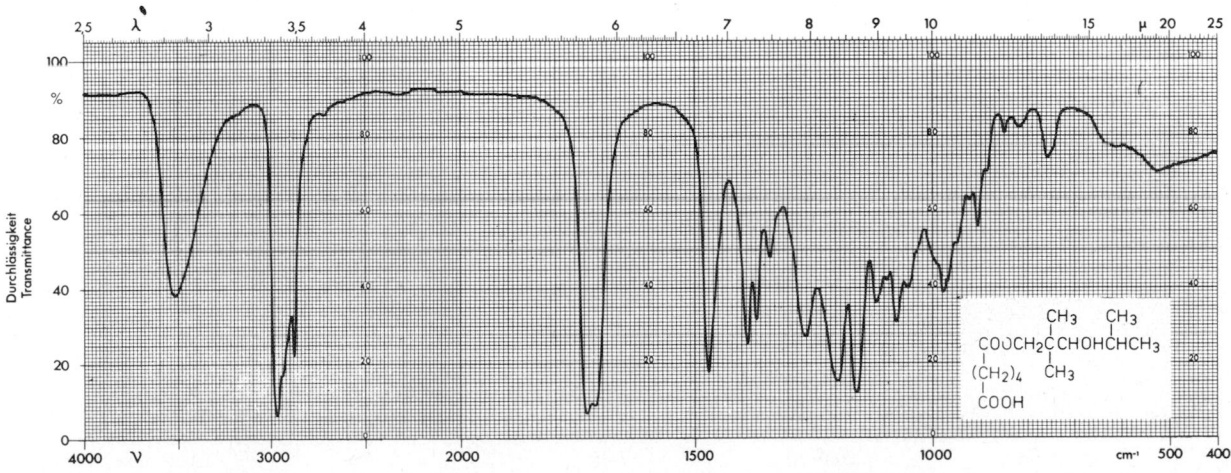

Verbindung:	2,2,4-Trimethyl-1,3-pentandiol-monoadipat			Compound:	2,2,4-trimethyl-1,3-pentandiol-monoadipate			5080
Formel:	$C_{14}H_{24}O_5$	M.:	272,4	Formula:	$C_{14}H_{24}O_5$	M. w.:	272,4	
Handelsname:	TMPDM-Adipate	Herst.:	Eastman	Tradename:	TMPDM-Adipate	Manuf.:	Eastman	
Präparation:	Kapill. Film	Dez. Nr.:	2.2.17	Preparation:	Capill. Film	Dec. No.:	2.2.17	

Weichmacher
2. Aliphatische Di- und Tricarbonsäureester
2.3. Azelainsäureester

Plasticizers
2. Aliphatic Di- and Tricarboxylic Acid Esters
2.3. Azelaic Acid Esters

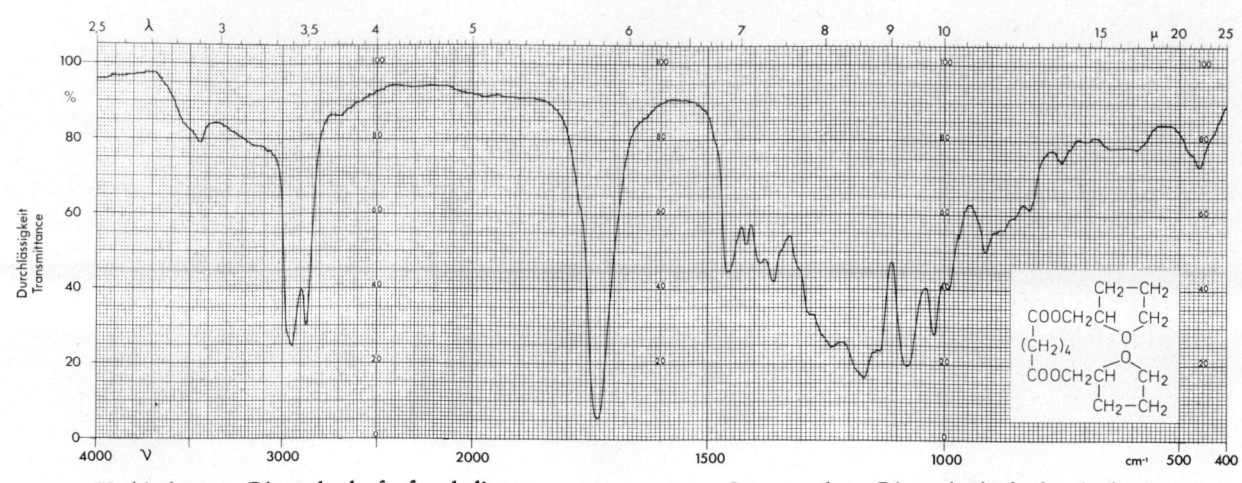

5081	Verbindung:	**Ditetrahydrofurfuryladipat**			Compound:	**Ditetrahydrofurfuryl adipate**		
	Formel:	$C_{16}H_{26}O_6$	M.:	**314,4**	Formula:	$C_{16}H_{26}O_6$	M. w.:	**314,4**
	Handelsname:		Herst.:	**Eastman**	Tradename:		Manuf.:	**Eastman**
	Präparation:	**Kapill. Film**	Dez. Nr.:	**2.2.18**	Preparation:	**Capill. Film**	Dec. No.:	**2.2.18**

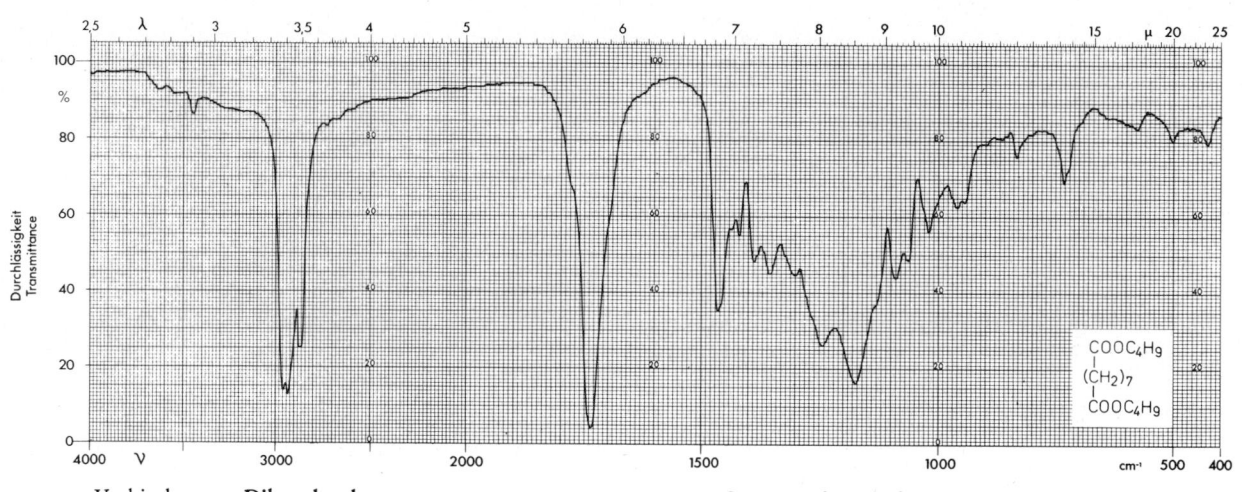

5082	Verbindung:	**Dibutylazelat**			Compound:	**Dibutyl azelate**		
	Formel:	$C_{17}H_{32}O_4$	M.:	**300,5**	Formula:	$C_{17}H_{32}O_4$	M. w.:	**300,5**
	Handelsname:		Herst.:	**BASF**	Tradename:		Manuf.:	**BASF**
	Präparation:	**Kapill. Film**	Dez. Nr.:	**2.3.1**	Preparation:	**Capill. Film**	Dec. No.:	**2.3.1**

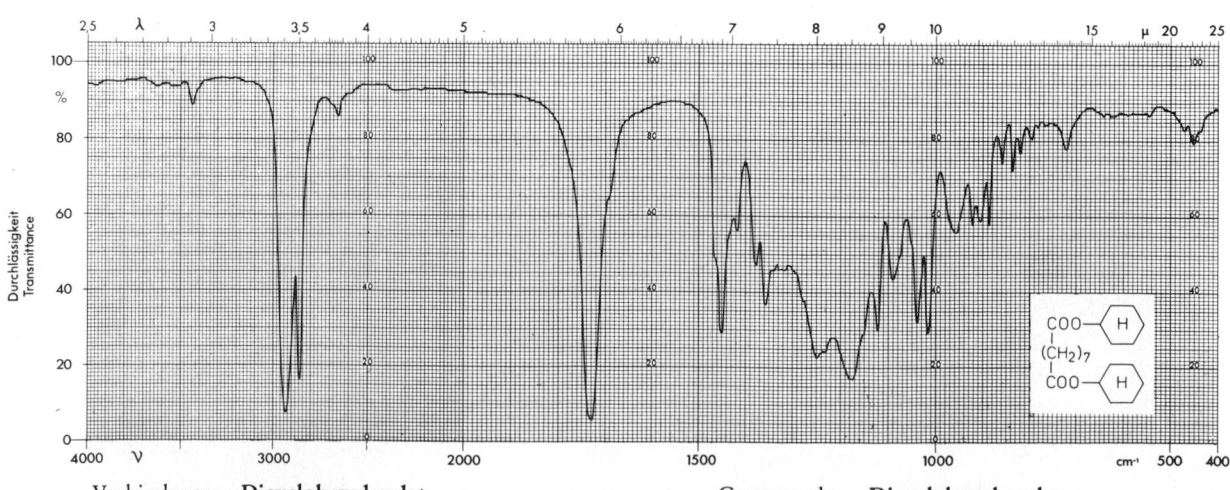

5083	Verbindung:	**Dicyclohexylazelat**			Compound:	**Dicyclohexyl azelate**		
	Formel:	$C_{21}H_{36}O_4$	M.:	**352,4**	Formula:	$C_{21}H_{36}O_4$	M. w.:	**352,4**
	Handelsname:	**Morflex X-1114**	Herst.:	**Pfizer**	Tradename:	**Morflex X-1114**	Manuf.:	**Pfizer**
	Präparation:	**Kapill. Film**	Dez. Nr.:	**2.3.2**	Preparation:	**Capill. Film**	Dec. No.:	**2.3.2**

Weichmacher
2. Aliphatische Di- und Tricarbonsäureester
2.3. Azelainsäureester

Plasticizers
2. Aliphatic Di- and Tricarboxylic Acid Esters
2.3. Azelaic Acid Esters

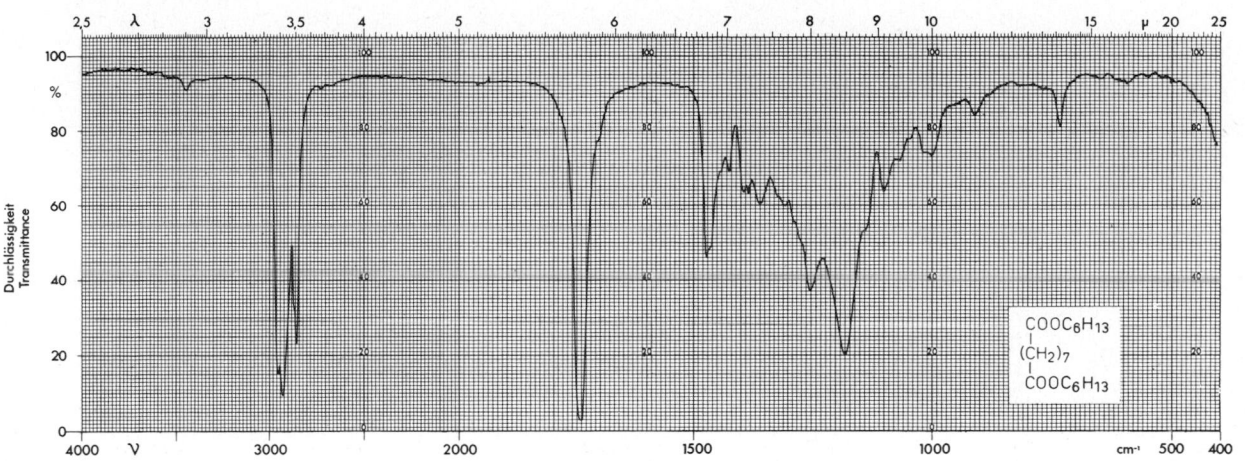

Verbindung:	Di-n-hexylazelat			Compound:	Di-n-hexyl azelate			5084
Formel:	C$_{21}$H$_{40}$O$_4$	M.:	356,6	Formula:	C$_{21}$H$_{40}$O$_4$	M. w.:	356,6	
Handelsname:	Plastolein 9051	Herst.:	Emery	Tradename:	Plastolein 9051	Manuf.:	Emery	
Präparation:	Kapill. Film	Dez. Nr.:	2.3.3	Preparation:	Capill. Film	Dec. No.:	2.3.3	

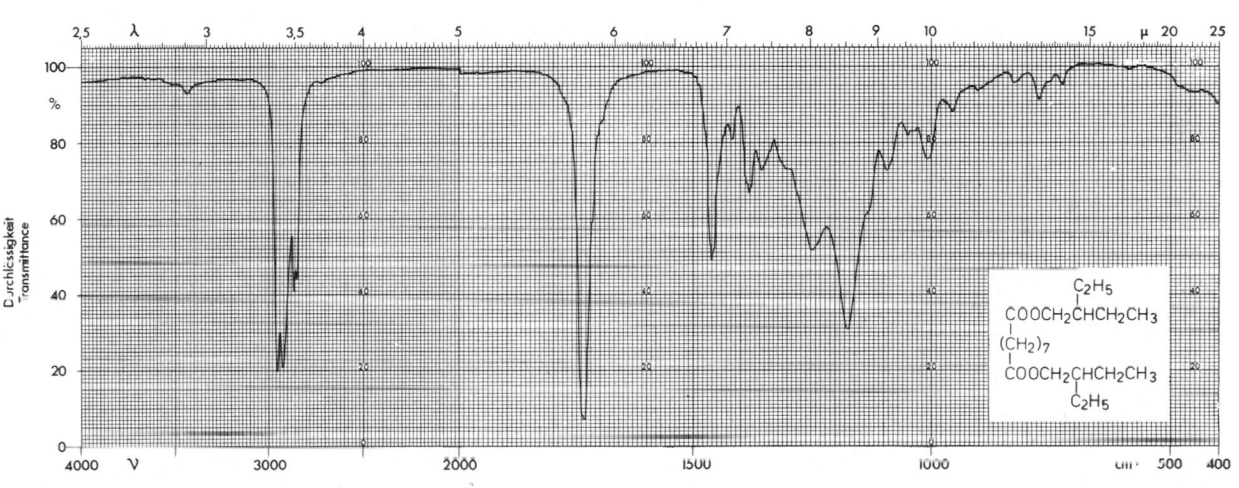

Verbindung:	Di 2 ethylbutylazelat			Compound:	Di-2-ethylbutyl azelate			5085
Formel:	C$_{21}$H$_{40}$O$_4$	M.:	356,6	Formula:	C$_{21}$H$_{40}$O$_4$	M. w.:	356,6	
Handelsname:	Plastolein 9050	Herst.:	Emery	Tradename:	Plastolein 9050	Manuf.:	Emery	
Präparation:	Capill. Film	Dez. Nr.:	2.3.4	Preparation:	Kapill. Film	Dec. No.:	2.3.4	

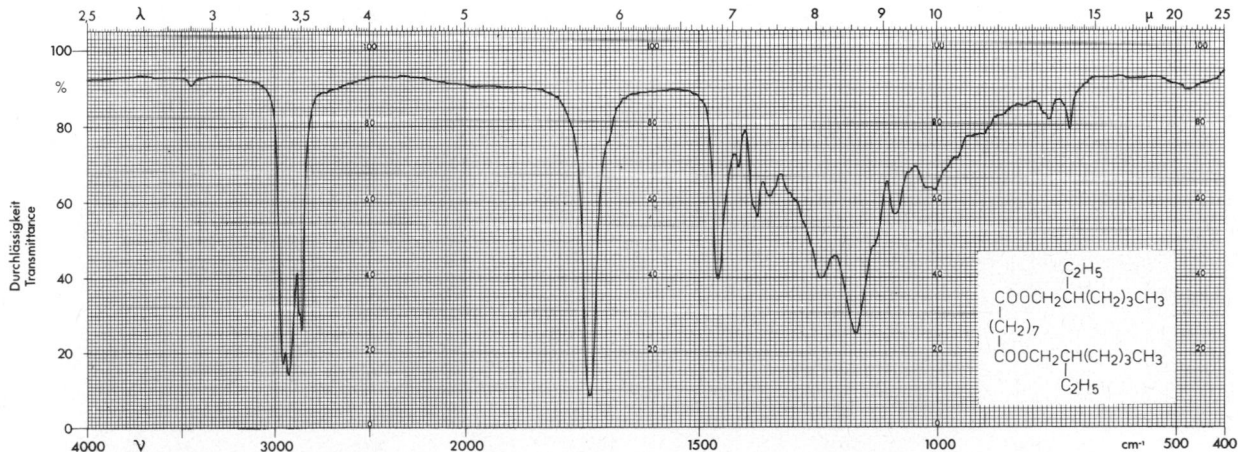

Verbindung:	Di-2-ethylhexylazelat			Compound:	Di-2-ethylhexyl azelate			5086
Formel:	C$_{25}$H$_{48}$O$_4$	M.:	412,7	Formula:	C$_{25}$H$_{48}$O$_4$	M. w.:	412,7	
Handelsname:	Flexol Z-88	Herst.:	Union Carb.	Tradename:	Flexol Z-88	Manuf.:	Union Carb.	
Präparation:	Kapill. Film	Dez. Nr.:	2.3.5	Preparation:	Capill. Film	Dec. No.:	2.3.5	

Weichmacher
2. Aliphatische Di- und Tricarbonsäureester
2.4. Sebacinsäureester

Plasticizers
2. Aliphatic Di- and Tricarboxylic Acid Esters
2.4. Sebacic Acid Esters

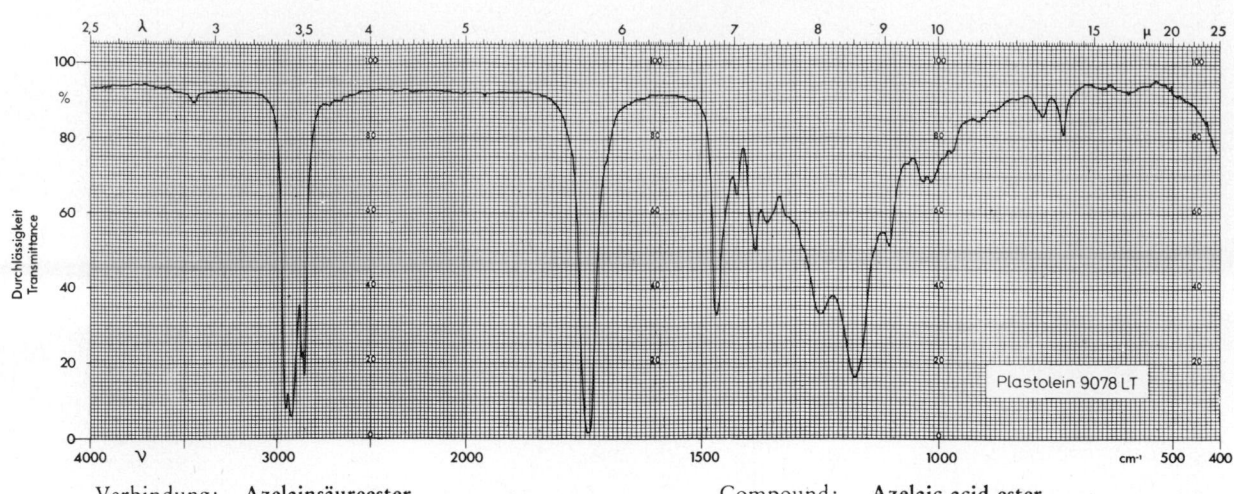

5087
Verbindung:	**Azelainsäureester**			Compound:	**Azelaic acid ester**	
Formel:	**Plastolein 9078 LT**	M.:	**410**	Formula:	**Plastolein 9078 LT**	M. w.: **410**
Handelsname:		Herst.:	**Emery**	Tradename:		Manuf.: **Emery**
Präparation:	**Kapill. Film**	Dez. Nr.:	**2.3.6**	Preparation:	**Capill. Film**	Dec. No.: **2.3.6**

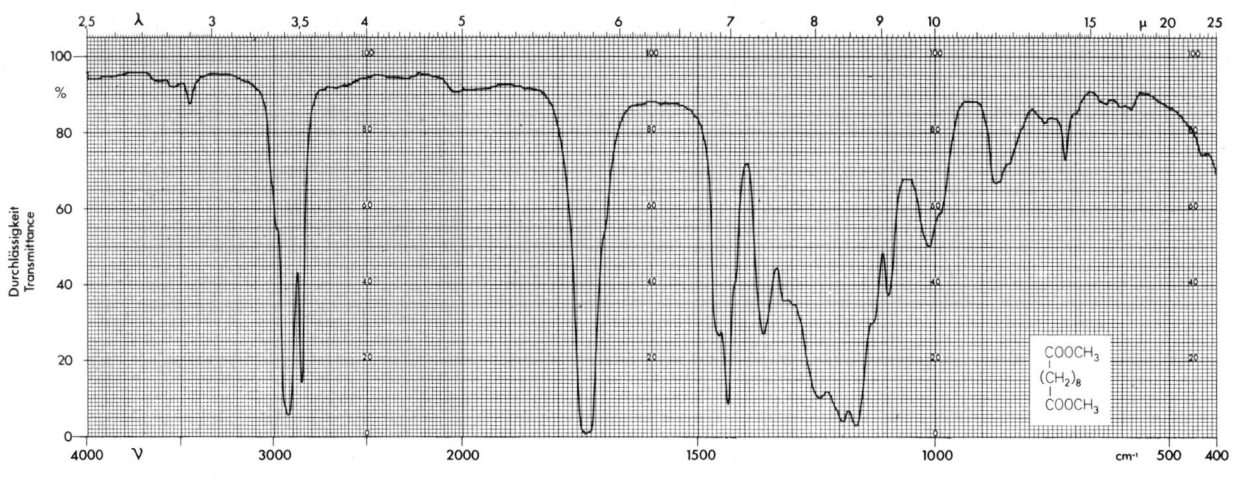

5088
Verbindung:	**Dimethylsebacat**			Compound:	**Dimethyl sebacate**	
Formel:	**C₁₂H₂₂O₄**	M.:	**230,2**	Formula:	**C₁₂H₂₂O₄**	M. w.: **230,2**
Handelsname:		Herst.:	**Bosch**	Tradename:		Manuf.: **Bosch**
Präparation:	**Kapill. Film**	Dez. Nr.:	**2.4.1**	Preparation:	**Capill. Film**	Dec. No.: **2.4.1**

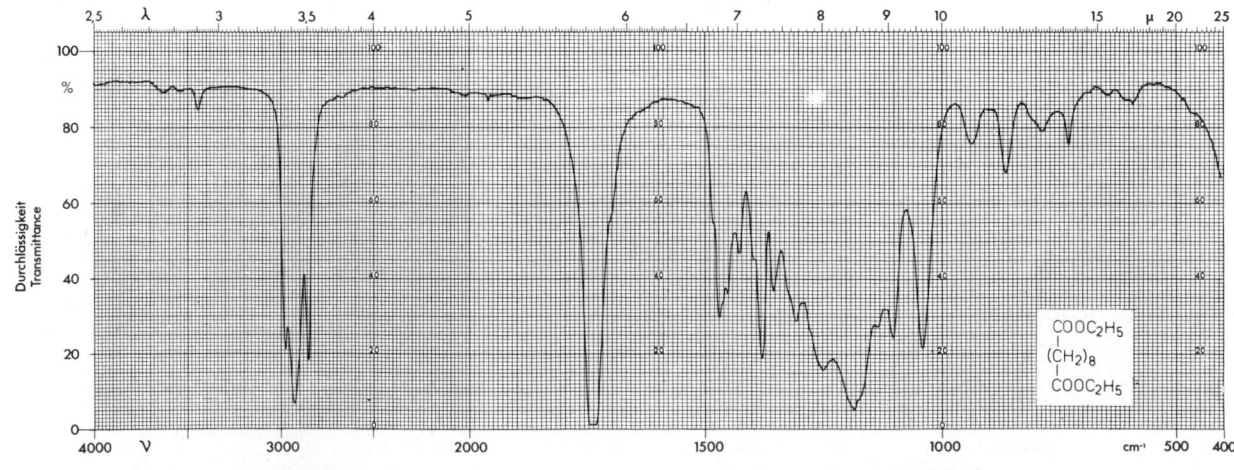

5089
Verbindung:	**Diethylsebacat**			Compound:	**Diethyl sebacate**	
Formel:	**C₁₄H₂₆O₄**	M.:	**258,3**	Formula:	**C₁₄H₂₆O₄**	M. w.: **258,3**
Handelsname:	**Reomol DES**	Herst.:	**Geigy**	Tradename:	**Reomol DES**	Manuf.: **Geigy**
Präparation:	**Kapill. Film**	Dez. Nr.:	**2.4.2**	Preparation:	**Capill. Film**	Dec. No.: **2.4.2**

Weichmacher
2. Aliphatische Di- und Tricarbonsäureester
2.4. Sebacinsäureester

Plasticizers
2. Aliphatic Di- and Tricarboxylic Acid Esters
2.4. Sebacic Acid Esters

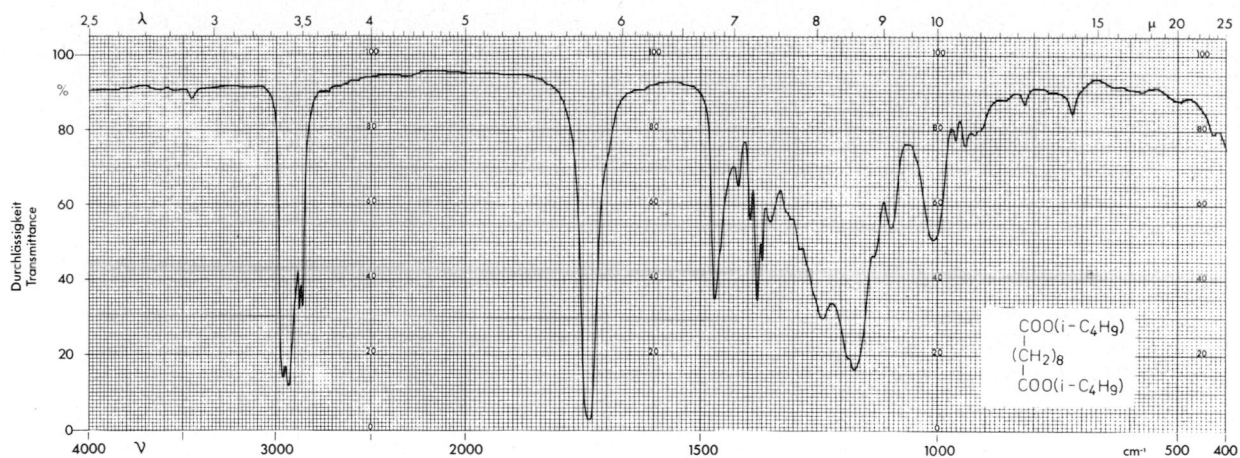

Verbindung: **Diisobutylsebacat**

Formel: $C_{18}H_{34}O_4$ M.: **314,5**

Handelsname: Herst.: **Bosch**

Präparation: **Kapill. Film** Dez. Nr.: **2.4.3**

Compound: **Diisobutyl sebacate** **5090**

Formula: $C_{18}H_{34}O_4$ M. w.: **314,5**

Tradename: Manuf.: **Bosch**

Preparation: **Capill. Film** Dec. No.: **2.4.3**

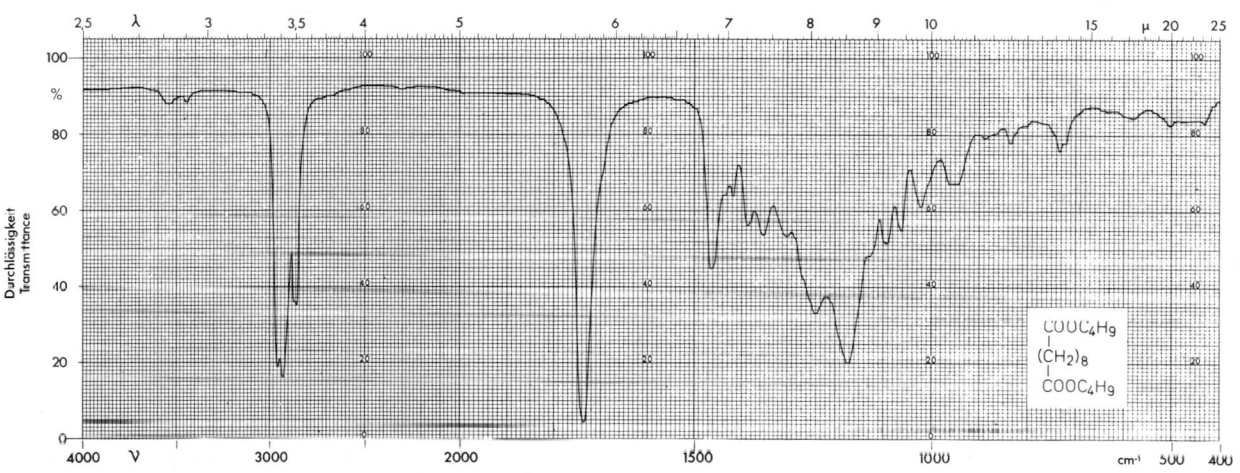

Verbindung: **Dibutylsebacat**

Formel: $C_{18}H_{34}O_4$ M.: **314,5**

Handelsname: Herst.: **Bosch**

Präparation: **Kapill. Film** Dez. Nr.: **2.4.4**

Compound: **Dibutyl sebacate** **5091**

Formula: $C_{18}H_{34}O_4$ M. w.: **314,5**

Tradename: Manuf.: **Bosch**

Preparation: **Capill. Film** Dec. No.: **2.4.4**

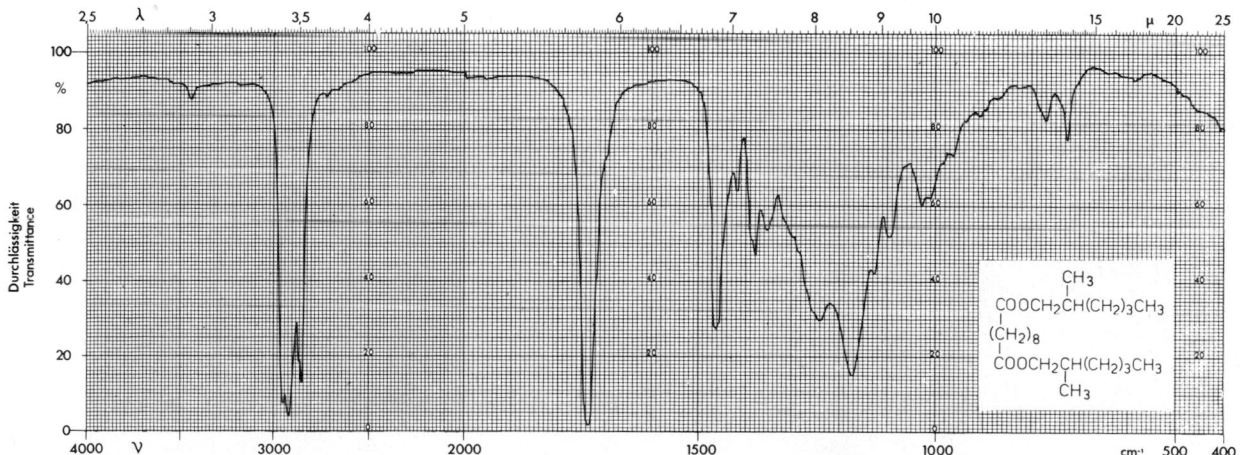

Verbindung: **Di-2-ethylhexylsebacat**

Formel: $C_{26}H_{50}O_4$ M.: **426,7**

Handelsname: **Reomol DOS** Herst.: **Geigy**

Präparation: **Kapill. Film** Dez. Nr.: **2.4.5**

Compound: **Di-(2-ethylhexyl) sebacate** **5092**

Formula: $C_{26}H_{50}O_4$ M. w.: **426,7**

Tradename: **Reomol DOS** Manuf.: **Geigy**

Preparation: **Capill. Film** Dec. No:. **2.4.5**

Weichmacher
2. Aliphatische Di- und Tricarbonsäureester
2.4. Sebacinsäureester

Plasticizers
2. Aliphatic Di- and Tricarboxylic Acid Esters
2.4. Sebacic Acid Esters

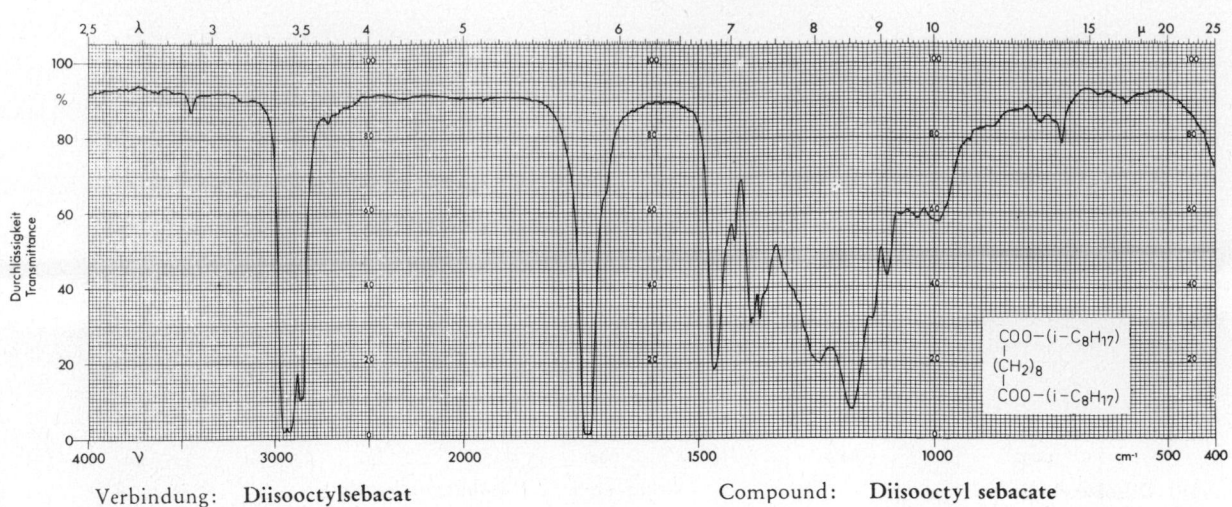

$$COO-(i-C_8H_{17})$$
$$|$$
$$(CH_2)_8$$
$$|$$
$$COO-(i-C_8H_{17})$$

5093	Verbindung:	Diisooctylsebacat		Compound:	Diisooctyl sebacate	
	Formel:	$C_{26}H_{50}O_4$	M.: 426,7	Formula:	$C_{26}H_{50}O_4$	M. w.: 426,7
	Handelsname:	Reomol DIOS	Herst.: Geigy	Tradename:	Reomol DIOS	Manuf.: Geigy
	Präparation:	Kapill. Film	Dez. Nr.: 2.4.6	Preparation:	Capill. Film	Dec. No.: 2.4.6

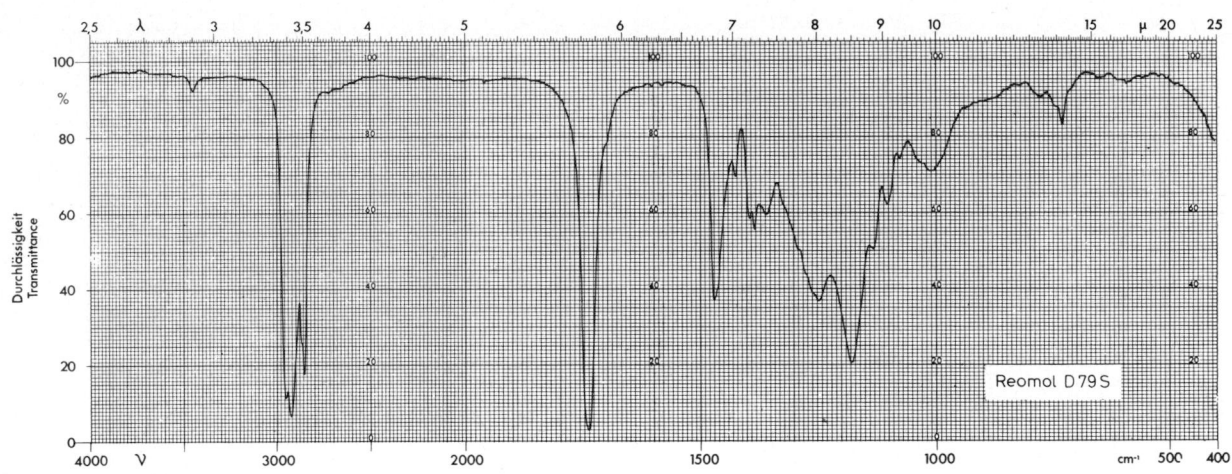

Reomol D 79 S

5094	Verbindung:	Gemisch von C_8-Alkohol-Sebacaten		Compound:	Mixed C_8-alcohol sebacate	
	Formel:	$C_{26}H_{50}O_4$	M.: 426,7	Formula:	$C_{26}H_{50}O_4$	M. w.: 426,7
	Handelsname:	Reomol D 79 S	Herst.: Geigy	Tradename:	Reomol D 79 S	Manuf.: Geigy
	Präparation:	Kapill. Film	Dez. Nr.: 2.4.7	Preparation:	Capill. Film	Dec. No.: 2.4.7

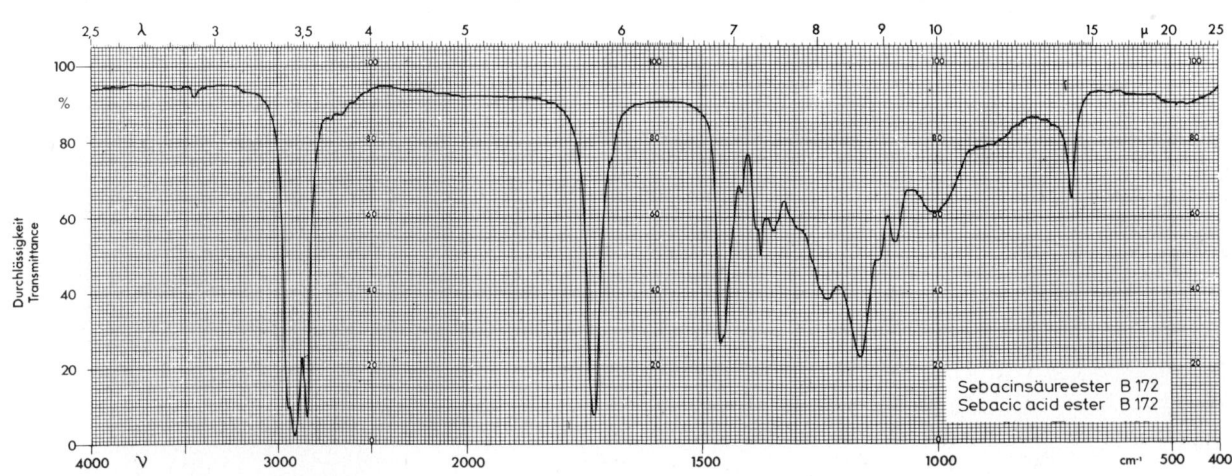

Sebacinsäureester B 172
Sebacic acid ester B 172

5095	Verbindung:	Fettalkoholsebacat		Compound:	Fatty alcohol sebacate	
	Formel:	$\sim C_{46}H_{90}O_4$	M.: $\sim$ 670	Formula:	$\sim C_{46}H_{90}O_4$	M. w.: $\sim$ 670
	Handelsname:	Sebacinsäureester B 172	Herst.: Dehydag	Tradename:	Sebacinsäureester B 172	Manuf.: Dehydag
	Präparation:	Kapill. Film	Dez. Nr.: 2.4.8	Preparation:	Capill. Film	Dec. No.: 2.4.8

Weichmacher
2. Aliphatische Di- und Tricarbonsäureester
2.5. Wein- und Citronensäureester

Plasticizers
2. Aliphatic Di- and Tricarboxylic Acid Esters
2.5. Tartaric and Citric Acid Esters

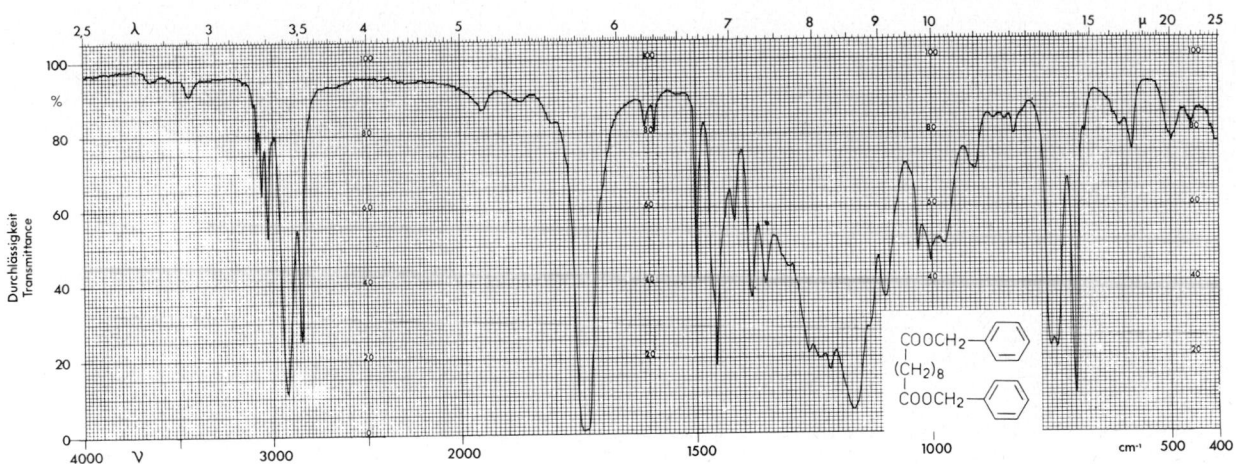

Verbindung:	Dibenzylsebacat			Compound:	Dibenzyl sebacate			5096
Formel:	$C_{24}H_{30}O_4$	M.:	382,5	Formula:	$C_{24}H_{30}O_4$	M. w.:	382,5	
Handelsname:	Harflex 90	Herst.:	Harchem	Tradename:	Harflex 90	Manuf.:	Harchem	
Präparation:	Kapill. Film	Dez. Nr.:	2.4.9	Preparation:	Capill. Film	Dec. No.:	2.4.9	

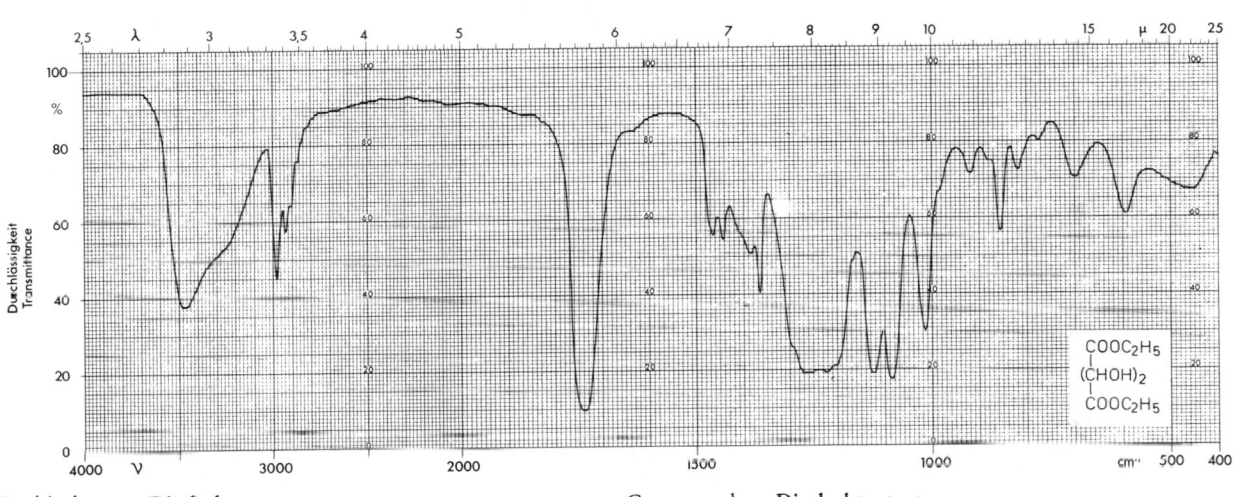

Verbindung:	Diethyltartrat			Compound:	Diethyl tartrate			5097
Formel:	$C_8H_{14}O_6$	M.:	206,2	Formula:	$C_8H_{14}O_6$	M. w.:	206,2	
Handelsname:		Herst.:	Eastman	Tradename:		Manuf.:	Eastman	
Präparation:	Kapill. Film	Dez. Nr.:	2.5.1	Preparation:	Capill. Film	Dec. No.:	2.5.1	

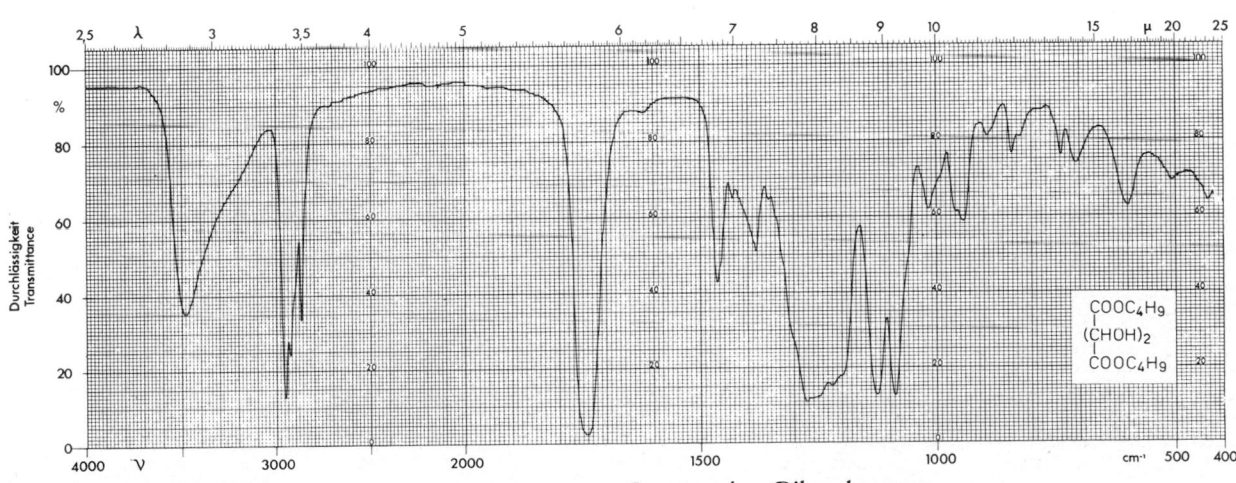

Verbindung:	Dibutyltartrat			Compound:	Dibutyl tartrate			5098
Formel:	$C_{12}H_{22}O_6$	M.:	262,3	Formula:	$C_{12}H_{22}O_6$	M. w.:	262,3	
Handelsname:		Herst.:	DCL-Bisol	Tradename:		Manuf.:	DCL-Bisol	
Präparation:	Kapill. Film	Dez. Nr.:	2.5.2	Preparation:	Capill. Film	Dec. No.:	2.5.2	

Weichmacher
2. Aliphatische Di- und Tricarbonsäureester
2.5. Wein- und Citronensäureester

Plasticizers
2. Aliphatic Di- and Tricarboxylic Acid Esters
2.5. Tartaric and Citric Acid Esters

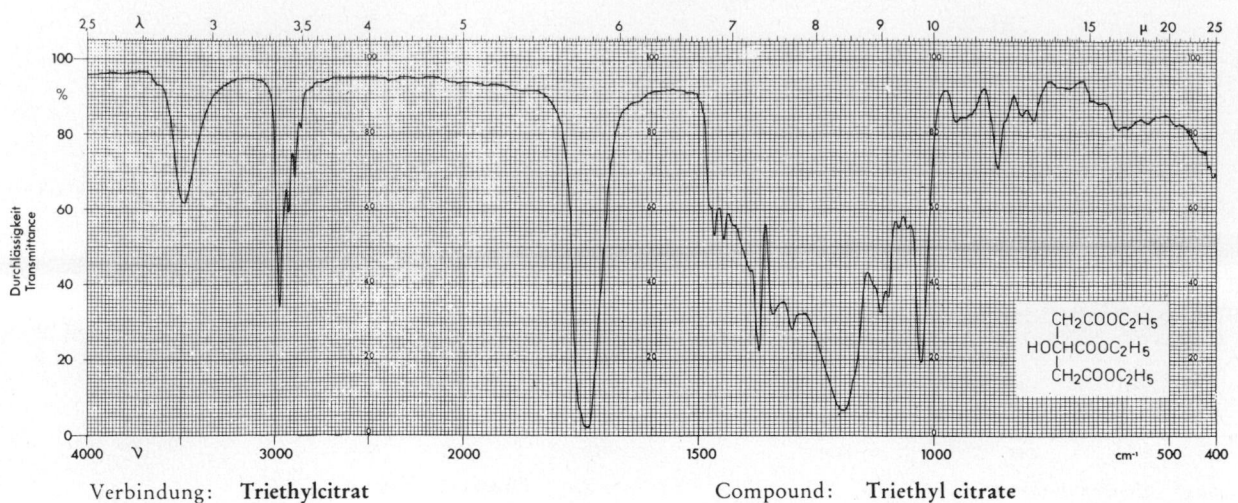

5099

Verbindung:	**Triethylcitrat**			Compound:	**Triethyl citrate**		
Formel:	**C₁₂H₂₀O₇**	M.:	**276,3**	Formula:	**C₁₂H₂₀O₇**	M. w.:	**276,3**
Handelsname:	**Citroflex 2**	Herst.:	**Pfizer**	Tradename:	**Citroflex 2**	Manuf.:	**Pfizer**
Präparation:	**Kapill. Film**	Dez. Nr.:	**2.5.3**	Preparation:	**Capill. Film**	Dec. No:.	**2.5.3**

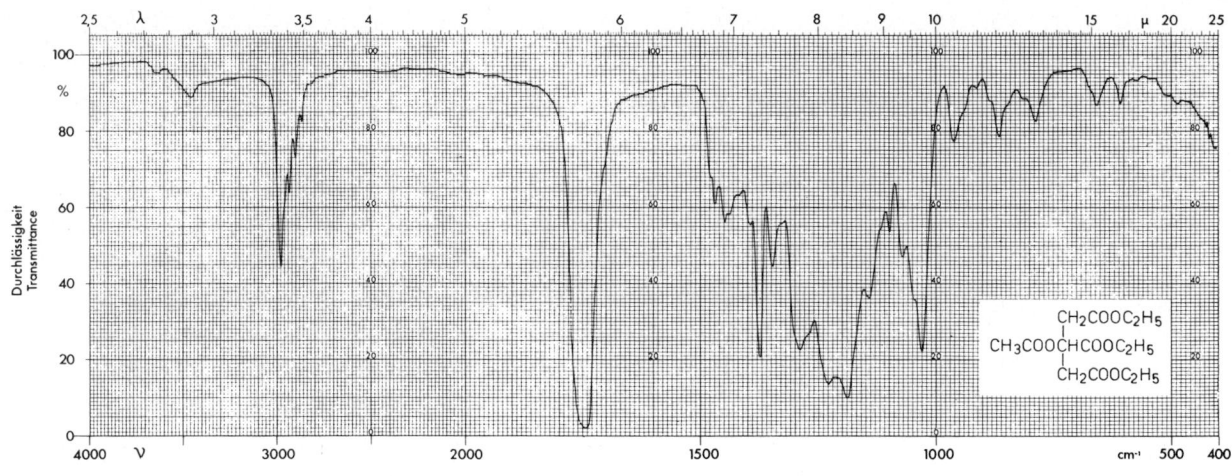

5100

Verbindung:	**Acetyltriethylcitrat**			Compound:	**Acetyl triethyl citrate**		
Formel:	**C₁₄H₂₂O₈**	M.:	**318,3**	Formula:	**C₁₄H₂₂O₈**	M. w.:	**318,3**
Handelsname:	**Citroflex A-2**	Herst.:	**Pfizer**	Tradename:	**Citroflex A-2**	Manuf.:	**Pfizer**
Präparation:	**Kapill. Film**	Dez. Nr.:	**2.5.4**	Preparation:	**Capill. Film**	Dec. No:.	**2.5.4**

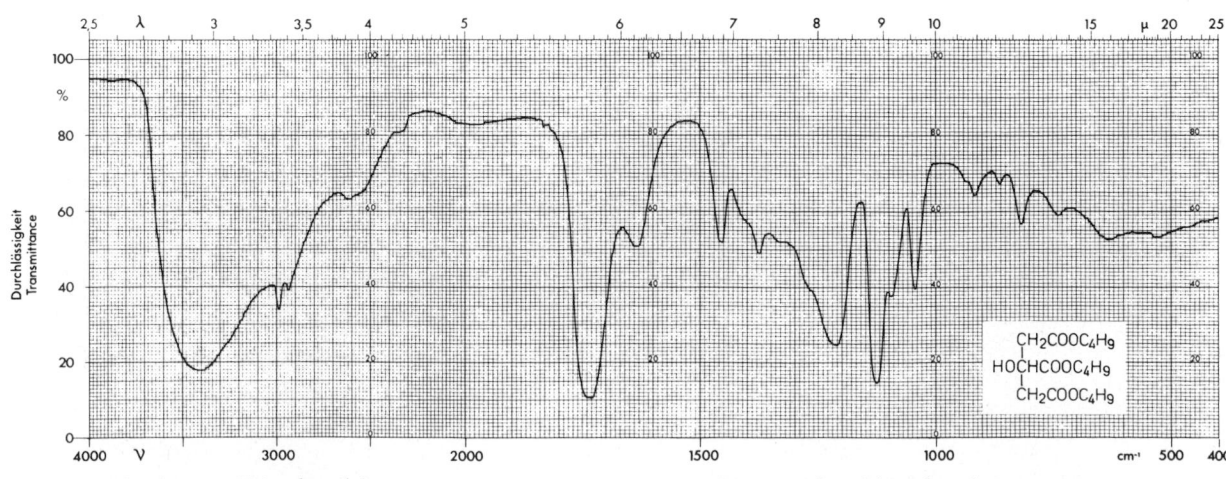

5101

Verbindung:	**Tri-n-butylcitrat**			Compound:	**Tri-n-butyl citrate**		
Formel:	**C₁₈H₃₂O₇**	M.:	**360,5**	Formula:	**C₁₈H₃₂O₇**	M. w.:	**360,5**
Handelsname:	**Citroflex 4**	Herst.:	**Pfizer**	Tradename:	**Citroflex 4**	Manuf.:	**Pfizer**
Präparation:	**Kapill. Film**	Dez. Nr.:	**2.5.5**	Preparation:	**Capill. Film**	Dec. No:.	**2.5.5**

Weichmacher
2. Aliphatische Di- und Tricarbonsäureester
2.5. Wein- und Citronensäureester

Plasticizers
2. Aliphatic Di- and Tricarboxylic Acid Esters
2.5. Tartaric and Citric Acid Esters

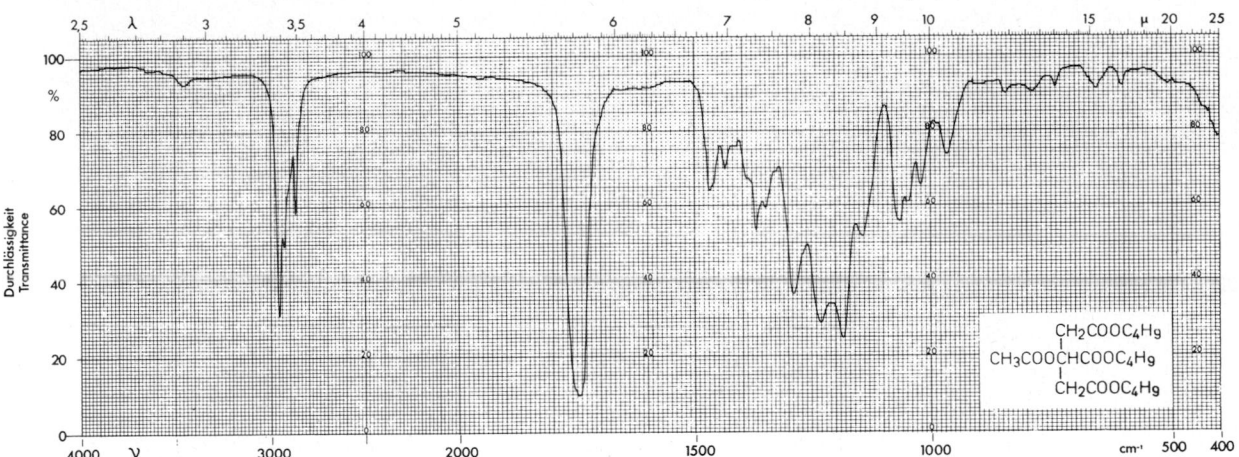

Verbindung:	Acetyltri-n-butylcitrat			Compound:	Acetyl tri-n-butyl citrate		5102
Formel:	$C_{20}H_{34}O_8$	M.:	402,5	Formula:	$C_{20}H_{34}O_8$	M. w.: 402,5	
Handelsname:	Citroflex A 4	Herst.:	Pfizer	Tradename:	Citroflex A 4	Manuf.: Pfizer	
Präparation:	Kapill. Film	Dez. Nr.:	2.5.6	Preparation:	Capill. Film	Dec. No:. 2.5.6	

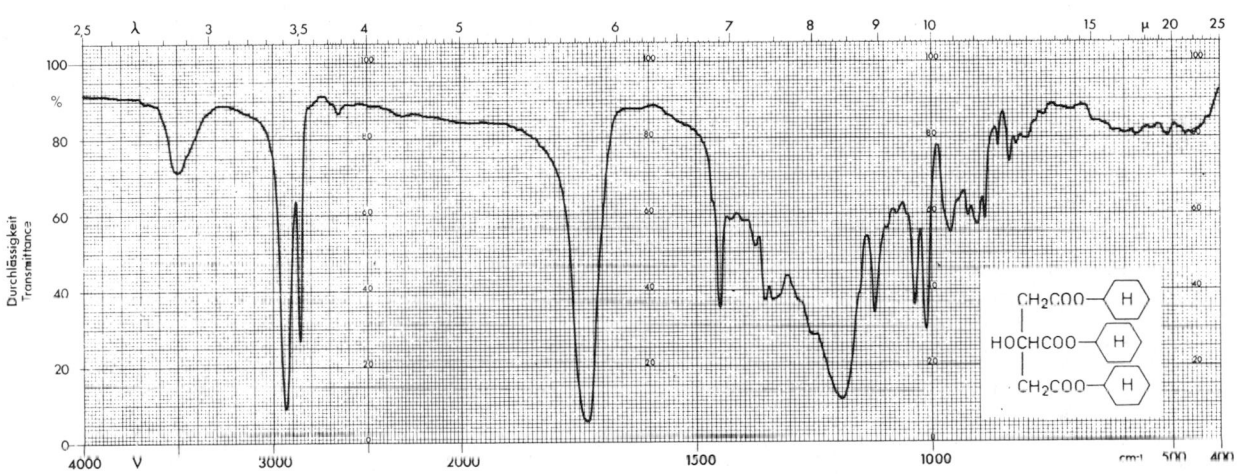

Verbindung:	Tricyclohexylcitrat			Compound:	Tricyclohexyl citrate		5103
Formel:	$C_{24}H_{38}O_7$	M.:	438,6	Formula:	$C_{24}H_{38}O_7$	M. w.: 438,6	
Handelsname:	Citroflex 6 R	Herst.:	Pfizer	Tradename:	Citroflex 6 R	Manuf.: Pfizer	
Präparation:	Kapill. Film	Dez. Nr.:	2.5.7	Preparation:	Capill. Film	Dec. No:. 2.5.7	

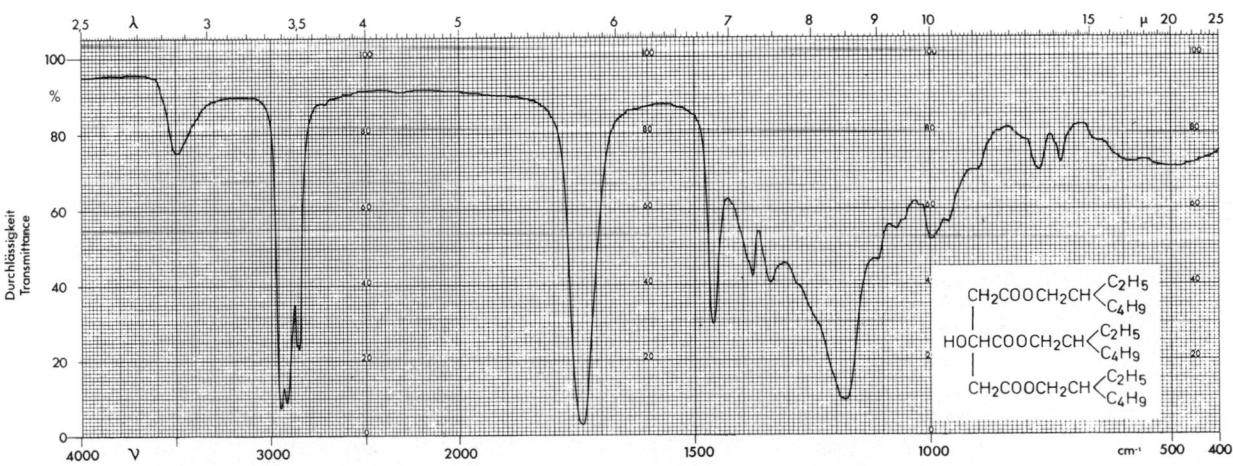

Verbindung:	Tri-(2-ethylhexyl)-citrat			Compound:	Tri(2-ethylhexyl) citrate		5104
Formel:	$C_{30}H_{56}O_7$	M.:	528,8	Formula:	$C_{30}H_{56}O_7$	M. w.: 528,8	
Handelsname:		Herst.:	Bosch	Tradename:		Manuf.: Bosch	
Präparation:	Kapill. Film	Dez. Nr.:	2.5.8	Preparation:	Capill. Film	Dec. No:. 2.5.8	

Weichmacher
2. Aliphatische Di- und Tricarbonsäureester
2.6. Aliph. Dicarbonsäurepolyester

Plasticizers
2. Aliphatic Di- and Tricarboxylic Acid Esters
2.6. Aliphatic Dicarbon Acid Polyesters

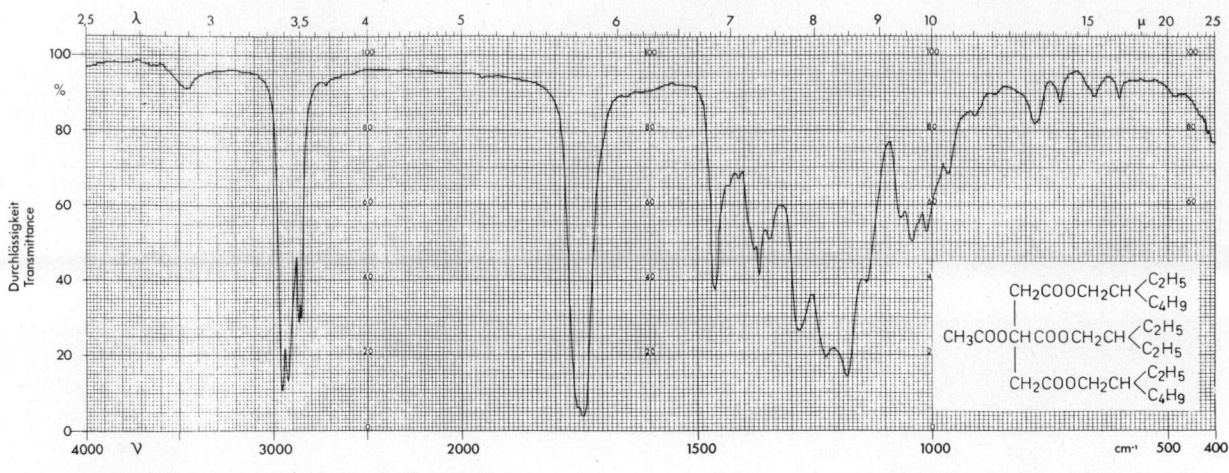

5105

Verbindung:	Acetyl-tri-(2-ethylhexyl)citrat			Compound:	Acetyl-tri(2-ethylhexyl) citrate		
Formel:	$C_{32}H_{58}O_4$	M.:	571,8	Formula:	$C_{32}H_{58}O_4$	M. w.:	571,8
Handelsname:	Citroflex A-8	Herst.:	Pfizer	Tradename:	Citroflex A-8	Manuf.:	Pfizer
Präparation:	Kapill. Film	Dez. Nr.:	2.5.9	Preparation:	Capill. Film	Dec. No:.	2.5.9

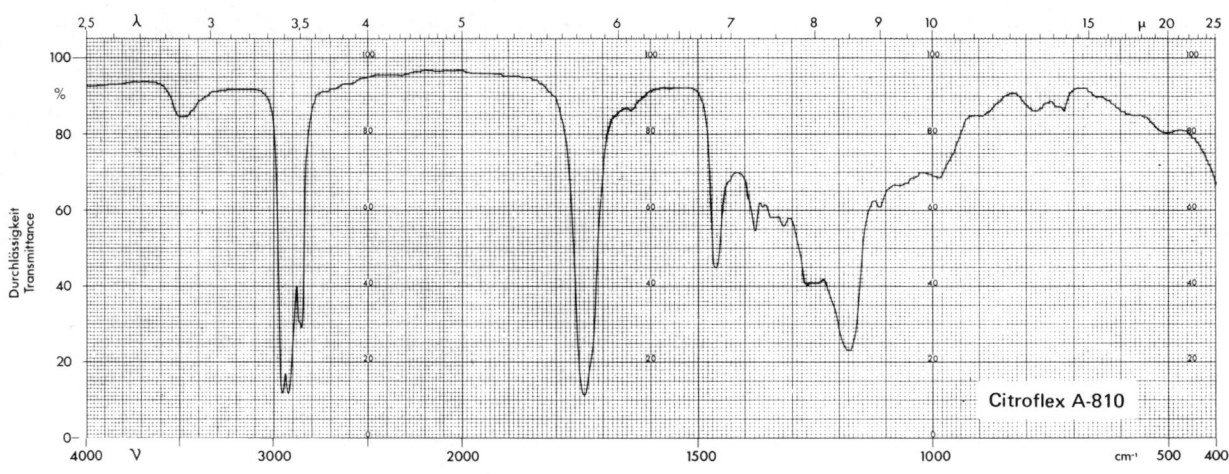

Citroflex A-810

5106

Verbindung:	Acetyltri-(n-octyl,n-decyl)-citrat			Compound:	Acetyl tri(n-octyl,n-decyl) citrate		
Formel:		M.:	~ 610	Formula:		M. w.:	~ 610
Handelsname:	Citroflex A-810	Herst.:	Pfizer	Tradename:	Citroflex A-810	Manuf.:	Pfizer
Präparation:	Kapill. Film	Dez. Nr.:	2.5.10	Preparation:	Capill. Film	Dec. No:.	2.5.10

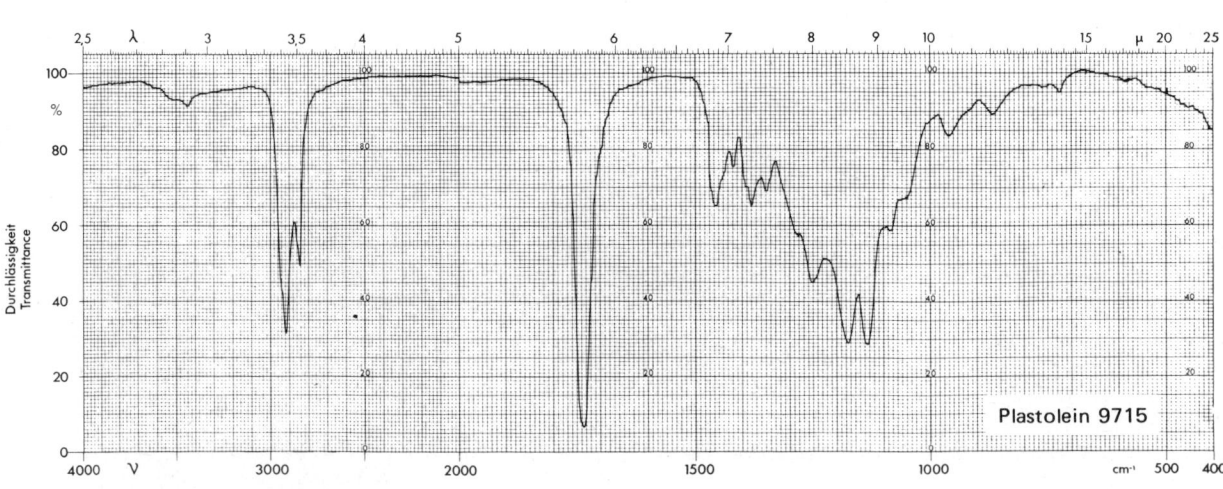

Plastolein 9715

5107

Verbindung:	Adipinsäurepolyester			Compound:	Adipic acid polyester		
Formel:		M.:	~ 1000	Formula:		M. w.:	~ 1000
Handelsname:	Plastolein 9715	Herst.:	Emery	Tradename:	Plastolein 9715	Manuf.:	Emery
Präparation:	Kapill. Film	Dez. Nr.:	2.6.1	Preparation:	Capill. Film	Dec. No:.	2.6.1

Weichmacher
2. Aliphatische Di- und Tricarbonsäureester
2.6. Aliph. Dicarbonsäurepolyester

Plasticizers
2. Aliphatic Di- and Tricarboxylic Acid Esters
2.6. Aliphatic Dicarbon Acid Polyesters

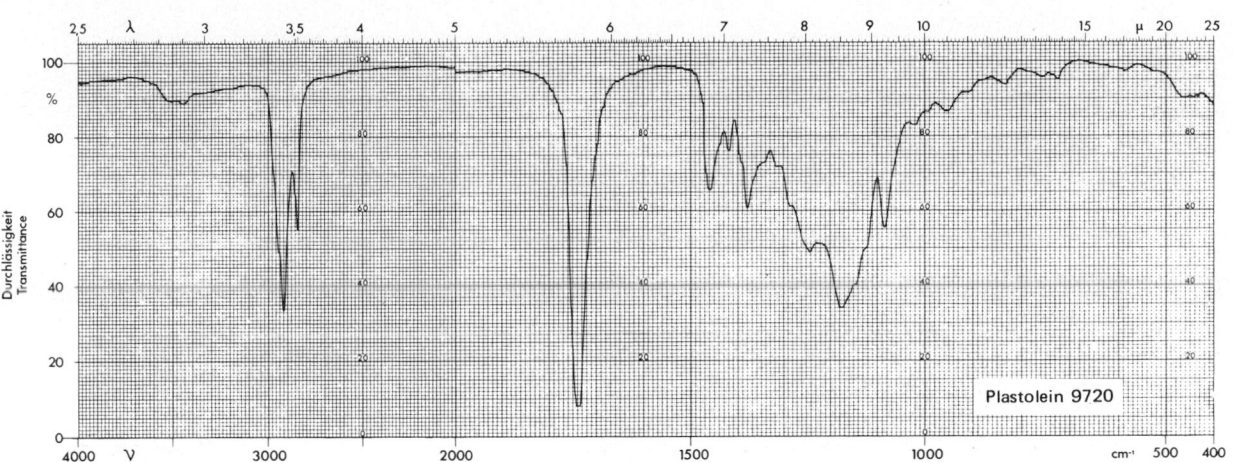

Verbindung:	Adipinsäurepolyester			Compound:	Adipic acid polyester			5108
Formel:		M.:	~ 800	Formula:		M. w.:	~ 800	
Handelsname:	Plastolein 9720	Herst.:	Emery	Tradename:	Plastolein 9720	Manuf.:	Emery	
Präparation:	Kapill. Film	Dez. Nr.:	2.6.2	Preparation:	Capill. Film	Dec. No.:	2.6.2	

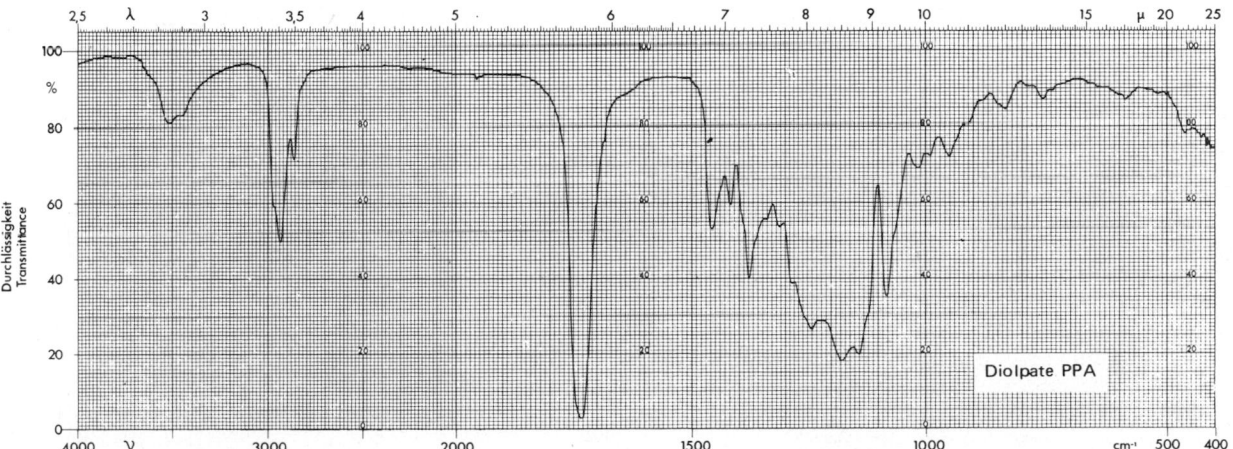

Verbindung:	Adipinsäureethylenglykolpolyester			Compound:	Adipic acid ethyleneglycol polyester			5109
Formel:		M.:	~ 1200	Formula:		M. w.:	~ 1200	
Handelsname:		Herst.:	Schuchardt	Tradename:		Manuf.:	Schuchardt	
Präparation:	Kapill. Film	Dez. Nr.:	2.6.3	Preparation:	Capill. Film	Dec. No.:	2.6.3	

Verbindung:	Adipinsäurepolyester			Compound:	Adipic acid polyester			5110
Formel:		M.:	~ 1600	Formula:		M. w.:	~ 1600	
Handelsname:	Diolpate PPA	Herst.:	Briggs	Tradename:	Diolpate PPA	Manuf.:	Briggs	
Präparation:	Kapill. Film	Dez. Nr.:	2.6.4	Preparation:	Capill. Film	Dec. No.:	2.6.4	

Weichmacher
2. Aliphatische Di- und Tricarbonsäureester
2.6. Aliph. Dicarbonsäurepolyester

Plasticizers
2. Aliphatic Di- and Tricarboxylic Acid Esters
2.6. Aliphatic Dicarbon Acid Polyesters

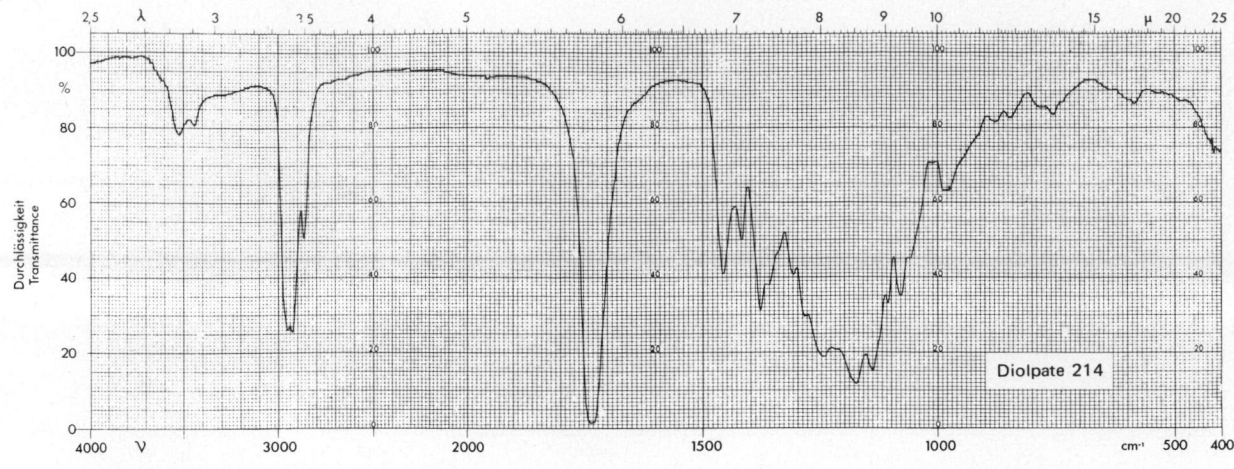

5111

Verbindung:	Adipinsäurepolyester			Compound:	Adipic acid polyester		
Formel:		M.:	~ 1150	Formula:		M. w.:	~ 1150
Handelsname:	Diolpate 214	Herst.:	Briggs	Tradename:	Diolpate 214	Manuf.:	Briggs
Präparation:	Kapill. Film	Dez. Nr.:	2.6.5	Preparation:	Capill. Film	Dec. No.:	2.6.5

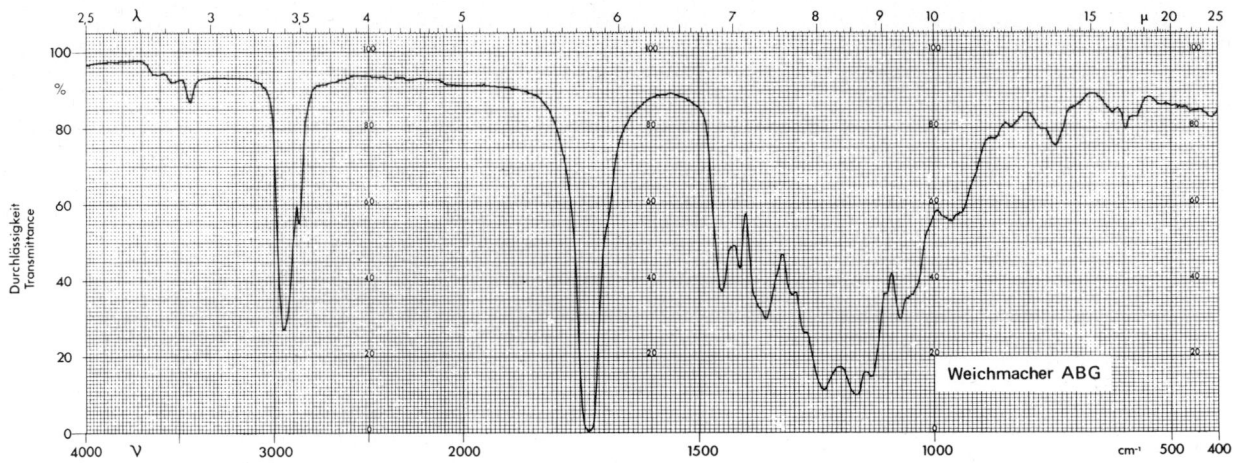

5112

Verbindung:	Adipinsäurebutylenglykolpolyester			Compound:	Adipic acid butyleneglycol polyester		
Formel:		M.:	~ 1700	Formula:		M. w.:	~ 1700
Handelsname:	Weichmacher ABG	Herst.:	BASF	Tradename:	Weichmacher ABG	Manuf.:	BASF
Präparation:	Kapill. Film	Dez. Nr.:	2.6.6	Preparation:	Capill. Film	Dec. No.:	2.6.6

5113

Verbindung:	Adipinsäurepolyester			Compound:	Adipic acid polyester		
Formel:		M.:	~ 1800	Formula:		M. w.:	~ 1800
Handelsname:	Ultramoll I	Herst.:	Bayer	Tradename:	Ultramoll I	Manuf.:	Bayer
Präparation:	Kapill. Film	Dez. Nr.:	2.6.7	Preparation:	Capill. Film	Dec. No.:	2.6.7

Weichmacher
2. Aliphatische Di- und Tricarbonsäureester
2.6. Aliph. Dicarbonsäurepolyester

Plasticizers
2. Aliphatic Di- and Tricarboxylic Acid Esters
2.6. Aliphatic Dicarbon Acid Polyesters

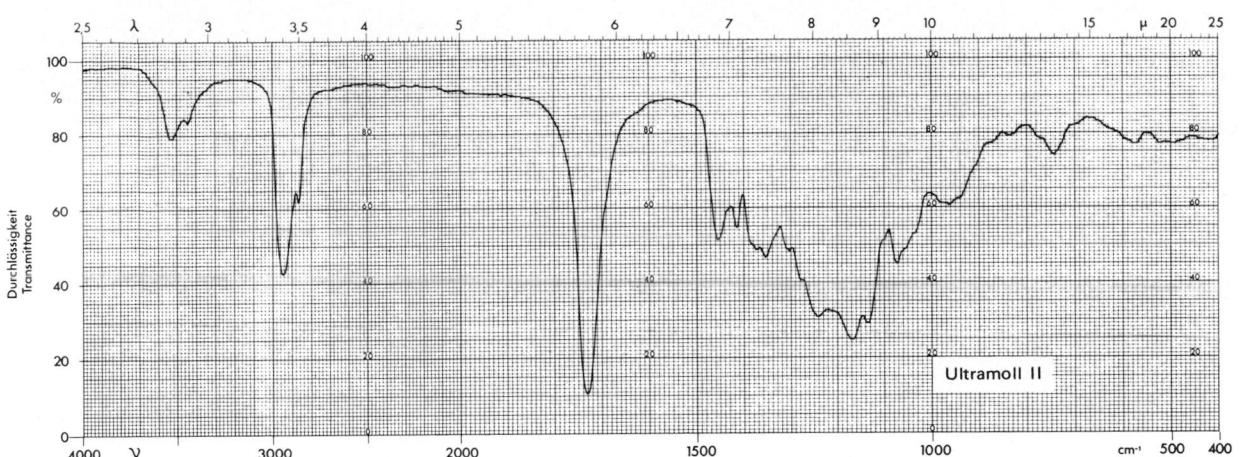

Verbindung:	Adipinsäurepolyester			Compound:	Adipic acid polyester			5114
Formel:		M.:	~ 2200	Formula:		M. w.:	~ 2200	
Handelsname:	Ultramoll II	Herst.:	Bayer	Tradename:	Ultramoll II	Manuf.:	Bayer	
Präparation:	Kapill. Film	Dez. Nr.:	2.6.8	Preparation:	Capill. Film	Dec. No.:	2.6.8	

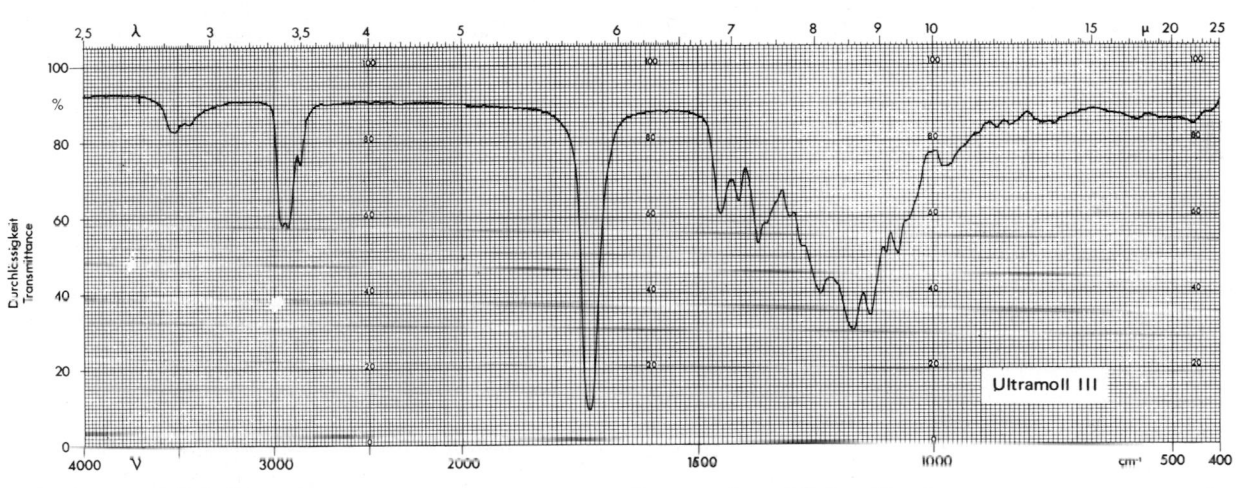

Verbindung:	Adipinsäurepolyester			Compound:	Adipic acid polyester			5115
Formel:		M.:	~ 1600	Formula:		M. w.:	~ 1600	
Handelsname:	Ultramoll III	Herst.:	Bayer	Tradename:	Ultramoll III	Manuf.:	Bayer	
Präparation:	Kapill. Film	Dez. Nr.:	2.6.9	Preparation:	Capill. Film	Dec. No.:	2.6.9	

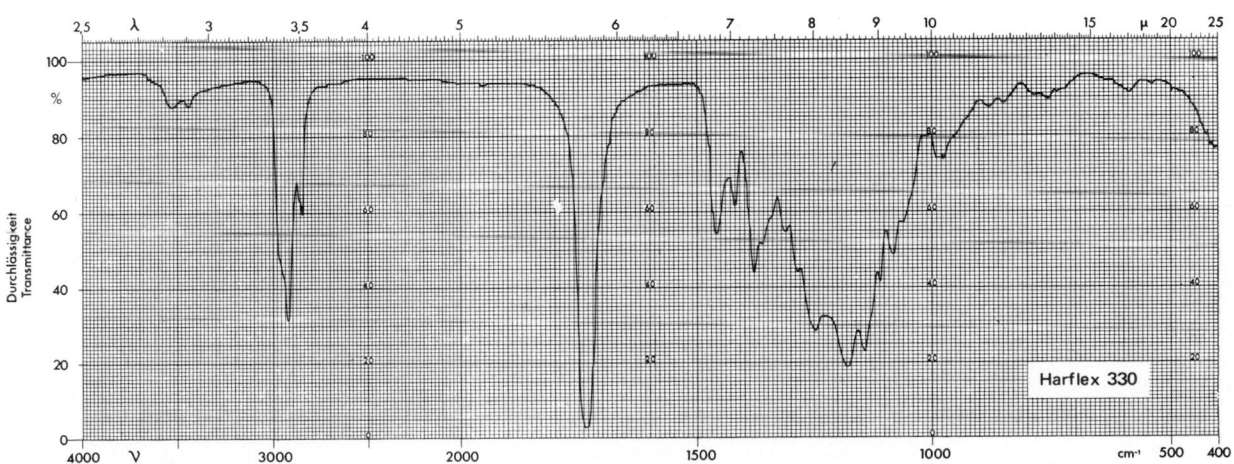

Verbindung:	Adipinsäurepolyester			Compound:	Adipic acid polyester			5116
Formel:		M.:		Formula:		M. w.:		
Handelsname:	Harflex 330	Herst.:	Harchem	Tradename:	Harflex 330	Manuf.:	Harchem	
Präparation:	Kapill. Film	Dez. Nr.:	2.6.10	Preparation:	Capill. Film	Dec. No.:	2.6.10	

Weichmacher
2. Aliphatische Di- und Tricarbonsäureester
2.6. Aliph. Dicarbonsäurepolyester

Plasticizers
2. Aliphatic Di- and Tricarboxylic Acid Esters
2.6. Aliphatic Dicarbon Acid Polyesters

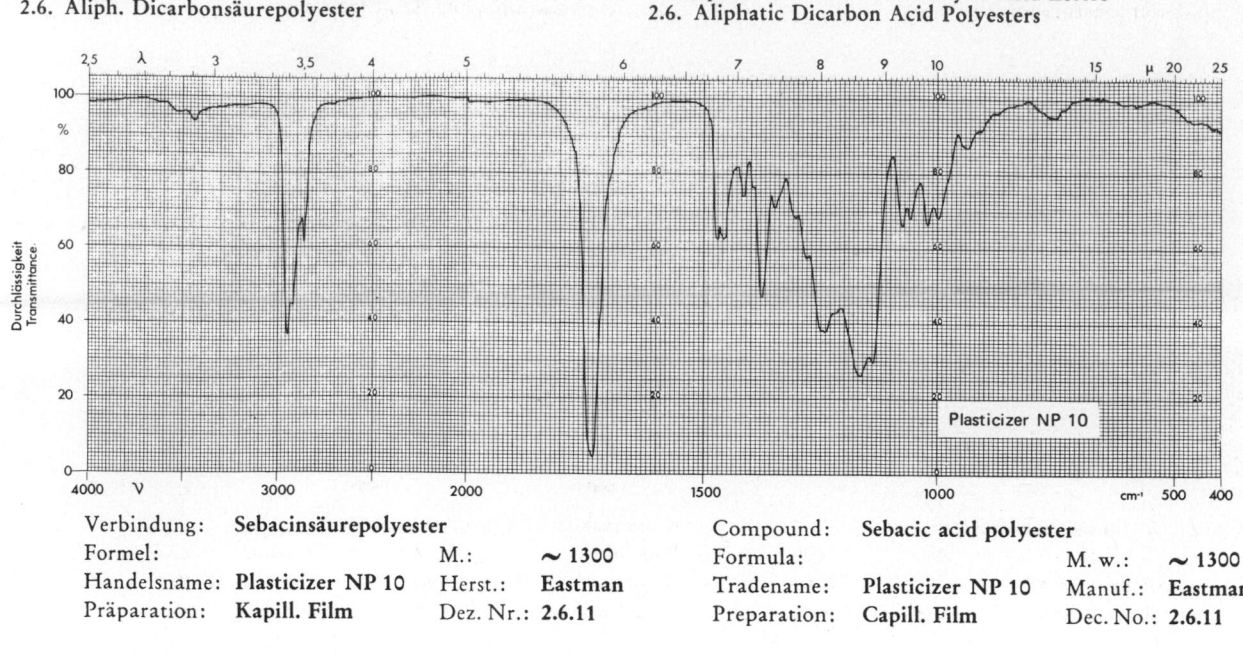

Plasticizer NP 10

5117	Verbindung:	Sebacinsäurepolyester			Compound:	Sebacic acid polyester		
	Formel:		M.:	~ 1300	Formula:		M. w.:	~ 1300
	Handelsname:	Plasticizer NP 10	Herst.:	Eastman	Tradename:	Plasticizer NP 10	Manuf.:	Eastman
	Präparation:	Kapill. Film	Dez. Nr.:	2.6.11	Preparation:	Capill. Film	Dec. No.:	2.6.11

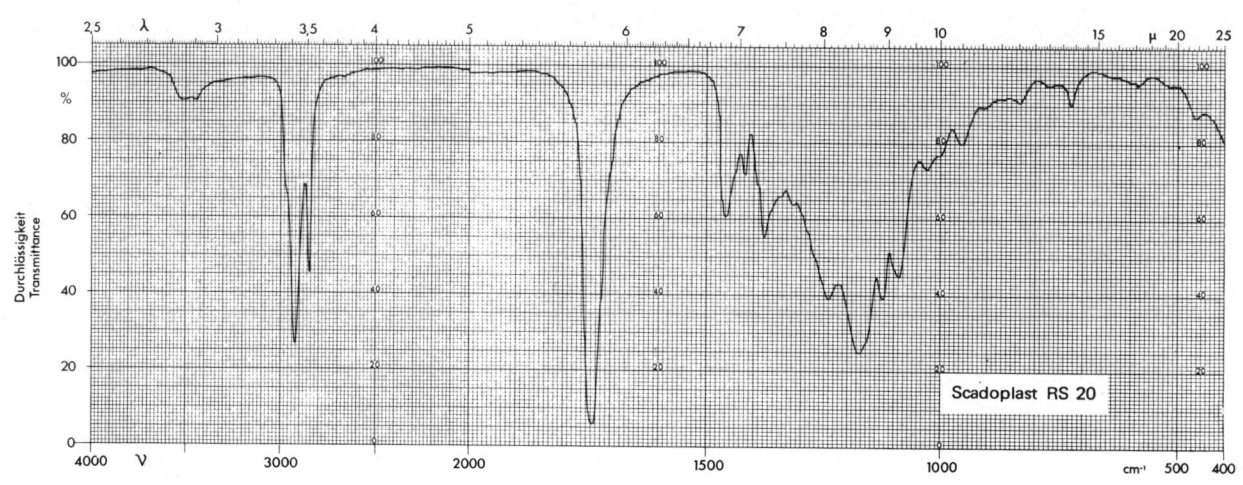

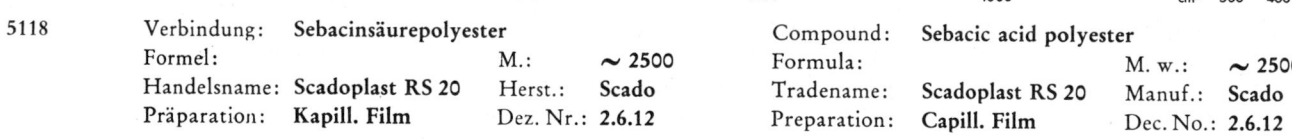

Scadoplast RS 20

5118	Verbindung:	Sebacinsäurepolyester			Compound:	Sebacic acid polyester		
	Formel:		M.:	~ 2500	Formula:		M. w.:	~ 2500
	Handelsname:	Scadoplast RS 20	Herst.:	Scado	Tradename:	Scadoplast RS 20	Manuf.:	Scado
	Präparation:	Kapill. Film	Dez. Nr.:	2.6.12	Preparation:	Capill. Film	Dec. No.:	2.6.12

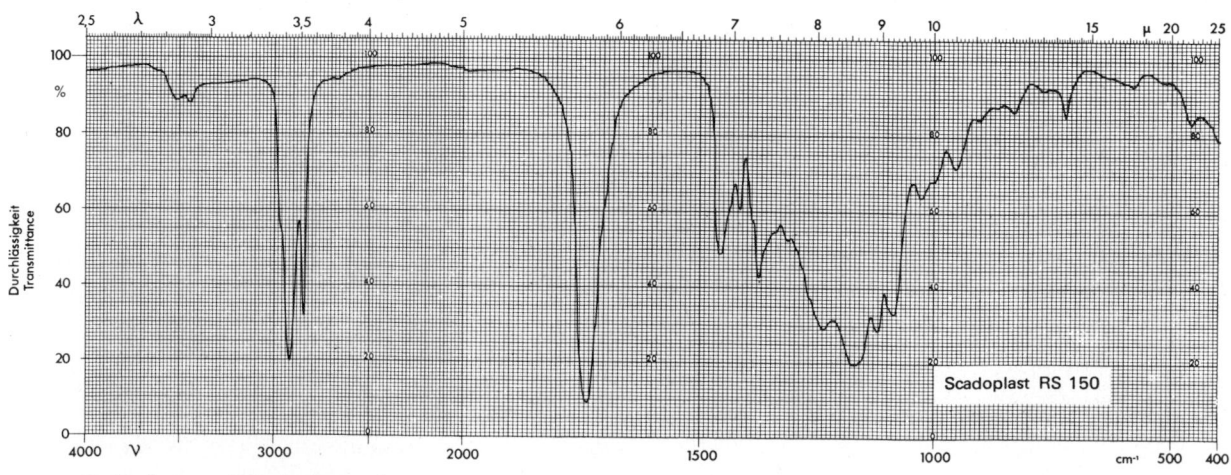

Scadoplast RS 150

5119	Verbindung:	Sebacinsäurepolyester			Compound:	Sebacic acid polyester		
	Formel:		M.:	~ 2650	Formula:		M. w.:	~ 2650
	Handelsname:	Scadoplast RS 150	Herst.:	Scado	Tradename:	Scadoplast RS 150	Manuf.:	Scado
	Präparation:	Kapill. Film	Dez. Nr.:	2.6.13	Preparation:	Capill. Film	Dec. No.:	2.6.13

Weichmacher
3. Aliphat. Monocarbonsäureester
3.1. C$_2$ ... C$_4$-Carbonsäureester

Plasticizers
3. Aliphatic Monocarboxylic Acid Esters
3.1. C$_2$ ... C$_4$-Carboxylic Acid Esters

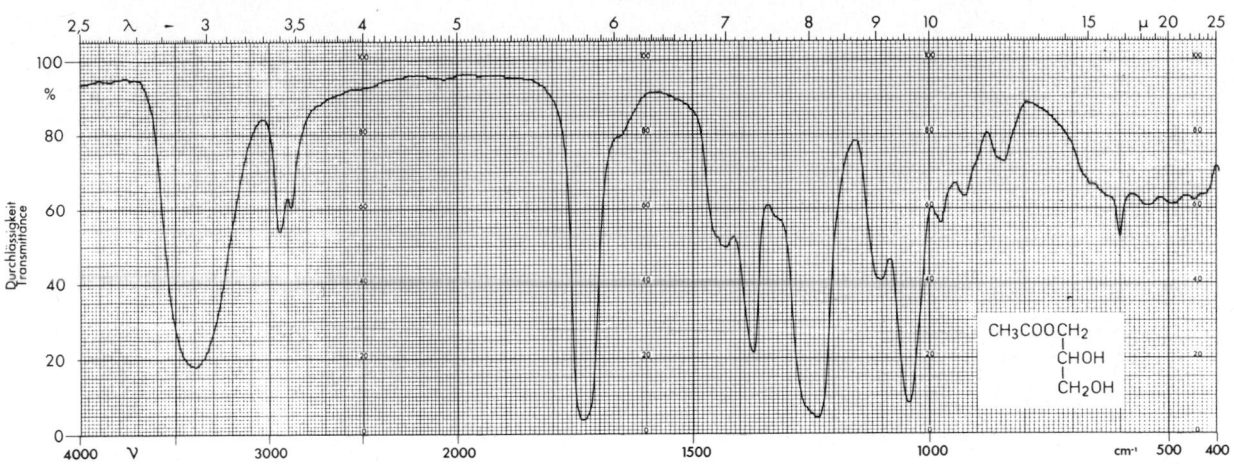

Verbindung:	Glycerinmonoacetat			Compound:	Glycerol monoacetate		5120
Formel:	C$_5$H$_{10}$O$_4$	M.:	134,1	Formula:	C$_5$H$_{10}$O$_4$	M. w.: 134,1	
Handelsname:	Acetin	Herst.:	Bayer	Tradename:	Acetin	Manuf.: Bayer	
Präparation:	Kapill. Film	Dez. Nr.:	3.1.1	Preparation:	Capill. Film	Dec. No:. 3.1.1	

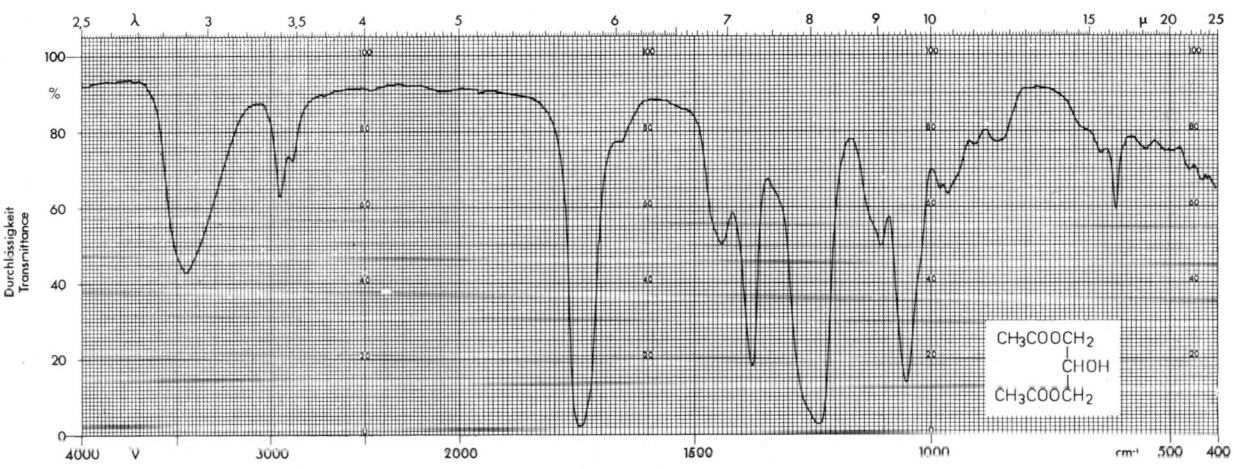

Verbindung:	Glycerindiacetat			Compound:	Glycerol diacetate		5121
Formel:	C$_7$H$_{12}$O$_5$	M.:	176,2	Formula:	C$_7$H$_{12}$O$_5$	M. w.: 176,2	
Handelsname:	Diacetin	Herst.:	Bayer	Tradename:	Diacetin	Manuf.: Bayer	
Präparation:	Kapill. Film	Dez. Nr.:	3.1.2	Preparation:	Capill. Film	Dec. No.: 3.1.2	

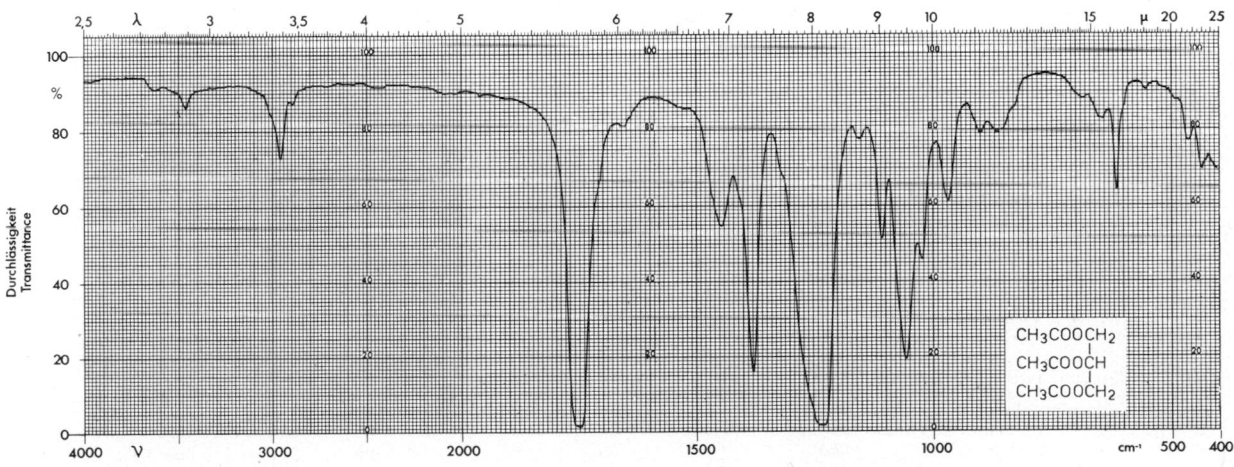

Verbindung:	Glycerintriacetat			Compound:	Glycerol triacetate		5122
Formel:	C$_9$H$_{14}$O$_6$	M.:	218,2	Formula:	C$_9$H$_{14}$O$_6$	M. w.: 218,2	
Handelsname:	Triacetin	Herst.:	Bayer	Tradename:	Triacetin	Manuf.: Bayer	
Präparation	Kapill. Film	Dez. Nr.:	3.1.3	Preparation:	Capill. Film	Dec. No:. 3.1.3	

Weichmacher
3. Aliphat. Monocarbonsäureester
3.1. C₂ ... C₄-Carbonsäureester

Plasticizers
3. Aliphatic Monocarboxylic Acid Esters
3.1. C₂ ... C₄-Carboxylic Acid Esters

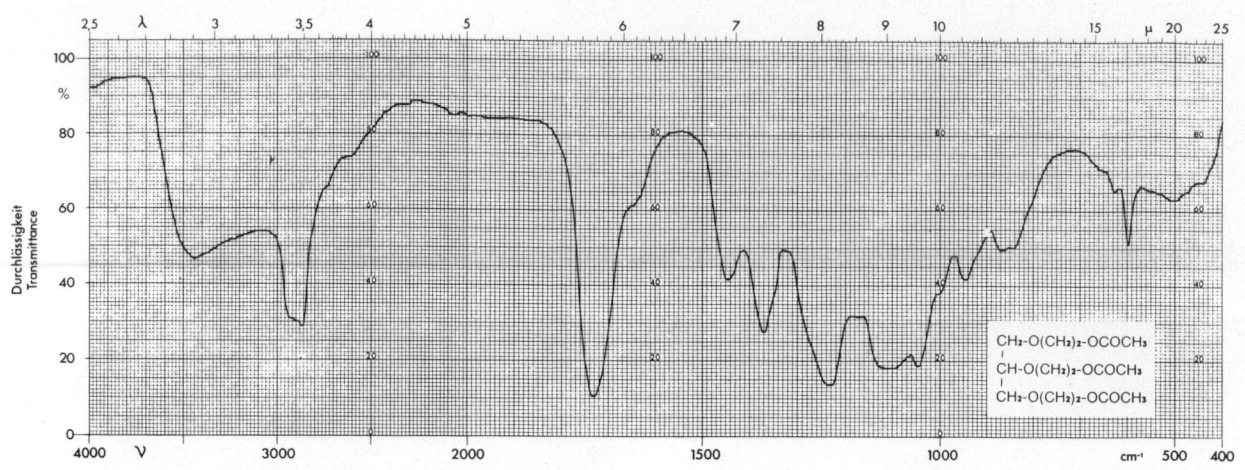

5123

	Verbindung:	Glycerintri-ethylenglykolacetatether			Compound:	Glycerol tri(ethyleneglycolacetate) ether
	Formel:	$C_{15}H_{26}O_9$	M.: 340,4		Formula:	$C_{15}H_{26}O_9$ M. w.: 340,4
	Handelsname:	Weichmacher 90	Herst.: BASF		Tradename:	Weichmacher 90 Manuf.: BASF
	Präparation:	Kapill. Film	Dez. Nr.: 3.1.4		Preparation:	Capill. Film Dec. No.: 3.1.4

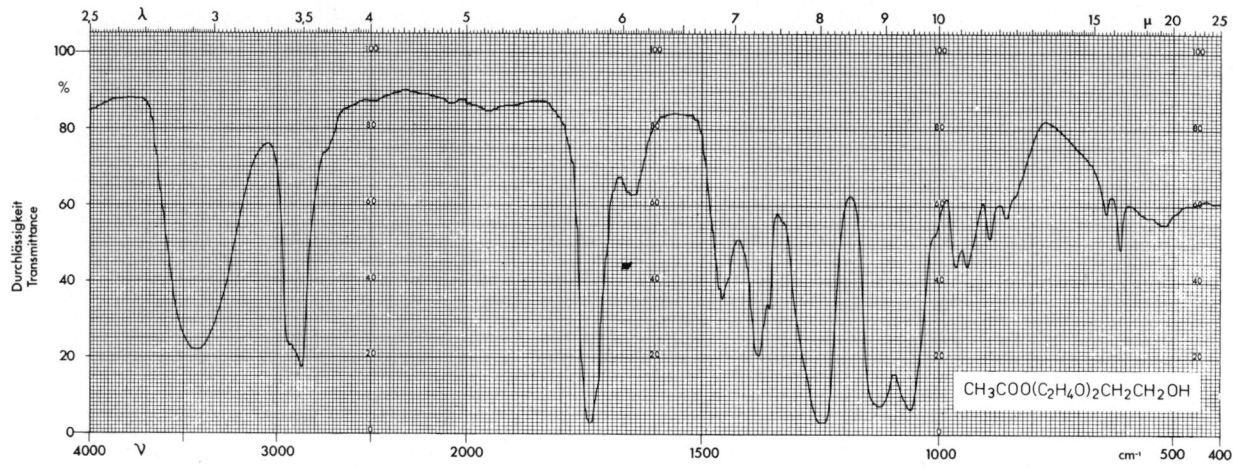

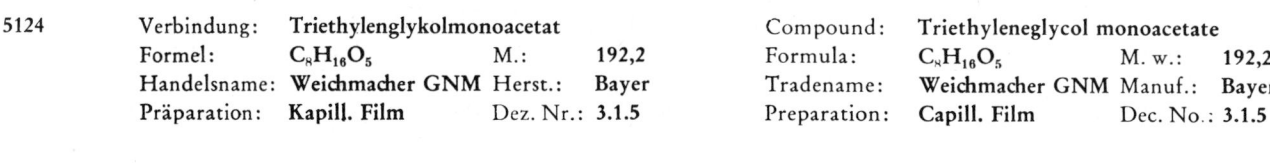

5124

	Verbindung:	Triethylenglykolmonoacetat			Compound:	Triethyleneglycol monoacetate
	Formel:	$C_8H_{16}O_5$	M.: 192,2		Formula:	$C_8H_{16}O_5$ M. w.: 192,2
	Handelsname:	Weichmacher GNM	Herst.: Bayer		Tradename:	Weichmacher GNM Manuf.: Bayer
	Präparation:	Kapill. Film	Dez. Nr.: 3.1.5		Preparation:	Capill. Film Dec. No.: 3.1.5

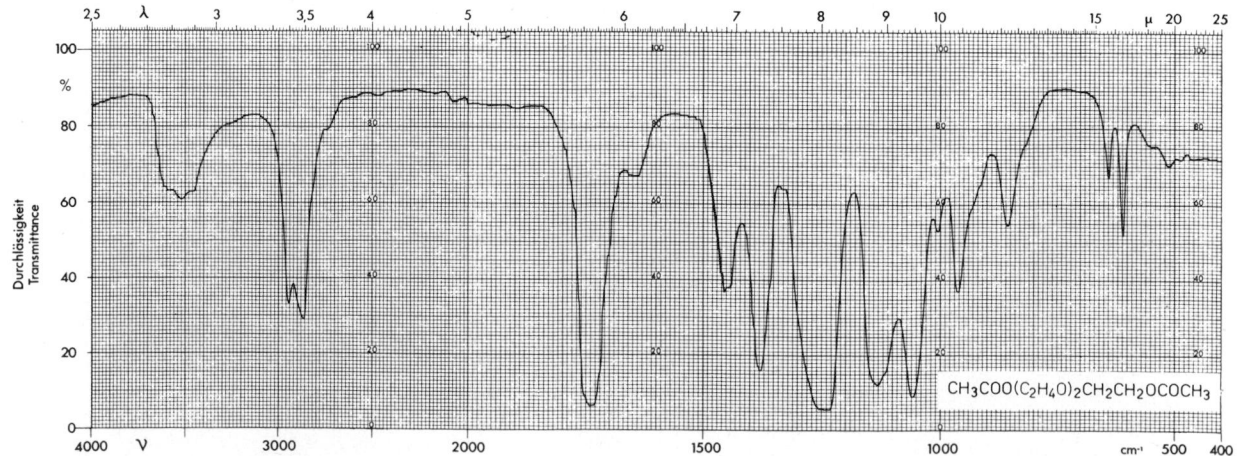

5125

	Verbindung:	Triethylenglykoldiacetat			Compound:	Triethyleneglycol diacetate
	Formel:	$C_{10}H_{18}O_6$	M.: 234,3		Formula:	$C_{10}H_{18}O_6$ M. w.: 234,3
	Handelsname:	Weichmacher GN	Herst.: Bayer		Tradename:	Weichmacher GN Manuf.: Bayer
	Präparation:	Kapill. Film	Dez. Nr.: 3.1.6		Preparation:	Capill. Film Dec. No.: 3.1.6

Weichmacher
3. Aliphat. Monocarbonsäureester
3.1. C₂ ... C₄-Carbonsäureester

Plasticizers
3. Aliphatic Monocarboxylic Acid Esters
3.1. C₂ ... C₄-Carboxylic Acid Esters

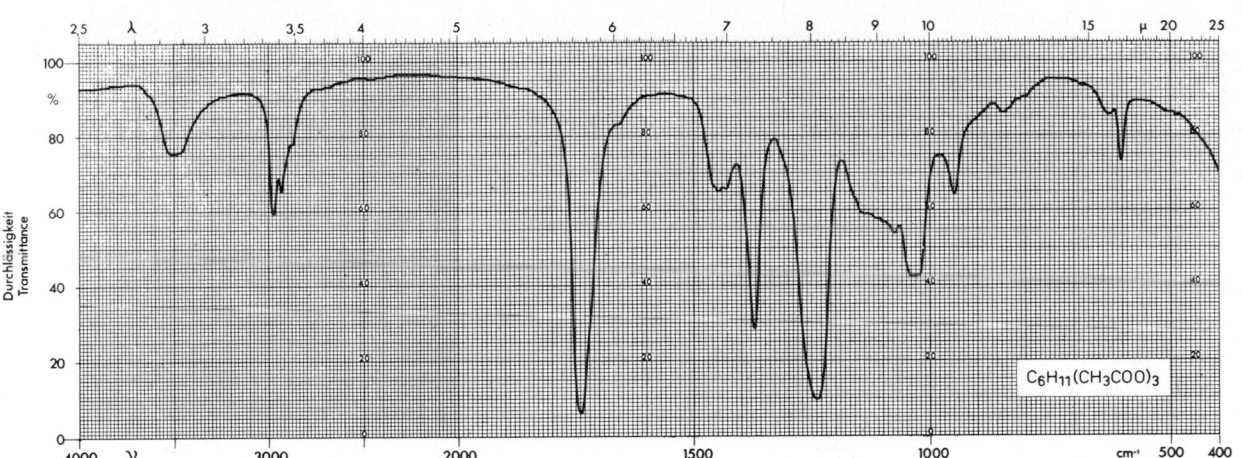

Verbindung:	**Hexantrioltriacetat**			Compound:	**Hexanetriol triacetate**			5126
Formel:	**C₁₂H₂₀O₆**	M.:	**250,3**	Formula:	**C₁₂H₂₀O₆**	M. w.:	**250,3**	
Handelsname:	**Triacetin H**	Herst.:	**Bayer**	Tradename:	**Triacetin H**	Manuf.:	**Bayer**	
Präparation:	**Kapill. Film**	Dez. Nr.:	**3.1.7**	Preparation:	**Capill. Film**	Dec. No.:	**3.1.7**	

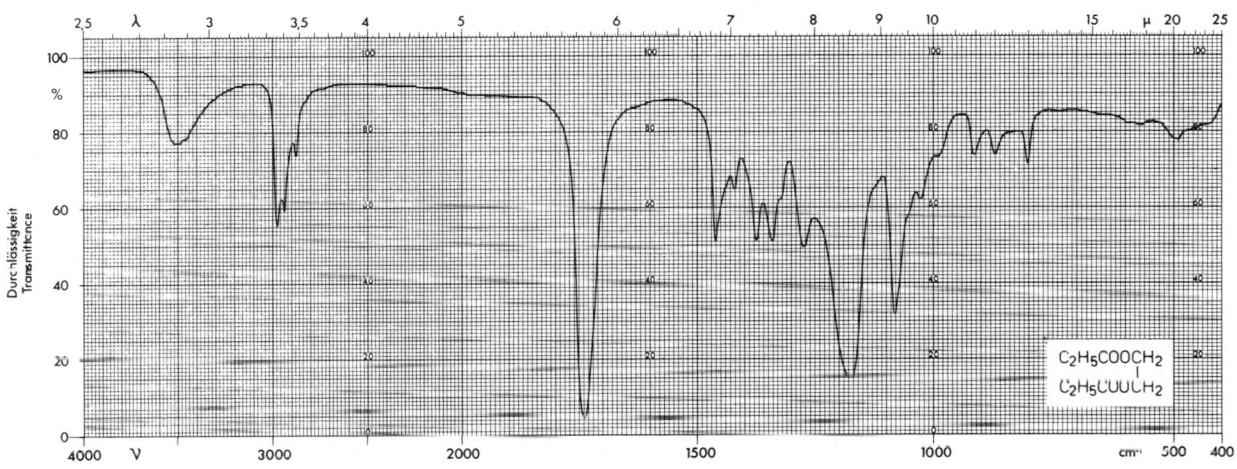

Verbindung:	**Ethylenglykoldipropionat**			Compound:	**Ethyleneglycol dipropionate**			5127
Formel:	**C₈H₁₄O₄**	M.:	**174,2**	Formula:	**C₈H₁₄O₄**	M. w.:	**174,2**	
Handelsname:		Herst.:	**Eastman**	Tradename:		Manuf.:	**Eastman**	
Präparation:	**Kapill. Film**	Dez. Nr.:	**3.1.8**	Preparation:	**Capill. Film**	Dec. No.:	**3.1.8**	

Verbindung:	**Diethylenglykoldipropionat**			Compound:	**Diethyleneglycol dipropionate**			5128
Formel:	**C₁₀H₁₈O₅**	M.:	**218,3**	Formula:	**C₁₀H₁₈O₅**	M. w.:	**218,3**	
Handelsname:		Herst.:	**Eastman**	Tradename:		Manuf.:	**Eastman**	
Präparation:	**Kapill. Film**	Dez. Nr.:	**3.1.9**	Preparation:	**Capill. Film**	Dec. No.:	**3.1.9**	

Weichmacher
3. Aliphat. Monocarbonsäureester
3.1. C₂ ... C₄-Carbonsäureester

Plasticizers
3. Aliphatic Monocarboxylic Acid Esters
3.1. C₂ ... C₄-Carboxylic Acid Esters

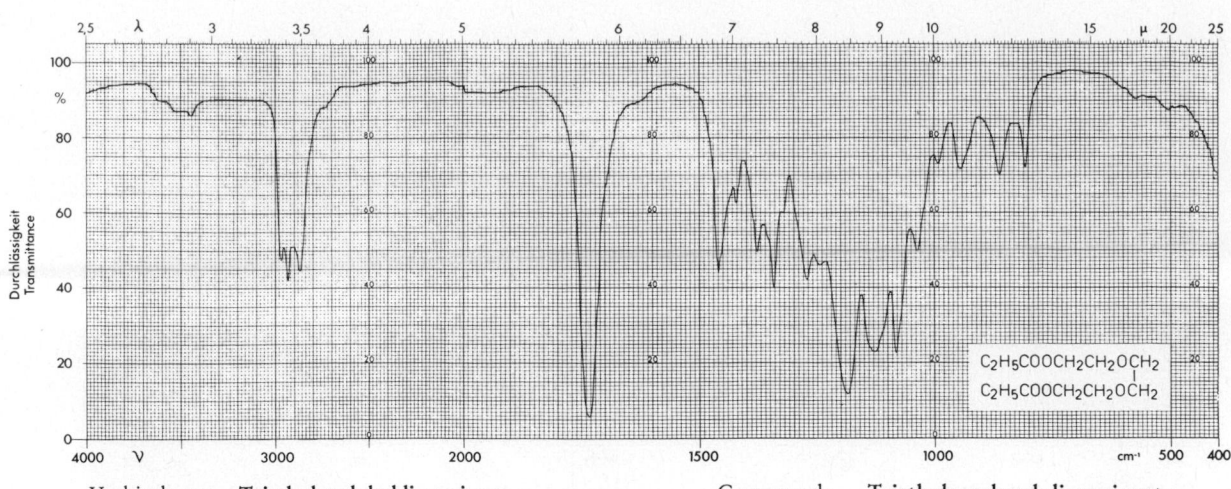

5129

Verbindung:	Triethylenglykoldipropionat			Compound:	Triethyleneglycol dipropionate		
Formel:	$C_{12}H_{22}O_6$	M.:	262,3	Formula:	$C_{12}H_{22}O_6$	M. w.:	262,3
Handelsname:		Herst.:	Eastman	Tradename:		Manuf.:	Eastman
Präparation:	Kapill. Film	Dez. Nr.:	3.1.10	Preparation:	Capill. Film	Dec. No.:	3.1.10

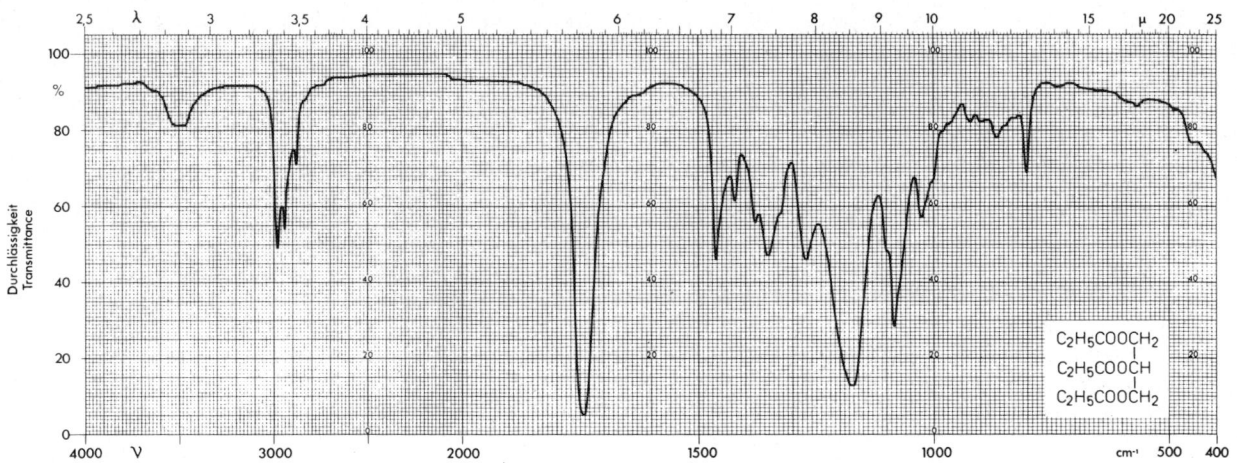

5130

Verbindung:	Glycerintripropionat			Compound:	Glycerol tripropionate		
Formel:	$C_{12}H_{20}O_6$	M.:	260,3	Formula:	$C_{12}H_{20}O_6$	M. w.:	260,3
Handelsname:	Tripropionin	Herst.:	Eastman	Tradename:	Tripropionin	Manuf.:	Eastman
Präparation:	Kapill. Film	Dez. Nr.:	3.1.11	Preparation:	Capill. Film	Dec. No.:	3.1.11

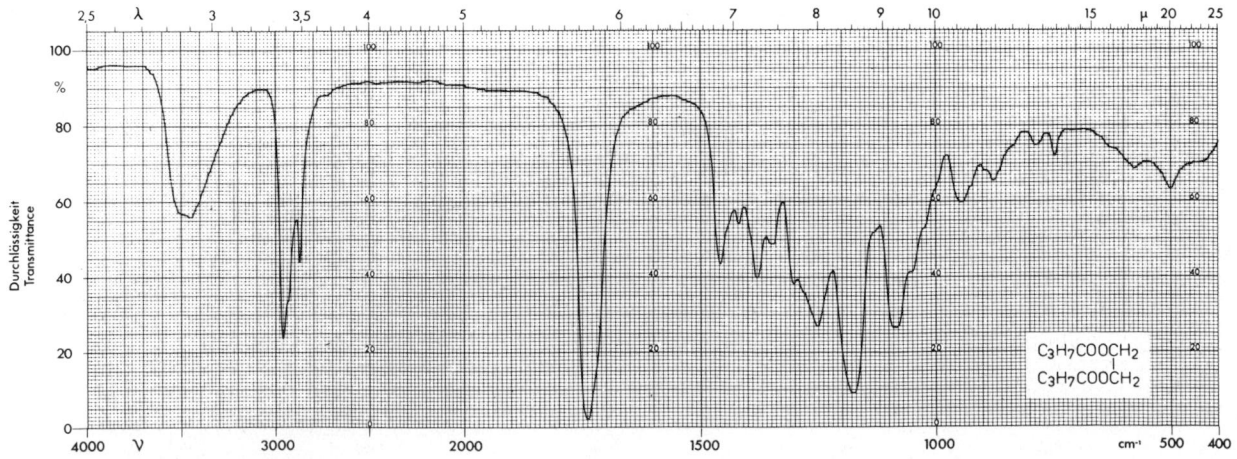

5131

Verbindung:	Ethylenglykoldibutyrat			Compound:	Ethylene glycol dibutyrate		
Formel:	$C_{10}H_{18}O_4$	M.:	202,2	Formula:	$C_{10}H_{18}O_4$	M. w.:	202,2
Handelsname:		Herst.:	Eastman	Tradename:		Manuf.:	Eastman
Präparation:	Kapill. Film	Dez. Nr.:	3.1.12	Preparation:	Capill. Film	Dec. No.:	3.1.12

Weichmacher
3. Aliphat. Monocarbonsäureester
3.1. C₂ ... C₄-Carbonsäureester

Plasticizers
3. Aliphatic Monocarboxylic Acid Esters
3.1. C₂ ... C₄-Carboxylic Acid Esters

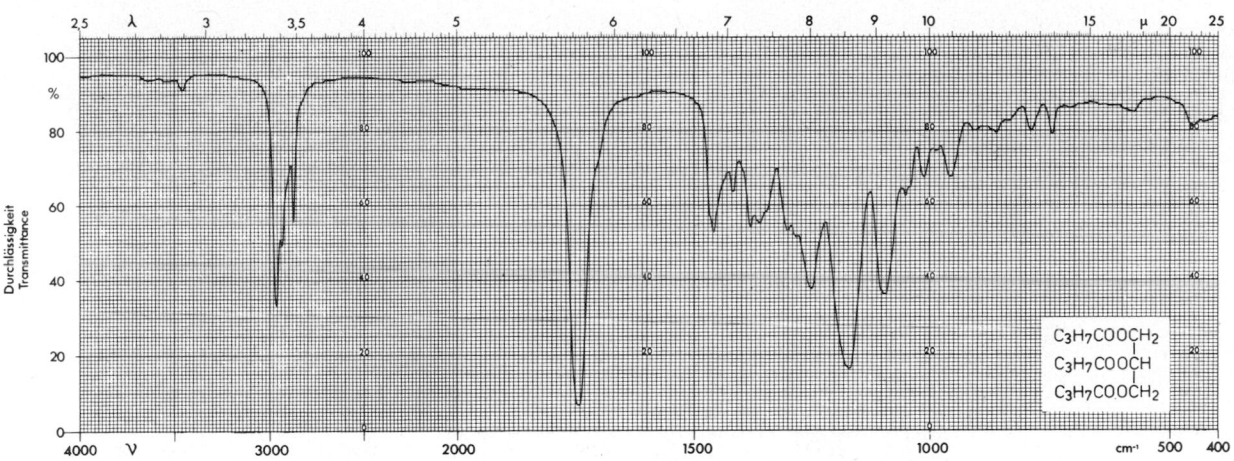

Verbindung:	Glycerintributyrat		Compound:	Glycerol tributyrate	5132
Formel:	$C_{15}H_{26}O_6$	M.: 302,4	Formula:	M. w.: $C_{15}H_{26}O_6$ 302,4
Handelsname:	Tri-n-butyrin	Herst.: Eastman	Tradename:	Manuf.: Tri-n-butyrin Eastman
Präparation:	Kapill. Film	Dez. Nr.: 3.1.13	Preparation:	Dec. No.: Capill. Film 3.1.13

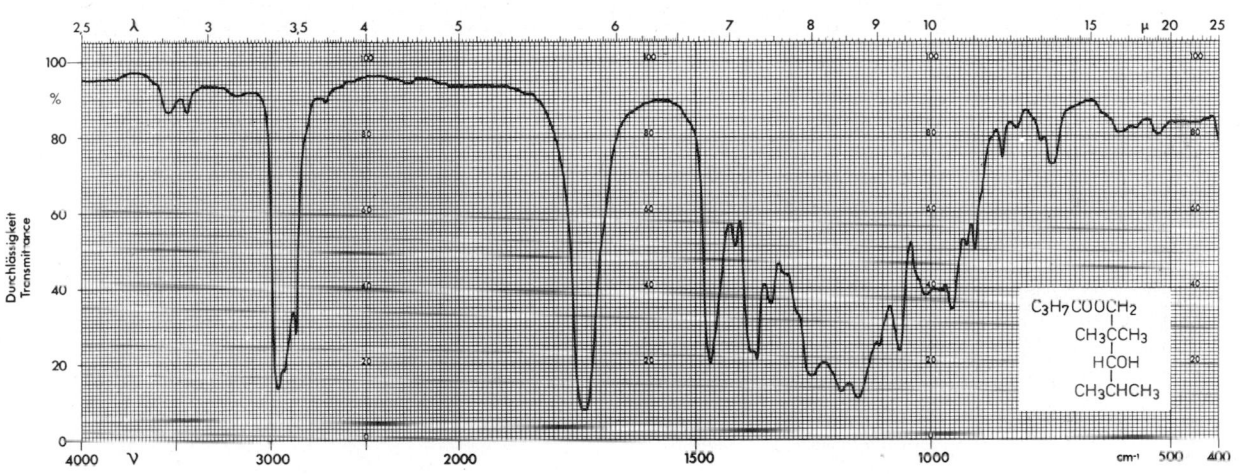

Verbindung:	2,2,4-Trimethyl-1,3-pentandiolmono- isobutyrat		Compound:	2,2,4-Trimethyl-1,3-pentandiol monoisobutyrate	5133
Formel:	$C_{12}H_{24}O_3$	M.: 216,3	Formula:	$C_{12}H_{24}O_3$ M. w.: 216,3
Handelsname:	TMPDMI	Herst.: Eastman	Tradename:	TMPDMI Manuf.: Eastman
Präparation:	Kapill. Film	Dez. Nr.: 3.1.14	Preparation:	Capill. Film Dec. No.: 3.1.14

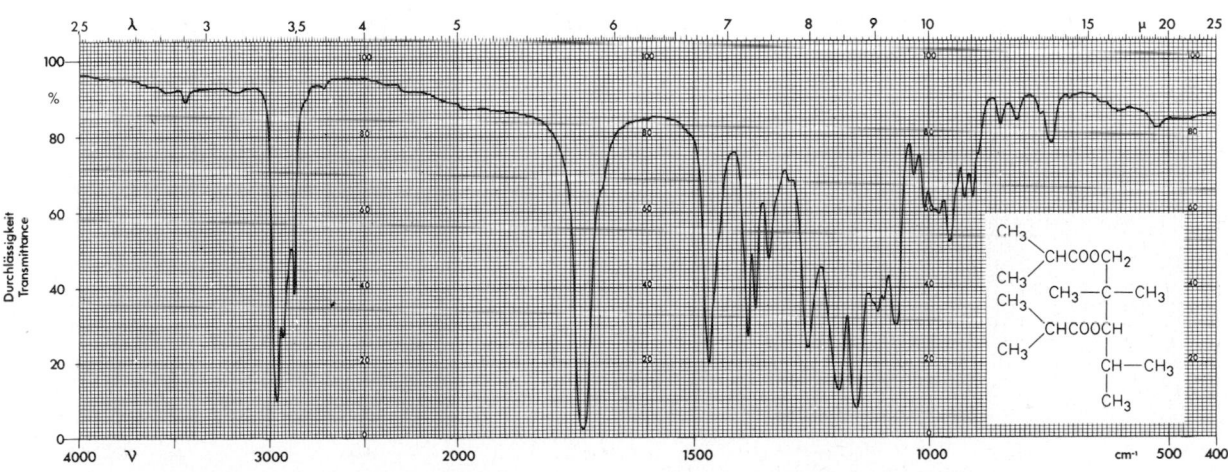

Verbindung:	2,2,4-Trimethyl-1,3-pentandioldiisobutyrat		Compound:	2,2,4-Trimethyl-1,3-pentanediol diisobutyrate	5134
Formel:	$C_{16}H_{30}O_4$	M.: 286,4	Formula:	$C_{16}H_{30}O_4$ M. w.: 286,4
Handelsname:	Texanol Isobutyrate	Herst.: Eastman	Tradename:	Texanol Isobutyrate Manuf.: Eastman
Präparation:	Kapill. Film	Dez. Nr.: 3.1.15	Preparation:	Capill. Film Dec. No.: 3.1.15

Weichmacher
3. Aliphat. Monocarbonsäureester
3.2. C$_5$ ... C$_{10}$-Carbonsäureester

Plasticizers
3. Aliphatic Monocarboxylic Acid Esters
3.2. C$_5$ ... C$_{10}$-Carboxylic Acid Esters

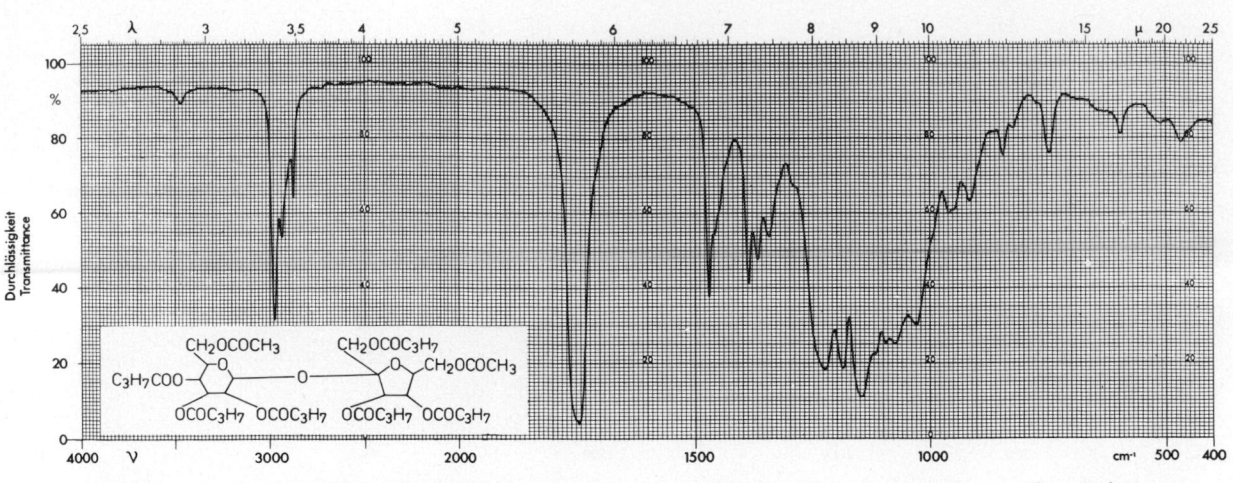

5135 | Verbindung: **Saccharosediacetathexaisobutyrat** | Compound: **Sucrose diacetate hexaisobutyrate**

Formel: **C$_{40}$H$_{62}$O$_{19}$** M.: **847**   Formula: **C$_{40}$H$_{62}$O$_{19}$** M. w.: **847**

Handelsname: **Saib 100** Herst.: **Eastman**   Tradename: **Saib 100** Manuf.: **Eastman**

Präparation: **Kapill. Film** Dez. Nr.: **3.1.16**   Preparation: **Capill. Film** Dec. No.: **3.1.16**

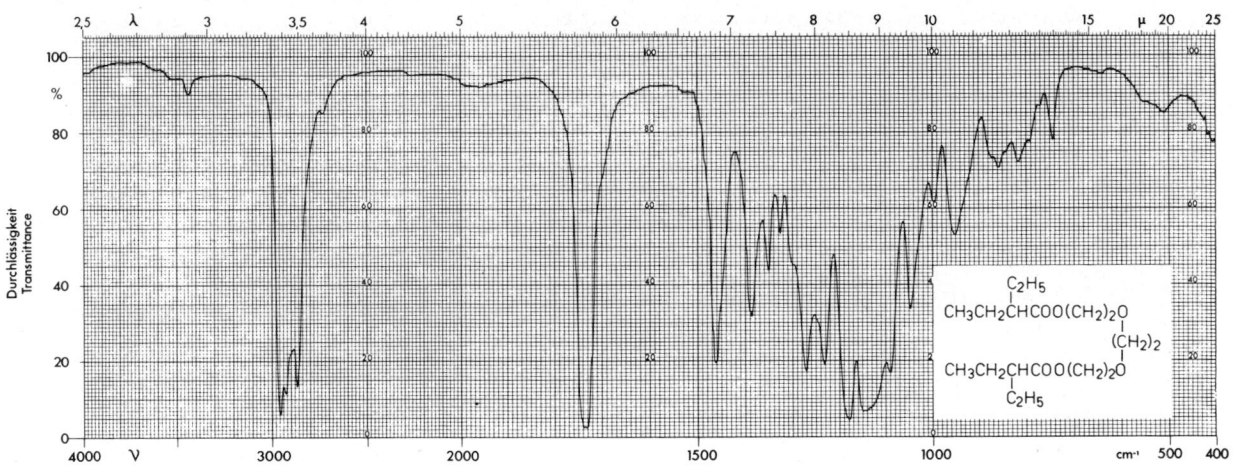

5136 | Verbindung: **Triethylenglykol-di-2-ethylbutyrat** | Compound: **Triethylene glycol-di-2-ethylhexylbutyrate**

Formel: **C$_{18}$H$_{34}$O$_6$** M.: **346,5**   Formula: **C$_{18}$H$_{34}$O$_6$** M. w.: **346,5**

Handelsname: **Flexol 36 H** Herst.: **Union Carb.**   Tradename: **Flexol 36 H** Manuf.: **Union Carb.**

Präparation: **Kapill. Film** Dez. Nr.: **3.2.1**   Preparation: **Capill. Film** Dec. No.: **3.2.1**

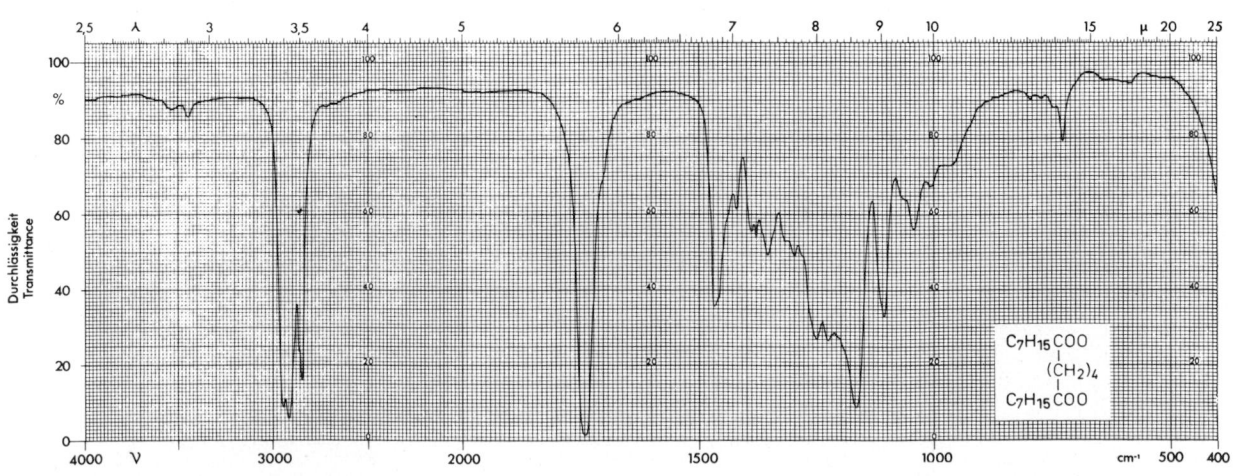

5137 | Verbindung: **Butandioldicaprylat** | Compound: **Butandiol dicaprylate**

Formel: **C$_{20}$H$_{38}$O$_4$** M.: **342,6**   Formula: **C$_{20}$H$_{38}$O$_4$** M. w.: **342,6**

Handelsname: **Rucoflex BD 8** Herst.: **Hooker**   Tradename: **Rucoflex BD 8** Manuf.: **Hooker**

Präparation: **Kapill. Film** Dez. Nr.: **3.2.2**   Preparation: **Capill. Film** Dec. No:. **3.2.2**

Weichmacher
3. Aliphat. Monocarbonsäureester
3.2. C₅ ... C₁₀-Carbonsäureester

Plasticizers
3. Aliphatic Monocarboxylic Acid Esters
3.2. C₅ ... C₁₀-Carboxylic Acid Esters

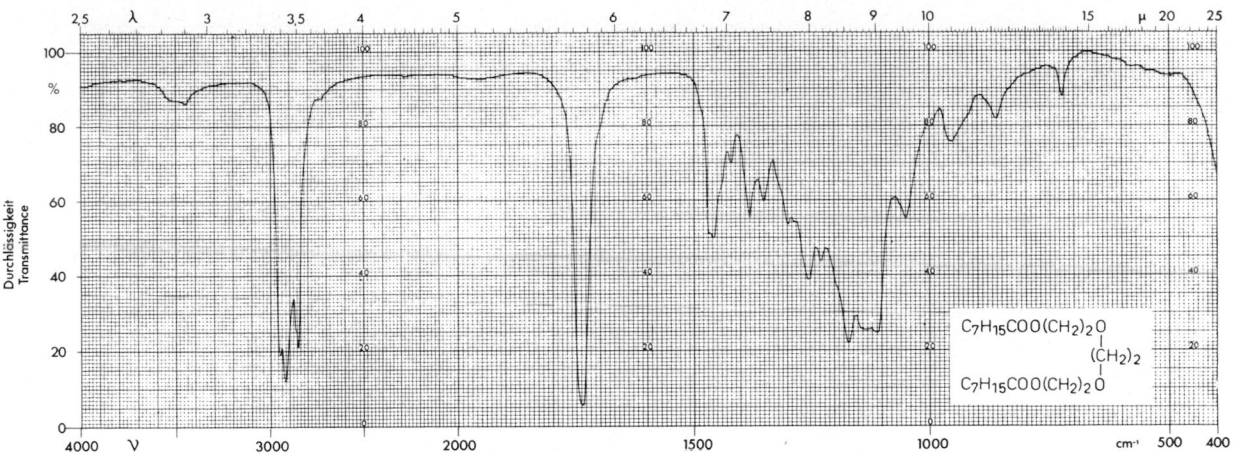

Verbindung:	Triethylenglykoldicaprylat		Compound:	Triethylene glycol dicaprylate		5138
Formel:	$C_{22}H_{42}O_6$	M.: 402,6	Formula:	$C_{22}H_{42}O_6$	M. w.: 402,6	
Handelsname:	Rucoflex TG 8	Herst.: Hooker	Tradename:	Rucoflex TG 8	Manuf.: Hooker	
Präparation:	Kapill. Film	Dez. Nr.: 3.2.3	Preparation:	Capill. Film	Dec. No.: 3.2.3	

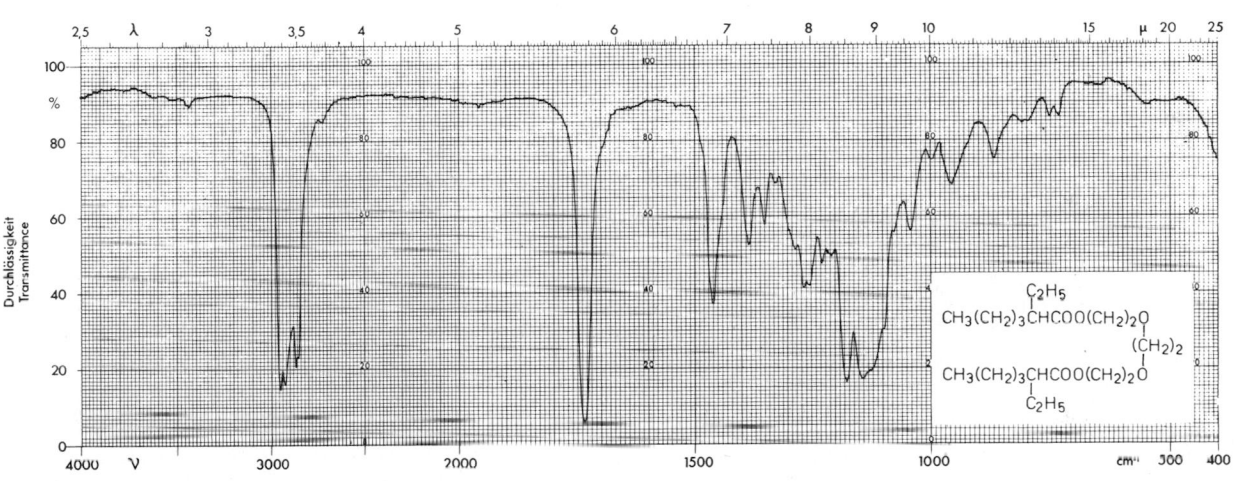

Verbindung:	Triethylenglykol-di-2-ethylhexoat		Compound:	Triethylene glycol-di-2-ethylhexoate		5139
Formel:	$C_{22}H_{42}O_6$	M.: 402,6	Formula:	$C_{22}H_{42}O_6$	M. w.: 402,6	
Handelsname:	Flexol 3 GO	Herst.: Union Carb.	Tradename:	Flexol 3 GO	Manuf.: Union Carb.	
Präparation:	Kapill. Film	Dez. Nr.: 3.2.4	Preparation:	Capill. Film	Dec. No.: 3.2.4	

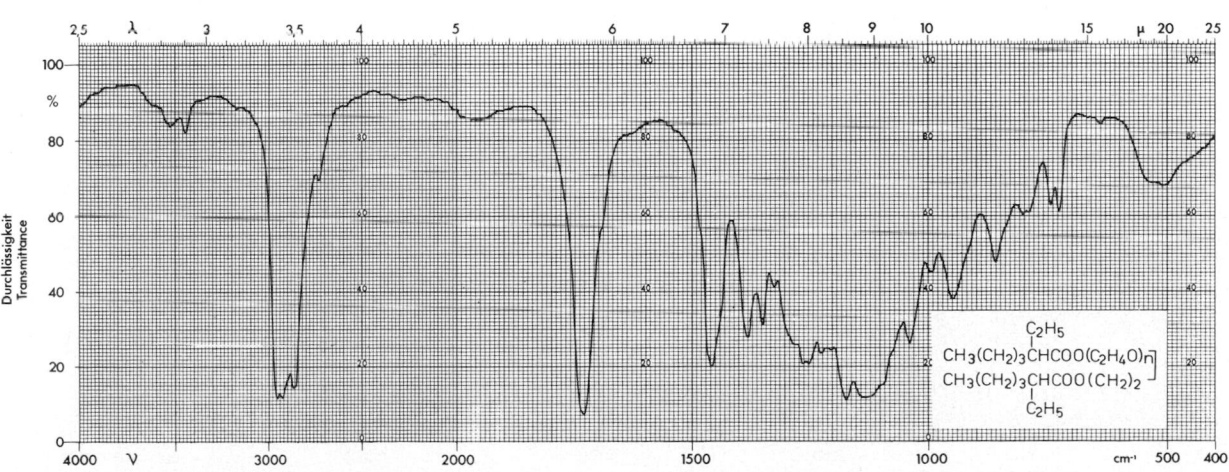

Verbindung:	Polyethylenglykol-di-2-ethylhexoat		Compound:	Polyethylene glycol-di-2-ethylhexoate		5140
Formel:		M.:	Formula:		M. w.:	
Handelsname:	Flexol 4 GO	Herst.: Union Carb.	Tradename:	Flexol 4 GO	Manuf.: Union Carb.	
Präparation:	Kapill. Film	Dez. Nr.: 3.2.5	Preparation:	Capill. Film	Dec. No.: 3.2.5	

Weichmacher
3. Aliphat. Monocarbonsäureester
3.2. C$_5$ ... C$_{10}$-Carbonsäureester

Plasticizers
3. Aliphatic Monocarboxylic Acid Esters
3.2. C$_5$ ... C$_{10}$-Carboxylic Acid Esters

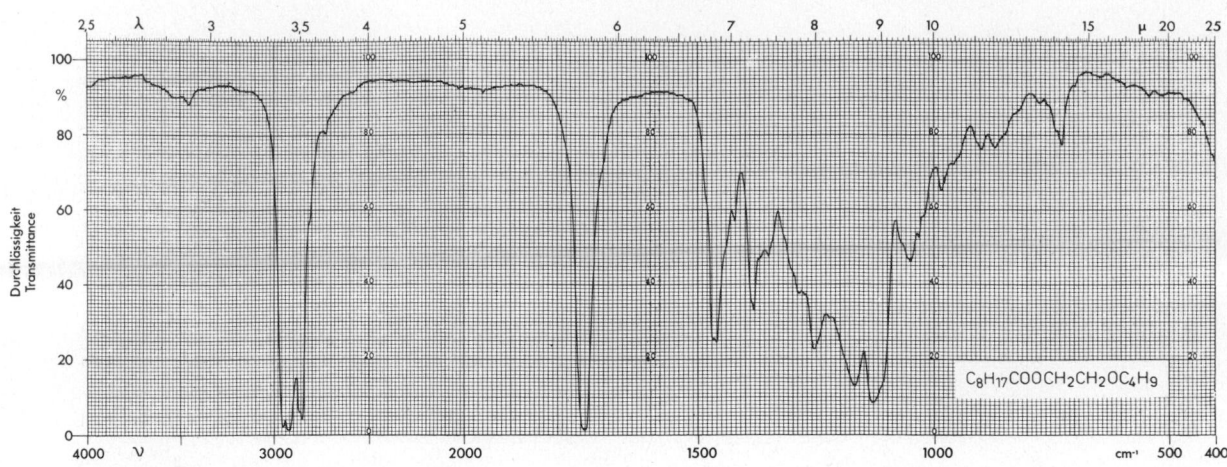

C$_8$H$_{17}$COOCH$_2$CH$_2$OC$_4$H$_9$

5141	Verbindung:	**2-Butoxyethylpelargonat**		Compound:	**2-Butoxyethyl pelargonate**	
	Formel:	**C$_{15}$H$_{30}$O$_3$**	M.: **258,6**	Formula:	**C$_{15}$H$_{30}$O$_3$**	M. w.: **258,6**
	Handelsname:	**Hallco 3425**	Herst.: **Hall**	Tradename:	**Hallco 3425**	Manuf.: **Hall**
	Präparation:	**Kapill. Film**	Dez. Nr.: **3.2.6**	Preparation:	**Capill. Film**	Dec. No.: **3.2.6**

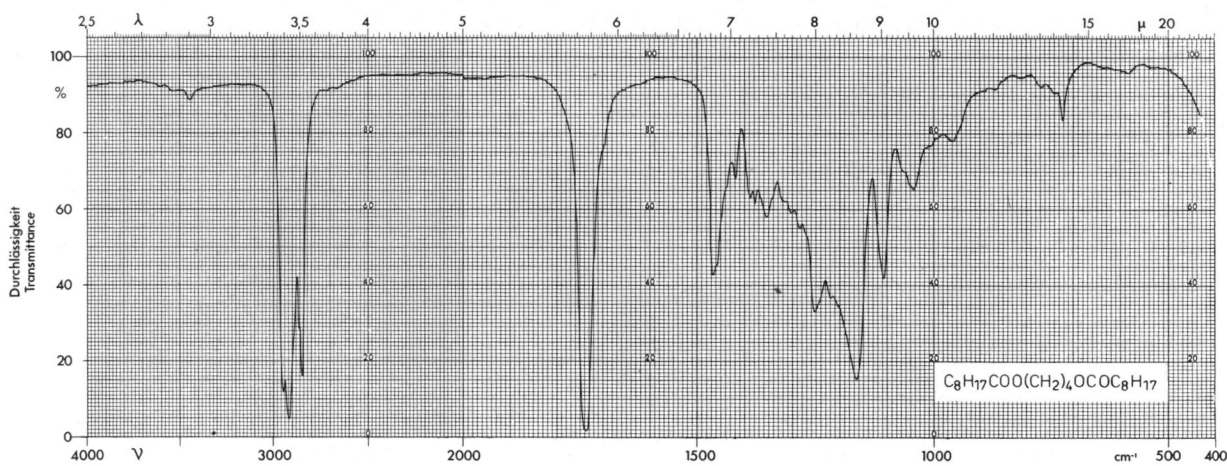

C$_8$H$_{17}$COO(CH$_2$)$_4$OCOC$_8$H$_{17}$

5142	Verbindung:	**Butandioldipelargonat**		Compound:	**Butanediol dipelargonate**	
	Formel:	**C$_{22}$H$_{42}$O$_4$**	M.: **372**	Formula:	**C$_{22}$H$_{42}$O$_4$**	M. w.: **372**
	Handelsname:	**Rucoflex BD-9**	Herst.: **Hooker**	Tradename:	**Rucoflex BD-9**	Manuf.: **Hooker**
	Präparation:	**Kapill. Film**	Dez. Nr.: **3.2.7**	Preparation:	**Capill. Film**	Dec. No:. **3.2.7**

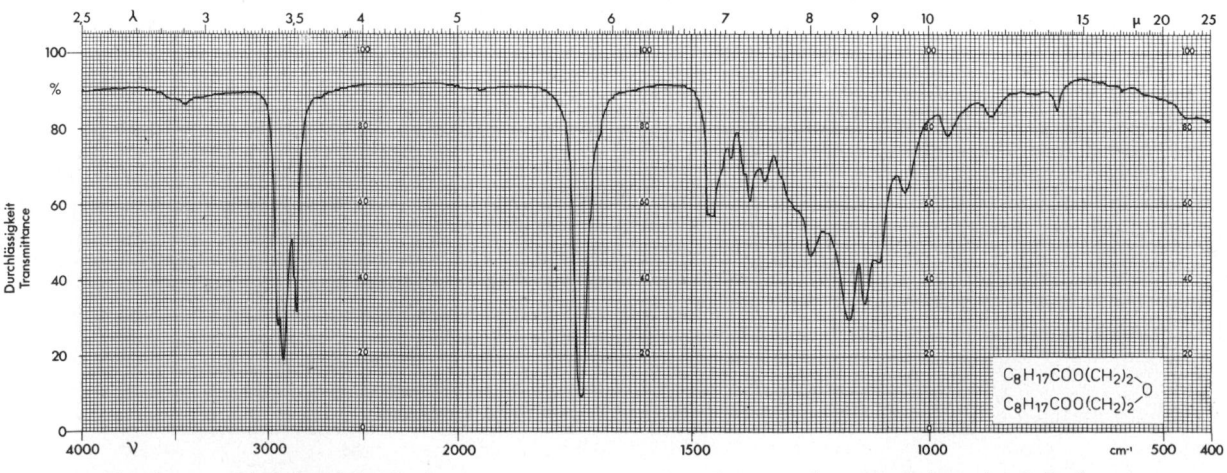

C$_8$H$_{17}$COO(CH$_2$)$_2$
C$_8$H$_{17}$COO(CH$_2$)$_2$ O

5143	Verbindung:	**Diethylenglykoldipelargonat**		Compound:	**Diethylene glycol dipelargonate**	
	Formel:	**C$_{22}$H$_{42}$O$_5$**	M.: **386,6**	Formula:	**C$_{22}$H$_{42}$O$_5$**	M. w.: **386,6**
	Handelsname:	**Plastolein 9055 DPG**	Herst.: **Emery**	Tradename:	**Plastolein 9055 DPG**	Manuf.: **Emery**
	Präparation:	**Kapill. Film**	Dez. Nr.: **3.2.8**	Preparation:	**Capill. Film**	Dec. No.: **3.2.8**

Weichmacher
3. Aliphat. Monocarbonsäureester
3.3. Laurin-, Myristin-, Palmitinsäureester

Plasticizers
3. Aliphatic Monocarboxylic Acid Esters
3.3. Lauric-, Myristic-, Palmitic-Acid Esters

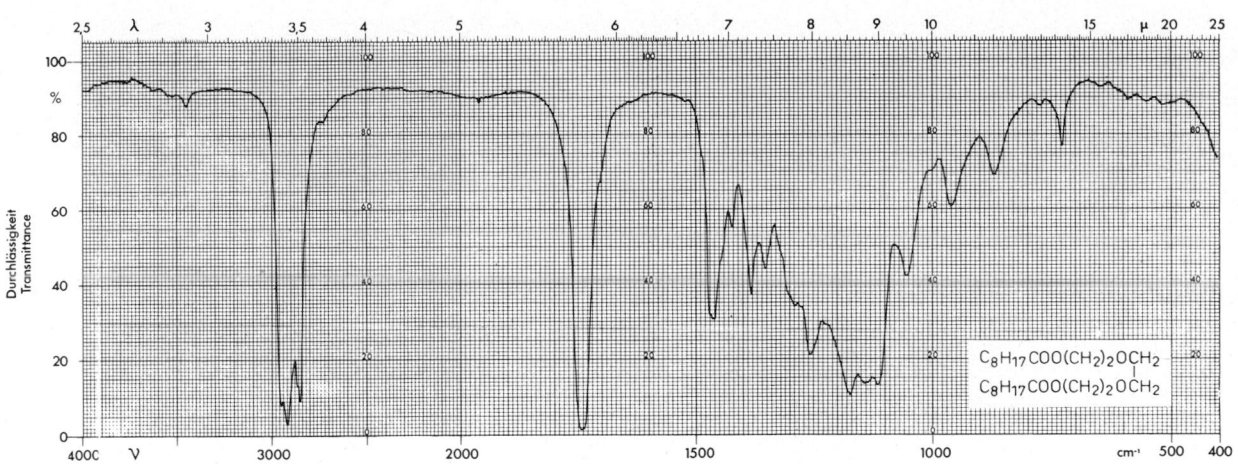

Verbindung:	**Triethylenglykoldipelargonate**		Compound:	**Triethylene glycol dipelargonate**		**5144**
Formel:	$C_{24}H_{46}O_6$	M.: **430,4**	Formula:	$C_{24}H_{46}O_6$	M. w.: **430,4**	
Handelsname:	**Plastolein 9404 TGP** Herst.:	**Emery**	Tradename:	**Plastolein 9404 TGP** Manuf.:	**Emery**	
Präparation:	**Kapill. Film**	Dez. Nr.: **3.2.9**	Preparation:	**Capill. Film**	Dec. No.: **3.2.9**	

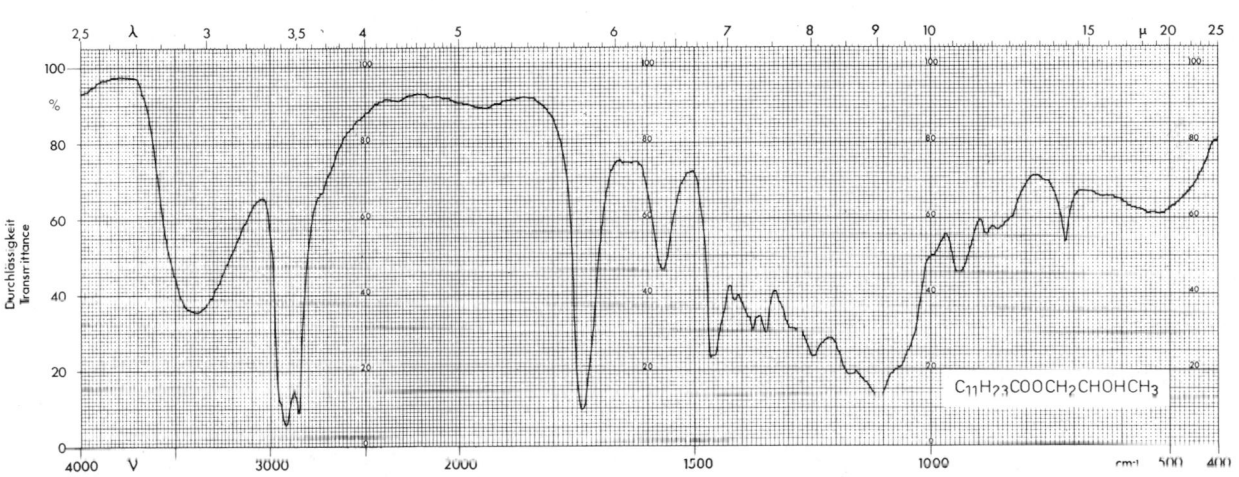

Verbindung:	**1,2-Propylenglykolmonolaurat**		Compound:	**1,2-Propylene glycol monolaurate**		**5145**
Formel:	$C_{15}H_{30}O_3$	M.: **258,6**	Formula:	$C_{15}H_{30}O_3$	M. w.: **258,6**	
Handelsname:	**Nopco 1325 L**	Herst.: **Nopco**	Tradename:	**Nopco 1325 L**	Manuf.: **Nopco**	
Präparation:	**Kapill. Film**	Dez. Nr.: **3.3.1**	Preparation:	**Capill. Film**	Dec. No.: **3.3.1**	

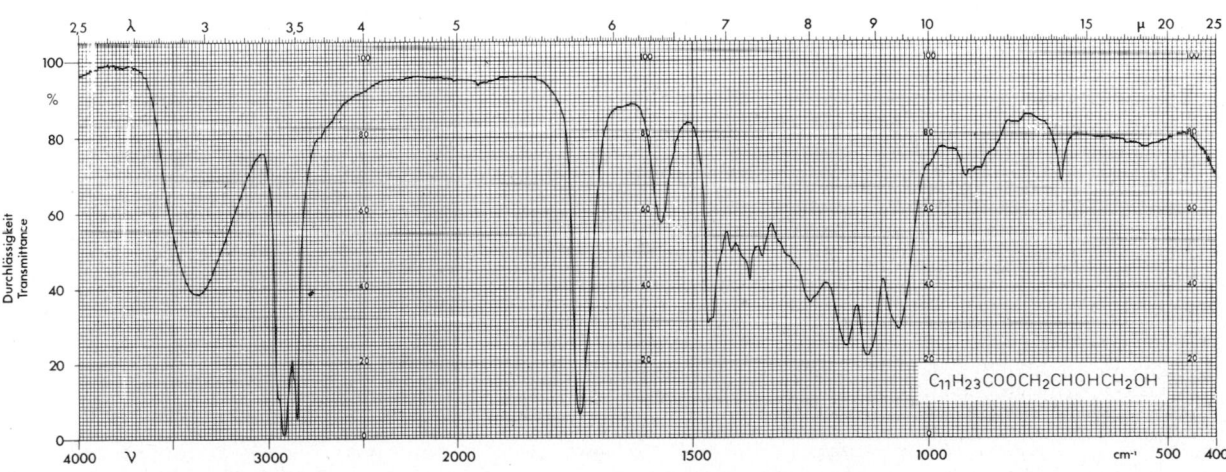

Verbindung:	**Glycerinmonolaurat**		Compound:	**Glycerol monolaurate**		**5146**
Formel:	$C_{15}H_{30}O_4$	M.: **274,6**	Formula:	$C_{15}H_{30}O_4$	M. w.: **274,6**	
Handelsname:	**Nopco 2225 L**	Herst.: **Nopco**	Tradename:	**Nopco 2225 L**	Manuf.: **Nopco**	
Präparation:	**Kapill. Film**	Dez. Nr.: **3.3.2**	Preparation:	**Capill. Film**	Dec. No:. **3.3.2**	

Weichmacher
3. Aliphat. Monocarbonsäureester
3.3. Laurin-, Myristin-, Palmitinsäureester

Plasticizers
3. Aliphatic Monocarboxylic Acid Esters
3.3. Lauric-, Myristic-, Palmitic-Acid Esters

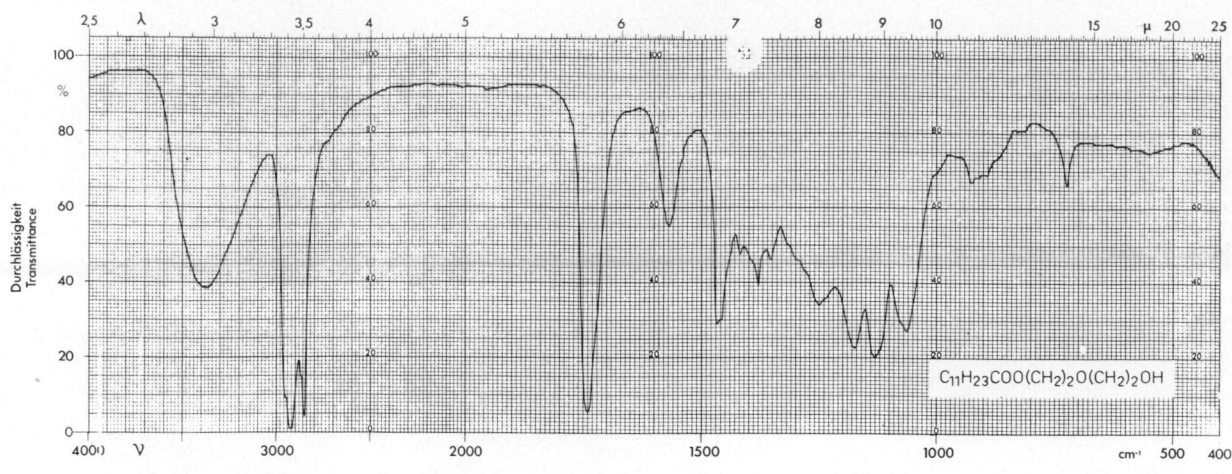

$C_{11}H_{23}COO(CH_2)_2O(CH_2)_2OH$

5147

Verbindung:	Diethylenglykolmonolaurat			Compound:	Diethylene glycol monolaurate	
Formel:	$C_{16}H_{32}O_4$	M.:	288,6	Formula:	$C_{16}H_{32}O_4$	M. w.: 288,6
Handelsname:	Nopalcol 1-L	Herst.:	Nopco	Tradename:	Nopalcol 1-L	Manuf.: Nopco
Präparation:	Kapill. Film	Dez. Nr.:	3.3.3	Preparation:	Capill. Film	Dec. No.: 3.3.3

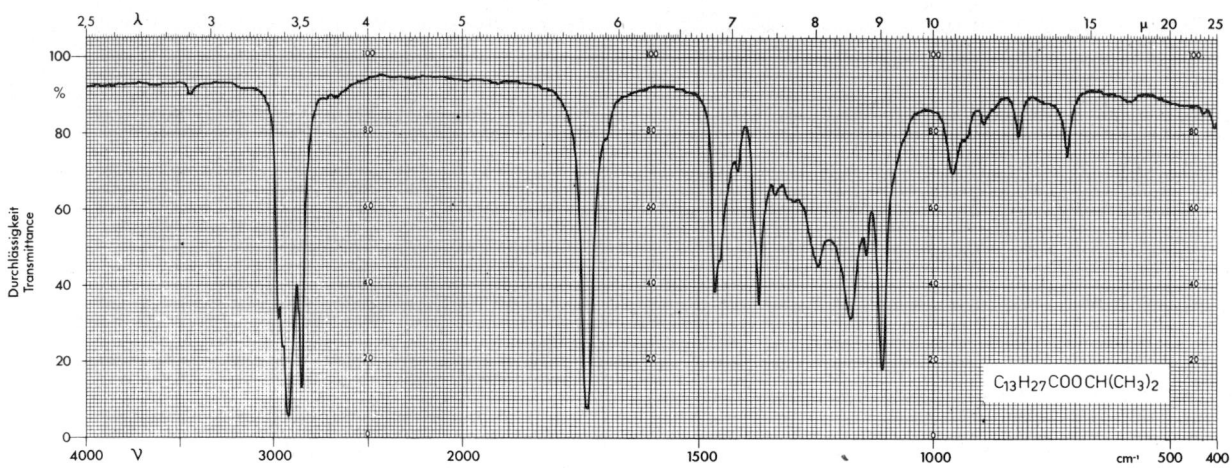

$C_{13}H_{27}COOCH(CH_3)_2$

5148

Verbindung:	Isopropylmyristat			Compound:	Isopropyl myristate	
Formel:	$C_{17}H_{34}O_2$	M.:	270,5	Formula:	$C_{17}H_{34}O_2$	M. w.: 270,5
Handelsname:		Herst.:	Kessler	Tradename:		Manuf.: Kessler
Präparation:	Kapill. Film	Dez. Nr.:	3.3.4	Preparation:	Capill. Film	Dec. No.: 3.3.4

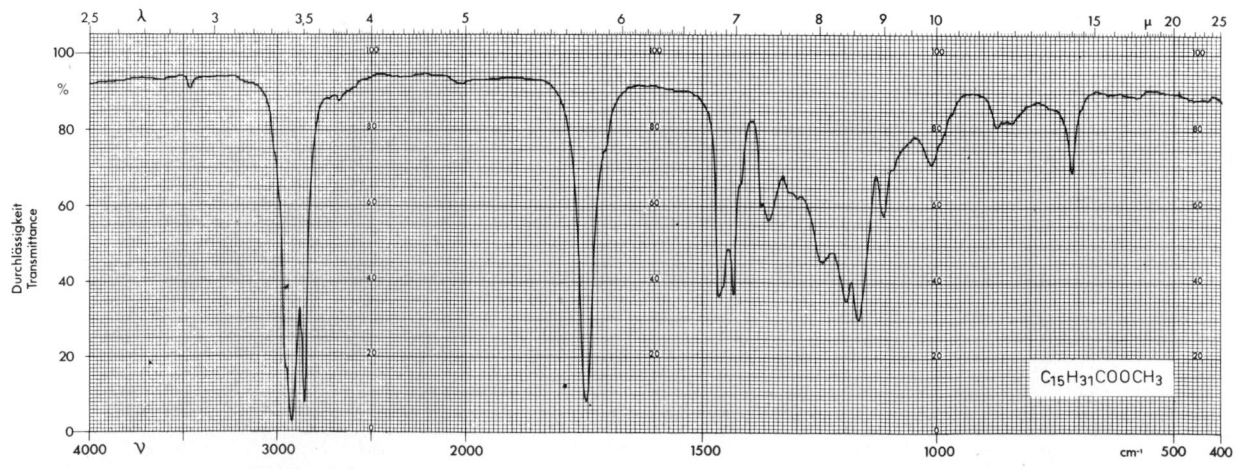

$C_{15}H_{31}COOCH_3$

5149

Verbindung:	Methylpalmitat			Compound:	Methyl palmitate	
Formel:	$C_{17}H_{34}O_2$	M.:	270,5	Formula:	$C_{17}H_{34}O_2$	M. w.: 270,5
Handelsname:		Herst.:	Bosch	Tradename:		Manuf.: Bosch
Präparation:	Kapill. Film	Dez. Nr.:	3.3.5	Preparation:	Capill. Film	Dec. No.: 3.3.5

Weichmacher
3. Aliphat. Monocarbonsäureester
3.3. Laurin-, Myristin-, Palmitinsäureester

Plasticizers
3. Aliphatic Monocarboxylic Acid Esters
3.3. Lauric-, Myristic-, Palmitic-Acid Esters

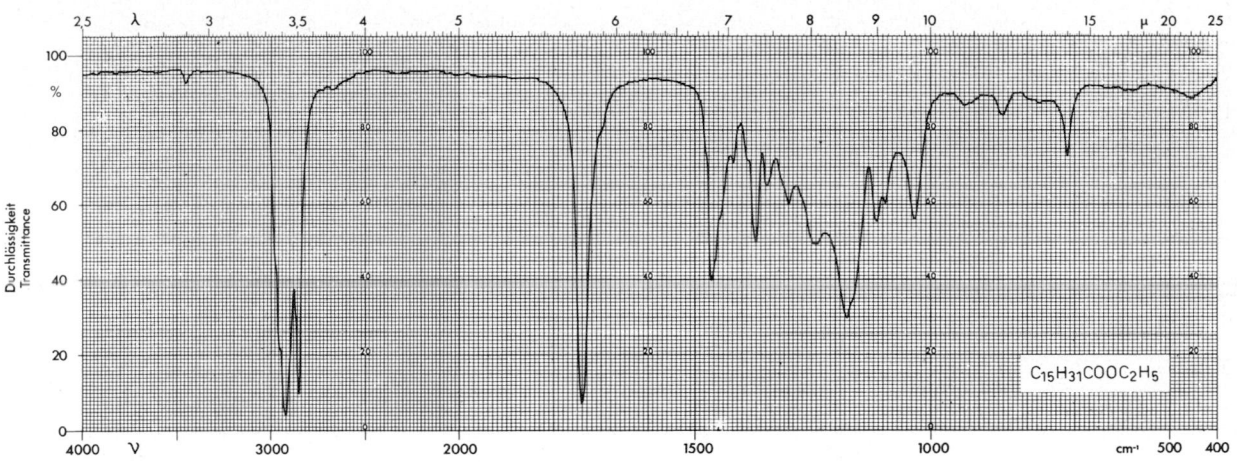

Verbindung:	**Ethylpalmitat**			Compound:	**Ethyl palmitate**			5150
Formel:	$C_{18}H_{36}O_2$	M.:	**284,5**	Formula:	$C_{18}H_{36}O_2$	M. w.:	**284,5**	
Handelsname:		Herst.:	**Bosch**	Tradename:		Manuf.:	**Bosch**	
Präparation:	**Kapill. Film**	Dez. Nr.:	**3.3.6**	Preparation:	**Capill. Film**	Dec. No.:	**3.3.6**	

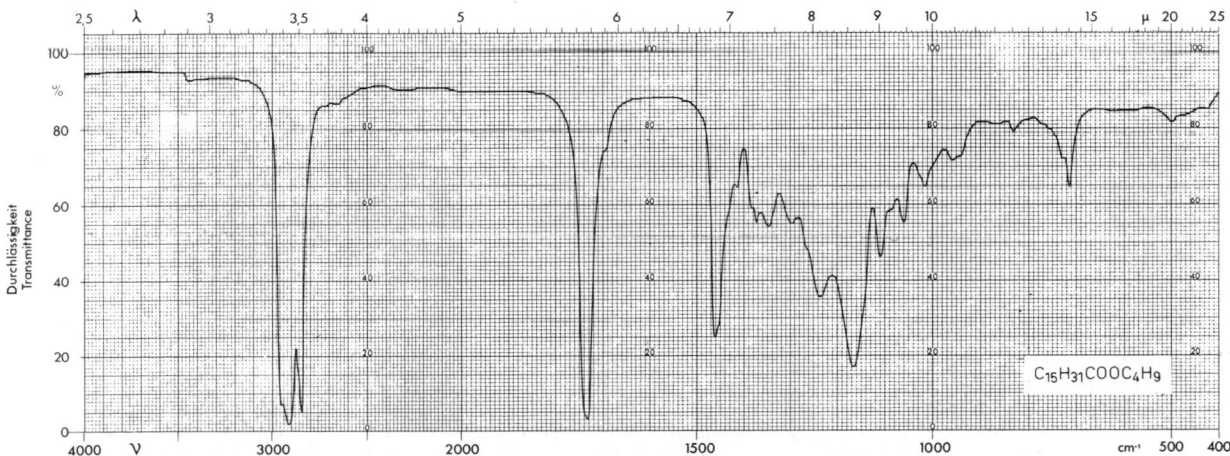

Verbindung:	**Isopropylpalmitat**			Compound:	**Isopropyl palmitate**			5151
Formel:	$C_{19}H_{38}O_2$	M.:	**298,5**	Formula:	$C_{19}H_{38}O_2$	M. w.:	**298,5**	
Handelsname:		Herst.:	**Kessler**	Tradename:		Manuf.:	**Kessler**	
Präparation:	**Kapill. Film**	Dez. Nr.:	**3.3.7**	Preparation:	**Capill. Film**	Dec. No.:	**3.3.7**	

Verbindung:	**n-Butylpalmitat**			Compound:	**n-Butyl palmitate**			5152
Formel:	$C_{20}H_{40}O_2$	M.:	**312,5**	Formula:	$C_{20}H_{40}O_2$	M. w.:	**312,5**	
Handelsname:		Herst.:	**Bosch**	Tradename:		Manuf.:	**Bosch**	
Präparation:	**Kapill. Film**	Dez. Nr.:	**3.3.8**	Preparation:	**Capill. Film**	Dec. No.:	**3.3.8**	

Weichmacher
3. Aliphat. Monocarbonsäureester
3.4. Ölsäureester

Plasticizers
3. Aliphatic Monocarboxylic Acid Esters
3.4. Oleic Acid Esters

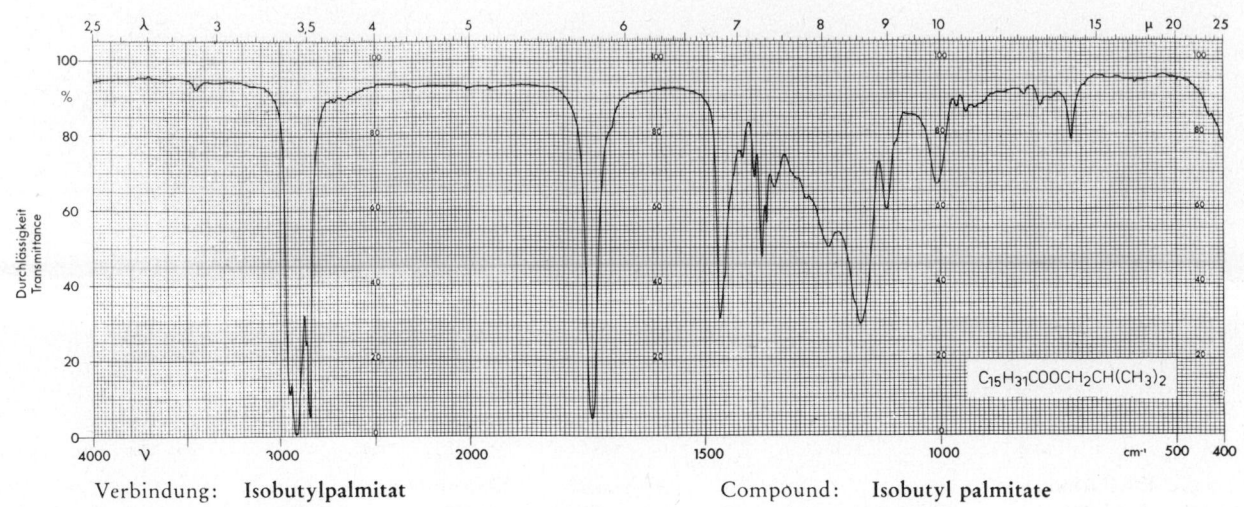

5153

Verbindung:	Isobutylpalmitat			Compound:	Isobutyl palmitate		
Formel:	C$_{20}$H$_{40}$O$_2$	M.:	312,5	Formula:	C$_{20}$H$_{40}$O$_2$	M. w.:	312,5
Handelsname:		Herst.:	Kessler	Tradename:		Manuf.:	Kessler
Präparation:	Kapill. Film	Dez. Nr.:	3.3.9	Preparation:	Capill. Film	Dec. No.:	3.3.9

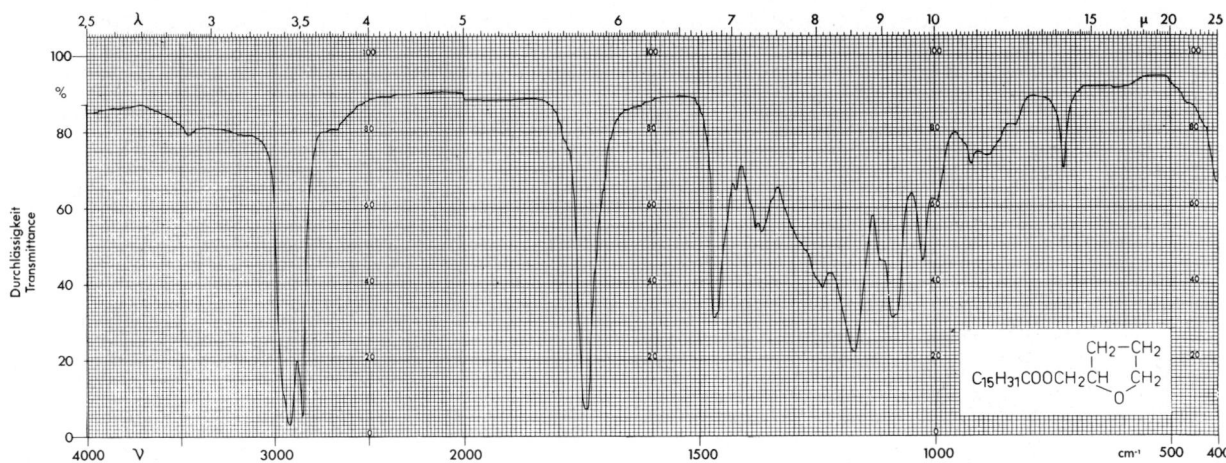

5154

Verbindung:	Tetrahydrofurfurylpalmitat			Compound:	Tetrahydrofurfuryl palmitate		
Formel:	C$_{21}$H$_{40}$O$_3$	M.:	340,5	Formula:	C$_{21}$H$_{40}$O$_3$	M. w.:	340,5
Handelsname:		Herst.:	Eastman	Tradename:		Manuf.:	Eastman
Präparation:	Kapill. Film	Dez. Nr.:	3.3.10	Preparation:	Capill. Film	Dec. No.:	3.3.10

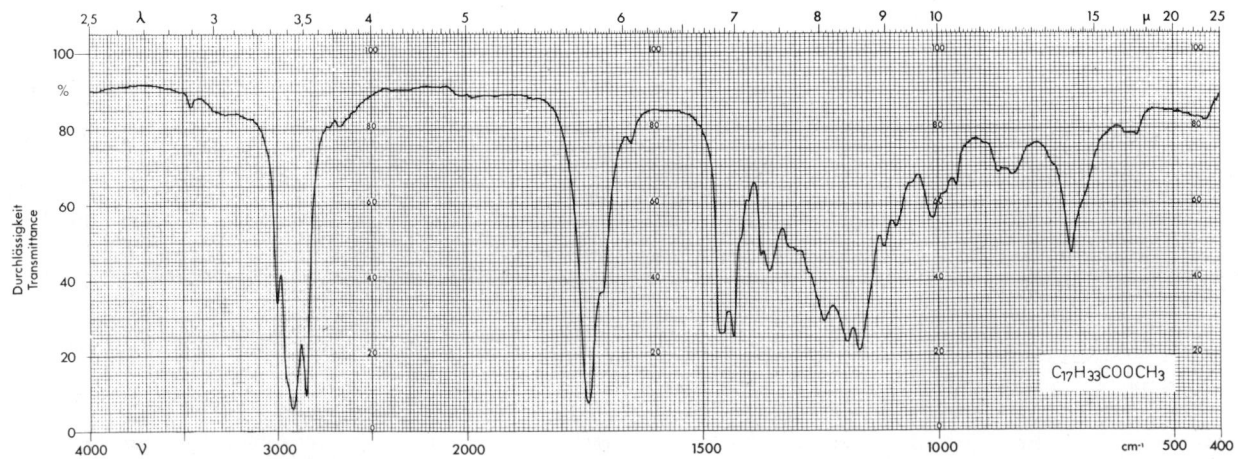

5155

Verbindung:	Methyloleat			Compound:	Methyl oleate		
Formel:	C$_{19}$H$_{36}$O$_2$	M.:	296,5	Formula:	C$_{19}$H$_{36}$O$_2$	M. w.:	296,5
Handelsname:	Nopco 2060	Herst.:	Nopco	Tradename:	Nopco 2060	Manuf.:	Nopco
Präparation:	Kapill. Film	Dez. Nr.:	3.4.1	Preparation:	Capill. Film	Dec. No.:	3.4.1

Weichmacher
3. Aliphat. Monocarbonsäureester
3.4. Ölsäureester

Plasticizers
3. Aliphatic Monocarboxylic Acid Esters
3.4. Oleic Acid Esters

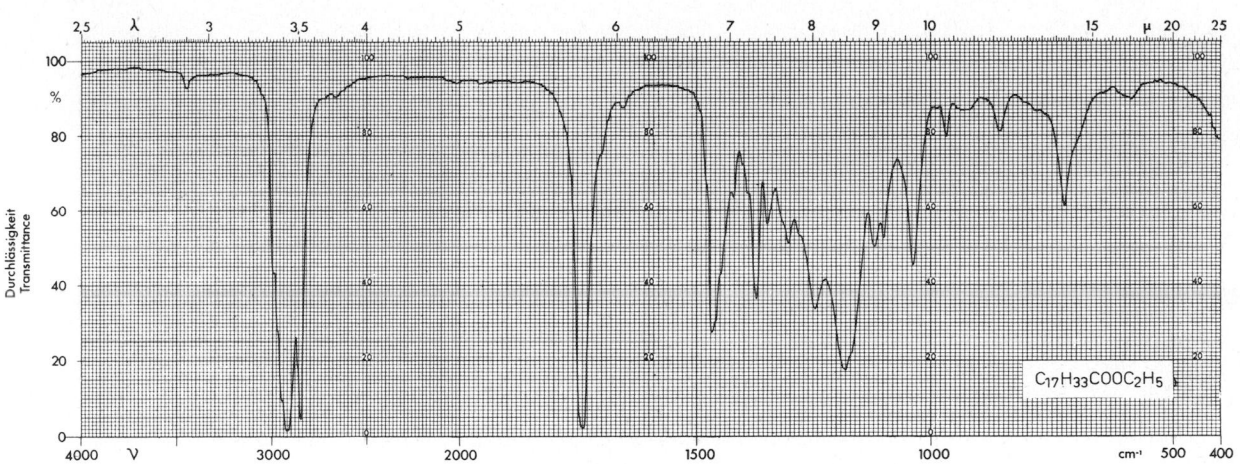

Verbindung: **Ethyloleat** Compound: **Ethyl oleate** **5156**
Formel: $C_{20}H_{38}O_2$ M.: **310,52** Formula: $C_{20}H_{38}O_2$ M. w.: **310,52**
Handelsname: Herst.: **DCL-Bisol** Tradename: Manuf.: **DCL-Bisol**
Präparation: **Kapill. Film** Dez. Nr.: **3.4.2** Preparation: **Capill. Film** Dec. No.: **3.4.2**

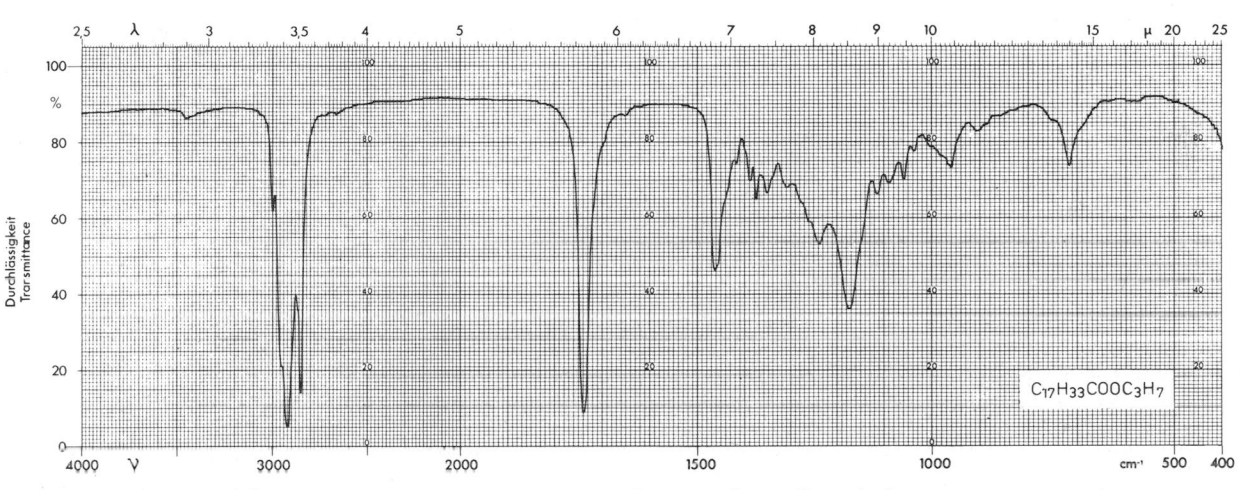

Verbindung: **n-Propyloleat** Compound: **n-Propyl oleate** **5157**
Formel: $C_{21}H_{40}O_2$ M.: **324,5** Formula: $C_{21}H_{40}O_2$ M. w.: **324,5**
Handelsname: Herst.: **Bosch** Tradename: Manuf.: **Bosch**
Präparation: **Kapill. Film** Dez. Nr.: **3.4.3** Preparation: **Capill. Film** Dec. No.: **3.4.3**

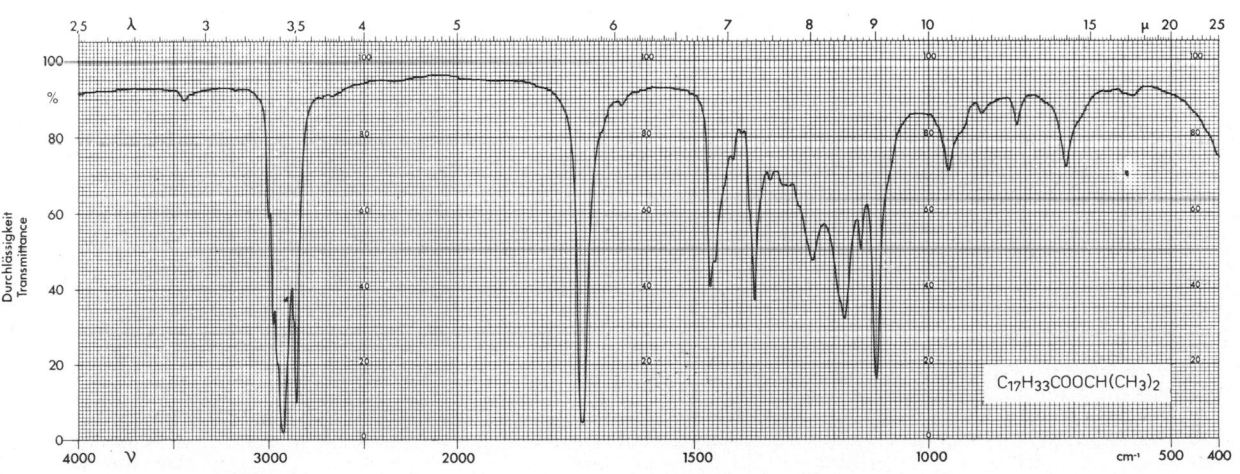

Verbindung: **Isopropyloleat** Compound: **Isopropyl oleate** **5158**
Formel: $C_{21}H_{40}O_2$ M.: **324,5** Formula: $C_{21}H_{40}O_2$ M. w.: **324,5**
Handelsname: Herst.: **Bosch** Tradename: Manuf.: **Bosch**
Präparation: **Kapill. Film** Dez. Nr.: Preparation: **Capill. Film** Dec. No.: **3.4.4**

Weichmacher
3. Aliphat. Monocarbonsäureester
3.4. Ölsäureester

Plasticizers
3. Aliphatic Monocarboxylic Acid Esters
3.4. Oleic Acid Esters

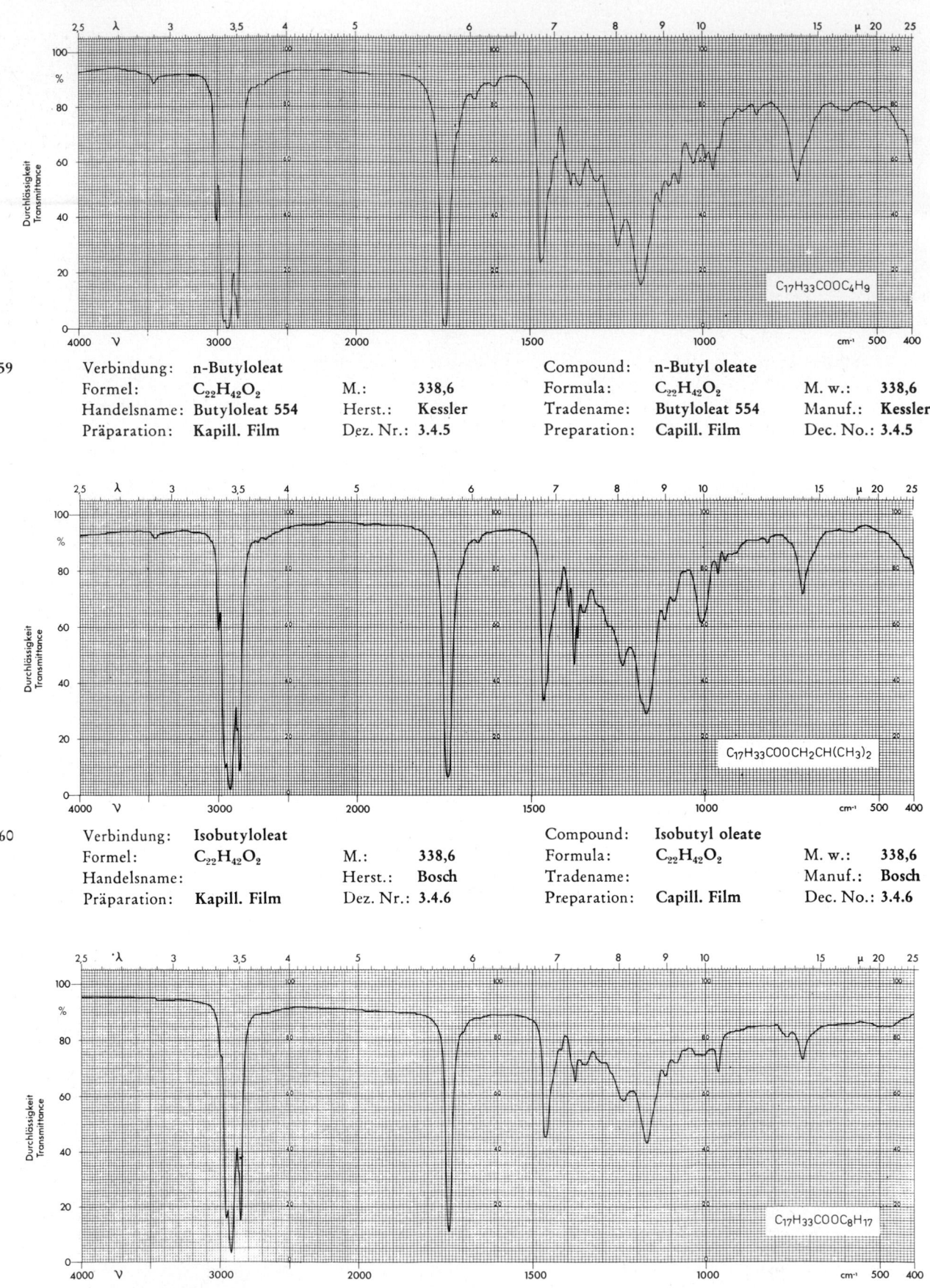

5159

Verbindung:	n-Butyloleat			Compound:	n-Butyl oleate		
Formel:	$C_{22}H_{42}O_2$	M.:	338,6	Formula:	$C_{22}H_{42}O_2$	M. w.:	338,6
Handelsname:	Butyloleat 554	Herst.:	Kessler	Tradename:	Butyloleat 554	Manuf.:	Kessler
Präparation:	Kapill. Film	Dez. Nr.:	3.4.5	Preparation:	Capill. Film	Dec. No.:	3.4.5

5160

Verbindung:	Isobutyloleat			Compound:	Isobutyl oleate		
Formel:	$C_{22}H_{42}O_2$	M.:	338,6	Formula:	$C_{22}H_{42}O_2$	M. w.:	338,6
Handelsname:		Herst.:	Bosch	Tradename:		Manuf.:	Bosch
Präparation:	Kapill. Film	Dez. Nr.:	3.4.6	Preparation:	Capill. Film	Dec. No.:	3.4.6

5161

Verbindung:	Octyloleat			Compound:	Octyl oleate		
Formel:	$C_{26}H_{51}O_2$	M.:	395,7	Formula:	$C_{26}H_{51}O_2$	M. w.:	395,7
Handelsname:		Herst.:	Bosch	Tradename:		Manuf.:	Bosch
Präparation:	Kapill. Film	Dez. Nr.:	3.4.7	Preparation:	Capill. Film	Dec. No.:	3.4.7

Weichmacher
3. Aliphat. Monocarbonsäureester
3.4. Ölsäureester

Plasticizers
3. Aliphatic Monocarboxylic Acid Esters
3.4. Oleic Acid Esters

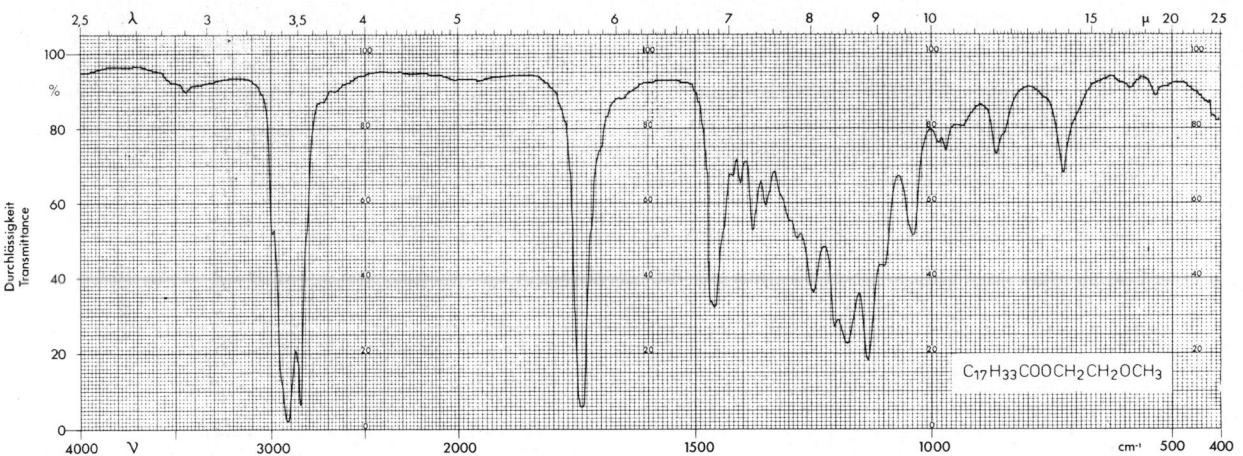

Verbindung:	Methoxyethyloleat			Compound:	Methoxyethyl oleate			5162
Formel:	$C_{21}H_{40}O_3$	M.:	340,6	Formula:	$C_{21}H_{40}O_3$	M. w.:	340,6	
Handelsname:	Kapsol	Herst.:	FMC	Tradename:	Kapsol	Manuf.:	FMC	
Präparation:	Kapill. Film	Dez. Nr.:	3.4.8	Preparation:	Capill. Film	Dec. No.:	3.4.8	

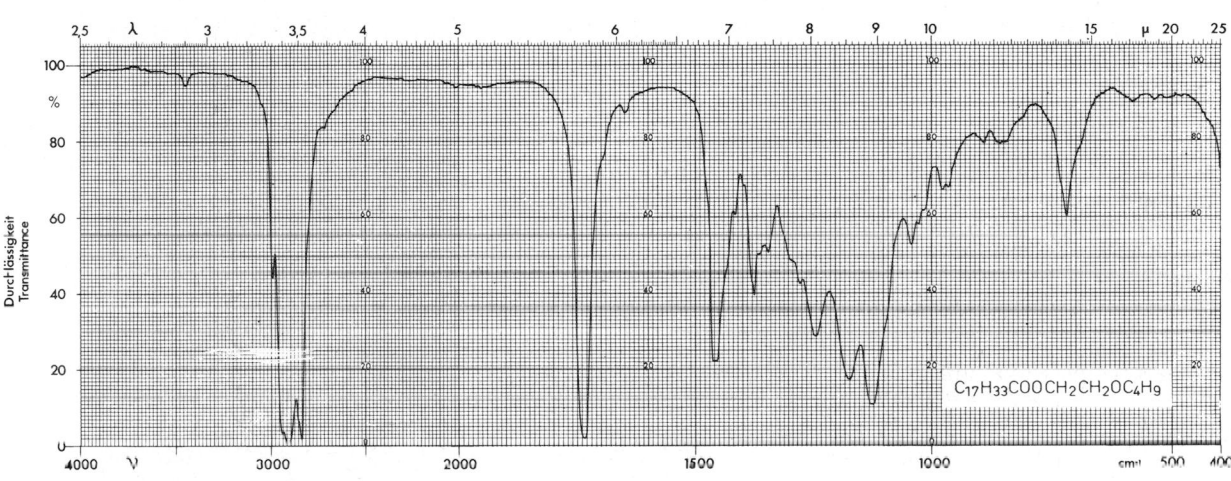

Verbindung:	Butoxyethyloleat			Compound:	Butoxyethyl oleate			5163
Formel:	$C_{24}H_{46}O_3$	M.:	382,6	Formula:	$C_{24}H_{46}O_3$	M. w.:	382,6	
Handelsname:		Herst.:	Kessler	Tradename:		Manuf.:	Kessler	
Präparation:	Kapill. Film	Dez. Nr.:	3.4.9	Preparation:	Capill. Film	Dec. No.:	3.4.9	

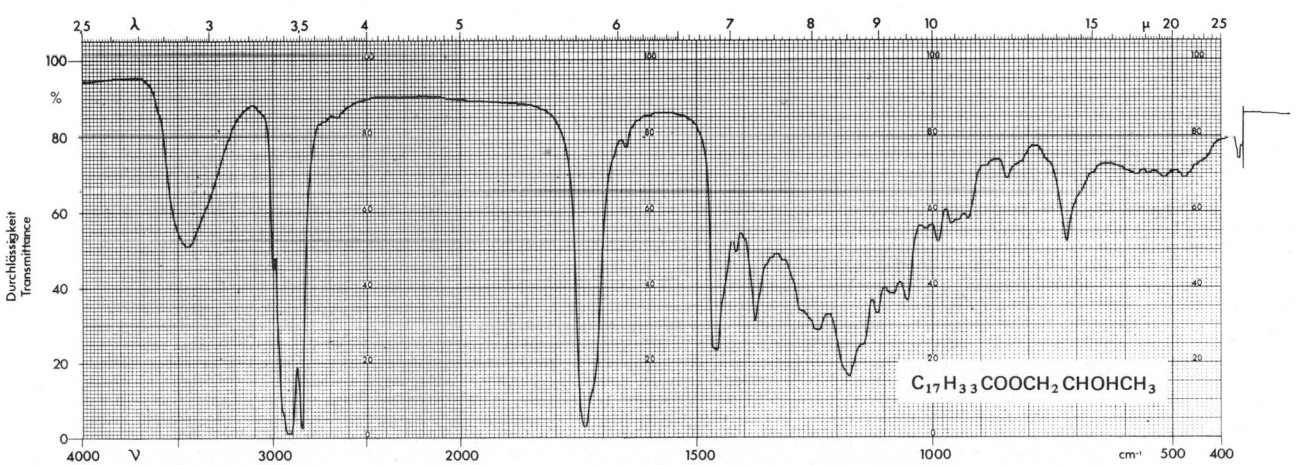

Verbindung:	1,2-Propylenglykolmonooleat			Compound:	1,2-Propylene glycol monooleate			5164
Formel:	$C_{21}H_{40}O_3$	M.:	340,6	Formula:	$C_{21}H_{40}O_3$	M. w.:	340,6	
Handelsname:		Herst.:	Bosch	Tradename:		Manuf.:	Bosch	
Präparation:	Kapill. Film	Dez. Nr.:	3.4.10	Preparation:	Capill. Film	Dec. No.:	3.4.10	

Weichmacher
3. Aliphat. Monocarbonsäureester
3.4. Ölsäureester

Plasticizers
3. Aliphatic Monocarboxylic Acid Esters
3.4. Oleic Acid Esters

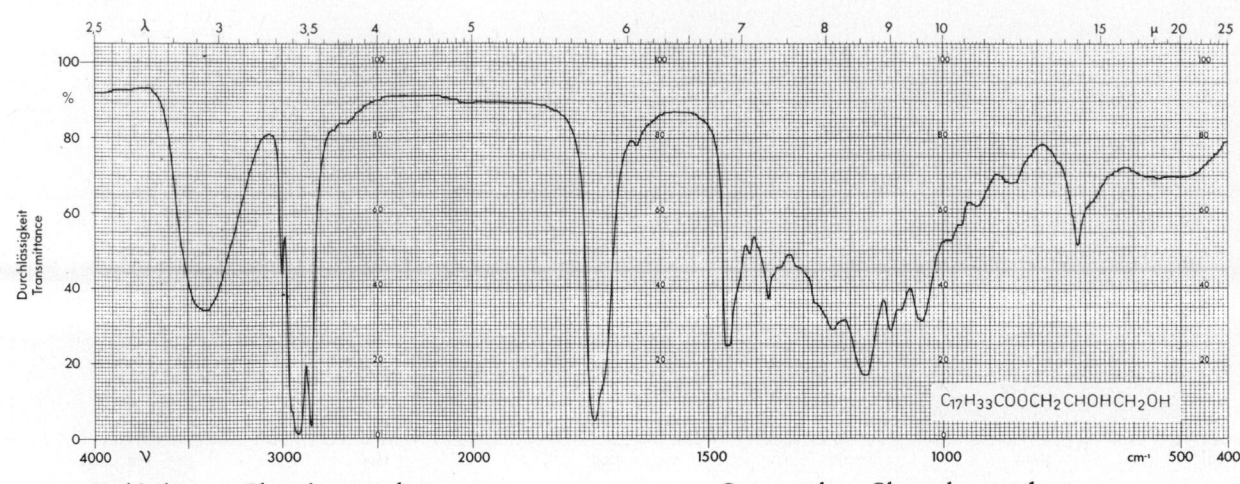

$C_{17}H_{33}COOCH_2CHOHCH_2OH$

5165	Verbindung:	**Glycerinmonooleat**			Compound:	**Glycerol monooleate**		
	Formel:	$C_{21}H_{40}O_3$	M.:	**356,6**	Formula:	$C_{21}H_{40}O_3$	M. w.:	**356,6**
	Handelsname:		Herst.:	**Bosch**	Tradename:		Manuf.:	**Bosch**
	Präparation:	**Kapill. Film**	Dez. Nr.:	**3.4.11**	Preparation:	**Capill. Film**	Dec. No.:	**3.4.11**

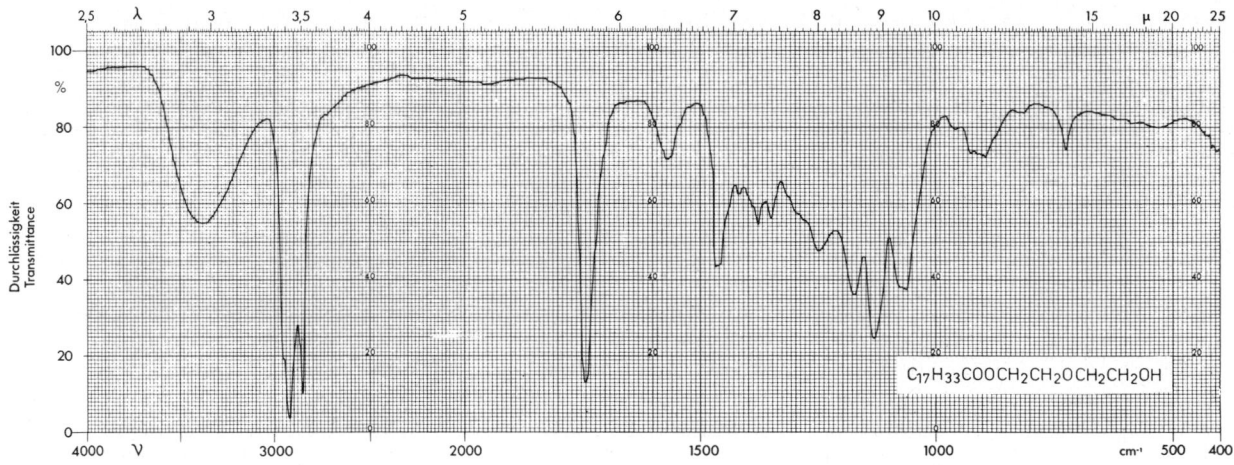

$C_{17}H_{33}COOCH_2CH_2OCH_2CH_2OH$

5166	Verbindung:	**Diethylenglykolmonooleat**			Compound:	**Diethylene glycol monooleate**		
	Formel:	$C_{22}H_{42}O_4$	M.:	**370,6**	Formula:	$C_{22}H_{42}O_4$	M. w.:	**370,6**
	Handelsname:		Herst.:	**Schuchardt**	Tradename:		Manuf.:	**Schuchardt**
	Präparation:	**Kapill. Film**	Dez. Nr.:	**3.4.12**	Preparation:	**Capill. Film**	Dec. No.:	**3.4.12**

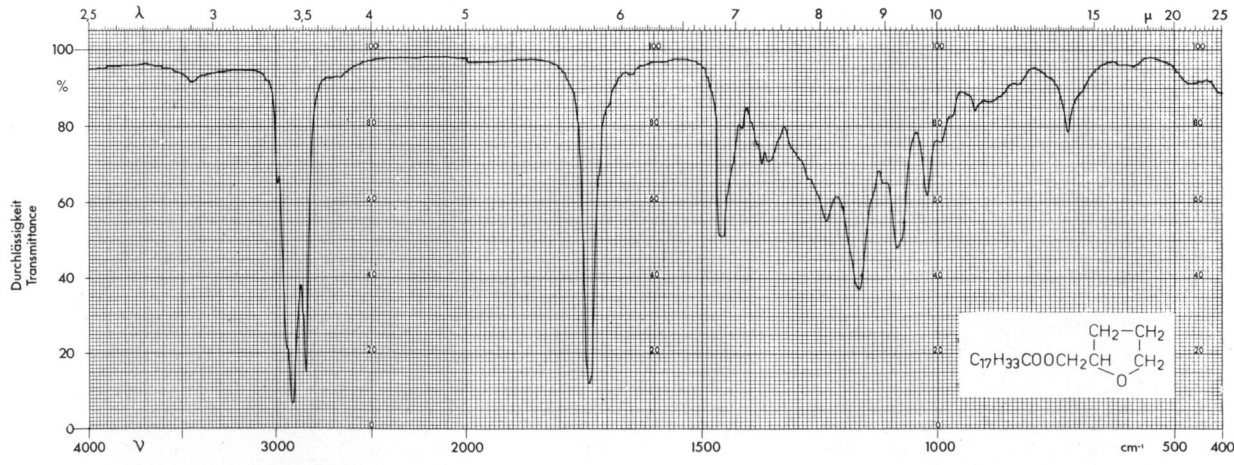

5167	Verbindung:	**Tetrahydrofurfuryloleat**			Compound:	**Tetrahydrofurfuryl oleate**		
	Formel:	$C_{23}H_{42}O_3$	M.:	**366,6**	Formula:	$C_{23}H_{42}O_3$	M. w.:	**366,6**
	Handelsname:	**Plastolein 9250**	Herst.:	**Emery**	Tradename:	**Plastolein 9250**	Manuf.:	**Emery**
	Präparation:	**Kapill. Film**	Dez. Nr.:	**3.4.13**	Preparation:	**Capill. Film**	Dec. No.:	**3.4.13**

Weichmacher
3. Aliphat. Monocarbonsäureester
3.5. Stearinsäureester

Plasticizers
3. Aliphatic Monocarboxylic Acid Esters
3.5. Stearic Acid Esters

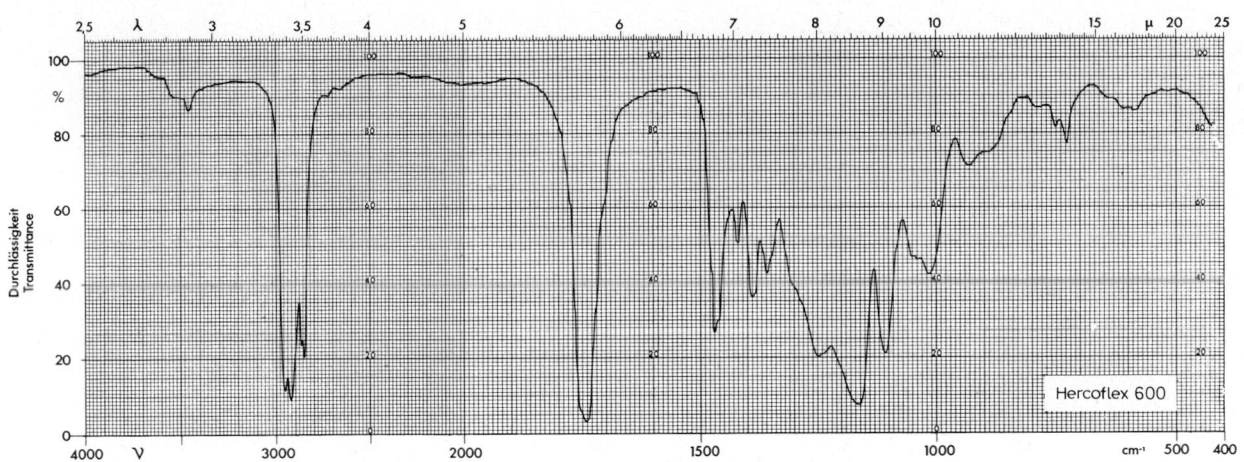

Verbindung:	Pentaerythritvorlauffettsäureester		Compound:	Pentarythrol fatty acid ester		5168
Formel:	Edenol PV	M.:	Formula:	Edenol PV	M. w.:	
Handelsname:		Herst.: **Dehydag**	Tradename:		Manuf.: **Dehydag**	
Präparation:	**Kapill. Film**	Dez. Nr.: **3.4.14**	Preparation:	**Capill. Film**	Dec. No.: **3.4.14**	

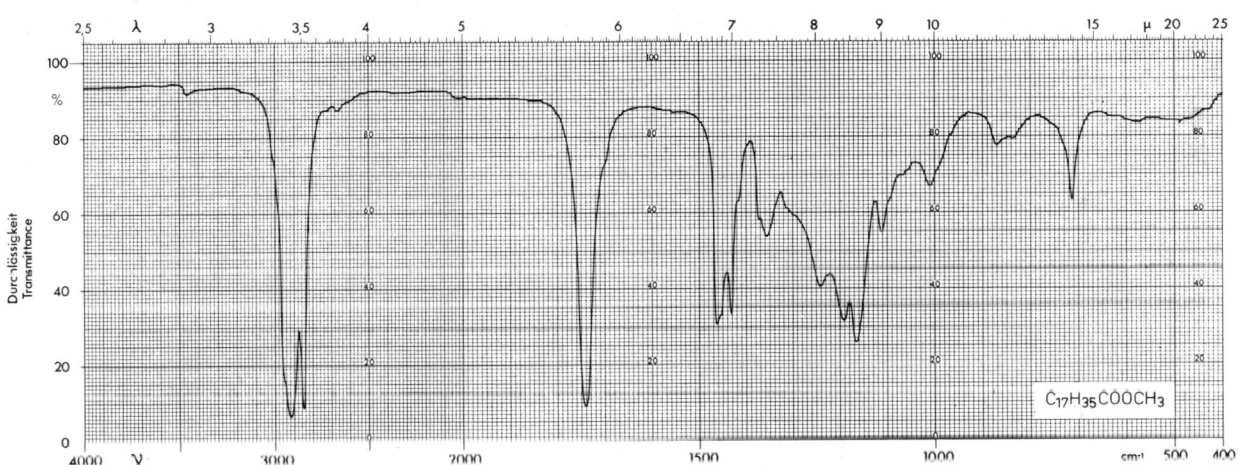

Verbindung:	**Methylstearat**		Compound:	**Methyl stearate**		5169
Formel:	$C_{19}H_{38}O_2$	M.: **298,5**	Formula:	$C_{19}H_{38}O_2$	M. w.: **298,5**	
Handelsname:		Herst.: **Bosch**	Tradename:		Manuf.: **Bosch**	
Präparation:	**Kapill. Film**	Dez. Nr.: **3.5.1**	Preparation:	**Capill. Film**	Dec. No.: **3.5.1**	

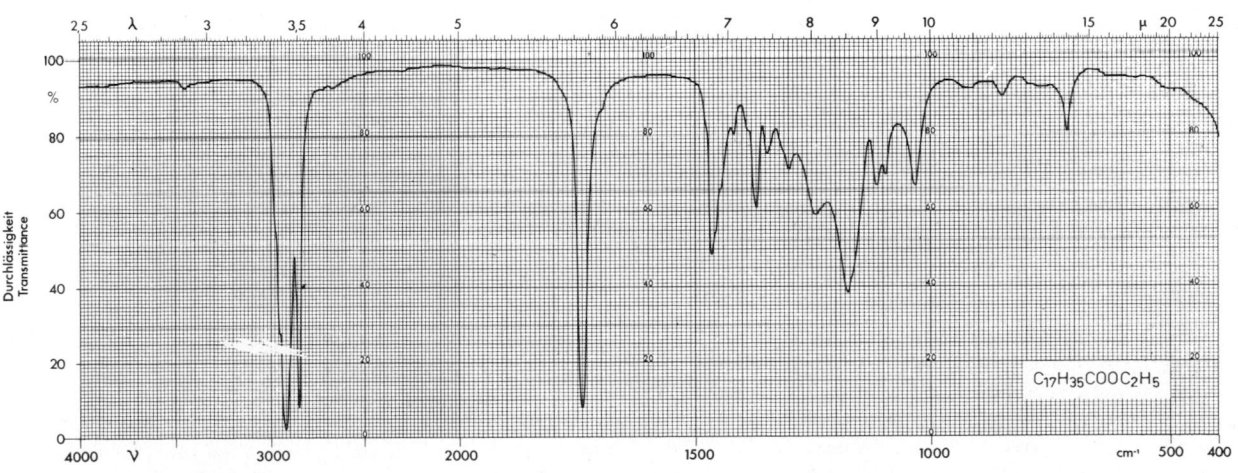

Verbindung:	**Ethylstearat**		Compound:	**Ethyl stearate**		5170
Formel:	$C_{20}H_{40}O_2$	M.: **312,5**	Formula:	$C_{20}H_{40}O_2$	M. w.: **312,5**	
Handelsname:		Herst.: **Bosch**	Tradename:		Manuf.: **Bosch**	
Präparation:	**Kapill. Film**	Dez. Nr.: **3.5.2**	Preparation:	**Capill. Film**	Dec. No.: **3.5.2**	

Weichmacher
3. Aliphat. Monocarbonsäureester
3.5. Stearinsäureester

Plasticizers
3. Aliphatic Monocarboxylic Acid Esters
3.5. Stearic Acid Esters

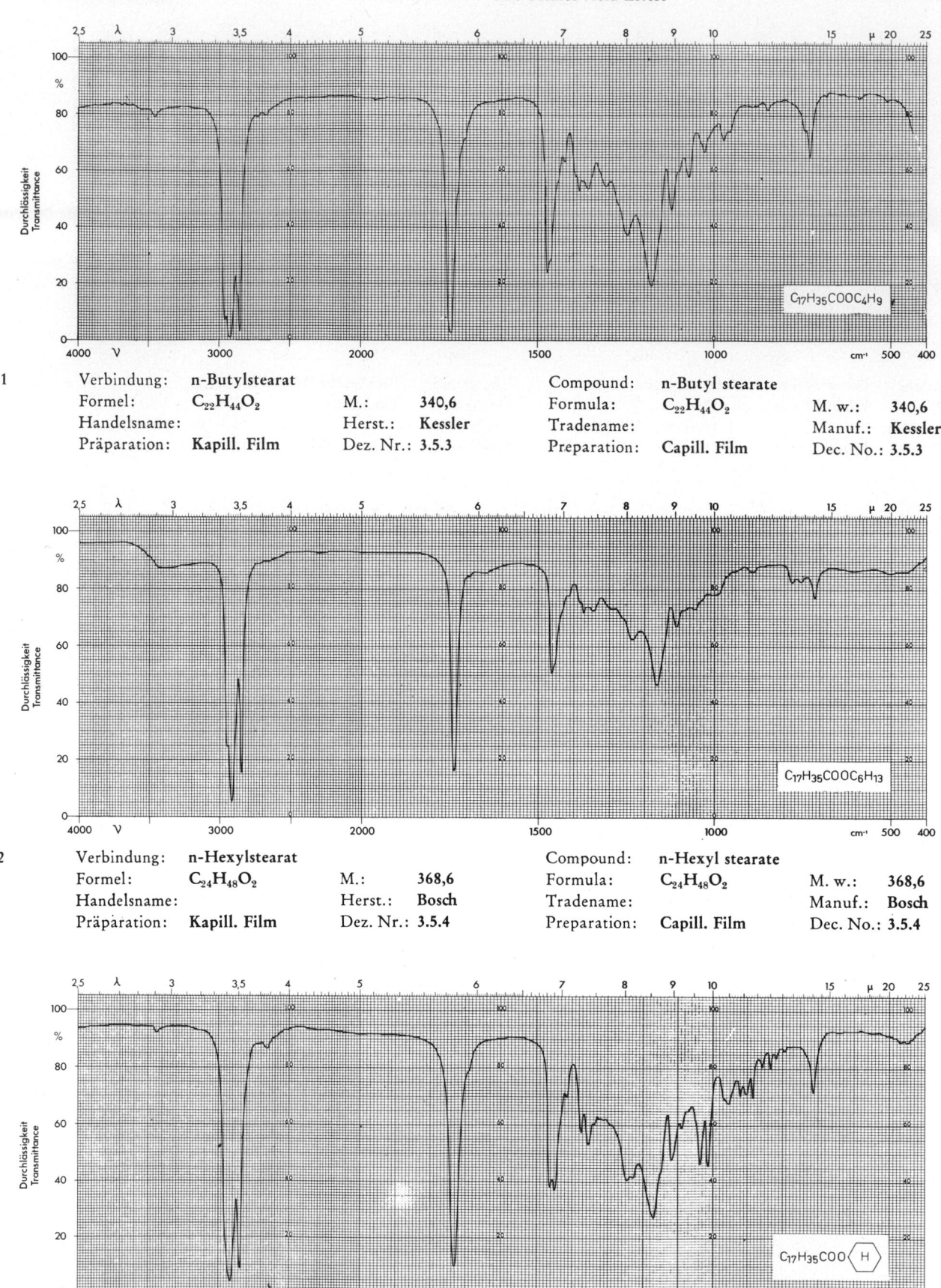

5171

Verbindung:	**n-Butylstearat**		Compound:	**n-Butyl stearate**	
Formel:	$C_{22}H_{44}O_2$	M.: **340,6**	Formula:	$C_{22}H_{44}O_2$	M. w.: **340,6**
Handelsname:		Herst.: **Kessler**	Tradename:		Manuf.: **Kessler**
Präparation:	**Kapill. Film**	Dez. Nr.: **3.5.3**	Preparation:	**Capill. Film**	Dec. No.: **3.5.3**

5172

Verbindung:	**n-Hexylstearat**		Compound:	**n-Hexyl stearate**	
Formel:	$C_{24}H_{48}O_2$	M.: **368,6**	Formula:	$C_{24}H_{48}O_2$	M. w.: **368,6**
Handelsname:		Herst.: **Bosch**	Tradename:		Manuf.: **Bosch**
Präparation:	**Kapill. Film**	Dez. Nr.: **3.5.4**	Preparation:	**Capill. Film**	Dec. No.: **3.5.4**

5173

Verbindung:	**Cyclohexylstearat**		Compound:	**Cyclohexyl stearate**	
Formel:	$C_{24}H_{46}O_2$	M.: **366,6**	Formula:	$C_{24}H_{46}O_2$	M. w.: **366,6**
Handelsname:		Herst.: **Bosch**	Tradename:		Manuf.: **Bosch**
Präparation:	**Kapill. Film**	Dez. Nr.: **3.5.5**	Preparation:	**Capill. Film**	Dec. No.: **3.5.5**

Weichmacher
3. Aliphat. Monocarbonsäureester
3.5. Stearinsäureester

Plasticizers
3. Aliphatic Monocarboxylic Acid Esters
3.5. Stearic Acid Esters

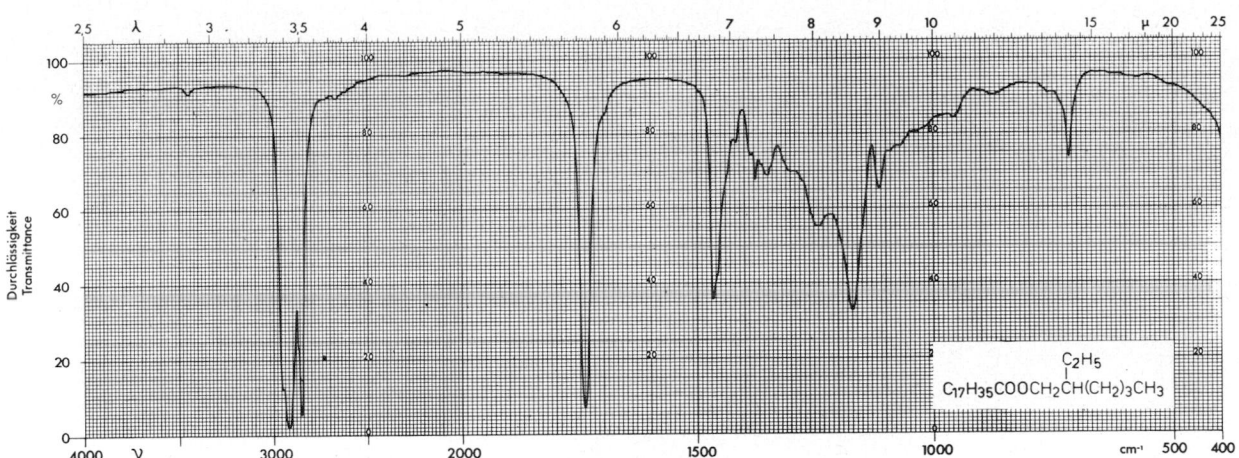

Verbindung:	2-Ethylhexylstearat			Compound:	2-Ethylhexyl stearate			5174
Formel:	$C_{26}H_{52}O_2$	M.:	396,7	Formula:	$C_{26}H_{52}O_2$	M. w.:	396,7	
Handelsname:		Herst.:	Bosch	Tradename:		Manuf.:	Bosch	
Präparation:	Kapill. Film	Dez. Nr.:	3.5.6	Preparation:	Capill. Film	Dec. No.:	3.5.6	

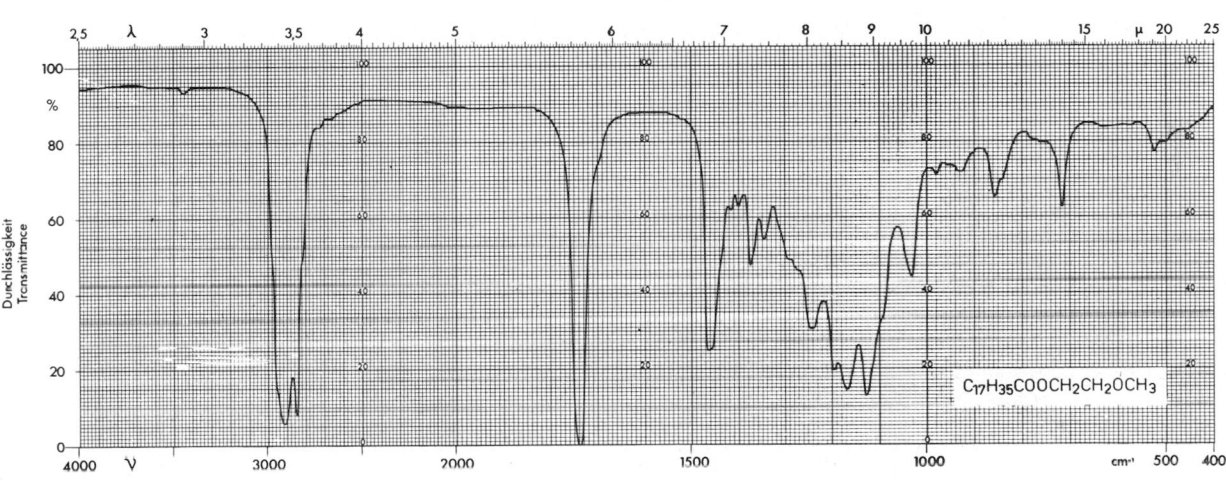

Verbindung:	Methoxyethylstearat			Compound:	Methoxyethyl stearate			5175
Formel:	$C_{21}H_{42}O_3$	M.:	342,6	Formula:	$C_{21}H_{42}O_3$	M. w.:	342,6	
Handelsname:		Herst.:	Bosch	Tradename:		Manuf.:	Bosch	
Präparation:	Kapill. Film	Dez. Nr.:	3.5.7	Preparation:	Capill. Film	Dec. No.:	3.5.7	

Verbindung:	Butoxyethylstearat			Compound:	Butoxyethyl stearate			5176
Formel:	$C_{24}H_{48}O_3$	M.:	384,6	Formula:	$C_{24}H_{48}O_3$	M. w.:	384,6	
Handelsname:	KP 23	Herst.:	FMC	Tradename:	KP 23	Manuf.:	FMC	
Präparation:	Kapill. Film	Dez. Nr.:	3.5.8	Preparation:	Capill. Film	Dec. No.:	3.5.8	

Weichmacher
3. Aliphat. Monocarbonsäureester
3.5. Stearinsäureester

Plasticizers
3. Aliphatic Monocarboxylic Acid Esters
3.5. Stearic Acid Esters

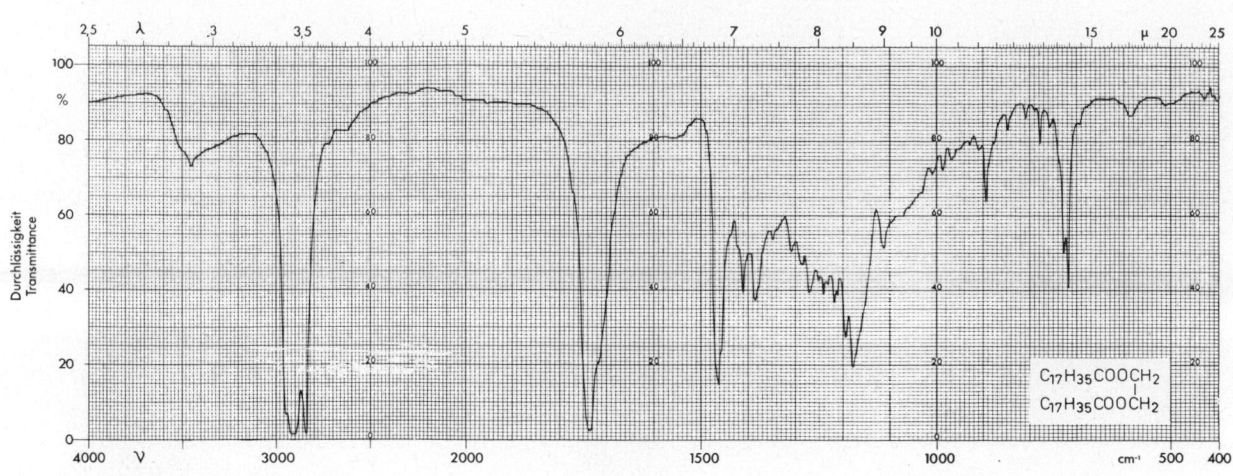

5177

Verbindung:	Ethylenglykoldistearat			Compound:	Ethylene glycol distearate	
Formel:	$C_{38}H_{74}O_2$	M.:	563	Formula:	$C_{38}H_{74}O_2$	M. w.: 563
Handelsname:		Herst.:	Schuchardt	Tradename:		Manuf.: Schuchardt
Präparation:	Kapill. Film	Dez. Nr.:	3.5.9	Preparation:	Capill. Film	Dec. No.: 3.5.9

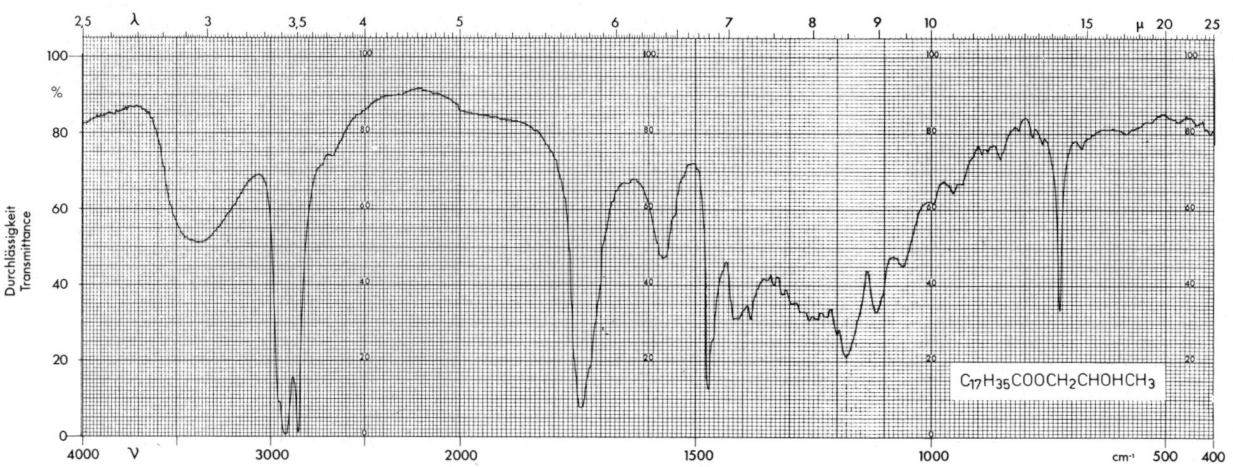

5178

Verbindung:	1,2-Propylenglykolmonostearat			Compound:	1,2-Propylene glycol monostearate	
Formel:	$C_{21}H_{42}O_3$	M.:	342,6	Formula:	$C_{21}H_{42}O_3$	M. w.: 342,6
Handelsname:		Herst.:	Kessler	Tradename:		Manuf.: Kessler
Präparation:	Kapill. Film	Dez. Nr.:	3.5.10	Preparation:	Capill. Film	Dec. No.: 3.5.10

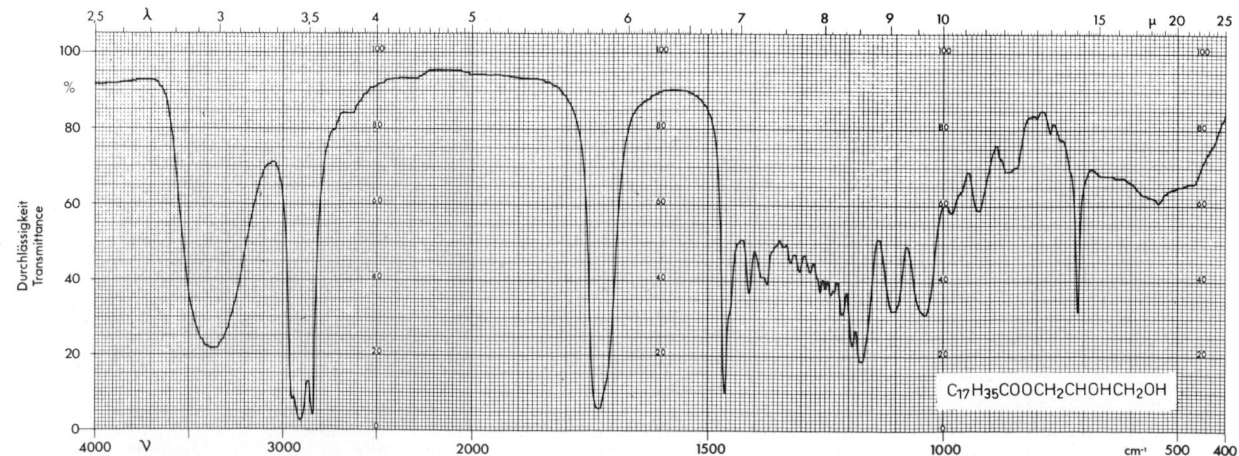

5179

Verbindung:	Glycerinmonostearat			Compound:	Glycerol monostearate	
Formel:	$C_{21}H_{42}O_4$	M.:	358,6	Formula:	$C_{21}H_{42}O_4$	M. w.: 358,6
Handelsname:	Nopco 2225-P	Herst.:		Tradename:	Nopco 2225-P	Manuf.:
Präparation:	Kapill. Film	Dez. Nr.:	3.5.11	Preparation:	Capill. Film	Dec. No.: 3.5.11

Weichmacher
3. Aliphat. Monocarbonsäureester
3.5. Stearinsäureester

Plasticizers
3. Aliphatic Monocarboxylic Acid Esters
3.5. Stearic Acid Esters

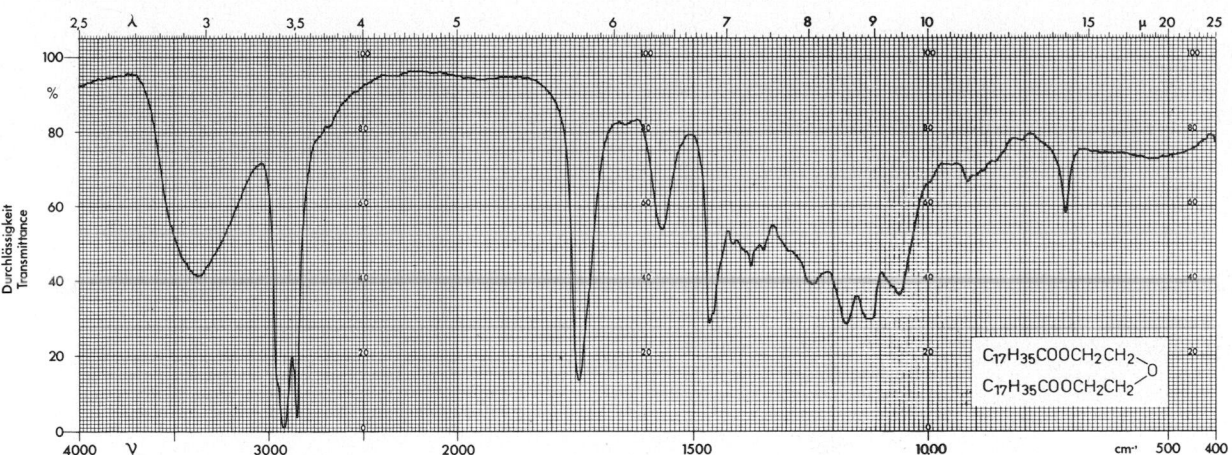

Verbindung:	Diethylenglykoldistearat		Compound:	**Diethylene glycol distearate**		5180
Formel:	$C_{40}H_{78}O_5$	M.: **639,1**	Formula:	$C_{40}H_{78}O_5$	M. w.: **639,1**	
Handelsname: **Nopalcol 1-S**		Herst.: **Nopco**	Tradename: **Nopalcol 1-S**		Manuf.: **Nopco**	
Präparation: **Kapill. Film**		Dez. Nr.: **3.5.12**	Preparation: **Capill. Film**		Dec. No.: **3.5.12**	

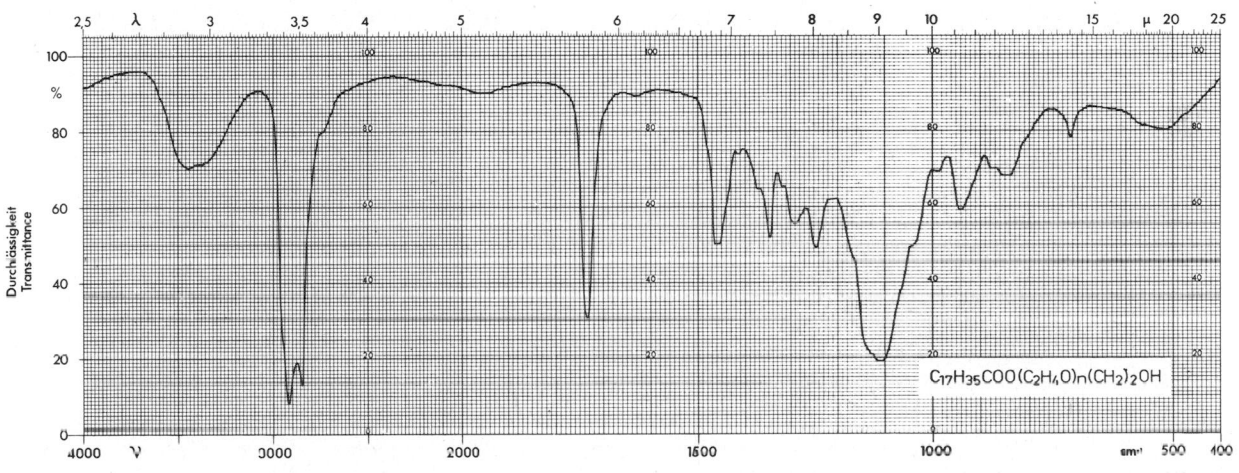

Verbindung:	**Polyethylenglykol(400)-monostearat**		Compound:	**Polyethylene glycol(400)monostearate**		5181
Formel:		M.: **∼ 700**	Formula:		M. w.: **∼ 700**	
Handelsname:		Herst.: **Kessler**	Tradename:		Manuf.: **Kessler**	
Präparation: **Kapill. Film**		Dez. Nr.: **3.5.13**	Preparation: **Capill. Film**		Dec. No.: **3.5.13**	

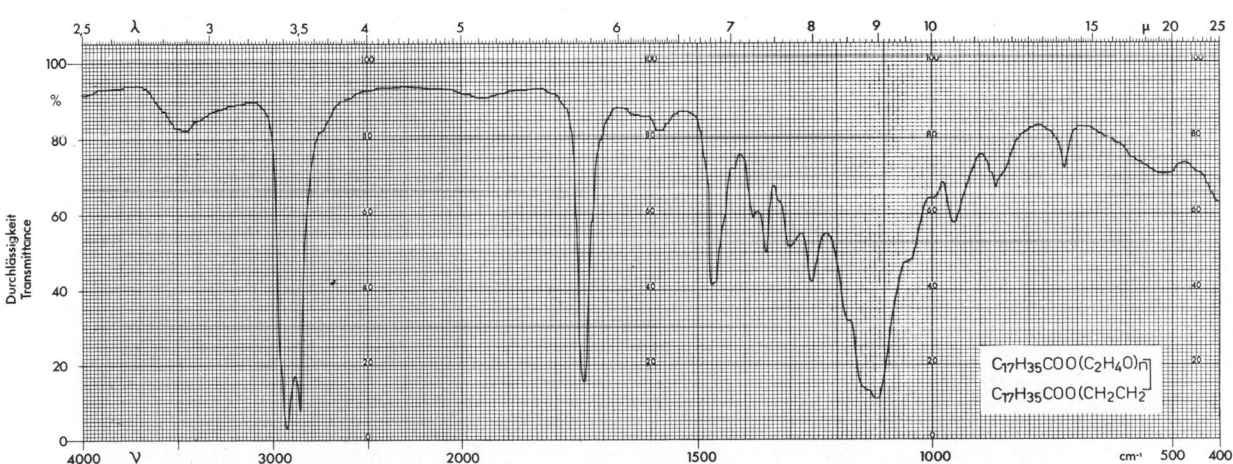

Verbindung:	**Polyethylenglykol(400)-distearat**		Compound:	**Polyethylene glycol(400)distearate**		5182
Formel:		M.: **∼ 1000**	Formula:		M. w.: **∼ 1000**	
Handelsname:		Herst.: **Kessler**	Tradename:		Manuf.: **Kessler**	
Präparation: **Kapill. Film**		Dez. Nr.: **3.5.14**	Preparation: **Capill. Film**		Dec. No.: **3.5.14**	

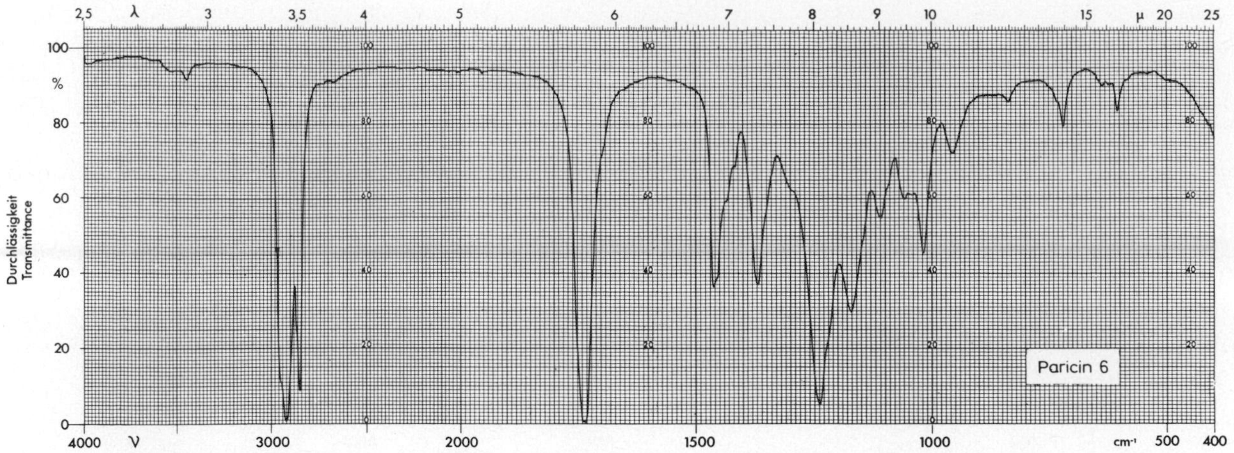

Weichmacher
3. Aliphat. Monocarbonsäureester
3.6. Ricinolsäureester

Plasticizers
3. Aliphatic Monocarboxylic Acid Esters
3.6. Ricinoleic Acid Esters

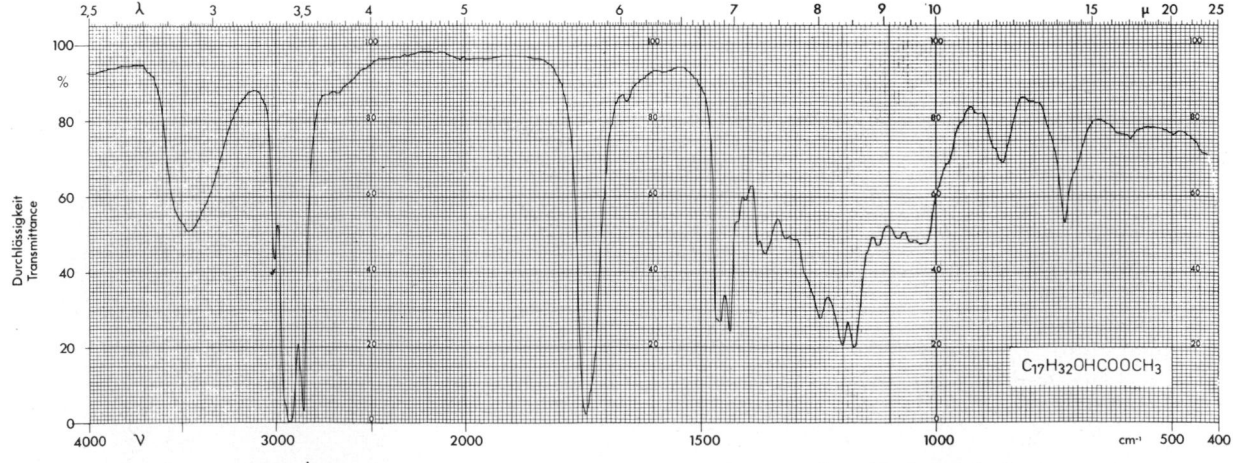

5183

Verbindung:	Butylacetoxystearat			
Formel:	$C_{24}H_{46}O_4$	M.:	**398,6**	
Handelsname:	Paricin 6	Herst.:	Baker	
Präparation:	Kapill. Film	Dez. Nr.:	3.5.15	

Compound:	Butyl acetoxystearate			
Formula:	$C_{24}H_{46}O_4$	M. w.:	**398,6**	
Tradename:	Paricin 6	Manuf.:	Baker	
Preparation:	Capill. Film	Dec. No.:	3.5.15	

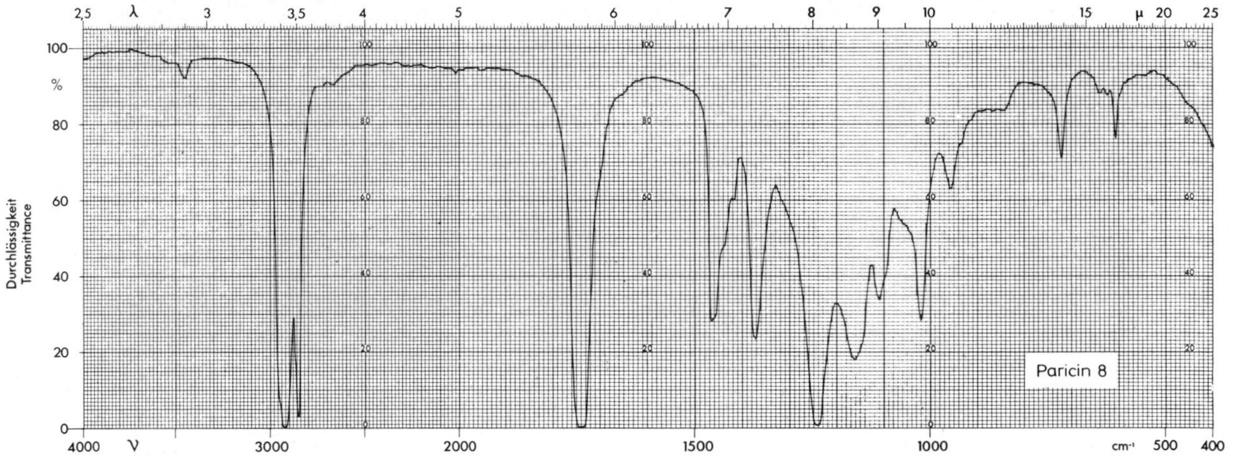

5184

Verbindung:	Glycerintriacetoxystearat			
Formel:	$C_{63}H_{116}O_{12}$	M.:	**1065,6**	
Handelsname:	Paricin 8	Herst.:	Baker	
Präparation:	Kapill. Film	Dez. Nr.:	3.5.16	

Compound:	Glyceroltriacetoxy stearate			
Formula:	$C_{63}H_{116}O_{12}$	M. w.:	**1065,6**	
Tradename:	Paricin 8	Manuf.:	Baker	
Preparation:	Capill. Film	Dec. No.:	3.5.16	

5185

Verbindung:	Methylricinolat			
Formel:	$C_{19}H_{36}O_3$	M.:	**312,5**	
Handelsname:	Nopco 1060 C	Herst.:	Nopco	
Präparation:	Kapill. Film	Dez. Nr.:	3.6.1	

Compound:	Methyl ricinoleate			
Formula:	$C_{19}H_{36}O_3$	M. w.:	312,5	
Tradename:	Nopco 1060 C	Manuf.:	Nopco	
Preparation:	Capill. Film	Dec. No.:	3.6.1	

Weichmacher
3. Aliphat. Monocarbonsäureester
3.6. Ricinolsäureester

Plasticizers
3. Aliphatic Monocarboxylic Acid Esters
3.6. Ricinoleic Acid Esters

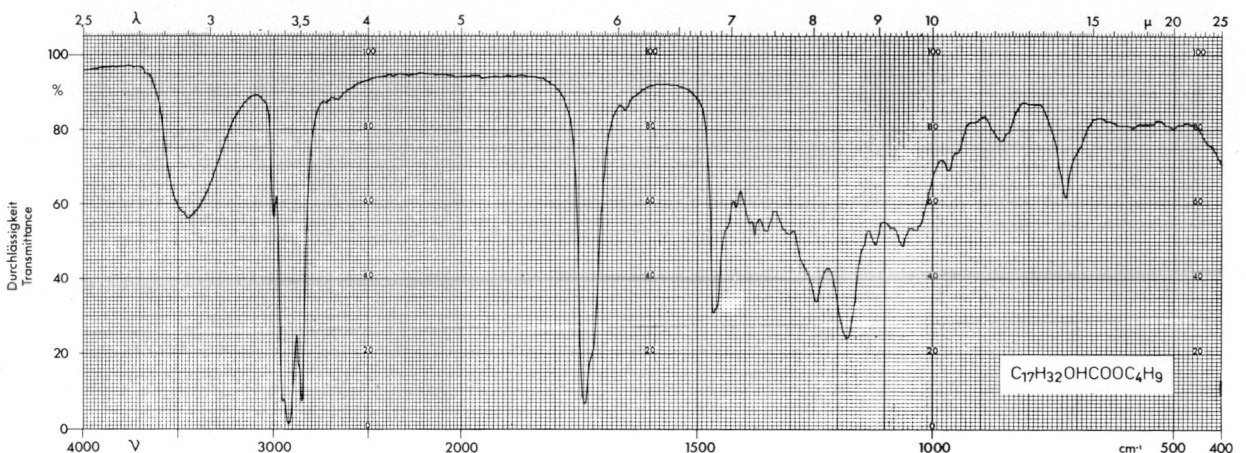

Verbindung:	Butylricinolat			Compound:	Butyl ricinoleate			5186
Formel:	$C_{22}H_{42}O_3$	M.:	354,6	Formula:	$C_{22}H_{42}O_3$	M. w.:	354,6	
Handelsname:	Flexricin P-3	Herst.:	Baker	Tradename:	Flexricin P-3	Manuf.:	Baker	
Präparation:	Kapill. Film	Dez. Nr.:	3.6.2	Preparation:	Capill. Film	Dec. No.:	3.6.2	

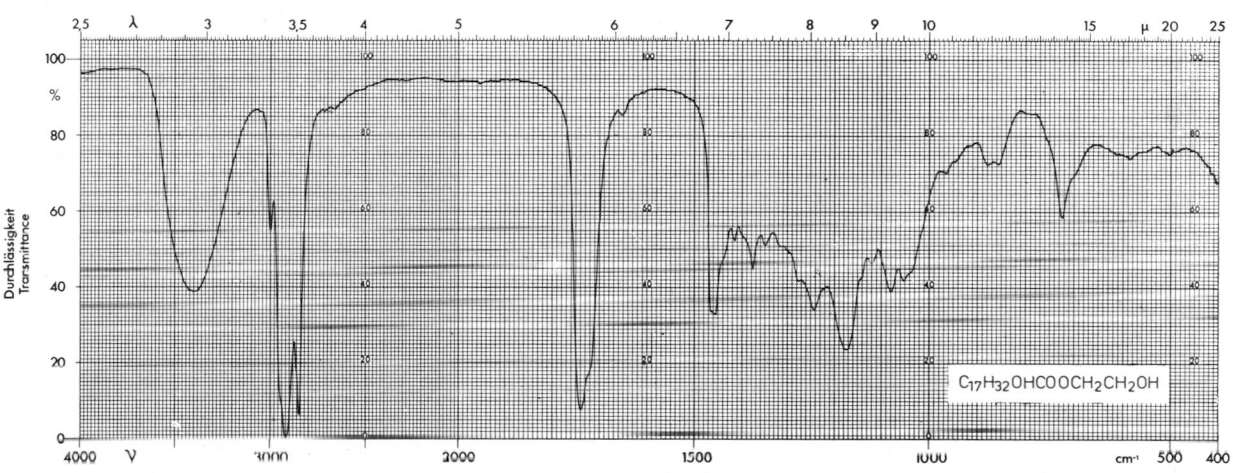

Verbindung:	Ethylenglykolmonoricinolat			Compound:	Ethylene glycol monoricinoleate			5187
Formel:	$C_{20}H_{38}O_4$	M.:	342,6	Formula:	$C_{20}H_{38}O_4$	M. w.:	342,6	
Handelsname:	Flexricin 15	Herst.:	Baker	Tradename:	Flexricin 15	Manuf.:	Baker	
Präparation:	Kapill. Film	Dez. Nr.:	3.6.3	Preparation:	Capill. Film	Dec. No.:	3.6.3	

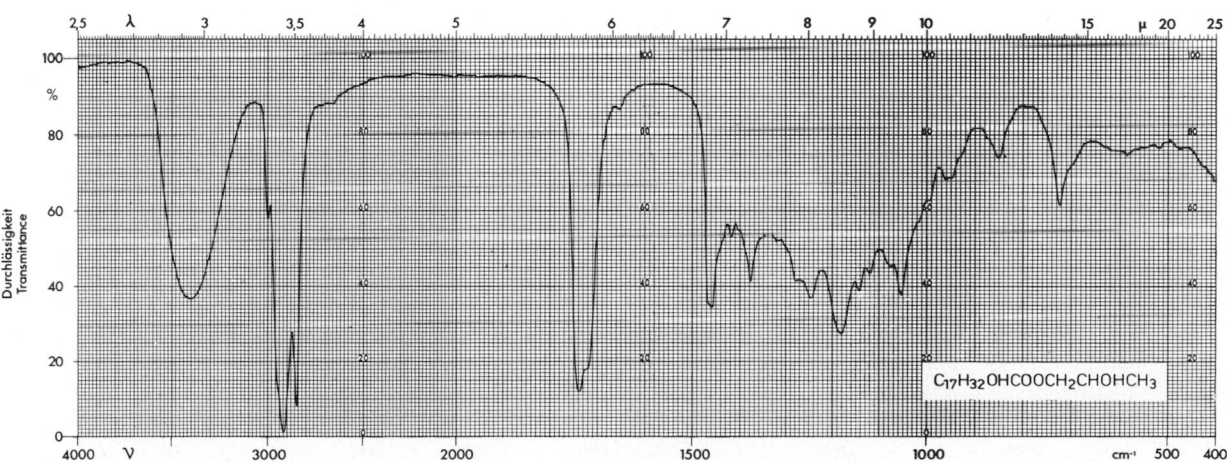

Verbindung:	1,2-Propylenglykolmonoricinolat			Compound:	1,2-Propylene glycol monoricinoleate			5188
Formel:	$C_{21}H_{40}O_4$	M.:	356,6	Formula:	$C_{21}H_{40}O_4$	M. w.:	356,6	
Handelsname:	Flexricin 9	Herst.:	Baker	Tradename:	Flexricin 9	Manuf.:	Baker	
Präparation:	Kapill. Film	Dez. Nr.:	3.6.4	Preparation:	Capill. Film	Dec. No.:	3.6.4	

Weichmacher
3. Aliphat. Monocarbonsäureester
3.6. Ricinolsäureester

Plasticizers
3. Aliphatic Monocarboxylic Acid Esters
3.6. Ricinoleic Acid Esters

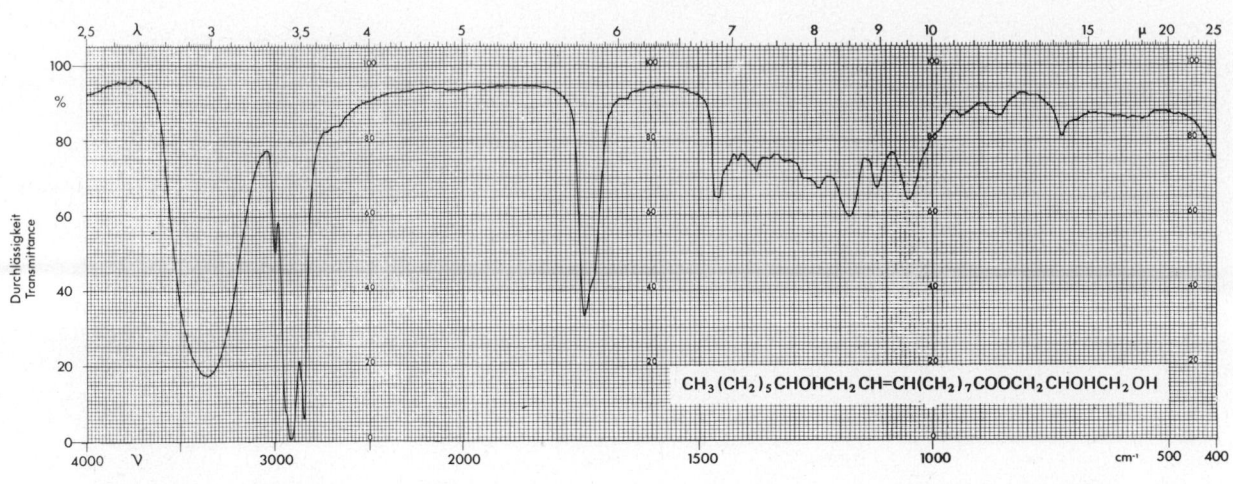

$CH_3(CH_2)_5CHOHCH_2CH=CH(CH_2)_7COOCH_2CHOHCH_2OH$

5189	Verbindung:	Glycerinmonoricinolat	Compound:	Glycerol monoricinoleate	
	Formel: $C_{21}H_{40}O_5$	M.: 372,6	Formula: $C_{21}H_{40}O_5$	M. w.: 372,6	
	Handelsname: Flexricin 13	Herst.: Baker	Tradename: Flexricin 13	Manuf.: Baker	
	Präparation: Kapill. Film	Dez. Nr.: 3.6.5	Preparation: Capill. Film	Dec. No.: 3.6.5	

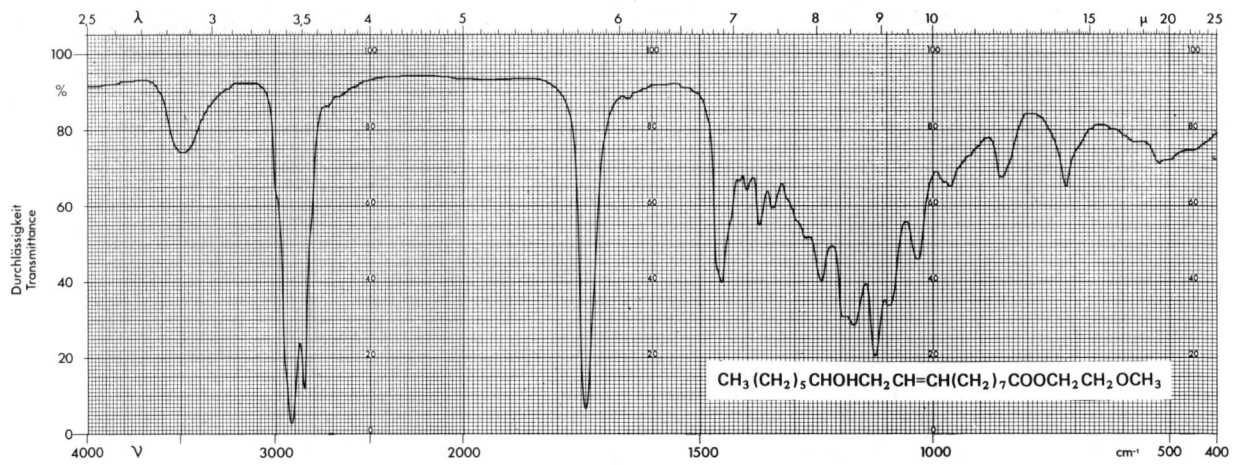

$CH_3(CH_2)_5CHOHCH_2CH=CH(CH_2)_7COOCH_2CH_2OCH_3$

5190	Verbindung:	Methoxyethylricinolat	Compound:	Methoxyethyl ricinoleate	
	Formel: $C_{21}H_{40}O_4$	M.: 356,6	Formula: $C_{21}H_{40}O_4$	M. w.: 356,6	
	Handelsname: Flexricin P-1 C	Herst.: Baker	Tradename: Flexricin P-1 C	Manuf.: Baker	
	Präparation: Kapill. Film	Dez. Nr.: 3.6.6	Preparation: Capill. Film	Dec. No.: 3.6.6	

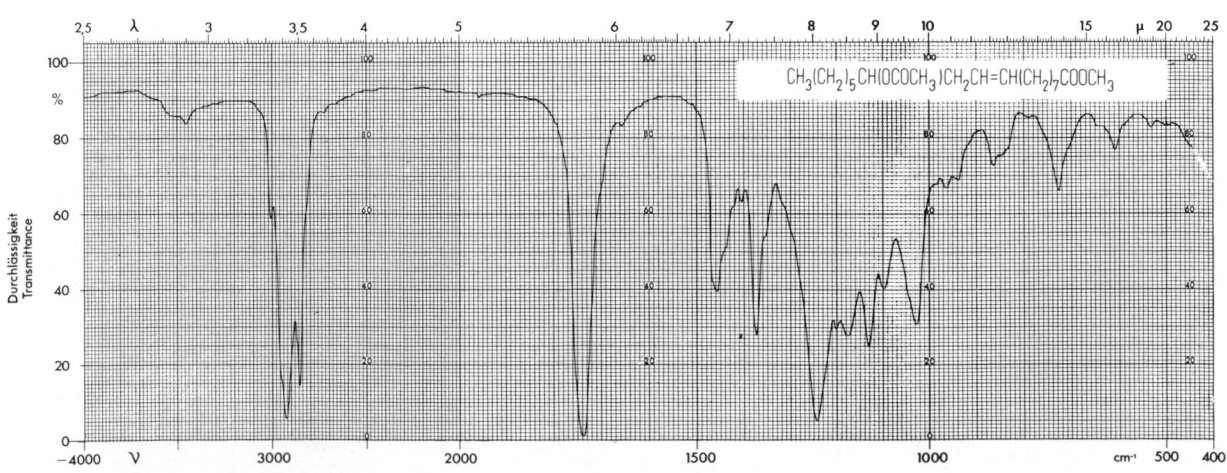

$CH_3(CH_2)_5CH(OCOCH_3)CH_2CH=CH(CH_2)_7COOCH_3$

5191	Verbindung:	Methylacetylricinolat	Compound:	Methyl acetyl ricinoleate	
	Formel: $C_{21}H_{38}O_4$	M.: 354,6	Formula: $C_{21}H_{38}O_4$	M. w.: 354,6	
	Handelsname: Flexricin P 4	Herst.: Baker	Tradename: Flexricin P 4	Manuf.: Baker	
	Präparation: Kapill. Film	Dez. Nr.: 3.6.7	Preparation: Capill. Film	Dec. No.: 3.6.7	

Weichmacher
3. Aliphat. Monocarbonsäureester
3.6. Ricinolsäureester

Plasticizers
3. Aliphatic Monocarboxylic Acid Esters
3.6. Ricinoleic Acid Esters

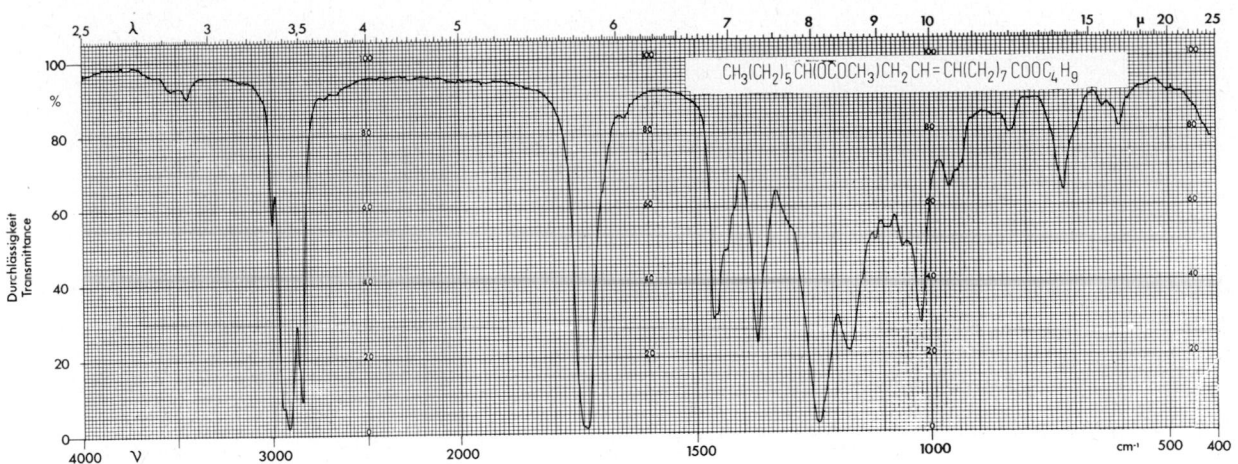

$CH_3(CH_2)_5 CH(OCOCH_3)CH_2 CH=CH(CH_2)_7 COOC_4H_9$

Verbindung:	Butylacetylricinolat		
Formel:	$C_{24}H_{44}O_4$	M.:	396,6
Handelsname:	Flexricin P 6	Herst.:	Baker
Präparation:	Kapill. Film	Dez. Nr.:	3.6.8

Compound:	Butyl acetyl ricinoleate			5192
Formula:	$C_{24}H_{44}O_4$	M. w.:	396,6	
Tradename:	Flexricin P 6	Manuf.:	Baker	
Preparation:	Capill. Film	Dec. No.:	3.6.8	

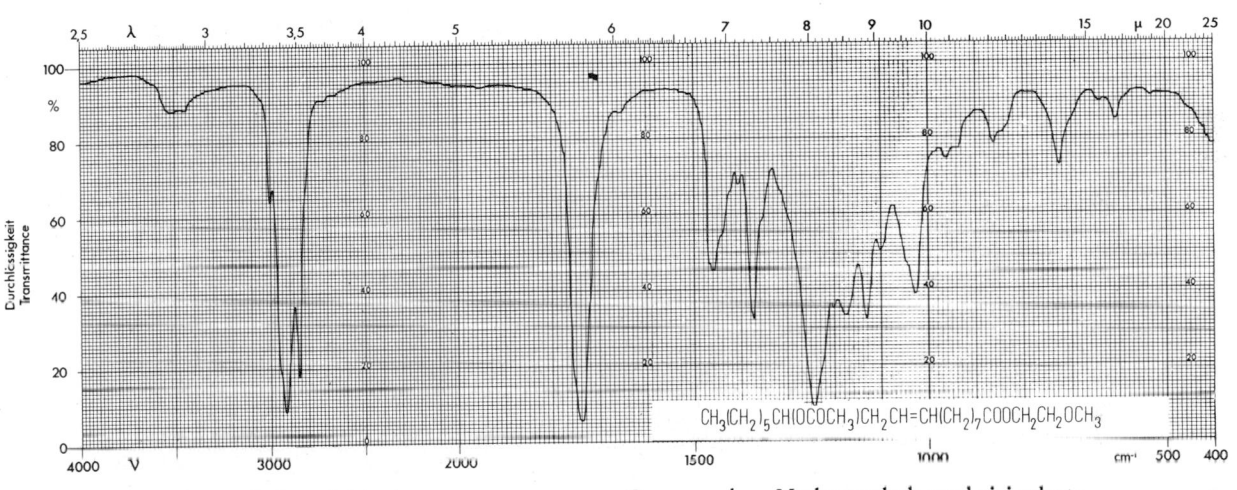

$CH_3(CH_2)_5 CH(OCOCH_3)CH_2 CH=CH(CH_2)_7 COOCH_2CH_2OCH_3$

Verbindung:	Methoxyethylacetylricinolat		
Formel:	$C_{23}H_{42}O_5$	M.:	398,6
Handelsname:	KP 120	Herst.:	FMC
Präparation:	Kapill. Film	Dez. Nr.:	3.6.9

Compound:	Methoxyethylacetyl ricinoleate			5193
Formula:	$C_{23}H_{42}O_5$	M. w.:	398,6	
Tradename:	KP 120	Manuf.:	FMC	
Preparation:	Capill. Film	Dec. No.:	3.6.9	

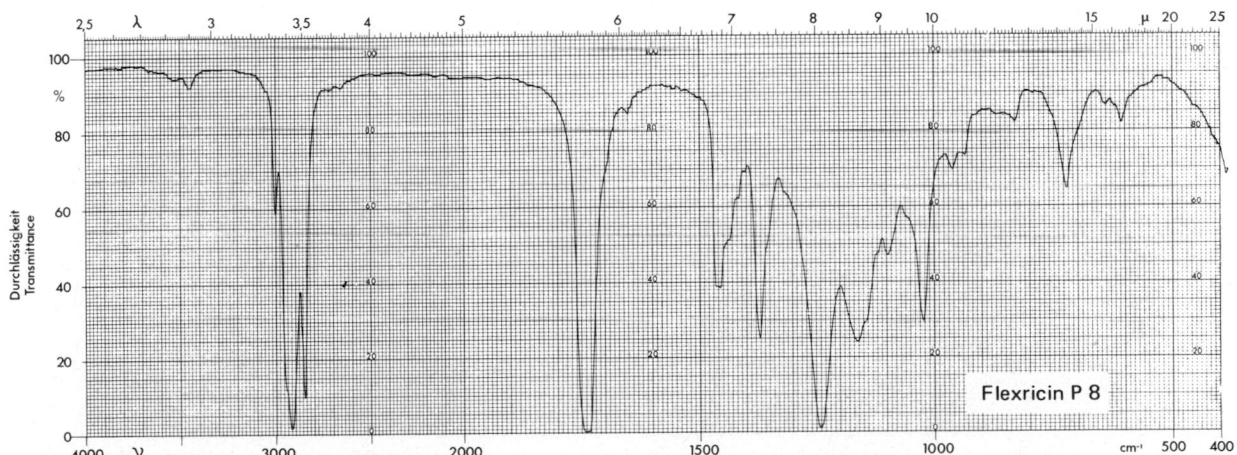

Flexricin P 8

Verbindung:	Glycerin-tri-acetylricinolat		
Formel:	$C_{63}H_{110}O_2$	M.:	1059,6
Handelsname:	Flexricin P-8	Herst.:	Baker
Präparation:	Kapill. Film	Dez. Nr.:	3.6.10

Compound:	Glycerol triacetyl ricinoleate			5194
Formula:	$C_{63}H_{110}O_2$	M. w.:	1059,6	
Tradename:	Flexricin P-8	Manuf.:	Baker	
Preparation:	Capill. Film	Dec. No.:	3.6.10	

Weichmacher
3. Aliphat. Monocarbonsäureester
3.8. Sonstige Ester

Plasticizers
3. Aliphatic Monocarboxylic Acid Esters
3.8. Miscellaneos Esters

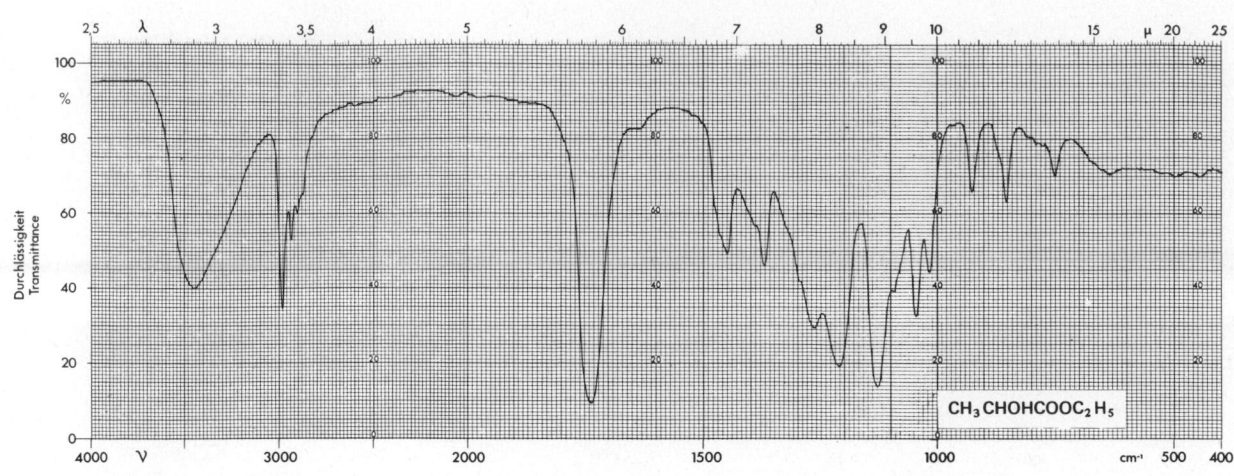

$CH_3CHOHCOOC_2H_5$

5195	Verbindung:	**Ethyllactat**			Compound:	**Ethyl lactate**		
	Formel:	$C_5H_{10}O_3$	M.:	**118,1**	Formula:	$C_5H_{10}O_3$	M. w.:	**118,1**
	Handelsname:	**Lactonal**	Herst.:	**Boehringer**	Tradename:	**Lactonal**	Manuf.:	**Boehringer**
	Präparation:	**Kapill. Film**	Dez. Nr.:	**3.8.1**	Preparation:	**Capill. Film**	Dec. No.	**3.8.1**

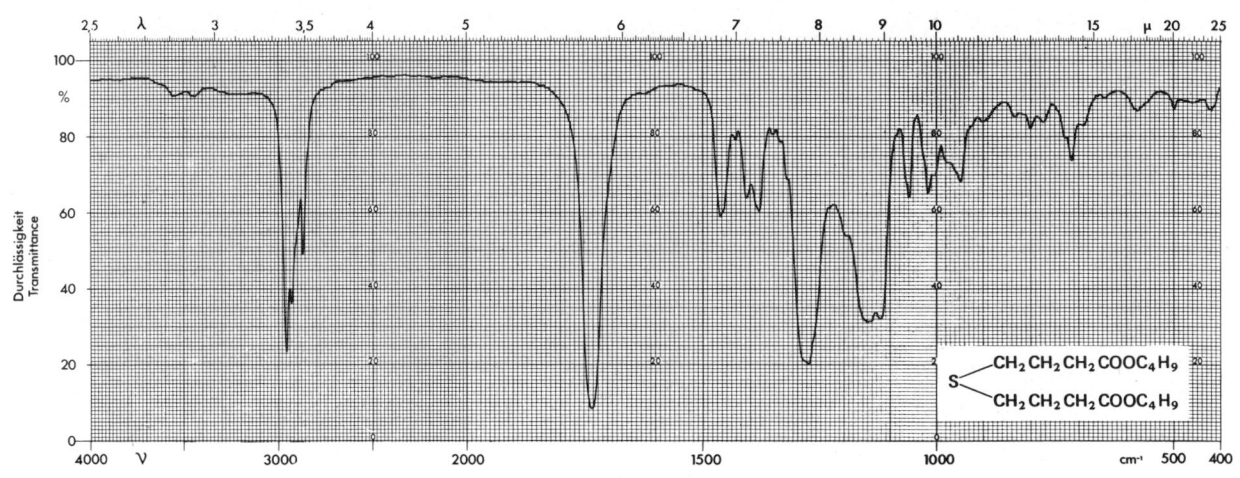

$$S\begin{cases} CH_2CH_2CH_2COOC_4H_9 \\ CH_2CH_2CH_2COOC_4H_9 \end{cases}$$

5196	Verbindung:	**Dibutylthiodibutyrat**			Compound:	**Dibutyl thiodibutyrate**		
	Formel:	$C_{16}H_{32}O_4S$	M.:	**320,5**	Formula:	$C_{16}H_{32}O_4S$	M. w.:	**320,5**
	Handelsname:		Herst.:		Tradename:		Manuf.:	
	Präparation:	**Kapill. Film**	Dez. Nr.:	**3.8.2**	Preparation:	**Capill. Film**	Dec. No.:	**3.8.2**

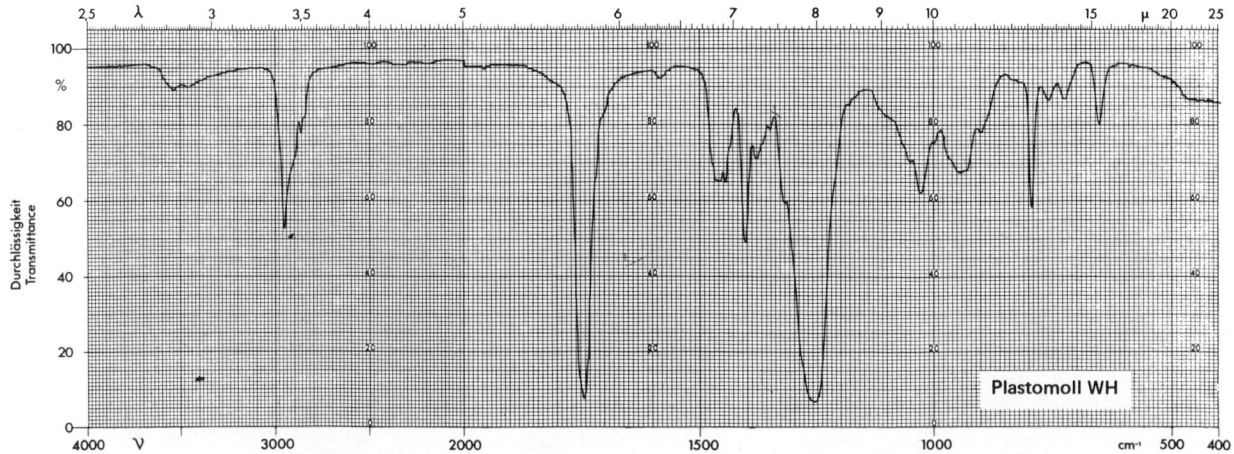

Plastomoll WH

5197	Verbindung:	**Dichlorbutandiol-bis-butylcarbonat**			Compound:	**Dichlorobutanediol-bis-butylcarbonate**		
	Formel:		M.:		Formula:		M. w.:	
	Handelsname:	**Plastomoll WH**	Herst.:	**BASF**	Tradename:	**Plastomoll WH**	Manuf.:	**BASF**
	Präparation:	**Kapill. Film**	Dez. Nr.:	**3.8.3**	Preparation:	**Capill. Film**	Dec. No.:	**3.8.3**

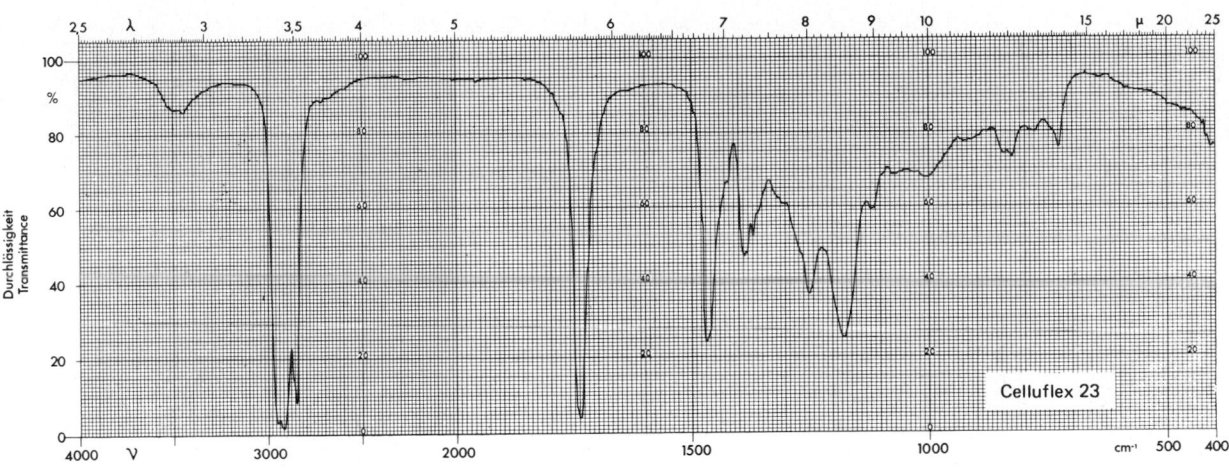

Verbindung:	Alkylepoxystearat			Compound:	Alkyl epoxy stearate			5198
Formel:		M.:	~ 400	Formula:		M. w.:	~ 400	
Handelsname:	Celluflex 23	Herst.:	Celanese	Tradename:	Celluflex 23	Manuf.:	Celanese	
Präparation:	Kapill. Film	Dez. Nr.:	4.1	Preparation:	Capill. Film	Dec. No.:	4.1	

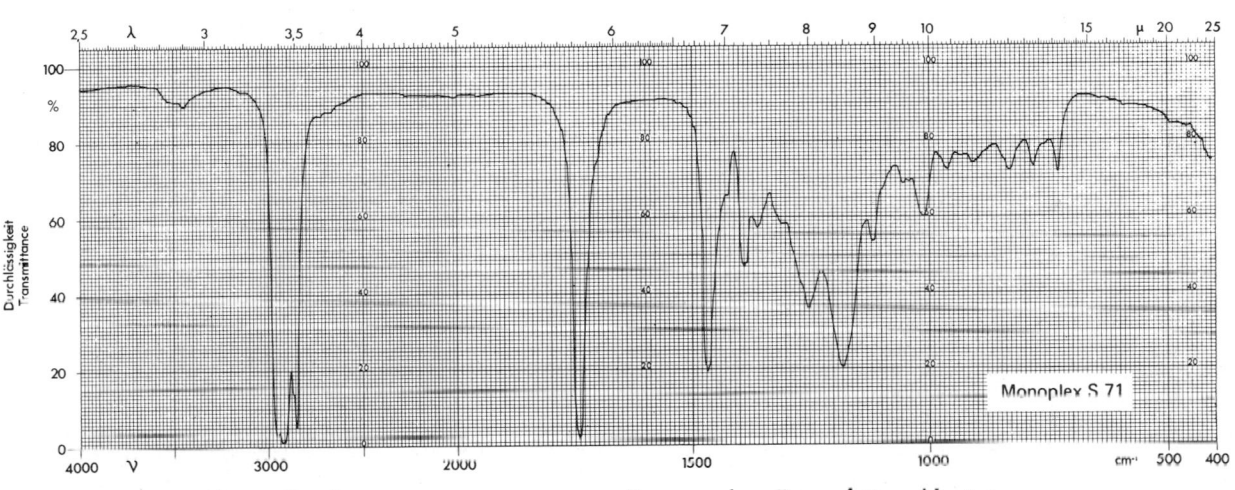

Verbindung:	Epoxydierter Fettsäureester			Compound:	Epoxy fatty acid ester			5199
Formel:		M.:	~ 360	Formula:		M. w.:	~ 360	
Handelsname:	Monoplex S 71	Herst.:	Rohm & Haas	Tradename:	Monoplex S 71	Manuf.:	Rohm & Haas	
Präparation:	Kapill. Film	Dez. Nr.:	4.2	Preparation:	Capill. Film	Dec. No.:	4.2	

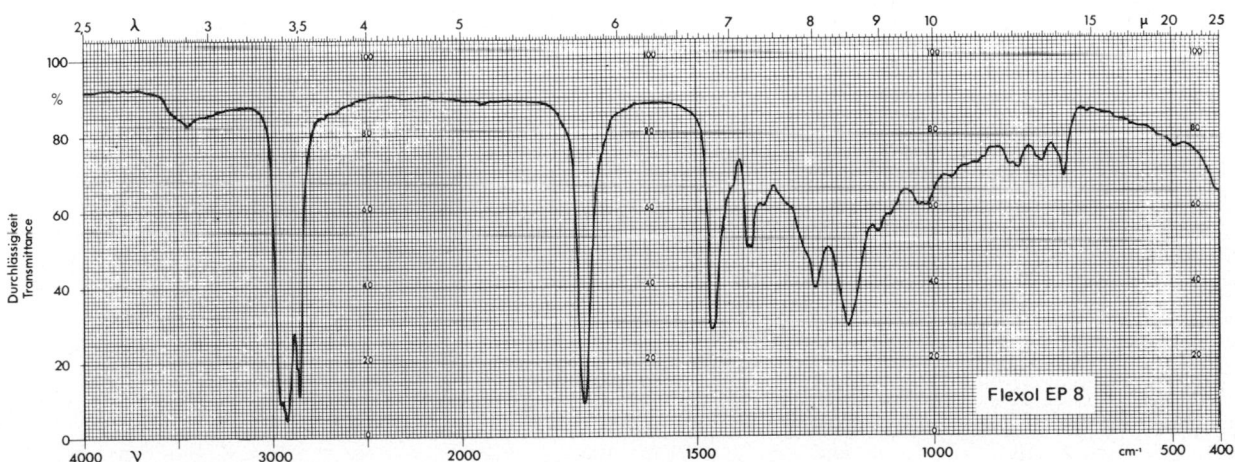

Verbindung:	2-Ethylhexylepoxytallat			Compound:	2-Ethylhexyl epoxytallate			5200
Formel:		M.:	~ 385	Formula:		M. w.:	~ 385	
Handelsname:	Flexol EP 8	Herst.:	Carbide	Tradename:	Flexol EP 8	Manuf.:	Carbide	
Präparation:	Kapill. Film	Dez. Nr.:	4.3	Preparation:	Capill. Film	Dec. No.:	4.3	

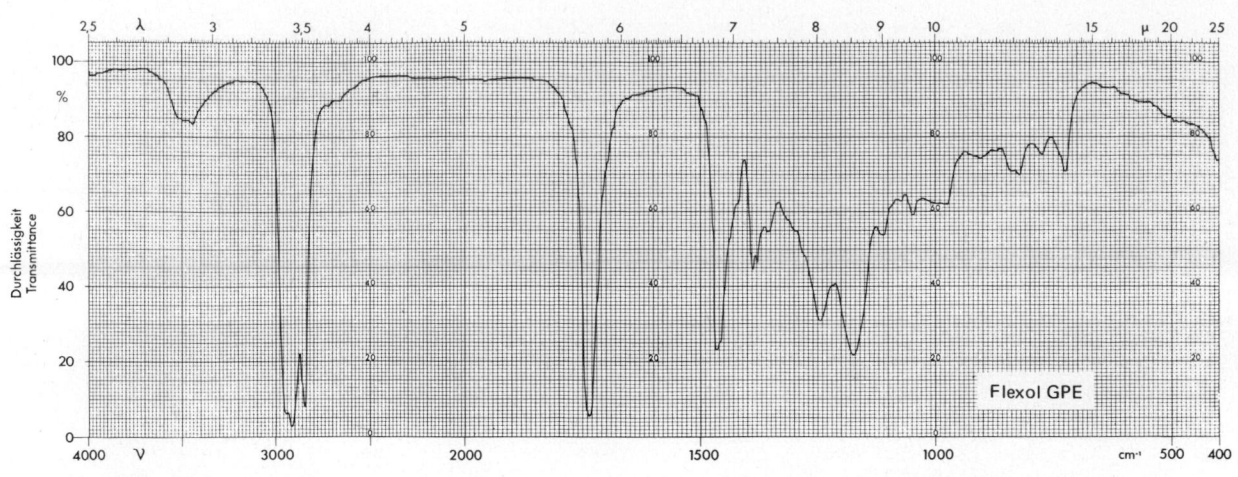

5201	Verbindung:	Epoxydierter Fettsäureester		Compound:	Epoxidized fatty acid ester	
	Formel:		M.: ∼ 350	Formula:		M. w.: ∼ 350
	Handelsname:	Flexol GPE	Herst.: Carbide	Tradename:	Flexol GPE	Manuf.: Carbide
	Präparation:	Kapill. Film	Dez. Nr.: 4.4	Preparation:	Capill. Film	Dec. No.: 4.4

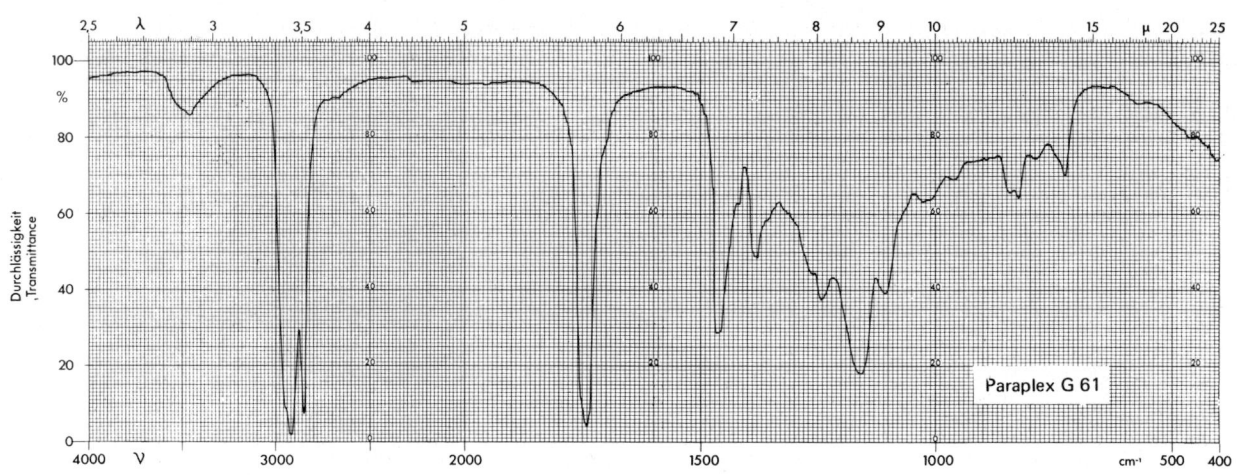

5202	Verbindung:	Epoxydiertes Fettsäuretriglycerid		Compound:	Epoxidized fatty acid triglyceride	
	Formel:		M.: ∼ 1000	Formula:		M. w.: ∼ 1000
	Handelsname:	Paraplex G 61	Herst.: Rohm & Haas	Tradename:	Paraplex G 61	Manuf.: Rohm & Haas
	Präparation:	Kapill. Film	Dez. Nr.: 4.5	Preparation:	Capill. Film	Dec. No:. 4.5

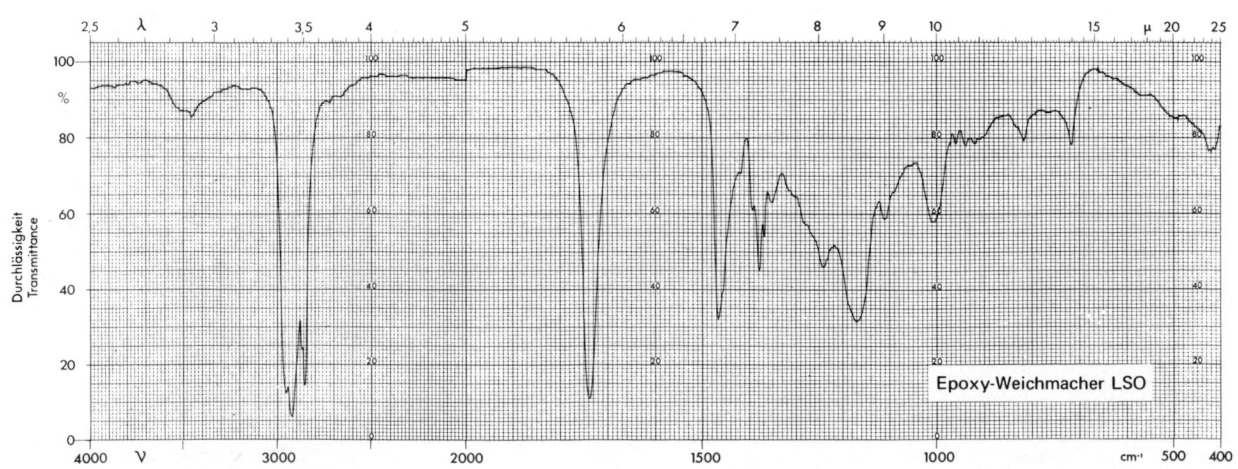

5203	Verbindung:	Epoxydierter Fettsäureester		Compound:	Epoxidized fatty acid ester	
	Formel:		M.: ∼ 285	Formula:		M. w.: ∼ 285
	Handelsname:	Epoxy-Weichmacher LSO	Herst.: Bärlocher	Tradename:	Epoxy-Weichmacher LSO	Manuf.: Bärlocher
	Präparation:	Kapill. Film	Dez. Nr.: 4.6	Preparation:	Capill. Film	Dec. No.: 4.6

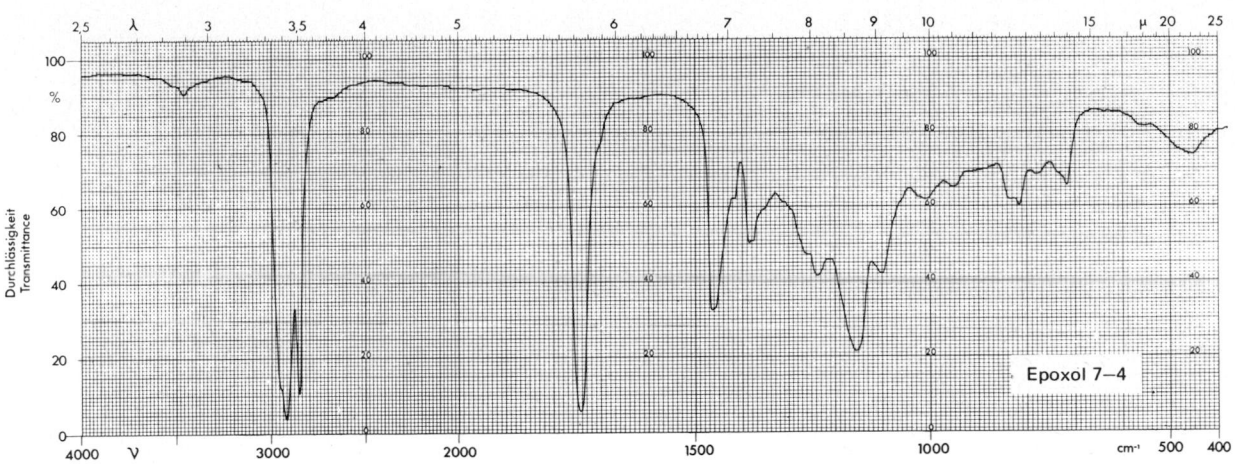

Verbindung:	Epoxydiertes Sojaöl			Compound:	Epoxidized soy bean oil			5204
Formel:		M.:	~ 950	Formula:		M. w.:	~ 950	
Handelsname:	EPOXOL 7-4	Herst.:	Swift	Tradename:	EPOXOL 7-4	Manuf.:	Swift	
Präparation:	Kapill. Film	Dez. Nr.:	4.7	Preparation:	Capill. Film	Dec. No.:	4.7	

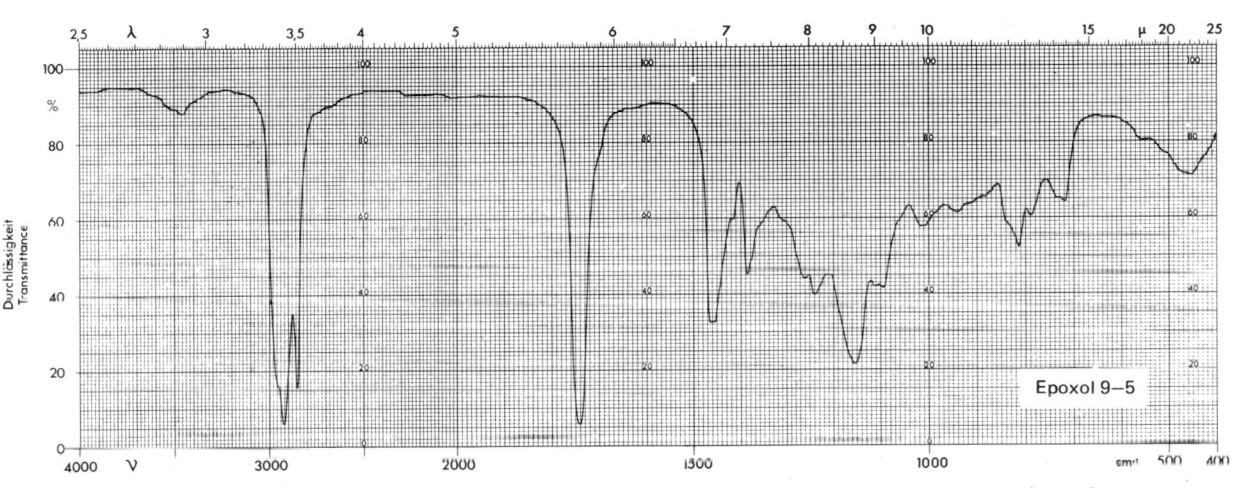

Verbindung:	Epoxydiertes Fettsäuretriglycerid			Compound:	Epoxidized fatty acid triglyceride			5205
Formel:		M.:	~ 980	Formula:		M. w.:	~ 980	
Handelsname:	EPOXOL 9-5	Herst.:	Swift	Tradename:	EPOXOL 9-5	Manuf.:	Swift	
Präparation:	Kapill. Film	Dez. Nr.:	4.8	Preparation:	Capill. Film	Dec. No.:	4.8	

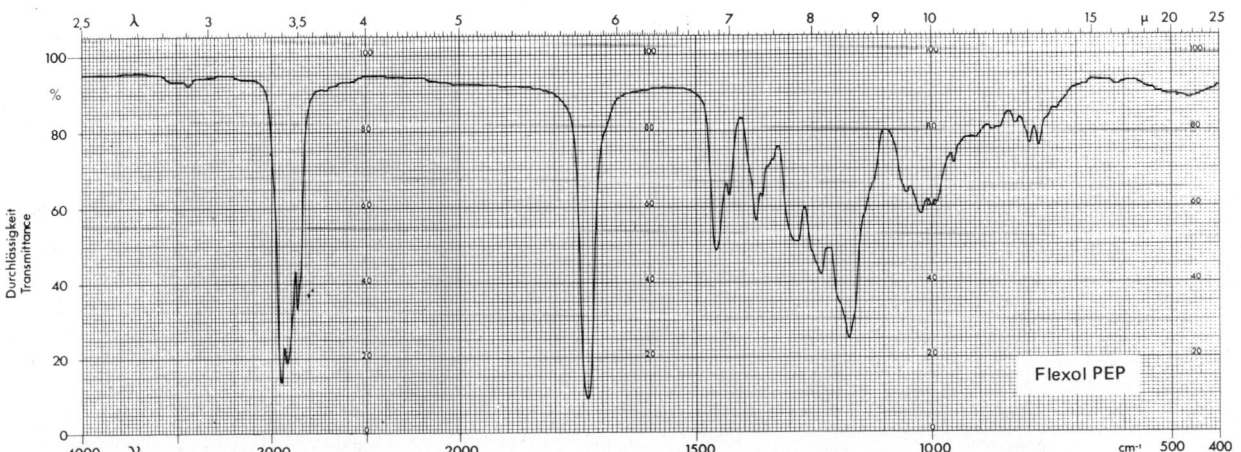

Verbindung:	Epoxytetrahydrophthalat			Compound:	Epoxy tetrahydro phthalate			5206
Formel:		M.:		Formula:		M. w.:		
Handelsname:	Flexol PEP	Herst.:	Carbide	Tradename:	Flexol PEP	Manuf.:	Carbide	
Präparation:	Kapill. Film	Dez. Nr.:	4.9	Preparation:	Capill. Film	Dec. No.:	4.9	

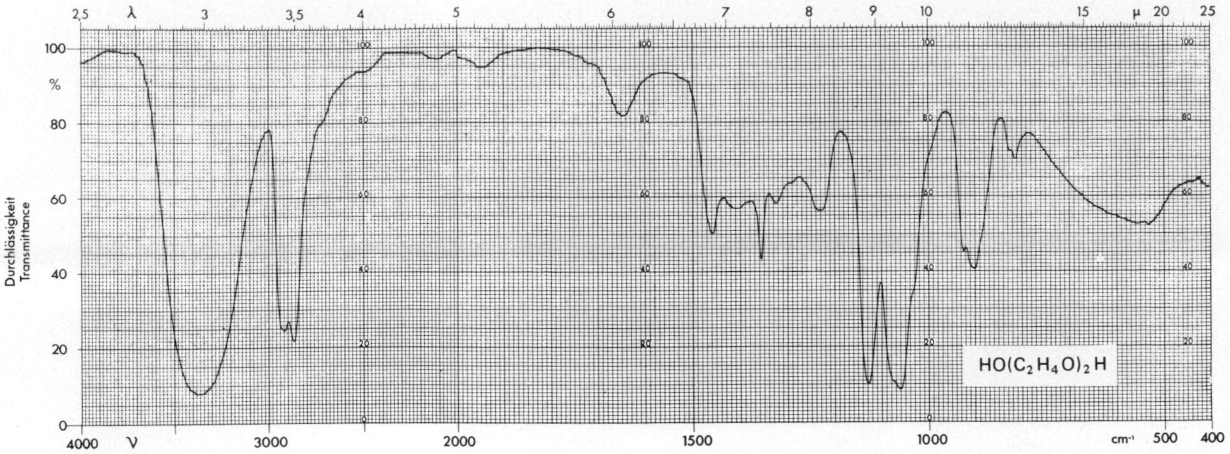

Weichmacher
5. Glykole und Ether
5.1. Äthylen- und Polyethylenglykole

Plasticizers
5. Glycols and Ethers
5.1. Ethylene- and Polyethylene Glycols

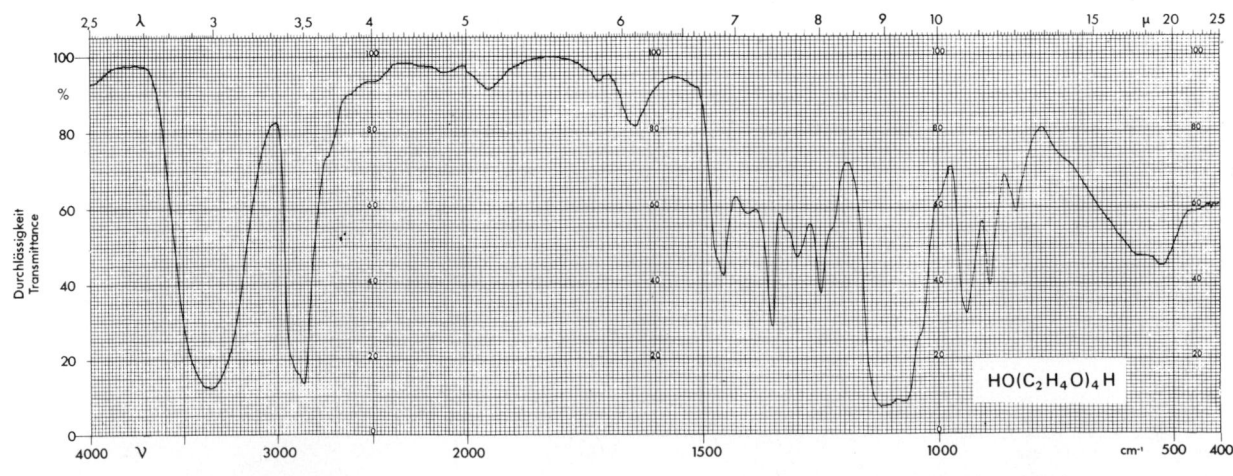

5207

Verbindung:	Diethylenglykol			Compound:	Diethylene glycol		
Formel:	$C_4H_{10}O_3$	M.:	106,1	Formula:	$C_4H_{10}O_3$	M. w.:	106,1
Handelsname:	Diglykol	Herst.:	BASF	Tradename:	Diglykol	Manuf.:	BASF
Präparation:	Kapill. Film	Dez. Nr.:	5.1.1	Preparation:	Capill. Film	Dec. No.:	5.1.1

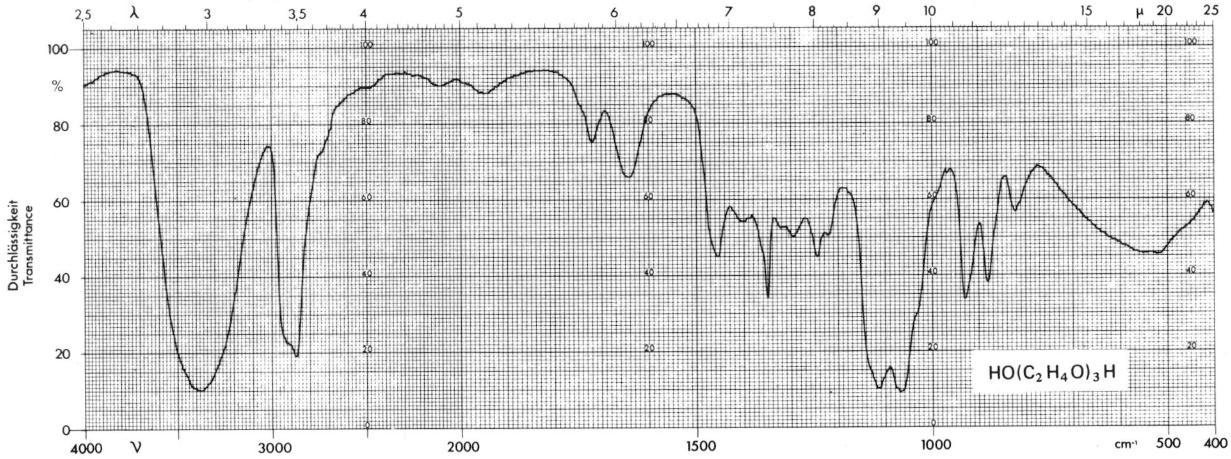

5208

Verbindung:	Triethylenglykol			Compound:	Triethylene glycol		
Formel:	$C_6H_{14}O_4$	M.:	150,2	Formula:	$C_6H_{14}O_4$	M. w.:	150,2
Handelsname:	Triglykol	Herst.:	BASF	Tradename:	Triglykol	Manuf.:	BASF
Präparation:	Kapill. Film	Dez. Nr.:	5.1.2	Preparation:	Capill. Film	Dec. No.:	5.1.2

5209

Verbindung:	Tetraethylenglykol			Compound:	Tetraethylene glycol		
Formel:	$C_8H_{18}O_5$	M.:	194	Formula:	$C_8H_{18}O_5$	M. w.:	194
Handelsname:	Diol 4 P	Herst.:	BASF	Tradename:	Diol 4 P	Manuf.:	BASF
Präparation:	Kapill. Film	Dez. Nr.:	5.1.3	Preparation:	Capill. Film	Dec. No.:	5.1.3

Weichmacher
5. Glykole und Ether
5.1. Äthylen- und Polyethylenglykole

Plasticizers
5. Glycols and Ethers
5.1. Ethylene- and Polyethylene Glycols

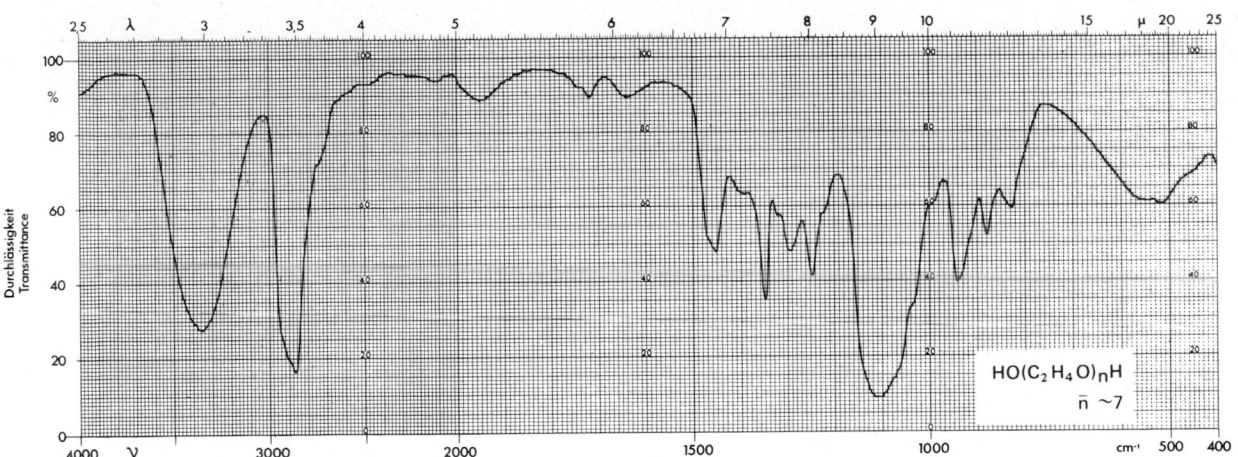

Verbindung:	Polyethylenglykol			Compound:	Polyethylene glycol			5210
Formel:	$C_nH_{2n+2}O_{n/2+1}$	M.:	~ 300	Formula:	$C_nH_{2n+2}O_{n/2+1}$	M. w.:	~ 300	
Handelsname:	Polyglykol 300	Herst.:	Hoechst	Tradename:	Polyglykol 300	Manuf.:	Hoechst	
Präparation:	Kapill. Film	Dez. Nr.:	5.1.4	Preparation:	Capill. Film	Dec. No.:	5.1.4	

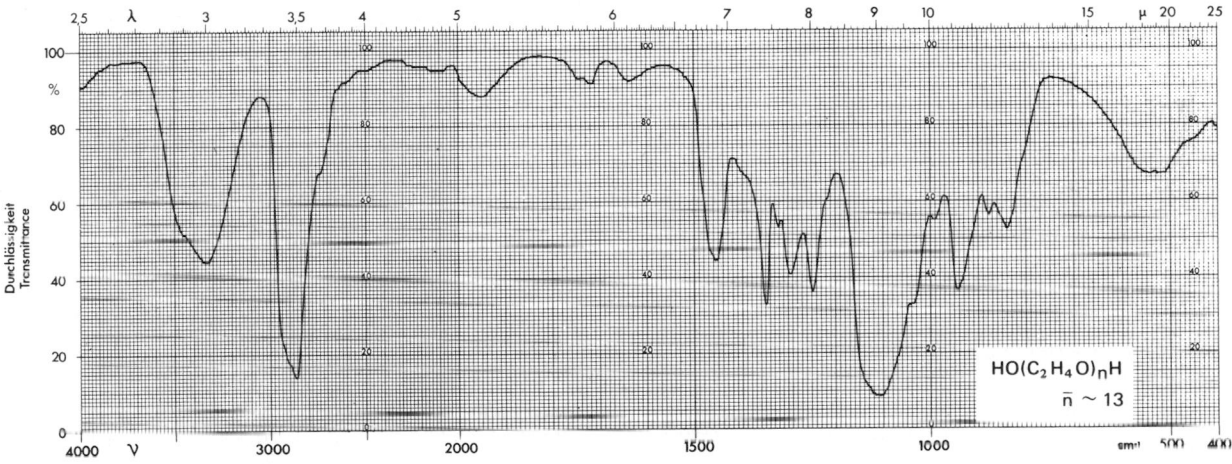

Verbindung:	Polyethylenglykol			Compound:	Polyethylene glycol			5211
Formel:	$C_nH_{2n+2}O_{n/2+1}$	M.:	~ 600	Formula:	$C_nH_{2n+2}O_{n/2+1}$	M. w.:	~ 600	
Handelsname:	Polyglykol 600	Herst.:	Hoechst	Tradename:	Polyglykol 600	Manuf.:	Hoechst	
Präparation:	Kapill. Film	Dez. Nr.:	5.1.5	Preparation:	Capill. Film	Dec. No.:	5.1.5	

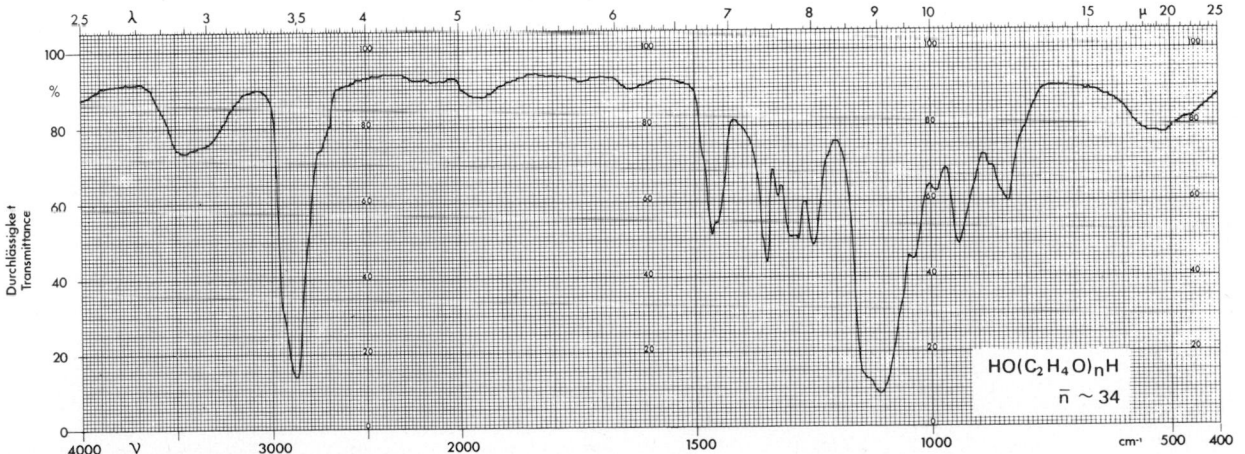

Verbindung:	Polyethylenglykol			Compound:	Polyethylene glycol			5212
Formel:	$C_nH_{2n+2}O_{n/2+1}$	M.:	~ 1500	Formula:	$C_nH_{2n+2}O_{n/2+1}$	M. w.:	~ 1500	
Handelsname:	Polyglykol 1500	Herst.:	Hoechst	Tradename:	Polyglykol 1500	Manuf.:	Hoechst	
Präparation:	Kapill. Film	Dez. Nr.:	5.1.6	Preparation:	Capill. Film	Dec. No.:	5.1.6	

Weichmacher
5. Glykole und Ether
5.2. Polypropylenglykole

Plasticizers
5. Glycols and Ethers
5.2. Polypropylene Glycols

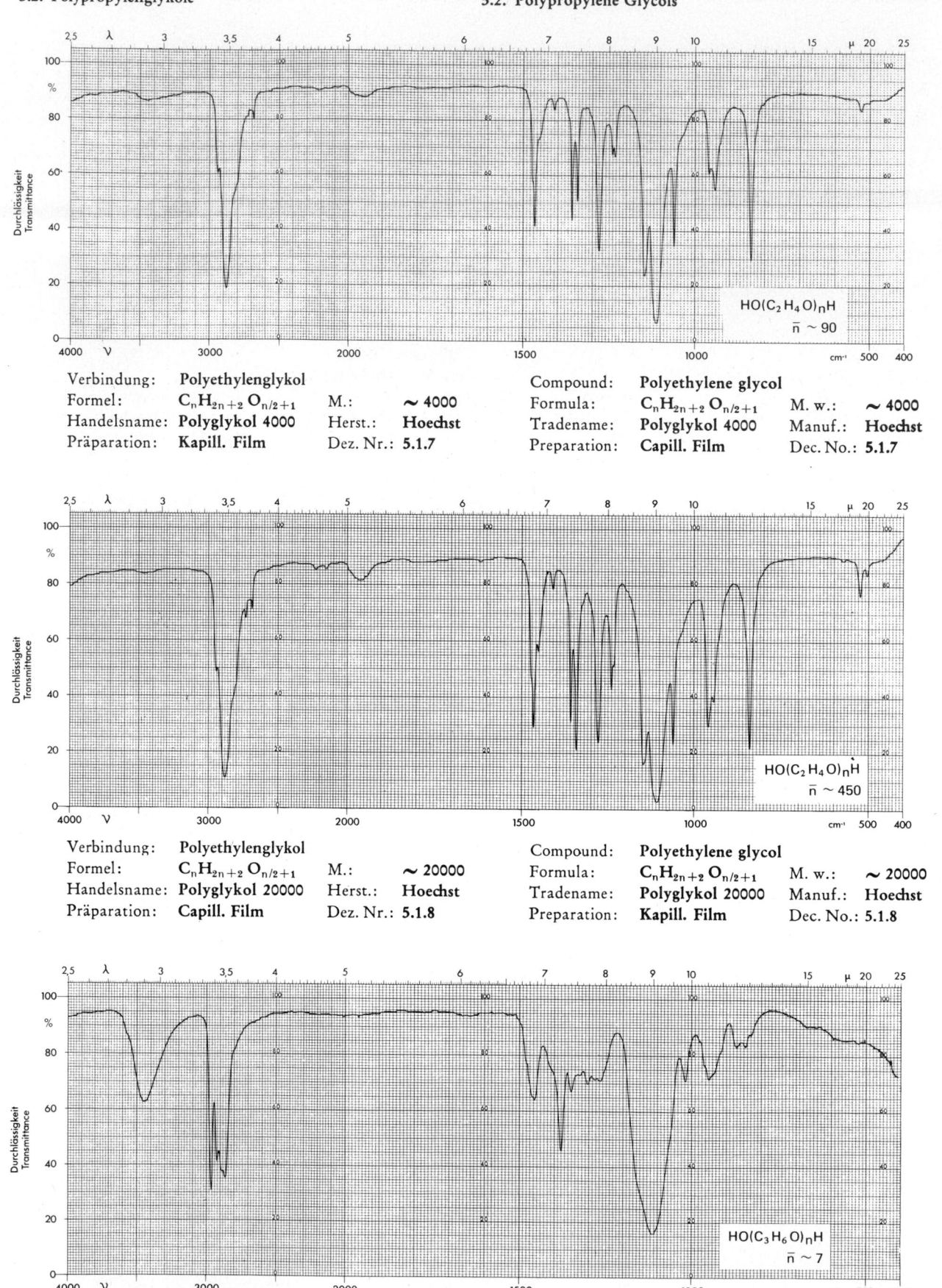

$HO(C_2H_4O)_nH$

$\bar{n} \sim 90$

5213	Verbindung:	Polyethylenglykol			Compound:	Polyethylene glycol		
	Formel:	$C_nH_{2n+2}O_{n/2+1}$	M.:	~ 4000	Formula:	$C_nH_{2n+2}O_{n/2+1}$	M. w.:	~ 4000
	Handelsname:	Polyglykol 4000	Herst.:	Hoechst	Tradename:	Polyglykol 4000	Manuf.:	Hoechst
	Präparation:	Kapill. Film	Dez. Nr.:	5.1.7	Preparation:	Capill. Film	Dec. No.:	5.1.7

$HO(C_2H_4O)_n\dot{H}$

$\bar{n} \sim 450$

5214	Verbindung:	Polyethylenglykol			Compound:	Polyethylene glycol		
	Formel:	$C_nH_{2n+2}O_{n/2+1}$	M.:	~ 20000	Formula:	$C_nH_{2n+2}O_{n/2+1}$	M. w.:	~ 20000
	Handelsname:	Polyglykol 20000	Herst.:	Hoechst	Tradename:	Polyglykol 20000	Manuf.:	Hoechst
	Präparation:	Capill. Film	Dez. Nr.:	5.1.8	Preparation:	Kapill. Film	Dec. No.:	5.1.8

$HO(C_3H_6O)_nH$

$\bar{n} \sim 7$

5215	Verbindung:	Polypropylenglykol			Compound:	Polypropylene glycol		
	Formel:	$C_nH_{2n+2}O_{n/3+1}$	M.:	~ 400	Formula:	$C_nH_{2n+2}O_{n/3+1}$	M. w.:	~ 400
	Handelsname:	Pluracol P 410	Herst.:	Wyandotte	Tradename:	Pluracol P 410	Manuf.:	Wyandotte
	Präparation:	Kapill. Film	Dez. Nr.:	5.2.1	Preparation:	Capill. Film	Dec. No:.	5.2.1

Weichmacher
5. Glykole und Ether
5.2. Polypropylenglykole

Plasticizers
5. Glycols and Ethers
5.2. Polypropylene Glycols

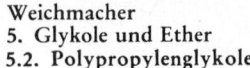

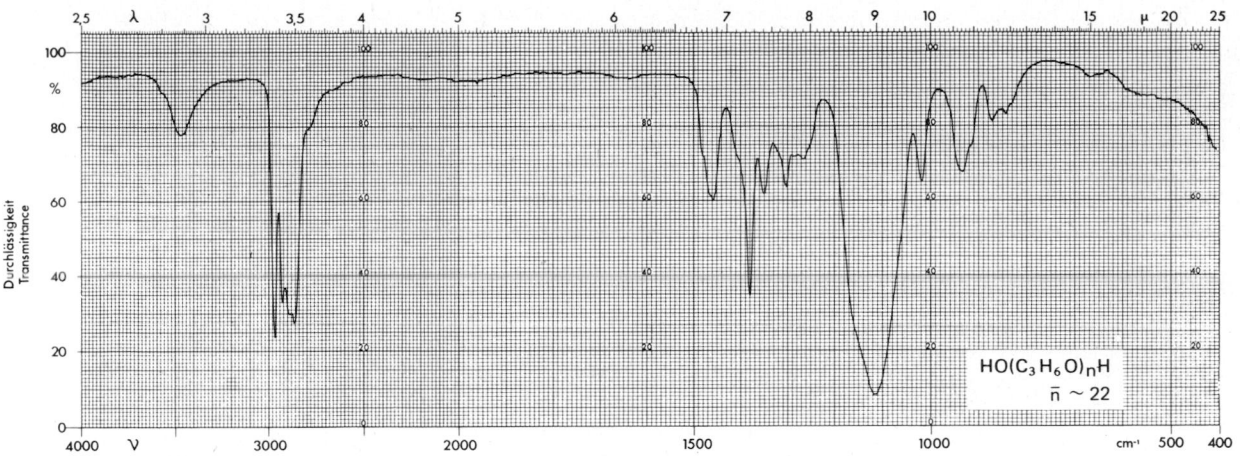

$HO(C_3H_6O)_nH$

$\bar{n} \sim 22$

Verbindung:	Polypropylenglykol			Compound:	Polypropylene glycol			5216
Formel:	$C_nH_{2n+2}O_{n/3+1}$	M.:	~ 1300	Formula:	$C_nH_{2n+2}O_{n/3+1}$	M. w.:	~ 1300	
Handelsname:	Pluracol P 1310	Herst.:	Wyandotte	Tradename:	Pluracol P 1310	Manuf.:	Wyandotte	
Präparation:	Kapill. Film	Dez. Nr.:	5.2.2	Preparation:	Capill. Film	Dec. No.:	5.2.2	

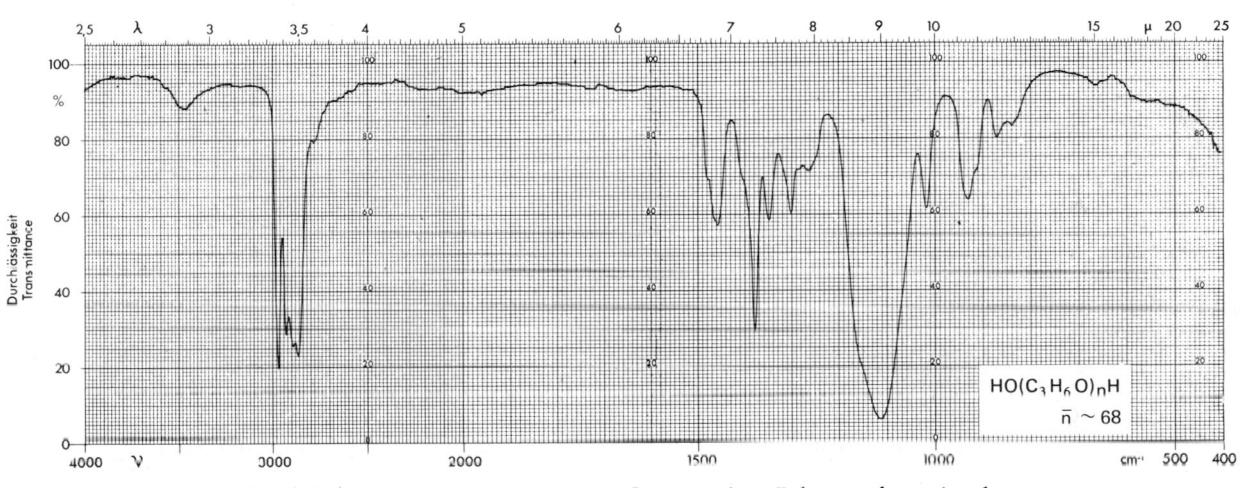

$HO(C_3H_6O)_nH$

$\bar{n} \sim 68$

Verbindung:	Polypropylenglykol			Compound:	Polypropylene glycol			5217
Formel:	$C_nH_{2n+2}O_{n/3+1}$	M.:	~ 4000	Formula:	$C_nH_{2n+2}O_{n/3+1}$	M. w.:	~ 4000	
Handelsname:	Polyglycol P 4000	Herst.:	Dow	Tradename:	Polyglycol P 4000	Manuf.:	Dow	
Präparation	Kapill. Film	Dez. Nr.:	5.2.3	Preparation:	Capill. Film	Dec. No.:	5.2.3	

Pluronic L 44

Verbindung:	Polyethylenoxidpolypropylenglykol		Compound:	Polyethyleneoxide polypropylene glycol		5218
Formel:	$HO[(C_2H_4O)_x(C_3H_6O)_y]H$	M.: ~ 2200	Formula:	$HO[(C_2H_4O)_x(C_3H_6O)_y]H$	M. w.: ~ 2200	
Handelsname:	Pluronic L 44	Herst.: Wyandotte	Tradename:	Pluronic L 44	Manuf.: Wyandotte	
Präparation:	Kapill. Film	Dez. Nr.: 5.2.4	Preparation:	Capill. Film	Dec. No.: 5.2.4	

Weichmacher
5. Glykole und Ether
5.3. Sonstige Diole und Triole

Plasticizers
5. Glycols and Ethers
5.3. Other Diols and Triols

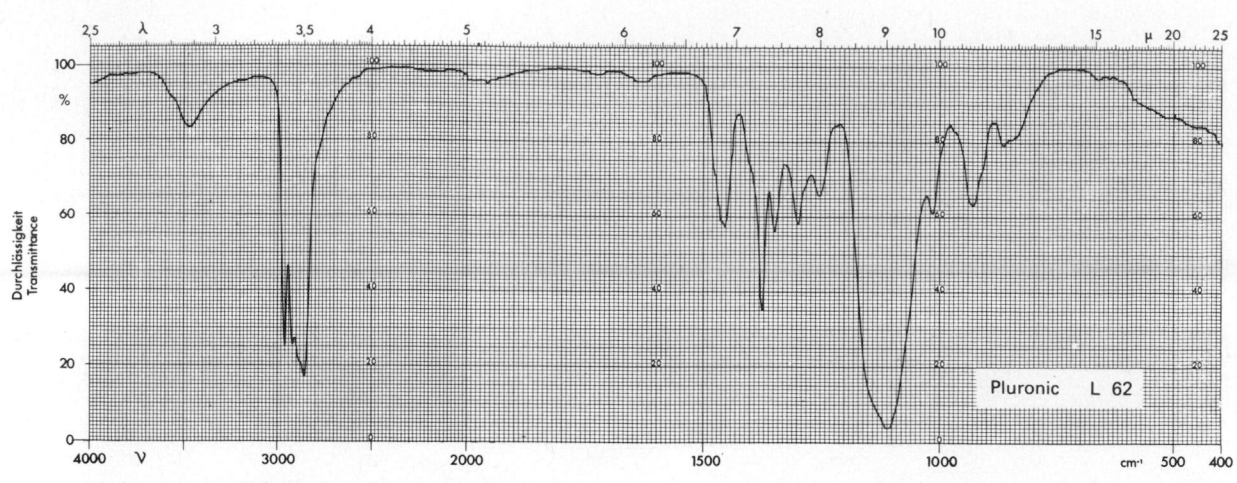

5219

Verbindung:	Polyethylenoxidpolypropylenglykol		Compound:	Polyethyleneoxide polypropylene glycol	
Formel:	HO[(C₂H₄O)ₓ(C₃H₆O)ᵧ]H M.: ~ 2000		Formula:	HO[(C₂H₄O)ₓ(C₃H₆O)ᵧ]H M. w.: ~ 2500	
Handelsname:	**Pluronic L 62**	Herst.: **Wyandotte**	Tradename:	**Pluronic L 62**	Manuf.: **Wyandotte**
Präparation:	**Kapill. Film**	Dez. Nr.: **5.2.5**	Preparation:	**Capill. Film**	Dec. No.: **5.2.5**

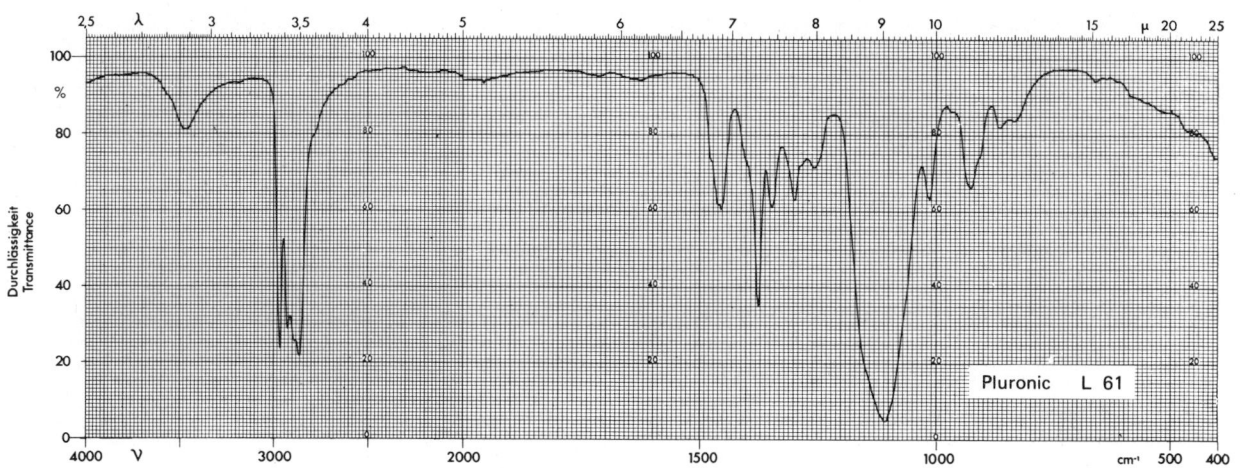

5220

Verbindung:	Polyethylenoxidpolypropylenglykol		Compound:	Polyethyleneoxide polypropylene glycol	
Formel:	HO[(C₂H₄O)ₓ(C₃H₆O)ᵧ]H M.: ~ 2000		Formula:	HO[(C₂H₄O)ₓ(C₃H₆O)ᵧ]H M. w.: ~ 2000	
Handelsname:	**Pluronic L 61**	Herst.: **Wyandotte**	Tradename:	**Pluronic L 61**	Manuf.: **Wyandotte**
Präparation:	**Kapill. Film**	Dez. Nr.: **5.2.6**	Preparation:	**Capill. Film**	Dec. No.: **5.2.6**

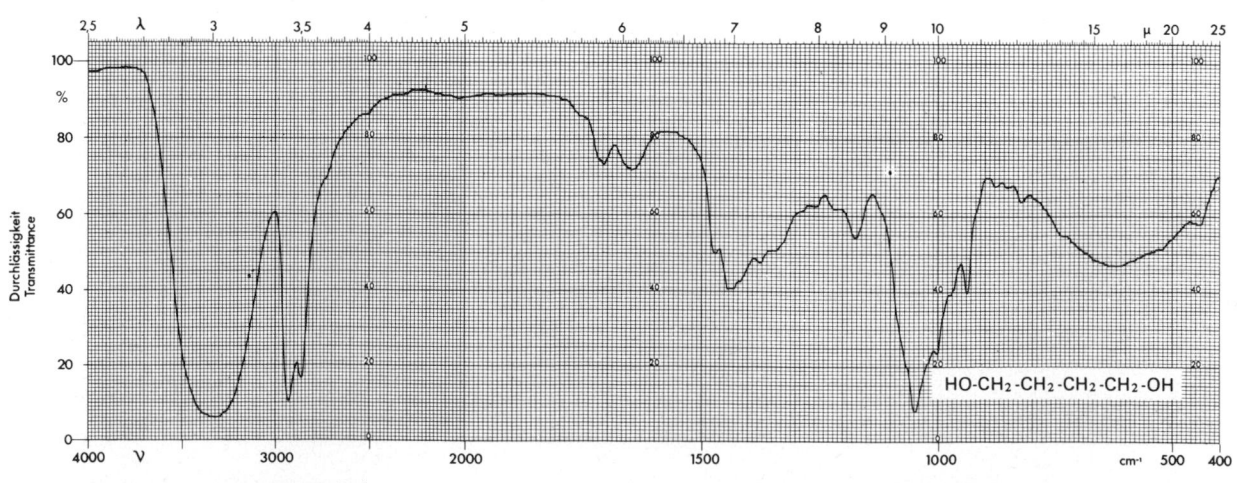

5221

Verbindung:	**1,4-Butandiol**		Compound:	**1,4-Butandiol**	
Formel:	**C₄H₁₀O₂**	M.: **90,1**	Formula:	**C₄H₁₀O₂**	M. w.: **90,1**
Handelsname:	**Diol 14 B**	Herst.: **BASF**	Tradename:	**Diol 14 B**	Manuf.: **BASF**
Präparation:	**Kapill. Film**	Dez. Nr.: **5.3.1**	Preparation:	**Capill. Film**	Dec. No:. **5.3.1**

Weichmacher
5. Glykole und Ether
5.3. Sonstige Diole und Triole

Plasticizers
5. Glycols and Ethers
5.3. Other Diols and Triols

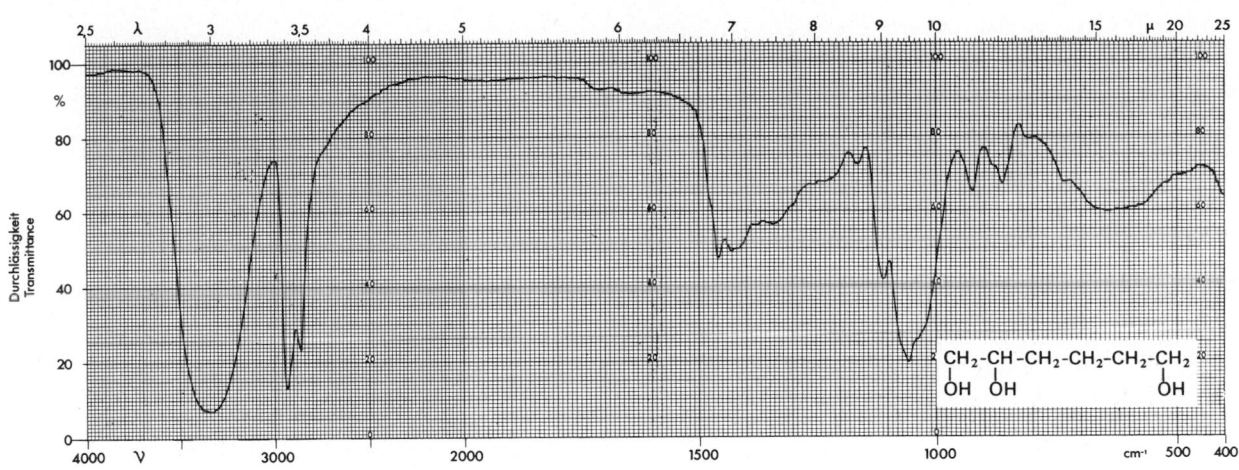

Verbindung:	Hexan 1,2,6-triol			Compound:	1,2,6-Hexanetriol		5222
Formel:	$C_6H_{14}O_3$	M.:	134,2	Formula:	$C_6H_{14}O_3$	M. w.: 134,2	
Handelsname:		Herst.:	Union Carb.	Tradename:		Manuf.: Union Carb.	
Präparation:	Kapill. Film	Dez. Nr.:	5.3.2	Preparation:	Capill. Film	Dec. No:. 5.3.2	

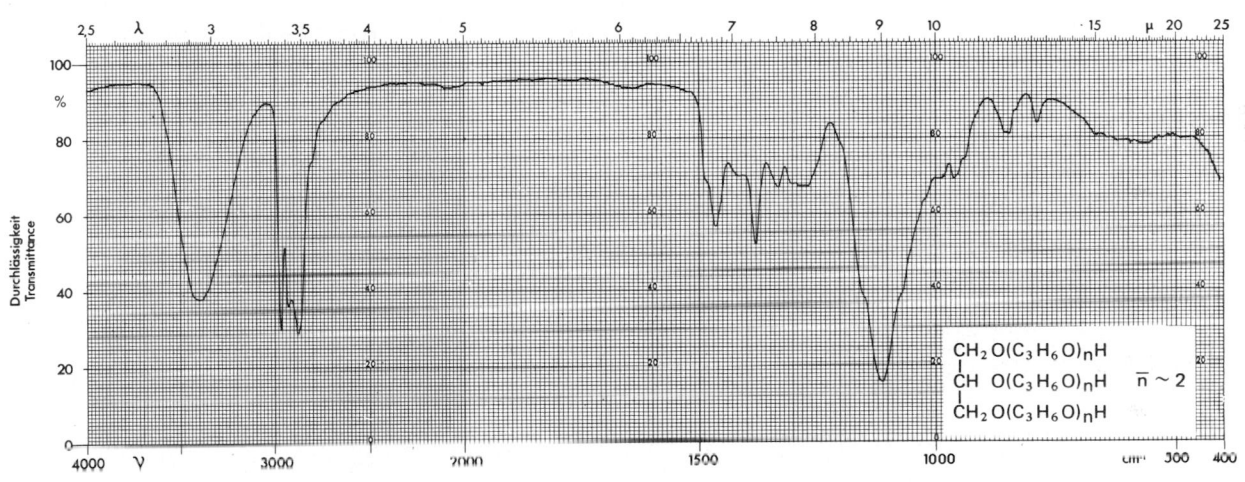

Verbindung	Glycerin-tri-polyoxypropylenether			Compound:	Glycerol tri(polyoxypropylene)ether		5223
Formel:		M.:	~ 350	Formula:		M. w.: ~ 350	
Handelsname:	Pluracol TP 340	Herst.:	Wyandotte	Tradename:	Pluracol TP 340	Manuf.: Wyandotte	
Präparation:	Kapill. Film	Dez. Nr.:	5.3.3	Preparation:	Capill. Film	Dec. No:. 5.3.3	

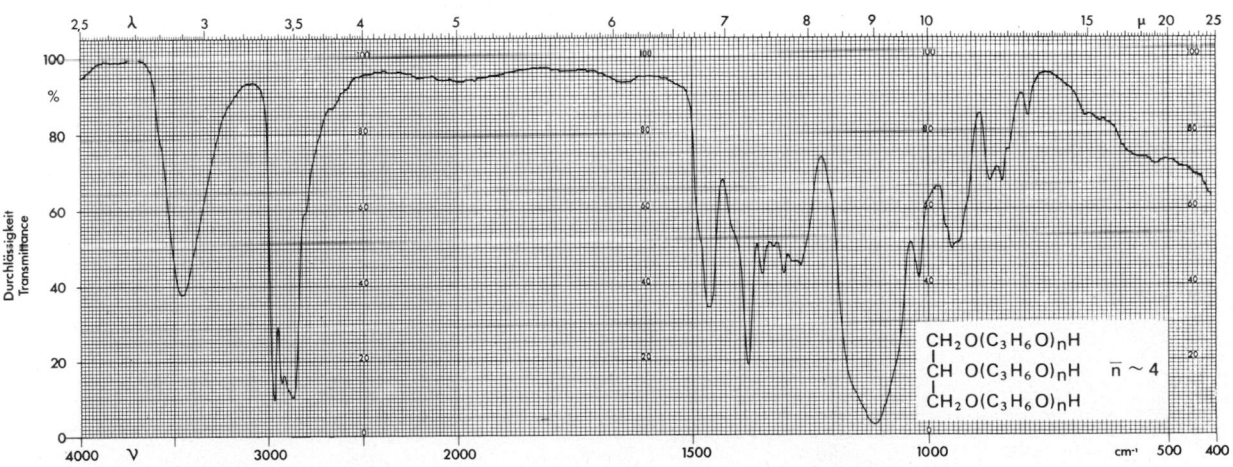

Verbindung:	Glycerin-tri-polyoxypropylenether			Compound:	Glycerol tri(polyoxypropylene)ether		5224
Formel:		M.:	~ 750	Formula:		M. w.: ~ 750	
Handelsname:	Pluracol TP 740	Herst.:		Tradename:	Pluracol TP 740	Manuf.:	
Präparation:	Kapill. Film	Dez. Nr.:	5.3.4	Preparation:	Capill. Film	Dec. No.: 5.3.4	

Weichmacher
5. Glykole und Ether
5.3. Sonstige Diole und Triole

Plasticizers
5. Glycols and Ethers
5.3. Other Diols and Triols

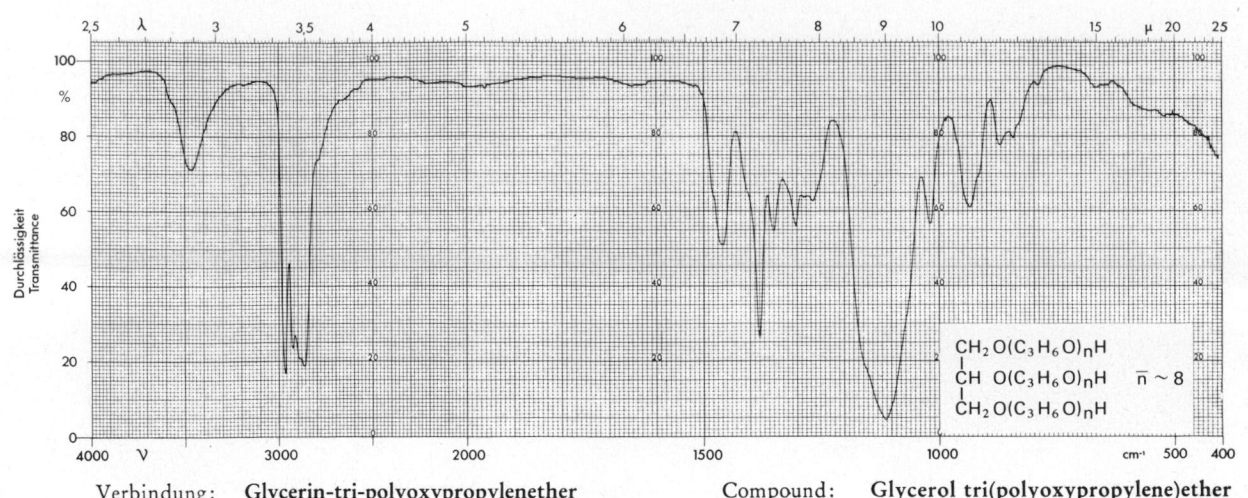

$$CH_2\,O(C_3H_6O)_nH$$
$$CH\;O(C_3H_6O)_nH \qquad \overline{n} \sim 8$$
$$CH_2\,O(C_3H_6O)_nH$$

5225

Verbindung:	Glycerin-tri-polyoxypropylenether	Compound:	Glycerol tri(polyoxypropylene)ether
Formel:	M.: ~ 1500	Formula:	M. w.: ~ 1500
Handelsname: Pluracol TP 1540	Herst.: Wyandotte	Tradename: Pluracol TP 1540	Manuf.: Wyandotte
Präparation: Kapill. Film	Dez. Nr.: 5.3.5	Preparation: Capill. Film	Dec. No.: 5.3.5

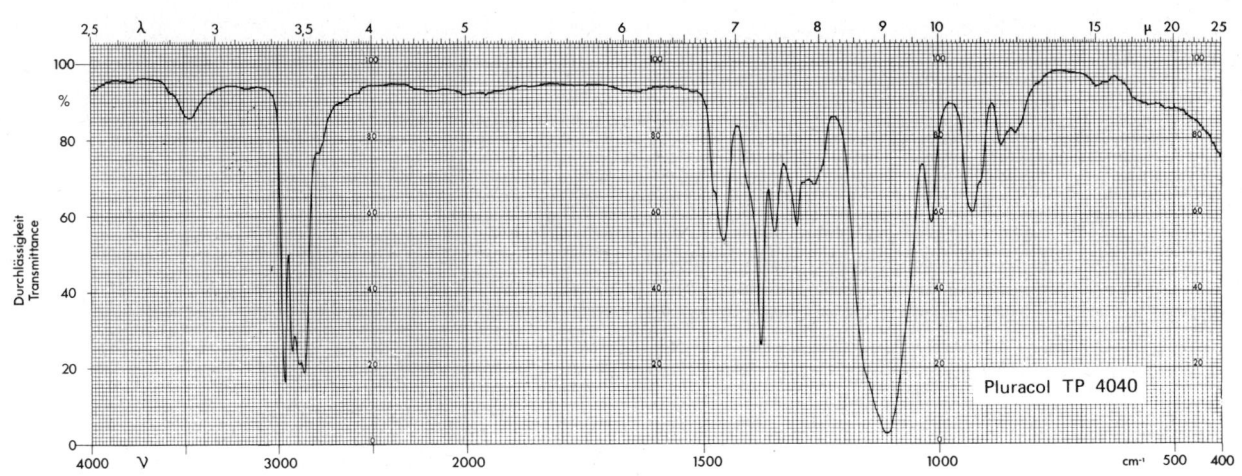

Pluracol TP 4040

5226

Verbindung:	Polytriol	Compound:	Polytriol
Formel:	M.: ~ 4000	Formula:	M. w.: ~ 4000
Handelsname: Pluracol TP 4040	Herst.: Wyandotte	Tradename: Pluracol TP 4040	Manuf.: Wyandotte
Präparation: Kapill. Film	Dez. Nr.: 5.3.6	Preparation: Capill. Film	Dec. No:. 5.3.6

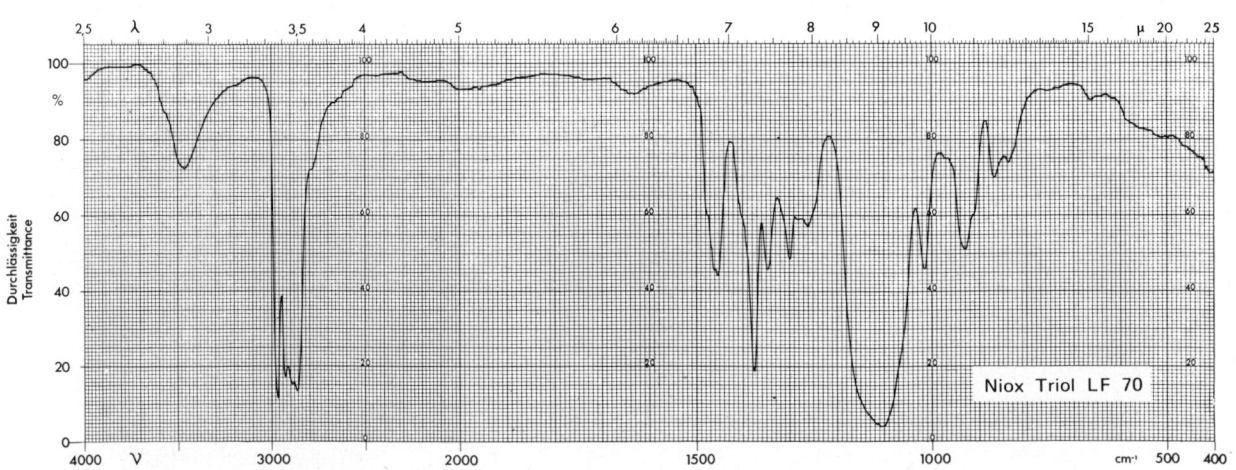

Niox Triol LF 70

5227

Verbindung:	Polytriol	Compound:	Polytriol
Formel:	M.: ~ 1550	Formula:	M. w.: ~ 1550
Handelsname: Niox Triol LF 70	Herst.: Union Carb.	Tradename: Niox Triol LF 70	Manuf.: Union Carb.
Präparation: Kapill. Film	Dez. Nr.: 5.3.7	Preparation: Capill. Film	Dec. No:. 5.3.7

Weichmacher
5. Glykole und Ether
5.4. Glykolether

Plasticizers
5. Glycols and Ethers
5.4. Glycol Ethers

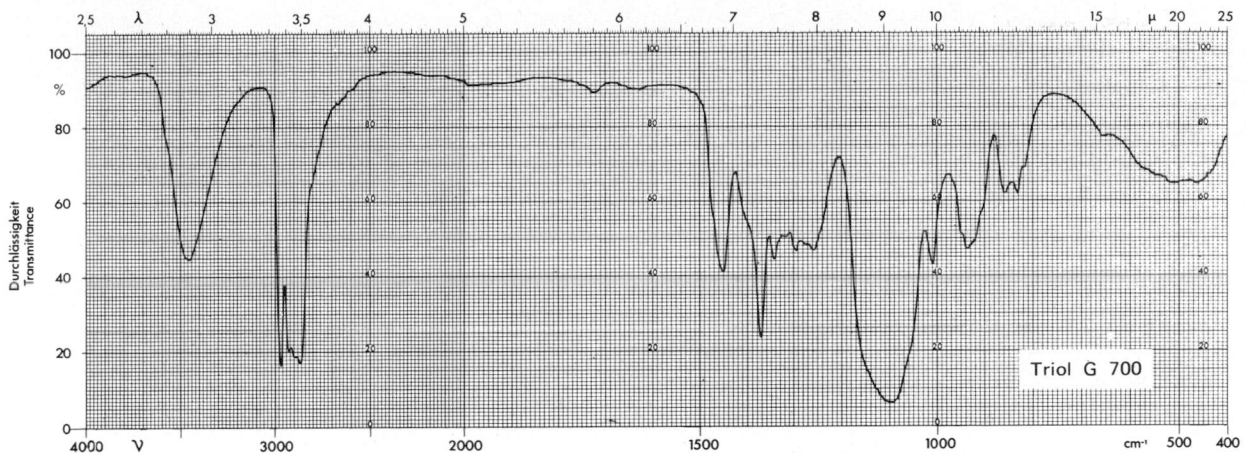

Verbindung:	Glycerintripolyoxypropylenether			Compound:	Glycerol tri(polyoxypropylene)ether			5228
Formel:		M.:	~ 700	Formula:		M. w.:	~ 700	
Handelsname:	Triol G 700	Herst.:	Jefferson	Tradename:	Triol G 700	Manuf.:	Jefferson	
Präparation:	Kapill. Film	Dez. Nr.:	5.3.8	Preparation:	Capill. Film	Dec. No:.	5.3.8	

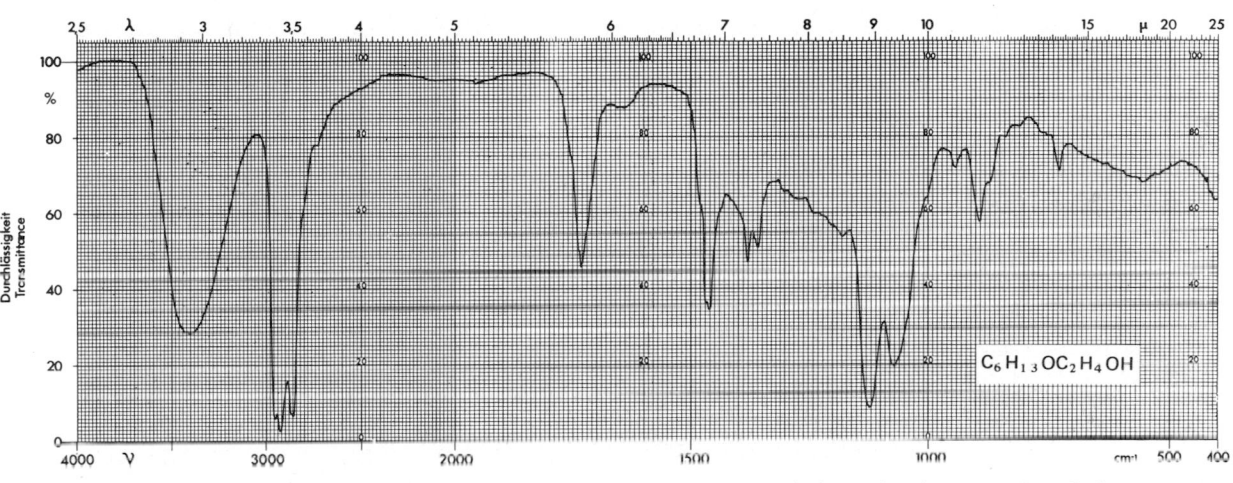

Verbindung:	Ethylenglykolmono-n-hexylether			Compound:	Ethylene glycol mono-n-hexylether			5229
Formel:	$C_8H_{18}O_2$	M.:	146,2	Formula:	$C_8H_{18}O_2$	M. w.:	146,2	
Handelsname:		Herst.:	Fluka	Tradename:		Manuf.:	Fluka	
Präparation:	Kapill. Film	Dez. Nr.:	5.4.1	Preparation:	Capill. Film	Dec. No:.	5.4.1	

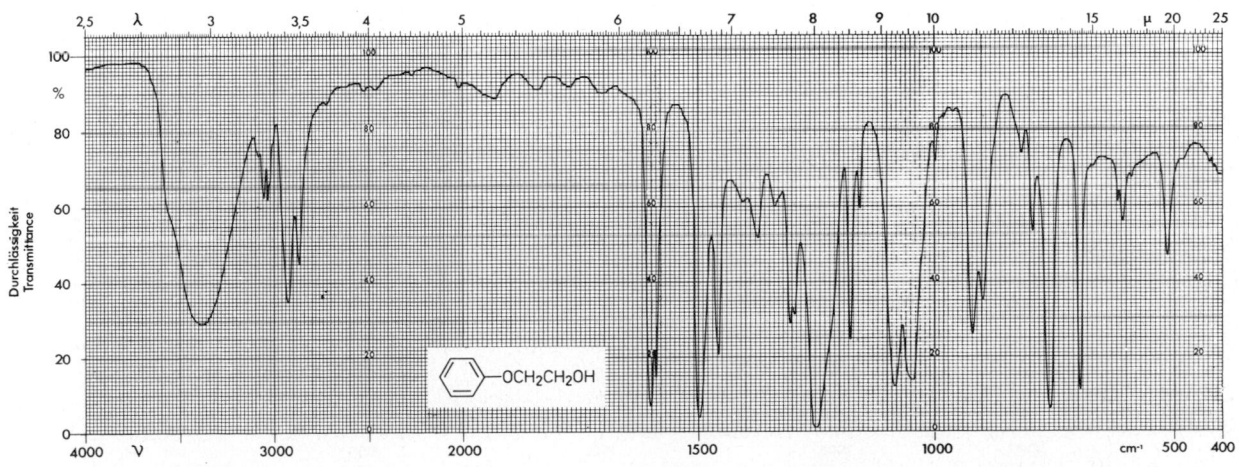

Verbindung:	Ethylenglykolmonophenylether			Compound:	Ethylene glycol monophenyl ether			5230
Formel:	$C_8H_{10}O_2$	M.:	138,2	Formula:	$C_8H_{10}O_2$	M. w.:	138,2	
Handelsname:		Herst.:	Fluka	Tradename:		Manuf.:	Fluka	
Präparation:	Kapill. Film	Dez. Nr.:	5.4.2	Preparation:	Capill. Film	Dec. No.:	5.4.2	

Weichmacher
5. Glykole und Ether
5.4. Glykolether

Plasticizers
5. Glycols and Ethers
5.4. Glycol Ethers

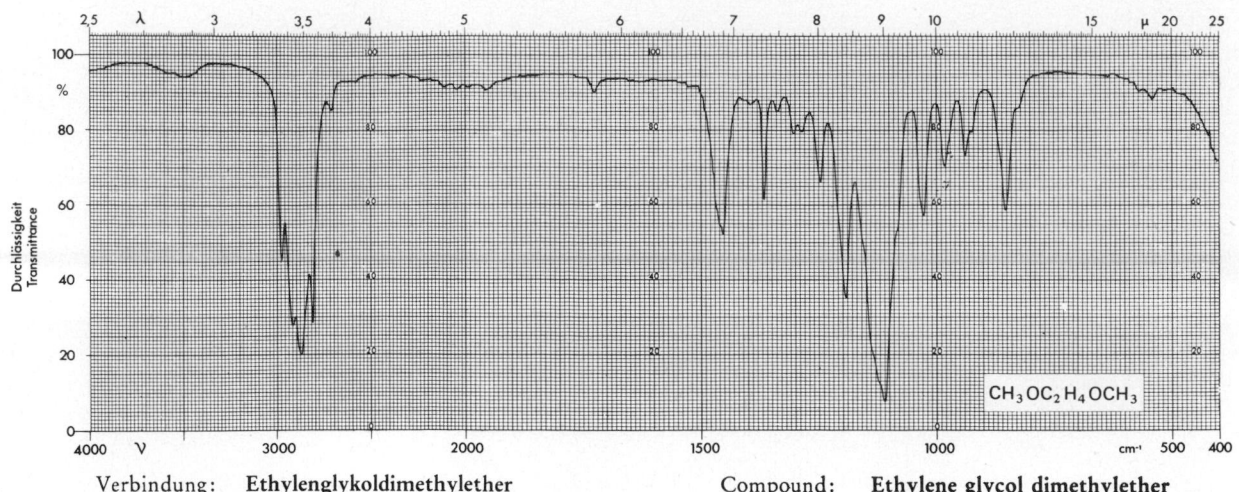

5231	Verbindung:	**Ethylenglykoldimethylether**			Compound:	**Ethylene glycol dimethylether**		
	Formel:	$C_4H_{10}O_2$	M.:	**90,1**	Formula:	$C_4H_{10}O_2$	M. w.:	**90,1**
	Handelsname:		Herst.:	**Fluka**	Tradename:		Manuf.:	**Fluka**
	Präparation:	**Kapill. Film**	Dez. Nr.:	**5.4.3**	Preparation:	**Capill. Film**	Dec. No.:	**5.4.3**

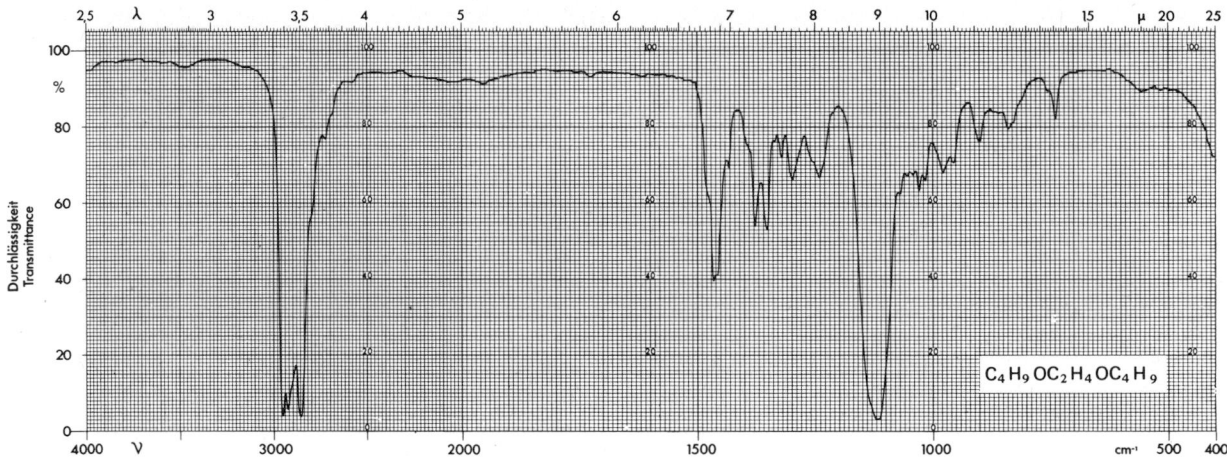

5232	Verbindung:	**Ethylenglykol-di-n-butylether**			Compound:	**Ethylene glycol di-n-butylether**		
	Formel:	$C_{10}H_{22}O_2$	M.:	**174,3**	Formula:	$C_{10}H_{22}O_2$	M. w.:	**174,3**
	Handelsname:		Herst.:	**Fluka**	Tradename:		Manuf.:	**Fluka**
	Präparation:	**Kapill. Film**	Dez. Nr.:	**5.4.4**	Preparation:	**Capill. Film**	Dec. No.:	**5.4.4**

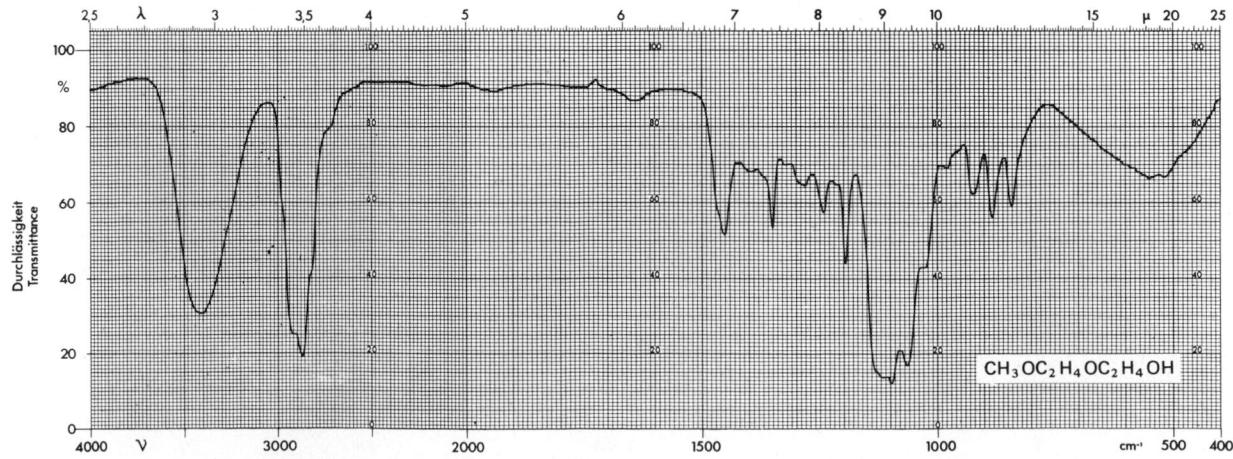

5233	Verbindung:	**Diethylenglykolmonomethylether**			Compound:	**Diethylene glycol monomethyl ether**		
	Formel:	$C_5H_{12}O_3$	M.:	**120,2**	Formula:	$C_5H_{12}O_3$	M. w.:	**120,2**
	Handelsname:	**Methyldiglykol**	Herst.:	**BASF**	Tradename:	**Methyldiglykol**	Manuf.:	**BASF**
	Präparation:	**Kapill. Film**	Dez. Nr.:	**5.4.5**	Preparation:	**Capill. Film**	Dec. No.:	**5.4.5**

Weichmacher
5. Glykole und Ether
5.4. Glykolether

Plasticizers
5. Glycols and Ethers
5.4. Glycol Ethers

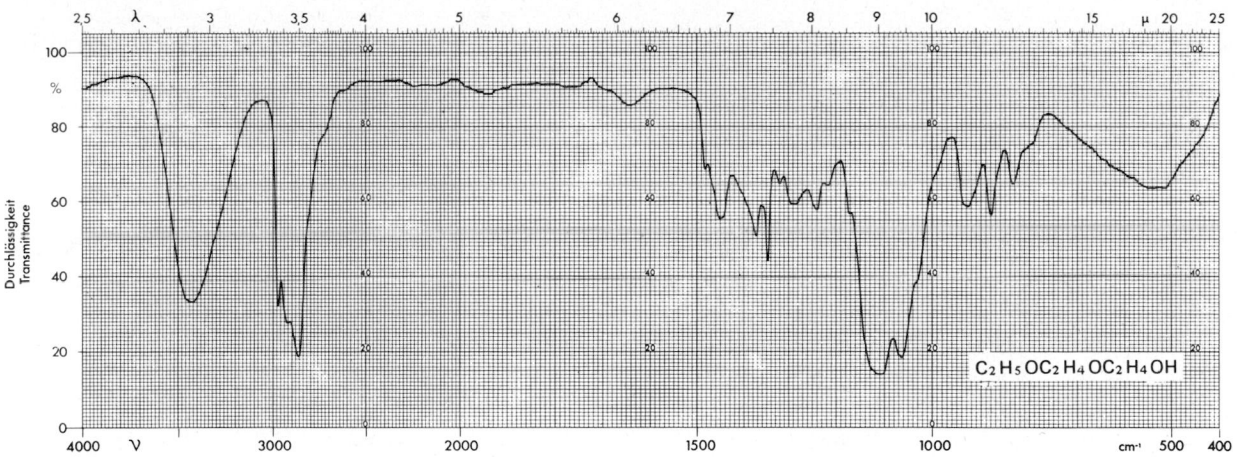

$C_2H_5OC_2H_4OC_2H_4OH$

Verbindung:	Diethylenglykolmonoethylether			Compound:	Diethylene glycol monoethyl ether		5234
Formel:	$C_6H_{14}O_3$	M.:	134,2	Formula:	$C_6H_{14}O_3$	M. w.: 134,2	
Handelsname:	Äthyldiglykol	Herst.:	BASF	Tradename:	Äthyldiglykol	Manuf.: BASF	
Präparation:	Kapill. Film	Dez. Nr.:	5.4.6	Preparation:	Capill. Film	Dec. No.: 5.4.6	

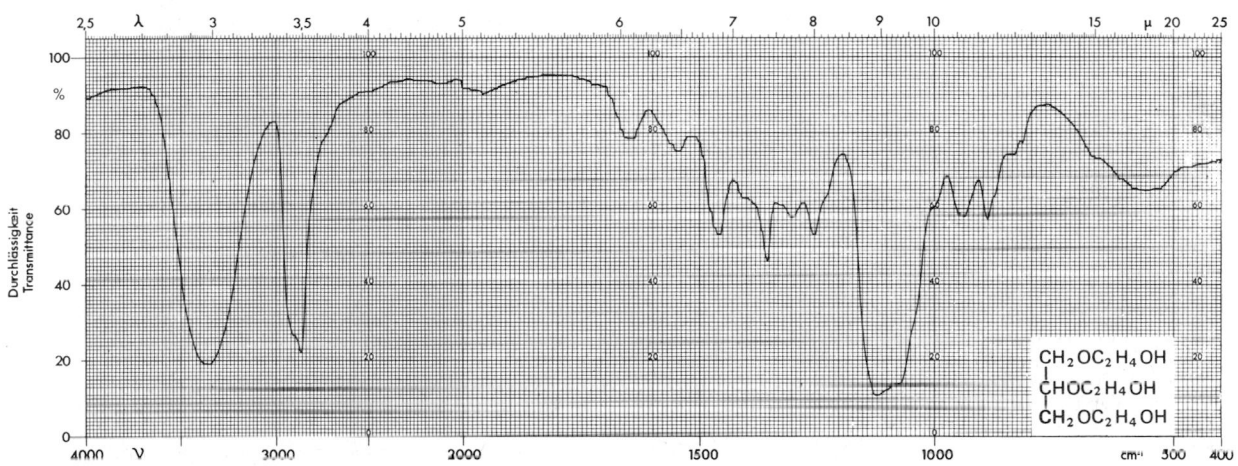

$CH_2OC_2H_4OH$
$CHOC_2H_4OH$
$CH_2OC_2H_4OH$

Verbindung:	Glycerintrioxyethylether			Compound:	Glycerol tri(oxyethyl ether)		5235
Formel:	$C_9H_{20}O_6$	M.:	224,3	Formula:	$C_9H_{20}O_6$	M. w.: 224,3	
Handelsname:	Weichmacher 9	Herst.:	BASF	Tradename:	Weichmacher 9	Manuf.: BASF	
Präparation:	Kapill. Film	Dez. Nr.:	5.4.7	Preparation:	Capill. Film	Dec. No.: 5.4.7	

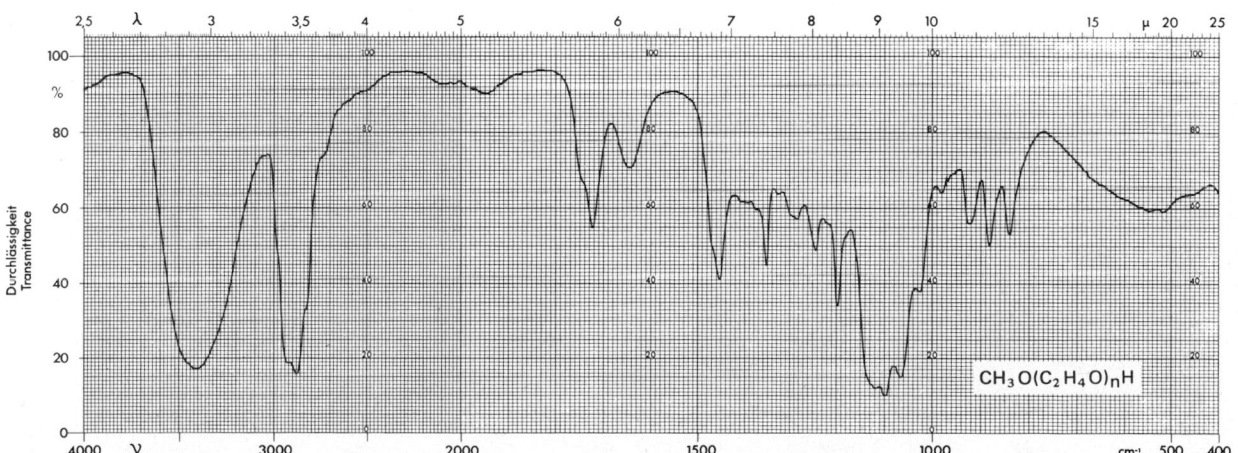

$CH_3O(C_2H_4O)_nH$

Verbindung:	Polyethylenglykolmonomethylether			Compound:	Polyethylene glycol monomethyl ether		5236
Formel:		M.:	~ 185	Formula:		M. w.: ~ 185	
Handelsname:	Methylpolyglykol	Herst.:	BASF	Tradename:	Methylpolyglykol	Manuf.: BASF	
Präparation:	Kapill. Film	Dez. Nr.:	5.4.8	Preparation:	Capill. Film	Dec. No.: 5.4.8	

Weichmacher
5. Glykole und Ether
5.4. Glykolether

Plasticizers
5. Glycols and Ethers
5.4. Glycol Ethers

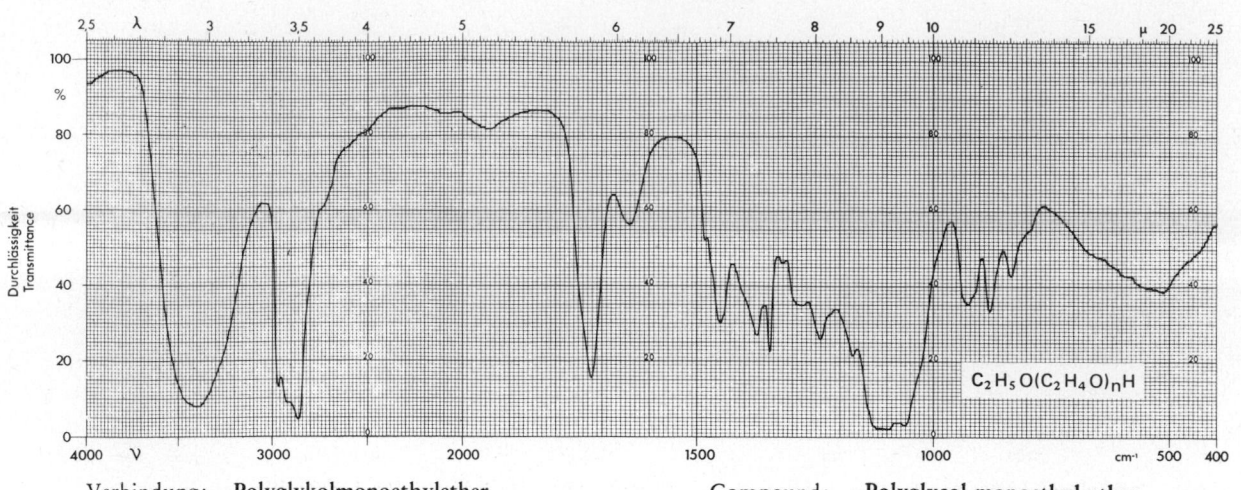

5237

Verbindung:	Polyglykolmonoethylether		Compound:	Polyglycol monoethyl ether	
Formel:		M.: ~ 195	Formula:		M. w.: ~ 195
Handelsname:	Äthylpolyglykol	Herst.: BASF	Tradename:	Äthylpolyglykol	Manuf.: BASF
Präparation:	Kapill. Film	Dez. Nr.: 5.4.9	Preparation:	Capill. Film	Dec. No.: 5.4.9

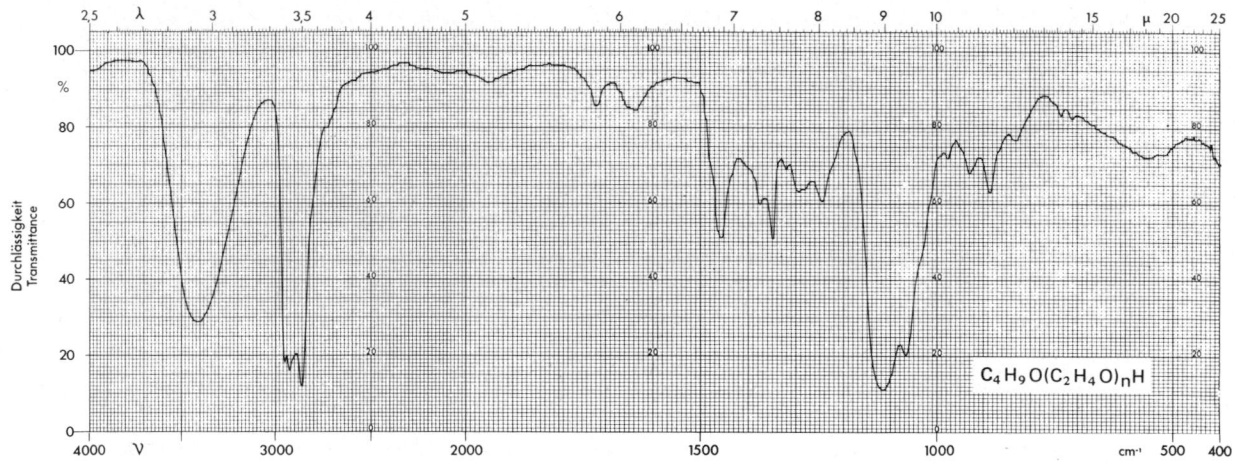

5238

Verbindung:	Polyglykolmonobutylether		Compound:	Polyglycol monobutylether	
Formel:		M.: ~ 200	Formula:		M. w.: ~ 200
Handelsname:	Butylpolyglykol	Herst.: Anorgana	Tradename:	Butylpolyglykol	Manuf.: Anorgana
Präparation:	Kapill. Film	Dez. Nr.: 5.4.10	Preparation:	Capill. Film	Dec. No.: 5.4.10

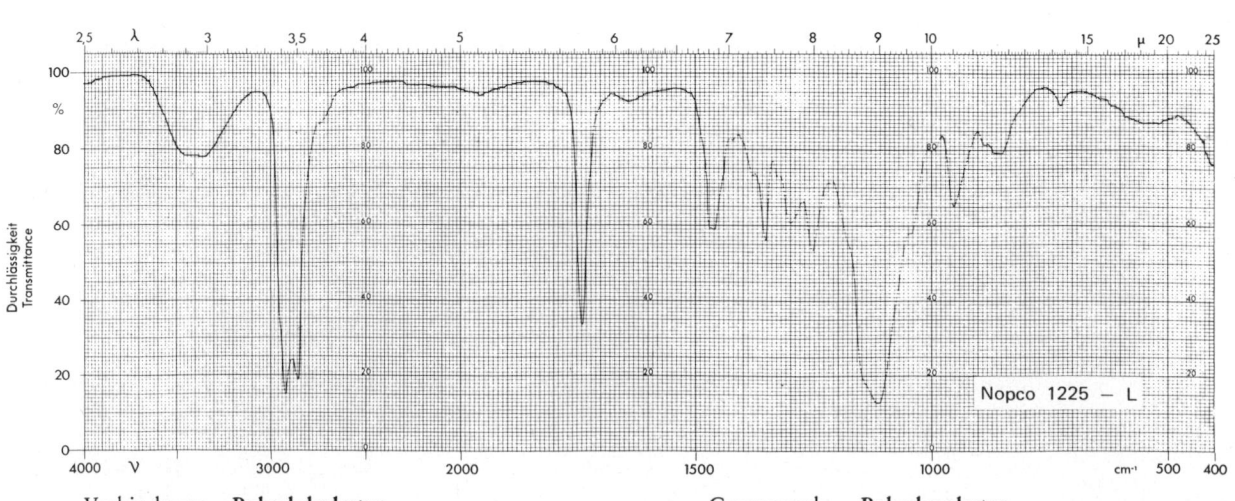

5239

Verbindung:	Polyglykolester		Compound:	Polyglycolester	
Formel:		M.: ~ 625	Formula:		M. w.: ~ 625
Handelsname:	Nopco 1225-L	Herst.: Nopco	Tradename:	Nopco 1225-L	Manuf.: Nopco
Präparation:	Kapill. Film	Dez. Nr.: 5.4.11	Preparation:	Capill. Film	Dec. No.: 5.4.11

Weichmacher
5. Glykole und Ether
5.4. Glykolether

Plasticizers
5. Glycols and Ethers
5.4. Glycol Ethers

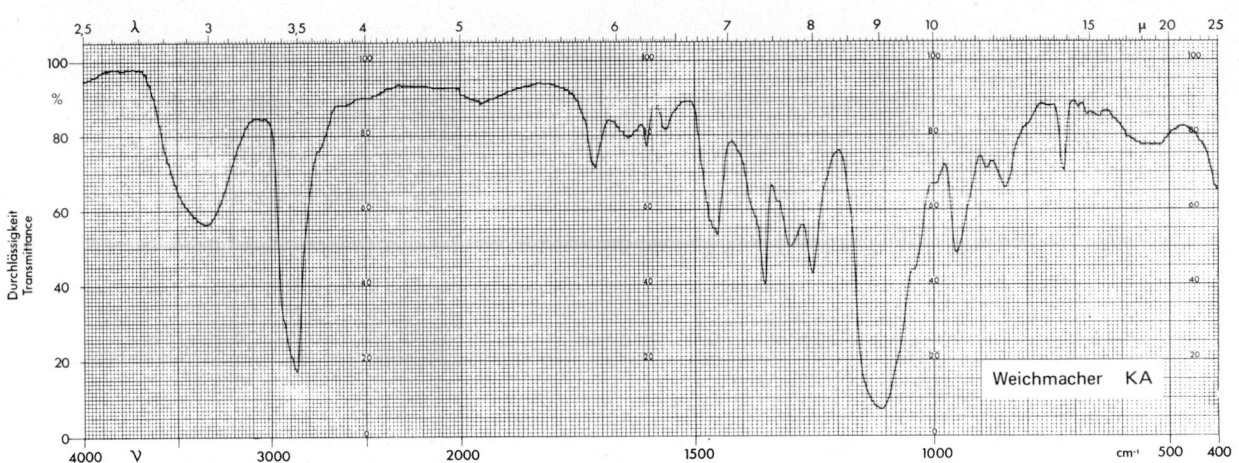

Verbindung:	Modifiz. Polyglykolether			Compound:	Modified polyglykolether			5240
Formel:		M.:	~ 935	Formula:		M. w.:	~ 935	
Handelsname:	Weichmacher KA	Herst.:	Bayer	Tradename:	Weichmacher KA	Manuf.:	Bayer	
Präparation:	Kapill. Film	Dez. Nr.:	5.4.12	Preparation:	Capill. Film	Dec. No.:	5.4.12	

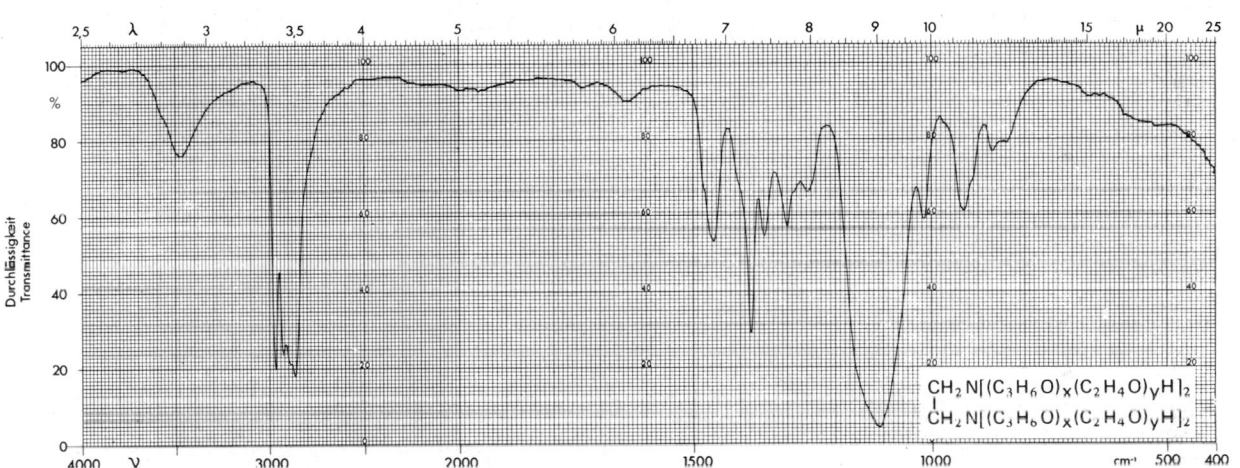

Verbindung:	Ethylendiamintetrapolyoxypropylen-polyethylenglycol			Compound:	Ethylene diamine tetra(polyoxypropylene polyethylene glycol)			5241
Formel:		M.:	~ 3400	Formula:		M. w.:	~ 3400	
Handelsname:	Tetronic 701	Herst.:	Wyandotte	Tradename:	Tetronic 701	Manuf.:	Wyandotte	
Präparation:	Kapill. Film	Dez. Nr.:	5.4.13	Preparation:	Capill. Film	Dec. No.:	5.4.13	

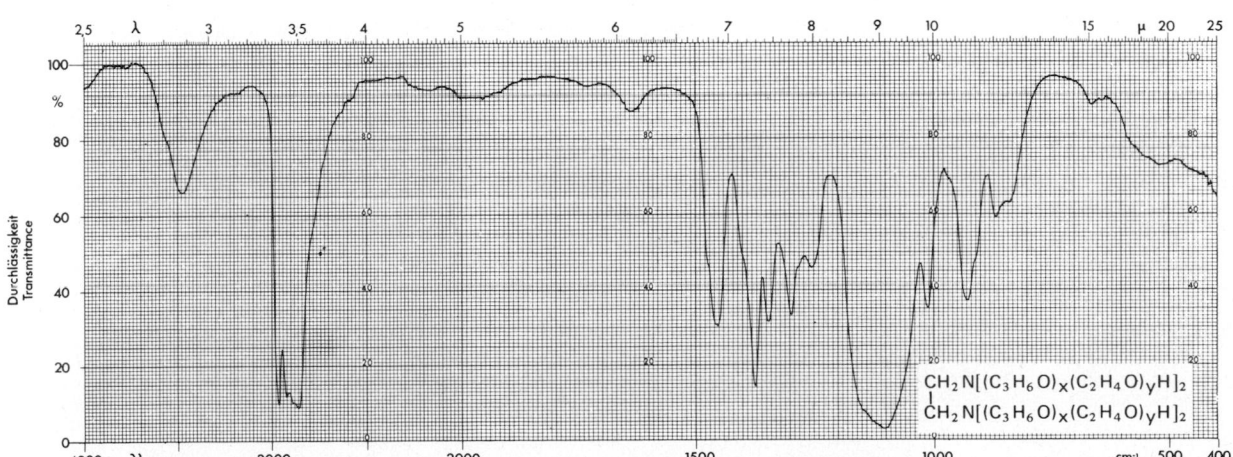

Verbindung:	Ethylendiamintetrapolyoxypropylen-polyethylenglycol			Compound:	Ethylene diamine tetra(polyoxyproplene polyethylene glycol)			5242
Formel:		M.:	~ 5000	Formula:		M. w.:	~ 5000	
Handelsname:	Tetronic 901	Herst.:	Wyandotte	Tradename:	Tetronic 901	Manuf.:	Wyandotte	
Präparation:	Kapill. Film	Dez. Nr.:	5.4.14	Preparation:	Capill. Film	Dec. No.:	5.4.14	

Weichmacher
5. Glykole und Ether
5.5. Sonstige Ether

Plasticizers
5. Glycols and Ethers
5.5. Other Ethers

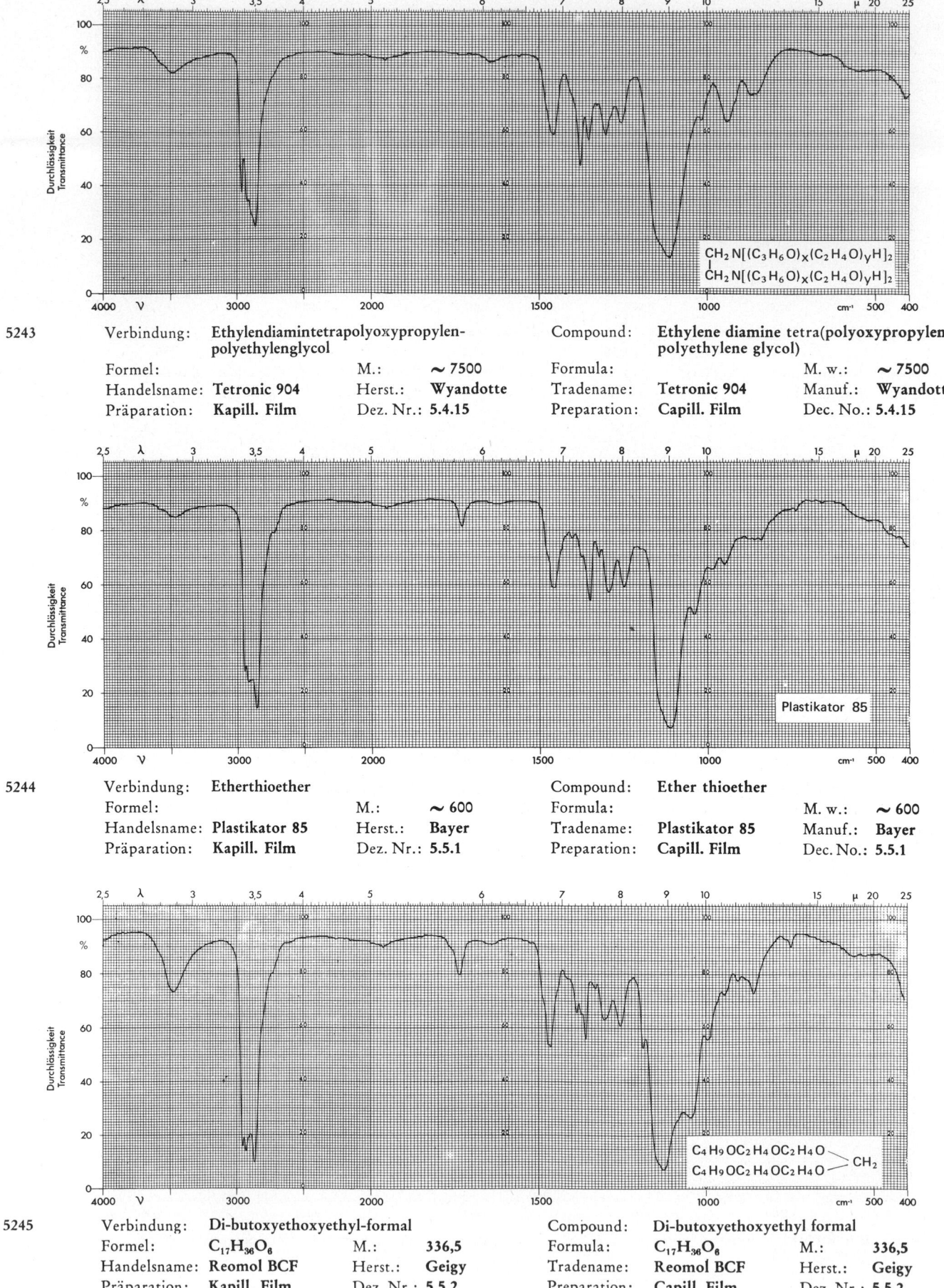

5243

Verbindung:	Ethylendiamintetrapolyoxypropylen-polyethylenglycol			Compound:	Ethylene diamine tetra(polyoxypropylene polyethylene glycol)		
Formel:		M.:	~ 7500	Formula:		M. w.:	~ 7500
Handelsname:	Tetronic 904	Herst.:	Wyandotte	Tradename:	Tetronic 904	Manuf.:	Wyandotte
Präparation:	Kapill. Film	Dez. Nr.:	5.4.15	Preparation:	Capill. Film	Dec. No.:	5.4.15

5244

Verbindung:	Etherthioether			Compound:	Ether thioether		
Formel:		M.:	~ 600	Formula:		M. w.:	~ 600
Handelsname:	Plastikator 85	Herst.:	Bayer	Tradename:	Plastikator 85	Manuf.:	Bayer
Präparation:	Kapill. Film	Dez. Nr.:	5.5.1	Preparation:	Capill. Film	Dec. No.:	5.5.1

5245

Verbindung:	Di-butoxyethoxyethyl-formal			Compound:	Di-butoxyethoxyethyl formal		
Formel:	$C_{17}H_{36}O_6$	M.:	336,5	Formula:	$C_{17}H_{36}O_6$	M.:	336,5
Handelsname:	Reomol BCF	Herst.:	Geigy	Tradename:	Reomol BCF	Herst.:	Geigy
Präparation:	Kapill. Film	Dez. Nr.:	5.5.2	Preparation:	Capill. Film	Dez. Nr.:	5.5.2

Weichmacher
5. Glykole und Ether
5.5. Sonstige Ether

Plasticizers
5. Glycols and Ethers
5.5. Other Ethers

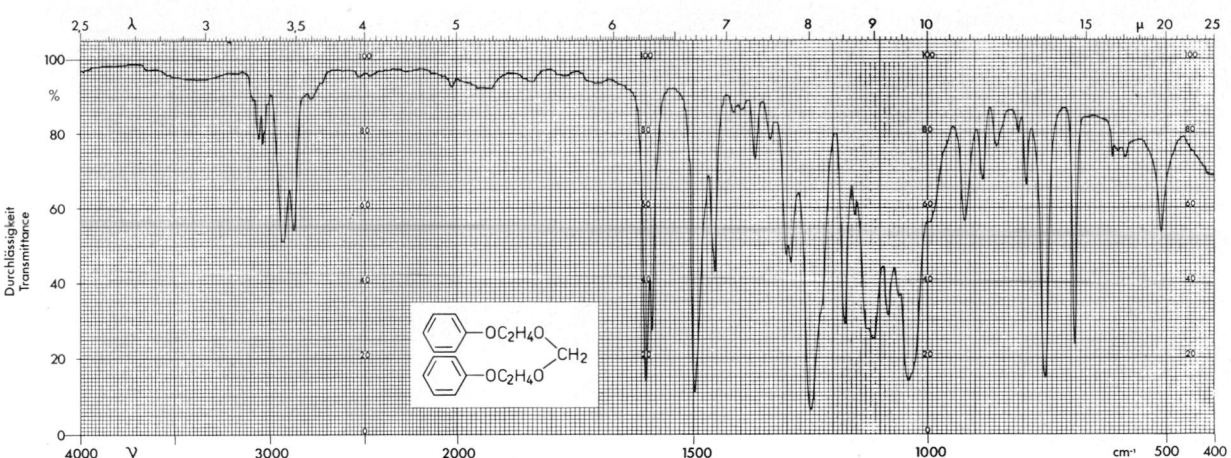

Verbindung:	Di-phenoxyethylformal			Compound:	Di-phenoxyethyl formal			5246
Formel:	$C_{17}H_{20}O_4$	M.:	**288,3**	Formula:	$C_{17}H_{20}O_4$	M. w.:	**288,3**	
Handelsname:	**Desavin**	Herst.:	**Bayer**	Tradename:	**Desavin**	Manuf.:	**Bayer**	
Präparation:	**Kapill. Film**	Dez. Nr.:	**5.5.3**	Preparation:	**Capill. Film**	Dec. No.:	**5.5.3**	

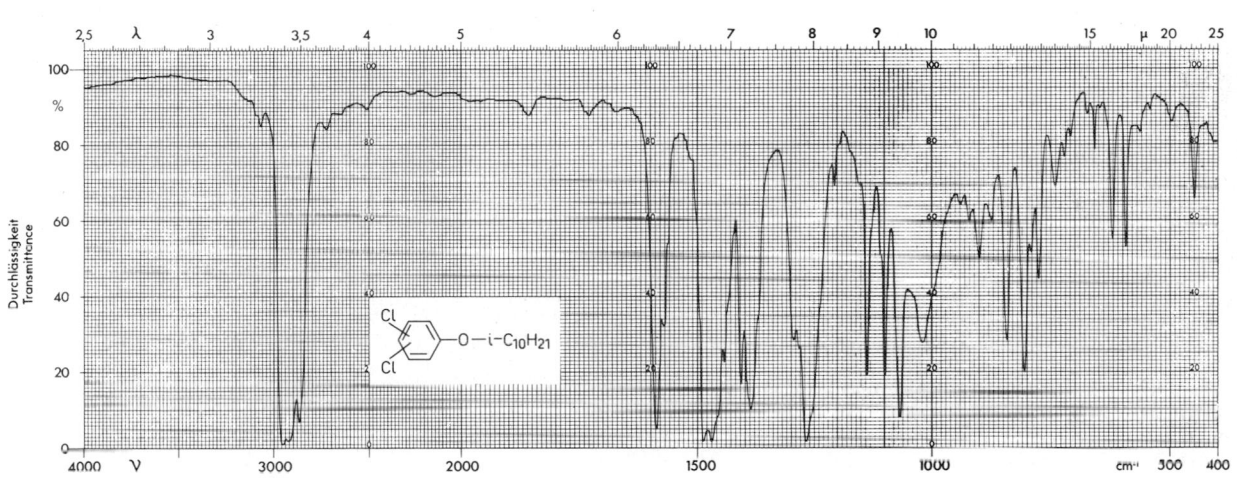

Verbindung:	**Dichlorphenylisodecylether**			Compound:	**Dichlorphenylisodecyl ether**			5247
Formel:	$C_{16}H_{24}OCl_2$	M.:	**303,3**	Formula:	$C_{16}H_{24}OCl_2$	M. w.:	**303,3**	
Handelsname:	**Mollan DCD**	Herst.:	**Oe-Stick**	Tradename:	**Mollan DCD**	Manuf.:	**Oe-Stick**	
Präparation:	**Kapill. Film**	Dez. Nr.:	**5.5.4**	Preparation:	**Capill. Film**	Dec. No.:	**5.5.4**	

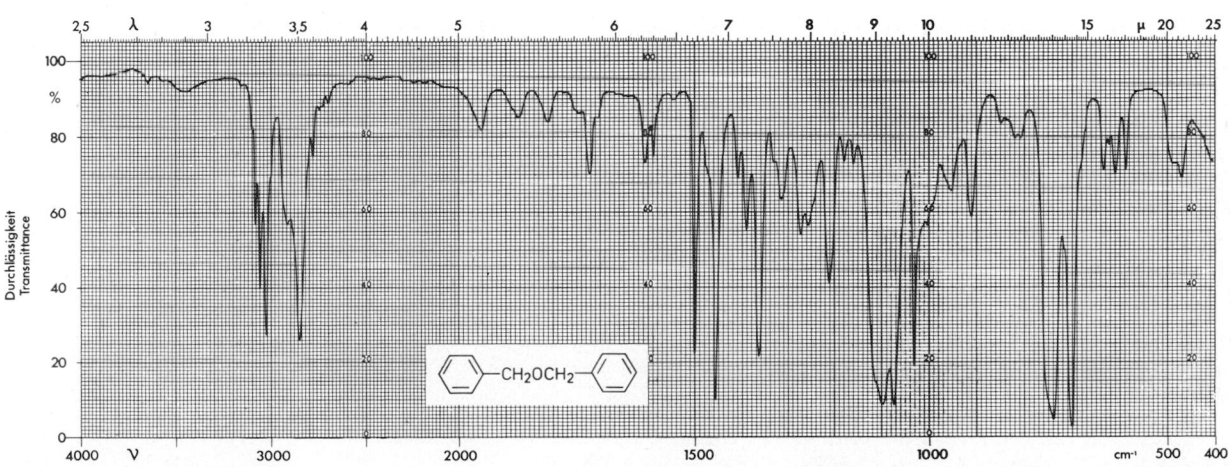

Verbindung:	**Dibenzylether**			Compound:	**Dibenzyl ether**			5248
Formel:	$C_{14}H_{14}O$	M.:	**198,4**	Formula:	$C_{14}H_{14}O$	M. w.:	**198,4**	
Handelsname:	**Plastoflex DBE**	Herst.:	**Advance**	Tradename:	**Plastoflex DBE**	Manuf.:	**Advance**	
Präparation:	**Kapill. Film**	Dez. Nr.:	**5.5.5**	Preparation:	**Capill. Film**	Dec. No.:	**5.5.5**	

Weichmacher
5. Glykole und Ether
5.5. Sonstige Ether

Plasticizers
5. Glycols and Ethers
5.5. Other Ethers

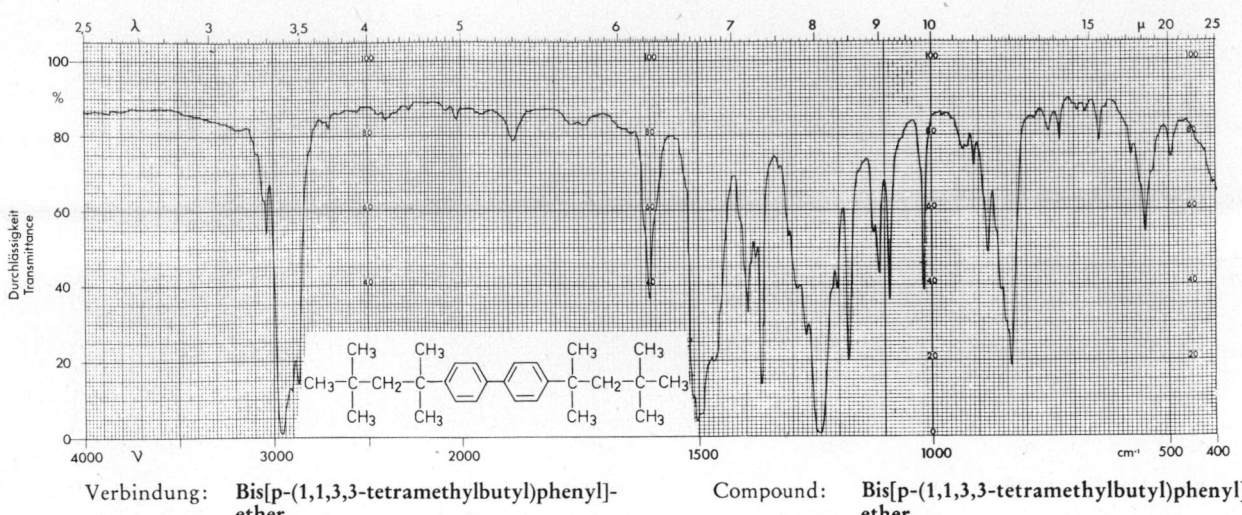

5249

Verbindung:	Bis[p-(1,1,3,3-tetramethylbutyl)phenyl]-ether		
Formel:	$C_{28}H_{42}O$	M.:	394,7
Handelsname:	Plastiflex 1099	Herst.:	Dow
Präparation:	Kapill. Film	Dez. Nr.:	5.5.6

Compound:	Bis[p-(1,1,3,3-tetramethylbutyl)phenyl]-ether		
Formula:	$C_{28}H_{42}O$	M. w.:	394,7
Tradename:	Plastiflex 1099	Manuf.:	Dow
Preparation:	Capill. Film	Dec. No.:	5.5.6

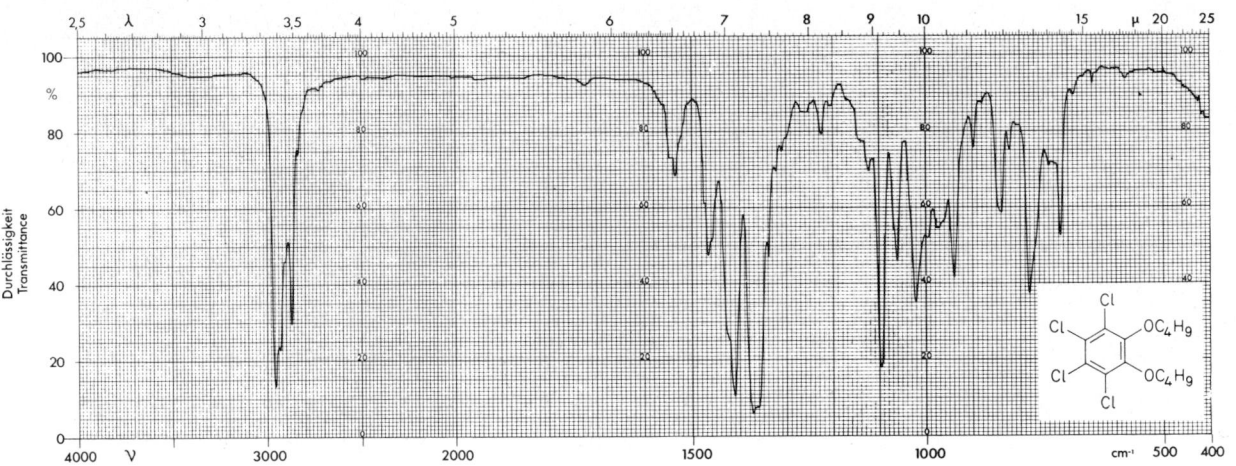

5250

Verbindung:	Tetrachlordibutoxybenzol		
Formel:	$C_{14}H_{18}O_2Cl_4$	M.:	360,1
Handelsname:	Jäganol CB	Herst.:	Jäger
Präparation:	Kapill. Film	Dez. Nr.:	5.5.7

Compound:	Tetrachlorodibutoxy benzene		
Formula:	$C_{14}H_{18}O_9Cl_4$	M. w.:	360,1
Tradename:	Jäganol CB	Manuf.:	Jäger
Preparation:	Capill. Film	Dec. No.:	5.5.7

5251

Verbindung:	Aromatischer Polyether		
Formel:		M.:	
Handelsname:	Plastikator FH	Herst.:	Bayer
Präparation:	Kapill. Film	Dez. Nr.:	5.5.8

Compound:	Aromatic polyether		
Formula:		M. w.:	
Tradename:	Plastikator FH	Manuf.:	Bayer
Preparation:	Capill. Film	Dec. No.:	5.5.8

Weichmacher
6. Phosphorsäureester
6.1. Phosphate

Plasticizers
6. Phosphoric Acid Esters
6.1. Phosphates

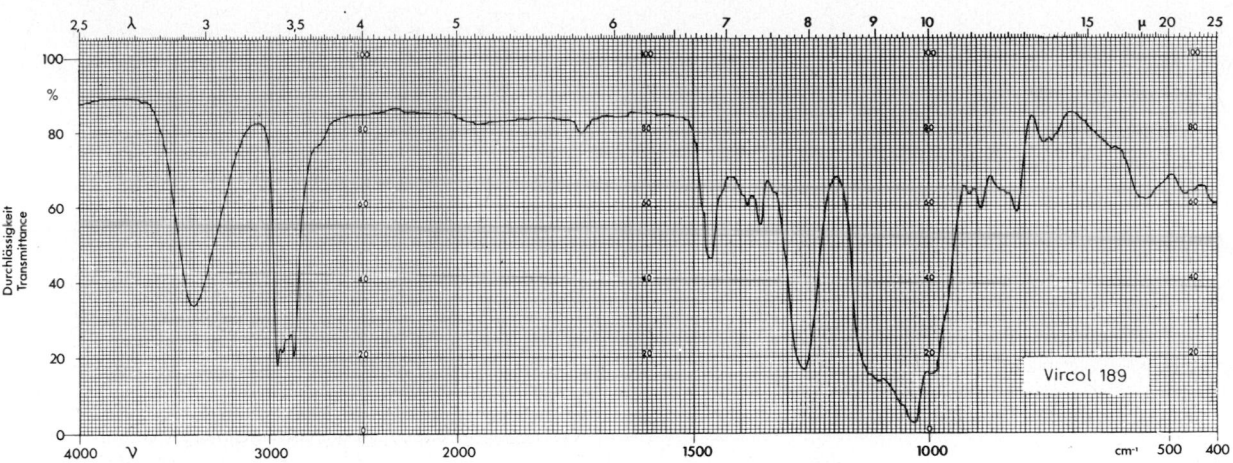

Verbindung:	Trialkylphosphat			Compound:	Trialkyl phosphate			5252
Formel:	Vircol 189	M.:	~ 340	Formula:	Vircol 189	M. w.:	~ 340	
Handelsname:		Herst.:	VC	Tradename:		Manuf.:	VC	
Präparation:	Kapill. Film	Dez. Nr.:	6.1.1	Preparation:	Capill. Film	Dec. No.:	6.1.1	

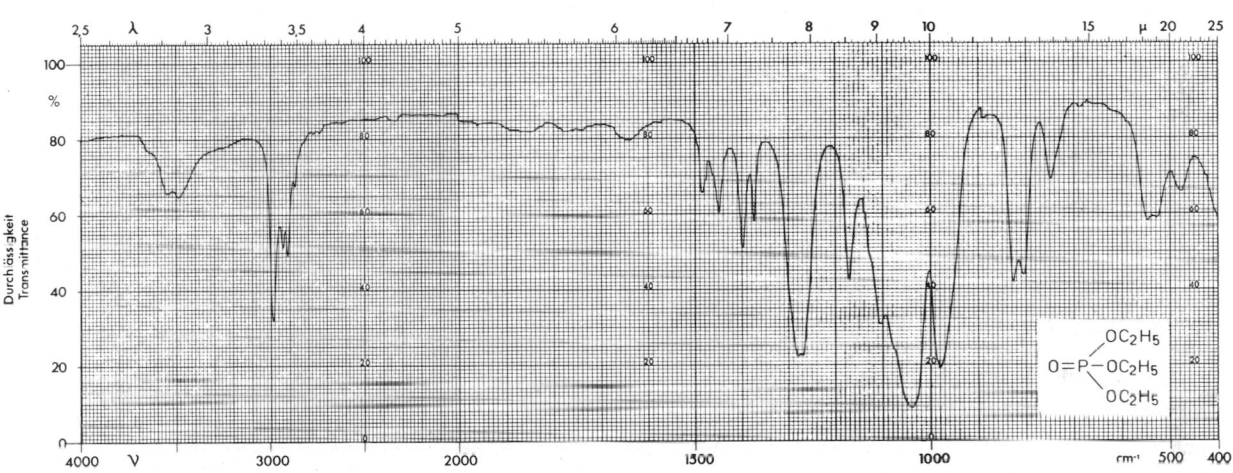

Verbindung:	Triethylphosphat			Compound:	Triethyl phosphate			5253
Formel:	$C_6H_{15}O_4P$	M.:	182,2	Formula:	$C_6H_{15}O_4P$	M. w.:	182,2	
Handelsname:		Herst.:	Eastman	Tradename:		Manuf.:	Eastman	
Präparation:	Kapill. Film	Dez. Nr.:	6.1.2	Preparation:	Capill. Film	Dec. No.:	6.1.2	

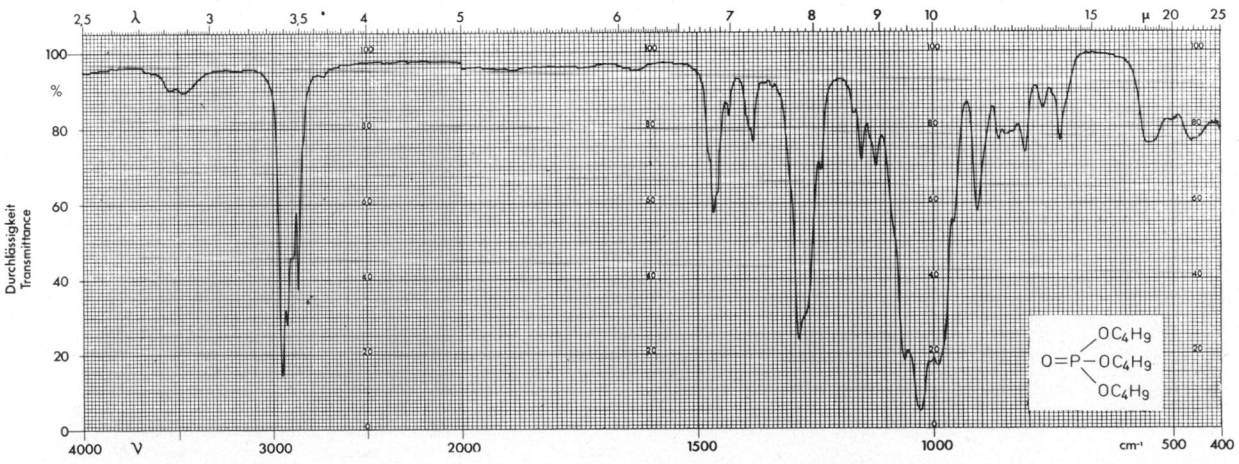

Verbindung:	Tributylphosphat			Compound:	Tributyl phosphate			5254
Formel:	$C_{12}H_{27}O_4P$	M.:	266,3	Formula:	$C_{12}H_{27}O_4P$	M. w.:	266,3	
Handelsname:		Herst.:	Bayer	Tradename:		Manuf.:	Bayer	
Präparation:	Kapill. Film	Dez. Nr.:	6.1.3	Preparation:	Capill. Film	Dec. No.:	6.1.3	

Weichmacher
6. Phosphorsäureester
6.1. Phosphate

Plasticizers
6. Phosphoric Acid Esters
6.1. Phosphates

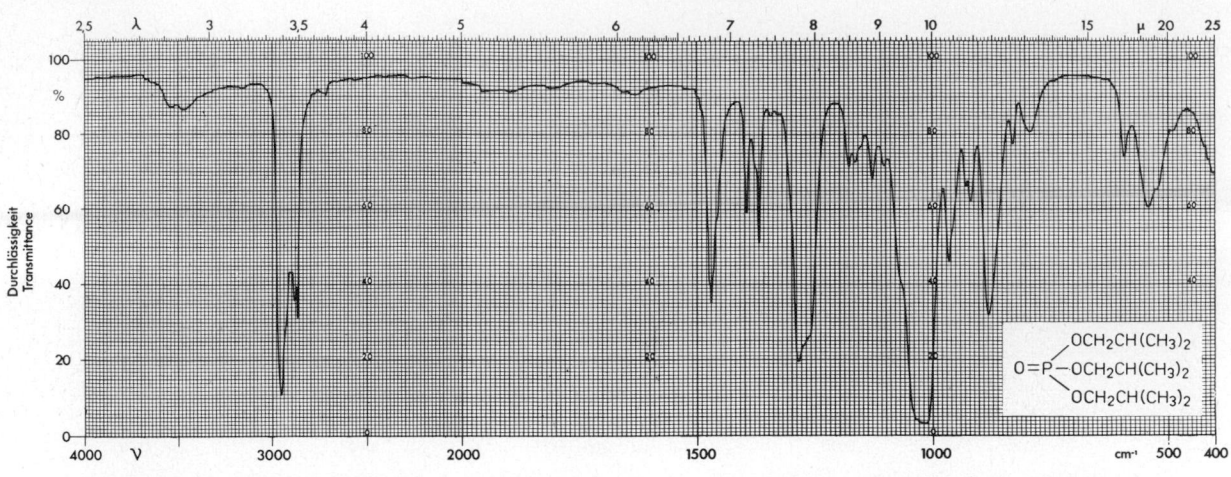

5255   Verbindung: **Triisobutylphosphat**   Compound: **Tri isobutyl phosphate**
Formel: $C_{12}H_{27}O_4P$ M.: **266,3**   Formula: $C_{12}H_{27}O_4P$ M. w.: **266,3**
Handelsname: Herst.: **Bayer**   Tradename: Manuf.: **Bayer**
Präparation: **Kapill. Film**   Dez. Nr.: **6.1.4**   Preparation: **Capill. Film**   Dec. No.: **6.1.4**

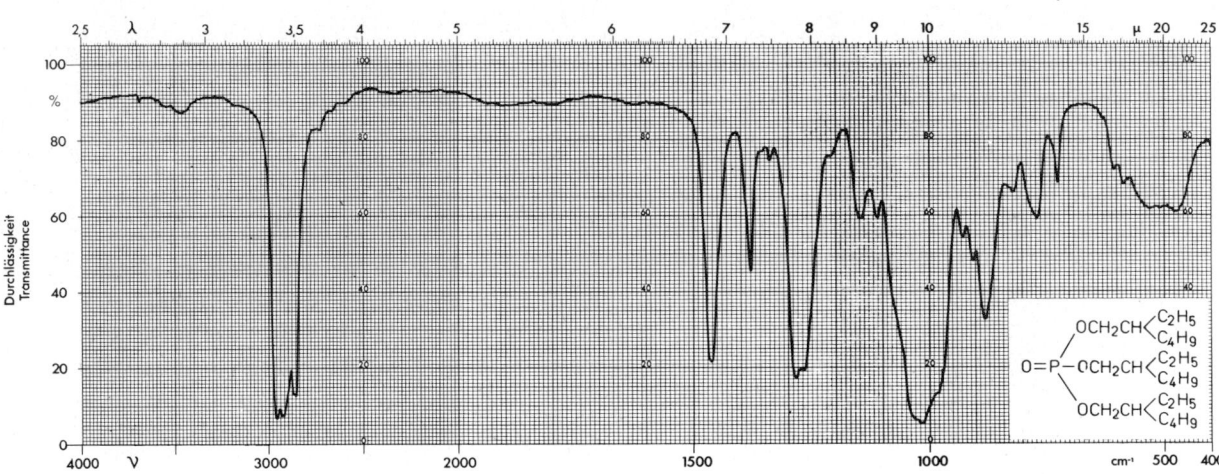

5256   Verbindung: **Tri-2-ethylhexylphosphat**   Compound: **Tri-2-ethylhexyl phosphate**
Formel: $C_{25}H_{51}O_4P$ M.: **446,6**   Formula: $C_{25}H_{51}O_4P$ M. w.: **446,6**
Handelsname: Herst.: **Heyden**   Tradename: Manuf.: **Heyden**
Präparation: **Kapill. Film**   Dez. Nr.: **6.1.5**   Preparation: **Capill. Film**   Dec. No.: **6.1.5**

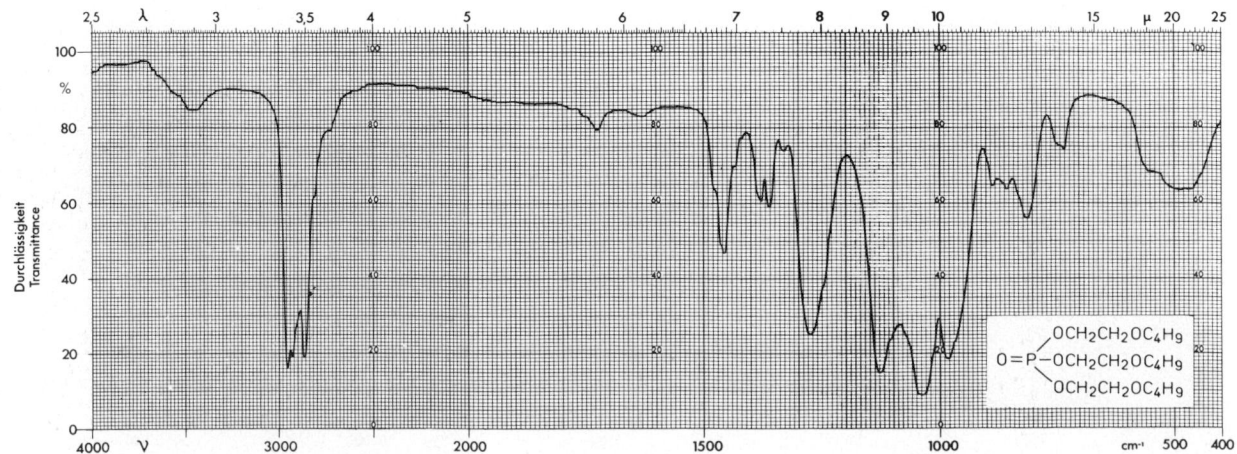

5257   Verbindung: **Tributoxyethylphosphat**   Compound: **Tributoxyethyl phosphate**
Formel: $C_{18}H_{39}O_7P$ M.: **398,5**   Formula: $C_{18}H_{39}O_7P$ M. w.: **398,5**
Handelsname: **KP 140**   Herst.: **FMC**   Tradename: **KP 140**   Manuf.: **FMC**
Präparation: **Kapill. Film**   Dez. Nr.: **6.1.6**   Preparation: **Capill. Film**   Dec. No.: **6.1.6**

Weichmacher
6. Phosphorsäureester
6.1. Phosphate

Plasticizers
6. Phosphoric Acid Esters
6.1. Phosphates

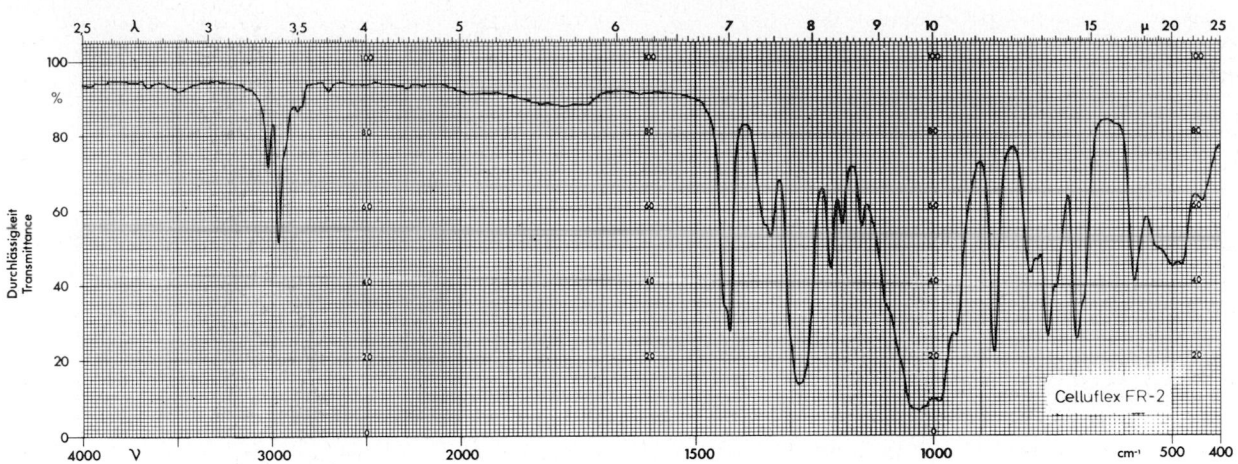

Verbindung:	Chloralkylarylphosphat			Compound:	Chloralkylaryl phosphate			5258
Formel:		M.:	~ 490	Formula:		M. w.:	~ 490	
Handelsname:	Celluflex FR-2	Herst.:	Celanese	Tradename:	Celluflex FR-2	Manuf.:	Celanese	
Präparation:	Kapill. Film	Dez. Nr.:	6.1.7	Preparation:	Capill. Film	Dec. No.:	6.1.7	

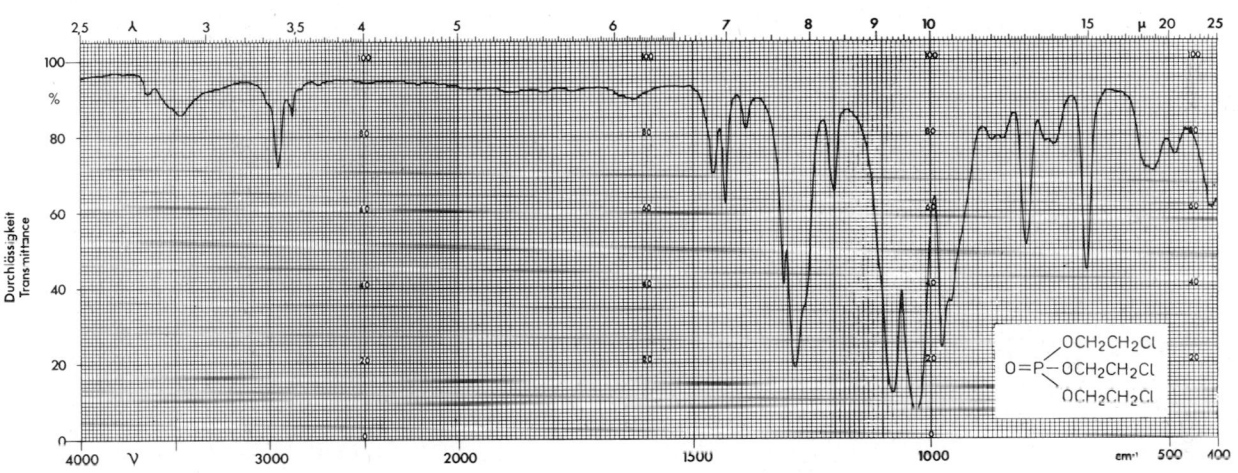

Verbindung:	Tri-2-chlorethylphosphat			Compound:	Tris(2-chloroethyl) phosphate			5259
Formel:	$C_6H_{12}O_4PCl_3$	M.:	285,7	Formula:	$C_6H_{12}O_4PCl_3$	M. w.:	285,7	
Handelsname:	Cetamoll Q	Herst.:	Bayer	Tradename:	Cetamoll Q	Manuf.:	Bayer	
Präparation:	Kapill. Film	Dez. Nr.:	6.1.8	Preparation:	Capill. Film	Dec. No.:	6.1.8	

Verbindung:	Triphenylphosphat			Compound:	Triphenyl phosphate			5260
Formel:	$C_{18}H_{15}O_4P$	M.:	326,3	Formula:	$C_{18}H_{15}O_4P$	M. w.:	326,3	
Handelsname:	Disflamoll TP	Herst.:	Bayer	Tradename:	Disflamoll TP	Manuf.:	Bayer	
Präparation:	Kapill. Film	Dez. Nr.:	6.1.9	Preparation:	Capill. Film	Dec. No.:	6.1.9	

Weichmacher
6. Phosphorsäureester
6.1. Phosphate

Plasticizers
6. Phosphoric Acid Esters
6.1. Phosphates

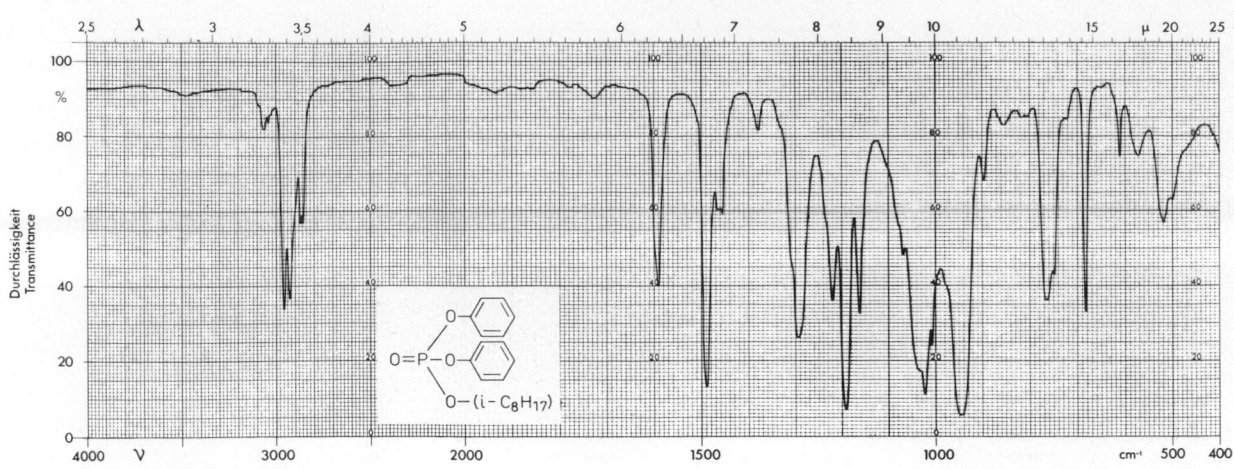

5261

Verbindung:	Octyldiphenylphosphat		Compound:	Octyl diphenyl phosphate	
Formel:	$C_{20}H_{27}O_4P$	M.: 362,4	Formula:	$C_{20}H_{27}O_4P$	M. w.: 362,4
Handelsname:	Santicizer 141	Herst.: Monsanto	Tradename:	Santicizer 141	Manuf.: Monsanto
Präparation:	Kapill. Film	Dez. Nr.: 6.1.10	Preparation:	Capill. Film	Dec. No:. 6.1.10

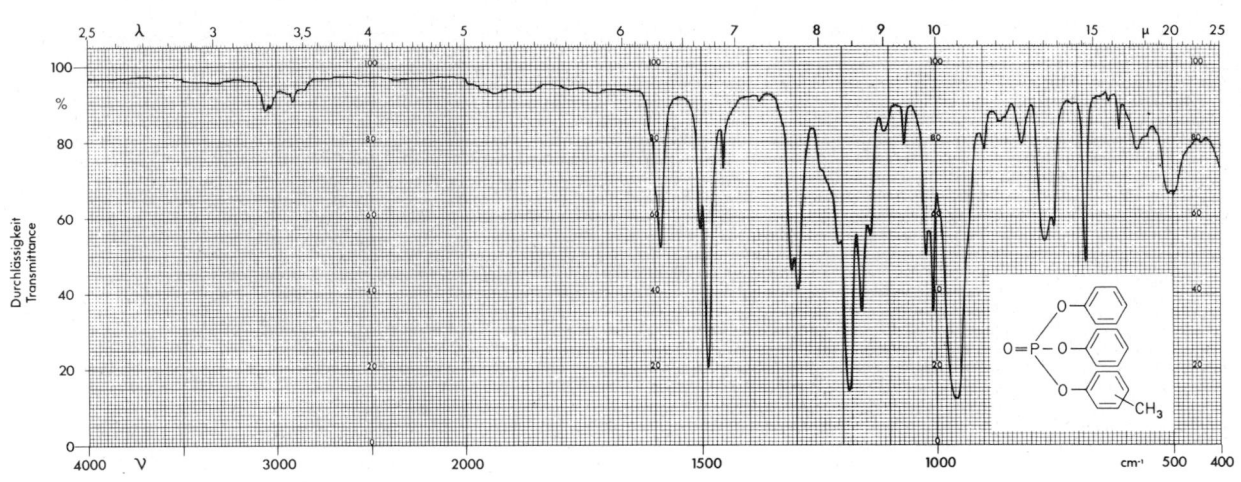

5262

Verbindung:	Kresyldiphenylphosphat		Compound:	Cresyl diphenyl phosphate	
Formel:	$C_{19}H_{17}O_4P$	M.: 340,3	Formula:	$C_{19}H_{17}O_4P$	M. w.: 340,3
Handelsname:	Disflamoll DBK	Herst.: Bayer	Tradename:	Disflamoll DBK	Manuf.: Bayer
Präparation:	Kapill. Film	Dez. Nr.: 6.1.11	Preparation:	Capill. Film	Dec. No:. 6.1.11

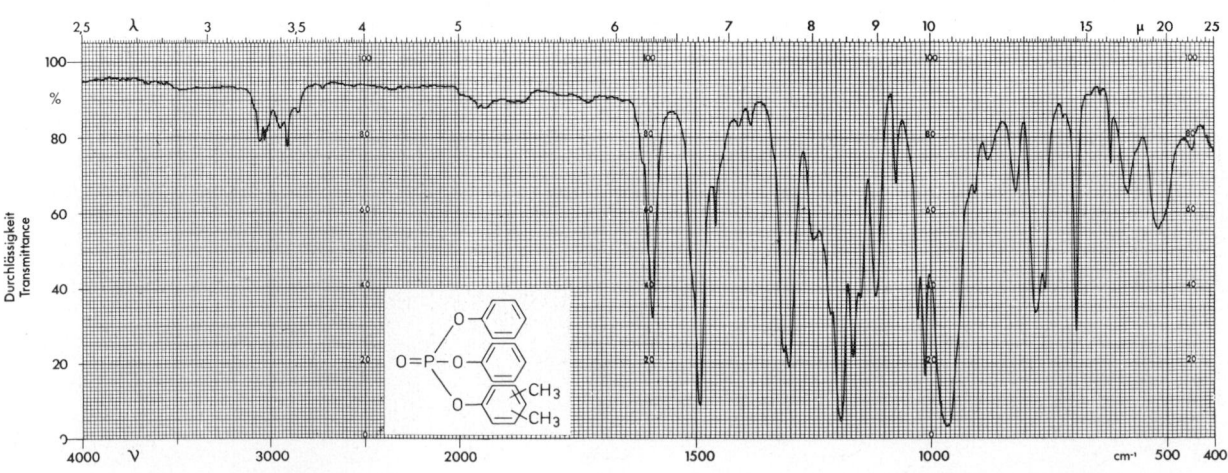

5263

Verbindung:	Xylyldiphenylphosphat		Compound:	Xylyl diphenyl phosphate	
Formel:	$C_{20}H_{19}O_4P$	M.: 354,4	Formula:	$C_{20}H_{19}O_4P$	M. w.: 354,4
Handelsname:	Disflamoll XDP	Herst.: Bayer	Tradename:	Disflamoll XDP	Manuf.: Bayer
Präparation:	Kapill. Film	Dez. Nr.: 6.1.12	Preparation:	Capill. Film	Dec. No.: 6.1.12

Weichmacher
6. Phosphorsäureester
6.1. Phosphate

Plasticizers
6. Phosphoric Acid Esters
6.1. Phosphates

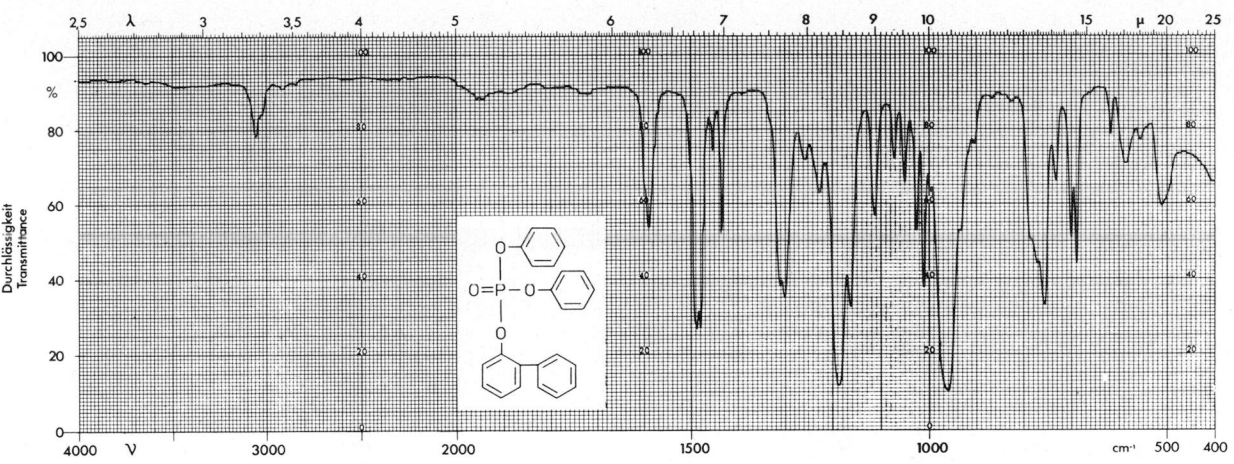

Verbindung:	Diphenylbiphenylyl-2-phosphat		Compound:	Diphenyl biphenylyl-2 phosphate		5264
Formel:	$C_{24}H_{19}O_4P$	M.: 402,4	Formula:	$C_{24}H_{19}O_4P$	M. w.: 402,4	
Handelsname:	Plasticizer 5	Herst.: Dow	Tradename:	Plasticizer 5	Manuf.: Dow	
Präparation:	Kapill. Film	Dez. Nr.: 6.1.13	Preparation:	Capill. Film	Dec. No.: 6.1.13	

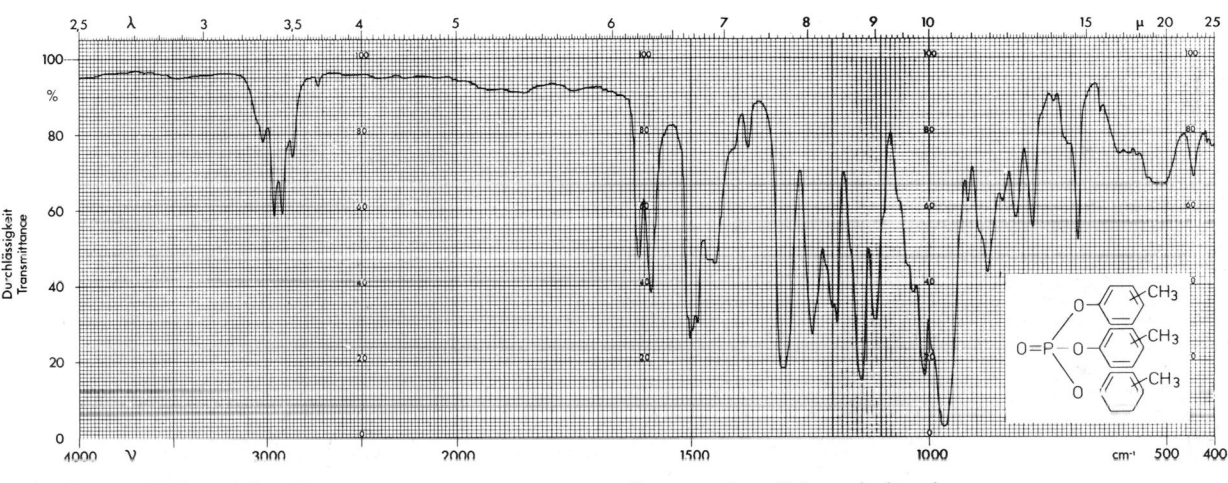

Verbindung:	Trikresylphosphat		Compound:	Tricresyl phosphate		5265
Formel:	$C_{21}H_{21}O_4P$	M.: 368,4	Formula:	$C_{21}H_{21}O_4P$	M. w.: 368,4	
Handelsname:	Celluflex 179 A	Herst.: Celanese	Tradename:	Celluflex 179 A	Manuf.: Celanese	
Präparation:	Kapill. Film	Dez. Nr.: 6.1.14	Preparation:	Capill. Film	Dec. No.: 6.1.14	

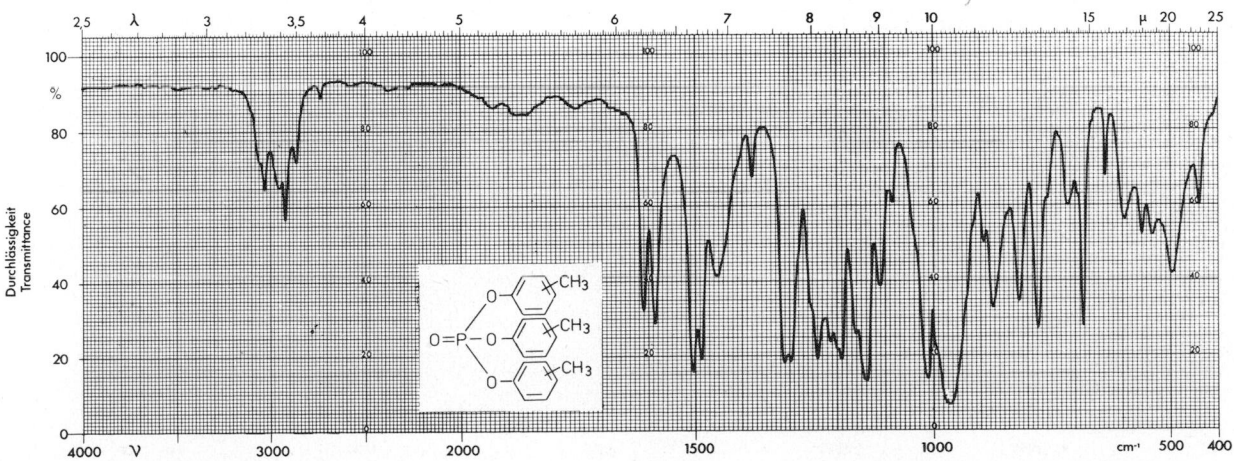

Verbindung:	Trikresylphosphat		Compound:	Tricresyl phosphate		5266
Formel:	$C_{21}H_{21}O_4P$	M.: 368,4	Formula:	$C_{21}H_{21}O_4P$	M. w.: 368,4	
Handelsname:		Herst.: Bosch	Tradename:		Manuf.: Bosch	
Präparation:	Kapill. Film	Dez. Nr.: 6.1.15	Preparation:	Capill. Film	Dec. No.: 6.1.15	

Weichmacher
6. Phosphorsäureester
6.2. Thiophosphate

Plasticizers
6. Phosphoric Acid Esters
6.2. Thiophosphates

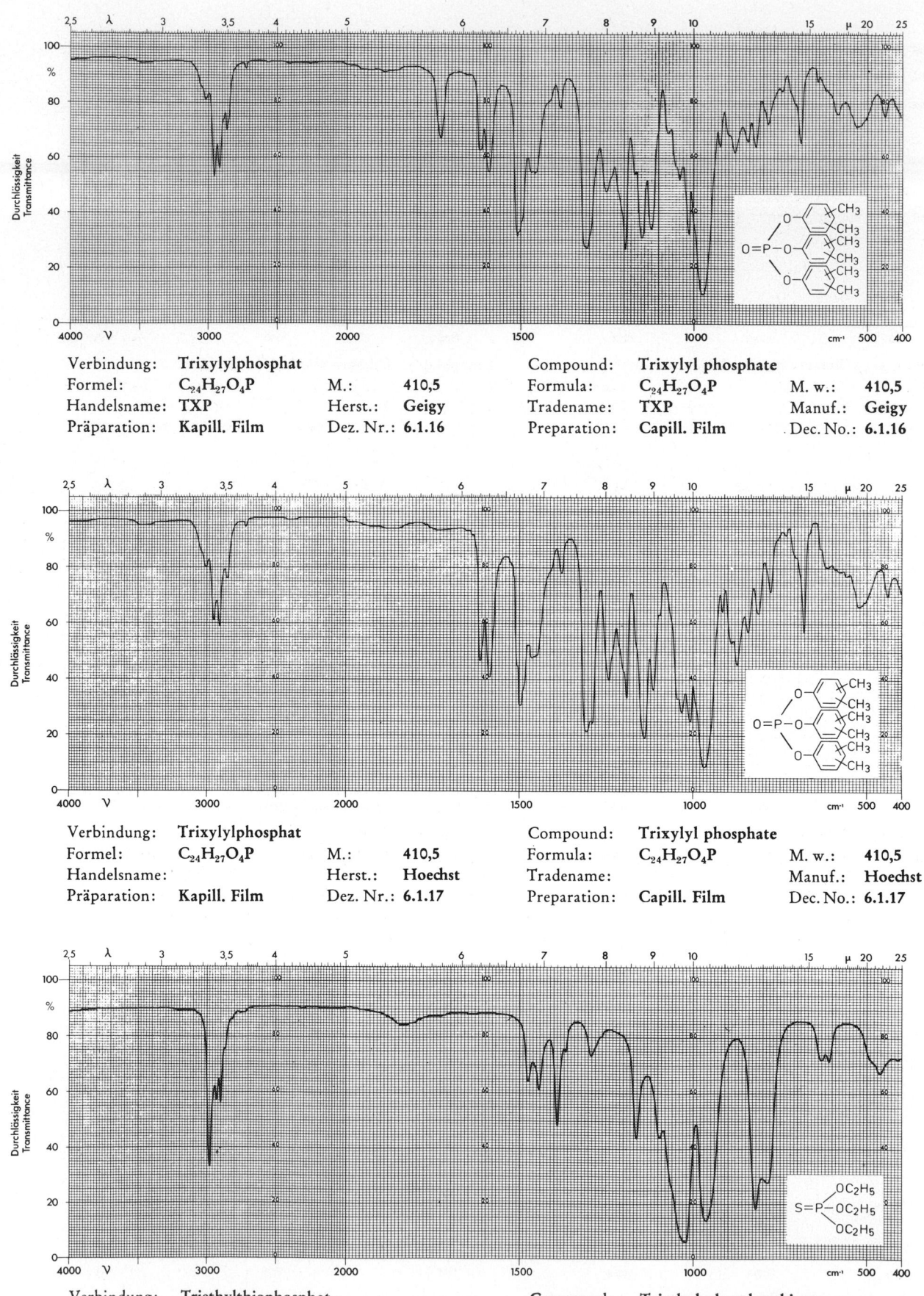

5267

Verbindung:	**Trixylylphosphat**		Compound:	**Trixylyl phosphate**	
Formel:	$C_{24}H_{27}O_4P$	M.: **410,5**	Formula:	$C_{24}H_{27}O_4P$	M. w.: **410,5**
Handelsname:	**TXP**	Herst.: **Geigy**	Tradename:	**TXP**	Manuf.: **Geigy**
Präparation:	**Kapill. Film**	Dez. Nr.: **6.1.16**	Preparation:	**Capill. Film**	Dec. No.: **6.1.16**

5268

Verbindung:	**Trixylylphosphat**		Compound:	**Trixylyl phosphate**	
Formel:	$C_{24}H_{27}O_4P$	M.: **410,5**	Formula:	$C_{24}H_{27}O_4P$	M. w.: **410,5**
Handelsname:		Herst.: **Hoechst**	Tradename:		Manuf.: **Hoechst**
Präparation:	**Kapill. Film**	Dez. Nr.: **6.1.17**	Preparation:	**Capill. Film**	Dec. No.: **6.1.17**

5269

Verbindung:	**Triethylthiophosphat**		Compound:	**Triethyl phosphorthioate**	
Formel:	$C_6H_{15}O_3PS$	M.: **198,2**	Formula:	$C_6H_{15}O_3PS$	M. w.: **198,2**
Handelsname:		Herst.: **VC**	Tradename:		Manuf.: **VC**
Präparation:	**Kapill. Film**	Dez. Nr.: **6.2.1**	Preparation:	**Capill. Film**	Dec. No:. **6.2.1**

Weichmacher
6. Phosphorsäureester
6.3. Phosphonate

Plasticizers
6. Phosphoric Acid Esters
6.3. Phosphonates

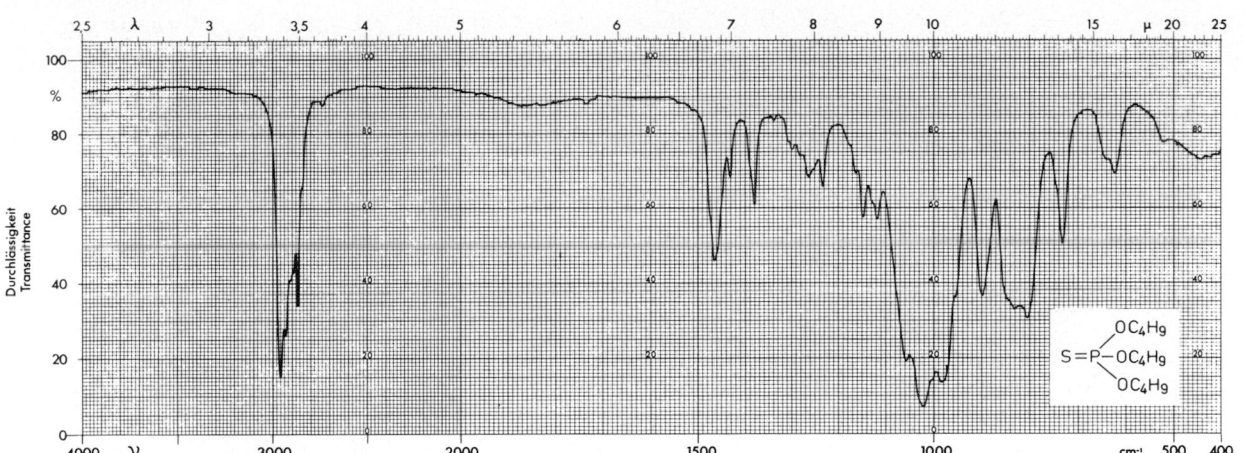

Verbindung:	**Tributylthiophosphat**			Compound:	**Tributyl phosphorthioate**			5270
Formel:	$C_{12}H_{27}O_3PS$	M.:	**282,3**	Formula:	$C_{12}H_{27}O_3PS$	M. w.:	**282,3**	
Handelsname:		Herst.:	**VC**	Tradename:		Manuf.:	**VC**	
Präparation:	**Kapill. Film**	Dez. Nr.:	**6.2.2**	Preparation:	**Capill. Film**	Dec. No.:	**6.2.2**	

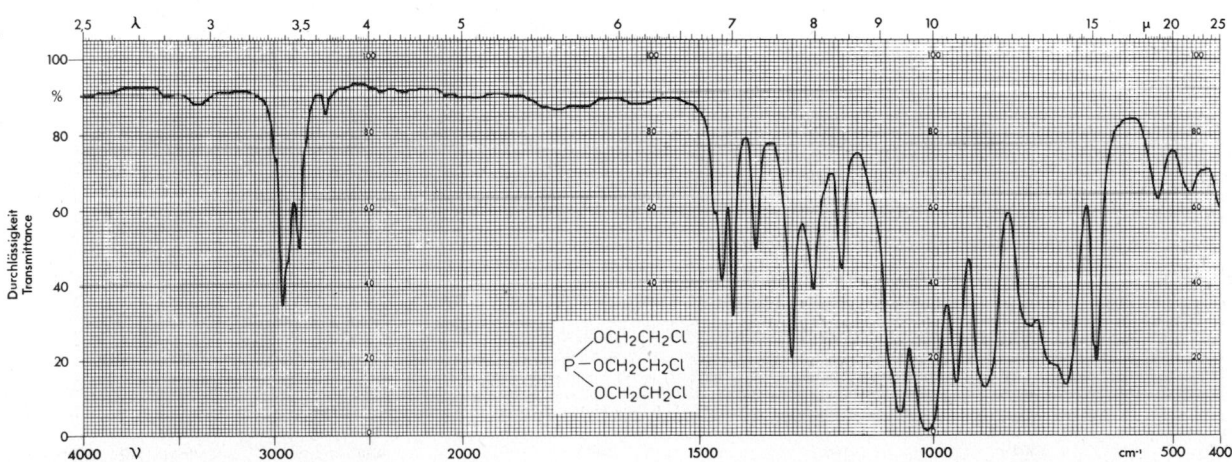

Verbindung:	**Triisooctylthiophosphat**			Compound:	**Triisooctyl phosphorthioate**			5271
Formel:	$C_{24}H_{51}O_3PS$	M.:	**451,7**	Formula:	$C_{24}H_{51}O_3PS$	M. w.:	**451,7**	
Handelsname:		Herst.:	**VC**	Tradename:		Manuf.:	**VC**	
Präparation:	**Kapill. Film**	Dez. Nr.:	**6.2.3**	Preparation:	**Capill. Film**	Dec. No.:	**6.2.3**	

Verbindung:	**Tri(2-chlorethyl)phosphit**			Compound:	**Tri(2-chloroethyl) phosphite**			5272
Formel:	$C_6H_{12}O_3PCl_3$	M.:	**269,7**	Formula:	$C_6H_{12}O_3PCl_3$	M. w.:	**269,7**	
Handelsname:		Herst.:	**VC**	Tradename:		Manuf.:	**VC**	
Präparation:	**Kapill. Film**	Dez. Nr.:	**6.3.1**	Preparation:	**Capill. Film**	Dec. No.:	**6.3.1**	

Weichmacher
6. Phosphorsäureester
6.3. Phosphonate

Plasticizers
6. Phosphoric Acid Esters
6.3. Phosphonates

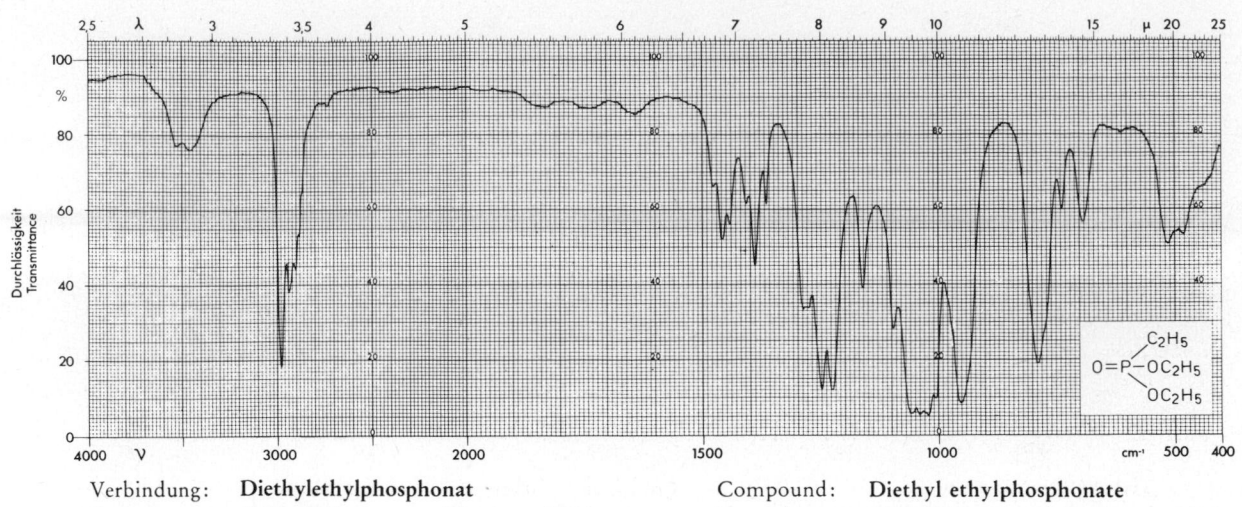

5273   Verbindung: **Diethylethylphosphonat**   Compound: **Diethyl ethylphosphonate**

Formel: $C_6H_{15}O_3P$ M.:   166,2   Formula: $C_6H_{15}O_3P$ M. w.:   166,2

Handelsname: Herst.:   **VC**   Tradename: Manuf.:   **VC**

Präparation: **Kapill. Film**   Dez. Nr.:   **6.3.2**   Preparation: **Capill. Film**   Dec. No.:   **6.3.2**

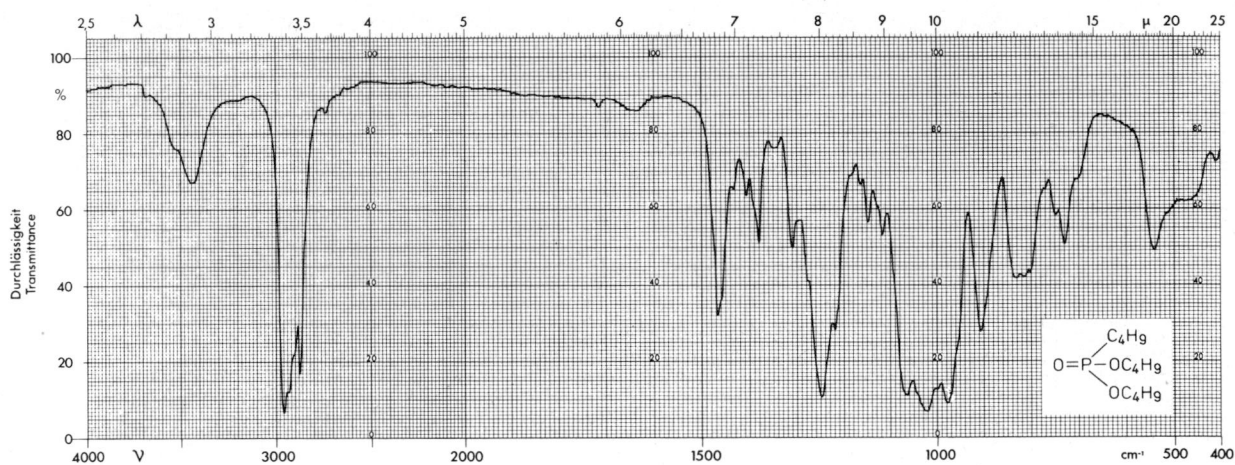

5274   Verbindung: **Dibutylbutylphosphonat**   Compound: **Dibutyl butylphosphonate**

Formel: $C_{12}H_{27}O_3P$ M.:   250,4   Formula: $C_{12}H_{27}O_3P$ M. w.:   250,4

Handelsname: Herst.:   **VC**   Tradename: Manuf.:   **VC**

Präparation: **Kapill. Film**   Dez. Nr.:   **6.3.3**   Preparation: **Capill. Film**   Dec. No.:   **6.3.3**

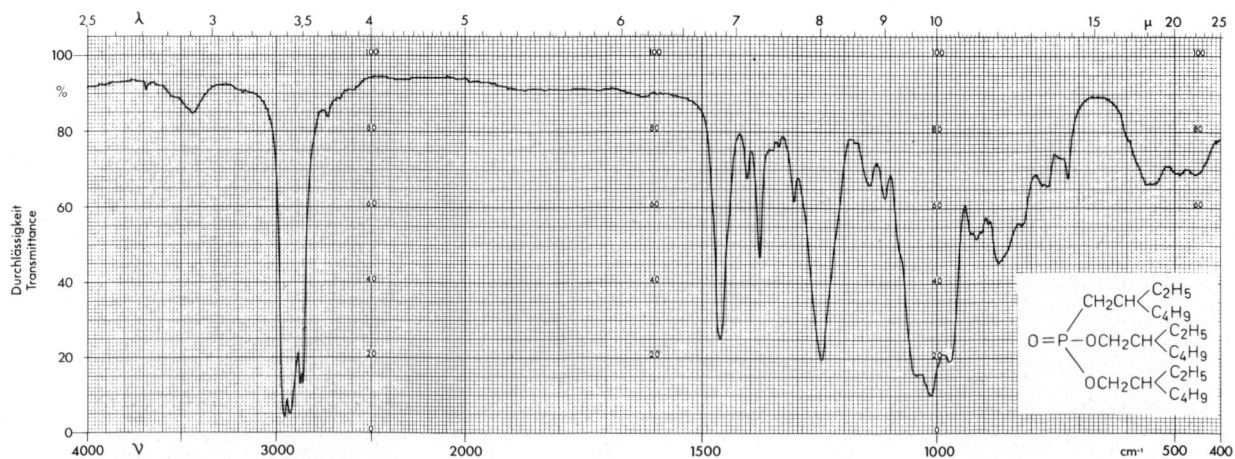

5275   Verbindung: **Di(2-ethylhexyl)-2-ethylhexylphosphonat**   Compound: **Di(2-ethylhexyl)-2-ethylhexylphosphonate**

Formel: $C_{24}H_{51}O_3P$ M.:   419,7   Formula: $C_{24}H_{51}O_3P$ M. w.:   419,7

Handelsname: Herst.:   **VC**   Tradename: Manuf.:   **VC**

Präparation: **Kapill. Film**   Dez. Nr.:   **6.3.4**   Preparation: **Capill. Film**   Dec. No.:   **6.3.4**

Weichmacher
7. Heterocyclische Verbindungen
7.1. Imidazoline und Piperidinderivate

Plasticizers
7. Heterocyclic Compounds
7.1. Imidazolines and Piperidine Derivatives

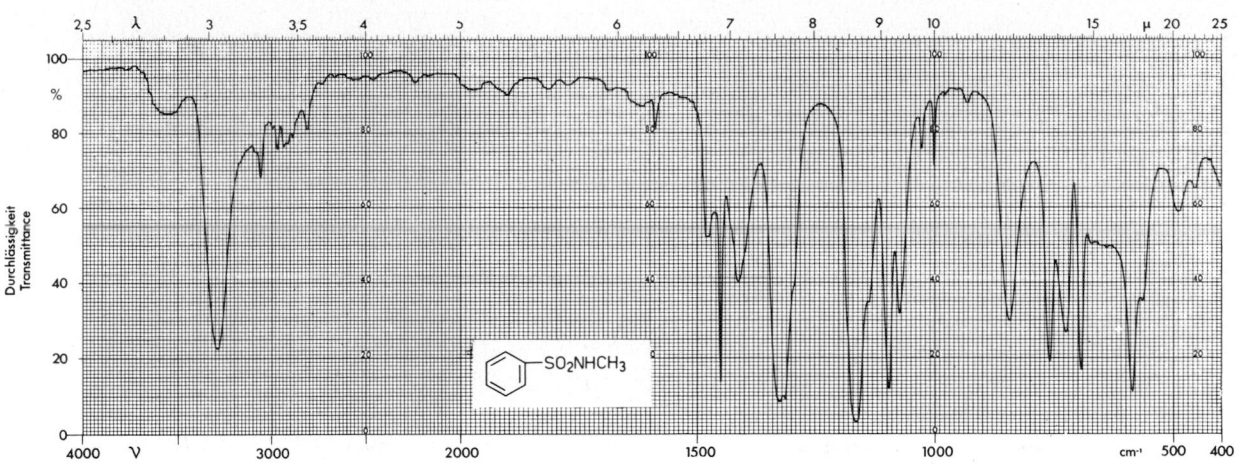

Verbindung:	Benzolsulfonmethylamid			Compound:	Benzenesulfonmethylamide		5276
Formel:	$C_7H_5O_2NS$	M.:	171,2	Formula:	$C_7H_5O_2NS$	M. w.: 171,2	
Handelsname:	Dellatol MMA	Herst.:	Bayer	Tradename:	Dellatol MMA	Manuf.: Bayer	
Präparation:	Kapill. Film	Dez. Nr.:	7.1.1	Preparation:	Capill. Film	Dec. No.: 7.1.1	

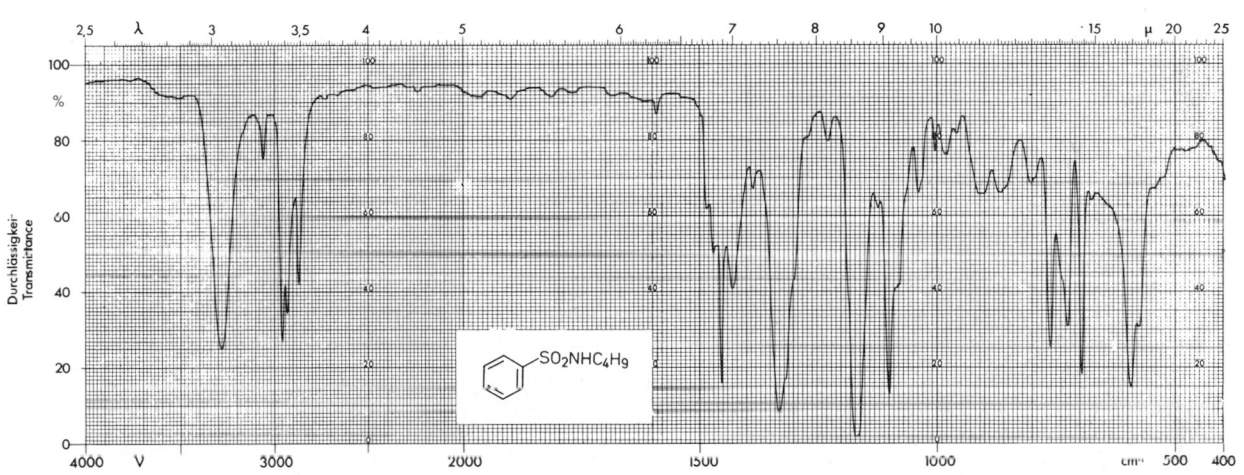

Verbindung:	Benzolsulfonbutylamid			Compound:	Benzenesulfonbutylamide		5277
Formel:	$C_{10}H_{15}O_2NS$	M.:	213,2	Formula:	$C_{10}H_{15}O_2NS$	M. w.: 213,2	
Handelsname:	Plastomoll BMB	Herst.:	BASF	Tradename:	Plastomoll BMB	Manuf.: BASF	
Präparation:	Kapill. Film	Dez. Nr.:	7.1.2	Preparation:	Capill. Film	Dec. No.: 7.1.2	

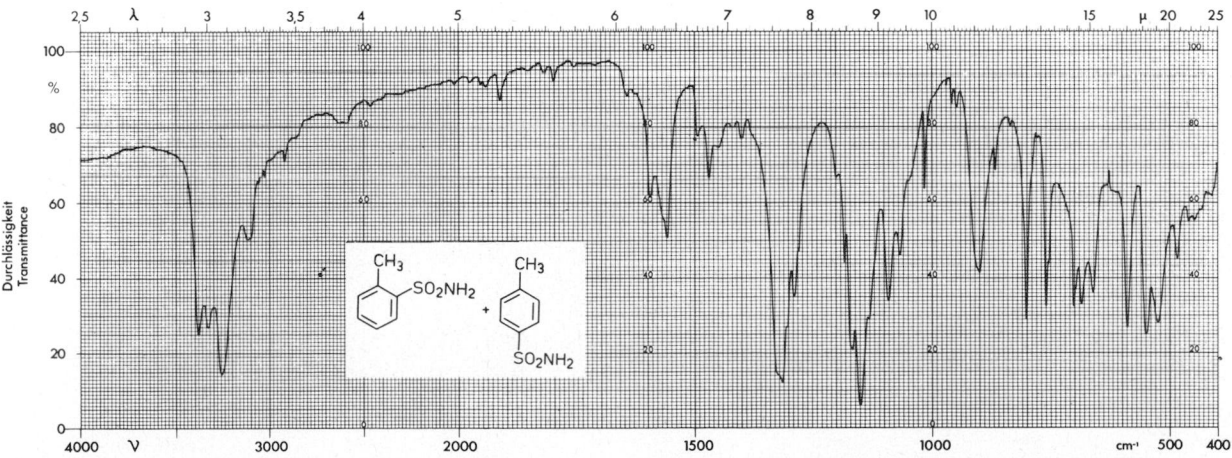

Verbindung:	Gemisch von o- und p-Toluolsulfonamid			Compound:	Mixture of o- and p-Toluenesulfonamide		5278
Formel:	$C_7H_9O_2NS$	M.:	171,2	Formula:	$C_7H_9O_2NS$	M. w.: 171,2	
Handelsname:	Santicizer 9	Herst.:	Monsanto	Tradename:	Santicizer 9	Manuf.: Monsanto	
Präparation:	Kapill. Film	Dez. Nr.:	7.1.3	Preparation:	Capill. Film	Dec. No.: 7.1.3	

Weichmacher
7. Heterocyclische Verbindungen
7.1. Imidazoline und Piperidinderivate

Plasticizers
7. Heterocyclic Compounds
7.1. Imidazolines and Piperidine Derivatives

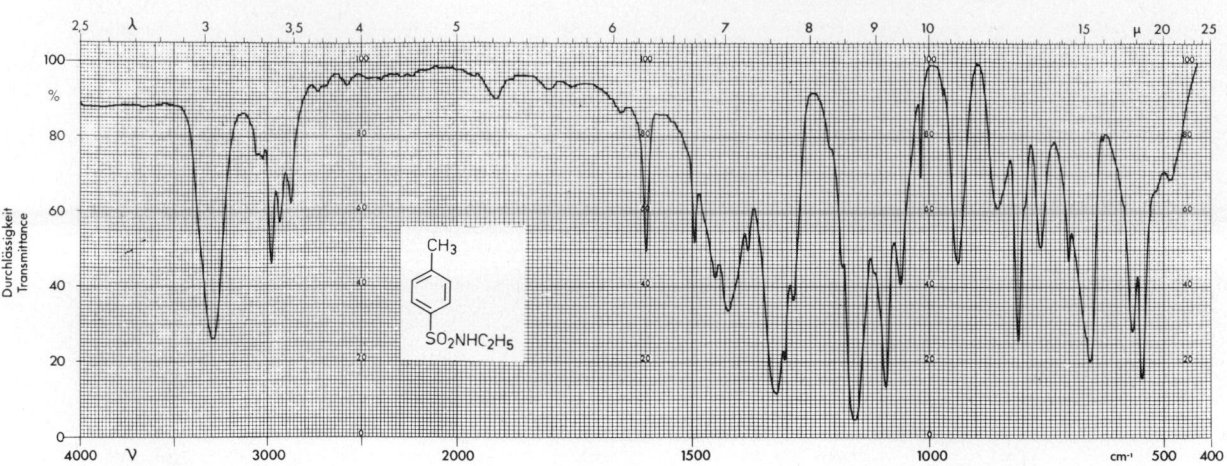

5279

Verbindung:	Tri(2-chlorethyl)phosphit			Compound:	N-ethyl-p-toluene sulfonamide		
Formel:	$C_9H_{13}O_9NS$	M.:	199,2	Formula:	$C_9H_{13}O_2NS$	M. w.:	199,2
Handelsname:	Santicizer 3	Herst.:	Monsanto	Tradename:	Santicizer 3	Manuf.:	Monsanto
Präparation:	Kapill. Film	Dez. Nr.:	7.1.4	Preparation:	Capill. Film	Dec. No.:	7.1.4

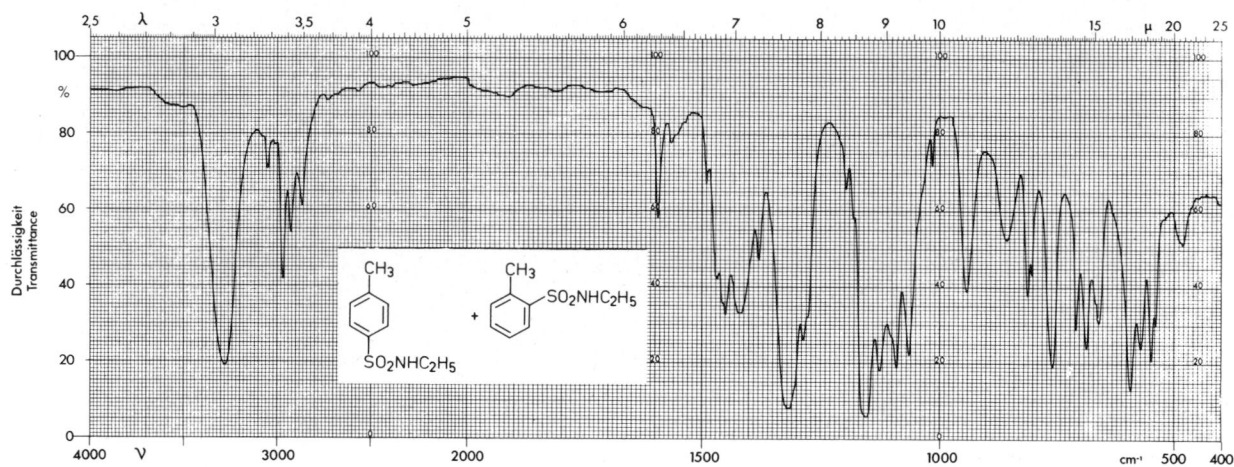

5280

Verbindung:	Gemisch von o- und p-Ethyl-toluolsulfon-amid			Compound:	Mixture of o- and p-N-ethyl-toluenesulfon-amide		
Formel:	$C_9H_{13}O_2NS$	M.:	199,2	Formula:	$C_9H_{13}O_2NS$	M. w.:	199,2
Handelsname:	Santicizer 8	Herst.:	Monsanto	Tradename:	Santicizer 8	Manuf.:	Monsanto
Präparation:	Kapill. Film	Dez. Nr.:	7.1.5	Preparation:	Capill. Film	Dec. No.:	7.1.5

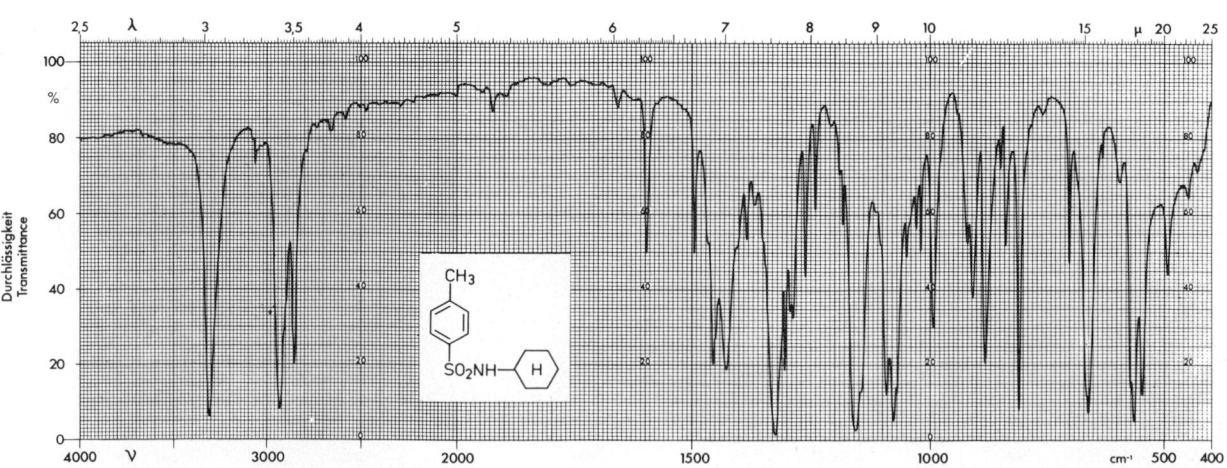

5281

Verbindung:	N-Cyclohexyl-p-toluolsulfonamid			Compound:	N-Cyclohexyl-p-toluenesulfonamide		
Formel:	$C_{13}H_{19}O_2NS$	M.:	253,3	Formula:	$C_{13}H_{19}O_2NS$	M. w.:	253,3
Handelsname:	Santicizer 1-H	Herst.:	Monsanto	Tradename:	Santicizer 1-H	Manuf.:	Monsanto
Präparation:	Kapill. Film	Dez. Nr.:	7.1.6	Preparation:	Capill. Film	Dec. No.:	7.1.6

Weichmacher
8. Kohlenwasserstoffe
8.1. Paraffinische und naphthenische Mineralöle

Plasticizers
8. Hydrocarbons
8.1. Paraffinic and Naphthenic Mineral Oils

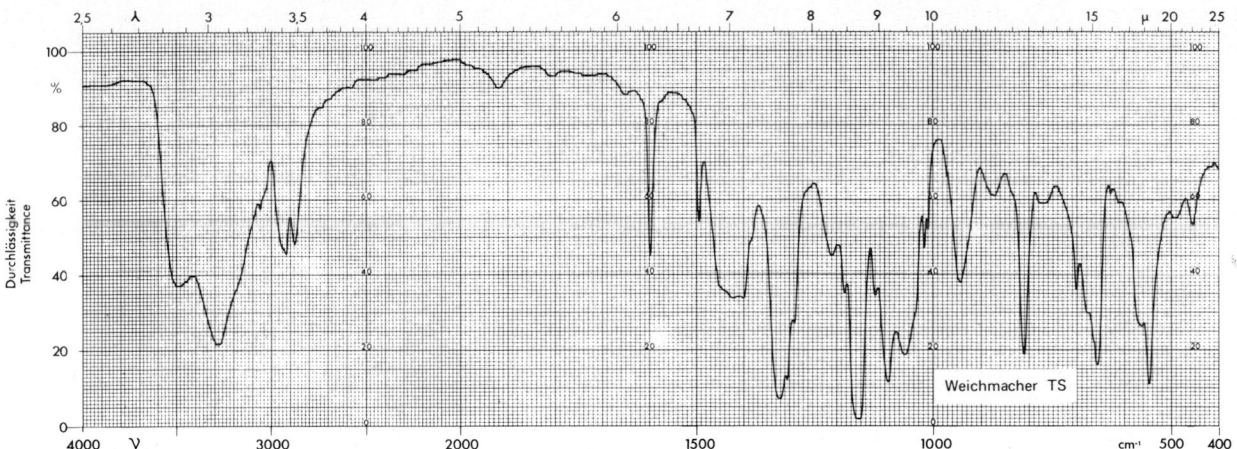

Verbindung:	Sulfonamid-Weichmacher		Compound:	Sulfonamide-plasticizer		5282
Formel:		M.:	Formula:		M. w.:	
Handelsname:	Weichmacher TS	Herst.: BASF	Tradename:	Weichmacher TS	Manuf.: BASF	
Präparation:	Kapill. Film	Dez. Nr.: 7.1.7	Preparation:	Capill. film	Dec. No.: 7.1.7	

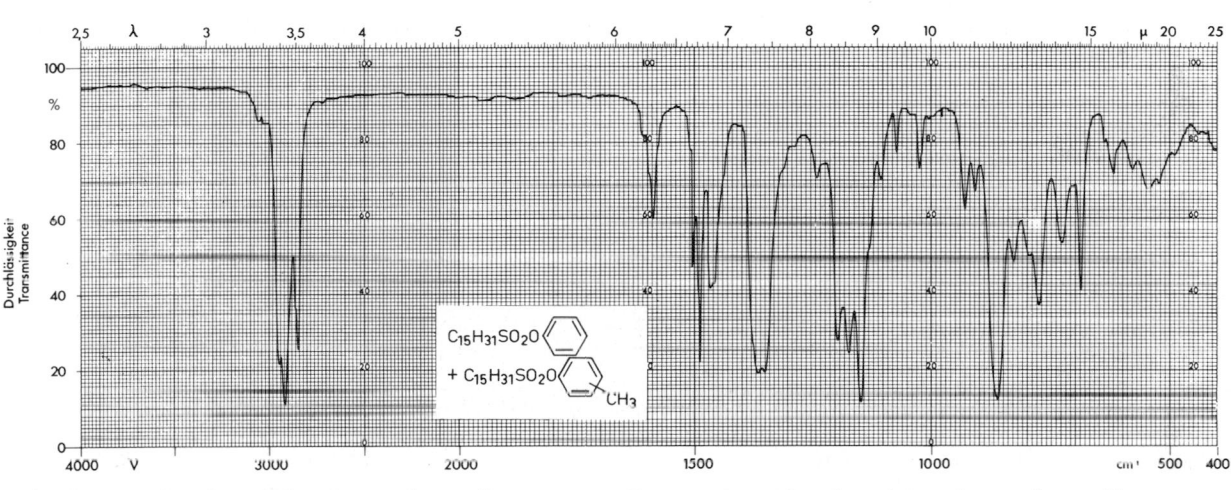

Verbindung:	Phenol- und Kresol-pentadecansulfonate		Compound:	Phenol- and Cresol-pentadecansulfonates		5283
Formel:		M.: ~ 400	Formula:		M. w.: ~ 400	
Handelsname:	Mesamoll	Herst.: Bayer	Tradename:	Mesamoll	Manuf.: Bayer	
Präparation:	Kapill. Film	Dez. Nr.: 7.2.1	Preparation:	Capill. film	Dec. No.: 7.2.1	

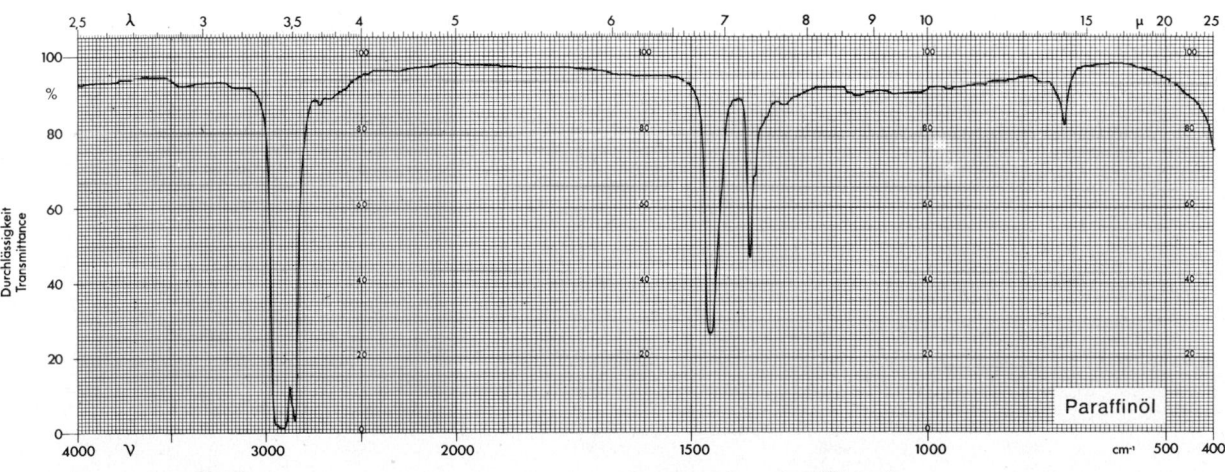

Verbindung:	Paraffinöl		Compound:	Paraffine oil		5284
		M.: ~ 380			M. w.: ~ 380	
Handelsname:	Weißöl 505	Herst.: Fuchs	Tradename:	Weißöl 505	Manuf.: Fuchs	
Präparation:	Kapill. Film 25 μ	Dez. Nr.: 8.1.1	Preparation:	Capill. film 25 μ	Dec. No.: 8.1.1	

Weichmacher
8. Kohlenwasserstoffe
8.1. Paraffinische und naphthenische Mineralöle

Plasticizers
8. Hydrocarbons
8.1. Paraffinic and Naphthenic Mineral Oils

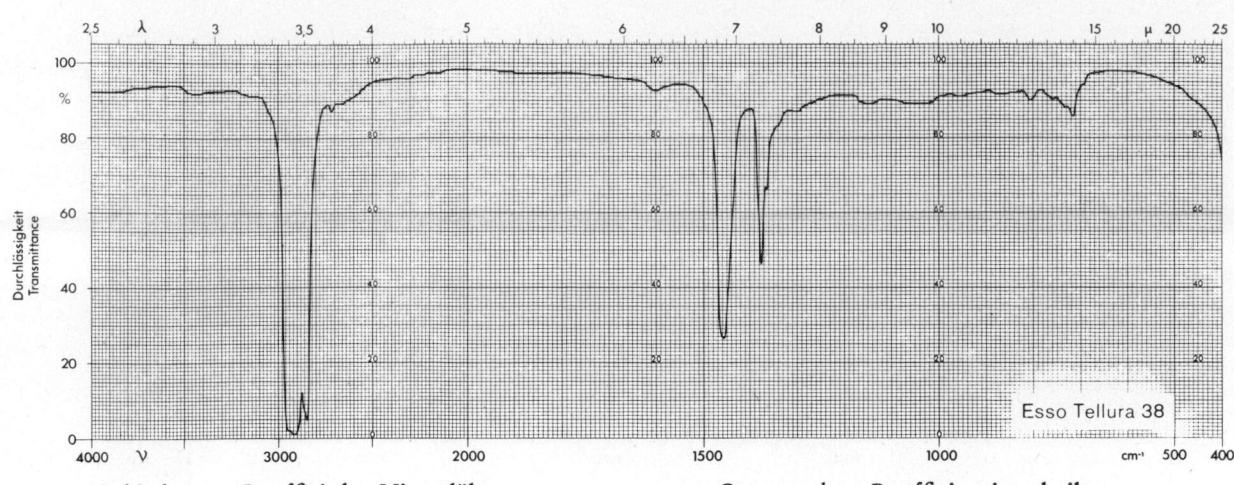

5285   Verbindung: **Paraffinisches Mineralöl**   Compound: **Paraffinic mineral oil**

	M.: **~ 325**		M. w.: **~ 325**
Handelsname: **Esso Tellura 38**	Herst.: **Esso**	Tradename: **Esso Tellura 38**	Manuf.: **Esso**
Präparation: **Kapill. Film 25 μ**	Dez. Nr.: **8.1.2**	Preparation: **Capill. film 25 μ**	Dec. No.: **8.1.2**

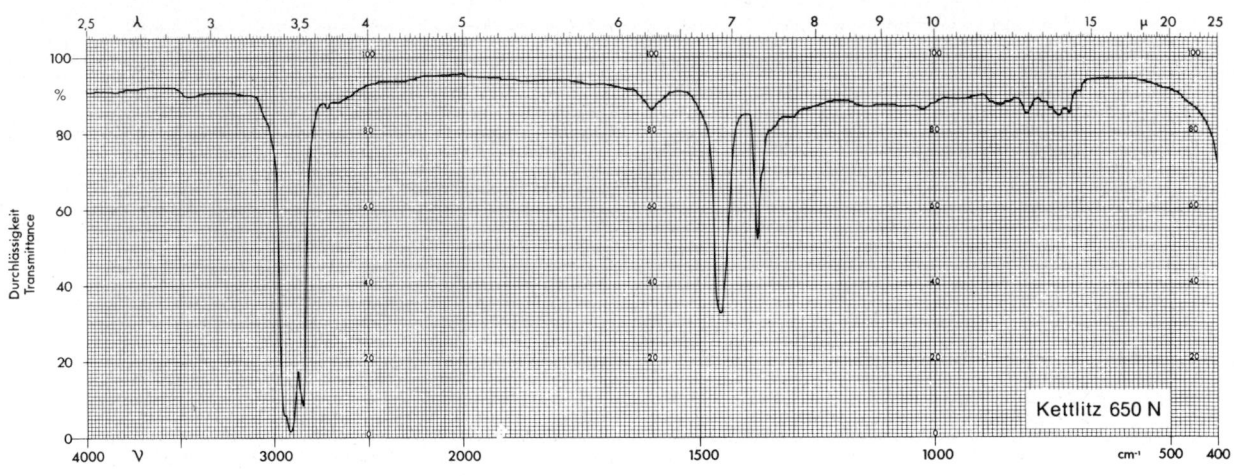

5286   Verbindung: **Naphthenisches Mineralöl**   Compound: **Naphthenic mineral oil**

	M.: **~ 370**		M. w.: **~ 370**
Handelsname: **Kettlitz 650 N**	Herst.: **Kettlitz**	Tradename: **Kettlitz 650 N**	Manuf.: **Kettlitz**
Präparation: **Kapill. Film 25 μ**	Dez. Nr.: **8.1.3**	Preparation: **Capill. film 25 μ**	Dec. No.: **8.1.3**

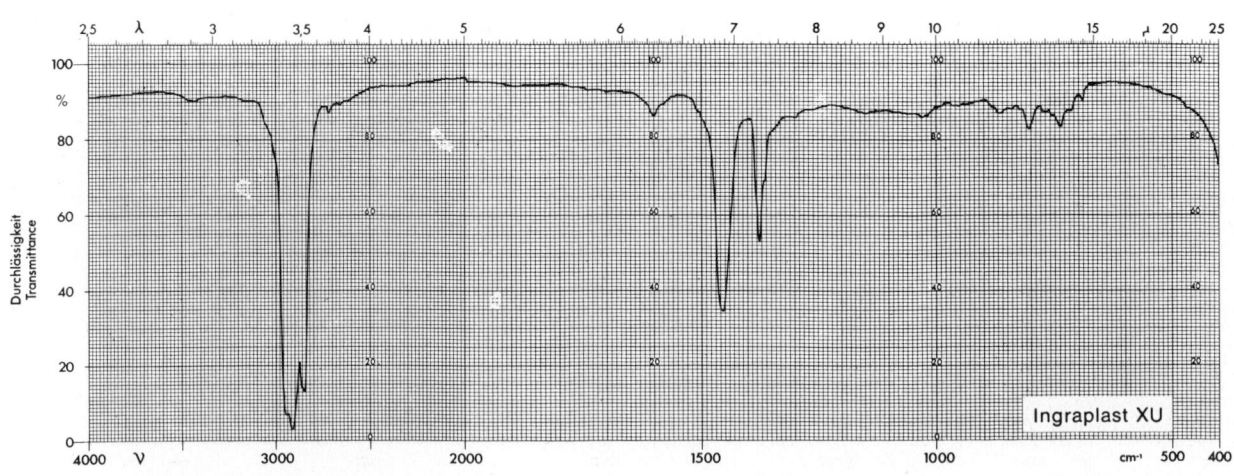

5287   Verbindung: **Naphthenisches Mineralöl**   Compound: **Naphthenic mineral oil**

	M.: **~ 290**		M. w.: **~ 290**
Handelsname: **Ingraplast XU**	Herst.: **Fuchs**	Tradename: **Ingraplast XU**	Manuf.: **Fuchs**
Präparation: **Kapill. Film 25 μ**	Dez. Nr.: **8.1.4**	Preparation: **Capill. film 25 μ**	Dec. No.: **8.1.4**

Weichmacher
8. Kohlenwasserstoffe
8.1. Paraffinische und naphthenische Mineralöle

Plasticizers
8. Hydrocarbons
8.1. Paraffinic and Naphthenic Mineral Oils

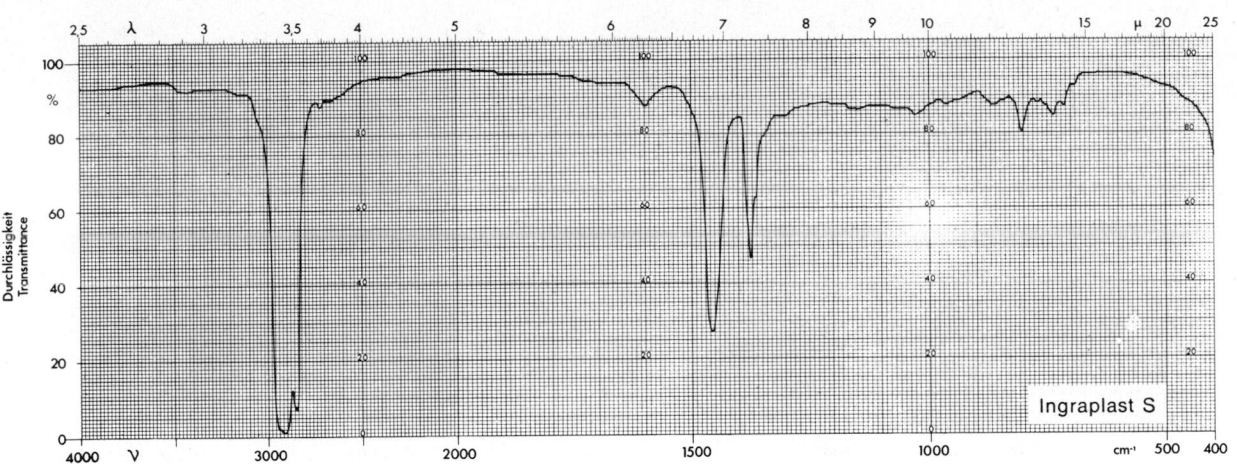

Verbindung: **Naphthenisches Mineralöl**   Compound: **Naphthenic mineral oil**   5288

M.:   **~ 380**   M. w.:   **~ 380**

Handelsname: **Ingraplast S**   Herst.:   **Fuchs**   Tradename: **Ingraplast S**   Manuf.:   **Fuchs**

Präparation: **Kapill. Film 25 μ**   Dez. Nr.: **8.1.5**   Preparation: **Capill. film 25 μ**   Dec. No.: **8.1.5**

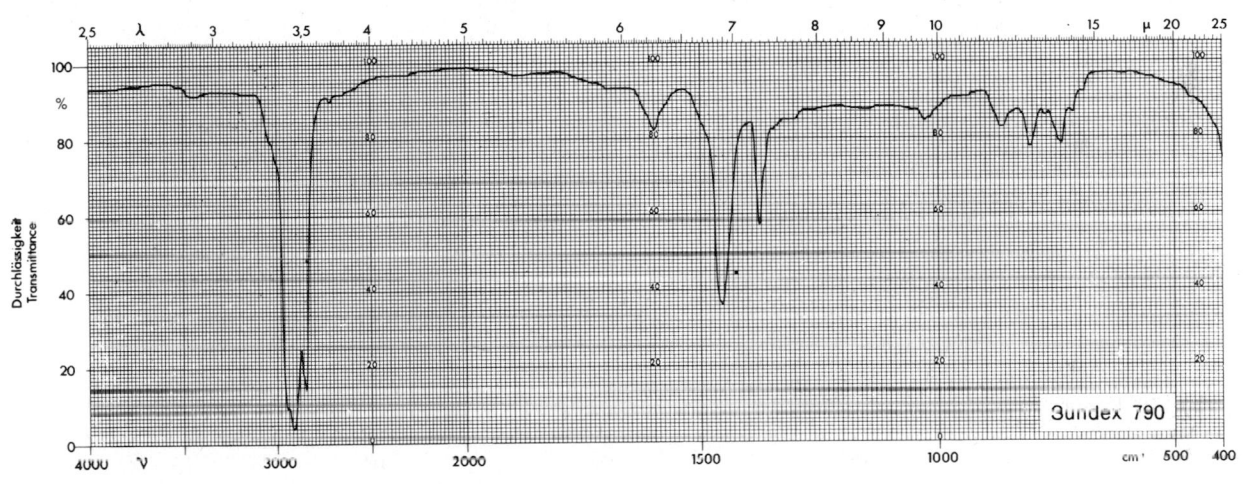

Verbindung: **Naphthenisches Mineralöl**   Compound: **Naphthenic mineral oil**   5289

M.:   **~ 345**   M. w.:   **~ 345**

Handelsname: **Sundex 790**   Herst.:   **Sun Oil**   Tradename: **Sundex 790**   Manuf.:   **Sun Oil**

Präparation: **Kapill. Film 25 μ**   Dez. Nr.: **8.1.6**   Preparation: **Capill. film 25 μ**   Dec. No.: **8.1.6**

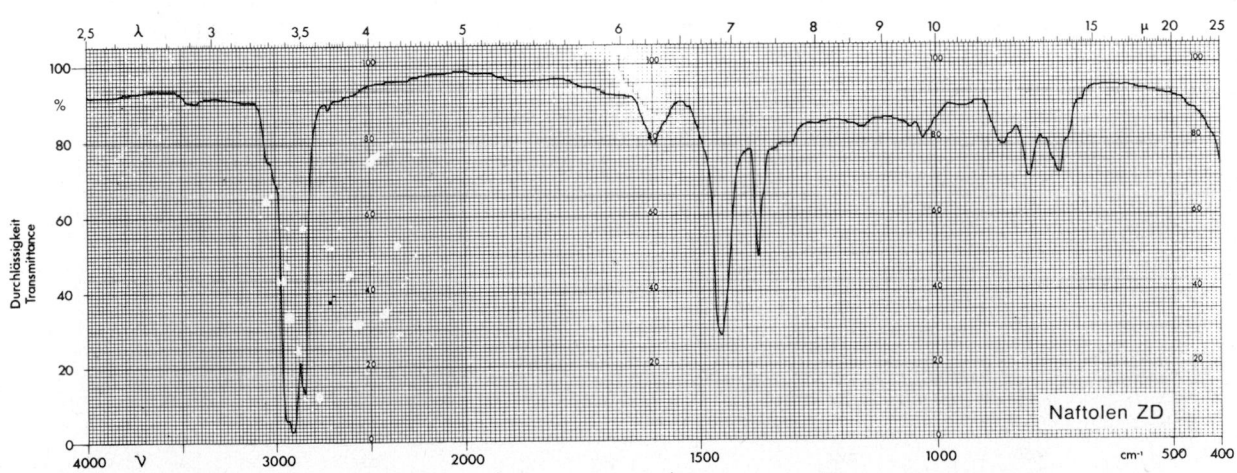

Verbindung: **Naphthenisches Mineralöl**   Compound: **Naphthenic mineral oil**   5290

M.:   **~ 320**   M. w.:   **~ 320**

Handelsname: **Naftolen ZD**   Herst.:   **Metallges.**   Tradename: **Naftolen ZD**   Manuf.:   **Metallges.**

Präparation: **Kapill. Film 25 μ**   Dez. Nr.: **8.1.7**   Preparation: **Capill. film 25 μ**   Dec. No.: **8.1.7**

Weichmacher
8. Kohlenwasserstoffe
8.2. Aromatische Öle

Plasticizers
8. Hydrocarbons
8.2. Aromatic Oils

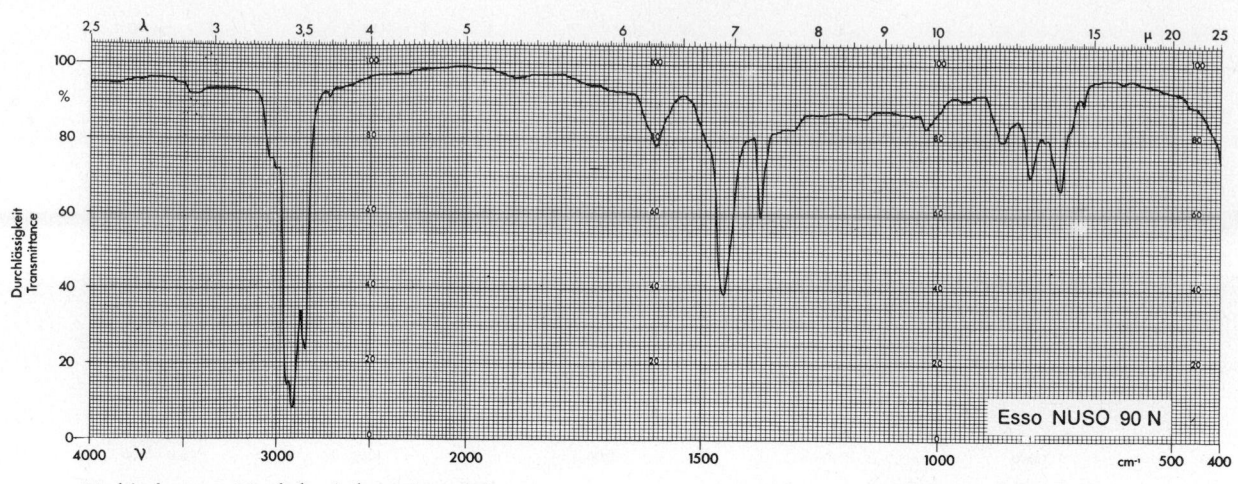

5291   Verbindung: **Naphthenisches Mineralöl**   Compound: **Naphthenic mineral oil**

M.:   ∼ 360   M. w.:   ∼ 360

Handelsname: **Esso NUSO 90 N**   Herst.:   **Esso**   Tradename: **Esso NUSO 90 N**   Manuf.:   **Esso**

Präparation: **Kapill. Film 25 μ**   Dez. Nr.: **8.1.8**   Preparation: **Capill. film 25 μ**   Dec. No.: **8.1.8**

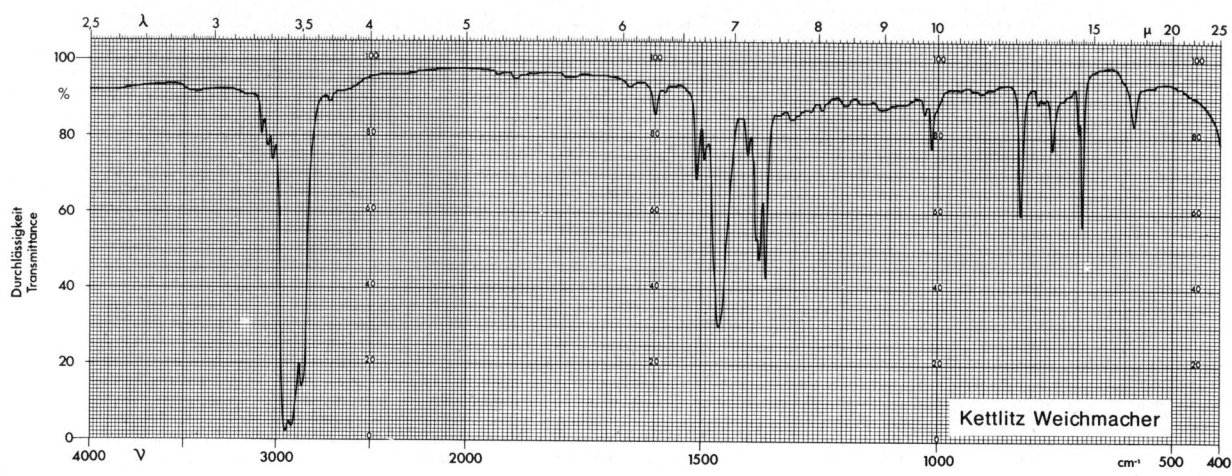

5292   Verbindung: **Aromatisches Mineralöl**   Compound: **Aromatic mineral oil**

M.:   ∼ 370   M. w.:   ∼ 370

Handelsname: **Kettlitz Weichmach.** Herst.:   **Kettlitz**   Tradename: **Kettlitz Weichmach.** Manuf.:   **Kettlitz**

Präparation: **Kapill. Film 25 μ**   Dez. Nr.: **8.2.1**   Preparation: **Capill. film 25 μ**   Dec. No.: **8.2.1**

5293   Verbindung: **Aromatisches Mineralöl**   Compound: **Aromatic mineral oil**

M.:   ∼ 305   M. w.:   ∼ 305

Handelsname: **Kettlitz NS**   Herst.:   **Kettlitz**   Tradename: **Kettlitz NS**   Manuf.:   **Kettlitz**

Präparation: **Kapill. Film 25 μ**   Dez. Nr.: **8.2.2**   Preparation: **Capill. film 25 μ**   Dec. No.: **8.2.2**

Weichmacher
8. Kohlenwasserstoffe
8.2. Aromatische Öle

Plasticizers
8. Hydrocarbons
8.2. Aromatic Oils

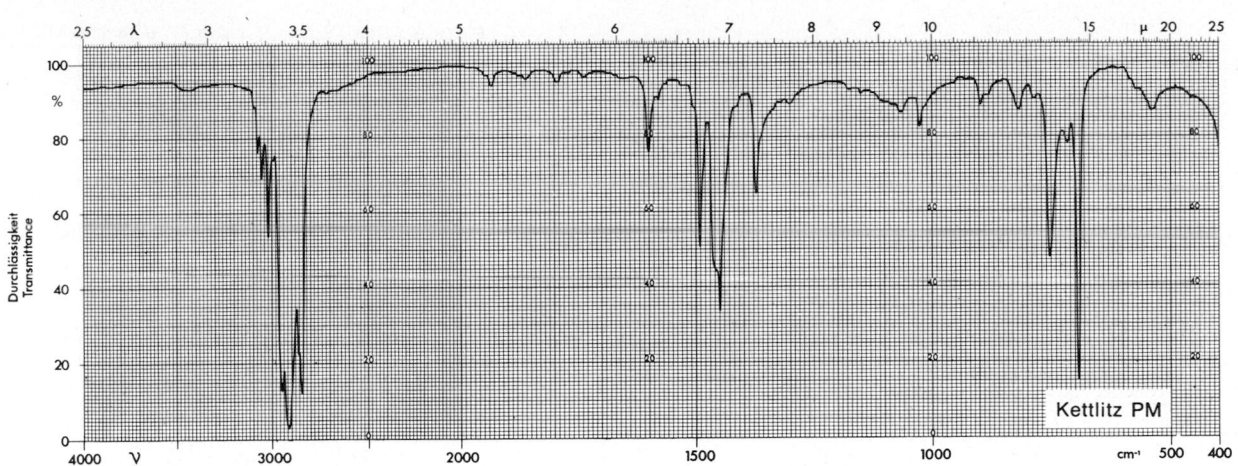

Kettlitz PM

Verbindung:	Aromatisches Mineralöl			Compound:	Aromatic mineral oil			5294
		M.:	~ 380			M. w.:	~ 380	
Handelsname:	Kettlitz PM	Herst.:	Kettlitz	Tradename:	Kettlitz PM	Manuf.:	Kettlitz	
Präparation:	Kapill. Film 25 μ	Dez. Nr.:	8.2.3	Preparation:	Capill. film 25 μ	Dec. No.:	8.2.3	

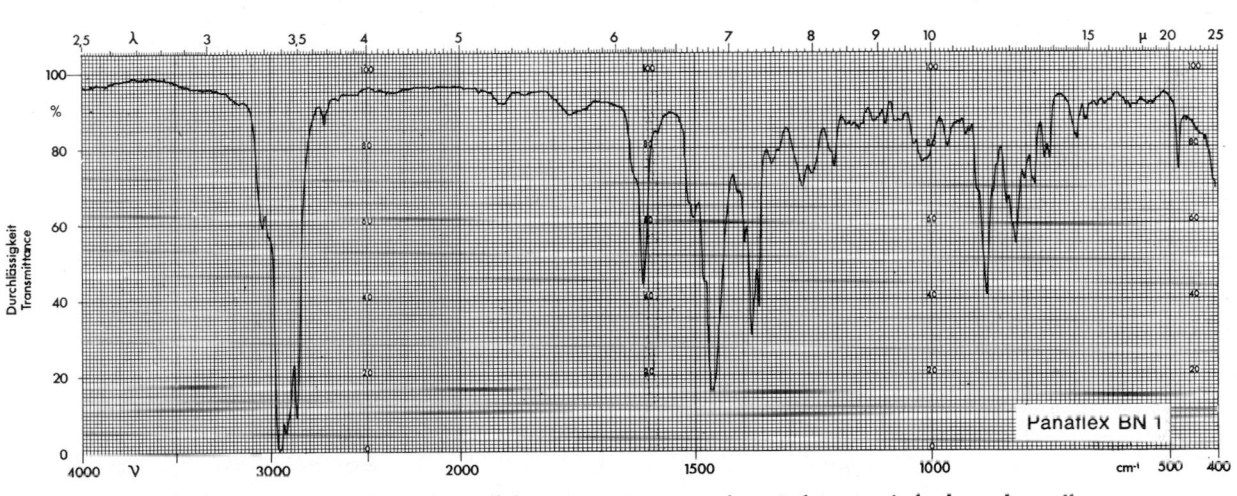

Panaflex BN 1

Verbindung:	Polyaromatisches Kohlenwasserstofföl			Compound:	Polyaromatic hydrocarbon oil			5295
		M.:	~ 280			M. w.:	~ 280	
Handelsname:	Panaflex BN 1	Herst.:	Amoco	Tradename:	Panaflex BN 1	Manuf.:	Amoco	
Präparation:	Kapill. Film 15 μ	Dez. Nr.:	8.2.4	Preparation:	Capill. film 15 μ	Dec. No.:	8.2.4	

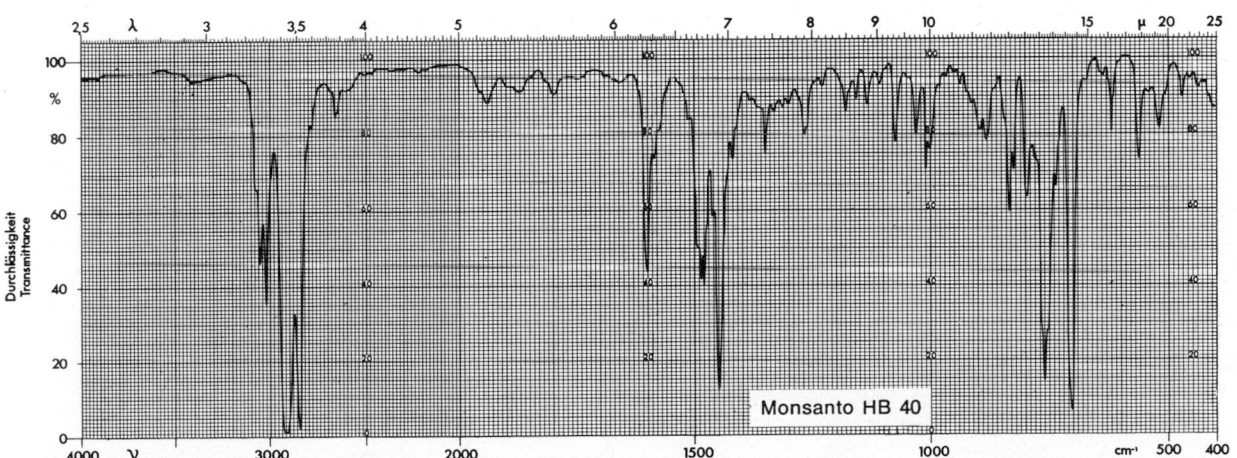

Monsanto HB 40

Verbindung:	Hydriertes Terphenyl			Compound:	Hydrogenated terphenyl			5296
		M.:	~ 240			M. w.:	~ 240	
Handelsname:	HB 40	Herst.:	Monsanto	Tradename:	HB 40	Manuf.:	Monsanto	
Präparation:	Kapill. Film	Dez. Nr.:	8.2.5	Preparation:	Capill. film	Dec. No.:	8.2.5	

Weichmacher
8. Kohlenwasserstoffe
8.3. Paraffinische Halogenkohlenwasserstoffe

Plasticizers
8. Hydrocarbons
8.3. Paraffinic Halogenated Hydrocarbons

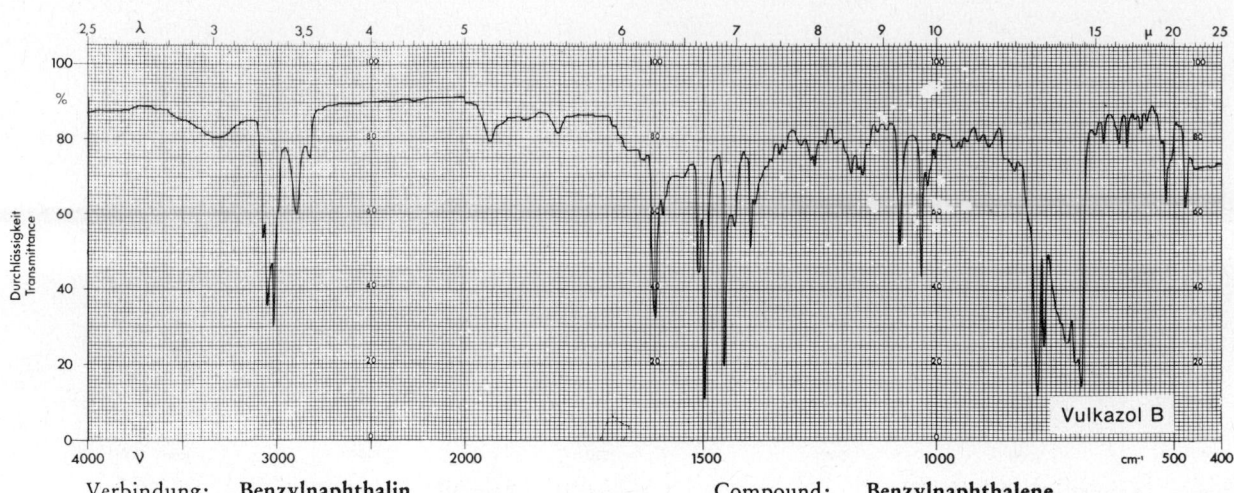

5297   Verbindung: **Benzylnaphthalin**

		M.:	**~ 218,3**	
Handelsname:	**Vulkazol B**	Herst.:	**Bayer**	
Präparation:	**Kapill. Film**	Dez. Nr.:	**8.2.6**	

Compound: **Benzylnaphthalene**

M. w.: **~ 218,3**
Tradename: **Vulkazol B**   Manuf.: **Bayer**
Preparation: **Capill. film**   Dec. No.: **8.2.6**

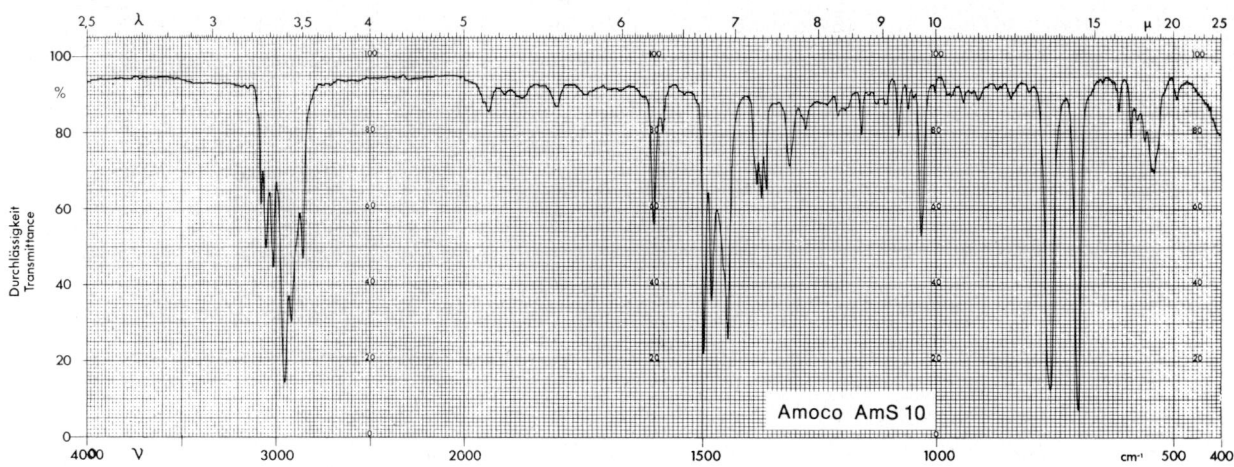

5298   Verbindung: **Poly-α-methylstyrol**

M.: **~ 330**
Handelsname: **Amoco AmS 10**   Herst.: **Amoco**
Präparation: **Kapill. Film**   Dez. Nr.: **8.2.7**

Compound: **Poly-α-methylstyrene**

M. w.: **~ 330**
Tradename: **Amoco AmS 10**   Manuf.: **Amoco**
Preparation: **Capill. film**   Dec. No.: **8.2.7**

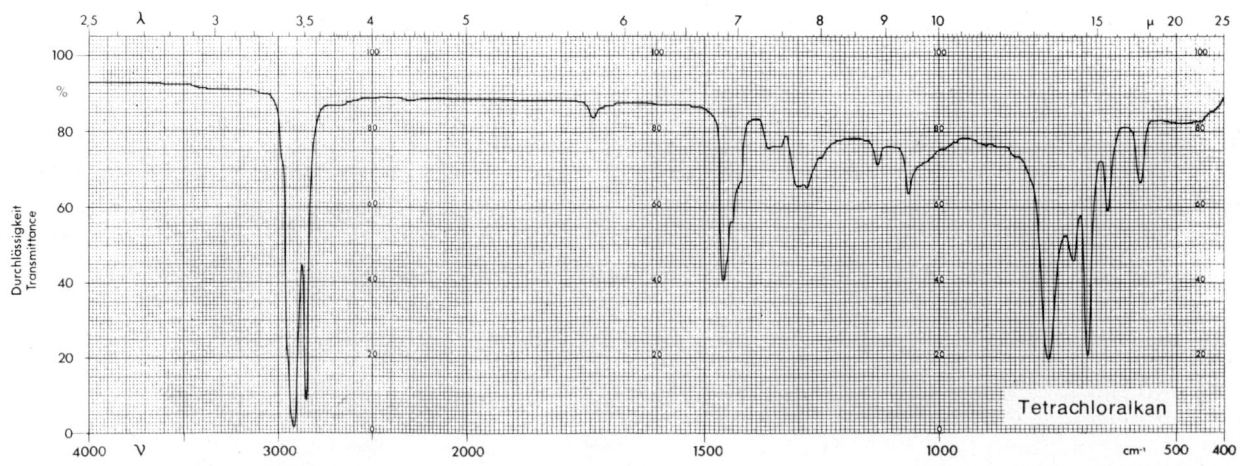

5299   Verbindung: **Chlorierte Paraffinkohlenwasserstoffe**

M.: **~ 310**
Handelsname: **Tetrachloralkan**   Herst.:
Präparation: **Kapill. Film**   Dez. Nr.: **8.3.1**

Compound: **Chlorinated paraffinic hydrocarbons**

M. w.: **~ 310**
Tradename: **Tetrachloralkan**   Manuf.:
Preparation: **Capill. film**   Dec. No.: **8.3.1**

Weichmacher
8. Kohlenwasserstoffe
8.4. Aromatische Halogenkohlenwasserstoffe

Plasticizers
8. Hydrocarbons
8.4. Aromatic Halogenated Hydrocarbons

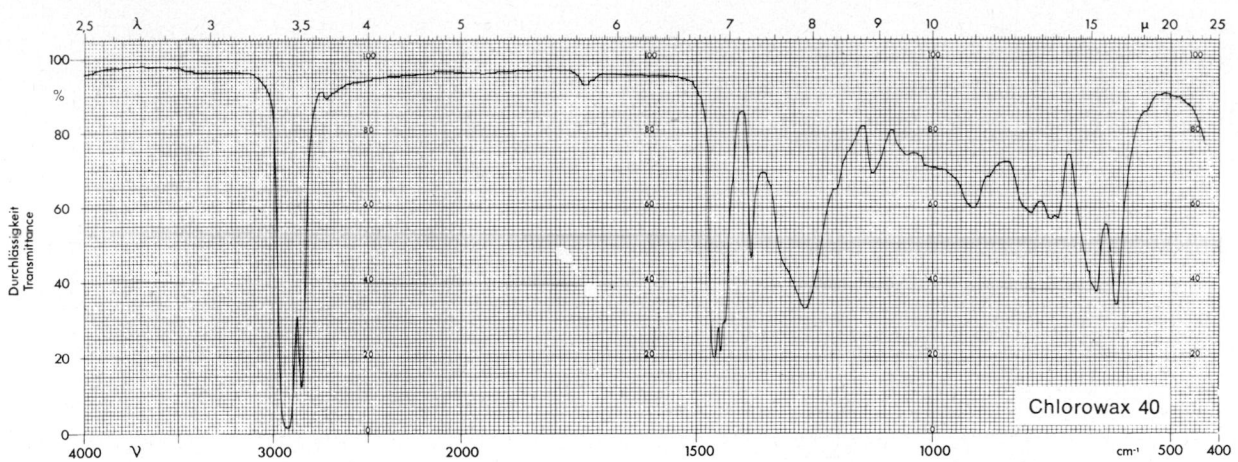

Verbindung:	Chlorierte Paraffinkohlenwasserstoffe		Compound:	Chlorinated paraffinic hydrocarbons		5300
	M.:	~ 590		M. w.:	~ 590	
Handelsname: Chlorowax 40	Herst.: Diamond		Tradename: Chlorowax 40	Manuf.: Diamond		
Präparation: Kapill. Film 6,5 μ	Dez. Nr.: 8.3.2		Preparation: Capill. film 6,5 μ	Dec. No.: 8.3.2		

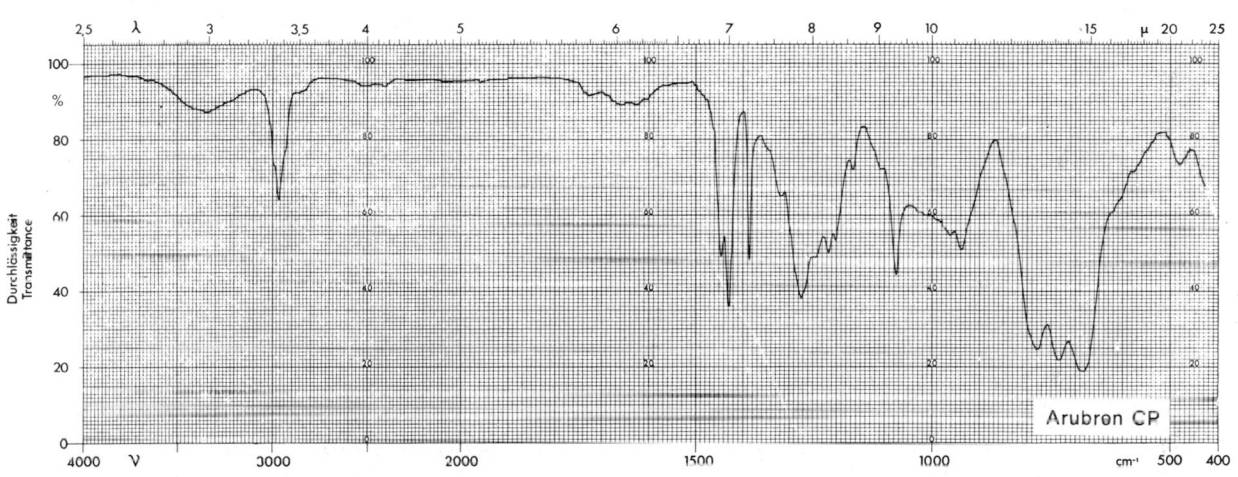

Verbindung:	Chlorierte Paraffinkohlenwasserstoffe		Compound:	Chlorinated paraffinic hydrocarbons		5301
	M.:	~ 465		M. w.:	~ 465	
Handelsname: Arubren CP	Herst.: Bayer		Tradename: Arubren CP	Manuf.: Bayer		
Präparation: Kapill. Film	Dez. Nr.: 8.3.3		Preparation: Capill. film	Dec. No.: 8.3.3		

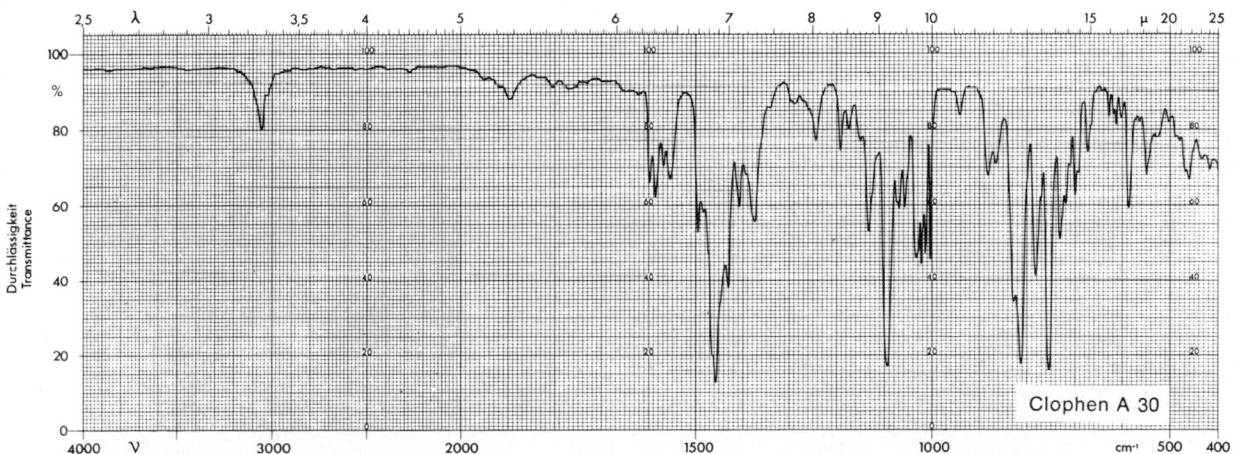

Verbindung:	Chloriertes Diphenyl		Compound:	Chlorinated diphenyl		5302
	M.:	~ 260		M. w.:	~ 260	
Handelsname: Clophen A 30	Herst.: Bayer		Tradename: Clophen A 30	Manuf.: Bayer		
Präparation: Kapill. Film 13 μ	Dez. Nr.: 8.4.1		Preparation: Capill. film 13 μ	Dec. No.: 8.4.1		

Weichmacher
8. Kohlenwasserstoffe
8.4. Aromatische Halogenkohlenwasserstoffe

Plasticizers
8. Hydrocarbons
8.4. Aromatic Halogenated Hydrocarbons

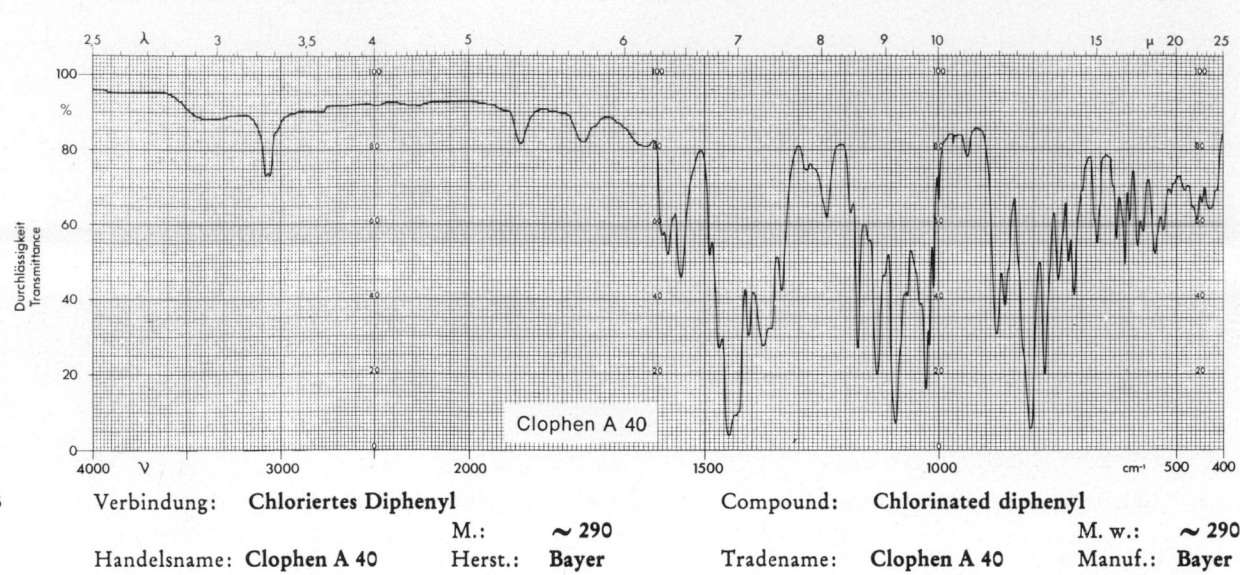

5303   Verbindung: **Chloriertes Diphenyl**   Compound: **Chlorinated diphenyl**

	M.: **~ 290**		M. w.: **~ 290**
Handelsname: **Clophen A 40**	Herst.: **Bayer**	Tradename: **Clophen A 40**	Manuf.: **Bayer**
Präparation: **Kapill. Film**	Dez. Nr.: **8.4.2**	Preparation: **Capill. film**	Dec. No.: **8.4.2**

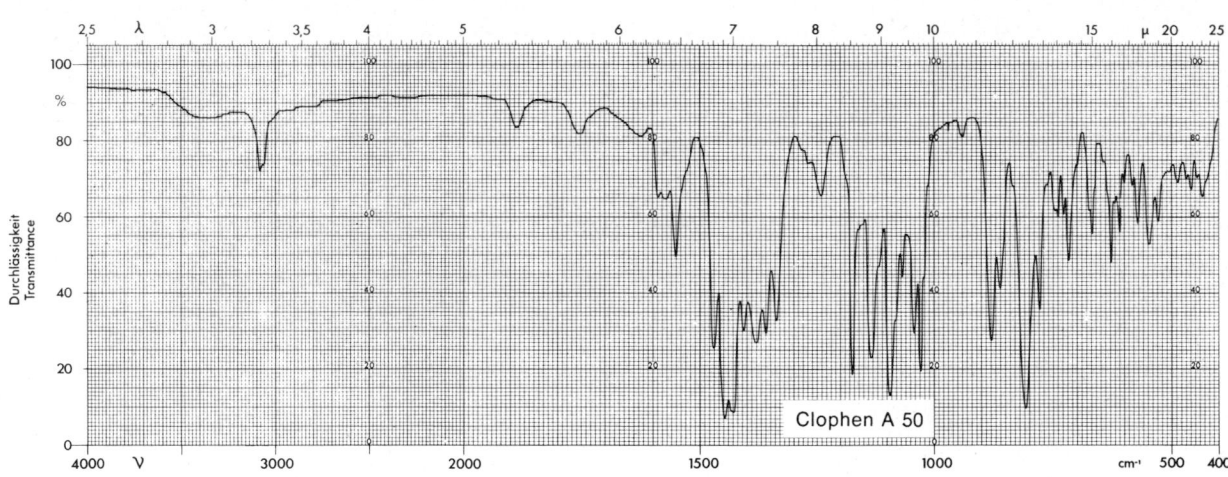

5304   Verbindung: **Chloriertes Diphenyl**   Compound: **Chlorinated diphenyl**

	M.: **~ 325**		M. w.: **~ 325**
Handelsname: **Clophen A 50**	Herst.: **Bayer**	Tradename: **Clophen A 50**	Manuf.: **Bayer**
Präparation: **Kapill. Film**	Dez. Nr.: **8.4.3**	Preparation: **Capill. film**	Dec. No.: **8.4.3**

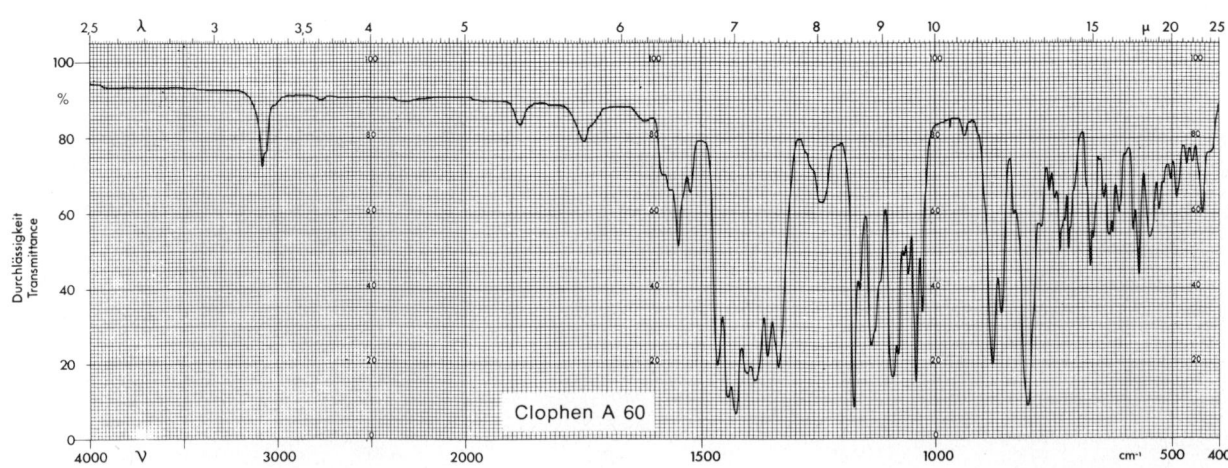

5305   Verbindung: **Chloriertes Diphenyl**   Compound: **Chlorinated diphenyl**

	M.: **~ 360**		M. w.: **~ 360**
Handelsname: **Clophen A 60**	Herst.: **Bayer**	Tradename: **Clophen A 60**	Manuf.: **Bayer**
Präparation: **Kapill. Film**	Dez. Nr.: **8.4.4**	Preparation: **Capill. film**	Dec. No.: **8.4.4**

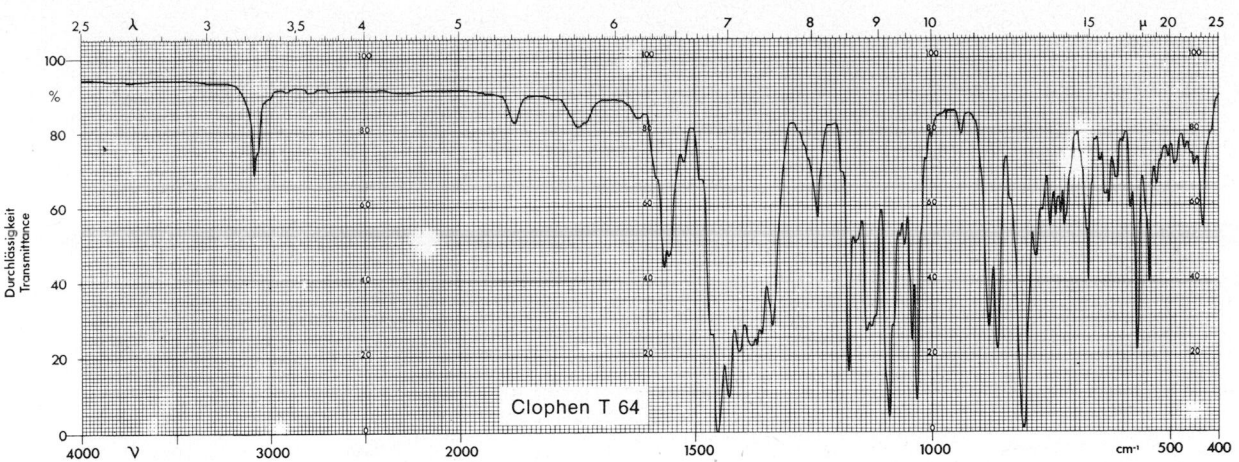

Verbindung:	Chlorierter, aromatischer Kohlenwasserstoff	Compound:	Chlorinated aromatic hydrocarbon	5306

M.: ~ 275   M. w.: ~ 275

Handelsname: Clophen T 64   Herst.: Bayer

Tradename: Clophen T 64   Manuf.: Bayer

Präparation: Kapill. Film   Dez. Nr.: 8.4.5

Preparation: Capill. film   Dec. No.: 8.4.5

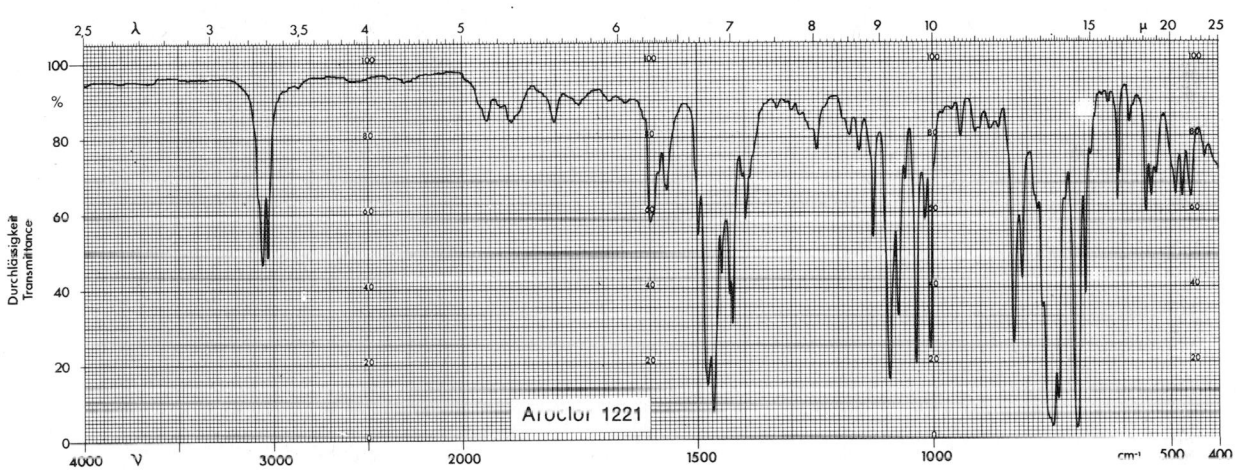

Verbindung:	Chloriertes Diphenyl	Compound:	Chlorinated diphenyl	5307

M.: ~ 190   M. w.: ~ 190

Handelsname: Aroclor 1221   Herst.: Monsanto

Tradename: Aroclor 1221   Manuf.: Monsanto

Präparation: Kapill. Film 13 μ   Dez. Nr.: 8.4.6

Preparation: Capill. film 13 μ   Dec. No.: 8.4.6

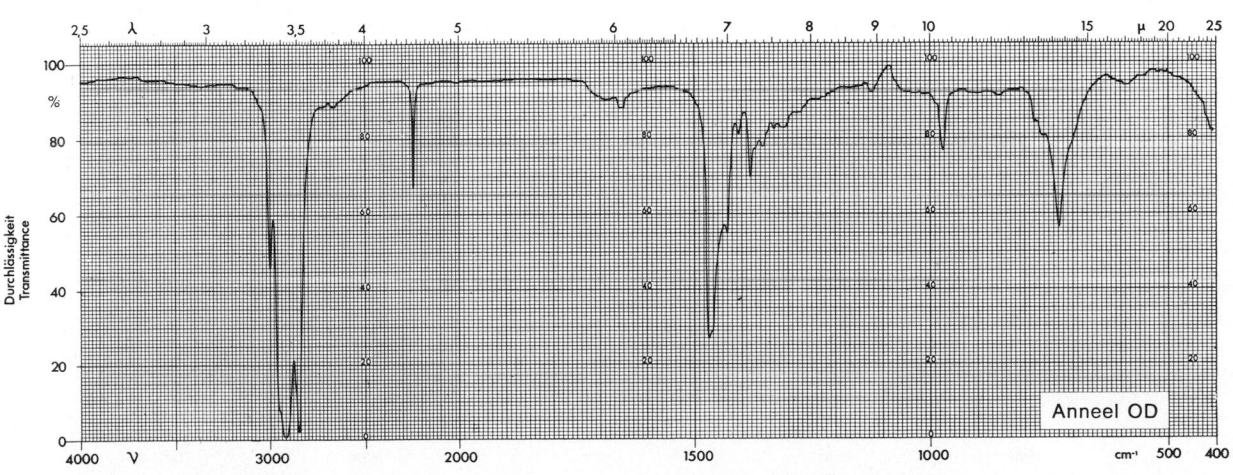

Verbindung:	Fettsäurenitril	Compound:	Fatty acid nitrile	5308

M.: ~ 265   M. w.: ~ 265

Handelsname: Aneel OD   Herst.: Armour

Tradename: Aneel OD   Manuf.: Armour

Präparation: Kapill. Film   Dez. Nr.: 9.1

Preparation: Capill. film   Dec. No.: 9.1

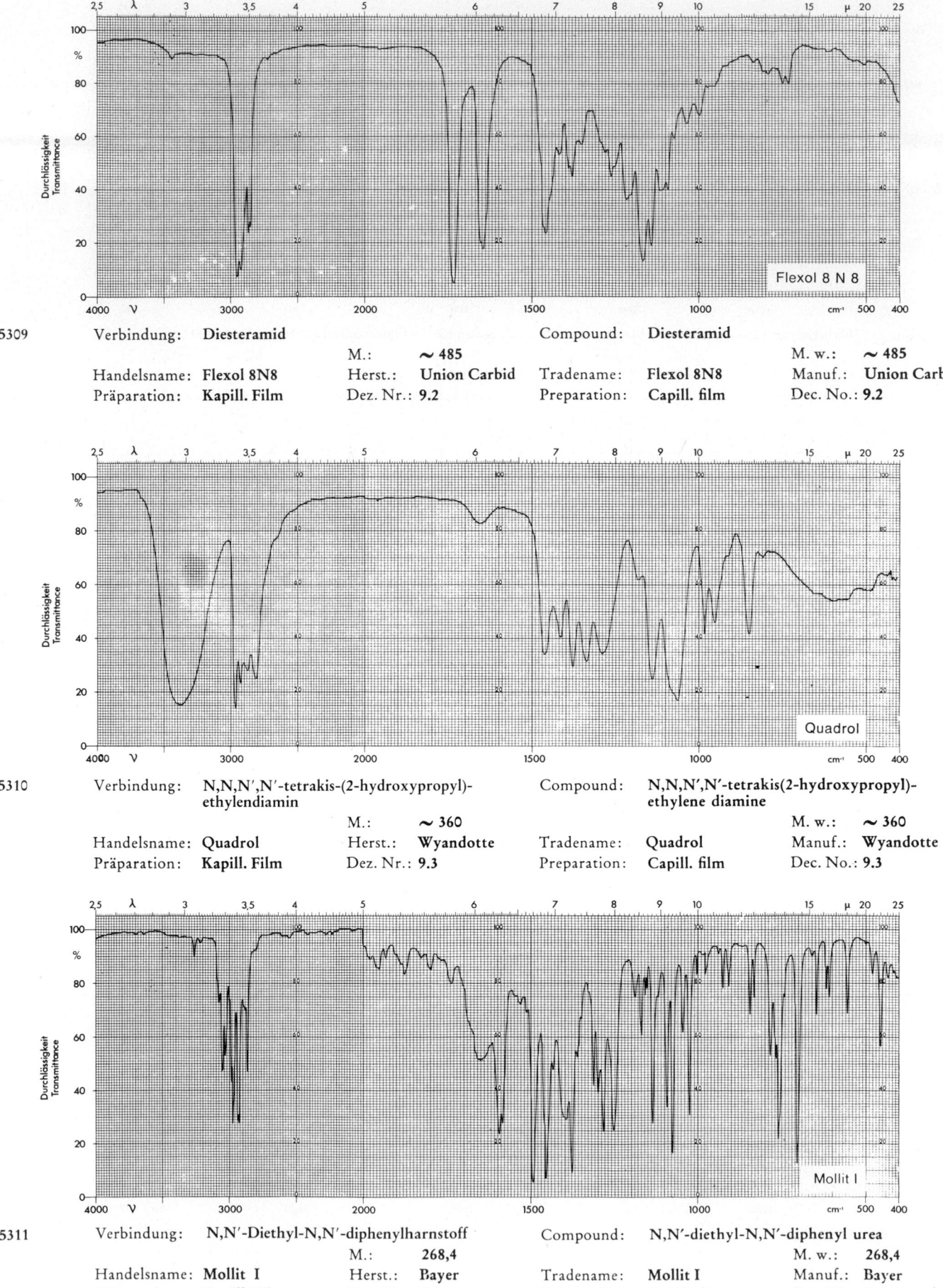

5309   Verbindung: **Diesteramid**   Compound: **Diesteramid**
                                    M.:   **~ 485**   M. w.:   **~ 485**
            Handelsname: **Flexol 8N8**   Herst.:   **Union Carbid**   Tradename: **Flexol 8N8**   Manuf.:   **Union Carbid**
            Präparation: **Kapill. Film**   Dez. Nr.:   **9.2**   Preparation: **Capill. film**   Dec. No.:   **9.2**

5310   Verbindung: **N,N,N′,N′-tetrakis-(2-hydroxypropyl)-**   Compound: **N,N,N′,N′-tetrakis(2-hydroxypropyl)-**
                            ethylendiamin   **ethylene diamine**
                                    M.:   **~ 360**   M. w.:   **~ 360**
            Handelsname: **Quadrol**   Herst.:   **Wyandotte**   Tradename: **Quadrol**   Manuf.:   **Wyandotte**
            Präparation: **Kapill. Film**   Dez. Nr.:   **9.3**   Preparation: **Capill. film**   Dec. No.:   **9.3**

5311   Verbindung: **N,N′-Diethyl-N,N′-diphenylharnstoff**   Compound: **N,N′-diethyl-N,N′-diphenyl urea**
                                    M.:   **268,4**   M. w.:   **268,4**
            Handelsname: **Mollit I**   Herst.:   **Bayer**   Tradename: **Mollit I**   Manuf.:   **Bayer**
            Präparation: **Kapill. Film**   Dez. Nr.:   **9.4**   Preparation: **Capill. film**   Dec. No.:   **9.4**

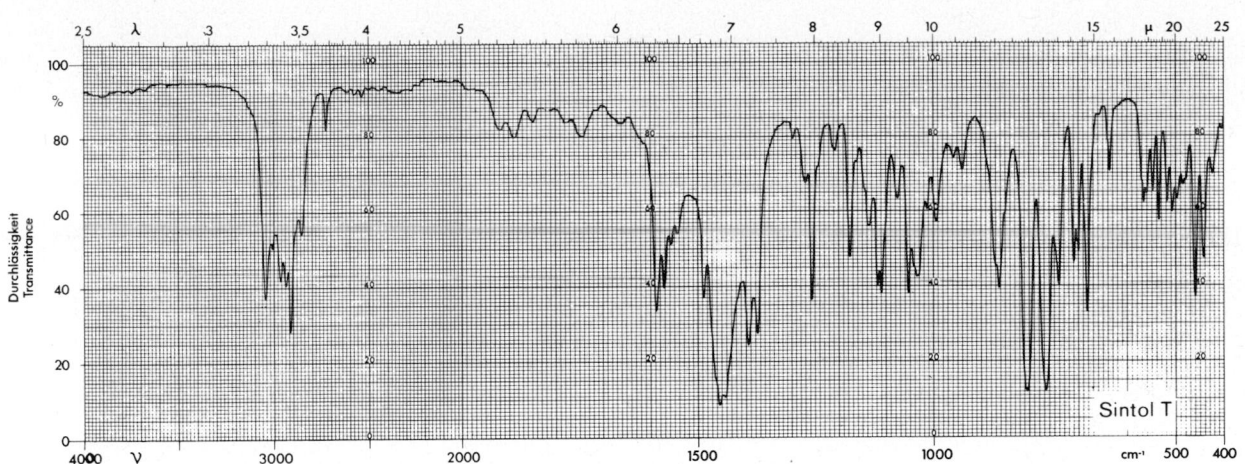

Verbindung:	Dimethylthianthren			Compound:	Dimethyl thianthrene			5312
		M.:	244,3			M. w.:	244,3	
Handelsname:	Sintol T	Herst.:	Bayer	Tradename:	Sintol T	Manuf.:	Bayer	
Präparation:	Kapill. Film	Dez. Nr.:	9.5	Preparation:	Capill. film	Dec. No.:	9.5	

Anorganische Füllstoffe und Pigmente

Inorganic Fillers and Pigments

Anorganische Füllstoffe und Pigmente
1. Füllstoffe
1.1. Kieselsäure

Inorganic Fillers and Pigments
1. Fillers
1.1. Silica

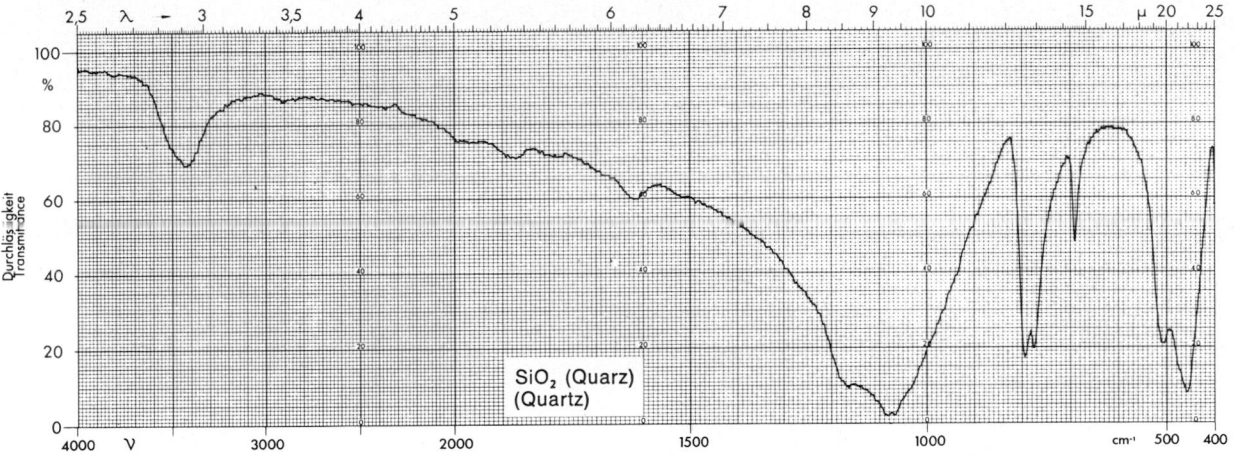

Siliciumdioxid (Quarz), SiO₂

Composition: Silicium dioxide (quartz), SiO₂

5400

| Handelsname: | Quarzmehl | Herst.: | Merck | Tradename: | Quartz powder | Manuf.: | Merck |
| Präparation: | KBr (2/1000) | Dez. Nr.: | 1.1.1 | Preparation: | KBr (2/1000) | Dec. No.: | 1.1.1 |

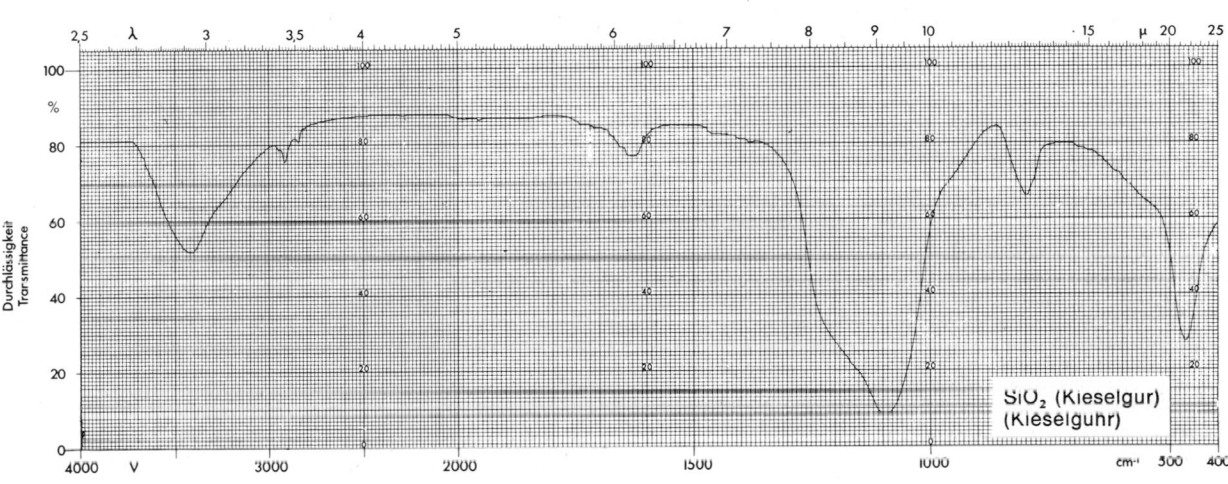

Zusammen-
setzung:

Siliciumdioxid (Diatomeenerde, amorph),
SiO₂

Composition: Silicium dioxide (diatomaceous earth,
amorphous), SiO₂

5401

| Handelsname: | Kieselgur | Herst.: | Freudenberg | Tradename: | Kieselgur | Manuf.: | Freudenberg |
| Präparation: | KBr (2/1000) | Dez. Nr.: | 1.1.2 | Preparation: | KBr (2/1000) | Dec. No.: | 1.1.2 |

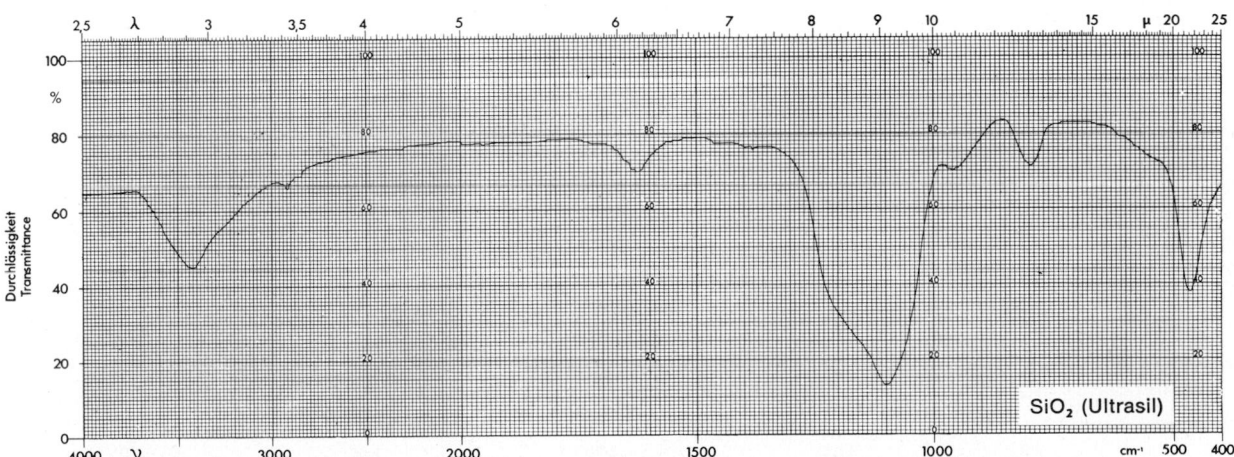

Zusammen-
setzung:

Siliciumdioxid (amorph), SiO₂

Composition: Silicium dioxide (amorphous), SiO₂

5402

| Handelsname: | Ultrasil VN 3 | Herst.: | Degussa | Tradename: | Ultrasil VN 3 | Manuf.: | Degussa |
| Präparation: | KBr (2/1000) | Dez. Nr.: | 1.1.3 | Preparation: | KBr (2/1000) | Dec. No.: | 1.1.3 |

Anorganische Füllstoffe und Pigmente
1. Füllstoffe
1.2. Tonminerale, Glimmer

Inorganic Fillers and Pigments
1. Fillers
1.2. Clay Minerals, Mica

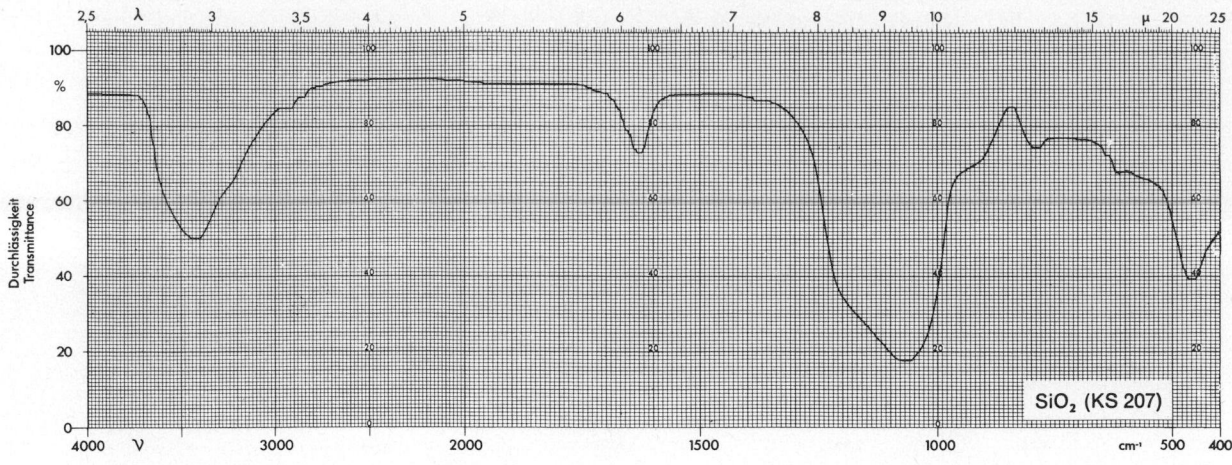

SiO₂ (KS 207)

5403   Zusammen-setzung: **Siliciumdioxid (amorph), SiO₂**   Composition: **Silicium dioxide (amorphous), SiO₂**

Handelsname: **Hoesch KS 207**   Herst.: **Hoesch**   Tradename: **Hoesch KS 207**   Manuf.: **Hoesch**

Präparation: **KBr (2/1000)**   Dez. Nr.: **1.1.4**   Preparation: **KBr (2/1000)**   Dec. No.: **1.1.4**

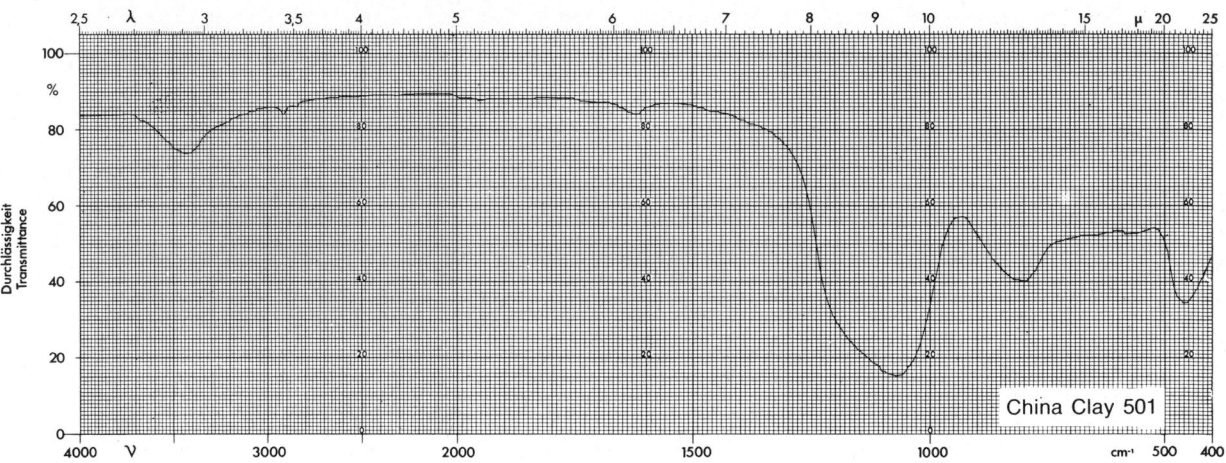

China Clay 501

5404   Zusammen-setzung: **SiO₂ (amorph) und Silikate**   Composition: **SiO₂ (amorphous) and silicates**

Handelsname: **China Clay 501**   Herst.: **E. Clays**   Tradename: **China Clay 501**   Manuf.: **E. Clays**

Präparation: **KBr (2/1000)**   Dez. Nr.: **1.1.5**   Preparation: **KBr (2/1000)**   Dec. No.: **1.1.5**

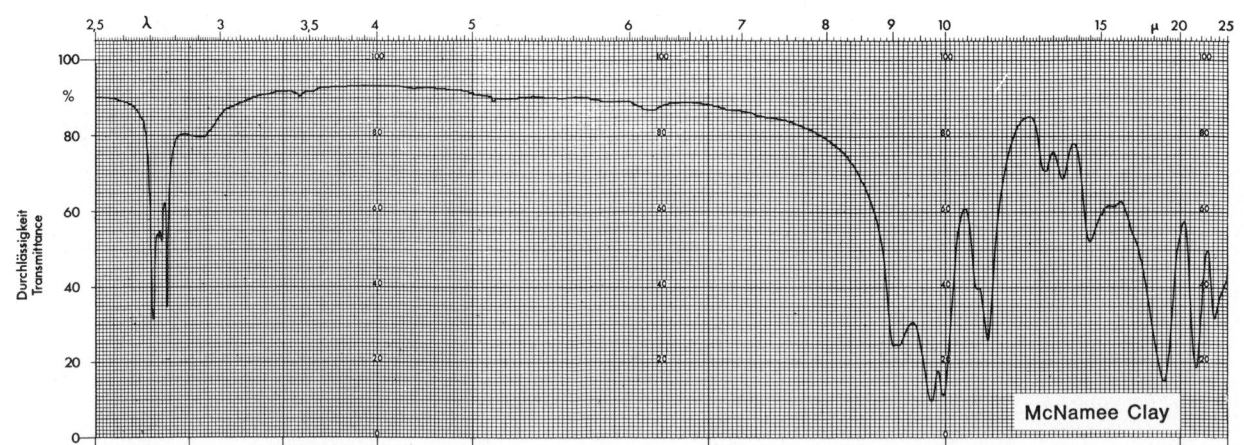

McNamee Clay

5405   Zusammen-setzung: **Kaolinit, Al₄[(OH)₈Si₄O₁₀]**   Composition: **Kaolinite, Al₄[(OH)₈Si₄O₁₀]**

Handelsname: **Mc Namee Clay**   Herst.: **Lehmann**   Tradename: **Mc Namee Clay**   Manuf.: **Lehmann**

Präparation: **KBr (1,5/1000)**   Dez. Nr.: **1.2.1**   Preparation: **KBr (1,5/1000)**   Dec. No.: **1.2.1**

Anorganische Füllstoffe und Pigmente
1. Füllstoffe
1.2. Tonminerale, Glimmer

Inorganic Fillers and Pigments
1. Fillers
1.2. Clay Minerals, Mica

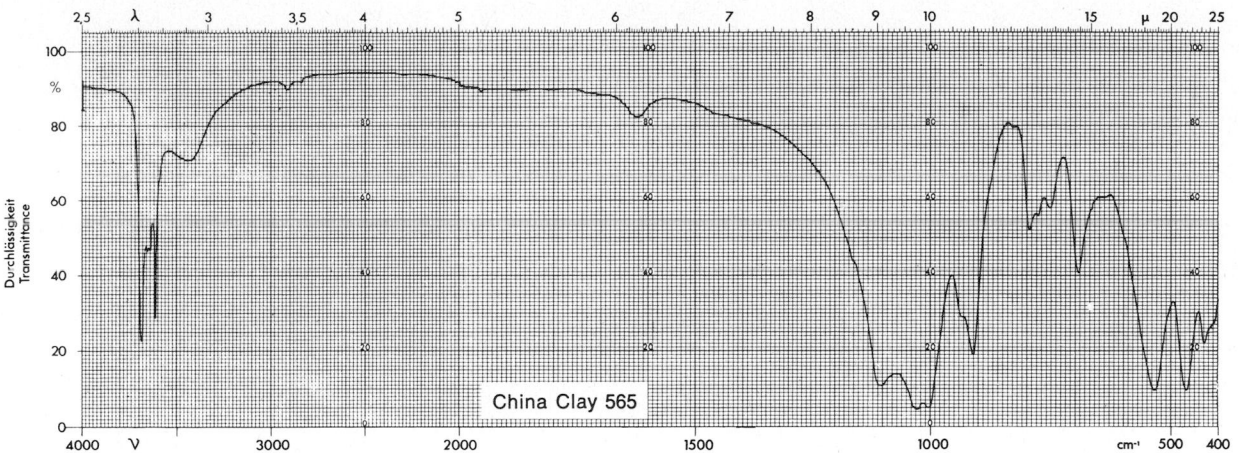

China Clay 565

Zusammensetzung:	**Kaolinit, Quarz**			Composition:	**Kaolinite, quartz**		5406
Handelsname:	**China Clay 565**	Herst.:	**E. Clays**	Tradename:	**China Clay 565**	Manuf.: **E. Clays**	
Präparation:	**KBr (2/1000)**	Dez. Nr.:	**1.2.2**	Preparation:	**KBr (2/1000)**	Dec. No.: **1.2.2**	

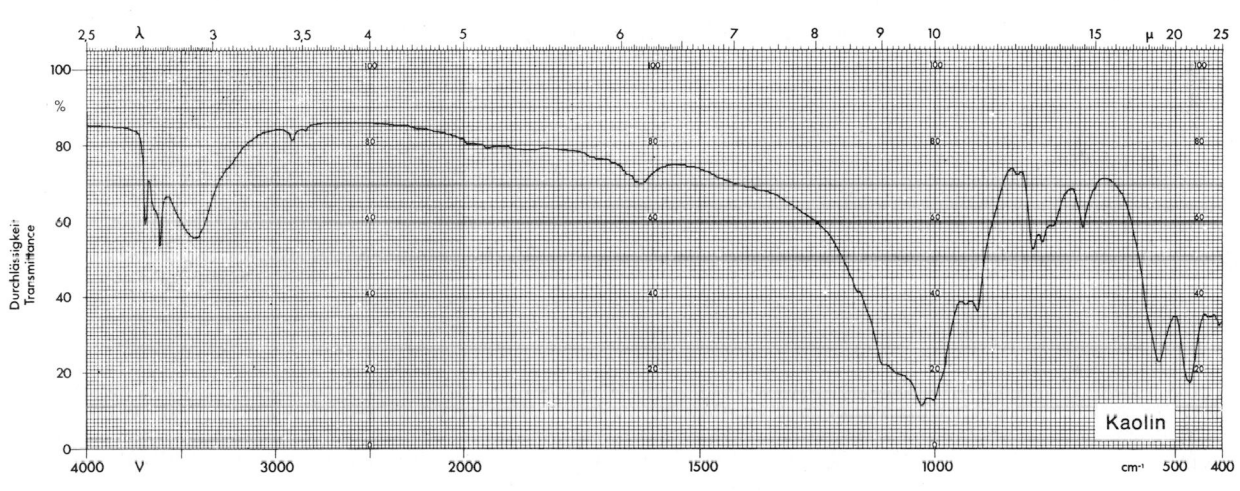

Kaolin

Zusammensetzung:	**Kaolinit, Quarz**			Composition:	**Kaolinite, quartz**		5407
Handelsname:	**Kaolin**	Herst.:	**Leun**	Tradename:	**Kaolin**	Manuf.: **Leun**	
Präparation:	**KBr (2/1000)**	Dez. Nr.:	**1.2.3**	Preparation:	**KBr (2/1000)**	Dec. No.: **1.2.3**	

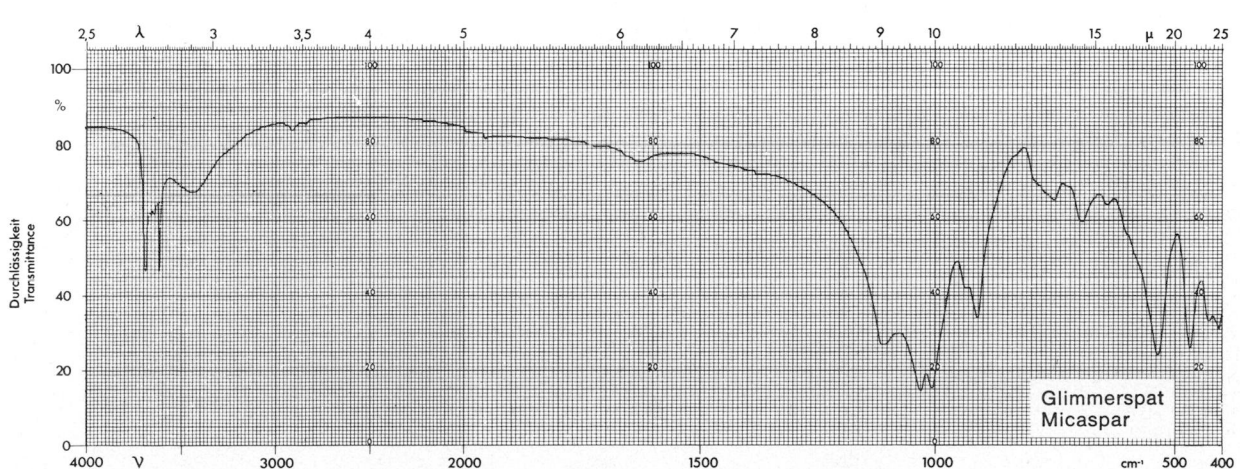

Glimmerspat
Micaspar

Zusammensetzung:	**Tonminerale, Quarz**			Composition:	**Clay minerals, quartz**		5408
Handelsname:	**Glimmerspat**	Herst.:	**Leun**	Tradename:	**Glimmerspat**	Manuf.: **Leun**	
Präparation:	**KBr (2/1000)**	Dez. Nr.:	**1.2.4**	Preparation:	**KBr (2/1000)**	Dec. No.: **1.2.4**	

Anorganische Füllstoffe und Pigmente
1. Füllstoffe
1.2. Tonminerale, Glimmer

Inorganic Fillers and Pigments
1. Fillers
1.2. Clay Minerals, Mica

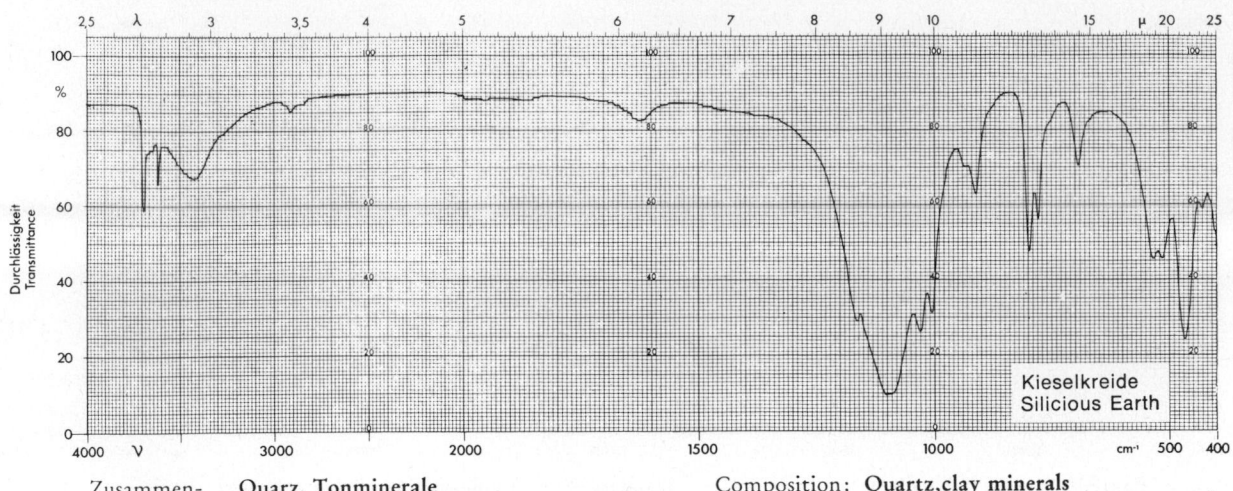

Kieselkreide
Silicious Earth

5409

Zusammensetzung:	Quarz, Tonminerale			Composition:	Quartz, clay minerals		
Handelsname:	Kieselkreide	Herst.:	Leun	Tradename:	Kieselkreide	Manuf.:	Leun
Präparation:	KBr (2/1000)	Dez. Nr.:	1.2.5	Preparation:	KBr (2/1000)	Dec. No.:	1.2.5

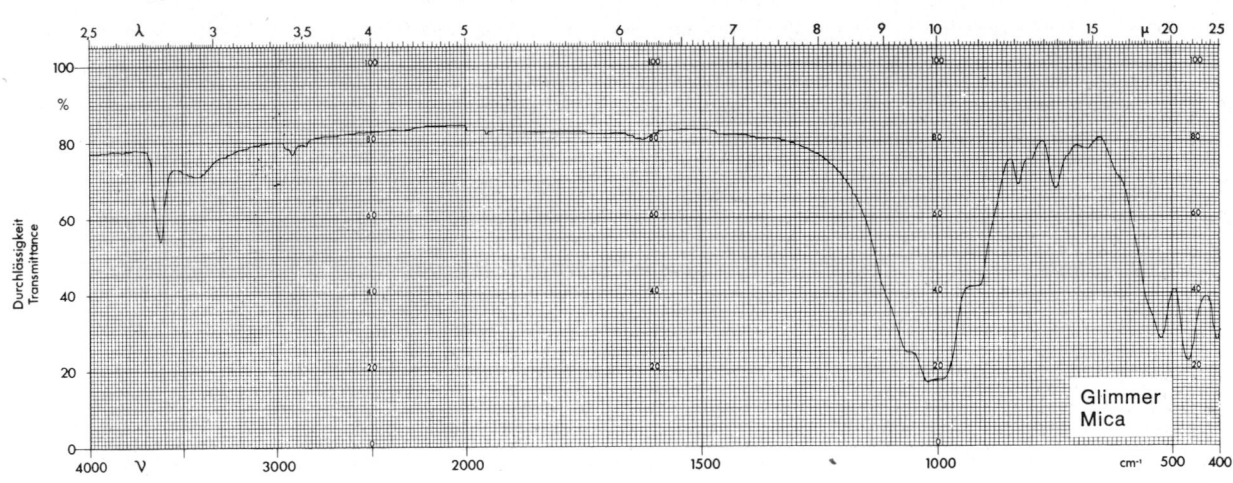

Glimmer
Mica

5410

Zusammensetzung:	Glimmer			Composition:	Mica		
Handelsname:	Mica Glimmer	Herst.:	Lehmann	Tradename:	Mica Glimmer	Manuf.:	Lehmann
Präparation:	KBr (2/1000)	Dez. Nr.:	1.2.6	Preparation:	KBr (2/1000)	Dec. No.:	1.2.6

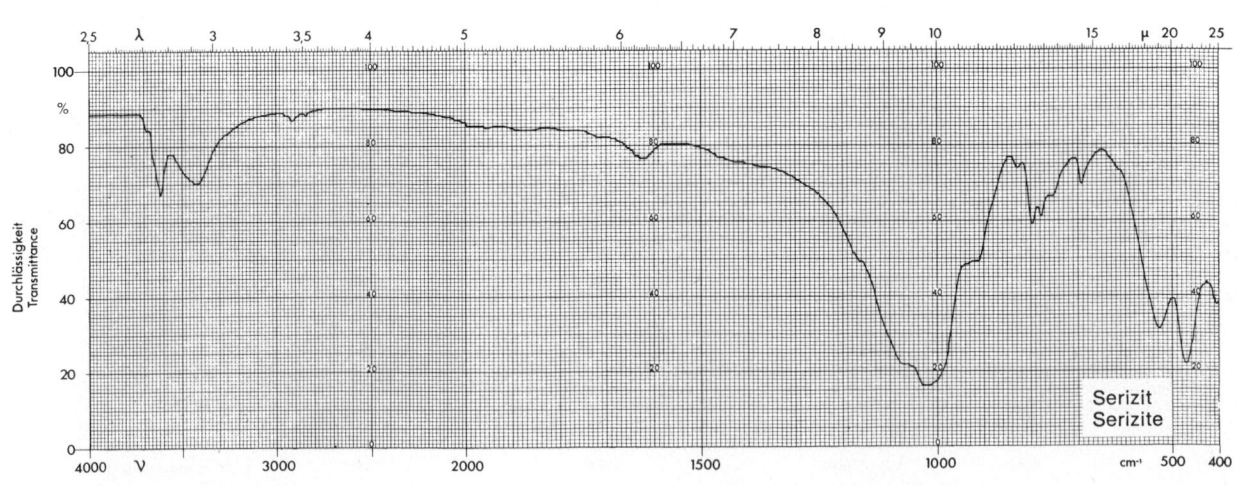

Serizit
Serizite

5411

Zusammensetzung:	Serizit			Composition:	Serizite		
Handelsname:	Serizit	Herst.:	Leun	Tradename:	Serizit	Manuf.:	Leun
Präparation:	KBr (2/1000)	Dez. Nr.:	1.2.7	Preparation:	KBr (2/1000)	Dec. No.:	1.2.7

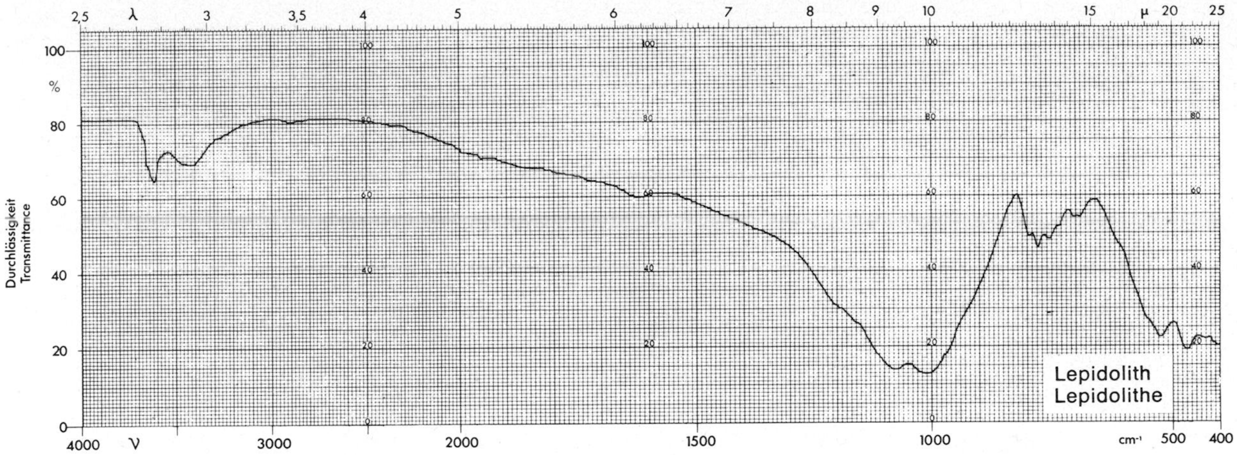

Anorganische Füllstoffe und Pigmente
1. Füllstoffe
1.2. Tonminerale, Glimmer

Inorganic Fillers and Pigments
1. Fillers
1.2. Clay Minerals, Mica

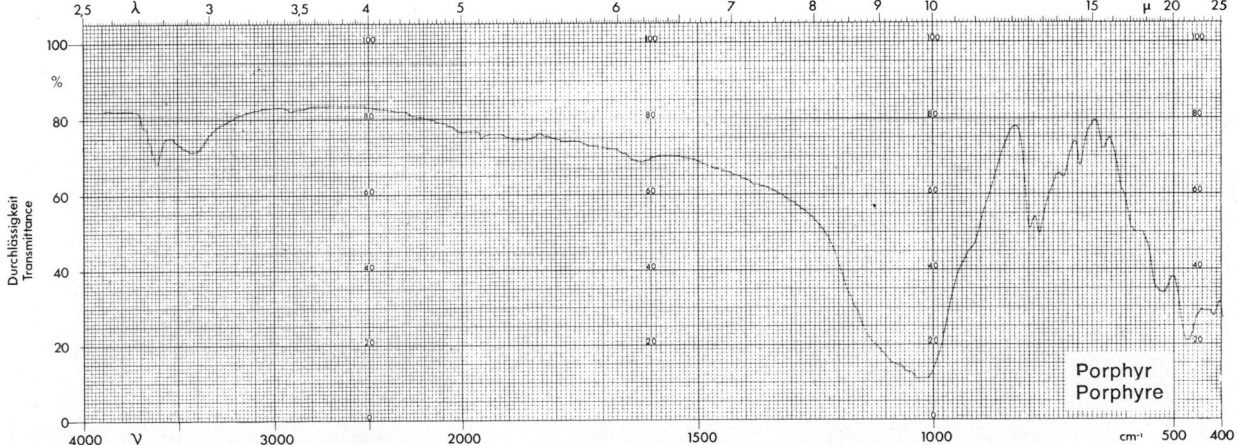

Zusammen-setzung: **Lepidolith, Al-K-Li-F-Silikat**

Composition: **Lepidolithe, Al-K-Li-F-silicate**

5412

Handelsname: **Lepidolith**	Herst.: **Leun**	Tradename: **Lepidolith**	Manuf.: **Leun**
Präparation: **KBr (2/1000)**	Dez. Nr.: **1.2.8**	Preparation: **KBr (2/1000)**	Dec. No.: **1.2.8**

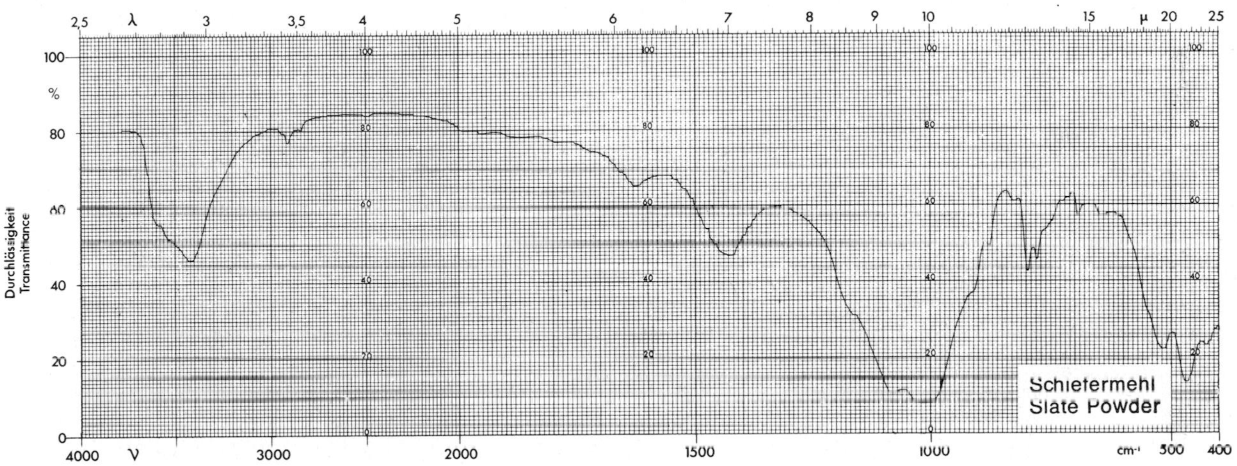

Zusammen-setzung: **Schiefermehl**

Composition: **Slate powder**

5413

Handelsname: **Schiefermehl**	Herst.: **Leun**	Tradename: **Schiefermehl**	Manuf.: **Leun**
Präparation: **KBr (2/1000)**	Dez. Nr.: **1.2.9**	Preparation: **KBr (2/1000)**	Dec. No.: **1.2.9**

Zusammen-setzung: **Porphyr, Al-K-Fe-Silikat**

Composition: **Porphyre, Al-K-Fe-silicate**

5414

Handelsname: **Porphyr**	Herst.: **Leun**	Tradename: **Porphyr**	Manuf.: **Leun**
Präparation: **KBr (2/1000)**	Dez. Nr. **1.2.10**	Preparation: **KBr (2/1000)**	Dec. No.: **1.2.10**

Anorganische Füllstoffe und Pigmente
1. Füllstoffe
1.3. Asbest

Inorganic Fillers and Pigments
1. Fillers
1.3. Asbestos

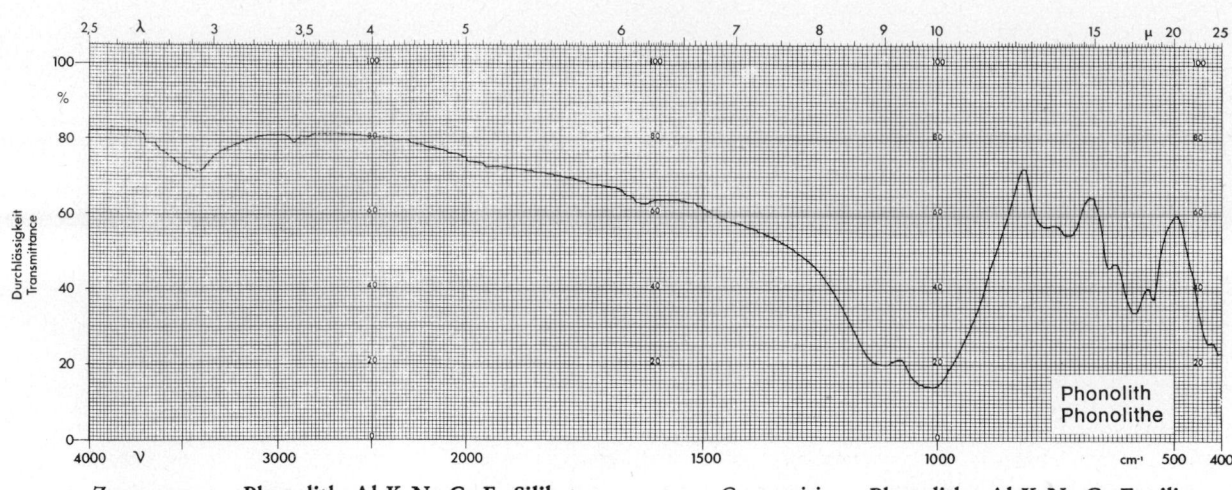

5415   Zusammen-   **Phonolith, Al-K-Na-Ca-Fe-Silikat**   Composition: **Phonolithe, Al-K-Na-Ca-Fe-silicate**
setzung:

Handelsname: **Phonolith**	Herst.: **Leun**	Tradename: **Phonolith**	Manuf.: **Leun**
Präparation: **KBr (2/1000)**	Dez. Nr.: **1.2.11**	Preparation: **KBr (2/1000)**	Dec. No.: **1.2.11**

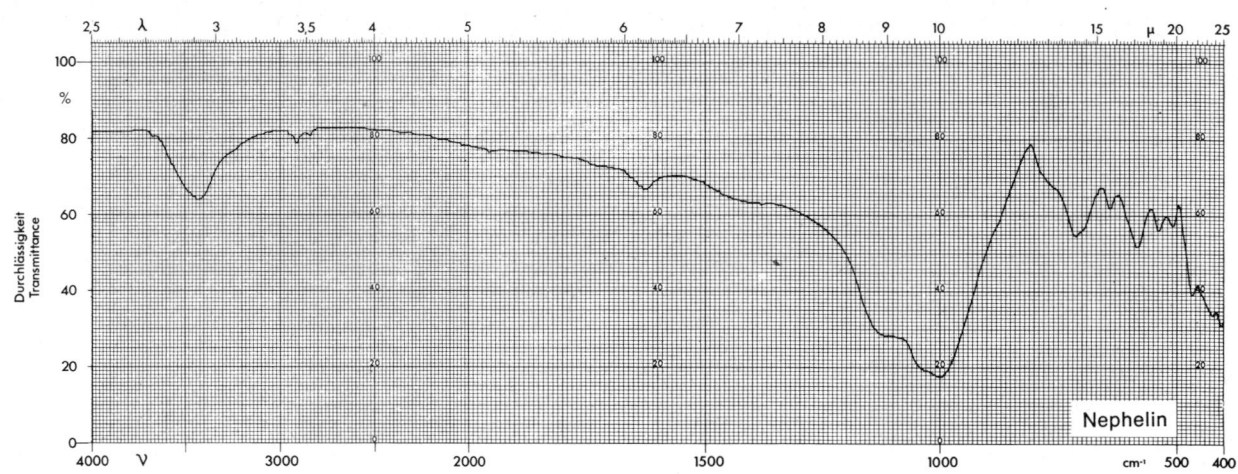

5416   Zusammen-   **Nephelin, K-Na-Al-Silikat**   Composition: **Nephelin, K-Na-Al-silicate**
setzung:

Handelsname: **Nephelin**	Herst.: **Leun**	Tradename: **Nephelin**	Manuf.: **Leun**
Präparation: **KBr (2/1000)**	Dez. Nr.: **1.2.12**	Preparation: **KBr (2/1000)**	Dec. No.: **1.2.12**

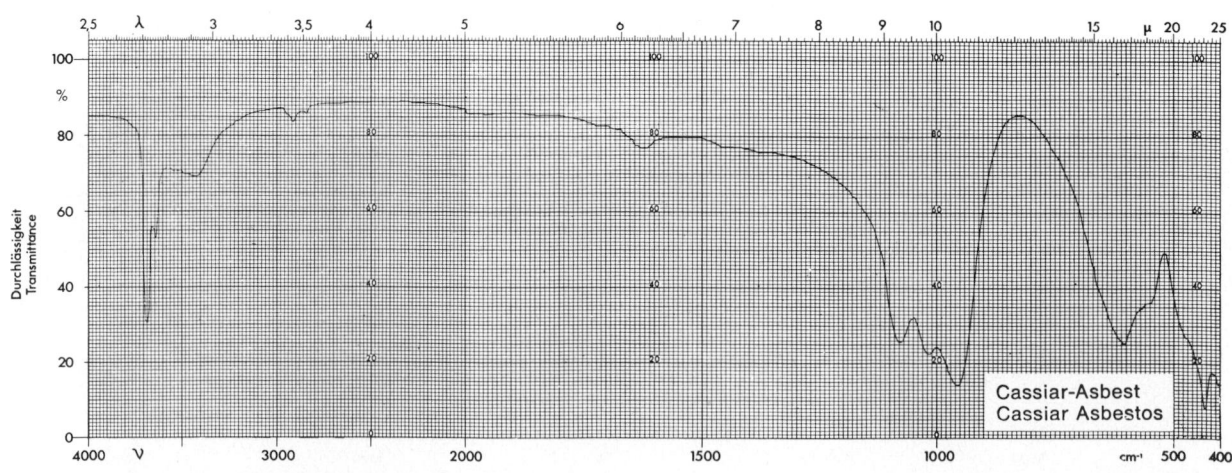

5417   Zusammen-   **Cassiar-Asbest, $Mg_6[(OH)_8Si_4O_{10}]$**   Composition: **Cassiar-asbestos, $Mg_6[(OH)_8Si_4O_{10}]$**
setzung:

Handelsname: **Cassiar-Asbest**	Herst.: **Hegeler**	Tradename: **Cassiar-Asbest**	Manuf.: **Hegeler**
Präparation: **KBr (2/1000)**	Dez. Nr.: **1.3.1**	Preparation: **KBr (2/1000)**	Dec. No.: **1.3.1**

Anorganische Füllstoffe und Pigmente
1. Füllstoffe
1.3. Asbest

Inorganic Fillers and Pigments
1. Fillers
1.3. Asbestos

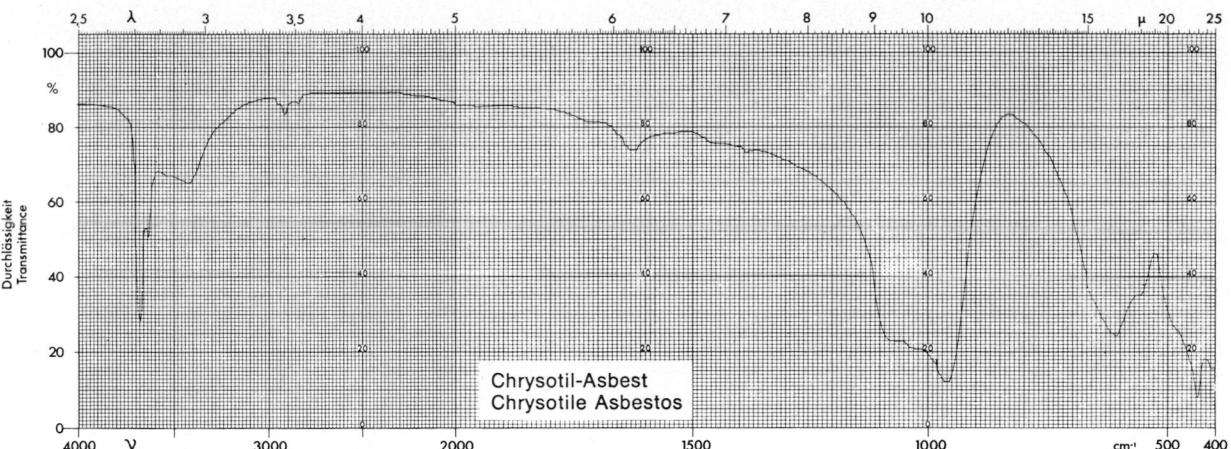

Chrysotil-Asbest
Chrysotile Asbestos

Zusammensetzung:	**Chrysotil-Asbest, Mg-Silikat**	Composition:	**Chrysotile asbestos, Mg-silicate**	5418
Handelsname:	**Rhod. Chrysot.-Asb.** Herst.: **Ostroff**	Tradename:	**Rhod. Chrysot.-Asb.** Manuf.: **Ostroff**	
Präparation:	**KBr (2/1000)** Dez. Nr.: **1.3.2**	Preparation:	**KBr (2/1000)** Dec. No.: **1.3.2**	

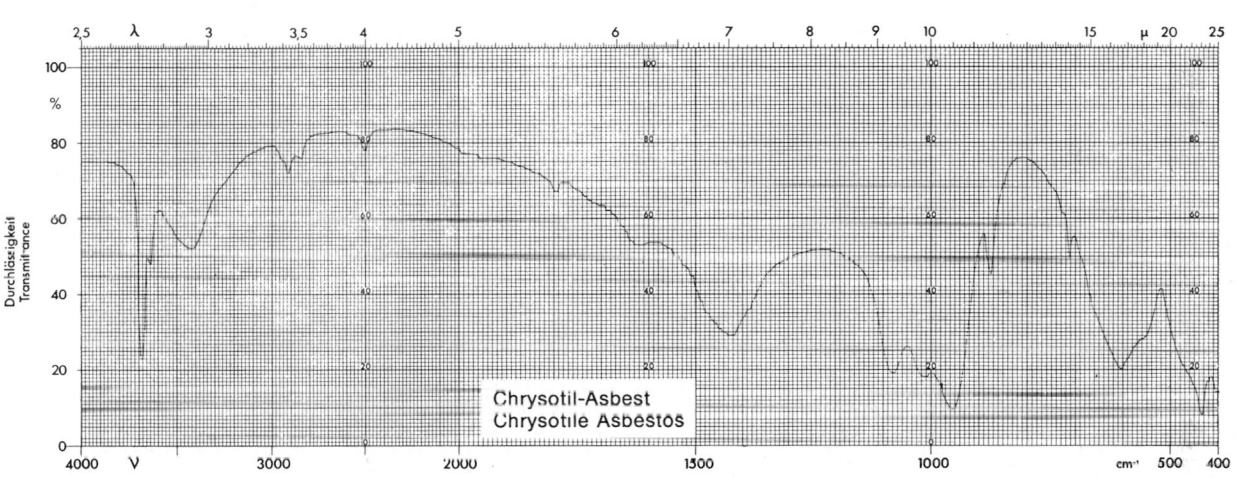

Chrysotil-Asbest
Chrysotile Asbestos

Zusammensetzung:	**Chrysotil-Asbest, Mg-Silikat**	Composition:	**Chrysotile asbestos, Mg-silicate**	5419
Handelsname:	**Südafr. Chrysot.-As.** Herst.: **Tropag**	Tradename:	**Südafr. Chrysot.-As.** Manuf.: **Tropag**	
Präparation:	**KBr (2/1000)** Dez. Nr.: **1.3.3**	Preparation:	**KBr (2/1000)** Dec. No.: **1.3.3**	

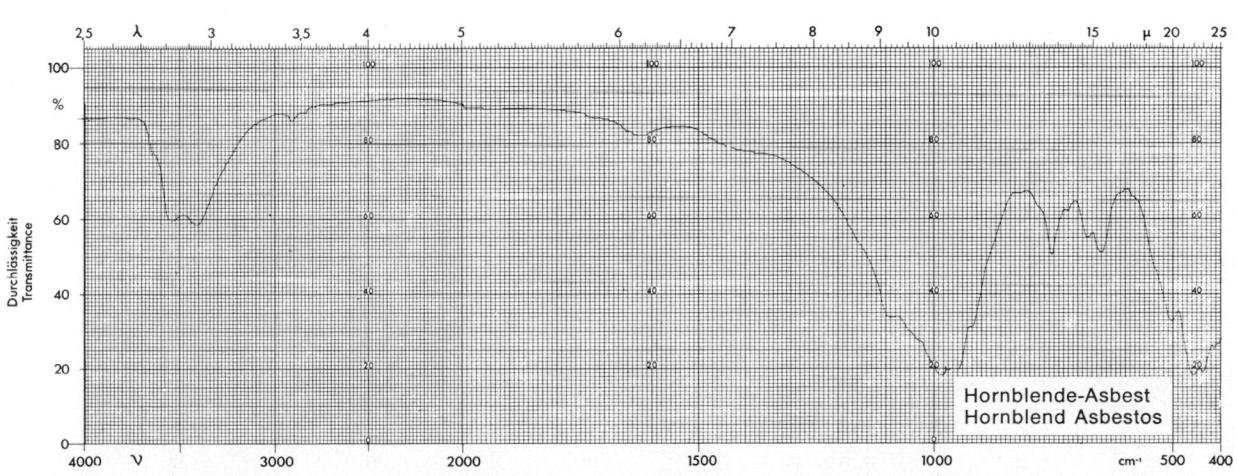

Hornblende-Asbest
Hornblend Asbestos

Zusammensetzung:	**Hornblende-Asbest, Mg-Al-Fe-Ca-Silikat**	Composition:	**Hornblend asbestos, Mg-Al-Fe-Ca-silicate**	5420
Handelsname:	**Mikro-Hornbl.-Asb.** Herst.: **Erbslöh**	Tradename:	**Mikro-Hornbl.-Asb.** Manuf.: **Erbslöh**	
Präparation:	**KBr (2/1000)** Dez. Nr.: **1.3.4**	Preparation:	**KBr (2/1000)** Dec. No.: **1.3.4**	

Anorganische Füllstoffe und Pigmente
1. Füllstoffe
1.3. Asbest

Inorganic Fillers and Pigments
1. Fillers
1.3. Asbestos

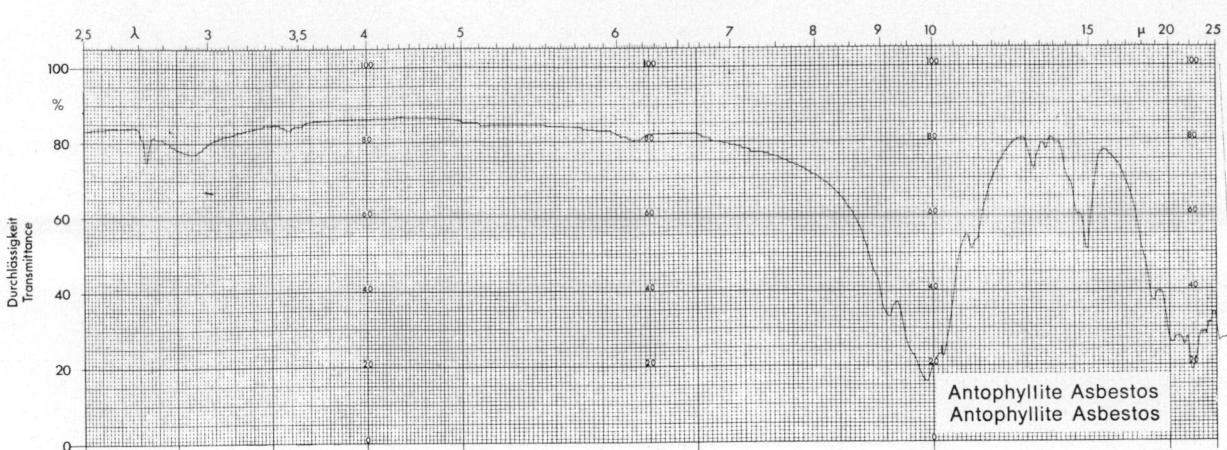

5421   Zusammen-setzung: **Anthophyllit-Asbest, Mg-Fe-Silikat**   Composition: **Anthophyllite asbestos, Mg-Fe-silicate**

Handelsname: **Ital. Anthophyll.-As.** Herst.: **Tropag**   Tradename: **Ital. Anthophyll.-As.** Manuf.: **Tropag**

Präparation: **KBr (2/1000)**   Dez. Nr.: **1.3.5**   Preparation: **KBr (2/1000)**   Dec. No.: **1.3.5**

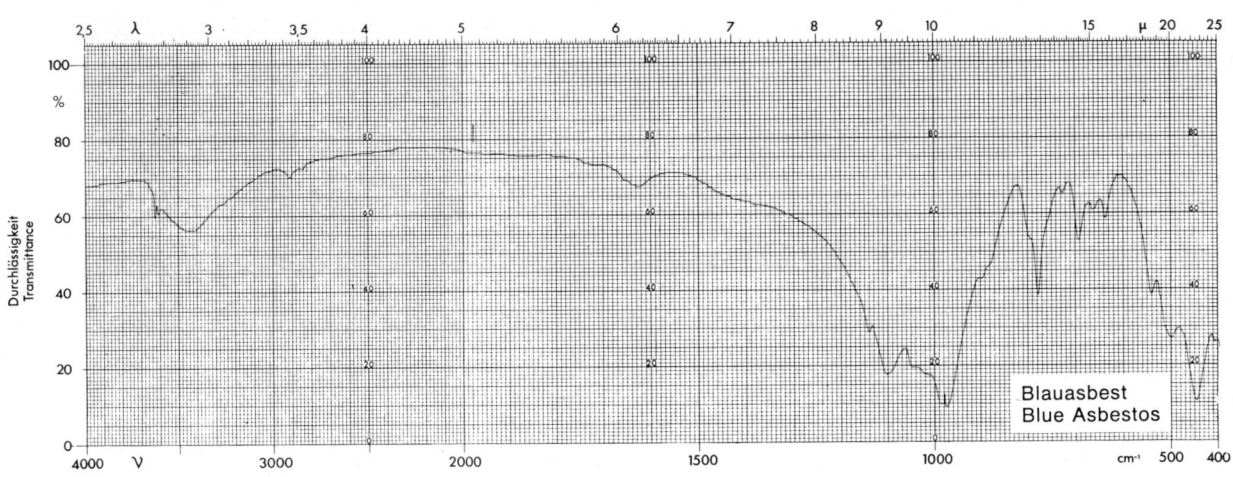

5422   Zusammen-setzung: **Blauasbest, Mg-Silikat**   Composition: **Blue asbestos, Mg-silicate**

Handelsname: **Blauasbest**   Herst.: **Tropag**   Tradename: **Blauasbest**   Manuf.: **Tropag**

Präparation: **KBr (2/1000)**   Dez. Nr.: **1.3.6**   Preparation: **KBr (2/1000)**   Dec. No.: **1.3.6**

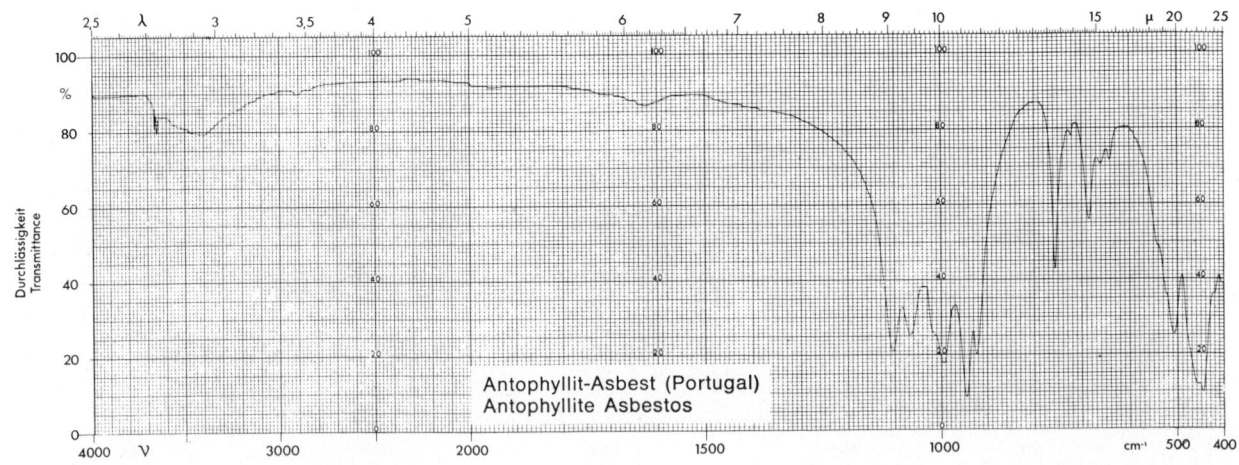

5423   Zusammen-setzung: **Anthophyllit-Asbest, Mg-Fe-Silikat**   Composition: **Anthophyllite asbestos, Mg-Fe-silicate**

Handelsname: **Port. Anthophyll.-As.** Herst.: **Tropag**   Tradename: **Port. Anthophyll.-As.** Manuf.: **Tropag**

Präparation: **KBr (2/1000)**   Dez. Nr.: **1.3.7**   Preparation: **KBr (2/1000)**   Dec. No.: **1.3.7**

Anorganische Füllstoffe und Pigmente
1. Füllstoffe
1.4. Andere Silikate

Inorganic Fillers and Pigments
1. Fillers
1.4. Other silicates

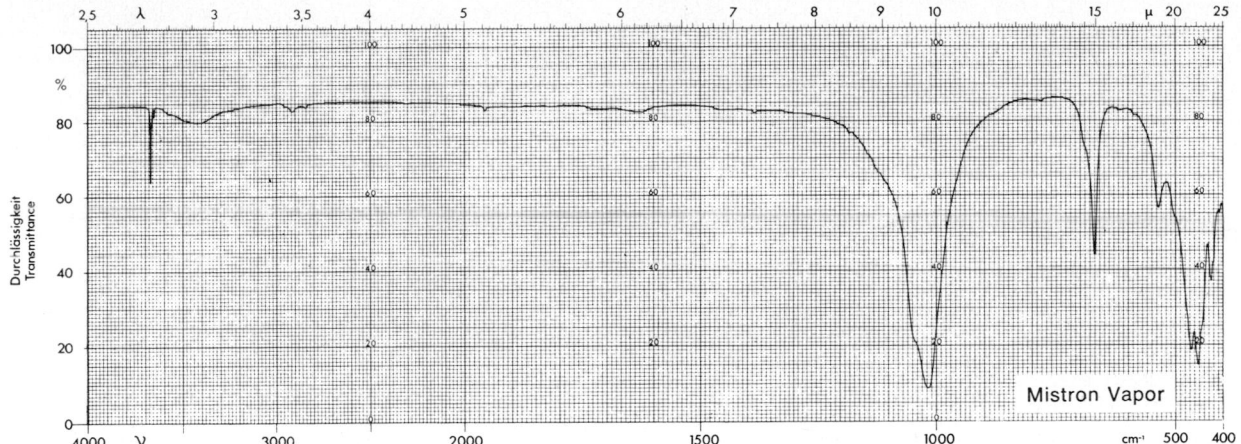

Zusammen-
setzung: **wasserhaltiges Mg-Silikat**

Composition: **Hydrated Mg silicate**

5424

Handelsname: **Mistron Vapor**	Herst.: **Chem. AG.**	Tradename: **Mistron Vapor**	Manuf.: **Chem. AG.**
Präparation: **KBr (1,5/1000)**	Dez. Nr.: **1.4.1**	Preparation: **KBr (1,5/1000)**	Dec. No.: **1.4.1**

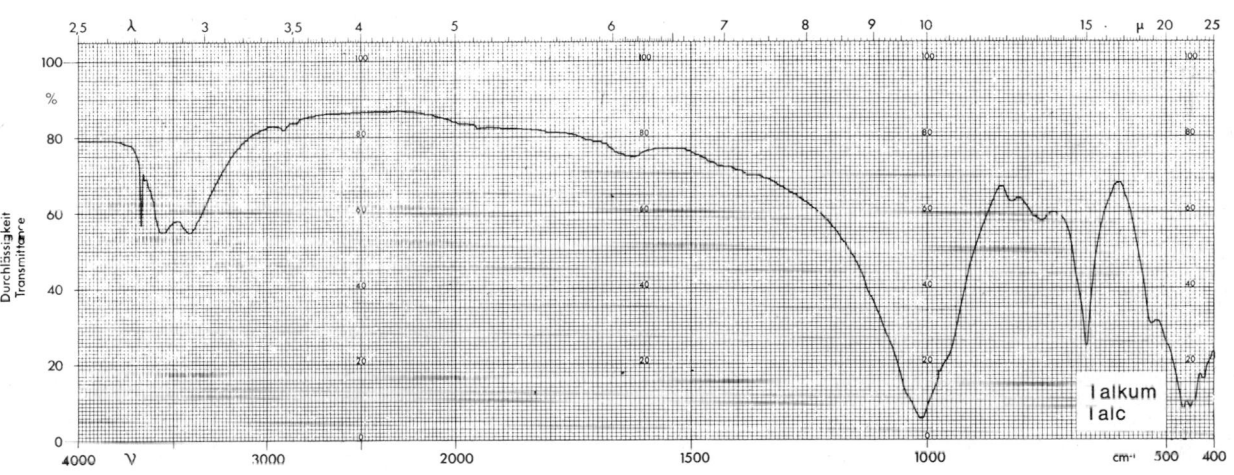

Zusammen-
setzung: **wasserhaltiges Mg-Silikat**

Composition: **Hydrated Mg silicate**

5425

Handelsname: **Talkum**	Herst.: **Leun**	Tradename: **Talc**	Manuf.: **Leun**
Präparation: **KBr (2/1000)**	Dez. Nr.: **1.4.2**	Preparation: **KBr (2/1000)**	Dec. No.: **1.4.2**

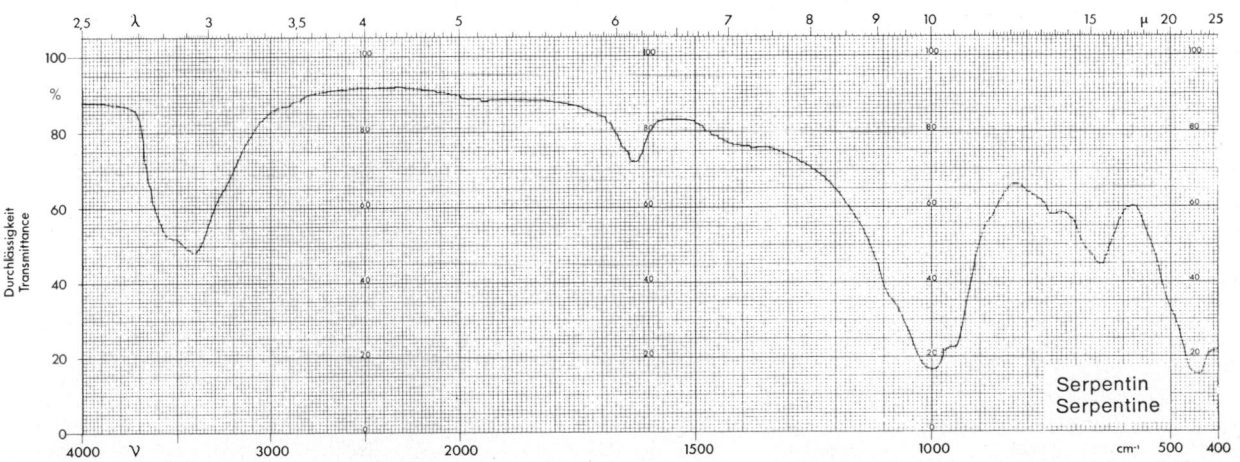

Zusammen-
setzung: **Serpentin, Mg-Fe-Al-Ca-Silikat**

Composition: **Serpentine, Mg-Fe-Al-Ca-silicate**

5426

Handelsname: **Serpentin**	Herst.: **Leun**	Tradename: **Serpentin**	Manuf.: **Leun**
Präparation: **KBr (2/1000)**	Dez. Nr.: **1.4.3**	Preparation: **KBr (2/1000)**	Dec. No.: **1.4.3**

Anorganische Füllstoffe und Pigmente
1. Füllstoffe
1.4. Andere Silikate

Inorganic Fillers and Pigments
1. Fillers
1.4. Other silicates

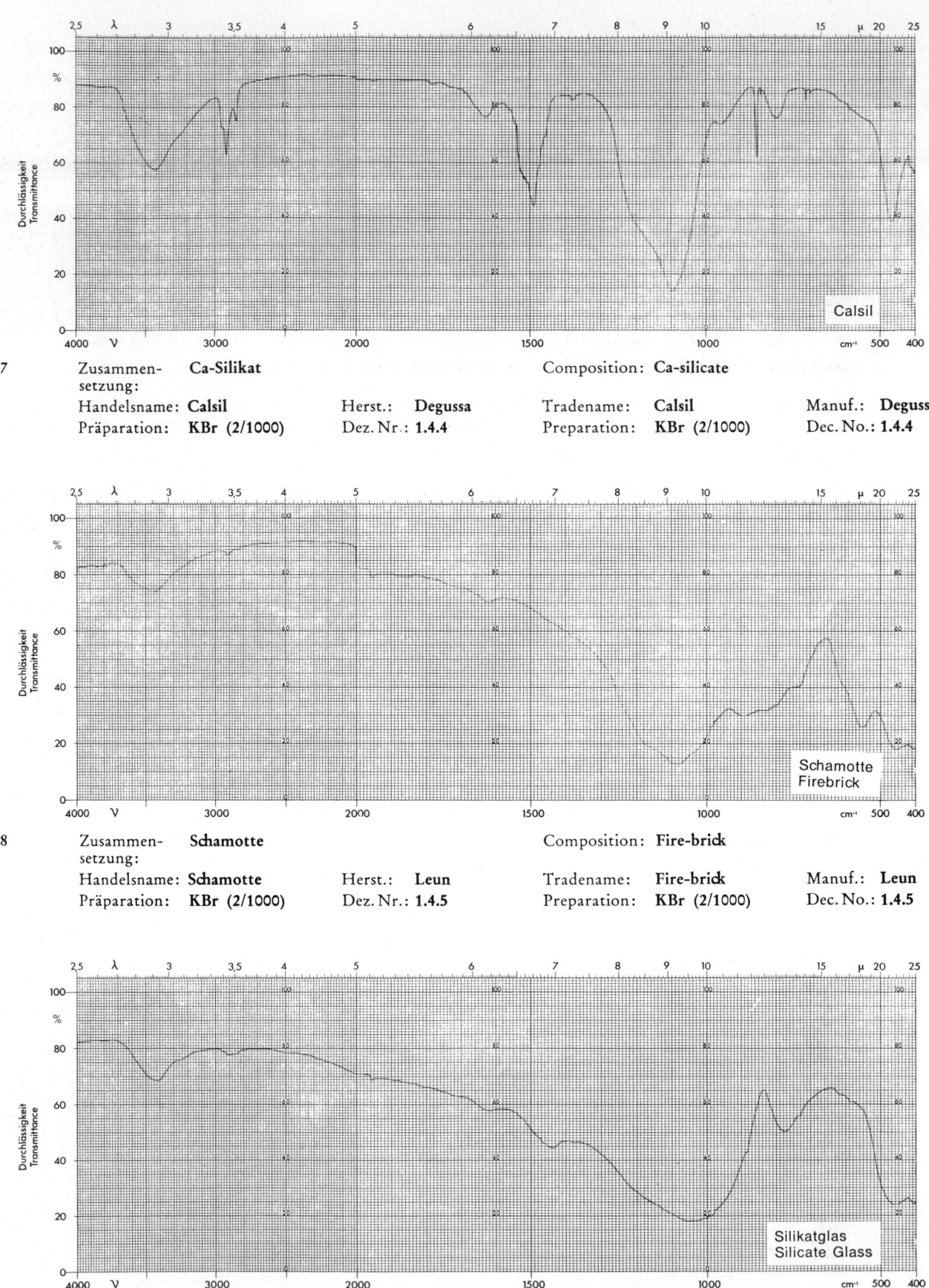

5427   Zusammen-   **Ca-Silikat**   Composition: **Ca-silicate**
         setzung:

Handelsname: **Calsil**   Herst.: **Degussa**   Tradename: **Calsil**   Manuf.: **Degussa**

Präparation: **KBr (2/1000)**   Dez. Nr.: **1.4.4**   Preparation: **KBr (2/1000)**   Dec. No.: **1.4.4**

5428   Zusammen-   **Schamotte**   Composition: **Fire-brick**
         setzung:

Handelsname: **Schamotte**   Herst.: **Leun**   Tradename: **Fire-brick**   Manuf.: **Leun**

Präparation: **KBr (2/1000)**   Dez. Nr.: **1.4.5**   Preparation: **KBr (2/1000)**   Dec. No.: **1.4.5**

5429   Zusammen-   **Silikatglas**   Composition: **Silicate glass**
         setzung:

Handelsname: **Glasfritte**   Herst.: **Leun**   Tradename: **Glass powder**   Manuf.: **Leun**

Präparation: **KBr (2/1000)**   Dez. Nr.: **1.4.6**   Preparation: **KBr (2/1000)**   Dec. No.: **1.4.6**

Anorganische Füllstoffe und Pigmente
1. Füllstoffe
1.5. Carbonate

Inorganic Fillers and Pigments
1. Fillers
1.5. Carbonates

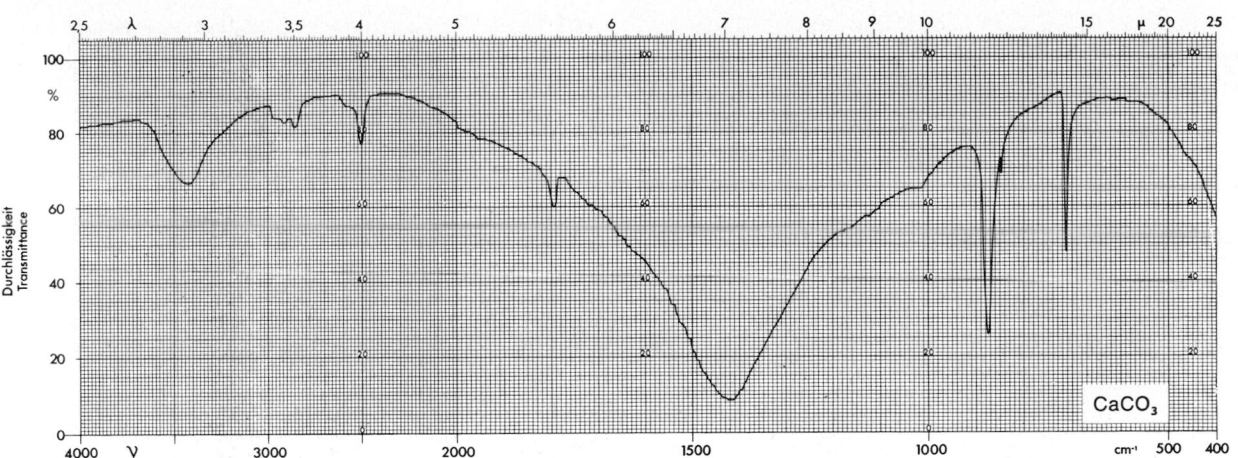

Zusammen-setzung:	Calciumcarbonat, CaCO₃			Composition:	Calcium carbonate, CaCO₃			5430

Zusammen-
setzung: **Calciumcarbonat, CaCO₃**

Handelsname: **Kalkspat** Herst.: **Leun**

Präparation: **KBr (2/1000)** Dez. Nr.: **1.5.1**

Composition: **Calcium carbonate, CaCO₃** 5430

Tradename: **Kalkspat** Manuf.: **Leun**

Preparation: **KBr (2/1000)** Dec. No:. **1.5.1**

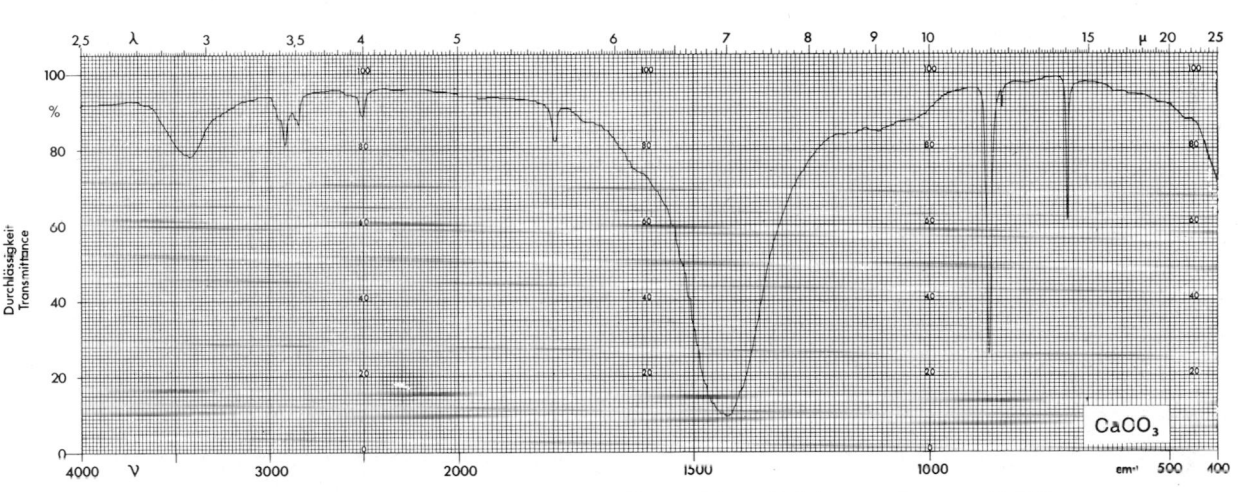

Zusammen-
setzung: **Calciumcarbonat, CaCO₃**

Handelsname: **Kreide Omya BSH** Herst.: **Omya**

Präparation: **KBr (2/1000)** Dez. Nr.: **1.5.2**

Composition: **Calcium carbonate, CaCO₃** 5431

Tradename: **Kreide Omya BSH** Manuf.: **Omya**

Preparation: **KBr (2/1000)** Dec. No:. **1.5.2**

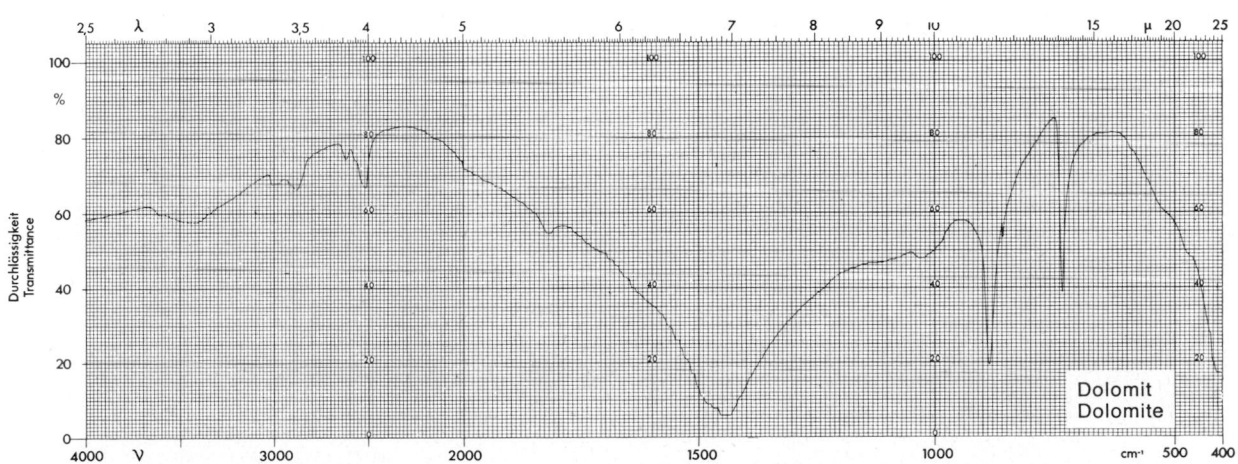

Zusammen-
setzung: **Dolomit, MgCa(CO₃)₂**

Handelsname: **Dolomit** Herst.: **Erbslöh**

Präparation: **KBr (2/1000)** Dez. Nr.: **1.5.3**

Composition: **Dolomite, MgCa(CO₃)₂** 5432

Tradename: **Dolomit** Manuf.: **Erbslöh**

Preparation: **KBr (2/1000)** Dec. No.: **1.5.3**

Anorganische Füllstoffe und Pigmente
1. Füllstoffe
1.6. Sulfate

Inorganic Fillers and Pigments
1. Fillers
1.6. Sulfates

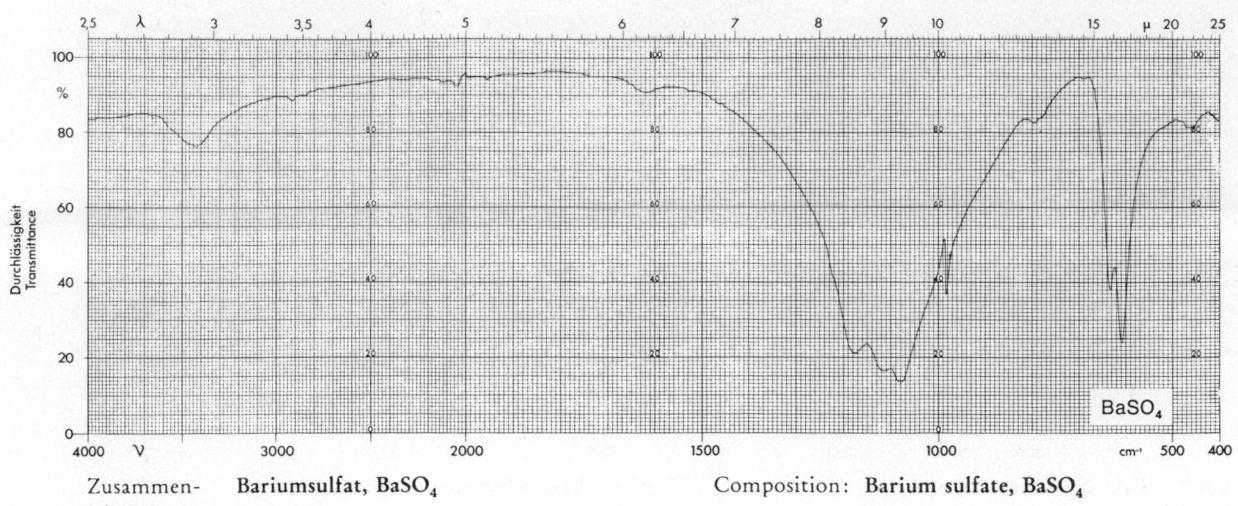

5433	Zusammen-setzung:	Bariumsulfat, BaSO₄		Composition:	Barium sulfate, BaSO₄	
	Handelsname:	**Schwerspat**	Herst.: **Leun**	Tradename:	**Barytes**	Manuf.: **Leun**
	Präparation:	**KBr (2/1000)**	Dez. Nr.: **1.6.1**	Preparation:	**KBr (2/1000)**	Dec. No.: **1.6.1**

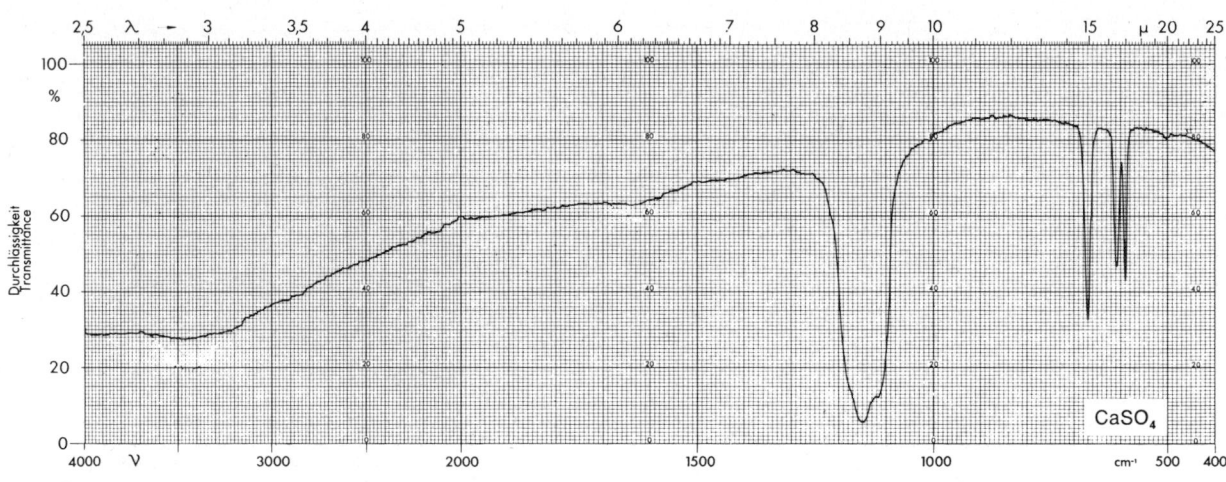

5434	Zusammen-setzung:	Calciumsulfat, CaSO₄		Composition:	Calcium sulfate, CaSO₄	
	Handelsname:	**Calciumsulfat**	Herst.: **Merck**	Tradename:	**Calciumsulfat**	Manuf.: **Merck**
	Präparation:	**KBr (2/1000)**	Dez. Nr.: **1.6.2**	Preparation:	**KBr (2/1000)**	Dec. No.: **1.6.2**

5435	Zusammen-setzung:	Calciumsulfat, CaSO₄ · 2 H₂O		Composition:	Calcium sulfate, CaSO₄ · 2 H₂O	
	Handelsname:	**Gips**	Herst.: **Riedel**	Tradename:	**Gypsum**	Manuf.: **Riedel**
	Präparation:	**KBr (2/1000)**	Dez. Nr.: **1.6.3**	Preparation:	**KBr (2/1000)**	Dec. No.: **1.6.3**

Anorg. Pigmente
2. Weißpigmente
2.1. Oxide

Inorganic Pigments
2. White Pigments
2.1. Oxides

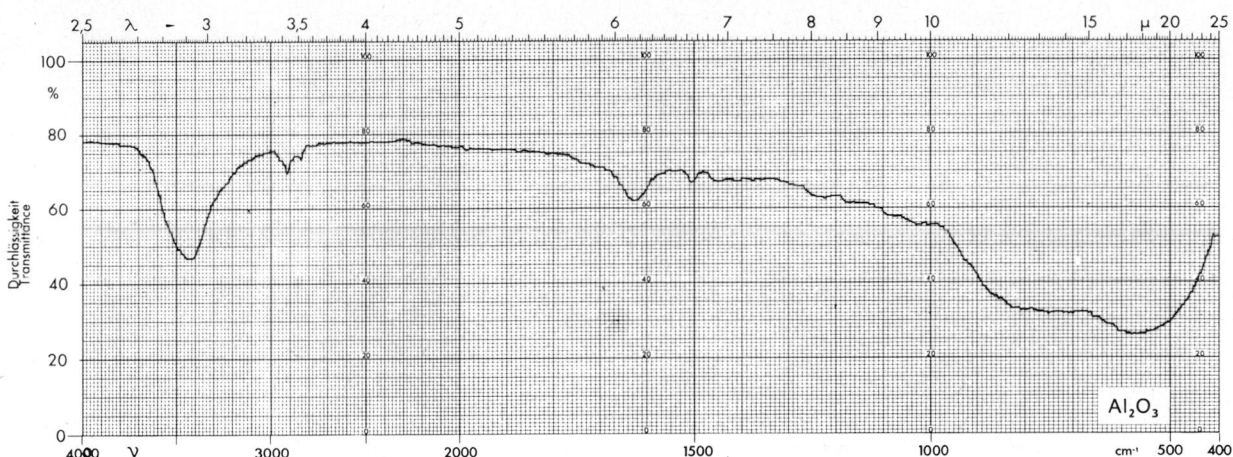

Zusammen-setzung:	**Aluminiumoxid, Al₂O₃**		Composition:	**Aluminium oxide, Al₂O₃**		5436
Handelsname:	**Korund**	Herst.: **Bosch**	Tradename:	**Korund**	Manuf.: **Bosch**	
Präparation:	**KBr (2/1000)**	Dez. Nr.: **1.7.1**	Preparation:	**KBr (2/1000)**	Dec. No.: **1.7.1**	

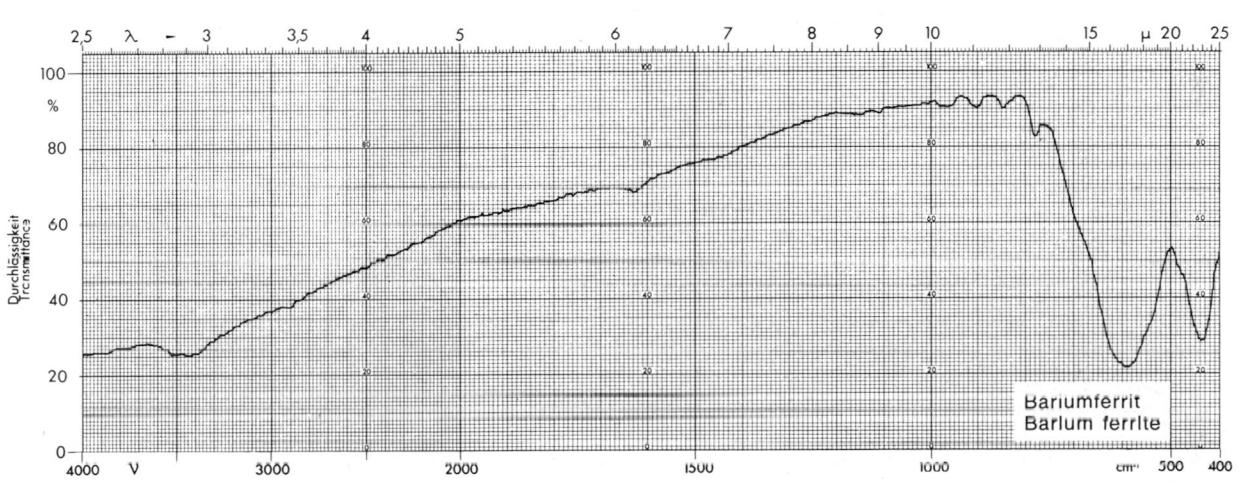

Zusammen-setzung:	**Bariumferrit, BaO · 6 Fe₂O₃**		Composition:	**Barium ferrite, BaO · 6 Fe₂O₃**		5437
Handelsname:	**Bariumferrit**	Herst.: **Bosch**	Tradename:	**Bariumferrit**	Manuf.: **Bosch**	
Präparation:	**KBr (2/1000)**	Dez. Nr.: **1.7.2**	Preparation:	**KBr (2/1000)**	Dec. No.: **1.7.2**	

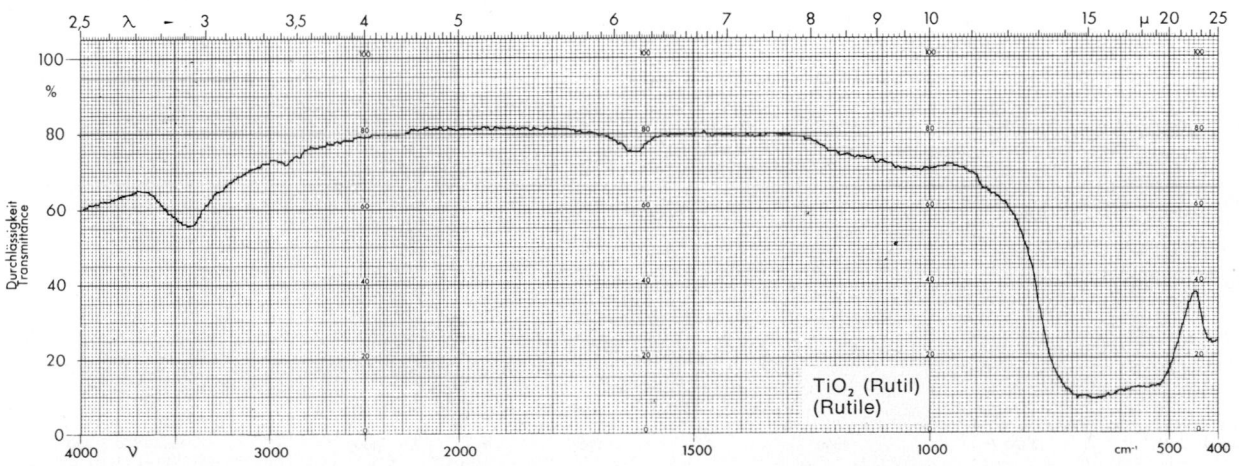

CI-Name:	**Pigmentweiß 6**	CI-No.: **77891**	CI-Name:	**Pigment White 6**	CI-No.: **77891**	5438
Zusammen-setzung:	**Titandioxid (Rutil), TiO₂**		Composition:	**Titanium dioxide (rutile), TiO₂**		
Handelsname:	**Titandioxid RN 56**	Herst.: **Siegle**	Tradename:	**Titandioxid RN 56**	Manuf.: **Siegle**	
Präparation:	**KBr (1,5/1000)**	Dez. Nr.: **2.1.1**	Preparation:	**KBr (1,5/1000)**	Dec. No.: **2.1.1**	

Anorg. Pigmente
2. Weißpigmente
2.1. Oxide

Inorganic Pigments
2. White Pigments
2.1. Oxides

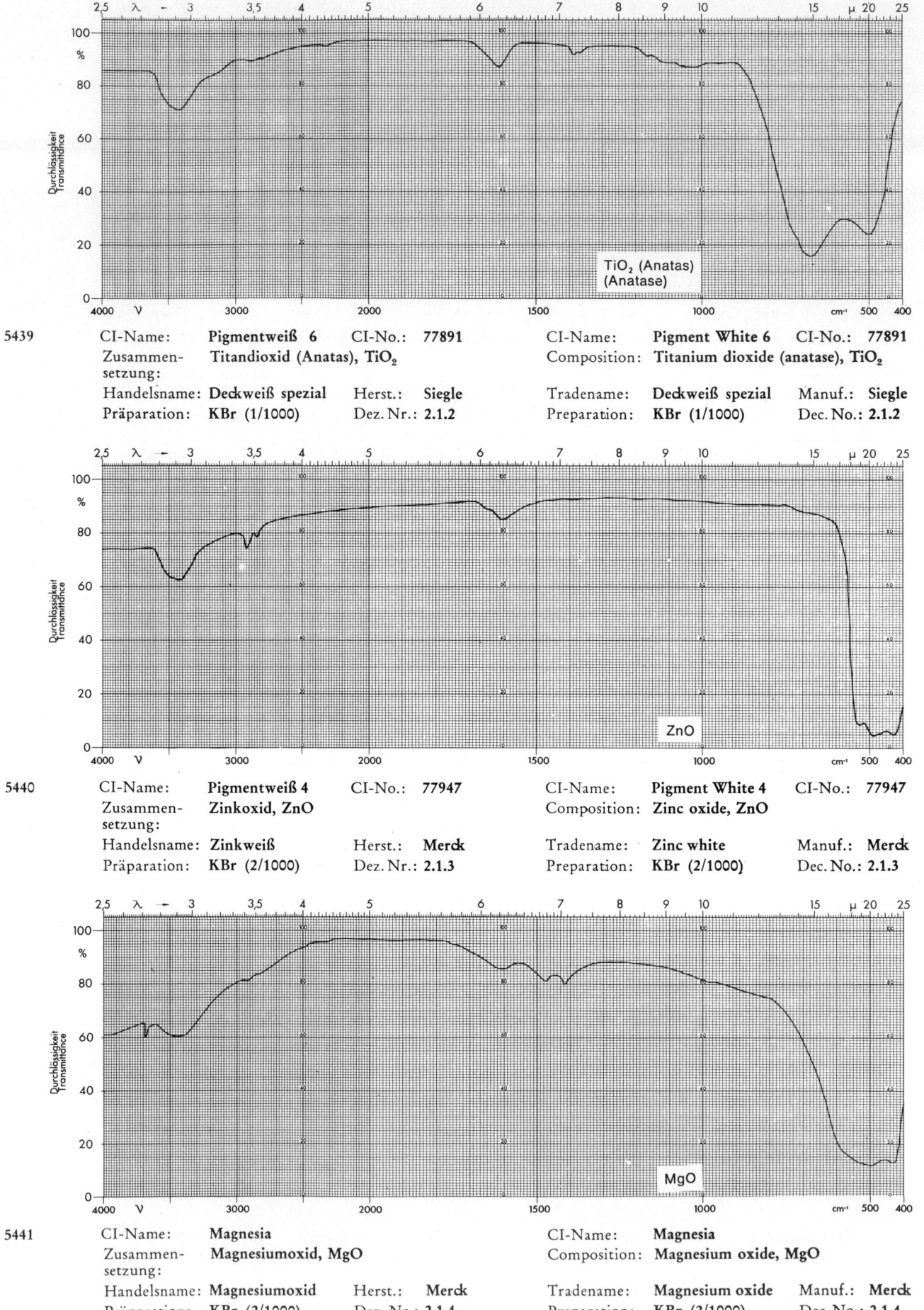

5439

	CI-Name:	**Pigmentweiß 6**	CI-No.:	**77891**	CI-Name:	**Pigment White 6**	CI-No.:	**77891**
	Zusammen-setzung:	**Titandioxid (Anatas), TiO₂**			Composition:	**Titanium dioxide (anatase), TiO₂**		
	Handelsname:	**Deckweiß spezial**	Herst.:	**Siegle**	Tradename:	**Deckweiß spezial**	Manuf.:	**Siegle**
	Präparation:	**KBr (1/1000)**	Dez. Nr.:	**2.1.2**	Preparation:	**KBr (1/1000)**	Dec. No.:	**2.1.2**

5440

	CI-Name:	**Pigmentweiß 4**	CI-No.:	**77947**	CI-Name:	**Pigment White 4**	CI-No.:	**77947**
	Zusammen-setzung:	**Zinkoxid, ZnO**			Composition:	**Zinc oxide, ZnO**		
	Handelsname:	**Zinkweiß**	Herst.:	**Merck**	Tradename:	**Zinc white**	Manuf.:	**Merck**
	Präparation:	**KBr (2/1000)**	Dez. Nr.:	**2.1.3**	Preparation:	**KBr (2/1000)**	Dec. No.:	**2.1.3**

5441

	CI-Name:	**Magnesia**			CI-Name:	**Magnesia**		
	Zusammen-setzung:	**Magnesiumoxid, MgO**			Composition:	**Magnesium oxide, MgO**		
	Handelsname:	**Magnesiumoxid**	Herst.:	**Merck**	Tradename:	**Magnesium oxide**	Manuf.:	**Merck**
	Präparation:	**KBr (2/1000)**	Dez. Nr.:	**2.1.4**	Preparation:	**KBr (2/1000)**	Dec. No.:	**2.1.4**

Anorg. Pigmente
2. Weißpigmente
2.2. Sulfate, Carbonate

Inorganic Pigments
2. White Pigments
2.2. Sulfates, Carbonates

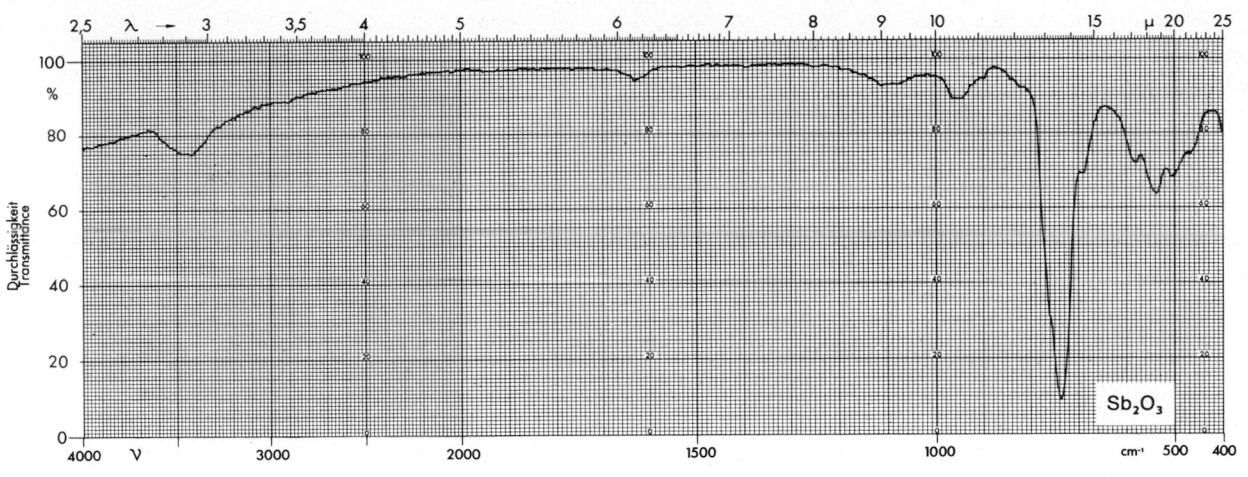

CI-Name:	Pigmentweiß 11	CI-No.:	77052	CI-Name:	Pigment White 11	CI-No.:	77052	5442

Zusammensetzung: **Antimonoxid, Sb₂O₃** — Composition: **Antimony oxide, Sb₂O₃**

Handelsname: **Antimonweiß** Herst.: **Siegle** Tradename: **Antimony white** Manuf.: **Siegle**
Präparation: **KBr (1,5/1000)** Dez. Nr.: **2.1.5** Preparation: **KBr (1,5/1000)** Dec. No.: **2.1.5**

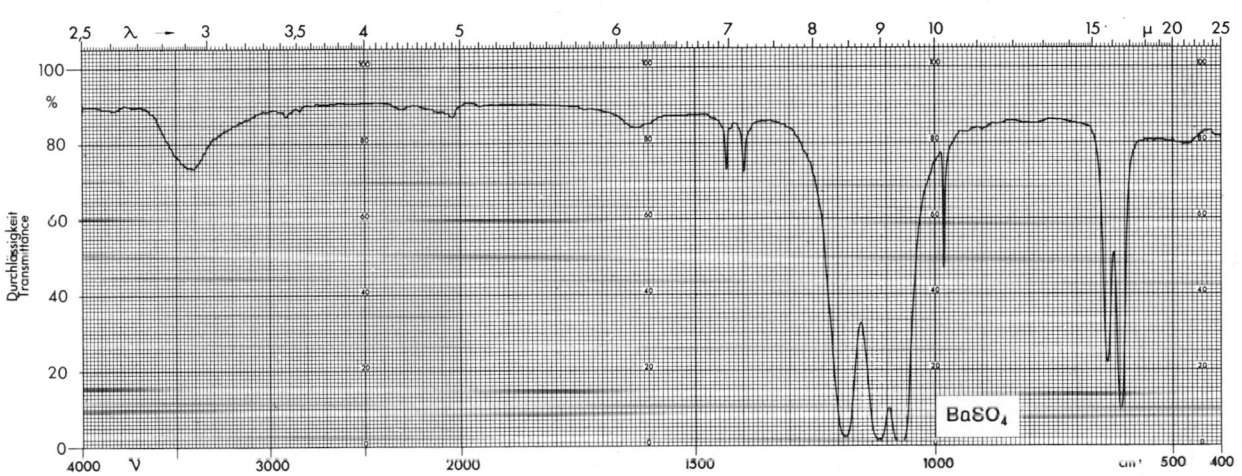

CI-Name:	Pigmentweiß 21	CI-No.:	77120	CI-Name:	Pigment White 21	CI-No.:	77120	5443

Zusammensetzung: **Bariumsulfat, BaSO₄** — Composition: **Barium sulfate, BaSO₄**

Handelsname: **Blanc fixe F** Herst.: **Siegle** Tradename: **Blanc fixe F** Manuf.: **Siegle**
Präparation: **KBr (3/1000)** Dez. Nr.: **2.2.1** Preparation: **KBr (3/1000)** Dec. No.: **2.2.1**

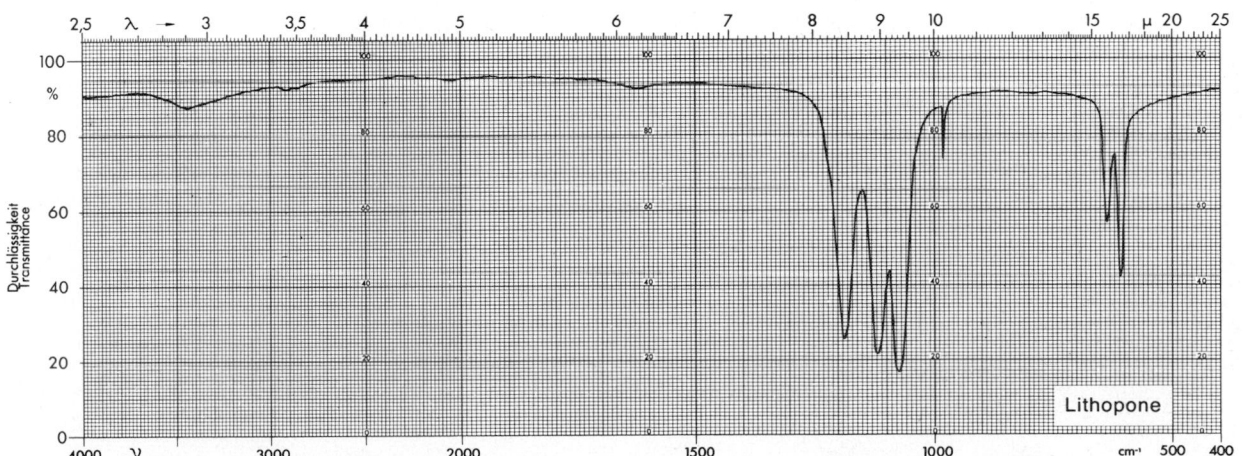

CI-Name:	Pigmentweiß 5	CI-No.:	77115	CI-Name:	Pigment White 5	CI-No.:	77115	5444

Zusammensetzung: **Lithopone, BaSO₄, ZnS** — Composition: **Lithopone, BaSO₄, ZnS**

Handelsname: **Zinkw. Grünsieg. GS** Herst.: **Siegle** Tradename: **Zinkw. Grünsieg. GS** Manuf.: **Siegle**
Präparation: **KBr (3/1000)** Dez. Nr.: **2.2.2** Preparation: **KBr (3/1000)** Dec. No.: **2.2.2**

Anorg. Pigmente
2. Weißpigmente
2.3. Sonstige

Inorganic Pigments
2. White Pigments
2.3. Miscellaneous

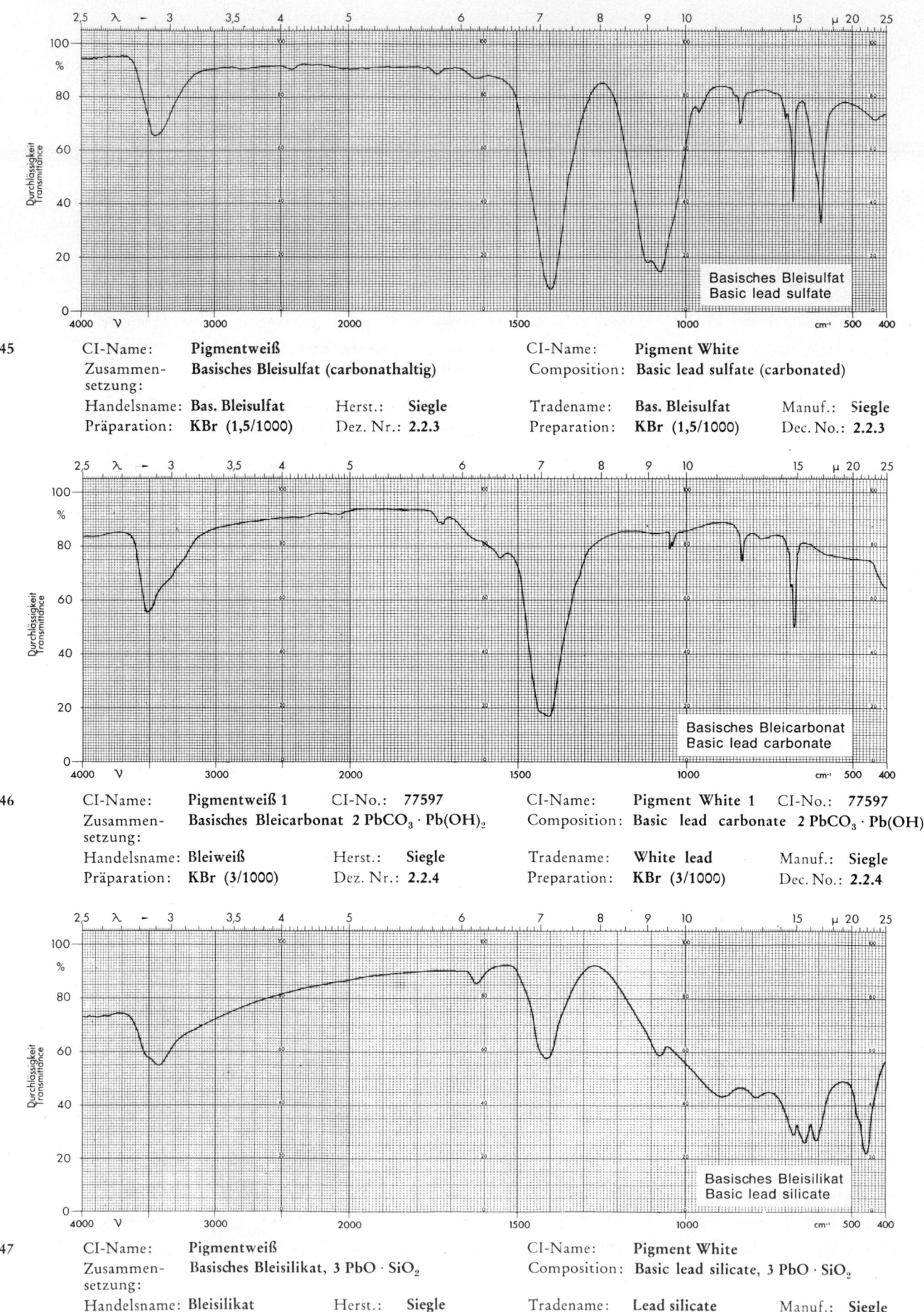

5445

CI-Name: **Pigmentweiß**
Zusammen-
setzung: **Basisches Bleisulfat (carbonathaltig)**
Handelsname: **Bas. Bleisulfat**   Herst.: **Siegle**
Präparation: **KBr (1,5/1000)**   Dez. Nr.: **2.2.3**

CI-Name: **Pigment White**
Composition: **Basic lead sulfate (carbonated)**
Tradename: **Bas. Bleisulfat**   Manuf.: **Siegle**
Preparation: **KBr (1,5/1000)**   Dec. No.: **2.2.3**

5446

CI-Name: **Pigmentweiß 1**   CI-No.: **77597**
Zusammen-
setzung: **Basisches Bleicarbonat 2 PbCO$_3$ · Pb(OH)$_2$**
Handelsname: **Bleiweiß**   Herst.: **Siegle**
Präparation: **KBr (3/1000)**   Dez. Nr.: **2.2.4**

CI-Name: **Pigment White 1**   CI-No.: **77597**
Composition: **Basic lead carbonate 2 PbCO$_3$ · Pb(OH)$_2$**
Tradename: **White lead**   Manuf.: **Siegle**
Preparation: **KBr (3/1000)**   Dec. No.: **2.2.4**

5447

CI-Name: **Pigmentweiß**
Zusammen-
setzung: **Basisches Bleisilikat, 3 PbO · SiO$_2$**
Handelsname: **Bleisilikat**   Herst.: **Siegle**
Präparation: **KBr (5/1000)**   Dez. Nr.: **2.3.1**

CI-Name: **Pigment White**
Composition: **Basic lead silicate, 3 PbO · SiO$_2$**
Tradename: **Lead silicate**   Manuf.: **Siegle**
Preparation: **KBr (5/1000)**   Dec. No.: **2.3.1**

Anorg. Pigmente
3. Gelbe, orange Pigmente
3.1. Chromate

Inorganic Pigments
3. Yellow orange Pigments
3.1. Chromates

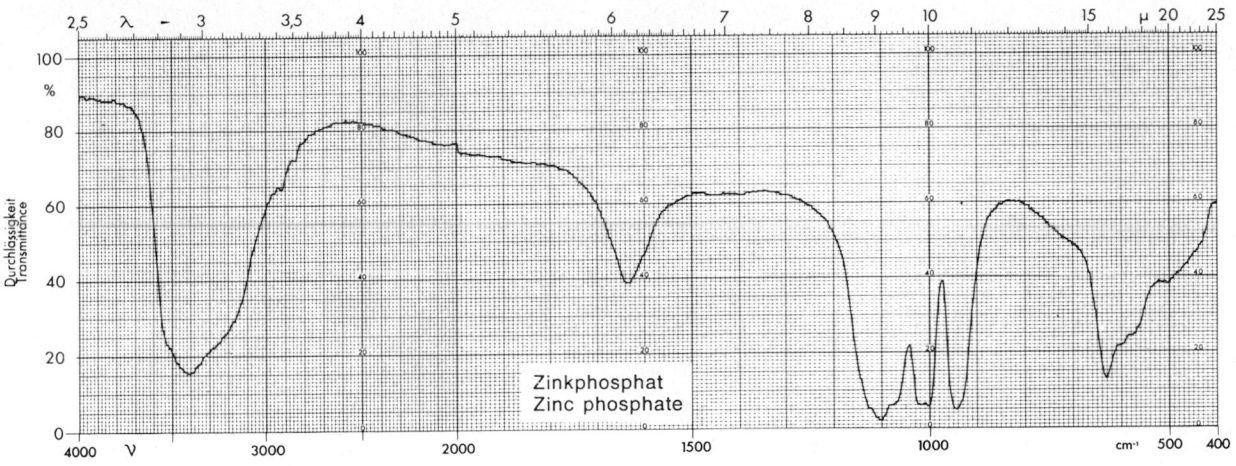

Zinkphosphat
Zinc phosphate

CI-Name: **Zinkphosphat ZNP**   CI-Name: **Zinc phosphate ZNP**   **5448**

Zusammen-setzung: **Zinkphosphat, $Zn_3(PO_4)_2 \cdot 4\,H_2O$**   Composition: **Zinc phosphate, $Zn_3(PO_4)_2 \cdot 4\,H_2O$**

Handelsname: **Zinkphosphat ZNP**   Herst.: **Siegle**   Tradename: **Zinkphosphat ZNP**   Manuf.: **Siegle**

Präparation: **KBr (3/1000)**   Dez. Nr.: **2.3.2**   Preparation: **KBr (3/1000)**   Dec. No.: **2.3.2**

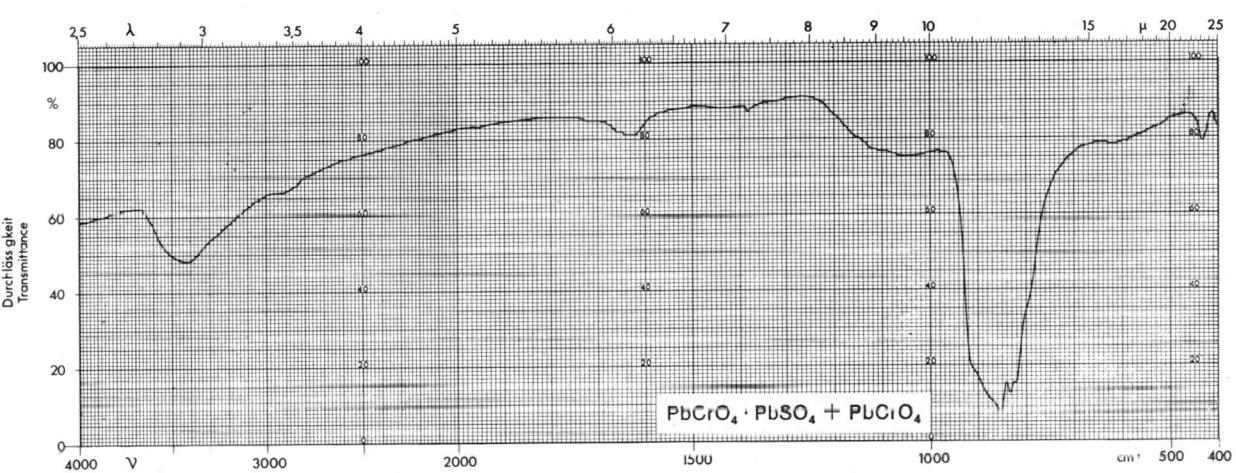

$PbCrO_4 \cdot PbSO_4 + PbCrO_4$

CI-Name: **Chromgelb 7520**   CI-Name: **Chrom. Yellow 7520**   **5449**

Zusammen-setzung: **Bleichromat, Bleichromatsulfat**   Composition: **Lead chromate, lead chromate-sulfate**

Handelsname: **Chromgelb 7520**   Herst.: **Siegle**   Tradename: **Chromgelb 7520**   Manuf.: **Siegle**

Präparation: **KBr (3/1000)**   Dez. Nr.: **3.1.1**   Preparation: **KBr (3/1000)**   Dec. No.: **3.1.1**

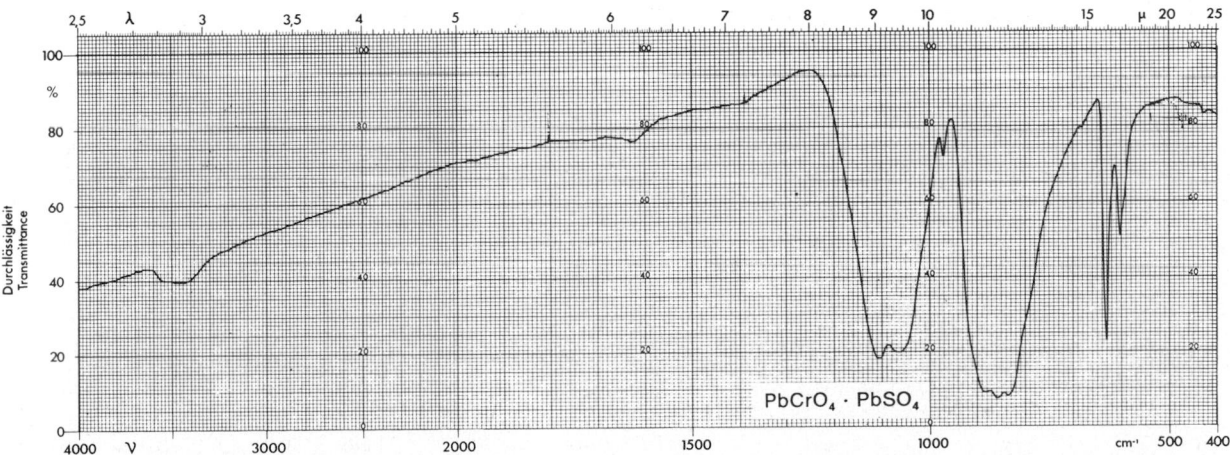

$PbCrO_4 \cdot PbSO_4$

CI-Name: **Pigmentgelb 34**   CI-No.: **77603**   CI-Name: **Pigment Yellow 34**   CI-No.: **77603**   **5450**

Zusammen-setzung: **Mischkristalle Bleichromatsulfat**   Composition: **Mixed crystals of lead chromate-sulfate**

Handelsname: **Chromgelb 51**   Herst.: **Siegle**   Tradename: **Chromgelb 51**   Manuf.: **Siegle**

Präparation: **KBr (5/1000)**   Dez. Nr.: **3.1.2**   Preparation: **KBr (5/1000)**   Dec. No.: **3.1.2**

Anorg. Pigmente
3. Gelbe, orange Pigmente
3.1. Chromate

Inorganic Pigments
3. Yellow orange Pigments
3.1. Chromates

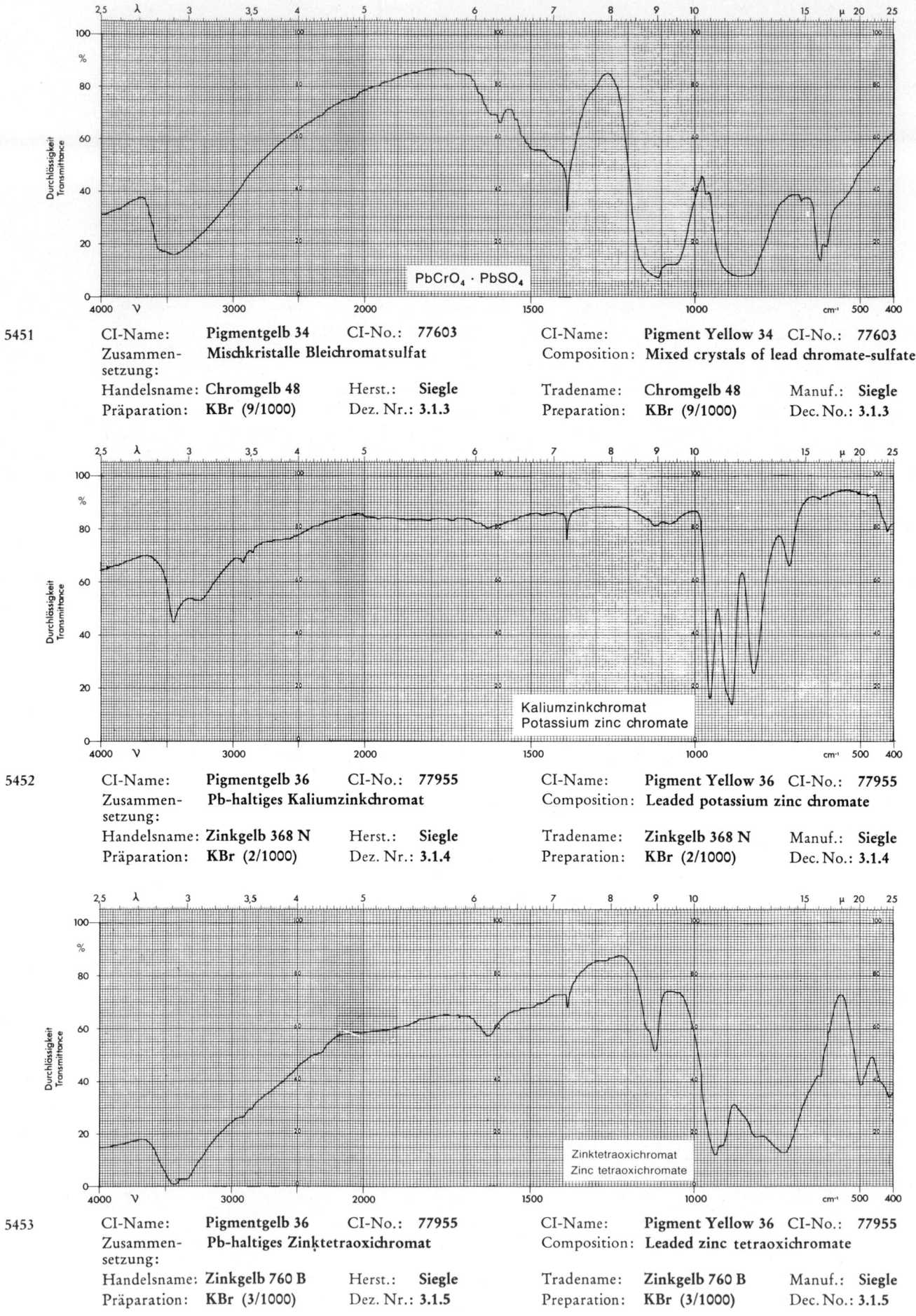

PbCrO₄ · PbSO₄

Kaliumzinkchromat
Potassium zinc chromate

Zinktetraoxichromat
Zinc tetraoxichromate

5451

CI-Name:	**Pigmentgelb 34**	CI-No.: **77603**
Zusammensetzung:	**Mischkristalle Bleichromatsulfat**	
Handelsname:	**Chromgelb 48**	Herst.: **Siegle**
Präparation:	**KBr (9/1000)**	Dez. Nr.: **3.1.3**

CI-Name:	**Pigment Yellow 34**	CI-No.: **77603**
Composition:	**Mixed crystals of lead chromate-sulfate**	
Tradename:	**Chromgelb 48**	Manuf.: **Siegle**
Preparation:	**KBr (9/1000)**	Dec. No.: **3.1.3**

5452

CI-Name:	**Pigmentgelb 36**	CI-No.: **77955**
Zusammensetzung:	**Pb-haltiges Kaliumzinkchromat**	
Handelsname:	**Zinkgelb 368 N**	Herst.: **Siegle**
Präparation:	**KBr (2/1000)**	Dez. Nr.: **3.1.4**

CI-Name:	**Pigment Yellow 36**	CI-No.: **77955**
Composition:	**Leaded potassium zinc chromate**	
Tradename:	**Zinkgelb 368 N**	Manuf.: **Siegle**
Preparation:	**KBr (2/1000)**	Dec. No.: **3.1.4**

5453

CI-Name:	**Pigmentgelb 36**	CI-No.: **77955**
Zusammensetzung:	**Pb-haltiges Zinktetraoxichromat**	
Handelsname:	**Zinkgelb 760 B**	Herst.: **Siegle**
Präparation:	**KBr (3/1000)**	Dez. Nr.: **3.1.5**

CI-Name:	**Pigment Yellow 36**	CI-No.: **77955**
Composition:	**Leaded zinc tetraoxichromate**	
Tradename:	**Zinkgelb 760 B**	Manuf.: **Siegle**
Preparation:	**KBr (3/1000)**	Dec. No.: **3.1.5**

Anorg. Pigmente
3. Gelbe, orange Pigmente
3.1. Chromate

Inorganic Pigments
3. Yellow, orange Pigments
3.1. Chromates

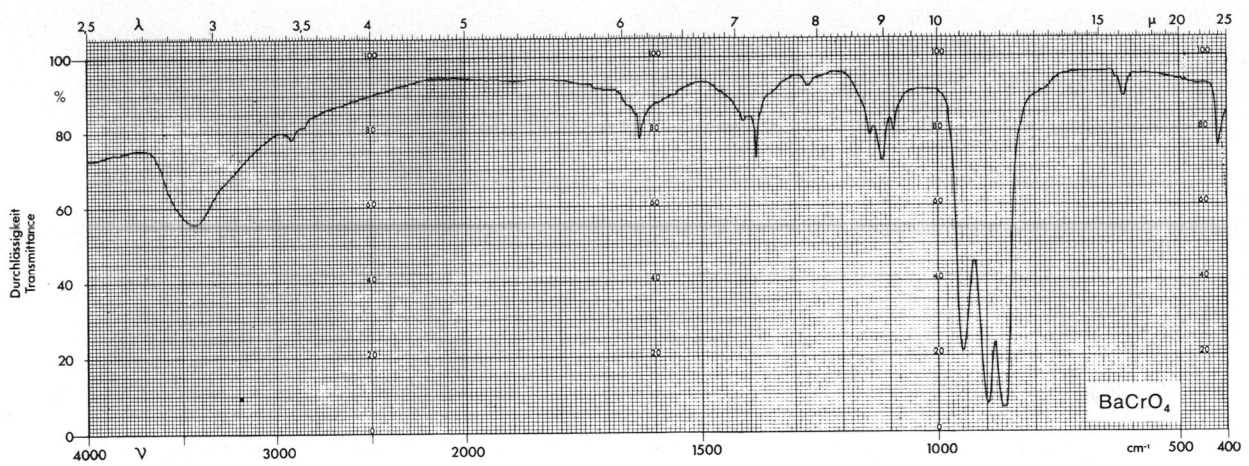

CI-Name:	**Pigmentgelb 31**	CI-No.:	**77103**	CI-Name:	**Pigment Yellow 31**	CI-No.:	**77103**	5454
Zusammensetzung:	**Bariumchromat, BaCrO₄**			Composition:	**Barium chromate, BaCrO₄**			
Handelsname:	**Bariumchr. 840 SV**	Herst.:	**Siegle**	Tradename:	**Bariumchr. 840 SV**	Manuf.:	**Siegle**	
Präparation:	**KBr (1/1000)**	Dez. Nr.:	**3.1.6**	Preparation:	**KBr (1/1000)**	Dec. No.:	**3.1.6**	

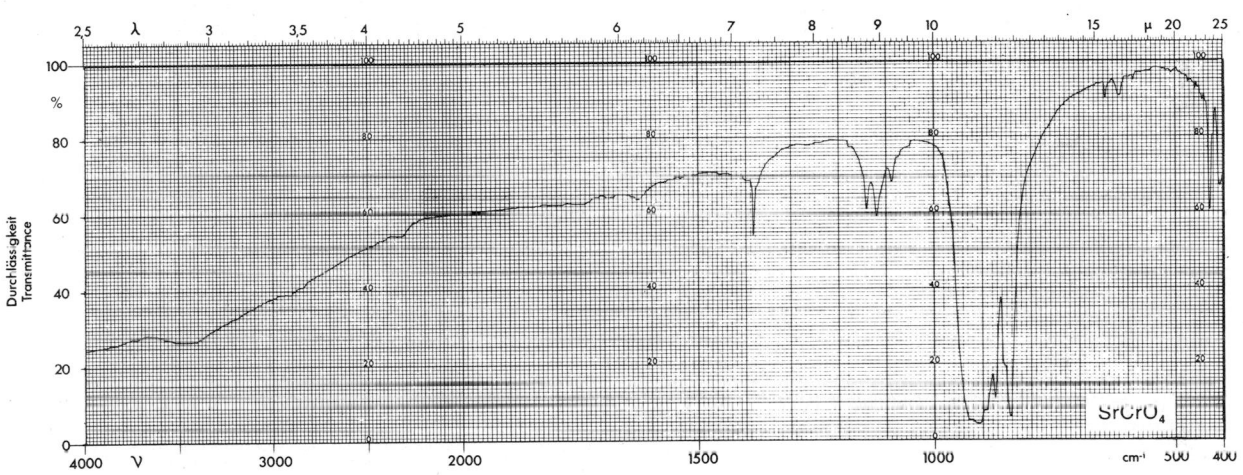

CI-Name:	**Pigmentgelb 32**	CI-No.:	**77839**	CI-Name:	**Pigment Yellow 32**	CI-No.:	**77839**	5455
Zusammensetzung:	**Strontiumchromat, SrCrO₄**			Composition:	**Strontium chromate, SrCrO₄**			
Handelsname:	**Strontiumchromat A**	Herst.:	**Siegle**	Tradename:	**Strontiumchromat A**	Manuf.:	**Siegle**	
Präparation:	**KBr (2/1000)**	Dez. Nr.:	**3.1.7**	Preparation:	**KBr (2/1000)**	Dec. No.	**3.1.7**	

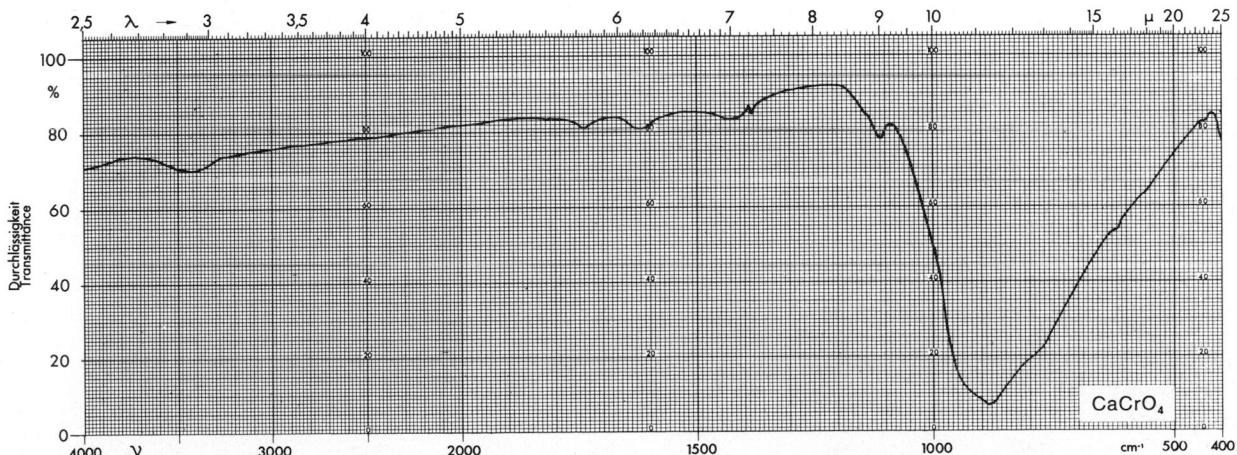

CI-Name:	**Pigmentgelb**			CI-Name:	**Pigment Yellow**			5456
Zusammensetzung:	**Calciumchromat, CaCrO₄**			Composition:	**Calcium chromate, CaCrO₄**			
Handelsname:	**Calciumchr. SII 1472**	Herst.:	**Siegle**	Tradename:	**Calciumchr. SII 1472**	Manuf.:	**Siegle**	
Präparation:	**KBr (3/1000)**	Dez. Nr.:	**3.1.8**	Preparation:	**KBr (3/1000)**	Dec. No.:	**3.1.8**	

Anorg. Pigmente
3. Gelbe, orange Pigmente
3.2. Antimonate

Inorganic Pigments
3. Yellow, orange Pigments
3.2. Antimonates

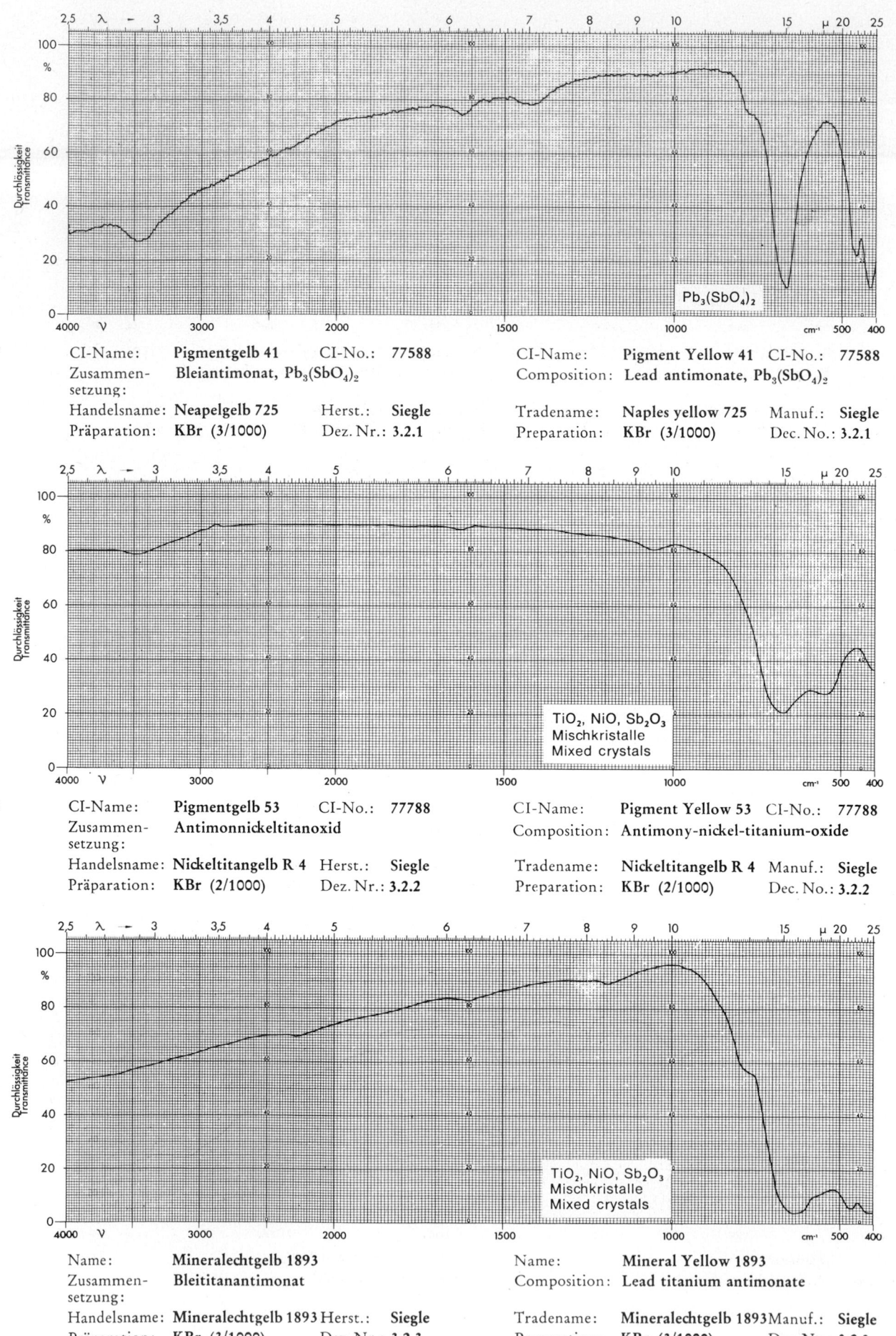

$Pb_3(SbO_4)_2$

TiO_2, NiO, Sb_2O_3
Mischkristalle
Mixed crystals

TiO_2, NiO, Sb_2O_3
Mischkristalle
Mixed crystals

5457

CI-Name:	**Pigmentgelb 41**	CI-No.:	**77588**	CI-Name:	**Pigment Yellow 41**	CI-No.: **77588**
Zusammen-setzung:	**Bleiantimonat, $Pb_3(SbO_4)_2$**			Composition:	**Lead antimonate, $Pb_3(SbO_4)_2$**	
Handelsname:	**Neapelgelb 725**	Herst.:	**Siegle**	Tradename:	**Naples yellow 725**	Manuf.: **Siegle**
Präparation:	**KBr (3/1000)**	Dez. Nr.:	**3.2.1**	Preparation:	**KBr (3/1000)**	Dec. No.: **3.2.1**

5458

CI-Name:	**Pigmentgelb 53**	CI-No.:	**77788**	CI-Name:	**Pigment Yellow 53**	CI-No.: **77788**
Zusammen-setzung:	**Antimonnickeltitanoxid**			Composition:	**Antimony-nickel-titanium-oxide**	
Handelsname:	**Nickeltitangelb R 4**	Herst.:	**Siegle**	Tradename:	**Nickeltitangelb R 4**	Manuf.: **Siegle**
Präparation:	**KBr (2/1000)**	Dez. Nr.:	**3.2.2**	Preparation:	**KBr (2/1000)**	Dec. No.: **3.2.2**

5459

Name:	**Mineralechtgelb 1893**		Name:	**Mineral Yellow 1893**
Zusammen-setzung:	**Bleititanantimonat**		Composition:	**Lead titanium antimonate**
Handelsname:	**Mineralechtgelb 1893**	Herst.: **Siegle**	Tradename:	**Mineralechtgelb 1893** Manuf.: **Siegle**
Präparation:	**KBr (3/1000)**	Dez. Nr.: **3.2.3**	Preparation:	**KBr (3/1000)** Dec. No.: **3.2.3**

Anorg. Pigmente
4. Braune, rote Pigmente
4.1. Eisenoxidpigmente

Inorganic Pigments
4. Brown, red Pigments
4.1. Iron Oxide Pigments

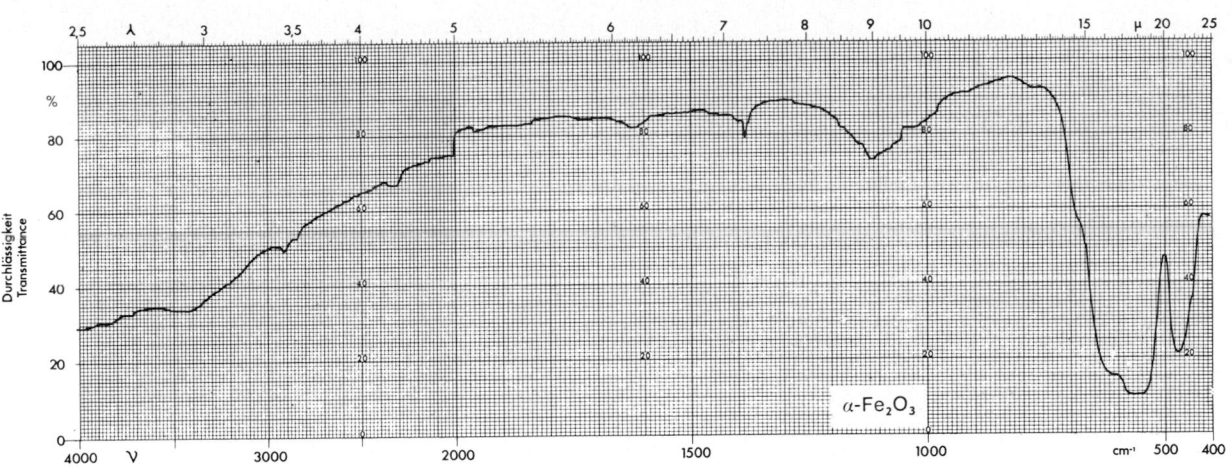

α-Fe$_2$O$_3$

Name:	**Eisenoxid**	
Zusammen-setzung:	**Eisen(III) oxid, α-Fe$_2$O$_3$**	
Handelsname: α-**Eisenoxid**	Herst.:	**Bayer**
Präparation: **KBr (3/1000)**	Dez. Nr.:	**4.1.1**

Name:	**Iron oxide**	
Composition:	**Iron(III) oxide, α-Fe$_2$O$_3$**	
Tradename: α-**Eisenoxid**	Manuf.:	**Bayer**
Preparation: **KBr (3/1000)**	Dec. No.:	**4.1.1**

5460

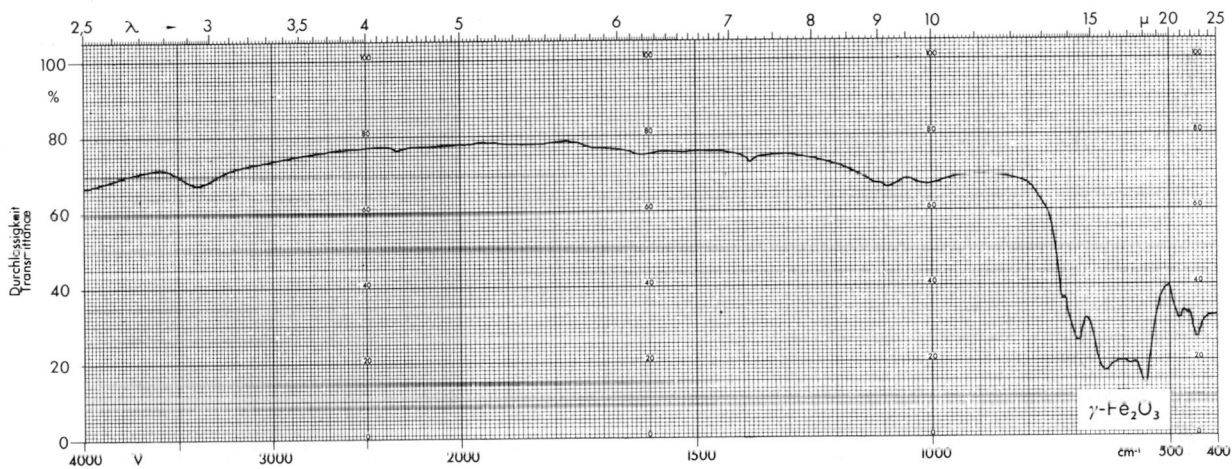

γ-Fe$_2$O$_3$

Name:	**Eisenoxid**	
Zusammen-setzung:	**Eisen(III)oxid, γ-Fe$_2$O$_3$**	
Handelsname: γ-**Eisenoxid**	Herst.:	**Bayer**
Präparation: **KBr (3/1000)**	Dez. Nr.:	**4.1.2**

Name:	**Iron oxide**	
Composition:	**Iron(III) oxide, γ-Fe$_2$O$_3$**	
Tradename: γ **Eisenoxid**	Manuf.:	**Bayer**
Preparation: **KBr (3/1000)**	Dec. No.:	**4.1.2**

5461

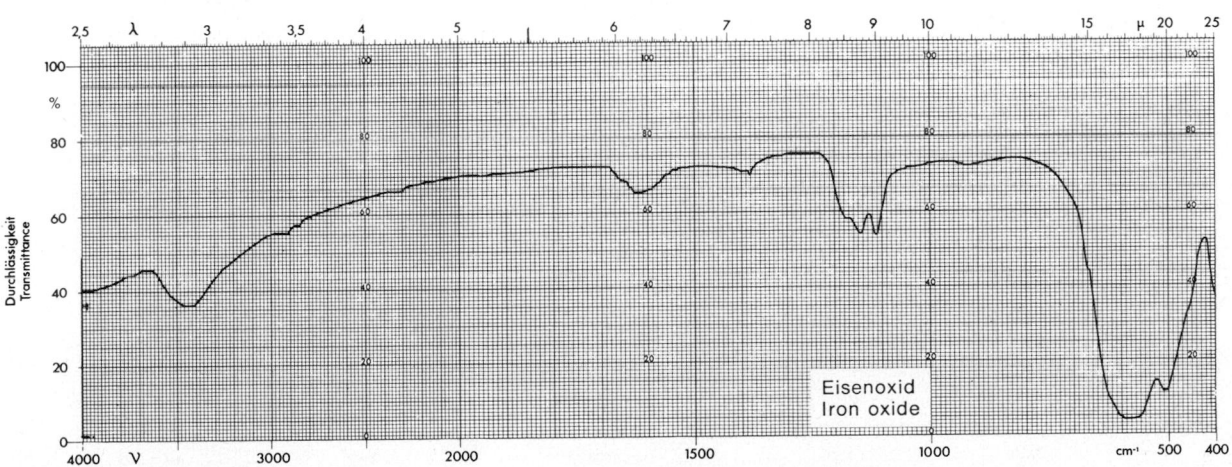

Eisenoxid
Iron oxide

CI-Name:	**Pigmentrot**	
Zusammen-setzung:	**Eisenoxid**	
Handelsname: **Eisenoxid WM SII 2132**	Herst.:	**Siegle**
Präparation: **KBr (3/1000)**	Dez. Nr.:	**4.1.3**

CI-Name:	**Pigment Red**	
Composition:	**Iron oxide**	
Tradename: **Eisenoxid WM SII 2132**	Manuf.:	**Siegle**
Preparation: **KBr (3/1000)**	Dec. No.:	**4.1.3**

5462

Anorg. Pigmente
4. Braune, rote Pigmente
4.1. Eisenoxidpigmente

Inorganic Pigments
4. Brown, red Pigments
4.1. Iron Oxide Pigments

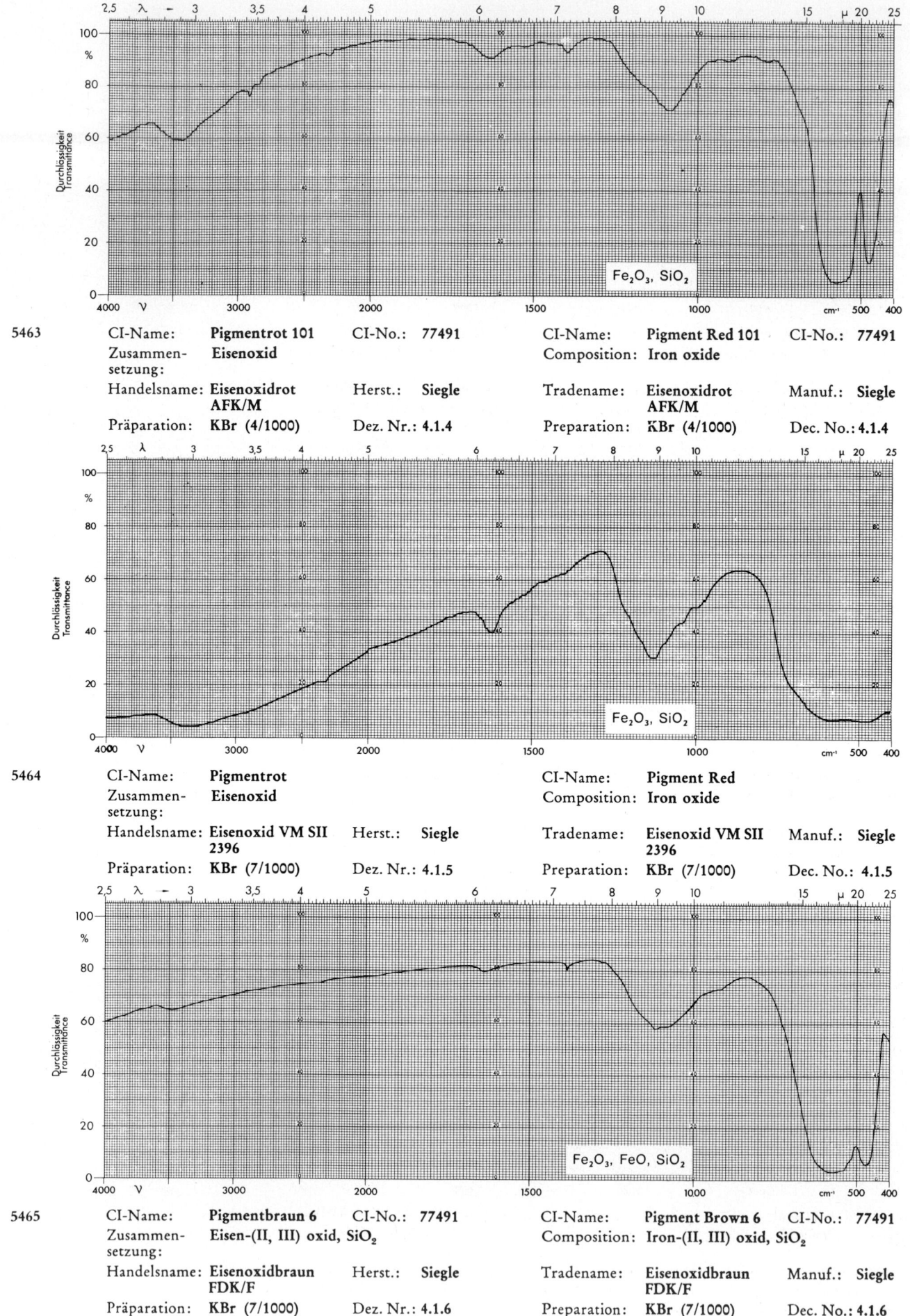

Fe₂O₃, SiO₂

Fe₂O₃, SiO₂

Fe₂O₃, FeO, SiO₂

5463

CI-Name:	**Pigmentrot 101**	CI-No.:	**77491**	
Zusammensetzung:	**Eisenoxid**			
Handelsname:	**Eisenoxidrot AFK/M**	Herst.:	**Siegle**	
Präparation:	**KBr (4/1000)**	Dez. Nr.:	**4.1.4**	

CI-Name:	**Pigment Red 101**	CI-No.:	**77491**
Composition:	**Iron oxide**		
Tradename:	**Eisenoxidrot AFK/M**	Manuf.:	**Siegle**
Preparation:	**KBr (4/1000)**	Dec. No.:	**4.1.4**

5464

CI-Name:	**Pigmentrot**		
Zusammensetzung:	**Eisenoxid**		
Handelsname:	**Eisenoxid VM SII 2396**	Herst.:	**Siegle**
Präparation:	**KBr (7/1000)**	Dez. Nr.:	**4.1.5**

CI-Name:	**Pigment Red**		
Composition:	**Iron oxide**		
Tradename:	**Eisenoxid VM SII 2396**	Manuf.:	**Siegle**
Preparation:	**KBr (7/1000)**	Dec. No.:	**4.1.5**

5465

CI-Name:	**Pigmentbraun 6**	CI-No.:	**77491**
Zusammensetzung:	**Eisen-(II, III) oxid, SiO₂**		
Handelsname:	**Eisenoxidbraun FDK/F**	Herst.:	**Siegle**
Präparation:	**KBr (7/1000)**	Dez. Nr.:	**4.1.6**

CI-Name:	**Pigment Brown 6**	CI-No.:	**77491**
Composition:	**Iron-(II, III) oxid, SiO₂**		
Tradename:	**Eisenoxidbraun FDK/F**	Manuf.:	**Siegle**
Preparation:	**KBr (7/1000)**	Dec. No.:	**4.1.6**

Anorg. Pigmente
4. Braune, rote Pigmente
4.1. Eisenoxidpigmente

Inorganic Pigments
4. Brown, red Pigments
4.1. Iron Oxide Pigments

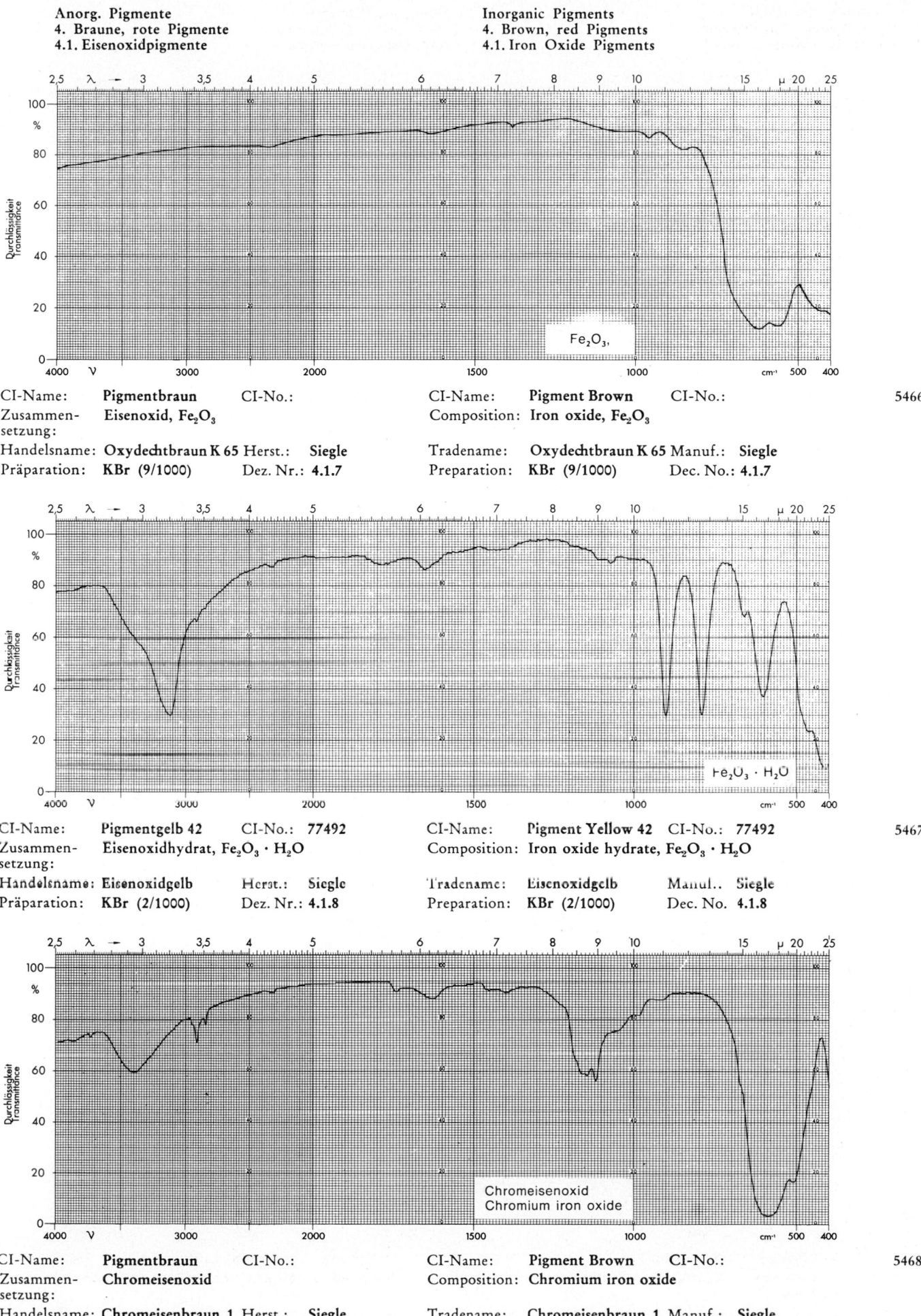

CI-Name:	**Pigmentbraun**	CI-No.:	CI-Name:	**Pigment Brown**	CI-No.:	5466
Zusammen-setzung:	Eisenoxid, Fe_2O_3		Composition:	Iron oxide, Fe_2O_3	
Handelsname:	**Oxydechtbraun K 65**	Herst.: **Siegle**	Tradename:	**Oxydechtbraun K 65**	Manuf.: **Siegle**
Präparation:	**KBr (9/1000)**	Dez. Nr.: **4.1.7**	Preparation:	**KBr (9/1000)**	Dec. No.: **4.1.7**

CI-Name:	**Pigmentgelb 42**	CI-No.: **77492**	CI-Name:	**Pigment Yellow 42**	CI-No.: **77492**	5467
Zusammen-setzung:	Eisenoxidhydrat, $Fe_2O_3 \cdot H_2O$		Composition:	Iron oxide hydrate, $Fe_2O_3 \cdot H_2O$	
Handelsname:	**Eisenoxidgelb**	Herst.: **Siegle**	Tradename:	**Eisenoxidgelb**	Manuf.: **Siegle**
Präparation:	**KBr (2/1000)**	Dez. Nr.: **4.1.8**	Preparation:	**KBr (2/1000)**	Dec. No. **4.1.8**

CI-Name:	**Pigmentbraun**	CI-No.:	CI-Name:	**Pigment Brown**	CI-No.:	5468
Zusammen-setzung:	**Chromeisenoxid**		Composition:	**Chromium iron oxide**	
Handelsname:	**Chromeisenbraun 1**	Herst.: **Siegle**	Tradename:	**Chromeisenbraun 1**	Manuf.: **Siegle**
Präparation:	**KBr (2/1000)**	Dez. Nr.: **4.1.9**	Preparation:	**KBr (2/1000)**	Dec. No.: **4.1.9**

Anorg. Pigmente
4. Braune, rote Pigmente
4.2. Bleiverbindungen

Inorganic Pigments
4. Brown, red Pigments
4.2. Lead Compounds

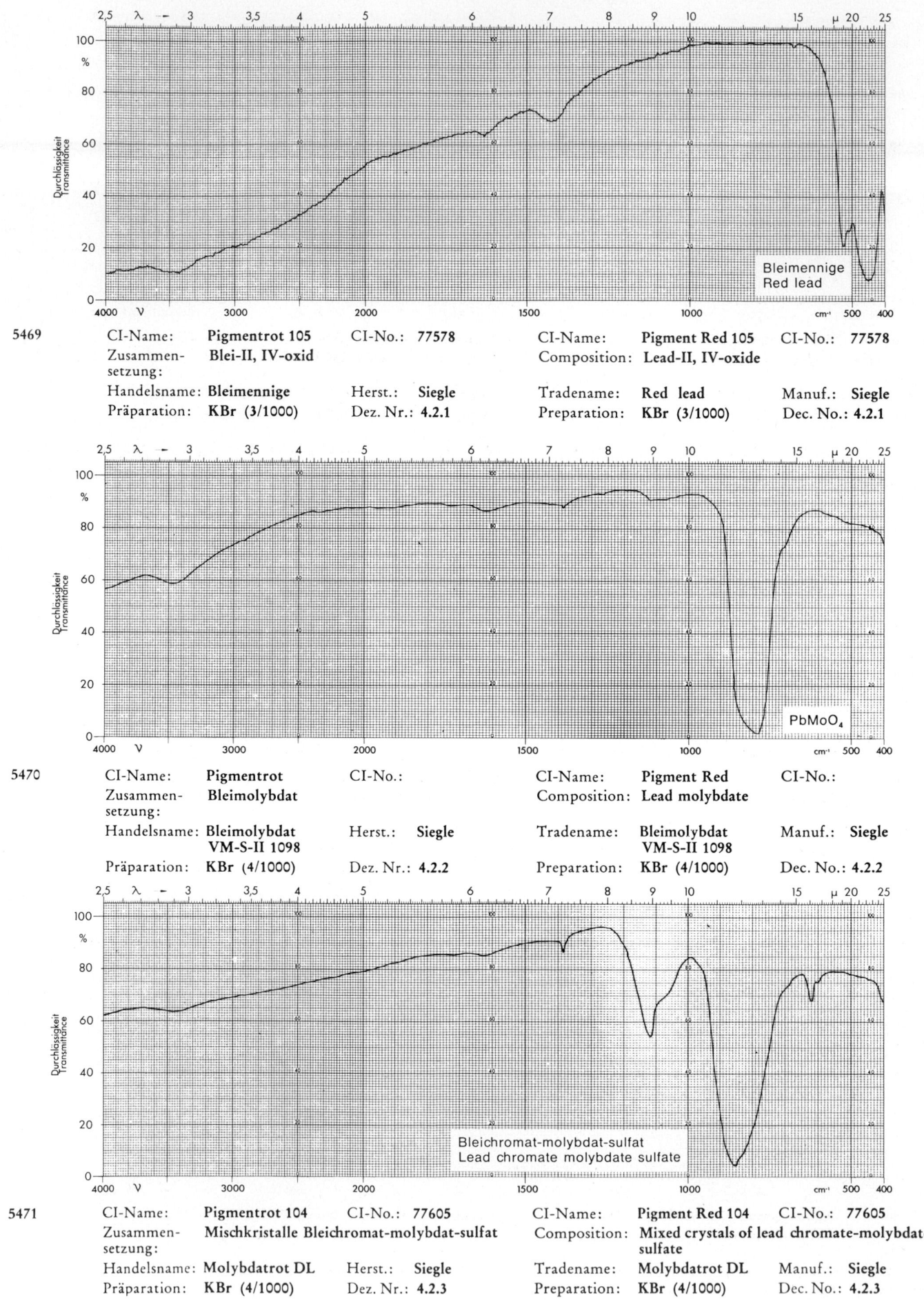

5469

	CI-Name:	**Pigmentrot 105**	CI-No.:	**77578**		CI-Name:	**Pigment Red 105**	CI-No.:	**77578**
	Zusammen-setzung:	**Blei-II, IV-oxid**				Composition:	**Lead-II, IV-oxide**		
	Handelsname:	**Bleimennige**	Herst.:	**Siegle**		Tradename:	**Red lead**	Manuf.:	**Siegle**
	Präparation:	**KBr (3/1000)**	Dez. Nr.:	**4.2.1**		Preparation:	**KBr (3/1000)**	Dec. No.:	**4.2.1**

5470

	CI-Name:	**Pigmentrot**	CI-No.:			CI-Name:	**Pigment Red**	CI-No.:	
	Zusammen-setzung:	**Bleimolybdat**				Composition:	**Lead molybdate**		
	Handelsname:	**Bleimolybdat VM-S-II 1098**	Herst.:	**Siegle**		Tradename:	**Bleimolybdat VM-S-II 1098**	Manuf.:	**Siegle**
	Präparation:	**KBr (4/1000)**	Dez. Nr.:	**4.2.2**		Preparation:	**KBr (4/1000)**	Dec. No.:	**4.2.2**

5471

	CI-Name:	**Pigmentrot 104**	CI-No.:	**77605**		CI-Name:	**Pigment Red 104**	CI-No.:	**77605**
	Zusammen-setzung:	**Mischkristalle Bleichromat-molybdat-sulfat**				Composition:	**Mixed crystals of lead chromate-molybdate-sulfate**		
	Handelsname:	**Molybdatrot DL**	Herst.:	**Siegle**		Tradename:	**Molybdatrot DL**	Manuf.:	**Siegle**
	Präparation:	**KBr (4/1000)**	Dez. Nr.:	**4.2.3**		Preparation:	**KBr (4/1000)**	Dec. No.:	**4.2.3**

Anorg. Pigmente
4. Braune, rote Pigmente
4.2. Bleiverbindungen

Inorganic Pigments
4. Brown, red Pigments
4.2. Lead Compounds

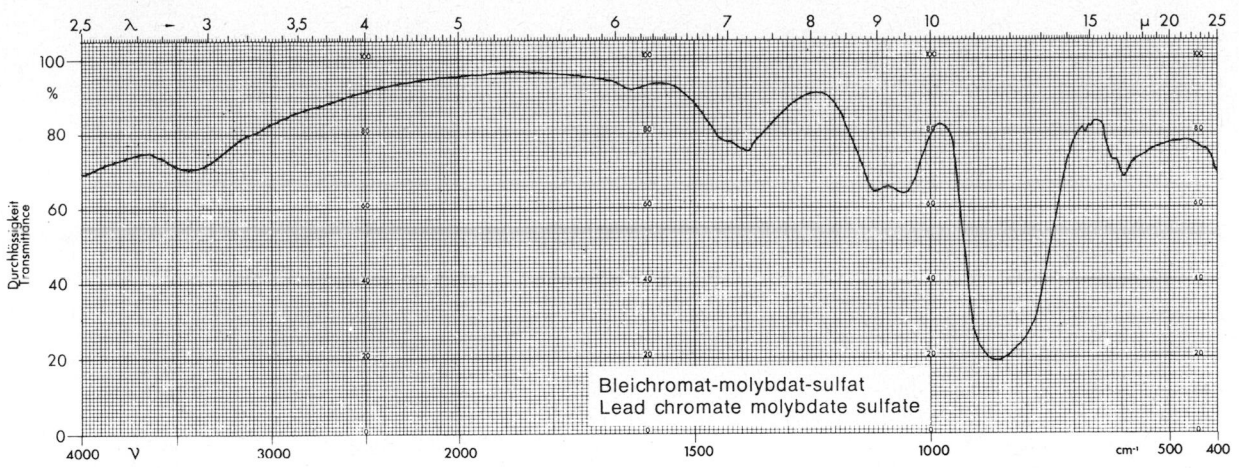

Bleichromat-molybdat-sulfat
Lead chromate molybdate sulfate

CI-Name:	Pigmentrot 104	CI-No.:	77605		CI-Name:	Pigment Red 104	CI-No.:	77605	5472

Zusammensetzung: **Mischkristalle Bleichromat-molybdat-sulfat**

Composition: **Mixed crystals of lead chromate-molybdate-sulfate**

Handelsname:	**Molybdatrot VM**	Herst.:	**Siegle**	Tradename:	**Molybdatrot VM**	Manuf.:	**Siegle**
Präparation:	**KBr (4/1000)**	Dez. Nr.:	**4.2.4**	Preparation:	**KBr (4/1000)**	Dec. No.:	**4.2.4**

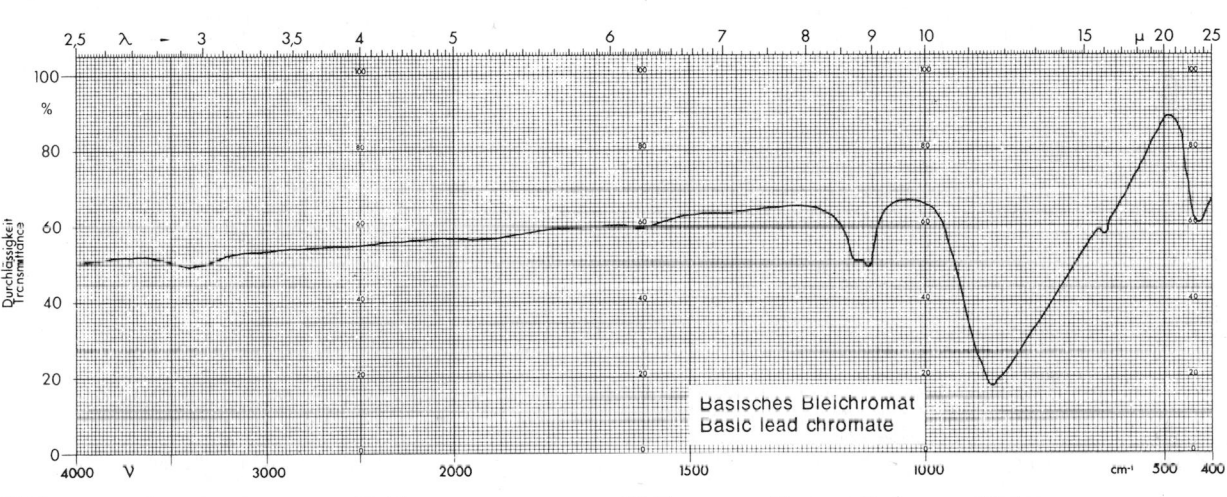

Basisches Bleichromat
Basic lead chromate

CI-Name:	Pigmentrot	CI-No.:		CI-Name:	Pigment Red	CI No.:	5473

Zusammensetzung: **Basisches Bleichromat**

Composition: **Basic lead chromate**

Handelsname:	**Chromrot 1**	Herst.:	**Siegle**	Tradename:	**Chromrot 1**	Manuf.:	**Siegle**
Präparation:	**KBr (3/1000)**	Dez. Nr.:	**4.2.5**	Preparation:	**KBr (3/1000)**	Dec. No.:	**4.2.5**

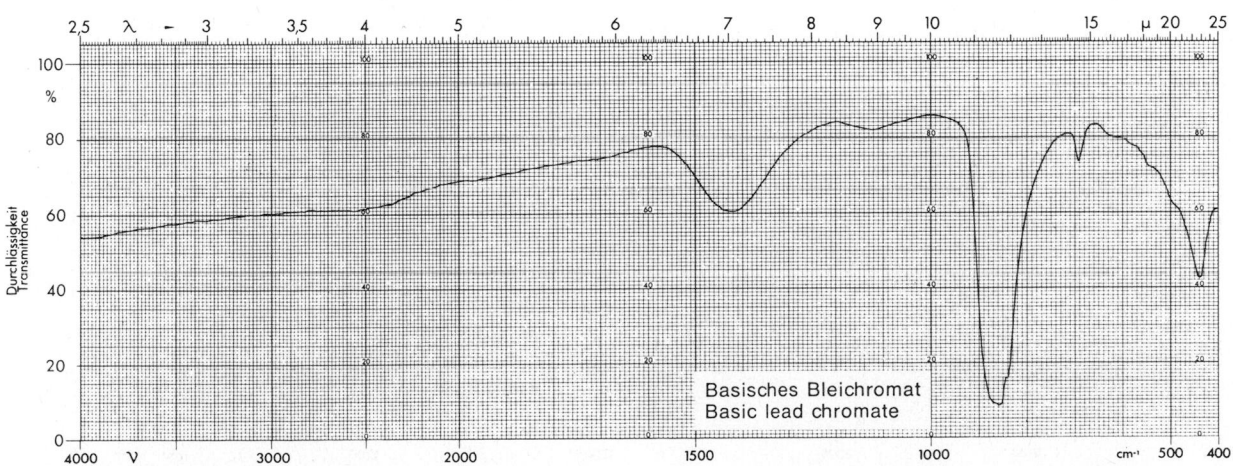

Basisches Bleichromat
Basic lead chromate

CI-Name:	Pigmentorange 21	CI-No.:	77601		CI-Name:	Pigment Orange 21	CI-No.:	77601	5474

Zusammensetzung: **Basisches Bleichromat**

Composition: **Basic lead chromate**

Handelsname:	**Chromorange 58**	Herst.:	**Siegle**	Tradename:	**Chromorange 58**	Manuf.:	**Siegle**
Präparation:	**KBr (3/1000)**	Dez. Nr.:	**4.2.6**	Preparation:	**KBr (3/1000)**	Dec. No:.	**4.2.6**

Anorg. Pigmente
5. Grüne Pigmente
5.2. Cobaltpigmente

Inorganic Pigments
5. Green Pigments
5.2. Cobalt Pigments

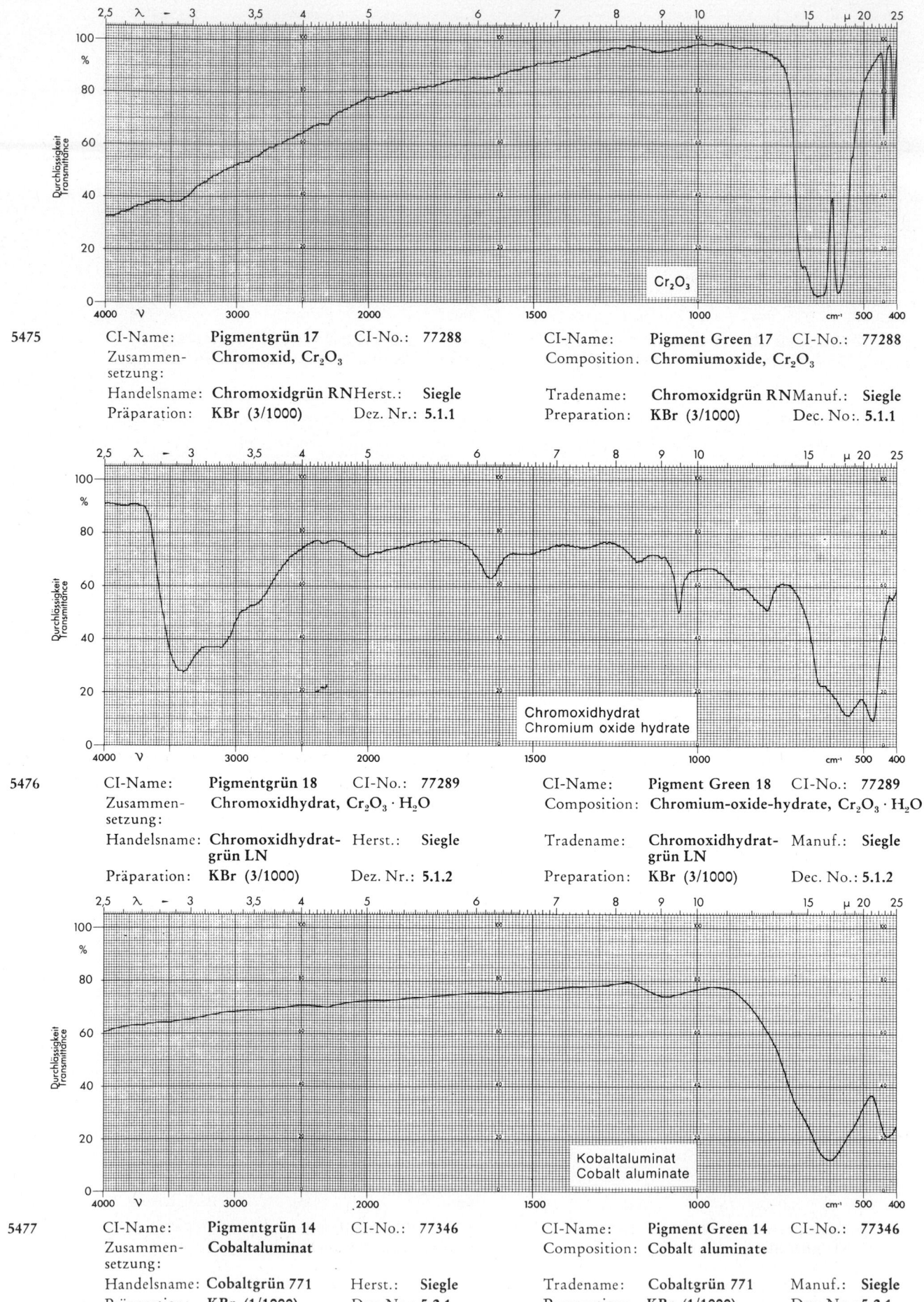

5475

CI-Name:	**Pigmentgrün 17**	CI-No.: **77288**		CI-Name:	**Pigment Green 17**	CI-No.: **77288**
Zusammen-setzung:	**Chromoxid, Cr₂O₃**			Composition.	**Chromiumoxide, Cr₂O₃**	
Handelsname:	**Chromoxidgrün RN**	Herst.: **Siegle**		Tradename:	**Chromoxidgrün RN**	Manuf.: **Siegle**
Präparation:	**KBr (3/1000)**	Dez. Nr.: **5.1.1**		Preparation:	**KBr (3/1000)**	Dec. No:. **5.1.1**

CI-Name: **Pigmentgrün 17** CI-No.: **77288** — Zusammensetzung: **Chromoxid, Cr_2O_3** — Handelsname: **Chromoxidgrün RN** Herst.: **Siegle** — Präparation: **KBr (3/1000)** Dez. Nr.: **5.1.1**

CI-Name: **Pigment Green 17** CI-No.: **77288** — Composition. **Chromiumoxide, Cr_2O_3** — Tradename: **Chromoxidgrün RN** Manuf.: **Siegle** — Preparation: **KBr (3/1000)** Dec. No:. **5.1.1**

Cr₂O₃

5476

Chromoxidhydrat
Chromium oxide hydrate

CI-Name: **Pigmentgrün 18** CI-No.: **77289** — Zusammensetzung: **Chromoxidhydrat, $Cr_2O_3 \cdot H_2O$** — Handelsname: **Chromoxidhydrat-grün LN** Herst.: **Siegle** — Präparation: **KBr (3/1000)** Dez. Nr.: **5.1.2**

CI-Name: **Pigment Green 18** CI-No.: **77289** — Composition: **Chromium-oxide-hydrate, $Cr_2O_3 \cdot H_2O$** — Tradename: **Chromoxidhydrat-grün LN** Manuf.: **Siegle** — Preparation: **KBr (3/1000)** Dec. No.: **5.1.2**

5477

Kobaltaluminat
Cobalt aluminate

CI-Name: **Pigmentgrün 14** CI-No.: **77346** — Zusammensetzung: **Cobaltaluminat** — Handelsname: **Cobaltgrün 771** Herst.: **Siegle** — Präparation: **KBr (1/1000)** Dez. Nr.: **5.2.1**

CI-Name: **Pigment Green 14** CI-No.: **77346** — Composition: **Cobalt aluminate** — Tradename: **Cobaltgrün 771** Manuf.: **Siegle** — Preparation: **KBr (1/1000)** Dec. No.: **5.2.1**

Anorg. Pigmente
6. Blaue Pigmente
6.1. Verschiedene

Inorganic Pigments
6. Blue Pigments
6.1. Miscellaneous

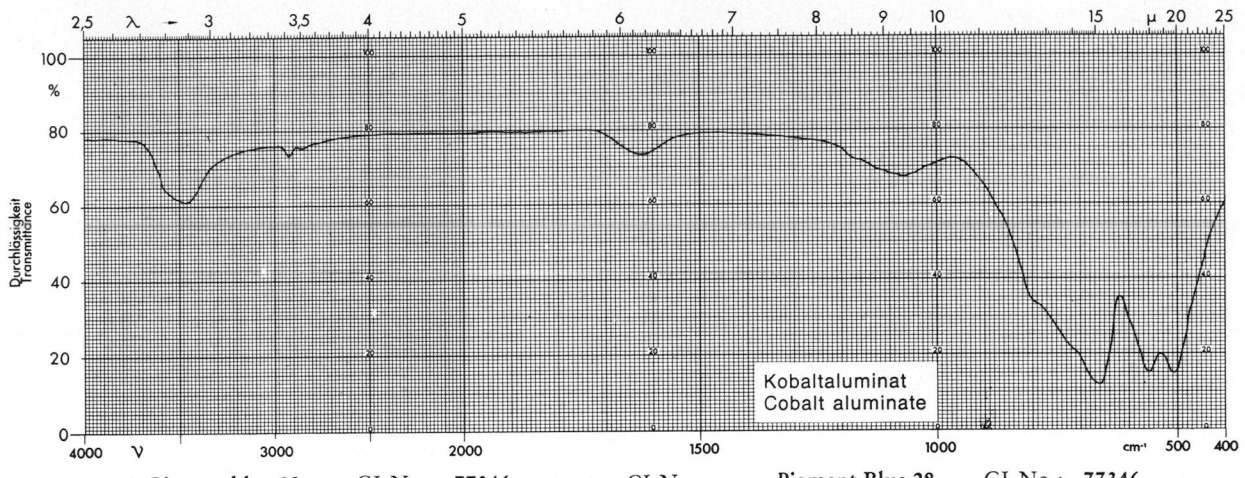

CI-Name:	Pigmentblau 28	CI-No.: 77346		CI-Name:	Pigment Blue 28	CI-No.: 77346	5478
Zusammensetzung:	Cobaltaluminat, CoO · Al₂O₃			Composition:	Cobalt aluminate, CoO · Al₂O₃		

CI-Name: **Pigmentblau 28**   CI-No.: **77346**   CI-Name: **Pigment Blue 28**   CI-No.: **77346**   5478
Zusammen- **Cobaltaluminat, CoO · Al₂O₃**   Composition: **Cobalt aluminate, CoO · Al₂O₃**
setzung:
Handelsname: **Cobaltblau 767**   Herst.: **Siegle**   Tradename: **Cobaltblau 767**   Manuf.: **Siegle**
Präparation: **KBr (3/1000)**   Dez. Nr.: **6.1.1**   Preparation: **KBr (3/1000)**   Dec. No:. **6.1.1**

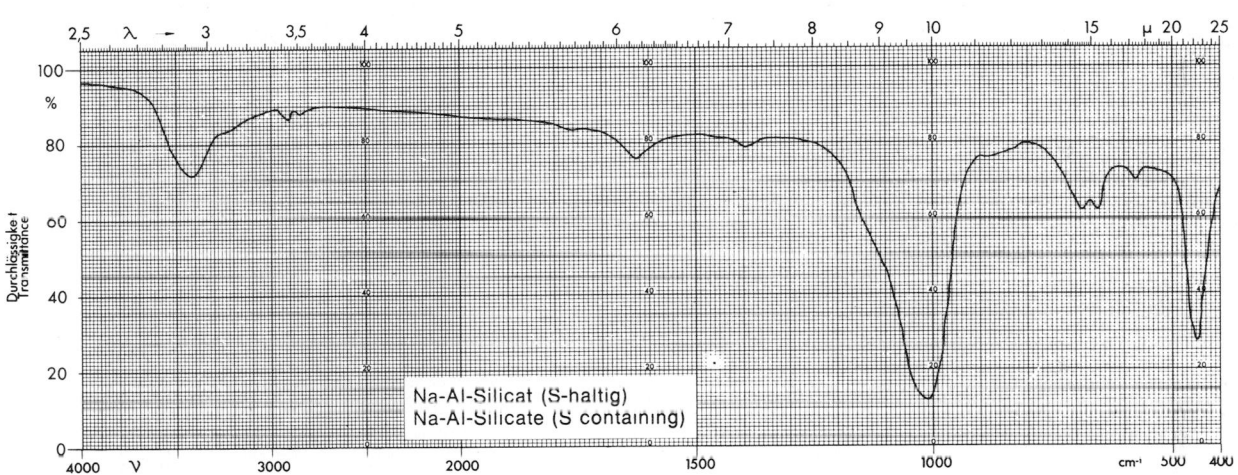

CI-Name: **Pigmentblau 29**   CI-No.: **77007**   CI-Name: **Pigment Blue 29**   CI-No.: **77007**   5479
Zusammen- **schwefelhaltiges Na-Al-Silikat**   Composition: **Sulfurous Na-Al-silicate**
setzung:
Handelsname: **Ultramarinblau 130** Herst.: **Siegle**   Tradename: **Ultramarinblau 130** Manuf.: **Siegle**
Präparation: **KBr (2/1000)**   Dez. Nr.: **6.1.2**   Preparation: **KBr (2/1000)**   Dec. No:. **6.1.2**

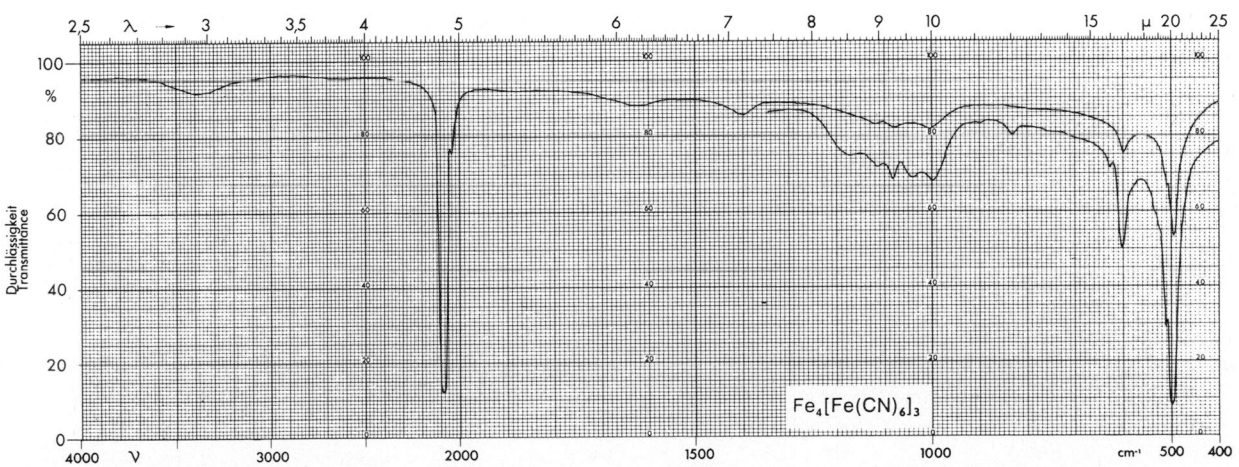

CI-Name: **Pigmentblau 27**   CI-No.: **77510**   CI-Name: **Pigment Blue 27**   CI-No.: **77510**   5480
Zusammen- **Ferri-ferrocyanid, Fe₄[Fe(CN)₆]₃**   Composition: **Ferric-ferrocyanide, Fe₄[Fe(CN)₆]₃**
setzung:
Handelsname: **Miloriblau R 28543** Herst.: **Siegle**   Tradename: **Miloriblau R 28543** Manuf.: **Siegle**
Präparation: **KBr (3/1000)**   Dez. Nr.: **6.1.3**   Preparation: **KBr (3/1000)**   Dec. No:. **6.1.3**

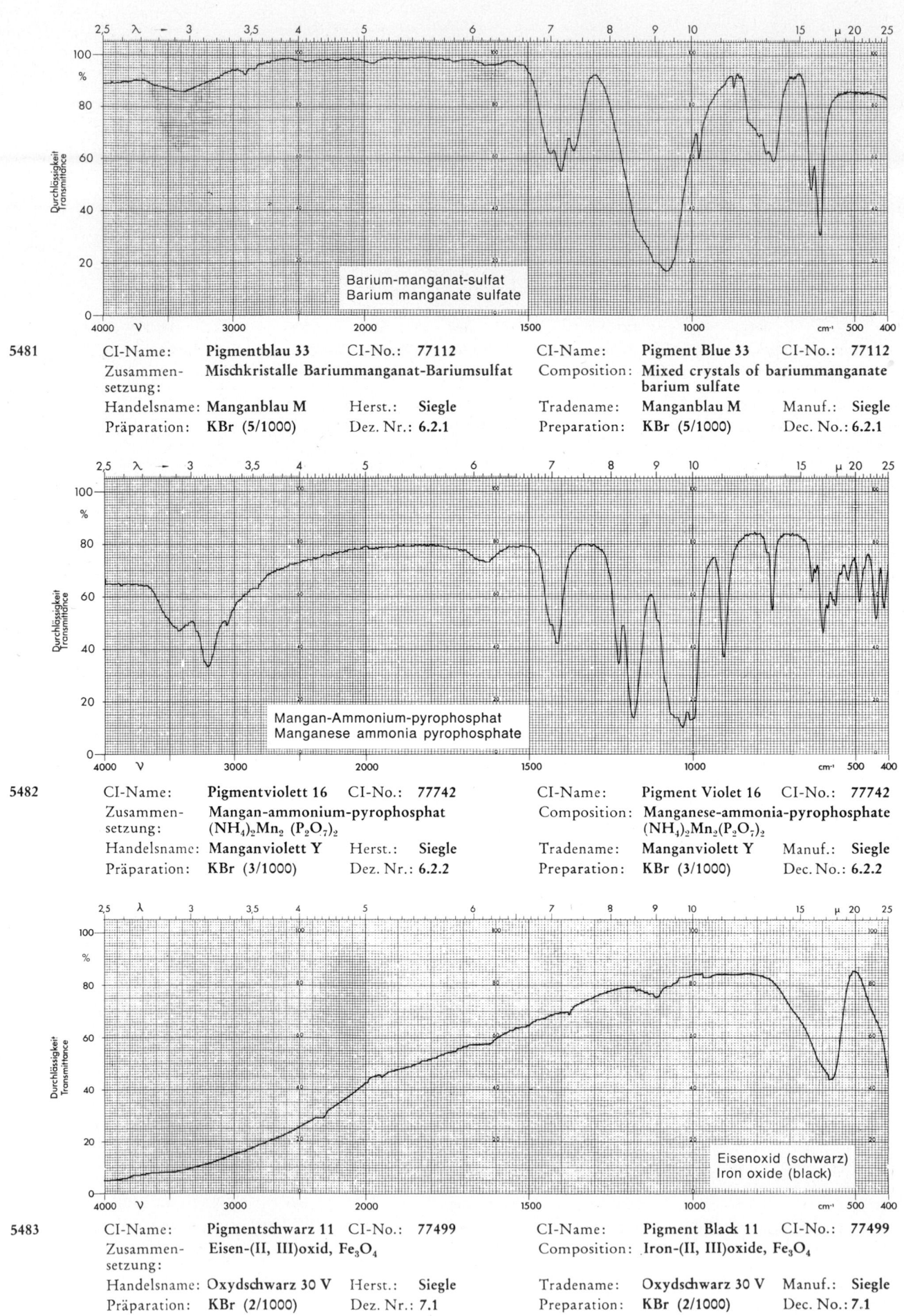

5481

CI-Name:	**Pigmentblau 33**	CI-No.: **77112**	CI-Name:	**Pigment Blue 33**	CI-No.: **77112**
Zusammen-setzung:	**Mischkristalle Bariummanganat-Bariumsulfat**		Composition:	**Mixed crystals of bariummanganate barium sulfate**	
Handelsname: **Manganblau M**		Herst.: **Siegle**	Tradename: **Manganblau M**		Manuf.: **Siegle**
Präparation: **KBr (5/1000)**		Dez. Nr.: **6.2.1**	Preparation: **KBr (5/1000)**		Dec. No.: **6.2.1**

5482

CI-Name:	**Pigmentviolett 16**	CI-No.: **77742**	CI-Name:	**Pigment Violet 16**	CI-No.: **77742**
Zusammen-setzung:	**Mangan-ammonium-pyrophosphat $(NH_4)_2Mn_2(P_2O_7)_2$**		Composition:	**Manganese-ammonia-pyrophosphate $(NH_4)_2Mn_2(P_2O_7)_2$**	
Handelsname: **Manganviolett Y**		Herst.: **Siegle**	Tradename: **Manganviolett Y**		Manuf.: **Siegle**
Präparation: **KBr (3/1000)**		Dez. Nr.: **6.2.2**	Preparation: **KBr (3/1000)**		Dec. No.: **6.2.2**

5483

CI-Name:	**Pigmentschwarz 11**	CI-No.: **77499**	CI-Name:	**Pigment Black 11**	CI-No.: **77499**
Zusammen-setzung:	**Eisen-(II, III)oxid, Fe_3O_4**		Composition:	**Iron-(II, III)oxide, Fe_3O_4**	
Handelsname: **Oxydschwarz 30 V**		Herst.: **Siegle**	Tradename: **Oxydschwarz 30 V**		Manuf.: **Siegle**
Präparation: **KBr (2/1000)**		Dez. Nr.: **7.1**	Preparation: **KBr (2/1000)**		Dec. No.: **7.1**

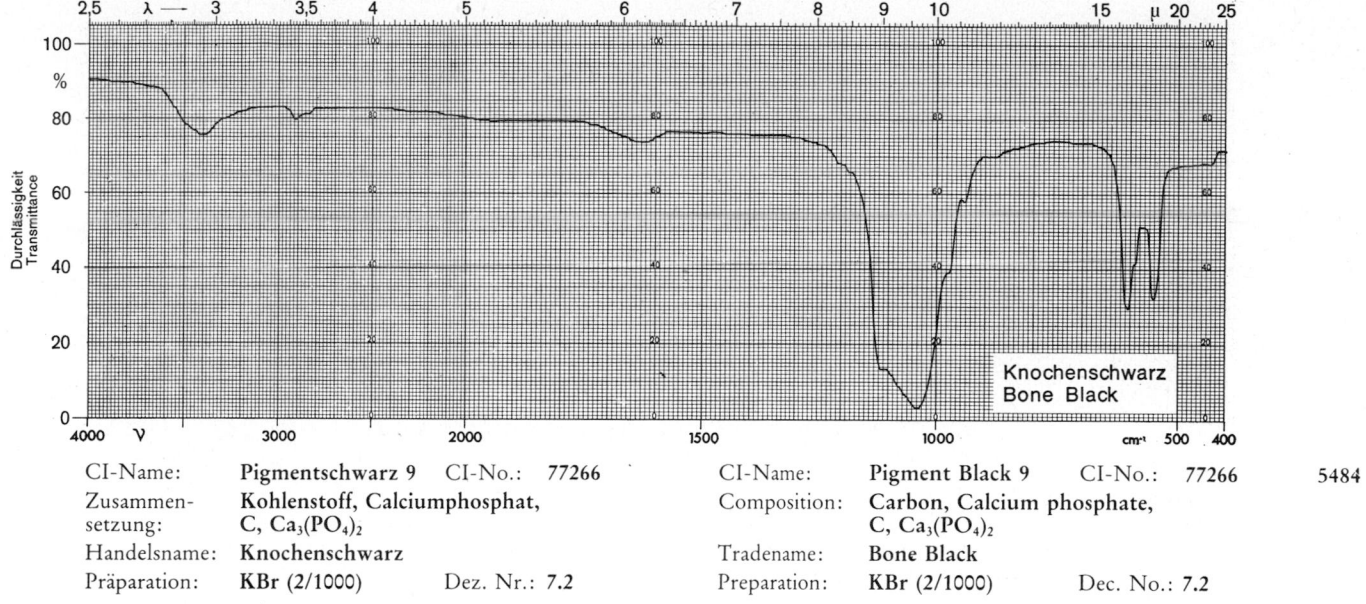

Knochenschwarz
Bone Black

CI-Name:	**Pigmentschwarz 9**	CI-No.: **77266**	CI-Name:	**Pigment Black 9**	CI-No.: **77266**
Zusammensetzung:	**Kohlenstoff, Calciumphosphat, C, Ca₃(PO₄)₂**		Composition:	**Carbon, Calcium phosphate, C, Ca₃(PO₄)₂**	
Handelsname:	**Knochenschwarz**		Tradename:	**Bone Black**	
Präparation:	**KBr (2/1000)**	Dez. Nr.: **7.2**	Preparation:	**KBr (2/1000)**	Dec. No.: **7.2**

CI-Name: **Pigmentschwarz 9** CI-No.: **77266**
Zusammensetzung: **Kohlenstoff, Calciumphosphat, C, Ca$_3$(PO$_4$)$_2$**
Handelsname: **Knochenschwarz**
Präparation: **KBr (2/1000)** Dez. Nr.: **7.2**

CI-Name: **Pigment Black 9** CI-No.: **77266**
Composition: **Carbon, Calcium phosphate, C, Ca$_3$(PO$_4$)$_2$**
Tradename: **Bone Black**
Preparation: **KBr (2/1000)** Dec. No.: **7.2**

5484

Organische Pigmente

Organic Pigments

Organische Pigmente
1. Monoazopigmente
1.1. KK Acetessigsäurearylide (ACES-arylide)

Organic Pigments
1. Monoazo Pigments
1.1. CC Acetoacetic-arylides (ACAA-arylides)

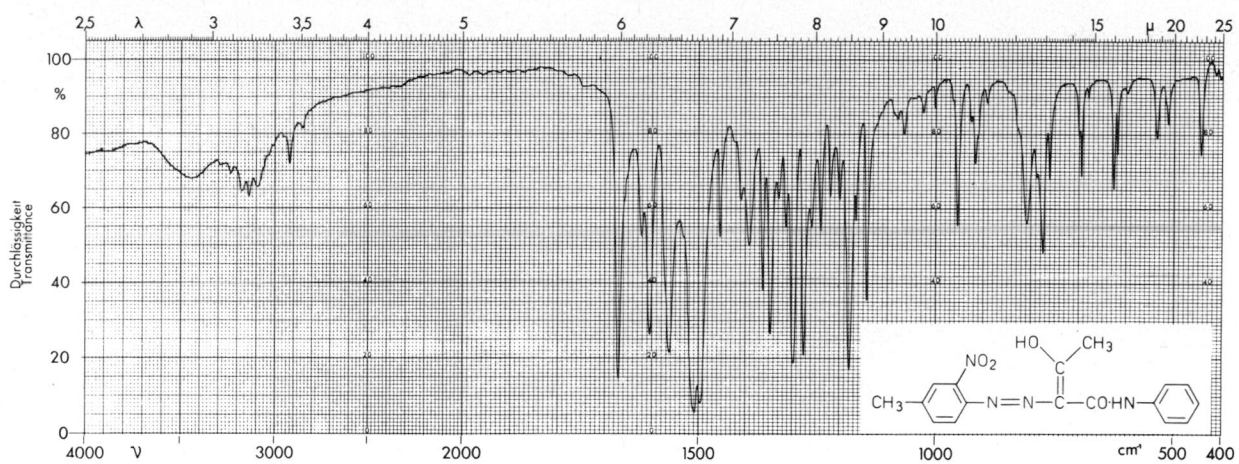

CI-Name: **Pigment Gelb 1**   CI-No.: **11680**
Zusammen-
setzung: **3-Nitro-4-toluidin → ACES-anilid**
Präparation: **KBr (1/1000)**   Dez. Nr.: **1.1.1**

CI-Name: **Pigment Yellow 1**   CI-No.: **11680**
Composition: **3-Nitro-4-toluidine → ACAA-anilide**
Preparation: **KBr (1/1000)**   Dec. No.: **1.1.1**

5500

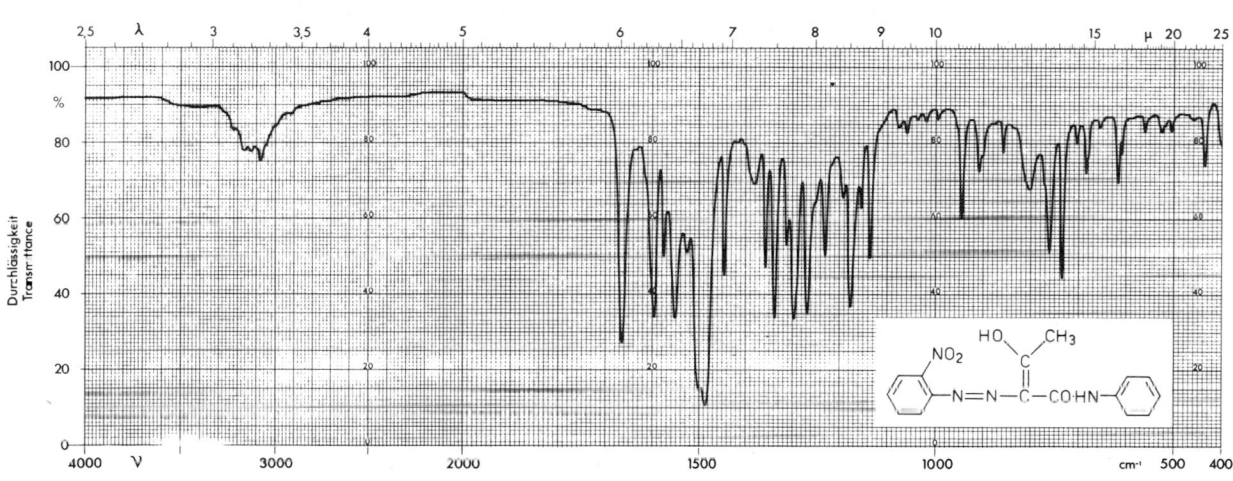

CI-Name: **Pigment Gelb 5**   CI-No.: **11660**
Zusammen-
setzung: **2-Nitroanilin → ACES-anilid**
Präparation: **KBr (2/1000)**   Dez. Nr.: **1.1.2**

CI-Name: **Pigment Yellow 5**   CI-No.: **11660**
Composition: **2-Nitroaniline → ACAA-anilide**
Preparation: **KBr (2/1000)**   Dec. No.: **1.1.2**

5501

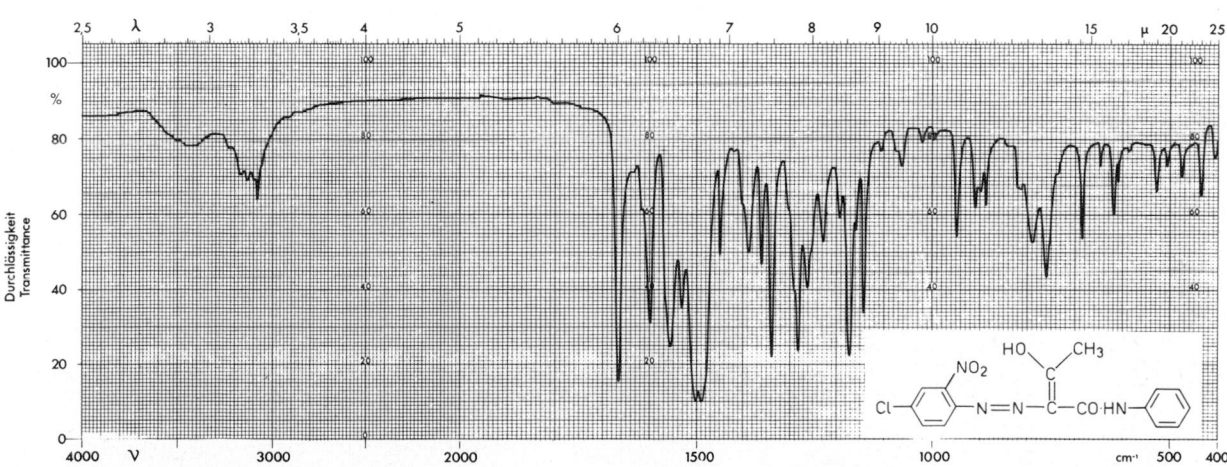

CI-Name: **Pigment Gelb 6**   CI-No.: **11670**
Zusammen-
setzung: **4-Chlor-2-nitroanilin → ACES-anilid**
Präparation: **KBr (2/1000)**   Dez. Nr.: **1.1.3**

CI-Name: **Pigment Yellow 6**   CI-No.: **11670**
Composition: **4-Chloro-2-nitroaniline → ACAA-anilide**
Preparation: **KBr (2/1000)**   Dec. No.: **1.1.3**

5502

Organische Pigmente
1. Monoazopigmente
1.1. KK Acetessigsäurearylide (ACES-arylide)

Organic Pigments
1. Monoazo Pigments
1.1. CC Acetoacetic-arylides (ACAA-arylides)

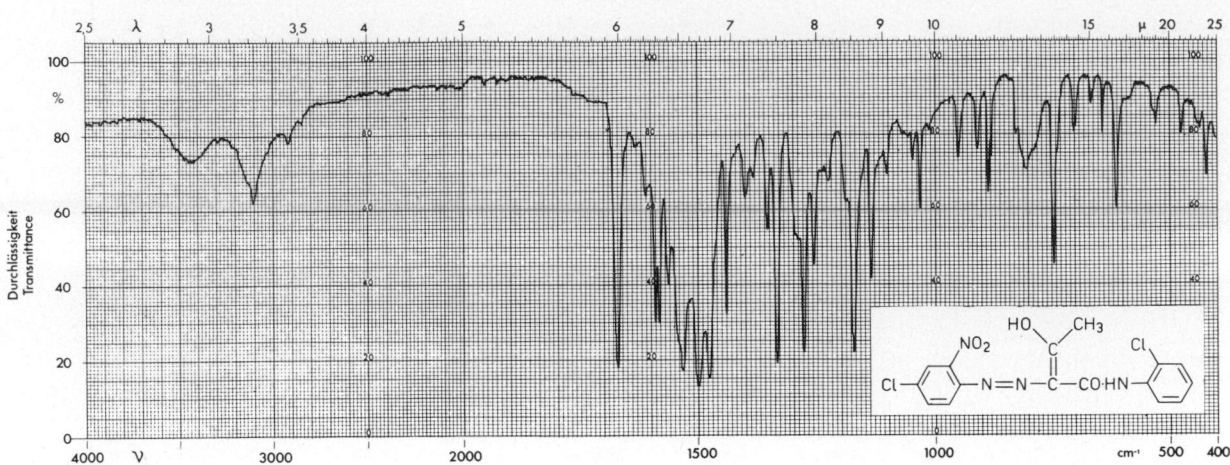

5503

CI-Name:	**Pigment Gelb 3** CI-No.: **11710**
Zusammensetzung:	**4-Chlor-2-nitroanilin → ACES-2-chloranilid**
Präparation:	**KBr (3/1000)** Dez. Nr.: **1.1.4**

CI-Name:	**Pigment Yellow 3** CI-No.: **11710**
Composition:	**4-Chloro-2-nitroaniline → ACAA-2-chloroanilide**
Preparation:	**KBr (3/1000)** Dec. No.: **1.1.4**

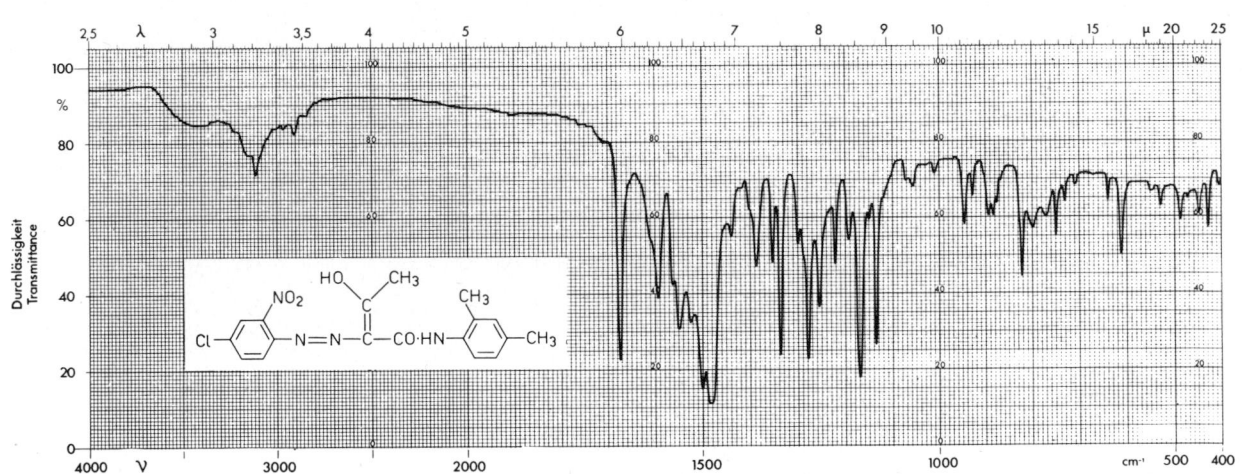

5504

CI-Name:	**Pigment Gelb 2** CI-No.: **11730**
Zusammensetzung:	**4-Chlor-2-nitroanilin → ACES-2,4-dimethylanilid**
Präparation:	**KBr (2/1000)** Dez. Nr.: **1.1.5**

CI-Name:	**Pigment Yellow 2** CI-No.: **11730**
Composition:	**4-Chloro-2-nitroaniline → ACAA-2,4-dimethylanilide**
Preparation:	**KBr (2/1000)** Dec. No.: **1.1.5**

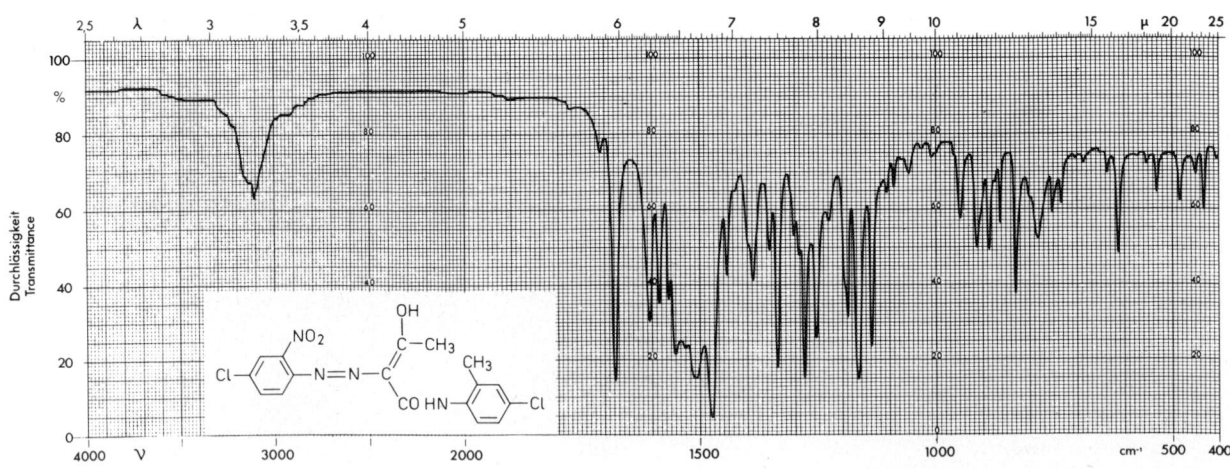

5505

CI-Name:	**Pigment Gelb 98** CI-No.: **11727**
Zusammensetzung:	**4-Chlor-2-nitroanilin → ACES-4-chlor-2-methylanilid**
Präparation:	**KBr (2/1000)** Dez. Nr.: **1.1.6**

CI-Name:	**Pigment Yellow 98** CI-No.: **11727**
Composition:	**4-Chloro-2-nitroaniline → ACAA-4-chloro-2-methylanilide**
Preparation:	**KBr (2/1000)** Dec. No.: **1.1.6**

Organische Pigmente
1. Monoazopigmente
1.1. KK Acetessigsäurearylide (ACES-arylide)

Organic Pigments
1. Monoazo Pigments
1.1. CC Acetoacetic-arylides (ACAA-arylides)

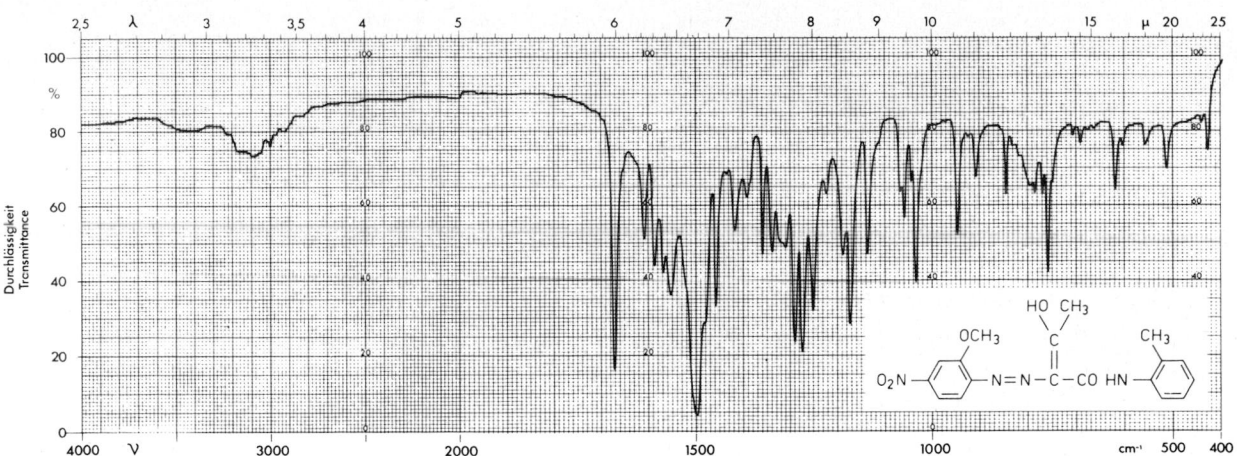

CI-Name: **Pigment Orange 1** CI-No.: **11725**
Zusammen-
setzung: **2-Methoxy-4-nitroanilin → ACES-
2-methylanilid**
Präparation: **KBr (2/1000)** Dez. Nr.: **1.1.7**

CI-Name: **Pigment Orange 1** CI-No.: **11725**
Composition: **2-Methoxy-4-nitroaniline → ACAA-
2-methylanilide**
Preparation: **KBr (2/1000)** Dec. No.: **1.1.7**

5506

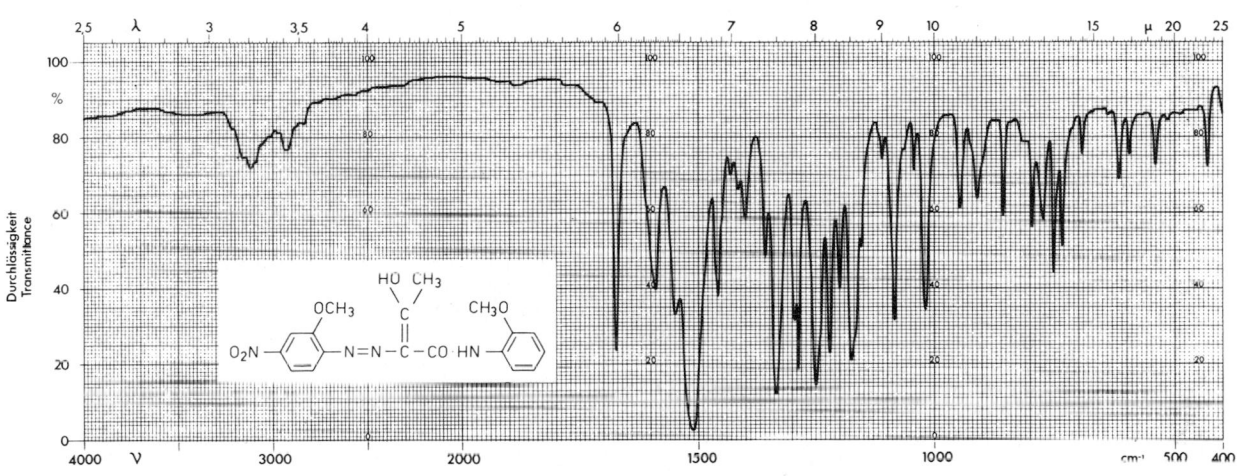

CI-Name: **Pigment Gelb 74**
Zusammen-
setzung: **2-Methoxy-4-nitroanilin → ACES-
2-methoxyanilid**
Präparation: **KBr (2/1000)** Dez. Nr.: **1.1.8**

CI-Name: **Pigment Yellow 74**
Composition: **2-Methoxy-4-nitroaniline → ACAA-
2-methoxyanilide**
Preparation: **KBr (2/1000)** Dec. No.: **1.1.8**

5507

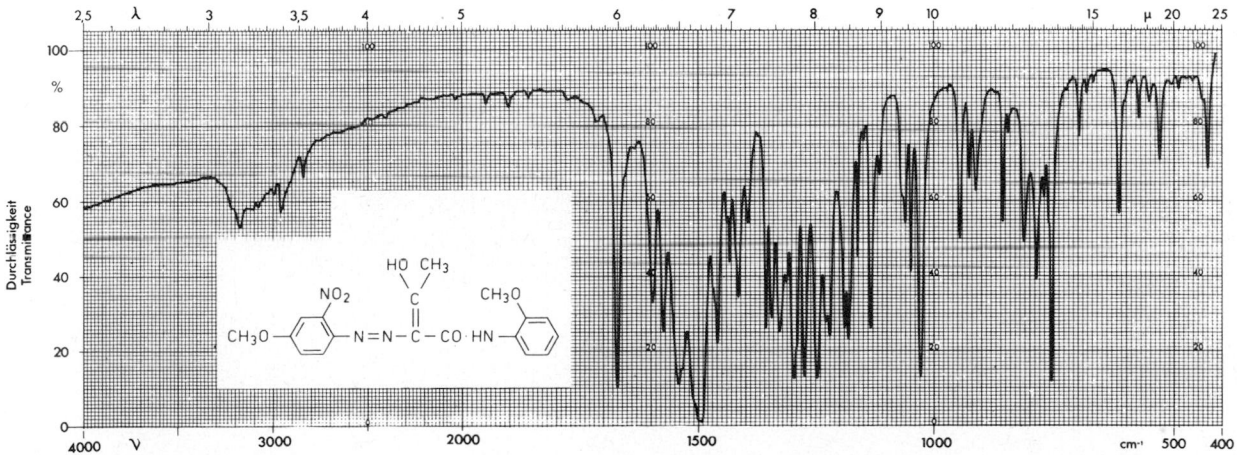

CI-Name: **Pigment Gelb 65** CI-No.: **11740**
Zusammen-
setzung: **4-Methoxy-2-nitroanilin → ACES-
2-methoxyanilid**
Präparation: **KBr (2/1000)** Dez. Nr.: **1.1.9**

CI-Name: **Pigment Yellow 65** CI-No.: **11740**
Composition: **4-Methoxy-2-nitroaniline → ACAA-
2-methoxyanilide**
Preparation: **KBr (2/1000)** Dec. No.: **1.1.9**

5508

Organische Pigmente
1. Monoazopigmente
1.1. KK Acetessigsäurearylide (ACES-arylide)

Organic Pigments
1. Monoazo Pigments
1.1. CC Acetoacetic-arylides (ACAA-arylides)

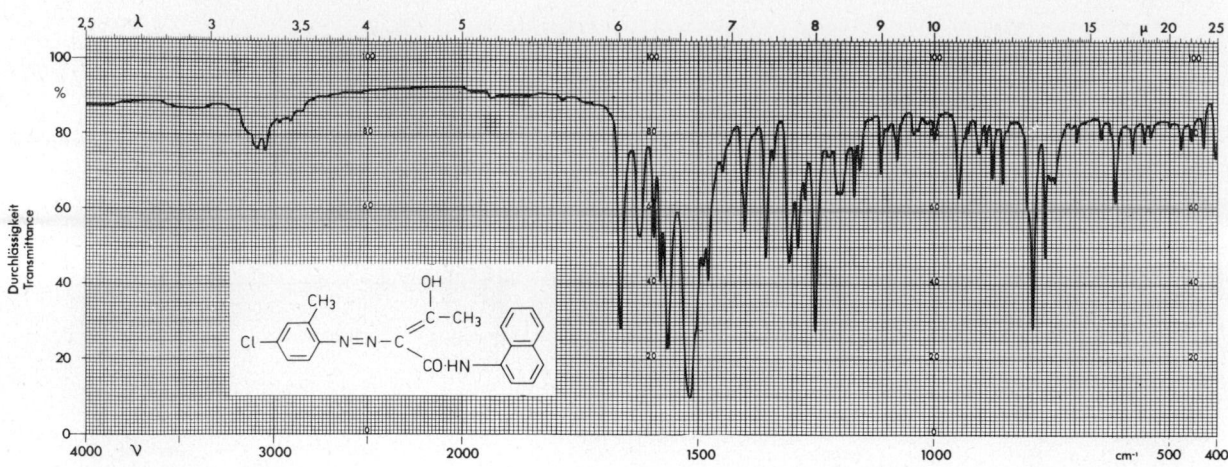

5509

CI-Name:	Pigment Gelb 25
Zusammensetzung:	4-Chlor-2-toluidin → ACES-1-naphthylamid
Präparation:	KBr (2/1000) Dez. Nr.: 1.1.10

CI-Name:	Pigment Yellow 25
Composition:	4-Chloro-2-toluidine → ACAA-1-naphthylamide
Preparation:	KBr (2/1000) Dec. No.: 1.1.10

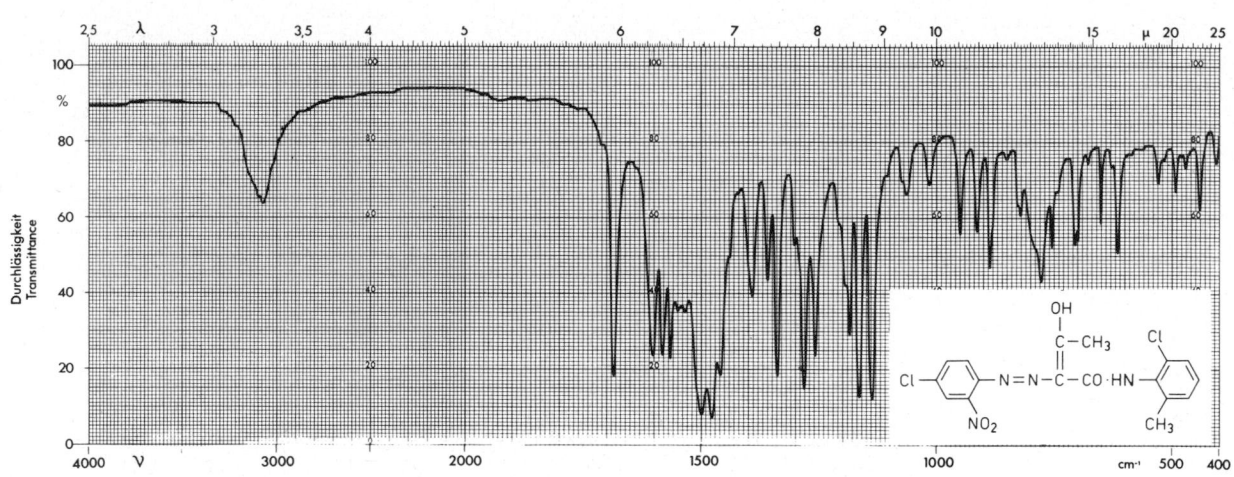

5510

CI-Name:	Pigment Gelb 82
Zusammensetzung:	4-Chlor-2-nitroanilin → ACES-6-chlor-2-methylanilin
Präparation:	KBr (2/1000) Dez. Nr.: 1.1.11

CI-Name:	Pigment Yellow 82
Composition:	4-Chloro-2-nitroaniline → ACAA-6-chloro-2-methylaniline
Preparation:	KBr (2/1000) Dec. No.: 1.1.11

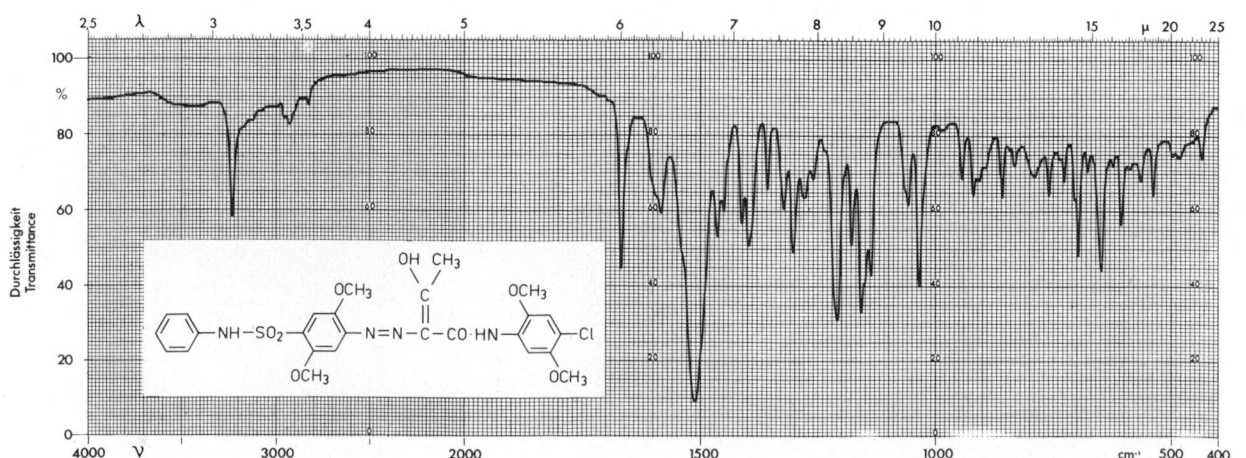

5511

CI-Name:	Pigment Gelb 97 CI-No.: 11767
Zusammensetzung:	2,5-Dimethoxy-4-N-phenyl-sulfonamido-anilin → ACES-4-chlor-2,5-dimethoxyanilid
Präparation:	KBr (2/1000) Dez. Nr.: 1.1.12

CI-Name:	Pigment Yellow 97 CI-No.: 11767
Composition:	2,5-Dimethoxy-4-N-phenyl-sulfonamido-aniline→ACAA-4-chloro-2,5-dimethoxy-anilide
Preparation:	KBr (2/1000) Dec. No.: 1.1.12

Organische Pigmente
1. Monoazopigmente
1.1. KK Acetessigsäurearylide (ACES-arylide)

Organic Pigments
1. Monoazo Pigments
1.1. CC Acetoacetic-arylides (ACAA-arylides)

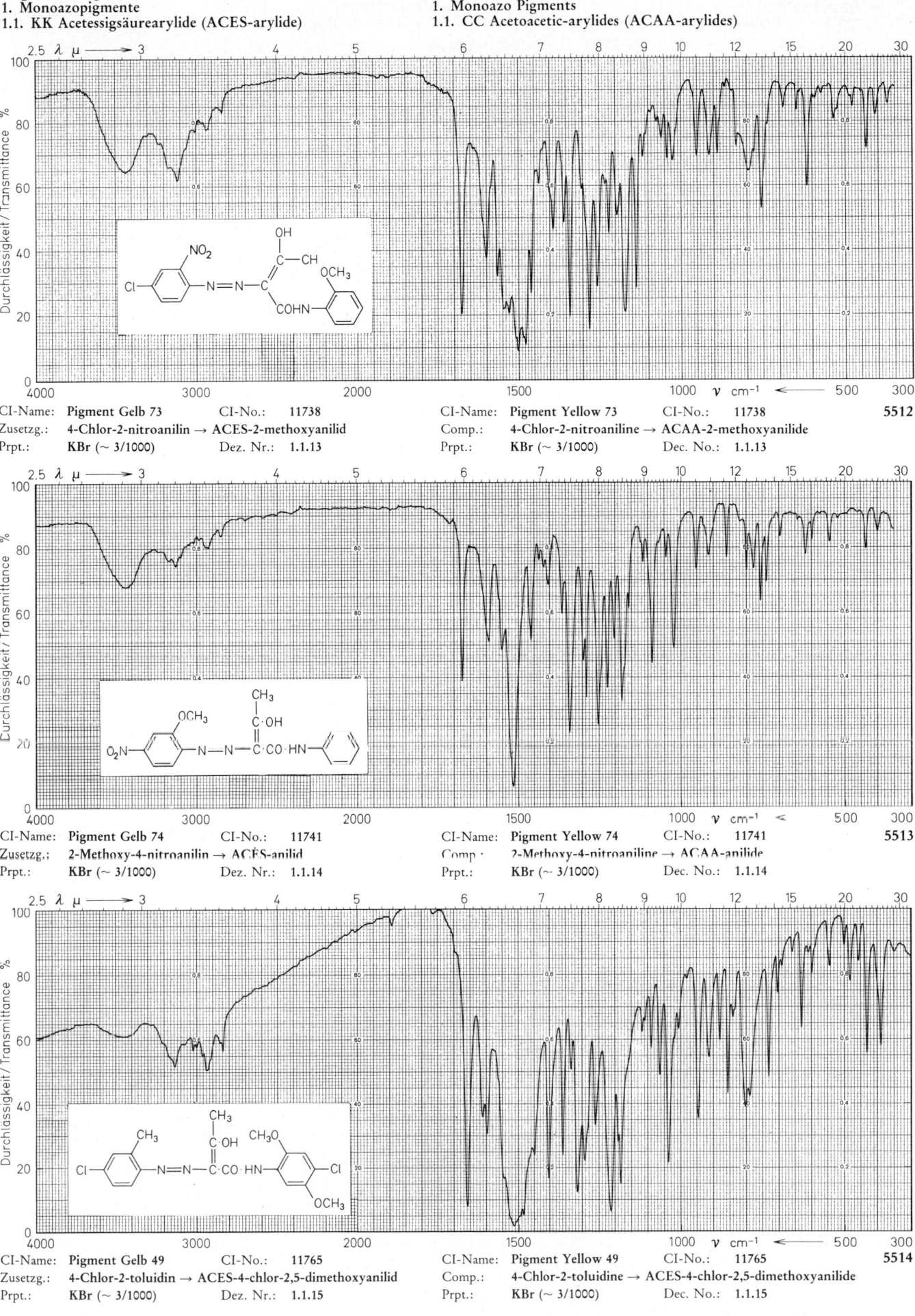

CI-Name: **Pigment Gelb 73** CI-No.: **11738**
Zusetzg.: **4-Chlor-2-nitroanilin → ACES-2-methoxyanilid**
Prpt.: **KBr (~ 3/1000)** Dez. Nr.: **1.1.13**

CI-Name: **Pigment Yellow 73** CI-No.: **11738** **5512**
Comp.: **4-Chlor-2-nitroaniline → ACAA-2-methoxyanilide**
Prpt.: **KBr (~ 3/1000)** Dec. No.: **1.1.13**

CI-Name: **Pigment Gelb 74** CI-No.: **11741**
Zusetzg.: **2-Methoxy-4-nitroanilin → ACES-anilid**
Prpt.: **KBr (~ 3/1000)** Dez. Nr.: **1.1.14**

CI-Name: **Pigment Yellow 74** CI-No.: **11741** **5513**
Comp.: **2-Methoxy-4-nitroaniline → ACAA-anilide**
Prpt.: **KBr (~ 3/1000)** Dec. No.: **1.1.14**

CI-Name: **Pigment Gelb 49** CI-No.: **11765**
Zusetzg.: **4-Chlor-2-toluidin → ACES-4-chlor-2,5-dimethoxyanilid**
Prpt.: **KBr (~ 3/1000)** Dez. Nr.: **1.1.15**

CI-Name: **Pigment Yellow 49** CI-No.: **11765** **5514**
Comp.: **4-Chlor-2-toluidine → ACES-4-chlor-2,5-dimethoxyanilide**
Prpt.: **KBr (~ 3/1000)** Dec. No.: **1.1.15**

Organische Pigmente
1. Monoazopigmente
1.2. KK β-Oxynaphtholsäurearylide (BONS-arylide)

Organic Pigments
1. Monoazo Pigments
1.2. CC β-Hydroxynaphthoic-arylides (BHNA-arylides)

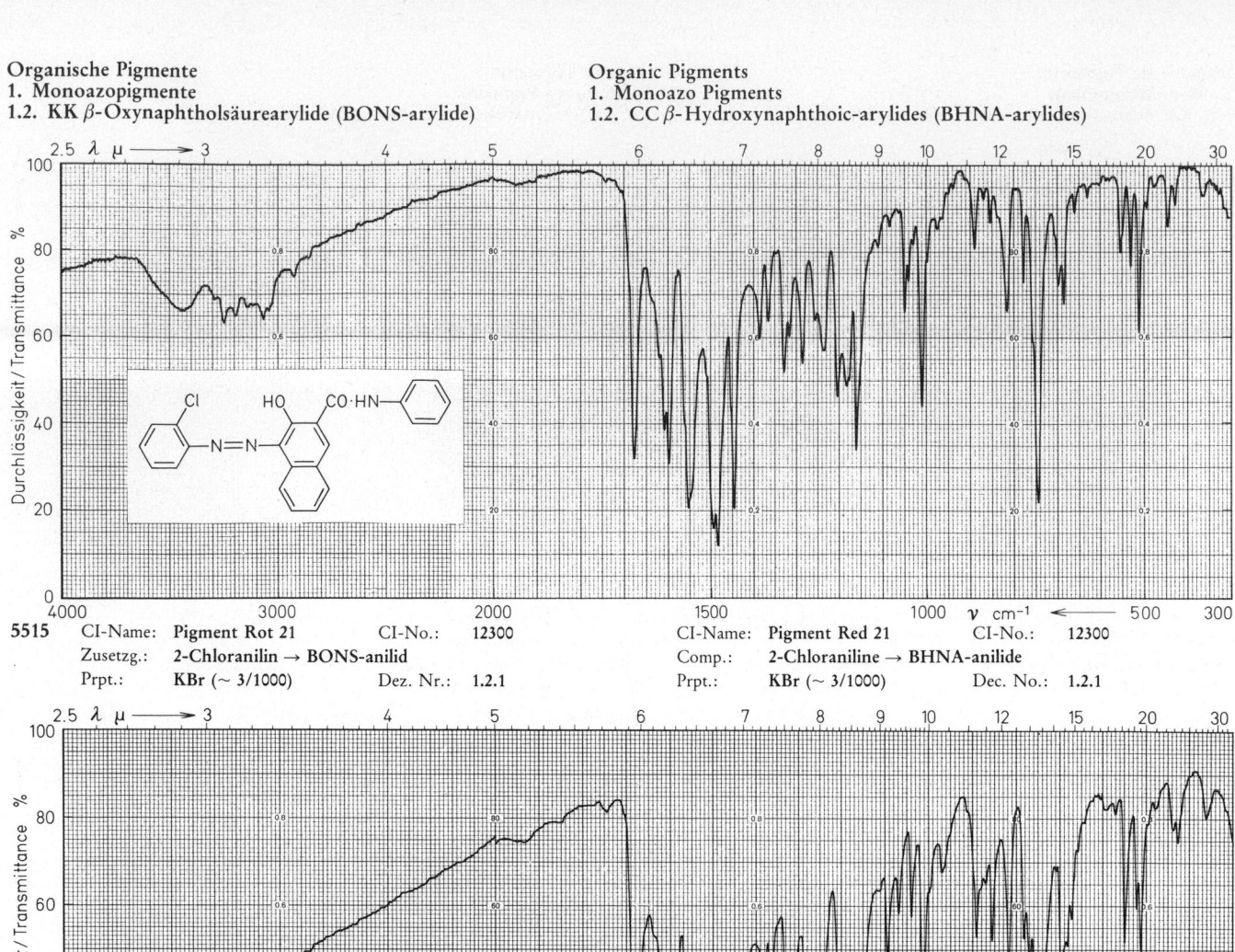

5515 CI-Name: **Pigment Rot 21**   CI-No.: **12300**   CI-Name: **Pigment Red 21**   CI-No.: **12300**

Zusetzg.: **2-Chloranilin → BONS-anilid**   Comp.: **2-Chloraniline → BHNA-anilide**

Prpt.: **KBr (~ 3/1000)**   Dez. Nr.: **1.2.1**   Prpt.: **KBr (~ 3/1000)**   Dec. No.: **1.2.1**

Pigment Orange 24

5516 CI-Name: **Pigment Orange 24**   CI-No.: **12365**   CI-Name: **Pigment Orange 24**   CI-No.: **12365**

Zusetzg.: **3-Chloranilin → BONS-anilid**   Comp.: **3-Chloraniline → BHNA-anilide**

Prpt.: **KBr (~ 3/1000)**   Dez. Nr.: **1.2.2**   Prpt.: **KBr (~ 3/1000)**   Dec. No.: **1.2.2**

Organische Pigmente
1. Monoazopigmente
1.2. KK β-Oxynaphtholsäurearylide (BONS-arylide)

Organic Pigments
1. Monoazo Pigments
1.2. CC β-Hydroxynaphthoic-arylides (BHNA-arylides)

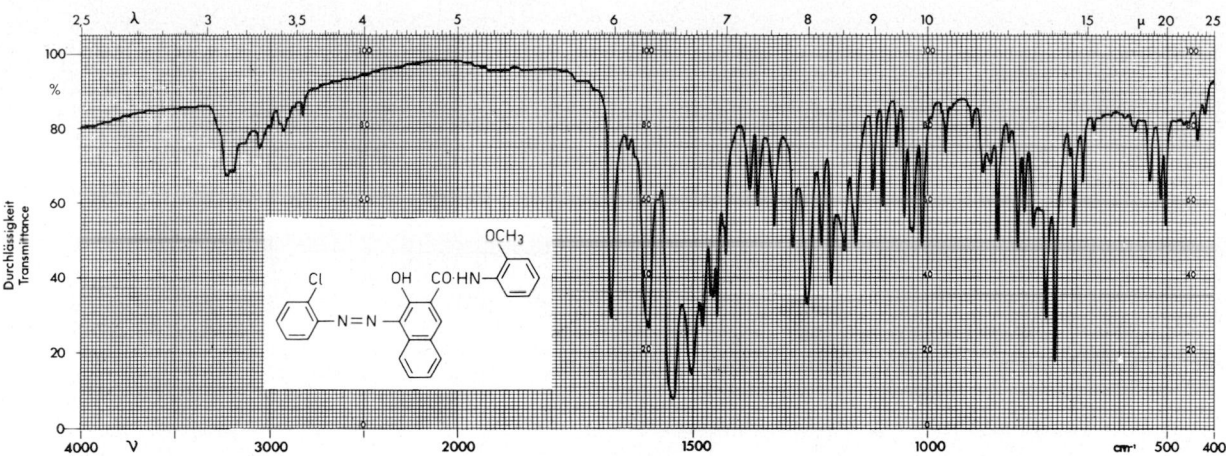

CI-Name:	CI-Name: 5517
Pigment Orange 4	Pigment Orange 4
Zusammen-setzung: 2-Chloranilin → BONS-2-methoxyanilid	Composition: 2-Chloroaniline → BHNA-2-methoxy-anilide
Präparation: KBr (2/1000) Dez.Nr.: 1.2.3	Preparation: KBr (2/1000) Dec.No.: 1.2.3

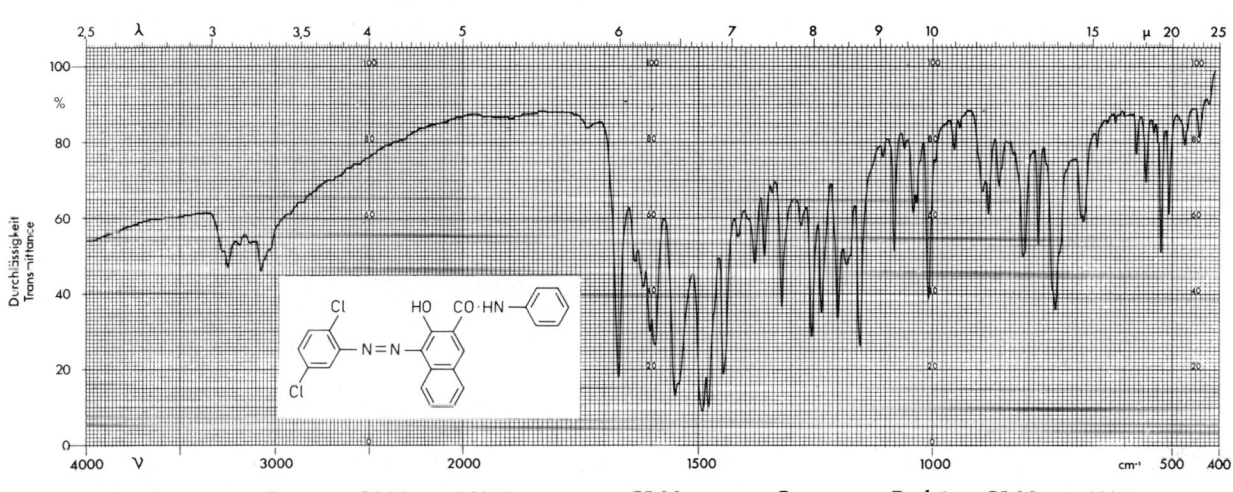

CI Name: Permanent Rot 2 CI-No.: 12310	CI-Name: Permanent Red 2 CI-No.: 12310 5518
Zusammen setzung: 2,5 Dichloranilin → BONS-anilid	Composition: 2,5-Dichloroaniline → BHNA-anilide
Präparation: KBr (2/1000) Dez.Nr.: 1.2.4	Preparation: KBr (2/1000) Dec.No.: 1.2.4

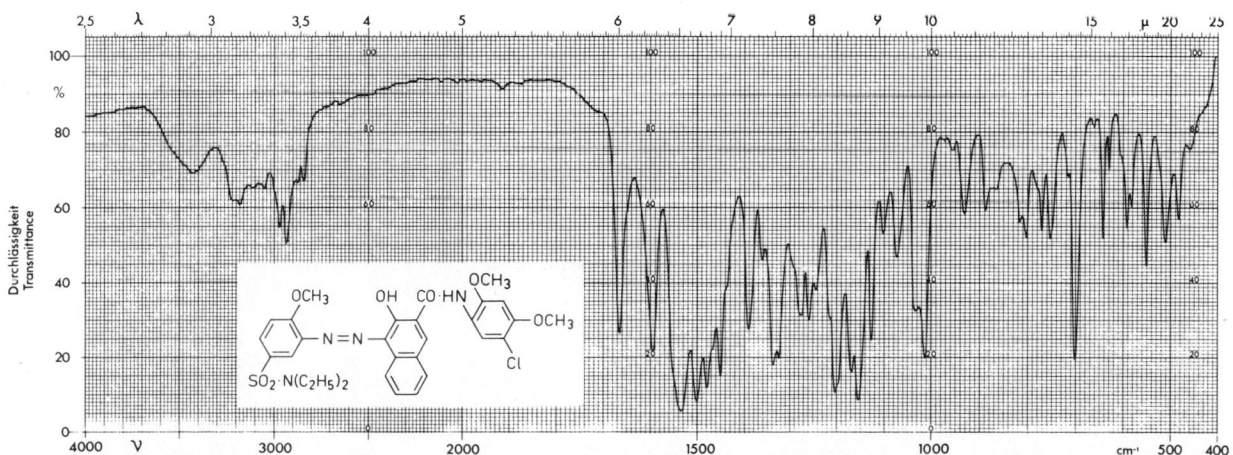

CI-Name: Pigment Rot 5 CI-No.: 12490	CI-Name: Pigment Red 5 CI-No.: 12490 5519
Zusammen-setzung: 2-Methoxy-5-N,N-dimethyl-sulfonamido-anilin → BONS-5-chlor-2,4-dimethoxyanilid	Composition: 2-Methoxy-5-N,N-dimethyl-sulfonamido aniline → BHNA-5-chloro-2,4-dimethoxy-anilide
Präparation: KBr (3/1000) Dez.Nr.: 1.2.5	Preparation: KBr (3/1000) Dec.No.: 1.2.5

Organische Pigmente
1. Monoazopigmente
1.2. KK β-Oxynaphtholsäurearylide (BONS-arylide)

Organic Pigments
1. Monoazo Pigments
1.2. CC β-Hydroxynaphthoic-arylides (BHNA-arylides)

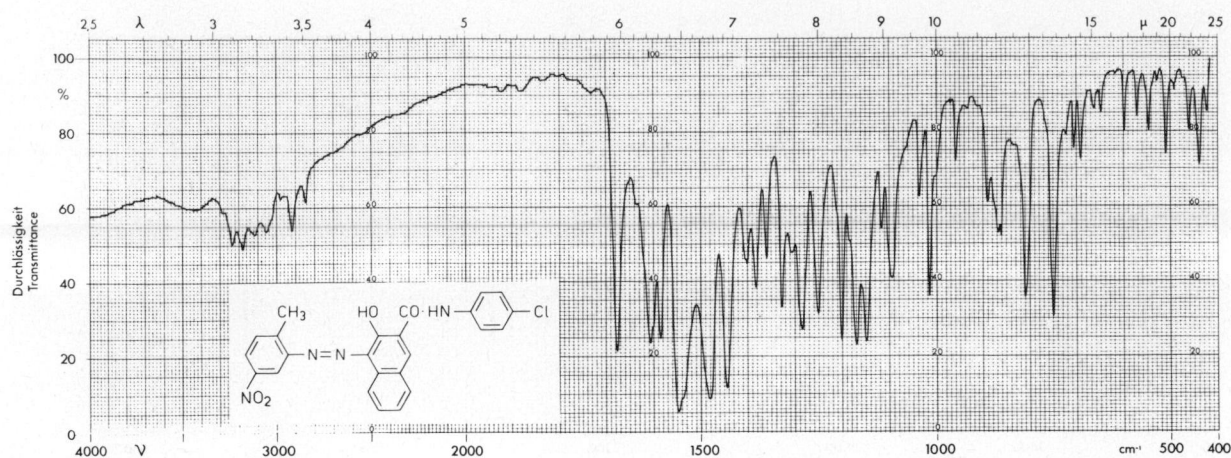

5520

CI-Name:	**Pigment Rot 7**	CI-No.:	**12420**
Zusammensetzung:	4-Chlor-2-toluidin → BONS-4-chlor-2-methylanilid		
Präparation:	**KBr (4/1000)**	Dez. Nr.:	**1.2.6**

CI-Name:	**Pigment Red 7**	CI-No.:	**12420**
Composition:	4-Chloro-2-toluidine → BHNA-4-chloro-2-methylanilide		
Preparation:	**KBr (4/1000)**	Dec. No.:	**1.2.6**

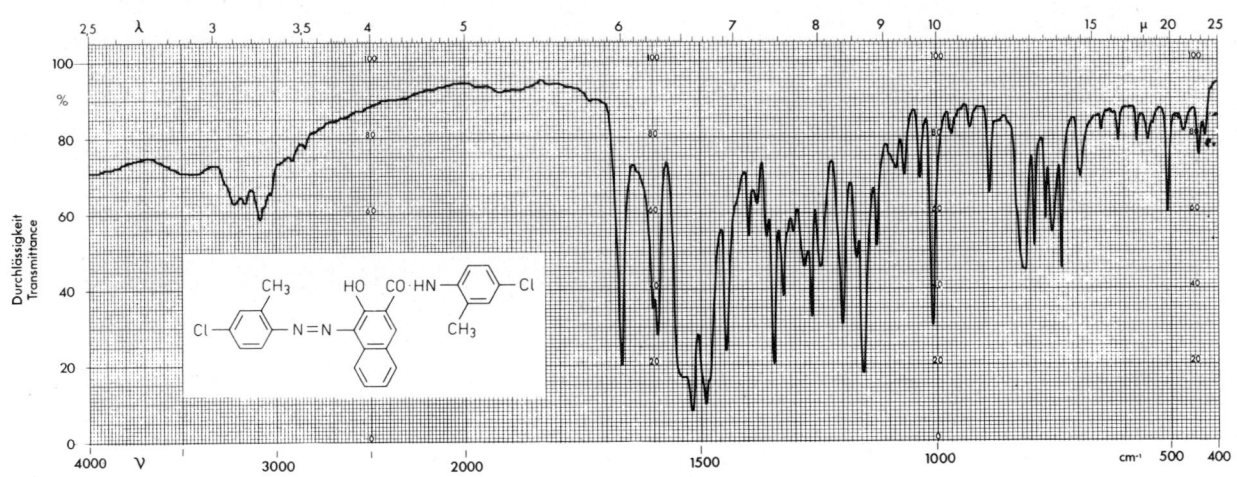

5521

CI-Name:	**Pigment Rot 8**	CI-No.:	**12335**
Zusammensetzung:	5-Nitro-2-toluidin → BONS-4-chloranilid		
Präparation:	**KBr (3,5/1000)**	Dez. Nr.:	**1.2.7**

CI-Name:	**Pigment Red 8**	CI-No.:	**12335**
Composition:	5-Nitro-2-toluidine → BHNA-4-chloro-anilide		
Preparation:	**KBr (3,5/1000)**	Dec. No.:	**1.2.7**

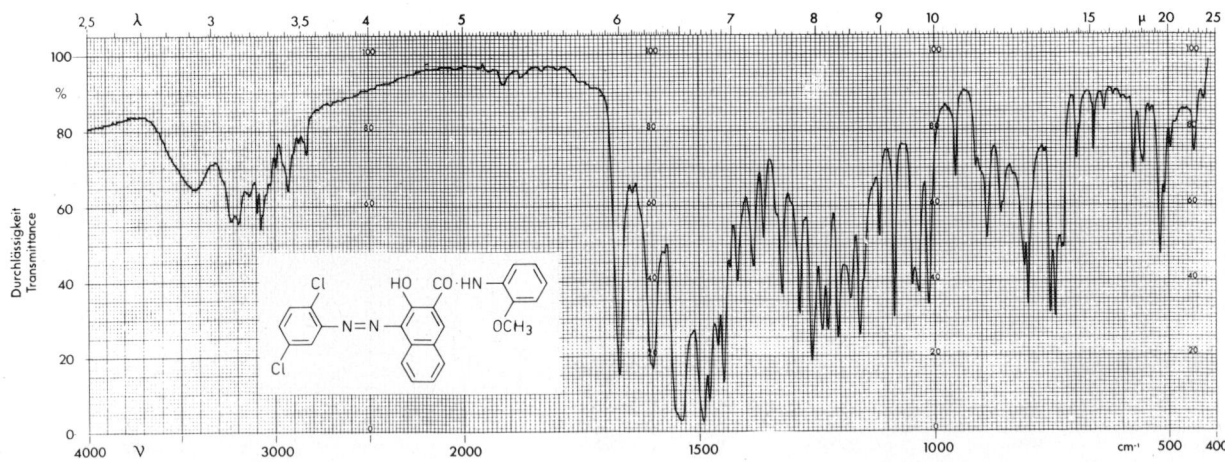

5522

CI-Name:	**Pigment Rot 9**		
Zusammensetzung:	2,5-Dichloranilin → BHNA-2-methoxy-anilid		
Präparation:	**KBr (3,5/1000)**	Dez. Nr.:	**1.2.8**

CI-Name:	**Pigment Red 9**		
Composition:	2,5-Dichloroaniline → BHNA-2-methoxy-anilide		
Preparation:	**KBr (3,5/1000)**	Dec. No.:	**1.2.8**

Organische Pigmente
1. Monoazopigmente
1.2. KK β-Oxynaphtholsäurearylide (BONS-arylide)

Organic Pigments
1. Monoazo Pigments
1.2. CC β-Hydroxynaphthoic-arylides (BHNA-arylides)

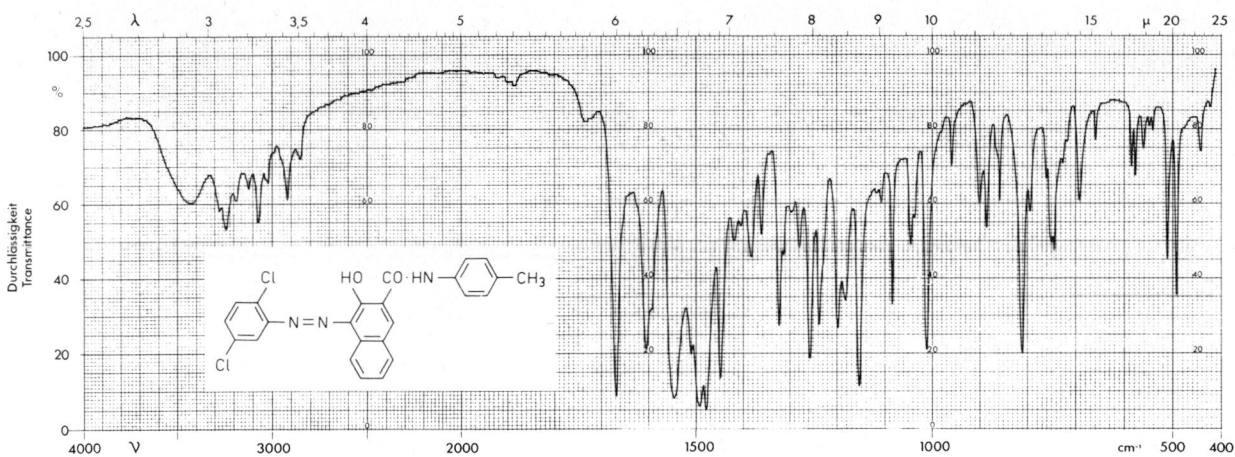

CI-Name: **Pigment Rot 10**   CI-No.: **12440**
Zusammensetzung: **2,5-Dichloranilin → BONS-4-methylanilid**
Präparation: **KBr (3,5/1000)**   Dez. Nr.: **1.2.9**

CI-Name: **Pigment Red 10**   CI-No.: **12440**
Composition: **2,5-Dichloroaniline → BHNA-4-methyl-anilide**
Preparation: **KBr (3,5/1000)**   Dec. No.: **1.2.9**

5523

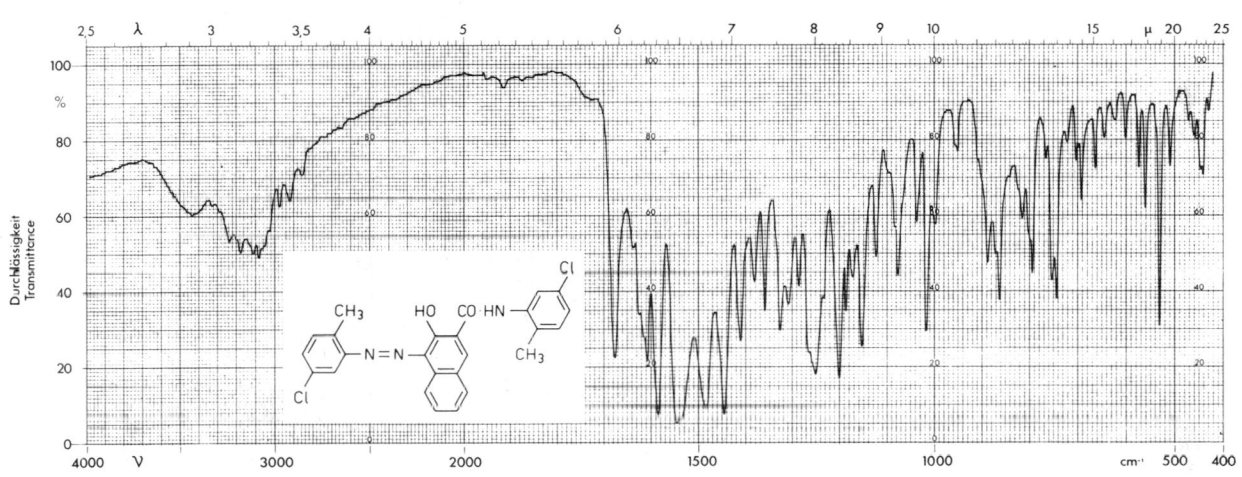

CI-Name: **Pigment Rot 11**   CI-No.: **12430**
Zusammensetzung: **5-Chlor-2-toluidin → BONS-5-chlor-2-methylanilid**
Präparation: **KBr (3,5/1000)**   Dez. Nr.: **1.2.10**

CI-Name: **Pigment Red 11**   CI-No.: **12430**
Composition: **5-Chloro-2-toluidine → BHNA-5-chloro-2-methylanilide**
Preparation: **KBr (3,5/1000)**   Dec. No.: **1.2.10**

5524

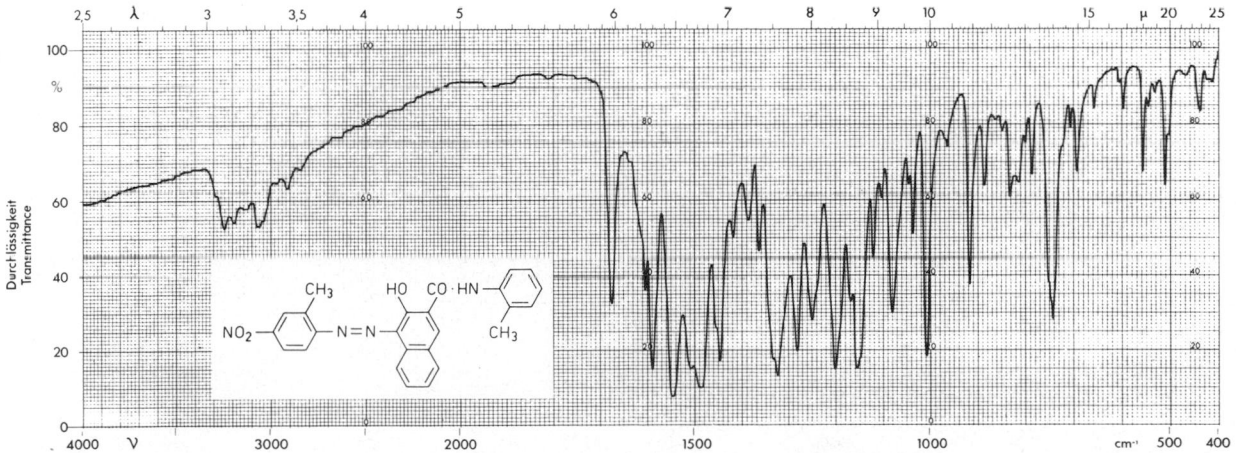

CI-Name: **Pigment Rot 12**   CI-No.: **12385**
Zusammensetzung: **4-Nitro-2-toluidin → BONS-2-methylanilid**
Präparation: **KBr (3,5/1000)**   Dez. Nr.: **1.2.11**

CI-Name: **Pigment Red 12**   CI-No.: **12385**
Composition: **4-Nitro-2-toluidine → BHNA-2-methyl-anilide**
Preparation: **KBr (3,5/1000)**   Dec. No.: **1.2.11**

5525

Organische Pigmente
1. Monoazopigmente
1.2. KK β-Oxynaphtholsäurearylide (BONS-arylide)

Organic Pigments
1. Monoazo Pigments
1.2. CC β-Hydroxynaphthoic-arylides (BHNA-arylides)

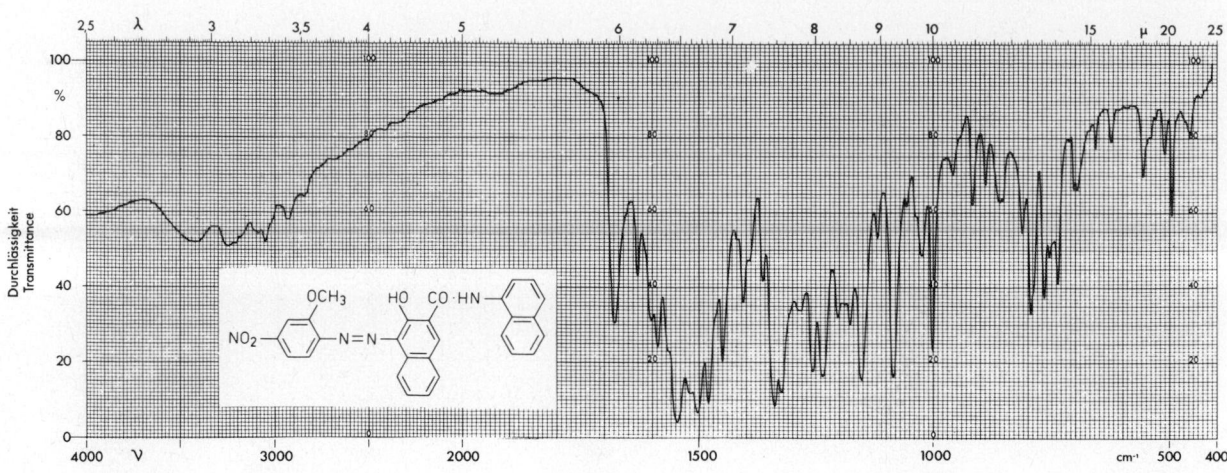

5526

CI-Name:	**Pigment Rot 16**	CI-No.:	**12500**
Zusammen-setzung:	**2-Methoxy-4-nitroanilin → BONS-1-naphthylamid**		
Präparation:	**KBr (3,5/1000)**	Dez. Nr.:	**1.2.12**

CI-Name:	**Pigment Red 16**	CI-No.:	**12500**
Composition:	**2-Methoxy-4-nitroaniline →BHNA-1-naphthylamide**		
Preparation:	**KBr (3,5/1000)**	Dec. No.:	**1.2.12**

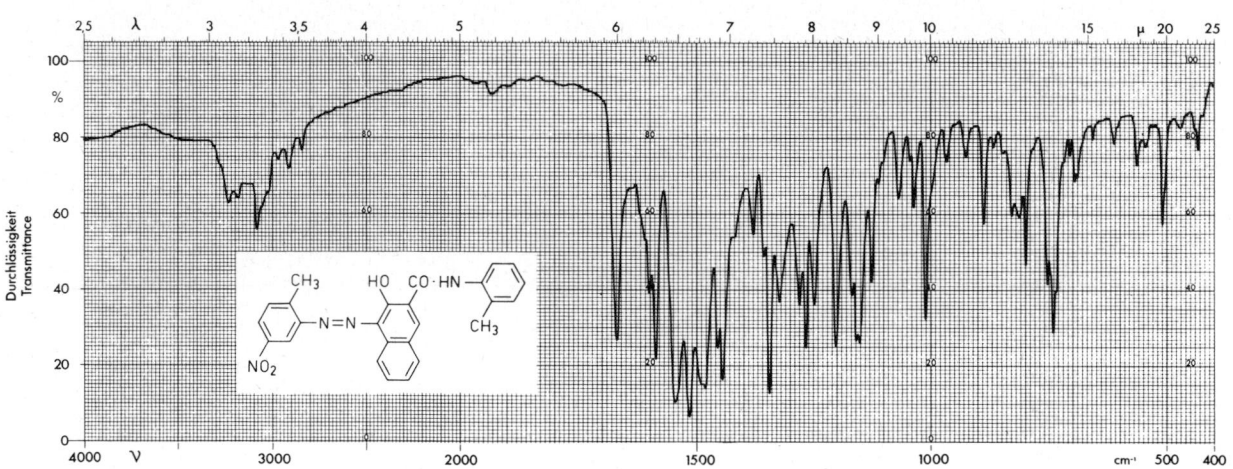

5527

CI-Name:	**Pigment Rot 17**	CI-No.:	**12390**
Zusammen-setzung:	**5-Nitro-2-toluidin → BONS-2-methylanilid**		
Präparation:	**KBr (3,5/1000)**	Dez. Nr.:	**1.2.13**

CI-Name:	**Pigment Red 17**	CI-No.:	**12390**
Composition:	**5-Nitro-2-toluidine → BHNA-2-methyl-anilide**		
Preparation:	**KBr (3,5/1000)**	Dec. No.:	**1.2.13**

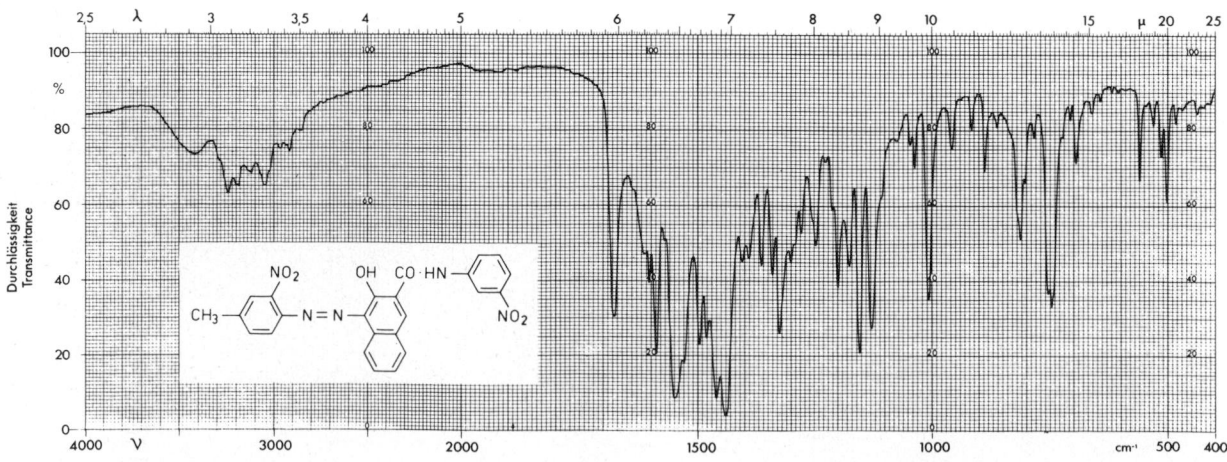

5528

CI-Name:	**Pigment Rot 18**	CI-No.:	**12350**
Zusammen-setzung:	**2-Nitro-4-toluidin → BONS-3-nitroanilid**		
Präparation:	**KBr (3,5/1000)**	Dez. Nr.:	**1.2.14**

CI-Name:	**Pigment Red 18**	CI-No.:	**12350**
Composition:	**2-Nitro-4-toluidine → BHNA-3-nitro-anilide**		
Preparation:	**KBr (3,5/1000)**	Dec. No.:	**1.2.14**

Organische Pigmente
1. Monoazopigmente
1.2. KK β-Oxynaphtolsäurearylide

Organic Pigments
1. Monoazo Pigments
1.2. CC β-Hydroxynaphtoic-arylides

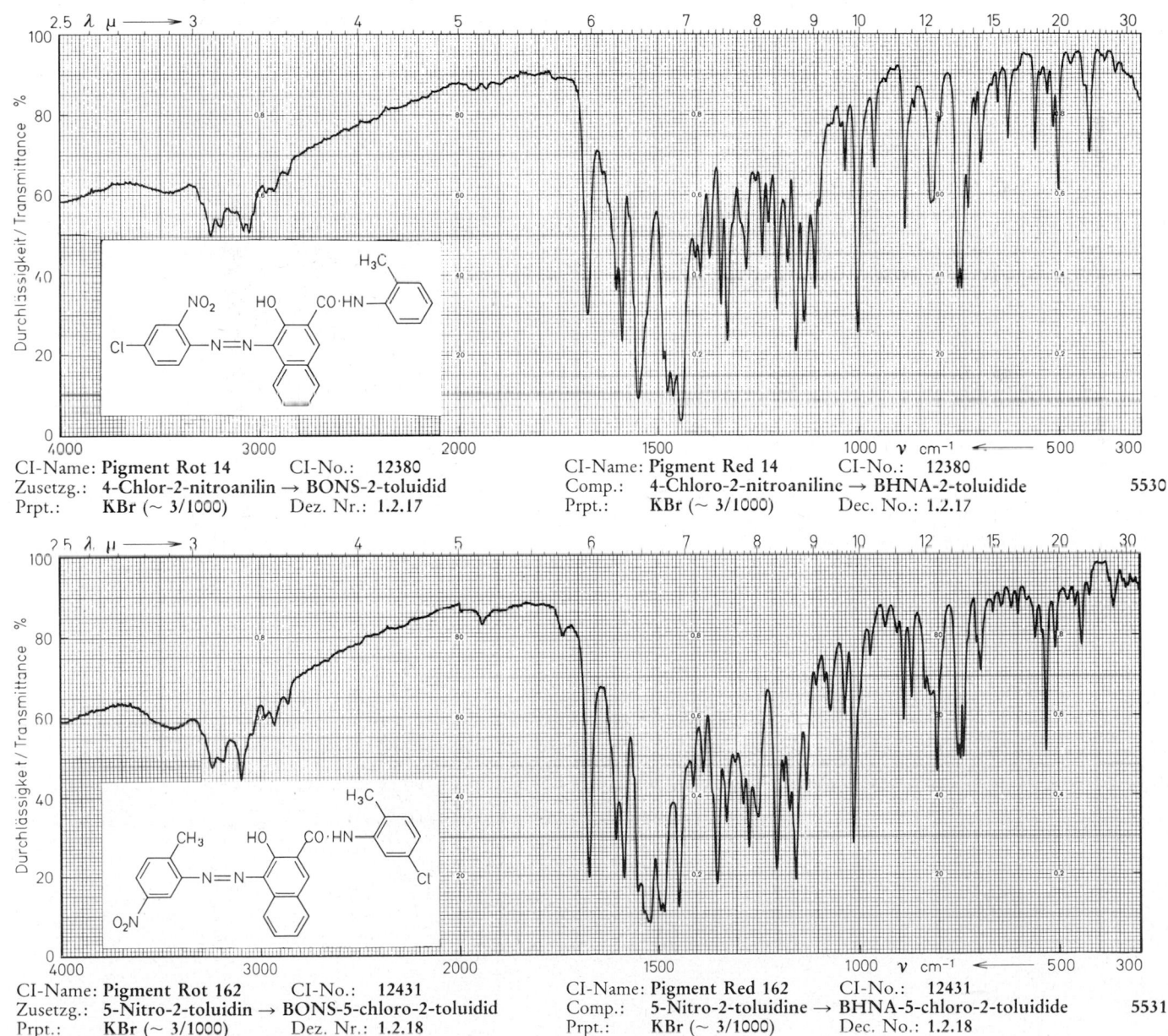

CI-Name: **Pigment Rot 14**   CI-No.: **12380**
Zusetzg.: **4-Chlor-2-nitroanilin → BONS-2-toluidid**
Prpt.: **KBr** (~ 3/1000)   Dez. Nr.: **1.2.17**

CI-Name: **Pigment Red 14**   CI-No.: **12380**
Comp.: **4-Chloro-2-nitroaniline → BHNA-2-toluidide**
Prpt.: **KBr** (~ 3/1000)   Dec. No.: **1.2.17**

5530

CI-Name: **Pigment Rot 162**   CI-No.: **12431**
Zusetzg.: **5-Nitro-2-toluidin → BONS-5-chloro-2-toluidid**
Prpt.: **KBr** (~ 3/1000)   Dez. Nr.: **1.2.18**

CI-Name: **Pigment Red 162**   CI-No.: **12431**
Comp.: **5-Nitro-2-toluidine → BHNA-5-chloro-2-toluidide**
Prpt.: **KBr** (~ 3/1000)   Dec. No.: **1.2.18**

5531

Sp. No. 5529: Während der Herstellung eliminiert – during production eliminated

Organische Pigmente
1. Monoazopigmente
1.2. KK β-Oxynaphtholsäurearylide (BONS-arylide)

Organic Pigments
1. Monoazo Pigments
1.2. CC β-Hydroxynaphthoic-arylides (BHNA-arylides)

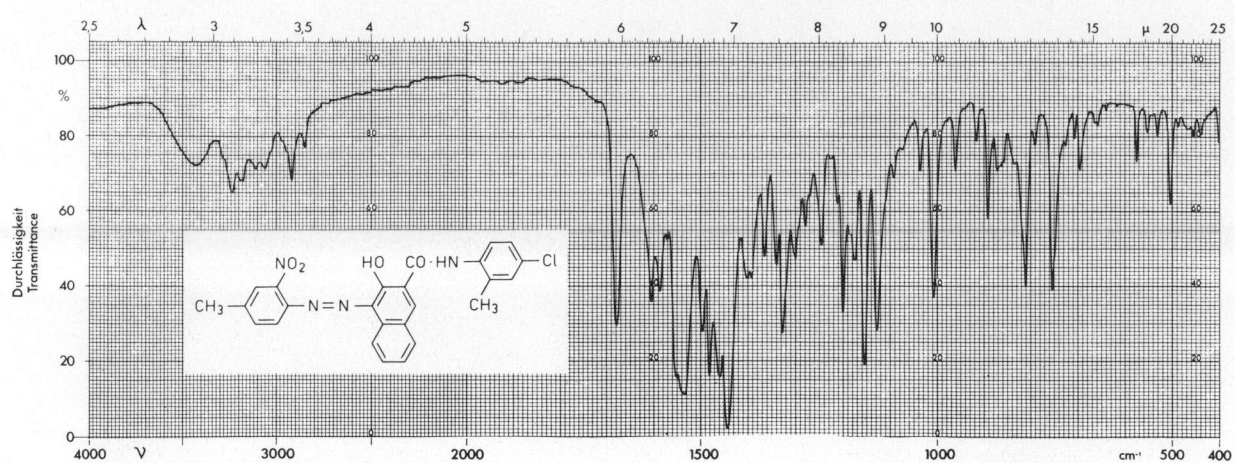

5532

Name:	**Sico Echtmaroon BMD**	Name:	**Sico Maroon BMD**
Zusammensetzung:	**2-Nitro-4-toluidin → BONS-4-chlor-2-methylanilid**	Composition:	**2-Nitro-4-toluidine → BHNA-4-chloro-2-methylanilide**
Präparation:	**KBr (3,5/1000)** Dez. Nr.: **1.2.15**	Preparation:	**KBr (3,5/1000)** Dec. No.: **1.2.15**

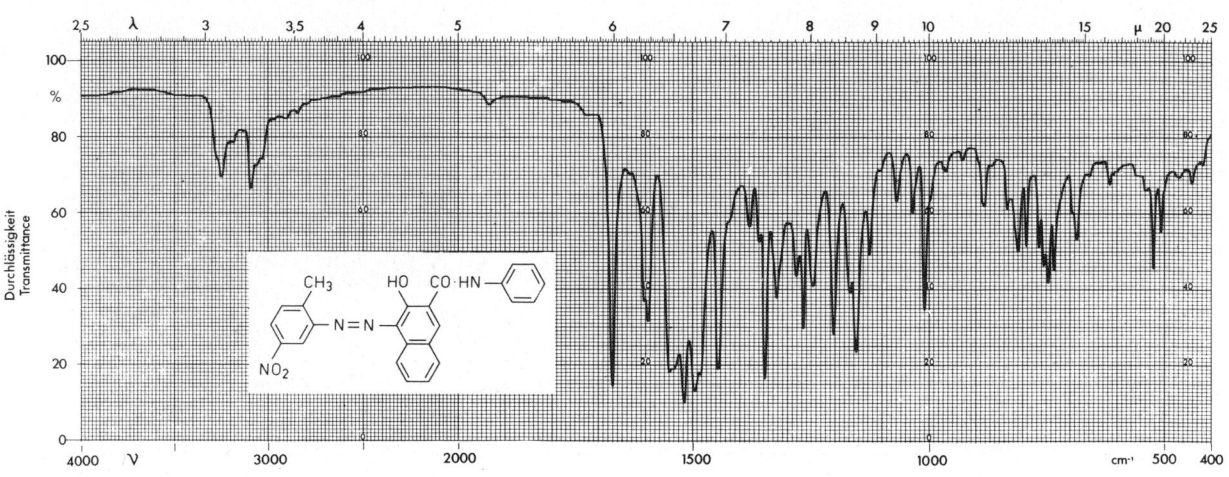

5533

CI-Name:	**Pigment Rot 22** CI-No.: **12315**	CI-Name:	**Pigment Red 22** CI-No.: **12315**
Zusammensetzung:	**5-Nitro-2-toluidin → BONS-anilid**	Composition:	**5-Nitro-2-toluidine → BHNA-anilide**
Präparation:	**KBr (3,5/1000)** Dez. Nr.: **1.2.19**	Preparation:	**KBr (3,5/1000)** Dec. No.: **1.2.19**

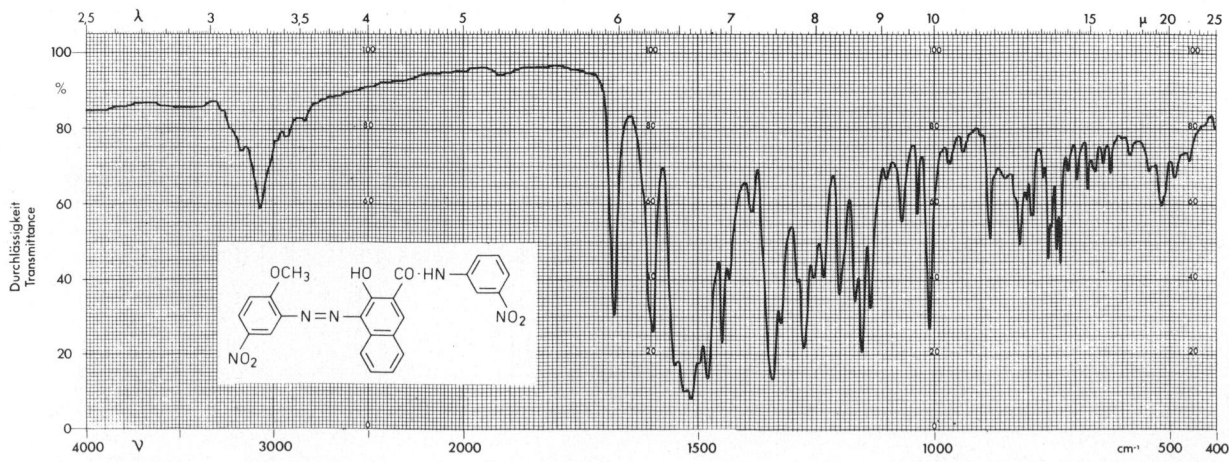

5534

CI-Name:	**Pigment Rot 23** CI-No.: **12355**	CI-Name:	**Pigment Red 23** CI-No.: **12355**
Zusammensetzung:	**2-Methoxy-5-nitroanilin → BONS-3-nitro-anilid**	Composition:	**2-Methoxy-5-nitroaniline → BHNA-3-nitroanilide**
Präparation:	**KBr (3,5/1000)** Dez. Nr.: **1.2.20**	Preparation:	**KBr (3,5/1000)** Dec. No.: **1.2.20**

Organische Pigmente
1. Monoazopigmente
1.2. KK β-Oxynaphtholsäurearylide (BONS-arylide)

Organic Pigments
1. Monoazo Pigments
1.2. CC β-Hydroxynaphthoic-arylides (BHNA-arylides)

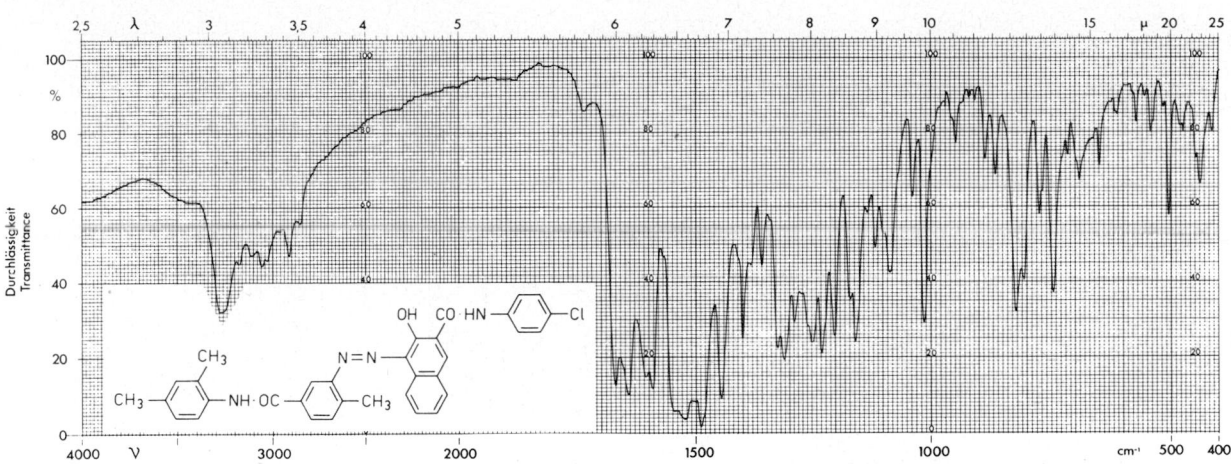

| CI-Name: | Pigment Rot 30 | CI-No.: | 12330 | | CI-Name: | Pigment Red 30 | CI-No.: | 12330 | 5535 |

CI-Name: **Pigment Rot 30** CI-No.: **12330**
Zusammensetzung: **3-Amino-4-methyl-N-(2',4'-xylyl)-benzamid → BONS-4-chloranilid**
Präparation: **KBr (3,5/1000)** Dez. Nr.: **1.2.21**

CI-Name: **Pigment Red 30** CI-No.: **12330**
Composition: **3-Amino-4-methyl-N-(2',4'-xylyl) benzamide → BHNA-4-chloroanilide**
Preparation: **KBr (3,5/1000)** Dec. No.: **1.2.21**

5535

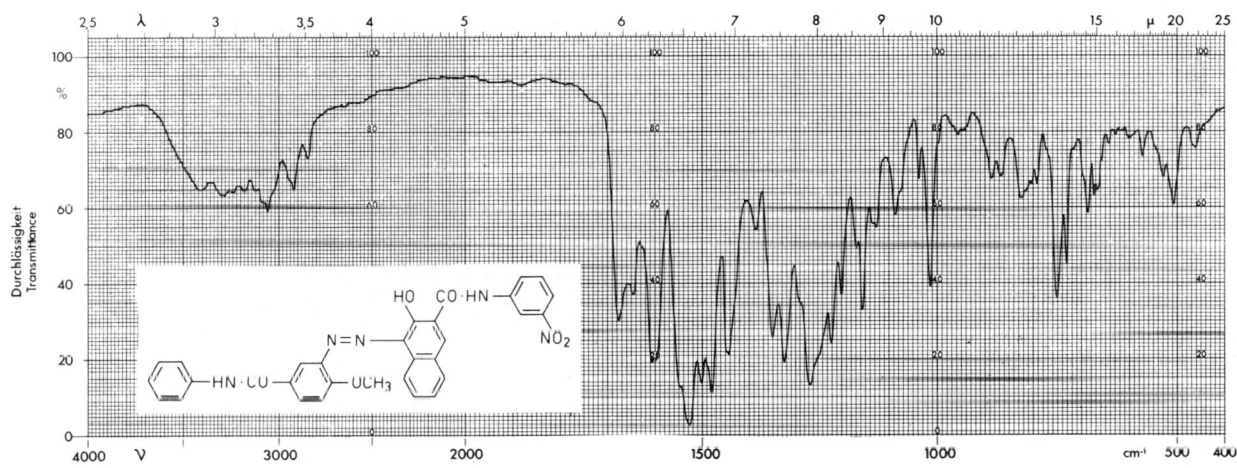

CI-Name: **Pigment Rot 31** CI-No.: **12360**
Zusammensetzung: **3-Amino-4-methoxybenzanilid → BONS-3-nitroanilid**
Präparation: **KBr (3,5/1000)** Dez. Nr.: **1.2.22**

CI-Name: **Pigment Red 31** CI-No.: **12360**
Composition: **3-Amino-4-methoxybenzanilide → BHNA-3-nitroanilide**
Preparation: **KBr (3,5/1000)** Dec. No.: **1.2.22**

5536

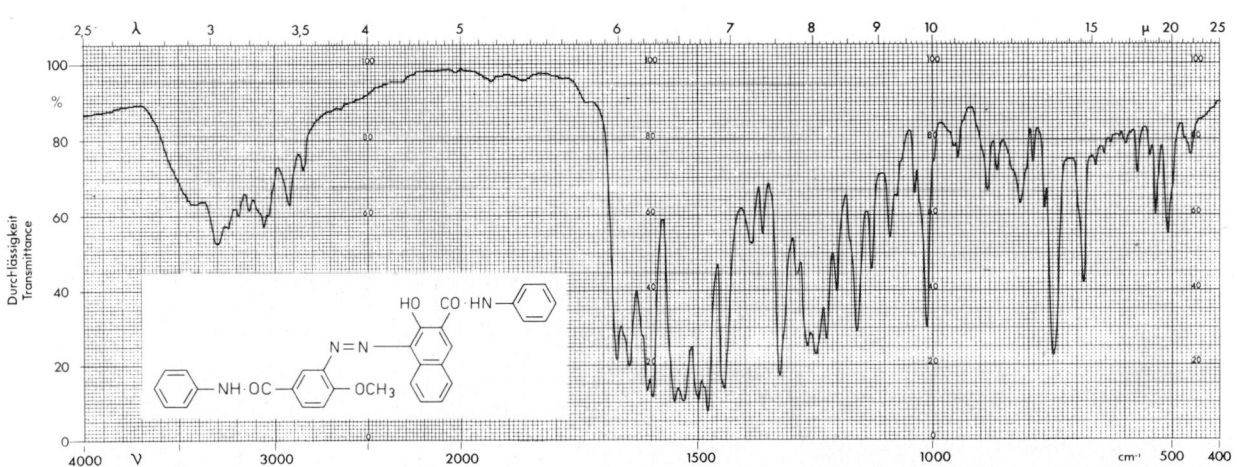

CI-Name: **Pigment Rot 32** CI-No.: **12320**
Zusammensetzung: **3-Amino-4-methoxybenzanilid → BONS-anilid**
Präparation: **KBr (3,5/1000)** Dez. Nr.: **1.2.23**

CI-Name: **Pigment Red 32** CI-No.: **12320**
Composition: **3-Amino-4-methoxybenzanilide → BHNA-anilide**
Preparation: **KBr (3,5/1000)** Dec. No.: **1.2.23**

5537

Organische Pigmente
1. Monoazopigmente
1.2. KK β-Oxynaphtholsäurearylide (BONS-arylide)

Organic Pigments
1. Monoazo Pigments
1.2. CC β-Hydroxynaphthoic-arylides (BHNA-arylides)

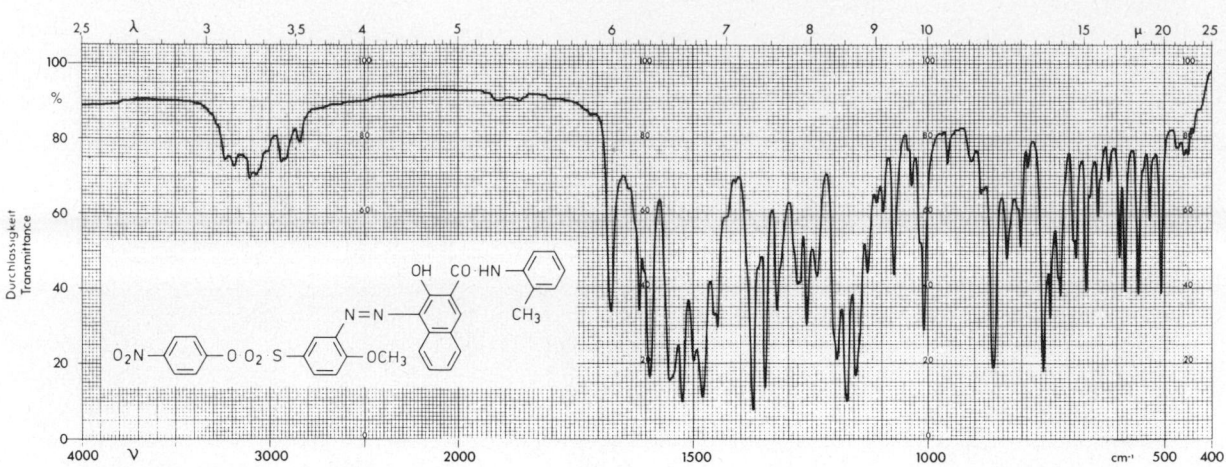

5538

CI-Name:	**Pigment Rot 95**	
Zusammen-setzung:	**4'-Nitrophenyl-(3-amino-4-methoxy-phenyl)-sulfonat → BONS-2-methylanilid**	
Präparation:	**KBr (3,5/1000)**	Dez. Nr.: **1.2.24**

CI-Name:	**Pigment Red 95**	
Composition:	**4'-Nitrophenyl-(3-amino-4-methoxy-phenyl) sulfonate → BHNA-2-methylanilide**	
Preparation:	**KBr (3,5/1000)**	Dec. No.: **1.2.24**

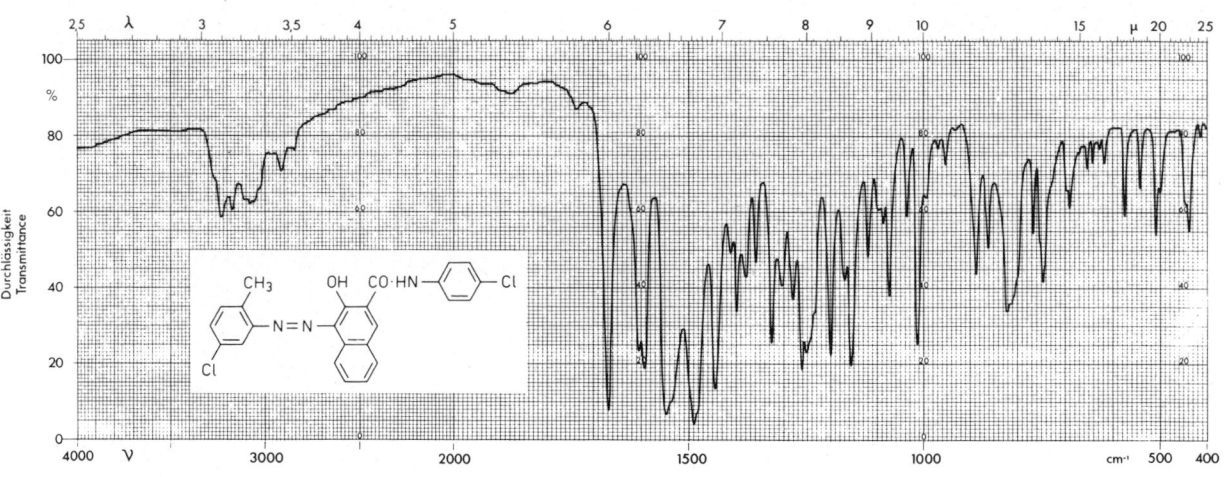

5539

CI-Name:	**Pigment Rot 96**	
Zusammen-setzung:	**5-Chlor-2-toluidin → BONS-4-chloranilid**	
Präparation:	**KBr (3,5/1000)**	Dez. Nr.: **1.2.25**

CI-Name:	**Pigment Red 96**	
Composition:	**5-Chloro-2-toluidine → BHNA-4-chloro-anilide**	
Preparation:	**KBr (3,5/1000)**	Dec. No.: **1.2.25**

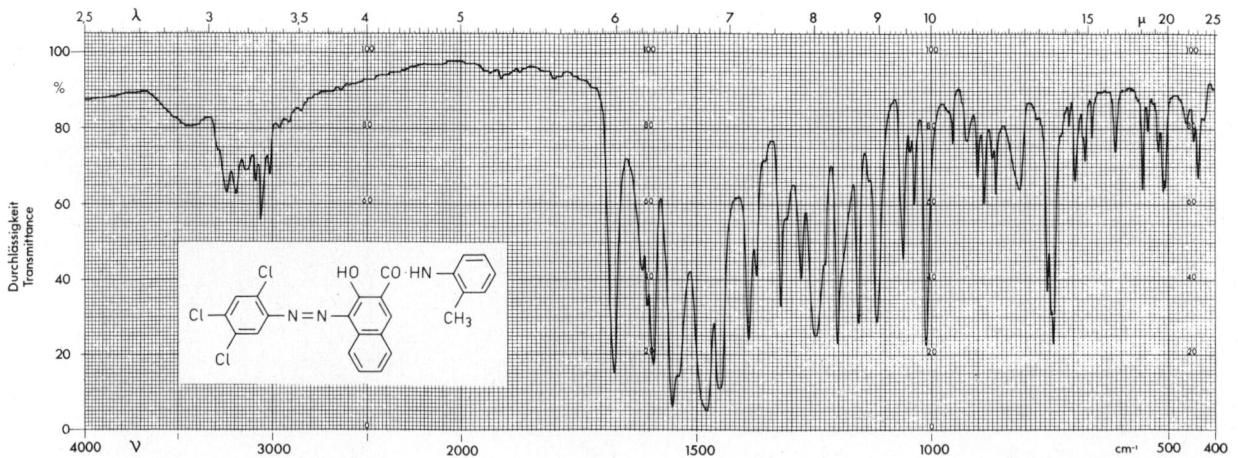

5540

CI-Name:	**Pigment Rot 112**	CI-No.:	**12370**
Zusammen-setzung:	**2,4,5-Trichloranilin → BONS-2-methyl-anilid**		
Präparation:	**KBr (3,5/1000)**	Dez. Nr.:	**1.2.26**

CI-Name:	**Pigment Red 112**	CI-No.:	**12370**
Composition:	**2,4,5-Trichloroaniline → BHNA-2-methyl-anilide**		
Preparation:	**KBr (3,5/1000)**	Dec. No.:	**1.2.26**

Organische Pigmente
1. Monoazopigmente
1.2. KK β-Oxynaphtholsäurearylide (BONS-arylide)

Organic Pigments
1. Monoazo Pigments
1.2. CC β-Hydroxynaphthoic-arylides (BHNA-arylides)

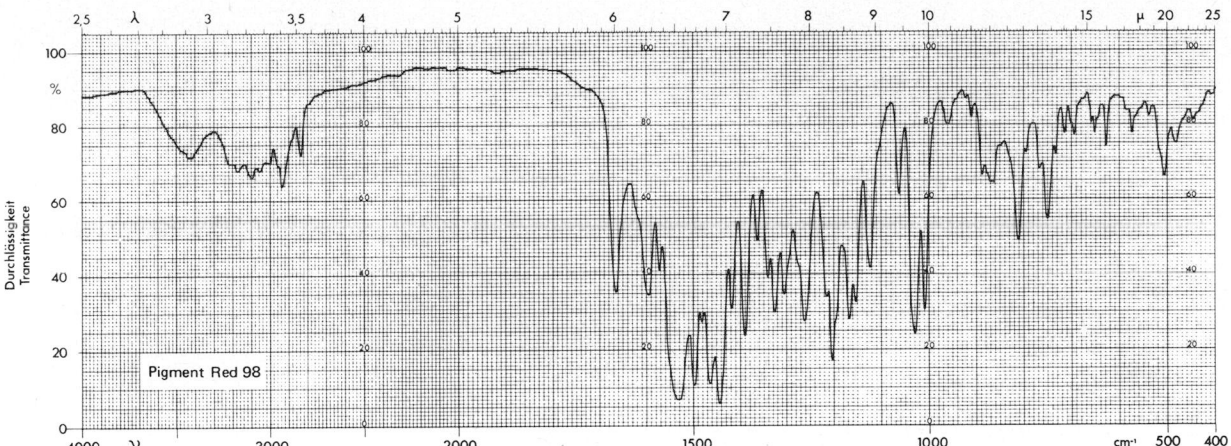

CI-Name: **Pigment Rot 98**

Zusammen-   **n. b.**
setzung:

Präparation: **KBr (3,5/1000)**   Dez. Nr.: **1.2.27**

CI-Name: **Pigment Red 98**

Composition: **n. k.**

Preparation: **KBr (3,5/1000)**   Dec. No.: **1.2.27**

5541

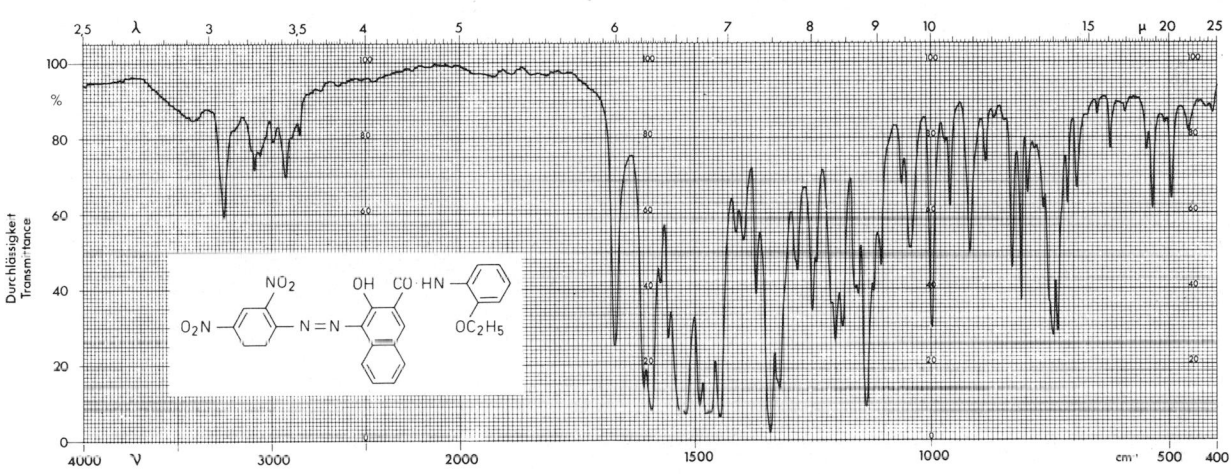

CI-Name: **Pigment Rot 136**

Zusammen-   **2,4-Dinitroanilin → BONS-2-ethoxyanilid**
setzung:

Präparation: **KBr (3,5/1000)**   Dez. Nr.: **1.1.28**

CI-Name: **Pigment Red 136**

Composition: **2,4-Dinitroaniline → BHNA-2-ethoxy-**
    anilide

Preparation: **KBr (3,5/1000)**   Dec. No.: **1.1.28**

5542

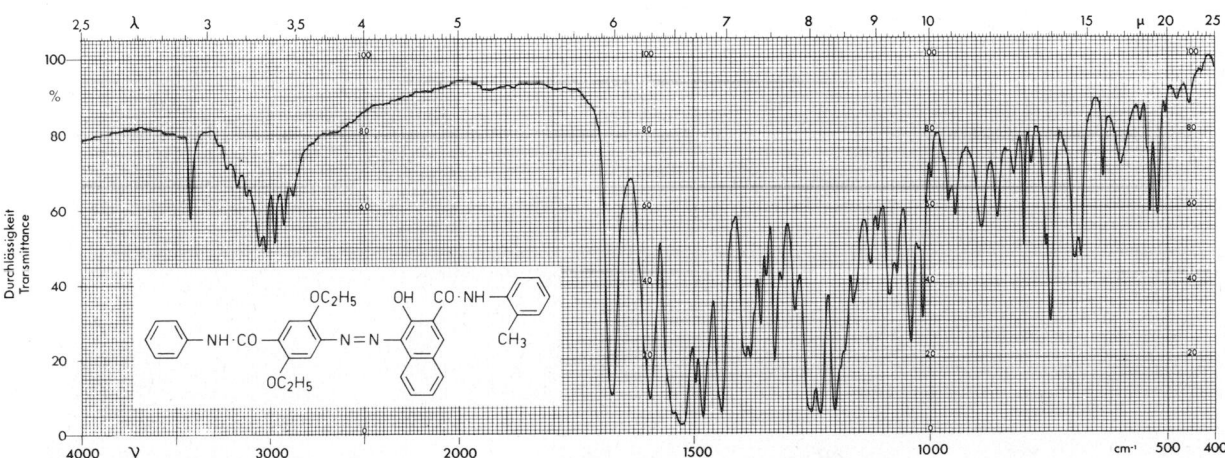

CI-Name: **Pigment Blau 23**

Zusammen-   **4-Amino-2,5-diethoxybenzanilid → BONS-**
setzung: **2-methylanilid**

Präparation: **KBr (3,5/1000)**   Dez. Nr.: **1.2.29**

CI-Name: **Pigment Blue 23**

Composition: **4-Amino-2,5-diethoxybenzanilide → BHNA-**
    2-methylanilide

Preparation: **KBr (3,5/1000)**   Dec. No.: **1.2.29**

5543

Organische Pigmente
1. Monoazopigmente
1.2. KK β-Oxynaphtholsäurearylide (BONS-arylide)

Organic Pigments
1. Monoazo Pigments
1.2. CC β-Hydroxynaphthoic-arylides (BHNA-arylides)

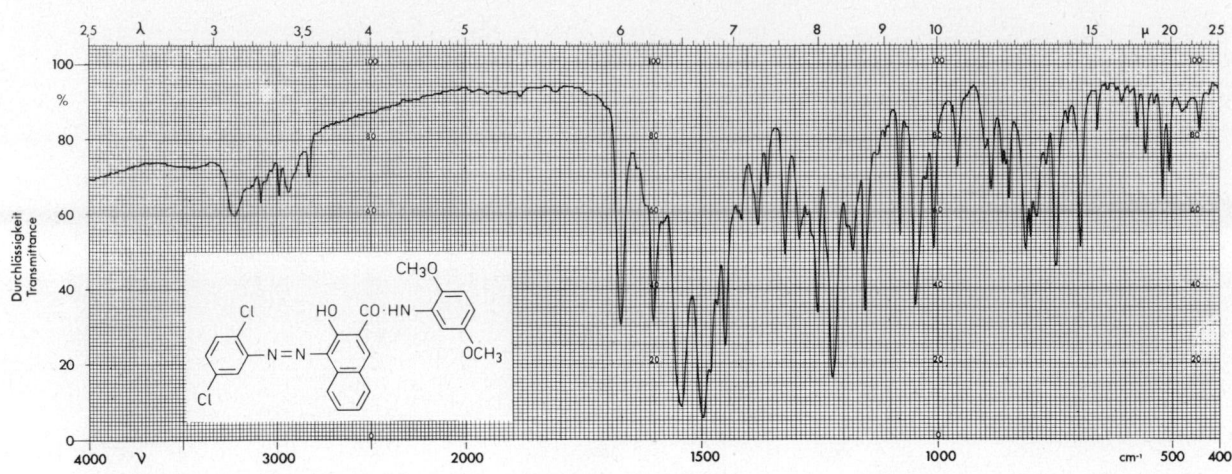

5544

CI-Name:	**Pigment Braun 1**	CI-No.:	**12480**
Zusammensetzung:	**2,5-Dichloranilin → BONS-2,5-dimethoxyanilid**		
Präparation:	**KBr (4,5/1000)**	Dez. Nr.:	**1.2.30**

CI-Name:	**Pigment Brown 1**	CI-No.:	**12480**
Composition:	**2,5-Dichloroaniline → BHNA-2,5-dimethoxyanilide**		
Preparation:	**KBr (4,5/1000)**	Dec. No.:	**1.2.30**

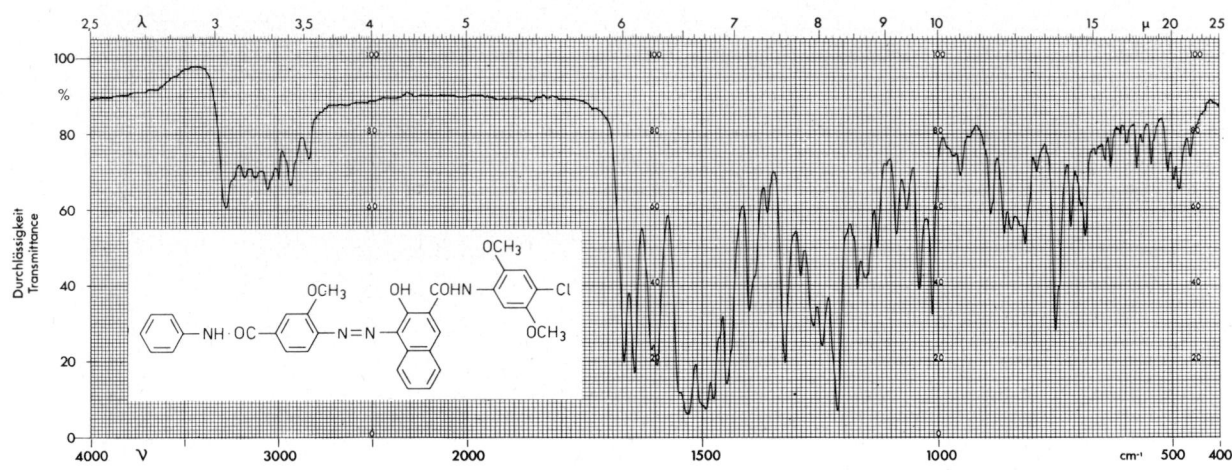

5545

CI-Name:	**Pigment Rot 146**
Zusammensetzung:	**4-Amino-3-methoxybenzanilid → BONS-4-chlor-2,5-dimethoxyanilid**
Präparation:	**KBr (3,5/1000)** Dez. Nr.: **1.2.31**

CI-Name:	**Pigment Red 146**
Composition:	**4-Amino-3-methoxybenzanilide → BHNA-4-chloro-2,5-dimethoxyanilide**
Preparation:	**KBr (3,5/1000)** Dec. No.: **1.2.31**

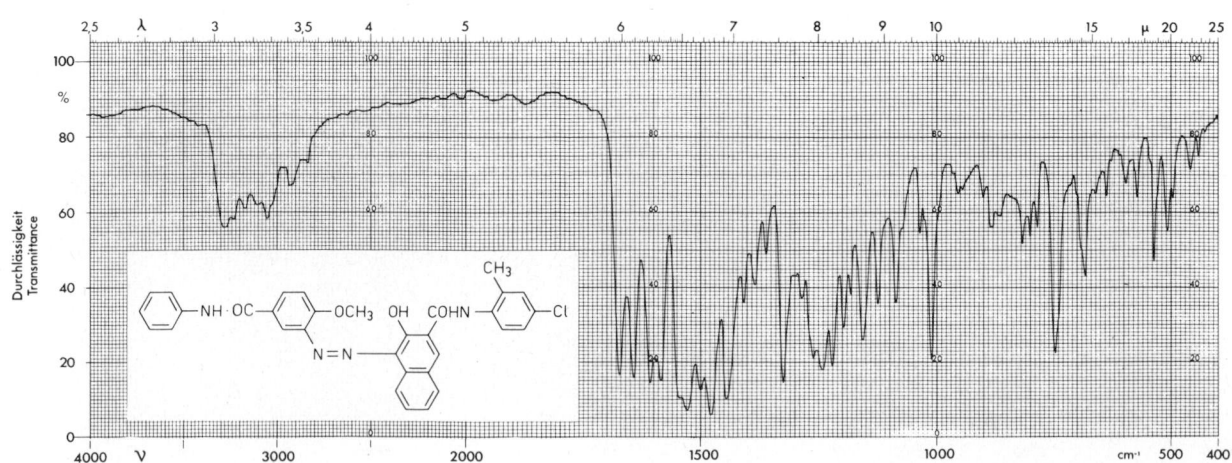

5546

CI-Name:	**Pigment Rot 147**
Zusammensetzung:	**3-Amino-4-methoxy-benzanilid → BONS-4-chlor-2-methylanilid**
Präparation:	**KBr (3,5/1000)** Dez. Nr.: **1.2.32**

CI-Name:	**Pigment Red 147**
Composition:	**3-Amino-4-methoxy-benzanilide → BHNA-4-chloro-2-methylanilide**
Preparation:	**KBr (3,5/1000)** Dec. No.: **1.2.32**

Organische Pigmente
1. Monoazopigmente
1.2. KK β-Oxynaphtolsäurearylide

Organic Pigments
1. Monoazo Pigments
1.2. CC β-Hydroxynaphtoic-arylides

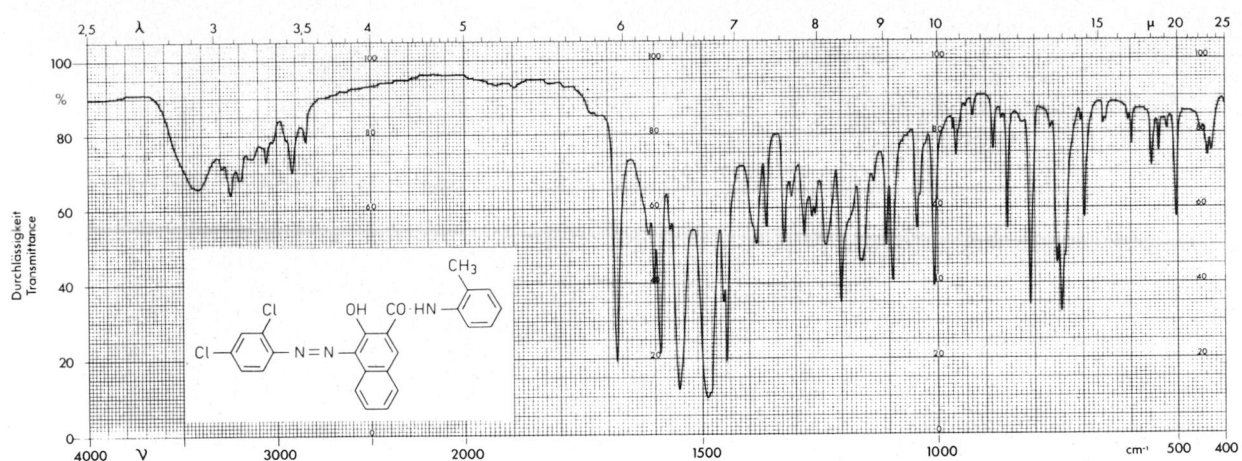

CI-Name: **Pigment Rot 148**

Zusammensetzung: 2,4-Dichloranilin → BONS-2-methylanilid

Präparation: **KBr (5/1000)**   Dez. Nr.: **1.2.33**

CI-Name: **Pigment Red 148**

Composition: **2,4-Dichloroaniline → BHNA-2-methyl-anilide**

Preparation: **KBr (5/1000)**   Dec. No.: **1.2.33**

5547

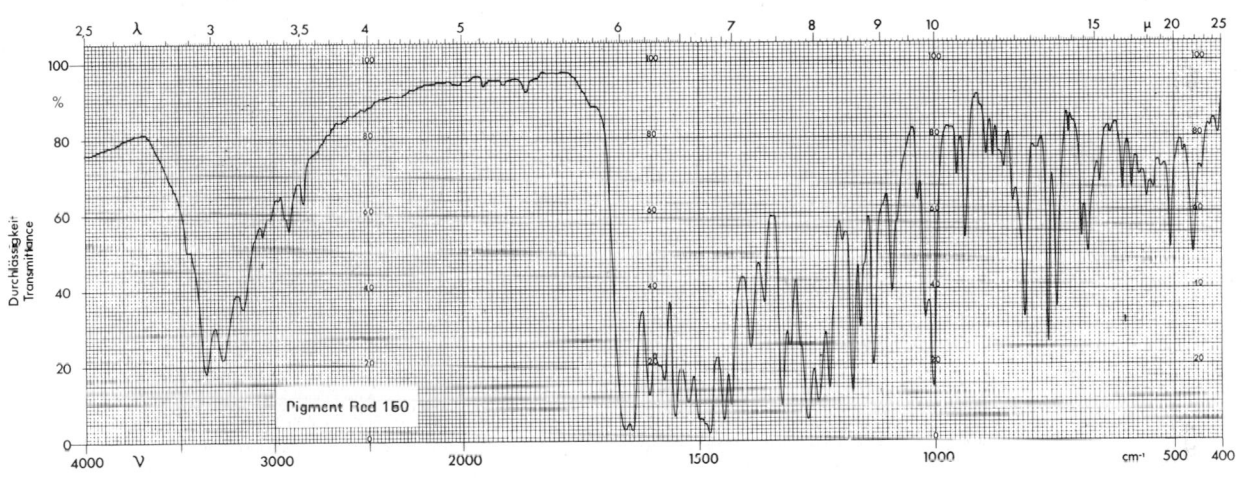

CI-Name: **Pigment Rot 150**

Zusammensetzung: **n. b.**

Präparation: **KBr (5/1000)**   Dez. Nr.: **1.2.34**

CI-Name: **Pigment Red 150**

Composition: **n. k.**

Preparation: **KBr (5/1000)**   Dec. No.: **1.2.34**

5548

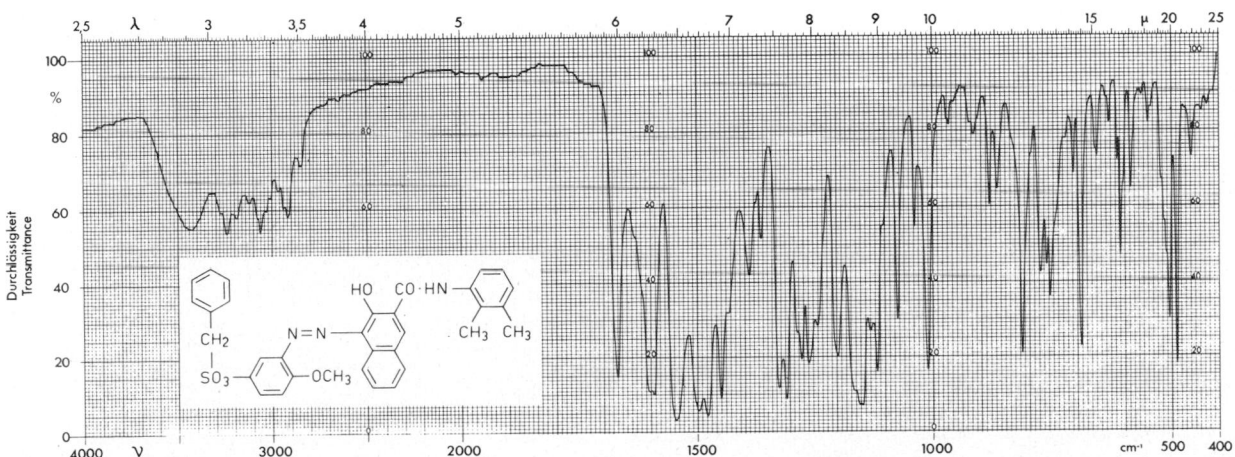

CI-Name: **Pigment Rot 163**   CI-No.: **12455**

Zusammensetzung: **3-Amino-4-methoxyphenylbenzyl-sulfon → BONS-2,3-dimethylanilid**

Präparation: **KBr (5/1000)**   Dez. Nr.: **1.2.35**

CI-Name: **Pigment Red 163**   CI-No.: **12455**

Composition: **3-Amino-4-methoxyphenylbenzyl sulfone → BHNA-2,3-dimethylanilide**

Preparation: **KBr (5/1000)**   Dec. No.: **1.2.35**

5549

Organische Pigmente
1. Monoazopigmente
1.3. KK β-Naphthol

Organic Pigments
1. Monoazo Pigments
1.3. CC β-Naphthol

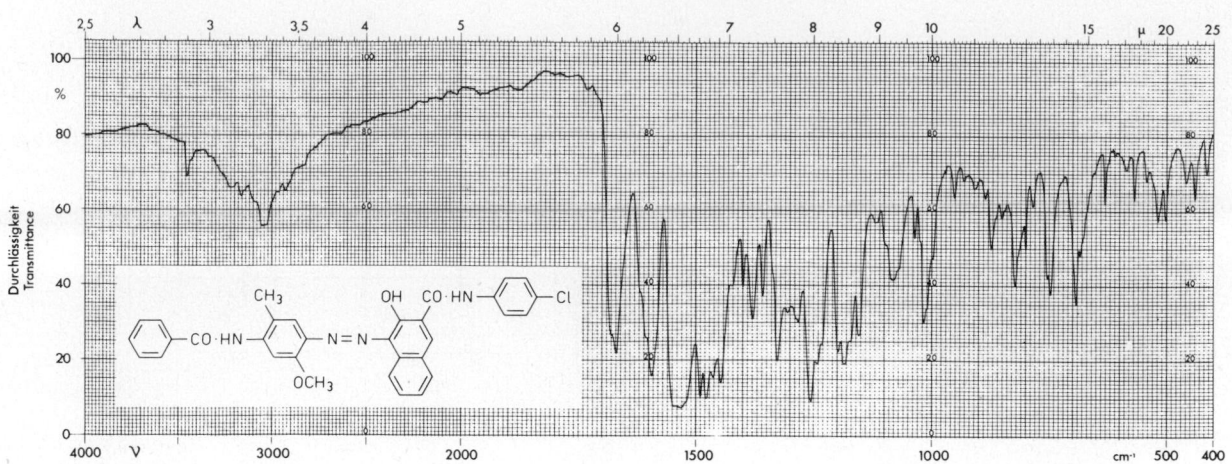

5550

Name: Heliofilviolett BV 150

Zusammen-
setzung: N-Benzoyl-2-methyl-5-methoxy-1,4-
phenylendiamin → BONS-4-chloranilid

Präparation: KBr (3,5/1000)   Dez. Nr.: 1.2.36

Name: Heliofilviolet BV 150

Composition: N-Benzoyl-2-methyl-5-methoxy-1,4-
phenylenediamine → BHNA-4-chloroanilide

Preparation: KBr (3,5/1000)   Dec. No.: 1.2.36

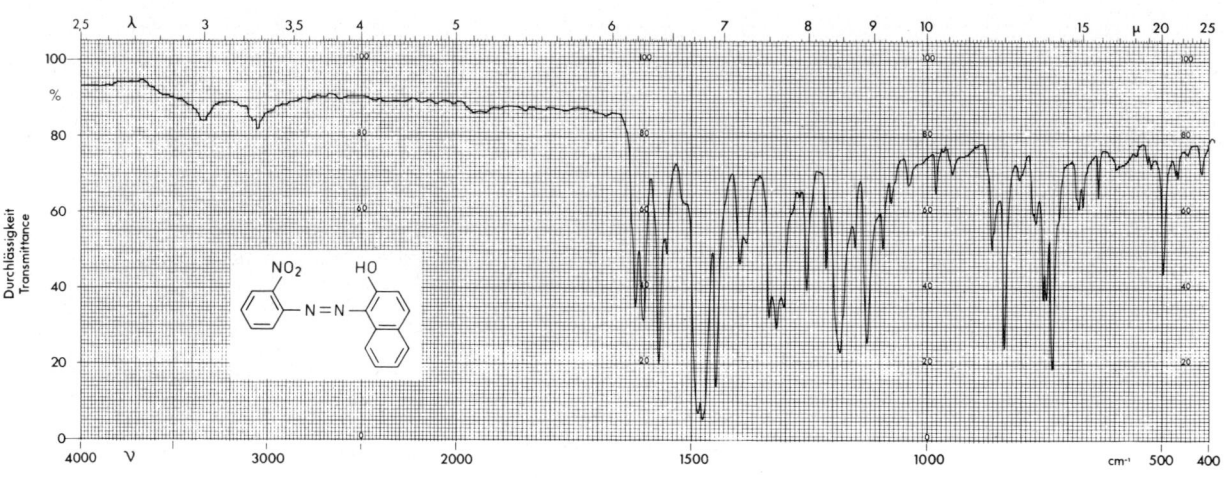

5551

CI-Name: Pigment Orange 2   CI-No.: 12060

Zusammen-
setzung: 2-Nitroanilin → 2-Naphthol

Präparation: KBr (3,5/1000)   Dez. Nr.: 1.3.1

CI-Name: Pigment Orange 2   CI-No.: 12060

Composition: 2-Nitroaniline → 2-Naphthol

Preparation: KBr (3,5/1000)   Dec. No.: 1.3.1

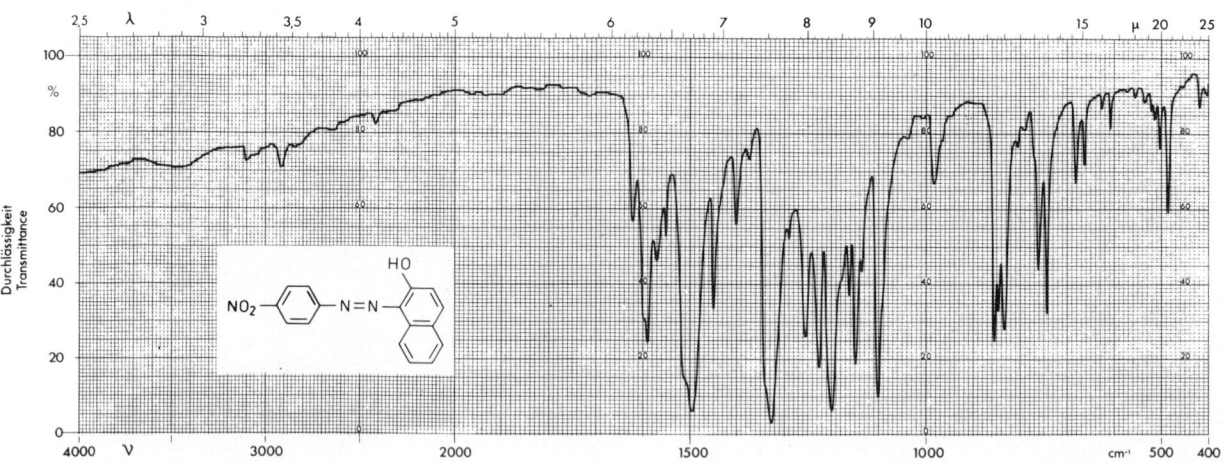

5552

CI-Name: Pigment Rot 1   CI-No.: 12070

Zusammen-
setzung: 4-Nitroanilin → 2-Naphthol

Präparation: KBr (3,5/1000)   Dez. Nr.: 1.3.2

CI-Name: Pigment Red 1   CI-No.: 12070

Composition: 4-Nitroaniline → 2-Naphthol

Preparation: KBr (3,5/1000)   Dec. No.: 1.3.2

Organische Pigmente
1. Monoazopigmente
1.3. KK β-Naphthol

Organic Pigments
1. Monoazo Pigments
1.3. CC β-Naphthol

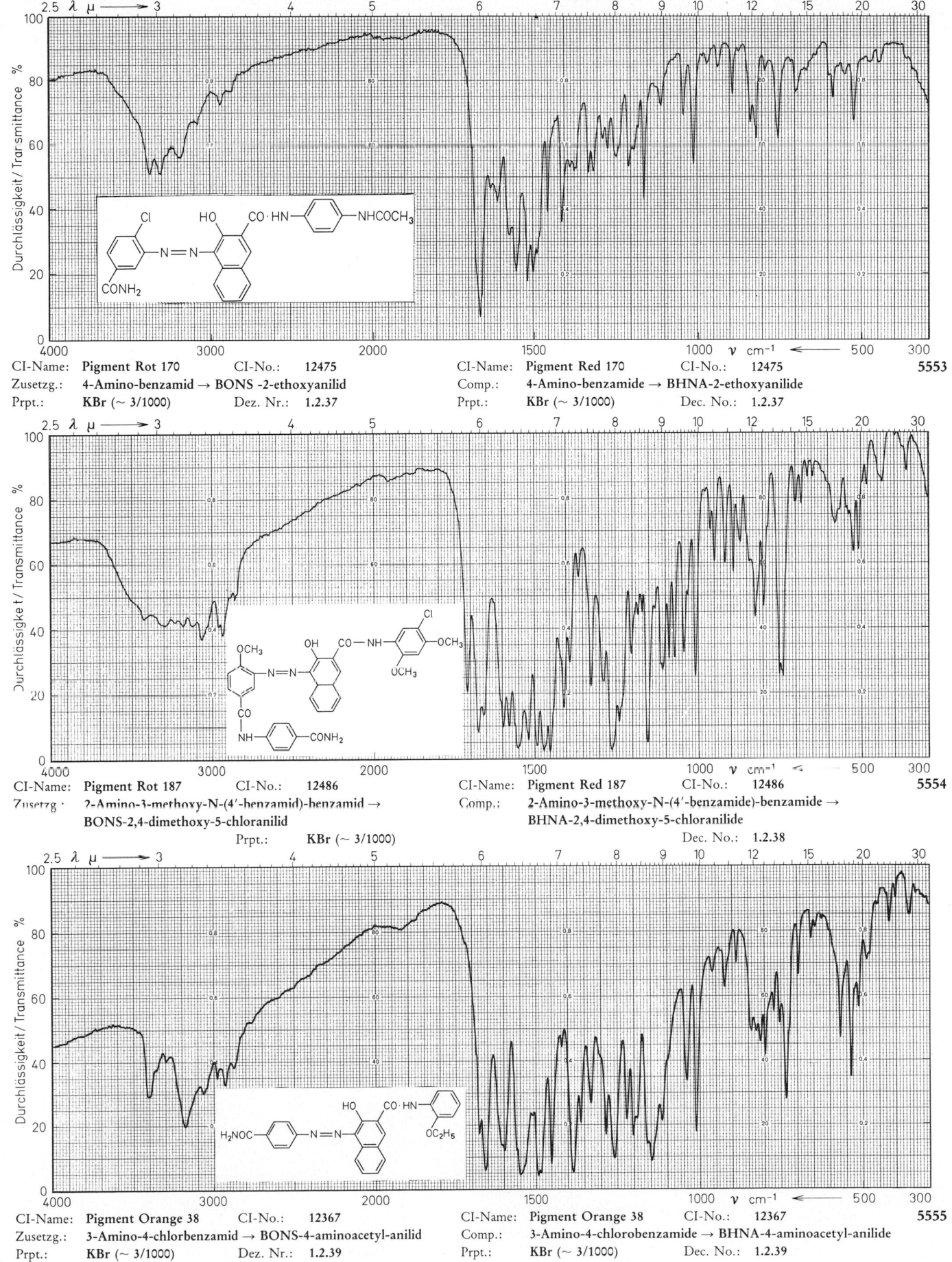

CI-Name: **Pigment Rot 170**   CI-No.: **12475**   CI-Name: **Pigment Red 170**   CI-No.: **12475**   **5553**
Zusetzg.: **4-Amino-benzamid → BONS -2-ethoxyanilid**   Comp.: **4-Amino-benzamide → BHNA-2-ethoxyanilide**
Prpt.: **KBr (~ 3/1000)**   Dez. Nr.: **1.2.37**   Prpt.: **KBr (~ 3/1000)**   Dec. No.: **1.2.37**

CI-Name: **Pigment Rot 187**   CI-No.: **12486**   CI-Name: **Pigment Red 187**   CI-No.: **12486**   **5554**
Zusetzg.: **2-Amino-3-methoxy-N-(4'-benzamid)-benzamid →**   Comp.: **2-Amino-3-methoxy-N-(4'-benzamide)-benzamide →**
BONS-2,4-dimethoxy-5-chloranilid   **BHNA-2,4-dimethoxy-5-chloranilide**
Prpt.: **KBr (~ 3/1000)**   Dec. No.: **1.2.38**

CI-Name: **Pigment Orange 38**   CI-No.: **12367**   CI-Name: **Pigment Orange 38**   CI-No.: **12367**   **5555**
Zusetzg.: **3-Amino-4-chlorbenzamid → BONS-4-aminoacetyl-anilid**   Comp.: **3-Amino-4-chlorobenzamide → BHNA-4-aminoacetyl-anilide**
Prpt.: **KBr (~ 3/1000)**   Dez. Nr.: **1.2.39**   Prpt.: **KBr (~ 3/1000)**   Dec. No.: **1.2.39**

Organische Pigmente
1. Monoazopigmente
1.3. KK β-Naphthol

Organic Pigments
1. Monoazo Pigments
1.3. CC β-Naphthol

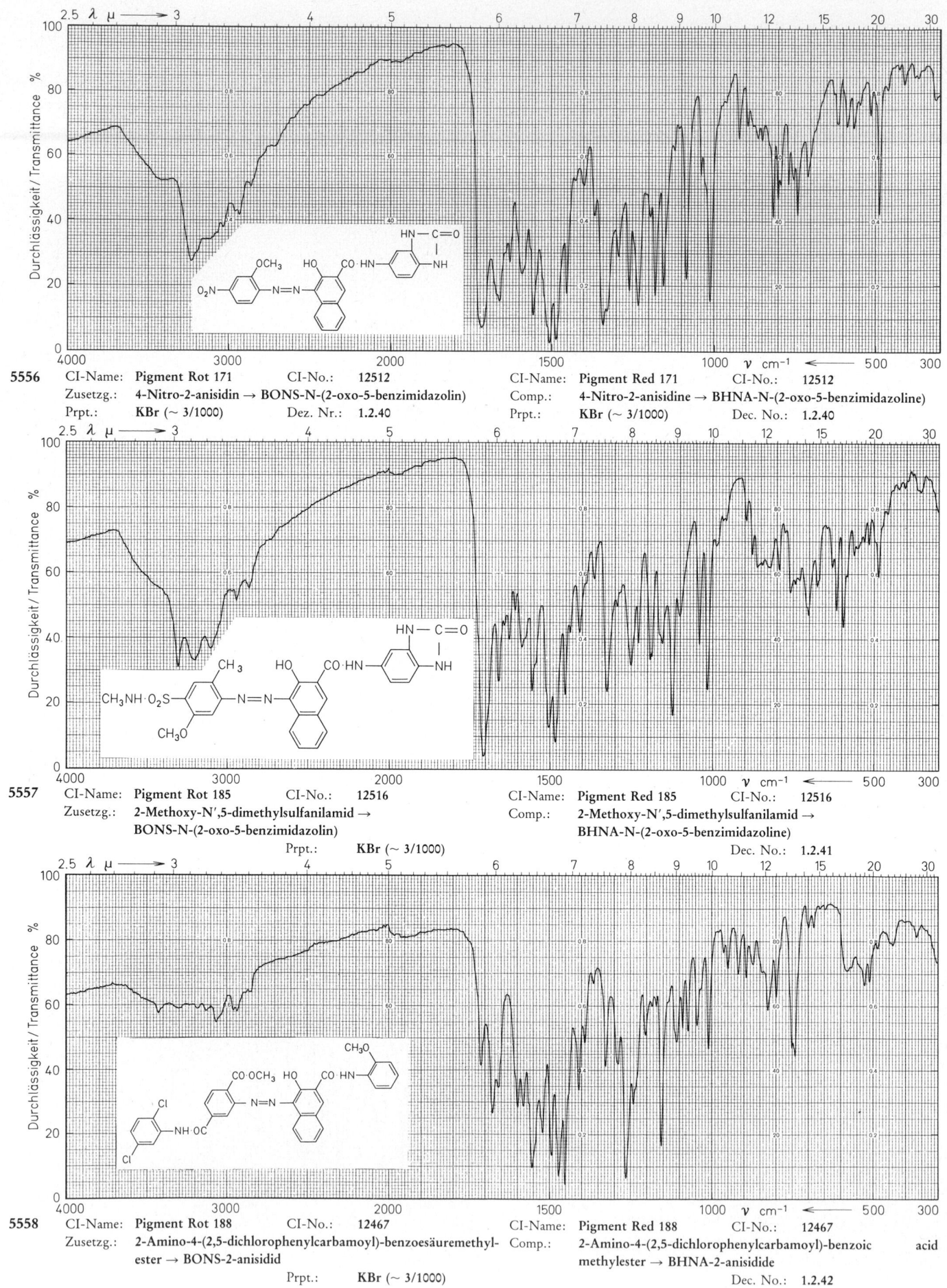

5556 CI-Name: **Pigment Rot 171**   CI-No.: **12512**   CI-Name: **Pigment Red 171**   CI-No.: **12512**
Zusetzg.: **4-Nitro-2-anisidin → BONS-N-(2-oxo-5-benzimidazolin)**   Comp.: **4-Nitro-2-anisidine → BHNA-N-(2-oxo-5-benzimidazoline)**
Prpt.: **KBr (~ 3/1000)**   Dez. Nr.: **1.2.40**   Prpt.: **KBr (~ 3/1000)**   Dec. No.: **1.2.40**

5557 CI-Name: **Pigment Rot 185**   CI-No.: **12516**   CI-Name: **Pigment Red 185**   CI-No.: **12516**
Zusetzg.: **2-Methoxy-N′,5-dimethylsulfanilamid →**   Comp.: **2-Methoxy-N′,5-dimethylsulfanilamid →**
BONS-N-(2-oxo-5-benzimidazolin)   **BHNA-N-(2-oxo-5-benzimidazoline)**
Prpt.: **KBr (~ 3/1000)**   Dec. No.: **1.2.41**

5558 CI-Name: **Pigment Rot 188**   CI-No.: **12467**   CI-Name: **Pigment Red 188**   CI-No.: **12467**
Zusetzg.: **2-Amino-4-(2,5-dichlorophenylcarbamoyl)-benzoesäuremethyl-**   Comp.: **2-Amino-4-(2,5-dichlorophenylcarbamoyl)-benzoic   acid**
ester → BONS-2-anisidid   **methylester → BHNA-2-anisidide**
Prpt.: **KBr (~ 3/1000)**   Dec. No.: **1.2.42**

Organische Pigmente
1. Monoazopigmente
1.3. KK β-Naphthol

Organic Pigments
1. Monoazo Pigments
1.3. CC β-Naphthol

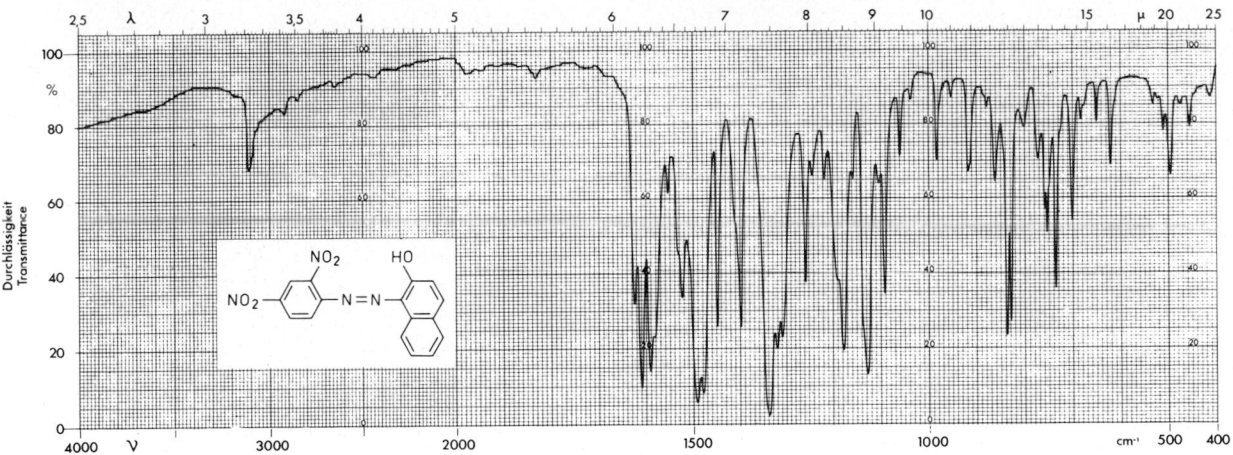

CI-Name: **Pigment Orange 5** CI-No.: **12075**
Zusammen-   **2,4-Dinitroanilin → 2-Naphthol**
setzung:
Präparation: **KBr (3,5/1000)**   Dez. Nr.: **1.3.3**

CI-Name: **Pigment Orange 5** CI-No.: **12075**
Composition: **2,4-Dinitroaniline → 2-Naphthol**
Preparation: **KBr (3,5/1000)**   Dec. No.: **1.3.3**

5559

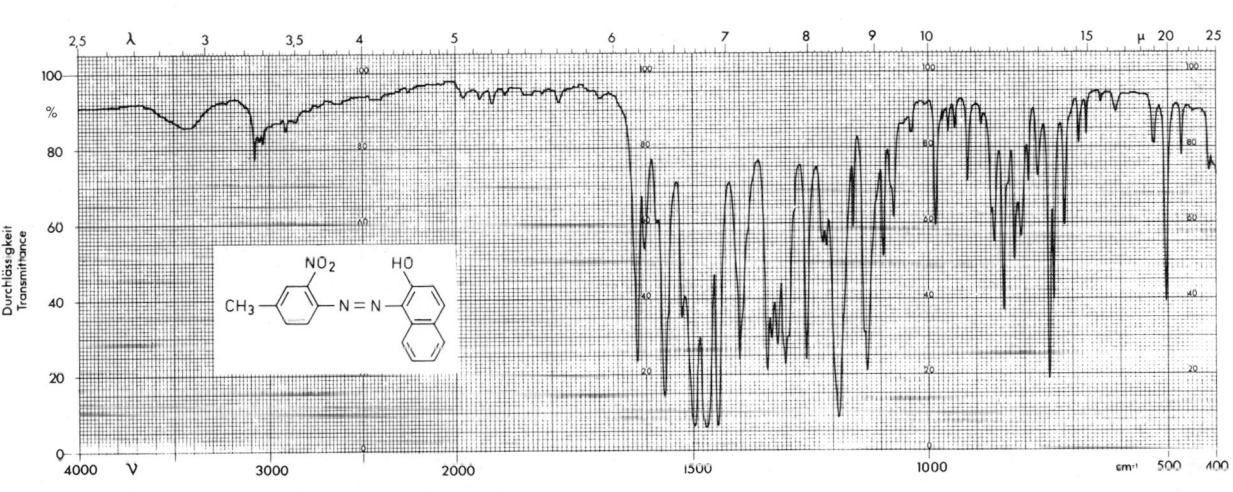

CI-Name: **Pigment Rot 3**   CI-No.: **12120**
Zusammen-   **4-Methyl-2-nitroanilin → 2-Naphthol**
setzung:
Präparation: **KBr (3,5/1000)**   Dez. Nr.: **1.3.4**

CI-Name: **Pigment Red 3**   CI-No.: **12120**
Composition: **4-Methyl-2-nitroaniline → 2-Naphthol**
Preparation: **KBr (3,5/1000)**   Dec. No.: **1.3.4**

5560

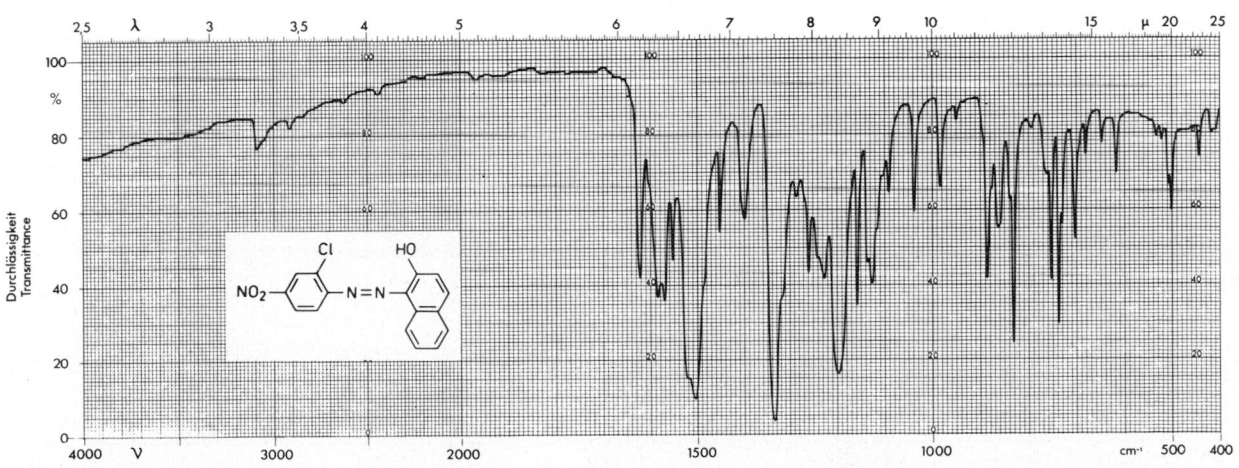

CI-Name: **Pigment Rot 4**   CI-No.: **12085**
Zusammen-   **2-Chlor-4-nitroanilin → 2-Naphthol**
setzung:
Präparation: **KBr (3,5/1000)**   Dez. Nr.: **1.3.5**

CI-Name: **Pigment Red 4**   CI-No.: **12085**
Composition: **2-Chloro-4-nitroaniline → 2-Naphthol**
Preparation: **KBr (3,5/1000)**   Dec. No.: **1.3.5**

5561

Organische Pigmente
1. Monoazopigmente
1.4. KK Phenylmethylpyrazolon

Organic Pigments
1. Monoazo Pigments
1.4. CC Phenylmethylpyrazolones

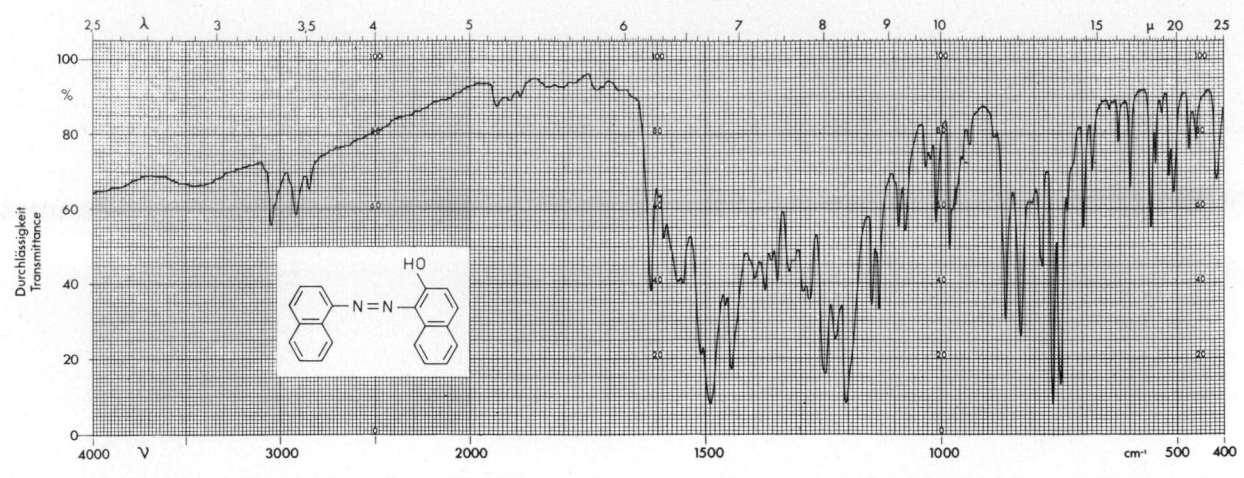

5562

CI-Name:	**Pigment Rot 40**	CI-No.:	**12170**
Zusammen-setzung:	**1-Naphthylamin → 2-Naphthol**		
Präparation:	**KBr (3,5/1000)**	Dez. Nr.:	**1.3.6**

CI-Name:	**Pigment Red 40**	CI-No.:	**12170**
Composition:	**1-Naphthylamine → 2-Naphthol**		
Preparation:	**KBr (3,5/1000)**	Dec. No.:	**1.3.6**

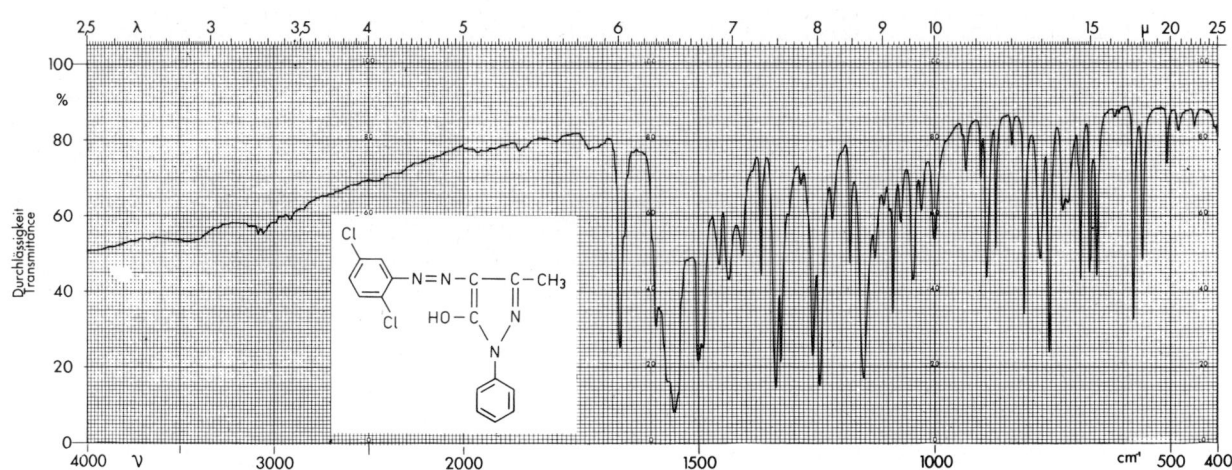

5563

CI-Name:	**Pigment Gelb 10**	CI-No.:	**12710**
Zusammen-setzung:	**2,5-Dichloranilin → 3-Methyl-1-phenyl-pyrazolon-5**		
Präparation:	**KBr (3/1000)**	Dez. Nr.:	**1.4.1**

CI-Name:	**Pigment Yellow 10**	CI-No.:	**12710**
Composition:	**2,5-Dichloro-aniline → 3-Methyl-1-phenyl-5-pyrazolone**		
Preparation:	**KBr (3/1000)**	Dec. No.:	**1.4.1**

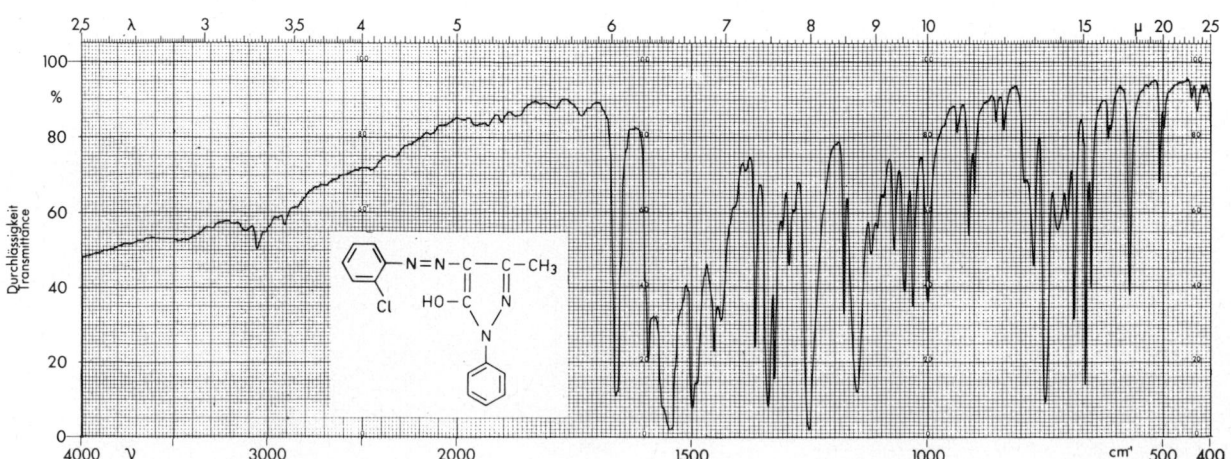

5564

CI-Name:	**Pigment Gelb 60**	CI-No.:	**12705**
Zusammen-setzung:	**2-Chloranilin → 3-Methyl-1-phenyl-pyrazolon-5**		
Präparation:	**KBr (4/1000)**	Dez. Nr.:	**1.4.2**

CI-Name:	**Pigment Yellow 60**	CI-No.:	**12705**
Composition:	**2-Chloroanilin → 3-Methyl-1-phenyl-5-pyrazolone**		
Preparation:	**KBr (4/1000)**	Dec. No.:	**1.4.2**

Organische Pigmente
1. Monoazopigmente
1.4. KK Phenylmethylpyrazolon

Organic Pigments
1. Monoazo Pigments
1.4. CC Phenylmethylpyrazolones

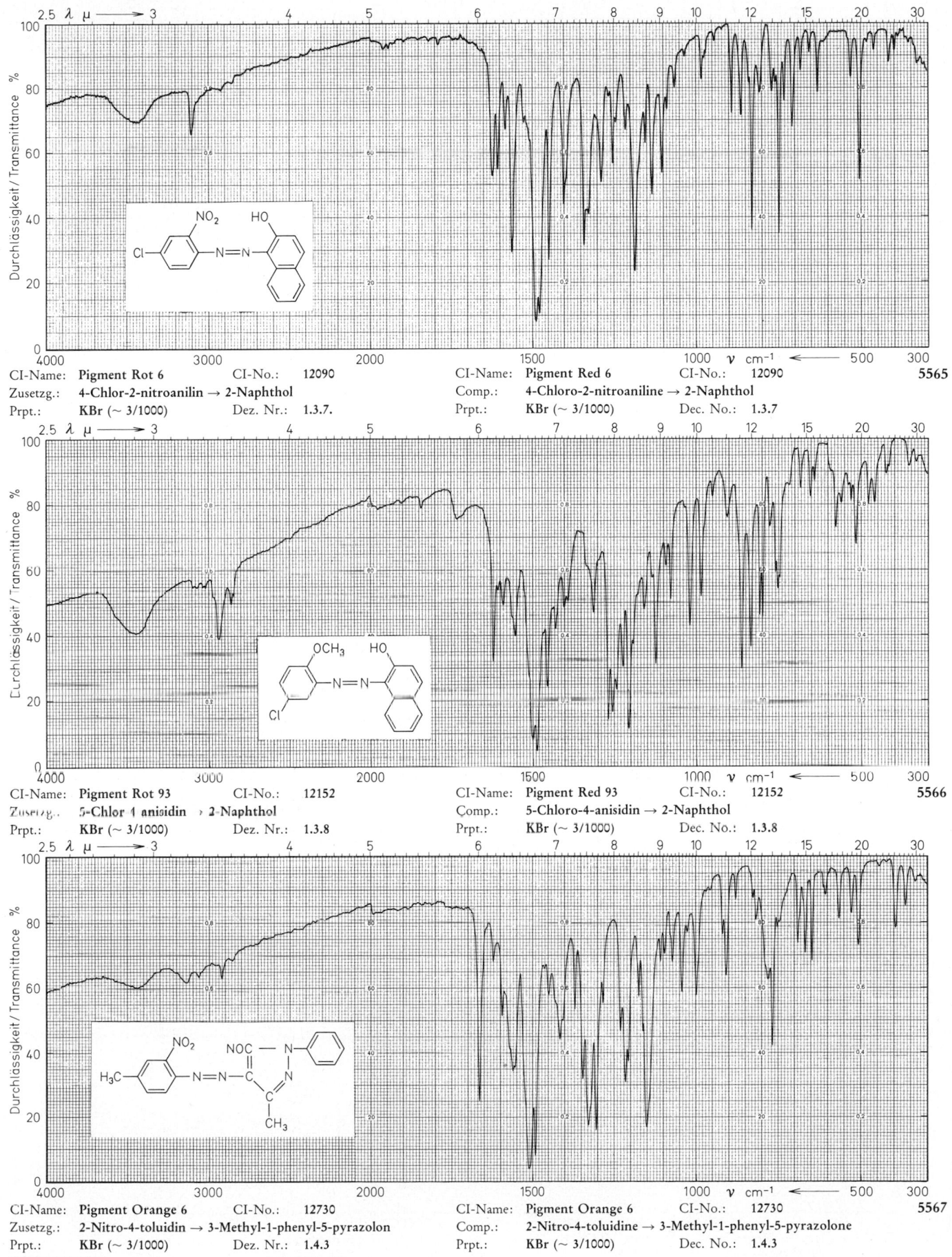

CI-Name: **Pigment Rot 6**   CI-No.: **12090**
Zusetzg.: **4-Chlor-2-nitroanilin → 2-Naphthol**
Prpt.: **KBr (~ 3/1000)**   Dez. Nr.: **1.3.7.**

CI-Name: **Pigment Red 6**   CI-No.: **12090**   **5565**
Comp.: **4-Chloro-2-nitroaniline → 2-Naphthol**
Prpt.: **KBr (~ 3/1000)**   Dec. No.: **1.3.7**

CI-Name: **Pigment Rot 93**   CI-No.: **12152**
Zusetzg.: **5-Chlor-4-anisidin → 2-Naphthol**
Prpt.: **KBr (~ 3/1000)**   Dez. Nr.: **1.3.8**

CI-Name: **Pigment Red 93**   CI-No.: **12152**   **5566**
Comp.: **5-Chloro-4-anisidin → 2-Naphthol**
Prpt.: **KBr (~ 3/1000)**   Dec. No.: **1.3.8**

CI-Name: **Pigment Orange 6**   CI-No.: **12730**
Zusetzg.: **2-Nitro-4-toluidin → 3-Methyl-1-phenyl-5-pyrazolon**
Prpt.: **KBr (~ 3/1000)**   Dez. Nr.: **1.4.3**

CI-Name: **Pigment Orange 6**   CI-No.: **12730**   **5567**
Comp.: **2-Nitro-4-toluidine → 3-Methyl-1-phenyl-5-pyrazolone**
Prpt.: **KBr (~ 3/1000)**   Dec. No.: **1.4.3**

Sp. No. 5568: Während der Herstellung eliminiert – during production eliminated

Organische Pigmente
1. Monoazopigmente
1.5. KK Benzimidazole

Organic Pigments
1. Monoazo Pigments
1.5. CC Benzimidazoles

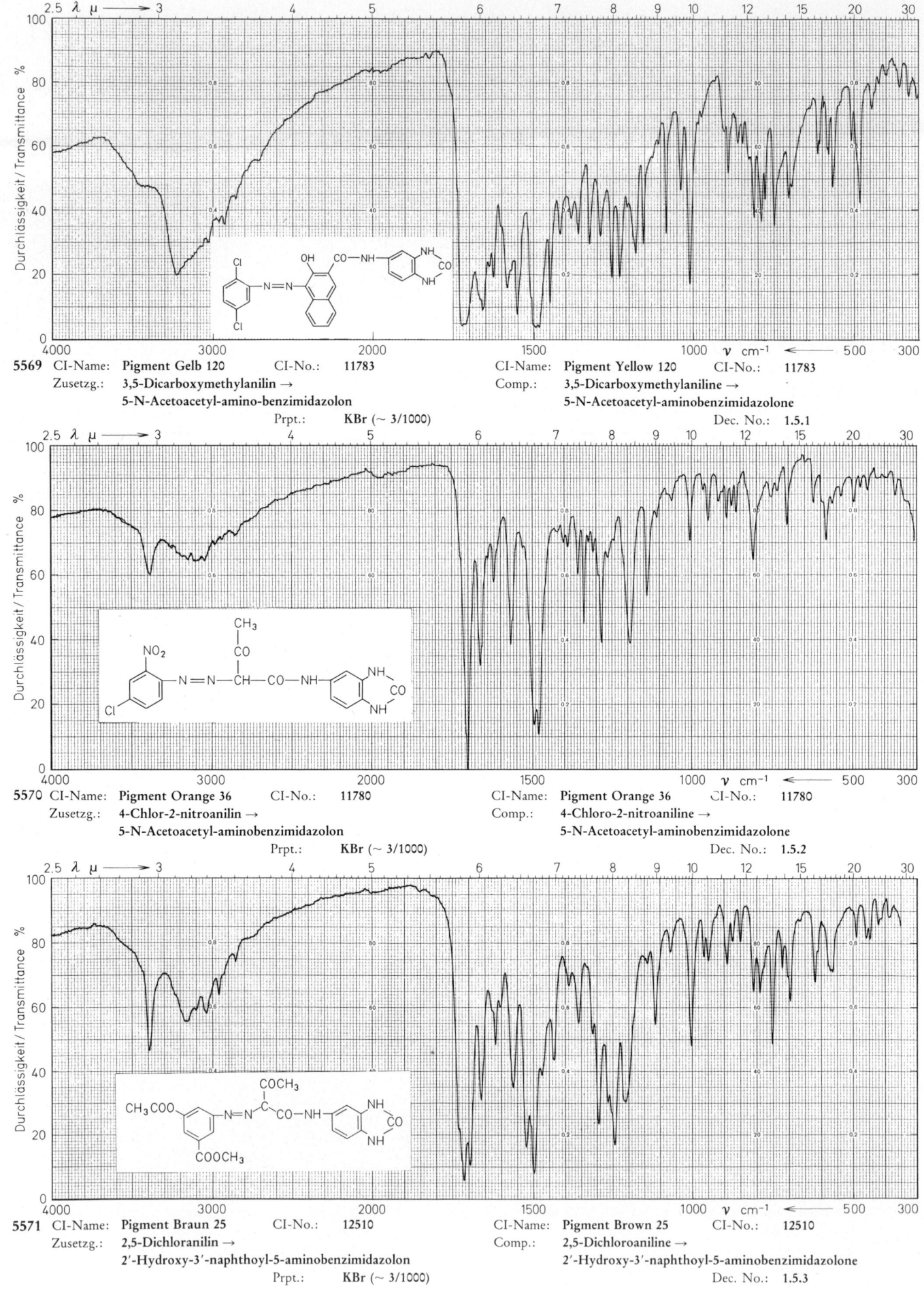

5569 CI-Name: **Pigment Gelb 120**   CI-No.: **11783**   CI-Name: **Pigment Yellow 120**   CI-No.: **11783**
        Zusetzg.: **3,5-Dicarboxymethylanilin** →   Comp.: **3,5-Dicarboxymethylaniline** →
                   5-N-Acetoacetyl-amino-benzimidazolon   **5-N-Acetoacetyl-aminobenzimidazolone**
                   Prpt.: **KBr (~ 3/1000)**   Dec. No.: **1.5.1**

5570 CI-Name: **Pigment Orange 36**   CI-No.: **11780**   CI-Name: **Pigment Orange 36**   CI-No.: **11780**
        Zusetzg.: **4-Chlor-2-nitroanilin** →   Comp.: **4-Chloro-2-nitroaniline** →
                   5-N-Acetoacetyl-aminobenzimidazolon   **5-N-Acetoacetyl-aminobenzimidazolone**
                   Prpt.: **KBr (~ 3/1000)**   Dec. No.: **1.5.2**

5571 CI-Name: **Pigment Braun 25**   CI-No.: **12510**   CI-Name: **Pigment Brown 25**   CI-No.: **12510**
        Zusetzg.: **2,5-Dichloranilin** →   Comp.: **2,5-Dichloroaniline** →
                   2'-Hydroxy-3'-naphthoyl-5-aminobenzimidazolon   **2'-Hydroxy-3'-naphthoyl-5-aminobenzimidazolone**
                   Prpt.: **KBr (~ 3/1000)**   Dec. No.: **1.5.3**

Organische Pigmente
1. Monoazopigmente
1.5. KK Benzimidazole

Organic Pigments
1. Monoazo Pigments
1.5. CC Benzimidazoles

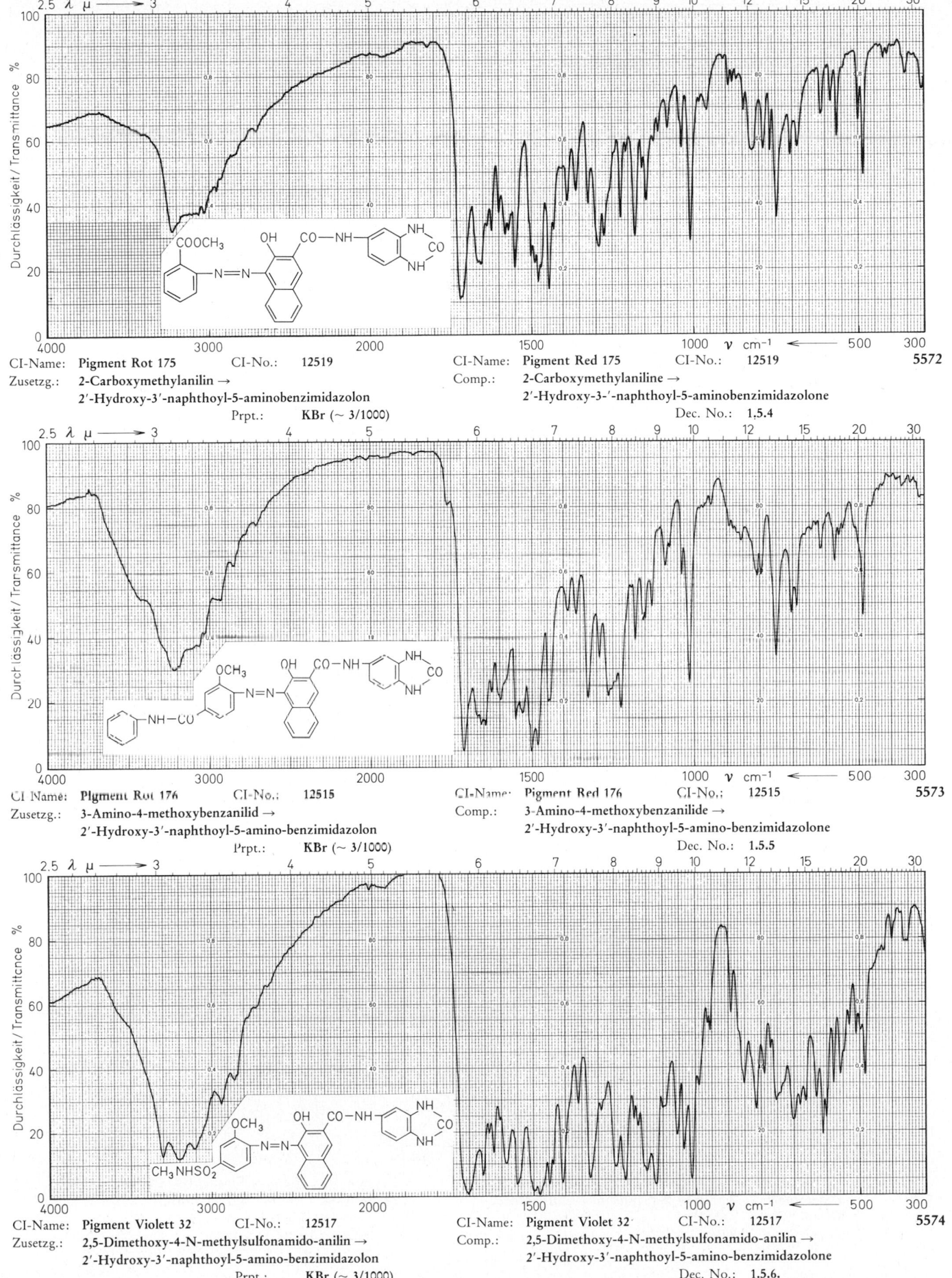

CI-Name: **Pigment Rot 175**   CI-No.: **12519**

CI-Name: **Pigment Red 175**   CI-No.: **12519**   **5572**

Zusetzg.: 2-Carboxymethylanilin →

Comp.: 2-Carboxymethylaniline →

2'-Hydroxy-3'-naphthoyl-5-aminobenzimidazolon

2'-Hydroxy-3-'-naphthoyl-5-aminobenzimidazolone

Prpt.: **KBr (~ 3/1000)**   Dec. No.: **1,5.4**

CI-Name: **Pigment Rot 176**   CI-No.: **12515**

CI-Name: **Pigment Red 176**   CI-No.: **12515**   **5573**

Zusetzg.: 3-Amino-4-methoxybenzanilid →

Comp.: 3-Amino-4-methoxybenzanilide →

2'-Hydroxy-3'-naphthoyl-5-amino-benzimidazolon

2'-Hydroxy-3'-naphthoyl-5-amino-benzimidazolone

Prpt.: **KBr (~ 3/1000)**   Dec. No.: **1.5.5**

CI-Name: **Pigment Violett 32**   CI-No.: **12517**

CI-Name: **Pigment Violet 32**   CI-No.: **12517**   **5574**

Zusetzg.: 2,5-Dimethoxy-4-N-methylsulfonamido-anilin →

Comp.: 2,5-Dimethoxy-4-N-methylsulfonamido-anilin →

2'-Hydroxy-3'-naphthoyl-5-amino-benzimidazolon

2'-Hydroxy-3'-naphthoyl-5-amino-benzimidazolone

Prpt.: **KBr (~ 3/1000)**   Dec. No.: **1.5.6.**

Organische Pigmente
2. Monoazofarblacke
2.2. Mit SO₃H-Gruppen

Organic Pigments
2. Monoazo-Salts
2.2. With SO₃H-Groups

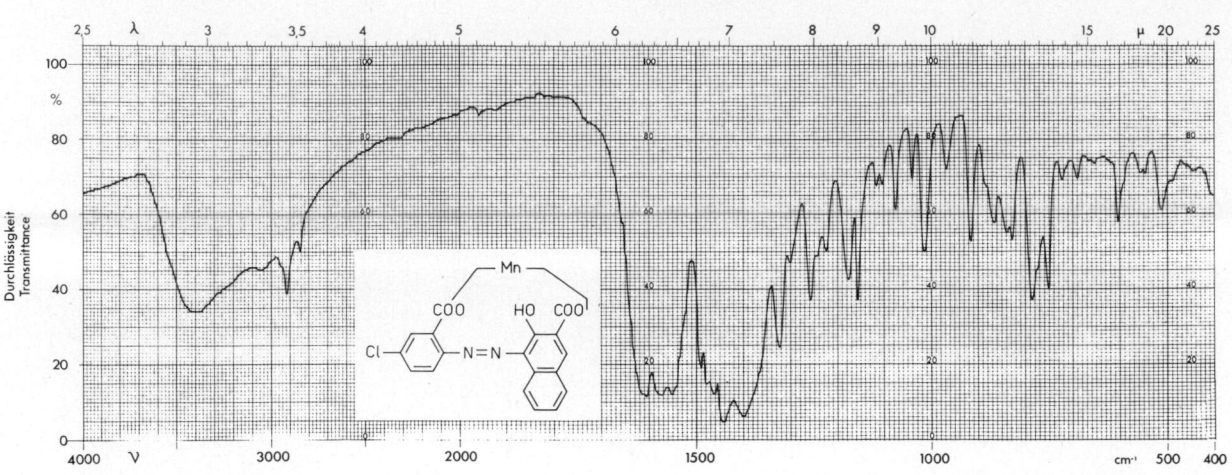

5575

CI-Name:	**Pigment Rot 55**	CI-No.:	**15820**

Zusammensetzung: **5-Chloranthranilsäure → BONS, Mn-Salz**

Präparation: **KBr (3,5/1000)**   Dez. Nr.: **2.1.1**

CI-Name: **Pigment Red 55** CI-No.: **15820**

Composition: **5-Chloroanthranilic acid → BHNA, Mn-salt**

Preparation: **KBr (3,5/1000)** Dec. No.: **2.1.1**

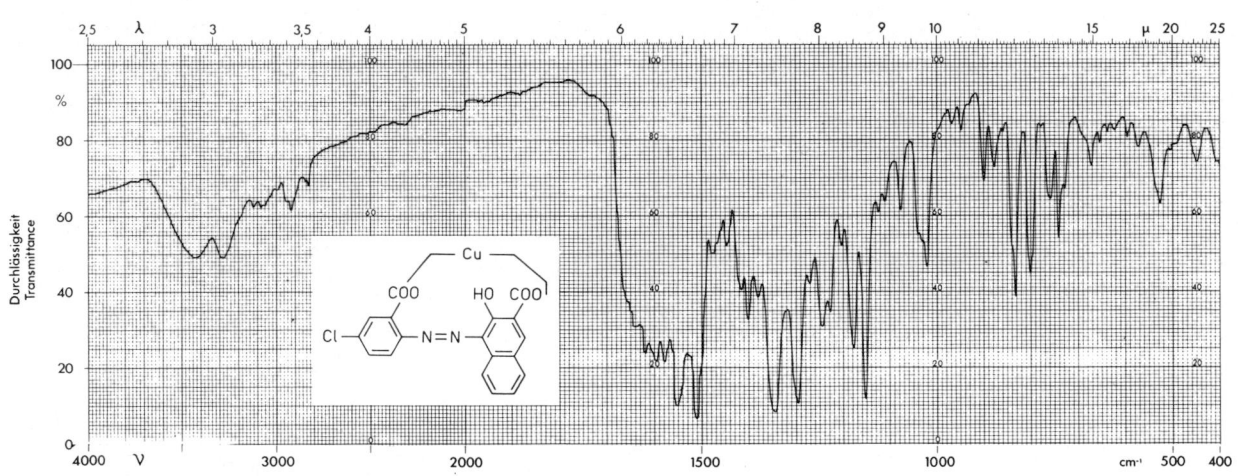

5576

CI-Name: **Pigment Rot 55** CI-No.: **15820**

Zusammensetzung: **5-Chloranthranilsäure → BONS, Cu-Salz**

Präparation: **KBr (3,5/1000)** Dez. Nr.: **2.1.2**

CI-Name: **Pigment Red 55** CI-No.: **15820**

Composition: **5-Chloroanthranilic acid → BHNA, Cu-salt**

Preparation: **KBr (3,5/1000)** Dec. No.: **2.1.2**

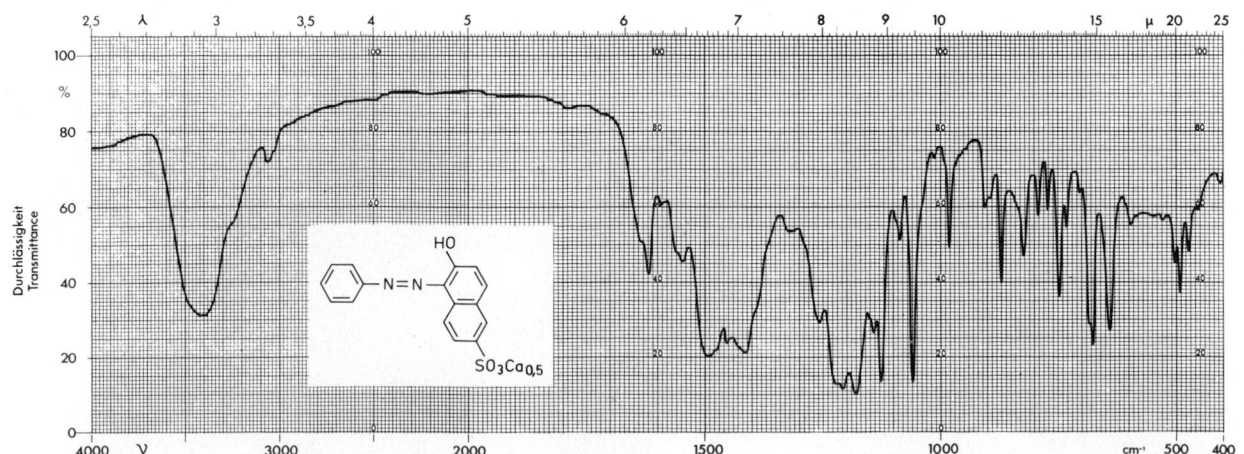

5577

CI-Name: **Pigment Orange 18** CI-No.: **15970**

Zusammensetzung: **Anilin → 2-Naphthol-6-sulfonsäure, Ca-Salz**

Präparation: **KBr (3,5/1000)** Dez. Nr.: **2.2.2**

CI-Name: **Pigment Orange 18** CI-No.: **15970**

Composition: **Aniline → 2-Naphthol-6-sulfonic acid, Ca-salt**

Preparation: **KBr (3,5/1000)** Dec. No.: **2.2.2**

Organische Pigmente
2. Monoazofarblacke
2.2. Mit SO₃H-Gruppen

Organic Pigments
2. Monoazo-Salts
2.2. With SO₃H-Groups

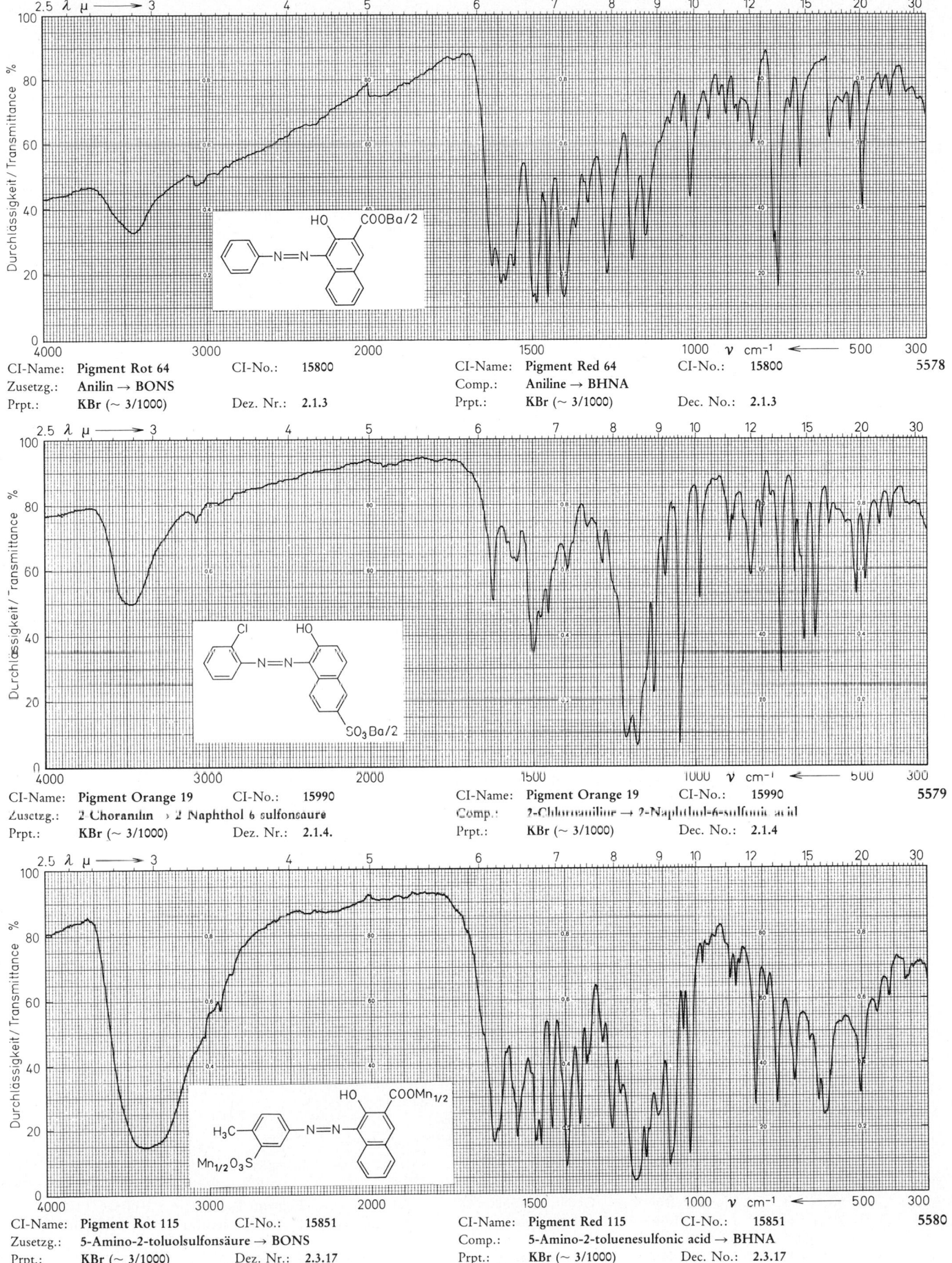

CI-Name: **Pigment Rot 64**   CI-No.:   **15800**   CI-Name: **Pigment Red 64**   CI-No.:   **15800**   **5578**
Zusetzg.:   **Anilin → BONS**   Comp.:   **Aniline → BHNA**
Prpt.:   **KBr (~ 3/1000)**   Dez. Nr.:   **2.1.3**   Prpt.:   **KBr (~ 3/1000)**   Dec. No.:   **2.1.3**

CI-Name: **Pigment Orange 19**   CI-No.:   **15990**   CI-Name: **Pigment Orange 19**   CI-No.:   **15990**   **5579**
Zusetzg.:   **2-Choranilin → 2-Naphthol 6-sulfonsäure**   Comp.:   **2-Chloroaniline → 2-Naphthol-6-sulfonic acid**
Prpt.:   **KBr (~ 3/1000)**   Dez. Nr.:   **2.1.4.**   Prpt.:   **KBr (~ 3/1000)**   Dec. No.:   **2.1.4**

CI-Name: **Pigment Rot 115**   CI-No.:   **15851**   CI-Name: **Pigment Red 115**   CI-No.:   **15851**   **5580**
Zusetzg.:   **5-Amino-2-toluolsulfonsäure → BONS**   Comp.:   **5-Amino-2-toluenesulfonic acid → BHNA**
Prpt.:   **KBr (~ 3/1000)**   Dez. Nr.:   **2.3.17**   Prpt.:   **KBr (~ 3/1000)**   Dec. No.:   **2.3.17**

Organische Pigmente
2. Monoazofarblacke
2.2. Mit SO₃H-Gruppen

Organic Pigments
2. Monoazo-Salts
2.2. With SO₃H-Groups

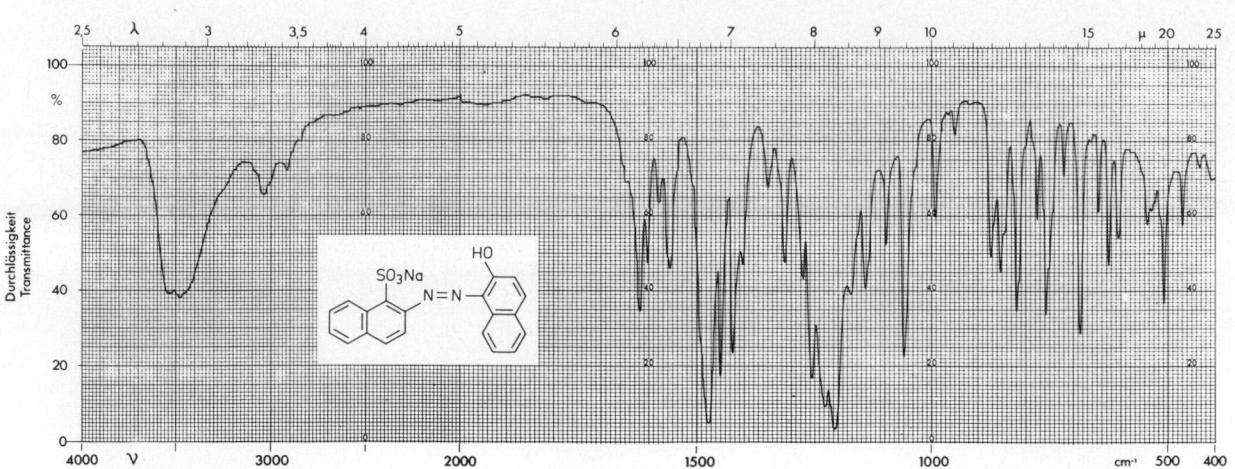

5581

CI-Name:	**Pigment Rot 49**	CI-No.:	**15630**
Zusammensetzung:	**2-Naphthylamin-1-sulfonsäure → 2-Naphthol, Na-Salz**		
Präparation:	**KBr (3,3/1000)**	Dez. Nr.:	**2.2.3**

CI-Name:	**Pigment Red 49**	CI-No.:	**15630**
Composition:	**2-Naphthylamine-1-sulfonic acid → 2-Naphthol, Na-salt**		
Preparation:	**KBr (3,3/1000)**	Dec. No.:	**2.2.3**

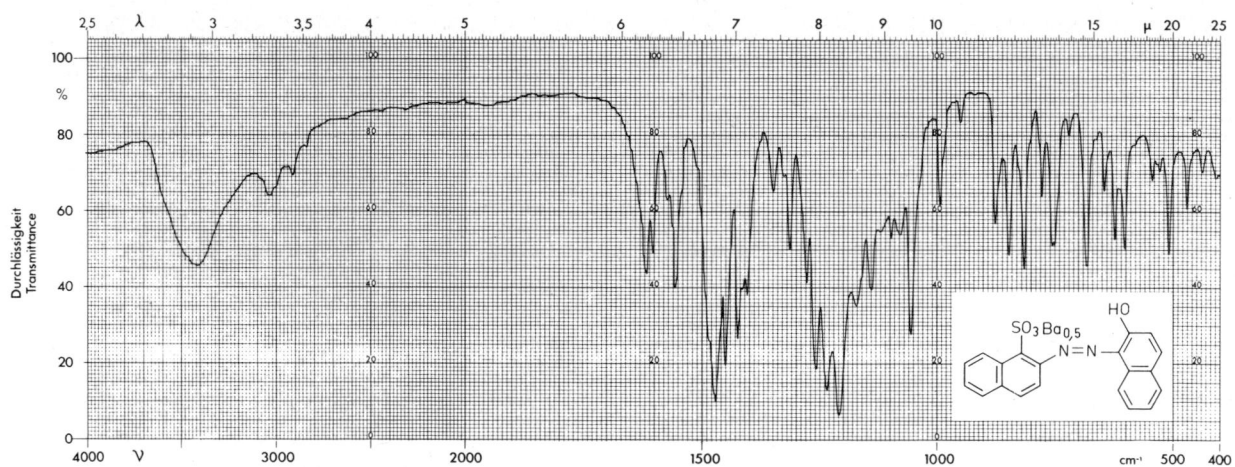

5582

CI-Name:	**Pigment Rot 49**	CI-No.:	**15630**
Zusammensetzung:	**2-Naphthylamin-1-sulfonsäure → 2-Naphthol, Ba-Salz**		
Präparation:	**KBr (3,3/1000)**	Dez. Nr.:	**2.2.4**

CI-Name:	**Pigment Red 49**	CI-No.:	**15630**
Composition:	**2-Naphthylamine-1-sulfonic acid → 2-Naphthol, Ba-salt**		
Preparation:	**KBr (3,3/1000)**	Dec. No.:	**2.2.4**

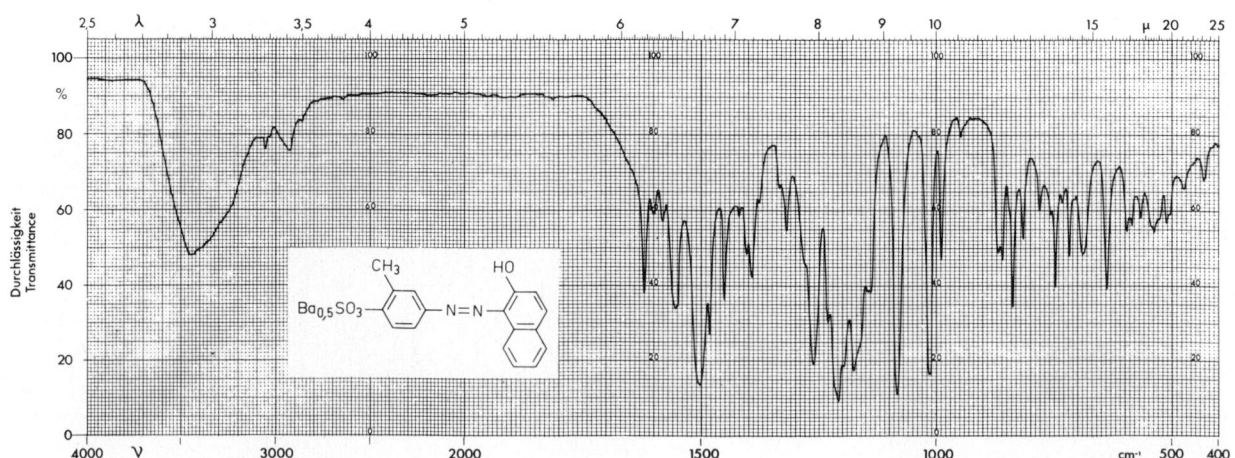

5583

CI-Name:	**Pigment Rot 51**	CI-No.:	**15580**
Zusammensetzung:	**2-Methylsulfanilsäure → 2-Naphthol, Ba-Salz**		
Präparation:	**KBr (3/1000)**	Dez. Nr.:	**2.2.5**

CI-Name:	**Pigment Red 51**	CI-No.:	**15580**
Composition:	**2-Methylsulfanilic acid → 2-Naphthol, Ba-salt**		
Preparation:	**KBr (3/1000)**	Dec. No.:	**2.2.5**

Organische Pigmente
2. Monoazofarblacke
2.2. Mit SO₃H-Gruppen

Organic Pigments
2. Monoazo-Salts
2.2. With SO₃H-Groups

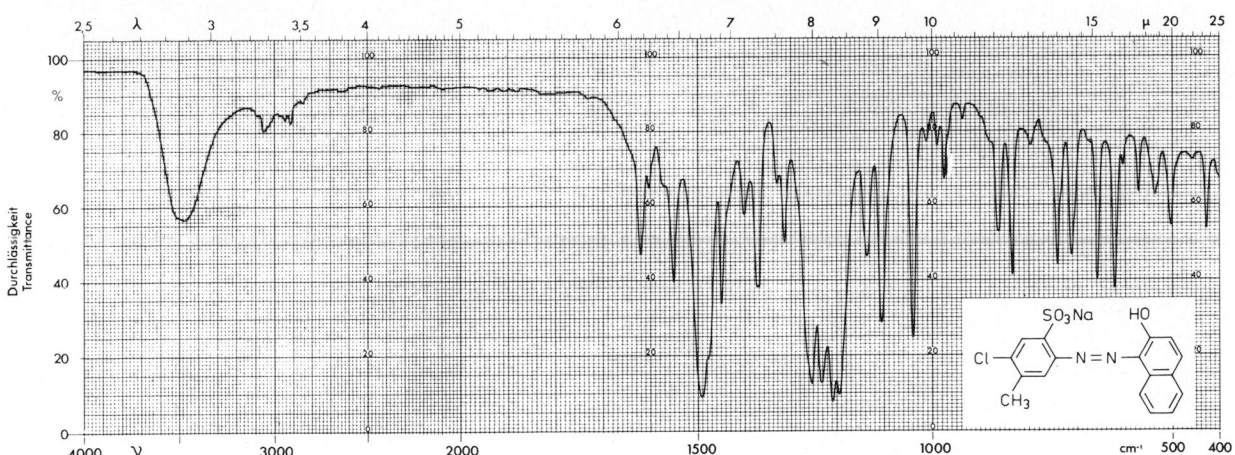

CI-Name:	**Pigment Rot 53**	CI-No.:	**15585**	CI-Name:	**Pigment Red 53**	CI-No.:	**15585**	**5584**

Zusammensetzung: **4-Chlor-3-toluidin-6-sulfonsäure → 2-Naphthol, Na-Salz**

Composition: **4-Chloro-3-toluidine-6-sulfonic acid → 2-Naphthol, Na-salt**

Präparation: **KBr (3,3/1000)**   Dez. Nr.: **2.2.6**

Preparation: **KBr (3,3/1000)**   Dec. No.: **2.2.6**

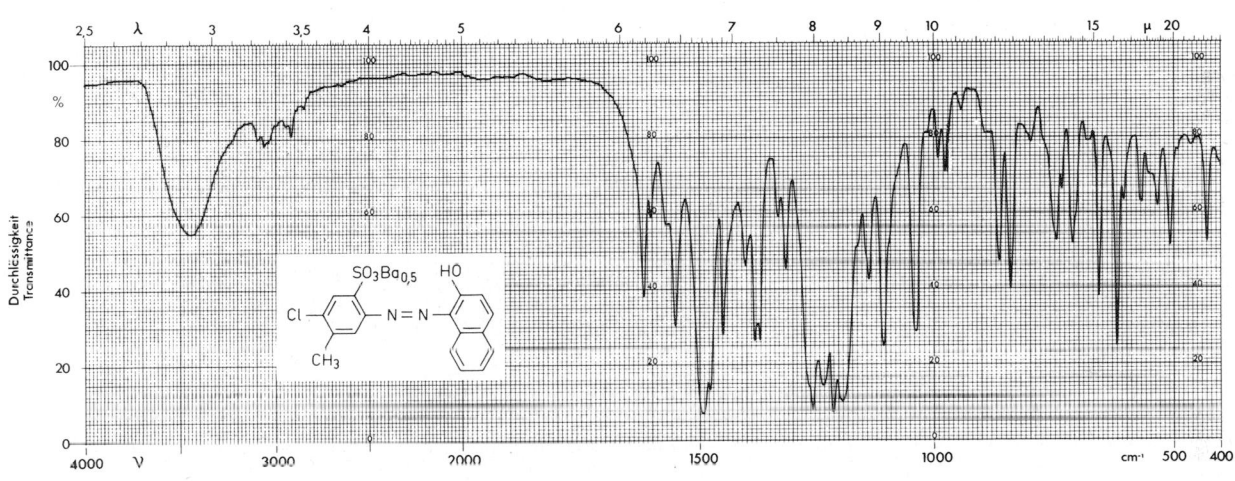

CI-Name:	**Pigment Rot 53**	CI-No.:	**15585**	CI-Name:	**Pigment Red 53**	CI-No.:	**15585**	**5585**

Zusammensetzung: **4-Chlor-3-toluidin-6-sulfonsäure → 2-Naphthol, Ba-Salz**

Composition: **4-Chloro-3-toluidine-6-sulfonic acid → 2-Naphthol, Ba-salt**

Präparation: **KBr (3,3/1000)**   Dez. Nr.: **2.2.7**

Preparation: **KBr (3,3/1000)**   Dec. No.: **2.2.7**

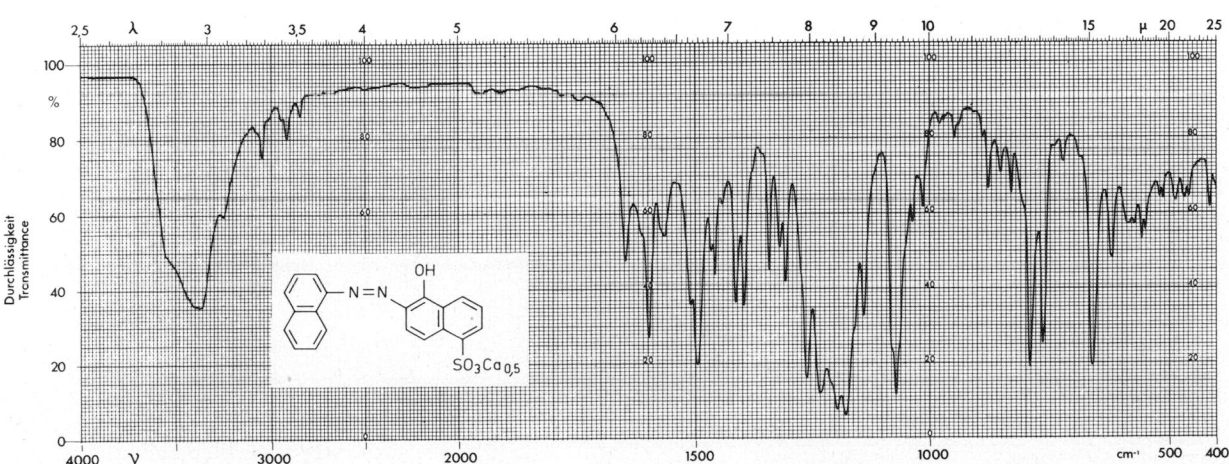

CI-Name:	**Pigment Rot 54**	CI-No.:	**14830**	CI-Name:	**Pigment Red 54**	CI-No.:	**14830**	**5586**

Zusammensetzung: **1-Naphthylamin → 1-Naphthol-5-sulfonsäure, Ca-Salz**

Composition: **1-Naphthylamine → 1-Naphthol-5-sulfonic acid, Ca-salt**

Präparation: **KBr (3,3/1000)**   Dez. Nr.: **2.2.20**

Preparation: **KBr (3,3/1000)**   Dec. No.: **2.2.20**

Organische Pigmente
2. Monoazofarblacke
2.2. Mit SO₃H-Gruppen

Organic Pigments
2. Monoazo-Salts
2.2. With SO₃H-Groups

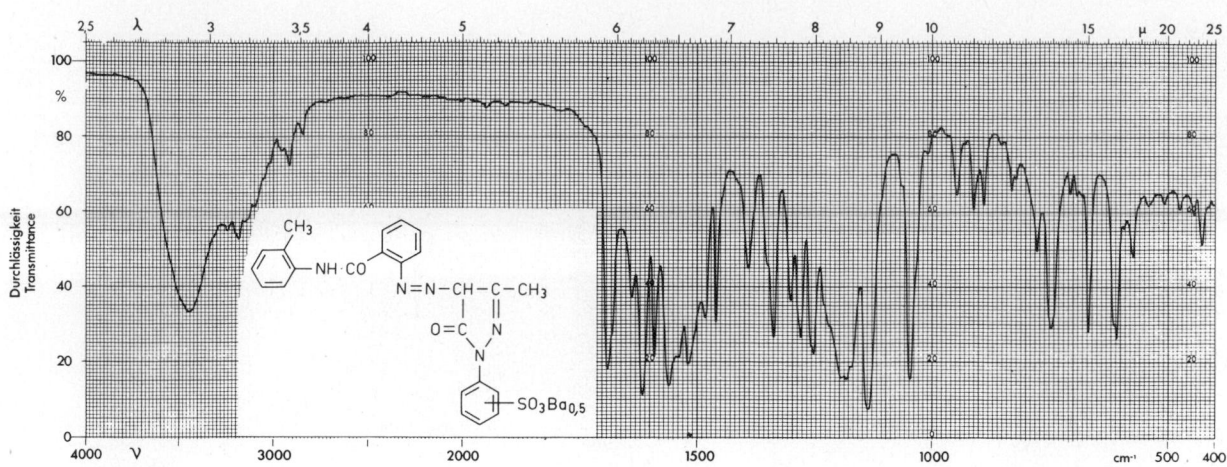

5587

CI-Name:	**Pigment Gelb 62**
Zusammensetzung:	**Anthranilsäure-2-toluidid → 3-Methyl-1-sulfophenylpyrazolon-5, Ba-Salz**
Präparation:	**KBr (3,3/1000)** Dez. Nr.: **2.2.8**

CI-Name:	**Pigment Yellow 62**
Composition:	**Anthranilic acid-2-toluidine → 3-Methyl-1-sulfophenyl-5-pyrazolone, Ba-salt**
Preparation:	**KBr (3,3/1000)** Dec. No.: **2.2.8**

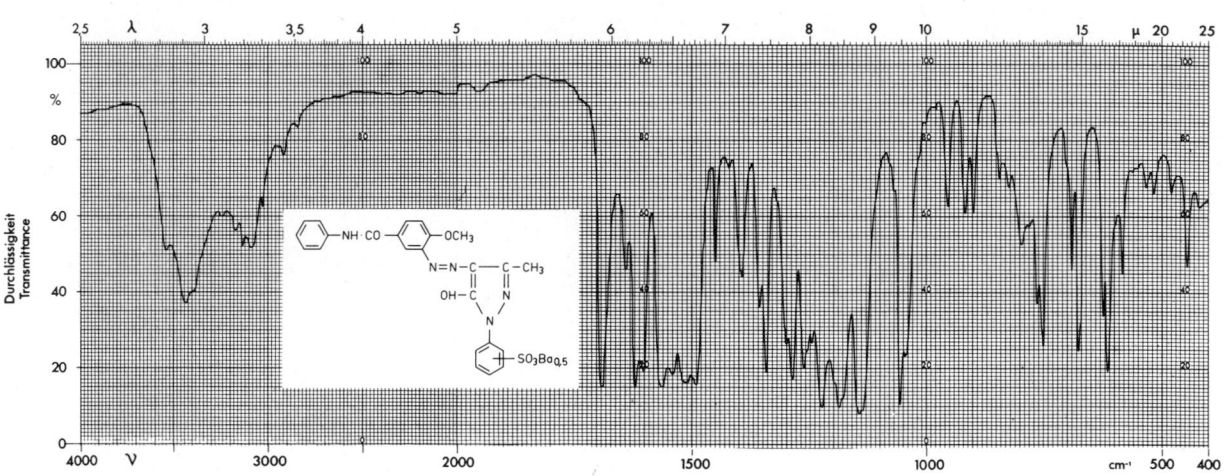

5588

CI-Name:	**Pigment Gelb 61**
Zusammensetzung:	**3-Amino-4-methoxybenzanilid → 3-Methyl-1-sulfophenylpyrazolon-5, Ba-Salz**
Präparation:	**KBr (3,3/1000)** Dez. Nr : **2.2.9**

CI-Name:	**Pigment Yellow 61**
Composition:	**3-Amino-4-methoxybenzanilide → 3-Methyl-1-sulfophenyl-5-pyrazolone, Ba-salt**
Preparation:	**KBr (3,3/1000)** Dec. No.: **2.2.9**

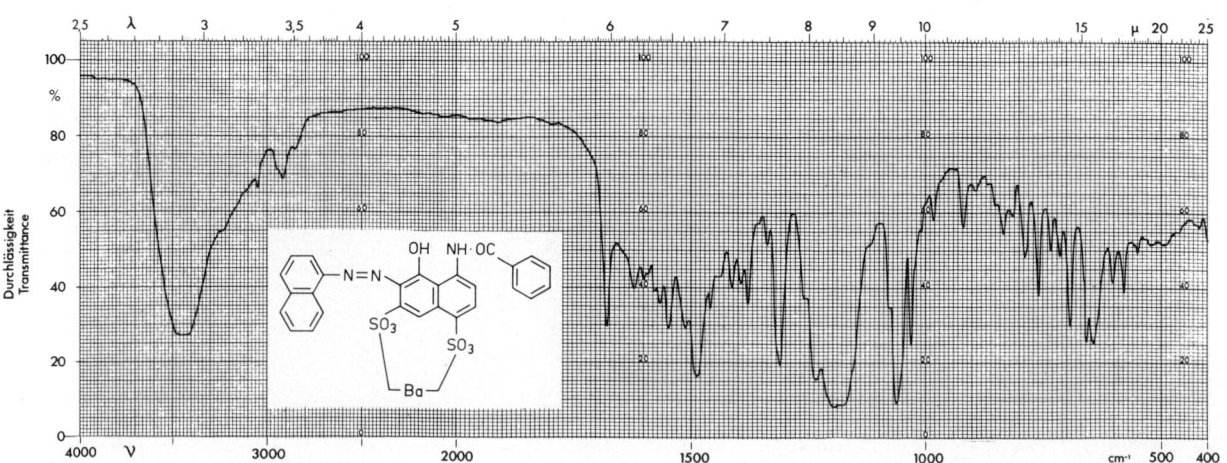

5589

CI-Name:	**Pigment Violett 8** CI-No.: **18005**
Zusammensetzung:	**1-Naphthylamin → N-Benzoyl-8-amino-1-naphthol-3,5-disulfonsäure, Ba-Salz**
Präparation:	**KBr (3,3/1000)** Dez. Nr.: **2.2.21**

CI-Name:	**Pigment Violet 8** CI-No.: **18005**
Composition:	**1-Naphthylamine → N-Benzoyl-8-amino-1-naphthol-3,5-disulfonic acid, Ba-salt**
Preparation:	**KBr (3,3/1000)** Dec. No.: **2.2.21**

Organische Pigmente
2. Monoazofarblacke
2.2. Mit SO₃H-Gruppen

Crganic Pigments
2. Monoazo-Salts
2.2. With SO₃H-Groups

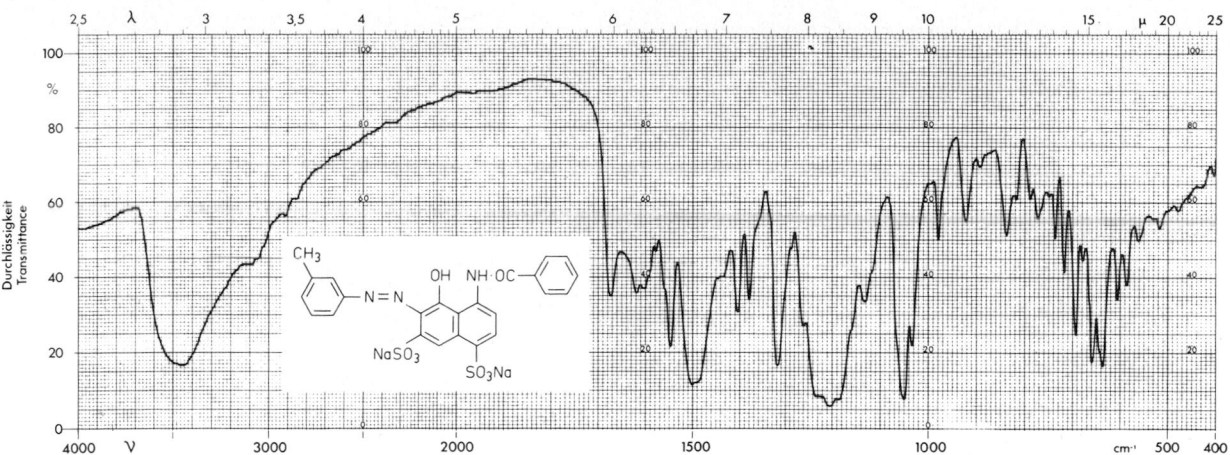

CI-Name: **Pigment Rot 66**   CI-No.: **18000**

Zusammensetzung: **3-Toluidin → N-Benzoyl-8-amino-1-naph-thol-3,5-disulfonsäure, Na-Salz**

Präparation: **KBr (3,3/1000)**   Dez. Nr.: **2.2.22**

CI-Name: **Pigment Red 66**   CI-No.: **18000**

Composition: **3-Toluidine → N-Benzoyl-8-amino-1-naph-thol-3,5-disulfonic acid, Na-sait**

Preparation: **KBr (3,3/1000)**   Dec. No.: **2.2.22**

5590

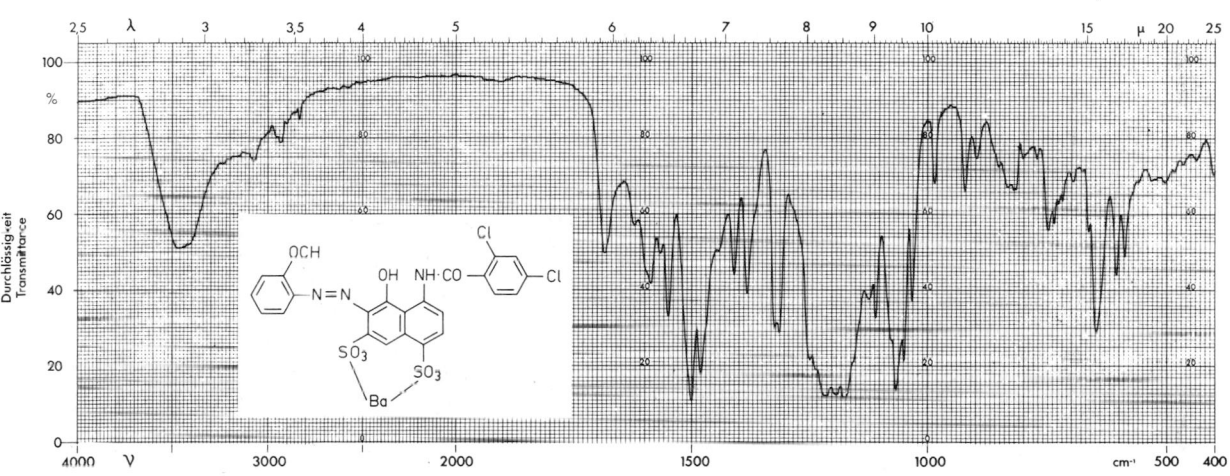

CI-Name: **Pigment Rot 67**   CI-No.: **18025**

Zusammensetzung: **2-Methoxyanilin → N-(2′,4′-Dichlorbenzoyl)-8-amino-1-naphthol-3,5-disulfonsäure, Ba-Salz**

Präparation: **KBr (3,3/1000)**   Dez. Nr.: **2.2.23**

CI-Name: **Pigment Red 67**   CI-No.: **18025**

Composition: **2-Methoxyaniline → N-(2′,4′-Dichlorobenzoyl)-8-amino-1-naphthol-3,5-disulfonic acid, Ba-salt**

Preparation: **KBr (3,3/1000)**   Dec. No.: **2.2.23**

5591

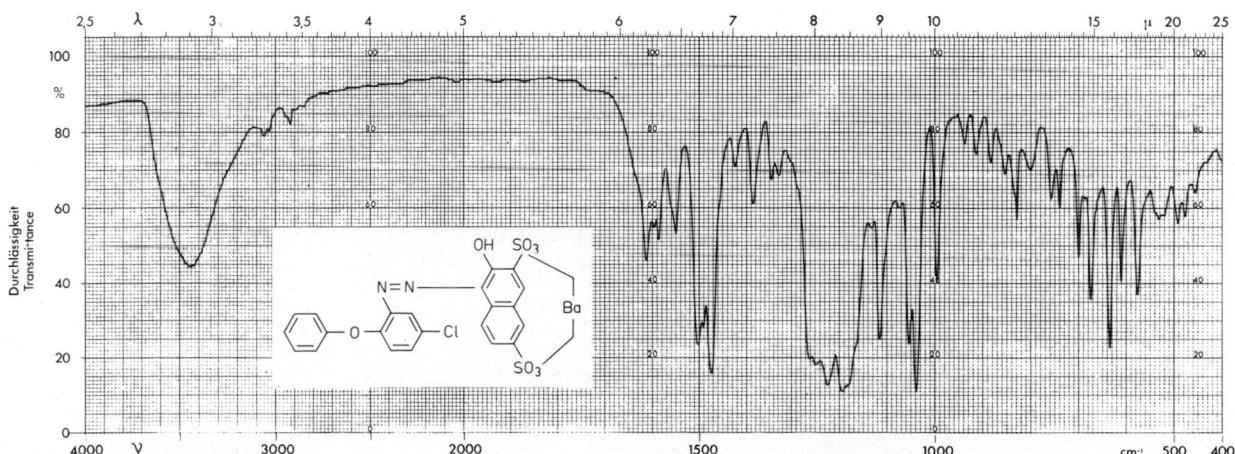

CI-Name: **Pigment Rot 94**

Zusammensetzung: **5-Chlor-2-phenoxyanilin → 2-Naphthol-3,6-disulfonsäure, Ba-Salz**

Präparation: **KBr (3,3/1000)**   Dez. Nr.: **2.2.10**

CI-Name: **Pigment Red 94**

Composition: **5-Chloro-2-phenoxyaniline → 2-Naphthol-3,6-disulfonic acid, Ba-salt**

Preparation: **KBr (3,3/1000)**   Dec. No.: **2.2.10**

5592

Organische Pigmente
2. Monoazofarblacke
2.2. Mit SO₃H-Gruppen

Organic Pigments
2. Monoazo-Salts
2.2. With SO₃H-Groups

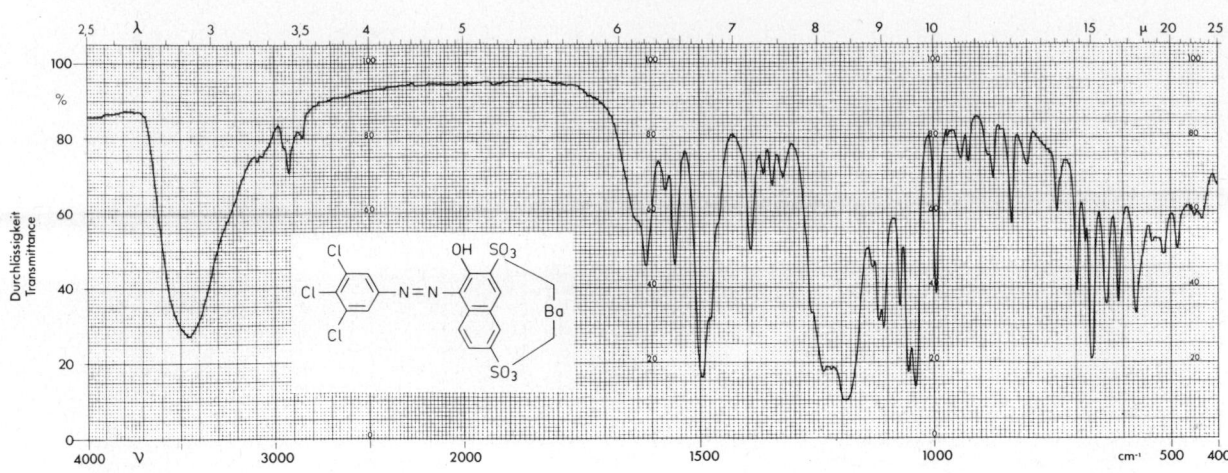

5593

CI-Name:	**Pigment Rot 120**	CI-Name:	**Pigment Red 120**
Zusammensetzung:	**3,4,5-Trichloranilin → 2-Methylnaphthalin-3,6-disulfonsäure, Ba-Salz**	Composition:	**3,4,5-Trichloroaniline → 2-Methyl-naphthalene-3,6-disulfonic acid, Ba-salt**
Präparation:	**KBr (3,3/1000)** Dez. Nr.: **2.2.11**	Preparation:	**KBr (3,3/1000)** Dec. No.: **2.2.11**

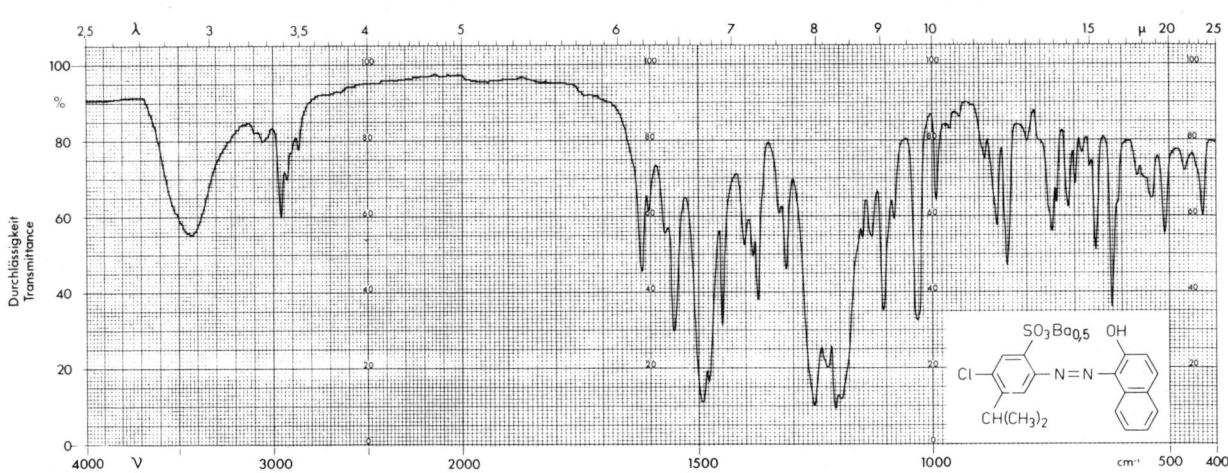

5594

CI-Name:	**Pigment Rot 117** CI-No.: 15603	CI-Name:	**Pigment Red 117** CI-No.: 15603
Zusammensetzung:	**2-Amino-5-chlor-4-isopropylbenzolsulfonsäure → 2-Naphthol, Ba-Salz**	Composition:	**2-Amino-5-chloro-4-isopropylbenzene-sulfonic acid → 2-Naphthol, Ba-salt**
Präparation:	**KBr (3,3/1000)** Dez. Nr : **2.2.12**	Preparation:	**KBr (3,3/1000)** Dec. No.: **2.2.12**

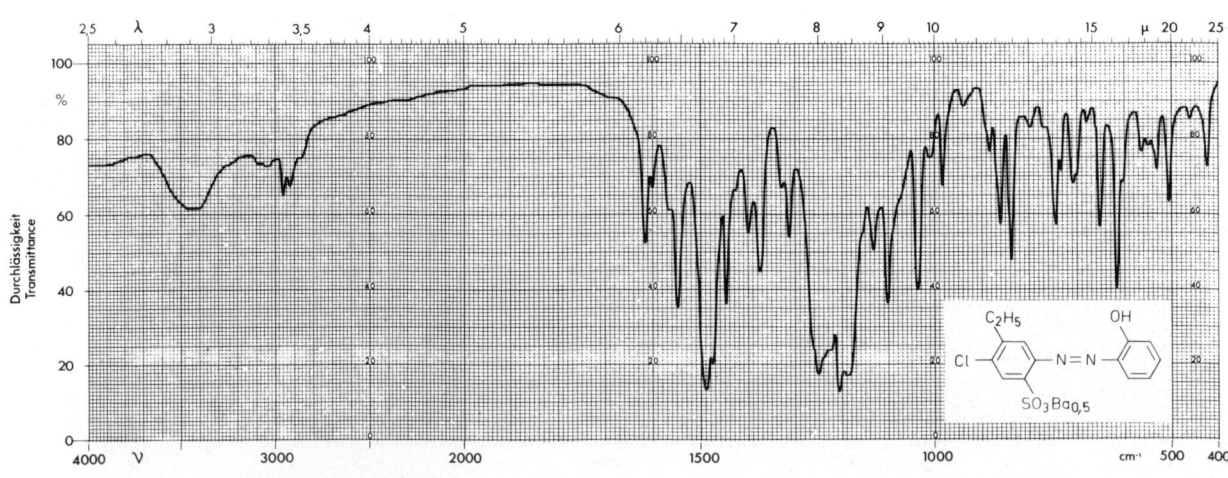

5595

Name:	**Clarion Rot 20-7150**	Name:	**Clarion Red 20-7150**
Zusammensetzung:	**2-Amino-4-ethyl-5-chlorbenzolsulfonsäure → Phenol, Ba-Salz**	Composition:	**2-Amino-5-chloro-4-ethylbenzene-sulfonic → Phenol, Ba-salt**
Präparation:	**KBr (3,5/1000)** Dez. Nr . **2.2.13**	Preparation:	**KBr (3,5/1000)** Dec. No.: **2.2.13**

Organische Pigmente
2. Monoazofarblacke
2.2. Mit SO₃H-Gruppen

Organic Pigments
2. Monoazo-Salts
2.2. With SO₃H-Groups

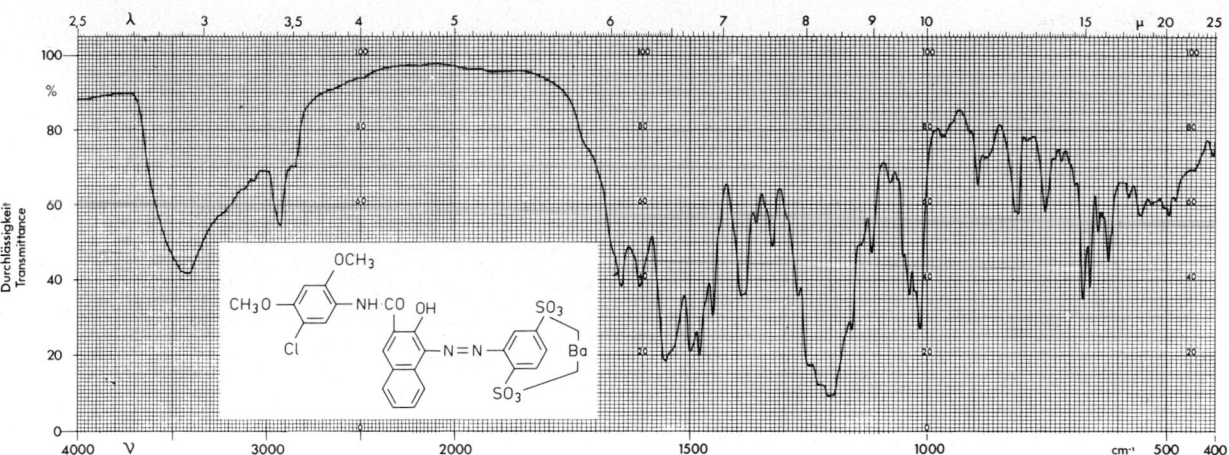

CI-Name: **Pigment Rot 133**
Zusammensetzung: **1-Amino-BONS-3'-chlor-4',6'-dimethoxy-anilid → 1,4-Benzoldisulfonsäure, Ba-Salz**
Präparation: **KBr (4/1000)**   Dez. Nr.: **2.2.14**

CI-Name: **Pigment Red 133**
Composition: **1-Amino-BHNA-3'-chloro-4',6'-dimethoxy-anilide → 1,4-Benzenedisulfonic acid, Ba-salt**
Preparation: **KBr (4/1000)**   Dec. No.: **2.2.14**

5596

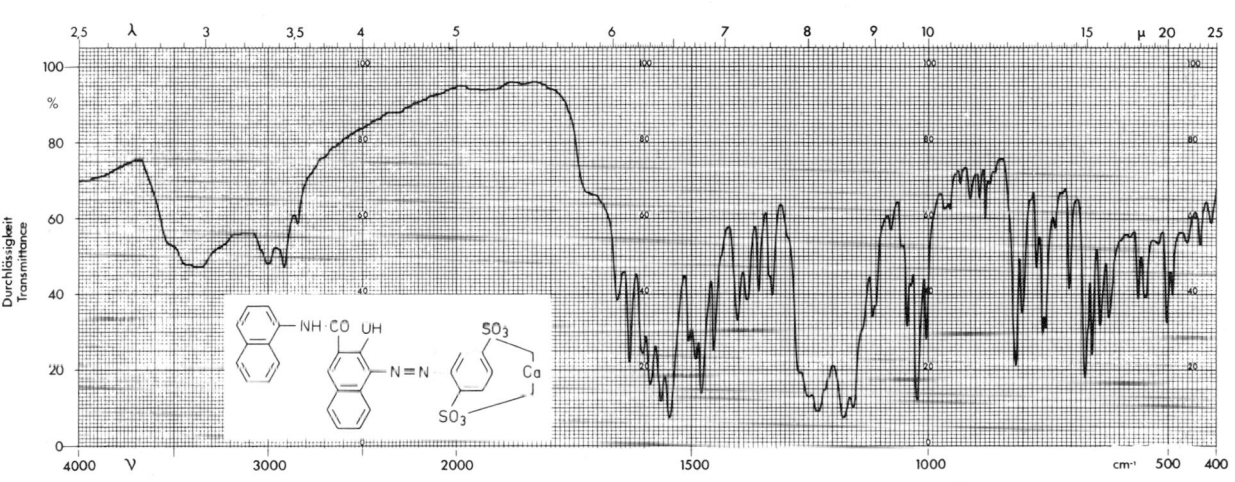

CI-Name: **Pigment Rot 134**
Zusammensetzung: **1-Amino-BONS-2'-naphthylamid → 1,4-Benzoldisulfonsäure, Ca Salz**
Präparation: **KBr (4/1000)**   Dez. Nr.: **2.2.15**

CI-Name: **Pigment Red 134**
Composition: **1-Amino-BHNA-2'-naphthylamide → 1,4-Benzenedisulfonic acid, Ca-salt**
Preparation: **KBr (4/1000)**   Dec. No.: **2.2.15**

5597

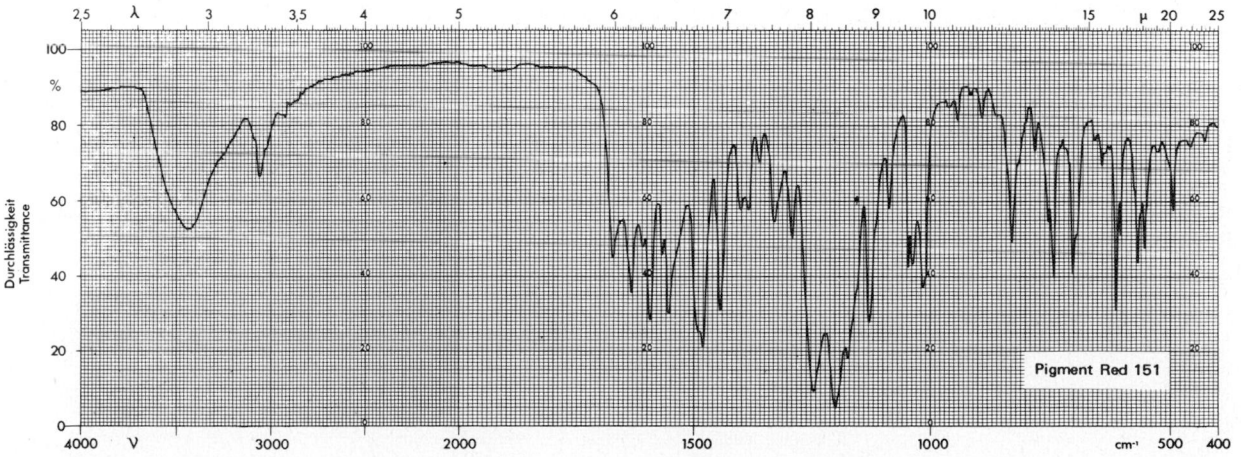

CI-Name: **Pigment Rot 151**   CI-No.: **15892**
Zusammensetzung: **n. b., Ba-Salz**
Präparation: **KBr (2/1000)**   Dez. Nr.: **2.2.16**

CI-Name: **Pigment Red 151**   CI-No.: **15892**
Composition: **n. k., Ba-salt**
Preparation: **KBr (2/1000)**   Dec. No.: **2.2.16**

5598

Organische Pigmente
2. Monoazofarblacke
2.2. Mit SO₃H-Gruppen

Organic Pigments
2. Monoazo-Salts
2.2. With SO₃H-Groups

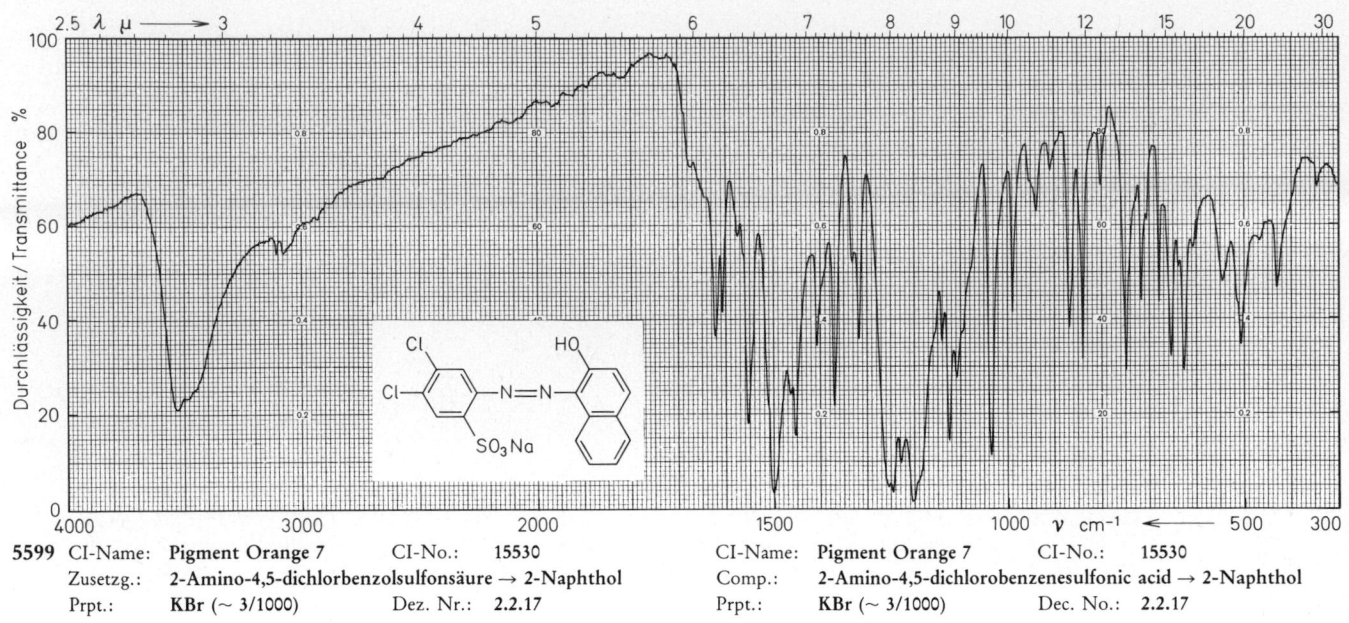

5599 CI-Name: **Pigment Orange 7**   CI-No.: **15530**
Zusetzg.: **2-Amino-4,5-dichlorbenzolsulfonsäure → 2-Naphthol**
Prpt.: **KBr (∼ 3/1000)**   Dez. Nr.: **2.2.17**

CI-Name: **Pigment Orange 7**   CI-No.: **15530**
Comp.: **2-Amino-4,5-dichlorobenzenesulfonic acid → 2-Naphthol**
Prpt.: **KBr (∼ 3/1000)**   Dec. No.: **2.2.17**

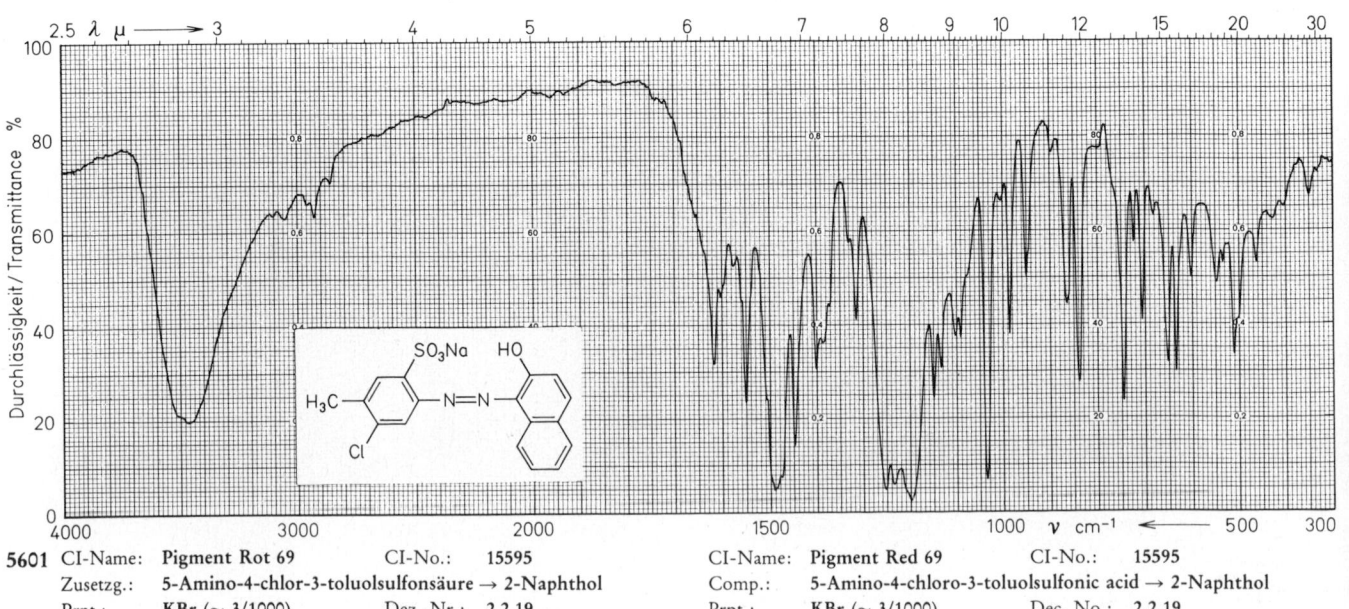

5601 CI-Name: **Pigment Rot 69**   CI-No.: **15595**
Zusetzg.: **5-Amino-4-chlor-3-toluolsulfonsäure → 2-Naphthol**
Prpt.: **KBr (∼ 3/1000)**   Dez.-Nr.: **2.2.19**

CI-Name: **Pigment Red 69**   CI-No.: **15595**
Comp.: **5-Amino-4-chloro-3-toluolsulfonic acid → 2-Naphthol**
Prpt.: **KBr (∼ 3/1000)**   Dec. No.: **2.2.19**

Sp. No. 5600: Während der Herstellung eliminiert – during production eliminated

Organische Pigmente
2. Monoazofarblacke
2.3. Mit COOH- und SO₃H-Gruppen

Organic Pigments
2. Monoazo-Salts
2.3. With COOH- and SO₃H-Groups

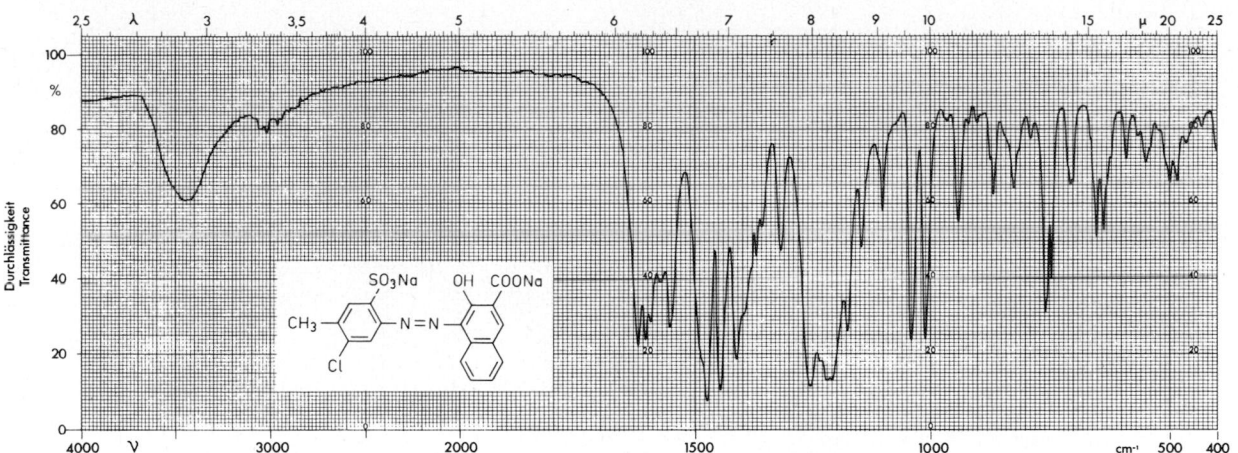

CI-Name: **Pigment Rot 48**   CI-No.: **15865**

CI-Name: **Pigment Red 48**   CI-No.: **15865**   5602

Zusammensetzung: 5-Chlor-4-toluidin-2-sulfonsäure → BONS, Na-Salz

Composition: 5-Chloro-4-toluidine-2-sulfonic acid → BHNA, Na-salt

Präparation: **KBr (3,3/1000)**   Dez. Nr.: **2.3.1**

Preparation: **KBr (3,3/1000)**   Dec. No.: **2.3.1**

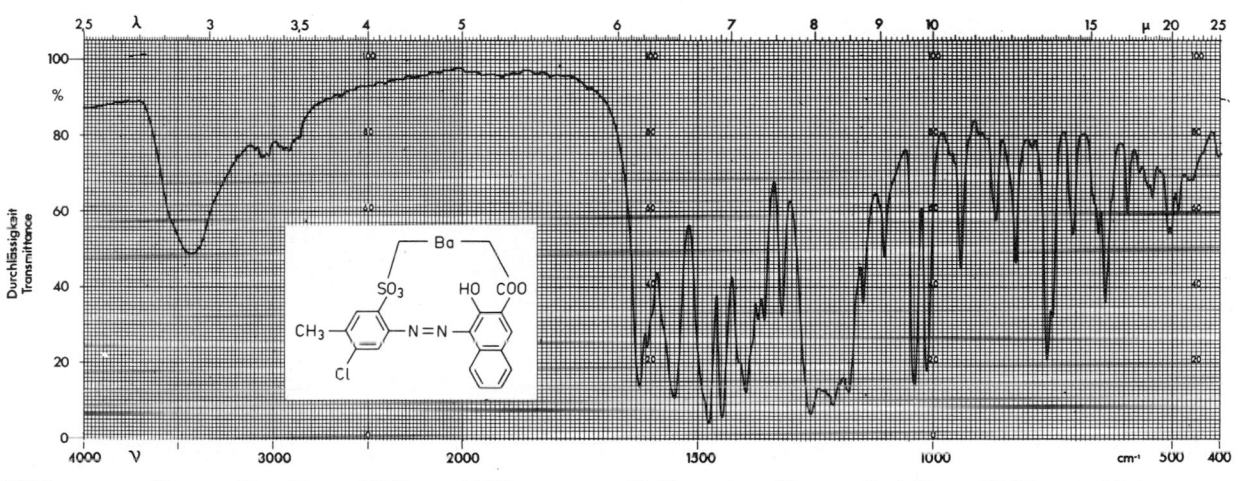

CI-Name: **Pigment Rot 48**   CI-No.: **15865**

CI-Name: **Pigment Red 48**   CI-No.: **5865**   5603

Zusammensetzung: 5-Chlor-4-toluidin-2-sulfonsäure → BONS, Ba-Salz

Composition: 5-Chloro-4-toluidine-2-sulfonic acid → BHNA, Ba-salt

Präparation: **KBr (3,3/1000)**   Dez. Nr.: **2.3.2**

Preparation: **KBr (3,3/1000)**   Dec. No.: **2.3.2**

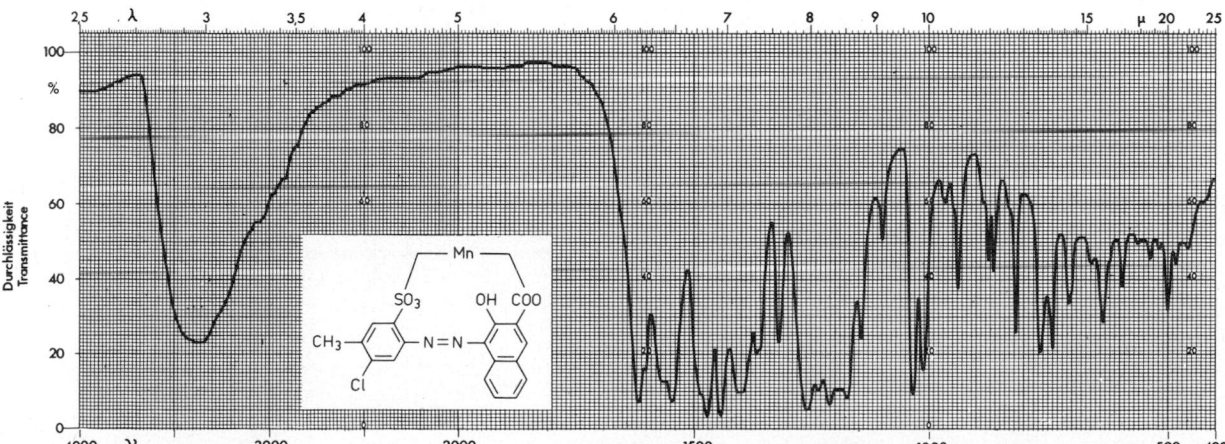

CI-Name: **Pigment Rot 48**   CI-No.: **15865**

CI-Name: **Pigment Red 48**   CI-No.: **15865**   5604

Zusammensetzung: 5-Chlor-4-toluidin-2-sulfonsäure → BONS, Mn-Salz

Composition: 5-Chloro-4-toluidine-2-sulfonic acid → BHNA, Mn-salt

Präparation: **KBr (5/1000)**   Dez. Nr.: **2.3.3**

Preparation: **KBr (5/1000)**   Dec. No.: **2.3.3**

Organische Pigmente
2. Monoazofarblacke
2.3. Mit COOH- und SO₃H-Gruppen

Organic Pigments
2. Monoazo-Salts
2.3. With COOH- and SO₃H-Groups

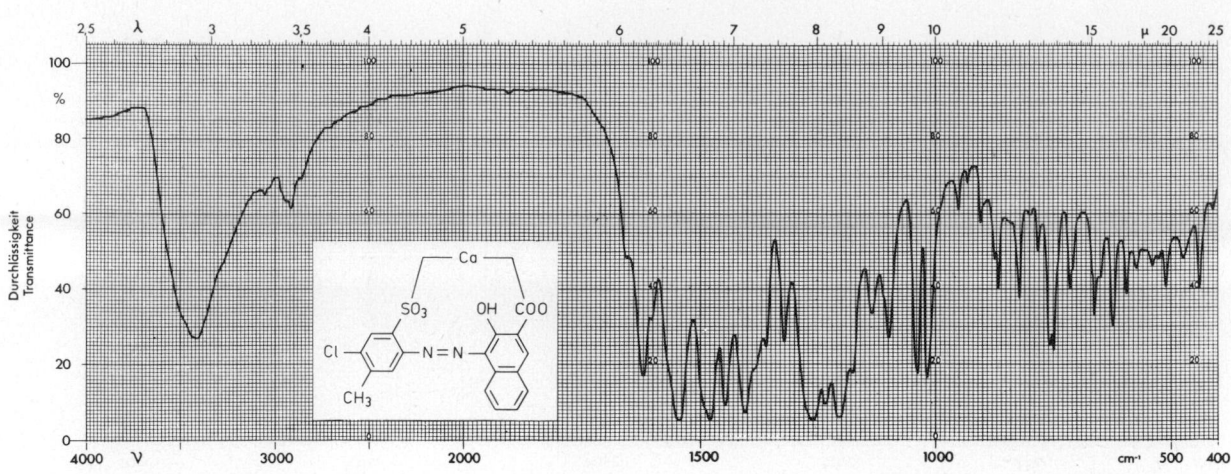

5605

CI-Name:	Pigment Rot 52	CI-No.:	15860
Zusammen-setzung:	6-Chlor-3-toluidin-4-sulfonsäure → BONS, Ca-Salz		
Präparation:	KBr (5/1000)	Dez. Nr.:	2.3.4

CI-Name:	Pigment Red 52	CI-No.:	15860
Composition:	6-Chloro-3-toluidine-4-sulfonic acid → BHNA, Ca-salt		
Preparation:	KBr (5/1000)	Dec. No.:	2.3.4

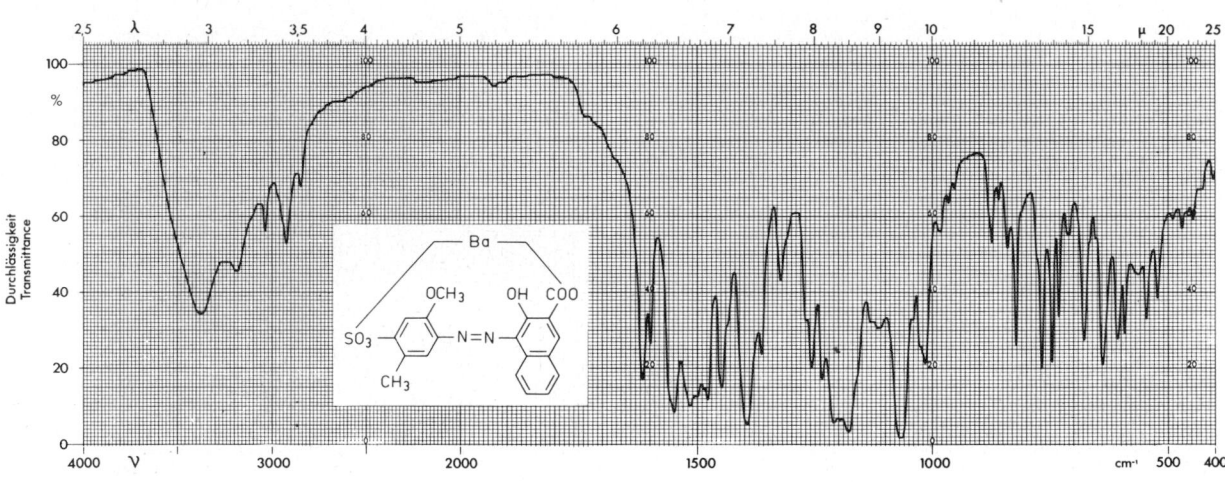

5606

CI-Name:	Pigment Rot 57	CI-No.:	15870
Zusammen-setzung:	2-Methyl-5-methoxylsulfanilsäure → BONS, Ba-Salz		
Präparation:	KBr (5/1000)	Dez. Nr.:	2.3.5

CI-Name:	Pigment Red 56	CI-No.:	15870
Composition:	2-Methyl-5-methoxysulfanilic acid → BHNA, Ba-salt		
Preparation:	KBr (5/1000)	Dec. No.:	2.3.5

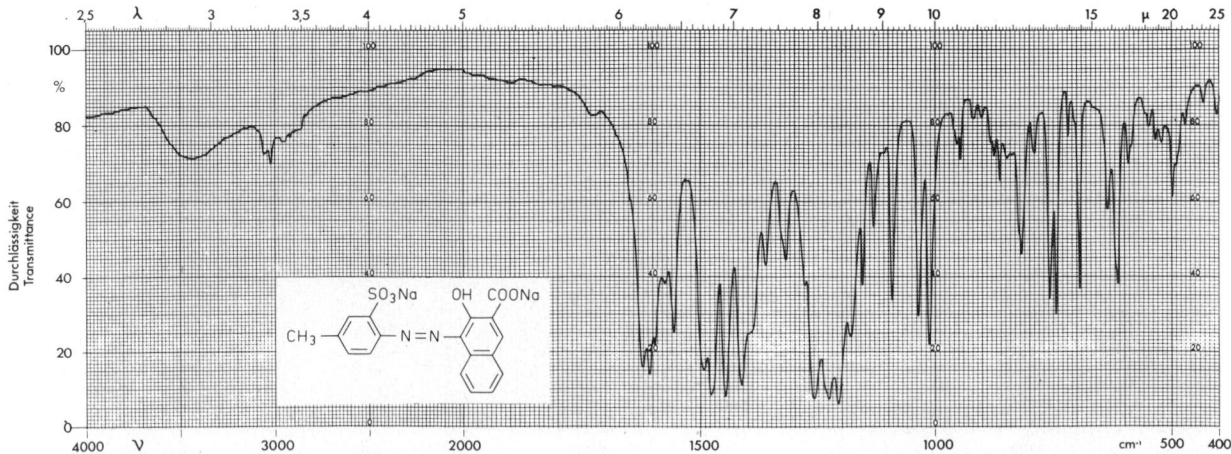

5607

CI-Name:	Pigment Rot 57	CI-No.:	15850
Zusammen-setzung:	4-Toluidin-3-sulfonsäure → BONS, Na-Salz		
Präparation:	KBr (5/1000)	Dez. Nr.:	2.3.6

CI-Name:	Pigment Red 57	CI-No.:	15850
Composition:	4-Toluidine-3-sulfonic acid → BHNA, Na-salt		
Preparation:	KBr (5/1000)	Dec. No.:	2.3.6

Organische Pigmente
2. Monoazofarblacke
2.3. Mit COOH- und SO₃H-Gruppen

Organic Pigments
2. Monoazo-Salts
2.3. With COOH- and SO₃H-Groups

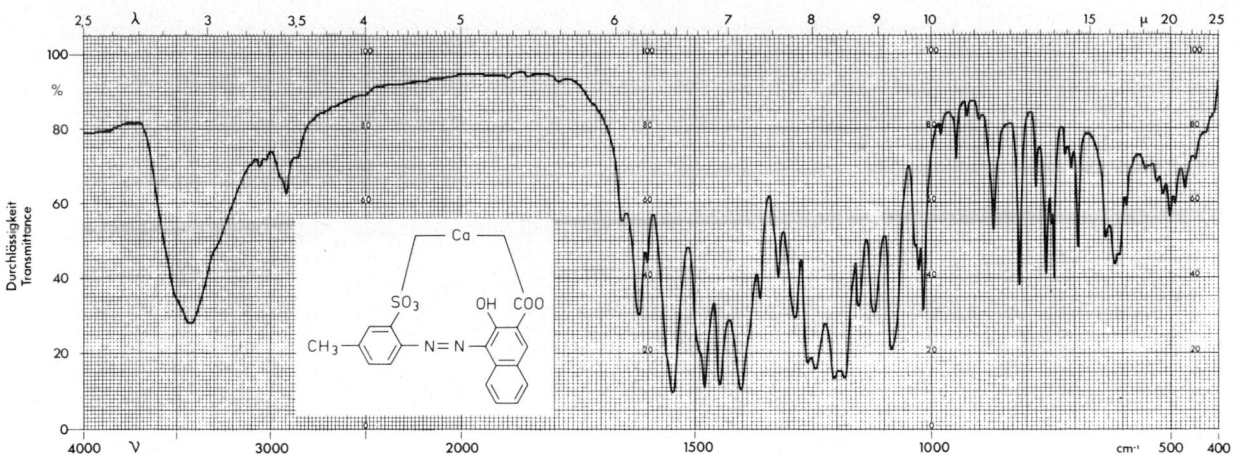

CI-Name:	**Pigment Rot 57**	CI-No.:	**15850**		CI-Name:	**Pigment Red 57**	CI-No.:	**15850**	**5608**

Zusammensetzung: **4-Toluidin-3-sulfonsäure → BONS, Ca-Salz**

Composition: **4-Toluidine-3-sulfonic acid → BHNA, Ca-salt**

Präparation: **KBr (5/1000)** Dez. Nr.: **2.3.7**

Preparation: **KBr (5/1000)** Dec. No.: **2.3.7**

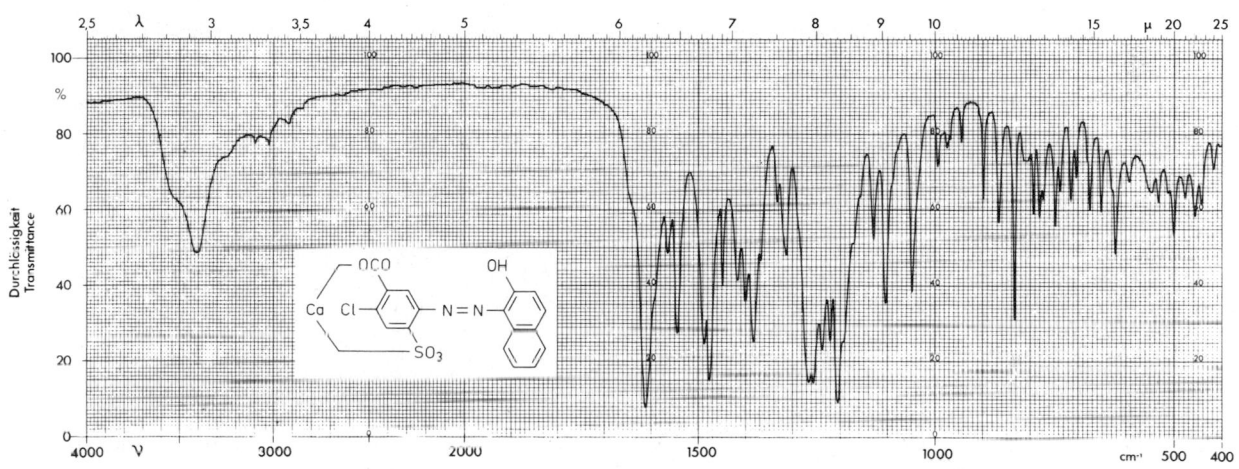

CI-Name: **Pigment Rot 68** CI-No.: **15525** CI-Name: **Pigment Red 68** CI-No.: **15525** **5609**

Zusammensetzung: **2-Amino-4-carboxy-5-chlorbenzolsulfonsäure → 2-Naphthol, Ca-Salz**

Composition: **2-Amino-4-carboxy-5-chlorobenzenesulfonic acid → 2-Naphthol, Ca-salt**

Präparation: **KBr (5/1000)** Dez. Nr.: **2.3.8**

Preparation: **KBr (5/1000)** Dec. No.: **2.3.8**

CI-Name: **Pigment Rot 58** CI-No.: **15825** CI-Name: **Pigment Red 58** CI-No.: **15825** **5610**

Zusammensetzung: **3-Amino-5-chlorbenzolsulfonsäure → BONS, Na-Salz**

Composition: **3-Amino-5-chlorobenzenesulfonic acid → BHNA, Na-salt**

Präparation: **KBr (5/1000)** Dez. Nr.: **2.3.9**

Preparation: **KBr (5/1000)** Dec. No.: **2.3.9**

Organische Pigmente
2. Monoazofarblacke
2.3. Mit COOH- und SO₃H-Gruppen

Organic Pigments
2. Monoazo-Salts
2.3. With COOH- and SO₃H-Groups

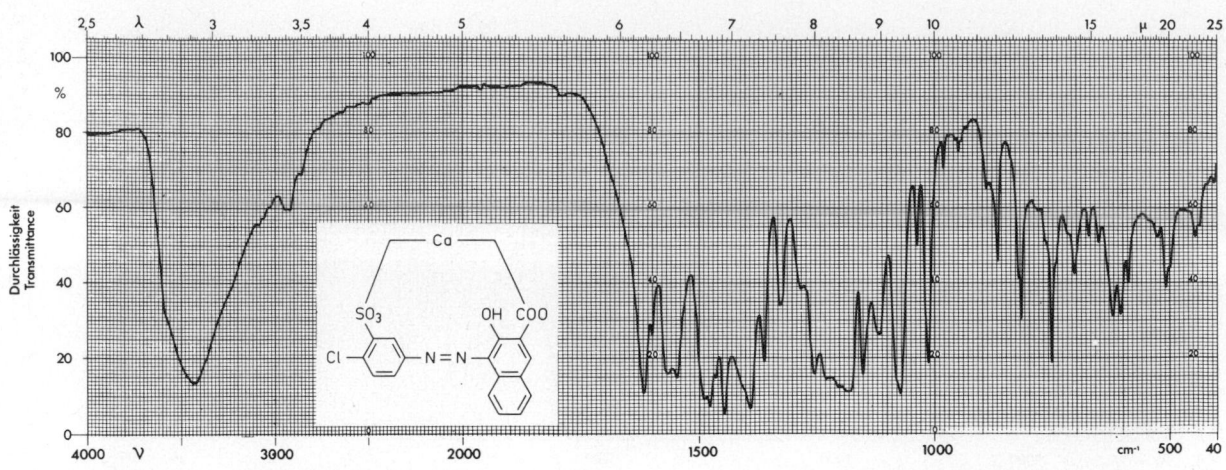

5611

CI-Name:	Pigment Rot 58	CI-No.:	**15825**
Zusammen-setzung:	3-Amino-5-chlorbenzolsulfon-säure → BONS, Ca-Salz		
Präparation:	KBr (5/1000)	Dez. Nr.:	**2.3.10**

CI-Name:	**Pigment Red 58**	CI-No.:	**15825**
Composition:	3-Amino-5-chlorobenzenesulfonic acid → BHNA, Ca-salt		
Preparation:	**KBr (5/1000)**	Dec. No.:	**2.3.10**

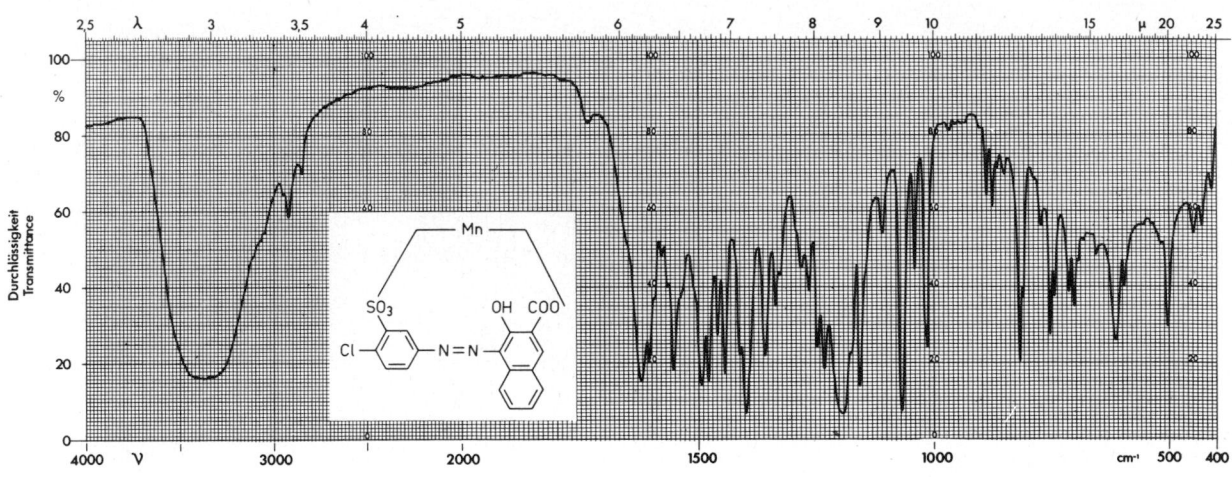

5612

CI-Name:	Pigment Rot 58	CI-No.:	**15825**
Zusammen-setzung:	3-Amino-5-chlorbenzolsulfon-säure → BONS, Mn-Salz		
Präparation:	KBr (5/1000)	Dez. Nr.:	**2.3.11**

CI-Name:	**Pigment Red 58**	CI-No.:	**15825**
Composition:	3-Amino-5-chlorobenzenesulfonic acid → BHNA, Mn-salt		
Preparation:	**KBr (5/1000)**	Dec. No.:	**2.3.11**

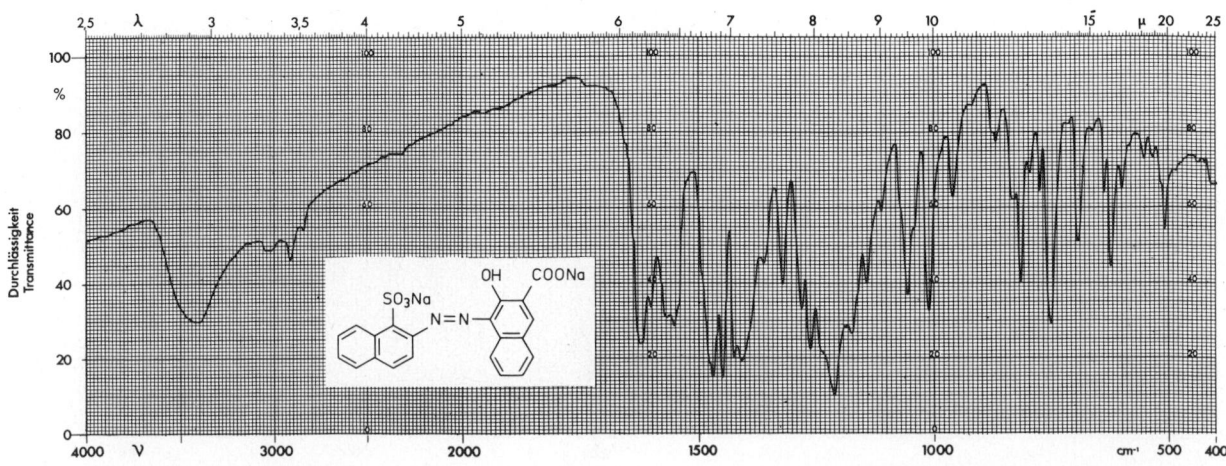

5613

CI-Name:	Pigment Rot 63	CI-No.:	**15580**
Zusammen-setzung:	2-Amino-1-naphthalinsulfon-säure → BONS, Na-Salz		
Präparation:	KBr (5/1000)	Dez. Nr.:	**2.3.12**

CI-Name:	**Pigment Red 63**	CI-No.:	**15580**
Composition:	2-Amino-1-naphthalenesulfonic acid → BHNA, Na-salt		
Preparation:	**KBr (5/1000)**	Dec. No.:	**2.3.12**

Organische Pigmente
2. Monoazofarblacke
2.3. Mit COOH- und SO₃H-Gruppen

Organic Pigments
2. Monoazo-Salts
2.3. With COOH- and SO₃H-Groups

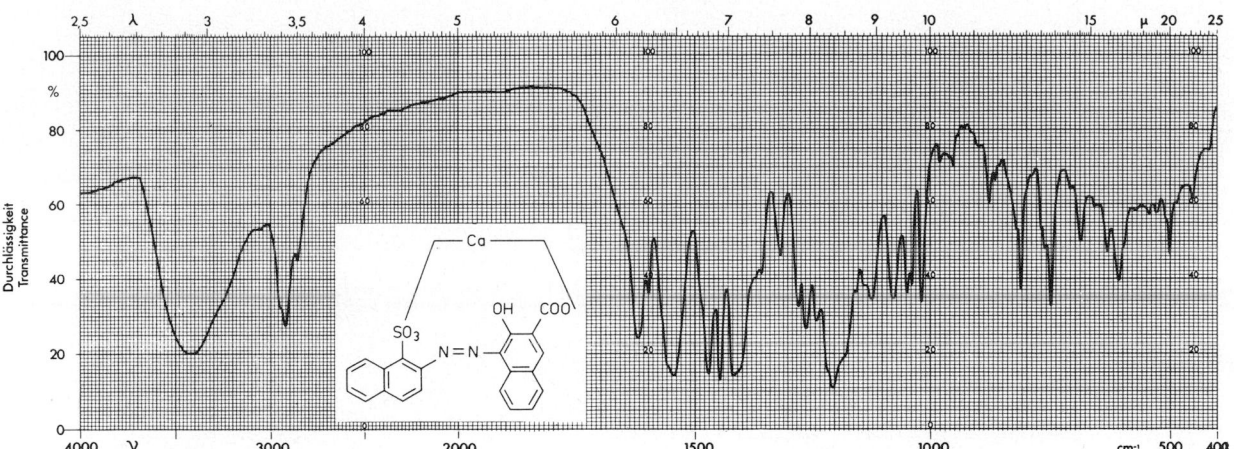

CI-Name: Pigment Rot 63   CI-No.:   15580
Zusammen-   2-Amino-1-naphthalinsulfon-
setzung: säure → BONS, Ca-Salz
Präparation: KBr (5/1000)   Dec. No.: 2.3.13

CI-Name: Pigment Red 63   CI-No.:   15580   5614
Composition: 2-Amino-1-naphthalenesulfonic
                acid → BHNA, Ca-salt
Preparation: KBr (5/1000)   Dez. Nr.: 2.3.13

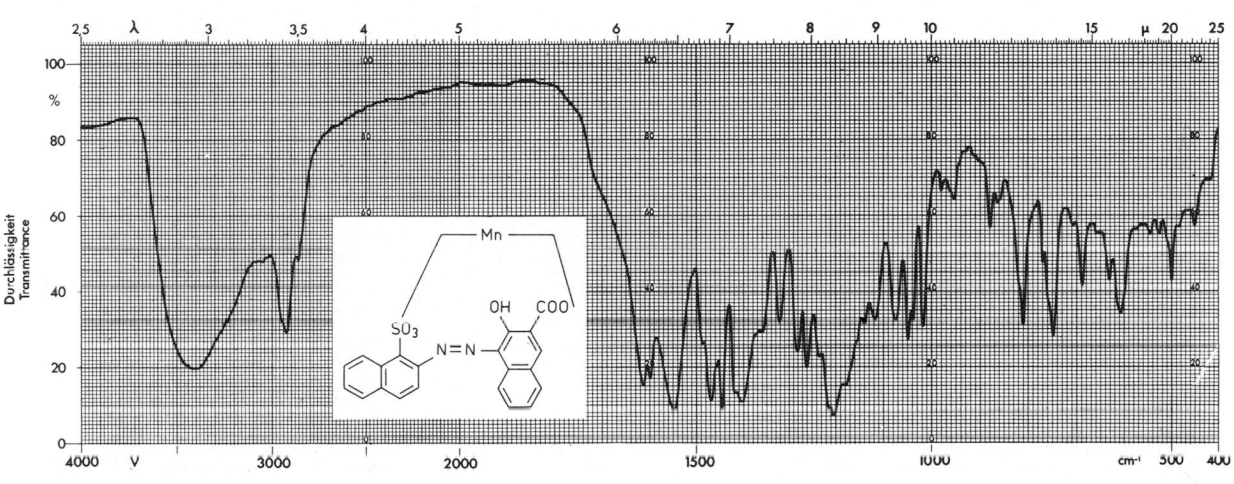

CI-Name: Pigment Rot 63   CI-No.:   15580
Zusammen-   2-Amino-1-naphthalinsulfon-
setzung: säure → BONS, Mn-Salz
Präparation: KBr (3,5/1000)   Dez. Nr.: 2.3.14

CI-Name: Pigment Red 63   CI-No.:   15580   5615
Composition: 2-Amino-1-naphthalenesulfonic
                acid → BHNA, Mn-salt
Preparation: KBr (3,5/1000)   Dec. No.: 2.3.14

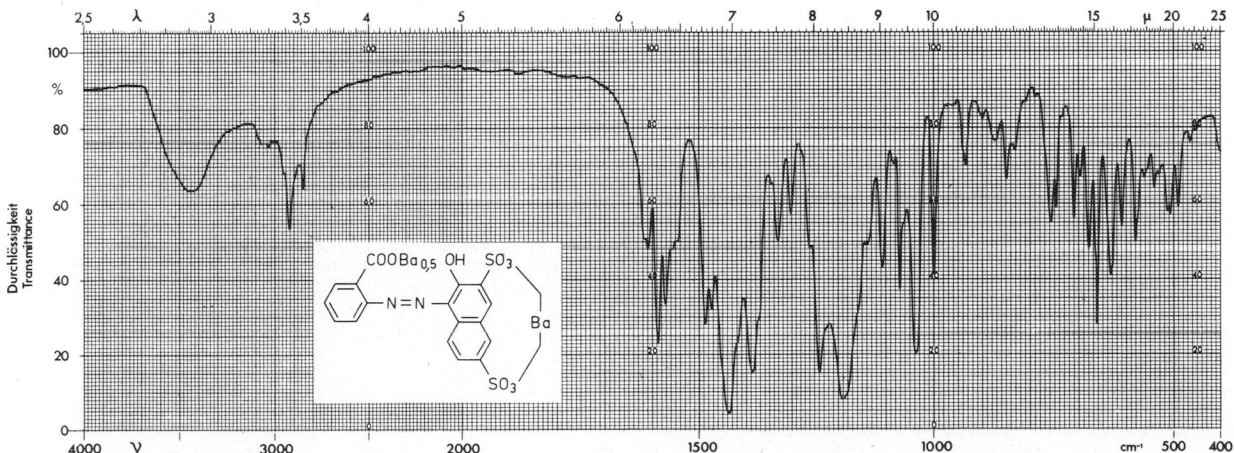

CI-Name: Pigment Rot 60   CI-No.:   16105
Zusammen-   Anthranilsäure → 2-Hydroxy-3,6-naphtha-
setzung: lindisulfonsäure, Ba-Salz
Präparation: KBr (3,3/1000)   Dez. Nr.: 2.3.15

CI-Name: Pigment Red 60   CI-No.:   16105   5616
Composition: Anthranilic acid → 2-Hydroxy-3,6-naphtha-
                lenedisulfonic acid, Ba-salt
Preparation: KBr (3,3/1000)   Dec. No.: 2.3.15

Organische Pigmente
2. Monoazofarblacke
2.4. Chelate

Organic Pigments
2. Monoazo-Salts
2.4. Chelates

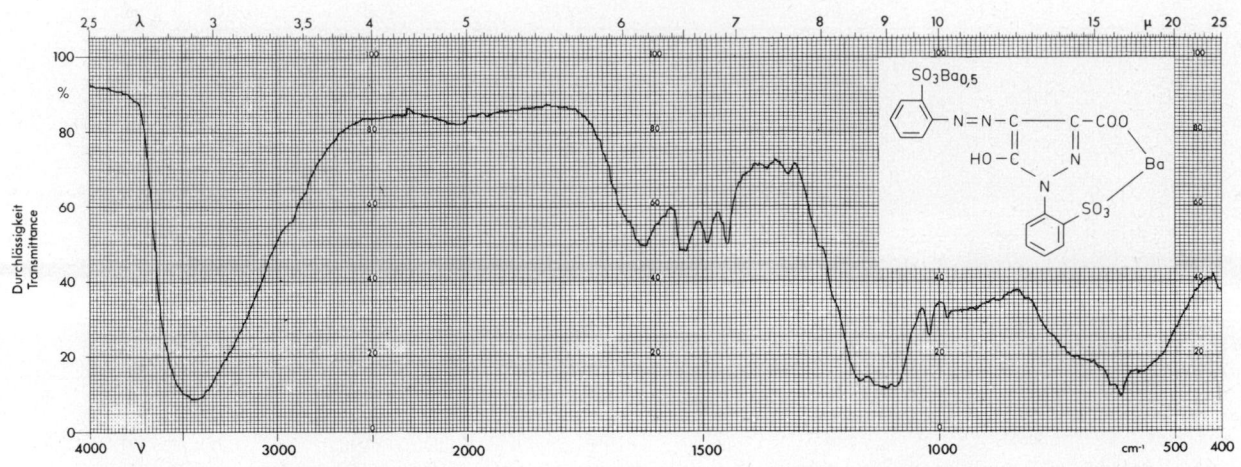

5617

CI-Name:	Echtgelblack 20	CI-No.:	19120

Zusammen-setzung: 2-Aminobenzolsulfonsäure → 1-(2'-Sulfophenyl)pyrazolon-5-(3-carbonsäure), Ba-Salz

Präparation: KBr (3,5/1000)   Dez. Nr.: 2.3.16

CI-Name: Yellow pigment 20   CI-No.: 19120

Composition: 2-Aminobenzenesulfonic acid → 1-(2'-Sulfophenyl)-5-pyrazolone-3-carboxylic acid, Ba-salt

Preparation: KBr (3,5/1000)   Dec. No:. 2.3.16

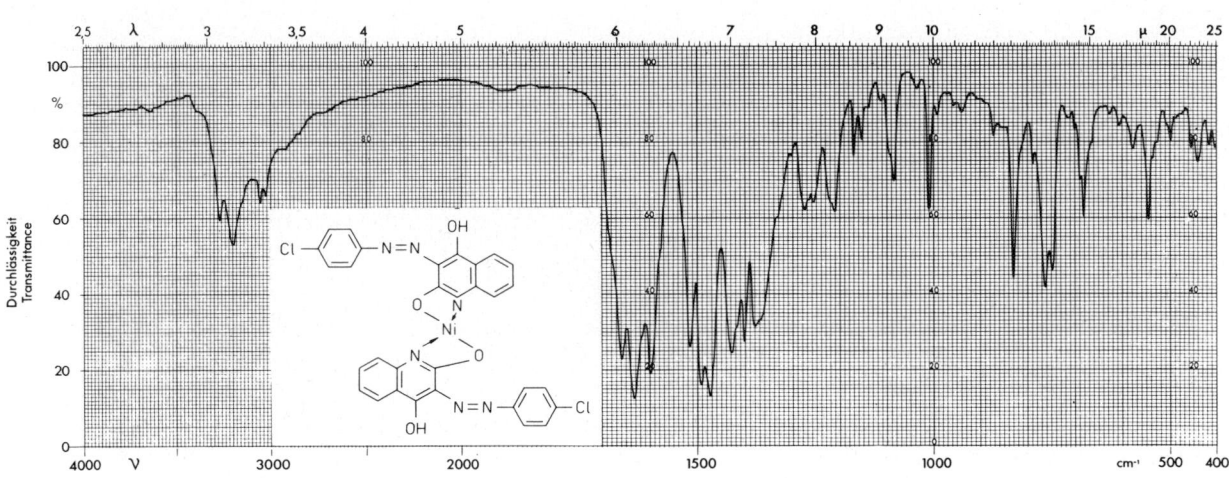

5618

CI-Name: Pigment Grün 10   CI-No.: 12775

Zusammen-setzung: 4-Chloranilin → 2,4-Dihydroxychinolin, Ni-Komplex

Präparation: KBr (3/1000)   Dez. Nr.: 2.4.1

CI-Name: Pigment Green 10   CI-No.: 12775

Composition: 4-Chloroaniline → 2,4-Dihydroxyquinoline, Ni-complex

Preparation: KBr (3/1000)   Dec. No.: 2.4.1

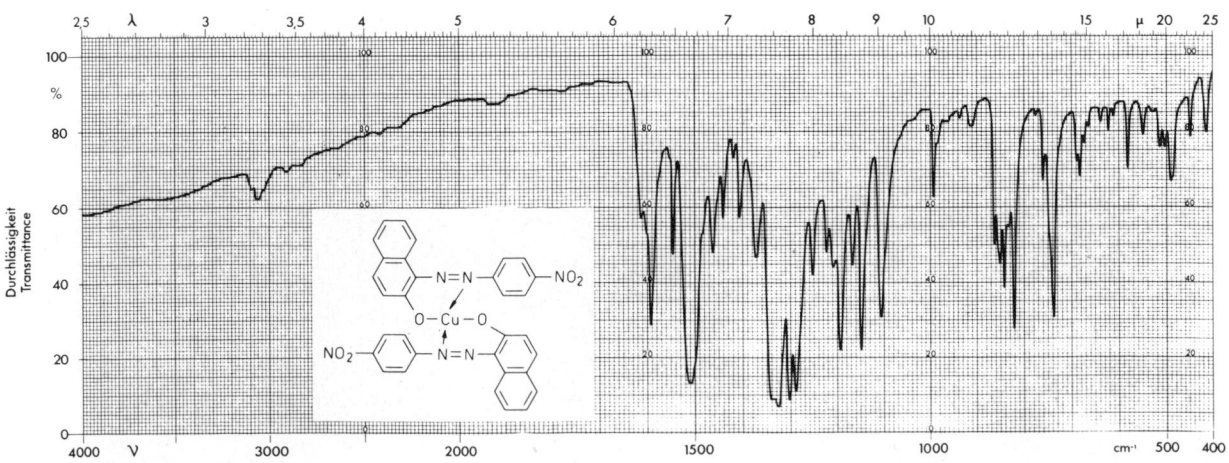

5619

CI-Name: Pigment Braun 2   CI-No.: 12071

Zusammen-setzung: 4-Nitroanilin → 2-Naphthol, Cu-Komplex

Präparation: KBr (4/1000)   Dez. Nr.: 2.4.2

CI-Name: Pigment Brown 2   CI-No.: 12071

Composition: 4-Nitroaniline → 2-Naphthol, Cu-complex

Preparation: KBr (4/1000)   Dec. No:. 2.4.2

Organische Pigmente
3. Disazopigmente
3.1. KK Acetessigsäurearylide

Organic Pigments
3. Disazo Pigments
3.1. CC Acetoacetic-arylides

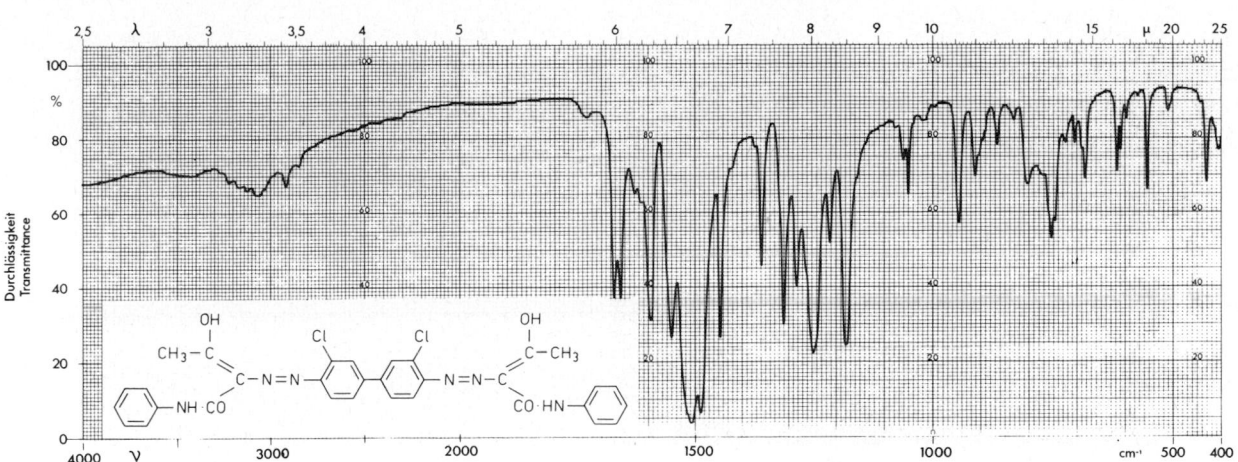

CI-Name: **Pigment Gelb 12**   CI-Nr.: **21090**
Zusammen-setzung: **3,3'-Dichlorbenzidin → ACES-anilid**
Präparation: **KBr (1,5/1000)**   Dez. Nr.: **3.1.1**

CI-Name: **Pigment Yellow 12** CI-No.: **21090**
Composition: **3,3'-Dichlorobenzidine → ACAA-anilide**
Preparation: **KBr (1,5/1000)**   Dec. No.: **3.1.1**

5620

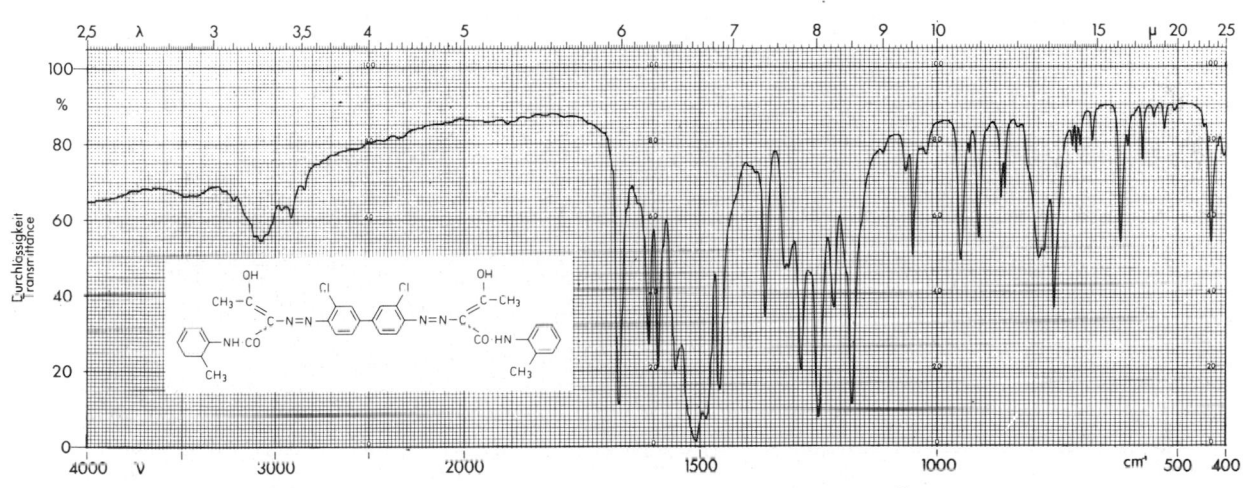

CI-Name: **Pigment Gelb 14**   CI-Nr.: **21095**
Zusammen-setzung: **3,3'-Dichlorbenzidin → ACES-2-methyl-anilid**
Präparation: **KBr (1,5/1000)**   Dez. Nr.: **3.1.2**

CI-Name: **Pigment Yellow 14** CI-No.: **21095**
Composition: **3,3'-Dichlorobenzidine → ACAA-2-methyl-anilide**
Preparation: **KBr (1,5/1000)**   Dec. No.: **3.1.2**

5621

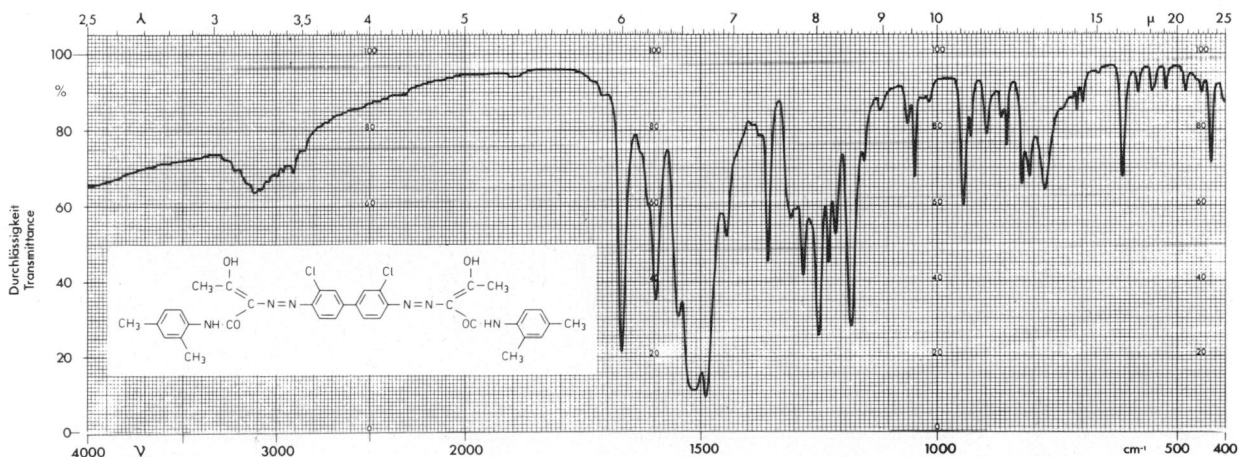

CI-Name: **Pigment Gelb 13**   CI-Nr.: **21000**
Zusammen-setzung: **3,3'-Dichlorbenzidin → ACES-2,4-dimethyl-anilid**
Präparation: **KBr (1,5/1000)**   Dez. Nr.: **3.1.3**

CI-Name: **Pigment Yellow 13** CI-No.: **21000**
Composition: **3,3'-Dichlorobenzidine → ACAA-2,4-dimethylanilide**
Preparation: **KBr (1,5/1000)**   Dec. No.: **3.1.3**

5622

Organische Pigmente
3. Disazopigmente
3.1. KK Acetessigsäurearylide

Organic Pigments
3. Disazo Pigments
3.1. CC Acetoacetic-arylides

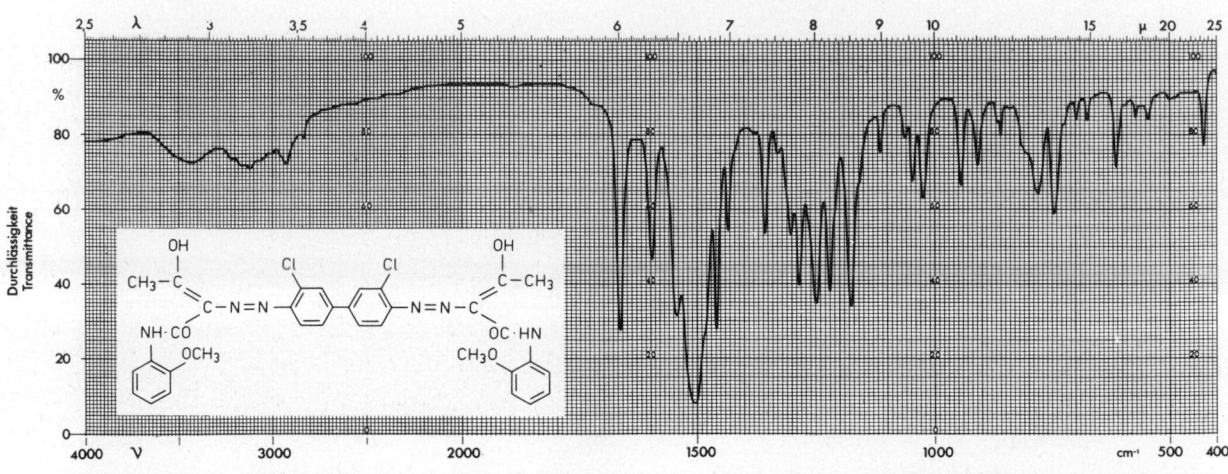

5623

CI-Name: **Pigment Gelb 17** CI-No.: **21105**

Zusammensetzung: **3,3'-Dichlorbenzidin → ACES-2-methoxyanilid**

Präparation: **KBr (1,5/1000)** Dez. Nr.: **3.1.4**

CI-Name: **Pigment Yellow 17** CI-No.: **21105**

Composition: **3,3'-Dichlorobenzidine → ACAA-2-methoxyanilide**

Preparation: **KBr (1,5/1000)** Dec. No.: **3.1.4**

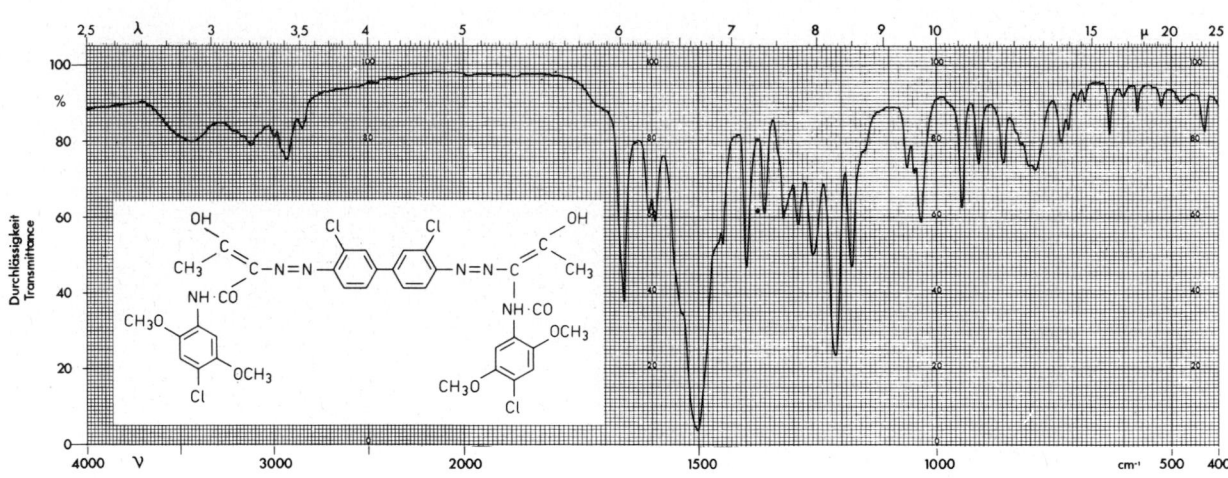

5624

CI-Name: **Pigment Gelb 83**

Zusammensetzung: **3,3'-Dichlorbenzidin → ACES-4-chlor-2,5-methoxyanilid**

Präparation: **KBr (1,5/1000)** Dez. Nr.: **3.1.5**

CI-Name: **Pigment Yellow 83**

Composition: **3,3'-Dichlorobenzidine → ACAA-4-chloro-2,5-dimethoxyanilide**

Preparation: **KBr (1,5/1000)** Dec. No.: **3.1.5**

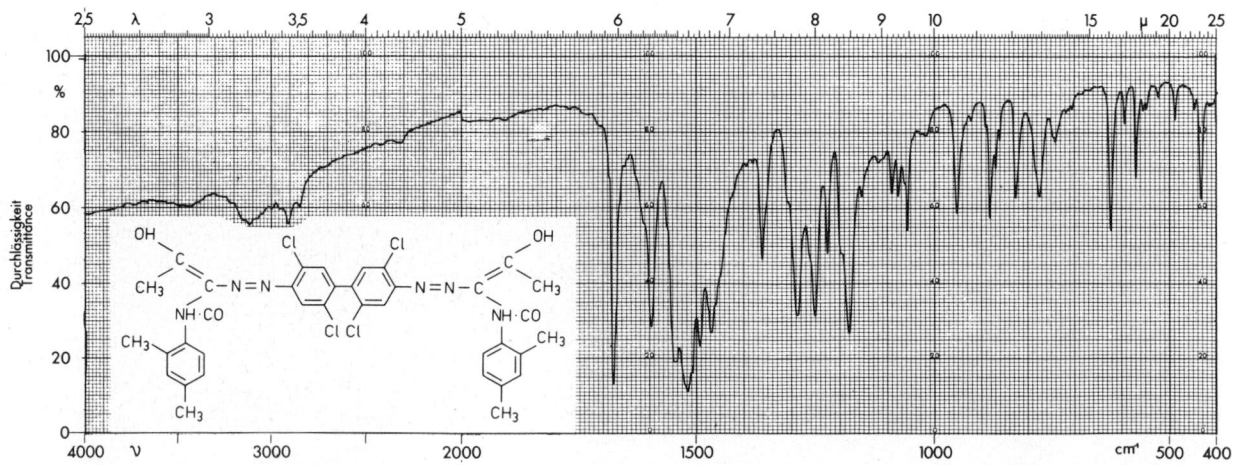

5625

CI-Name: **Pigment Gelb 81**

Zusammensetzung: **2,2'5,5'-Tetrachlorbenzidin → ACES-2,4-dimethylanilid**

Präparation: **KBr (2/1000)** Dez. Nr.: **3.1.6**

CI-Name: **Pigment Yellow 81**

Composition: **2,2'5,5'-Tetrachlorobenzidine → ACAA-2,4-dimethylanilide**

Preparation: **KBr (2/1000)** Dec. No.: **3.1.6**

Organische Pigmente
3. Disazopigmente
3.1. KK Acetessigsäurearylide

Organic Pigments
3. Disazo Pigments
3.1. CC Acetoacetic-arylides

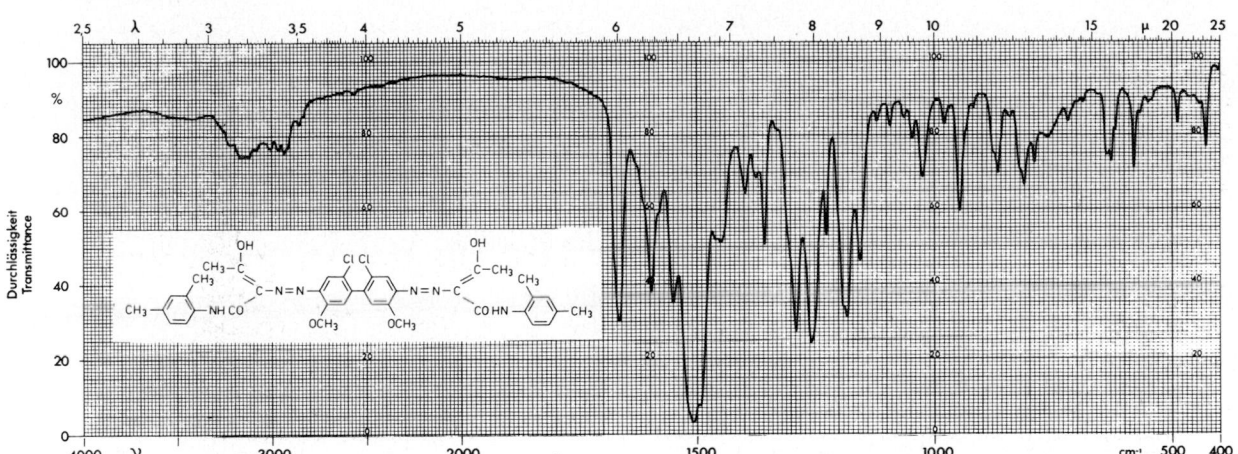

CI-Name: **Pigment Gelb 15**   CI-No.: **21220**
Zusammensetzung: **2,2'-Dichlor-5,5'-dimethoxybenzidin → ACES-2,4-dimethylanilid**
Präparation: **KBr (1,7/1000)**   Dez. Nr.: **3.1.7**

CI-Name: **Pigment Yellow 15** CI-No.: **21220**
Composition: **2,2'-Dichloro-5,5'-dimethoxybenzidine → ACAA-2,4-dimethylanilide**
Preparation: **KBr (1,7/1000)**   Dec. No.: **3.1.7**

5626

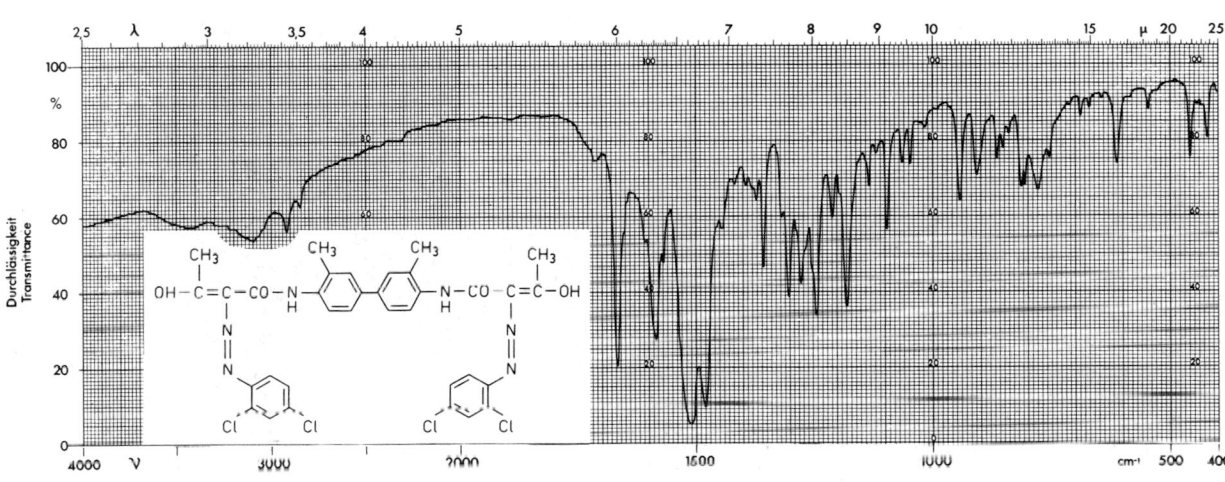

CI-Name: **Pigment Gelb 16**   CI-No.: **20040**
Zusammensetzung: **2,4-Dichloranilin → N,N'-Diacetoacetyl-3,3'-dimethylbenzidin**
Präparation: **KBr (1,7/1000)**   Dez. Nr.: **3.1.14**

CI-Name: **Pigment Yellow 16** CI-No.: **20040**
Composition: **2,4-Dichloroaniline → N,N'-Diacetoacetyl-3,3'-dimethylbenzidine**
Preparation: **KBr (1,7/1000)**   Dec. No.: 3.1.14

5627

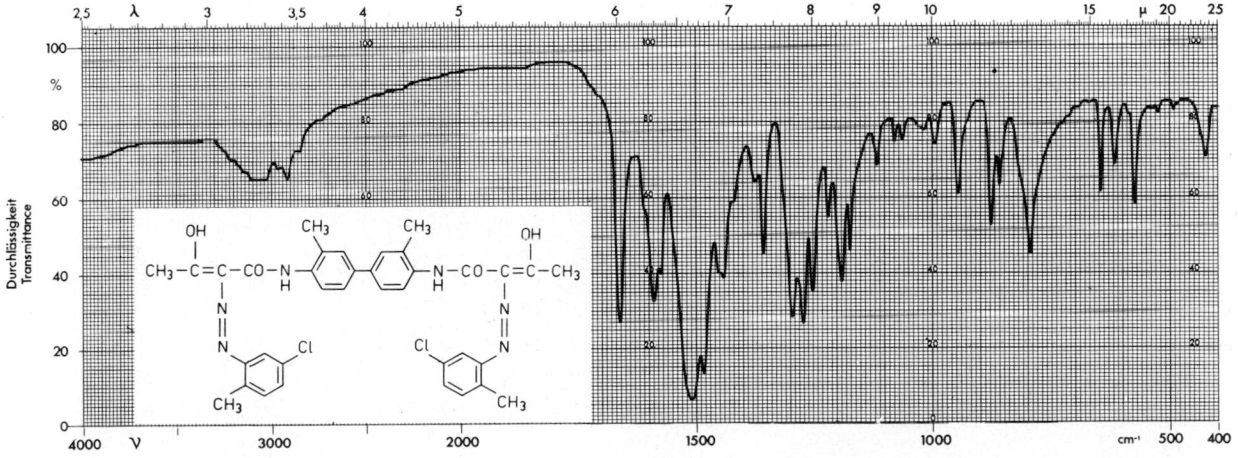

CI-Name: **Pigment Gelb 77**   CI-No.: **20045**
Zusammensetzung: **2,5-Dichloranilin → N,N'-Diacetoacetyl-3,3'-dimethylbenzidin**
Präparation: **KBr (1,7/1000)**   Dez. Nr.: **3.1.15**

CI-Name: **Pigment Yellow 77** CI-No.: **20045**
Composition: **2,5-Dichloroaniline → N,N'-Diacetoacetyl-3,3'-dimethylbenzidine**
Preparation: **KBr (1,7/1000)**   Dec. No.: 3.1.15

5628

Organische Pigmente
3. Disazopigmente
3.2. KK Pyrazolone

Organic Pigments
3. Disazo Pigments
3.2. CC Pyrazolones

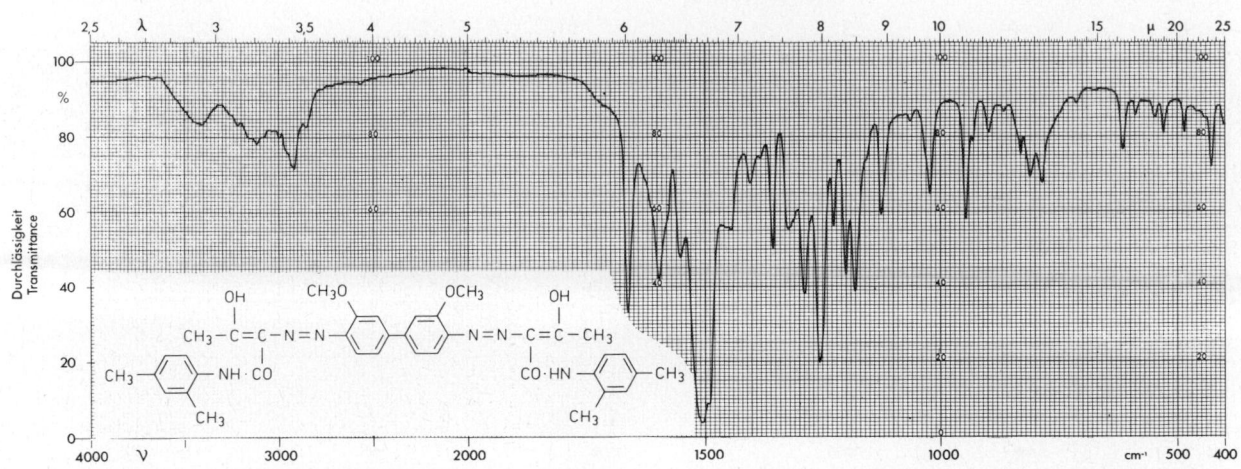

5629

CI-Name:	**Pigment Orange 14** CI-No.: **21165**	CI-Name:	**Pigment Orange 14** CI-No.: **21165**
Zusammensetzung:	**3,3'-Dimethoxybenzidin → ACES-2,4-dimethylanilid**	Composition:	**3,3'-Dimethoxybenzidine → ACAA-2,4-dimethylanilide**
Präparation:	**KBr (1,8/1000)** Dez. Nr.: 3.1.8	Preparation:	**KBr (1,8/1000)** Dec. No.: 3.1.8

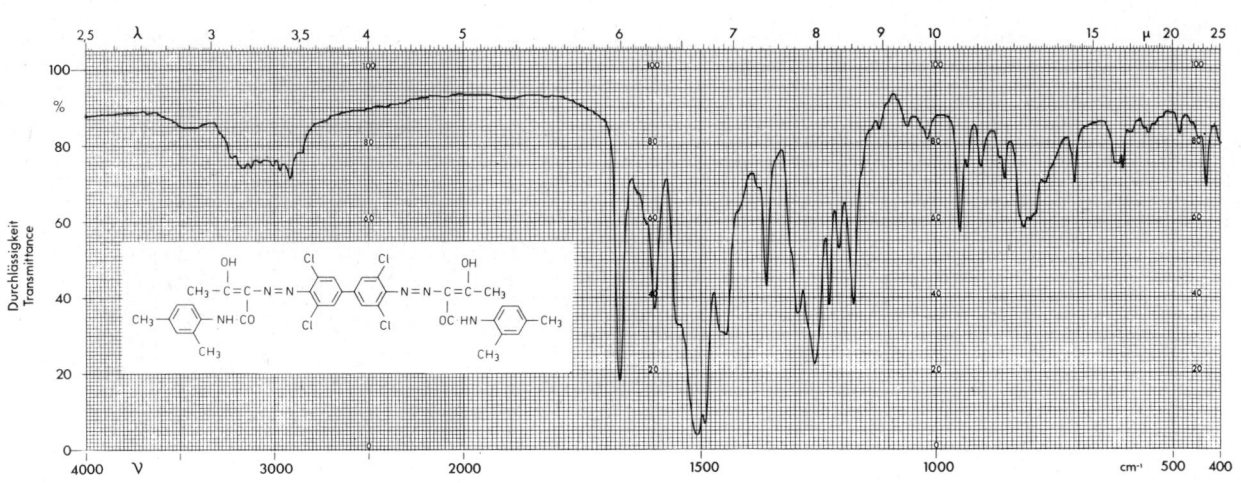

5630

Name:	Pigment Gelb 81 CI-No.: 21127	Name:	Pigment Yellow 81 CI-No.: 21127
Zusammensetzung:	**3,3',5,5'-Tetrachlorbenzidin → ACES-2,4-dimethylanilid**	Composition:	**3,3',5,5'-Tetrachlorobenzidine → ACAA-2,4-dimethylanilide**
Präparation:	**KBr (2/1000)** Dez. Nr.: 3.1.9	Preparation:	**KBr (2/1000)** Dec. No.: 3.1.9

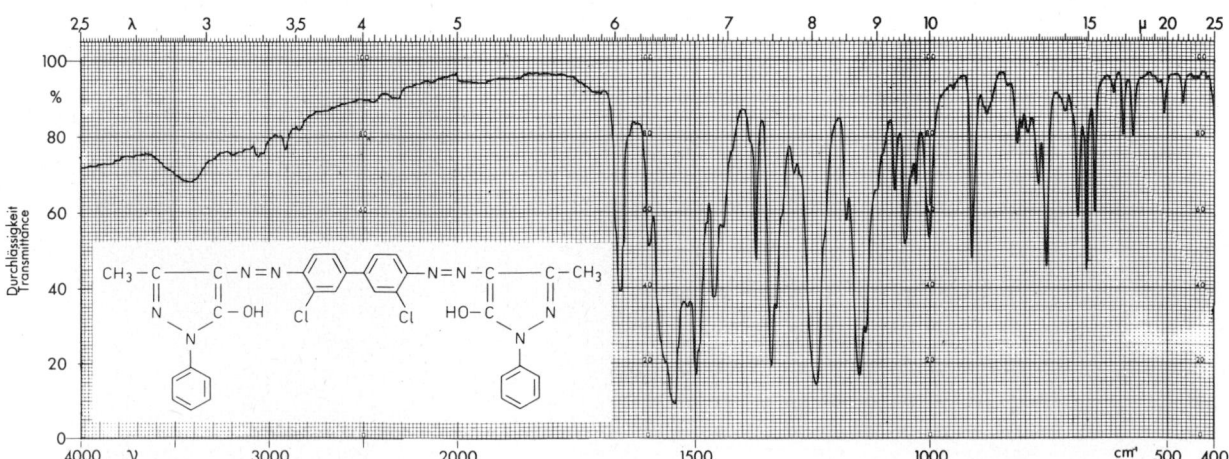

5631

CI-Name:	**Pigment Orange 13** CI-No.: **21110**	CI-Name:	**Pigment Orange 13** CI-No.: **21110**
Zusammensetzung:	**3,3'-Dichlorbenzidin → 3-Methyl-1-phenyl-pyrazolon-5**	Composition:	**3,3'-Dichlorobenzidine → 3-Methyl-1-phenyl-5-pyrazolone**
Präparation:	**KBr (2/1000)** Dez. Nr.: **3.2.1**	Preparation:	**KBr (2/1000)** Dec. No.: **3.2.1**

Organische Pigmente
3. Disazopigmente
3.2. KK Pyrazolone

Organic Pigments
3. Diazo Pigments
3.2. CC Pyrazolones

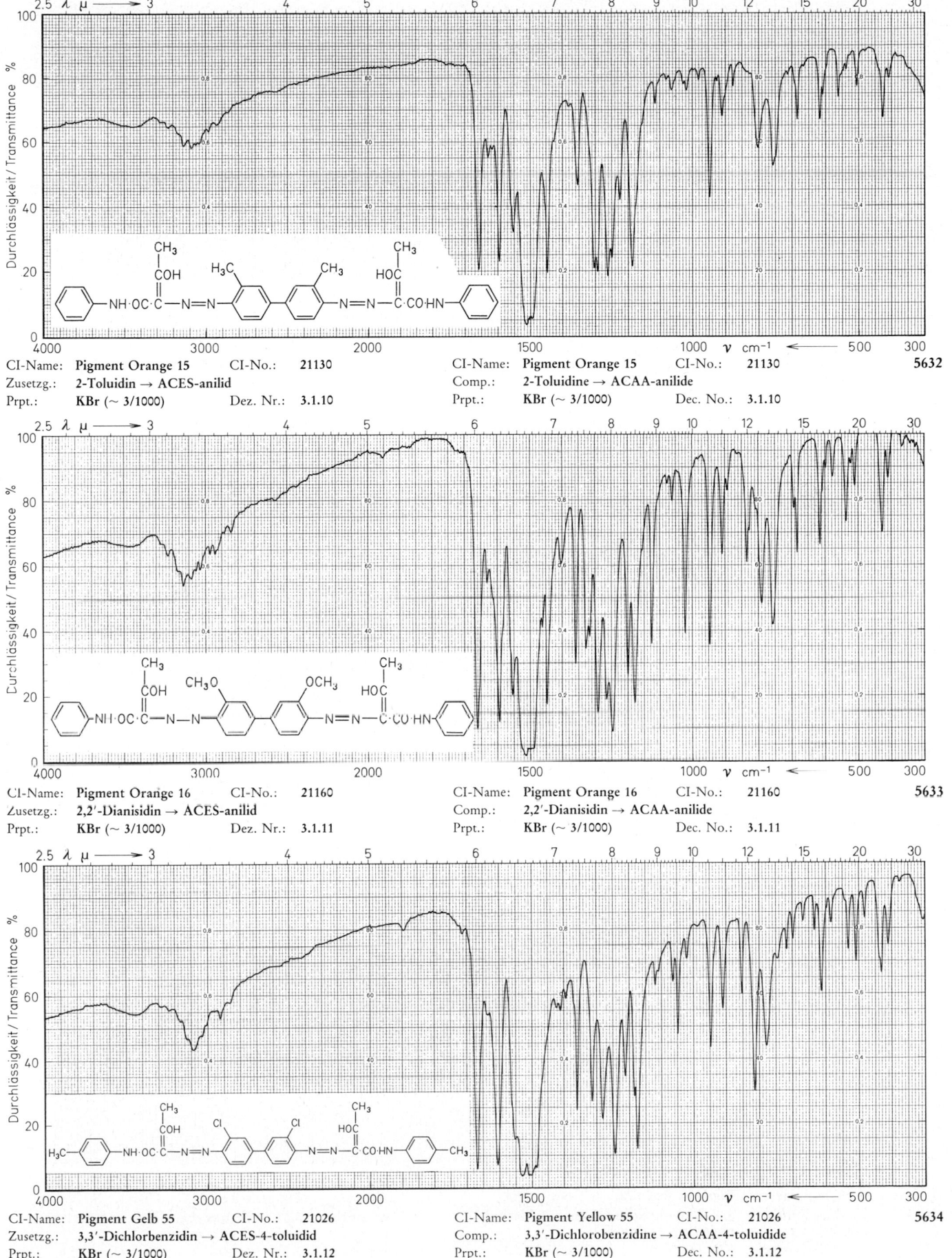

CI-Name: **Pigment Orange 15** CI-No.: **21130**
Zusetzg.: **2-Toluidin → ACES-anilid**
Prpt.: **KBr (~ 3/1000)** Dez. Nr.: **3.1.10**

CI-Name: **Pigment Orange 15** CI-No.: **21130**
Comp.: **2-Toluidine → ACAA-anilide**
Prpt.: **KBr (~ 3/1000)** Dec. No.: **3.1.10**

5632

CI-Name: **Pigment Orange 16** CI-No.: **21160**
Zusetzg.: **2,2′-Dianisidin → ACES-anilid**
Prpt.: **KBr (~ 3/1000)** Dez. Nr.: **3.1.11**

CI-Name: **Pigment Orange 16** CI-No.: **21160**
Comp.: **2,2′-Dianisidin → ACAA-anilide**
Prpt.: **KBr (~ 3/1000)** Dec. No.: **3.1.11**

5633

CI-Name: **Pigment Gelb 55** CI-No.: **21026**
Zusetzg.: **3,3′-Dichlorbenzidin → ACES-4-toluidid**
Prpt.: **KBr (~ 3/1000)** Dez. Nr.: **3.1.12**

CI-Name: **Pigment Yellow 55** CI-No.: **21026**
Comp.: **3,3′-Dichlorobenzidine → ACAA-4-toluidide**
Prpt.: **KBr (~ 3/1000)** Dec. No.: **3.1.12**

5634

Organische Pigmente
3. Disazopigmente
3.2. KK Pyrazolone

Organic Pigments
3. Disazo Pigments
3.2. CC Pyrazolones

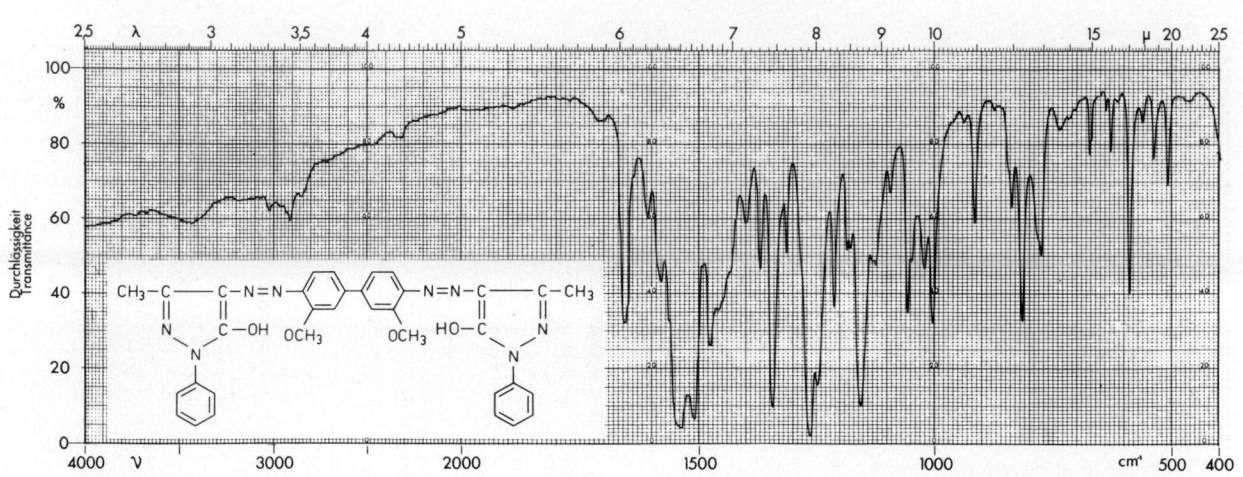

5635

CI-Name: **Pigment Rot 37** CI-No.: **21205**
Zusammen-
setzung: **3,3′-Dimethoxybenzidin → 3-Methyl-1-
(4′-toluyl)-pyrazolon-5**
Präparation: **KBr (2/1000)**   Dez. Nr.: **3.2.2**

CI-Name: **Pigment Red 37** CI-No.: **21205**
Composition: **3,3′-Dimethoxybenzidine → 3-Methyl-1-
(4′-tolyl)-pyrazolone-5**
Preparation: **KBr (2/1000)**   Dec. No.: **3.2.2**

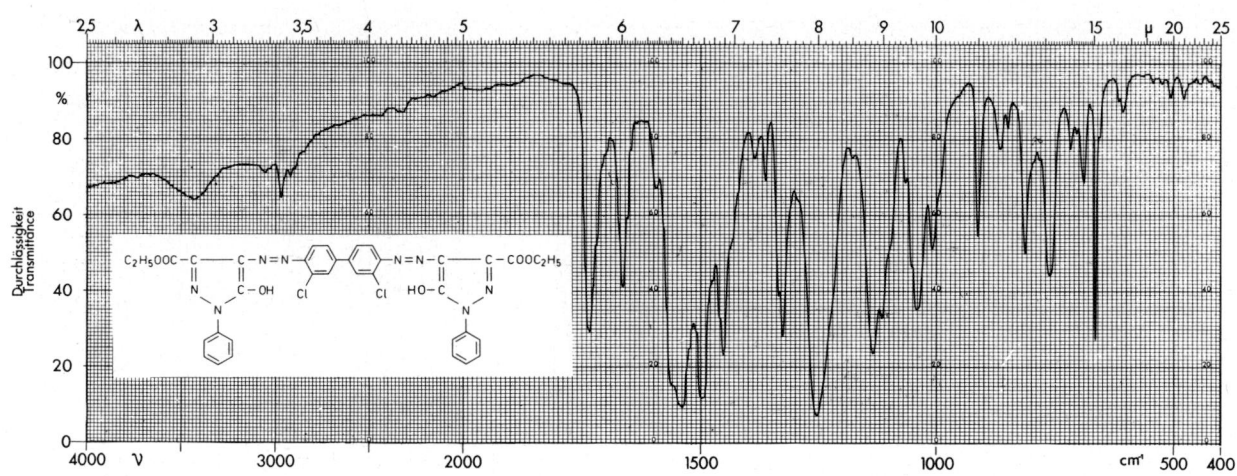

5636

CI-Name: **Pigment Rot 38** CI-No.: **21120**
Zusammen-
setzung: **3,3′-Dichlorbenzidin → 3-Carboxyethyl-
1-phenylpyrazolon-5**
Präparation: **KBr (2,0/1000)**   Dez. Nr.: **3.2.3**

CI-Name: **Pigment Red 38** CI-No.: **21120**
Composition: **3,3′-Dichlorobenzidine → 3-Carboxyethyl-
1-phenyl-5-pyrazolone**
Preparation: **KBr (2,0/1000)**   Dec. No.: **3.2.3**

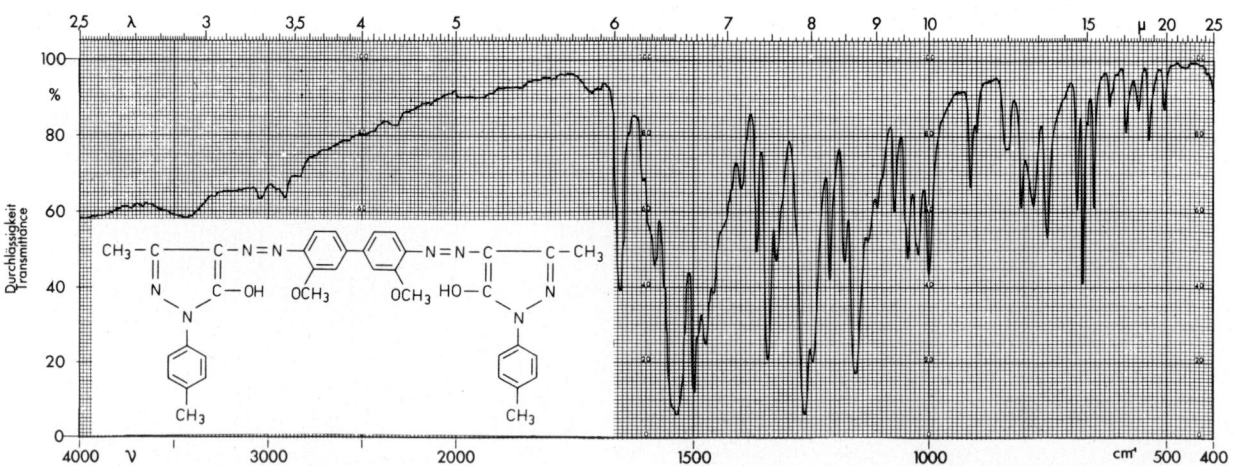

5637

CI-Name: **Pigment Rot 128** CI-No.: 21200
Zusammen-
setzung: **3,3′-Dimethoxybenzidin → 3-Methyl-1-
phenylpyrazolon-5**
Präparation: **KBr (2/1000)**   Dez. Nr.: **3.2.4**

CI-Name: **Pigment Red 128** CI-Nr.: 21200
Composition: **3,3′-Dimethoxybenzidine → 3-Methyl-1-
phenyl-5-pyrazolone**
Preparation: **KBr (2/1000)**   Dec. No.: **3.2.4**

Organische Pigmente
3. Disazopigmente
3.2. KK Pyrazolone

Organic Pigments
3. Diazo Pigments
3.2. CC Pyrazolones

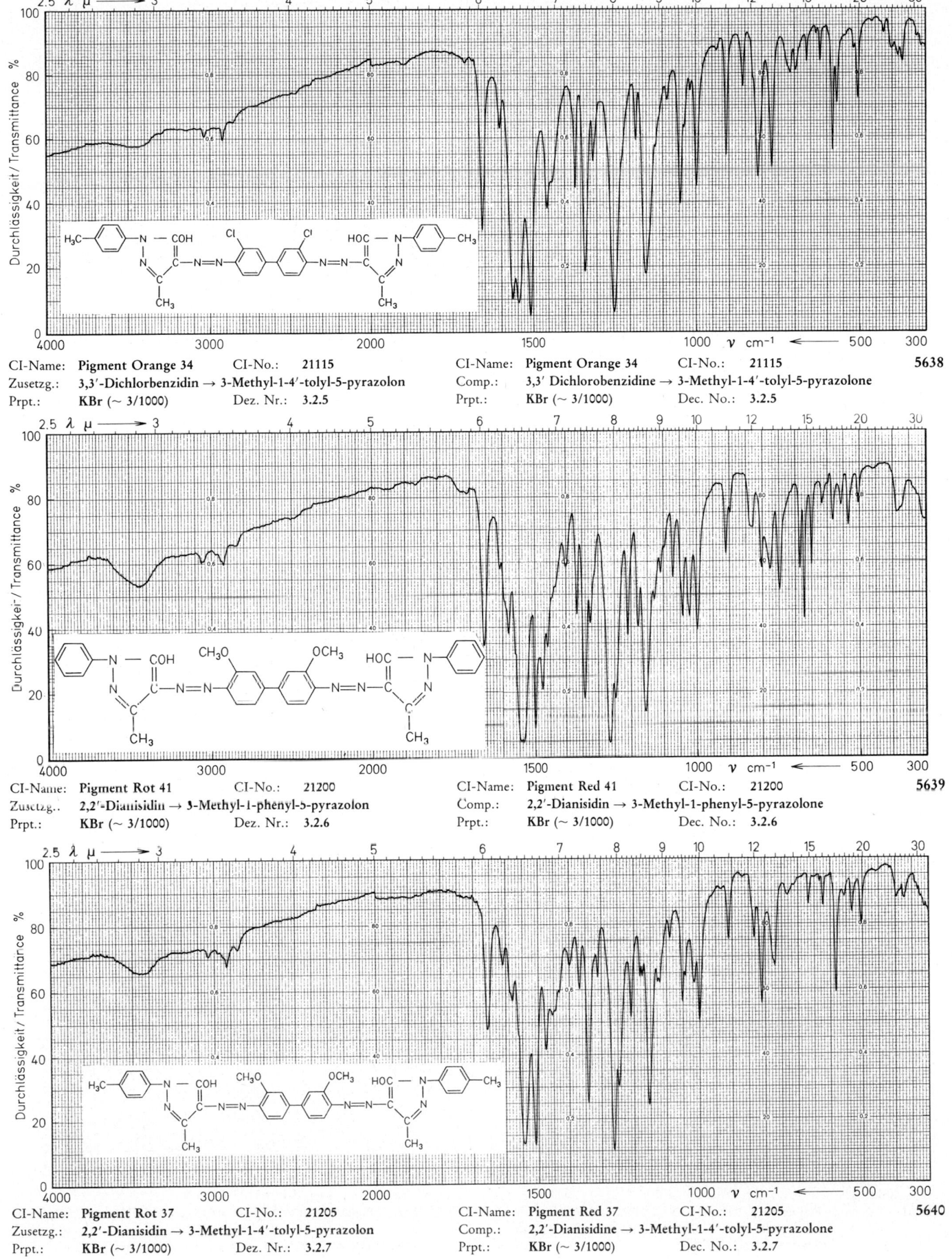

CI-Name: **Pigment Orange 34** CI-No.: **21115**
Zusetzg.: **3,3'-Dichlorbenzidin → 3-Methyl-1-4'-tolyl-5-pyrazolon**
Prpt.: **KBr (~ 3/1000)** Dez. Nr.: **3.2.5**

CI-Name: **Pigment Orange 34** CI-No.: **21115**
Comp.: **3,3' Dichlorobenzidine → 3-Methyl-1-4'-tolyl-5-pyrazolone**
Prpt.: **KBr (~ 3/1000)** Dec. No.: **3.2.5**

5638

CI-Name: **Pigment Rot 41** CI-No.: **21200**
Zusetzg.: **2,2'-Dianisidin → 3-Methyl-1-phenyl-5-pyrazolon**
Prpt.: **KBr (~ 3/1000)** Dez. Nr.: **3.2.6**

CI-Name: **Pigment Red 41** CI-No.: **21200**
Comp.: **2,2'-Dianisidin → 3-Methyl-1-phenyl-5-pyrazolone**
Prpt.: **KBr (~ 3/1000)** Dec. No.: **3.2.6**

5639

CI-Name: **Pigment Rot 37** CI-No.: **21205**
Zusetzg.: **2,2'-Dianisidin → 3-Methyl-1-4'-tolyl-5-pyrazolon**
Prpt.: **KBr (~ 3/1000)** Dez. Nr.: **3.2.7**

CI-Name: **Pigment Red 37** CI-No.: **21205**
Comp.: **2,2'-Dianisidine → 3-Methyl-1-4'-tolyl-5-pyrazolone**
Prpt.: **KBr (~ 3/1000)** Dec. No.: **3.2.7**

5640

Organische Pigmente
3. Diazopigmente
3.3. KK Naphthole

Organic Pigments
3. Diazo Pigments
3.3. CC Naphtholes

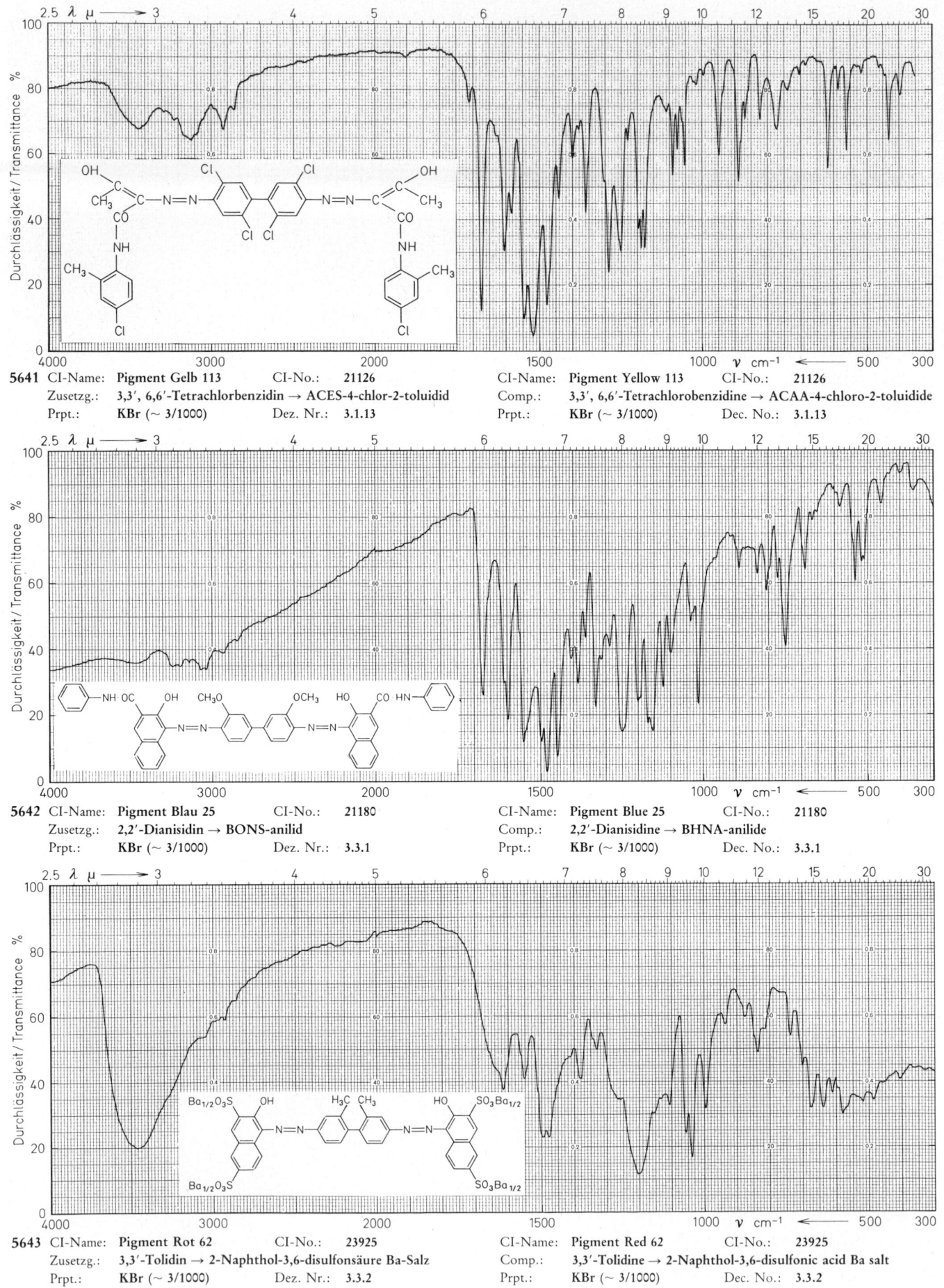

5641 CI-Name: **Pigment Gelb 113**   CI-No.: **21126**
   Zusetzg.: **3,3′, 6,6′-Tetrachlorbenzidin → ACES-4-chlor-2-toluidid**
   Prpt.: **KBr (~ 3/1000)**   Dez. Nr.: **3.1.13**

CI-Name: **Pigment Yellow 113**   CI-No.: **21126**
Comp.: **3,3′, 6,6′-Tetrachlorobenzidine → ACAA-4-chloro-2-toluidide**
Prpt.: **KBr (~ 3/1000)**   Dec. No.: **3.1.13**

5642 CI-Name: **Pigment Blau 25**   CI-No.: **21180**
   Zusetzg.: **2,2′-Dianisidin → BONS-anilid**
   Prpt.: **KBr (~ 3/1000)**   Dez. Nr.: **3.3.1**

CI-Name: **Pigment Blue 25**   CI-No.: **21180**
Comp.: **2,2′-Dianisidine → BHNA-anilide**
Prpt.: **KBr (~ 3/1000)**   Dec. No.: **3.3.1**

5643 CI-Name: **Pigment Rot 62**   CI-No.: **23925**
   Zusetzg.: **3,3′-Tolidin → 2-Naphthol-3,6-disulfonsäure Ba-Salz**
   Prpt.: **KBr (~ 3/1000)**   Dez. Nr.: **3.3.2**

CI-Name: **Pigment Red 62**   CI-No.: **23925**
Comp.: **3,3′-Tolidine → 2-Naphthol-3,6-disulfonic acid Ba salt**
Prpt.: **KBr (~ 3/1000)**   Dec. No.: **3.3.2**

Organische Pigmente
3. Disazopigmente
3.4. Sonstige

Organic Pigments
3. Disazo Pigments
3.4. Miscellaneous

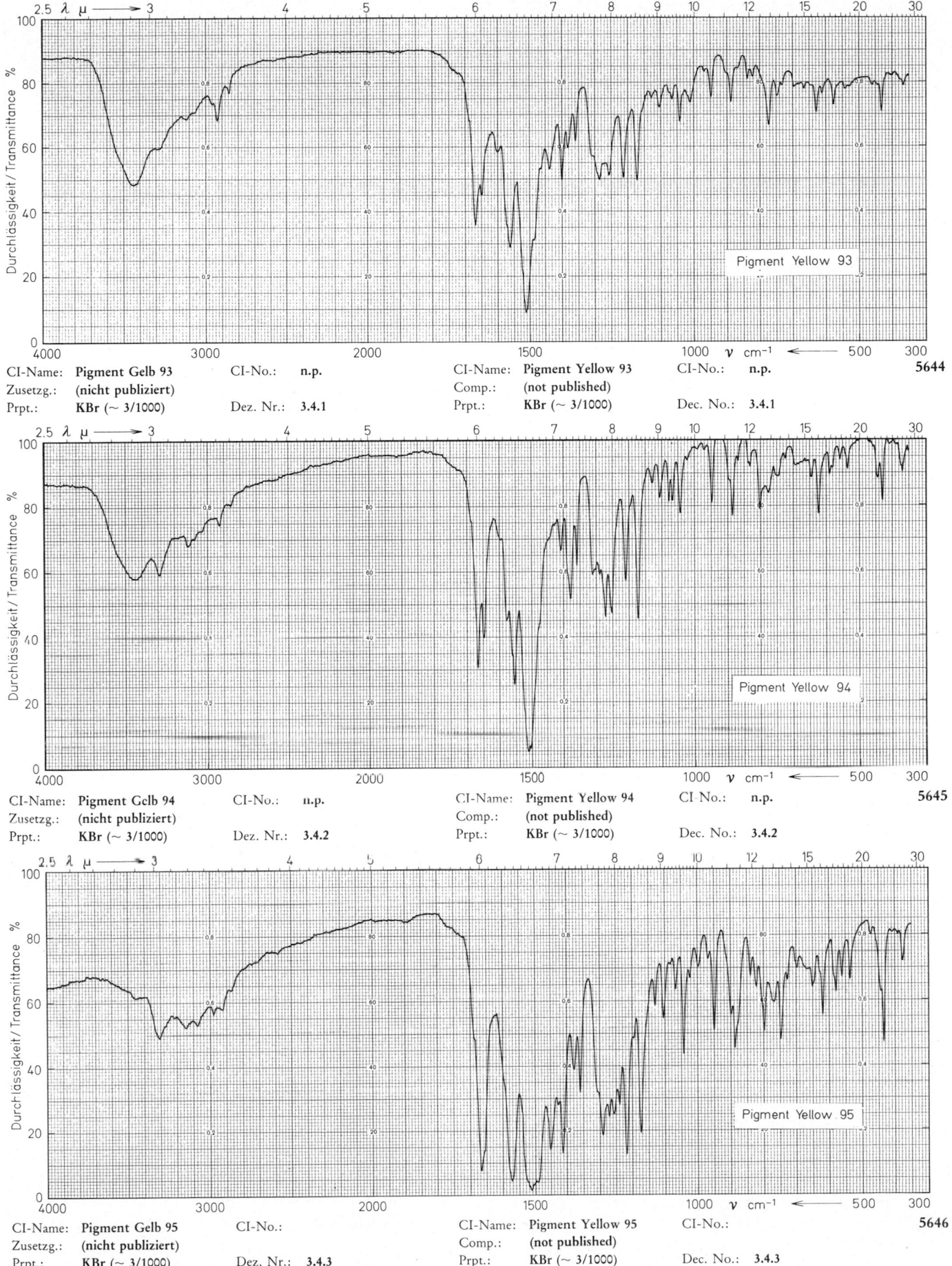

Pigment Yellow 93

CI-Name: **Pigment Gelb 93**	CI-No.: **n.p.**
Zusetzg.: **(nicht publiziert)**	
Prpt.: **KBr (~ 3/1000)**	Dez. Nr.: **3.4.1**

CI-Name: **Pigment Yellow 93**	CI-No.: **n.p.**
Comp.: **(not published)**	
Prpt.: **KBr (~ 3/1000)**	Dec. No.: **3.4.1**

5644

Pigment Yellow 94

CI-Name: **Pigment Gelb 94**	CI-No.: **n.p.**
Zusetzg.: **(nicht publiziert)**	
Prpt.: **KBr (~ 3/1000)**	Dez. Nr.: **3.4.2**

CI-Name: **Pigment Yellow 94**	CI-No.: **n.p.**
Comp.: **(not published)**	
Prpt.: **KBr (~ 3/1000)**	Dec. No.: **3.4.2**

5645

Pigment Yellow 95

CI-Name: **Pigment Gelb 95**	CI-No.:
Zusetzg.: **(nicht publiziert)**	
Prpt.: **KBr (~ 3/1000)**	Dez. Nr.: **3.4.3**

CI-Name: **Pigment Yellow 95**	CI-No.:
Comp.: **(not published)**	
Prpt.: **KBr (~ 3/1000)**	Dec. No.: **3.4.3**

5646

Organische Pigmente
3. Diazopigmente
3.4. Sonstige

Organic Pigments
3. Disazo Pigments
3.4. Miscellaneous

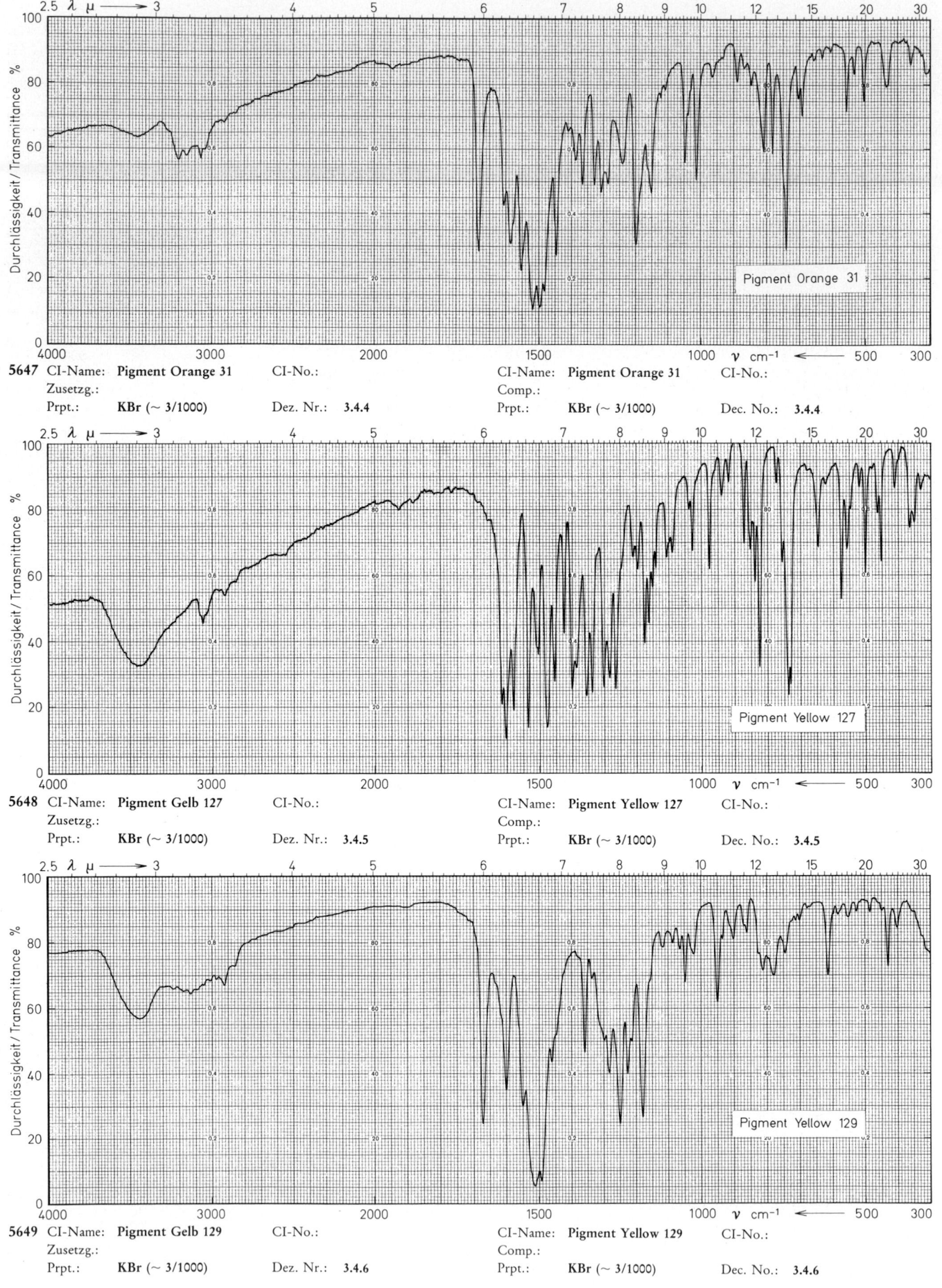

5647 CI-Name: **Pigment Orange 31**   CI-No.:
Zusetzg.:
Prpt.: **KBr (~ 3/1000)**   Dez. Nr.: **3.4.4**

CI-Name: **Pigment Orange 31**   CI-No.:
Comp.:
Prpt.: **KBr (~ 3/1000)**   Dec. No.: **3.4.4**

5648 CI-Name: **Pigment Gelb 127**   CI-No.:
Zusetzg.:
Prpt.: **KBr (~ 3/1000)**   Dez. Nr.: **3.4.5**

CI-Name: **Pigment Yellow 127**   CI-No.:
Comp.:
Prpt.: **KBr (~ 3/1000)**   Dec. No.: **3.4.5**

5649 CI-Name: **Pigment Gelb 129**   CI-No.:
Zusetzg.:
Prpt.: **KBr (~ 3/1000)**   Dez. Nr.: **3.4.6**

CI-Name: **Pigment Yellow 129**   CI-No.:
Comp.:
Prpt.: **KBr (~ 3/1000)**   Dec. No.: **3.4.6**

Organische Pigmente
3. **Diazopigmente**
3.4. **Sonstige**

Organic Pigments
3. **Disazo Pigments**
3.4. **Miscellaneous**

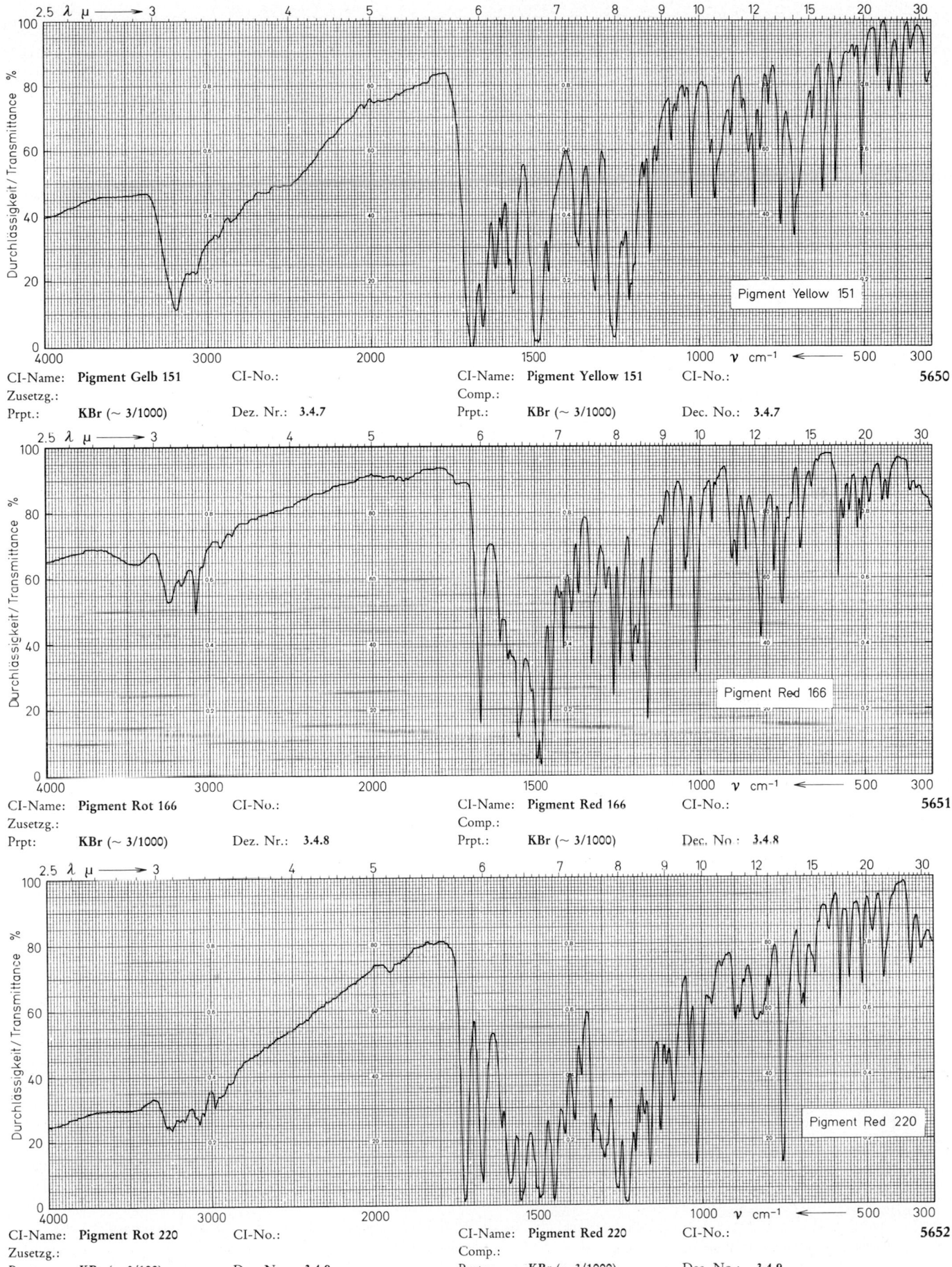

CI-Name: **Pigment Gelb 151**   CI-No.:   CI-Name: **Pigment Yellow 151**   CI-No.:   **5650**
Zusetzg.:   Comp.:
Prpt.: **KBr (~ 3/1000)**   Dez. Nr.: **3.4.7**   Prpt.: **KBr (~ 3/1000)**   Dec. No.: **3.4.7**

CI-Name: **Pigment Rot 166**   CI-No.:   CI-Name: **Pigment Red 166**   CI-No.:   **5651**
Zusetzg.:   Comp.:
Prpt: **KBr (~ 3/1000)**   Dez. Nr.: **3.4.8**   Prpt.: **KBr (~ 3/1000)**   Dec. No.: **3.4.8**

CI-Name: **Pigment Rot 220**   CI-No.:   CI-Name: **Pigment Red 220**   CI-No.:   **5652**
Zusetzg.:   Comp.:
Prpt.: **KBr (~ 3/100)**   Dez. Nr.: **3.4.9**   Prpt.: **KBr (~ 3/1000)**   Dec. No.: **3.4.9**

Organische Pigmente
3. Disazopigmente
3.4. Sonstige

Organic Pigments
3. Disazo Pigments
3.4. Miscellaneous

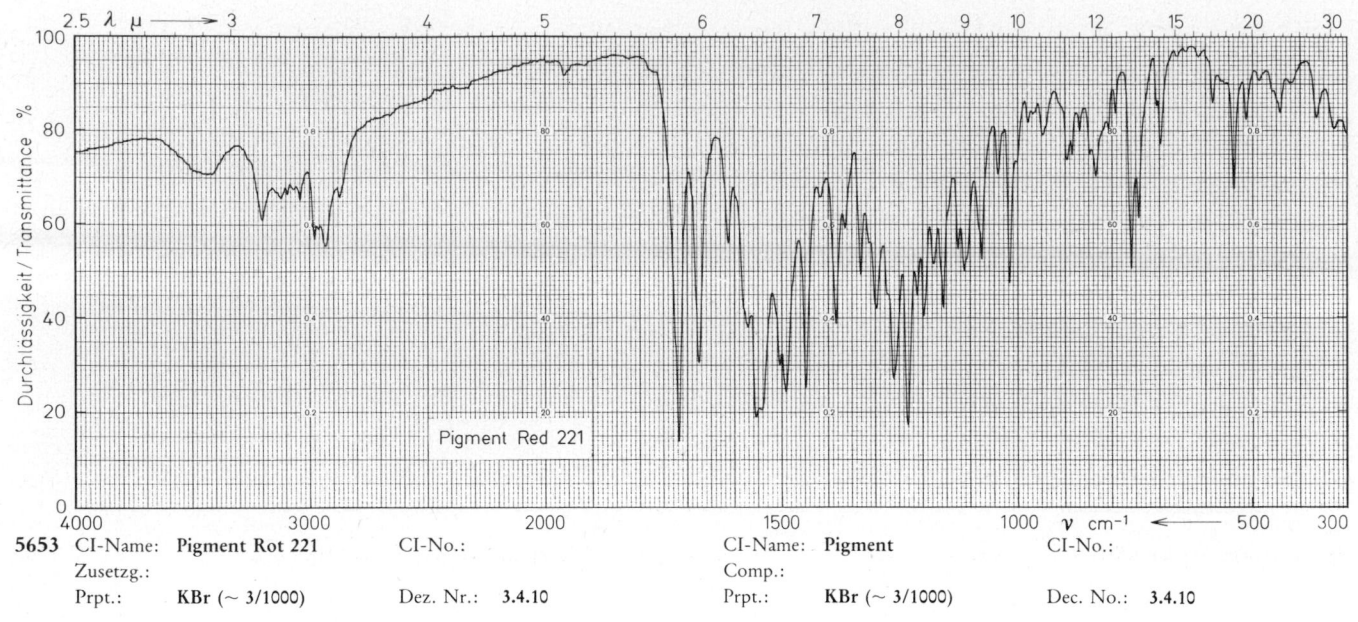

5653 CI-Name: **Pigment Rot 221**   CI-No.:

Zusetzg.:

Prpt.:   **KBr (~ 3/1000)**   Dez. Nr.:   **3.4.10**

CI-Name: **Pigment**   CI-No.:

Comp.:

Prpt.:   **KBr (~ 3/1000)**   Dec. No.:   **3.4.10**

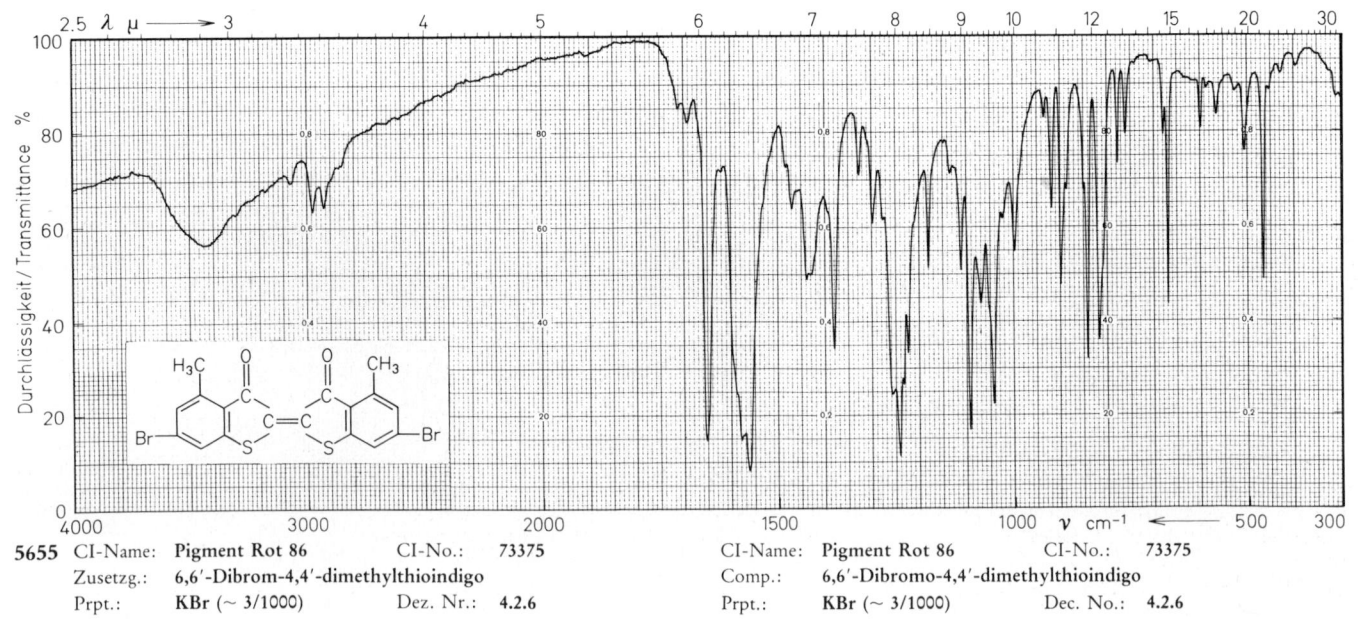

5655 CI-Name: **Pigment Rot 86**   CI-No.:   **73375**

Zusetzg.:   **6,6′-Dibrom-4,4′-dimethylthioindigo**

Prpt.:   **KBr (~ 3/1000)**   Dez. Nr.:   **4.2.6**

CI-Name: **Pigment Rot 86**   CI-No.:   **73375**

Comp.:   **6,6′-Dibromo-4,4′-dimethylthioindigo**

Prpt.:   **KBr (~ 3/1000)**   Dec. No.:   **4.2.6**

Sp. No. 5654: Während der Herstellung eliminiert – during production eliminated

Organische Pigmente
4. Indigo-Pigmente
4.1. Indigo und Derivate

Organic Pigments
4. Indigo Pigments
4.1. Indigo and Derivatives

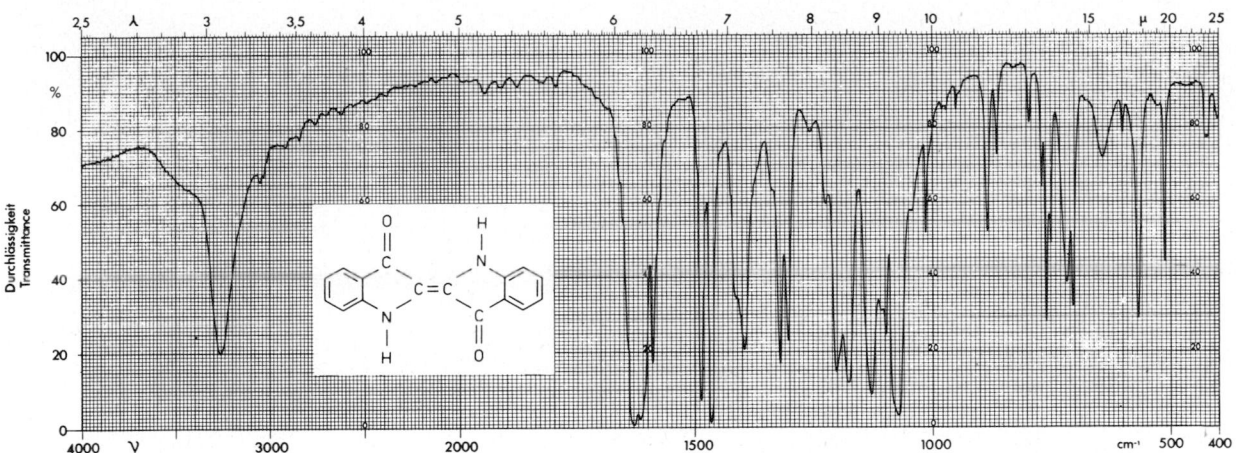

CI-Name: **VAT Blau 1**   CI-No.: **73000**   CI-Name: **Vat Blue 1**   CI-No.: **73000**   5656
Zusammen-   **Indigo**   Composition: **Indigo**
setzung:
Präparation: **KBr (1,5/1000)**   Dez. Nr.: **4.1.1**   Preparation: **KBr (1,5/1000)**   Dec. No.: **4.1.1**

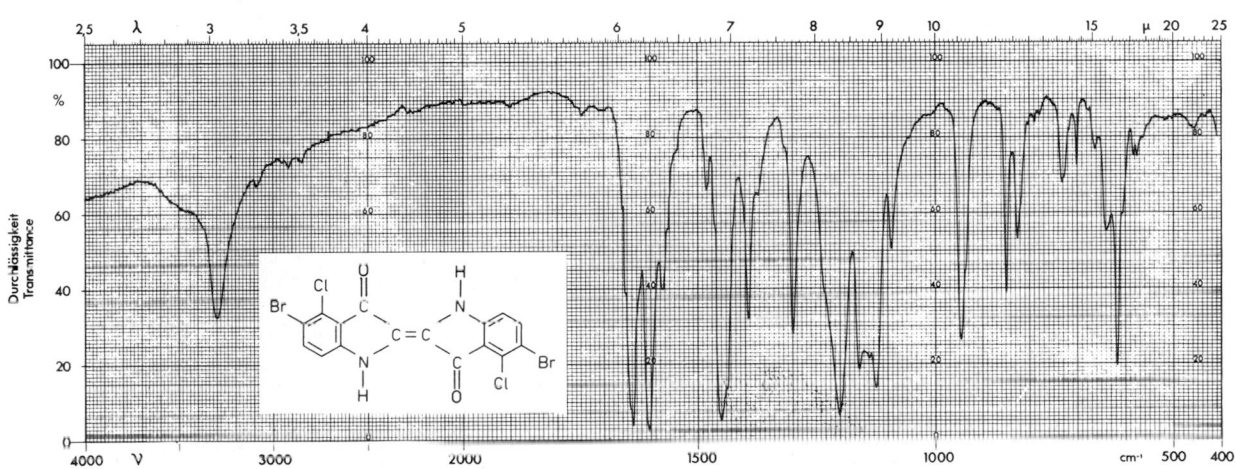

CI-Name: **VAT Blau 2**   CI-No.: **73045**   CI-Name: **Vat Blue 2**   CI-No.: **73045**   5657
Zusammen- **5,5'-Dibrom-4,4'-dichlorindigo**   Composition: **5,5'-Dibromo-4,4'-dichloroindigo**
setzung:
Präparation: **KBr (2,3/1000)**   Dez. Nr.: **4.1.2**   Preparation: **KBr (2,3/1000)**   Dec. No.: **4.1.2**

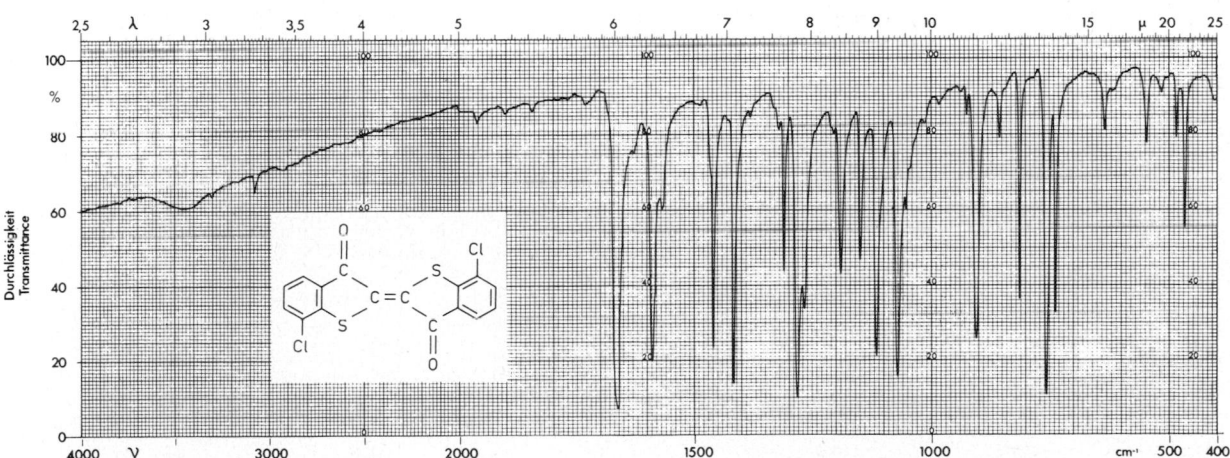

CI-Name: **Pigment Rot 87**   CI-No.: **73310**   CI-Name: **Pigment Red 87**   CI-No.: **73310**   5658
Zusammen- **7,7'-Dichlorthioindigo**   Composition: **7,7'-Dichlorothioindigo**
setzung:
Präparation: **KBr (2,5/1000)**   Dez. Nr.: **4.2.1**   Preparation: **KBr (2,5/1000)**   Dec. No.: **4.2.1**

Organische Pigmente
4. Indigo-Pigmente
4.2. Thioindigoderivate

Organic Pigments
4. Indigo Pigments
4.2. Thioindigo Derivatives

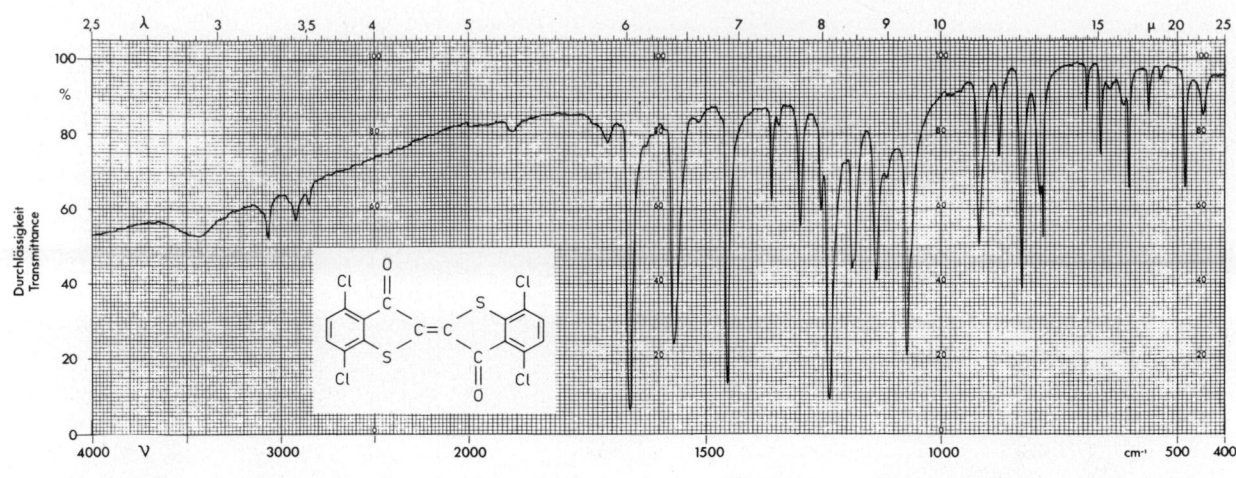

5659

CI-Name:	**Pigment Rot 88**	CI-No.: 73321
Zusammensetzung:	**4,4′,7,7′-Tetrachlorthioindigo**	
Präparation:	**KBr (2,1/1000)**	Dez. Nr.: **4.2.2**

CI-Name:	**Pigment Red 88**	CI-No.: 73321
Composition:	**4,4′,7,7′-Tetrachlorothioindigo**	
Preparation:	**KBr (2,1/1000)**	Dec. No.: **4.2.2**

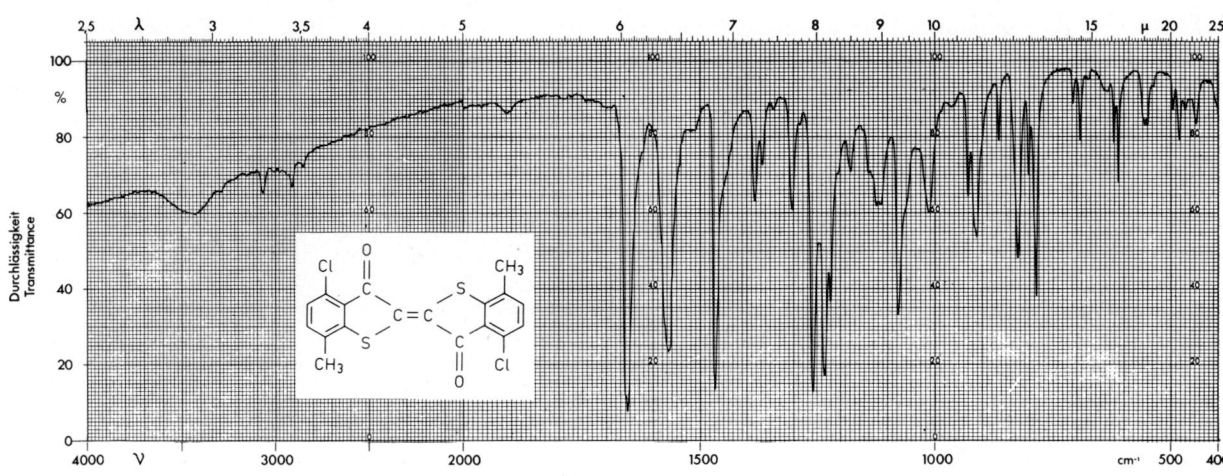

5660

CI-Name:	Pigment Rot 198	CI-No.: 73390
Zusammensetzung:	**4,4′-Dichlor-7,7′-dimethylthioindigo**	
Präparation:	**KBr (2,6/1000)**	Dez. Nr.: **4.2.3**

CI-Name:	Pigment Red 198	CI-No.: 73390
Composition:	**4,4′-Dichloro-7,7′-dimethylthioindigo**	
Preparation:	**KBr (2,6/1000)**	Dec. No.: **4.2.3**

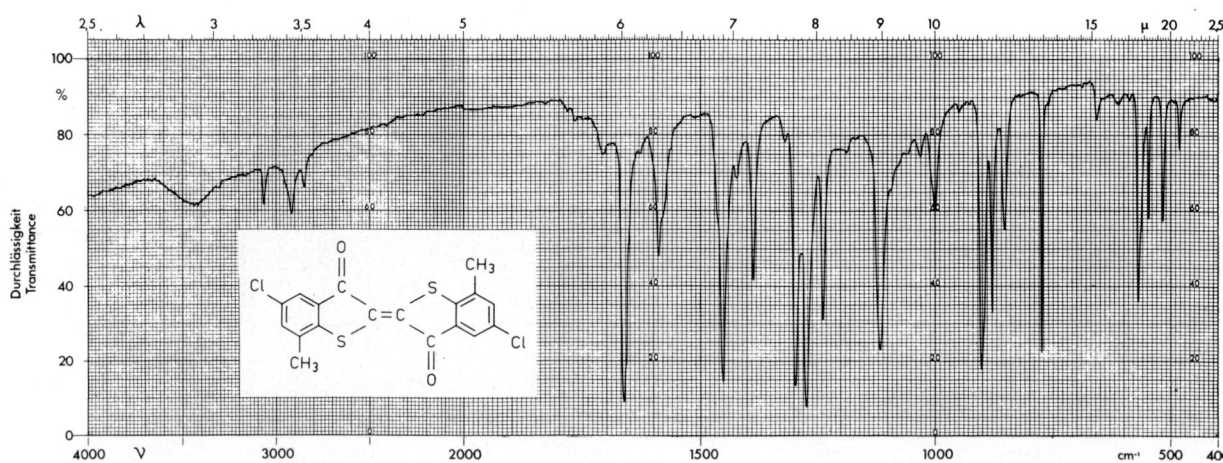

5661

CI-Name:	Pigment Violett 36	CI-No.: 73385
Zusammensetzung:	**5,5′-Dichlor-7,7′-dimethylthioindigo**	
Präparation:	**KBr (2,5/1000)**	Dez. Nr.: **4.2.4**

CI-Name:	Pigment Violet 36	CI-No.: **73385**
Composition:	**5,5′-Dichloro-7,7′-dimethylthioindigo**	
Preparation:	**KBr (2,5/1000)**	Dec. No.: **4.2.4**

Organische Pigmente
4. Indigo-Pigmente
4.2. Thioindigoderivate

Organic Pigments
4. Indigo Pigments
4.2. Thioindigo Derivatives

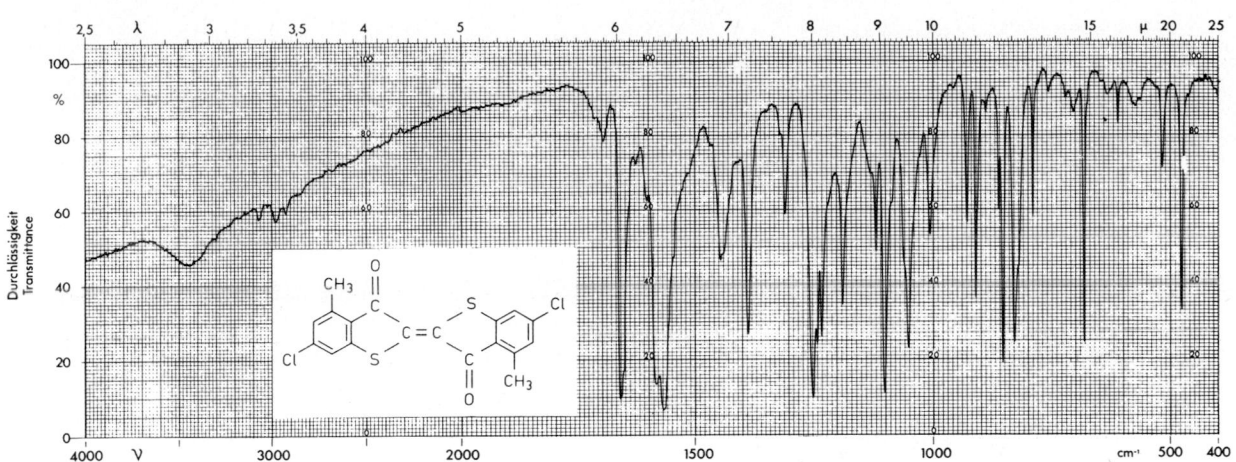

CI-Name: Pigment Rot 181   CI-No.:   **73360**
Zusammensetzung: **6,6′-Dichlor-4,4′-dimethylthioindigo**
Präparation: **KBr (3/1000)**   Dez. Nr.: **4.2.5**

CI-Name: **Vat Red 1**   CI-No.:   **73360**
Composition: **6,6′-Dichloro-4,4′-dimethylthioindigo**
Preparation: **KBr (3/1000)**   Dec. No.: **4.2.5**

5662

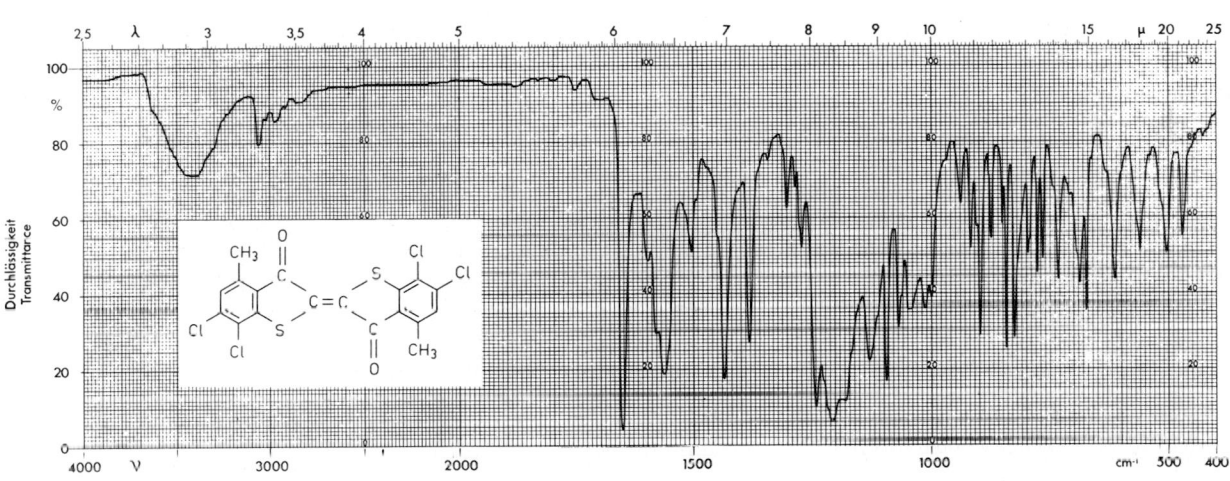

CI-Name: **VAT Rot 2**   CI-No.:   **73365**
Zusammensetzung: **5,5′,6,6′-Tetrachlor-4,4′-dimethylthioindigo**
Präparation: **KBr (6/1000)**   Dez. Nr.: 4.2.7

CI-Name: **Vat Red 2**   CI-No.:   **73365**
Composition: **5,5′,6,6′-Tetrachloro-4,4′-dimethylthioindigo**
Preparation: **KBr (6/1000)**   Dec. No.: 4.2.7

5663

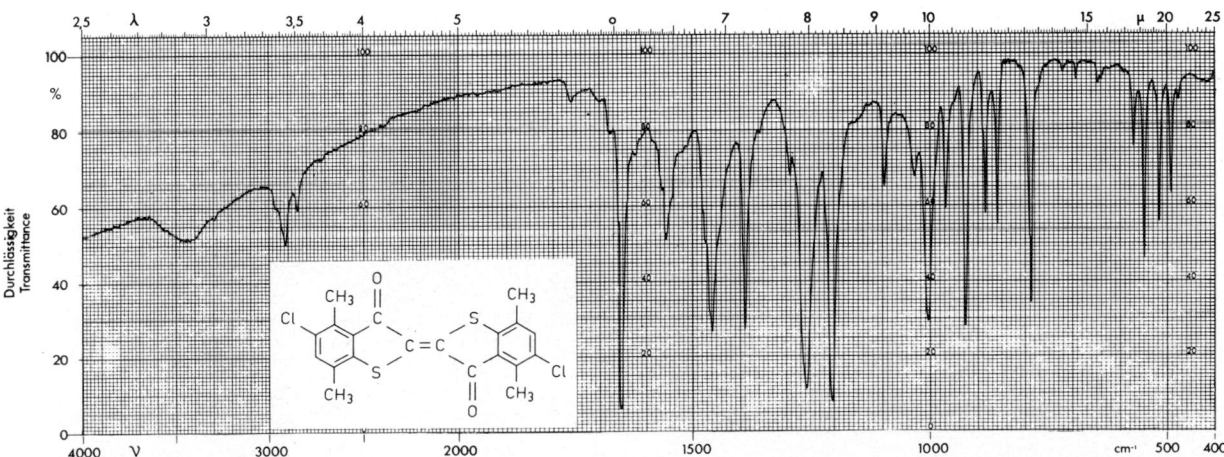

CI-Name: Pigment Violett 38   CI-No.:   **73395**
Zusammensetzung: **5,5′-Dichlor-4,4′,7,7′-tetramethylthioindigo**
Präparation: **KBr (3,3/1000)**   Dez. Nr.: 4.2.8

CI-Name: Pigment Violet 38   CI-No.:   **73395**
Composition: **5,5′-Dichloro-4,4′,7,7′-tetramethylthioindigo**
Preparation: **KBr (3,3/1000)**   Dec. No.: 4.2.8

5664

Organische Pigmente
5. Pigmente mit Kondens. Ringen
5.1. Einfache Anthrachinone

Organic Pigments
5. Pigments with condensed Rings
5.1. Anthraquinones

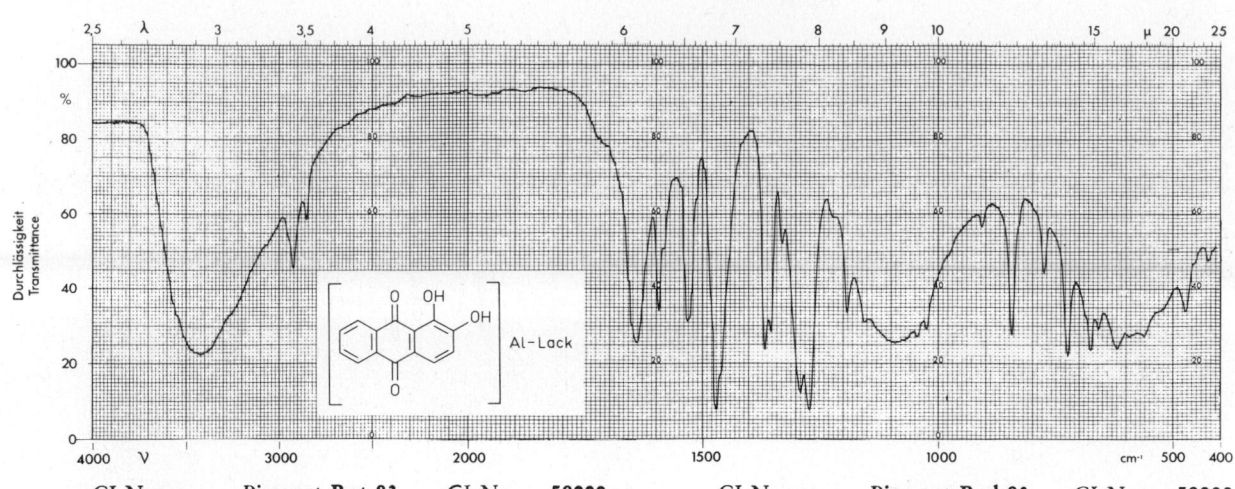

5665

CI-Name:	**Pigment Rot 83**	CI-No.:	**58000**
Zusammen-setzung:	**Alizarin, Al-Lack**		
Präparation:	**KBr (3/1000)**	Dez. Nr.:	**5.1.1**

CI-Name:	**Pigment Red 83**	CI-No.:	**58000**
Composition:	**Alizarin, Al-lake**		
Preparation:	**KBr (3/1000)**	Dec. No.:	**5.1.1**

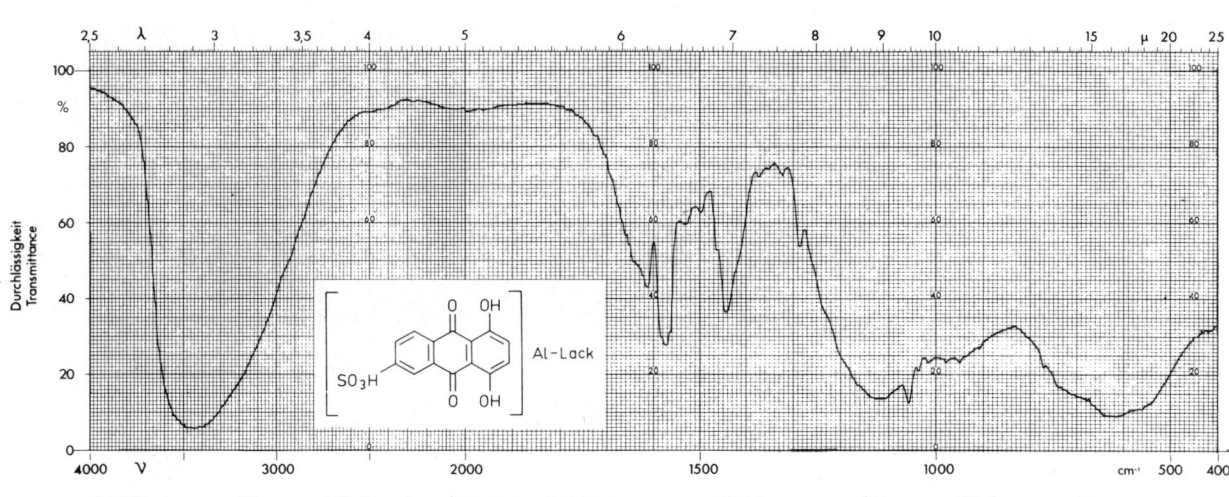

5666

CI-Name:	**Pigment Violett 6**	CI-No.:	**58060**
Zusammen-setzung:	**Chinizarin-6-sulfonsäure, Al-Lack**		
Präparation:	**KBr (4/1000)**	Dez. Nr.:	**5.1.2**

CI-Name:	**Pigment Violet 6**	CI-No.:	**58060**
Composition:	**Quinizarin-6-sulfonic acid, Al-lake**		
Preparation:	**KBr (4/1000)**	Dec. No.:	**5.1.2**

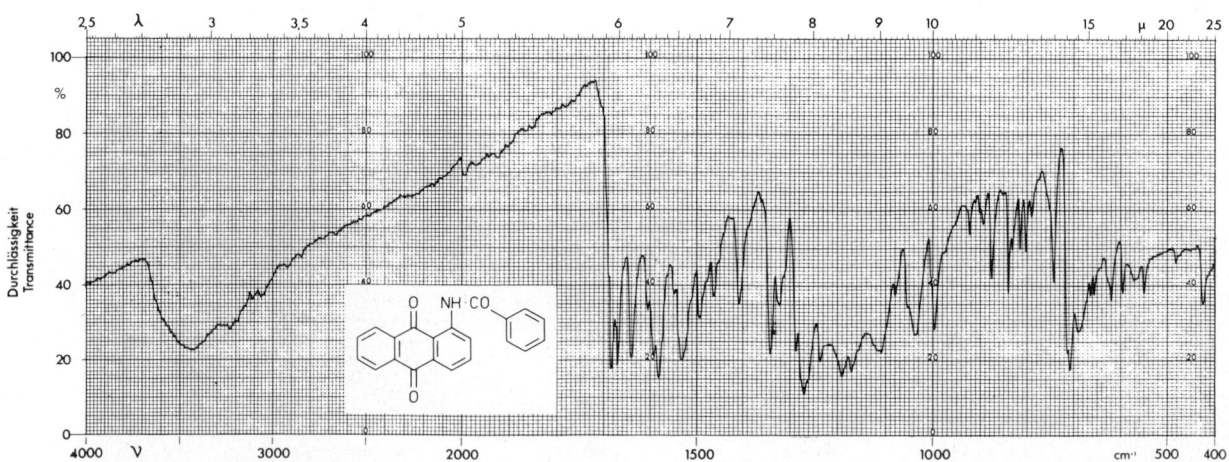

5667

CI-Name:	**(Pigmosol Gelb G)**	CI-No.:	**60515**
Zusammen-setzung:	**N-Benzoyl-1-amino-9,10-anthrachinon**		
Präparation:	**KBr (11/1000)**	Dez. Nr.:	5.1.6

CI-Name:	**(Pigmosol Yellow G)**	CI-No.:	**60515**
Composition:	**N-Benzoyl-1-amino-9,10-anthraquinone**		
Preparation:	**KBr (11/1000)**	Dec. No.:	5.1.6

Organische Pigmente
5. Pigmente mit Kondens. Ringen
5.1. Einfache Anthrachinone

Organic Pigments
5. Pigments with condensed Rings
5.1. Anthraquinones

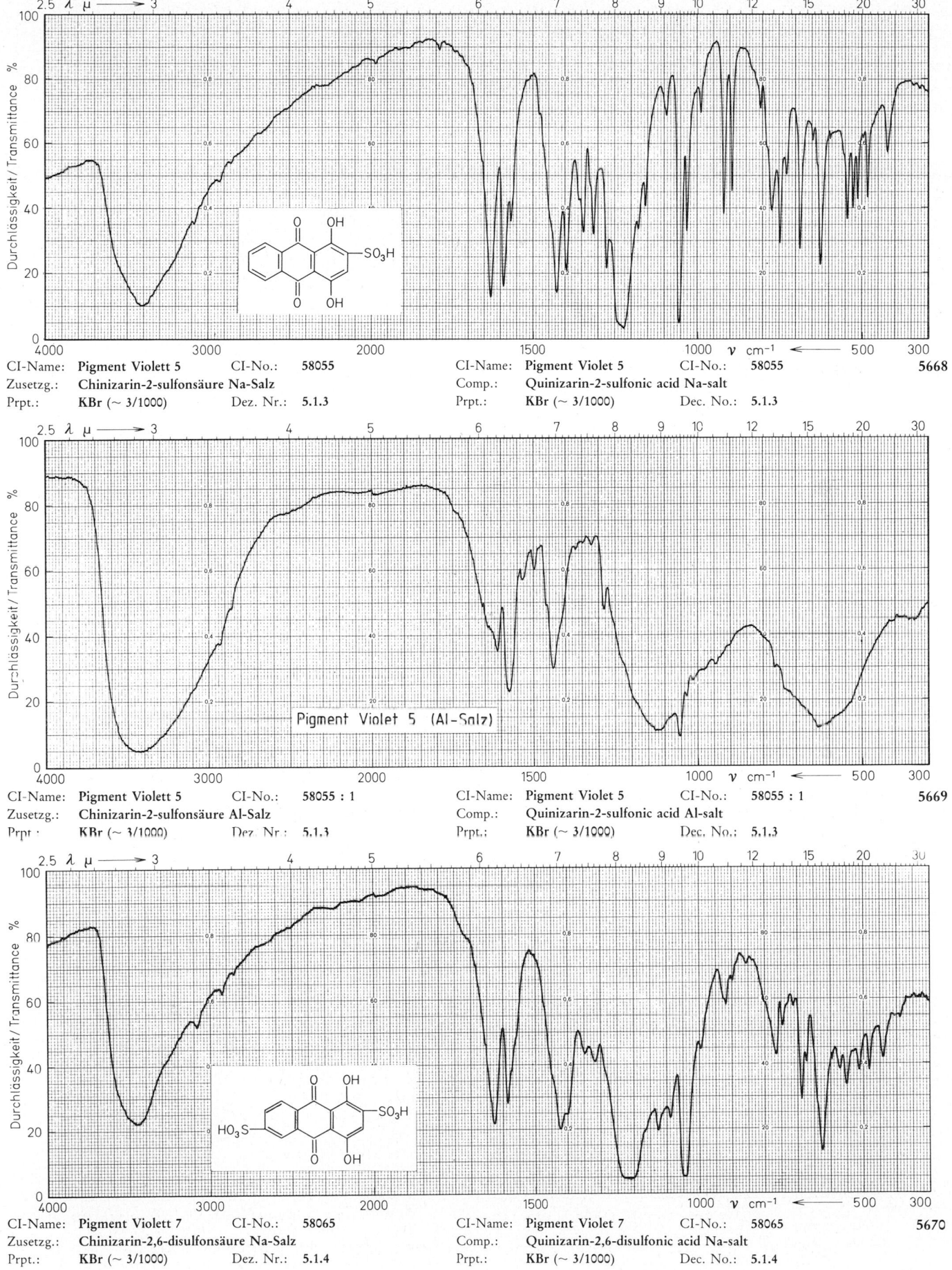

CI-Name: **Pigment Violett 5**　　CI-No.: **58055**
Zusetzg.: **Chinizarin-2-sulfonsäure Na-Salz**
Prpt.: **KBr (~ 3/1000)**　　Dez. Nr.: **5.1.3**

CI-Name: **Pigment Violet 5**　　CI-No.: **58055**
Comp.: **Quinizarin-2-sulfonic acid Na-salt**
Prpt.: **KBr (~ 3/1000)**　　Dec. No.: **5.1.3**

5668

Pigment Violet 5 (Al-Salz)

CI-Name: **Pigment Violett 5**　　CI-No.: **58055 : 1**
Zusetzg.: **Chinizarin-2-sulfonsäure Al-Salz**
Prpt.: **KBr (~ 3/1000)**　　Dez. Nr.: **5.1.3**

CI-Name: **Pigment Violet 5**　　CI-No.: **58055 : 1**
Comp.: **Quinizarin-2-sulfonic acid Al-salt**
Prpt.: **KBr (~ 3/1000)**　　Dec. No.: **5.1.3**

5669

CI-Name: **Pigment Violett 7**　　CI-No.: **58065**
Zusetzg.: **Chinizarin-2,6-disulfonsäure Na-Salz**
Prpt.: **KBr (~ 3/1000)**　　Dez. Nr.: **5.1.4**

CI-Name: **Pigment Violet 7**　　CI-No.: **58065**
Comp.: **Quinizarin-2,6-disulfonic acid Na-salt**
Prpt.: **KBr (~ 3/1000)**　　Dec. No.: **5.1.4**

5670

Organische Pigmente
5. Pigmente mit Kondens. Ringen
5.1. Einfache Anthrachinone

Organic Pigments
5. Pigments with condensed Rings
5.1. Anthraquinones

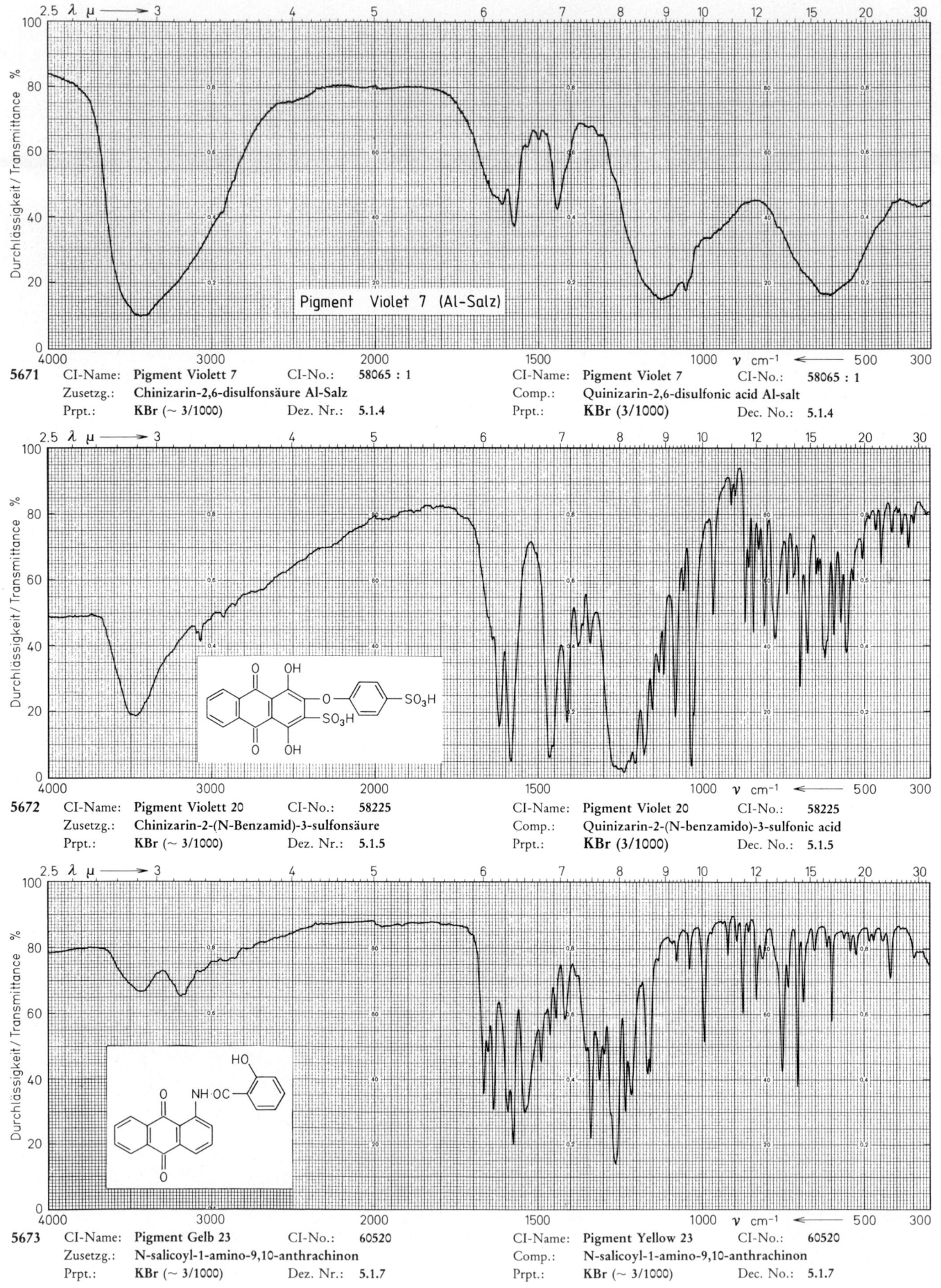

Pigment Violet 7 (Al–Salz)

5671

CI-Name:	**Pigment Violett 7**	CI-No.:	**58065 : 1**		CI-Name:	**Pigment Violet 7**	CI-No.:	**58065 : 1**
Zusetzg.:	**Chinizarin-2,6-disulfonsäure Al-Salz**				Comp.:	**Quinizarin-2,6-disulfonic acid Al-salt**		
Prpt.:	**KBr (~ 3/1000)**	Dez. Nr.:	**5.1.4**		Prpt.:	**KBr (3/1000)**	Dec. No.:	**5.1.4**

5672

CI-Name:	**Pigment Violett 20**	CI-No.:	**58225**		CI-Name:	**Pigment Violet 20**	CI-No.:	**58225**
Zusetzg.:	**Chinizarin-2-(N-Benzamid)-3-sulfonsäure**				Comp.:	**Quinizarin-2-(N-benzamido)-3-sulfonic acid**		
Prpt.:	**KBr (~ 3/1000)**	Dez. Nr.:	**5.1.5**		Prpt.:	**KBr (3/1000)**	Dec. No.:	**5.1.5**

5673

CI-Name:	**Pigment Gelb 23**	CI-No.:	**60520**		CI-Name:	**Pigment Yellow 23**	CI-No.:	**60520**
Zusetzg.:	**N-salicoyl-1-amino-9,10-anthrachinon**				Comp.:	**N-salicoyl-1-amino-9,10-anthrachinon**		
Prpt.:	**KBr (~ 3/1000)**	Dez. Nr.:	**5.1.7**		Prpt.:	**KBr (~ 3/1000)**	Dec. No.:	**5.1.7**

Organische Pigmente
5. Pigmente mit Kondens. Ringen
5.1. Einfache Anthrachinone

Organic Pigments
5. Pigments with condensed Rings
5.1. Anthraquinones

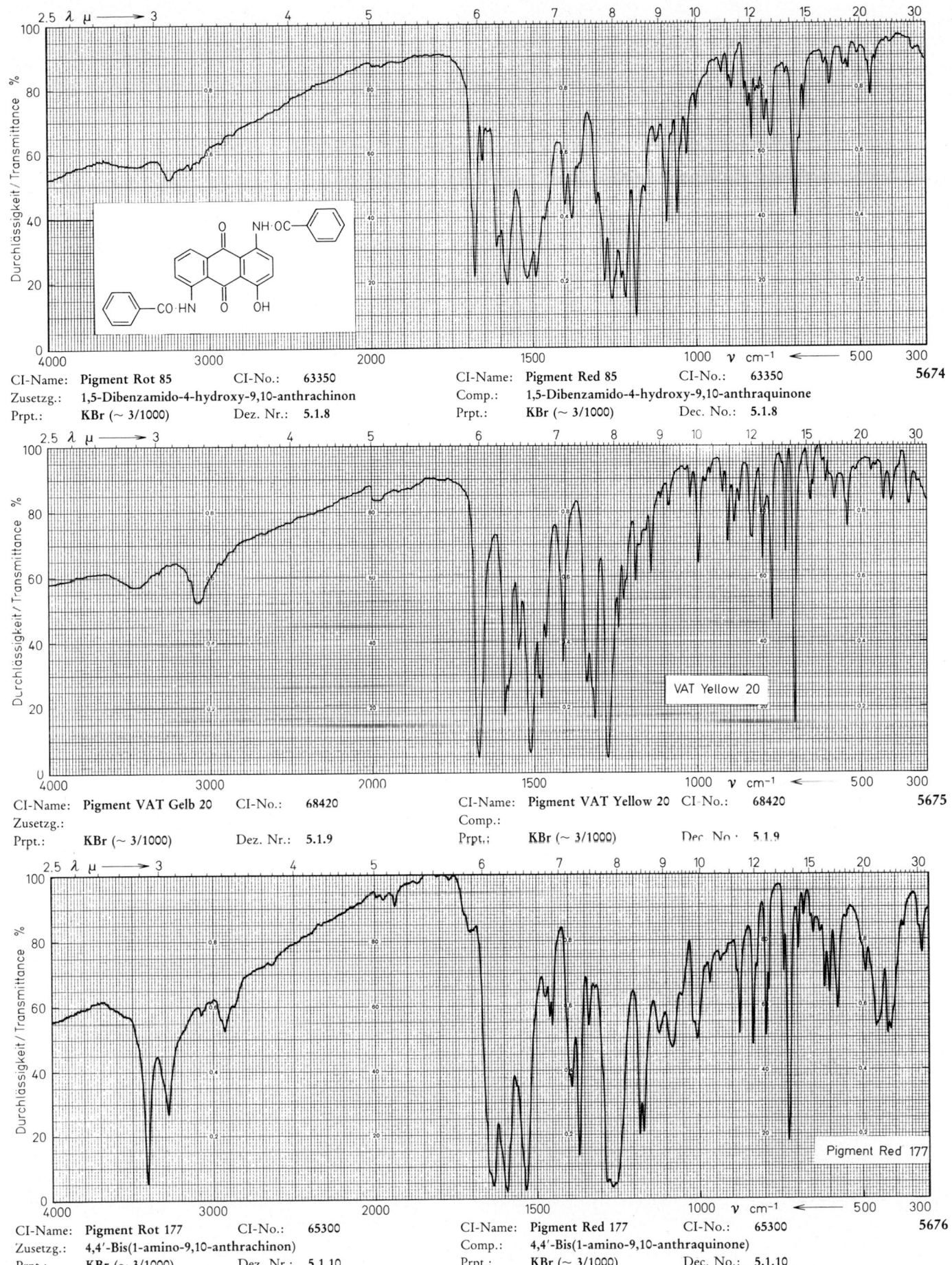

CI-Name: **Pigment Rot 85**   CI-No.: **63350**
Zusetzg.: **1,5-Dibenzamido-4-hydroxy-9,10-anthrachinon**
Prpt.: **KBr (~ 3/1000)**   Dez. Nr.: **5.1.8**

CI-Name: **Pigment Red 85**   CI-No.: **63350**   **5674**
Comp.: **1,5-Dibenzamido-4-hydroxy-9,10-anthraquinone**
Prpt.: **KBr (~ 3/1000)**   Dec. No.: **5.1.8**

VAT Yellow 20

CI-Name: **Pigment VAT Gelb 20**   CI-No.: **68420**
Zusetzg.:
Prpt.: **KBr (~ 3/1000)**   Dez. Nr.: **5.1.9**

CI-Name: **Pigment VAT Yellow 20**   CI-No.: **68420**   **5675**
Comp.:
Prpt.: **KBr (~ 3/1000)**   Dec. No.: **5.1.9**

Pigment Red 177

CI-Name: **Pigment Rot 177**   CI-No.: **65300**
Zusetzg.: **4,4'-Bis(1-amino-9,10-anthrachinon)**
Prpt.: **KBr (~ 3/1000)**   Dez. Nr.: **5.1.10**

CI-Name: **Pigment Red 177**   CI-No.: **65300**   **5676**
Comp.: **4,4'-Bis(1-amino-9,10-anthraquinone)**
Prpt.: **KBr (~ 3/1000)**   Dec. No.: **5.1.10**

Organische Pigmente
5. Pigmente mit Kondens. Ringen
5.2. Kondensierte Anthrachinone

Organic Pigments
5. Pigments with condensed Rings
5.2. Condensed Anthraquinones

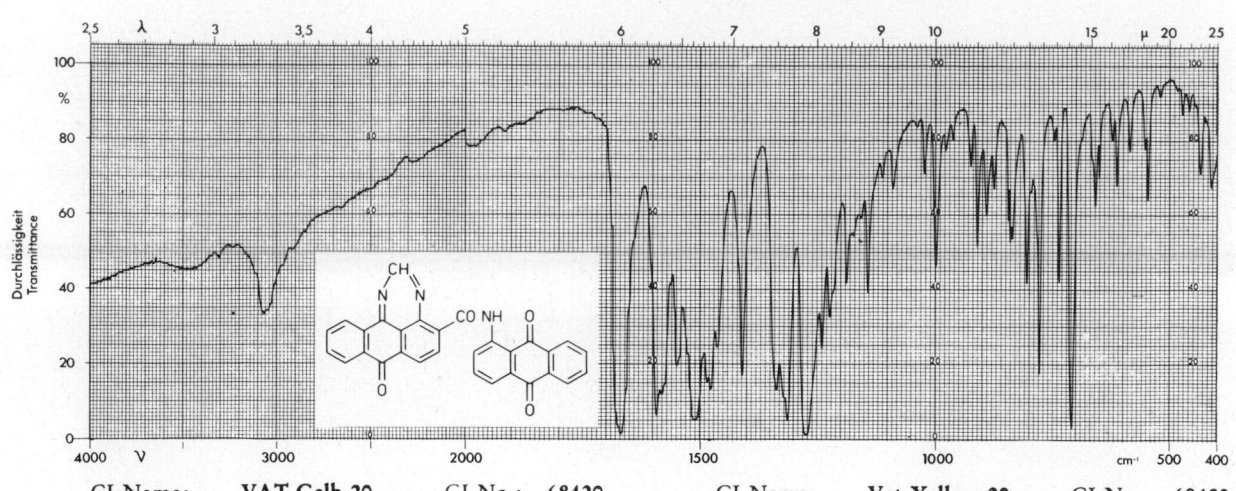

5677

	CI-Name:	VAT Gelb 20	CI-No.:	68420
Zusammensetzung:		Anthrapyrimidinpigment		
Präparation:	KBr (3/1000)		Dez. Nr.:	5.1.11

	CI-Name:	Vat Yellow 20	CI-No.:	68420
Composition:		Anthrapyrimidine pigment		
Preparation:	KBr (3/1000)		Dec. No.:	5.1.11

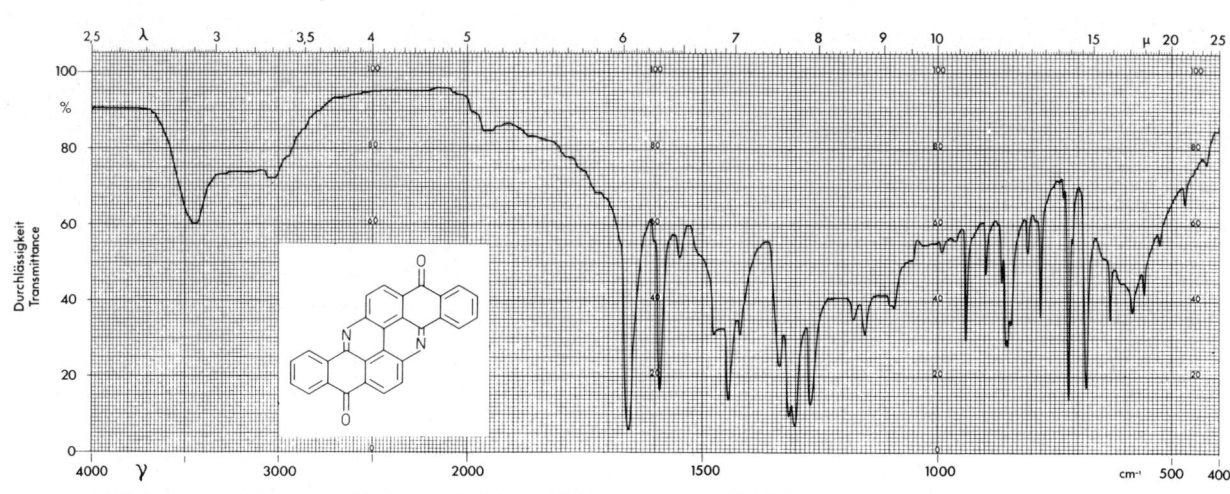

5678

	CI-Name:	Pigment Gelb 24	CI-No.:	70600
Zusammensetzung:		Flavanthron		
Präparation:	KBr (4/1000)		Dez. Nr.:	5.2.1

	CI-Name:	Pigment Yellow 24	CI-No.:	70600
Composition:		Flavanthrone		
Preparation:	KBr (4/1000)		Dec. No.:	5.2.1

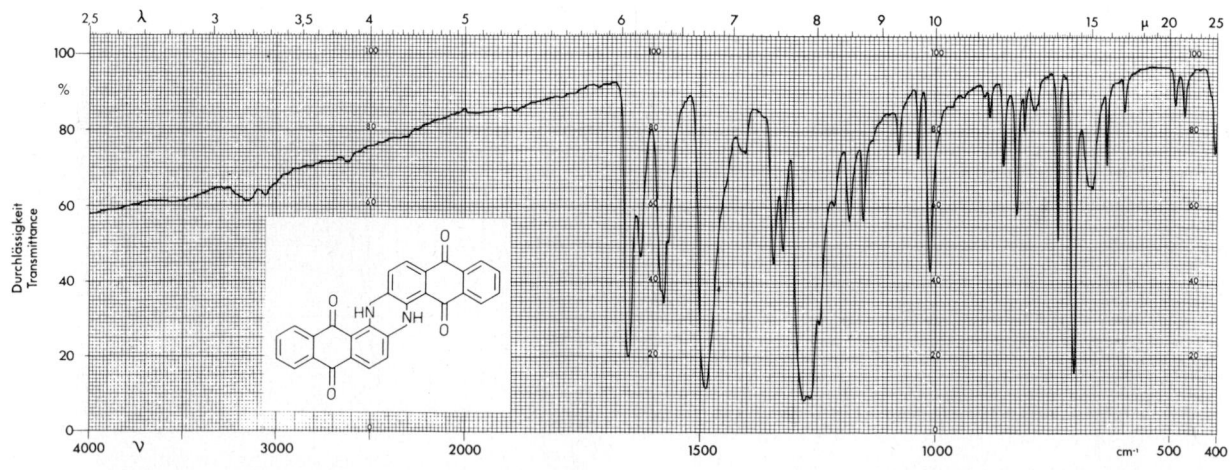

5679

	CI-Name:	Pigment Blau 60	CI-No.:	69800
Zusammensetzung:		Indanthron		
Präparation:	KBr (2,4/1000)		Dez. Nr.:	5.2.2

	CI-Name:	Pigment Blue 60	CI-No.:	69800
Composition:		Indanthrone		
Preparation:	KBr (2,4/1000)		Dec. No.:	5.2.2

Organische Pigmente
5. Pigmente mit Kondens. Ringen
5.2. Kondensierte Anthrachinone

Organic Pigments
5. Pigments with condensed Rings
5.2. Condensed Anthraquinones

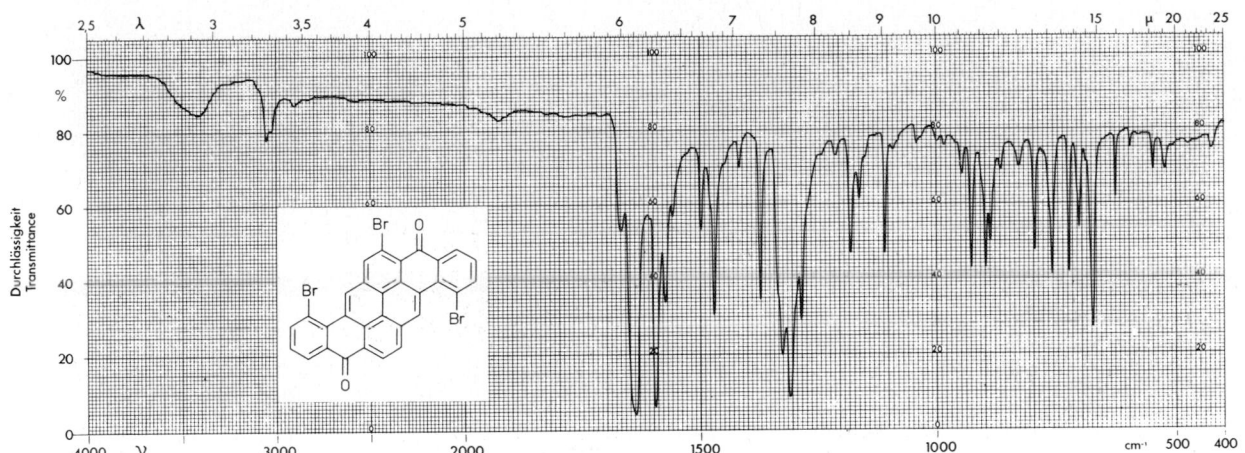

CI-Name: Pigment Rot 216   CI-No.: **59710**
Zusammensetzung: **4,8,8′-Tribrompyranthron**
Präparation: **KBr (1,8/1000)**   Dez. Nr.: **5.2.6**

CI-Name: Pigment Red 216   CI-No.: **59710**
Composition: **4,8,8′-Tribromopyranthrone**
Preparation: **KBr (1,8/1000)**   Dec. No.: **5.2.6**

5680

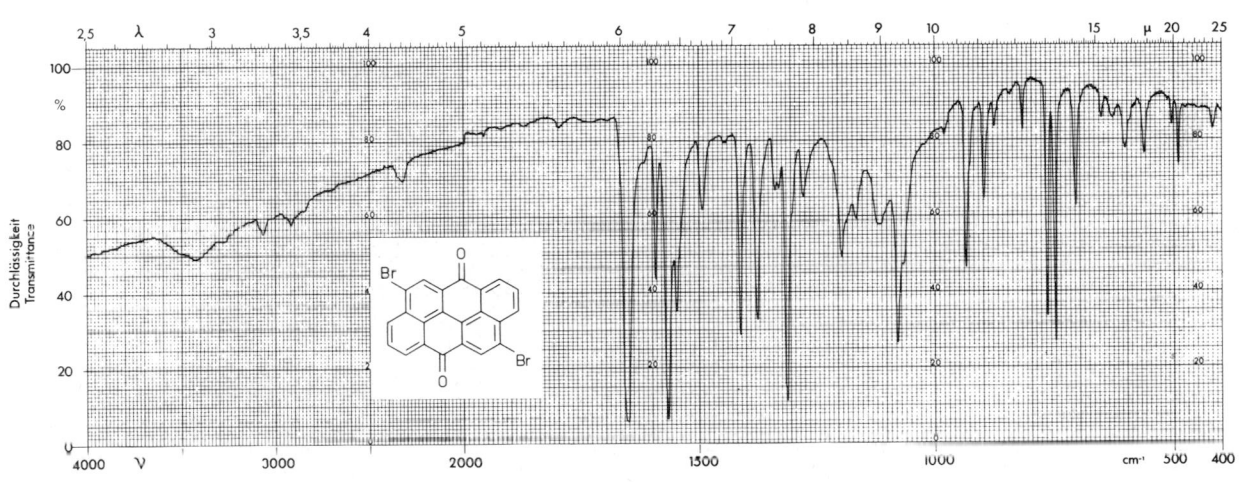

CI-Name: Pigment Rot 168   CI-No.: **59300**
Zusammensetzung: **2,7-Dibromanthanthron**
Präparation: **KBr (1,8/1000)**   Dez. Nr.: **5.2.7**

CI-Name: Pigment Red 168   CI-No.: **59300**
Composition: **2,7-Dibromoanthanthrone**
Preparation: **KBr (1,8/1000)**   Dec. No.: **5.2.7**

5681

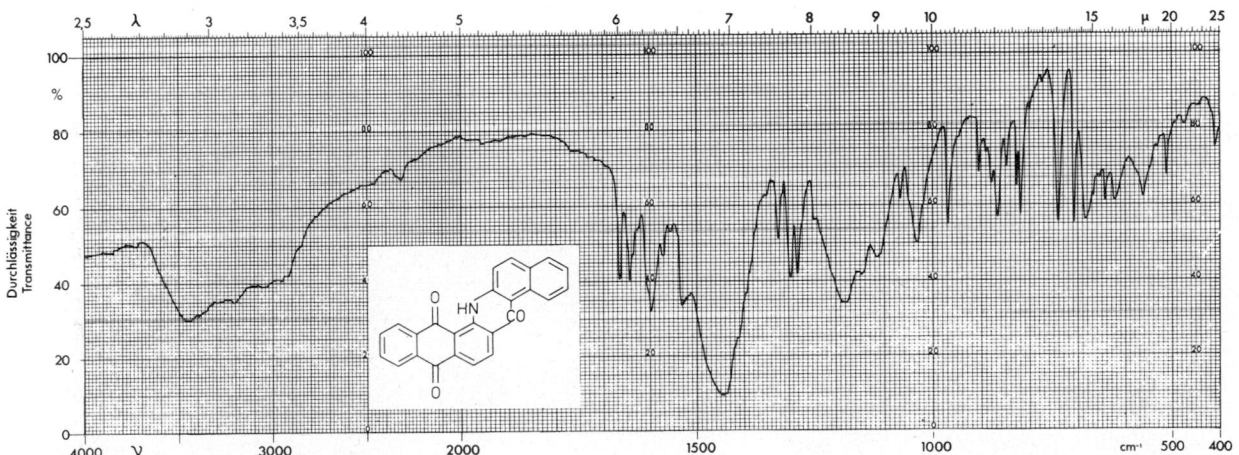

CI-Name: **VAT Rot 35**   CI-No.: **68000**
Zusammensetzung: **3,8,16-Trioxo-3,8,9,16-tetrahydronaphtha-lino[2,3-c]benz[k]acridin**
Präparation: **KBr (5/1000)**   Dez. Nr.: **5.2.8**

CI-Name: Vat Red 35   CI-No.: **68000**
Composition: **3,8,16-Trioxo-3,8,9,16-tetrahydronaphtha-lino[2,3-c]benz[k]acridine**
Preparation: **KBr (5/1000)**   Dec. No.: **5.2.8**

5682

Organische Pigmente
5. Pigmente mit Kondens. Ringen
5.2. Kondensierte Anthrachinone

Organic Pigments
5. Pigments with condensed Rings
5.2. Condensed Anthraquinones

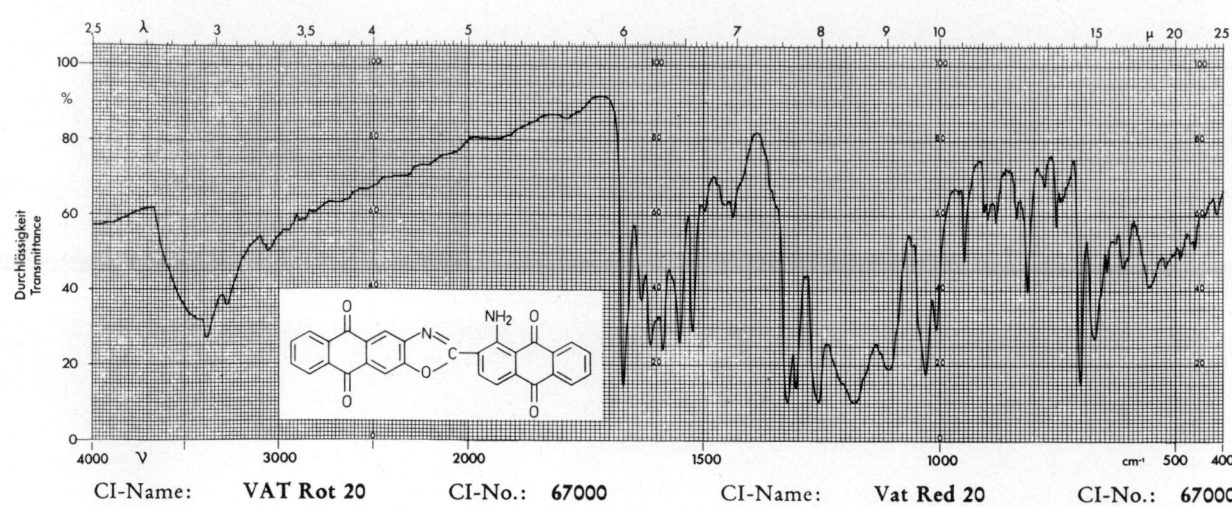

5683

CI-Name:	**VAT Rot 20**	CI-No.:	**67000**	CI-Name:	**Vat Red 20**	CI-No.:	**67000**
Zusammen-setzung:	**Oxazoloanthrachinonpigment**			Composition:	**Oxazoloanthraquinone pigment**		
Präparation:	**KBr (6,5/1000)**	Dez. Nr.:	**5.2.9**	Preparation:	**KBr (6,5/1000)**	Dec. No.:	**5.2.9**

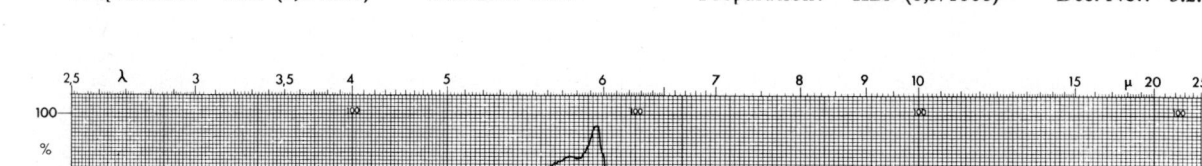
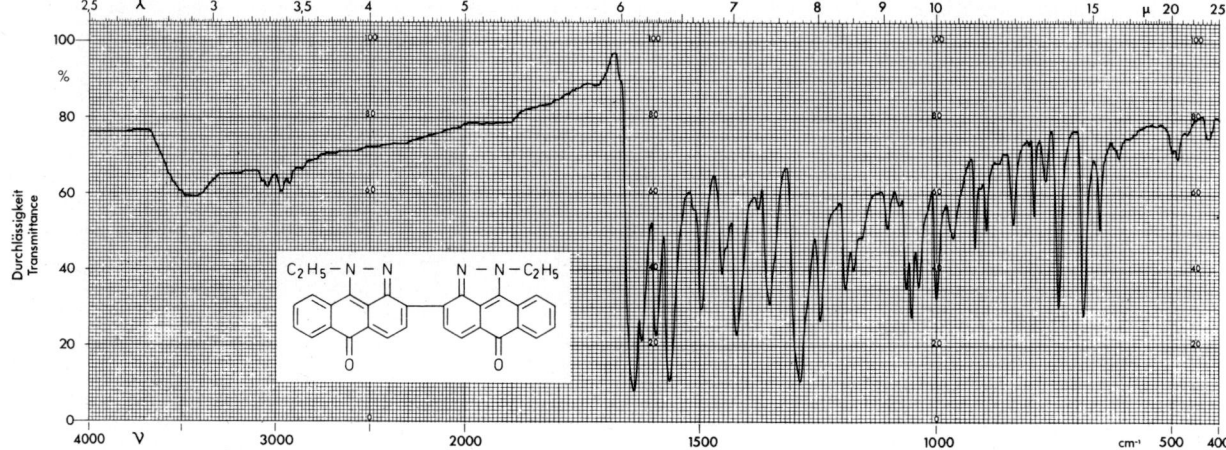

5684

CI-Name:	**VAT Rot 13**	CI-No.:	**70320**	CI-Name:	**Vat Red 13**	CI-No.:	**70320**
Zusammen-setzung:	**N,N′-Diethyldipyrazolanthronyl**			Composition:	**N,N′-Diethyldipyrazoleanthronyle**		
Präparation:	**KBr (9/1000)**	Dez. Nr.:	**5.2.10**	Preparation:	**KBr (9/1000)**	Dec. No.:	**5.2.10**

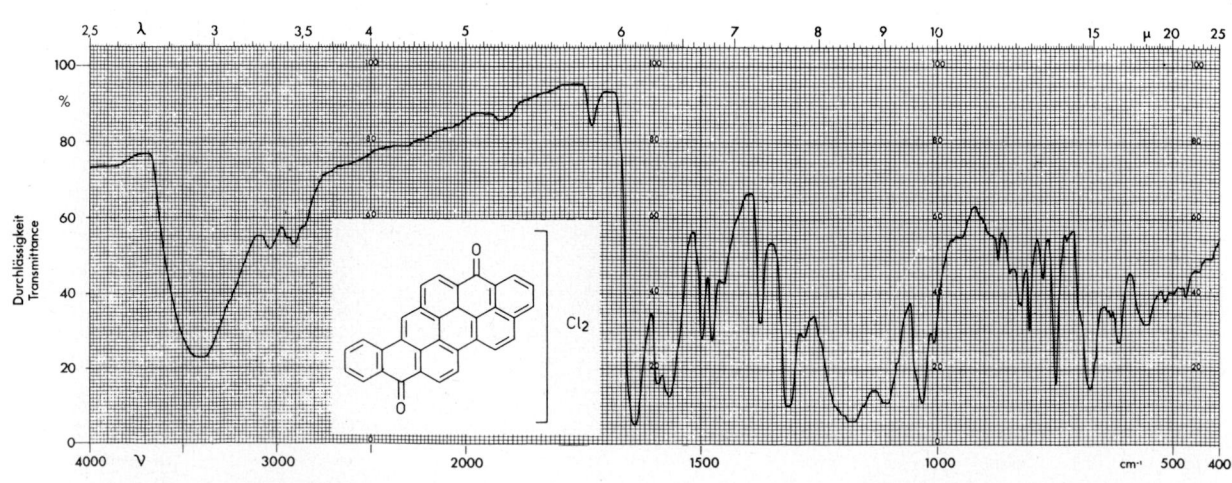

5685

CI-Name:	**VAT Violett 1**	CI-No.:	**60010**	CI-Name:	**Vat Violet 1**	CI-No.:	**60010**
Zusammen-setzung:	**Dichlorisoviolanthron**			Composition:	**Dichloroisoviolanthrone**		
Präparation:	**KBr (11/1000)**	Dez. Nr.:	**5.2.11**	Preparation:	**KBr (11/1000)**	Dec. No.:	**5.2.11**

Organische Pigmente
5. Pigmente mit Kondens. Ringen
5.2. Kondensierte Anthrachinone

Organic Pigments
5. Pigments with condensed Rings
5.2. Condensed Anthraquinones

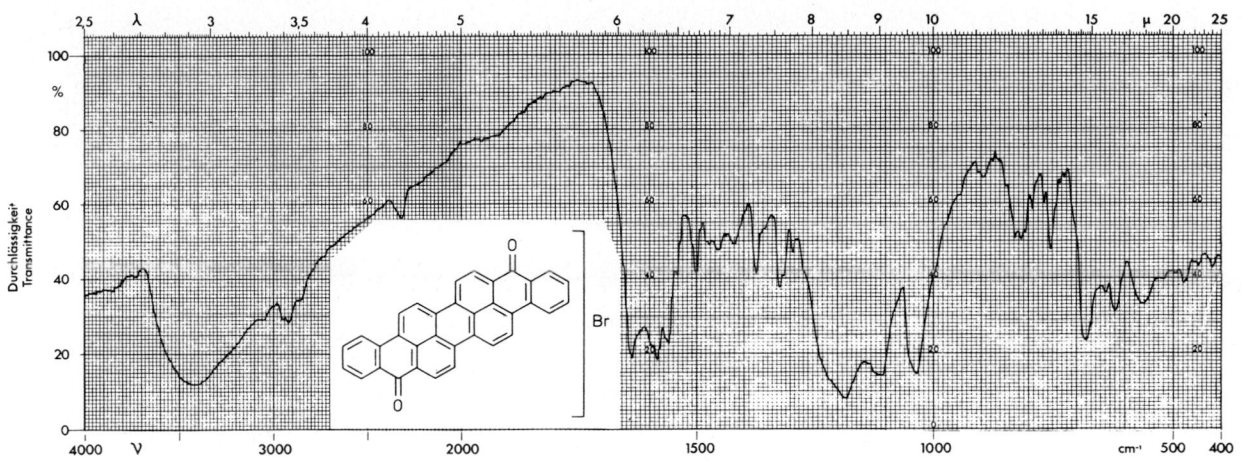

CI-Name: **VAT Violett 9**   CI-No.: **60005**   CI-Name: **Vat Violet 9**   CI-No.: **60005**   5686
Zusammen-
setzung: **Bromisoviolanthron**   Composition: **Bromoisoviolanthrone**
Präparation: **KBr (11/1000)**   Dez. Nr.: 5.2.12   Preparation: **KBr (11/1000)**   Dec. No.: 5.2.12

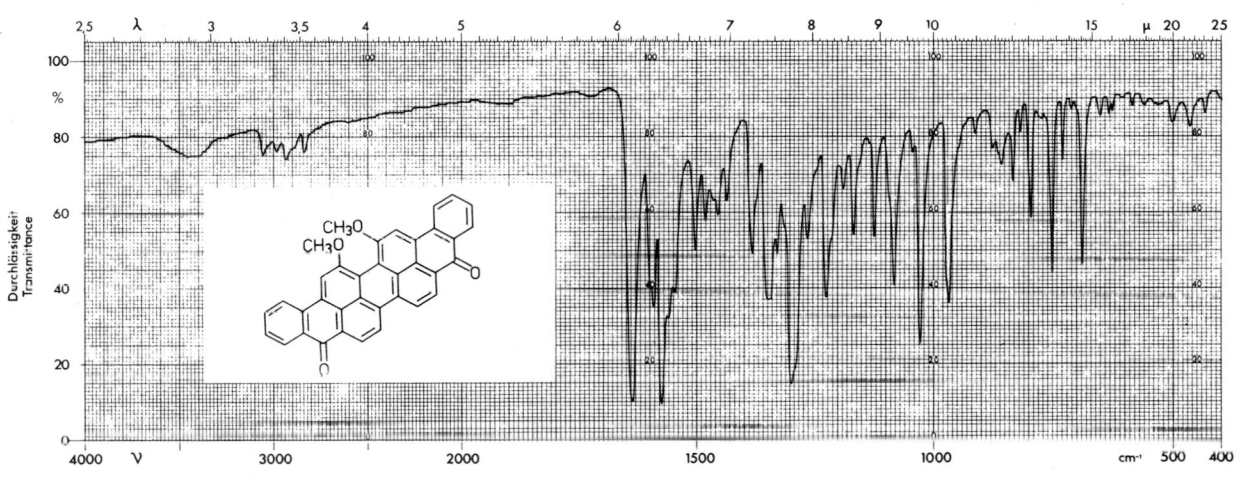

CI-Name: **VAT Grün 1**   CI-No.: **59825**   CI-Name: **Vat Green 1**   CI-No.: **59825**   5687
Zusammen-
setzung: **12,12′-Dimethoxyviolanthron**   Composition: **12,12′-Dimethoxyviolanthrone**
Präparation: **KBr (5/1000)**   Dez. Nr.: 5.2.13   Preparation: **KBr (5/1000)**   Dec. No.: 5.2.13

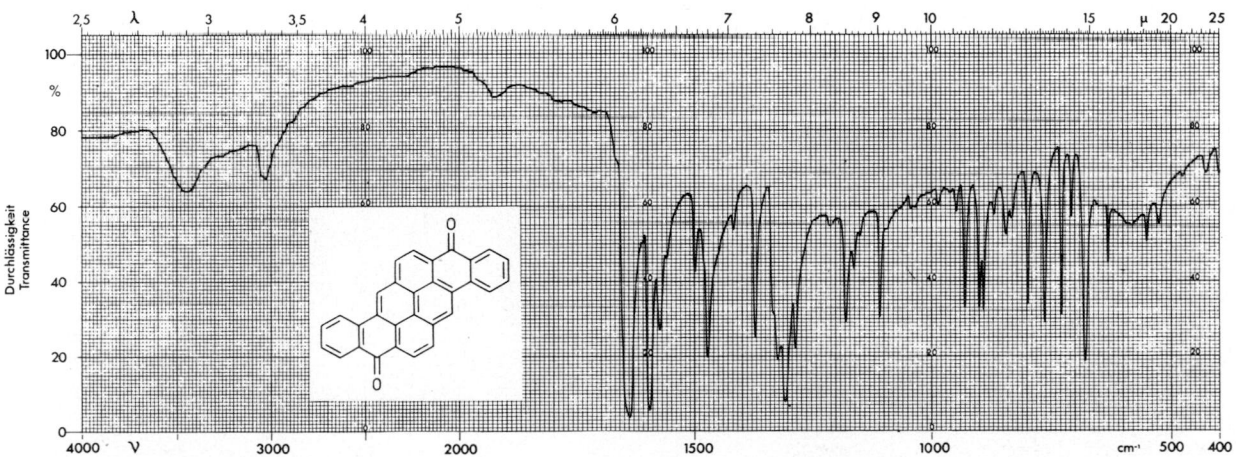

CI-Name: Pigment Orange 40   CI-No.: **59700**   CI-Name: Pigment Orange 40   CI-No.: **59700**   5688
Zusammen-
setzung: **Pyranthron**   Composition: **Pyranthrone**
Präparation: **KBr (6/1000)**   Dez. Nr.: 5.2.5   Preparation: **KBr (6/1000)**   Dec. No.: 5.2.5

Organische Pigmente
5. Pigmente mit Kondens. Ringen
5.3. Naphthoylenbenzimidazole

Organic Pigments
5. Pigments with condensed Rings
5.3. Naphthoic-benzimidazoles

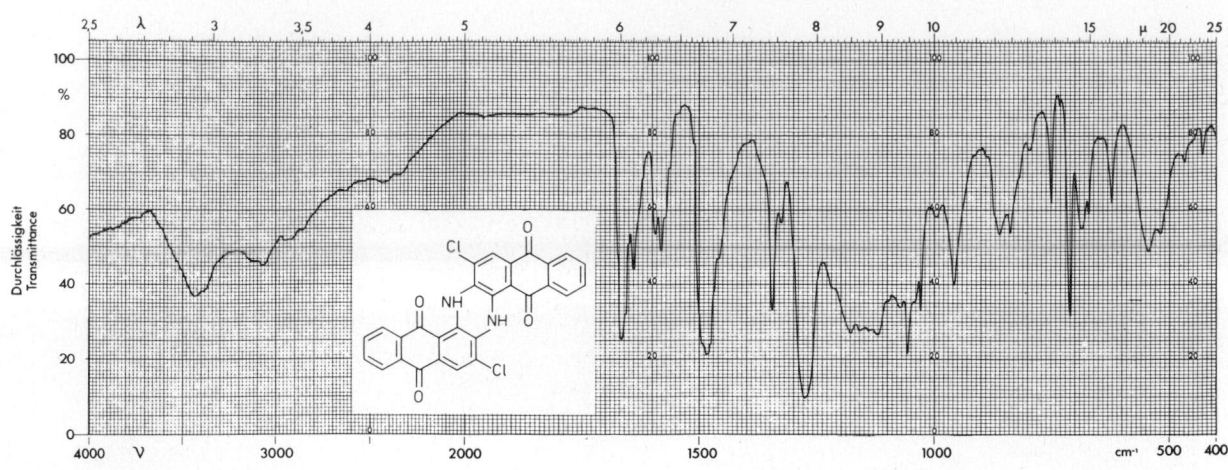

5689

CI-Name:	Pigment Blau 64	CI-No.:	**69825**	CI-Name:	Pigment Blue 64	CI-No.:	**69825**
Zusammen-setzung:	**3,3'-Dichlorindanthron**			Composition:	**3,3'-Dichloroindanthrone**		
Präparation:	**KBr** (3,3/1000)	Dez. Nr.:	5.2.4	Preparation:	**KBr** (3,3/1000)	Dec. No.:	5.2.4

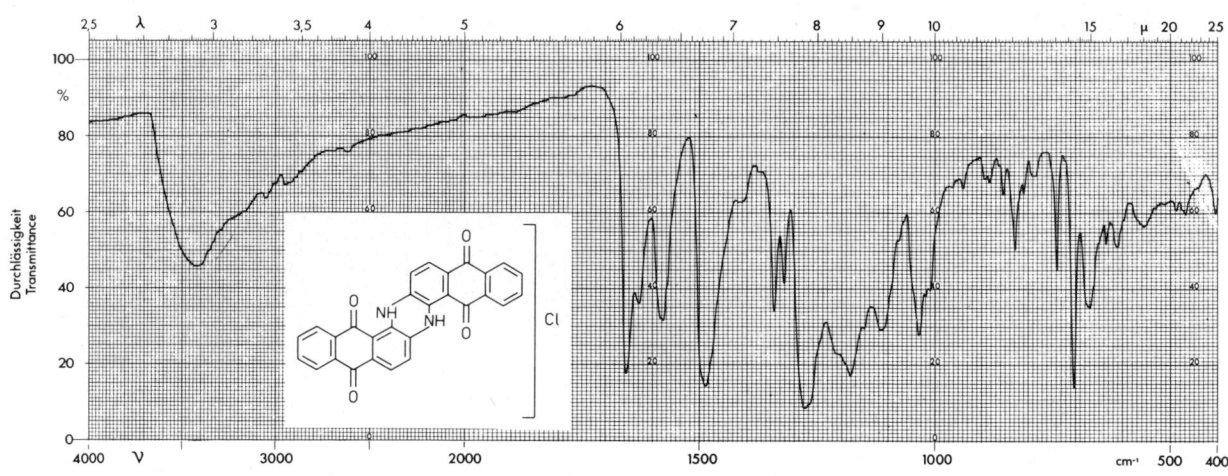

5690

CI-Name:	**Pigment Blau 22**	CI-No.:	**69810**	CI-Name:	**Pigment Blue 22**	CI-No.:	**69810**
Zusammen-setzung:	**Chlorindanthron**			Composition:	**Chloroindanthrone**		
Präparation:	**KBr** (3/1000)	Dez. Nr.:	5.2.3	Preparation:	**KBr** (3/1000)	Dec. No.:	5.2.3

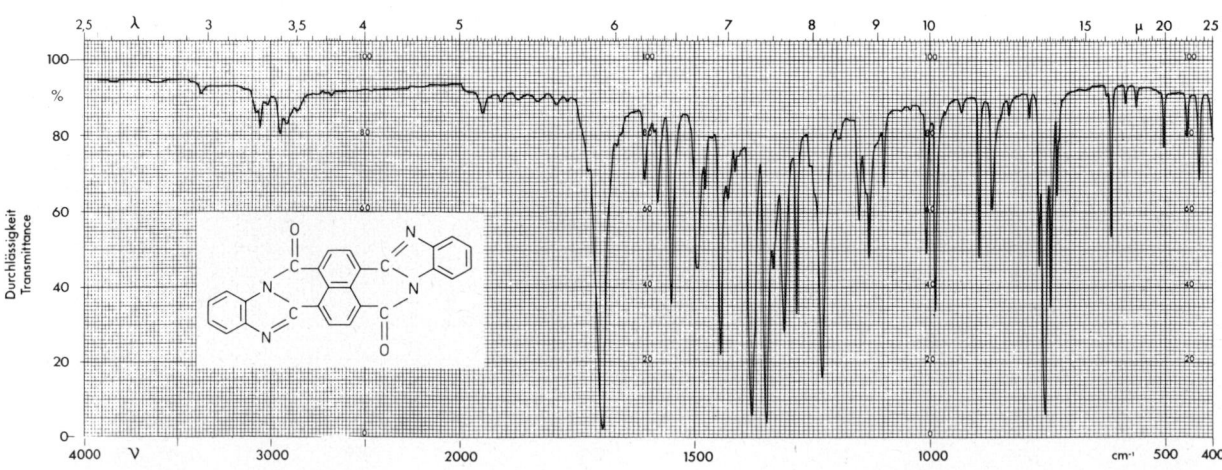

5691

CI-Name:	Pigment Orange 34	CI-No.:	**71105**	CI-Name:	Pigment Orange 34	CI-No.: **71105**
Zusammen-setzung:	**Dibenzimidazolo[1,2-e, 1',2'-m]-4,9-diaza-3,8-pyrenchinon**			Composition:	**Dibenzimidazolo[1,2-e, 1',2'-m]-4,9-diaza-3,8-pyrenequinone**	
Präparation:	**KBr** (1,8/1000)	Dez. Nr.:	**5.3.1**	Preparation:	**KBr** (1,8/1000)	Dec. No.: **5.3.1**

Organische Pigmente
5. Pigmente mit Kondens. Ringen
5.4. Perylene

Organic Pigments
5. Pigments with condensed Rings
5.4. Perylenes

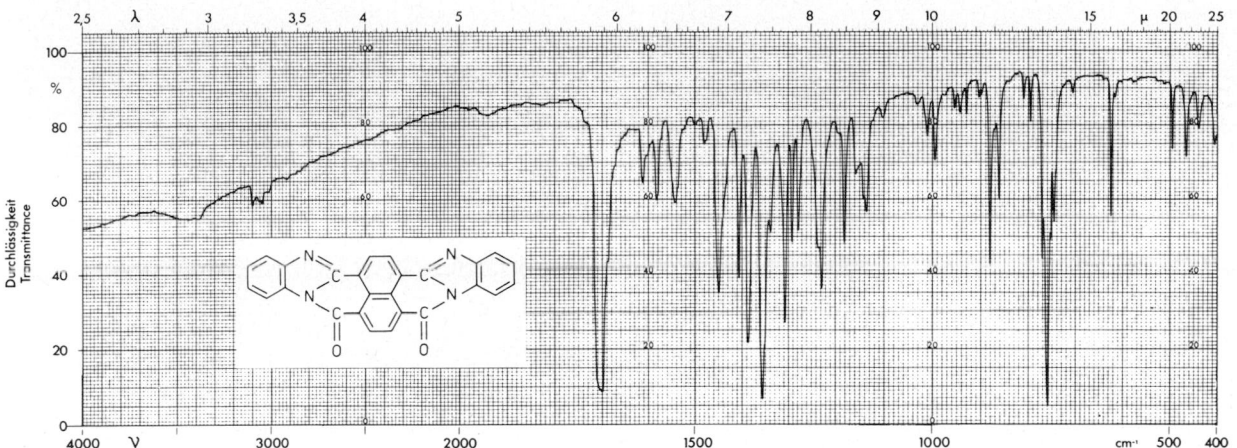

CI-Name: Pigment Rot 194   CI-No.: **71100**
Zusammen-setzung: **Dibenzimidazolo[1,2-e, 2',1'-l]-4,9-diaza-3,10-pyrenchinon**
Präparation: **KBr (1,7/1000)**   Dez. Nr.: **5.3.2**

CI-Name: Pigment Red 194   CI-No.: **71100**
Composition: **Dibenzimidazolo[1,2-e, 2',1'-l]-4,9-diaza-3,10-pyrenequinone**
Preparation: **KBr (1,7/1000)**   Dec. No.: **5.3.2**

5692

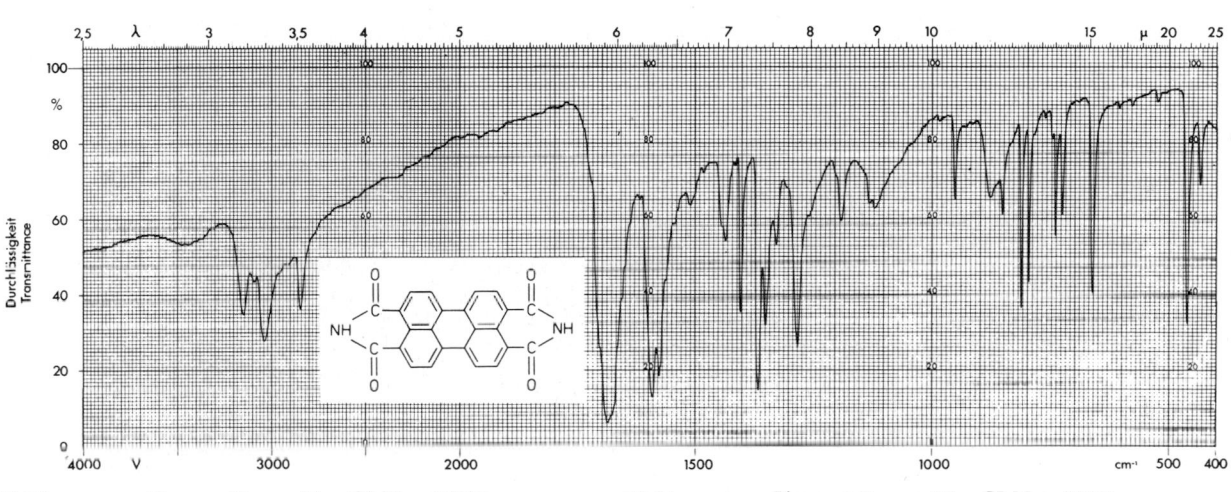

CI-Name: Pigment Braun 26   CI-No.: 71129
Zusammen-setzung: **Perylen-3,4,9,10-tetracarbonsäurediimid**
Präparation: **KBr (1,6/1000)**   Dez. Nr.: **5.4.1**

CI-Name: Pigment Brown 26   CI-No.: 71129
Composition: **Perylene-3,4,9,10-tetracarbonic acid diimide**
Preparation: **KBr (1,6/1000)**   Dec. No.: **5.4.1**

5693

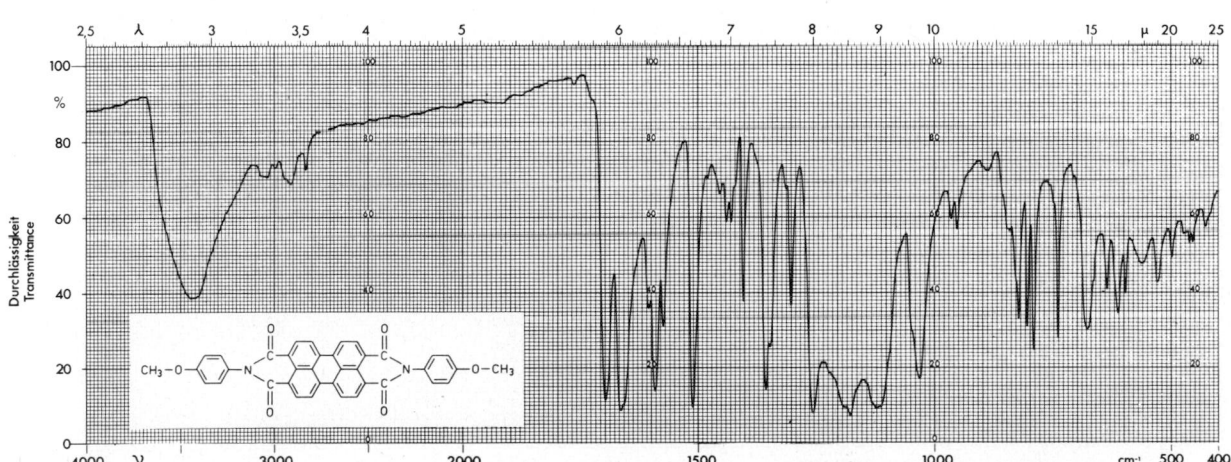

CI-Name: Pigment Red 190   CI-No.: **71140**
Zusammen-setzung: **N,N'-Di-4'-anisylperylen-3,4,9,10-tetra-carbonsäurediimid**
Präparation: **KBr (9/1000)**   Dez. Nr.: **5.4.2**

CI-Name: Pigment Rot 190   CI-No.: **71140**
Composition: **N,N'-Di-4'-anisylperylene-3,4,9,10-tetra-carbonic acid diimide**
Preparation: **KBr (9/1000)**   Dec. No.: **5.4.2**

5694

Organische Pigmente
5. Pigmente mit Kondens. Ringen
5.4. Perylene

Organic Pigments
5. Pigments with condensed Rings
5.4. Perylenes

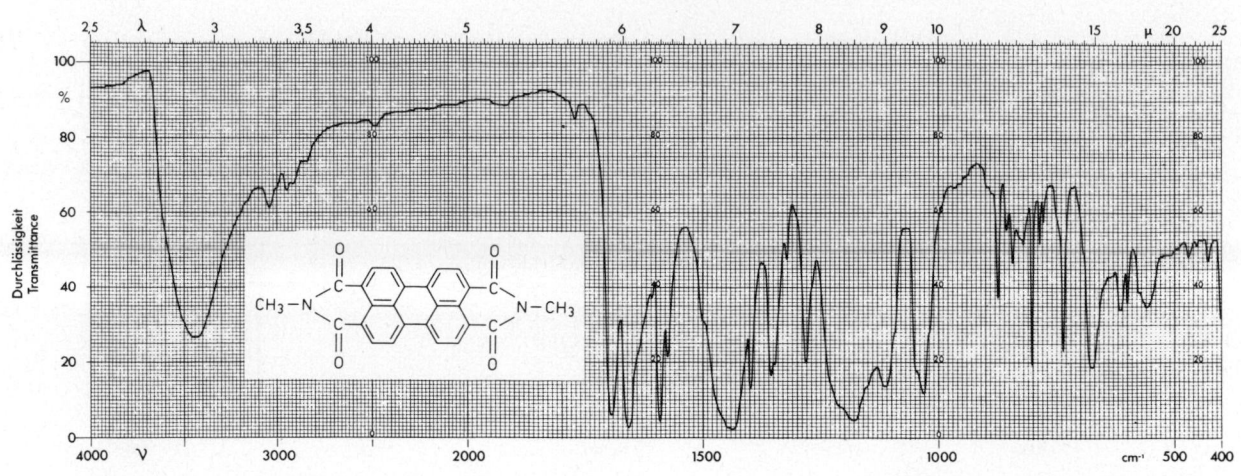

5695

CI-Name:	Pigment Rot 179	CI-No.:	**71130**
Zusammen-setzung:	N,N′-Dimethylperylen-3,4,9,10-tetra-carbonsäurediimid		
Präparation:	KBr (9/1000)	Dez. Nr..	**5.4.3**

CI-Name:	Pigment Red 179	CI-No.:	**71130**
Composition:	N,N′-Dimethylperylene-3,4,9,10-tetra-carbonic acid diimide		
Preparation:	KBr (9/1000)	Dec. No.:	**5.4.3**

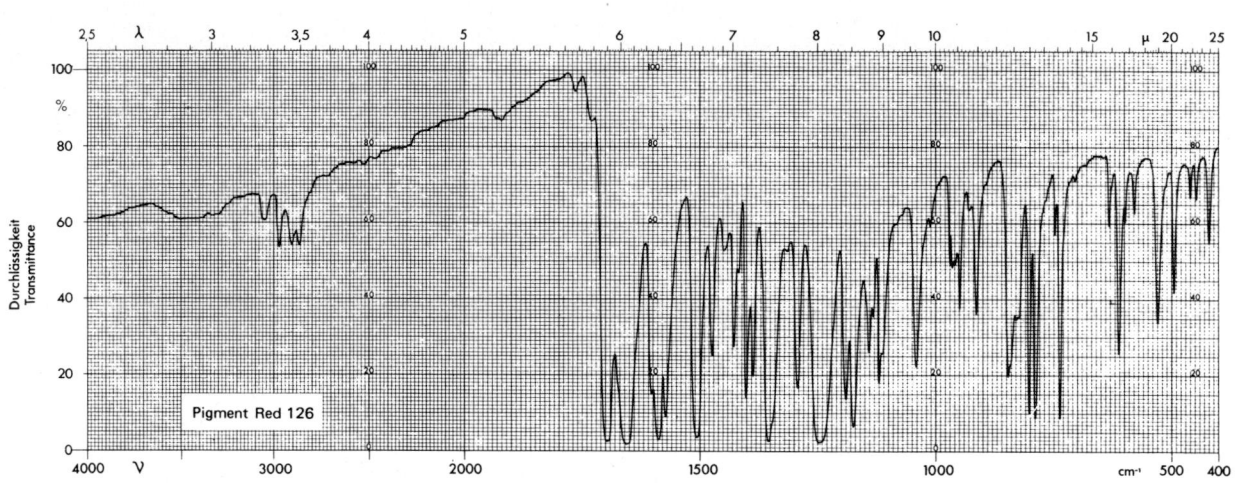

5696

CI-Name:	**Pigment Rot 126**
Zusammen-setzung:	**Perylenpigment**
Präparation:	**KBr (6,5/1000)**	Dez. Nr.:	**5.4.4**

CI-Name:	**Pigment Red 126**
Composition:	**Perylene pigment**
Preparation:	**KBr (6,5/1000)**	Dec. No.:	**5.4.4**

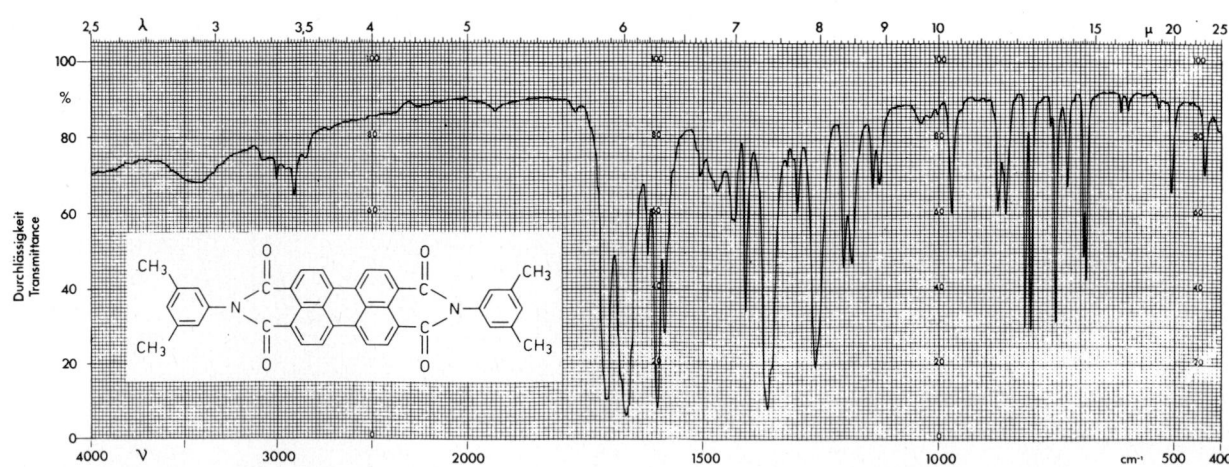

5697

CI-Name:	**Pigment Rot 149**
Zusammen-setzung:	**N,N′-Di-3′,5′-xylylperylen-3,4,9,10-tetra-carbonsäurediimid**
Präparation:	**KBr (2/1000)**	Dez. Nr.:	**5.4.5**

CI-Name:	**Pigment Red 149**
Composition:	**N,N′-Di-3′,5′-xylylperylene-3,4,9,10-tetra-carbonic acid diimide**
Preparation:	**KBr (2/1000)**	Dec. No.:	**5.4.5**

Organische Pigmente
5. Pigmente mit Kondens. Ringen
5.4. Perylene

Organic Pigments
5. Pigments with condensed Rings
5.4. Perylenes

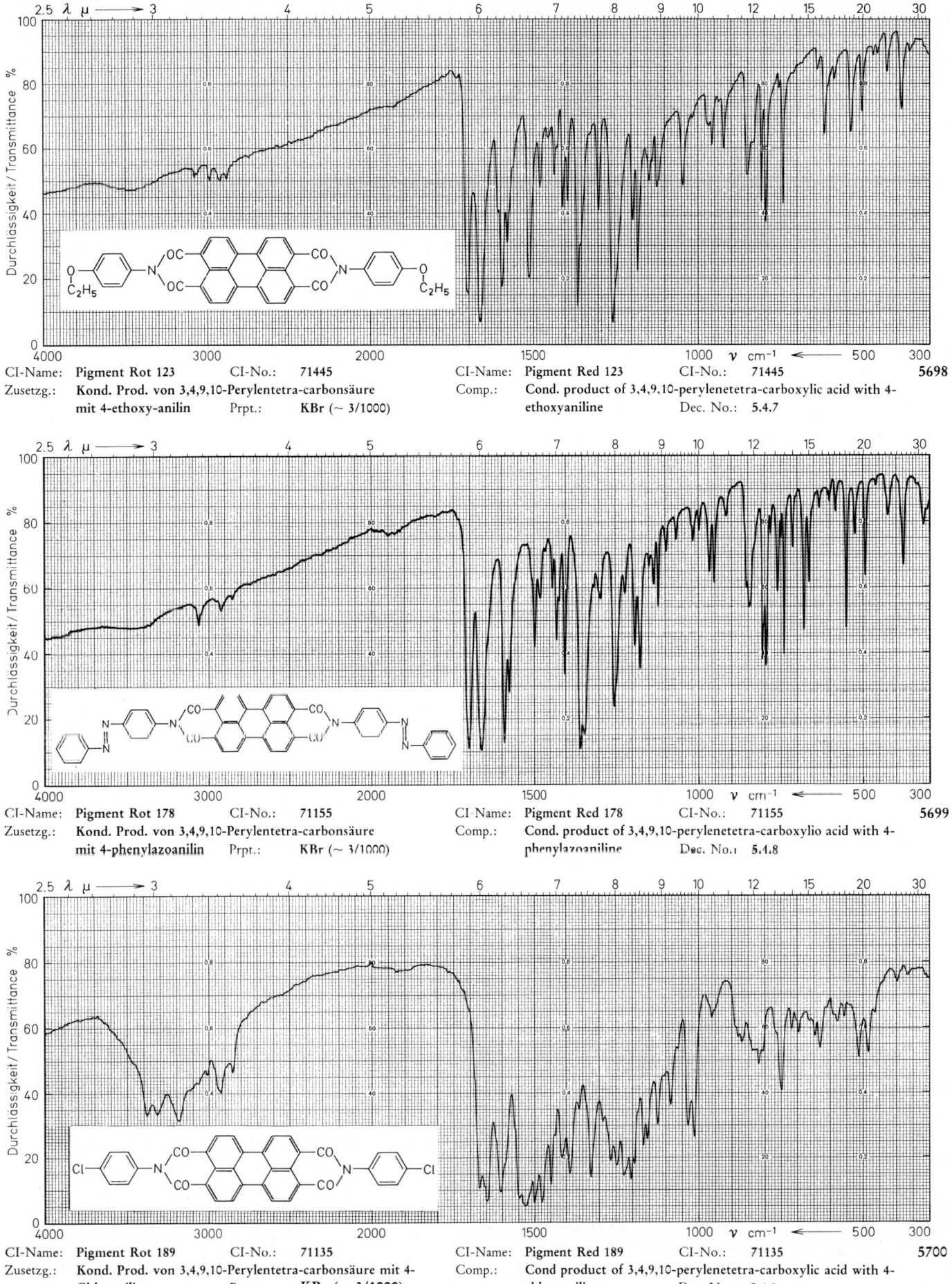

CI-Name: **Pigment Rot 123**   CI-No.: **71445**

Zusetzg.: **Kond. Prod. von 3,4,9,10-Perylentetra-carbonsäure**
mit 4-ethoxy-anilin   Prpt.: **KBr (~ 3/1000)**

CI-Name: **Pigment Red 123**   CI-No.: **71445**   **5698**

Comp.: **Cond. product of 3,4,9,10-perylenetetra-carboxylic acid with 4-**
ethoxyaniline   Dec. No.: **5.4.7**

CI-Name: **Pigment Rot 178**   CI-No.: **71155**

Zusetzg.: **Kond. Prod. von 3,4,9,10-Perylentetra-carbonsäure**
mit 4-phenylazoanilin   Prpt.: **KBr (~ 3/1000)**

CI-Name: **Pigment Red 178**   CI-No.: **71155**   **5699**

Comp.: **Cond. product of 3,4,9,10-perylenetetra-carboxylic acid with 4-**
phenylazoaniline   Dec. No.: **5.4.8**

CI-Name: **Pigment Rot 189**   CI-No.: **71135**

Zusetzg.: **Kond. Prod. von 3,4,9,10-Perylentetra-carbonsäure mit 4-**
Chloranilin   Prpt.: **KBr (~ 3/1000)**

CI-Name: **Pigment Red 189**   CI-No.: **71135**   **5700**

Comp.: **Cond product of 3,4,9,10-perylenetetra-carboxylic acid with 4-**
chloroaniline   Dec. No.: **5.4.9**

Organische Pigmente
5. Pigmente mit Kondens. Ringen
5.5. Chinacridone

Organic Pigments
5. Pigments with condensed Rings
5.5. Quinacridones

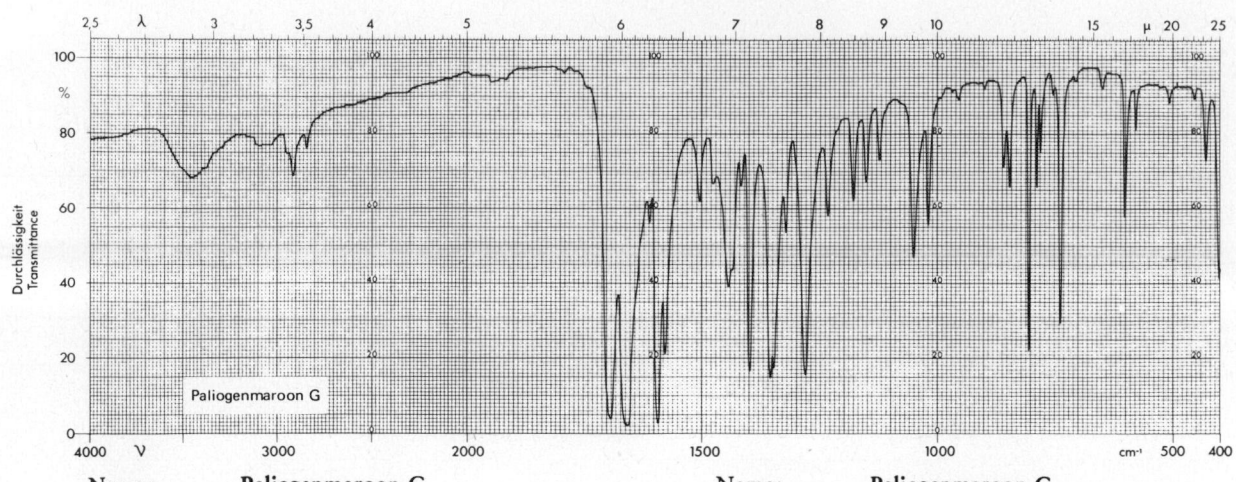

5701

Name:	**Paliogenmaroon G**		Name:	**Paliogenmaroon G**
Zusammen-setzung:	**Perylenpigment**		Composition:	**Perylene pigment**
Präparation:	**KBr (2,6/1000)**	CI-No.: **5.4.6**	Preparation:	**KBr (2,6/1000)** CI-No.: **5.4.6**

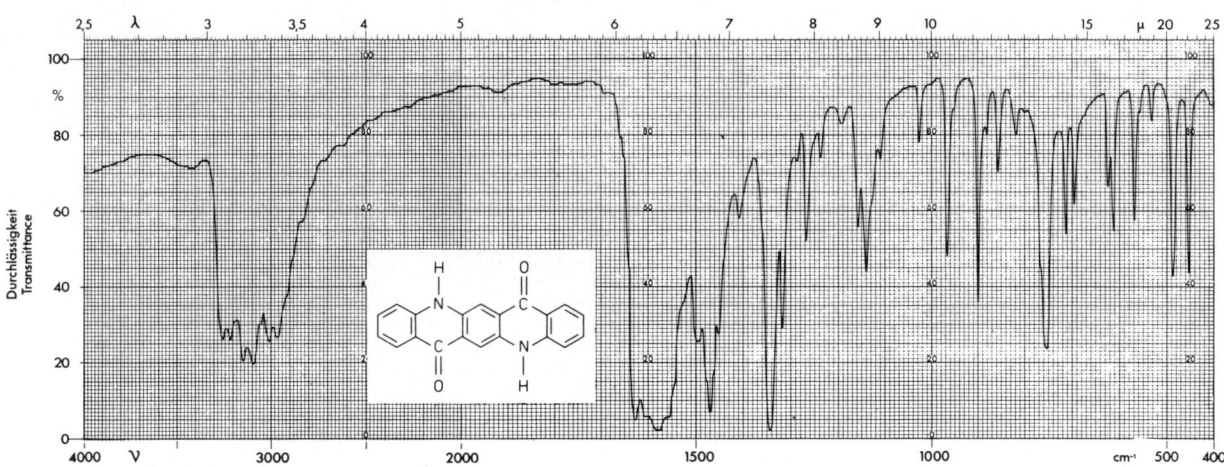

5702

CI-Name:	**Pigment Violett 19** CI-No.: **46500**	CI-Name:	**Pigment Violet 19** CI-No.: **46500**
Zusammen-setzung:	7,14-Dioxo-5,7,12,14-tetrahydrochinolino-[2,3-b]acridin, γ-Form	Composition:	7,14-Dioxo-5,7,12,14-tetrahydroquinolino-[2,3-b]acridine, γ-form
Präparation:	**KBr (2,2/1000)** CI-No.: **5.5.1**	Preparation:	**KBr (2,2/1000)** CI-No.: **5.5.1**

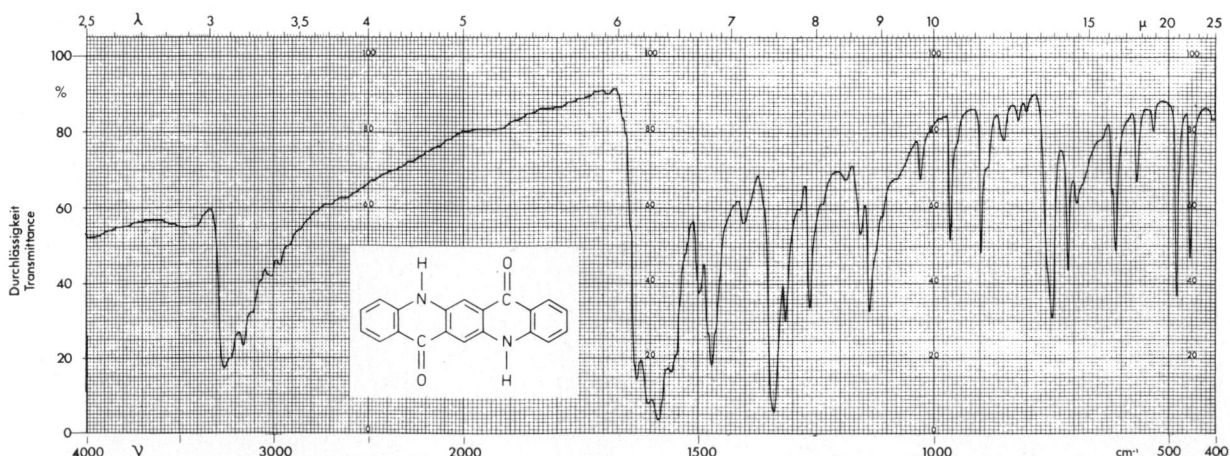

5703

CI-Name:	**Pigment Violett 19** CI-No.: **46500**	CI-Name:	**Pigment Violet 19** CI-No.: **46500**
Zusammen-setzung:	7,14-Dioxo-5,7,12,14-tetrahydrochinolino-[2,3-b]acridin, β-Form	Composition:	7,14-Dioxo-5,7,12,14-tetrahydroquinolino-[2,3-b]acridine, β-form
Präparation:	**KBr (2,2/1000)** Dez. Nr.: **5.5.1**	Preparation:	**KBr (2,2/1000)** Dec. No.: **5.5.1**

Organische Pigmente
5. Pigmente mit Kondens. Ringen
5.6. Dioxazine

Organic Pigments
5. Pigments with condensed Rings
5.6. Dioxazines

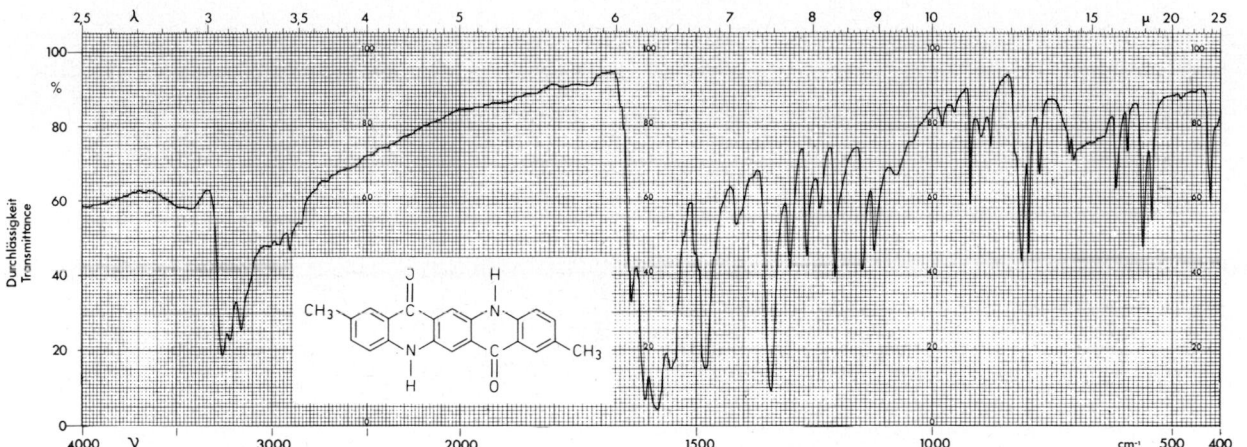

CI-Name: **Pigment Rot 122**   CI-No.: **46500**

Zusammen-   **2,9-Dimethyl-7,14-dioxo-5,7,12,14-tetra-**
setzung: **hydrochinolino[2,3-b]acridin**

Präparation: **KBr (2/1000)**   Dez. Nr.: **5.5.2**

CI-Name: **Pigment Red 122**   CI-No.: **46500**   5704

Composition: **2,9-Dimethyl-7,14-dioxo-5,7,12,14,tetra-**
             hydroquinolino[2,3-b]acridine

Preparation: **KBr (2/1000)**   Dec. No.: **5.5.2**

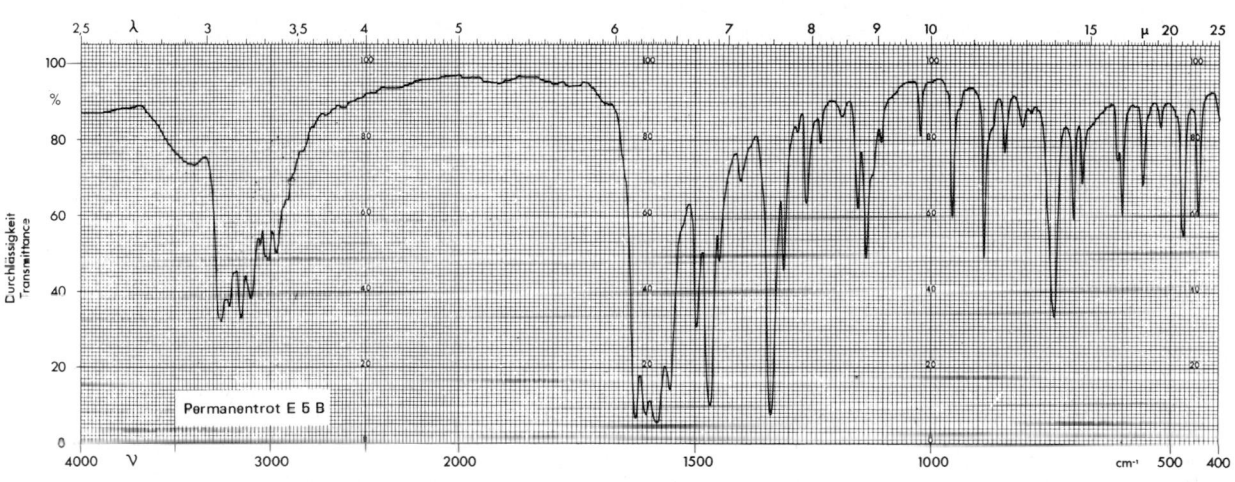

CI-Name: Pigment Violett 19   CI-No.: 46500

Zusammen-   **Chinacridonpigment**
setzung:

Präparation: **KBr (2/1000)**   Dez. Nr. 5.5.3

CI-Name: Pigment Violet 19   CI-No.: 46500   5705

Composition: **Chinacridone pigment**

Preparation: **KBr (2/1000)**   Dec. No.: 5.5.3

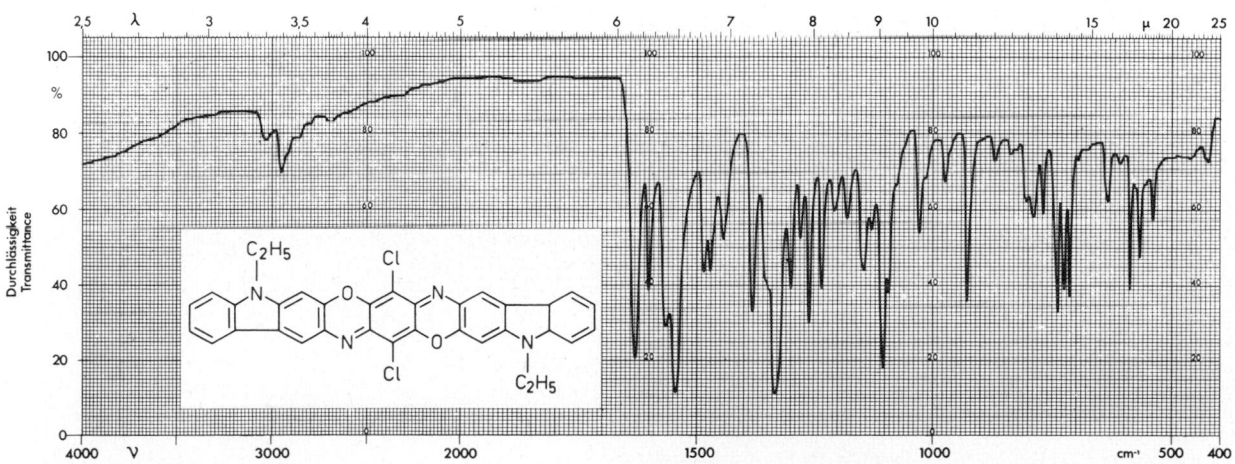

CI-Name: **Pigment Violett 23**

Zusammen-   **Dioxazinpigment**
setzung:

Präparation: **KBr (3/1000)**   Dez. Nr.: **5.6.1**

CI-Name: **Pigment Violet 23**   5706

Composition: **Dioxazine pigment**

Preparation: **KBr (3/1000)**   Dec. No.: **5.6.1**

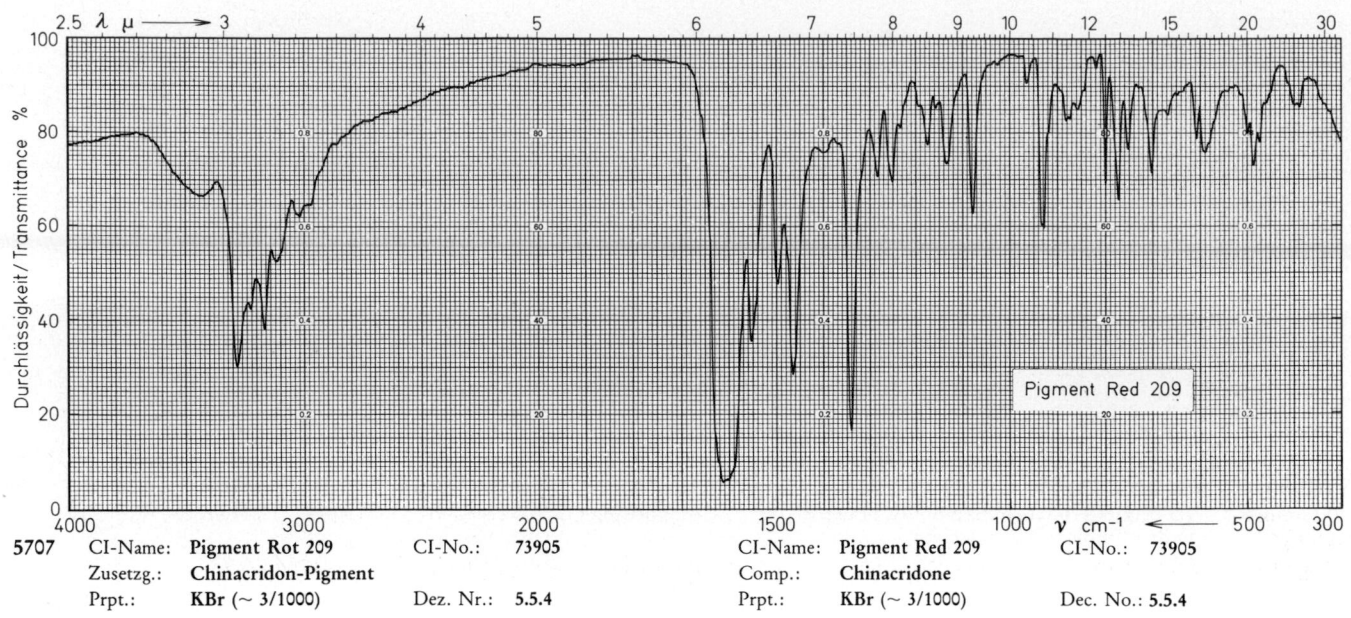

5707

CI-Name:	**Pigment Rot 209**	CI-No.:	**73905**
Zusetzg.:	**Chinacridon-Pigment**		
Prpt.:	**KBr (~ 3/1000)**	Dez. Nr.:	**5.5.4**

CI-Name:	**Pigment Red 209**	CI-No.:	**73905**
Comp.:	**Chinacridone**		
Prpt.:	**KBr (~ 3/1000)**	Dec. No.:	**5.5.4**

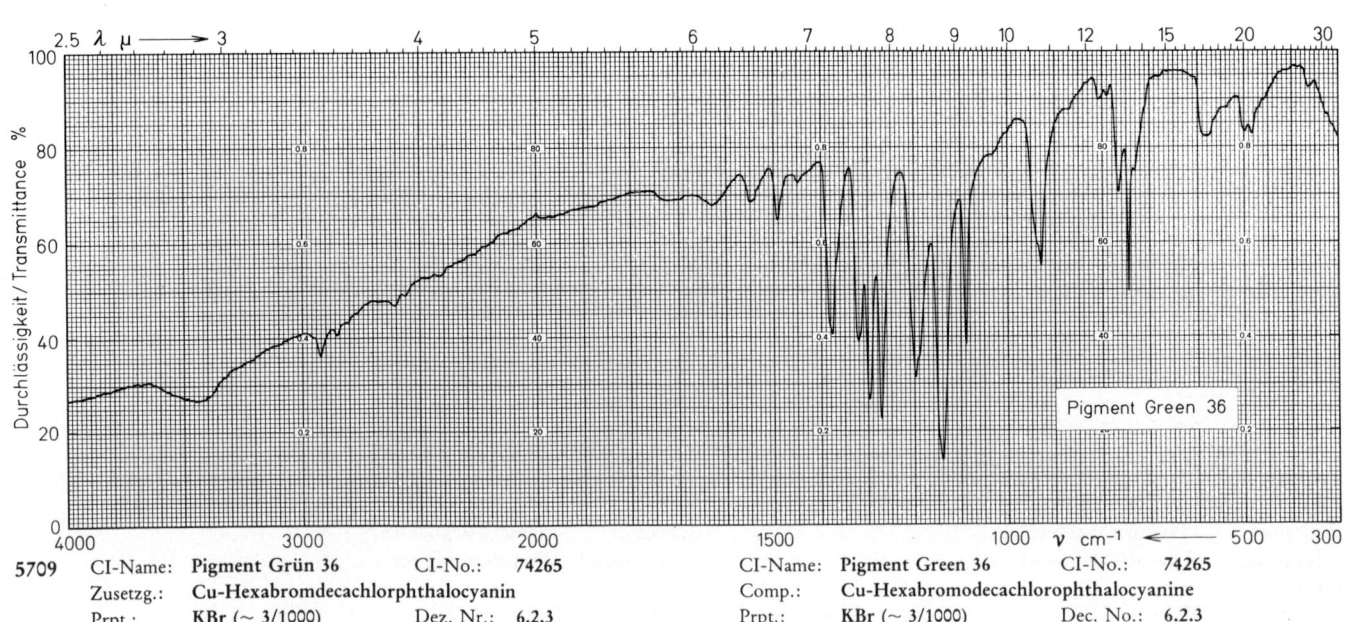

5709

CI-Name:	**Pigment Grün 36**	CI-No.:	**74265**
Zusetzg.:	**Cu-Hexabromdecachlorphthalocyanin**		
Prpt.:	**KBr (~ 3/1000)**	Dez. Nr.:	**6.2.3**

CI-Name:	**Pigment Green 36**	CI-No.:	**74265**
Comp.:	**Cu-Hexabromodecachlorophthalocyanine**		
Prpt.:	**KBr (~ 3/1000)**	Dec. No.:	**6.2.3**

Organische Pigmente
6. Phthalocyaninpigmente
6.1. Cu-Phthalocyanine

Organic Pigments
6. Phthalocyanine Pigments
6.1. Cu-Phthalocyanines

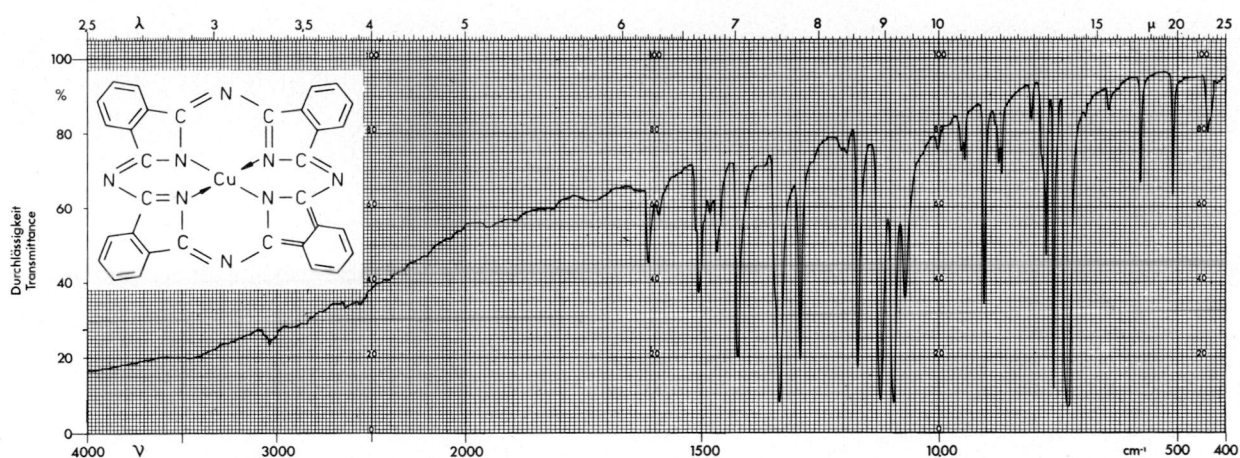

CI-Name: **Pigment Blau 15** CI-No.: **74160** CI-Name: **Pigment Blue 15** CI-No.: **74160** 5710
Zusammen- **Cu-Phthalocyanin, α-Form** Composition: **Cu-Phthalocyanine, α-form**
setzung:
Präparation: **KBr (3/1000)** Dez. Nr.: **6.1.1** Preparation: **KBr (3/1000)** Dec. No.: **6.1.1**

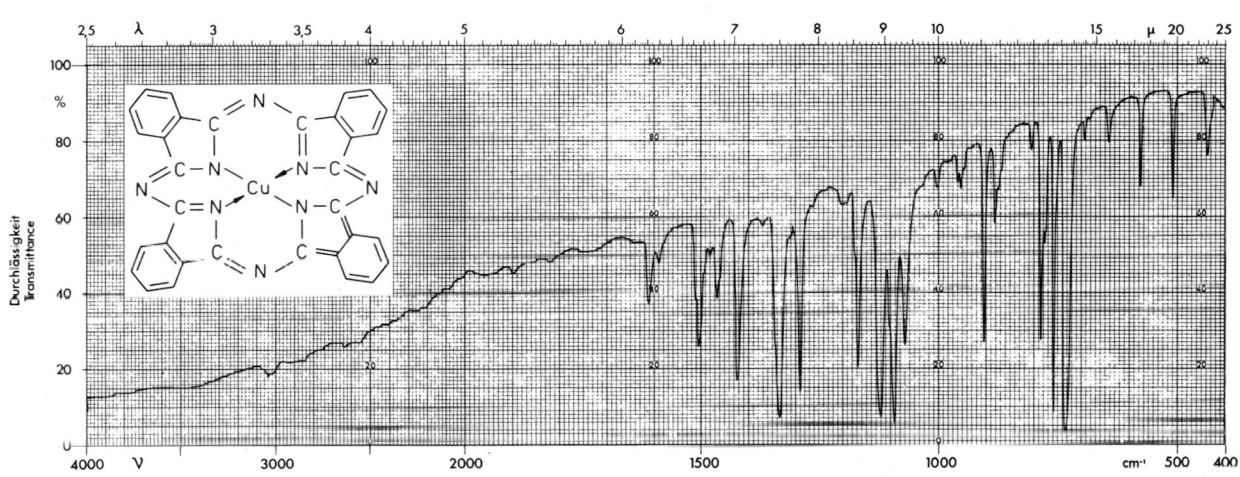

CI-Name: **Pigment Blau 15** CI-No.: **74160** CI-Name: **Pigment Blue 15** CI-No.: **74160** 5711
Zusammen- **Cu-Phthalocyanin, β-Form** Composition: **Cu-Phthalocyanine, β-form**
setzung:
Präparation: **KBr (3/1000)** Dez. Nr.: **6.1.1** Preparation: **KBr (3/1000)** Dec. No.: **6.1.1**

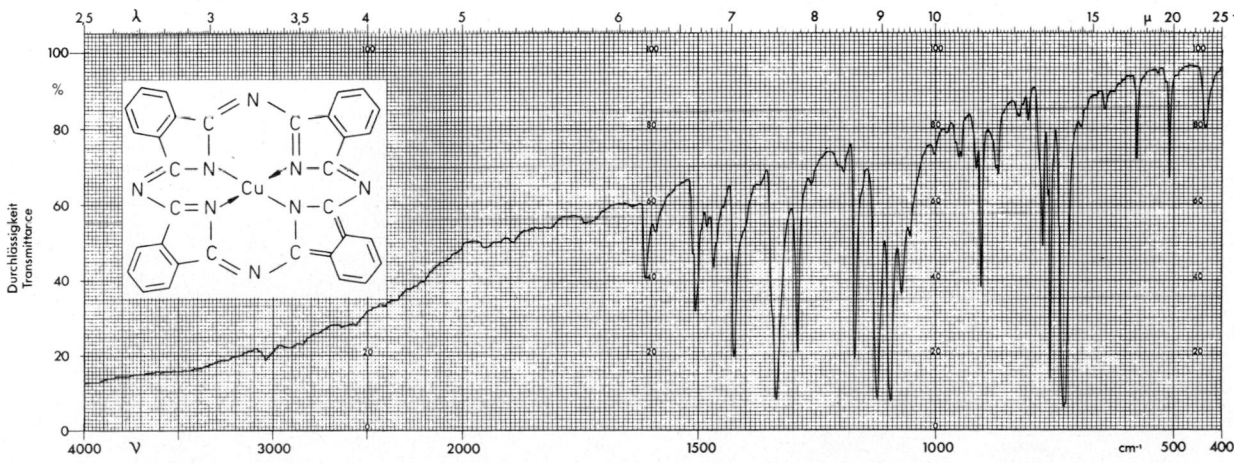

CI-Name: **Pigment Blau 15** CI-No.: **74160** CI-Name: **Pigment Blue 15** CI-No.: **74160** 5712
Zusammen- **Cu-Phthalocyanin, α-Form** Composition: **Cu-Phthalocyanine, α-form**
setzung:
Präparation: **KBr (3/1000)** Dez. Nr.: **6.1.1** Preparation: **KBr (3/1000)** Dec. No.: **6.1.1**

Organische Pigmente
6. Phthalocyaninpigmente
6.3. Metallfreie Phthalocyanine

Organic Pigments
6. Phthalocyanine Pigments
6.3. Metal-free Phthalocyanines

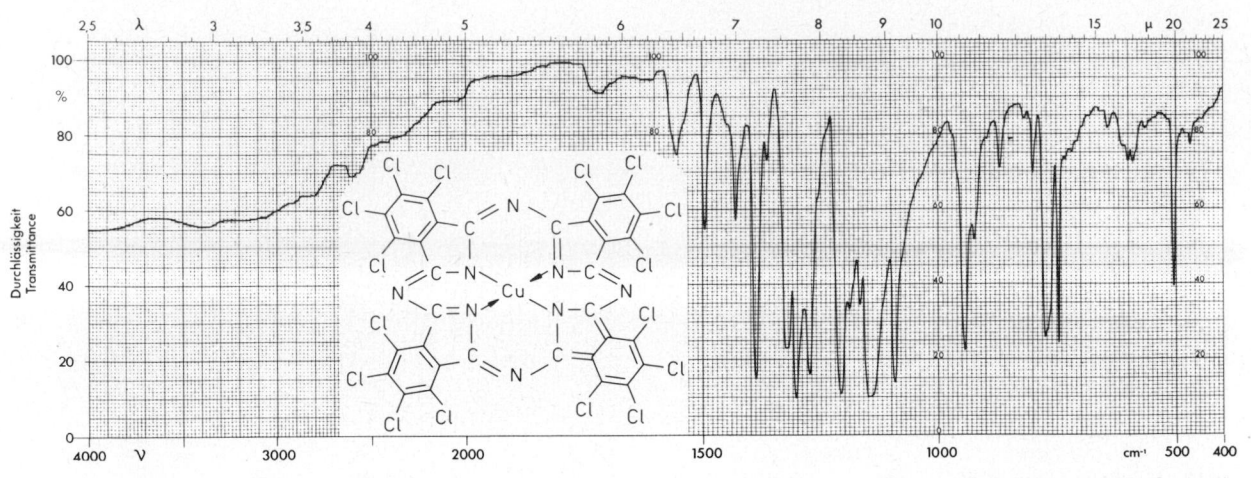

5713

	CI-Name:	**Pigment Grün 7**	CI-No.:	**74260**
	Zusammen-setzung:	**Cu-Hexadecachlorphthalocyanin**		
	Präparation:	**KBr (4,5/1000)**	Dez. Nr.:	**6.2.1**

	CI-Name:	**Pigment Green 7**	CI-No.:	**74260**
	Composition:	**Cu-Hexadecachlorophthalocyanine**		
	Preparation:	**KBr (4,5/1000)**	Dec. No.:	**6.2.1**

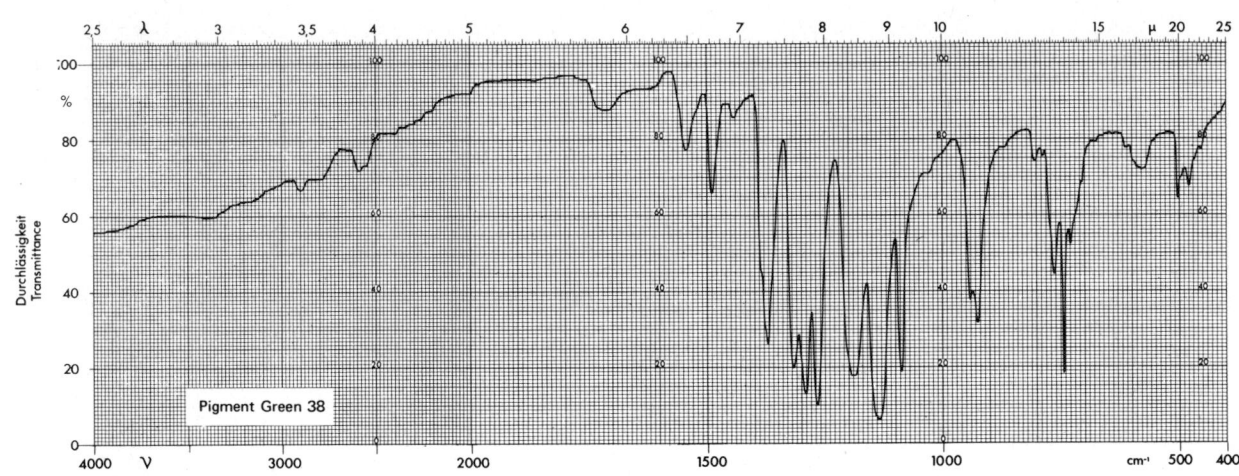

Pigment Green 38

5714

	CI-Name:	**Pigment Grün 38**
	Zusammen-setzung:	
	Präparation:	**KBr (6,5/1000)**	Dez. Nr.:	**6.2.2**

	CI-Name:	**Pigment Green 38**
	Composition:	
	Preparation:	**KBr (6,5/1000)**	Dec. No.:	**6.2.2**

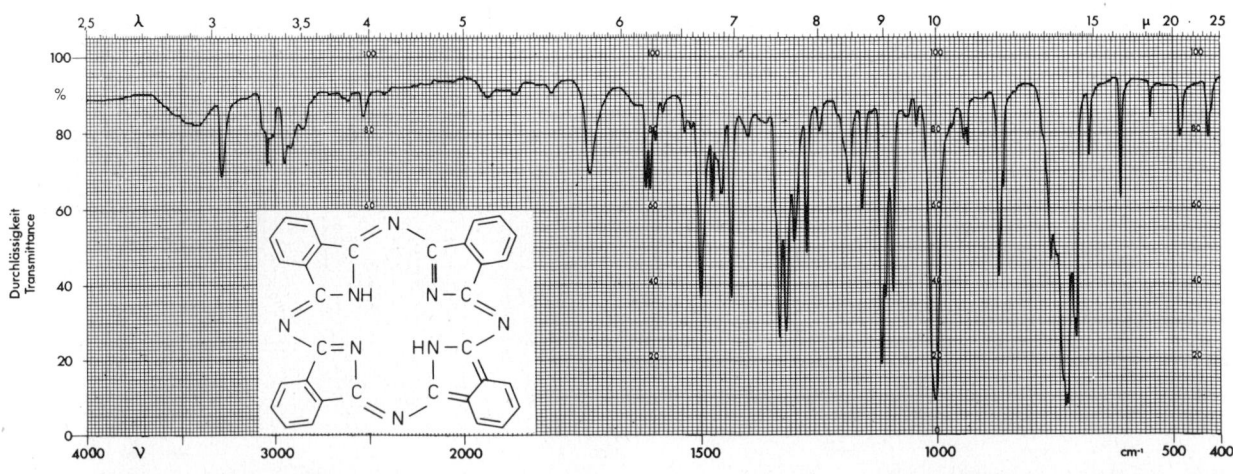

5715

	CI-Name:	**Pigment Blau 16**	CI-No.:	**74100**
	Zusammen-setzung:	Phthalocyanin		
	Präparation:	**KBr (2,2/1000)**	Dez. Nr.:	**6.3.1**

	CI-Name:	**Pigment Blue 16**	CI-No.:	**74100**
	Composition:	Phthalocyanine		
	Preparation:	**KBr (2,2/1000)**	Dec. No.:	**6.3.1**

Organische Pigmente
7. Sonstige Pigmente
7.1. PWMo-Säure-Lacke von Triphenylmethanen

Organic Pigments
7. Miscellaneous Pigmets
7.1. PWMo-Acid-Lakes of Triphenylmethanes

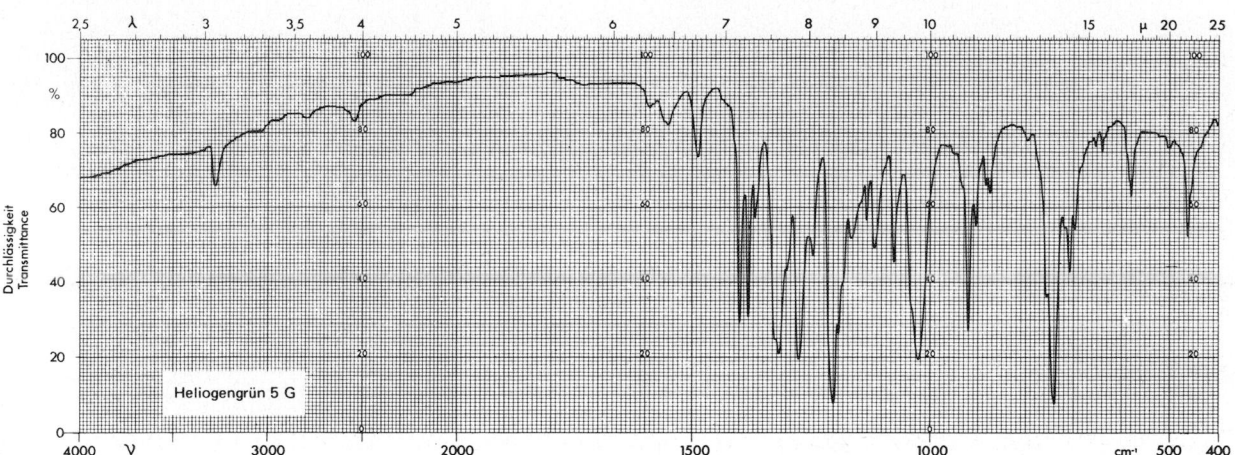

Name: **Heliogen Grün 5 G**
Zusammensetzung: Halogeniertes metallfreies Phthalocyanin
Präparation: **KBr (3/1000)**   Dez. Nr.: **6.3.2**

Name: **Heliogen Green 5 G**
Composition: Halogenated metalfree phthalocyanine
Preparation: **KBr (3/1000)**   Dec. No.: **6.3.2**

5716

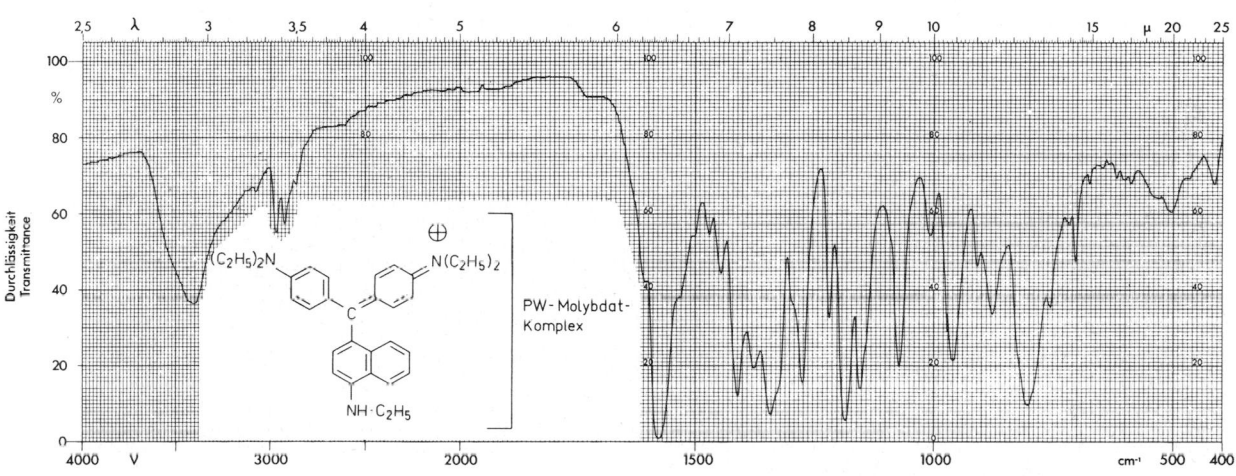

CI-Name: **Pigment Blau 1**   CI-No.: **42595**
Zusammensetzung: **PW-Molybdat-Komplex von Bis(4,N,N-diethylaminophenyl)-4'-N-Ethylamino-naphthalin-methan (Victoriareinblau BO)**
Präparation: **KBr (3/1000)**   Dez. Nr.: **7.1.1**

CI-Name: **Pigment Blue 1**   CI-No.: **42595**
Composition: **PW-molybdato-complex of bis(4-N,N-diethylaminophenyl)-4'N-ethylamino-naphthalene-methane (Victoria Blue BO)**
Preparation: **KBr (3/1000)**   Dec. No.: **7.1.1**

5717

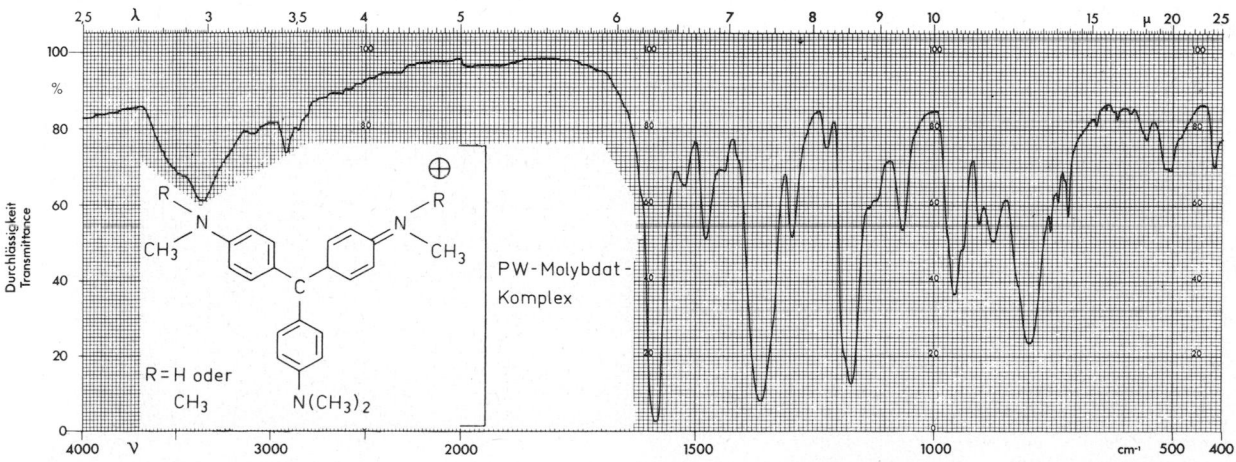

CI-Name: **Pigment Violett 3**   CI-No.: **42535**
Zusammensetzung: **PW-Molybdat-Komplex eines Gemisches von N-tetra, penta, hexa-methylierten Tri-4-aminophenylmethanen (Methylviolett)**
Präparation: **KBr (3,3/1000)**   Dez. Nr.: **7.1.2**

CI-Name: **Pigment Violet 3**   CI-No.: **42535**
Composition: **PW-molybdato-complex of a mixture of N-tetra, penta, hexa-methylated tri-4-aminophenyl methanes (Methyl violet)**
Preparation: **KBr (3,3/1000)**   Dec. No.: **7.1.2**

5718

Organische Pigmente
7. Sonstige Pigmente
7.1. PWMo-Säure-Lacke von Triphenylmethanen

Organic Pigments
7. Miscellaneous Pigmets
7.1. PWMo-Acid-Lakes of Triphenylmethanes

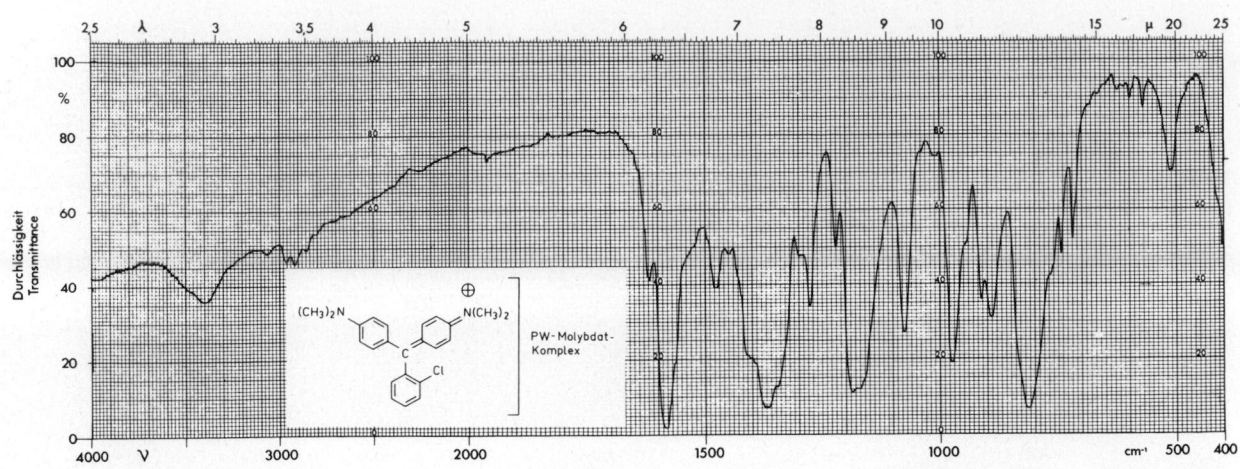

5719

CI-Name: **Pigment Blau 9**   CI-No.: **42025**
Zusammen-setzung: **PW-Molybdat-Komplex von Bis(4-N,N-dimethylaminophenyl)-2″-chlorphenyl-methan**
Präparation: **KBr (3,3/1000)**   Dez. Nr.: **7.1.3**

CI-Name: **Pigment Blue 9**   CI-No.: **42025**
Composition: **PW-molybdato complex of bis(4-N,N-dimethylaminophenyl)-2″-chlorophenyl-methane**
Preparation: **KBr (3,3/1000)**   Dec. No.: **7.1.3**

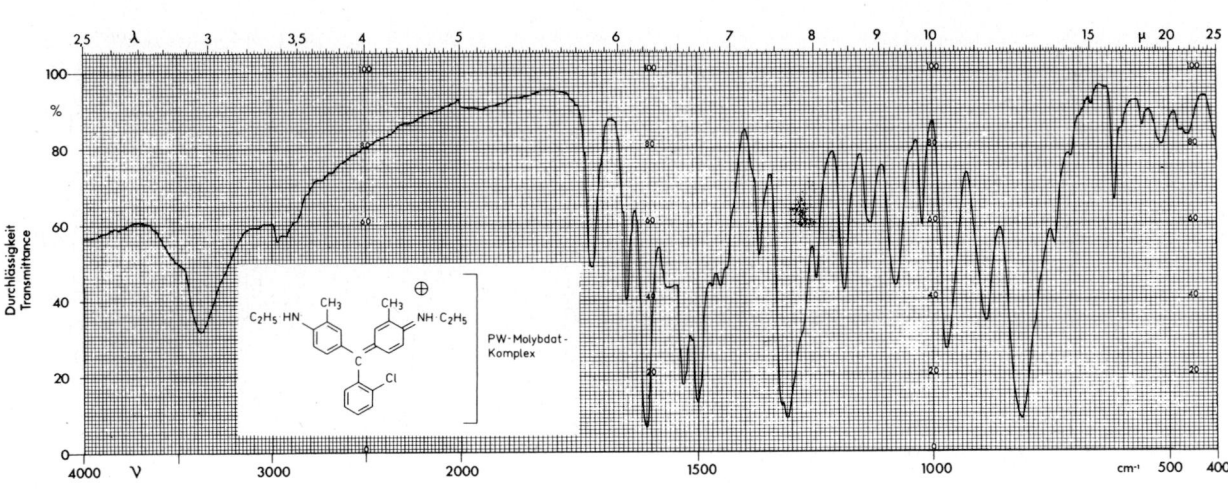

5720

CI-Name: **Pigment Blau 3**   CI-No.: **42140**
Zusammen-setzung: **PW-Molybdat-Komplex von Bis(4-N-ethyl-amino-3-methylphenyl)-2″-chlorphenyl-methan**
Präparation: **KBr (3/1000)**   Dec. No.: **7.1.4**

CI-Name: **Pigment Blue 3**   CI-No.: **42140**
Composition: **PW-molybdato complex of bis(4-N-ethyl-amino-3-methylphenyl)-2″-chlorophenyl-methan**
Preparation: **KBr (3/1000)**   Dez. Nr.: **7.1.4**

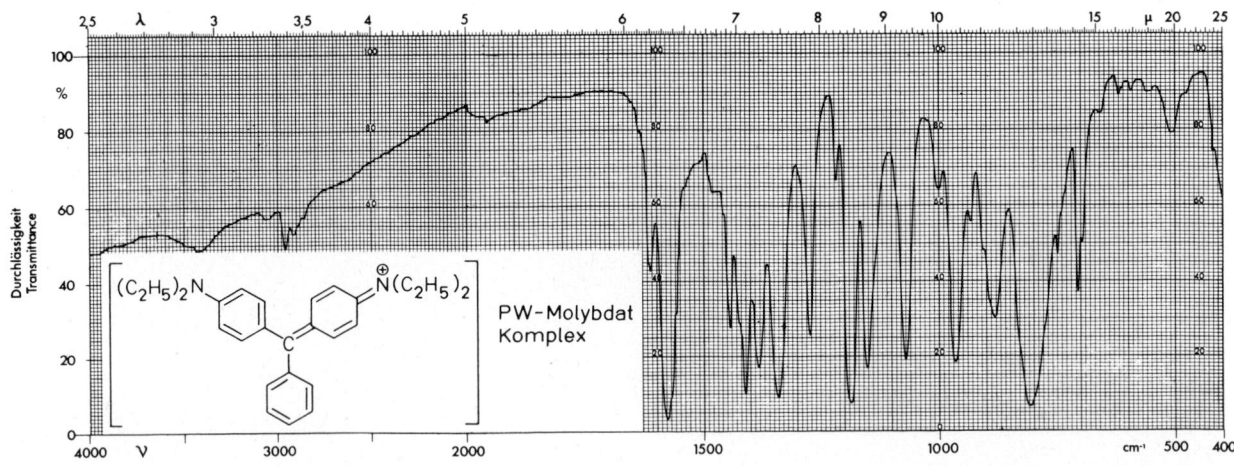

5721

CI-Name: **Pigment Grün 1**   CI-No.: **42040**
Zusammen-setzung: **PW-Molybdat-Komplex von Bis(4-N,N-diethylaminophenyl)-phenylmethan**
Präparation: **KBr (3,6/1000)**   Dez. Nr.: **7.1.5**

CI-Name: **Pigment Green 1**   CI-No.: **42040**
Composition: **PW-molybdato complex of bis(4-N,N-diethylaminophenyl)-phenyl-methane**
Preparation: **KBr (3,6/1000)**   Dec. No.: **7.1.5**

Organische Pigmente
7. Sonstige Pigmente
7.2. PWMo-Säure-Lacke von Xanthenen

Organic Pigments
7. Miscellaneous Pigmets
7.2. PWMo-Acid-Lakes of Xanthenes

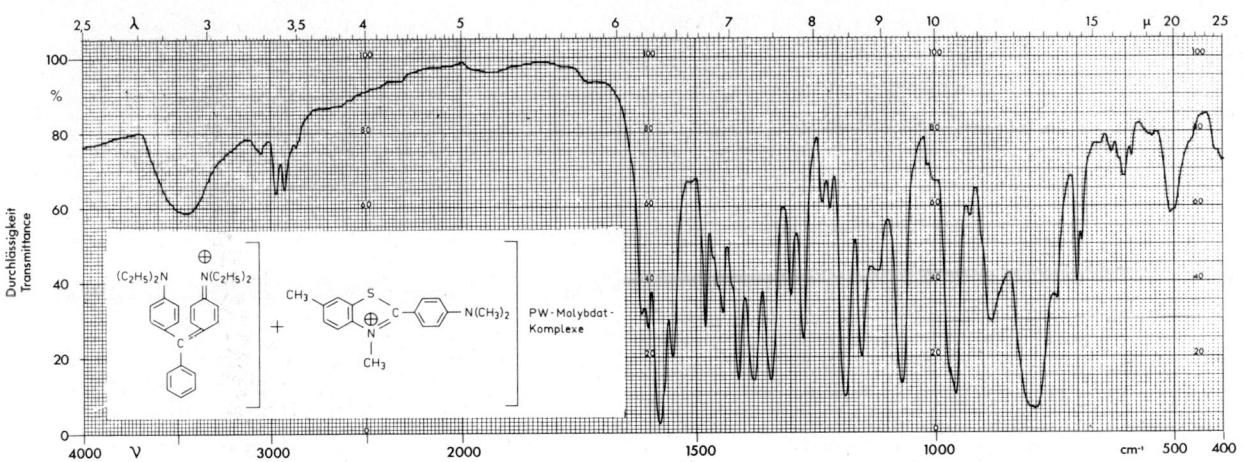

CI-Name: **Pigment Grün 2**   CI-No.: **42040 + 49005**
Zusammensetzung: **Gemisch aus Pigment Grün 1 (7.1.5) und Pigment Gelb 18 (7.8.1)**
Präparation: **KBr (3,1/1000)**   Dez. Nr.: **7.1.6**

CI-Name: **Pigment Green 2**   CI-No.: **42040 + 49005**
Composition: **Mixture of Pigment Green 1 (7.1.5) and Pigment Yellow 18 (7.8.1)**
Preparation: **KBr (3,1/1000)**   Dec. No.: **7.1.6**

5722

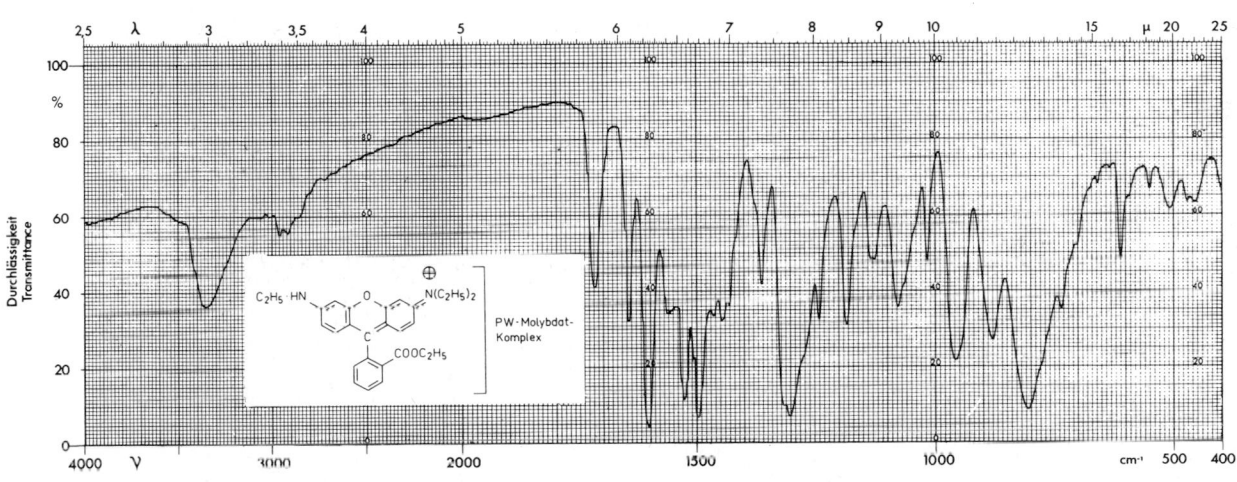

CI-Name: **Pigment Rot 81**   CI-No.: **45160**
Zusammensetzung: **PW-Molybdat-Komplex von Rhodamin 4 G**
Präparation: **KBr (3/1000)**   Dez. Nr.: **7.2.1**

CI-Name: **Pigment Red 81**   CI-No.: **45160**
Composition: **PW-molybdato-complex of Rhodamine 4 G**
Preparation: **KBr (3/1000)**   Dec. No.: **7.2.1**

5723

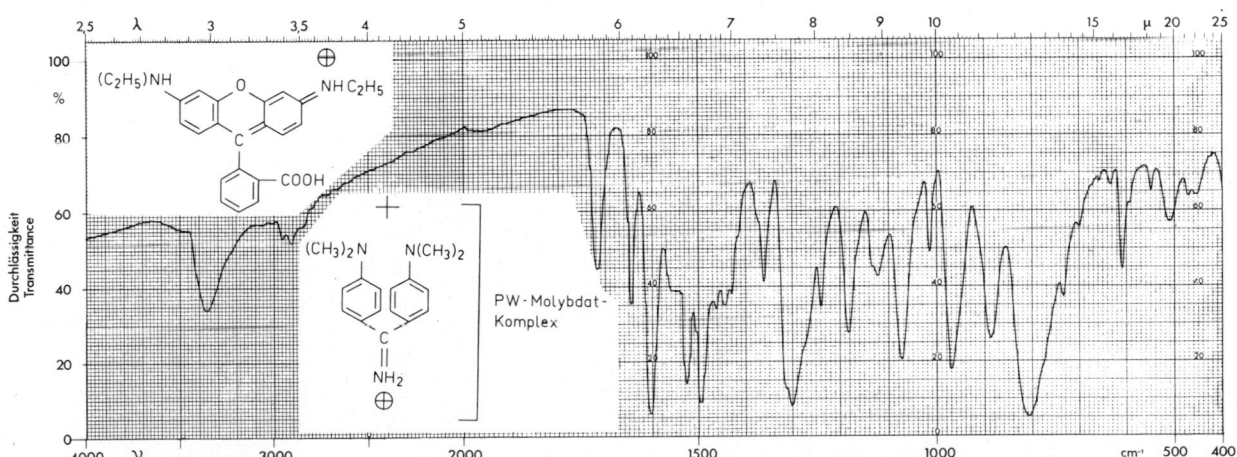

CI-Name: **Pigment Rot 82**   CI-No.: **45150 + 41000**
Zusammensetzung: **Gemisch der PW-Molybdat-Komplexe von Rhodamin G (93 %) und Auramin O (7 %)**
Präparation: **KBr (3/1000)**   Dez. Nr.: **7.2.2**

CI-Name: **Pigment Red 82**   CI-No.: **45150 + 41000**
Composition: **Mixture of PW-molybdato-complexes of Rhodamine G (93 %) and Auramine O (7 %)**
Preparation: **KBr (3/1000)**   Dec. No.: **7.2.2**

5724

Organische Pigmente
7. Sonstige Pigmente
7.3. Farblacke von Triphenylmethanen (TPM)
    mit sauren Gruppen

Organic Pigments
7. Miscellaneous Pigmets
7.3. Lakes of Triphenylmethanes (TPM)
    with Acid Groups

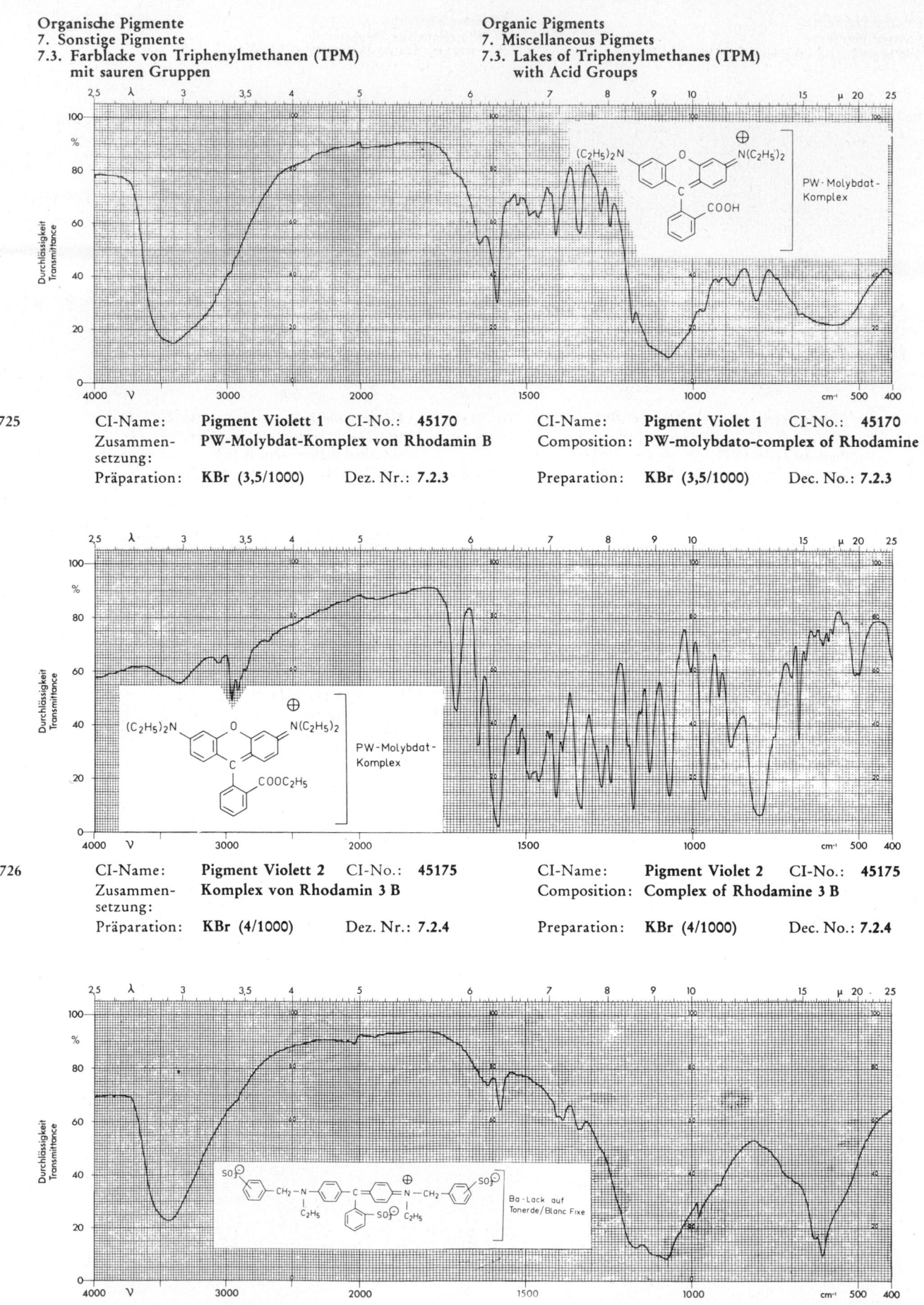

5725
CI-Name:	**Pigment Violett 1**	CI-No.:	**45170**
Zusammensetzung:	PW-Molybdat-Komplex von Rhodamin B
Präparation:	**KBr (3,5/1000)**	Dez. Nr.:	**7.2.3**

CI-Name:	**Pigment Violet 1**	CI-No.:	**45170**
Composition:	**PW-molybdato-complex of Rhodamine B**
Preparation:	**KBr (3,5/1000)**	Dec. No.:	**7.2.3**

5726
CI-Name:	**Pigment Violett 2**	CI-No.:	**45175**
Zusammensetzung:	**Komplex von Rhodamin 3 B**
Präparation:	**KBr (4/1000)**	Dez. Nr.:	**7.2.4**

CI-Name:	**Pigment Violet 2**	CI-No.:	**45175**
Composition:	**Complex of Rhodamine 3 B**
Preparation:	**KBr (4/1000)**	Dec. No.:	**7.2.4**

5727
CI-Name:	**Pigment Blau 24**	CI-No.:	**42090**
Zusammensetzung:	Bis(4-N-ethyl-N-sulfobenzyl-aminophenyl)-2″-sulfophenyl-methan, Ba-Lack
Präparation:	**KBr (6/1000)**	Dez. Nr.:	**7.3.1**

CI-Name:	**Pigment Blue 24**	CI-No.:	**42090**
Composition:	**Bis(4-N-ethyl-N-sulfobenzyl aminophenyl)-2″-sulfophenyl-methane, Ba-lake**
Preparation:	**KBr (6/1000)**	Dec. No.:	**7.3.1**

Organische Pigmente
7. Sonstige Pigmente
7.3. Farblacke von Triphenylmethanen (TPM)
   mit sauren Gruppen

Organic Pigments
7. Miscellaneous Pigmets
7.3. Lakes of Triphenylmethanes (TPM)
   with Acid Groups

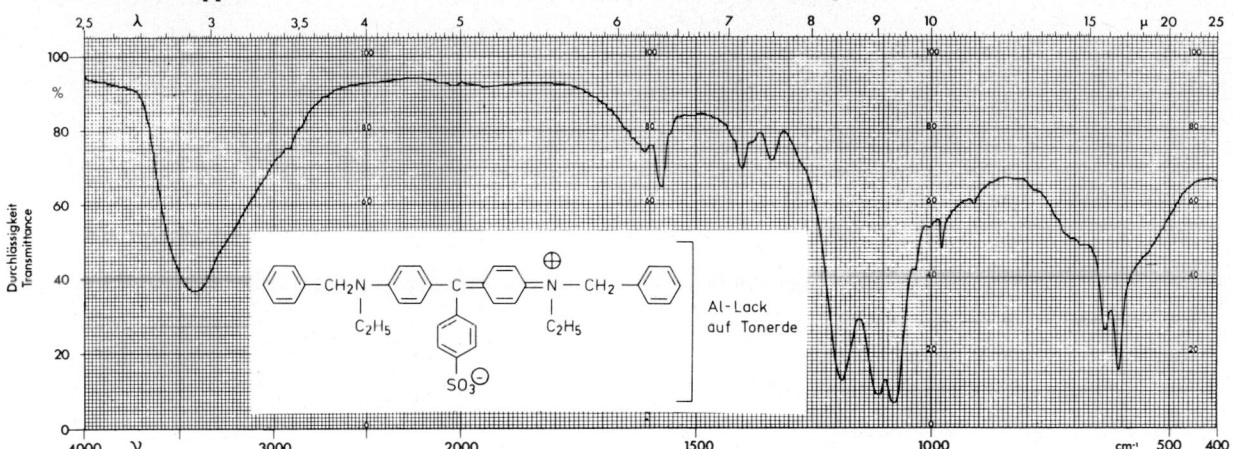

CI-Name:	(Viridin Lack)	CI-No.: 42095 + 10316	CI-Name:	(Viridin Lake)	CI-No.: 42095 + 10316	5728
Zusammensetzung:	Bis(4-N-ethyl-N-benzylaminophenyl)-4″-sulfophenyl-methan, Al-Lack auf Tonerde		Composition:	Bis(4-N-ethyl-N-benzylaminophenyl)-4″-sulfophenyl-methane, Al-lake on alumina		
Präparation:	KBr (3/1000)	Dez. Nr.: 7.3.2	Preparation:	KBr (3/1000)	Dec. No.: 7.3.2	

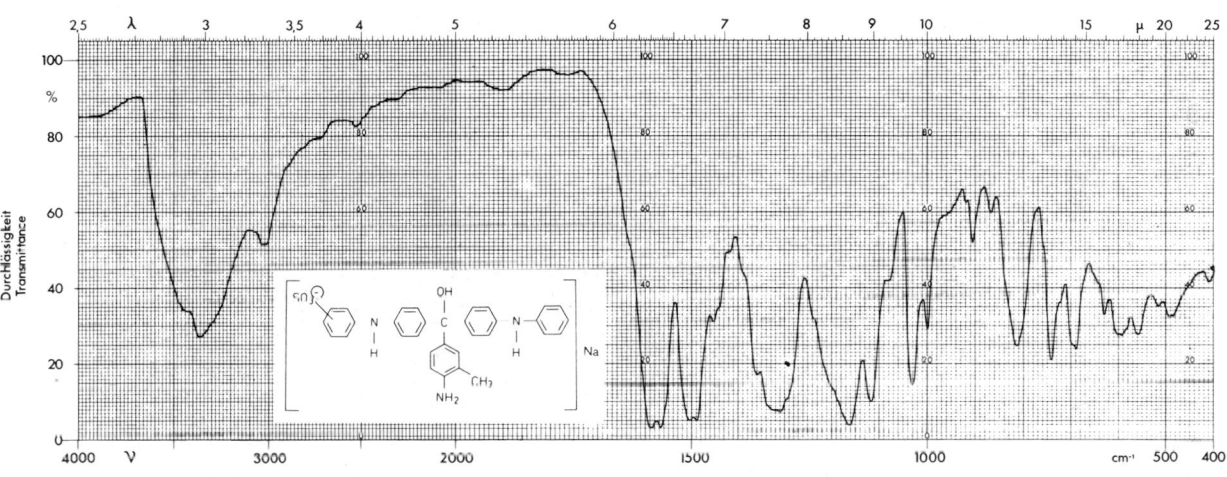

CI-Name:	Pigment Blau 19	CI-No.: 42750 A	CI-Name:	Pigment Blue 19	CI-No.: 42750 A	5729
Zusammensetzung:	4-(Amino-3-toluyl)-4′-N-phenylaminophenyl-4″-N-sulfophenylaminophenyl-methan, Na-Salz		Composition:	4-(Amino-3-tolyl)-4′-N-phenylaminophenyl-4″-N-sulfophenylaminophenyl-methane, Na-salt		
Präparation:	KBr (3/1000)	Dez. Nr.: 7.3.3	Präparation:	KBr (3/1000)	Dec. No.: 7.3.3	

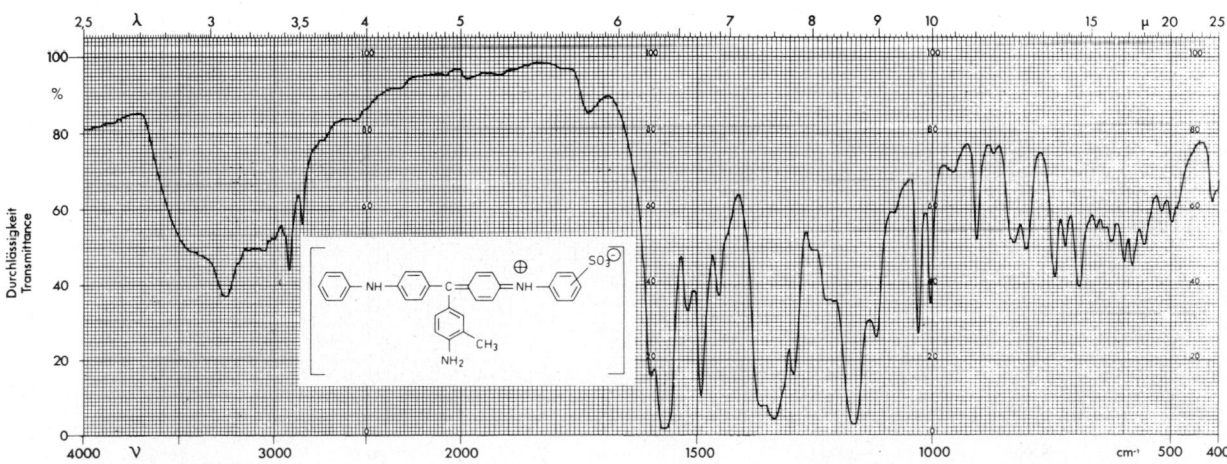

CI-Name:	ACID Blau 110	CI-No.: 42750	CI-Name:	Acid Blue 110	CI-No.: 42750	5730
Zusammensetzung:	4-(Amino-3-toluyl)-4′-N-phenylaminophenyl-4″-N-sulfophenylaminophenyl-methan, freie Säure		Composition:	4-(Amino-3-tolyl)-4′-N-phenylaminophenyl-4″-N-sulfophenylaminophenyl-methane, free acid		
Präparation:	KBr (3/1000)	Dez. Nr.: 7.3.4	Preparation:	KBr (3/1000)	Dec. No.: 7.3.4	

Organische Pigmente
7. Sonstige Pigmente
7.3. Farblacke von Triphenylmethanen (TPM)
   mit sauren Gruppen

Organic Pigments
7. Miscellaneous Pigmets
7.3. Lakes of Triphenylmethanes (TPM)
   with Acid Groups

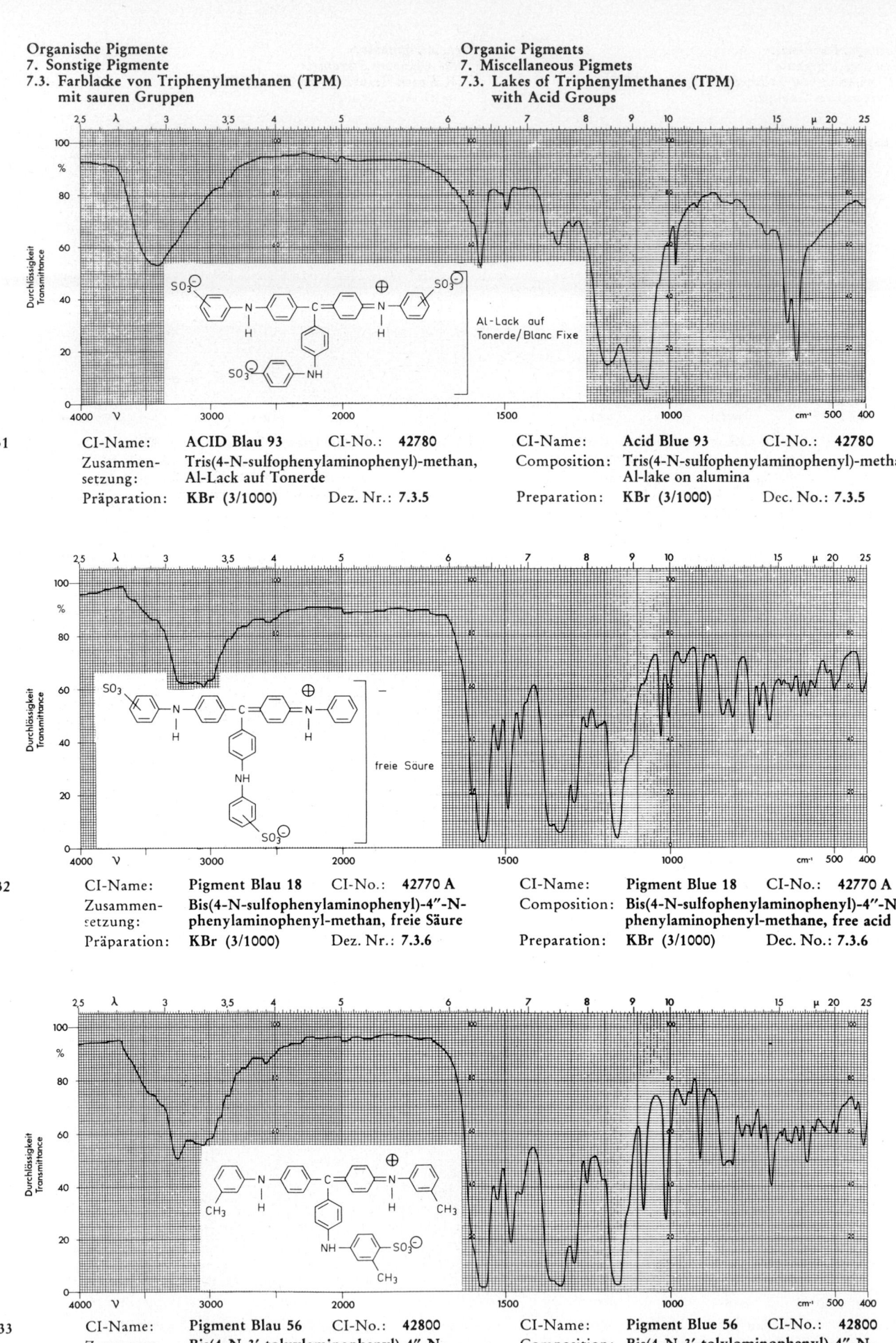

5731

CI-Name:	**ACID Blau 93**	CI-No.:	**42780**
Zusammen-setzung:	**Tris(4-N-sulfophenylaminophenyl)-methan, Al-Lack auf Tonerde**		
Präparation:	**KBr (3/1000)**	Dez. Nr.:	**7.3.5**

CI-Name:	Acid Blue 93	CI-No.:	**42780**
Composition:	Tris(4-N-sulfophenylaminophenyl)-methane, Al-lake on alumina		
Preparation:	**KBr (3/1000)**	Dec. No.:	**7.3.5**

5732

CI-Name:	**Pigment Blau 18**	CI-No.:	**42770 A**
Zusammen-setzung:	**Bis(4-N-sulfophenylaminophenyl)-4″-N-phenylaminophenyl-methan, freie Säure**		
Präparation:	**KBr (3/1000)**	Dez. Nr.:	**7.3.6**

CI-Name:	**Pigment Blue 18**	CI-No.:	**42770 A**
Composition:	**Bis(4-N-sulfophenylaminophenyl)-4″-N-phenylaminophenyl-methane, free acid**		
Preparation:	**KBr (3/1000)**	Dec. No.:	**7.3.6**

5733

CI-Name:	**Pigment Blau 56**	CI-No.:	**42800**
Zusammen-setzung:	**Bis(4-N-3′-toluylaminophenyl)-4″-N-(4‴-sulfo-3‴-toluylaminophenyl)methan**		
Präparation:	**KBr (1,7/1000)**	Dez. Nr.:	**7.3.7**

CI-Name:	**Pigment Blue 56**	CI-No.:	**42800**
Composition:	**Bis(4-N-3′-tolylominophenyl)-4″-N-(4‴-sulfo-3‴-tolylaminophenyl)methane**		
Preparation:	**KBr (1,7/1000)**	Dec. No.:	**7.3.7**

Organische Pigmente
7. Sonstige Pigmente
7.4. Xanthene mit sauren Gruppen

Organic Pigments
7. Miscellaneous Pigmets
7.4. Xanthenes with Acid Groups

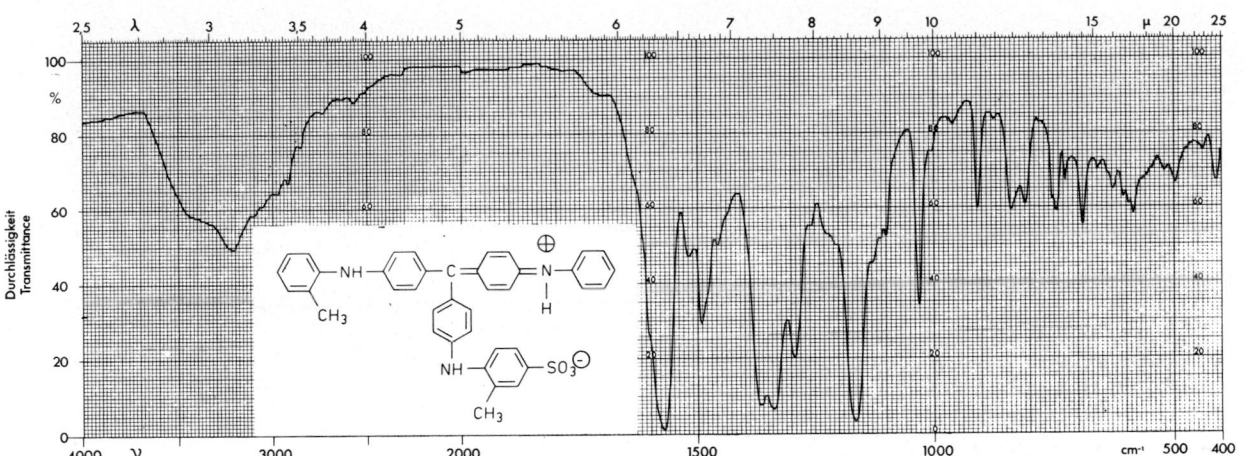

CI-Name: **Pigment Blau 57** CI-No.: **42795**

Zusammensetzung: **4-N-Phenylaminophenyl-4′-N-(2″-toluyl-aminophenyl)-4‴-N-(4⁗-sulfo-2⁗-toluylaminophenyl)methan**

Präparation: **KBr (1,7/1000)** Dez. Nr.: **7.3.8**

CI-Name: **Pigment Blue 57** CI-No.: **42795** 5734

Composition: **4-N-Phenylaminophenyl-4′-N-(2″-tolyl-aminophenyl)-4‴-N-(4⁗-sulfo-2⁗-tolyl-aminophenyl)methane**

Preparation: **KBr (1,7/1000)** Dec. No.: **7.3.8**

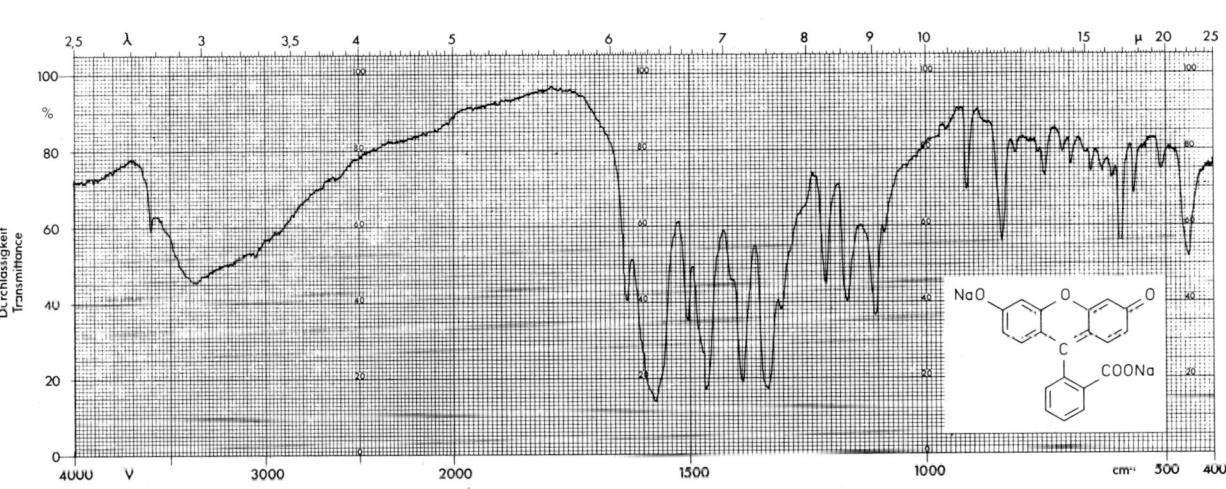

CI-Name: **ACID Gelb 73** CI-No.: **45350**

Zusammensetzung: **Fluorescein, Na-Salz**

Präparation: **KBr (3/1000)** Dez. Nr.: **7.4.1**

CI-Name: **Acid Yellow 73** CI-No.: **45350** 5735

Composition: **Fluorescein, Na-salt**

Preparation: **KBr (3/1000)** Dec. No.: **7.4.1**

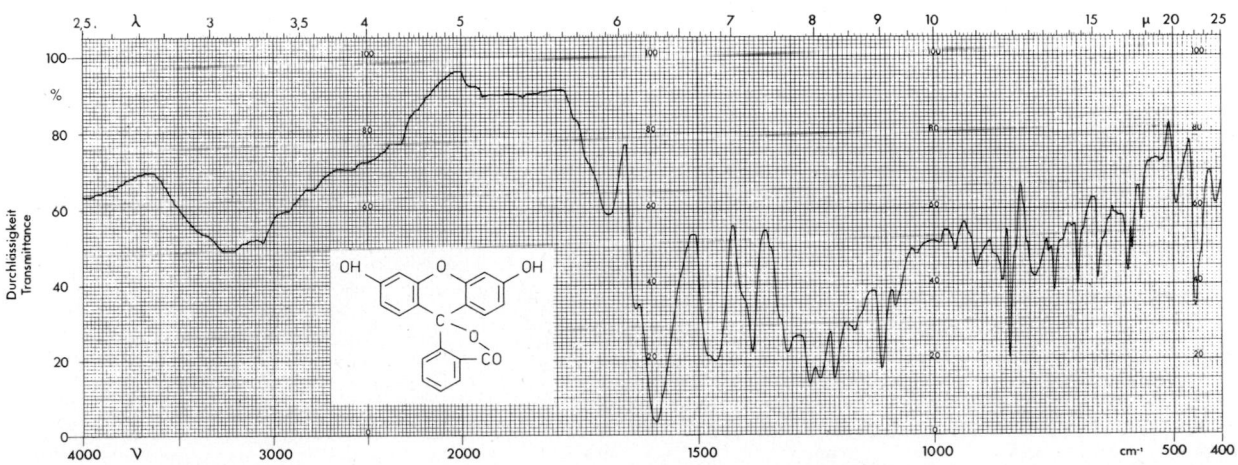

CI-Name: **ACID Gelb 73** CI-No.: **45350**

Zusammensetzung: **Fluorescein**

Präparation: **KBr (3/1000)** Dez. Nr.: **7.4.2**

CI-Name: **Acid Yellow 73** CI-No.: **45350** 5736

Composition: **Fluorescein**

Preparation: **KBr (3/1000)** Dec. No.: **7.4.2**

Organische Pigmente
7. Sonstige Pigmente
7.5. Diphenylmethane

Organic Pigments
7. Miscellaneous Pigmets
7.5. Diphenylmethanes

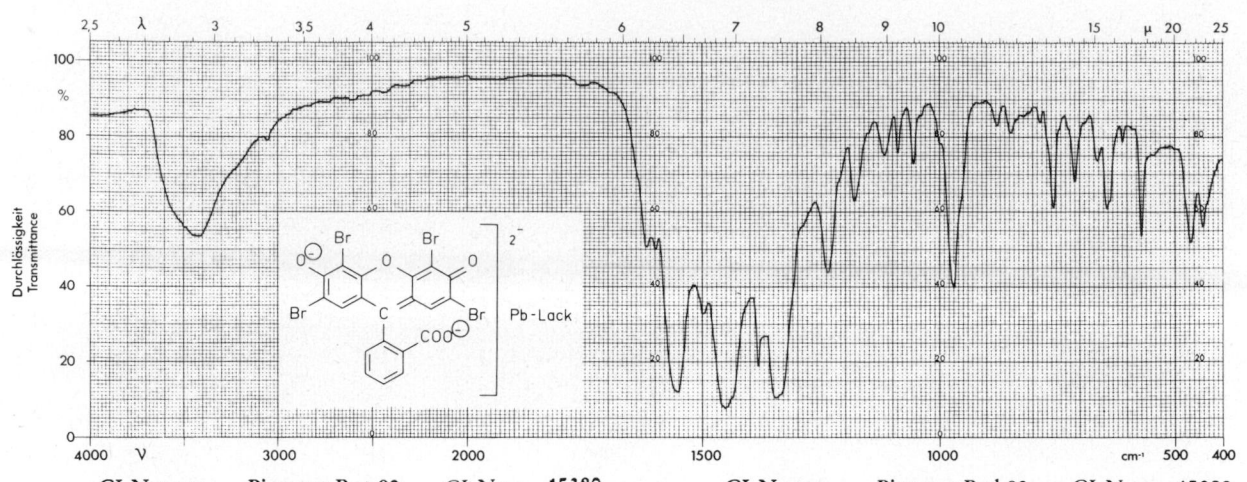

5737

| CI-Name: | Pigment Rot 90 | CI-No.: | 45380 |
| CI-Name: | Pigment Red 90 | CI-No.: | 45380 |

Zusammensetzung: **2,4,5,7-Tetrabromfluorescein, Pb-Salz**

Composition: **2,4,5,7-Tetrabromo fluorescein, Pb-salt**

Präparation: **KBr (3,5/1000)**　Dez. Nr.: **7.4.3**

Preparation: **KBr (3,5/1000)**　Dec. No.: **7.4.3**

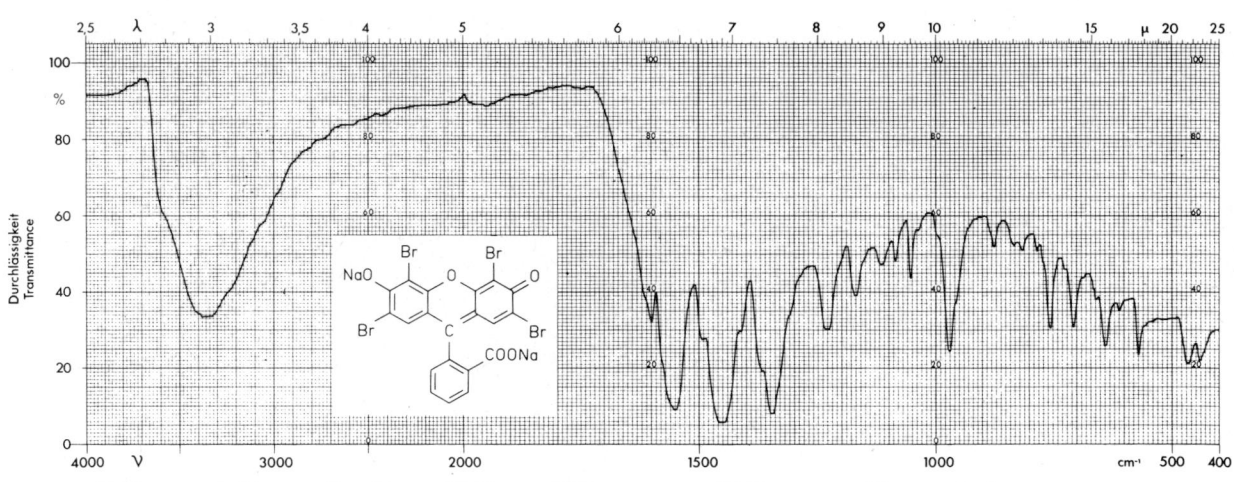

5738

| CI-Name: | **Pigment Rot 90** | CI-No.: | **45380** |
| CI-Name: | **Pigment Red 90** | CI-No.: | **45380** |

Zusammensetzung: **2,4,5,7-Tetrabromfluorescein Na-Salz (Eosin A)**

Composition: **2,4,5,7-Tetrabromo-fluorescein Na-salt (Eosin A)**

Präparation: **KBr (15/1000)**　Dez. Nr.: **7.4.4**

Präparation: **KBr (15/1000)**　Dec. No.: **7.4.4**

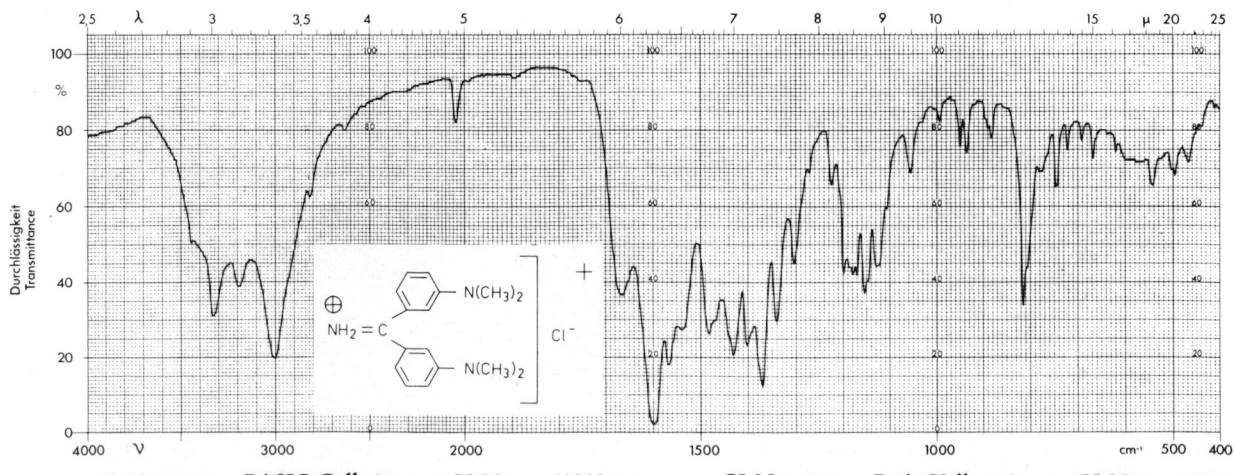

5739

CI-Name:	**BASIC Gelb 2**	CI-No.:	**41000**
	Auramin O		
CI-Name:	**Basic Yellow 2**	CI-No.:	**41000**

Zusammensetzung: **Auramin O**

Composition: **Auramin O**

Präparation: **KBr (3,5/1000)**　Dez. Nr.: **7.5.1**

Preparation: **KBr (3,5/1000)**　Dec. No.: **7.5.1**

Organische Pigmente
7. Sonstige Pigmente
7.7. Nitropigmente

Organic Pigments
7. Miscellaneous Pigmets
7.7. Nitro Pigments

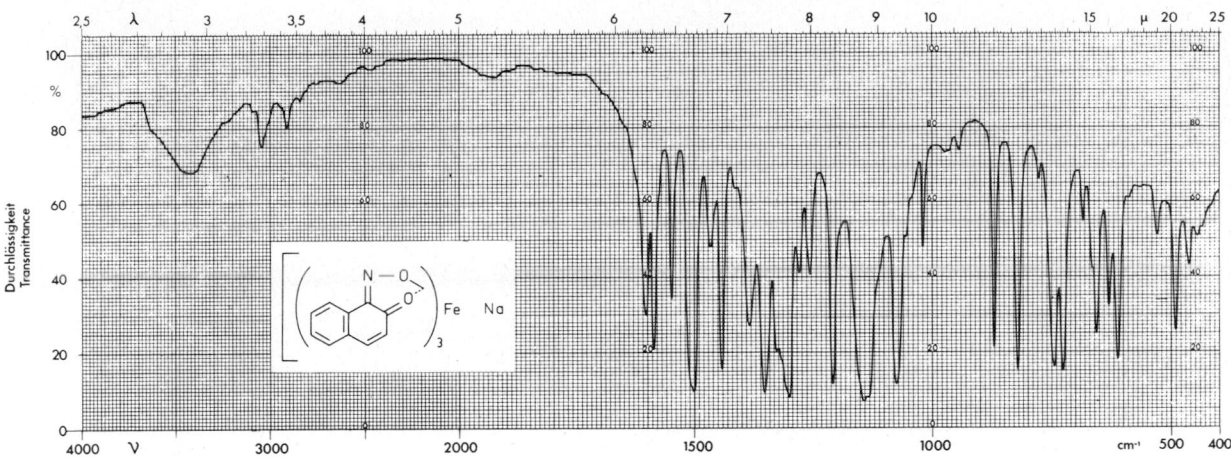

CI-Name: **Pigment Grün 8** CI-No.: **10006**
Zusammensetzung: **1-Nitroso-2-naphthol, Fe-Na-Chelat**
Präparation: **KBr (3,6/1000)** Dez. Nr.: **7.6.1**

CI-Name: **Pigment Green 8** CI-No.: **10006**
Composition: **1-Nitroso-2-naphthol, Fe-Na-Chelate**
Preparation: **KBr (3,6/1000)** Dec. No.: **7.6.1**

5740

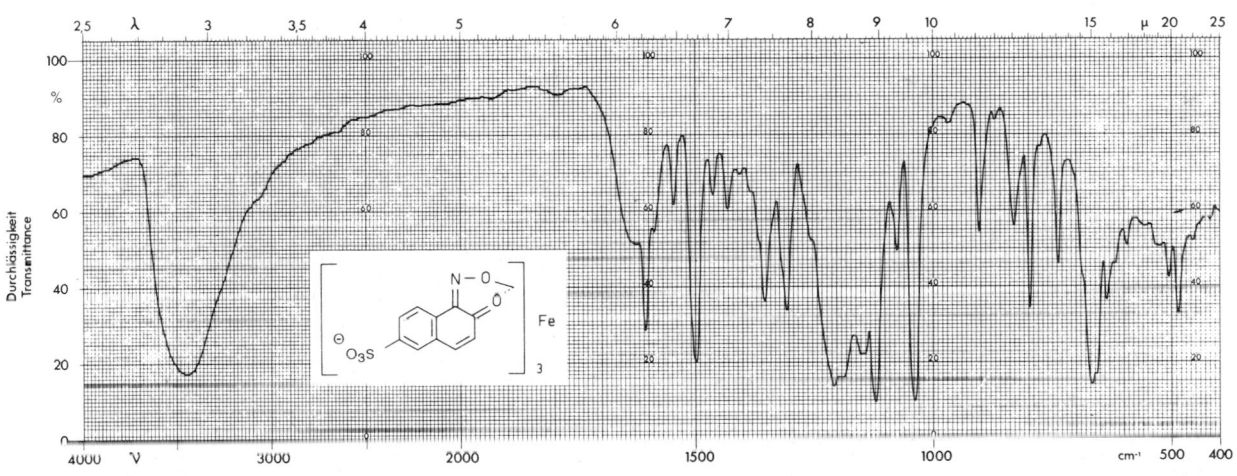

CI-Name: **Pigment Green 12** CI-No.: **10020**
Zusammensetzung: **1-Nitroso-2-naphthol-6-sulfonsäure, Fe-Na-Chelat**
Präparation: **KBr (6,6/1000)** Dez. Nr.: **7.6.2**

CI-Name: **Pigment Grün 12** CI-No.: **10020**
Composition: **1-Nitroso-2-naphthol-6-sulfonic acid, Fe-Na-Chelate**
Preparation: **KBr (6,6/1000)** Dec. No.: **7.6.2**

5741

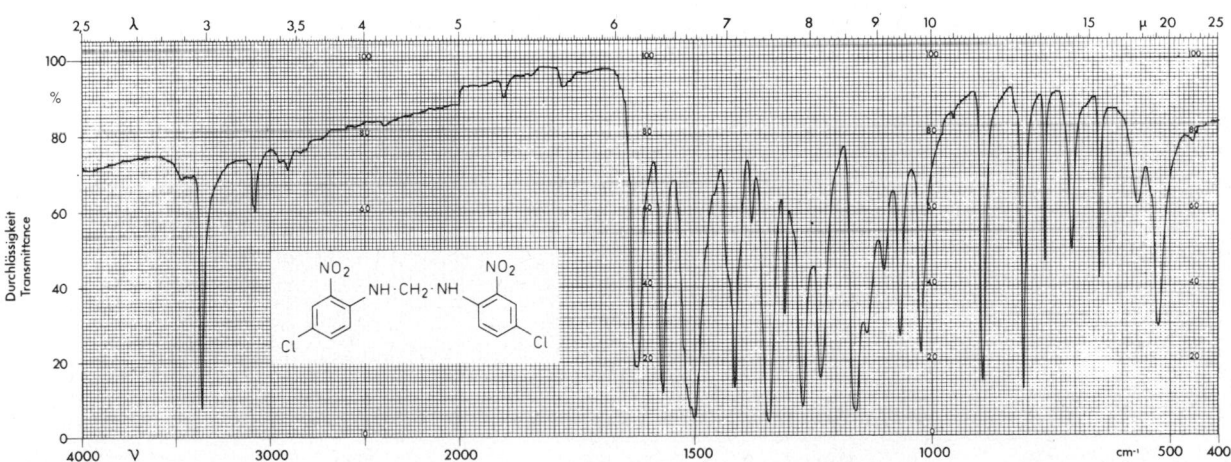

CI-Name: **Pigment Gelb 11** CI-No.: **10325**
Zusammensetzung: **N,N'-Di-4-chlor-2-nitrophenyl-methylendiamin**
Präparation: **KBr (3,6/1000)** Dez. Nr.: **7.7.1**

CI-Name: **Pigment Yellow 11** CI-No.: **10325**
Composition: **N,N'-Di-4-chloro-2-nitrophenyl-methylendiamine**
Preparation: **KBr (3,6/1000)** Dec. No.: **7.7.1**

5742

Organische Pigmente
7. Sonstige Pigmente
7.8. Thiazolpigmente

Organic Pigments
7. Miscellaneous Pigmets
7.8. Thiazole Pigments

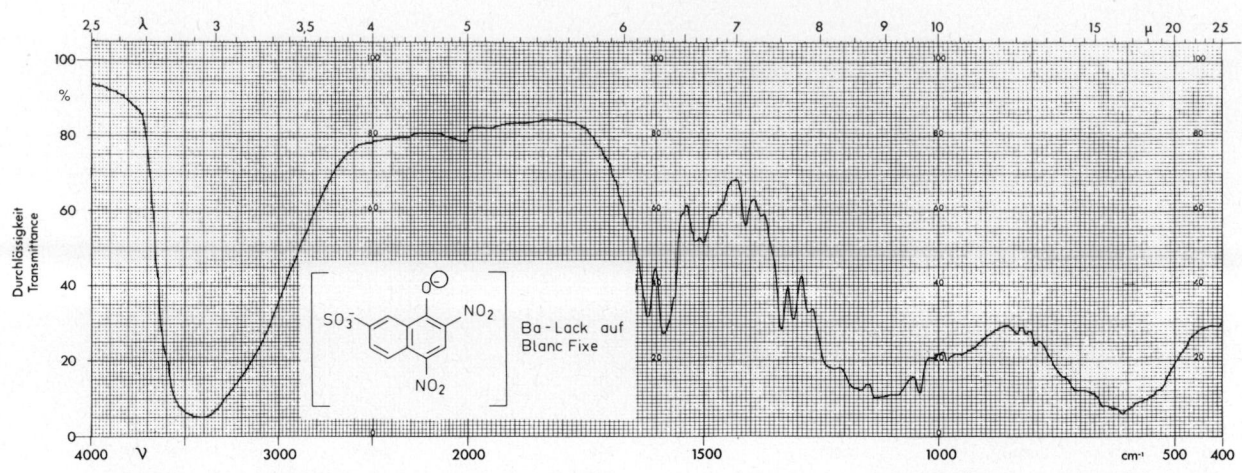

5743

CI-Name:	**ACID Gelb 1**	CI-No.:	**10316**	
Zusammensetzung:	**2,4-Dinitro-1-naphthol-7-sulfonsäure, Ba-Lack auf Blanc fixe**			
Präparation:	**KBr (4/1000)**	Dez. Nr.:	**7.7.2**	

CI-Name:	**Acid Yellow 1**	CI-No.:	**10316**	
Composition:	**2,4-Dinitro-1-naphthol-7-sulfonic acid, Ba-lake on Blanc fixe**			
Preparation:	**KBr (4/1000)**	Dec. No.:	**7.7.2**	

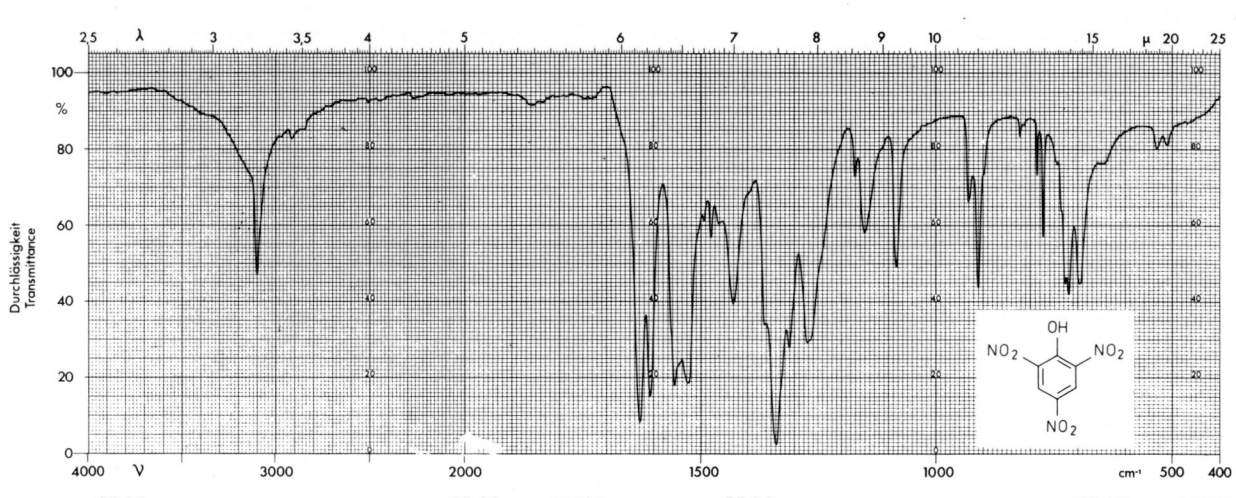

5744

CI-Name:		CI-No.:	**10305**
Zusammensetzung:	**Pikrinsäure**		
Präparation:	**KBr (10/1000)**	Dez. Nr.:	**7.7.3**

CI-Name:		CI-No.:	**10305**
Composition:	**Picric acid**		
Preparation:	**KBr (10/1000)**	Dec. No.:	**7.7.3**

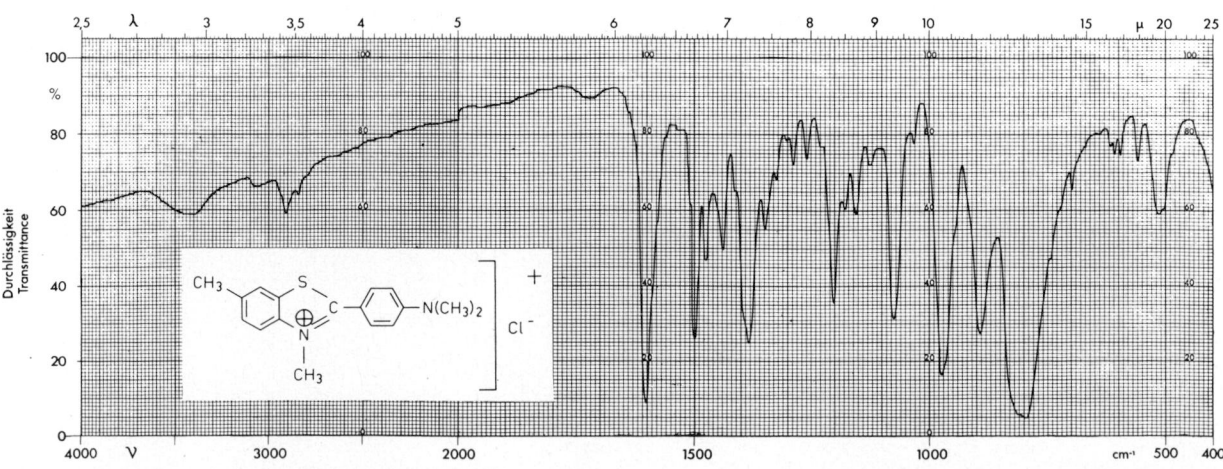

5745

CI-Name:	**Pigment Gelb 18**	CI-No.:	**49005**
Zusammensetzung:	**2-(4'-N,N-Dimethylaminophenyl)-3,6-dimethylthiazoliniumchlorid**		
Präparation:	**KBr (3,6/1000)**	Dez. Nr.:	**7.8.1**

CI-Name:	**Pigment Yellow 18**	CI-No.:	**49005**
Composition:	**2-(4'-N,N-Dimethylaminophenyl)-3,6-dimethylthiazolinium chloride**		
Preparation:	**KBr (3,6/1000)**	Dec. No.:	**7.8.1**

Organische Pigmente
7. Sonstige Pigmente
7.9. Azinpigmente

Organic Pigments
7. Miscellaneous Pigmets
7.9. Azine Pigments

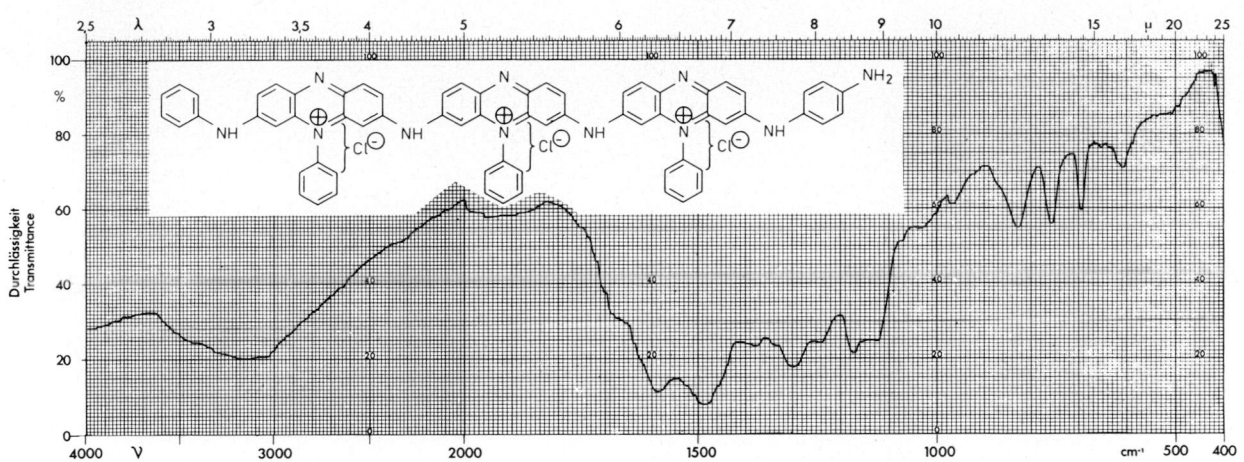

CI-Name: **Pigment Schwarz 1** CI-No.: **50440**
Zusammensetzung: **N-Phenyl-2-aminophenazonium-chlorid-Derivat**
Präparation: **KBr (3/1000)** Dez. Nr.: **7.9.1**

CI-Name: **Pigment Black 1** CI-No.: **50440**
Composition: **N-Phenyl-2-aminophenazonium-chloride derivative**
Preparation: **KBr (3/1000)** Dec. No.: **7.9.1**

5746

UV-Stabilisatoren
UV-Stabilizers

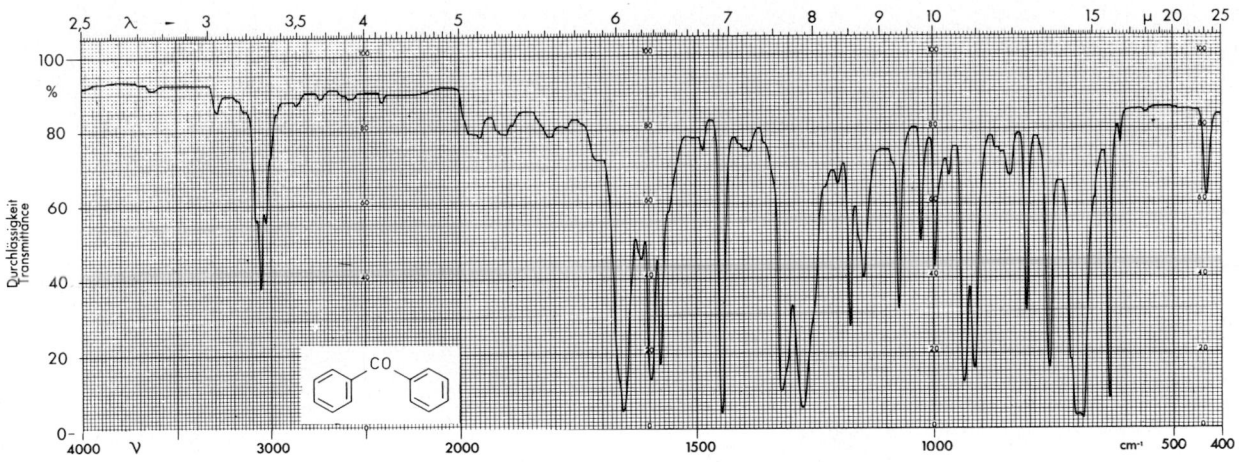

Verbindung:	Benzophenon			Compound:	Benzophenone			5800
Formel:	$C_{13}H_{10}O$	M.:	182,2	Formula:	$C_{13}H_{10}O$	M. w.:	182,2	
Handelsname:	Benzophenon	Herst.:	Eastman	Tradename:	Benzophenone	Manuf.:	Eastman	
Präparation:	Schmelzfilm	Dez. Nr.:	1.1	Preparation:	Melting film	Dec. No.:	1.1	

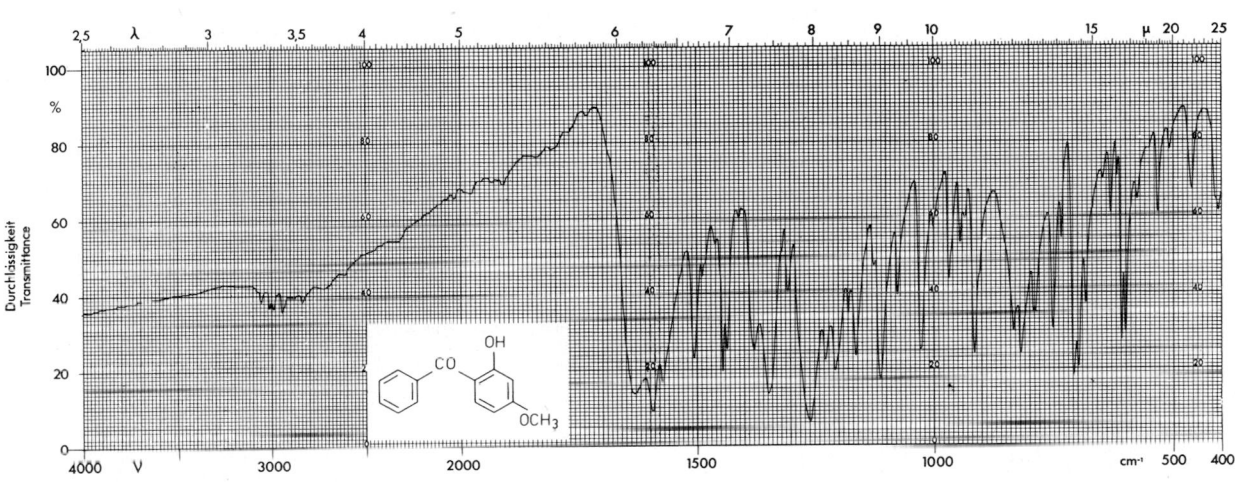

Verbindung:	2-Hydroxy-4-methoxy-benzophenon			Compound:	2-Hydroxy-4-methoxy-benzophenone			5801
Formel:	$C_{14}H_{12}O_3$	M.:	228,2	Formula:	$C_{14}H_{12}O_3$	M. w.:	228,2	
Handelsname:	Advastab 45	Herst.:	Advance	Tradename:	Advastab 45	Manuf.:	Advance	
Präparation:	KBr (6/1000)	Dez. Nr.:	1.2	Preparation:	KBr (6/1000)	Dec. No.:	1.2	

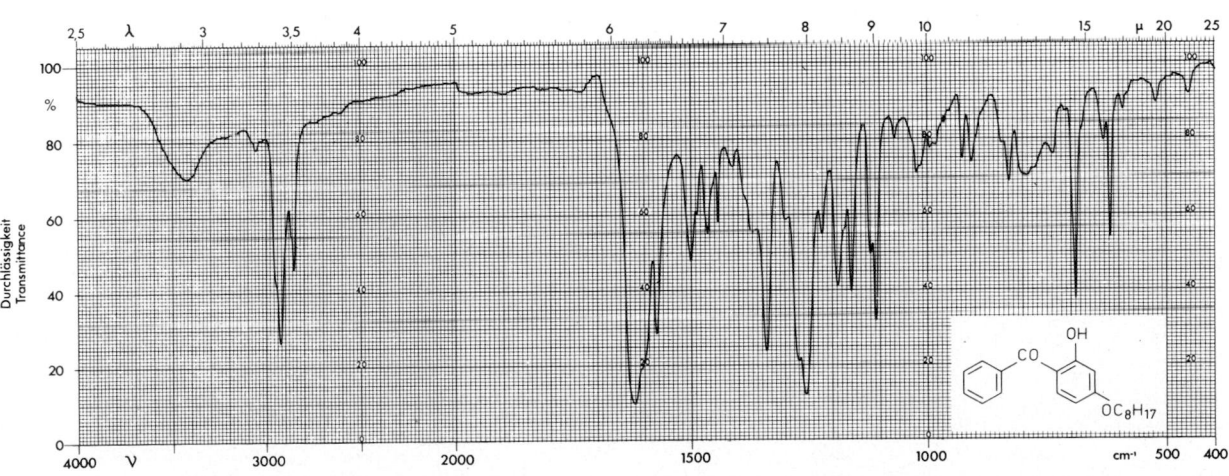

Verbindung:	2-Hydroxy-4-n-octyloxy-benzophenon			Compound:	2-Hydroxy-4-n-octoxy-benzophenone			5802
Formel:	$C_{21}H_{26}O_3$	M.:	326,2	Formula:	$C_{21}H_{26}O_3$	M. w.:	326,2	
Handelsname:	Cyasorb UV 531	Herst.:	Cyanamid	Tradename:	Cyasorb UV 531	Manuf.:	Cyanamid	
Präparation:	KBr (3/1000)	Dez. Nr.:	1.3	Preparation:	KBr (3/1000)	Dec. No.:	1.3	

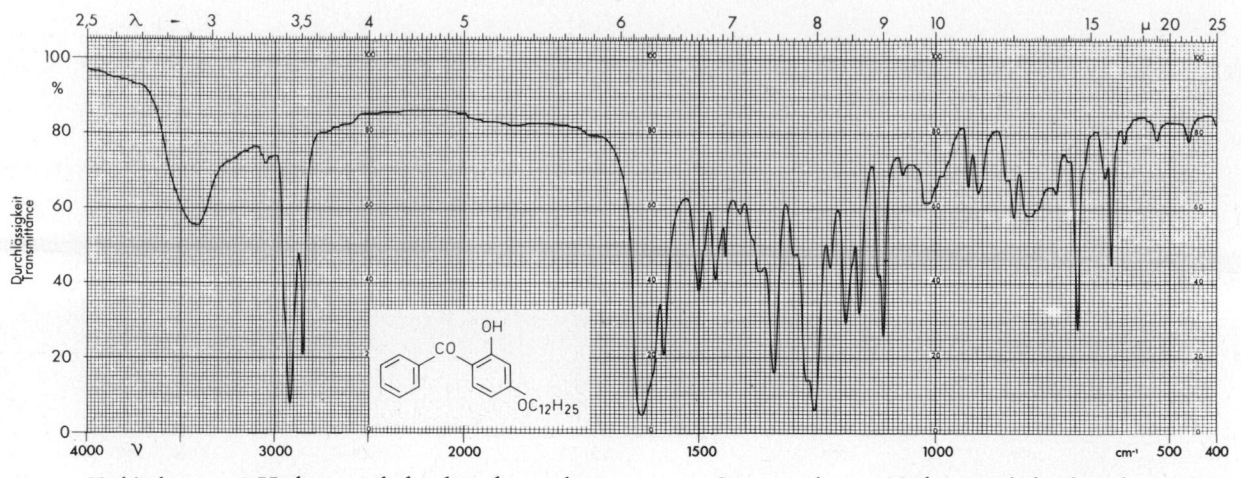

5803

Verbindung:	2-Hydroxy-4-dodecyloxy-benzophenon		
Formel:	C₂₅H₃₄O₃	M.:	382,5
Handelsname:	Inhibitor DOBP	Herst.:	Eastman
Präparation:	KBr (2,5/1000)	Dez. Nr.:	1.4

Compound:	2-Hydroxy-4-dodecyloxy-benzophenone		
Formula:	C₂₅H₃₄O₃	M. w.:	382,5
Tradename:	Inhibitor DOBP	Manuf.:	Eastman
Preparation:	KBr (2.5/1000)	Dec. No.:	1.4

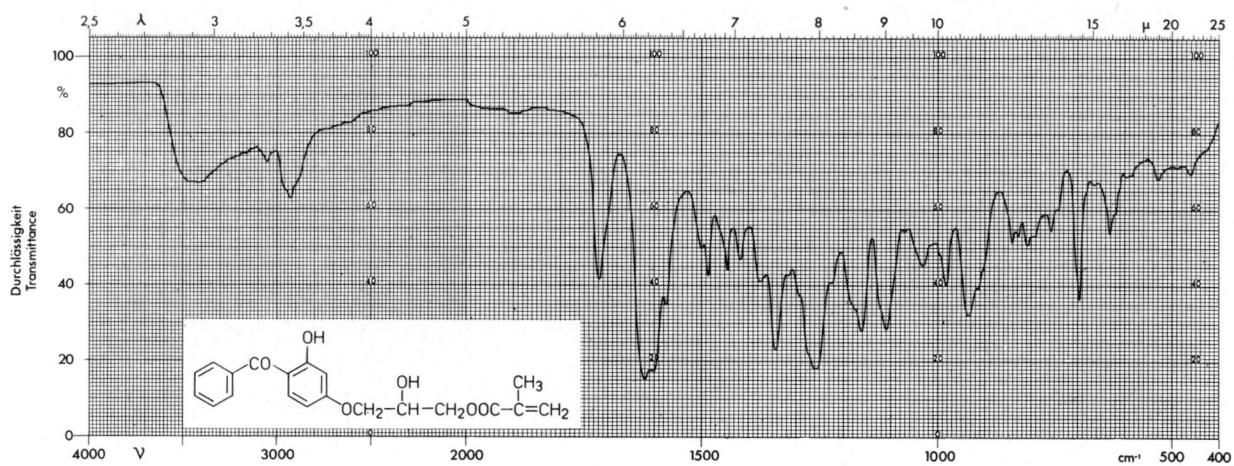

5804

Verbindung:	2-Hydroxy-4(2-hydroxy-3-methacryloxy)-propoxybenzophenon		
Formel:	C₂₀H₂₀O₆	M.:	357,3
Handelsname:	Permasorb MA	Herst.:	National
Präparation:	KBr (3/1000)	Dez. Nr.:	1.5

Compound:	2-Hydroxy-4(2-hydroxy-3-methacryloxy)-propoxybenzophenone		
Formula:	C₂₀H₂₀O₆	M. w.:	357,3
Tradename:	Permasorb MA	Manuf.:	National
Preparation:	KBr (3/1000)	Dec. No.:	1.5

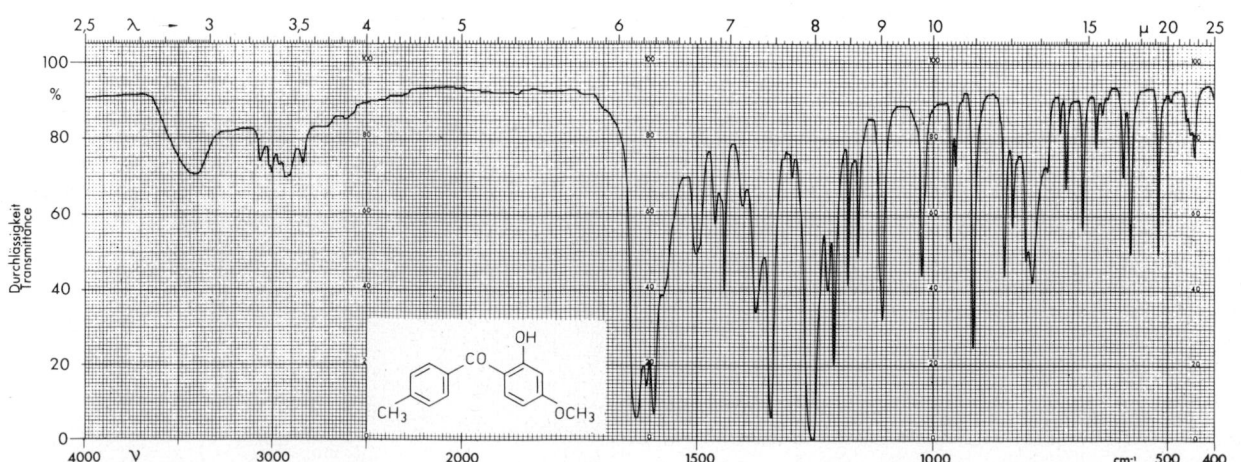

5805

Verbindung:	2-Hydroxy-4-methoxy-4'-methylbenzo-phenon		
Formel:	C₁₅H₁₄O₃	M.:	242,2
Handelsname:	Uvistat 2211	Herst.:	Ward
Präparation:	KBr (3,3/1000)	Dez. Nr.:	1.6

Compound:	2-Hydroxy-4-methoxy-4'-methylbenzo-phenone		
Formula:	C₁₅H₁₄O₃	M. w.:	242,2
Tradename:	Uvistat 2211	Manuf.:	Ward
Preparation:	KBr (3.3/1000)	Dec. No.:	1.6

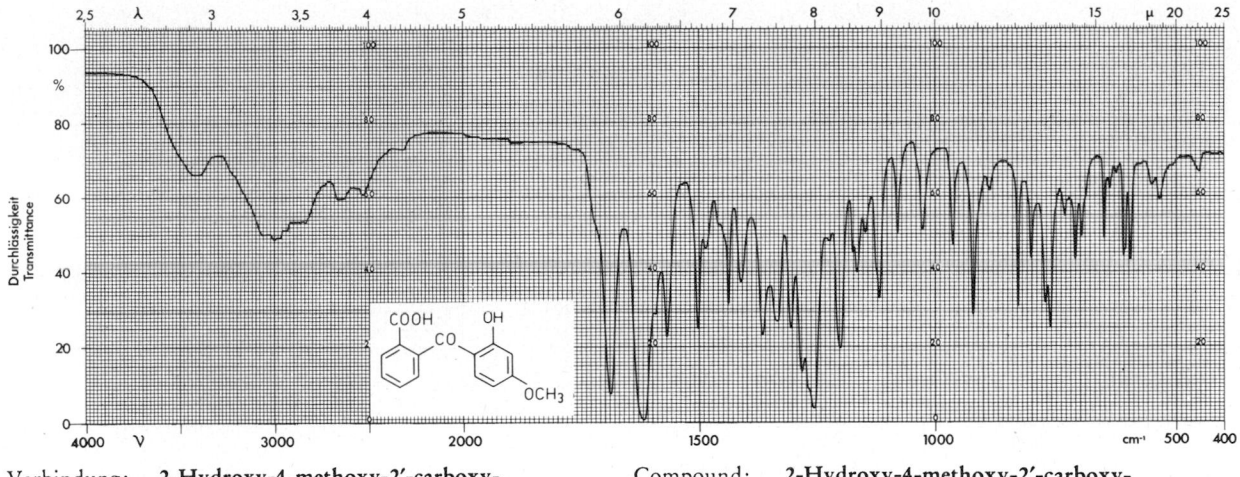

Verbindung:	2-Hydroxy-4-methoxy-2'-carboxy-benzophenon			Compound:	2-Hydroxy-4-methoxy-2'-carboxy-benzophenone			5806
Formel:	$C_{15}H_{12}O_5$	M.:	272,2	Formula:	$C_{15}H_{12}O_5$	M. w.:	272,2	
Handelsname:	Cyasorb UV 207	Herst.:	Cyanamid	Tradename:	Cyasorb UV 207	Manuf.:	Cyanamid	
Präparation:	KBr (1,5/1000)	Dez. Nr.:	1.7	Preparation:	KBr (1.5/1000)	Dec. No.:	1.7	

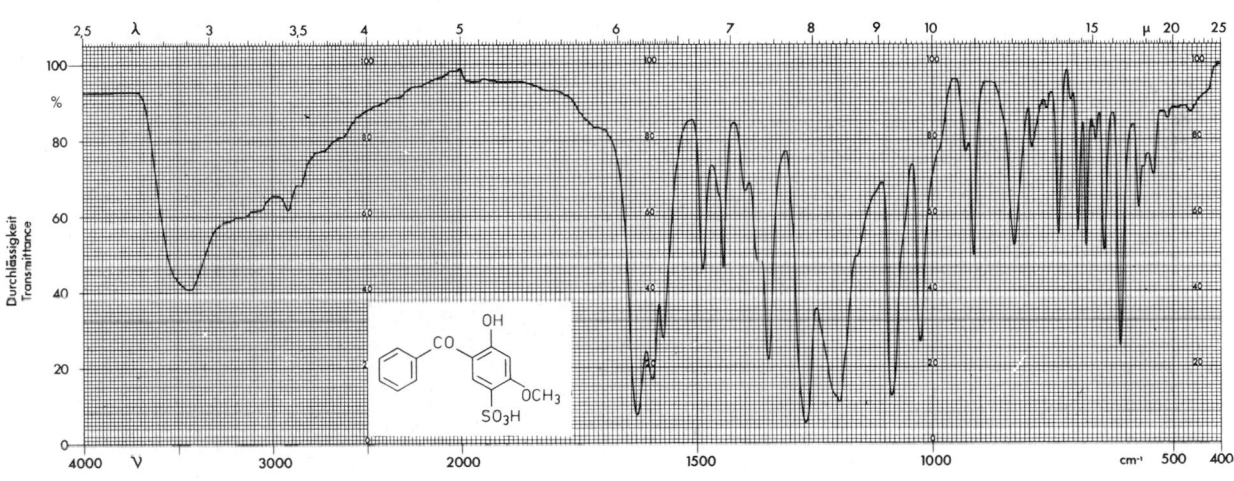

Verbindung:	2-Hydroxy-4-methoxy-5-sulfonsäure-benzophenon			Compound:	2-Hydroxy-4-methoxy-5 sulfonic acid-benzophenone			5807
Formel:	$C_{14}H_{12}O_6S$	M.:	308,2	Formula:	$C_{14}H_{12}O_6S$	M. w.:	308,2	
Handelsname:	Cyasorb UV 284	Herst.:	Cyanamid	Tradename:	Cyasorb UV 284	Manuf.:	Cyanamid	
Präparation:	KBr (6/1000)	Dez. Nr.:	1.8	Preparation:	KBr (6/1000)	Dec. No.:	1.8	

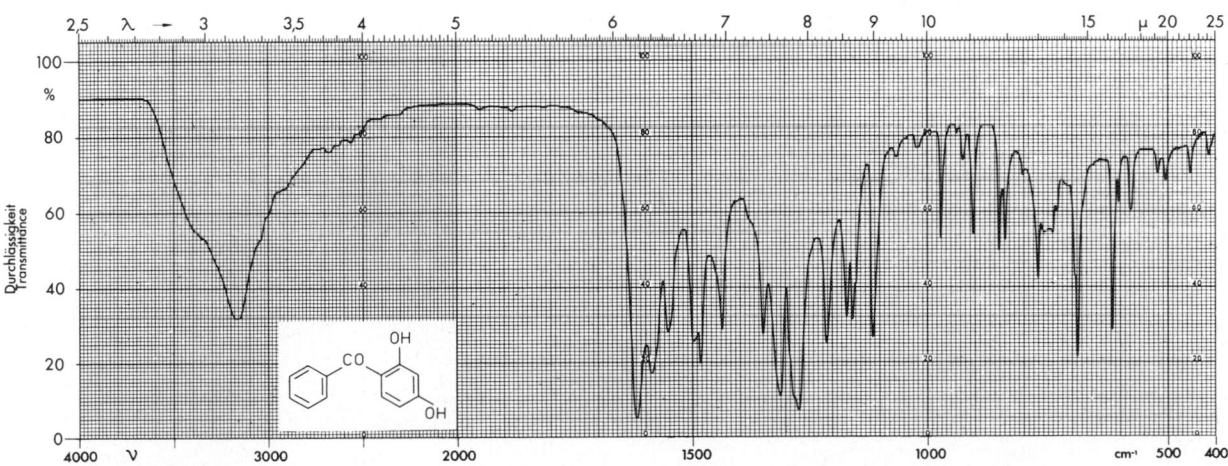

Verbindung:	2,4-Dihydroxybenzophenon			Compound:	2,4-Dihydroxybenzophenone			5808
Formel:	$C_{13}H_{10}O_3$	M.:	214,2	Formula:	$C_{13}H_{10}O_3$	M. w.:	214,2	
Handelsname:	Inhibitor DHBP	Herst.:	Eastman	Tradename:	Inhibitor DHBP	Manuf.:	Eastman	
Präparation:	KBr (2/1000)	Dez. Nr.:	1.9	Preparation:	KBr (2/1000)	Dec. No.:	1.9	

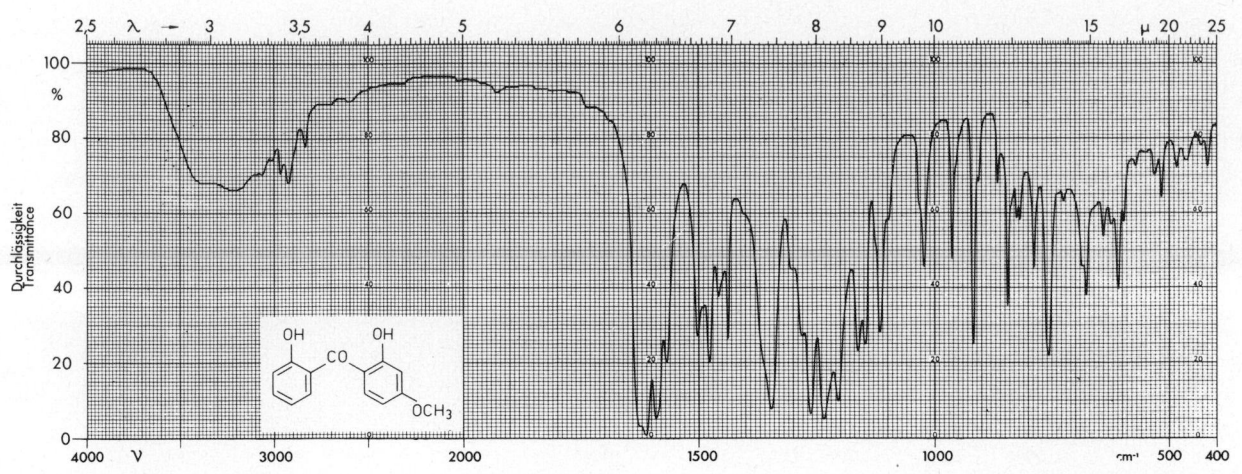

5809   Verbindung: **2,2′-Dihydroxy-4-methoxy-benzophenon**   Compound: **2,2′-Dihydroxy-4-methoxy-benzophenone**

Formel:	$C_{14}H_{12}O_4$	M.:	**244,2**	Formula:	$C_{14}H_{12}O_4$
Handelsname:	**Advastab 47**	Herst.:	**Advance**	Tradename:	**Advastab 47**
Präparation:	**KBr (3/1000)**	Dez.Nr.:	**1.10**	Preparation:	**KBr (3/1000)**

Formel: $C_{14}H_{12}O_4$ M.: **244,2**   Formula: $C_{14}H_{12}O_4$ M. w.: **244,2**
Handelsname: **Advastab 47**   Herst.: **Advance**   Tradename: **Advastab 47**   Manuf.: **Advance**
Präparation: **KBr (3/1000)**   Dez.Nr.: **1.10**   Preparation: **KBr (3/1000)**   Dec.No.: **1.10**

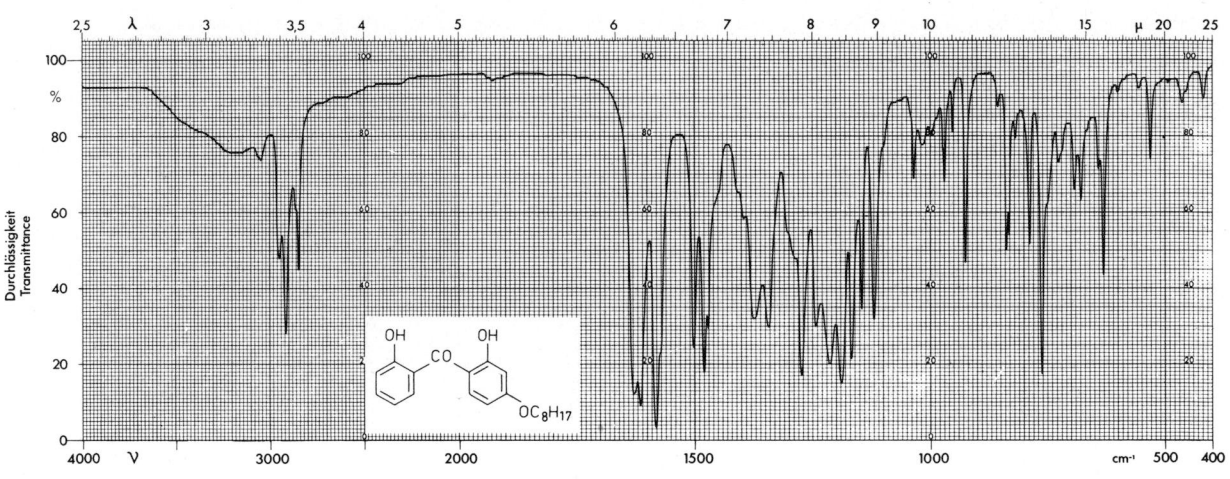

5810   Verbindung: **2,2′-Dihydroxy-4-octoxy-benzophenon**   Compound: **2,2′-Dihydroxy-4-octoxy-benzophenone**

Formel: $C_{21}H_{27}O_4$ M.: **343,3**   Formula: $C_{21}H_{27}O_4$ M. w.: **343,3**
Handelsname: **Cyasorb UV 314**   Herst.: **Cyanamid**   Tradename: **Cyasorb UV 314**   Manuf.: **Cyanamid**
Präparation: **KBr (3,3/1000)**   Dez.Nr.: **1.11**   Preparation: **KBr (3.3/1000)**   Dec.No.: **1.11**

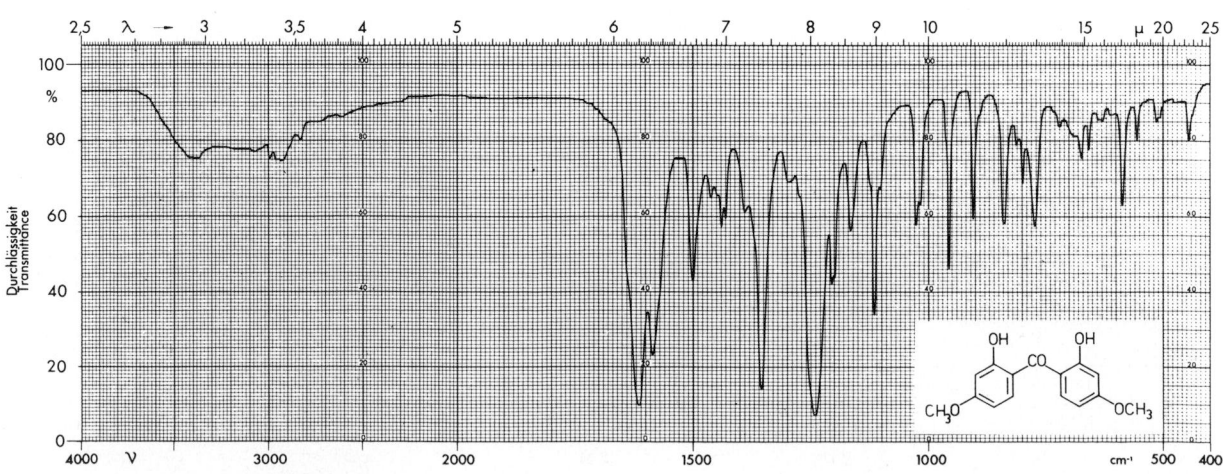

5811   Verbindung: **2,2′-Dihydroxy-4,4′-dimethoxy-benzophenon**   Compound: **2,2′-Dihydroxy-4,4′-dimethoxy-benzophenone**

Formel: $C_{15}H_{14}O_5$ M.: **274,2**   Formula: $C_{15}H_{14}O_5$ M. w.: **274,2**
Handelsname: **Uvinol D 49**   Herst.: **Gen. Aniline**   Tradename: **Uvinol D 49**   Manuf.: **Gen. Aniline**
Präparation: **KBr (6/1000)**   Dez.Nr.: **1.12**   Preparation: **KBr (6/1000)**   Dec.No.: **1.12**

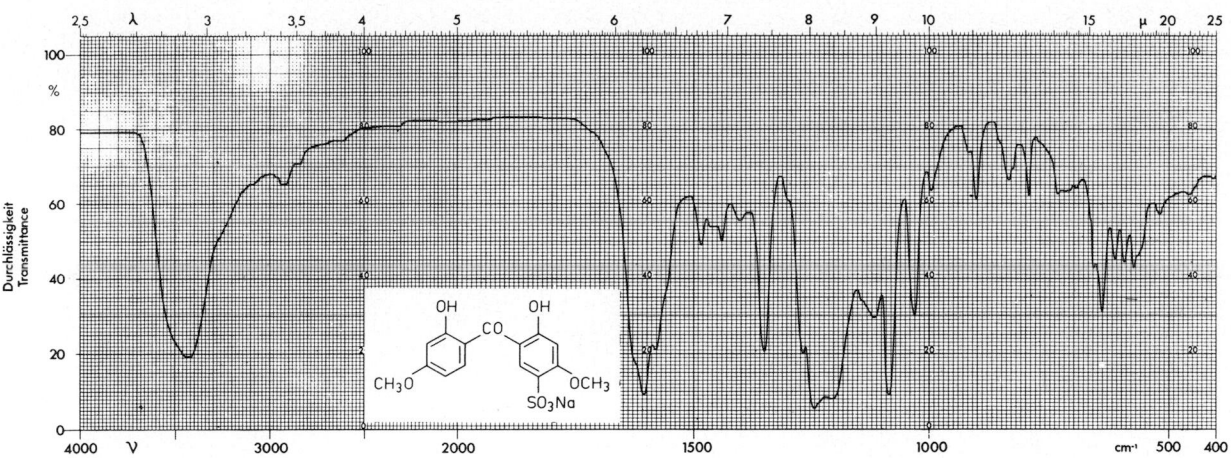

Verbindung: **2,2'-Dihydroxy-4,4'-dimethoxy-5-sulfo-benzophenon-Na**

Compound: **2,2'-Dihydroxy-4,4'-dimethoxy-5-sulfo-benzophenone-Na**

5812

Formel:	$C_{15}H_{13}O_8SNa$	M.:	**376**
Handelsname:	**Uvinol DS 49**	Herst.:	**Gen. Aniline**
Präparation:	**KBr (6/1000)**	Dez. Nr.:	**1.13**

Formula:	$C_{15}H_{13}O_8SNa$	M. w.:	**376**
Tradename:	**Uvinol DS 49**	Manuf.:	**Gen. Aniline**
Preparation:	**KBr (6/1000)**	Dec. No.:	**1.13**

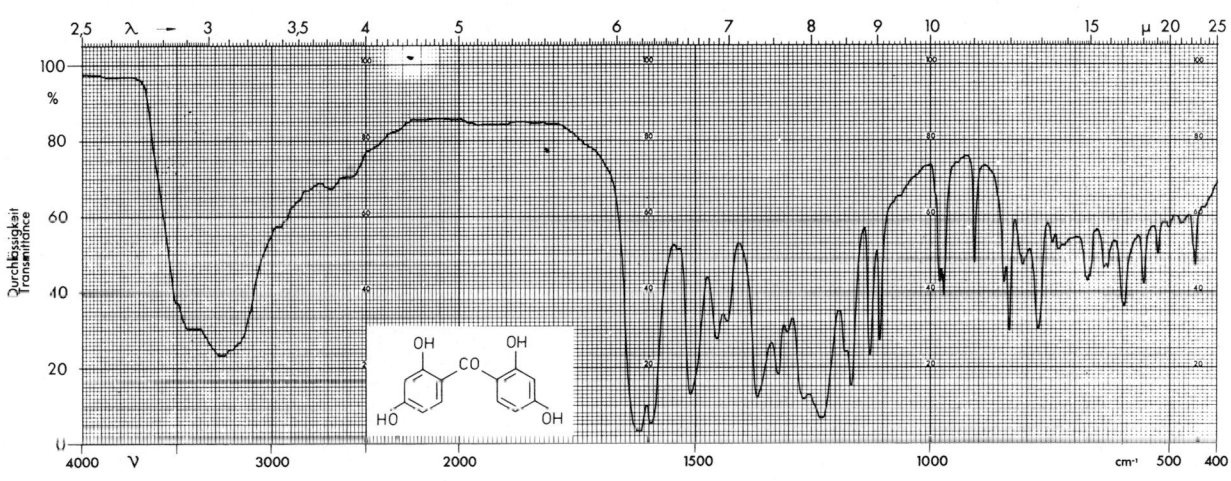

Verbindung: **2,2',4,4'-Tetrahydroxy-benzophenon**

Compound: **2,2',4,4'-Tetrahydroxy-benzophenone**

5813

Formel:	$C_{13}H_{10}O_5$	M.:	**246,2**
Handelsname:	**Uvinol D 50**	Herst.:	**Gen. Aniline**
Präparation:	**KBr (3/1000)**	Dez. Nr.:	**1.14**

Formula:	$C_{13}H_{10}O_5$	M. w.:	**246,2**
Tradename:	**Uvinol D 50**	Manuf.:	**Gen. Aniline**
Preparation:	**KBr (3/1000)**	Dec. No.:	**1.14**

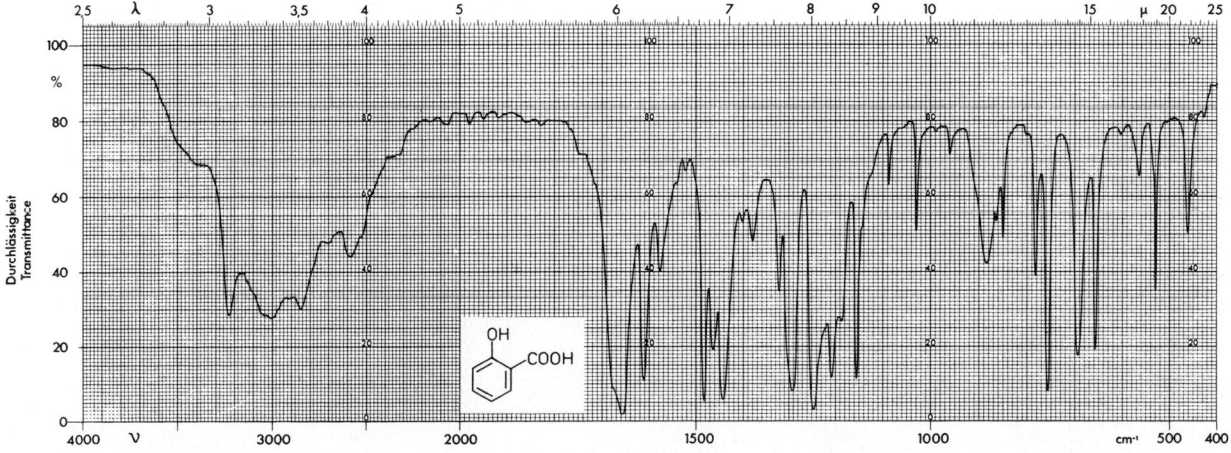

Verbindung: **Salicylsäure**

Compound: **Salicylic acid**

5814

Formel:	$C_7H_6O_3$	M.:	**138,0**
Handelsname:	**Salicylsäure**	Herst.:	**Merck**
Präparation:	**KBr (3/1000)**	Dez. Nr.:	**2.1**

Formula:	$C_7H_6O_3$	M. w.:	**138,0**
Tradename:	**Salicylic acid**	Manuf.:	**Merck**
Preparation:	**KBr (3/1000)**	Dec. No.:	**2.1**

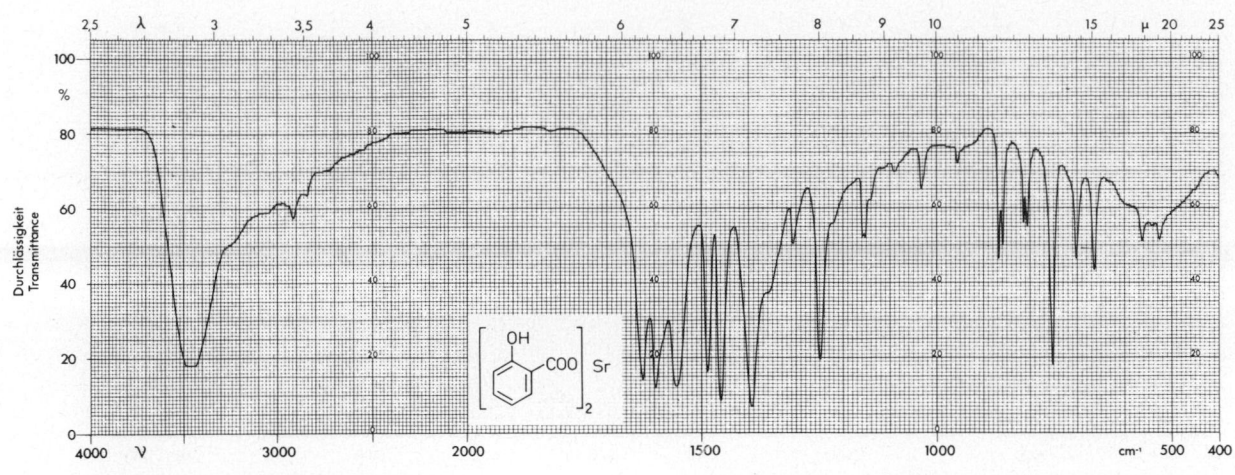

5815	Verbindung:	**Strontiumsalicylat**			Compound:	**Strontium salicylate**		
	Formel:	$C_{14}H_{10}O_6Sr$	M.:	**361,6**	Formula:	$C_{14}H_{10}O_6Sr$	M. w.:	**361,6**
	Handelsname:	**Sunkem SRS**	Herst.:	**Sun Chem.**	Tradename:	**Sunkem SRS**	Manuf.:	**Sun Chem.**
	Präparation:	**KBr (2,5/1000)**	Dez. Nr.:	**2.2**	Preparation:	**KBr (2.5/1000)**	Dec. No.:	**2.2**

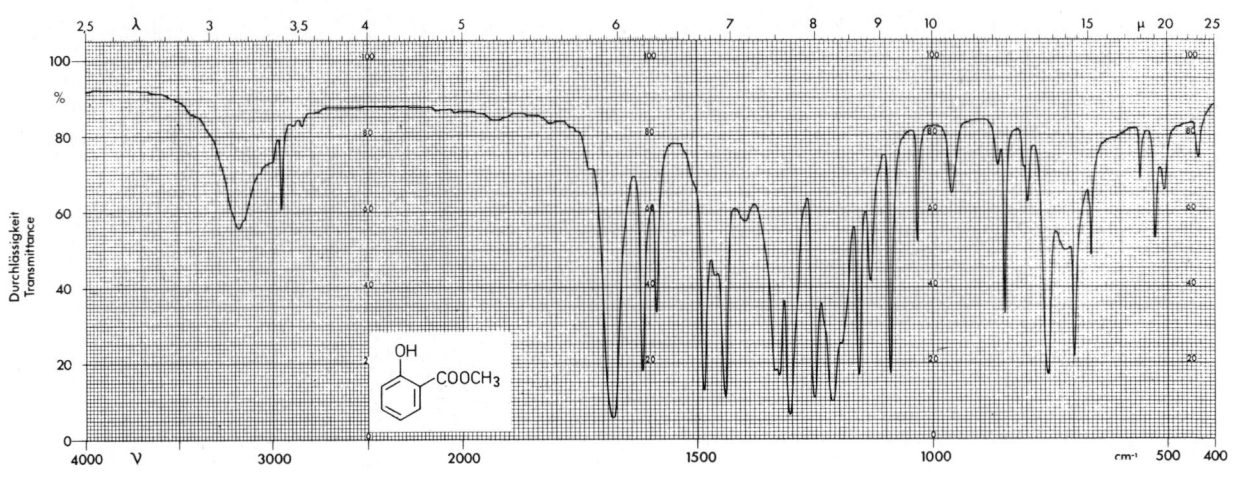

5816	Verbindung:	**Methylsalicylat**			Compound:	**Methyl salicylate**		
	Formel:	$C_8H_8O_3$	M.:	**152,1**	Formula:	$C_8H_8O_3$	M. w.:	**152,1**
	Handelsname:	**Sunkem MS**	Herst.:	**Sun Chem.**	Tradename:	**Sunkem MS**	Manuf.:	**Sun Chem.**
	Präparation:	**Kapill. Film**	Dez. Nr.:	**2.3**	Preparation:	**Capill. Film**	Dec. No.:	**2.3**

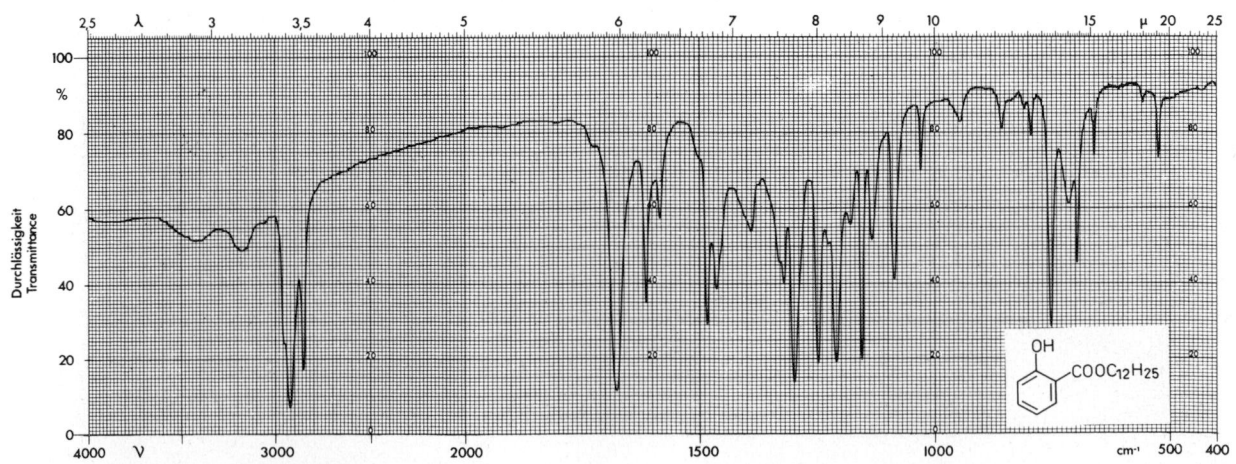

5817	Verbindung:	**Dodecylsalicylat**			Compound:	**Dodecyl salicylate**		
	Formel:	$C_{19}H_{30}O_3$	M.:	**322,4**	Formula:	$C_{19}H_{30}O_3$	M. w.:	**322,4**
	Handelsname:	**Sunkem DDS**	Herst.:	**Sun Chem.**	Tradename:	**Sunkem DDS**	Manuf.:	**Sun Chem.**
	Präparation:	**KBr (3/1000)**	Dez. Nr.:	**2.4**	Preparation:	**KBr (3/1000)**	Dec. No.:	**2.4**

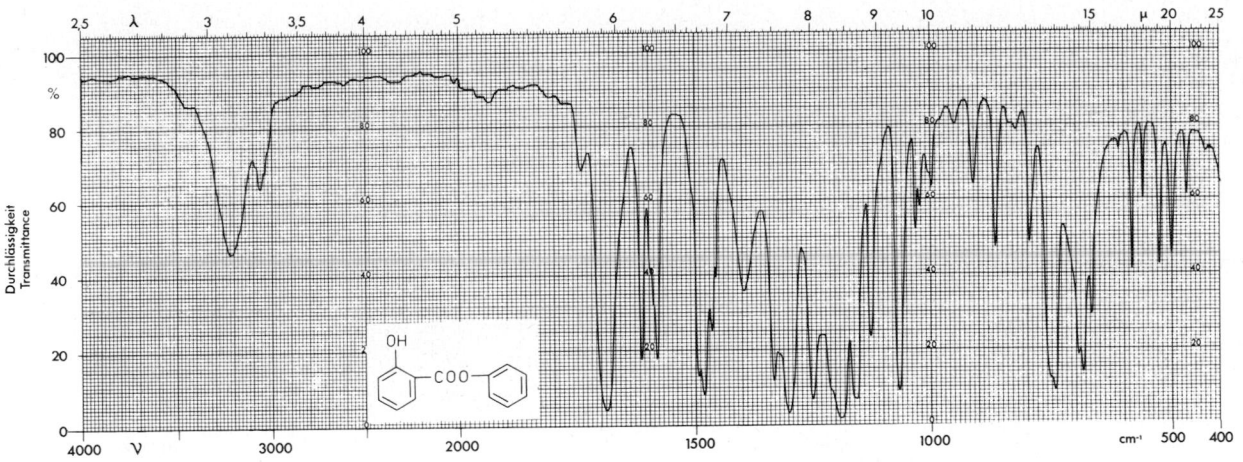

Verbindung:	**Phenylsalicylat**			Compound:	**Phenyl salicylate**			**5818**
Formel:	$C_{13}H_{10}O_3$	M.:	**214,2**	Formula:	$C_{13}H_{10}O_3$	M. w.:	**214,2**	
Handelsname:	**Salol**	Herst.:	**Bayer**	Tradename:	**Salol**	Manuf.:	**Bayer**	
Präparation:	**Schmelzfilm**	Dez. Nr.:	**2.5**	Preparation:	**Melting film**	Dec. No.:	**2.5**	

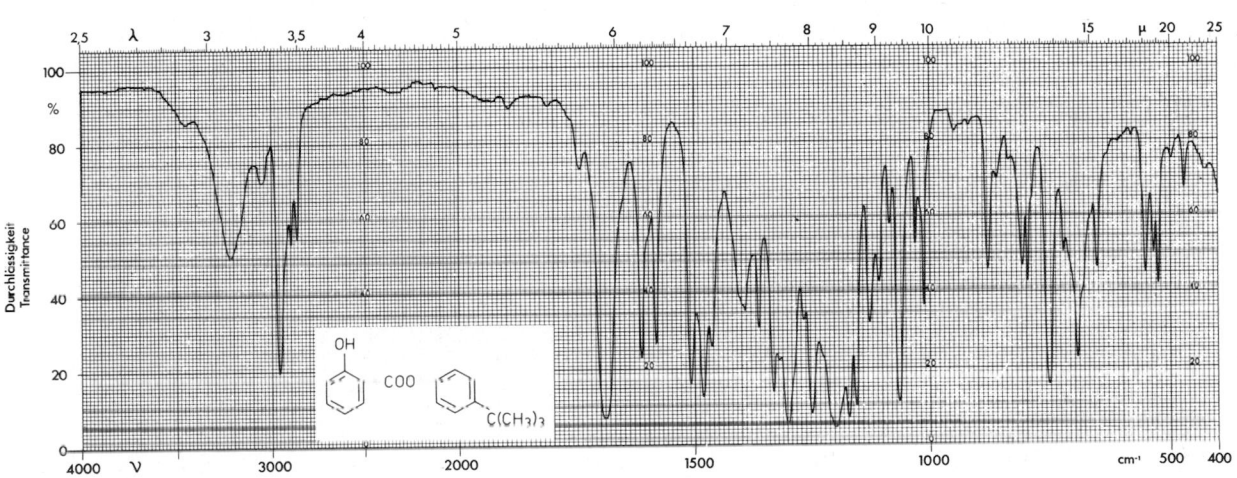

Verbindung:	**4-tert.-Butylphenylsalicylat**			Compound:	**4-tert.-Butylphenylsalicylate**			**5819**
Formel:	$C_{17}H_{18}O_3$	M.:	**270,2**	Formula:	$C_{17}H_{18}O_3$	M. w.:	**270,2**	
Handelsname:	**Light Absorber TBS**	Herst.:	**Dow**	Tradename:	**Light Absorber TBS**	Manuf.:	**Dow**	
Präparation:	**Schmelzfilm**	Dez. Nr.:	**2.6**	Preparation:	**Melting film**	Dec. No.:	**2.6**	

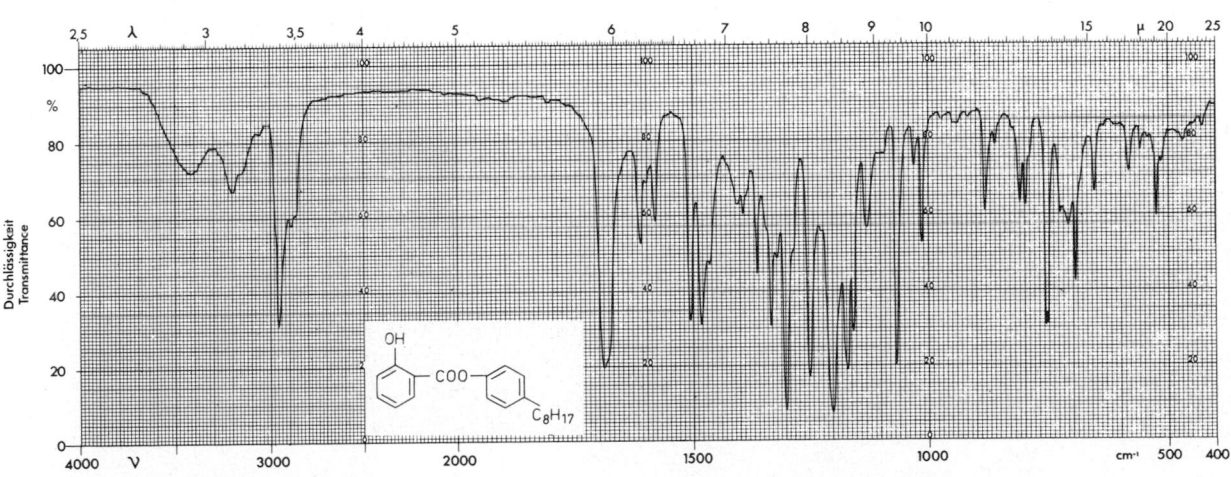

Verbindung:	**4-Octylphenylsalicylat**			Compound:	**4-Octylphenylsalicylate**			**5820**
Formel:	$C_{21}H_{26}O_3$	M.:	**326,3**	Formula:	$C_{21}H_{26}O_3$	M. w.:	**326,3**	
Handelsname:	**Eastman OPS**	Herst.:	**Eastman**	Tradename:	**Eastman OPS**	Manuf.:	**Eastman**	
Präparation:	**KBr (6/1000)**	Dez. Nr.:	**2.7**	Preparation:	**KBr (6/1000)**	Dec. No.:	**2.7**	

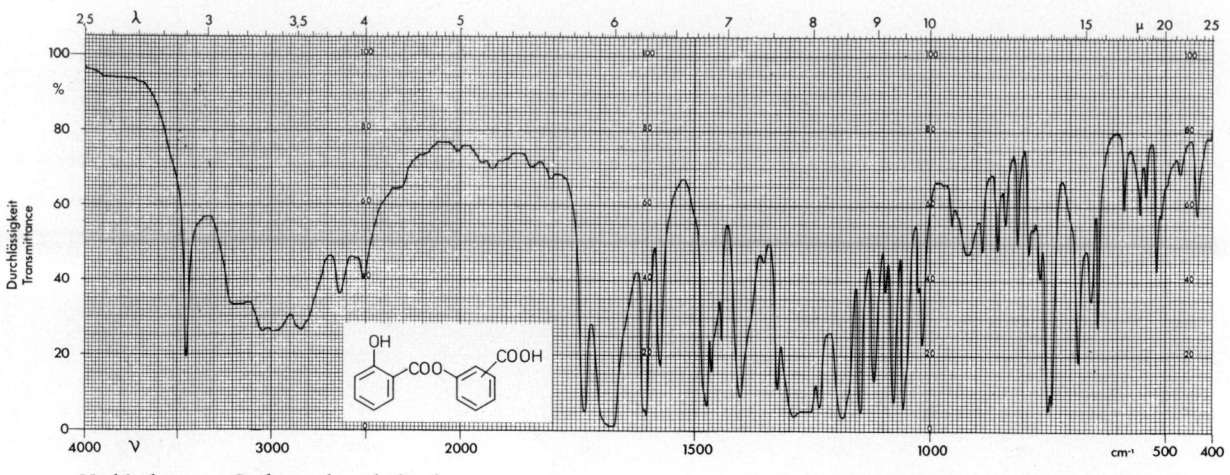

5821

Verbindung:	Carboxyphenylsalicylat			Compound:	Carboxylphenylsalicylate		
Formel:	$C_{14}H_{10}O_5$	M.:	258,2	Formula:	$C_{14}H_{10}O_5$	M. w.:	258,2
Handelsname:	Sunkem CPS	Herst.:	Sun Chem.	Tradename:	Sunkem CPS	Manuf.:	Sun Chem.
Präparation:	KBr (5/1000)	Dez. Nr.:	2.8	Preparation:	KBr (5/1000)	Dec. No.:	2.8

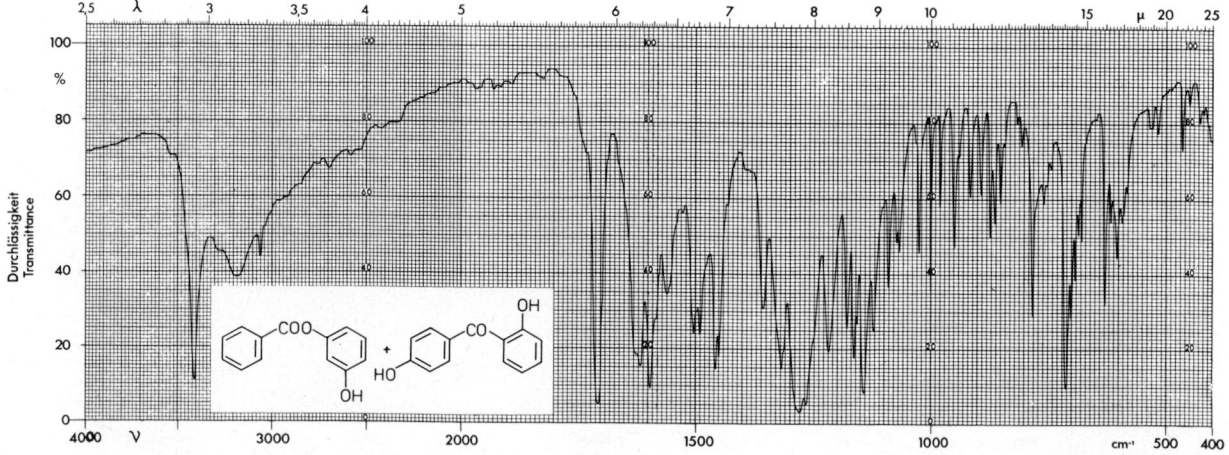

5822

Verbindung:	Resorcinmonobenzoat			Compound:	Resorcinol monobenzoate		
Formel:	$C_{13}H_{10}O_3$	M.:	214,2	Formula:	$C_{13}H_{10}O_3$	M. w.:	214,2
Handelsname:	Eastman RMB	Herst.:	Eastman	Tradename:	Eastman RMB	Manuf.:	Eastman
Präparation:	KBr (3,3/1000)	Dez. Nr.:	2.9	Preparation:	KBr (3.3/1000)	Dec. No.:	2.9

5823

Verbindung:	Gemisch aus Resorcinmonobenzoat und 2,4'-Dihydroxybenzophenon			Compound:	Mixture of Resorcinolmonobenzoate and 2,4'-Dihydroxybenzophenone		
Formel:		M.:		Formula:		M. w.:	
Handelsname:	Permyl B 100	Herst.:	Bärlocher	Tradename:	Permyl B 100	Manuf.:	Bärlocher
Präparation:	KBr (4/1000)	Dez. Nr.:	2.10	Preparation:	KBr (4/1000)	Dec. No.:	2.10

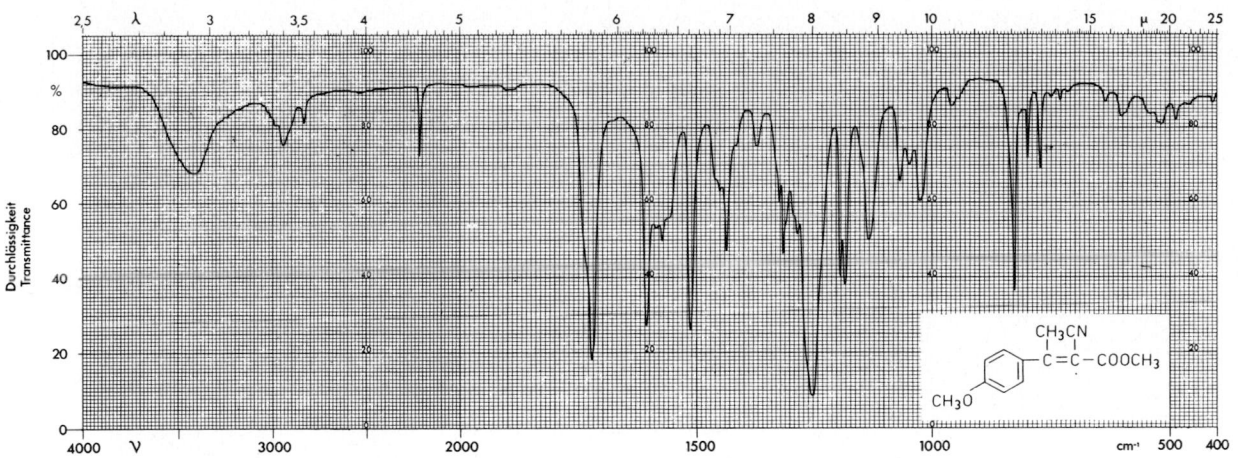

Verbindung:	α-Cyan-β-methyl-4-methoxy-zimtsäure methylester			Compound:	α-Cyano-β-methyl-4-methoxy-methyl cinnamate			5824
Formel:	$C_{13}H_{13}NO_3$	M.:	231,2	Formula:	$C_{13}H_{13}NO_3$	M. w.:	231,2	
Handelsname:	UV-Absorber 318	Herst.:	Bayer	Tradename:	UV-Absorber 318	Manuf.:	Bayer	
Präparation:	KBr (7/1000)	Dez. Nr.:	3.1	Preparation:	KBr (7/1000)	Dec. No.:	3.1	

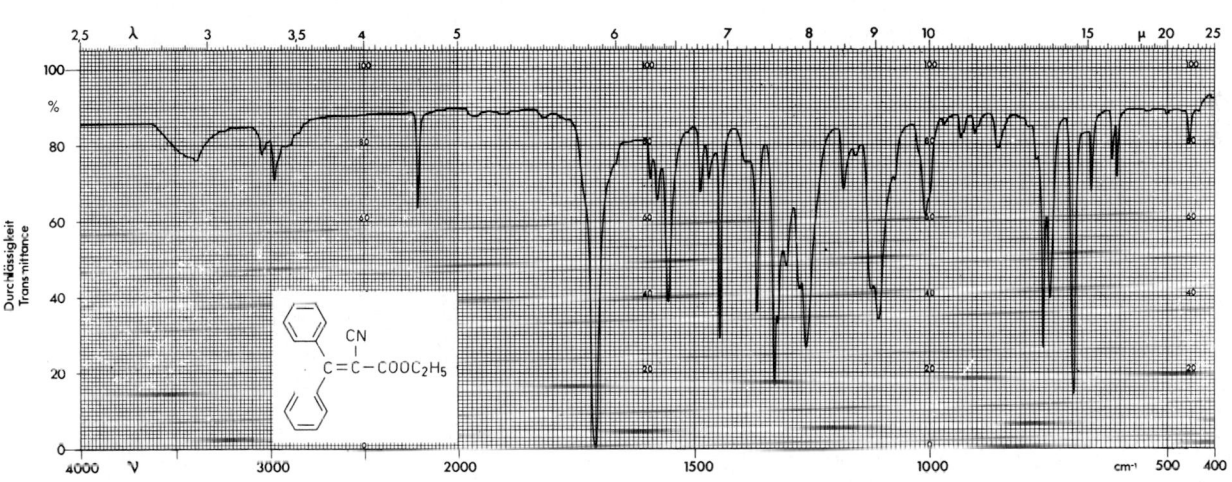

Verbindung:	α-Cyan-β-phenyl ethylcinnamat			Compound:	α-Cyano-β-phenyl-ethylcinnamate			5825
Formel:	$C_{18}H_{15}NO_2$	M.:	277,2	Formula:	$C_{18}H_{15}NO_2$	M. w.:	277,2	
Handelsname:	Uvinol N 35	Herst.:	Gen. Aniline	Tradename:	Uvinol N 35	Manuf.:	Gen. Aniline	
Präparation:	KBr (7/1000)	Dez. Nr.:	3.2	Preparation:	KBr (7/1000)	Dec. No.:	3.2	

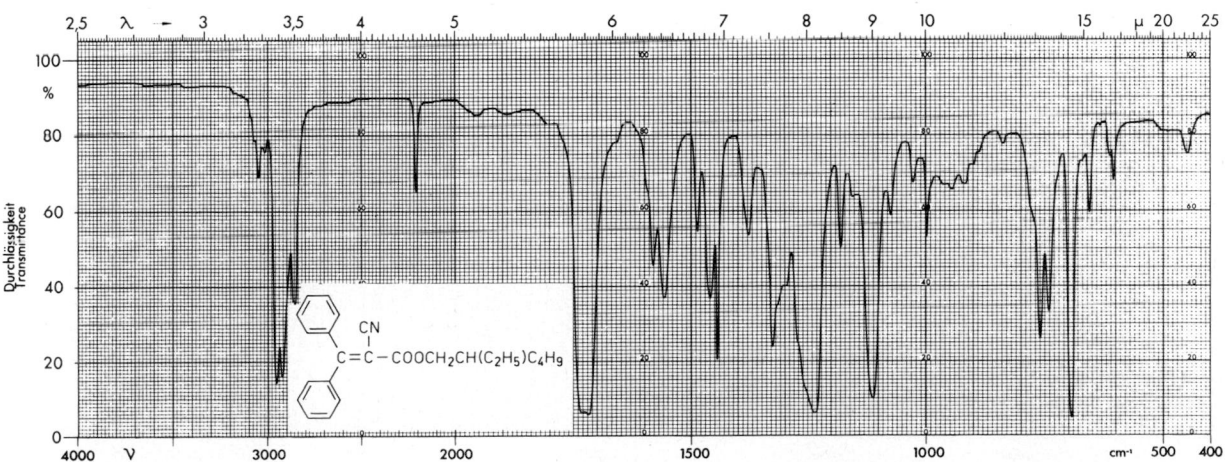

Verbindung:	α-Cyan-β-phenyl-(2-ethylhexyl)-cinnamat			Compound:	α-Cyano-β-phenyl-(2-ethylhexyl) cinnamate			5826
Formel:	$C_{24}H_{27}NO_2$	M.:	361,3	Formula:	$C_{24}H_{27}NO_2$	M. w.:	361,3	
Handelsname:	Uvinol N 539	Herst.:	Gen. Aniline	Tradename:	Uvinol N 539	Manuf.:	Gen. Aniline	
Präparation:	Kapill. Film	Dez. Nr.:	3.3	Preparation:	Capill. Film	Dec. No.:	3.3	

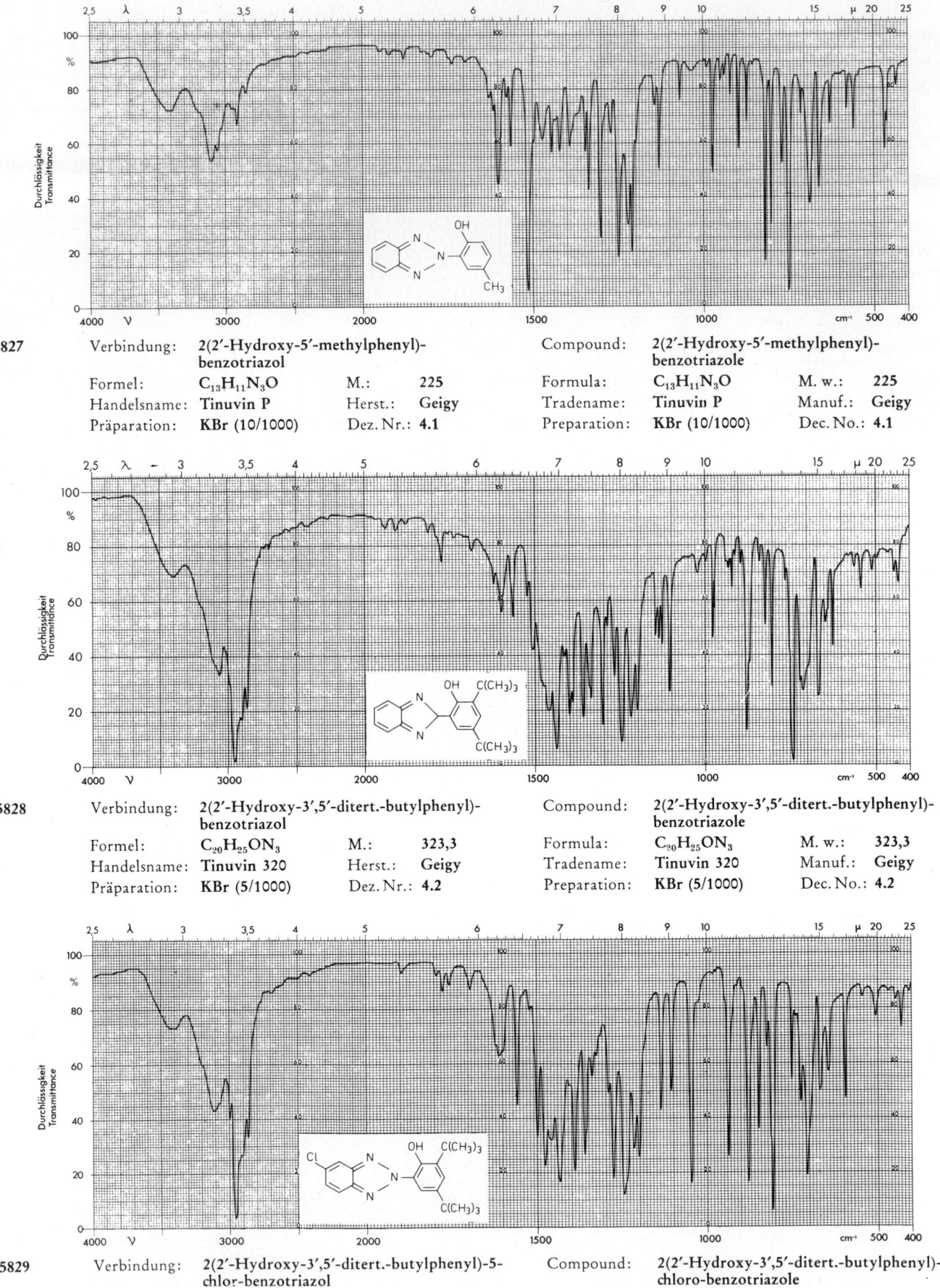

5827

Verbindung:	2(2'-Hydroxy-5'-methylphenyl)-benzotriazol			Compound:	2(2'-Hydroxy-5'-methylphenyl)-benzotriazole		
Formel:	$C_{13}H_{11}N_3O$	M.:	225	Formula:	$C_{13}H_{11}N_3O$	M. w.:	225
Handelsname:	Tinuvin P	Herst.:	Geigy	Tradename:	Tinuvin P	Manuf.:	Geigy
Präparation:	KBr (10/1000)	Dez. Nr.:	4.1	Preparation:	KBr (10/1000)	Dec. No.:	4.1

5828

Verbindung:	2(2'-Hydroxy-3',5'-ditert.-butylphenyl)-benzotriazol			Compound:	2(2'-Hydroxy-3',5'-ditert.-butylphenyl)-benzotriazole		
Formel:	$C_{20}H_{25}ON_3$	M.:	323,3	Formula:	$C_{20}H_{25}ON_3$	M. w.:	323,3
Handelsname:	Tinuvin 320	Herst.:	Geigy	Tradename:	Tinuvin 320	Manuf.:	Geigy
Präparation:	KBr (5/1000)	Dez. Nr.:	4.2	Preparation:	KBr (5/1000)	Dec. No.:	4.2

5829

Verbindung:	2(2'-Hydroxy-3',5'-ditert.-butylphenyl)-5-chlor-benzotriazol			Compound:	2(2'-Hydroxy-3',5'-ditert.-butylphenyl)-5-chloro-benzotriazole		
Formel:	$C_{20}H_{24}N_3OCl$	M.:	357,8	Formula:	$C_{20}H_{24}N_3OCl$	M. w.:	357,8
Handelsname:	Tinuvin 327	Herst.:	Geigy	Tradename:	Tinuvin 327	Manuf.:	Geigy
Präparation:	KBr (3/1000)	Dez. Nr.:	4.3	Preparation:	KBr (3/1000)	Dec. No.:	4.3

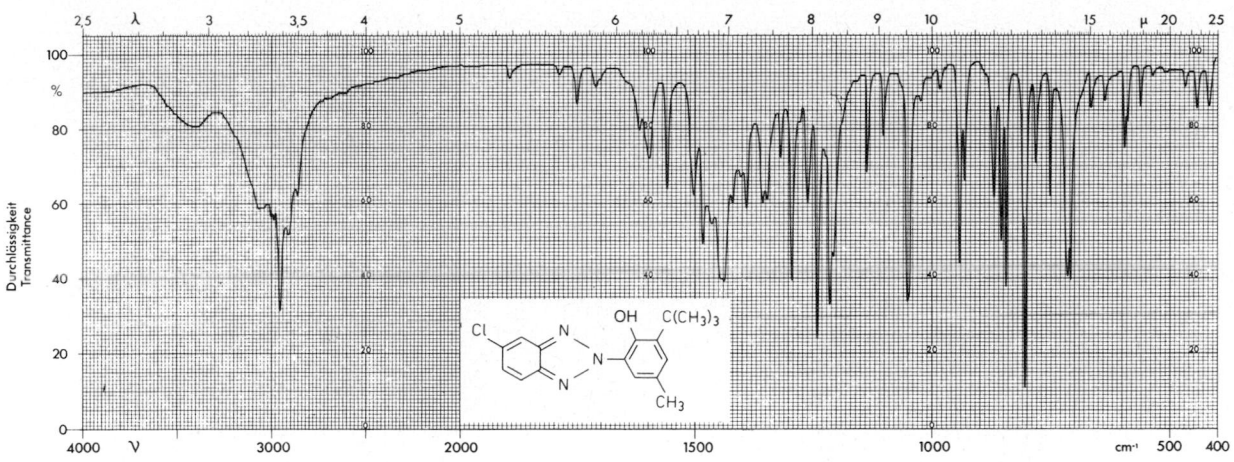

Verbindung:	2(2'-Hydroxy-3'-tert.-butyl-5'-methyl-phenyl)-5-chlor-benzotriazol	Compound:	2(2'-Hydroxy-3'-tert.-butyl-5'-methyl-phenyl)-5-chloro-benzotriazole

5830

Formel:	$C_{17}H_{18}N_3OCl$	M.:	315,7	Formula:	$C_{17}H_{18}N_3OCl$
Handelsname:	Tinuvin 326	Herst.:	Geigy	Tradename:	Tinuvin 326
Präparation:	KBr (3/1000)	Dez. Nr.:	4.4	Preparation:	KBr (3/1000)

M. w.: 315,7
Manuf.: Geigy
Dec. No.: 4.4

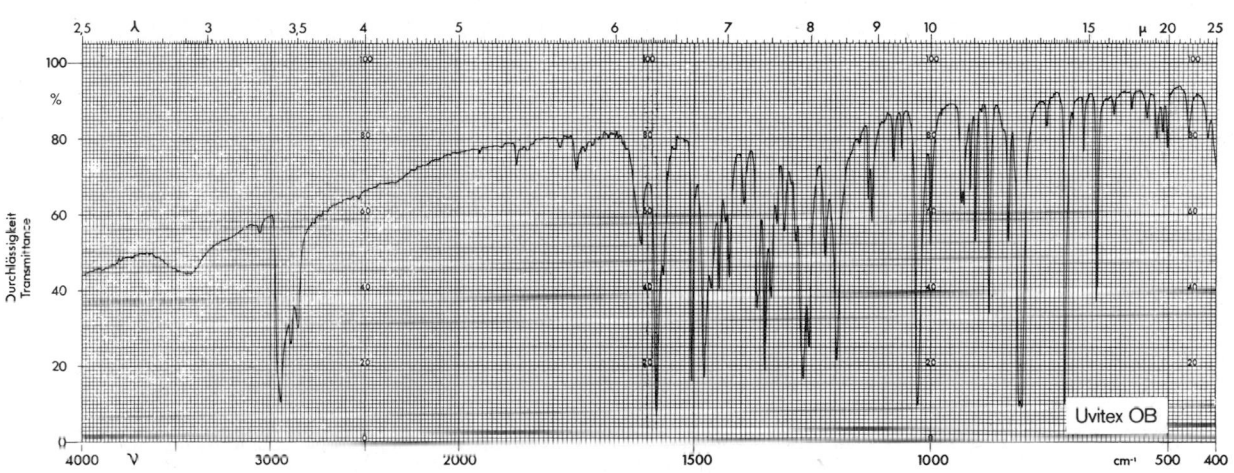

Verbindung:	Benzotriazolderivat	Compound:	Benzotriazole derivative
Formel:		M.:	Formula:
Handelsname:	Uvitex OB	Herst.: Ciba	Tradename: Uvitex OB
Präparation:	KBr (6/1000)	Dez. Nr.: 4.5	Preparation: KBr (6/1000)

5831

M. w.:
Manuf.: Ciba
Dec. No.: 4.5

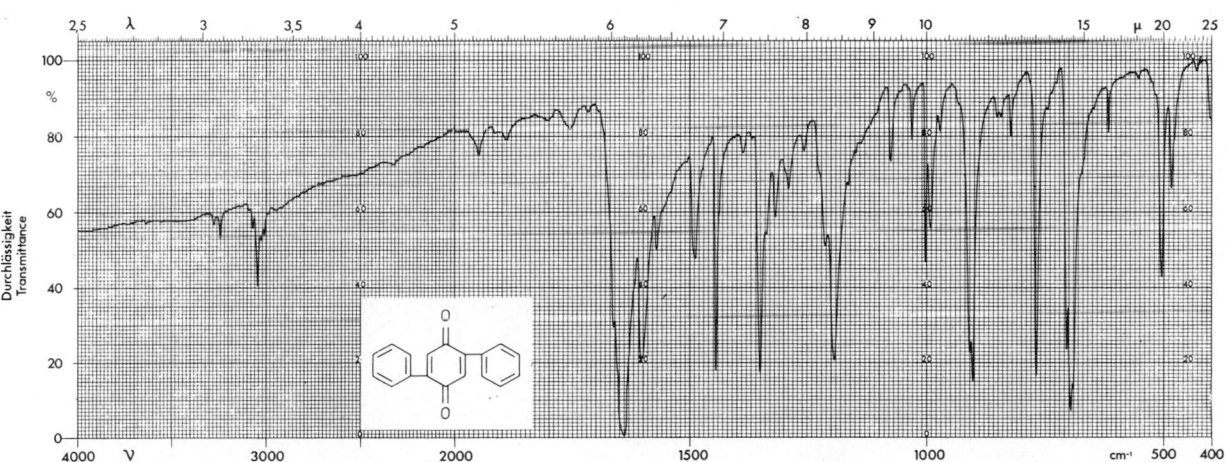

Verbindung:	2,5-Diphenyl-p-benzochinon	Compound:	2,5-Diphenyl-p-benzoquinone

5832

Formel:	$C_{18}H_{12}O_2$	M.: 260,3	Formula: $C_{18}H_{12}O_2$
Handelsname:	Eastman DPQ	Herst.: Eastman	Tradename: Eastman DPQ
Präparation:	KBr (6/1000)	Dez. Nr.: 5.1	Preparation: KBr (6/1000)

M. w.: 260,3
Manuf.: Eastman
Dec. No.: 5.1

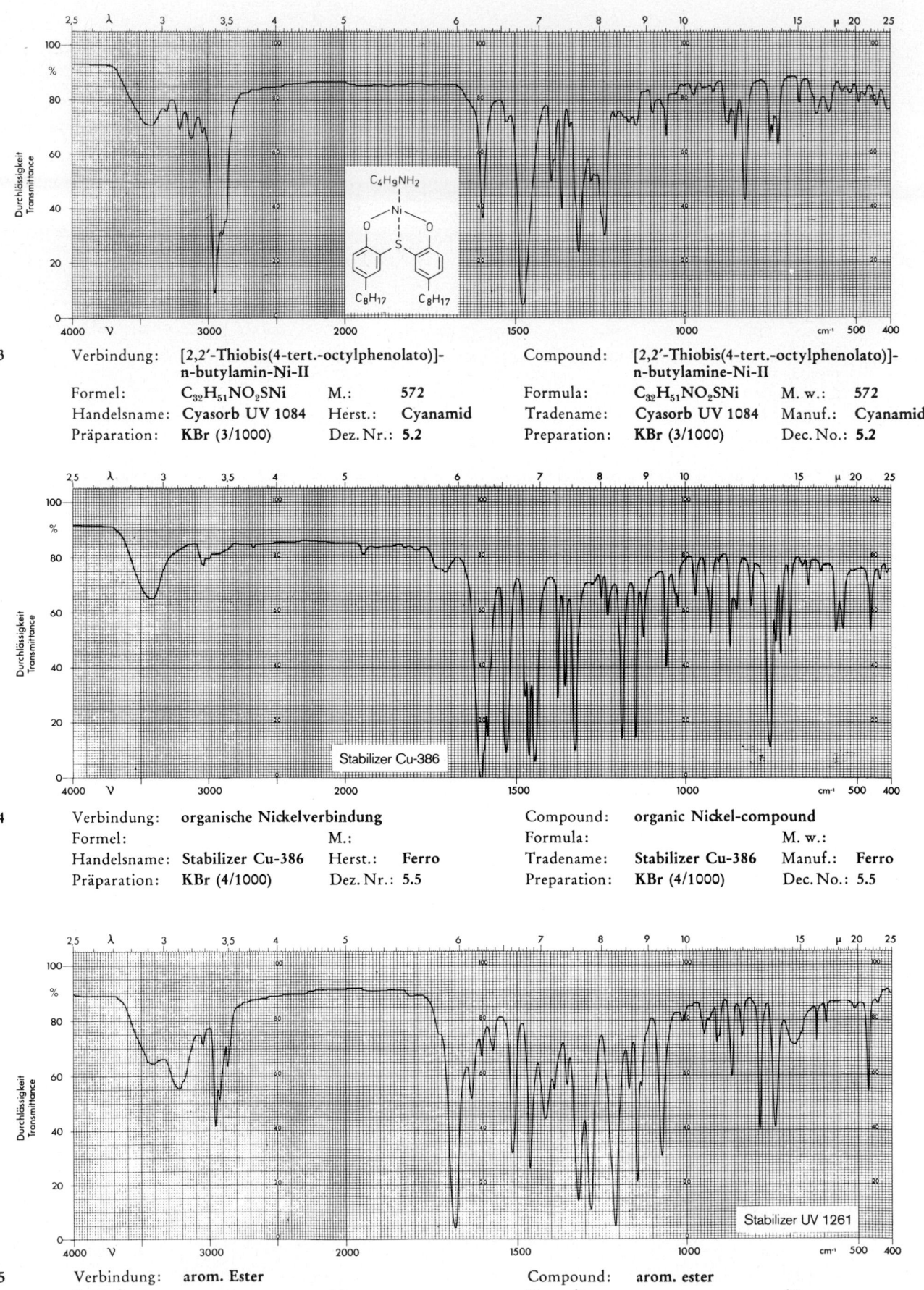

5833

Verbindung:	[2,2′-Thiobis(4-tert.-octylphenolato)]-n-butylamin-Ni-II		
Formel:	$C_{32}H_{51}NO_2SNi$	M.:	572
Handelsname:	Cyasorb UV 1084	Herst.:	Cyanamid
Präparation:	KBr (3/1000)	Dez. Nr.:	5.2

Compound:	[2,2′-Thiobis(4-tert.-octylphenolato)]-n-butylamine-Ni-II		
Formula:	$C_{32}H_{51}NO_2SNi$	M. w.:	572
Tradename:	Cyasorb UV 1084	Manuf.:	Cyanamid
Preparation:	KBr (3/1000)	Dec. No.:	5.2

5834

Verbindung:	organische Nickelverbindung		
Formel:		M.:	
Handelsname:	Stabilizer Cu-386	Herst.:	Ferro
Präparation:	KBr (4/1000)	Dez. Nr.:	5.5

Compound:	organic Nickel-compound		
Formula:		M. w.:	
Tradename:	Stabilizer Cu-386	Manuf.:	Ferro
Preparation:	KBr (4/1000)	Dec. No.:	5.5

5835

Verbindung:	arom. Ester		
Formel:		M.:	
Handelsname:	Stabilizer UV 1261	Herst.:	Stauffer Ch.
Präparation:	KBr (3/1000)	Dez. Nr.:	5.9

Compound:	arom. ester		
Formula:		M. w.:	
Tradename:	Stabilizer UV 1261	Manuf.:	Stauffer Ch.
Preparation:	KBr (3/1000)	Dec. No.:	5.9

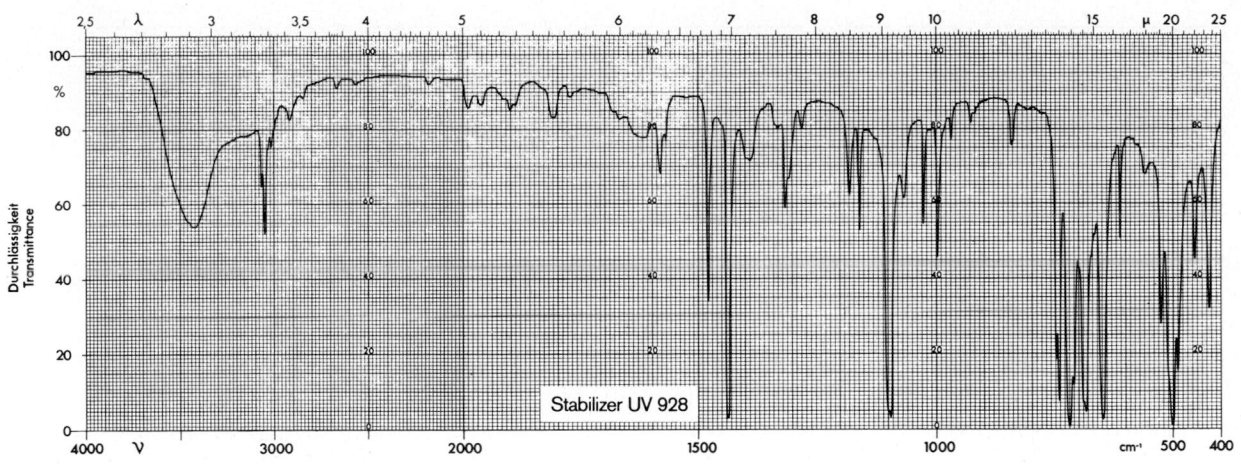

Verbindung:	org. P-S-Verbindung	Compound:	org. P,S compound	5836
Formel:	M.:	Formula:	M. w.:
Handelsname: **Stabilizer UV 928**	Herst.: **Stauffer Ch.**	Tradename: **Stabilizer UV 928**	Manuf.: **Stauffer Ch.**
Präparation: **KBr (3/1000)**	Dez. Nr.: 5.10	Preparation: **KBr (3/1000)**	Dec. No.: 5.10

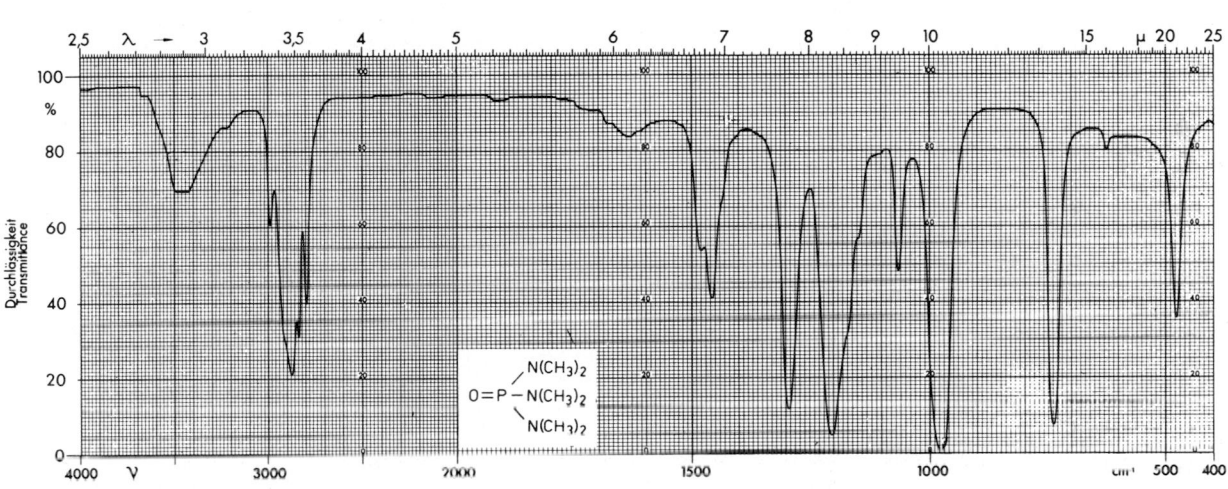

Verbindung:	**Hexamethylphosphorsäuretriamid**	Compound:	**Hexamethyl phosphoric acid trisamide**	5837
Formel:	$C_6H_{18}PON_3$	M.: **179,2**	Formula:	$C_6H_{18}PON_3$	M. w.: **179,2**
Handelsname: **Eastman HPT**	Herst.: **Eastman**	Tradename: **Eastman HPT**	Manuf.: **Eastman**
Präparation: **Kapill. Film**	Dez. Nr.: 5.11	Preparation: **Capill. Film**	Dec. No.: 5.11

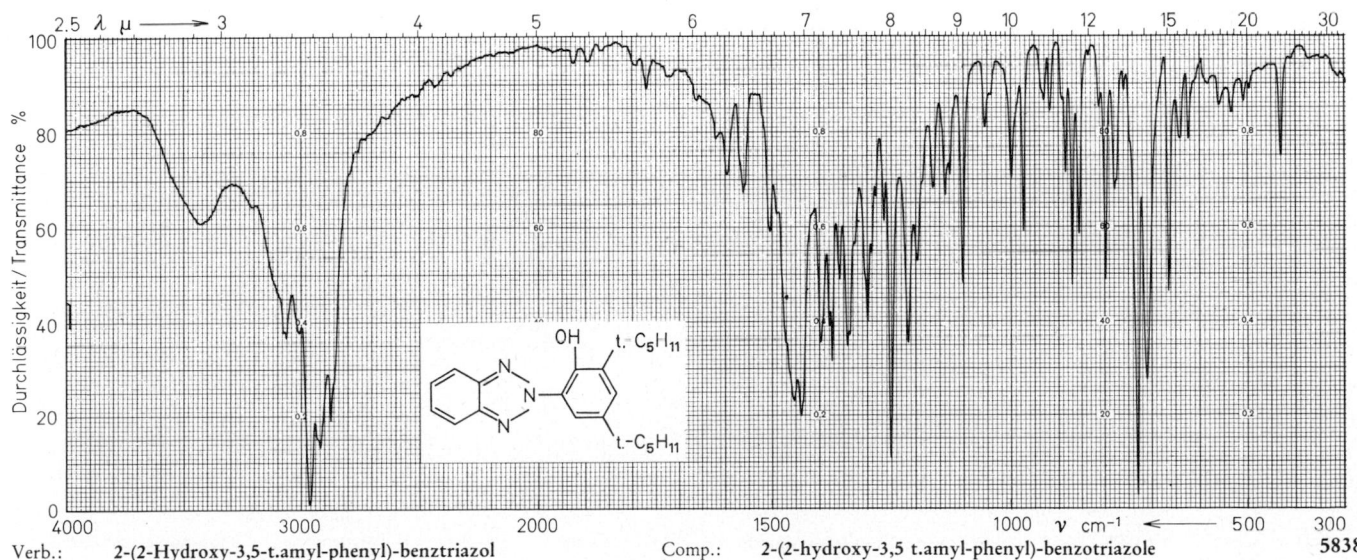

Verb.:	2-(2-Hydroxy-3,5-t.amyl-phenyl)-benztriazol	Comp.:	2-(2-hydroxy-3,5 t.amyl-phenyl)-benzotriazole	5838
Formel:	$C_{22}H_{29}N_3O$	M.: 352	Formula:	$C_{22}H_{29}N_3O$	M.w.: 352
Name:	Tinurin 328	Manuf.: Ciba	Prpt.: KBr 3/1000	Dec. No.:

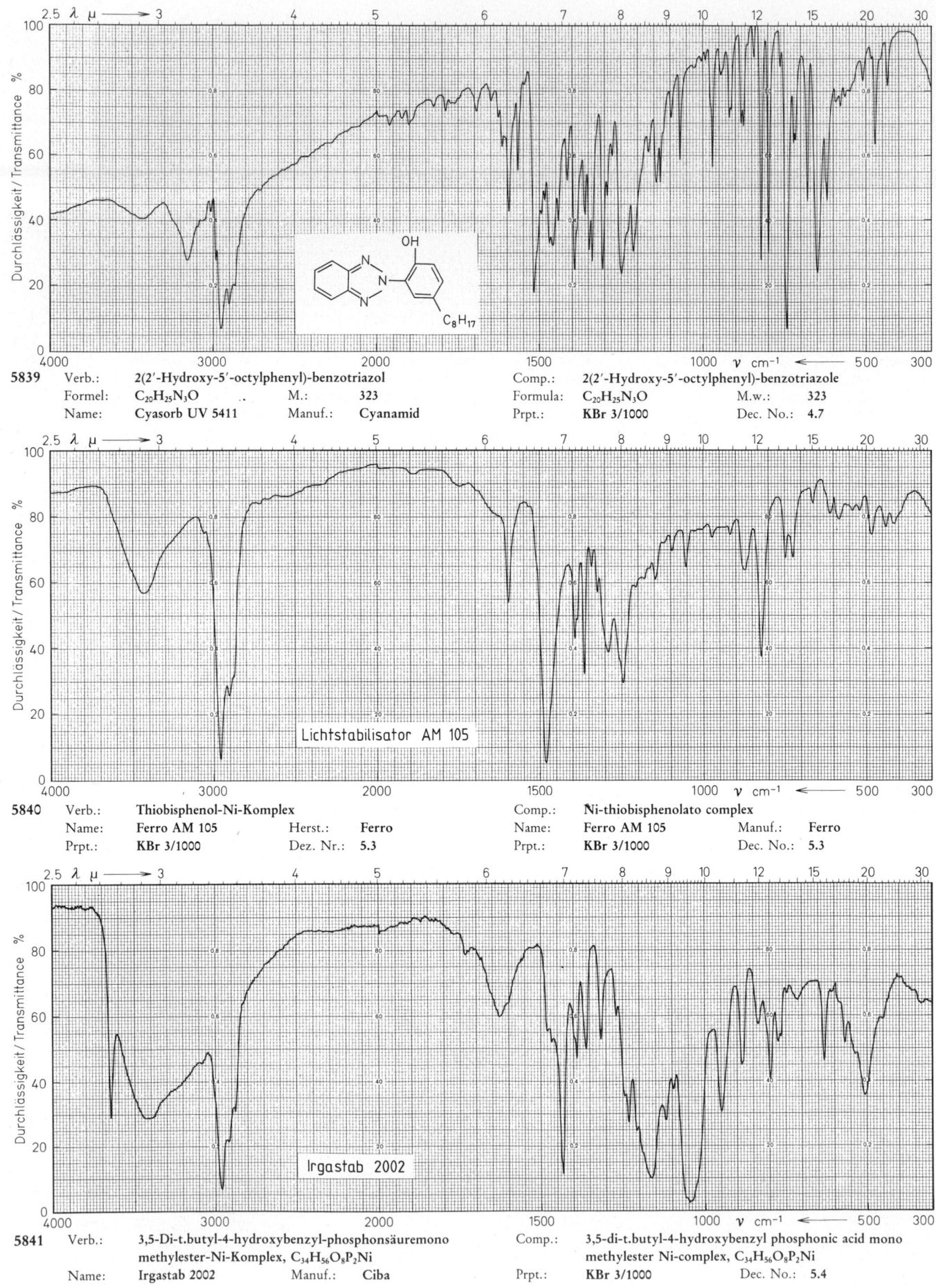

5839

Verb.:	2(2'-Hydroxy-5'-octylphenyl)-benzotriazol	Comp.:	2(2'-Hydroxy-5'-octylphenyl)-benzotriazole
Formel:	$C_{20}H_{25}N_3O$ M.: 323	Formula:	$C_{20}H_{25}N_3O$ M.w.: 323
Name:	Cyasorb UV 5411 Manuf.: Cyanamid	Prpt.:	KBr 3/1000 Dec. No.: 4.7

Lichtstabilisator AM 105

5840

Verb.:	Thiobisphenol-Ni-Komplex	Comp.:	Ni-thiobisphenolato complex
Name:	Ferro AM 105 Herst.: Ferro	Name:	Ferro AM 105 Manuf.: Ferro
Prpt.:	KBr 3/1000 Dez. Nr.: 5.3	Prpt.:	KBr 3/1000 Dec. No.: 5.3

Irgastab 2002

5841

Verb.:	3,5-Di-t.butyl-4-hydroxybenzyl-phosphonsäuremono methylester-Ni-Komplex, $C_{34}H_{56}O_8P_2Ni$	Comp.:	3,5-di-t.butyl-4-hydroxybenzyl phosphonic acid mono methylester Ni-complex, $C_{34}H_{56}O_8P_2Ni$
Name:	Irgastab 2002 Manuf.: Ciba	Prpt.:	KBr 3/1000 Dec. No.: 5.4

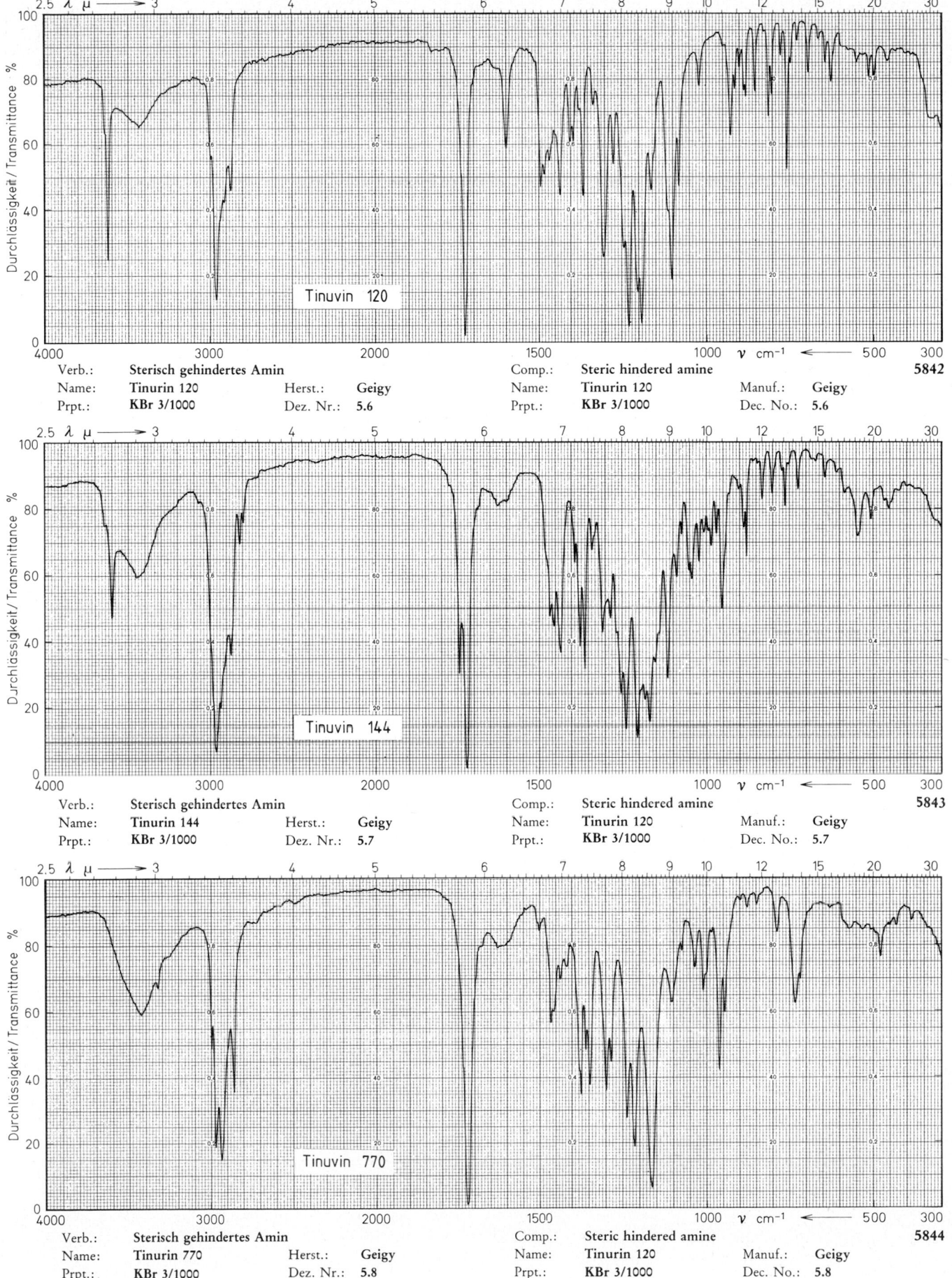

Verb.:	Sterisch gehindertes Amin			
Name:	Tinurin 120	Herst.:	Geigy	
Prpt.:	KBr 3/1000	Dez. Nr.:	5.6	

Comp.:	Steric hindered amine			5842
Name:	Tinurin 120	Manuf.:	Geigy	
Prpt.:	KBr 3/1000	Dec. No.:	5.6	

Tinuvin 120

Verb.:	Sterisch gehindertes Amin			
Name:	Tinurin 144	Herst.:	Geigy	
Prpt.:	KBr 3/1000	Dez. Nr.:	5.7	

Comp.:	Steric hindered amine			5843
Name:	Tinurin 120	Manuf.:	Geigy	
Prpt.:	KBr 3/1000	Dec. No.:	5.7	

Tinuvin 144

Verb.:	Sterisch gehindertes Amin			
Name:	Tinurin 770	Herst.:	Geigy	
Prpt.:	KBr 3/1000	Dez. Nr.:	5.8	

Comp.:	Steric hindered amine			5844
Name:	Tinurin 120	Manuf.:	Geigy	
Prpt.:	KBr 3/1000	Dec. No.:	5.8	

Tinuvin 770

Optische Aufheller

Fluorescent Whitening Agents

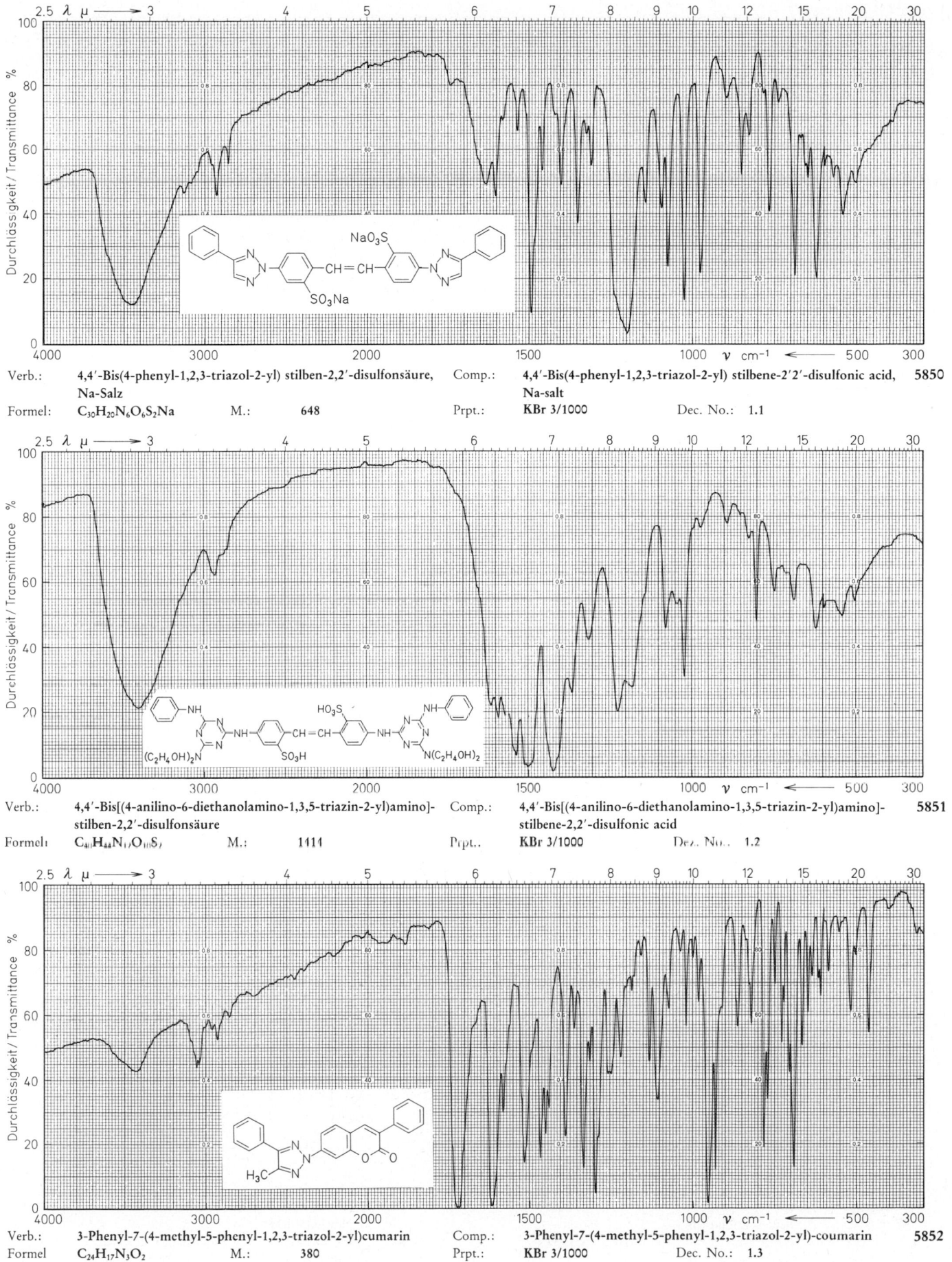

Verb.:   **4,4′-Bis(4-phenyl-1,2,3-triazol-2-yl) stilben-2,2′-disulfonsäure, Na-Salz**   Comp.:   **4,4′-Bis(4-phenyl-1,2,3-triazol-2-yl) stilbene-2′2′-disulfonic acid, Na-salt**   **5850**

Formel: $C_{30}H_{20}N_6O_6S_2Na$ M.:   **648**   Prpt.:   **KBr 3/1000**   Dec. No.:   **1.1**

Verb.:   **4,4′-Bis[(4-anilino-6-diethanolamino-1,3,5-triazin-2-yl)amino]-stilben-2,2′-disulfonsäure**   Comp.:   **4,4′-Bis[(4-anilino-6-diethanolamino-1,3,5-triazin-2-yl)amino]-stilbene-2,2′-disulfonic acid**   **5851**

Formel: $C_{40}H_{44}N_{12}O_{10}S_2$ M.:   **1111**   Prpt.:   **KBr 3/1000**   Dec. No.:   **1.2**

Verb.:   **3-Phenyl-7-(4-methyl-5-phenyl-1,2,3-triazol-2-yl)cumarin**   Comp.:   **3-Phenyl-7-(4-methyl-5-phenyl-1,2,3-triazol-2-yl)-coumarin**   **5852**

Formel $C_{24}H_{17}N_3O_2$ M.:   **380**   Prpt.:   **KBr 3/1000**   Dec. No.:   **1.3**

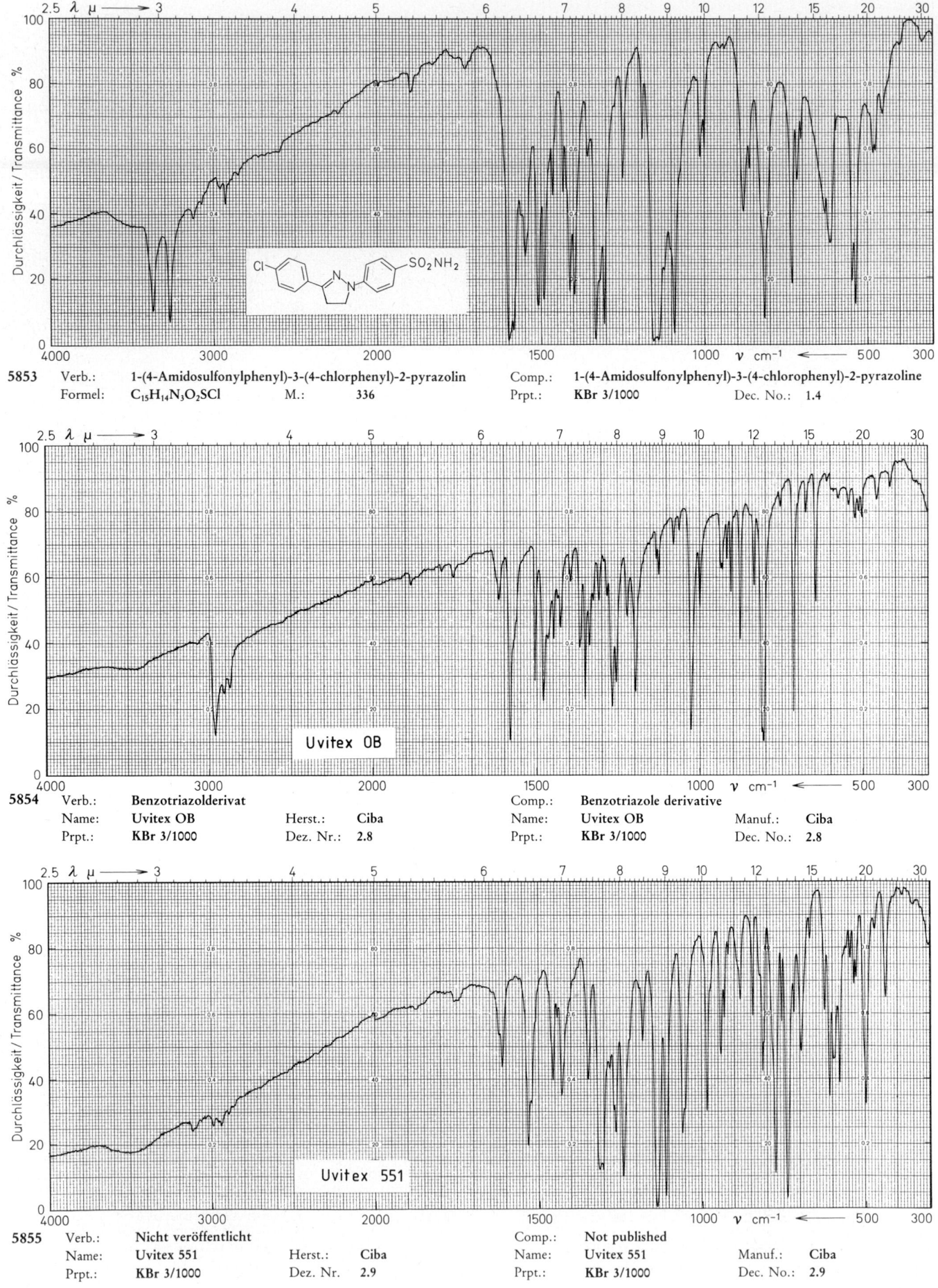

5853 Verb.: 1-(4-Amidosulfonylphenyl)-3-(4-chlorphenyl)-2-pyrazolin   Comp.: 1-(4-Amidosulfonylphenyl)-3-(4-chlorophenyl)-2-pyrazoline
Formel: C$_{15}$H$_{14}$N$_3$O$_2$SCl   M.:   336   Prpt.: KBr 3/1000   Dec. No.: 1.4

Uvitex OB

5854 Verb.: Benzotriazolderivat   Comp.: Benzotriazole derivative
Name: Uvitex OB   Herst.: Ciba   Name: Uvitex OB   Manuf.: Ciba
Prpt.: KBr 3/1000   Dez. Nr.: 2.8   Prpt.: KBr 3/1000   Dec. No.: 2.8

Uvitex 551

5855 Verb.: Nicht veröffentlicht   Comp.: Not published
Name: Uvitex 551   Herst.: Ciba   Name: Uvitex 551   Manuf.: Ciba
Prpt.: KBr 3/1000   Dez. Nr. 2.9   Prpt.: KBr 3/1000   Dec. No.: 2.9

Optische Aufheller   Fluorescent Whitening Agents

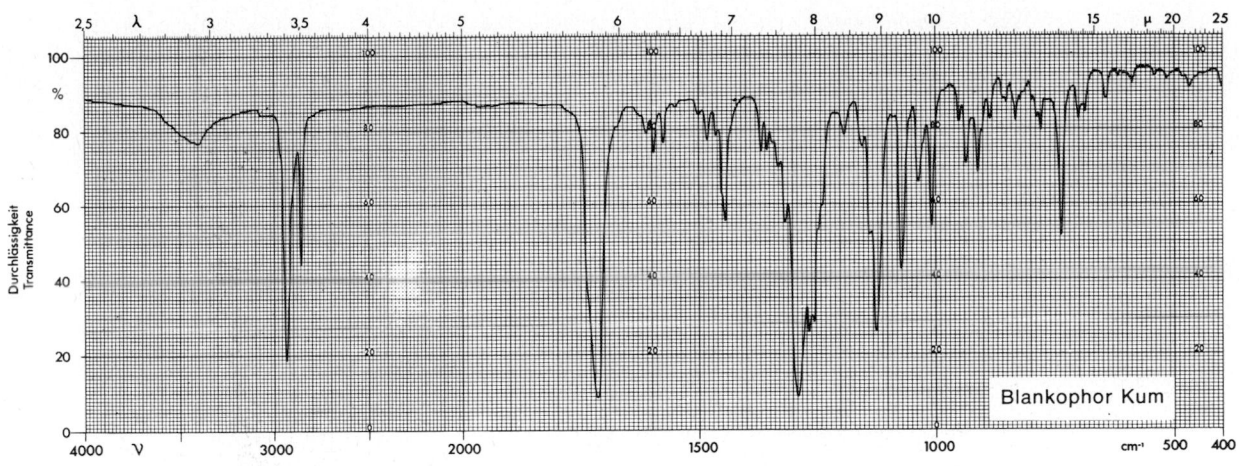

Handelsname: **Blankophor Kum**   Tradename: **Blankophor Kum**   5856
Hersteller: **Bayer**   Manufacturer: **Bayer**
Präparation: **fest / KBr**   Dez. Nr.: 2.1   Preparation: **solid / KBr**   Dec. No.: 2.1

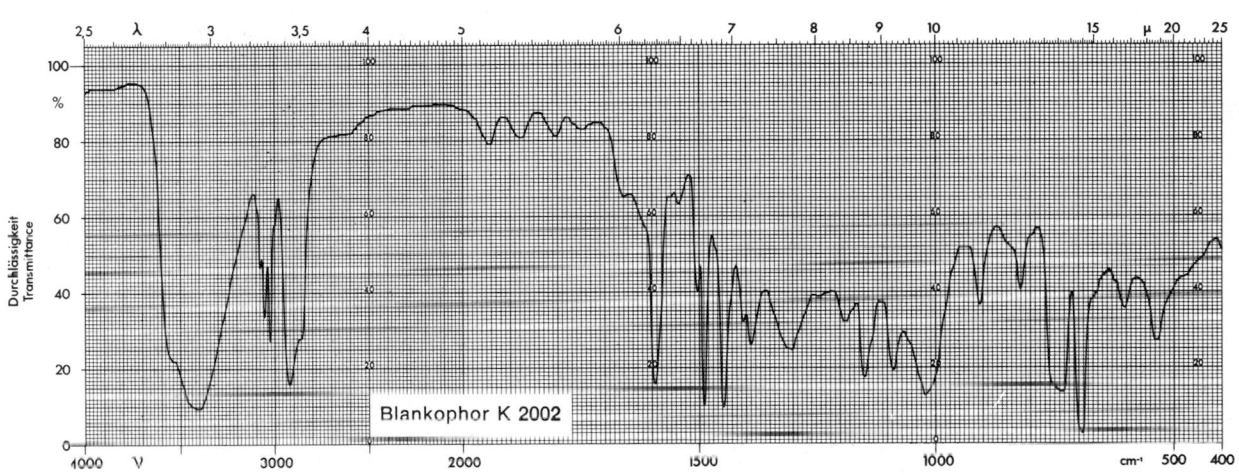

Handelsname: **Blankophor K 2002**   Tradename: **Blankophor K 2002**   5857
Hersteller: **Bayer**   Manufacturer: **Bayer**
Präparation: **fest / KBr**   Dez. Nr.: 2.2   Preparation: **solid / KBr**   Dec. No.: 2.2

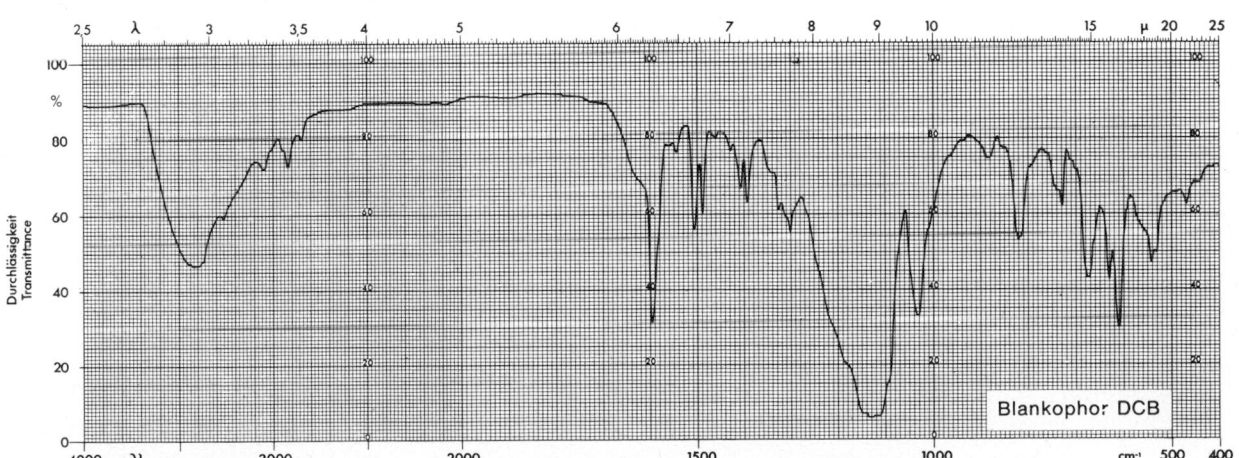

Handelsname: **Blankophor DCB**   Tradename: **Blankophor DCB**   5858
Hersteller: **Bayer**   Manufacturer: **Bayer**
Präparation: **fest / KBr**   Dez. Nr.: 2.3   Preparation: **solid / KBr**   Dec. No.: 2.3

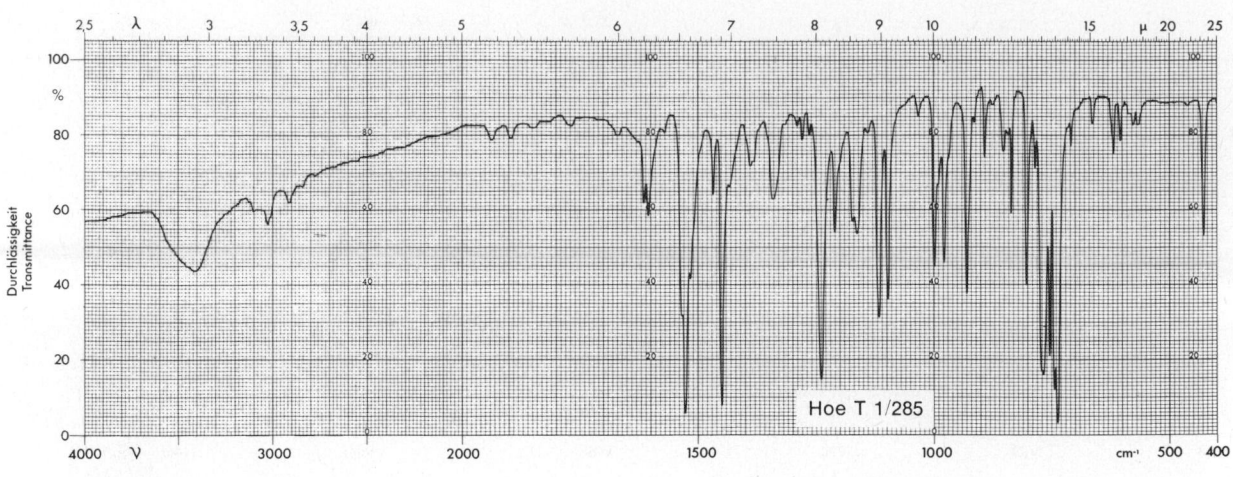

5859   Handelsname: **Hoe T 1/285**   Tradename: **Hoe T 1/285**
             Hersteller: **Hoechst**   Manufacturer: **Hoechst**
             Präparation: **fest / KBr**   Dez. Nr.: **2.4**   Preparation: **solid / KBr**   Dec. No.: **2.4**

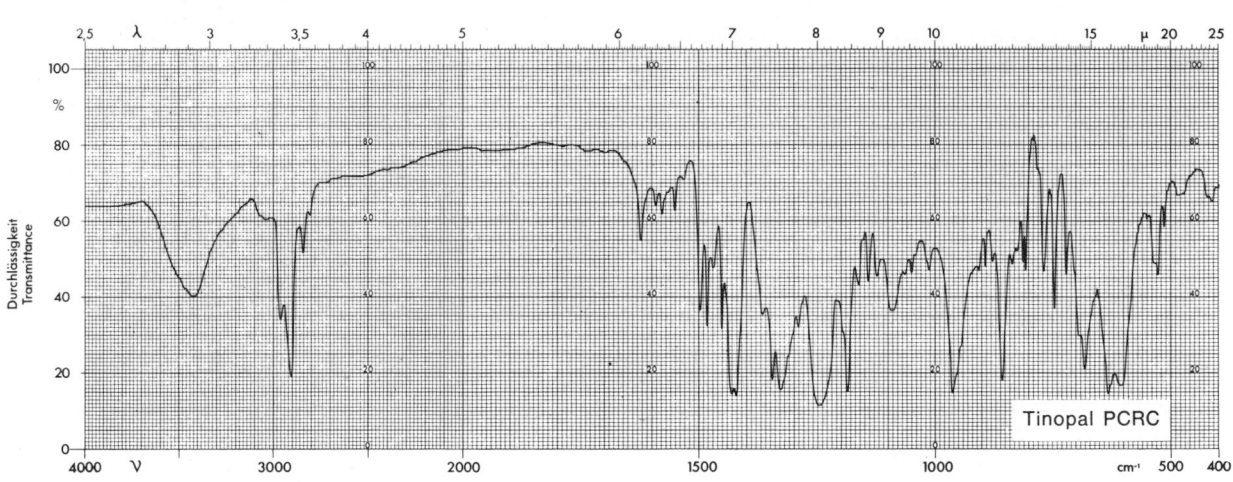

5860   Handelsname: **Tinopal PCR C**   Tradename: **Tinopal PCR C**
             Hersteller: **Geigy**   Manufacturer: **Geigy**
             Präparation: **fest / KBr**   Dez. Nr.: **2.5**   Preparation: **solid / KBr**   Dec. No.: **2.5**

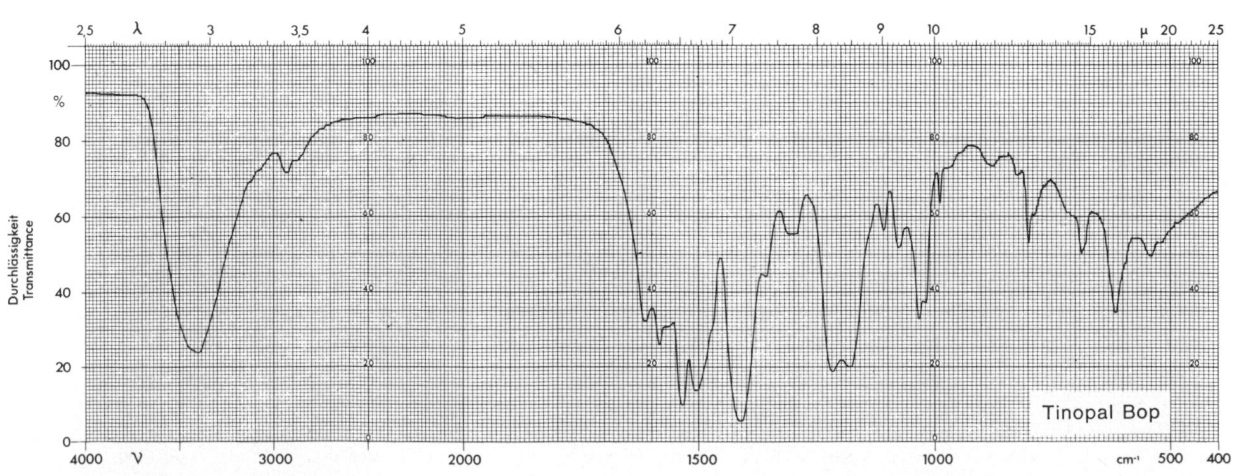

5861   Handelsname: **Tinopal Bop**   Tradename: **Tinopal Bop**
             Hersteller: **Geigy**   Manufacturer: **Geigy**
             Präparation: **fest / KBr**   Dez. Nr.: **2.6**   Preparation: **solid / KBr**   Dec. No.: **2.6**

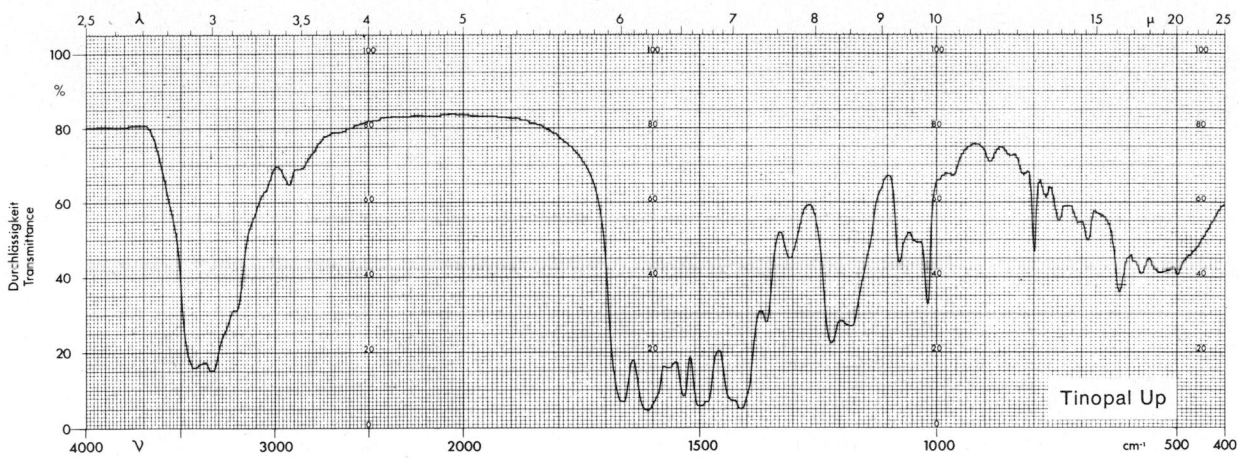

Handelsname: **Tinopal Up**   Tradename: **Tinopal Up**
Hersteller: **Geïgy**   Manufacturer: **Geigy**
Präparation: **fest / KBr**   Dez. Nr.: **2.7**   Präparation: **solid / KBr**   Dec. No.: **2.7**

Antioxidantien
Antioxidants

Antioxidantien
1. Phenole
1.1. Monophenole

Antioxidants
1. Phenols
1.1. Monophenols

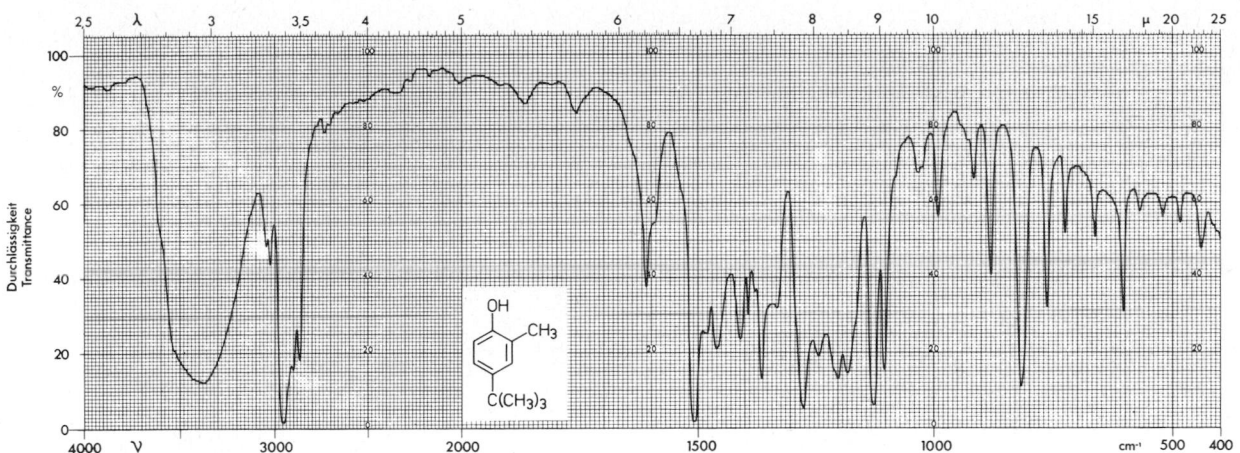

Verbindung:	2-Methyl-4-t.butylphenol			Compound:	2-Methyl-4-t.butyl phenol			5900
Formel:	C₁₁H₁₆O	M.:	164,2	Formula:	C₁₁H₁₆O	M. w.:	164,2	
Handelsname:	4-Tertiärbutyl-orthokresol	Herst.:	Hüls	Tradename:	4-Tertiärbutyl-orthocresol	Manuf.:	Hüls	
Präparation:	Kapill. Film	Dez. Nr.:	1.1.1	Preparation:	Capill. film	Dec. No.:	1.1.1	

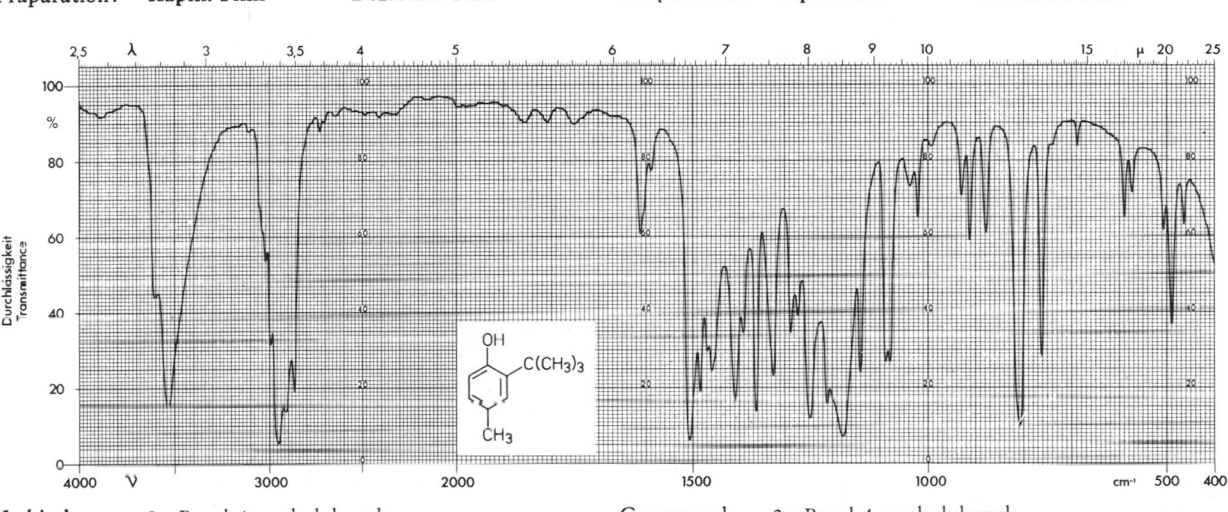

Verbindung:	2 t.Butyl 4 methylphenol			Compound:	2-t.Butyl-4-methylphenol			5901
Formel:	C₁₁H₁₆O	M.:	164,2	Formula:	C₁₁H₁₆O	M. w.:	164,2	
Handelsname:	2-Tertiärbutyl-parakresol	Herst.:	Hüls	Tradename:	2-Tertiärbutyl-paracresol	Manuf.:	Hüls	
Präparation:	Schmelzfilm	Dez. Nr.:	1.1.2	Preparation:	Melting film	Dec. No.:	1.1.2	

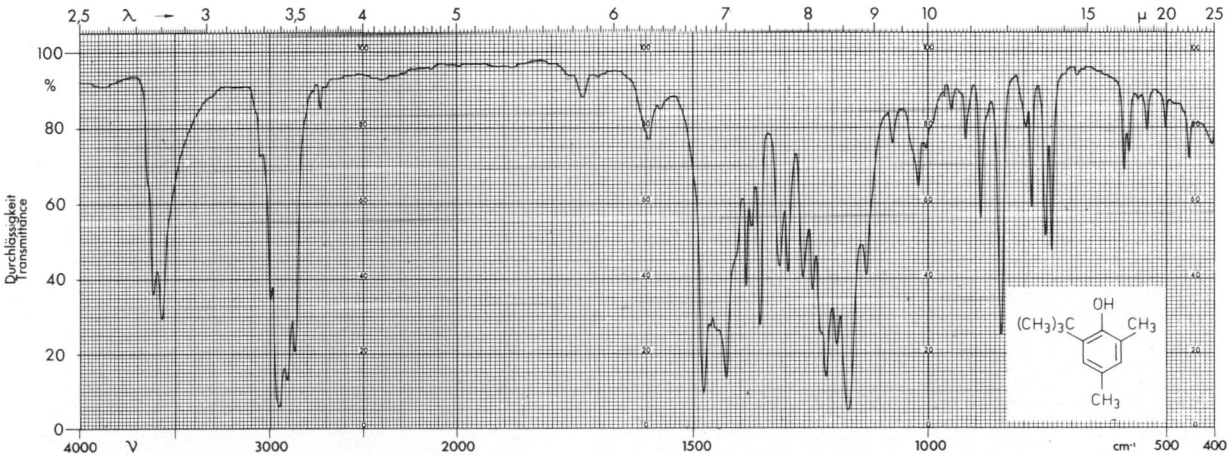

Verbindung:	2,4-Dimethyl-6-t.butylphenol			Compound:	2,4-Dimethyl-6-t.butylphenol			5902
Formel:	C₁₂H₁₈O	M.:	178,2	Formula:	C₁₂H₁₈O	M. w.:	178,2	
Handelsname:	Topanol A	Herst.:	ICI	Tradename:	Topanol A	Manuf.:	ICI	
Präparation:	Kapill. Film	Dez. Nr.:	1.1.3	Preparation:	Capill. film	Dec. No.:	1.1.3	

Antioxidantien
1. Phenole
1.1. Monophenole

Antioxidants
1. Phenols
1.1. Monophenols

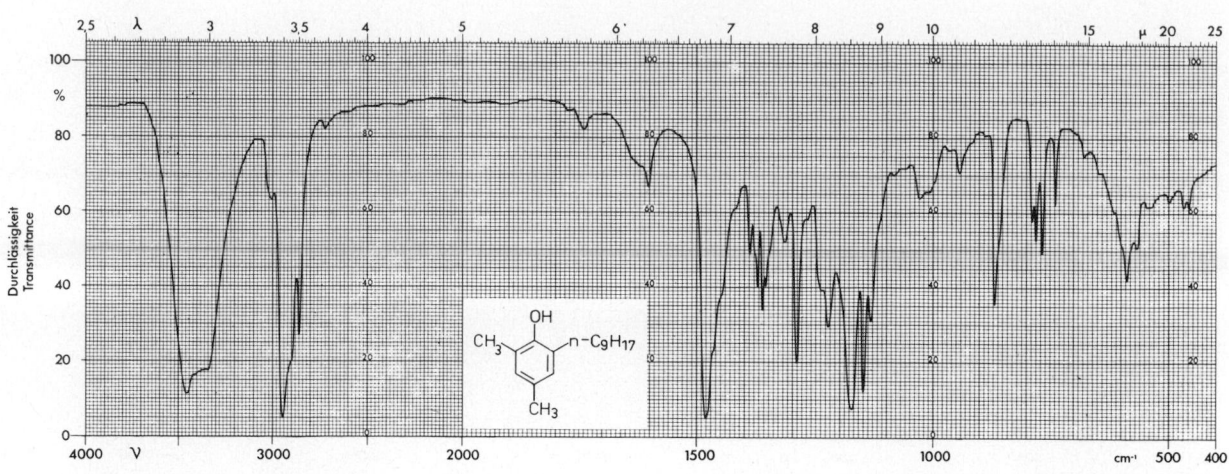

5903   Verbindung: **2,4-Dimethyl-6-nonylenphenol**   Compound: **2,4-Dimethyl-6-nonylene-phenol**

Formel:	$C_{17}H_{26}O$	M.:	**246,3**		
Handelsname:	**Nonox WSO**	Herst.:	**ICI**		
Präparation:	**KBr (6/1000)**	Dez. Nr.:	**1.1.4**		

Formula:	$C_{17}H_{26}O$	M. w.:	**246,3**
Tradename:	**Nonox WSO**	Manuf.:	**ICI**
Preparation:	**KBr (6/1000)**	Dec. No.:	**1.1.4**

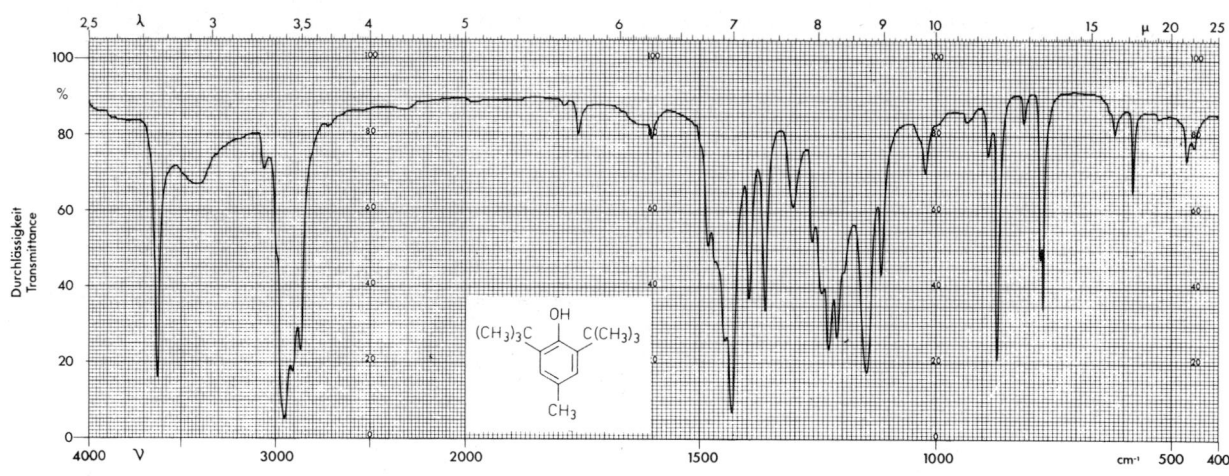

5904   Verbindung: **2,6-Di-t.butyl-4-methylphenol**   Compound: **2,6-Di-t.butyl-4-methylphenol**

Formel:	$C_{15}H_{24}O$	M.:	**220,2**
Handelsname:	**ASM KB**	Herst.:	**Bayer**
Präparation:	**KBr (6/1000)**	Dez. Nr.:	**1.1.5**

Formula:	$C_{15}H_{24}O$	M. w.:	**220,2**
Tradename:	**ASM KB**	Manuf.:	**Bayer**
Preparation:	**KBr (6/1000)**	Dec. No.:	**1.1.5**

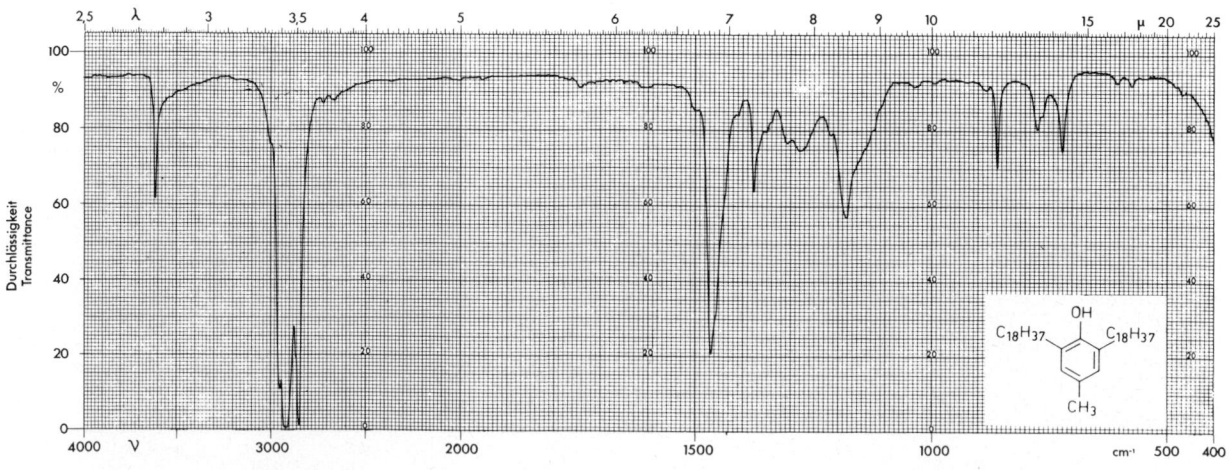

5905   Verbindung: **2,6-Dioctadecyl-4-methylphenol**   Compound: **2,6-Dioctadecyl-4-methylphenol**

Formel:	$C_{43}H_{80}O$	M.:	**612,0**
Handelsname:	**Inhibitor DOPC**	Herst.:	**Eastman**
Präparation:	**Kapill. Film**	Dez. Nr.:	**1.1.6**

Formula:	$C_{43}H_{80}O$	M. w.:	**612,0**
Tradename:	**Inhibitor DOPC**	Manuf.:	**Eastman**
Preparation:	**Capill. film**	Dec. No.:	**1.1.6**

Antioxidantien
1. Phenole
1.1. Monophenole

Antioxidants
1. Phenols
1.1. Monophenols

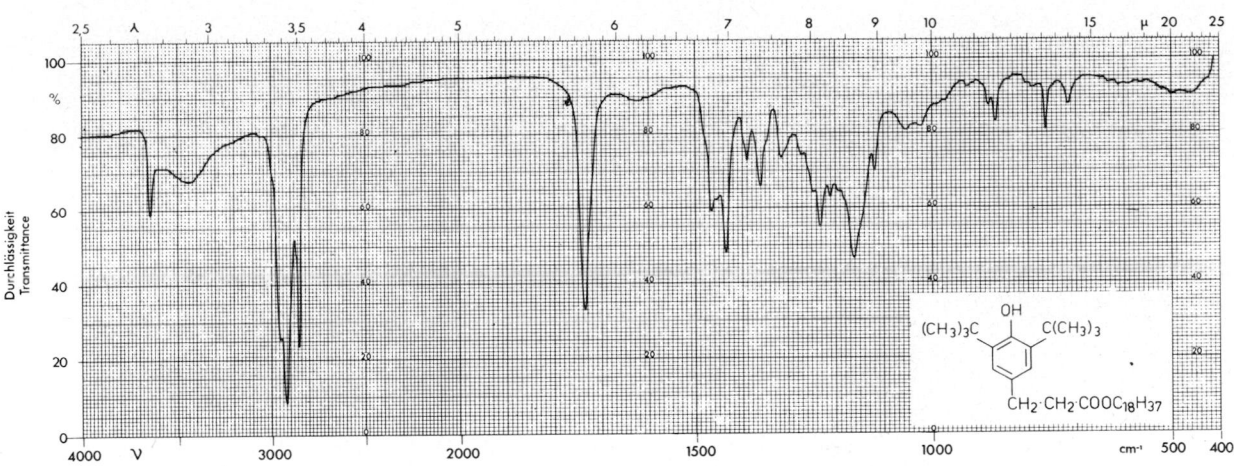

Verbindung: β-(3,5-Di-t.butyl-4-hydroxyphenyl)-propionsäure-n-octadecylester

Compound: β-(3,5-Di-t.butyl-4-hydroxyphenyl)-propionic octadecyl ester

5906

Formel: $C_{35}H_{62}O_3$	**M.:** **530,8**	**Formula:** $C_{35}H_{62}O_3$	**M. w.:** **530,8**
Handelsname: **Irganox 1076**	**Herst.:** **Geigy**	**Tradename:** **Irganox 1076**	**Manuf.:** **Geigy**
Präparation: **KBr (3/1000)**	**Dez. Nr.:** **1.1.7**	**Preparation:** **KBr (3/1000)**	**Dec. No.:** **1.1.7**

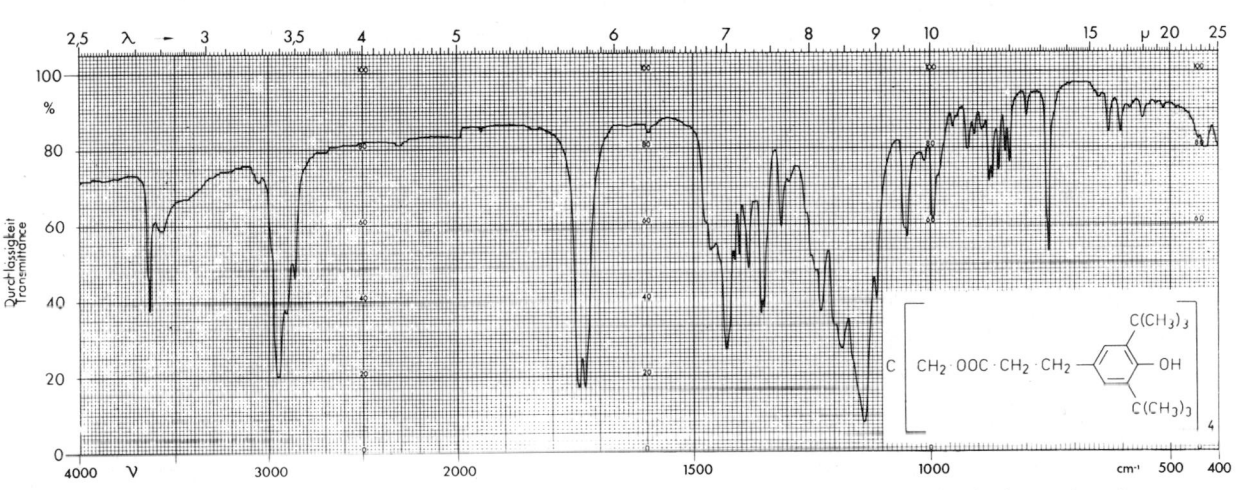

Verbindung: β-(3,5-Di-t.butyl 4 hydroxyphenyl) propionsäureester von Pentaerythrit

Compound: β-(3,5-Di-t.butyl-4-hydroxyphenyl)-propionic pentaerythrolester

5907

Formel: $C_{73}H_{108}O_{12}$	**M.:** **1177,4**	**Formula:** $C_{73}H_{108}O_{12}$	**M. w.:** **1177,4**
Handelsname: **Irganox 1010**	**Herst.:** **Geigy**	**Tradename:** **Irganox 1010**	**Manuf.:** **Geigy**
Präparation: **KBr (5/1000)**	**Dez. Nr.:** **1.3.15**	**Preparation:** **KBr (5/1000)**	**Dec. No.:** **1.3.15**

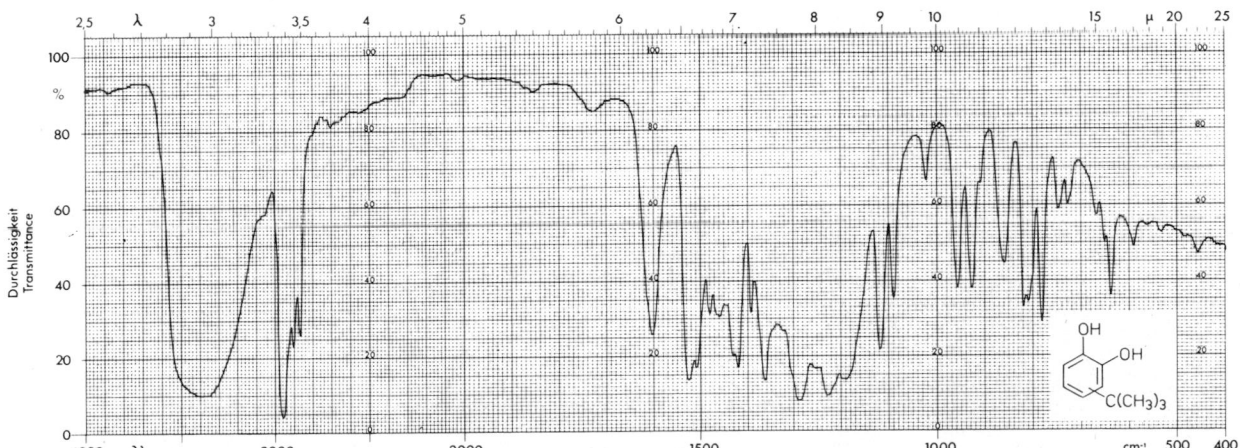

Verbindung: t.Butylbrenzkatechin

Compound: t.Butylbrenzcatechole

5908

Formel: $C_{10}H_{14}O_2$	**M.:** **166,2**	**Formula:** $C_{10}H_{14}O_2$	**M. w.:** **166,2**
Handelsname:	**Herst.:** **Schuchardt**	**Tradename:**	**Manuf.:** **Schuchardt**
Präparation: **Schmelzfilm**	**Dez. Nr.:** **1.2.1**	**Preparation:** **Melting film**	**Dec. No.:** **1.2.1**

Antioxidantien
1. Phenole
1.2. Di-, Trihydroxybenzole

Antioxidants
1. Phenols
1.2. Di-, Trihydroxybenzenes

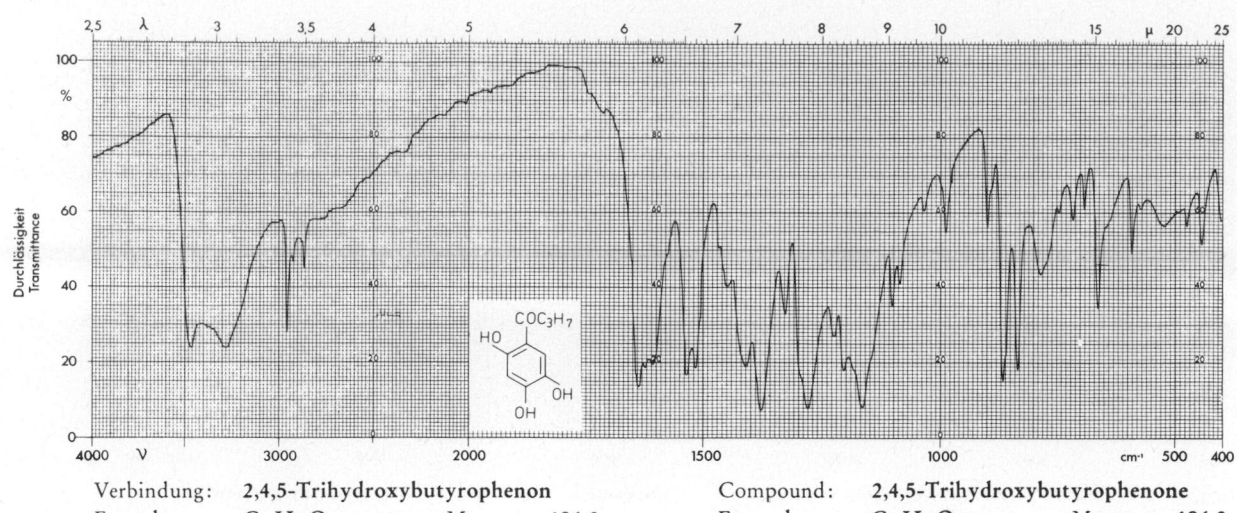

5909 Verbindung: 2,4,5-Trihydroxybutyrophenon
Formel: C₁₀H₁₂O₄   M.: 196,2
Handelsname: Inhibitor THBP   Herst.: Eastman
Präparation: KBr (5/1000)   Dez.Nr.: 1.2.2

Compound: 2,4,5-Trihydroxybutyrophenone
Formula: C₁₀H₁₂O₄   M. w.: 196,2
Tradename: Inhibitor THBP   Manuf.: Eastman
Preparation: KBr (5/1000)   Dec.No.: 1.2.2

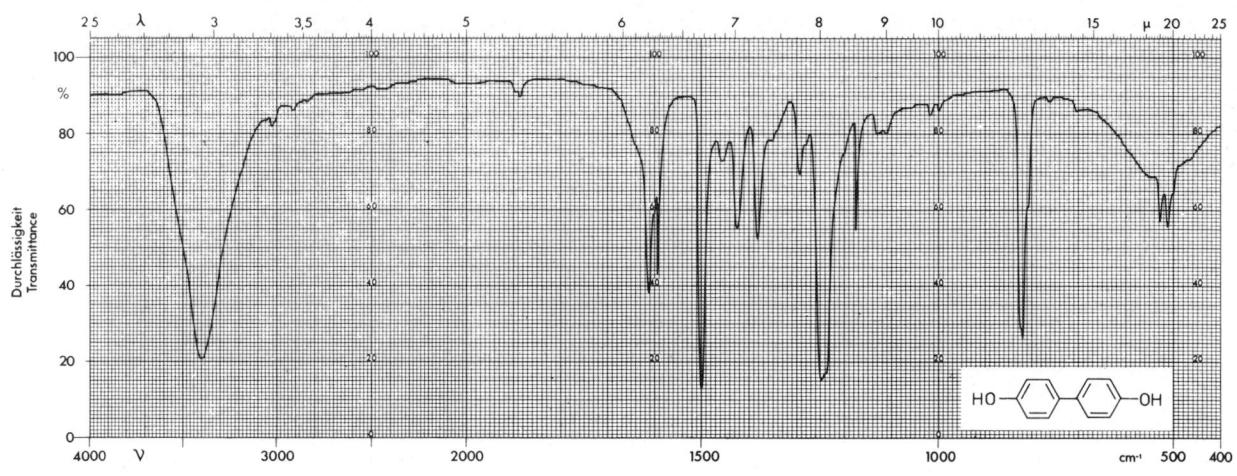

5910 Verbindung: 4,4'-Dihydroxydiphenyl
Formel: C₁₂H₁₀O₂   M.: 186,2
Handelsname: ASM DOD   Herst.: Bayer
Präparation: KBr (6/1000)   Dez.Nr.: 1.3.1

Compound: 4,4'-Dihydroxydiphenyl
Formula: C₁₂H₁₀O₂   M. w.: 186,2
Tradename: ASM DOD   Manuf.: Bayer
Preparation: KBr (6/1000)   Dec.No.: 1.3.1

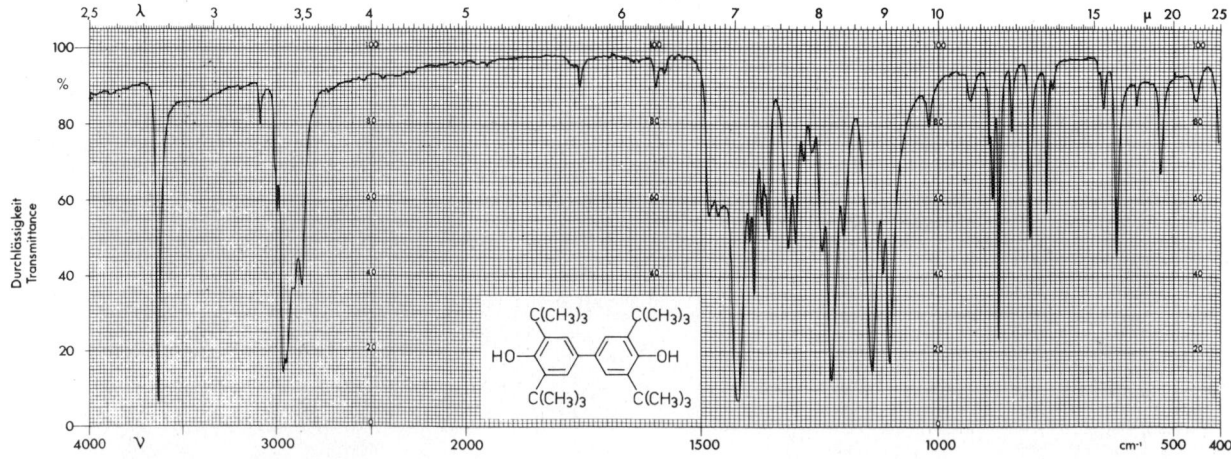

5911 Verbindung: 4,4'-Bis(2,6-di-t.butylphenol)
Formel: C₂₈H₄₂O₂   M.: 410,6
Handelsname: Antioxydant 712   Herst.: Ethyl
Präparation: KBr (6/1000)   Dez.Nr.: 1.3.2

Compound: 4,4'-Bis(2,6-di-t.butylphenol)
Formula: C₂₈H₄₂O₂   M. w.: 410,6
Tradename: Antioxydant 712   Manuf.: Ethyl
Preparation: KBr (6/1000)   Dec.No.: 1.3.2

Antioxidantien
1. Phenole
1.3. Bisphenole

Antioxidants
1. Phenols
1.3. Bisphenols

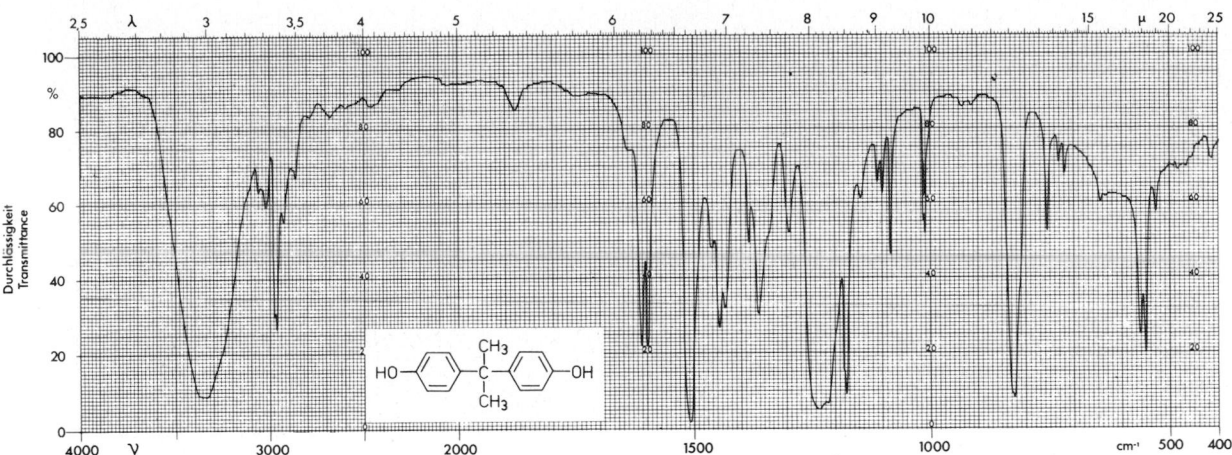

Verbindung: **Bis(4-hydroxyphenyl)-2-propan**

Formel: $C_{15}H_{16}O_2$ M.: **228,3**

Handelsname: **Bisphenol A**   Herst.: **Bayer**

Präparation: **KBr (6/1000)**   Dez. Nr.: **1.3.3**

Compound: **Bis(4-hydroxyphenyl)-2-propane**

Formula: $C_{15}H_{16}O_2$ M. w.: **228,3**

Tradename: **Bisphenol A**   Manuf.: **Bayer**

Preparation: **KBr (6/1000)**   Dec. No.: **1.3.3**

5912

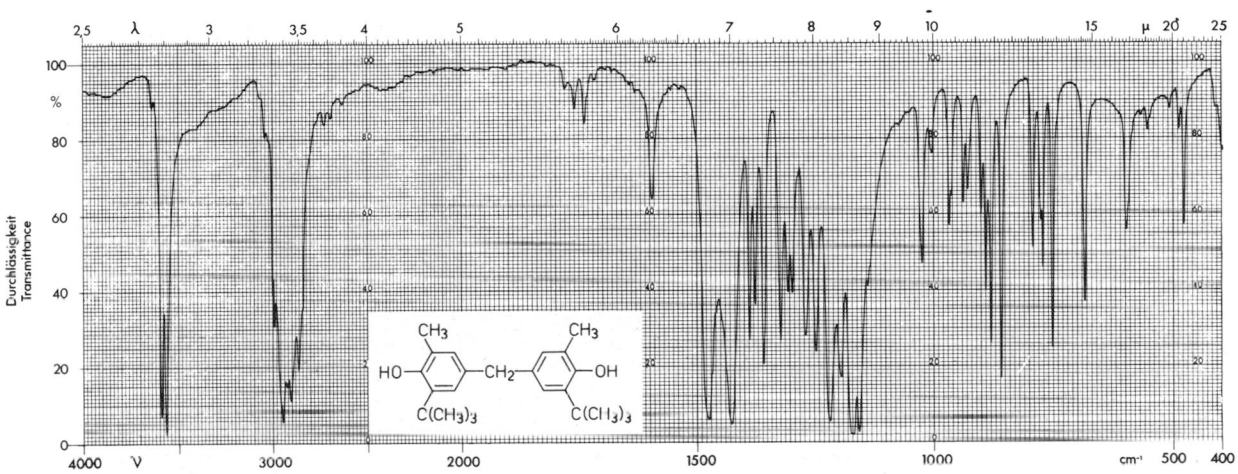

Verbindung: **4,4'-Methylenbis(2-methyl-6-t.butylphenol)**

Formel: $C_{23}H_{32}O_2$ M.: **340,4**

Handelsname: **Antioxydant 720**   Herst.: **Ethyl**

Präparation: **KBr (10/1000)**   Dez. Nr.: **1.3.4**

Compound: **4,4'-Methylenebis(2-methyl-6-t.butylphenol)**

Formula: $C_{23}H_{32}O_2$ M. w.: **340,4**

Tradename: **Antioxydant 720**   Manuf.: **Ethyl**

Preparation: **KBr (10/1000)**   Dec. No.: **1.3.4**

5913

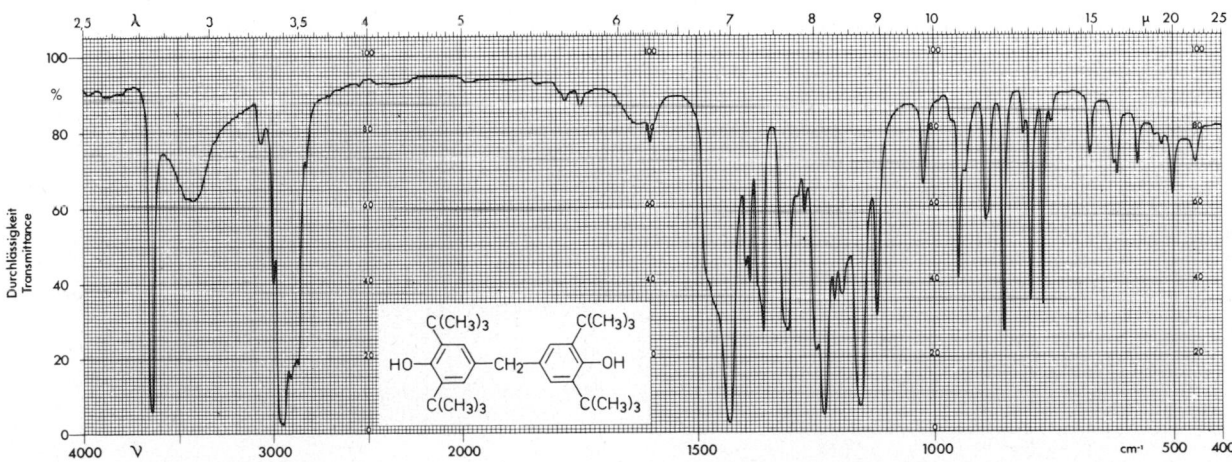

Verbindung: **4,4'-Methylenbis(2,6-di-t.butylphenol)**

Formel: $C_{29}H_{44}O_2$ M.: **424,6**

Handelsname: **Antioxydant 702**   Herst.: **Ethyl**

Präparation: **KBr (10/1000)**   Dez. Nr.: **1.3.5**

Compound: **4,4'-Methylenebis(2,6-di-t.butylphenol)**

Formula: $C_{29}H_{44}O_2$ M. w.: **424,6**

Tradename: **Antioxydant 702**   Manuf.: **Ethyl**

Preparation: **KBr (10/1000)**   Dec. No.: **1.3.5**

5914

Antioxidantien
1. Phenole
1.3. Bisphenole

Antioxidants
1. Phenols
1.3. Bisphenols

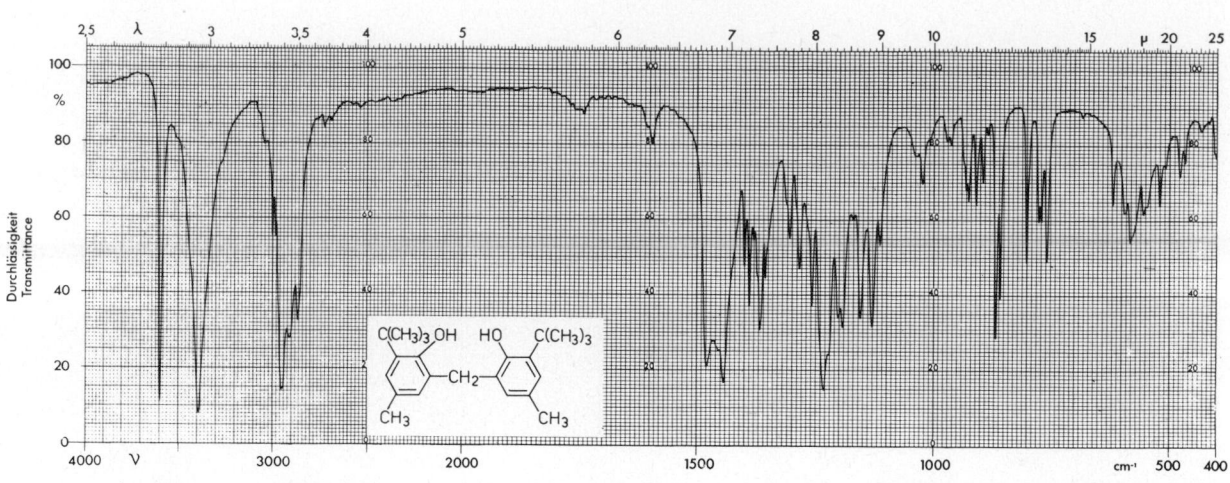

5915

Verbindung:	2,2'-Methylenbis(4-methyl-6-t.butylphenol)		Compound:	2,2'-Methylenebis(4-methyl-6-t.butylphenol)	
Formel:	$C_{23}H_{32}O_2$	M.: 340,4	Formula:	$C_{23}H_{32}O_2$	M. w.: 340,4
Handelsname:	CAO 5	Herst.: Catalin	Tradename:	CAO 5	Manuf.: Catalin
Präparation:	KBr (10/1000)	Dez. Nr.: 1.3.6	Preparation:	KBr (10/1000)	Dec. No.: 1.3.6

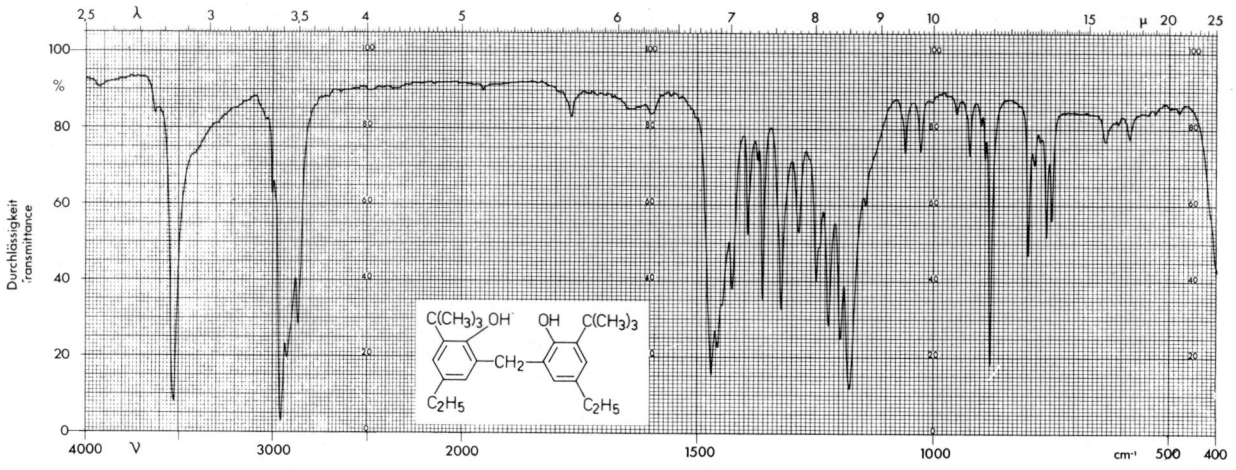

5916

Verbindung:	2,2'-Methylenbis(4-ethyl-6-t.butylphenol)		Compound:	2,2'-Methylenebis(4-ethyl-6-t.butylphenol)	
Formel:	$C_{25}H_{36}O_2$	M.: 368,4	Formula:	$C_{25}H_{36}O_2$	M. w.: 368,4
Handelsname:	Antioxydant 425	Herst.: Cyanamid	Tradename:	Antioxydant 425	Manuf.: Cyanamid
Präparation:	KBr (10/1000)	Dez. Nr.: 1.3.7	Preparation:	KBr (10/1000)	Dec. No.: 1.3.7

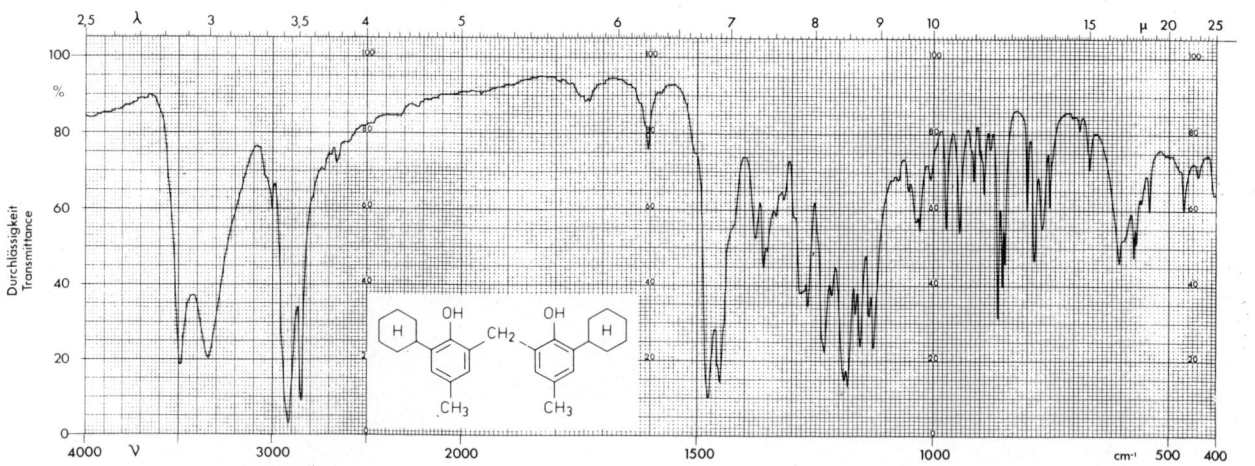

5917

Verbindung:	2,2'-Methylenbis(4-methyl-6-cyclohexyl-phenol)		Compound:	2,2'-Methylenebis(4-methyl-6-cyclohexyl-phenol)	
Formel:	$C_{27}H_{36}O_2$	M.: 392,4	Formula:	$C_{27}H_{36}O_2$	M. w.: 392,4
Handelsname:	ASM ZKF	Herst.: Bayer	Tradename:	ASM ZKF	Manuf.: Bayer
Präparation:	KBr (11/1000)	Dez. Nr.: 1.3.8	Preparation:	KBr (11/1000)	Dec. No.: 1.3.8

Antioxidantien
1. Phenole
1.3. Bisphenole

Antioxidants
1. Phenols
1.3. Bisphenols

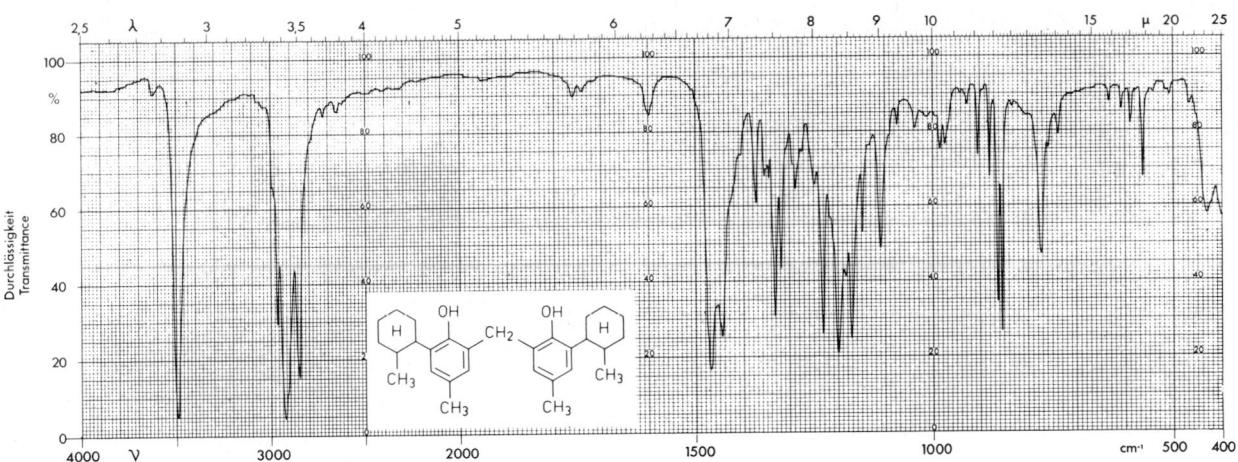

Verbindung: **2,2'-Methylenbis(4-methyl-6-methyl-cyclohexylphenol)**

Formel: $C_{29}H_{40}O_2$ M.: **420,6**

Handelsname: **Nonox WSP**   Herst.: **ICI**

Präparation: **KBr (6/1000)**   Dez. Nr.: **1.3.9**

Compound: **2,2'-Methylenebis(4-methyl-6-methyl-cyclohexylphenol)**

Formula: $C_{29}H_{40}O_2$ M. w.: **420,6**

Tradename: **Nonox WSP**   Manuf.: **ICI**

Preparation: **KBr (6/1000)**   Dec. No.: **1.3.9**

5918

Verbindung: **4,4'-Butylidenbis(3-methyl-6-t.butyl-phenol)**

Formel: $C_{26}H_{38}O_2$ M.: **382,4**

Handelsname: **Santowhite Powder**   Herst.: **Monsanto**

Präparation: **KBr (3/1000)**   Dez. Nr.: **1.3.10**

Compound: **4,4'-Butylidenebis(3-methyl-6-t.butyl-phenol)**

Formula: $C_{26}H_{38}O_2$ M. w.: **382,4**

Tradename: **Santowhite Powder**   Manuf.: **Monsanto**

Preparation: **KBr (3/1000)**   Dec. No.: **1.3.10**

5919

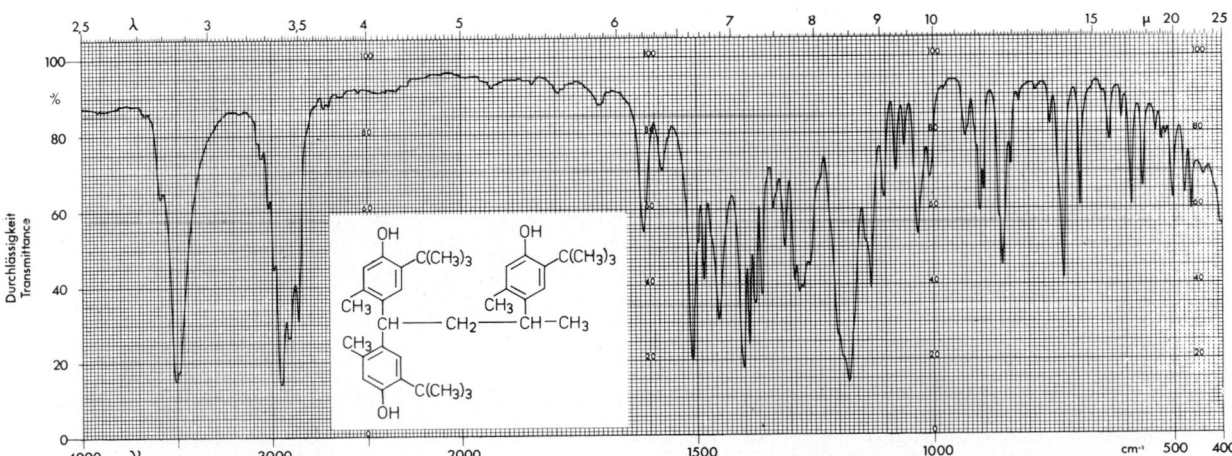

Verbindung: **1,1,3-Tris(2'-methyl-4'-hydroxy-5'-t.butyl-phenyl)butan**

Formel: $C_{37}H_{52}O_3$ M.: **544,7**

Handelsname: **Antioxidant CA**   Herst.: **ICI**

Präparation: **KBr (10/1000)**   Dez. Nr.: 1.3.13

Compound: **1,1,3-Tris(2'-methyl-4'-hydroxy-5'-t.butyl-phenyl)butane**

Formula: $C_{37}H_{52}O_3$ M. w.: **544,7**

Tradename: **Antioxidant CA**   Manuf.: **ICI**

Preparation: **KBr (10/1000)**   Dec. No.: 1.3.13

5920

Antioxidantien
1. Phenole
1.3. Bisphenole

Antioxidants
1. Phenols
1.3. Bisphenols

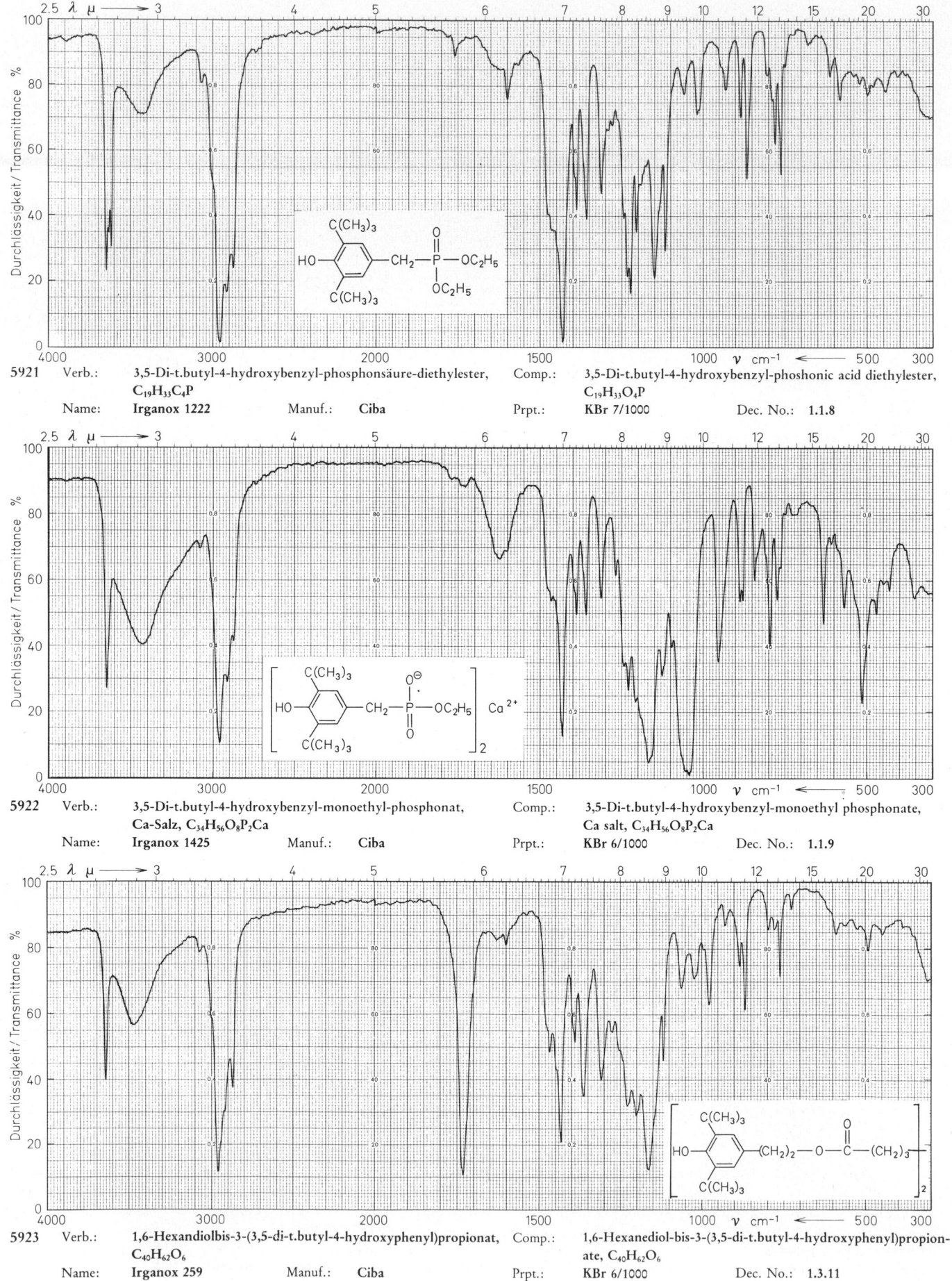

5921 Verb.: **3,5-Di-t.butyl-4-hydroxybenzyl-phosphonsäure-diethylester,** C₁₉H₃₃C₄P

Comp.: **3,5-Di-t.butyl-4-hydroxybenzyl-phoshonic acid diethylester,** $C_{19}H_{33}O_4P$

Name: **Irganox 1222** Manuf.: **Ciba** Prpt.: **KBr 7/1000** Dec. No.: **1.1.8**

5922 Verb.: **3,5-Di-t.butyl-4-hydroxybenzyl-monoethyl-phosphonat, Ca-Salz,** $C_{34}H_{56}O_8P_2Ca$

Comp.: **3,5-Di-t.butyl-4-hydroxybenzyl-monoethyl phosphonate, Ca salt,** $C_{34}H_{56}O_8P_2Ca$

Name: **Irganox 1425** Manuf.: **Ciba** Prpt.: **KBr 6/1000** Dec. No.: **1.1.9**

5923 Verb.: **1,6-Hexandiolbis-3-(3,5-di-t.butyl-4-hydroxyphenyl)propionat,** $C_{40}H_{62}O_6$

Comp.: **1,6-Hexanediol-bis-3-(3,5-di-t.butyl-4-hydroxyphenyl)propionate,** $C_{40}H_{62}O_6$

Name: **Irganox 259** Manuf.: **Ciba** Prpt.: **KBr 6/1000** Dec. No.: **1.3.11**

Antioxidantien
1. Phenole
1.3. Bisphenole

Antioxidants
1. Phenols
1.3 Bisphenols

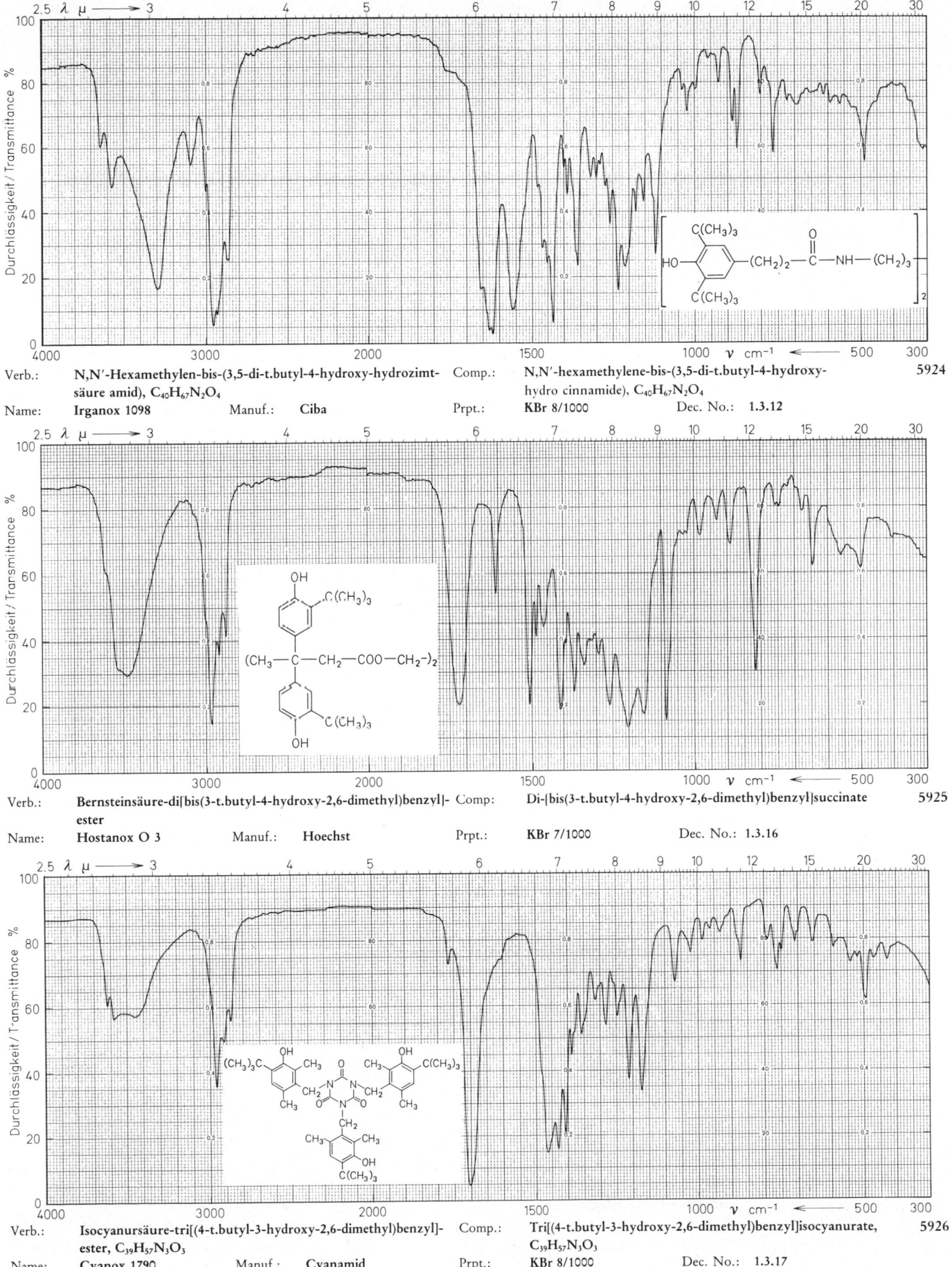

Verb.: N,N'-Hexamethylen-bis-(3,5-di-t.butyl-4-hydroxy-hydrozimt-   **Comp.:** N,N'-hexamethylene-bis-(3,5-di-t.butyl-4-hydroxy-   5924
säure amid), $C_{40}H_{67}N_2O_4$ hydro cinnamide), $C_{40}H_{67}N_2O_4$

Name: Irganox 1098   **Manuf.:** Ciba   **Prpt.:** KBr 8/1000   **Dec. No.:** 1.3.12

Verb.: Bernsteinsäure-di[bis(3-t.butyl-4-hydroxy-2,6-dimethyl)benzyl]-   **Comp:** Di-[bis(3-t.butyl-4-hydroxy-2,6-dimethyl)benzyl]succinate   5925
ester

Name: Hostanox O 3   **Manuf.:** Hoechst   **Prpt.:** KBr 7/1000   **Dec. No.:** 1.3.16

Verb.: Isocyanursäure-tri[(4-t.butyl-3-hydroxy-2,6-dimethyl)benzyl]-   **Comp.:** Tri[(4-t.butyl-3-hydroxy-2,6-dimethyl)benzyl]isocyanurate,   5926
ester, $C_{39}H_{57}N_3O_3$ $C_{39}H_{57}N_3O_3$

Name: Cyanox 1790   **Manuf.:** Cyanamid   **Prpt.:** KBr 8/1000   **Dec. No.:** 1.3.17

Antioxidantien
1. Phenole
1.4. Thiobisphenole

Antioxidants
1. Phenols
1.4. Thiobisphenols

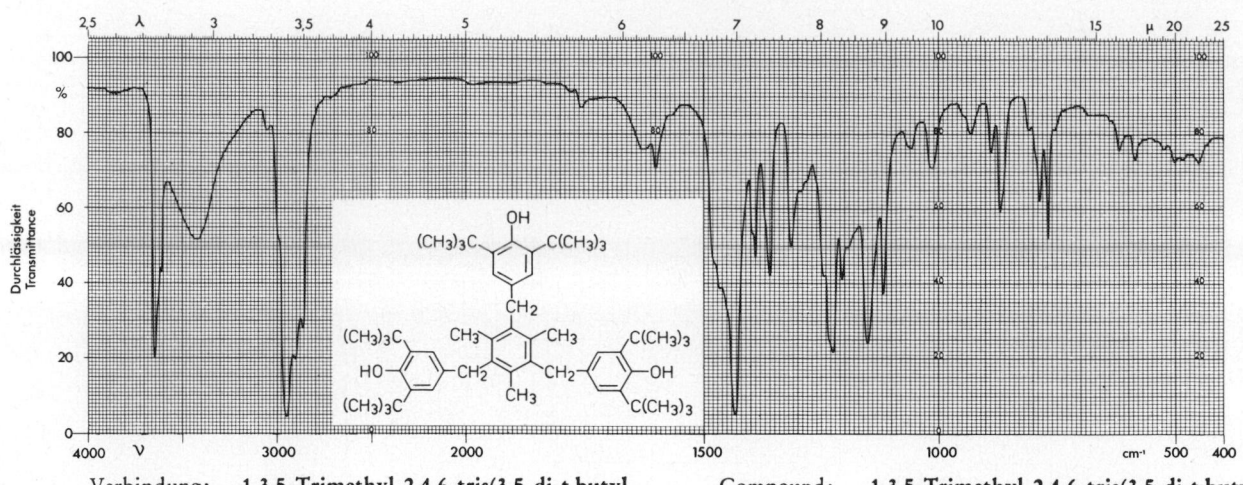

5927

	Verbindung:	1,3,5-Trimethyl-2,4,6-tris(3,5-di-t.butyl-4-hydroxybenzyl)benzol		Compound:	1,3,5-Trimethyl-2,4,6-tris(3,5-di-t.butyl-4-hydroxybenzyl)benzene
Formel:	$C_{54}H_{78}O_3$	M.: 774,0	Formula:	$C_{54}H_{78}O_3$	M. w.: 774,0
Handelsname:	Ionox 330	Herst.: Shell	Tradename:	Ionox 330	Manuf.: Shell
Präparation:	KBr (10/1000)	Dez. Nr.: 1.3.14	Preparation:	KBr (10/1000)	Dec. No.: 1.3.14

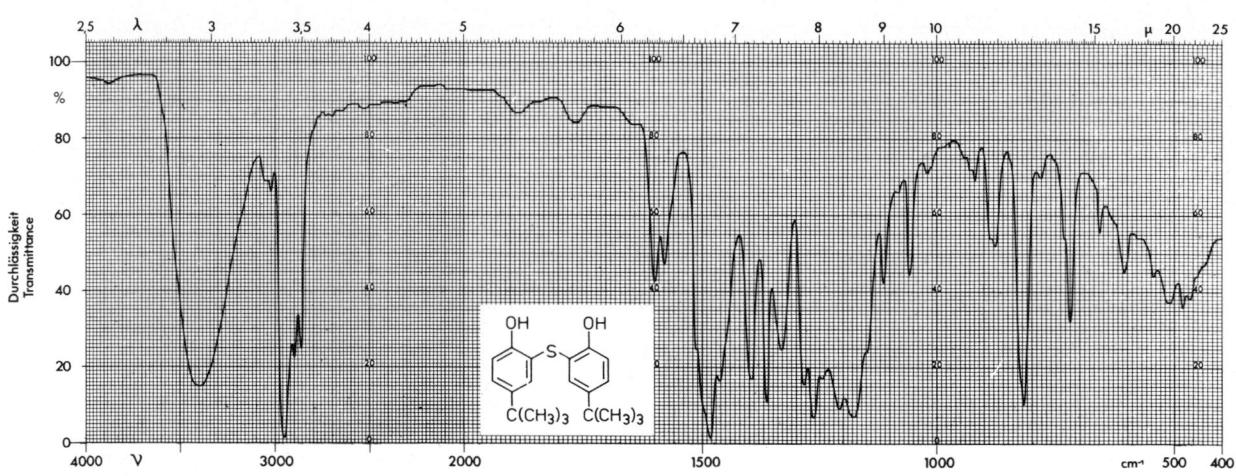

5928

	Verbindung:	2,2'-Thiobis(4-t.butylphenol)		Compound:	2,2'-Thiobis(4-t.butylphenol)
Formel:	$C_{20}H_{26}O_2S$	M.: 330,4	Formula:	$C_{20}H_{26}O_2S$	M. w.: 330,4
Handelsname:	Stabilisator BS	Herst.: Cassella	Tradename:	Stabilisator BS	Manuf.: Cassella
Präparation:	Schmelzfilm	Dez. Nr.: 1.4.1	Preparation:	Melting film	Dec. No.: 1.4.1

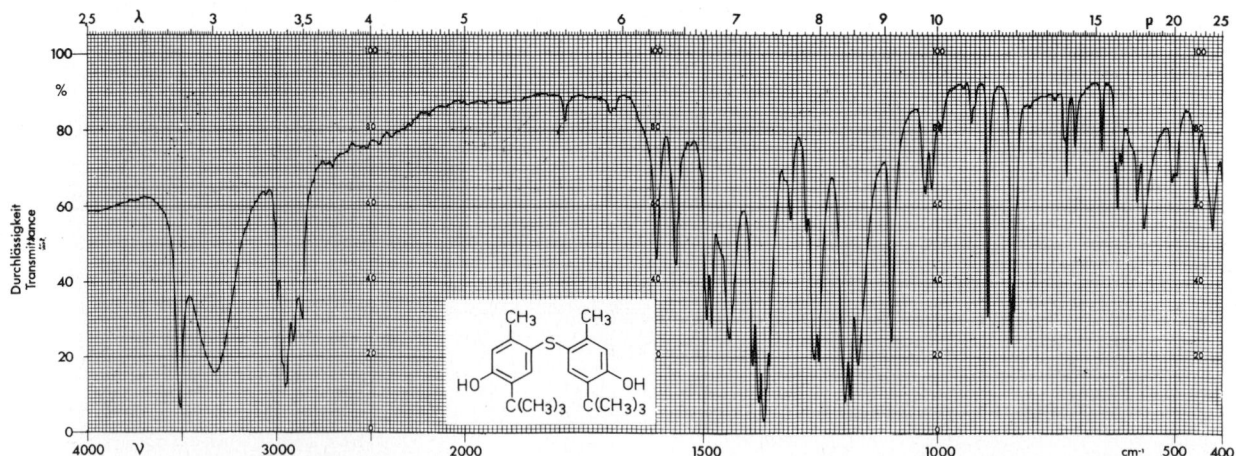

5929

	Verbindung:	4,4'-Thiobis(3-methyl-6-t.butylphenol)		Compound:	4,4'-Thiobis(3-methyl-6-t.butyl-phenol)
Formel:	$C_{22}H_{30}O_2S$	M.: 358,4	Formula:	$C_{22}H_{30}O_2S$	M. w.: 358,4
Handelsname:	Santowhite Crystals	Herst.: Monsanto	Tradename:	Santowhite Crystals	Manuf.: Monsanto
Präparation:	KBr (8/1000)	Dez. Nr.: 1.4.2	Preparation:	KBr (8/1000)	Dec. No.: 1.4.2

Antioxidantien
1. Phenole
1.4. Thiobisphenole

Antioxidants
1. Phenols
1.4. Thiobisphenols

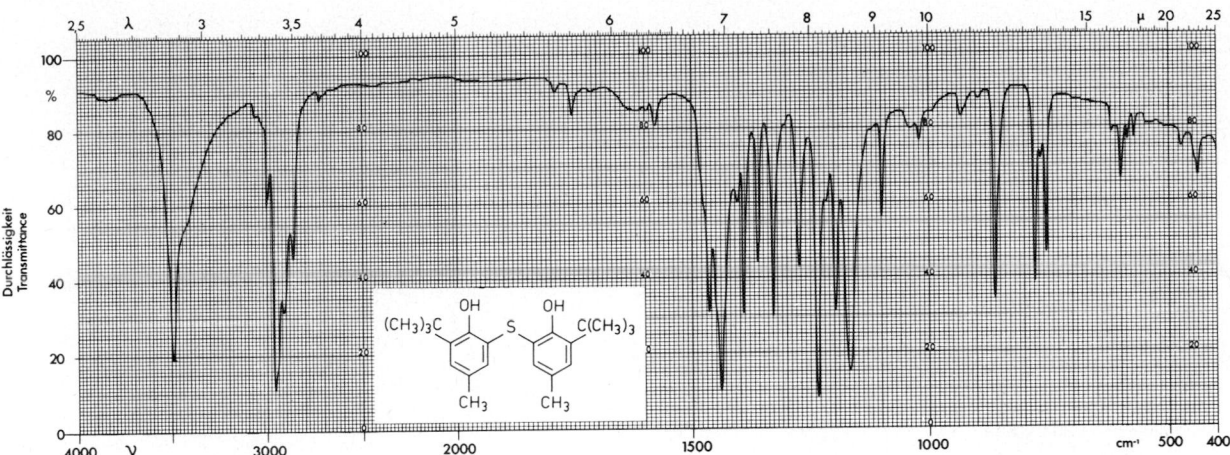

Verbindung:	2,2'-Thiobis(4-methyl-6-t.butylphenol)	Compound:	2,2'-Thiobis(4-methyl-6-t.butylphenol)
Formel: $C_{22}H_{30}O_2S$	M.: 358,4	Formula: $C_{22}H_{30}O_2S$	M. w.: 358,4
Handelsname: CAO 4	Herst.: Catalin	Tradename: CAO 4	Manuf.: Catalin
Präparation: KBr (5/1000)	Dez. Nr.: 1.4.3	Preparation: KBr (5/1000)	Dec. No.: 1.4.3

5930

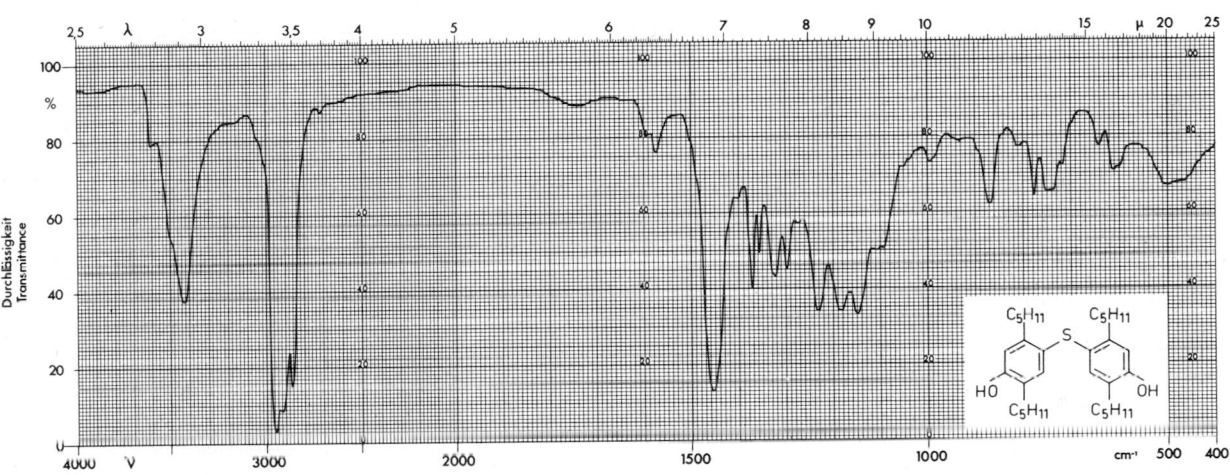

Verbindung:	4,4'-Thiobis[2,5-di(2-methylbutyl)phenol]	Compound:	4,4'-Thiobis[2,5-di(2-methylbutyl) phenol]
Formel: $C_{32}H_{50}O_2S$	M.: 498,7	Formula: $C_{32}H_{50}O_2S$	M. w.: 498,7
Handelsname: Santowhite L	Herst.: Monsanto	Tradename: Santowhite L	Manuf.: Monsanto
Präparation: Kapill. Film	Dez. Nr.: 1.4.4	Preparation: Capill. film	Dec. No.: 1.4.4

5931

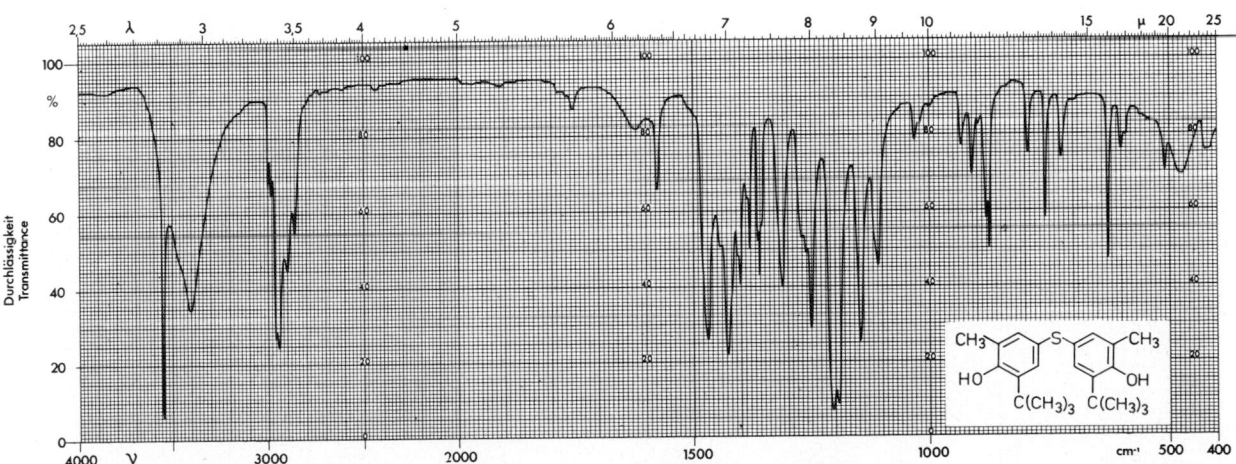

Verbindung:	4,4' Thiobis(2-methyl-6-t.butylphenol)	Compound:	4,4'-Thiobis(2-methyl-6-t.butyl-phenol)
Formel: $C_{22}H_{30}O_2S$	M.: 358,4	Formula: $C_{22}H_{30}O_2S$	M. w.: 358,4
Handelsname: Antioxidant 736	Herst.: Ethyl	Tradename: Antioxidant 736	Manuf.: Ethyl
Präparation: KBr (6/1000)	Dez. Nr.: 1.4.5	Preparation: KBr (6/1000)	Dec. No.: 1.4.5

5932

Antioxidantien
1. Phenole
1.4. Thiobisphenole

Antioxidants
1. Phenols
1.4. Thiobisphenols

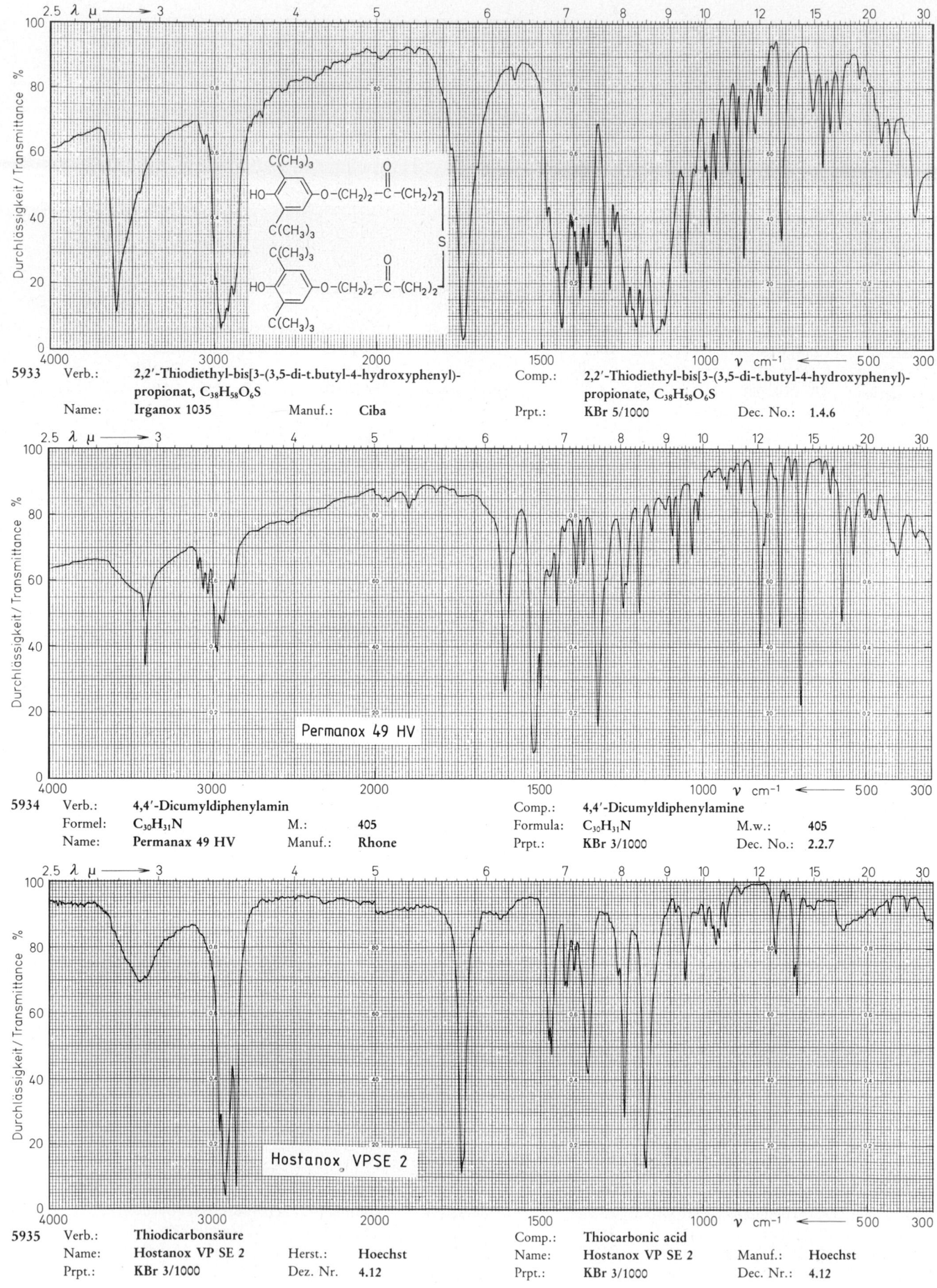

5933 Verb.: **2,2′-Thiodiethyl-bis[3-(3,5-di-t.butyl-4-hydroxyphenyl)-propionat, C₃₈H₅₈O₆S**
Name: **Irganox 1035** Manuf.: **Ciba**

Comp.: **2,2′-Thiodiethyl-bis[3-(3,5-di-t.butyl-4-hydroxyphenyl)-propionate, C₃₈H₅₈O₆S**
Prpt.: **KBr 5/1000** Dec. No.: **1.4.6**

5934 Verb.: **4,4′-Dicumyldiphenylamin**
Formel: **C₃₀H₃₁N** M.: **405**
Name: **Permanax 49 HV** Manuf.: **Rhone**

Comp.: **4,4′-Dicumyldiphenylamine**
Formula: **C₃₀H₃₁N** M.w.: **405**
Prpt.: **KBr 3/1000** Dec. No.: **2.2.7**

5935 Verb.: **Thiodicarbonsäure**
Name: **Hostanox VP SE 2** Herst.: **Hoechst**
Prpt.: **KBr 3/1000** Dez. Nr. **4.12**

Comp.: **Thiocarbonic acid**
Name: **Hostanox VP SE 2** Manuf.: **Hoechst**
Prpt.: **KBr 3/1000** Dec. Nr.: **4.12**

Antioxidantien
1. Phenole
1.5. Phenolether

Antioxidants
1. Phenols
1.5. Phenolethers

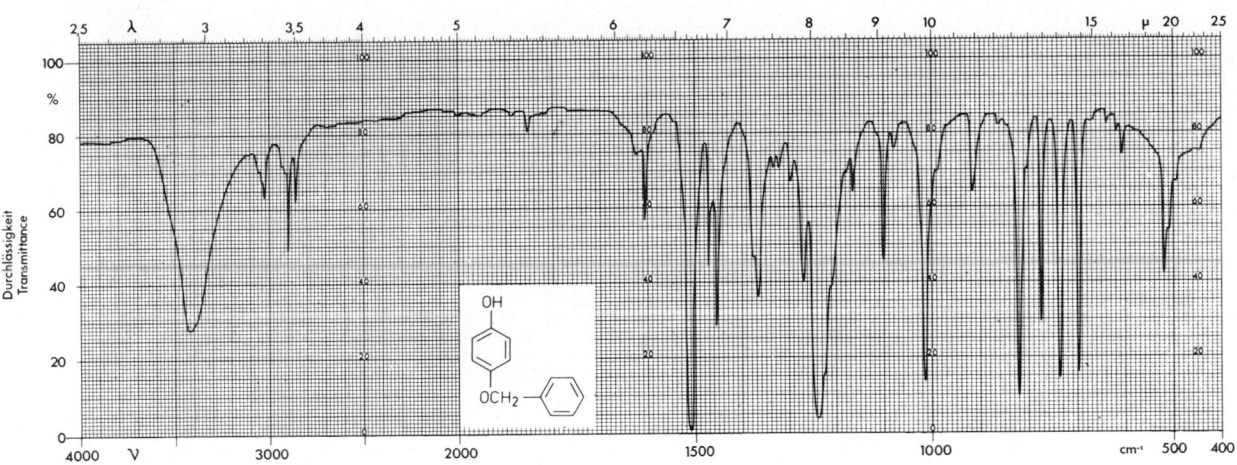

Verbindung: **4-Benzoxyphenol**
Formel: **C₁₃H₁₂O₂** M.: **200,2**
Handelsname: **Agerite Alba** Herst.: **Vanderbilt**
Präparation: **KBr (6/1000)** Dez. Nr.: **1.5.1**

Compound: **4-Benzoxy-phenol**
Formula: **C₁₃H₁₂O₂** M. w.: **200,2**
Tradename: **Agerite Alba** Manuf.: **Vanderbilt**
Preparation: **KBr (6/1000)** Dec. No.: **1.5.1**

5936

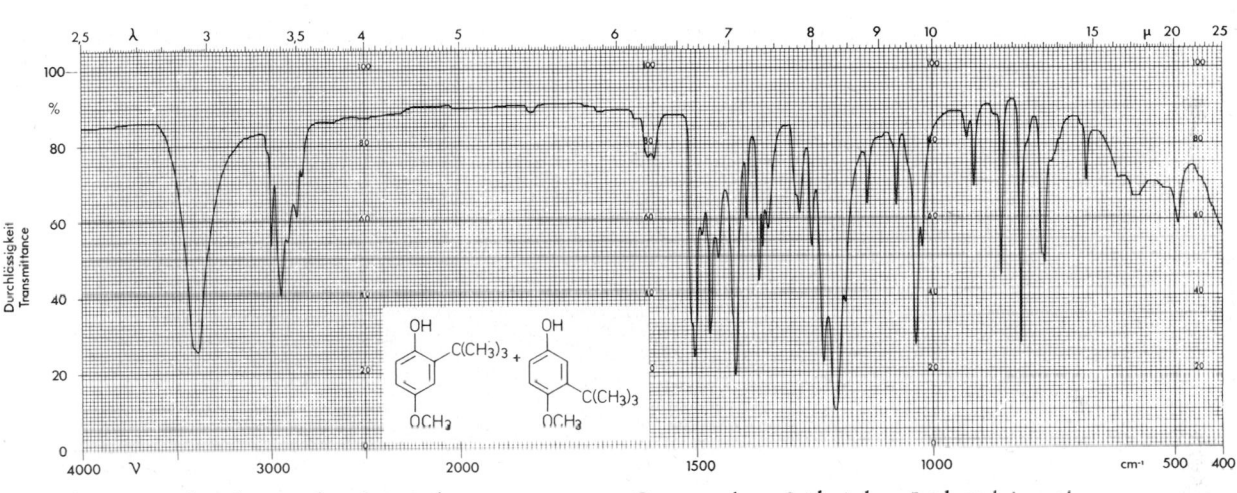

Verbindung: **2-t.butyl- u. 3-t.butyl-4-methoxy-phenol**
Formel: **C₁₁H₁₆O₂** M.: **180,2**
Handelsname: **BHA Tenox** Herst.: **Eastman**
Präparation: **KBr (6/1000)** Dez. Nr.: **1.5.2**

Compound: **2-t.butyl- a. 3-t.butyl-4-methoxy-phenol**
Formula: **C₁₁H₁₆O₂** M. w.: **180,2**
Tradename: **BHA Tenox** Manuf.: **Eastman**
Preparation: **KBr (6/1000)** Dec. No.: **1.5.2**

5937

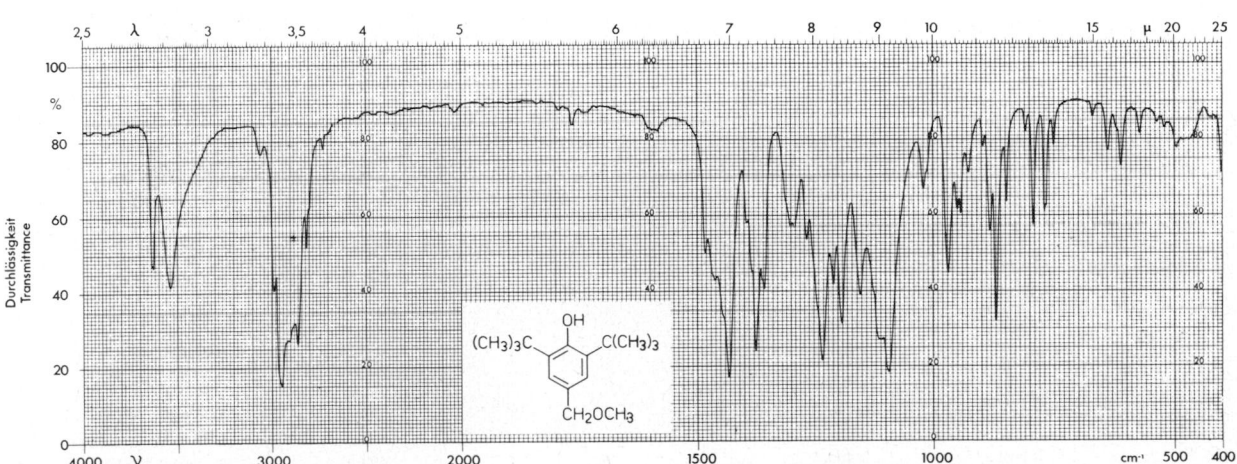

Verbindung: **2,6-Di-t.butyl-α-methoxy-p-kresol**
Formel: **C₁₆H₂₆O₂** M.: **250,3**
Handelsname: **Antioxidant 762** Herst.: **Ethyl**
Präparation: **KBr (5/1000)** Dez. Nr.: **1.5.3**

Compound: **2,6-Di-t.butyl-α-methoxy-p-cresol**
Formula: **C₁₆H₂₆O₂** M. w.: **250,3**
Tradename: **Antioxidant 762** Manuf.: **Ethyl**
Preparation: **KBr (5/1000)** Dec. No.: **1.5.3**

5938

Antioxidantien
1. Phenole
1.6. Aminophenole

Antioxidants
1. Phenols
1.6. Aminophenols

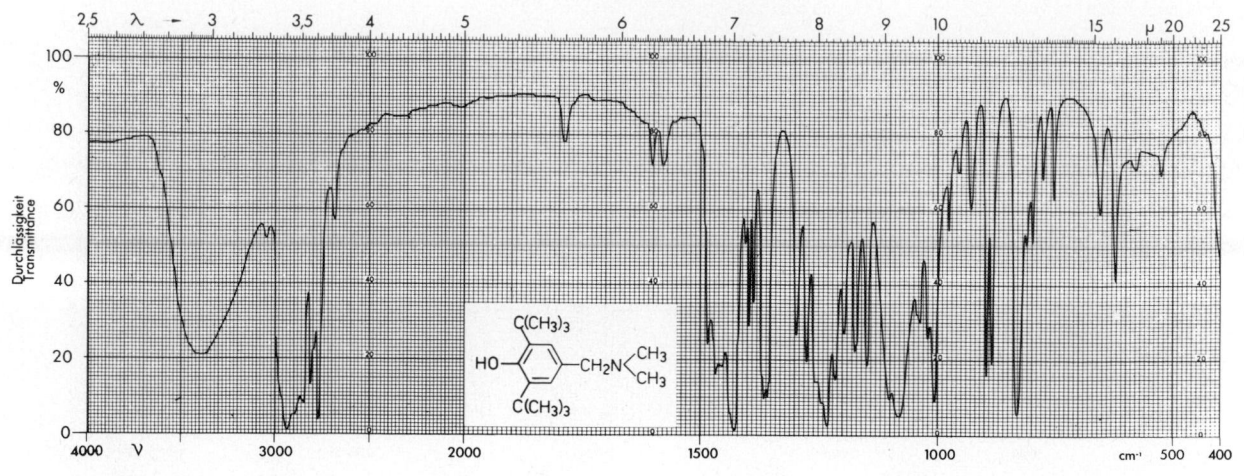

5939

Verbindung:	2,6-Di-t.butyl-α-dimethylamino-p-kresol		Compound:	2,6-Di-t.butyl-α-di-methyl-amino-p-cresol	
Formel:	C₁₇H₂₉ON	M.: 263,4	Formula:	C₁₇H₂₉ON	M. w.: 263,4
Handelsname:	Antioxidant 703	Herst.: Ethyl	Tradename:	Antioxidant 703	Manuf.: Ethyl
Präparation:	KBr (6/1000)	Dez. Nr.: 1.6.1	Preparation:	KBr (6/1000)	Dec. No.: 1.6.1

Verbindung: 2,6-Di-t.butyl-α-dimethylamino-p-kresol
Formel: $C_{17}H_{29}ON$ M.: 263,4
Handelsname: Antioxidant 703   Herst.: Ethyl
Präparation: KBr (6/1000)   Dez. Nr.: 1.6.1

Compound: 2,6-Di-t.butyl-α-di-methyl-amino-p-cresol
Formula: $C_{17}H_{29}ON$ M. w.: 263,4
Tradename: Antioxidant 703   Manuf.: Ethyl
Preparation: KBr (6/1000)   Dec. No.: 1.6.1

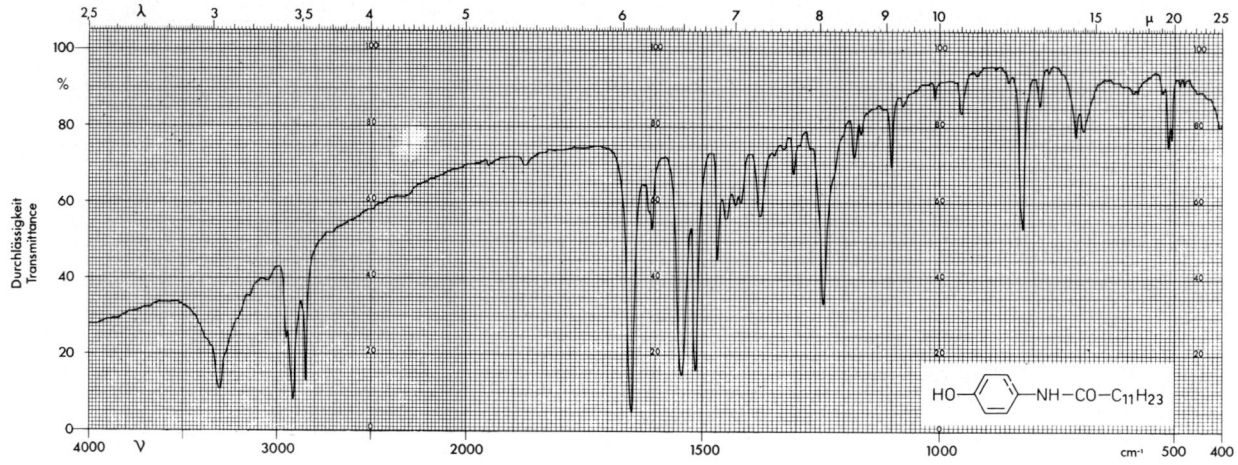

5940

Verbindung: N-Lauroyl-4-aminophenol
Formel: $C_{18}H_{29}NO_2$ M.: 291,4
Handelsname: Suconox-12   Herst.: Miles
Präparation: KBr (6/1000)   Dez. Nr.: 1.6.2

Compound: N-Lauroyl-4-amino-phenol
Formula: $C_{18}H_{29}NO_2$ M. w.: 291,4
Tradename: Suconox-12   Manuf.: Miles
Preparation: KBr (6/1000)   Dec. No.: 1.6.2

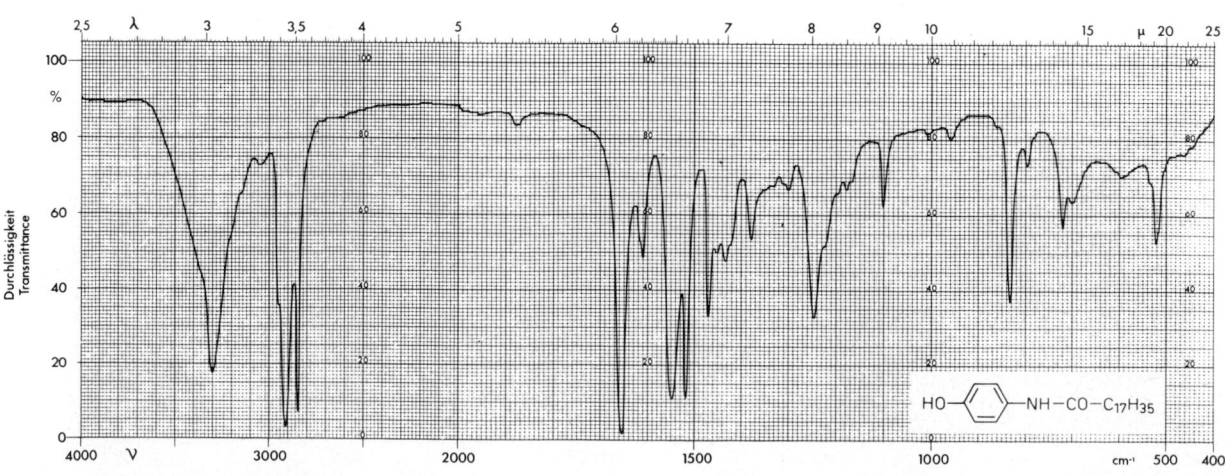

5941

Verbindung: N-Stearoyl-4-aminophenol
Formel: $C_{24}H_{41}NO_2$ M.: 375,5
Handelsname: Suconox-18   Herst.: Miles
Präparation: KBr (6/1000)   Dez. Nr.: 1.6.3

Compound: N-Stearoyl-4-amino-phenol
Formula: $C_{24}H_{41}NO_2$ M. w.: 375,5
Tradename: Suconox-18   Manuf.: Miles
Preparation: KBr (6/1000)   Dec. No.: 1.6.3

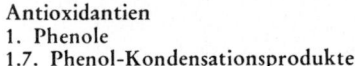

Antioxidantien
1. Phenole
1.7. Phenol-Kondensationsprodukte

Antioxidants
1. Phenols
1.7. Phenol Condensation Products

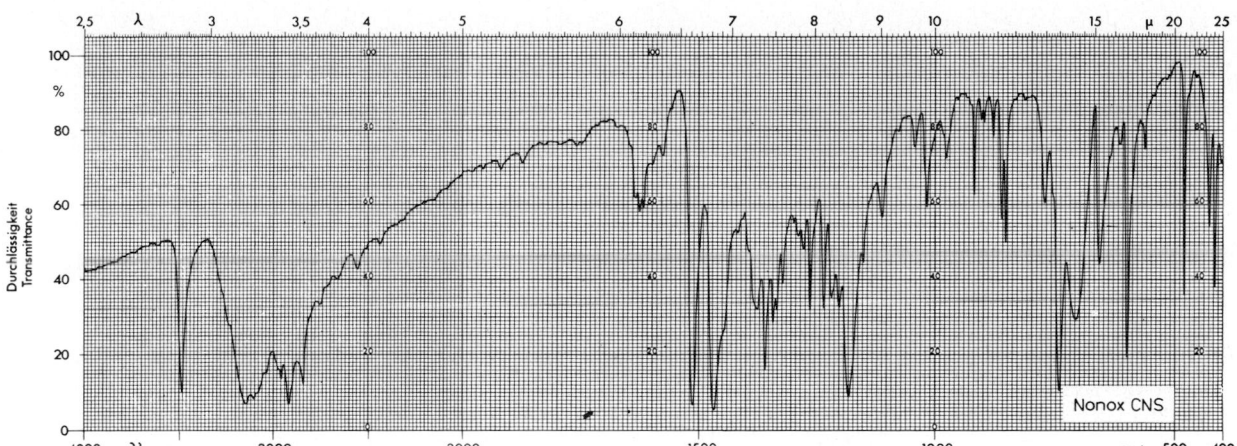

					5942
Verbindung:	N-haltige phenolische Verbindung		Compound:	Phenolic compound containing N	
Formel:		M.:	Formula:		M. w.:
Handelsname:	Nonox CNS	Herst.: ICI	Tradename:	Nonox CNS	Manuf.: ICI
Präparation:	KBr (7/1000)	Dez. Nr.: 1.6.4	Preparation:	KBr (7/1000)	Dec. No.: 1.6.4

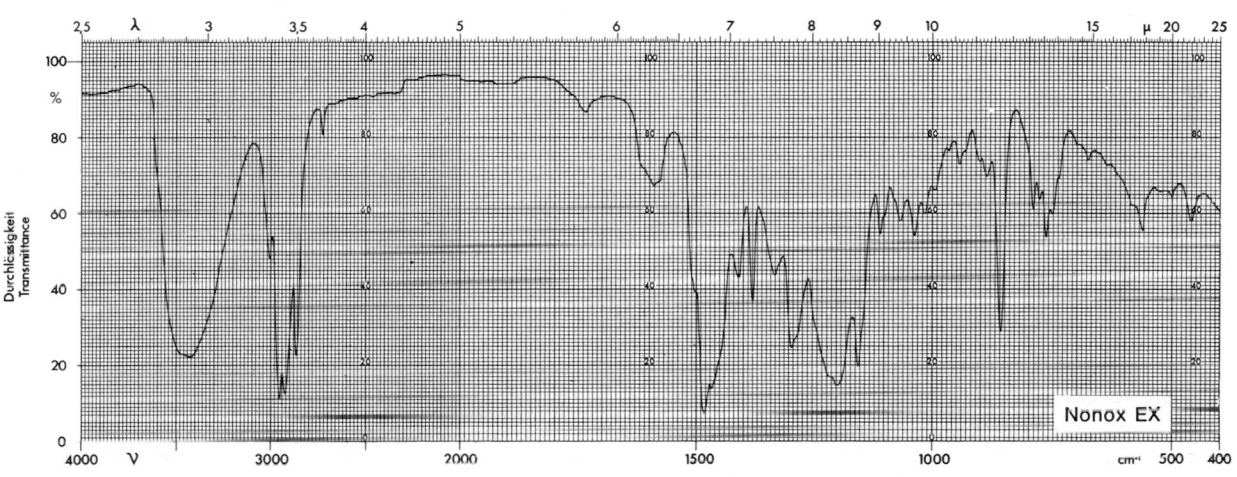

					5943
Verbindung:	Phenolkondensationsprodukt		Compound:	Phenol condensation product	
Formel:		M.:	Formula:		M. w.:
Handelsname:	Nonox EX	Herst.: ICI	Tradename:	Nonox EX	Manuf.: ICI
Präparation:	Kapill. Film	Dez. Nr.: 1.7.1	Preparation:	Capill. film	Dec. No.: 1.7.1

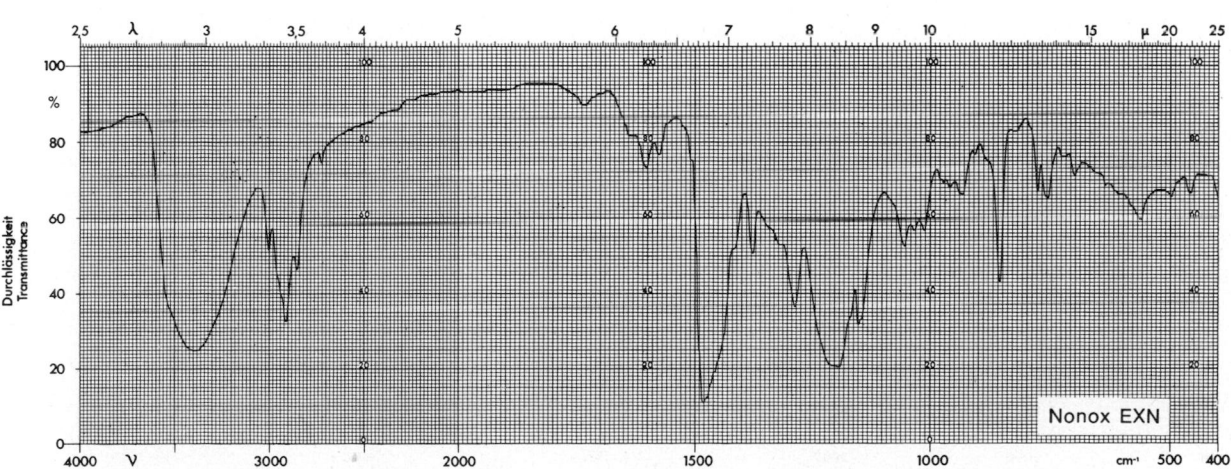

					5944
Verbindung:	Phenolkondensationsprodukt		Compound:	Phenol condensation product	
Formel:		M.:	Formula:		M. w.:
Handelsname:	Nonox EXN	Herst.: ICI	Tradename:	Nonox EXN	Manuf.: ICI
Präparation:	KBr (10/1000)	Dez. Nr.: 1.7.2	Preparation:	KBr (10/1000)	Dec. No.: 1.7.2

Antioxidantien
1. Phenole
1.8. Sonstige Phenole

Antioxidants
1. Phenols
1.8. Miscellaneous Phenols

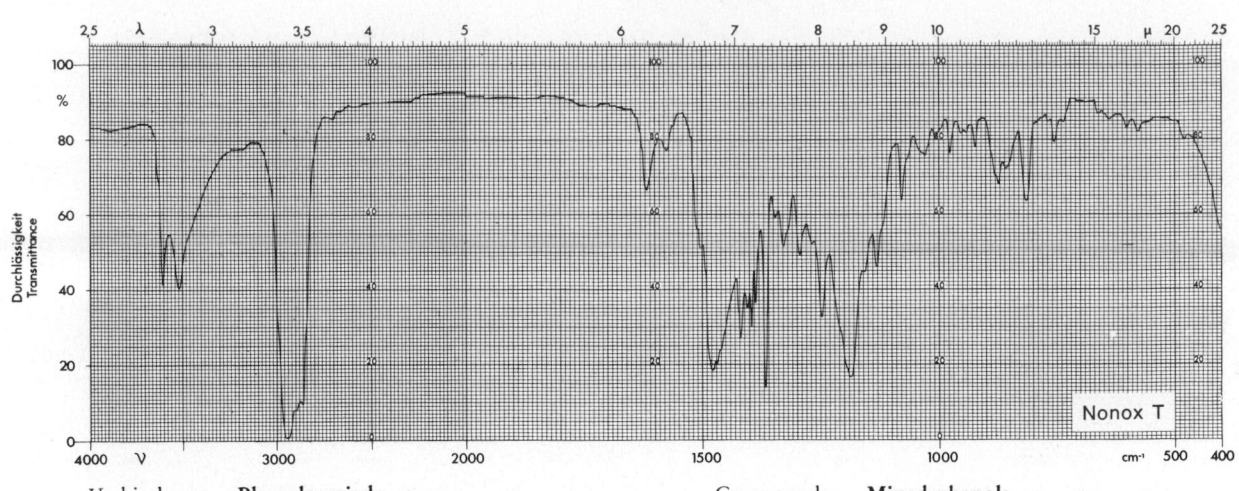

5945

Verbindung:	**Phenolgemisch**			Compound:	**Mixed phenols**	
Formel:		M.:		Formula:		M. w.:
Handelsname:	**Nonox T**	Herst.:	**ICI**	Tradename:	**Nonox T**	Manuf.: **ICI**
Präparation:	**Kapill. Film**	Dez. Nr.:	**1.8.1**	Preparation:	**Capill. film**	Dec. No.: **1.8.1**

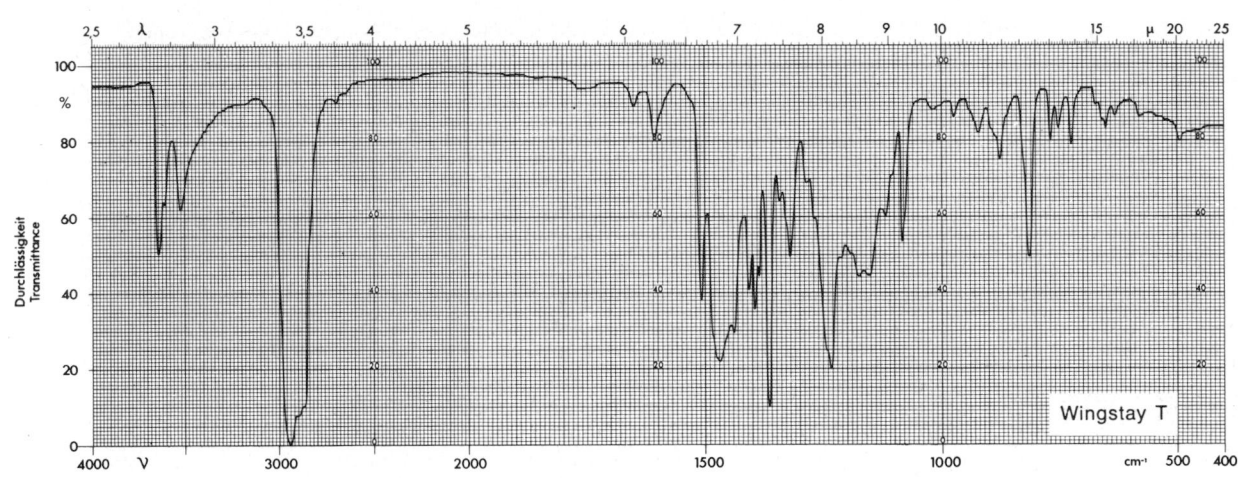

5946

Verbindung:	**Alkyliertes Phenol**			Compound:	**Alkylated phenol**	
Formel:		M.:		Formula:		M. w.:
Handelsname:	**Wingstay T**	Herst.:	**Goodyear**	Tradename:	**Wingstay T**	Manuf.: **Goodyear**
Präparation:	**Kapill. Film**	Dez. Nr.:	**1.8.2**	Preparation:	**Capill. film**	Dec. No.: **1.8.2**

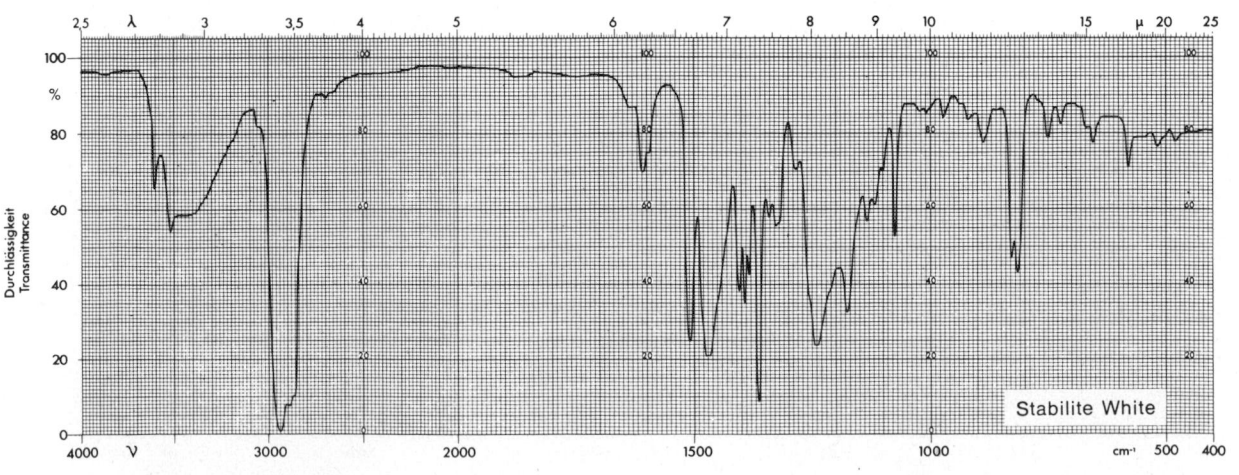

5947

Verbindung:	**Polyalkylphenol**			Compound:	**Polyalkylphenol**	
Formel:		M.:		Formula:		M. w.:
Handelsname:	**Stabilite White**	Herst.:	**Hall Comp.**	Tradename:	**Stabilite White**	Manuf.: **Hall Comp.**
Präparation:	**Kapill. Film**	Dez. Nr.:	**1.8.3**	Preparation:	**Capill. film**	Dec. No.: **1.8.3**

Antioxidantien
1. Phenole
1.8. Sonstige Phenole

Antioxidants
1. Phenols
1.8. Miscellaneous Phenols

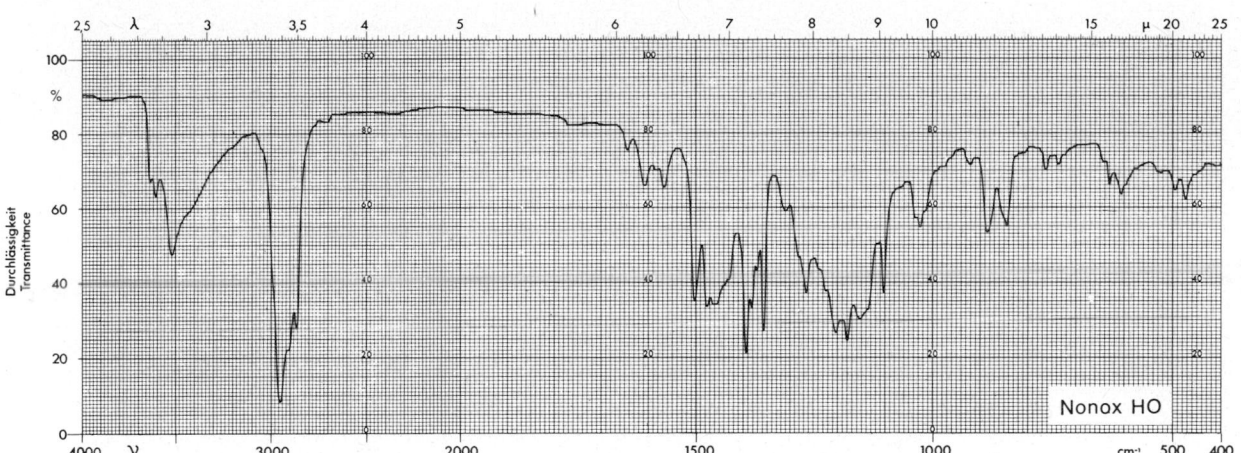

Verbindung:	Phenolgemisch	M.:		Compound:	Mixture of phenols	M. w.:		5948
Formel:				Formula:				
Handelsname:	Nonox HO	Herst.:	ICI	Tradename:	Nonox HO	Manuf.:	ICI	
Präparation:	Kapill. Film	Dez. Nr.:	1.8.4	Preparation:	Capill. film	Dec. No.:	1.8.4	

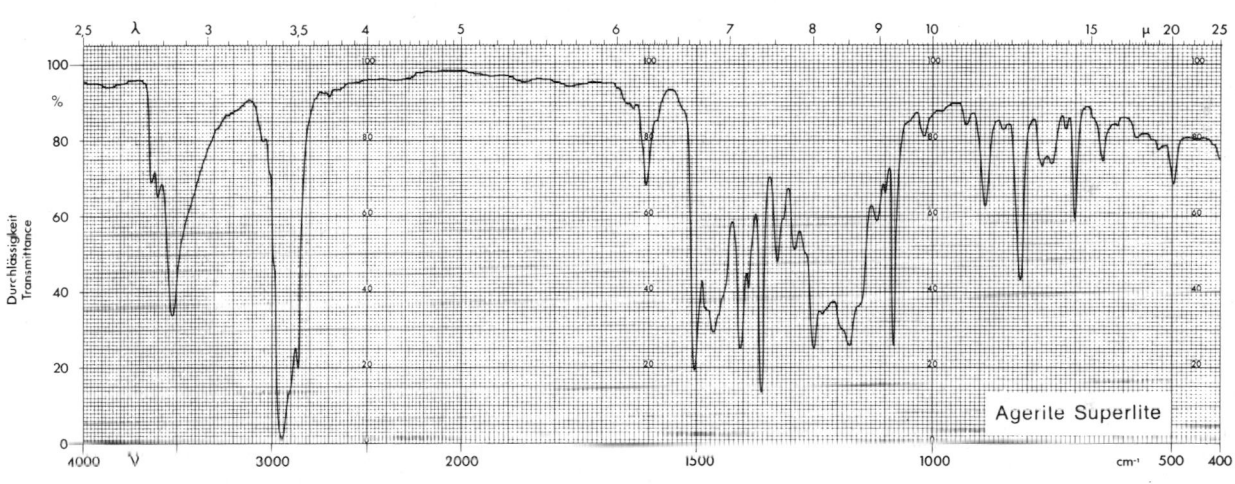

Verbindung:	Alkyliertes Polyphenol	M.:		Compound:	Alkylated polyphenol	M. w.:		5949
Formel:				Formula:				
Handelsname:	Agerite Superlite	Herst.:	Vanderbilt	Tradename:	Agerite Superlite	Manuf.:	Vanderbilt	
Präparation:	Kapill. Film	Dez. Nr.:	1.8.5	Preparation:	Capill. film	Dec. No.:	1.8.5	

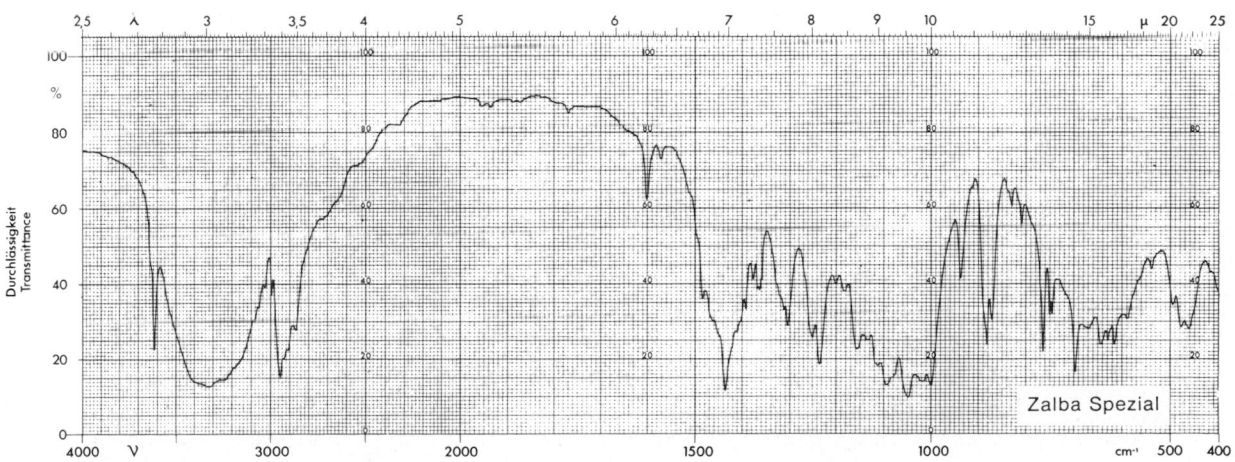

Verbindung:	Phenol-Verbindung	M.:		Compound:	Phenolic compound	M. w.:		5950
Formel:				Formula:				
Handelsname:	Zalba Spezial	Herst.:	Du Pont	Tradename:	Zalba Spezial	Manuf.:	Du Pont	
Präparation:	KBr (12/1000)	Dez. Nr.:	1.8.6	Preparation:	KBr (12/1000)	Dec. No.:	1.8.6	

Antioxidantien
1. Phenole
1.8. Sonstige Phenole

Antioxidants
1. Phenols
1.8. Miscellaneous Phenols

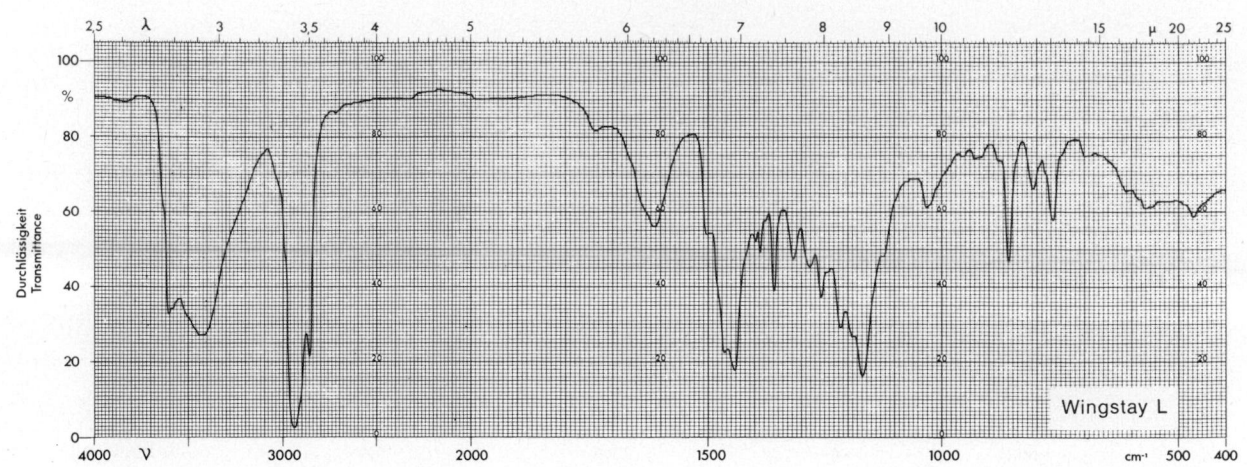

5951

Verbindung:	**Phenolkondensationsprodukt**		M.:			
Formel:			M.:			
Handelsname:	**Wingstay L**		Herst.:	**Goodyear**		
Präparation:	**KBr (6/1000)**		Dez. Nr.:	**1.8.7**		

Compound:	**Phenol condensation product**		
Formula:		M. w..	
Tradename:	**Wingstay L**	Manuf.:	**Goodyear**
Preparation:	**KBr (6/1000)**	Dec. No.:	**1.8.7**

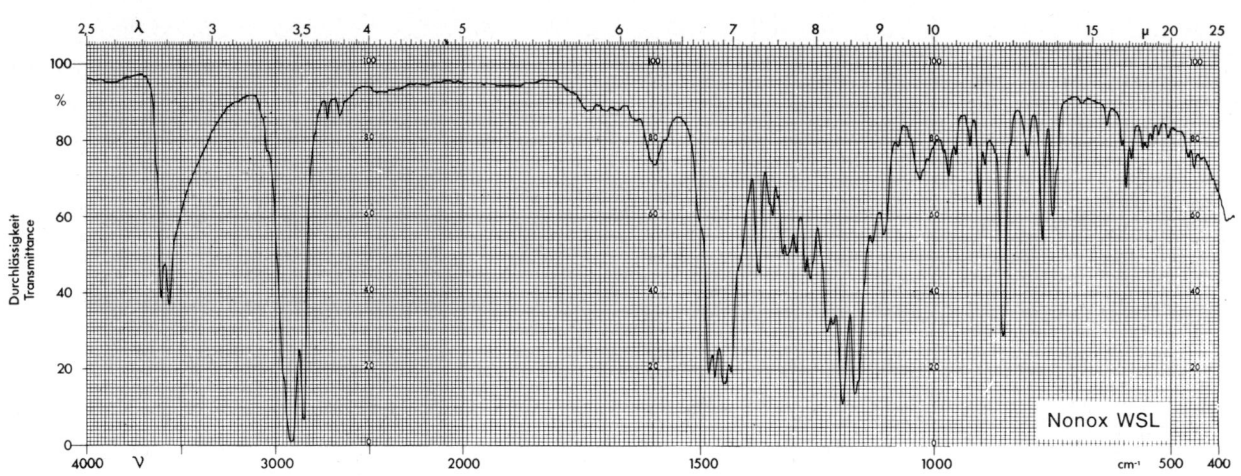

5952

Verbindung:	**Cyclohexylierte Phenole**		
Formel:		M.:	
Handelsname:	**Nonox WSL**	Herst.:	**ICI**
Präparation:	**Kapill. Film**	Dez. Nr.:	**1.8.8**

Compound:	**Cyclohexylated phenols**		
Formula:		M. w.:	
Tradename:	**Nonox WSL**	Manuf.:	**ICI**
Preparation:	**Capill. film**	Dec. No.:	**1.8.8**

5953

Verbindung:	**Styrolisiertes Phenol**		
Formel:		M.:	
Handelsname:	**Styphen 1**	Herst.:	**Dow**
Präparation:	**Kapill. Film**	Dez. Nr.:	**1.8.9**

Compound:	**Styrenated phenol**		
Formula:		M. w.:	
Tradename:	**Styphen 1**	Manuf.:	**Dow**
Preparation:	**Capill. film**	Dec. No.:	**1.8.9**

Antioxidantien
1. Phenole
1.8. Sonstige Phenole

Antioxidants
1. Phenols
1.8. Miscellaneous Phenols

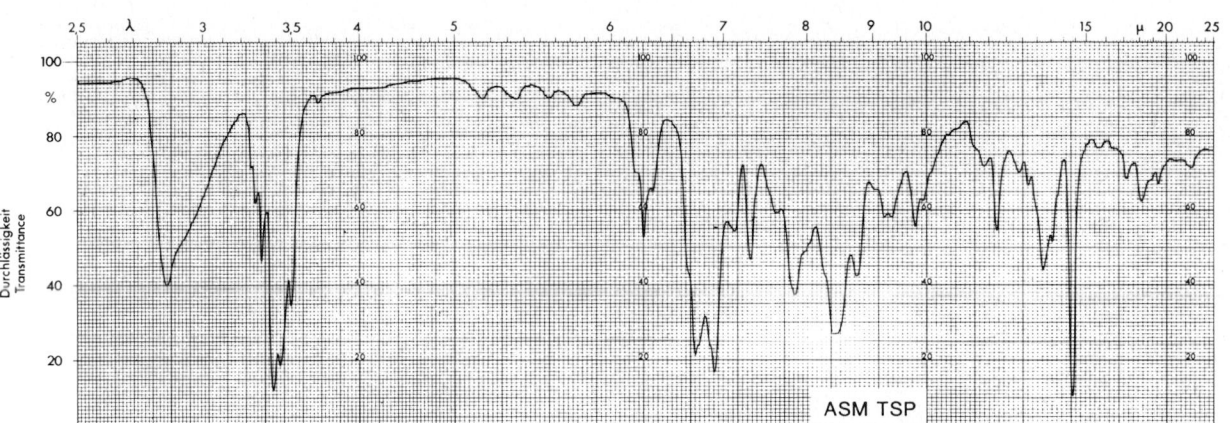

Verbindung:	Alkylierte und aralkylierte Phenole		Compound:	Alkylated and aralkylated phenols		5954
Formel:		M.:	Formula:		M. w.:	
Handelsname:	ASM TSP	Herst.: Bayer	Tradename:	ASM TSP	Manuf.: Bayer	
Präparation:	Kapill. Film	Dez. Nr.: 1.8.10	Preparation:	Capill. film	Dec. No.: 1.8.10	

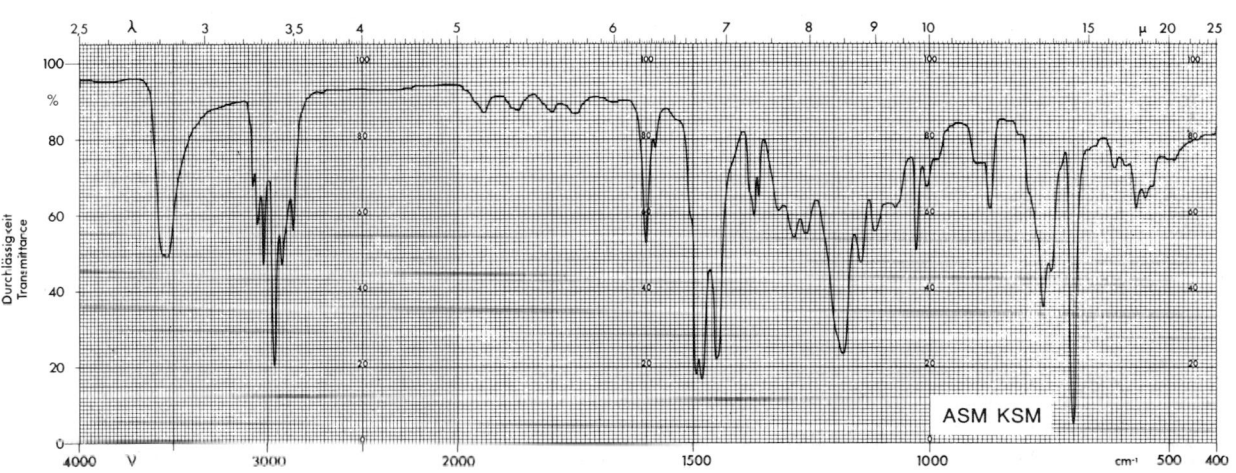

Verbindung:	Gemisch aralkylierter Phenole		Compound:	Mixture of aralkylated phenols		5955
Formel:		M.:	Formula:		M. w.:	
Handelsname:	ASM KSM	Herst.: Bayer	Tradename:	ASM KSM	Manuf.: Bayer	
Präparation:	Schmelzfilm	Dez. Nr.: 1.8.11	Preparation:	Melting film	Dec. No.: 1.8.11	

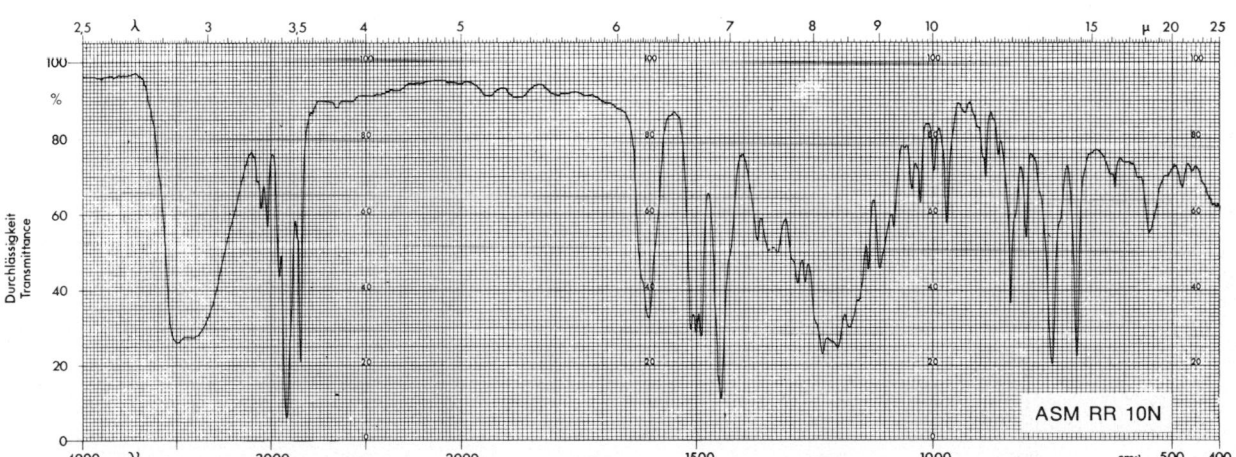

Verbindung:	Gemisch alkylierter Phenole		Compound:	Mixture of alkylated phenols		5956
Formel:		M.:	Formula:		M. w.:	
Handelsname:	ASM RR 10 N	Herst.· Bayer	Tradename:	ASM RR 10 N	Manuf.: Bayer	
Präparation:	Kapill. Film	Dez. Nr.: 1.8.12	Preparation:	Capill. film	Dec. No.: 1.8.12	

Antioxidantien
2. Amine
2.1. Naphthylamine

Antioxidants
2. Amines
2.1. Naphthylamines

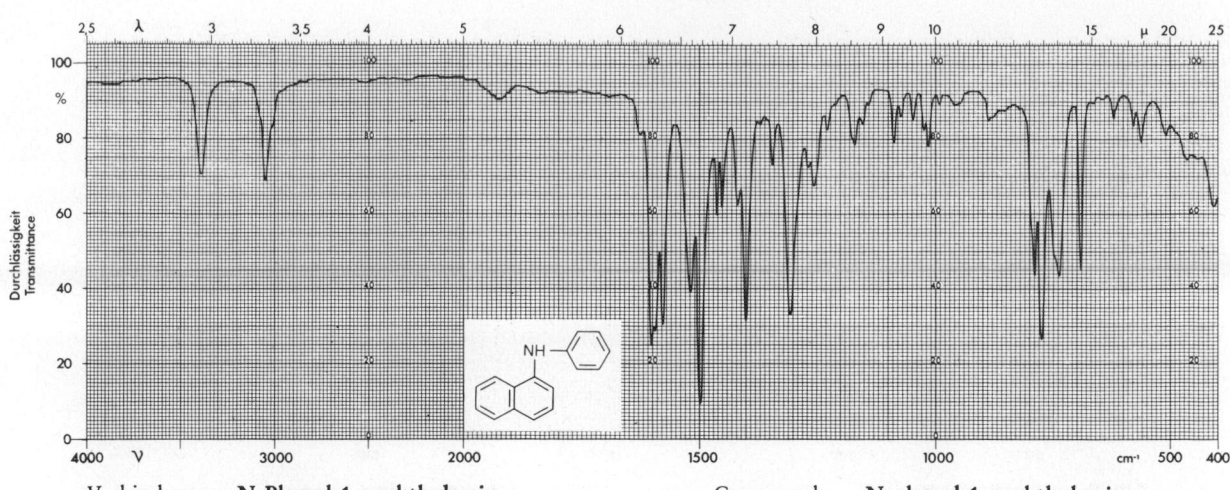

5957   Verbindung: **N-Phenyl-1-naphthylamin**   Compound: **N-phenyl-1-naphthylamine**

Formel:	$C_{16}H_{13}N$	M.:	**219,2**	Formula:	$C_{16}H_{13}N$	M. w.: **219,2**
Handelsname:	**ASM PAN**	Herst.:	**Bayer**	Tradename:	**ASM PAN**	Manuf.: **Bayer**
Präparation:	**Schmelzfilm**	Dez. Nr.:	**2.1.1**	Preparation:	**Melting film**	Dec. No.: **2.1.1**

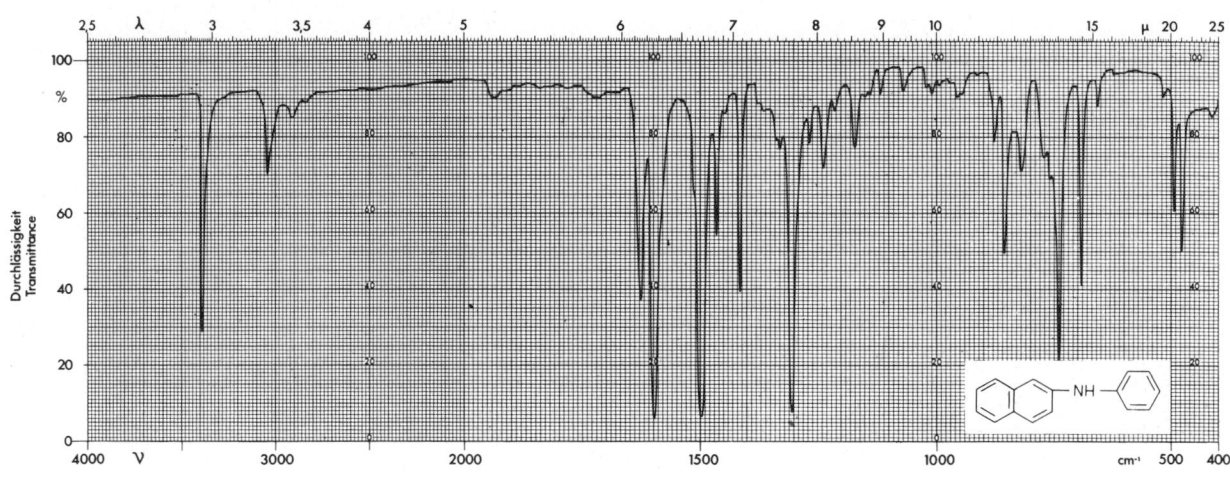

5958   Verbindung: **N-Phenyl-2-naphtylamin**   Compound: **N-phenyl-2-naphtylamine**

Formel:	$C_{16}H_{13}N$	M.:	**219,2**	Formula:	$C_{16}H_{13}N$	M. w.: **219,2**
Handelsname:	**Nonox D**	Herst.:	**ICI**	Tradename:	**Nonox D**	Manuf.: **ICI**
Präparation:	**KBr (3/1000)**	Dez. Nr.:	**2.1.2**	Preparation:	**KBr (3/1000)**	Dec. No.: **2.1.2**

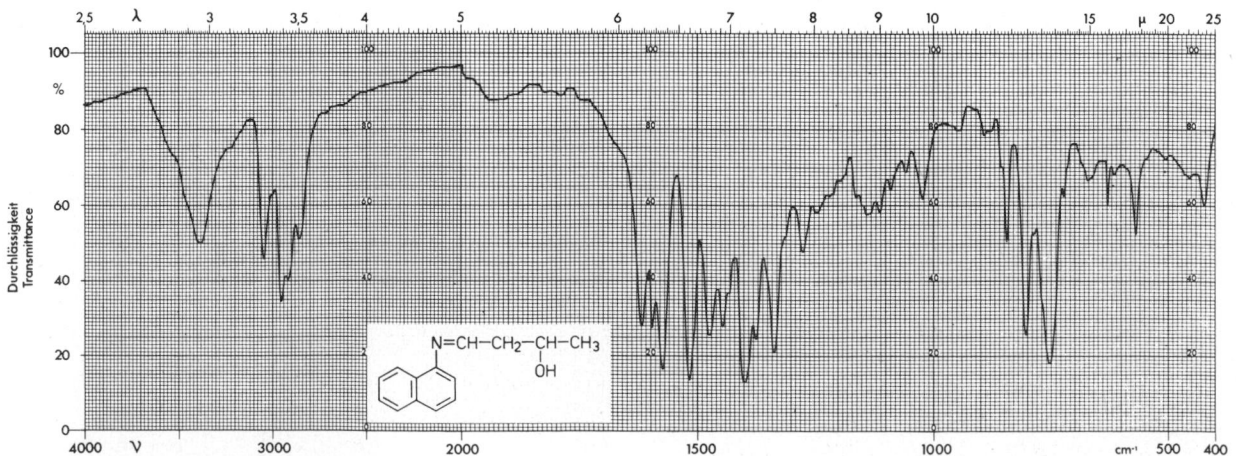

5959   Verbindung: **Aldol-1-naphthylamin**   Compound: **Aldol-1-naphthylamine**

Formel:	$C_{14}H_{15}NO$	M.:	**213,2**	Formula:	$C_{14}H_{15}NO$	M. w.: **213,2**
Handelsname:	**Agerite Resin**	Herst.:	**Vanderbilt**	Tradename:	**Agerite Resin**	Manuf.: **Vanderbilt**
Präparation:	**KBr (3/1000)**	Dez. Nr.:	**2.1.3**	Preparation:	**KBr (3/1000)**	Dec. No.: **2.1.3**

Antioxidantien
2. Amine
2.2. Diphenylamine

Antioxidants
2. Amines
2.2. Diphenylamines

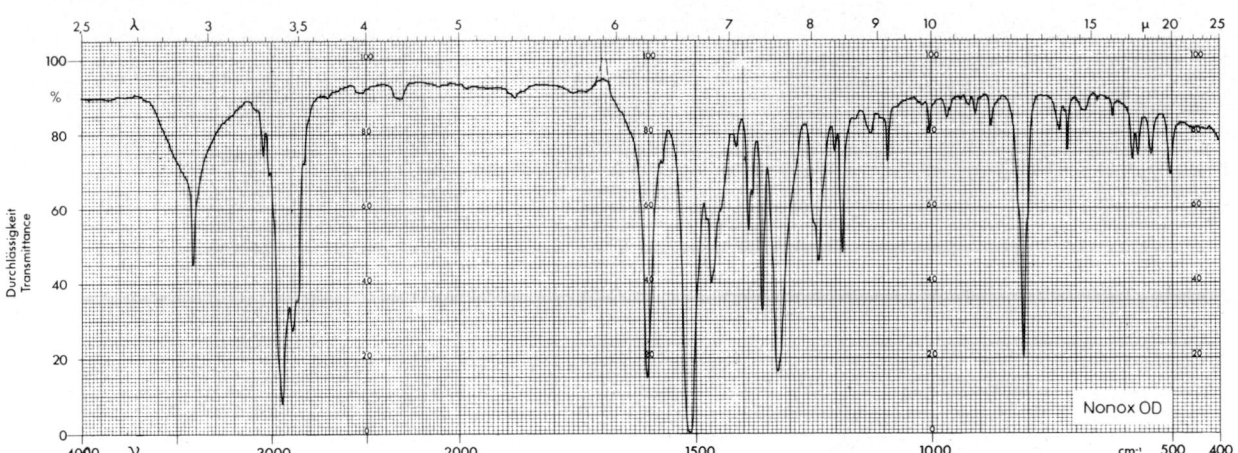

Verbindung: **Octyliertes Diphenylamin**   Compound: **Octylated diphenylamine**   5960
Formel: M.:   Formula: M. w.:
Handelsname: **Nonox OD**   Herst.: **ICI**   Tradename: **Nonox OD**   Manuf.: **ICI**
Präparation: **KBr (3/1000)**   Dez. Nr.: **2.2.1**   Preparation: **KBr (3/1000)**   Dec. No.: **2.2.1**

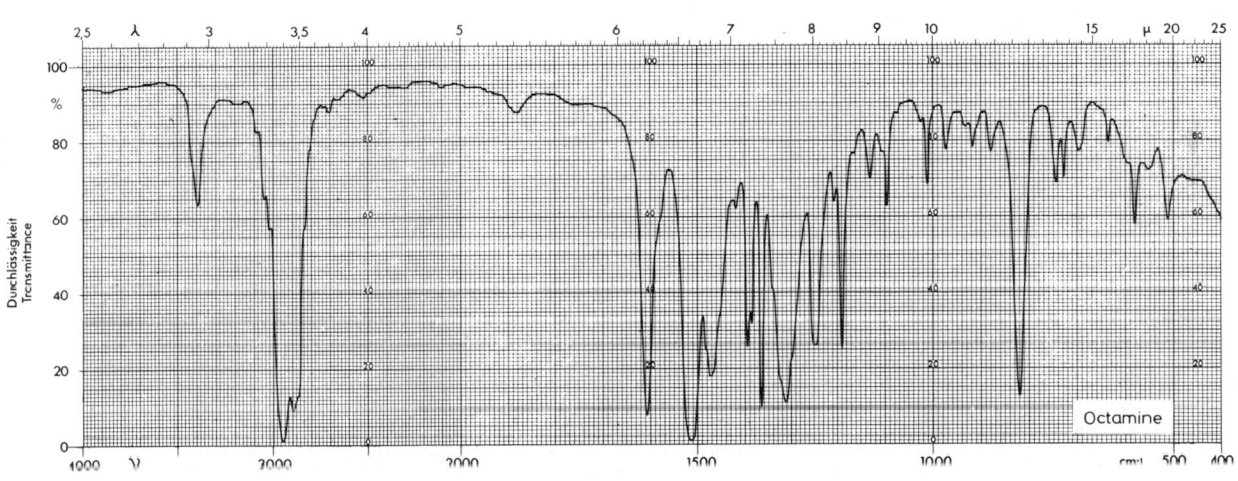

Verbindung: **Octyliertes Diphenylamin**   Compound: **Octylated diphenylamine**   5961
Formel: M.:   Formula: M. w.:
Handelsname: **Octamine**   Herst.: **Bayer**   Tradename: **Octamine**   Manuf.: **Bayer**
Präparation: **Schmelzfilm**   Dez. Nr.: **2.2.2**   Preparation: **Melting film**   Dec. No.: **2.2.2**

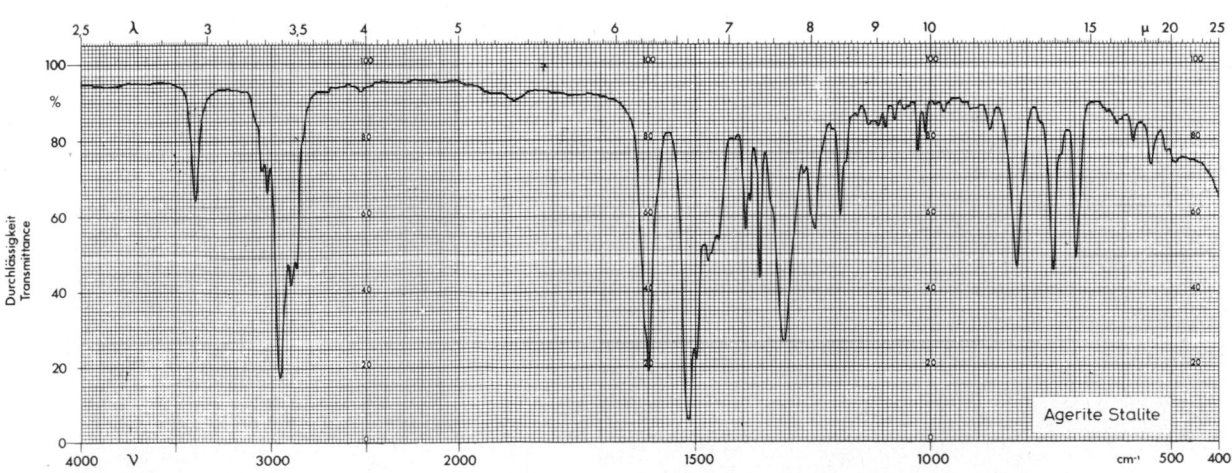

Verbindung: **Mono + Dioctyldiphenylamin**   Compound: **Mono + dioctyl diphenylamine**   5962
Formel: M.:   Formula: M. w.:
Handelsname: **Agerite Stalite**   Herst.: **Vanderbilt**   Tradename: **Agerite Stalite**   Manuf.: **Vanderbilt**
Präparation: **Kapill. Film**   Dez. Nr.: **2.2.3**   Preparation: **Capill. film**   Dec. No.: **2.2.3**

Antioxidantien
2. Amine
2.2. Diphenylamine

Antioxidants
2. Amines
2.2. Diphenylamines

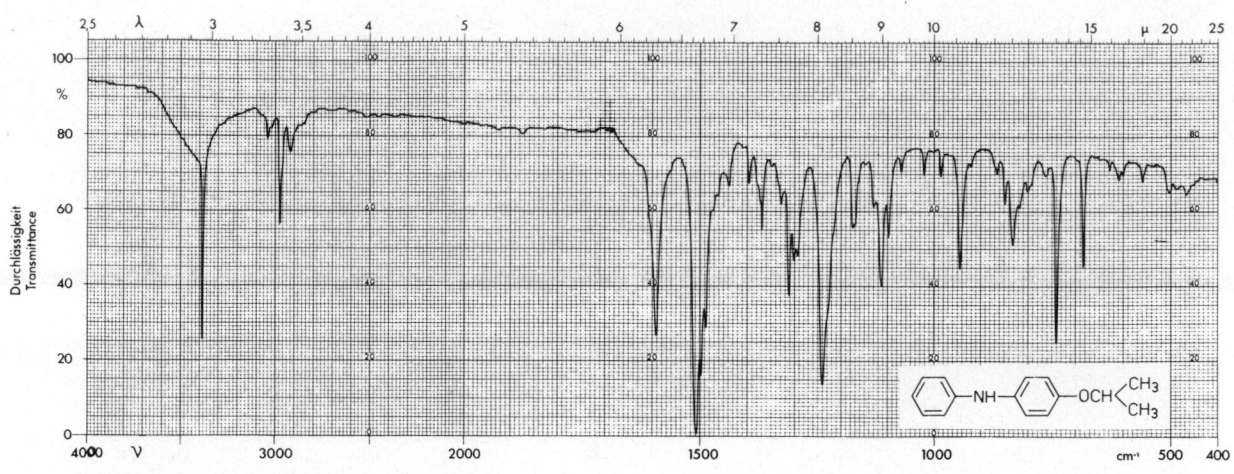

5963	Verbindung:	**4-Isopropoxydiphenylamin**		Compound:	**4-Isopropoxy-diphenylamine**	
	Formel:	$C_{15}H_{17}NO$	M.: **227,2**	Formula:	$C_{15}H_{17}NO$	M. w.: **227,2**
	Handelsname: **Agerite Iso**	Herst.: **Vanderbilt**		Tradename: **Agerite Iso**	Manuf.: **Vanderbilt**	
	Präparation: **KBr (3/1000)**	Dez. Nr.: **2.2.4**		Preparation: **KBr (3/1000)**	Dec. No.: **2.2.4**	

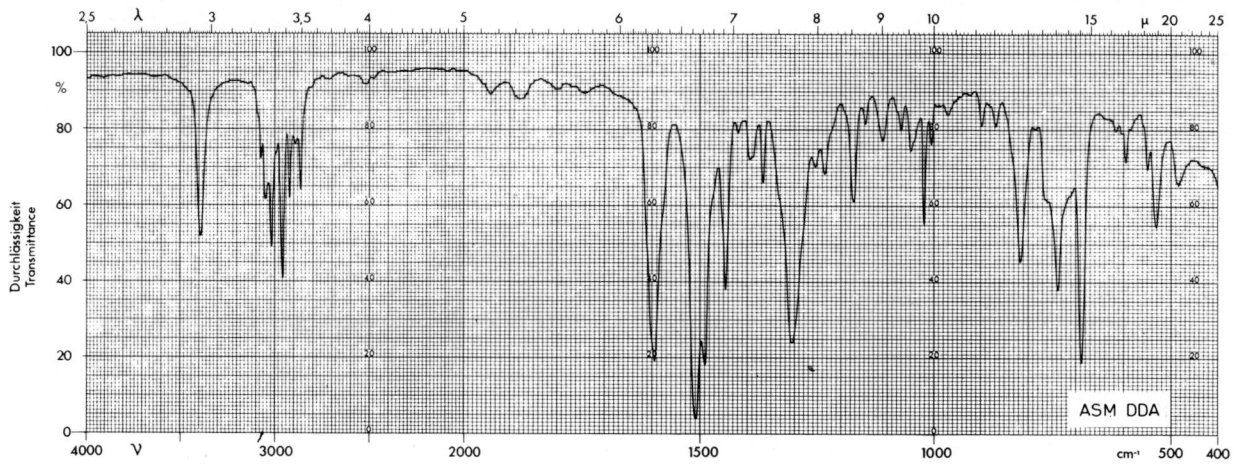

5964	Verbindung:	**Diphenylaminderivat**		Compound:	**Diphenylamine derivate**	
	Formel:		M.:	Formula:		M. w.:
	Handelsname: **ASM DDA**	Herst.: **Bayer**		Tradename: **ASM DDA**	Manuf.: **Bayer**	
	Präparation: **Kapill. Film**	Dez. Nr.: **2.2.5**		Preparation: **Capill. film**	Dec. No.: **2.2.5**	

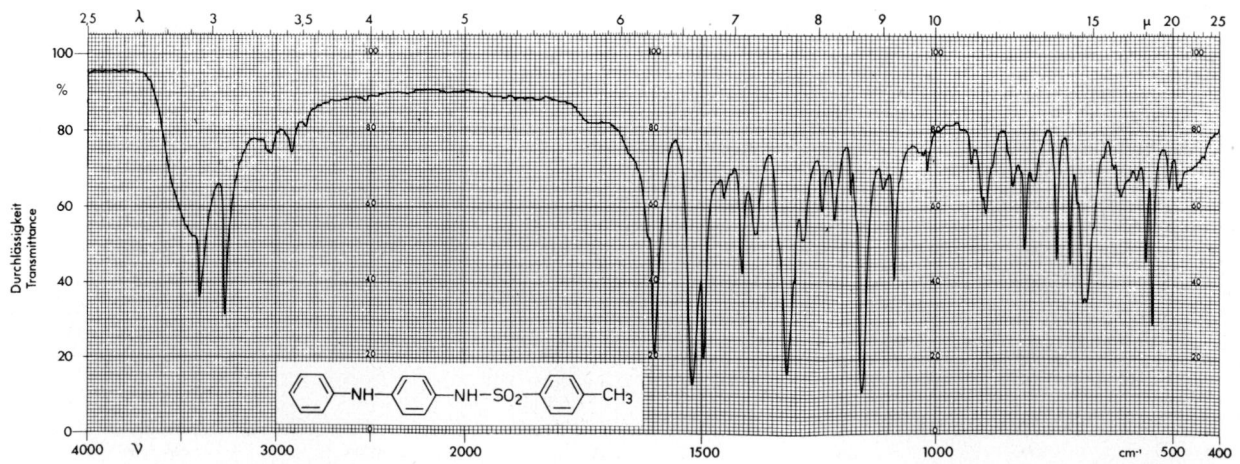

5965	Verbindung:	**4-(p-toluolsulfonamido)diphenylamin**		Compound:	**4-(p-toluenesulfonylamide)diphenylamine**	
	Formel:	$C_{19}H_{18}O_2N_2S$	M.: **338,3**	Formula:	$C_{19}H_{18}O_2N_2S$	M. w.: **338,3**
	Handelsname: **Aranox**	Herst.: **Naugatuck**		Tradename: **Aranox**	Manuf.: **Naugatuck**	
	Präparation: **KBr (7/1000)**	Dez. Nr.: **2.2.6**		Preparation: **KBr (7/1000)**	Dec. No.: **2.2.6**	

Antioxidantien
2. Amine
2.3. Phenylendiamine

Antioxidants
2. Amines
2.3. Phenylenediamines

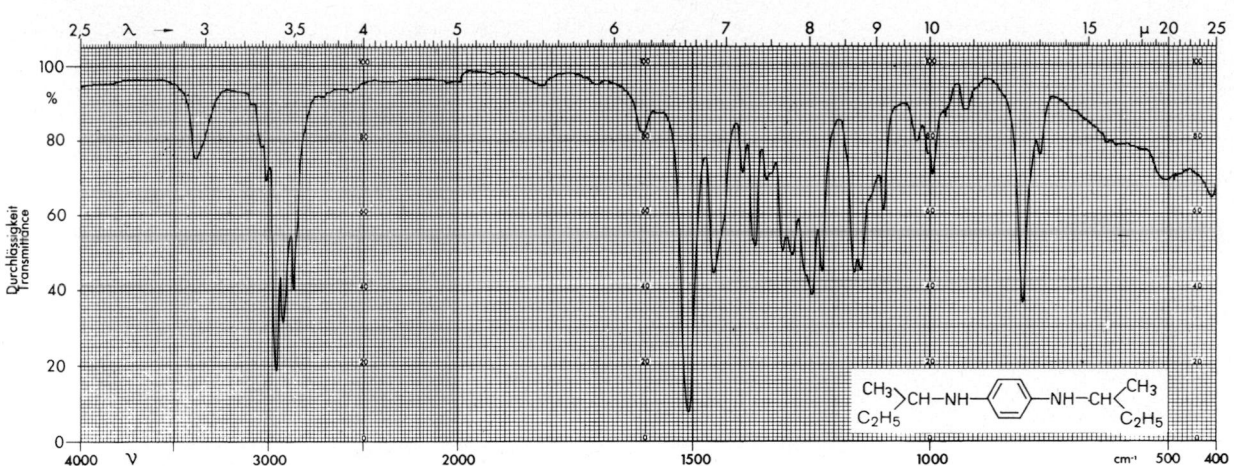

Verbindung: N,N'-di-sec.butyl-p-phenylendiamin
Formel: C₁₄H₂₄N₂   M.: 220,3
Handelsname: Tenamene 2   Herst.: Eastman
Präparation: Kapill. Film   Dez. Nr.: 2.3.1

Compound: N,N'-di-sec.butyl-p-phenylene-diamine
Formula: C₁₄H₂₄N₂   M. w.: 220,3
Tradename: Tenamene 2   Manuf.: Eastman
Preparation: Capill. film   Dec. No.: 2.3.1

5966

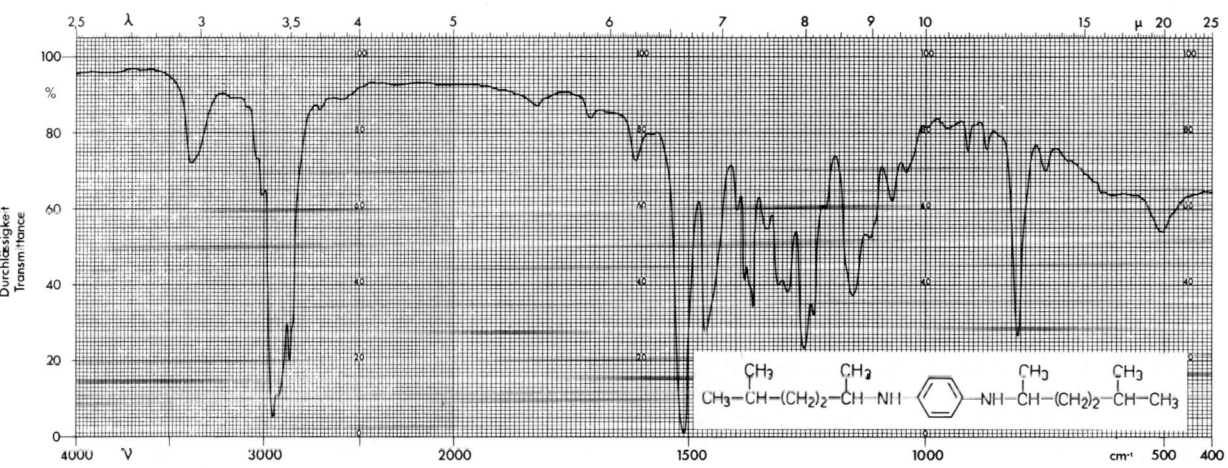

Verbindung: N,N'-Bis(1,4-dimethylpentyl)-p-phenylen-diamin
Formel: C₂₀H₃₆N₂   M.: 304,4
Handelsname: Santoflex 77   Herst.: Monsanto
Präparation: Kapill. Film   Dez. Nr.: 2.3.2

Compound: N,N'-Bis(1,4-di-methylpentyl)-p-phenylene-diamine
Formula: C₂₀H₃₆N₂   M. w.: 304,4
Tradename: Santoflex 77   Manuf.: Monsanto
Preparation: Capill. film   Dec. No.: 2.3.2

5967

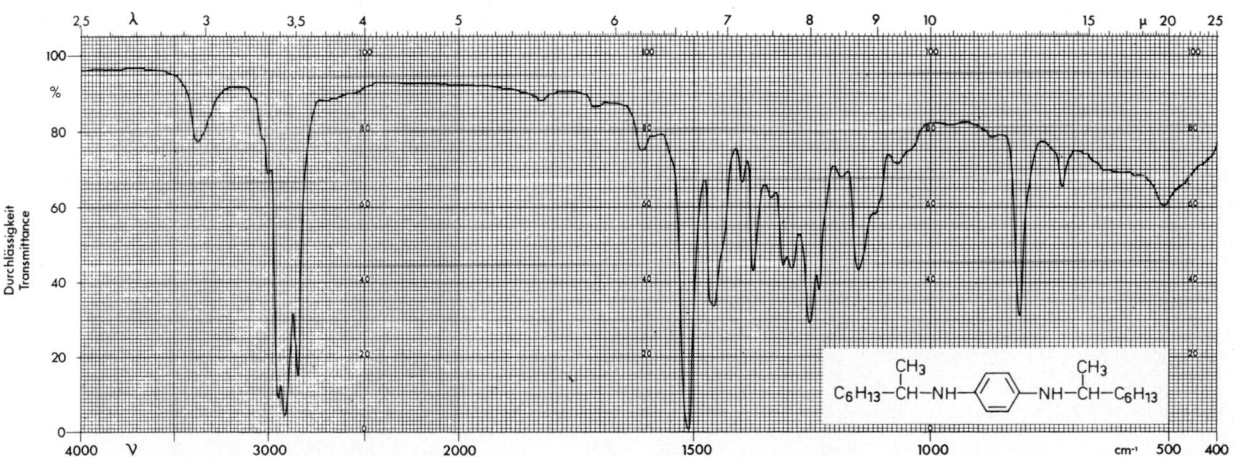

Verbindung: Di-2-octyl-p-phenylendiamin
Formel: C₂₂H₄₀N₂   M.: 332,5
Handelsname: UOP 288   Herst.: United Organic Products
Präparation: Kapill. Film   Dez. Nr.: 2.3.3

Compound: Di-2-octyl-p-phenylene-diamine
Formula: C₂₂H₄₀N₂   M. w.: 332,5
Tradename: UOP 288   Manuf.: United Organic Products
Preparation: Capill. film   Dec. No.: 2.3.3

5968

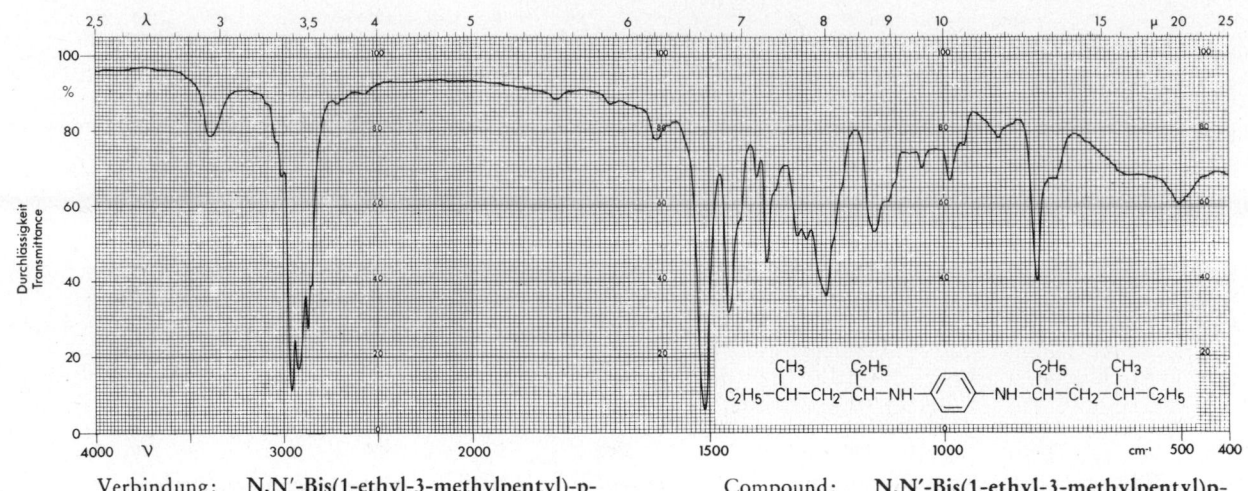

5969

Verbindung:	N,N′-Bis(1-ethyl-3-methylpentyl)-p-phenylendiamin			Compound:	N,N′-Bis(1-ethyl-3-methylpentyl)p-phenylenediamine		
Formel:	C$_{22}$H$_{40}$N$_2$	M.:	332,4	Formula:	C$_{22}$H$_{40}$N$_2$	M. w.:	332,4
Handelsname:	Santoflex 17	Herst.:	Monsanto	Tradename:	Santoflex 17	Manuf.:	Monsanto
Präparation:	Kapill. Film	Dez. Nr.:	2.3.4	Preparation:	Capill. film	Dec. No.:	2.3.4

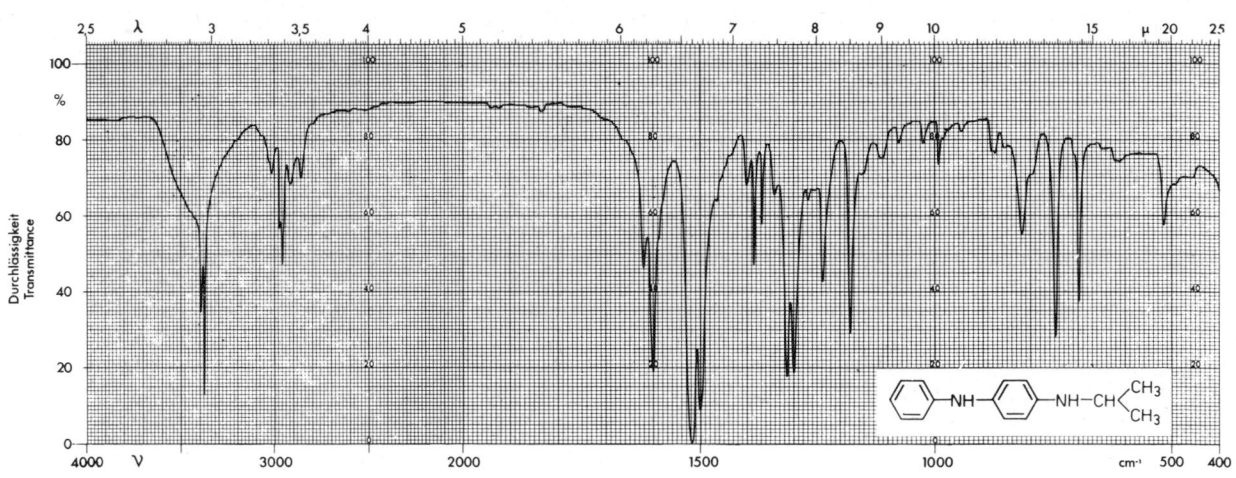

5970

Verbindung:	N-Phenyl-N′-isopropyl-p-phenylendiamin			Compound:	N-phenyl-N′-isopropyl-p-phenylene diamine		
Formel:	C$_{15}$H$_{18}$N$_2$	M.:	226,2	Formula:	C$_{15}$H$_{18}$N$_2$	M. w.:	226,2
Handelsname:	ASM 4010 NA	Herst.:	Bayer	Tradename:	ASM 4010 NA	Manuf.:	Bayer
Präparation:	KBr (6/1000)	Dez. Nr.:	2.3.5	Preparation:	KBr (6/1000)	Dec. No.:	2.3.5

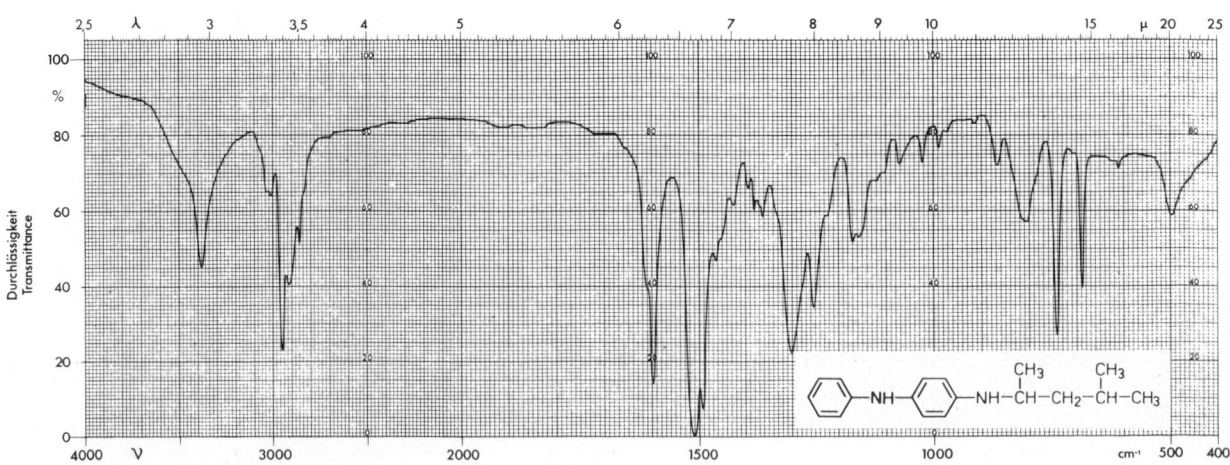

5971

Verbindung:	N-(1,3-Dimethylbutyl)-N′-phenyl-p-phenylendiamin			Compound:	N-(1,3-dimethylbutyl)-N′-phenyl-p-phenylene diamine		
Formel:	C$_{18}$H$_{24}$N$_2$	M.:	268,3	Formula:	C$_{18}$H$_{24}$N$_2$	M. w.:	268,3
Handelsname:	Santoflex 13 Flakes	Herst.:	Monsanto	Tradename:	Santoflex 13 Flakes	Manuf.:	Monsanto
Präparation:	KBr (3/1000)	Dez. Nr.:	2.3.6	Preparation:	KBr (3/1000)	Dec. No.:	2.3.6

Antioxidantien
2. Amine
2.3. Phenylendiamine

Antioxidants
2. Amines
2.3. Phenylenediamines

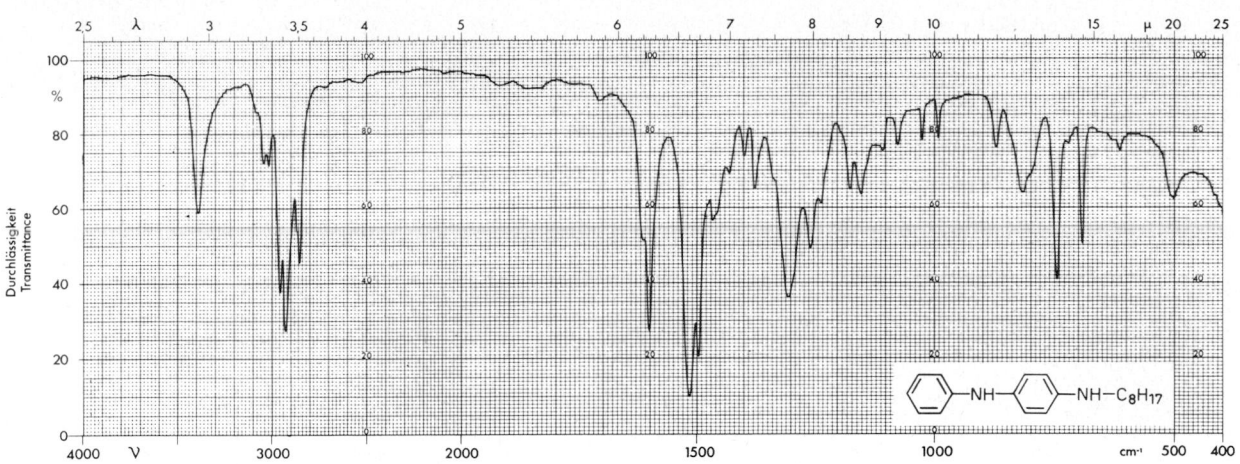

Verbindung:	N-Octyl-N′-phenyl-p-phenylendiamin		Compound:	N-octyl-N′-phenyl-p-phenylenediamine		5972
Formel:	$C_{20}H_{28}N_2$	M.: 296,3	Formula:	$C_{20}H_{28}N_2$	M. w.: 296,3	
Handelsname:	UOP 688	Herst.: United Orga-nic Products	Tradename:	UOP 688	Manuf.: United Orga-nic Products	
Präparation:	Kapill. Film	Dez. Nr.: 2.3.7	Preparation:	Capill. film	Dec. No.: 2.3.7	

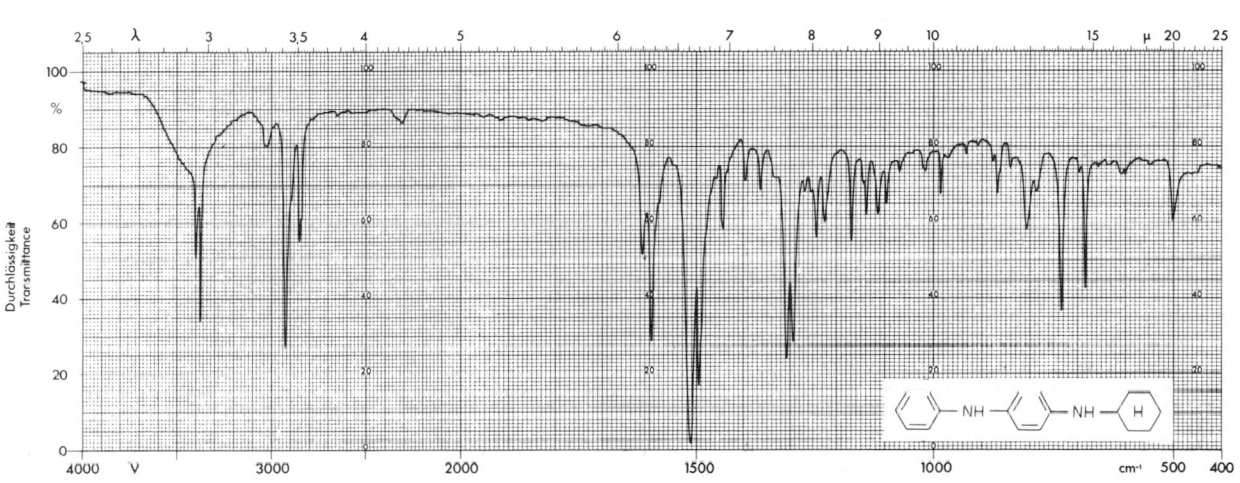

Verbindung:	N-Phenyl-N′-cyclohexyl-p-phenylendiamin		Compound:	N-phenyl-N′-cyclohexyl-p-phenylene-diamine		5973
Formel:	$C_{18}H_{22}N_2$	M.: 266,3	Formula:	$C_{18}H_{22}N_2$	M. w.: 266,3	
Handelsname:	ASM 4010	Herst.: Bayer	Tradename:	ASM 4010	Manuf.: Bayer	
Präparation:	KBr (5/1000)	Dez. Nr.: 2.3.8	Preparation:	KBr (5/1000)	Dec. No.: 2.3.8	

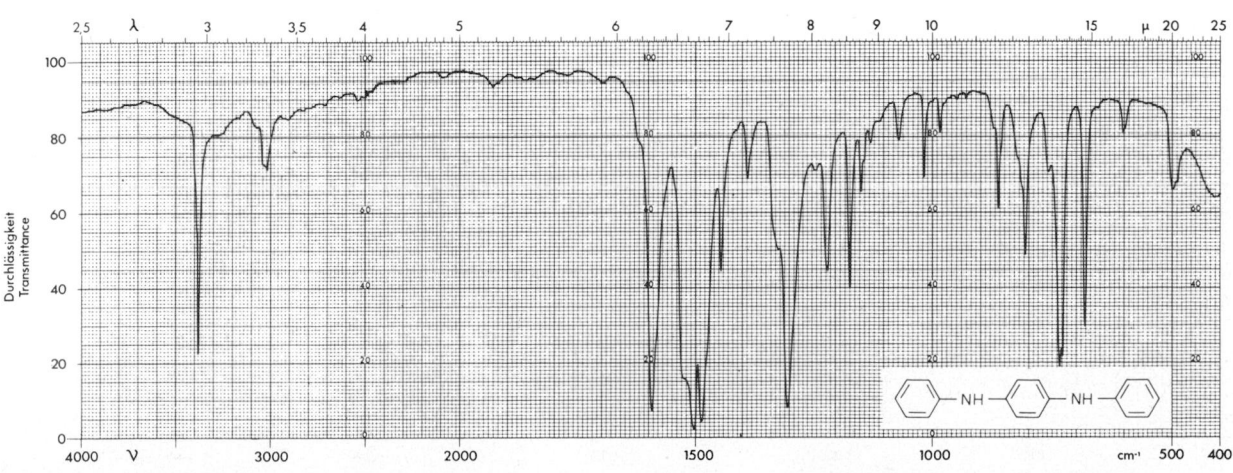

Verbindung:	N,N′-Diphenyl-p-phenylendiamin		Compound:	N,N′-Diphenyl-p-phenylenediamine		5974
Formel:	$C_{18}H_{16}N_2$	M.: 260,3	Formula:	$C_{18}H_{16}N_2$	M. w.: 260,3	
Handelsname:	Nonox DPPD	Herst.: ICI	Tradename:	Nonox DPPD	Manuf.: ICI	
Präparation:	KBr (6/1000)	Dez. Nr.: 2.3.9	Preparation:	KBr (6/1000)	Dec. No.: 2.3.9	

Antioxidantien
2. Amine
2.4. Diarylethylendiamine

Antioxidants
2. Amines
2.4. Diarylethylenediamines

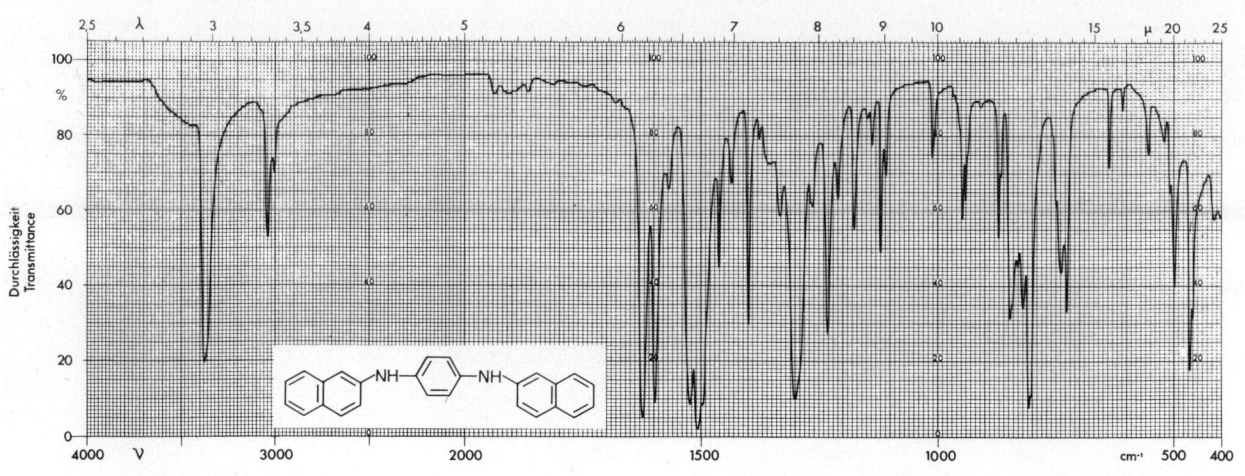

5975   Verbindung: **N,N'-Di-2-naphtyl-p-phenylendiamin**
Formel: **C₂₆H₂₀N₂**   M.: **360,4**
Handelsname: **ASM DNP**   Herst.: **Bayer**
Präparation: **KBr (5/1000)**   Dez. Nr.: **2.3.10**

Compound: **N,N'-Di-2-naphthyl-p-phenylenediamine**
Formula: **C₂₆H₂₀N₂**   M. w.: **360,4**
Tradename: **ASM DNP**   Manuf.: **Bayer**
Preparation: **KBr (5/1000)**   Dec. No.: **2.3.10**

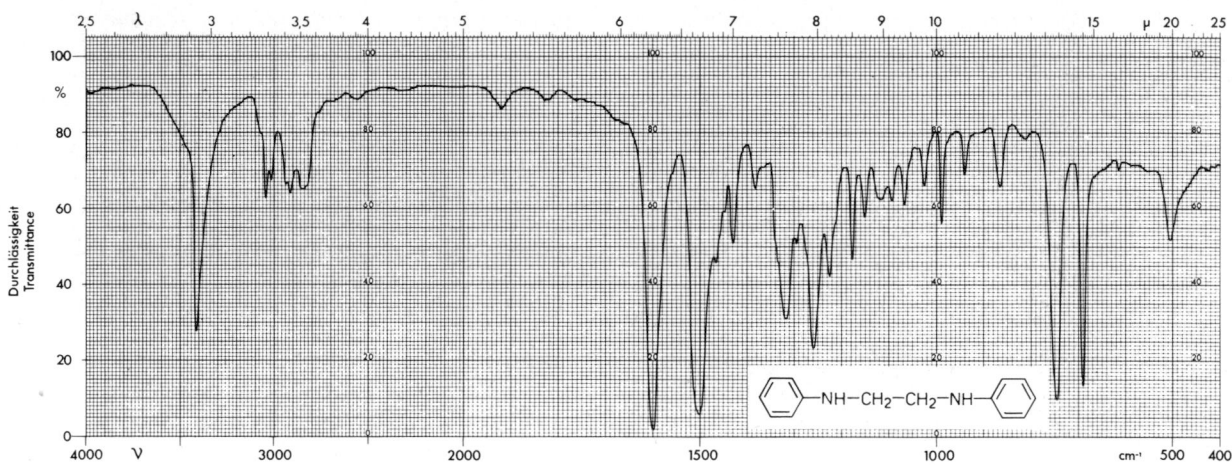

Verbindung: **N,N'-Diphenylethylendiamin**
Formel: **C₁₄H₁₆N₂**   M.: **212,2**
Handelsname: **Stabilite**   Herst.: **Hall**
Präparation: **KBr (6/1000)**   Dez. Nr.: **2.4.1**

Compound: **N,N'-Diphenyl-ethylenediamine**
Formula: **C₁₄H₁₆N₂**   M. w.: **212,2**
Tradename: **Stabilite**   Manuf.: **Hall**
Preparation: **KBr (6/1000)**   Dec. No.: **2.4.1**

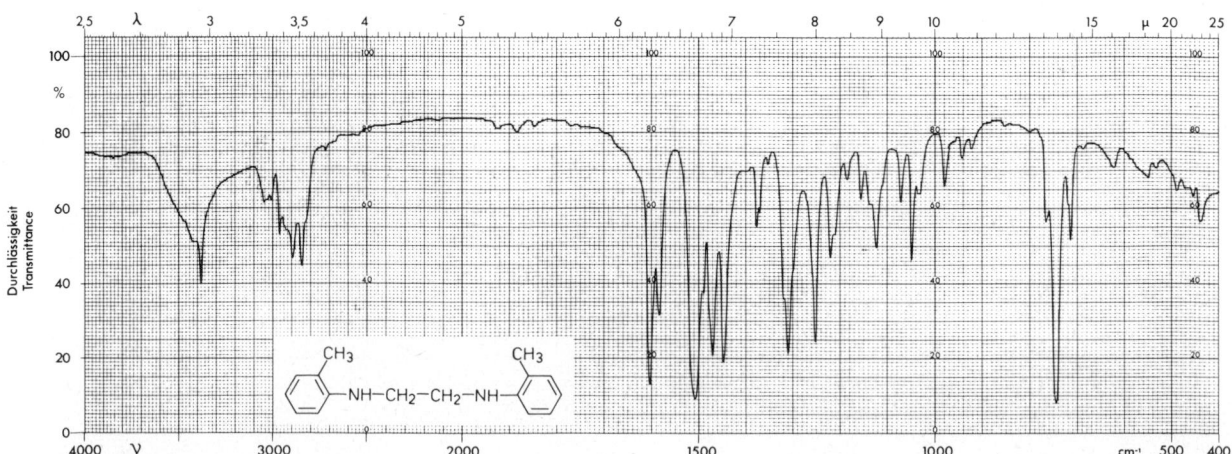

5977   Verbindung: **N,N'-2-Methylphenyl-ethylendiamin**
Formel: **C₁₆H₂₀N₂**   M.: **240,3**
Handelsname: **Stabilite Alba**   Herst.: **Hall**
Präparation: **KBr (2/1000)**   Dez. Nr.: **2.4.2**

Compound: **N,N'-2-Methylphenyl-ethylenediamine**
Formula: **C₁₆H₂₀N₂**   M. w.: **240,3**
Tradename: **Stabilite Alba**   Manuf.: **Hall**
Preparation: **KBr (2/1000)**   Dec. No.: **2.4.2**

Antioxidantien
2. Amine
2.5. Sonstige Amine und Amingemische

Antioxidants
2. Amines
2.5. Miscellaneous Amines and Amine Mixtures

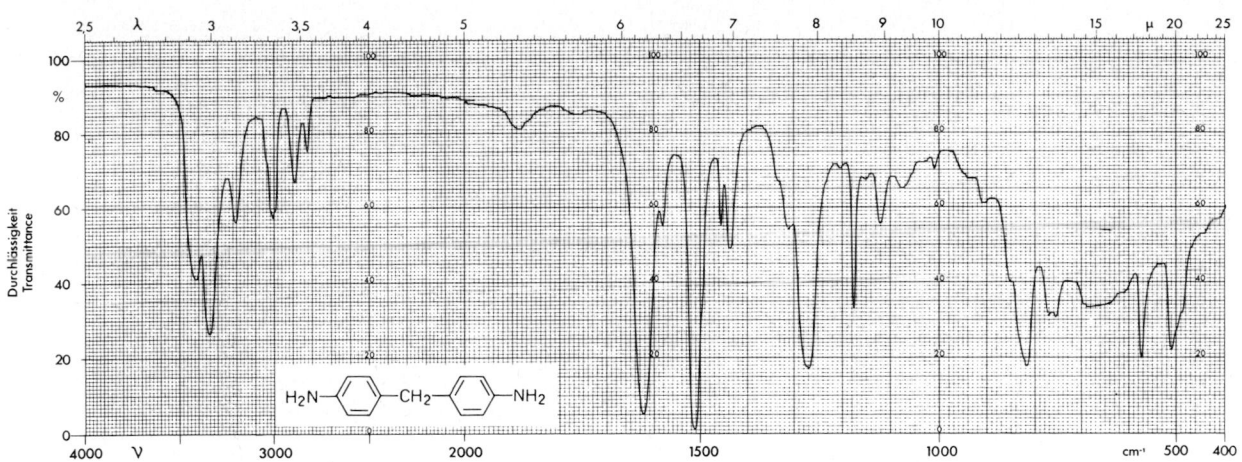

Verbindung:	4,4′-Diaminodiphenylmethan			Compound:	4,4′-Diamino-diphenylmethane	5978
Formel:	$C_{13}H_{14}N_2$	M.:	198,2	Formula:	$C_{13}H_{14}N_2$	M. w.:	198,2
Handelsname:	Tonox	Herst.:	Naugatuck	Tradename:	Tonox	Manuf.:	Naugatuck
Präparation:	Schmelzfilm	Dez. Nr.:	2.5.1	Preparation:	Melting film	Dec. No.:	2.5.1

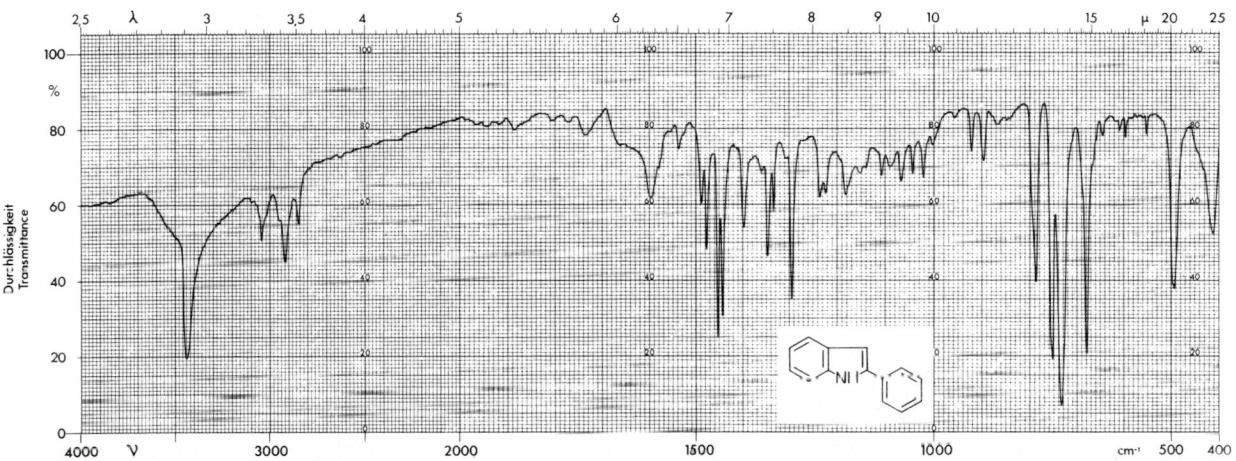

Verbindung:	2-Phenylindol			Compound:	2-Phenylindole	5979
Formel:	$C_{14}H_{11}N$	M.:	193,2	Formula:	$C_{14}H_{11}N$	M. w.:	193,2
Handelsname:	Stabilisator I	Herst.:	Bayer	Tradename:	Stabilisator I	Manuf.:	Bayer
Präparation:	KBr (6/1000)	Dez. Nr.:	2.5.2	Preparation:	KBr (6/1000)	Dec. No.:	2.5.2

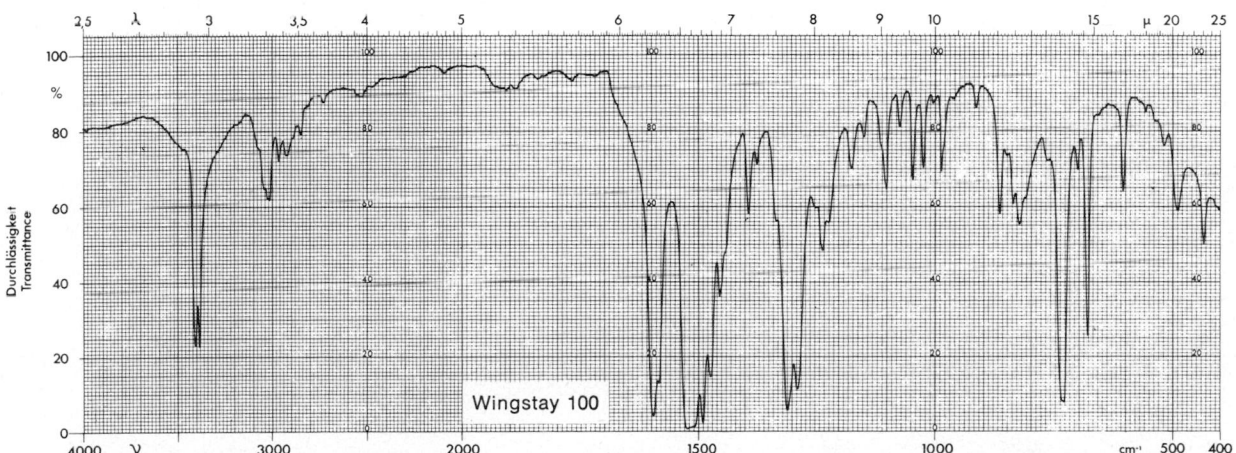

Verbindung:	Gemisch von Diaryl-p-phenylendiaminen			Compound:	Mixture of di-aryl-p-phenylenediamines	5980
Formel:		M.:		Formula:		M. w.:
Handelsname:	Wingstay 100	Herst.:	Goodyear	Tradename:	Wingstay 100	Manuf.:	Goodyear
Präparation:	KBr (3/1000)	Dez. Nr.:	2.5.3	Preparation:	KBr (3/1000)	Dec. No.:	2.5.3

Antioxidantien
2. Amine
2.5. Sonstige Amine und Amingemische

Antioxidants
2. Amines
2.5. Miscellaneous Amines and Amine Mixtures

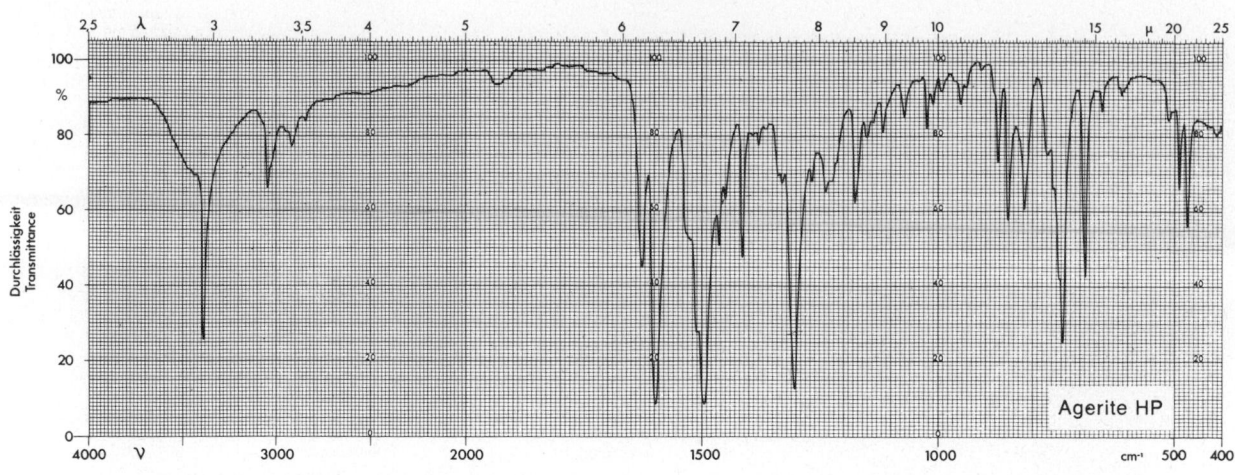

Agerite HP

5981

Verbindung:	Gemisch PBN+DPPD (2+1)		Compound:	Mixture PBN+DPPD (2+1)
Formel:		M.:	Formula:	M. w.:
Handelsname:	**Agerite HP**	Herst.: **Vanderbilt**	Tradename: **Agerite HP**	Manuf.: **Vanderbilt**
Präparation:	**KBr (6/1000)**	Dez. Nr.: **2.5.4**	Preparation: **KBr (6/1000)**	Dec. No.: **2.5.4**

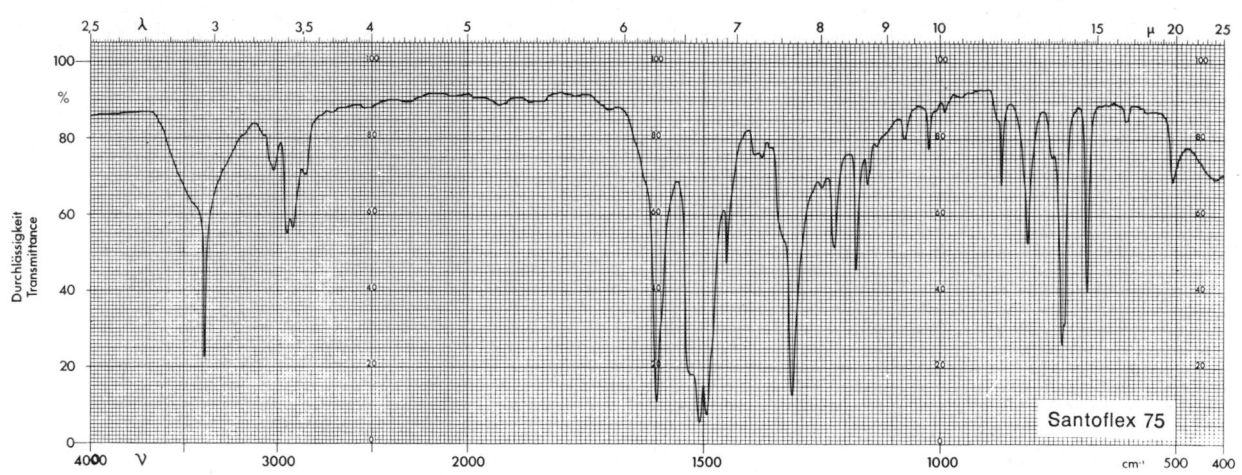

Santoflex 75

5982

Verbindung:	Gemisch DPPD+Santoflex DD (3+1)		Compound:	Mixture DPPD+Santoflex DD (3+1)
Formel:		M.:	Formula:	M. w.:
Handelsname:	**Santoflex 75**	Herst.: **Monsanto**	Tradename: **Santoflex 75**	Manuf.: **Monsanto**
Präparation:	**KBr (3/1000)**	Dez. Nr.: **2.5.5**	Preparation: **KBr (3/1000)**	Dec. No.: **2.5.5**

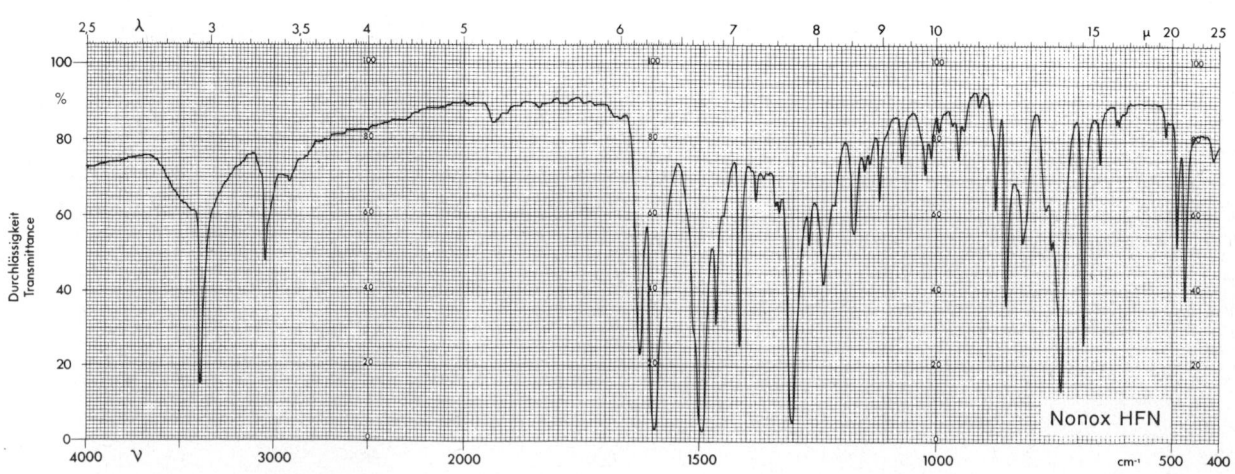

Nonox HFN

5983

Verbindung:	Gemisch aromatischer Amine		Compound:	Mixture of aromatic amines
Formel:		M.:	Formula:	M. w.:
Handelsname:	**Nonox HFN**	Herst.: **ICI**	Tradename: **Nonox HFN**	Manuf.: **ICI**
Präparation:	**KBr (5/1000)**	Dez. Nr.: **2.5.6**	Preparation: **KBr (5/1000)**	Dec. No.: **2.5.6**

Antioxidantien
2. Amine
2.6. Amin-Kondensationsprodukte

Antioxidants
2. Amines
2.6. Amine Condensation Products

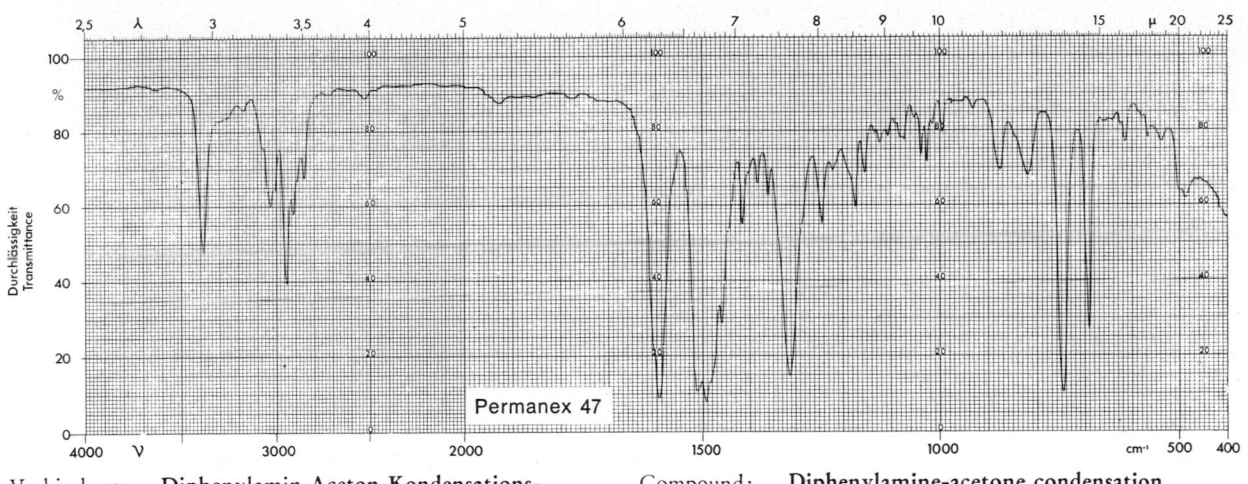

Verbindung: **Diphenylamin-Aceton-Kondensations-** **produkt**	Compound: **Diphenylamine-acetone condensation** **product**
Formel: M.:	Formula: M. w.:
Handelsname: **Permanex 47** Herst.: **Rhône-** **Poulenc**	Tradename: **Permanex 47** Manuf.: **Rhône-** **Poulenc**
Präparation: **Kapill. Film** Dez. Nr.: **2.6.1**	Preparation: **Capill. film** Dec. No.: **2.6.1**

5984

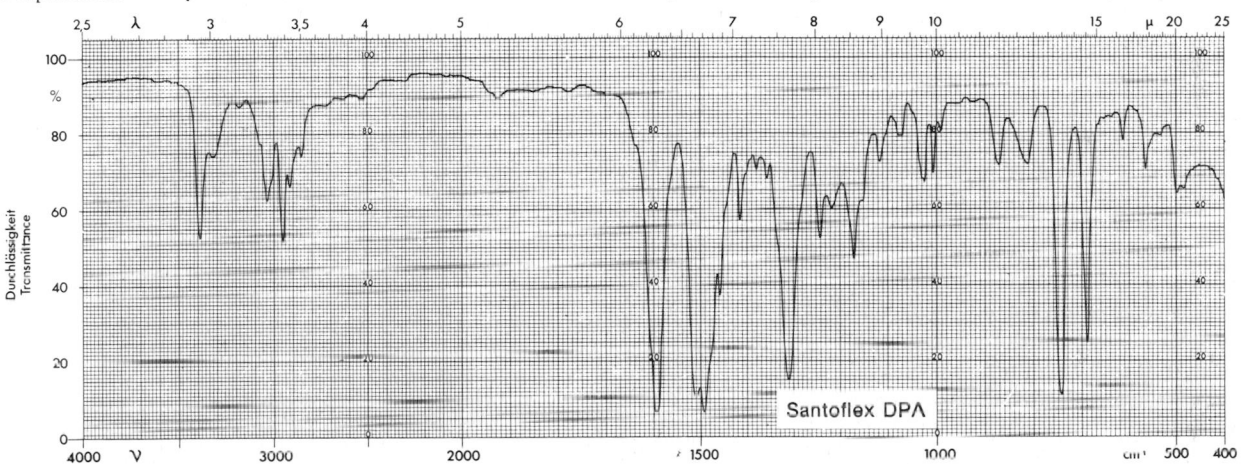

Verbindung: **Diphenylamin-Aceton-Kondensations-** **produkt**	Compound: **Diphenylamine-acetone condensation** **product**
Formel: M.:	Formula: M. w.:
Handelsname: **Santoflex DPA** Herst.: **Monsanto**	Tradename: **Santoflex DPA** Manuf.: **Monsanto**
Präparation: **Kapill. Film** Dez. Nr.: **2.6.2**	Preparation: **Capill. film** Dec. No.: **2.6.2**

5985

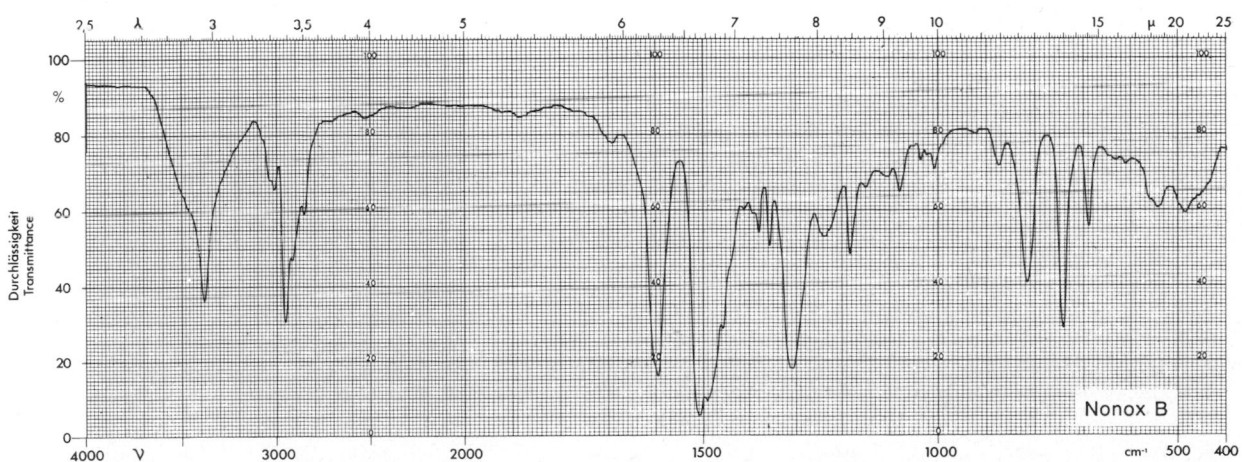

Verbindung: **Amin-Keton-Kondensationsprodukt**	Compound: **Amine-ketone-condensation product**
Formel: M.:	Formula: M. w.:
Handelsname: **Nonox B** Herst.: **ICI**	Tradename: **Nonox B** Manuf.: **ICI**
Präparation: **KBr (7/1000)** Dez. Nr.: **2.6.3**	Preparation: **KBr (7/1000)** Dec. No.: **2.6.3**

5986

Antioxidantien
2. Amine
2.6. Amin-Kondensationsprodukte

Antioxidants
2. Amines
2.6. Amine Condensation Products

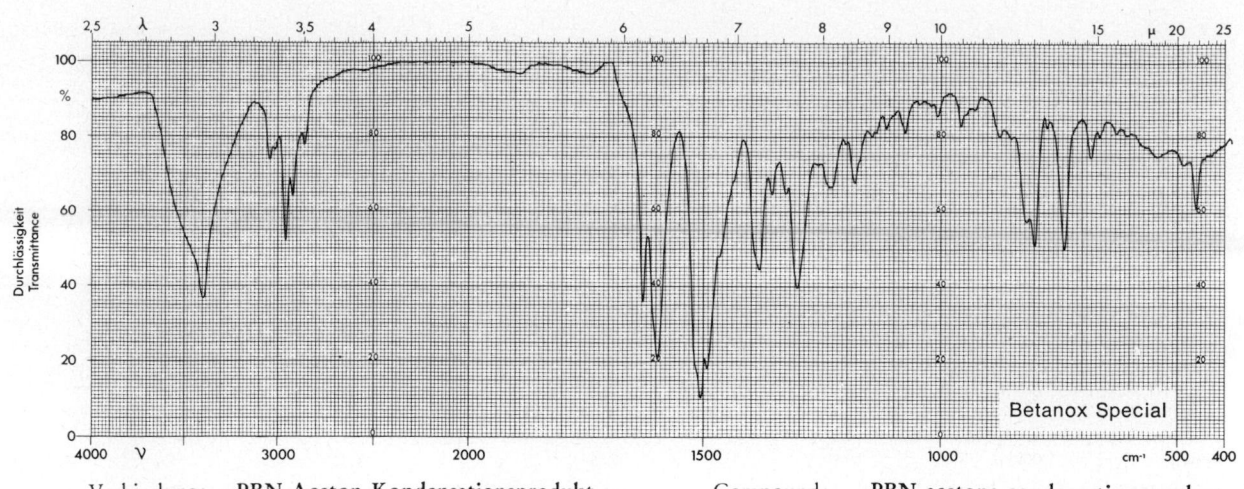

5987   Verbindung: **PBN-Aceton-Kondensationsprodukt**   Compound: **PBN-acetone-condensation product**

Formel:	M.:		Formula:	M. w.:
Handelsname: **Betanox Spezial**	Herst.: **Naugatuck**		Tradename: **Betanox Spezial**	Manuf.: **Naugatuck**
Präparation: **KBr (5/1000)**	Dez. Nr.: **2.6.4**		Preparation: **KBr (5/1000)**	Dec. No.: **2.6.4**

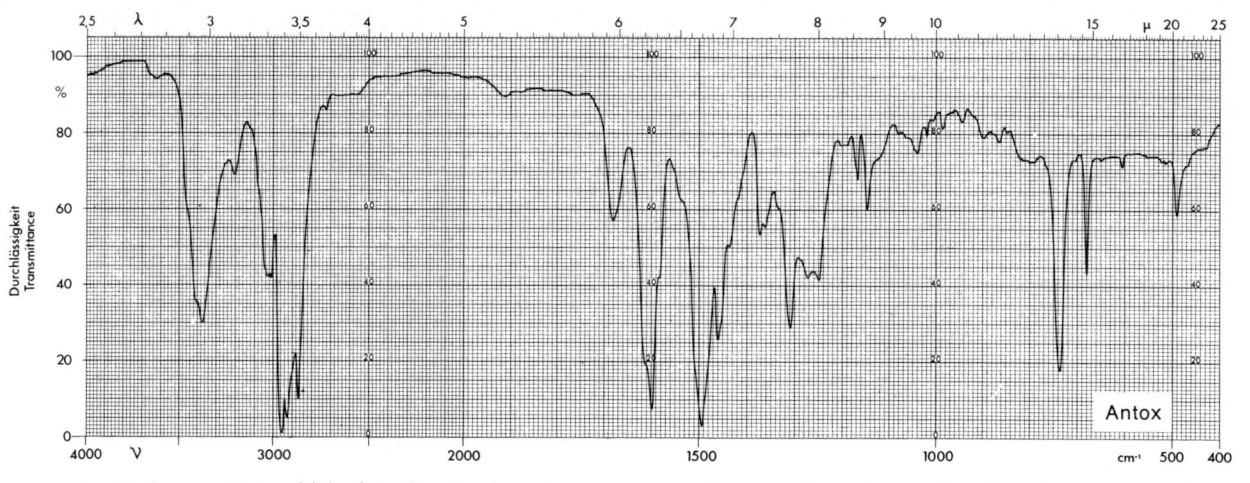

5988   Verbindung: **Butyraldehyd Anilin-Kondensations-produkt**   Compound: **Butyraldehyde aniline condensation product**

Formel:	M.:		Formula:	M. w.:
Handelsname: **Antox**	Herst.: **Du Pont**		Tradename: **Antox**	Manuf.: **Du Pont**
Präparation: **Kapill. Film**	Dez. Nr.: **2.6.5**		Preparation: **Capill. film**	Dec. No.: **2.6.5**

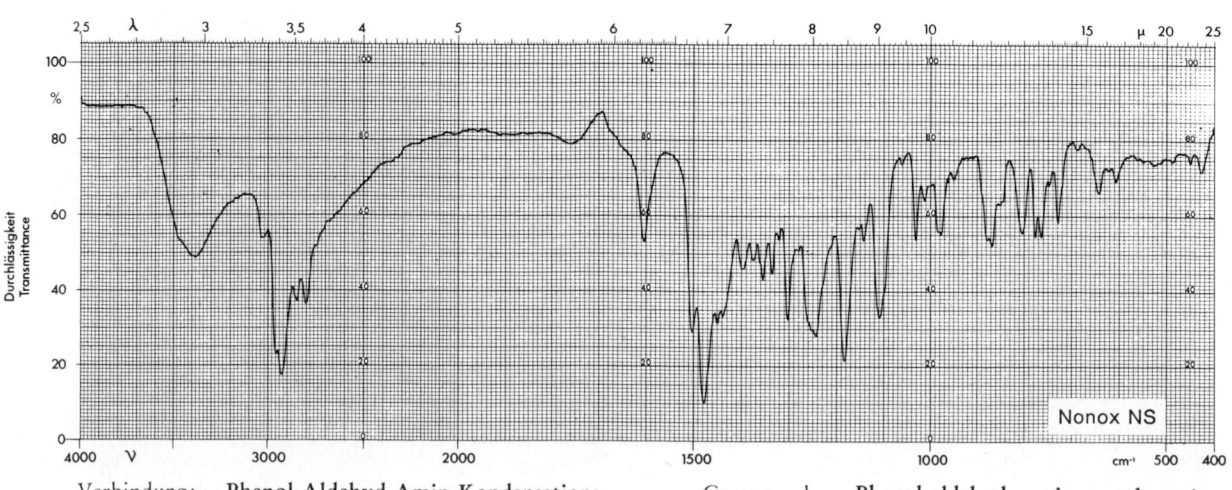

5989   Verbindung: **Phenol-Aldehyd-Amin-Kondensations-produkt**   Compound: **Phenol-aldehyde-amine-condensation product**

Formel:	M.:		Formula:	M. w.:
Handelsname: **Nonox NS**	Herst.: **ICI**		Tradename: **Nonox NS**	Manuf.: **ICI**
Präparation: **Kapill. Film**	Dez. Nr.: **2.6.6**		Preparation: **Capill. film**	Dec. No.: **2.6.6**

Antioxidantien
3. Sonstige N-haltige Verbindungen
3.1. Chinoline

Antioxidants
3. Other N-containing Substances
3.1. Quinolines

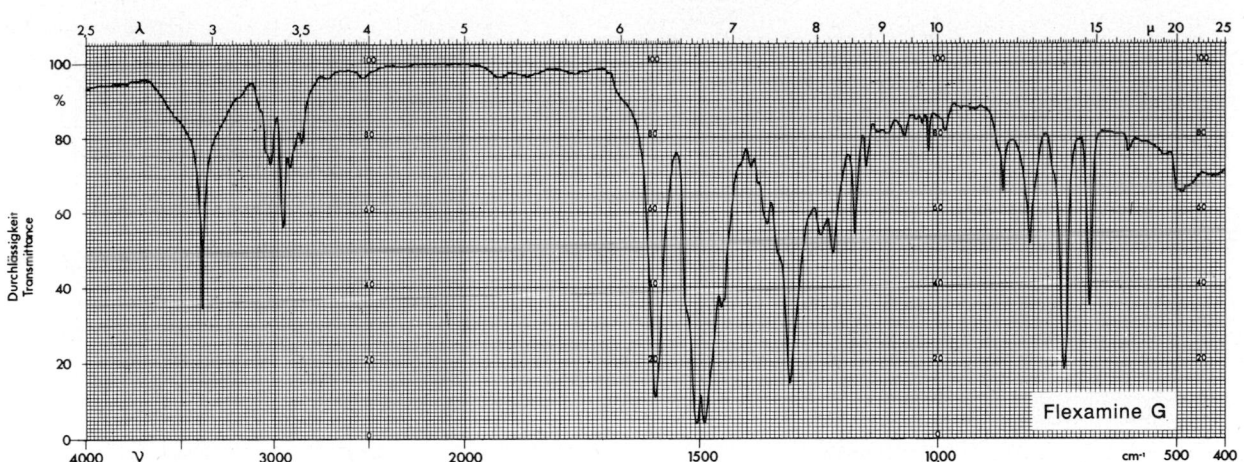

Verbindung:	Gemisch mit Diarylamin-Keton-Konden-sationsprodukt		Compound:	Mixture with diarylamine-ketone-condensation product		5990
Formel:		M.:	Formula:		M. w.:	
Handelsname:	Flexamine G	Herst.: Naugatuck	Tradename:	Flexamine G	Manuf.: Naugatuck	
Präparation:	KBr (5/1000)	Dez. Nr.: 2.6.7	Preparation:	KBr (5/1000)	Dec. No.: 2.6.7	

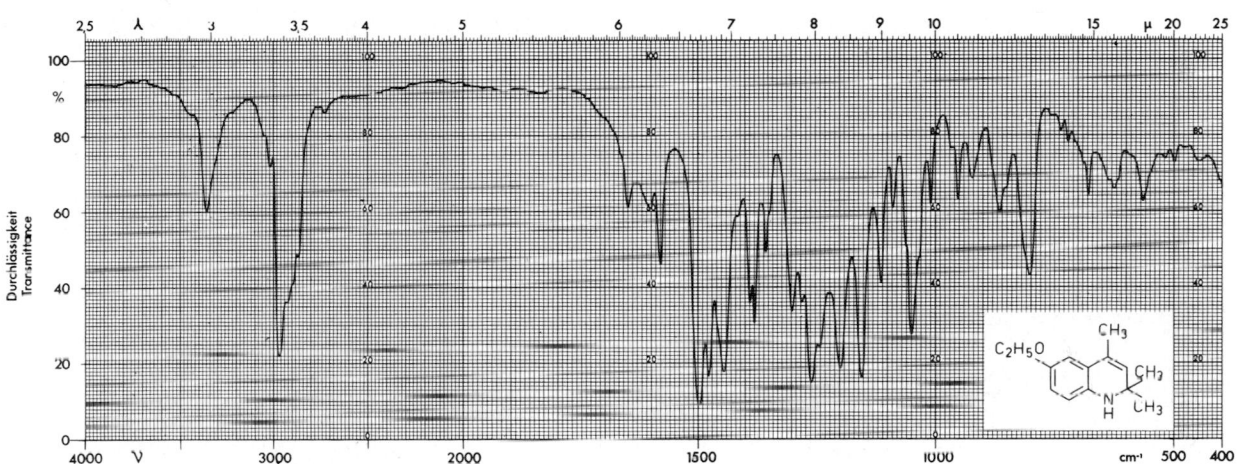

Verbindung:	6-Ethoxy-2,2,4-trimethyl-1,2-dihydro-chinolin		Compound:	6-Ethoxy-2,2,4-trimethyl-1,2-dihydro-quinoline		5991
Formel:	$C_{14}H_{19}ON$	M.: 217,3	Formula:	$C_{14}H_{19}ON$	M. w.: 217,3	
Handelsname:	Santoflex AW	Herst.: Monsanto	Tradename:	Santoflex AW	Manuf.: Monsanto	
Präparation:	Kapill. Film	Dez. Nr.: 3.1.1	Preparation:	Capill. film	Dec. No.: 3.1.1	

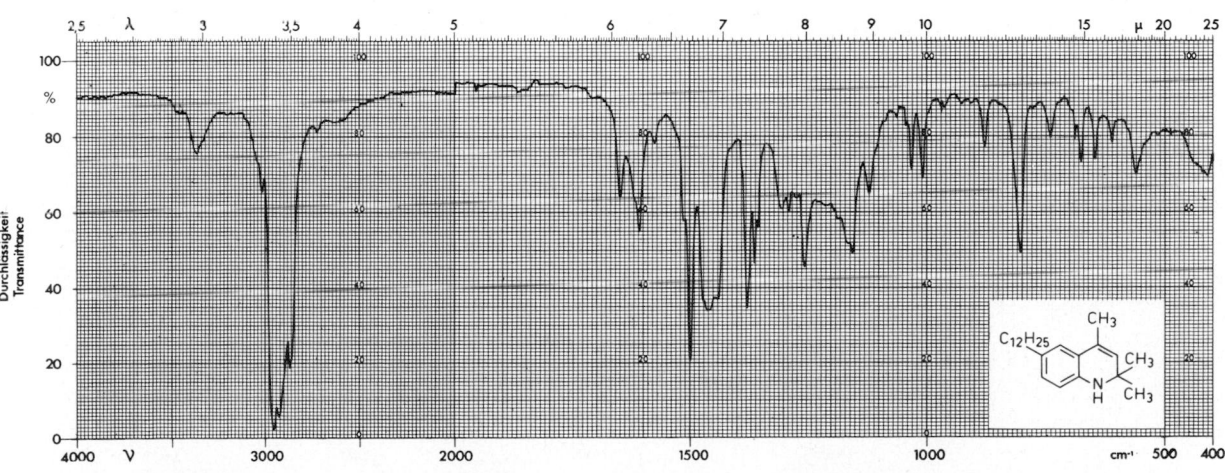

Verbindung:	6-Dodecyl-2,2,4-trimethyl-1,2-dihydro-chinolin		Compound:	6-Dodecyl-2,2,4-trimethyl-1,2-dihydro-quinoline		5992
Formel:	$C_{24}H_{39}N$	M.: 341,5	Formula:	$C_{24}H_{39}N$	M. w.: 341,5	
Handelsname:	Santoflex DD	Herst.: Monsanto	Tradename:	Santoflex DD	Manuf.: Monsanto	
Präparation:	Kapill. Film	Dez. Nr.: 3.1.2	Preparation:	Capill. film	Dec. No.: 3.1.2	

Antioxidantien
3. Sonstige N-haltige Verbindungen
3.2. Mercaptobenzimidazole

Antioxidants
3. Other N-containing Substances
3.2. Mercaptobenzimidazoles

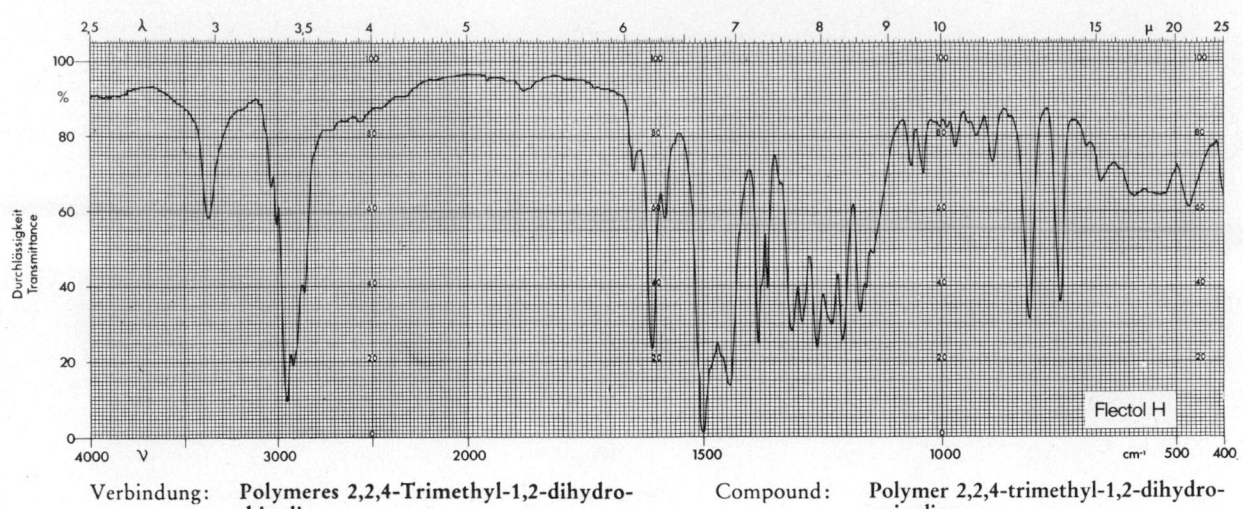

5993   Verbindung: **Polymeres 2,2,4-Trimethyl-1,2-dihydro-chinolin**   Compound: **Polymer 2,2,4-trimethyl-1,2-dihydro-quinoline**

Formel:	M.:	Formula:	M. w.:
Handelsname: **Flectol H**	Herst.: **Monsanto**	Tradename: **Flectol H**	Manuf.: **Monsanto**
Präparation: **KBr (6/1000)**	Dez. Nr.: **3.1.3**	Preparation: **KBr (6/1000)**	Dec. No.: **3.1.3**

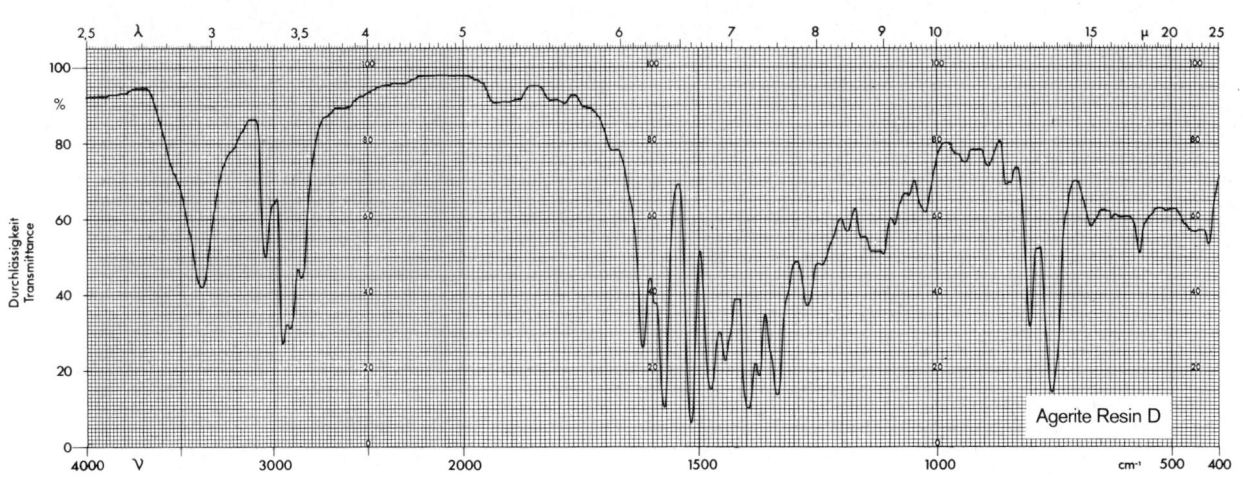

5994   Verbindung: **Polymeres 2,2,4-Trimethyl-1,2-dihydro-chinolin**   Compound: **Polymer 2,2,4-trimethyl-1,2-dihydro-quinoline**

Formel:	M.:	Formula:	M. w.:
Handelsname: **Agerite Resin D**	Herst.: **Vanderbilt**	Tradename: **Agerite Resin D**	Manuf.: **Vanderbilt**
Präparation: **KBr (6/1000)**	Dez. Nr.: **3.1.4**	Preparation: **KBr (6/1000)**	Dec. No.: **3.1.4**

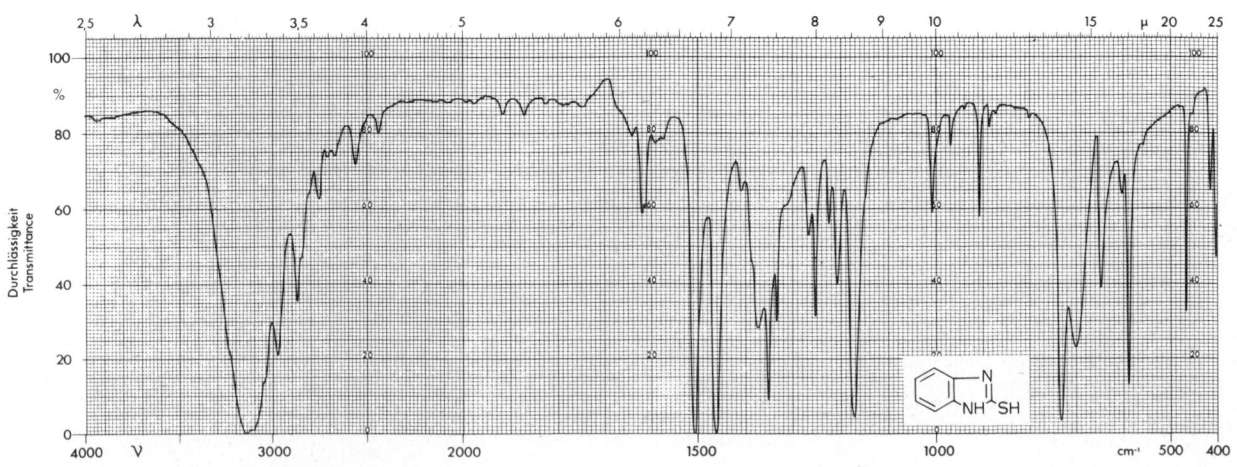

5995   Verbindung: **2-Mercaptobenzimidazol**   Compound: **2-Mercaptobenzimidazole**

Formel: $C_7H_6N_2S$	M.: **150,1**	Formula: $C_7H_6N_2S$	M. w.: **150,1**
Handelsname: **ASM MB**	Herst.: **Bayer**	Tradename: **ASM MB**	Manuf.: **Bayer**
Präparation: **KBr (3/1000)**	Dez. Nr.: **3.2.1**	Preparation: **KBr (3/1000)**	Dec. No.: **3.2.1**

Antioxidantien
3. Sonstige N-haltige Verbindungen
3.3. Harnstoff-, Carbodiimid-Derivate

Antioxidants
3. Other N-containing Substances
3.3. Urea and Carbodiimide Derivatives

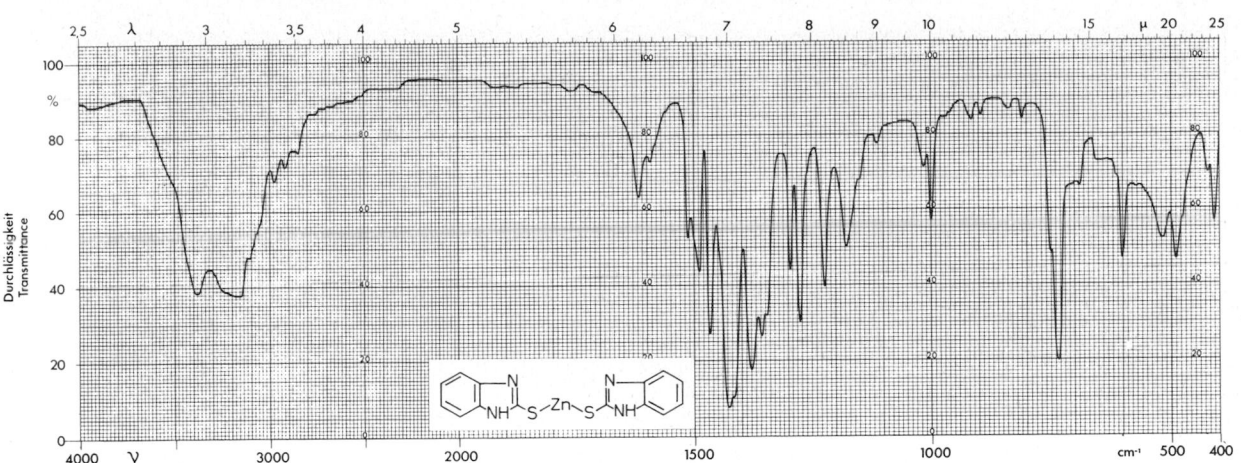

Verbindung:	Zn-2-Mercaptobenzimidazol			Compound:	Zn-2-mercaptobenzimidazole			5996
Formel:	$C_{14}H_{10}N_4S_2Zn$	M.:	363,6	Formula:	$C_{14}H_{10}N_4S_2Zn$	M. w.:	363,6	
Handelsname:	ASM ZMB	Herst.:	Bayer	Tradename:	ASM ZMB	Manuf.:	Bayer	
Präparation:	KBr (6/1000)	Dez. Nr.:	3.2.2	Preparation:	KBr (6/1000)	Dec. No.:	3.2.2	

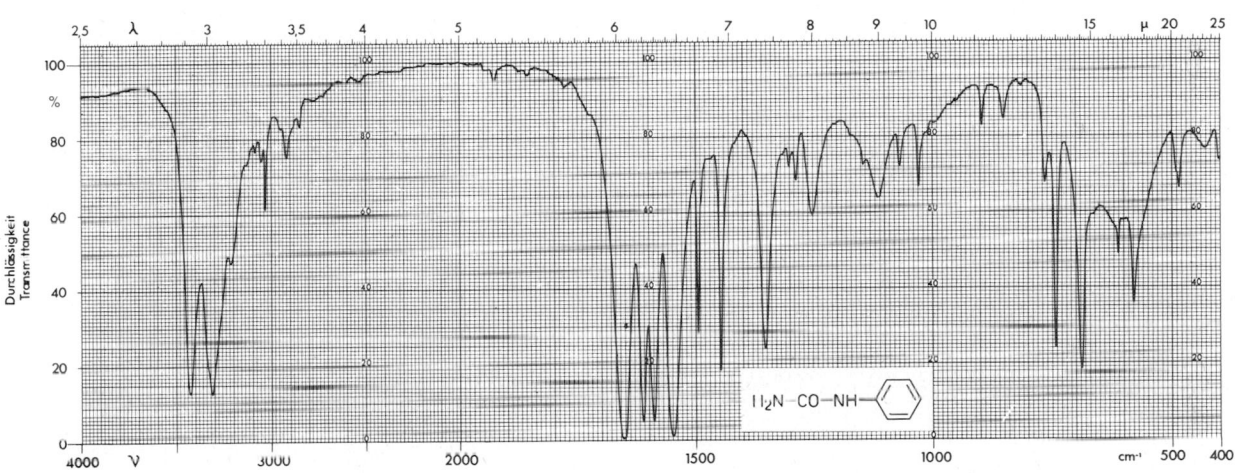

Verbindung:	Monophenylharnstoff			Compound:	Mono phenyl urea			5997
Formel:	$C_7H_8N_2O$	M.:	136,1	Formula:	$C_7H_8N_2O$	M. w.:	136,1	
Handelsname:	Stabilisator VH	Herst.:	Hüls	Tradename:	Stabilisator VH	Manuf.:	Hüls	
Präparation:	KBr (5/1000)	Dez. Nr.:	3.3.1	Preparation:	KBr (5/1000)	Dec. No.:	3.3.1	

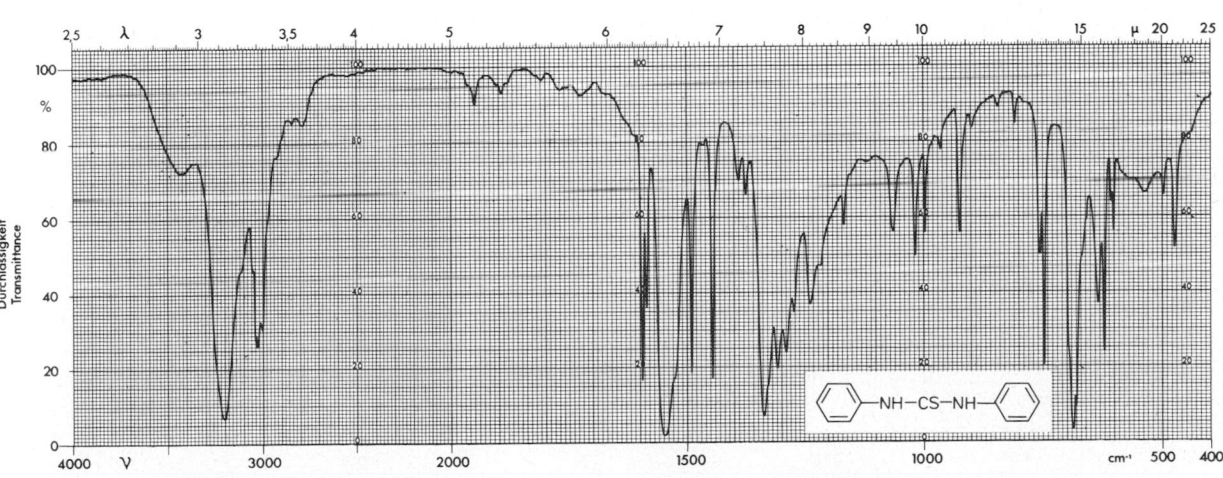

Verbindung:	N,N'-Diphenylthioharnstoff			Compound:	N,N'-Diphenyl thio urea			5998
Formel:	$C_{13}H_{12}N_2S$	M.:	228,2	Formula:	$C_{13}H_{12}N_2S$	M. w.:	228,2	
Handelsname:	Stabilisator C	Herst.:	Bayer	Tradename:	Stabilisator C	Manuf.:	Bayer	
Präparation:	KBr (5/1000)	Dez. Nr.:	3.3.2	Preparation:	KBr (5/1000)	Dec. No.:	3.3.2	

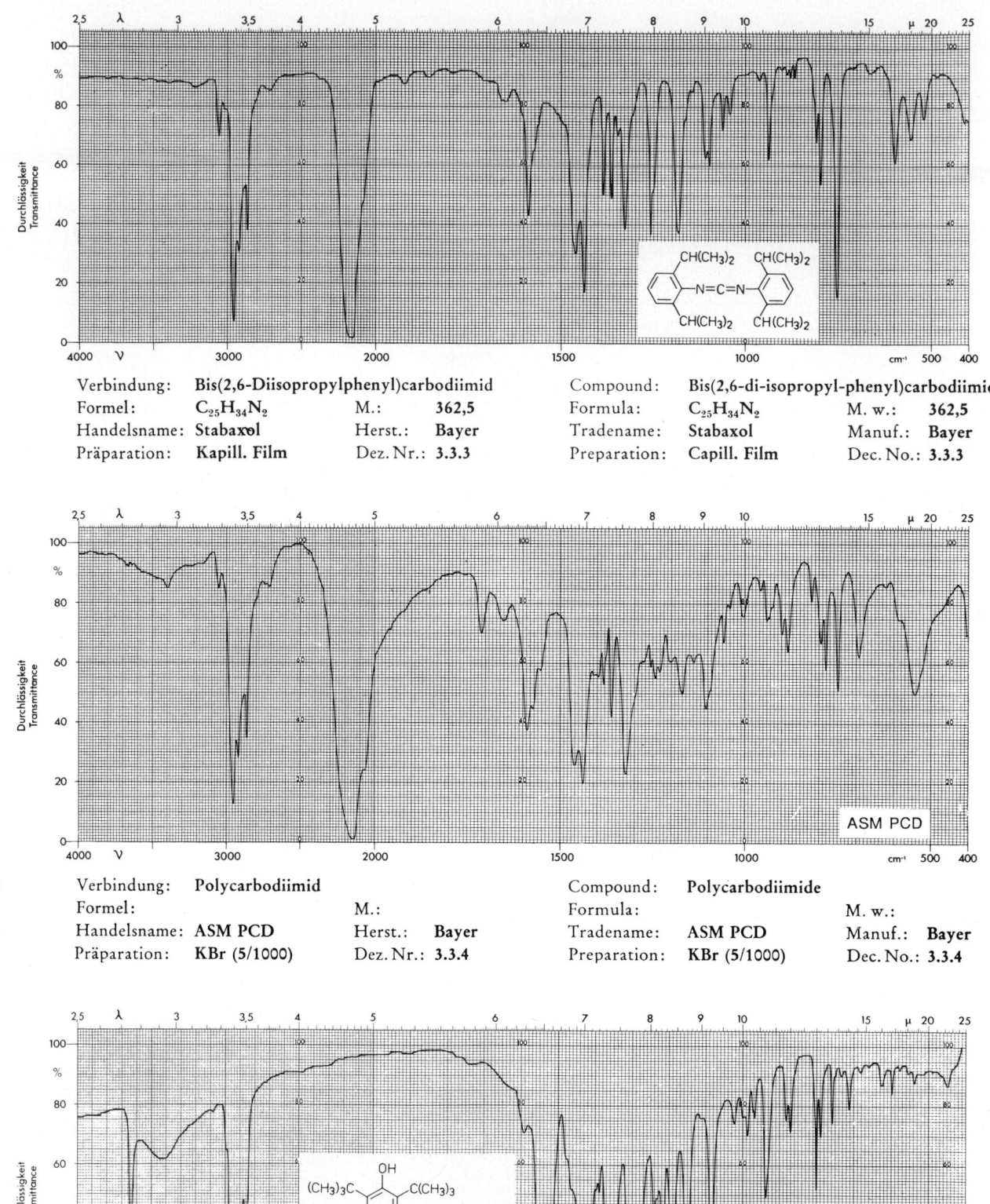

5999

Verbindung:	Bis(2,6-Diisopropylphenyl)carbodiimid	Compound:	Bis(2,6-di-isopropyl-phenyl)carbodiimide
Formel:	C₂₅H₃₄N₂ M.: 362,5	Formula:	C₂₅H₃₄N₂ M. w.: 362,5
Handelsname:	Stabaxol Herst.: Bayer	Tradename:	Stabaxol Manuf.: Bayer
Präparation:	Kapill. Film Dez. Nr.: 3.3.3	Preparation:	Capill. Film Dec. No.: 3.3.3

6000

Verbindung:	Polycarbodiimid	Compound:	Polycarbodiimide
Formel:	M.:	Formula:	M. w.:
Handelsname:	ASM PCD Herst.: Bayer	Tradename:	ASM PCD Manuf.: Bayer
Präparation:	KBr (5/1000) Dez. Nr.: 3.3.4	Preparation:	KBr (5/1000) Dec. No.: 3.3.4

6001

Verbindung:	2-n-Octylthio-4,6-di(4′-hydroxy-3′,5′-di-t.butylphenoxy)-1,3,5-triazin	Compound:	2-n-Octylthio-4,6-di(4′-hydroxy-3′,5′-di-t.butylphenoxy)-1,3,5 triazine
Formel:	C₃₉H₅₉N₃O₄S M.: 665,8	Formula:	C₃₉H₅₉N₃O₄S M. w.: 665,8
Handelsname:	Irganox 858 Herst.: Geigy	Tradename:	Irganox 858 Manuf.: Geigy
Präparation:	KBr (3/1000) Dez. Nr.: 4.1	Preparation:	KBr (3/1000) Dec. No.: 4.1

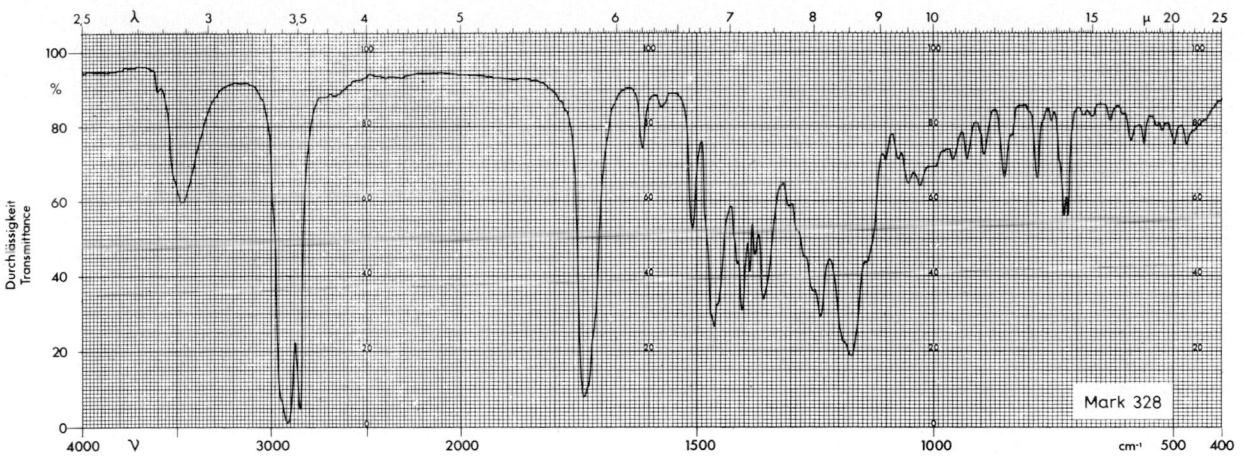

Verbindung: Phenolkondensationsprodukt + Thiodi-
propionsäuredialkylester

Compound: Phenol condensation product + Thiodi-
propionic alkylester   6002

Formel: M.:
Handelsname: Mark 328   Herst.: Argus
Präparation: Schmelzfilm   Dez. Nr.: 4.3

Formula: M. w.:
Tradename: Mark 328   Manuf.: Argus
Preparation: Melting film   Dec. No.: 4.3

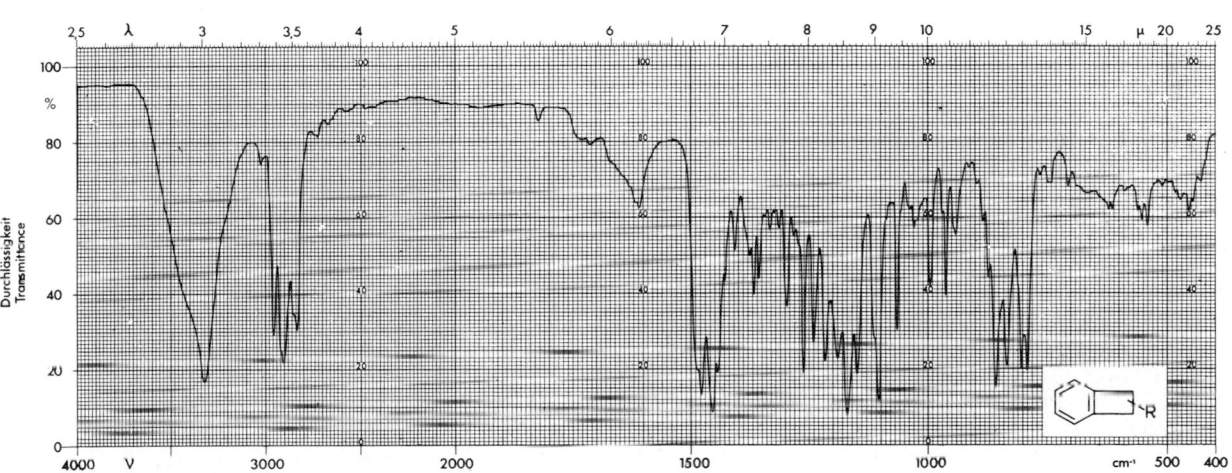

Verbindung: Benzocyclobutanderivat

Compound: Benzocyclobutane derivative   6003

Formel: M.:
Handelsname: KA 2009   Herst.: Bayer
Präparation: KBr (5/1000)   Dez. Nr.: 4.4

Formula: M. w.:
Tradename: KA 2009   Manuf.: Bayer
Preparation: KBr (5/1000)   Dec. No.: 4.4

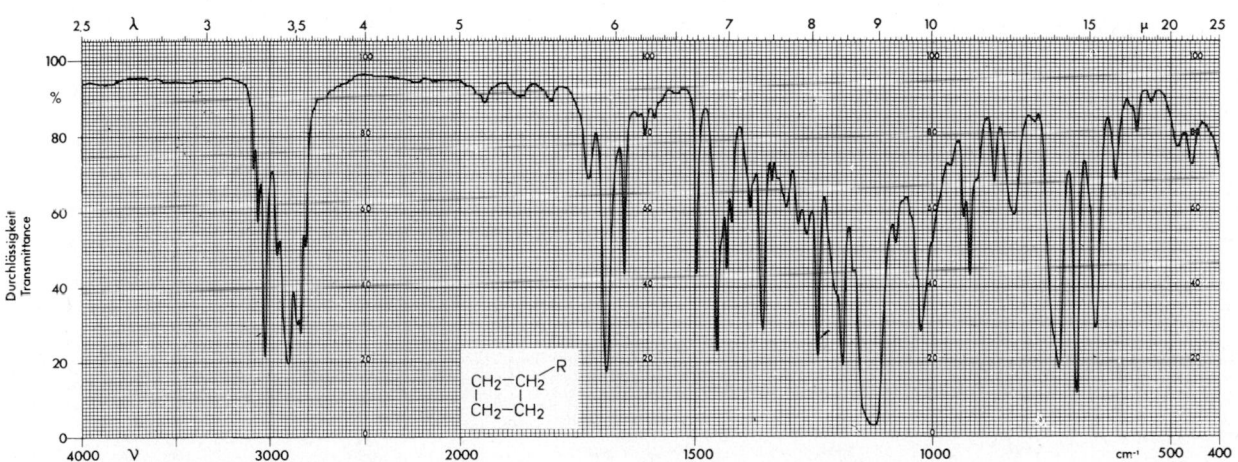

Verbindung: Cyclobutanderivat

Compound: Cyclobutane derivative   6004

Formel: M.:
Handelsname: KA 9019   Herst.: Bayer
Präparation: Kapill. Film   Dez. Nr.: 4.5

Formula: M. w.:
Tradename: KA 9019   Manuf.: Bayer
Preparation: Capill. Film   Dec. No.: 4.5

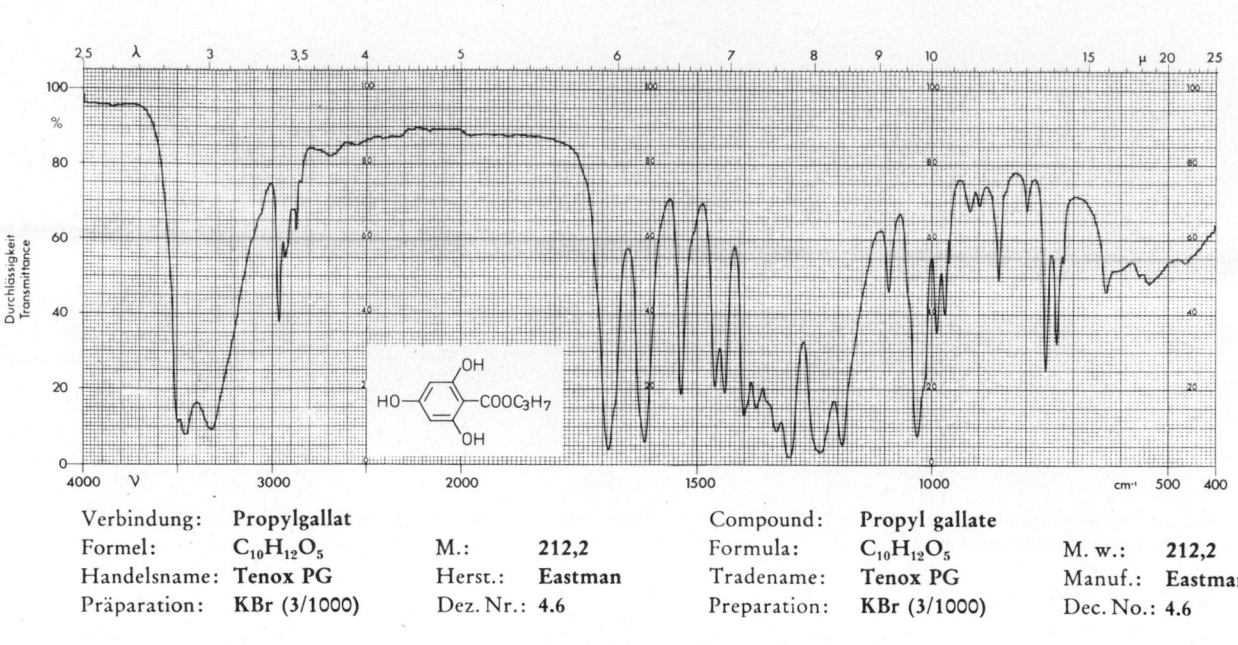

6005   Verbindung: **Propylgallat**   Compound: **Propyl gallate**

Formel:	$C_{10}H_{12}O_5$	M.:	**212,2**	Formula:	$C_{10}H_{12}O_5$	M. w.:	**212,2**
Handelsname:	**Tenox PG**	Herst.:	**Eastman**	Tradename:	**Tenox PG**	Manuf.:	**Eastman**
Präparation:	**KBr (3/1000)**	Dez. Nr.:	**4.6**	Preparation:	**KBr (3/1000)**	Dec. No.:	**4.6**

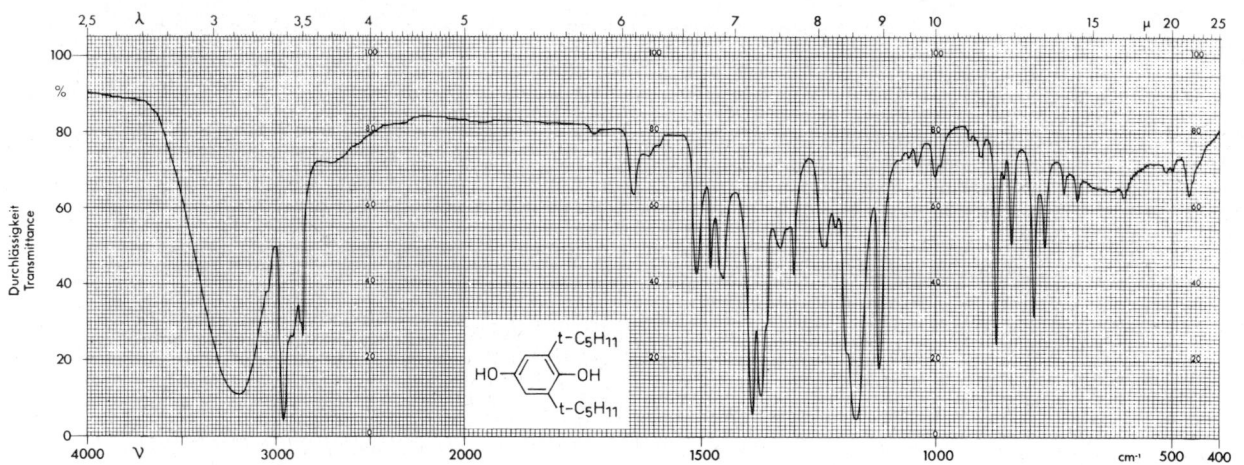

6006   Verbindung: **2,6-Di-t.amylhydrochinon**   Compound: **2,6-Di-t.amylhydroquinone**

Formel:	$C_{16}H_{26}O_2$	M.:	**250,3**	Formula:	$C_{16}H_{26}O_2$	M. w.:	**250,3**
Handelsname:	**Santovar**	Herst.:	**Monsanto**	Tradename:	**Santovar**	Manuf.:	**Monsanto**
Präparation:	**KBr (3/1000)**	Dez. Nr.:	**1.2.3**	Preparation:	**KBr (3/1000)**	Dec. No.:	**1.2.3**

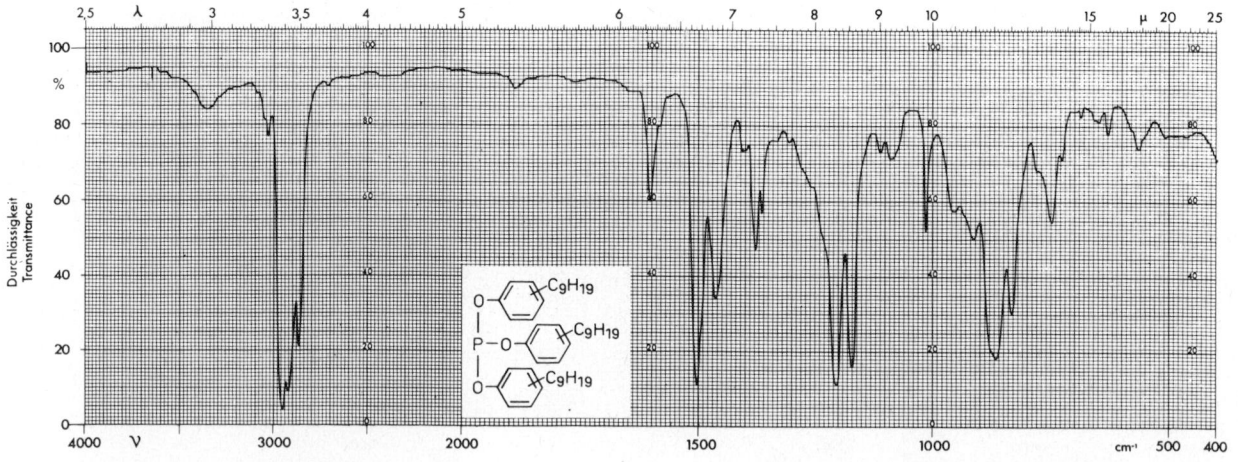

6007   Verbindung: **Trinonylphenylphosphit**   Compound: **Tri(nonylphenyl)phosphite**

Formel:	$C_{45}H_{69}O_3P$	M.:	**688,9**	Formula:	$C_{45}H_{69}O_3P$	M. w.:	**688,9**
Handelsname:	**Polygard**	Herst.:	**Naugatuck**	Tradename:	**Polygard**	Manuf.:	**Naugatuck**
Präparation:	**Kapill. Film**	Dez. Nr.:	**4.10**	Preparation:	**Capill. Film**	Dec. No.:	**4.10**

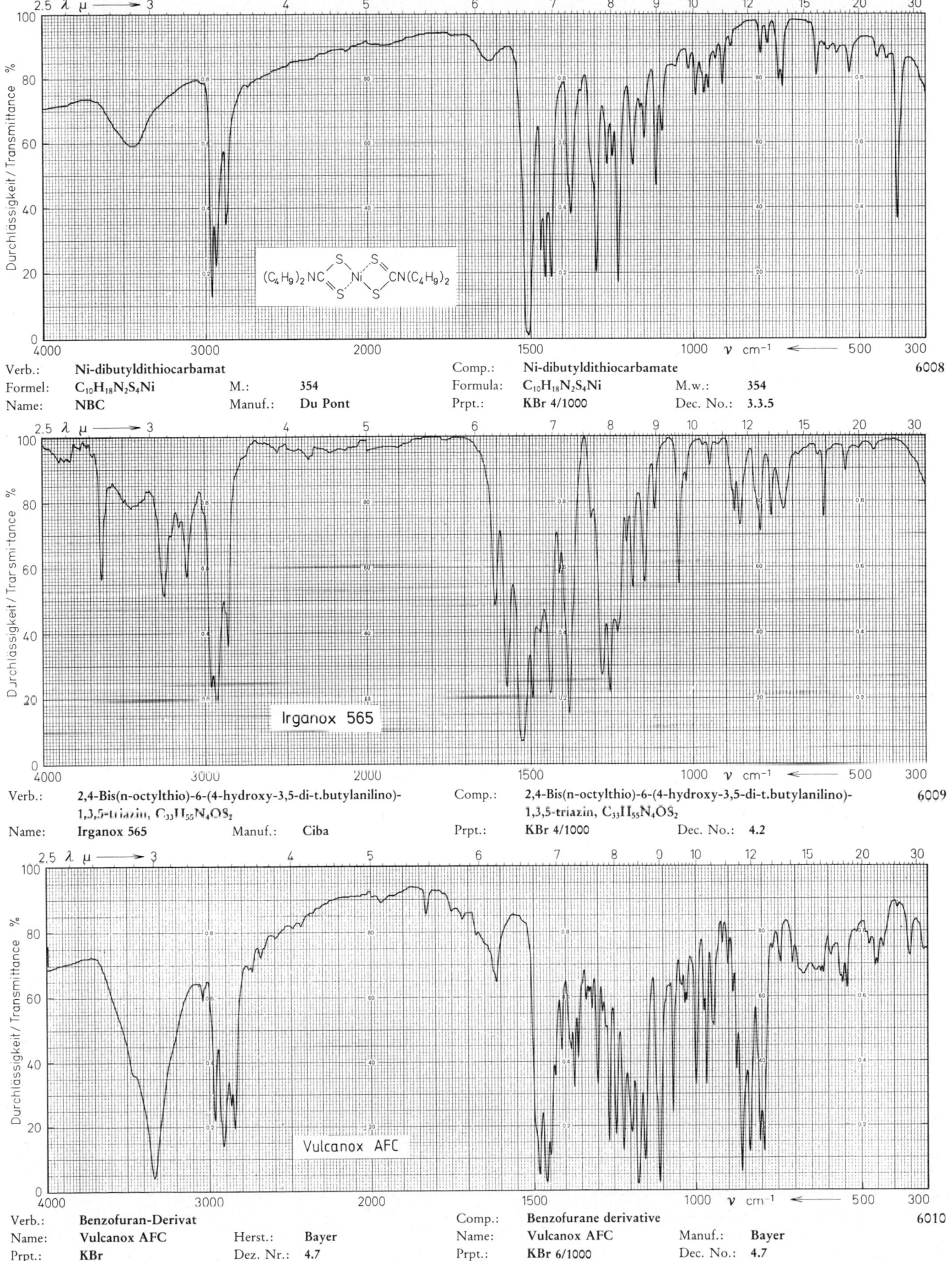

Verb.: **Ni-dibutyldithiocarbamat**
Formel: $C_{10}H_{18}N_2S_4Ni$ M.: **354**
Name: **NBC**   Manuf.: **Du Pont**

Comp.: **Ni-dibutyldithiocarbamate**
Formula: $C_{10}H_{18}N_2S_4Ni$ M.w.: **354**
Prpt.: **KBr 4/1000**   Dec. No.: **3.3.5**

6008

Irganox 565

Verb.: **2,4-Bis(n-octylthio)-6-(4-hydroxy-3,5-di-t.butylanilino)-1,3,5-triazin, $C_{33}H_{55}N_4OS_2$**
Name: **Irganox 565**   Manuf.: **Ciba**

Comp.: **2,4-Bis(n-octylthio)-6-(4-hydroxy-3,5-di-t.butylanilino)-1,3,5-triazin, $C_{33}H_{55}N_4OS_2$**
Prpt.: **KBr 4/1000**   Dec. No.: **4.2**

6009

Vulcanox AFC

Verb.: **Benzofuran-Derivat**
Name: **Vulcanox AFC**   Herst.: **Bayer**
Prpt.: **KBr**   Dez. Nr.: **4.7**

Comp.: **Benzofurane derivative**
Name: **Vulcanox AFC**   Manuf.: **Bayer**
Prpt.: **KBr 6/1000**   Dec. No.: **4.7**

6010

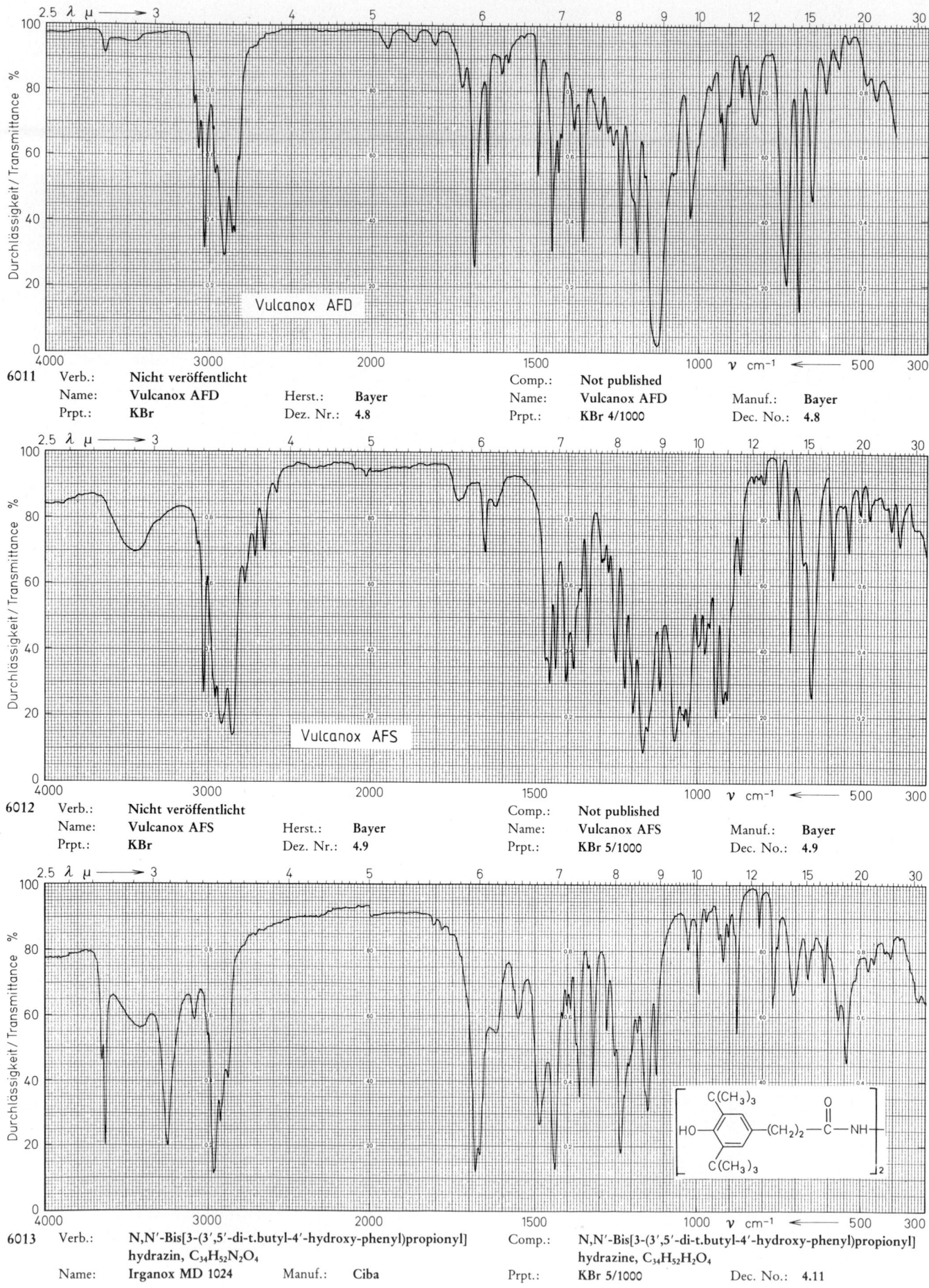

Vulcanox AFD

6011   Verb.:   **Nicht veröffentlicht**   Comp.:   **Not published**

     Name: **Vulcanox AFD**   Herst.:   **Bayer**   Name: **Vulcanox AFD**   Manuf.:   **Bayer**

     Prpt.:   **KBr**   Dez. Nr.:   **4.8**   Prpt.:   **KBr 4/1000**   Dec. No.:   **4.8**

Vulcanox AFS

6012   Verb.:   **Nicht veröffentlicht**   Comp.:   **Not published**

     Name: **Vulcanox AFS**   Herst.:   **Bayer**   Name: **Vulcanox AFS**   Manuf.:   **Bayer**

     Prpt.:   **KBr**   Dez. Nr.:   **4.9**   Prpt.:   **KBr 5/1000**   Dec. No.:   **4.9**

6013   Verb.:   **N,N′-Bis[3-(3′,5′-di-t.butyl-4′-hydroxy-phenyl)propionyl]**   Comp.:   **N,N′-Bis[3-(3′,5′-di-t.butyl-4′-hydroxy-phenyl)propionyl]**

           hydrazin, $C_{34}H_{52}N_2O_4$ **hydrazine, $C_{34}H_{52}H_2O_4$**

     Name: **Irganox MD 1024**   Manuf.:   **Ciba**   Prpt.:   **KBr 5/1000**   Dec. No.:   **4.11**

Stabilisatoren

Stabilizers

Stabilisatoren
1. Anorganische Stabilisatoren
1.1. Silikate

Stabilizers
1. Inorganic Stabilizers
1.1. Silicates

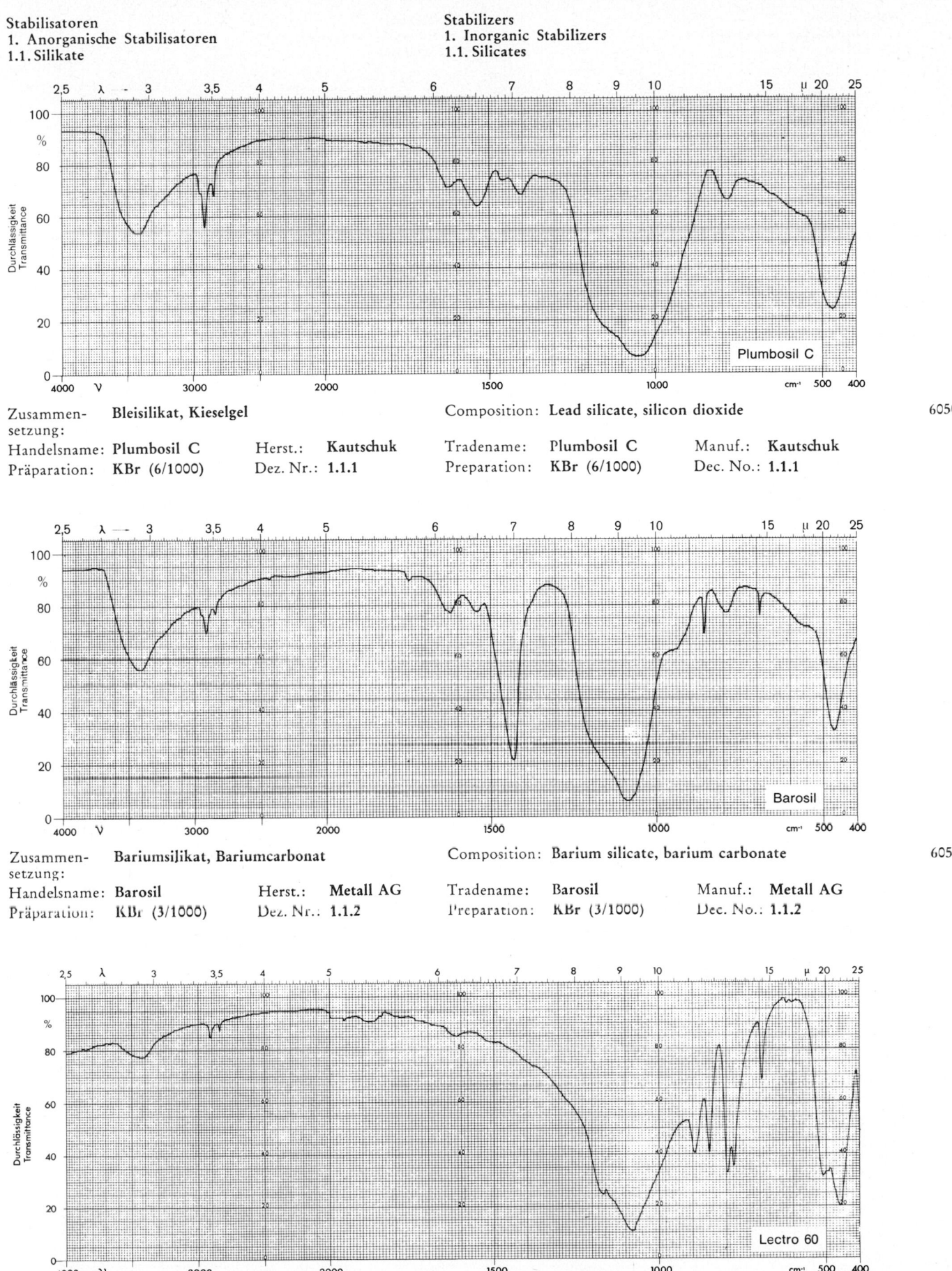

Zusammen-setzung:	**Bleisilikat, Kieselgel**		Composition:	**Lead silicate, silicon dioxide**		6050
Handelsname: **Plumbosil C**	Herst.: **Kautschuk**		Tradename: **Plumbosil C**	Manuf.: **Kautschuk**	
Präparation: **KBr (6/1000)**	Dez. Nr.: **1.1.1**		Preparation: **KBr (6/1000)**	Dec. No.: **1.1.1**	

Zusammen-setzung:	**Bariumsilikat, Bariumcarbonat**		Composition:	**Barium silicate, barium carbonate**		6051
Handelsname: **Barosil**	Herst.: **Metall AG**		Tradename: **Barosil**	Manuf.: **Metall AG**	
Präparation: **KBr (3/1000)**	Dez. Nr.: **1.1.2**		Preparation: **KBr (3/1000)**	Dec. No.: **1.1.2**	

Zusammen-setzung:	**Bleisilikat-Bleichlorid-Komplex**		Composition:	**Lead silicate-lead chloride-complex**		6052
Handelsname: **Lectro 60**	Herst.: **Kautschuk**		Tradename: **Lectro 60**	Manuf.: **Kautschuk**	
Präparation: **KBr (4/1000)**	Dez. Nr.: **1.1.3**		Preparation: **KBr (4/1000)**	Dec. No.: **1.1.3**	

Stabilisatoren
1. Anorganische Stabilisatoren
1.2. Sulfate

Stabilizers
1. Inorganic Stabilizers
1.2. Sulfates

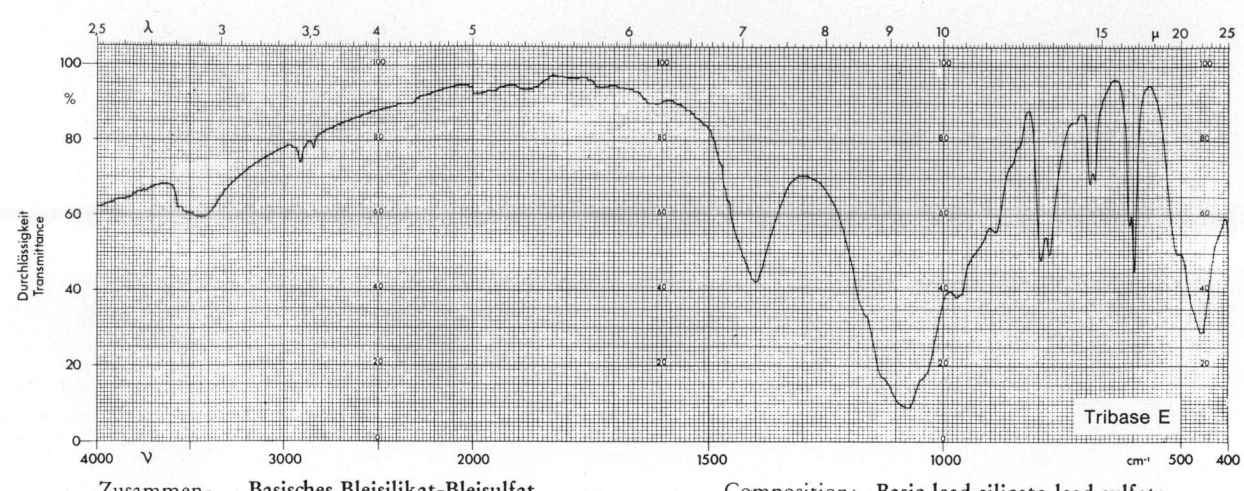

6053   Zusammensetzung: **Basisches Bleisilikat-Bleisulfat**   Composition: **Basic lead silicate-lead sulfate**

Handelsname: **Tribase E**   Herst.: **Kautschuk**   Tradename: **Tribase E**   Manuf.: **Kautschuk**

Präparation: **KBr (6/1000)**   Dez. Nr.: **1.1.4**   Preparation: **KBr (6/1000)**   Dec. No.: **1.1.4**

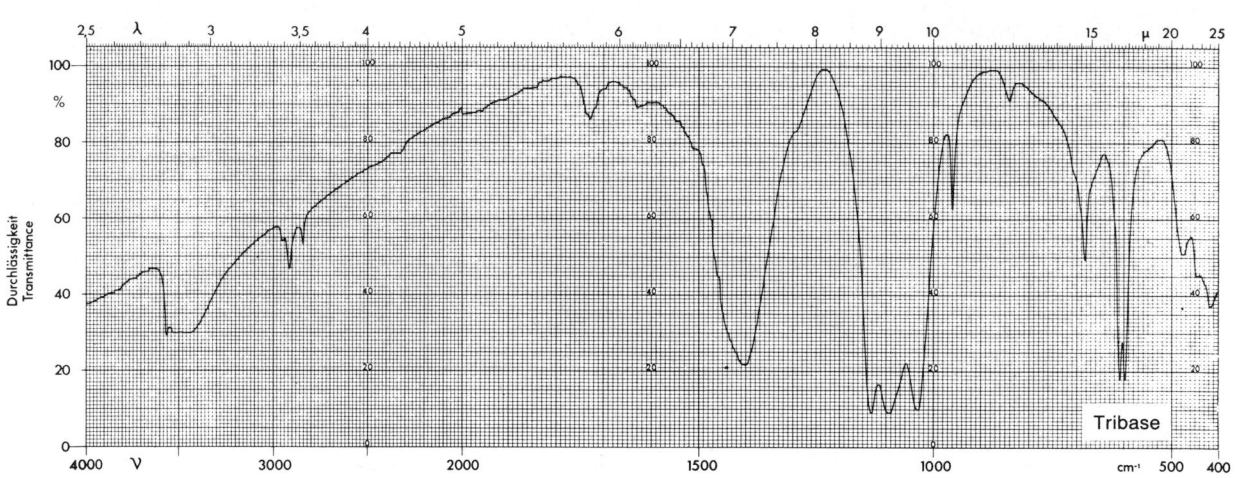

6054   Zusammensetzung: **3-basisches Bleisulfat**   Composition: **3-basic lead sulfate**

Handelsname: **Tribase**   Herst.: **Kautschuk**   Tradename: **Tribase**   Manuf.: **Kautschuk**

Präparation: **KBr (10/1000)**   Dez. Nr.: **1.2.1**   Preparation: **KBr (10/1000)**   Dec. No.: **1.2.1**

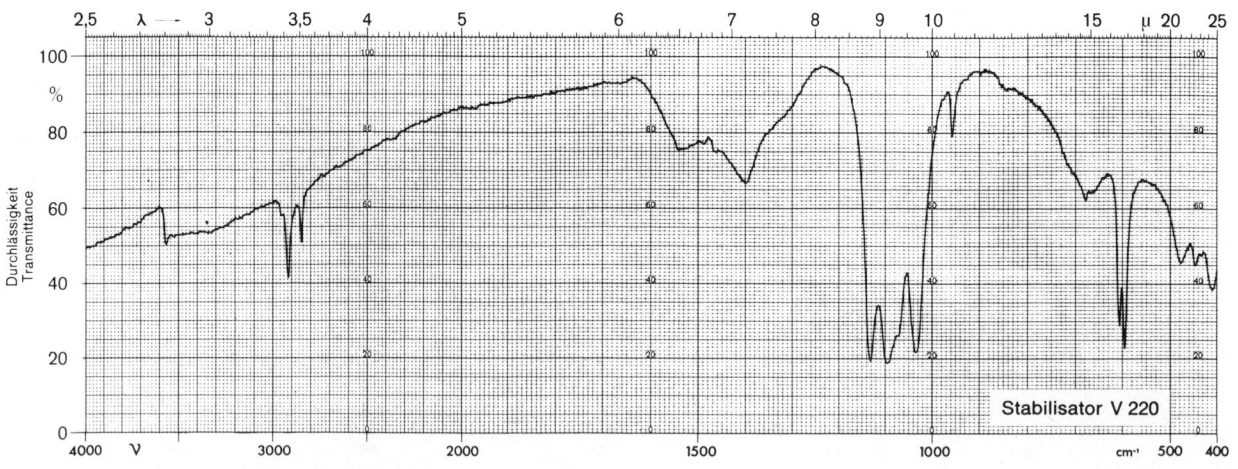

6055   Zusammensetzung: **2-basisches Bleisulfat mit Zusätzen**   Composition: **2-basic lead sulfate with additives**

Handelsname: **Stabilisator V 220**   Herst.: **Bärlocher**   Tradename: **Stabilisator V 220**   Manuf.: **Bärlocher**

Präparation: **KBr (6/1000)**   Dez. Nr.: **1.2.2**   Preparation: **KBr (6/1000)**   Dec. No.: **1.2.2**

Stabilisatoren
1. Anorganische Stabilisatoren
1.3. Phosphite, Phosphate

Stabilizers
1. Inorganic Stabilizers
1.3. Phosphites, Phosphates

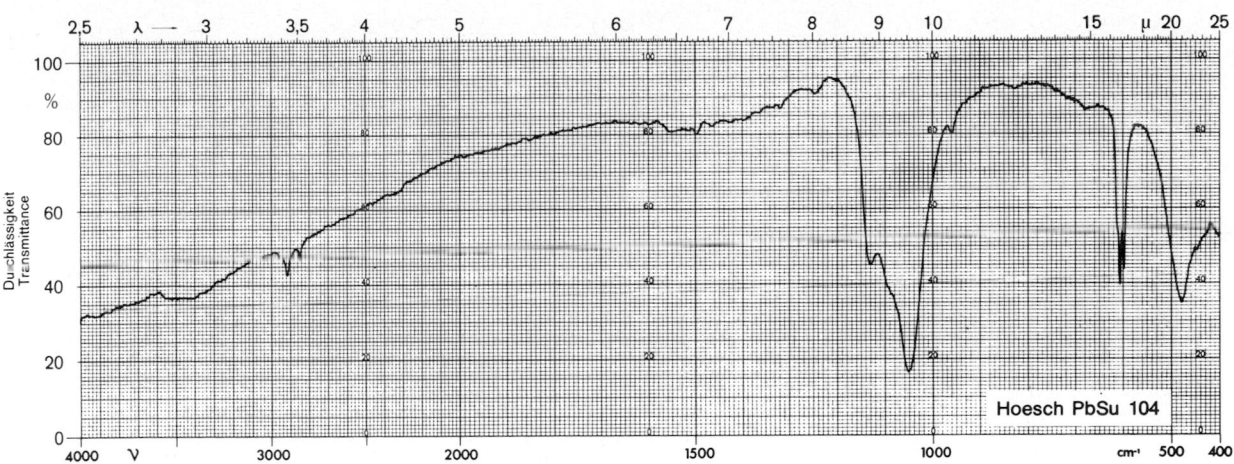

Zusammen-
setzung: **4-basisches Bleisulfat**

Handelsname: **Hoesch PbSu 104**   Herst.: **Hoesch**

Präparation: **KBr (6/1000)**   Dez. Nr.: **1.2.3**

Composition: **4-basic lead sulfate**

Tradename: Hoesch PbSu 104   Manuf.: **Hoesch**

Preparation: **KBr (6/1000)**   Dec. No.. **1.2.3**

6056

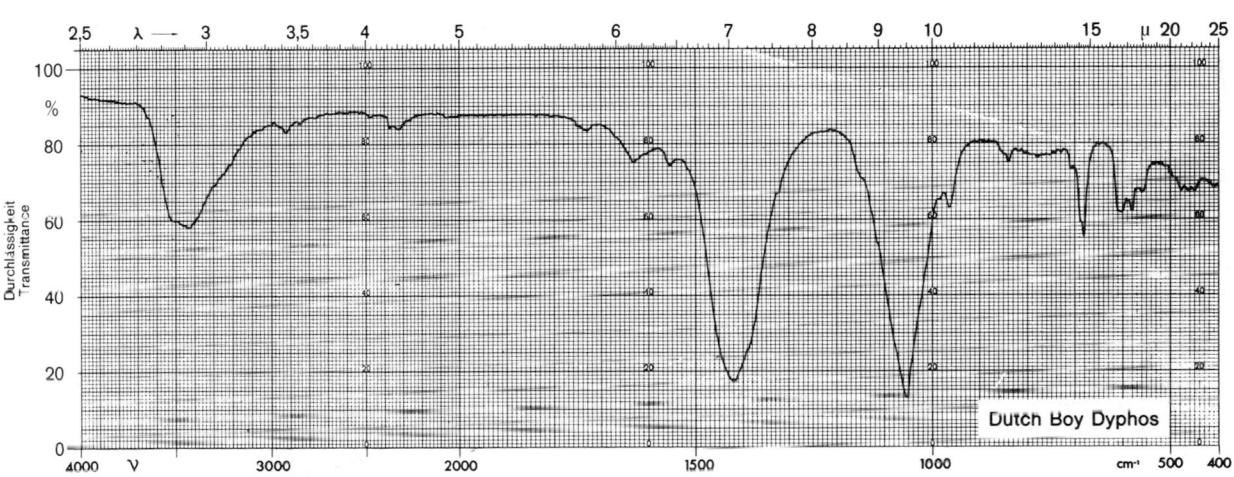

Zusammen-
setzung: **2-basisches Bleiphosphit**

Handelsname: **Dutch Boy Dyphos**   Herst.: **Kautschuk**

Präparation: **KBr (5/1000)**   Dez. Nr.: **1.3.1**

Composition: **2-basic lead phosphite**

Tradename: **Dutch Boy Dyphos**   Manuf.: **Kautschuk**

Preparation: **KBr (5/1000)**   Dec. No.: **1.3.1**

6057

Zusammen-
setzung: **Bleiphosphit mit Zusätzen**

Handelsname: **Hoesch Pb Lev 238**   Herst.: **Hoesch**

Präparation: **KBr (6/1000)**   Dez. Nr.: **1.3.2**

Composition: **Lead phosphite with additives**

Tradename: **Hoesch Pb Lev 238**   Manuf.: **Hoesch**

Preparation: **KBr (6/1000)**   Dec. No.: **1.3.2**

6058

Stabilisatoren
1. Anorganische Stabilisatoren
1.4. Carbonate, Oxidhydrate

Stabilizers
1. Inorganic Stabilizers
1.4. Carbonates, Oxidhydrates

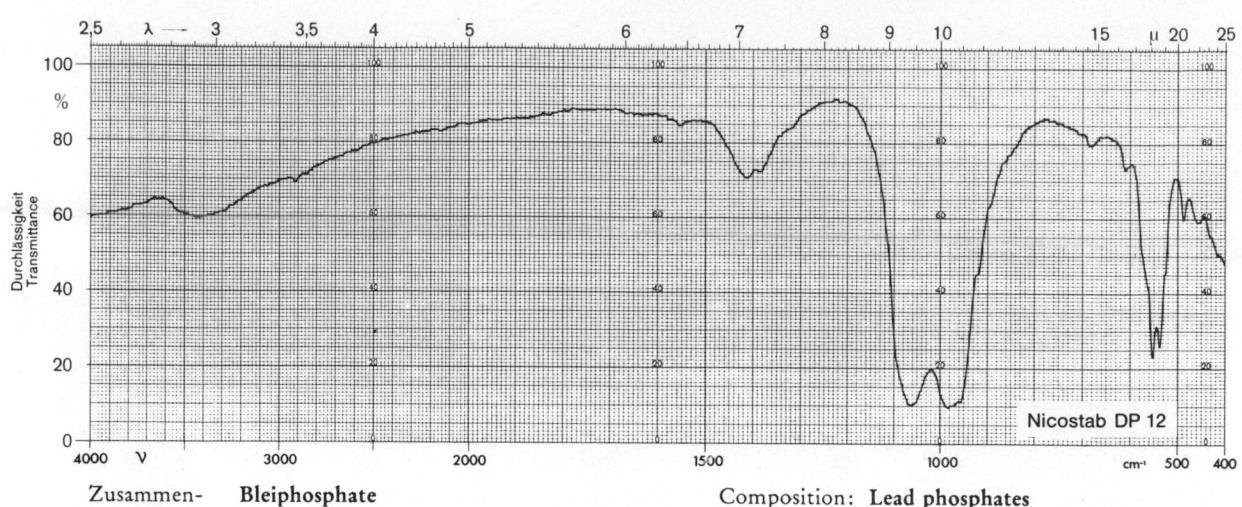

6059   Zusammen-   **Bleiphosphate**   Composition: **Lead phosphates**
       setzung:
       Handelsname: **Nicostab DP 12**   Herst.: **Argus**   Tradename: **Nicostab DP 12**   Manuf.: **Argus**
       Präparation: **KBr (6/1000)**   Dez. Nr.: **1.3.3**   Preparation: **KBr (6/1000)**   Dec. No.: **1.3.3**

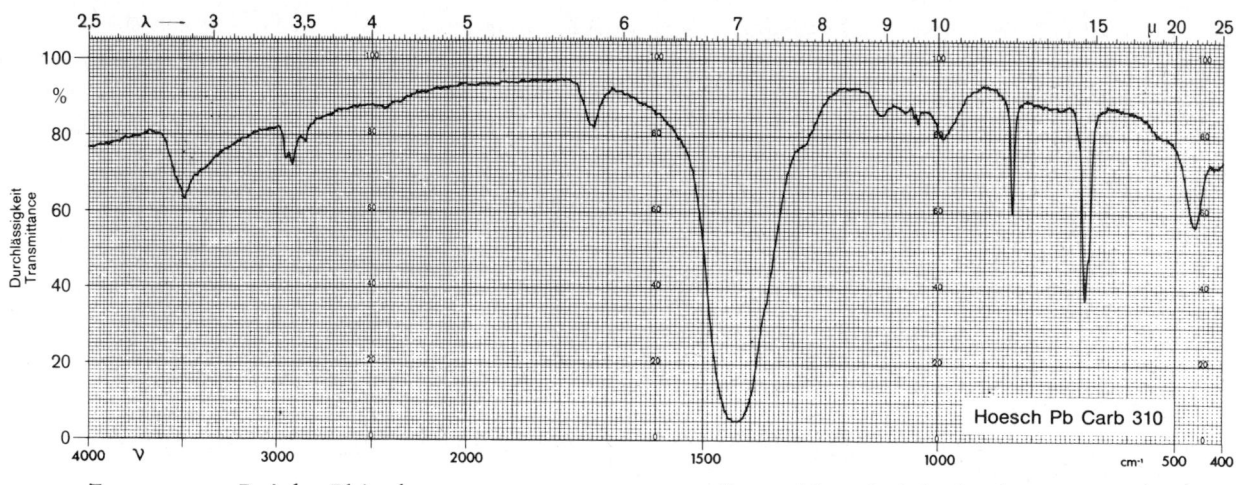

6060   Zusammen-   **Basisches Bleicarbonat**   Composition: **Basic lead carbonate**
       setzung:
       Handelsname: **Hoesch Pb Carb 310** Herst.: **Hoesch**   Tradename: **Hoesch Pb Carb 310** Manuf.: **Hoesch**
       Präparation: **KBr (6/1000)**   Dez. Nr.: **1.4.1**   Preparation: **KBr (6/1000)**   Dec. No.: **1.4.1**

6061   Zusammen-   **Manganoxidhydrat**   Composition: **Manganese oxide hydrate**
       setzung:
       Handelsname: **Stabilisator MOH** Herst.: **Hüls**   Tradename: **Stabilisator MOH** Manuf.: **Hüls**
       Präparation: **KBr (6/1000)**   Dez. Nr.: **1.4.2**   Preparation: **KBr (6/1000)**   Dec. No.: **1.4.2**

Stabilisatoren
2. Metallcarboxylat-Stabilisatoren
2.1. Metallsalze von Fettsäuren

Stabilizers
2. Metal Carboxylate Stabilizers
2.1. Metal Salts of Fatty Acids

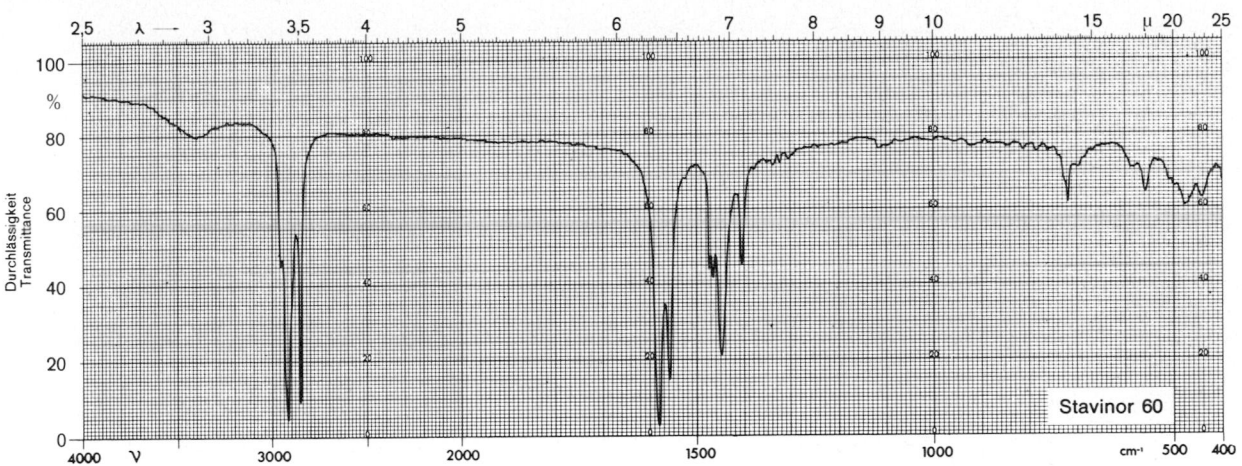

Stavinor 60

6062

Zusammen-setzung:	**Lithiumstearat**			Composition:	**Lithium stearate**		
Handelsname:	**Stavinor 60**	Herst.:	**Usines**	Tradename:	**Stavinor 60**	Manuf.:	**Usines**
Präparation:	**KBr (6/1000)**	Dez. Nr.:	**2.1.1**	Preparation:	**KBr (6/1000)**	Dec. No.:	**2.1.1**

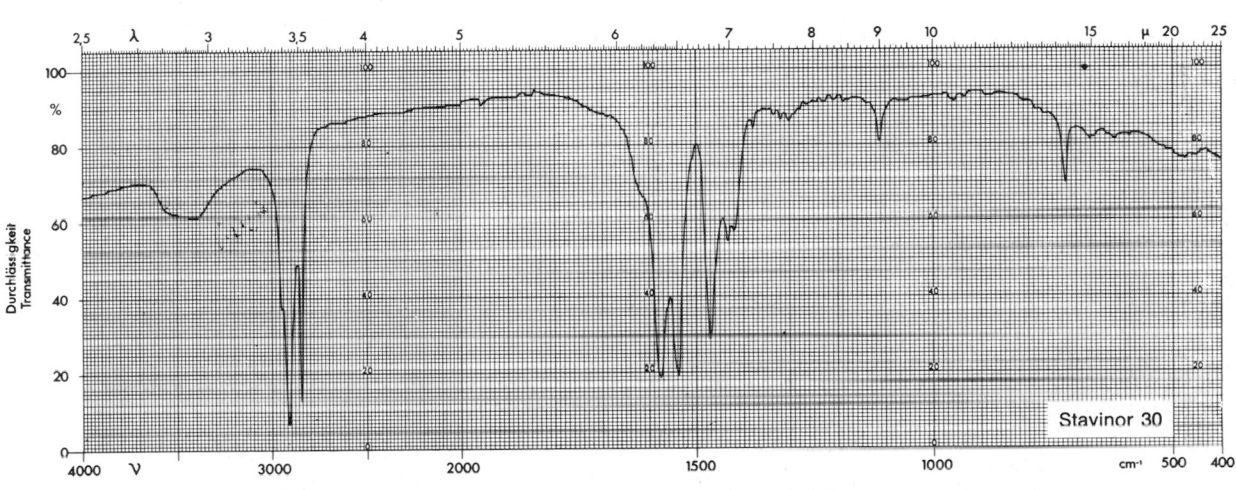

Stavinor 30

6063

Zusammen-setzung:	**Calciumstearat**			Composition:	**Calcium stearate**		
Handelsname:	**Stavinor 30**	Herst.:	**Usines**	Tradename:	**Stavinor 30**	Manuf.:	**Usines**
Präparation:	**KBr (6/1000)**	Dez. Nr.:	**2.1.2**	Preparation:	**KBr (6/1000)**	Dec. No.:	**2.1.2**

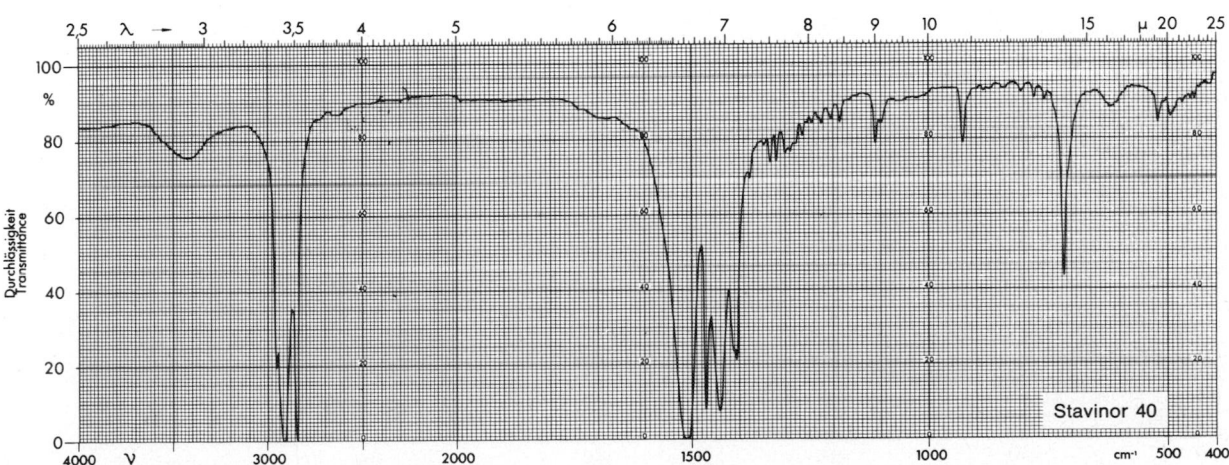

Stavinor 40

6064

Zusammen-setzung:	**Bariumstearat**			Composition:	**Barium stearate**		
Handelsname:	**Stavinor 40**	Herst.:	**Usines**	Tradename:	**Stavinor 40**	Manuf.:	**Usines**
Präparation:	**KBr (6/1000)**	Dez. Nr.:	**2.1.3**	Preparation:	**KBr (6/1000)**	Dec. No.:	**2.1.3**

Stabilisatoren
2. Metallcarboxylat-Stabilisatoren
2.1. Metallsalze von Fettsäuren

Stabilizers
2. Metal Carboxylate Stabilizers
2.1. Metal Salts of Fatty Acids

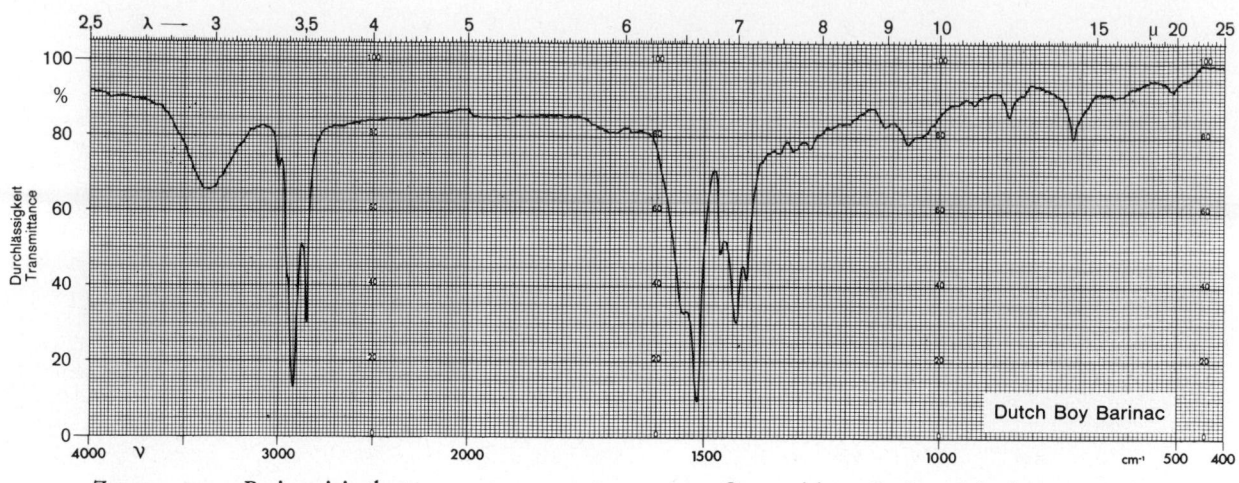

6065

Zusammen-setzung:	**Bariumricinoleat**		Composition:	**Barium ricinoleate**
Handelsname:	**Dutch Boy Barinac**	Herst.: **Kautschuk**	Tradename: **Dutch Boy Barinac**	Manuf.: **Kautschuk**
Präparation:	**KBr (4/1000)**	Dez. Nr.: **2.1.4**	Preparation: **KBr (4/1000)**	Dec. No.: **2.1.4**

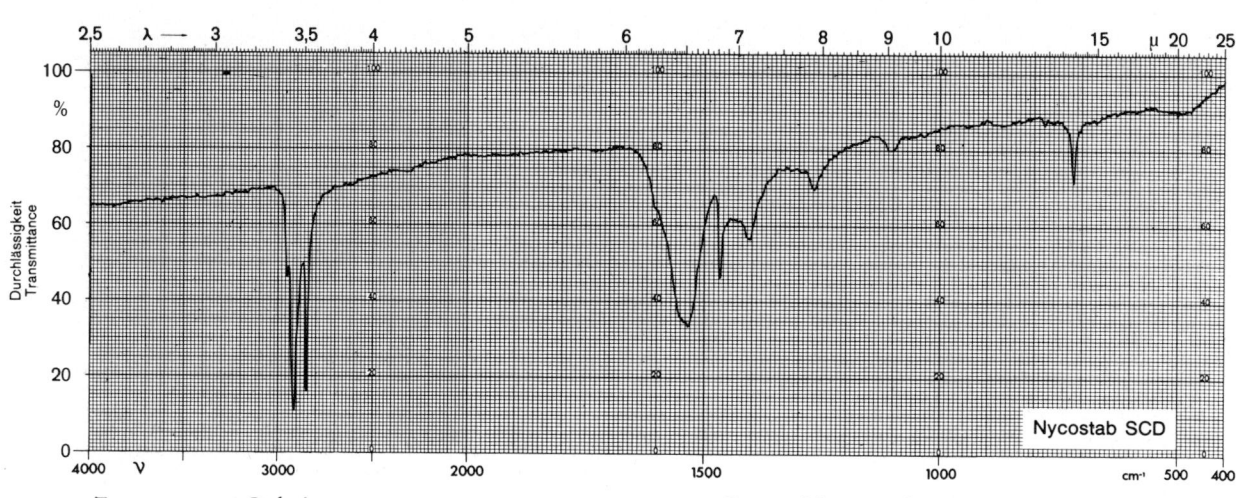

6066

Zusammen-setzung:	**Cadmiumstearat**		Composition:	**Cadmium stearate**
Handelsname:	**Nycostab SCD**	Herst.: **Argus**	Tradename: **Nycostab SCD**	Manuf.: **Argus**
Präparation:	**KBr (3/1000)**	Dez. Nr.: **2.1.5**	Preparation: **KBr (3/1000)**	Dec. No.: **2.1.5**

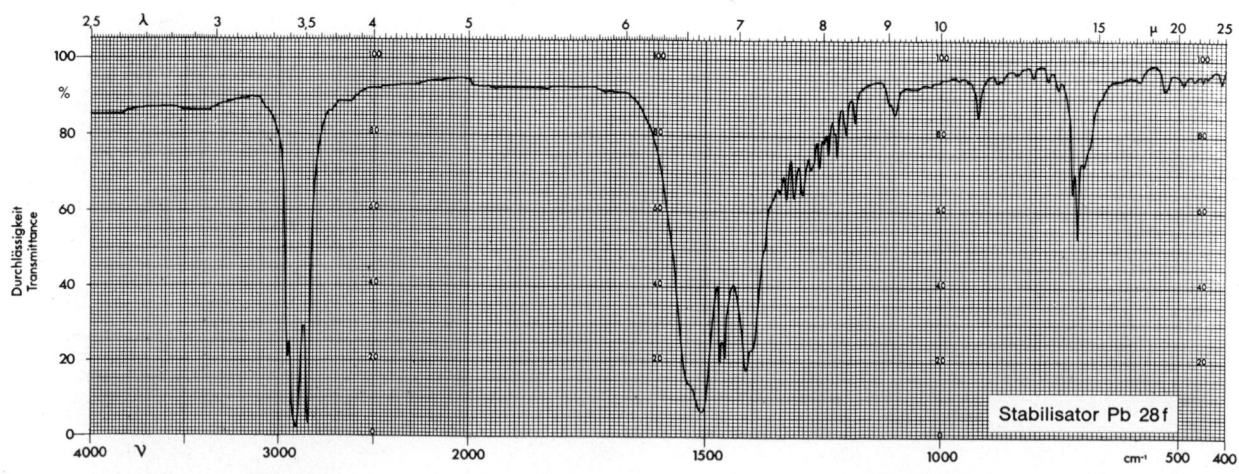

6067

Zusammen-setzung:	**Bleistearat**		Composition:	**Lead stearate**
Handelsname:	**Stabilisator Pb 28 f**	Herst.: **Bärlocher**	Tradename: **Stabilisator Pb 28 f**	Manuf.: **Bärlocher**
Präparation:	**Schmelzfilm**	Dez. Nr.: **2.1.6**	Preparation: **Melting film**	Dec. No.: **2.1.6**

Stabilisatoren
2. Metallcarboxylat-Stabilisatoren
2.1. Metallsalze von Fettsäuren

Stabilizers
2. Metal Carboxylate Stabilizers
2.1. Metal Salts of Fatty Acids

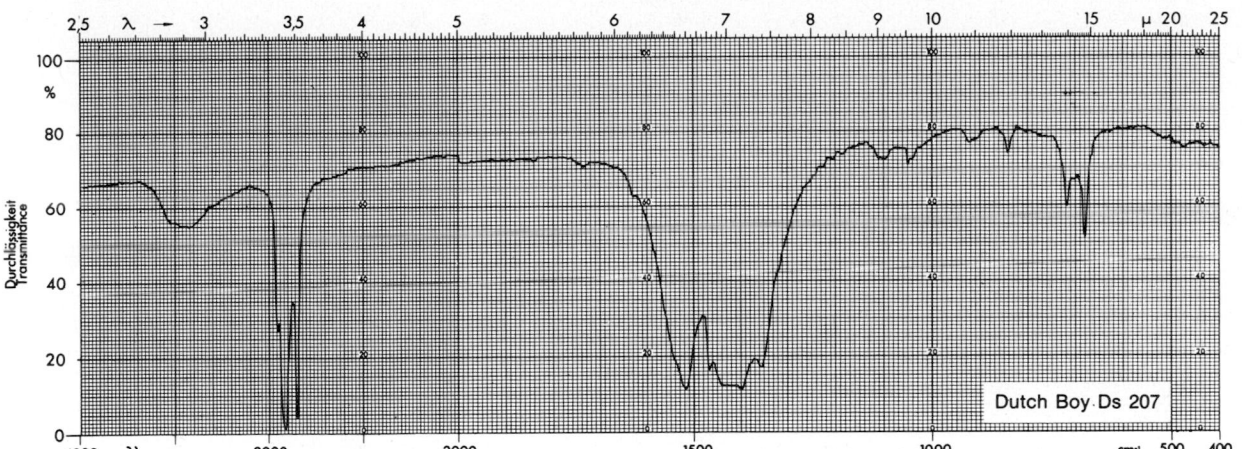

Dutch Boy Ds 207

Zusammensetzung:	2-basisches Bleistearat			Composition:	2-basic lead stearate		6068

Handelsname: **Dutch Boy Ds 207**   Herst.: **Kautschuk**   Tradename: **Dutch Boy Ds 207**   Manuf.: **Kautschuk**

Präparation: **KBr (6/1000)**   Dez. Nr.: **2.1.7**   Preparation: **KBr (6/1000)**   Dec. No.: **2.1.7**

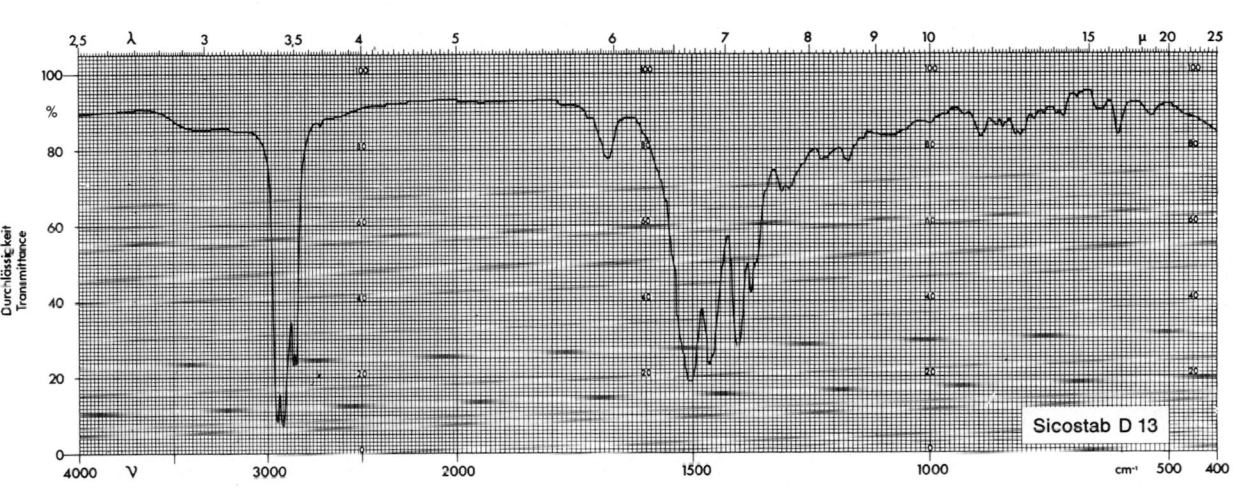

Sicostab D 13

Zusammensetzung:	Bleiseife (flüssig)		Composition:	Lead soap (liquid)		6069

Handelsname: **Sicostab D 13**   Herst.: **Siegle**   Tradename: **Sicostab D 13**   Manuf.: **Siegle**

Präparation: **Kapill. Film**   Dez. Nr.: **2.1.8**   Preparation: **Capill. film**   Dec. No.: **2.1.8**

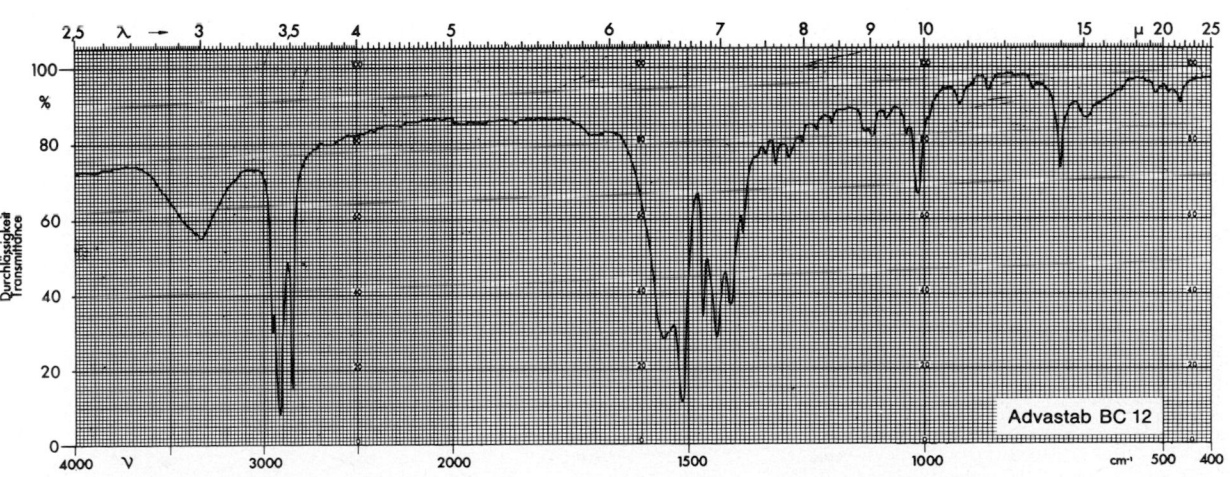

Advastab BC 12

Zusammensetzung:	Barium-Cadmium-Laurat		Composition:	Barium cadmium-laurate		6070

Handelsname: **Advastab BC 12**   Herst.: **Advance**   Tradename: **Advastab BC 12**   Manuf.: **Advance**

Präparation: **KBr (2/1000)**   Dez. Nr.: **2.1.9**   Preparation: **KBr (2/1000)**   Dec. No.: **2.1.9**

Stabilisatoren
2. Metallcarboxylat-Stabilisatoren
2.1. Metallsalze von Fettsäuren

Stabilizers
2. Metal Carboxylate Stabilizers
2.1. Metal Salts of Fatty Acids

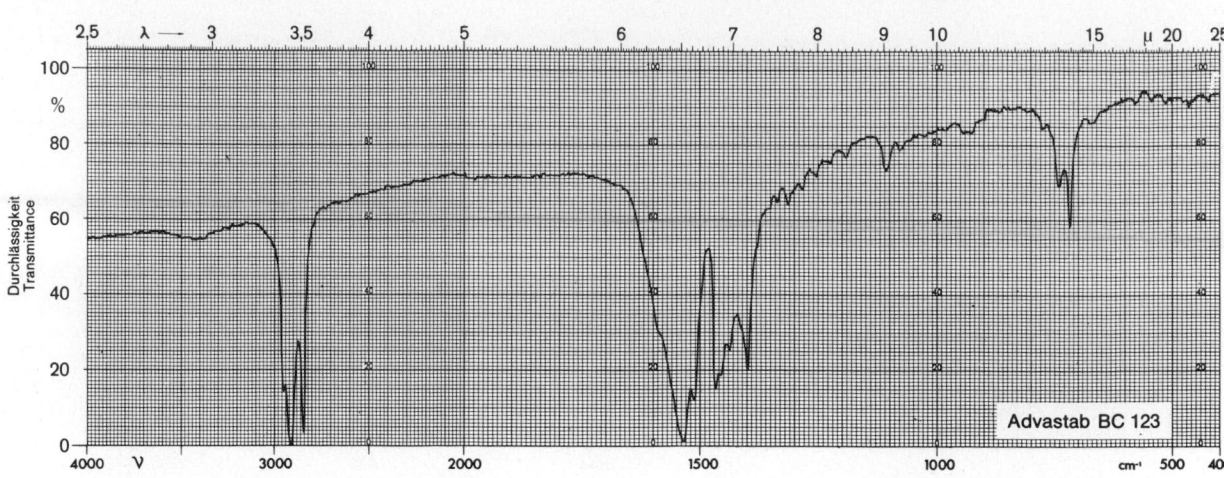

Advastab BC 123

6071 Zusammensetzung: **Barium-Cadmium-Seifen**

Composition: **Barium cadmium soaps**

Handelsname: **Advastab BC 123**   Herst.: **Advance**   Tradename: **Advastab BC 123**   Manuf.: **Advance**

Präparation: **KBr (5/1000)**   Dez. Nr.: **2.1.10**   Preparation: **KBr (5/1000)**   Dec. No.: **2.1.10**

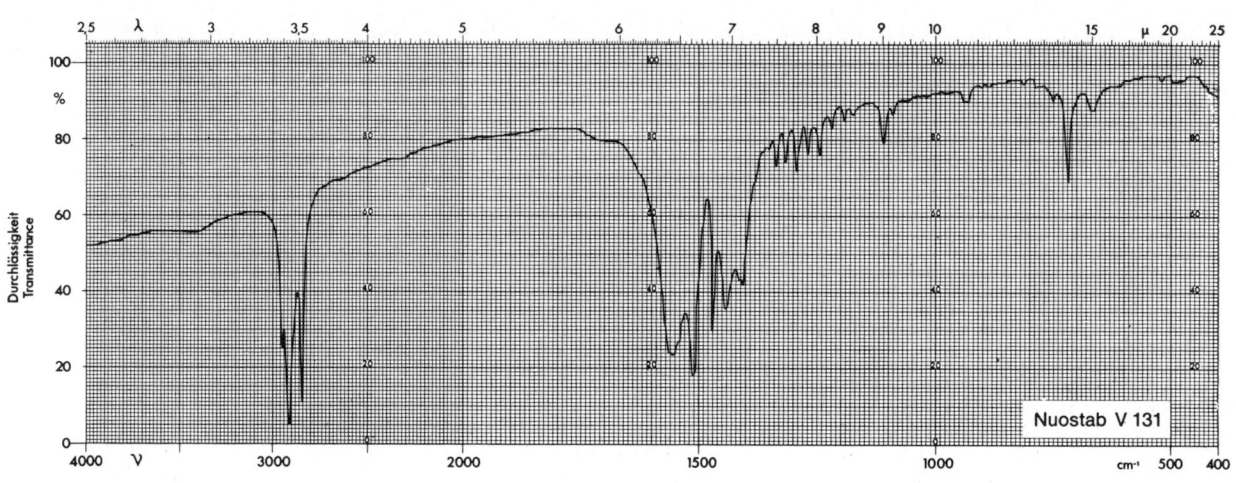

Nuostab V 131

6072 Zusammensetzung: **Barium-Cadmium-Seifen**

Composition: **Barium cadmium soaps**

Handelsname: **Nuostab V 131**   Herst.: **Siegle**   Tradename: **Nuostab V 131**   Manuf.: **Siegle**

Präparation: **KBr (3/1000)**   Dez. Nr.: **2.1.11**   Preparation: **KBr (3/1000)**   Dec. No.: **2.1.11**

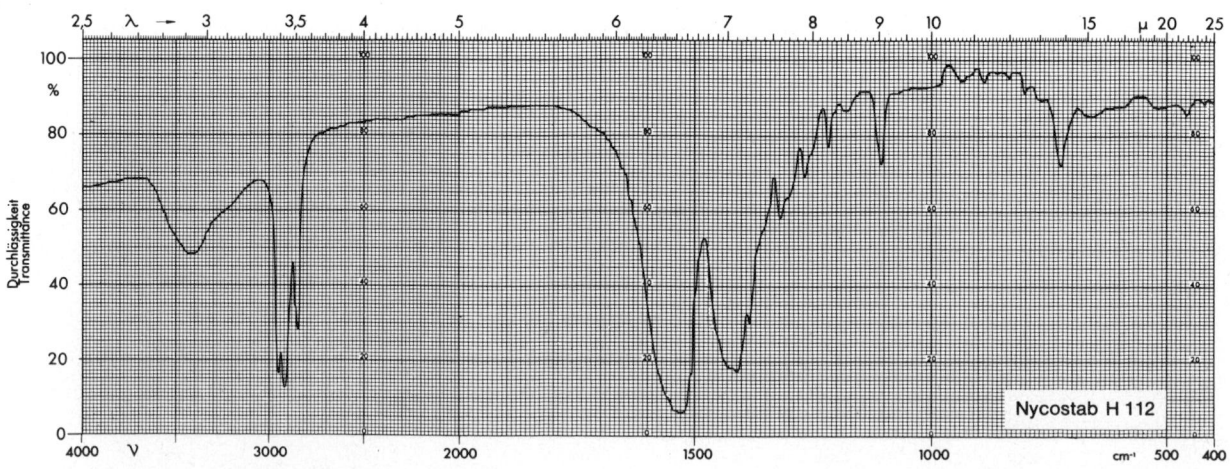

Nycostab H 112

6073 Zusammensetzung: **Barium-Cadmium-Seifen**

Composition: **Barium cadmium soaps**

Handelsname: **Nycostab H 112**   Herst.: **Argus**   Tradename: **Nycostab H 112**   Manuf.: **Argus**

Präparation: **KBr (5/1000)**   Dez. Nr.: **2.1.12**   Preparation: **KBr (5/1000)**   Dec. No.: **2.1.12**

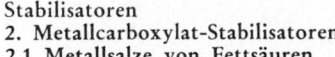

Stabilisatoren
2. Metallcarboxylat-Stabilisatoren
2.1. Metallsalze von Fettsäuren

Stabilizers
2. Metal Carboxylate Stabilizers
2.1. Metal Salts of Fatty Acids

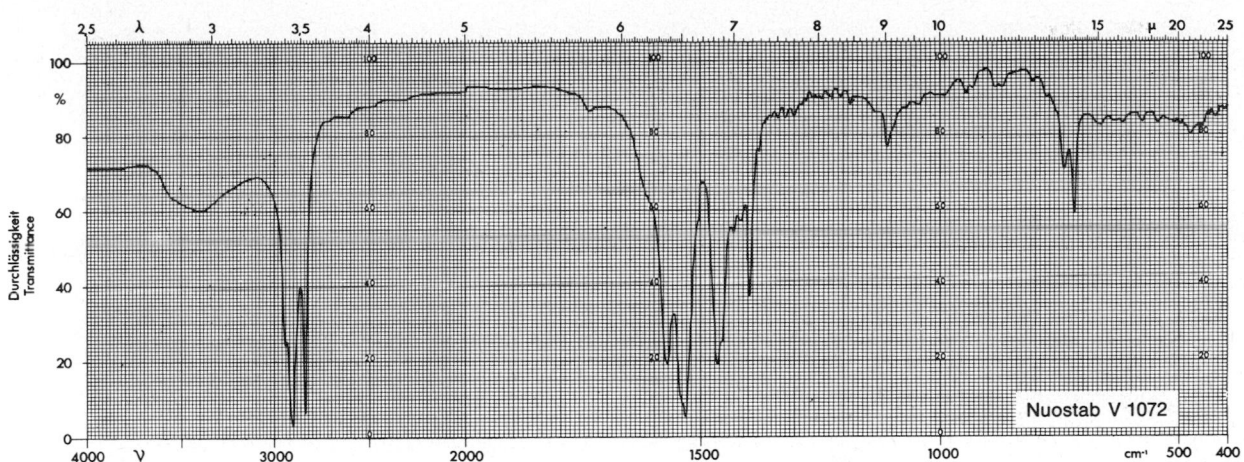

Zusammen- setzung:	Calcium-Zink-Stearat-Palmitat		Composition:	Calcium zinc stearate palmitate		6074
Handelsname:	Nuostab V 1072	Herst.: Siegle	Tradename:	Nuostab V 1072	Manuf.: Siegle	
Präparation:	KBr (5/1000)	Dez. Nr.: 2.1.13	Preparation:	KBr (5/1000)	Dec. No.: 2.1.13	

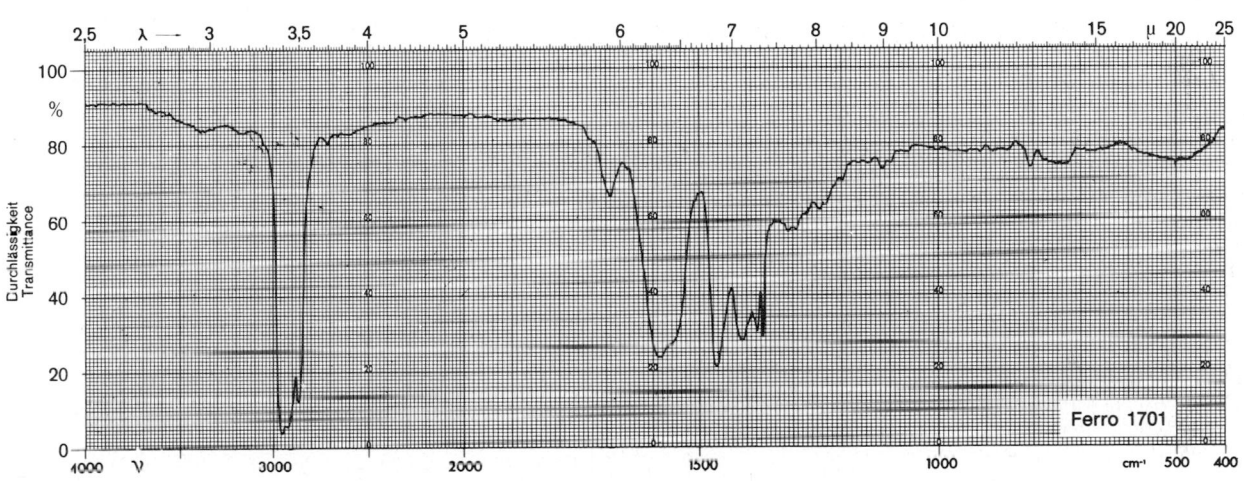

Zusammen- setzung:	Barium-Zink-Seifen		Composition:	Barium zinc soaps		6075
Handelsname:	Ferro 1701	Herst.: Bärlocher	Tradename:	Ferro 1701	Manuf.: Bärlocher	
Präparation:	Kapill. Film	Dez. Nr.: 2.1.14	Preparation:	Capill. film	Dec. No.: 2.1.14	

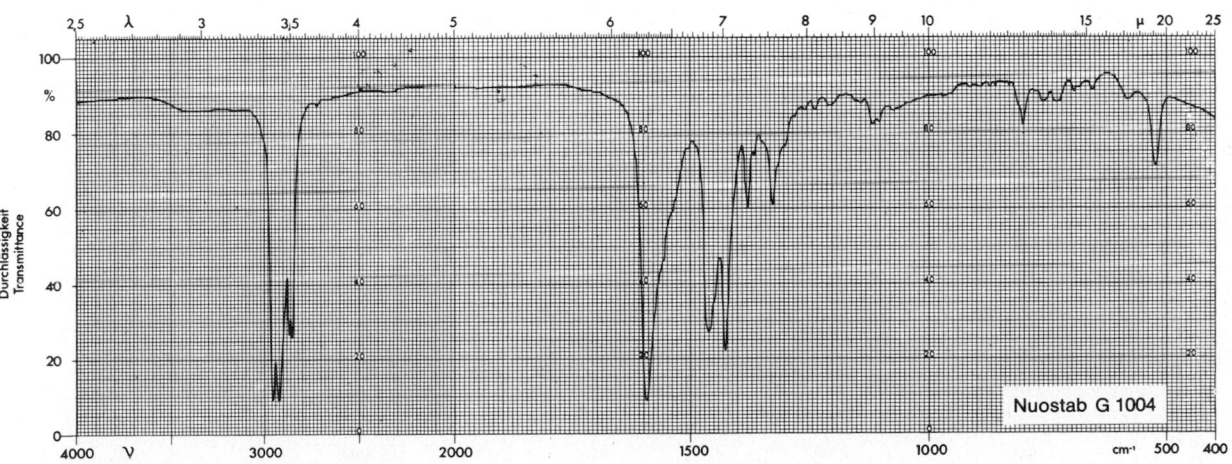

Zusammen- setzung:	Cadmium-Zink-Stabilisator		Composition:	Cadmium zinc stabilizer		6076
Handelsname:	Nuostab G 1004	Herst.: Siegle	Tradename:	Nuostab G 1004	Manuf.: Siegle	
Präparation:	Kapill. Film	Dez. Nr.: 2.1.15	Preparation:	Capill. film	Dec. No.: 2.1.15	

Stabilisatoren
2. Metallcarboxylat-Stabilisatoren
2.2. Metallsalze anderer Carbonsäuren

Stabilizers
2. Metal Carboxylate Stabilizers
2.2. Metal Salts of other Acids

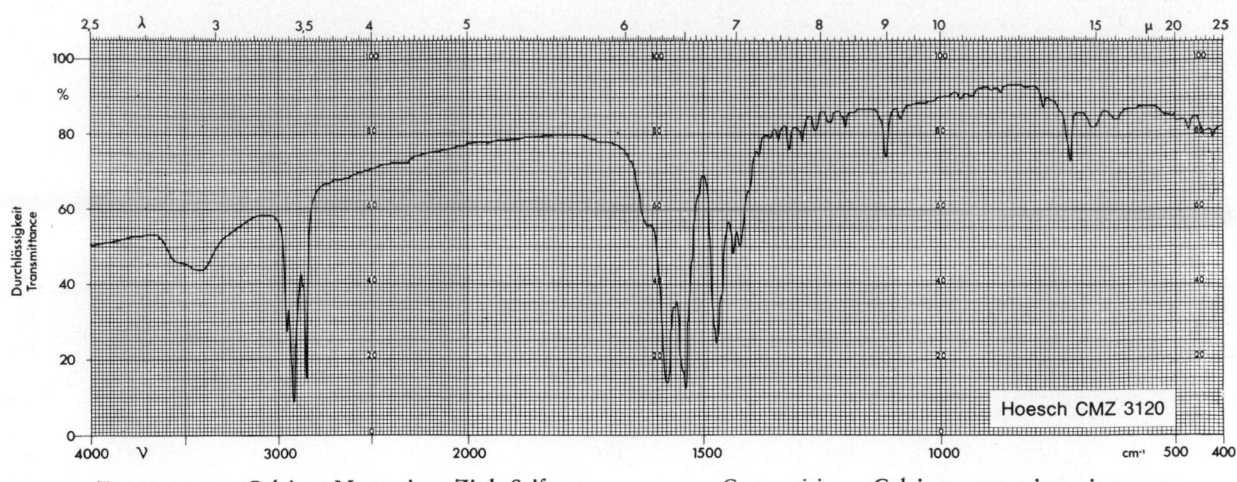

6077

Zusammen-setzung:	Calcium-Magnesium-Zink-Seifen		Composition:	Calcium magnesium zinc soaps	
Handelsname:	Hoesch CMZ 3120	Herst.: Hoesch	Tradename:	Hoesch CMZ 3120	Manuf.: Hoesch
Präparation:	KBr (5/1000)	Dez. Nr.: 2.1.16	Preparation:	KBr (5/1000)	Dec. No.: 2.1.16

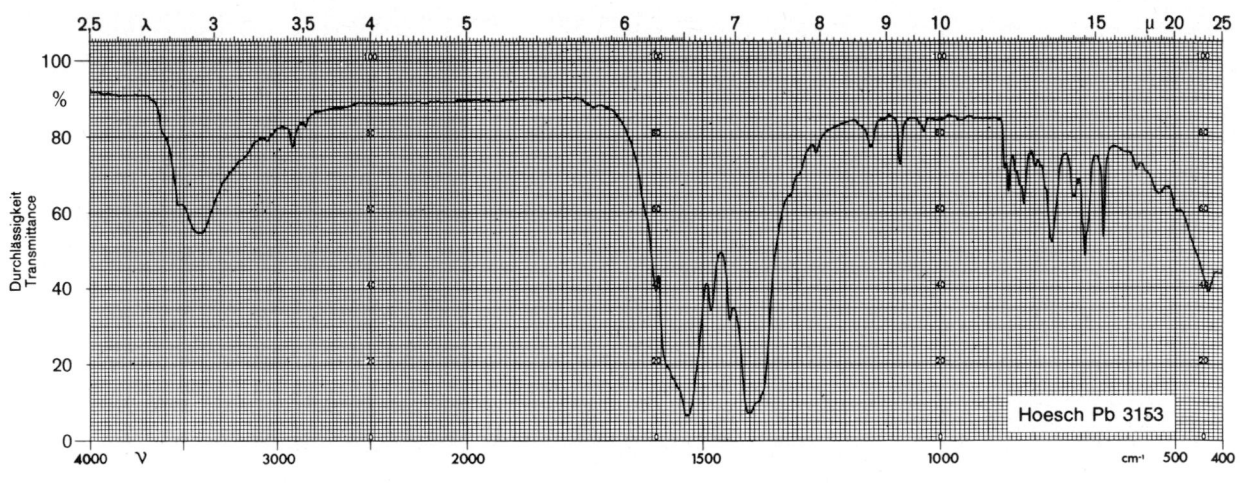

6078

Zusammen-setzung:	Bleiphthalat		Composition:	Lead phthalate	
Handelsname:	Hoesch Pb 3153	Herst.: Hoesch	Tradename:	Hoesch Pb 3153	Manuf.: Hoesch
Präparation:	KBr (3/1000)	Dez. Nr.: 2.2.1	Preparation:	KBr (3/1000)	Dec. No.: 2.2.1

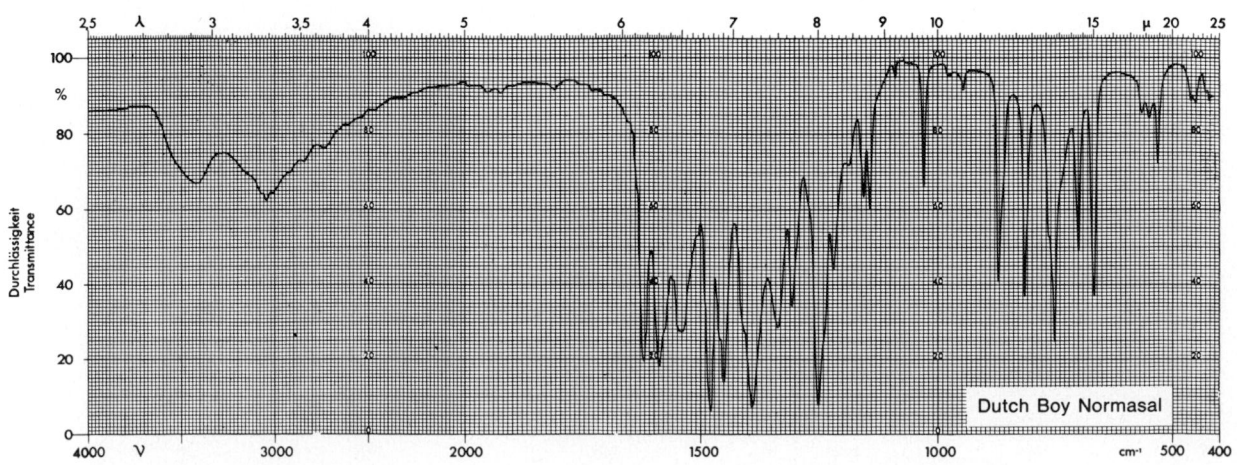

6079

Zusammen-setzung:	Bleisalicylat		Composition:	Lead salicylate	
Handelsname:	Dutch Boy Normasal	Herst.: Kautschuk	Tradename:	Dutch Boy Normasal	Manuf.: Kautschuk
Präparation:	KBr (5/1000)	Dez. Nr.: 2.2.2	Preparation:	KBr (5/1000)	Dec. No.: 2.2.2

Stabilisatoren
2. Metallcarboxylat-Stabilisatoren
2.3. Esterfreie Metallkomplex-Stabilisatoren

Stabilizers
2. Metal Carboxylate Stabilizers
2.3. Ester free Metal Complex Stabilizers

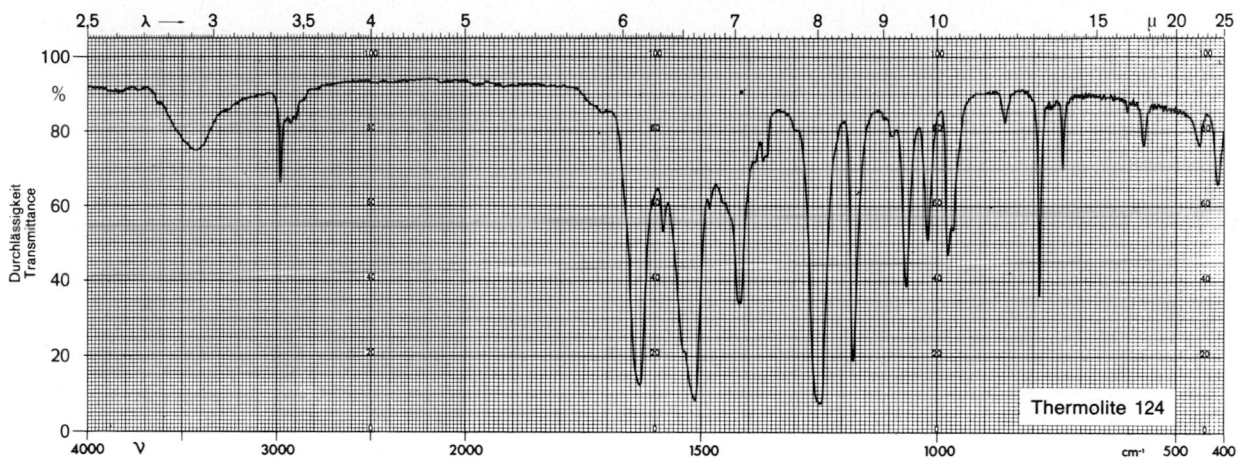

Zusammen-
setzung: **Calciumethylacetoacetat**

Composition: **Calcium ethylacetoacetate**

6080

Handelsname: **Thermolite 124**	Herst.: **M & T**	Tradename: **Thermolite 124**	Manuf.: **M & T**
Präparation: **KBr (3/1000)**	Dez. Nr.: **2.2.3**	Preparation: **KBr (3/1000)**	Dec. No.: **2.2.3**

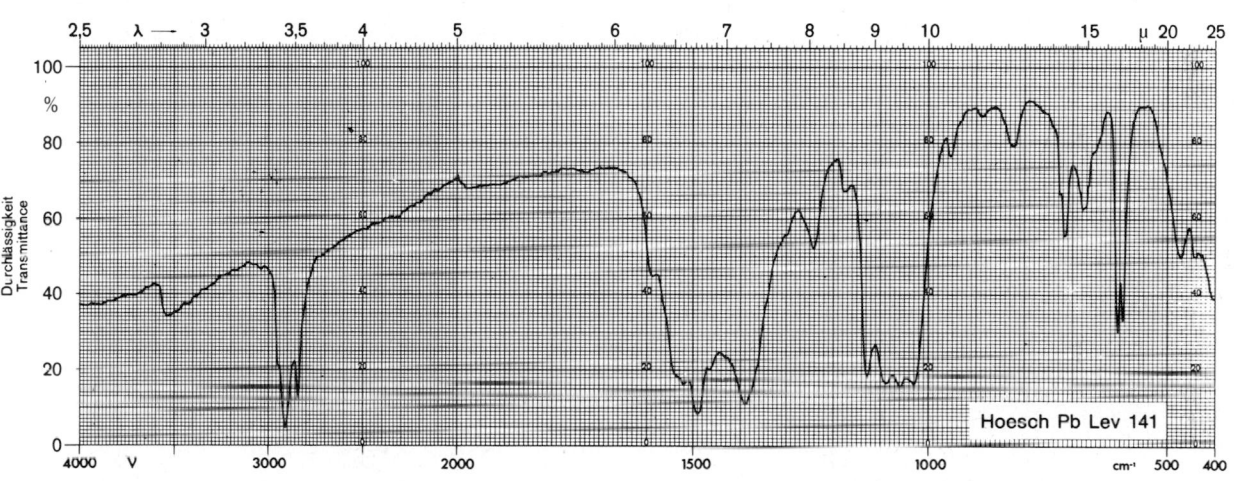

Zusammen-
setzung: **Blei-Sulfat-Stearat-Komplex**

Composition: **Lead sulfate stearate complex**

6081

Handelsname: **Hoesch Pb Lev 141**	Herst.: **Hoesch**	Tradename: **Hoesch Pb Lev 141**	Manuf.: **Hoesch**
Präparation: **KBr (5/1000)**	Dez. Nr.: **2.3.1**	Preparation: **KBr (5/1000)**	Dec. No.: **2.3.1**

Zusammen-
setzung: **Blei-Calcium-Seifen, basisches Bleiphosphit**

Composition: **Lead calcium soaps, basic lead phosphite**

6082

Handelsname: **Hoesch PbCa 3106**	Herst.: **Hoesch**	Tradename: **Hoesch PbCa 3106**	Manuf.: **Hoesch**
Präparation: **KBr (5/1000)**	Dez. Nr.: **2.3.2**	Preparation: **KBr (5/1000)**	Dec. No.: **2.3.2**

Stabilisatoren
2. Metallcarboxylat-Stabilisatoren
2.3. Esterfreie Metallkomplex-Stabilisatoren

Stabilizers
2. Metal Carboxylate Stabilizers
2.3. Ester free Metal Complex Stabilizers

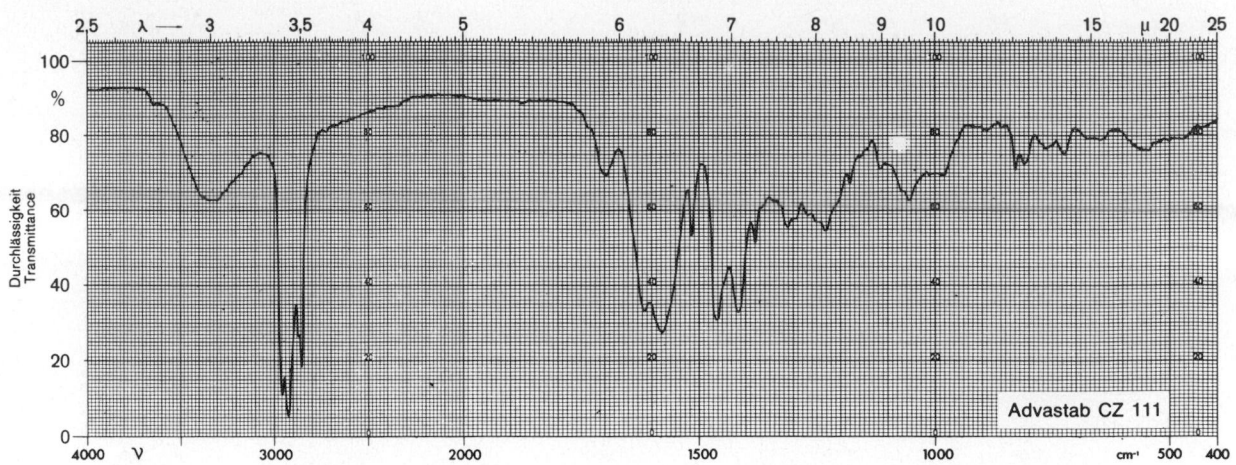

6083   Zusammen-   **Calcium-Zink-Stabilisator**   Composition: **Calcium zinc stabilizer**
setzung:

Handelsname: **Advastab CZ 111**   Herst.:   **Advance**   Tradename: **Advastab CZ 111**   Manuf.:   **Advance**
Präparation: **Kapill. Film**   Dez. Nr.:   **2.3.3**   Preparation: **Capill. film**   Dec. No.: **2.3.3**

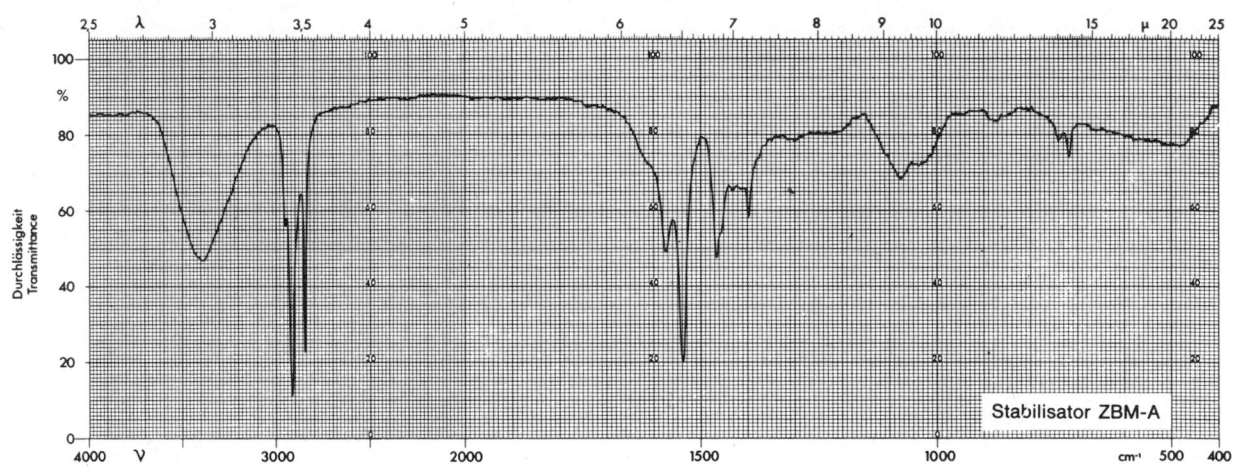

6084   Zusammen-   **Calcium-Zink-Stabilisator**   Composition: **Calcium zinc stabilizer**
setzung:

Handelsname: **Stabilisator ZBM-A**   Herst.:   **Bärlocher**   Tradename: **Stabilisator ZBM-A**   Manuf.:   **Bärlocher**
Präparation: **KBr (5/1000)**   Dez. Nr.:   **2.3.4**   Preparation: **KBr (5/1000)**   Dec. No.: **2.3.4**

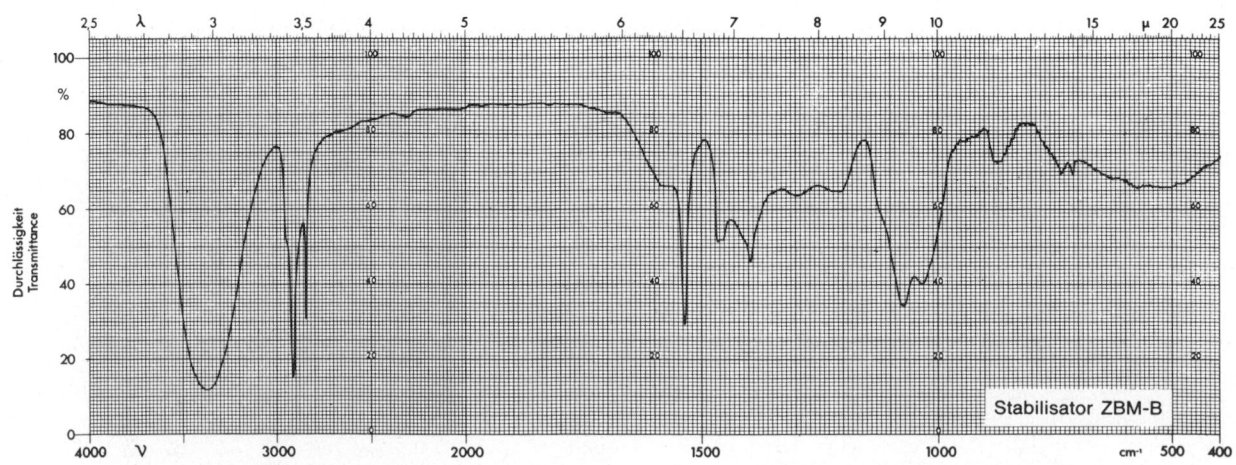

6085   Zusammen-   **Calcium-Zink-Stabilisator**   Composition: **Calcium zinc stabilizer**
setzung:

Handelsname: **Stabilisator ZBM-B**   Herst.:   **Bärlocher**   Tradename: **Stabilisator ZBM-B**   Manuf.:   **Bärlocher**
Präparation: **KBr (5/1000)**   Dez. Nr.:   **2.3.5**   Preparation: **KBr (5/1000)**   Dec. No.: **2.3.5**

Stabilisatoren
2. Metallcarboxylat-Stabilisatoren
2.3. Esterfreie Metallkomplex-Stabilisatoren

Stabilizers
2. Metal Carboxylate Stabilizers
2.3. Ester free Metal Complex Stabilizers

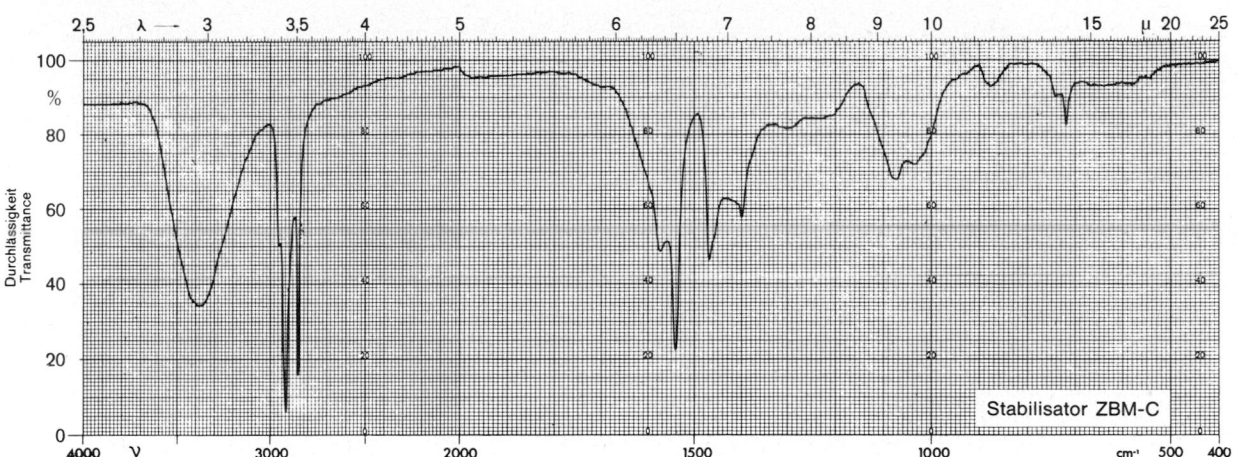

Zusammensetzung:	Calcium-Zink-Stabilisator		Composition:	Calcium zinc stabilizer		6086
Handelsname: Stabilisator ZBM-C	Herst.:	Bärlocher	Tradename:	Stabilisator ZBM-C	Manuf.:	Bärlocher
Präparation: KBr (5/1000)	Dez. Nr.:	2.3.6	Preparation:	KBr (5/1000)	Dec. No.:	2.3.6

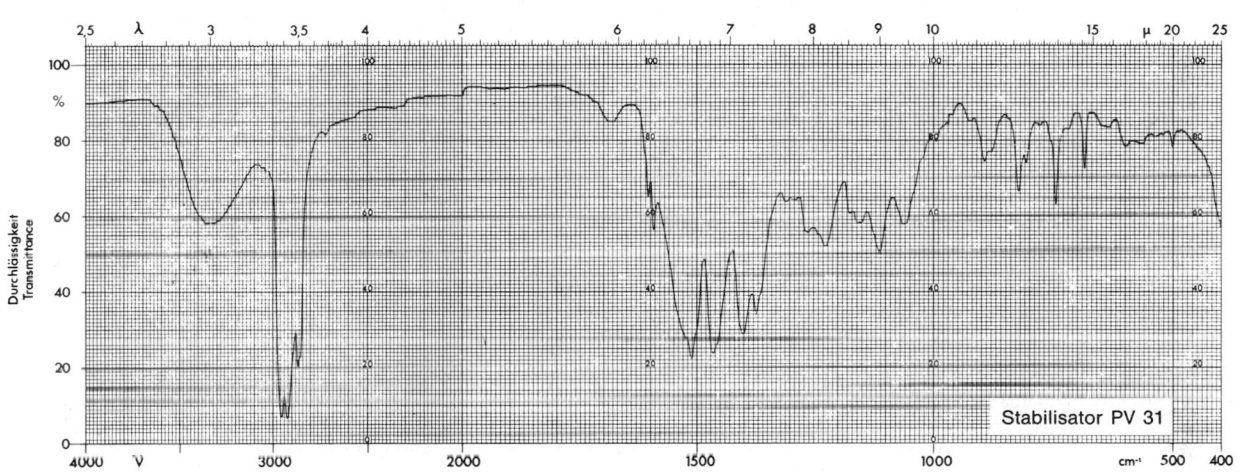

Zusammensetzung:	Ca-Pb-P-Komplex-Stabilisator		Composition:	Ca-Pb-P-complex stabilizer		6087
Handelsname: Stabilisator PV 31	Herst.:	Bärlocher	Tradename:	Stabilisator PV 31	Manuf.:	Bärlocher
Präparation: Kapill. Film	Dez. Nr.:	2.3.7	Preparation:	Capill. film	Dec. No.:	2.3.7

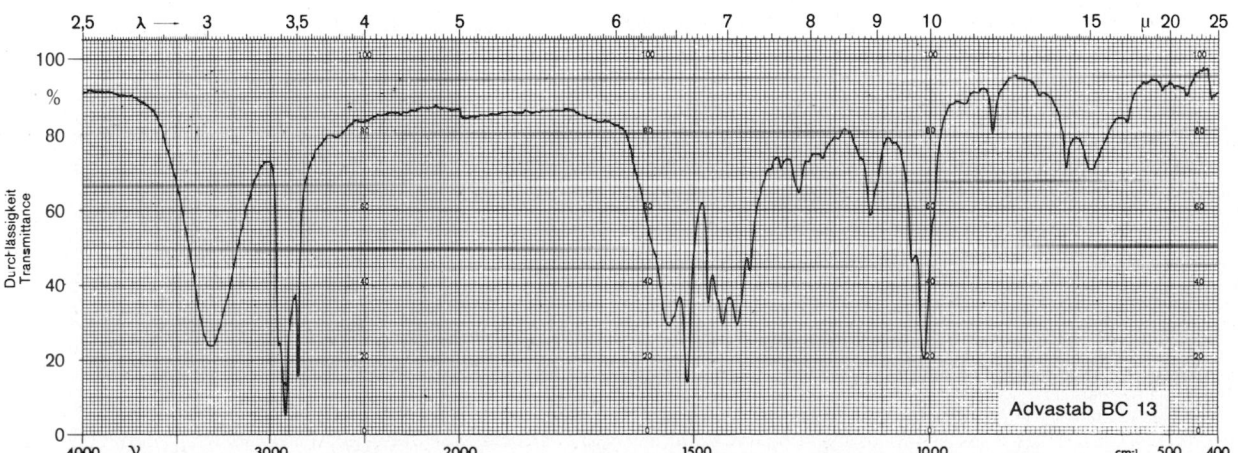

Zusammensetzung:	Barium-Cadmium-Calcium-Laurat		Composition:	Barium cadmium calcium laurate		6088
Handelsname: Advastab BC 13	Herst.:	Advance	Tradename:	Advastab BC 13	Manuf.:	Advance
Präparation: KBr (8/1000)	Dez. Nr.:	2.3.8	Preparation:	KBr (8/1000)	Dec. No.:	2.3.8

Stabilisatoren
2. Metallcarboxylat-Stabilisatoren
2.3. Esterfreie Metallkomplex-Stabilisatoren

Stabilizers
2. Metal Carboxylate Stabilizers
2.3. Ester free Metal Complex Stabilizers

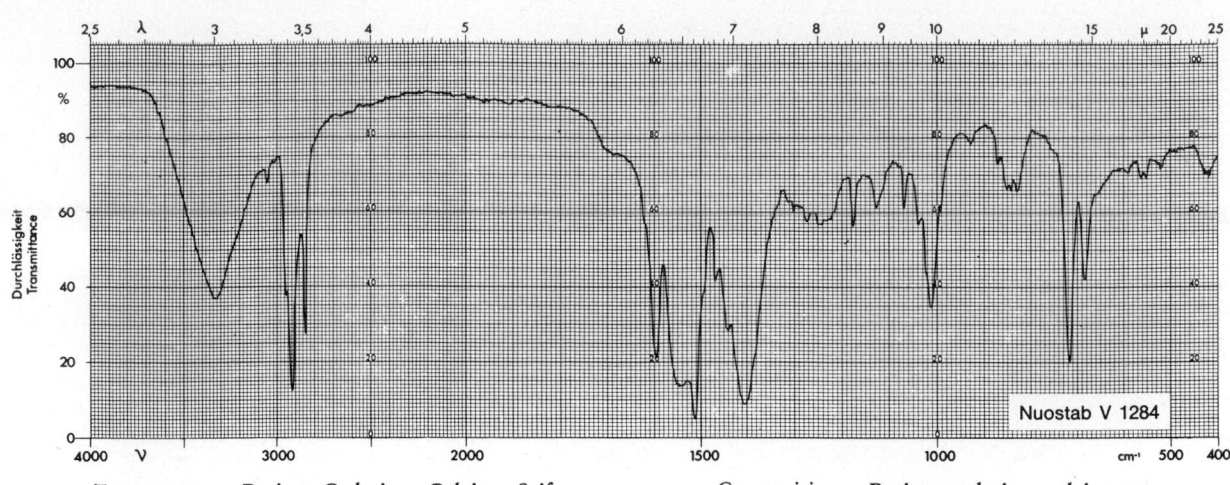

6089

Zusammensetzung:	Barium-Cadmium-Calcium-Seife		Composition:	Barium cadmium calcium soap	
Handelsname:	Nuostab V 1284	Herst.: Siegle	Tradename:	Nuostab V 1284	Manuf.: Siegle
Präparation:	KBr (6/1000)	Dez. Nr.: 2.3.9	Preparation:	KBr (6/1000)	Dec. No.: 2.3.9

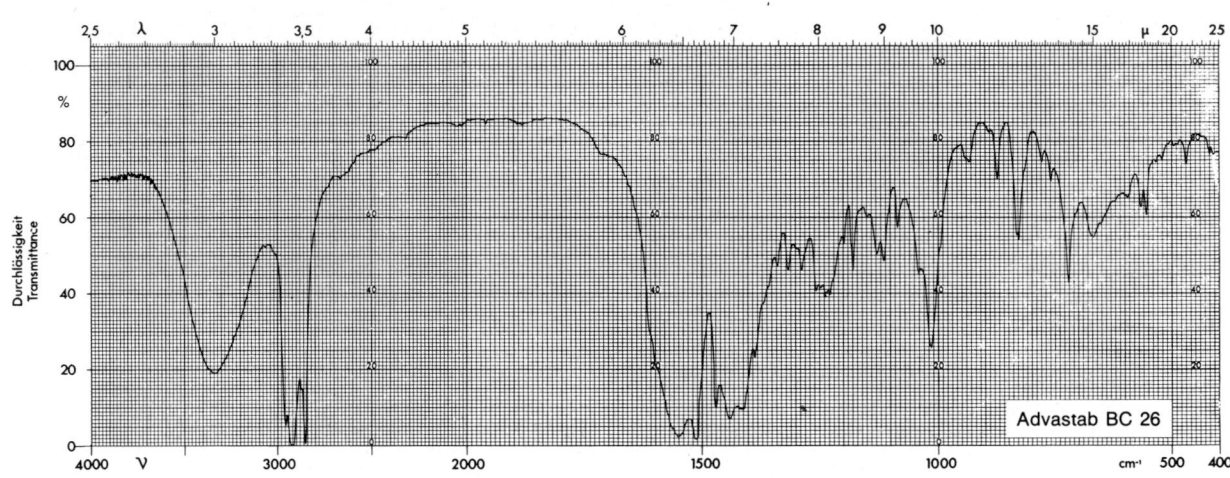

6090

Zusammensetzung:	Ba-Cd-Stabilisator		Composition:	Ba-Cd-stabilizer	
Handelsname:	Advastab BC 26	Herst.: Advance	Tradename:	Advastab BC 26	Manuf.: Advance
Präparation:	KBr (5/1000)	Dez. Nr.: 2.3.10	Preparation:	KBr (5/1000)	Dec. No.: 2.3.10

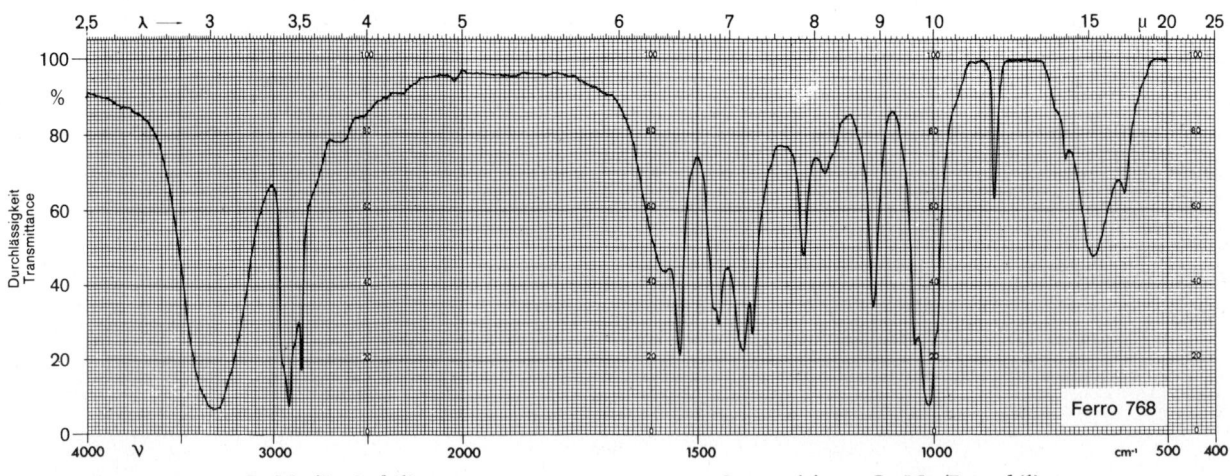

6091

Zusammensetzung:	Ca-Mg-Zn-Stabilisator		Composition:	Ca-Mg-Zn-stabilizer	
Handelsname:	Ferro 768	Herst.: Bärlocher	Tradename:	Ferro 768	Manuf.: Bärlocher
Präparation:	KBr (6/1000)	Dez. Nr.: 2.3.11	Preparation:	KBr (6/1000)	Dec. No.: 2.3.11

Stabilisatoren
2. Metallcarboxylat-Stabilisatoren
2.4. Esterhaltige Metallkomplex-Stabilisatoren

Stabilizers
2. Metal Carboxylate Stabilizers
2.4. Ester containing Metal Complex Stabilizers

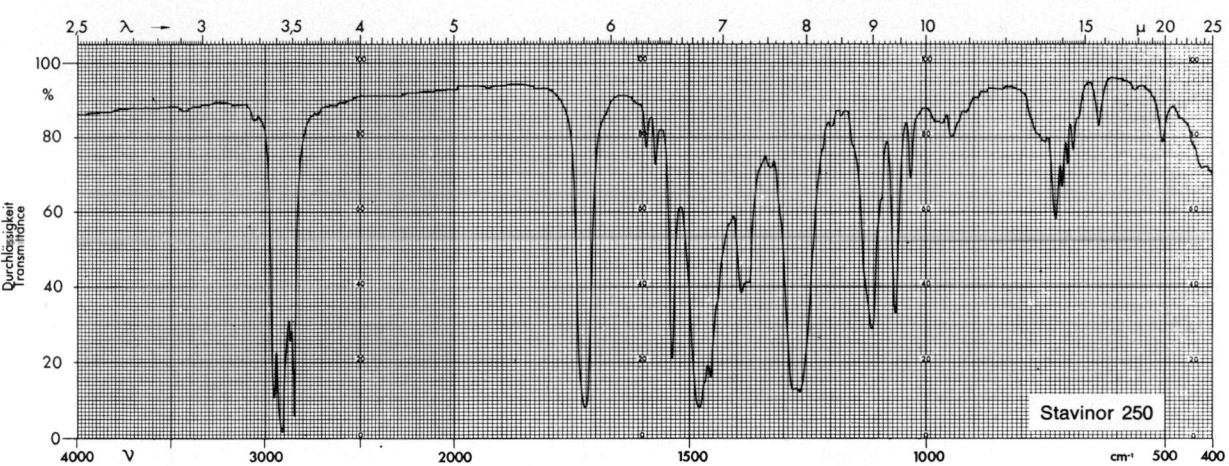

Zusammen-	Phthalester, Bleiseife		Composition:	Phthalic ester, lead soap		6092
setzung:						
Handelsname:	Stavinor 250	Herst.: Usines	Tradename:	Stavinor 250	Manuf.: Usines	
Präparation:	Kapill. Film	Dez. Nr.: 2.4.1	Preparation:	Capill. film	Dec. No.: 2.4.1	

Zusammen-	Zinkoctanoat, Dioctylphthalat		Composition:	Zinc octanoate, Dioctyl phthalate		6093
setzung:						
Handelsname:	Estabex Z 20	Herst.: Oxydo	Tradename:	Estabex Z 20	Manuf.: Oxydo	
Präparation:	Kapill. Film	Dez. Nr.: 2.4.2	Preparation:	Capill. film	Dec. No.: 2.4.2	

Zusammen-	Cadmium-Zink-Stabilisator		Composition:	Cadmium zinc stabilizer		6094
setzung:						
Handelsname:	Advastab C 86	Herst.: Advance	Tradename:	Advastab C 86	Manuf.: Advance	
Präparation:	Kapill. Film	Dez. Nr.: 2.4.3	Preparation:	Capill. film	Dec. No.: 2.4.3	

Stabilisatoren
2. Metallcarboxylat-Stabilisatoren
2.5. Phosphorhaltige Metallsalz-Stabilisatoren

Stabilizers
2. Metal Carboxylate Stabilizers
2.5. Phosphorus containing Metal Salts Stabilizers

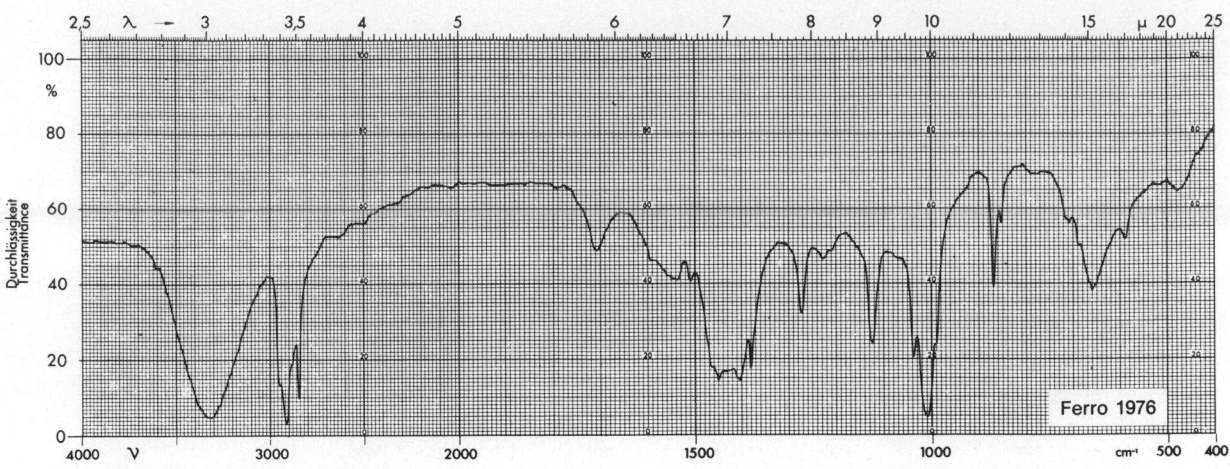

6095	Zusammen- setzung:	**Ca-Ba-Zn-Stabilisator**		Composition:	**Ca-Ba-Zn-stabilizer**	
	Handelsname:	**Ferro 1976**	Herst.: **Bärlocher**	Tradename:	**Ferro 1976**	Manuf.: **Bärlocher**
	Präparation:	**KBr (5/1000)**	Dez. Nr.: **2.4.4**	Preparation:	**KBr (5/1000)**	Dec. No.: **2.4.4**

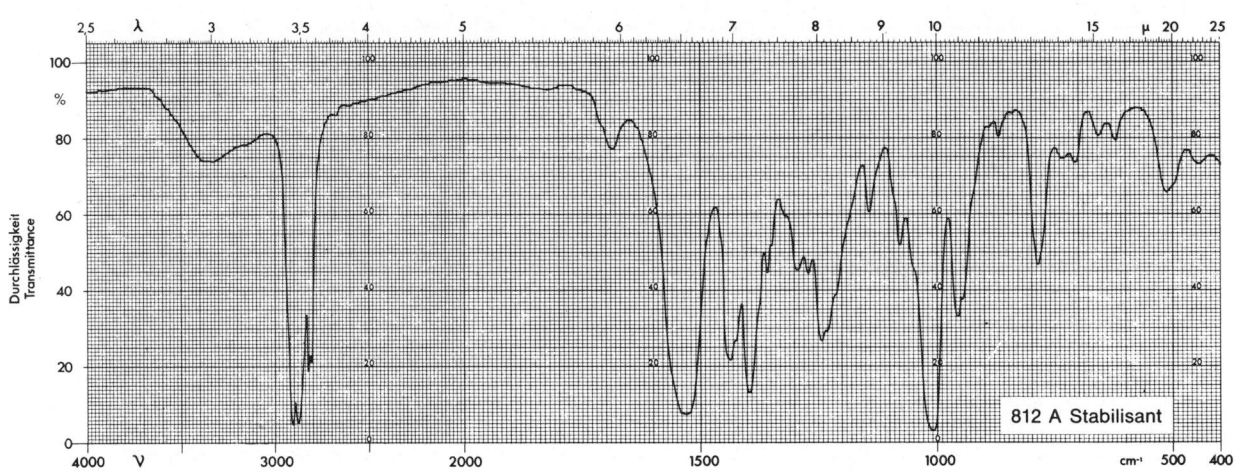

6096	Zusammen- setzung:	**Cadmiumseife, Alkylarylphosphat**		Composition:	**Cadmium soap, alkylarylphosphate**	
	Handelsname:	**812 A Stabilisant**	Herst.: **Argus**	Tradename:	**812 A Stabilisant**	Manuf.: **Argus**
	Präparation:	**Kapill. Film**	Dez. Nr.: **2.5.1**	Preparation:	**Capill. film**	Dec. No.: **2.5.1**

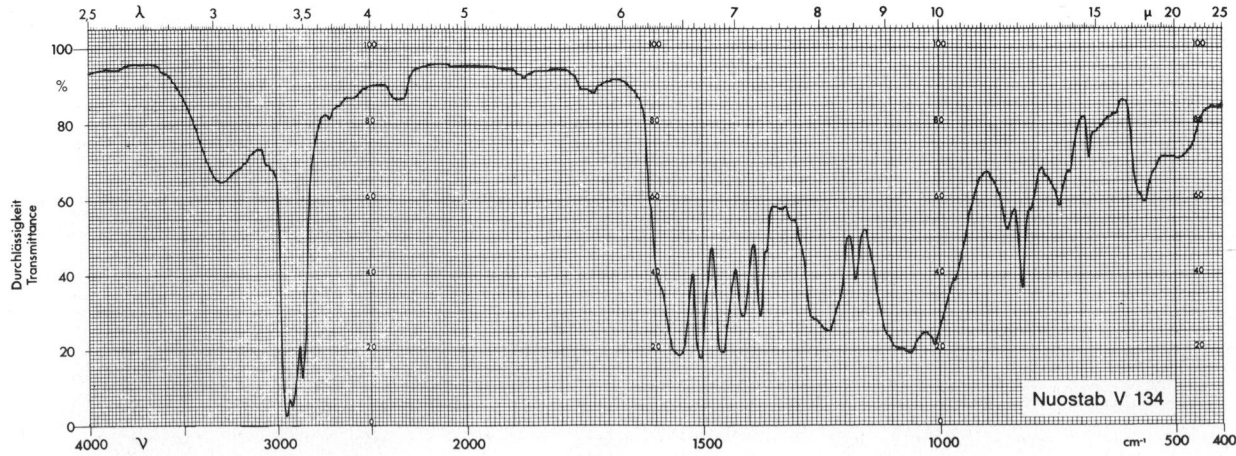

6097	Zusammen- setzung:	**Ba-Cd-P-Stabilisator**		Composition:	**Ba-Cd-P-stabilizer**	
	Handelsname:	**Nuostab V 134**	Herst.: **Siegle**	Tradename:	**Nuostab V 134**	Manuf.: **Siegle**
	Präparation:	**Kapill. Film**	Dez. Nr.: **2.5.2**	Preparation:	**Capill. film**	Dec. No.: **2.5.2**

Stabilisatoren
2. Metallcarboxylat-Stabilisatoren
2.5. Phosphorhaltige Metallsalz-Stabilisatoren

Stabilizers
2. Metal Carboxylate Stabilizers
2.5. Phosphorus containing Metal Salts Stabilizers

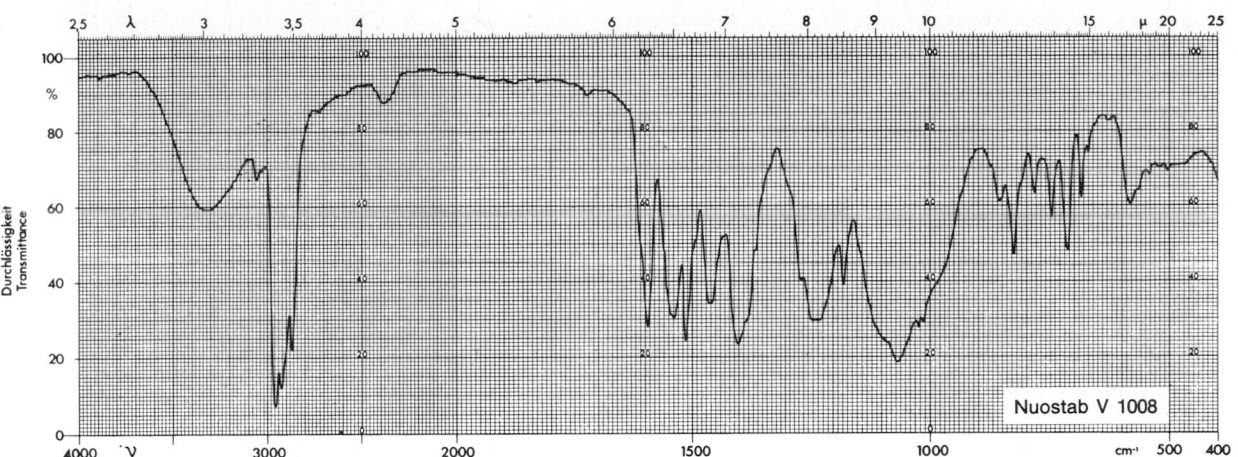

Nuostab V 1008

Zusammen-setzung:	Ba-Cd-P-Stabilisator		Composition:	Ba-Cd-P-stabilizer		6098
Handelsname:	Nuostab V 1008	Herst.: Siegle	Tradename:	Nuostab V 1008	Manuf.: Siegle	
Präparation:	Kapill. Film	Dez. Nr.: 2.5.3	Preparation:	Capill. film	Dec. No.: 2.5.3	

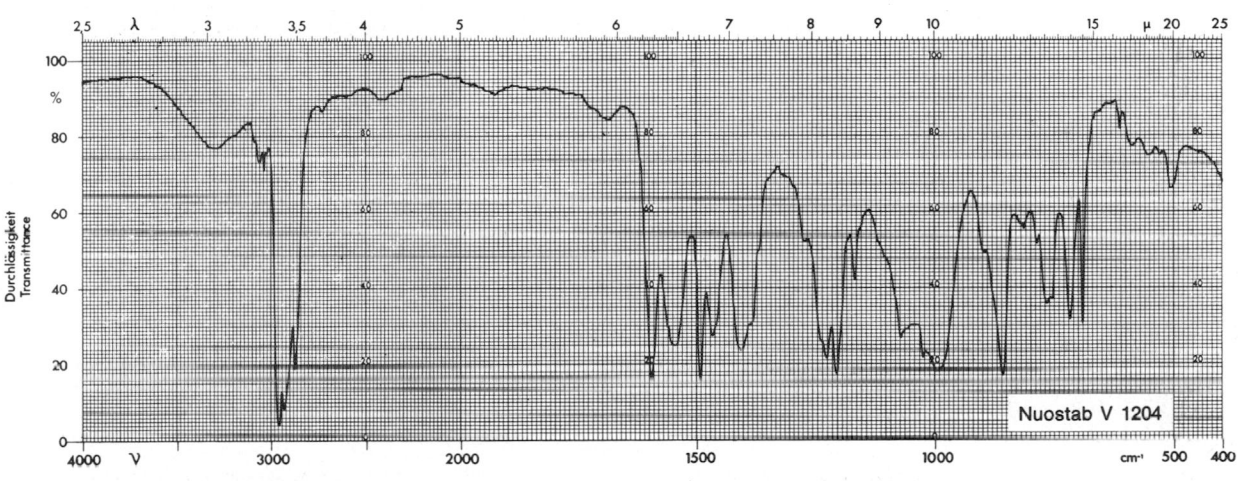

Nuostab V 1204

Zusammen-setzung:	Ba-Cd-P-Stabilisator		Composition:	Ba-Cd-P-stabilizer		6099
Handelsname:	Nuostab V 1204	Herst.: Siegle	Tradename:	Nuostab V 1204	Manuf.: Siegle	
Präparation:	Kapill. Film	Dez. Nr.: 2.5.4	Preparation:	Capill. film	Dec. No.: 2.5.4	

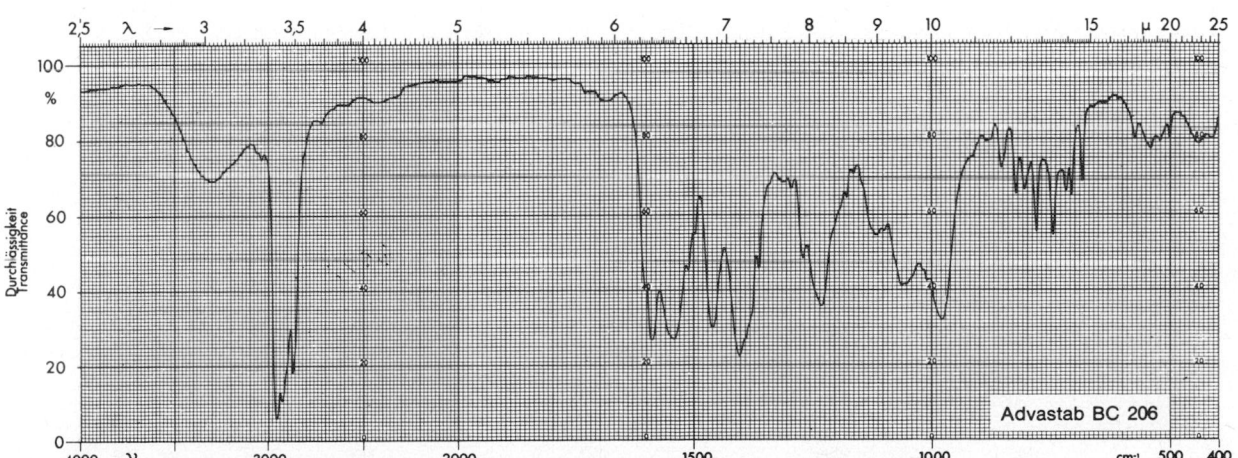

Advastab BC 206

Zusammen-setzung:	Ba-Cd-P-Stabilisator		Composition:	Ba-Cd-P-stabilizer		6100
Handelsname:	Advastab BC 206	Herst.: Advance	Tradename:	Advastab BC 206	Manuf.: Advance	
Präparation:	Kapill. Film	Dez. Nr.: 2.5.5	Preparation:	Capill. film	Dec. No.: 2.5.5	

Stabilisatoren
2. Metallcarboxylat-Stabilisatoren
2.5. Phosphorhaltige Metallsalz-Stabilisatoren

Stabilizers
2. Metal Carboxylate Stabilizers
2.5. Phosphorus containing Metal Salts Stabilizers

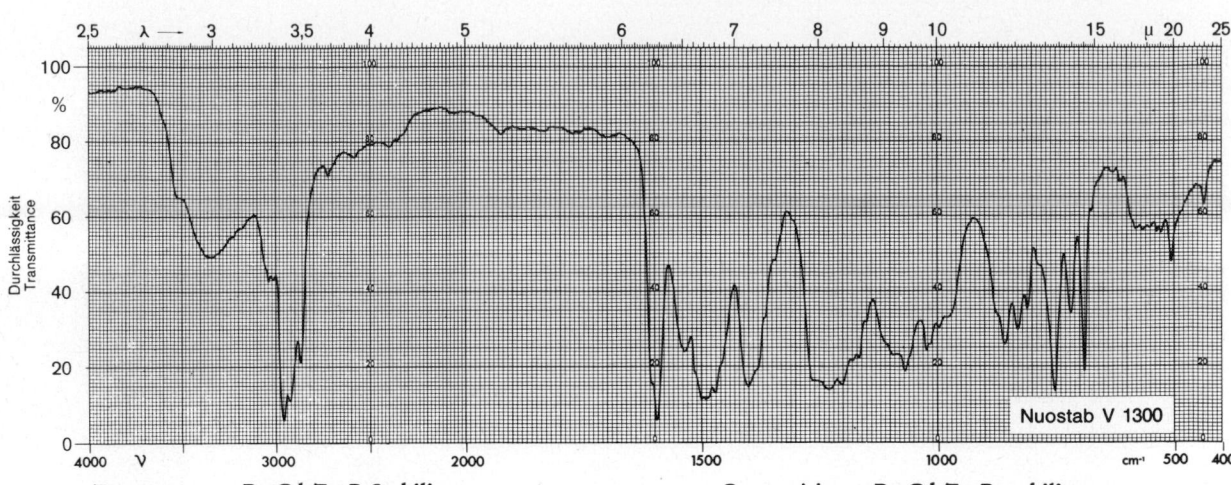

Nuostab V 1300

6101	Zusammen-setzung:	**Ba-Cd-Zn-P-Stabilisator**		Composition:	**Ba-Cd-Zn-P-stabilizer**	
	Handelsname:	**Nuostab V 1300**	Herst.: **Siegle**	Tradename:	**Nuostab V 1300**	Manuf.: **Siegle**
	Präparation:	**Kapill. Film**	Dez. Nr.: **2.5.6**	Preparation:	**Capill. film**	Dec. No.: **2.5.6**

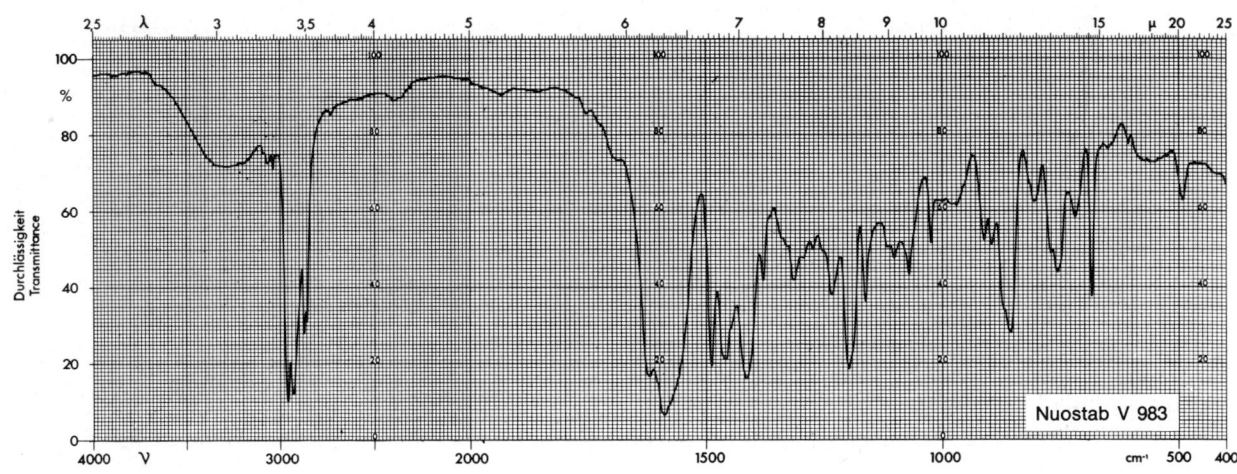

Nuostab V 983

6102	Zusammen-setzung:	**Ca-Zn-Mg-P-Stabilisator**		Composition:	**Ca-Zn-Mg-P-stabilizer**	
	Handelsname:	**Nuostab V 983**	Herst.: **Siegle**	Tradename:	**Nuostab V 983**	Manuf.: **Siegle**
	Präparation:	**Kapill. Film**	Dez. Nr.: **2.5.7**	Preparation:	**Capill. film**	Dec. No.: **2.5.7**

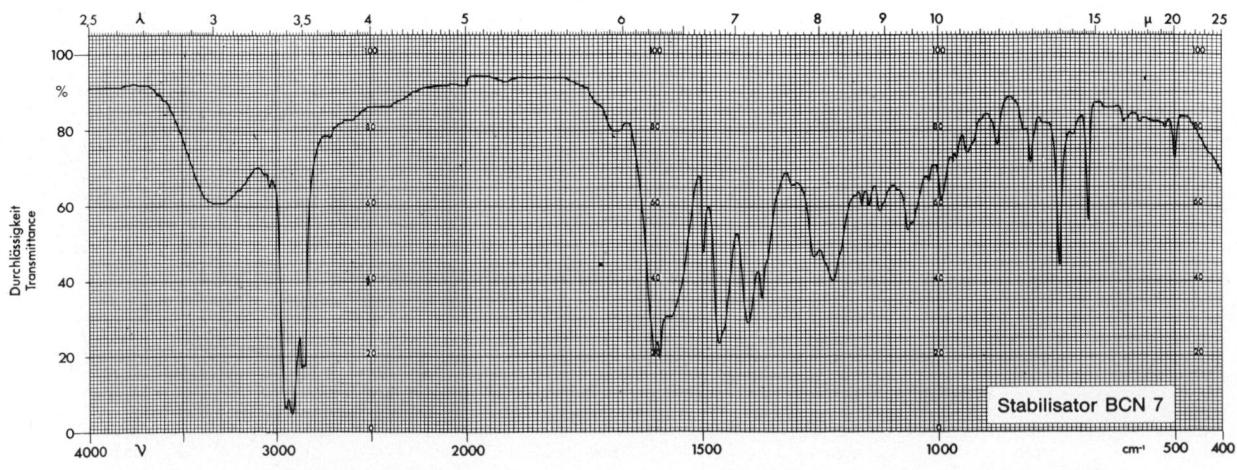

Stabilisator BCN 7

6103	Zusammen-setzung:	**Ca-Zn-Ba-Cd-P-Stabilisator**		Composition:	**Ca-Zn-Ba-Cd-P-stabilizer**	
	Handelsname:	Stabilisator BCN 7	Herst.: **Bärlocher**	Tradename:	**Stabilisator BCN 7**	Manuf.: **Bärlocher**
	Präparation:	**Kapill. Film**	Dez. Nr.: **2.5.8**	Preparation:	**Capill. film**	Dec. No.: **2.5.8**

Stabilisatoren
2. Metallcarboxylat-Stabilisatoren
2.6. Ester- und phosphorhaltige Metallsalz-Stabilisatoren

Stabilizers
2. Metal Carboxylate Stabilizers
2.6. Ester and Phosphorus containing Metal Salts Stabilizers

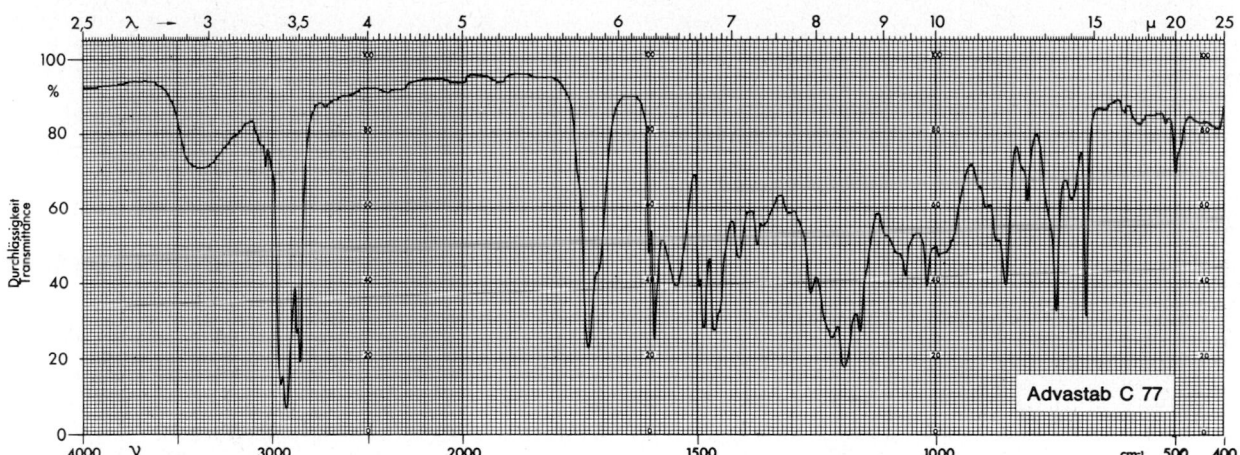

| Zusammen-setzung: | Ba-Cd-P-Stabilisator | | Composition: | Ba-Cd-P-stabilizer | | 6104 |

| Handelsname: | Advastab C 77 | Herst.: | Advance | Tradename: | Advastab C 77 | Manuf.: | Advance |
| Präparation: | Kapill. Film | Dez. Nr.: | 2.6.1 | Preparation: | Capill. film | Dec. No.: | 2.6.1 |

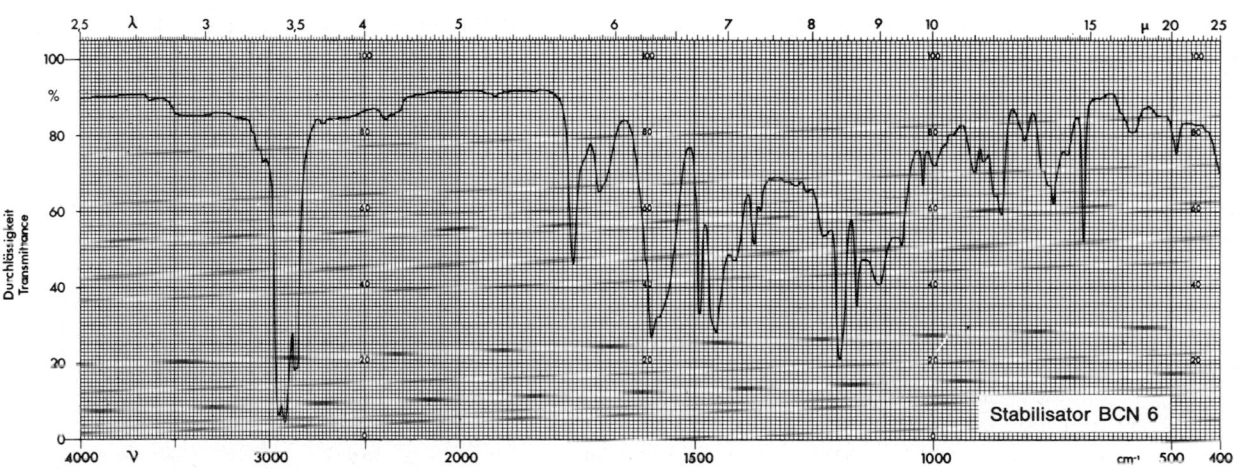

| Zusammen-setzung: | Ca-Zn-Cd-Mg-P-Stabilisator | | Composition: | Ca-Zn-Cd-Mg-P-stabilizer | | 6105 |

| Handelsname: | Stabilisator BCN 6 | Herst.: | Bärlocher | Tradename: | Stabilisator BCN 6 | Manuf.: | Bärlocher |
| Präparation: | Kapill. Film | Dez. Nr.: | 2.6.2 | Preparation: | Capill. film | Dec. No.: | 2.6.2 |

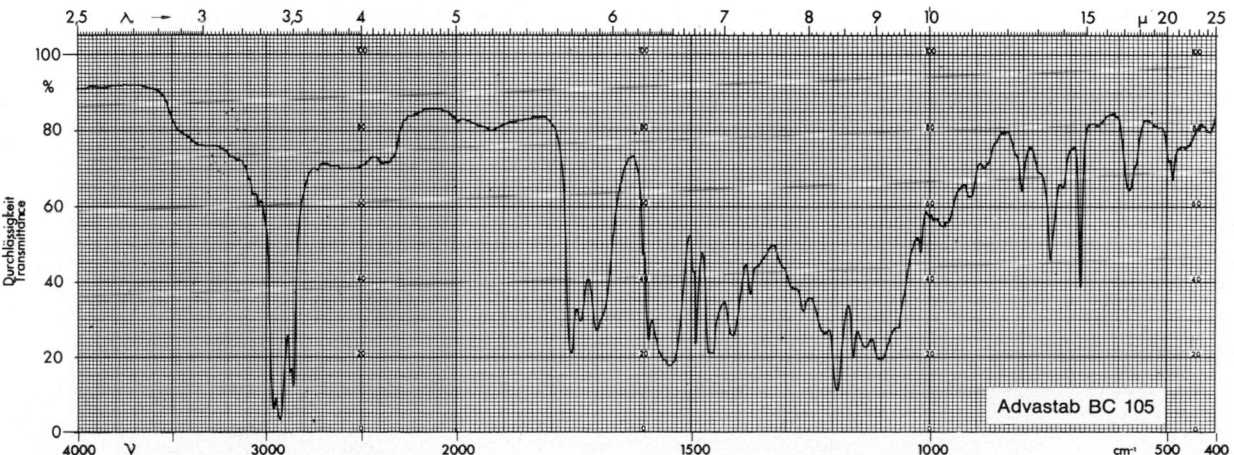

| Zusammen-setzung: | Ba-Cd-Na-Ca-P-Stabilisator | | Composition: | Ba-Cd-Na-Ca-P-stabilizer | | 6106 |

| Handelsname: | Advastab BC 105 | Herst.: | Advance | Tradename: | Advastab BC 105 | Manuf.: | Advance |
| Präparation: | Kapill. Film | Dez. Nr.: | 2.6.3 | Preparation: | Capill. film | Dec. No.: | 2.6.3 |

Stabilisatoren
2. Metallcarboxylat-Stabilisatoren
2.6. Ester- und phosphorhaltige Metallsalz-Stabilisatoren

Stabilizers
2. Metal Carboxylate Stabilizers
2.6. Ester and Phosphorus containing Metal Salts Stabilizers

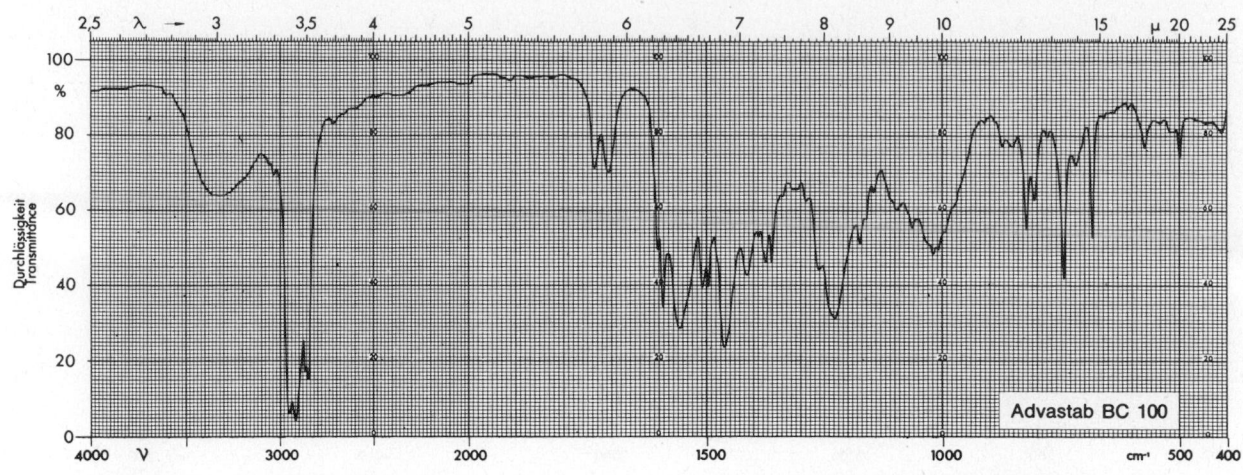

6107
Zusammen-setzung: **Ba-Cd-P-Stabilisator**

Handelsname: **Advastab BC 100** Herst.: **Advance**
Präparation: **Kapill. Film** Dez. Nr.: **2.6.4**

Composition: **Ba-Cd-P-stabilizer**

Tradename: **Advastab BC 100** Manuf.: **Advance**
Preparation: **Capill. film** Dec. No.: **2.6.4**

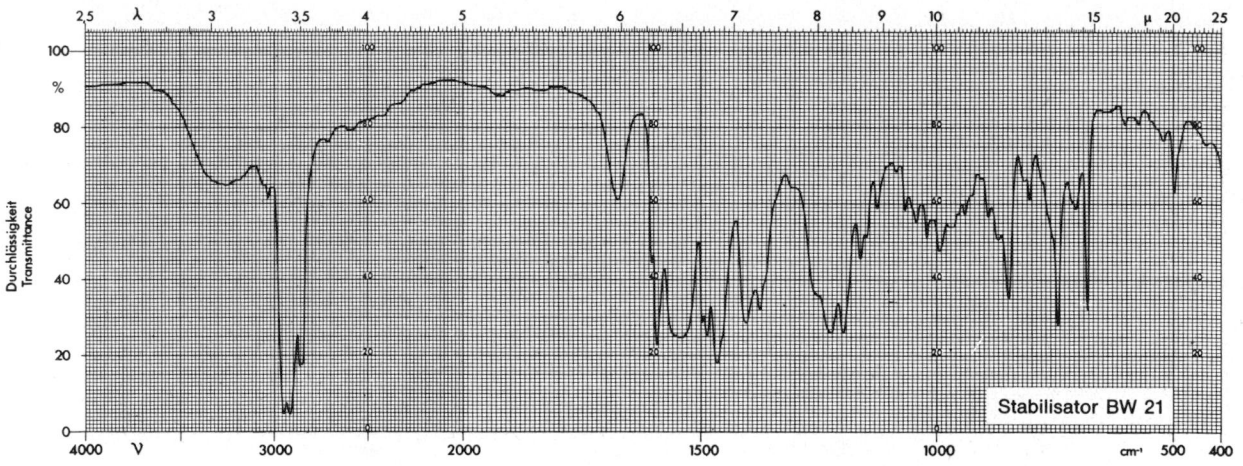

6108
Zusammen-setzung: **Ba-Cd-Ca-P-Stabilisator**

Handelsname: **Stabilisator BW 21** Herst.: **Bärlocher**
Präparation: **Kapill. Film** Dez. Nr.: **2.6.5**

Composition: **Ba-Cd-Ca-P-stabilizer**

Tradename: **Stabilisator BW 21** Manuf.: **Bärlocher**
Preparation: **Capill. film** Dec. No.: **2.6.5**

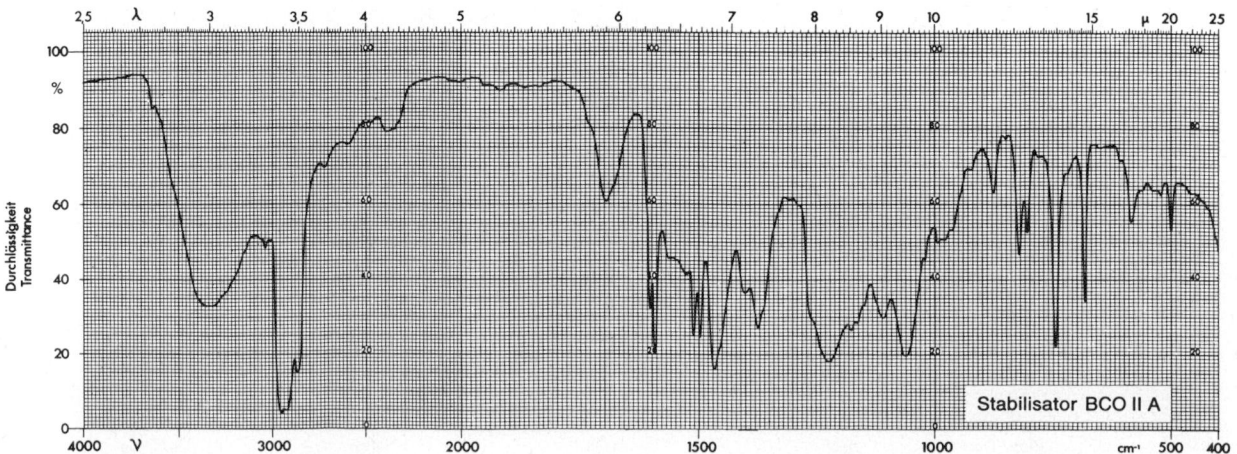

6109
Zusammen-setzung: **Ba-Cd-P-Stabilisator**

Handelsname: **Stabilisator BCO IIA** Herst.: **Bärlocher**
Präparation: **flüssig, ∼ 20 μ** Dez. Nr.: **2.6.6**

Composition: **Ba-Cd-P-stabilizer**

Tradename: **Stabilisator BCO IIA** Manuf.: **Bärlocher**
Preparation: **liquid, ∼ 20 μ** Dec. No.: **2.6.6**

Stabilisatoren
2. Metallcarboxylat-Stabilisatoren
2.6. Ester- und phosphorhaltige Metallsalz-Stabilisatoren

Stabilizers
2. Metal Carboxylate Stabilizers
2.6. Ester and Phosphorus containing Metal Salts Stabilizers

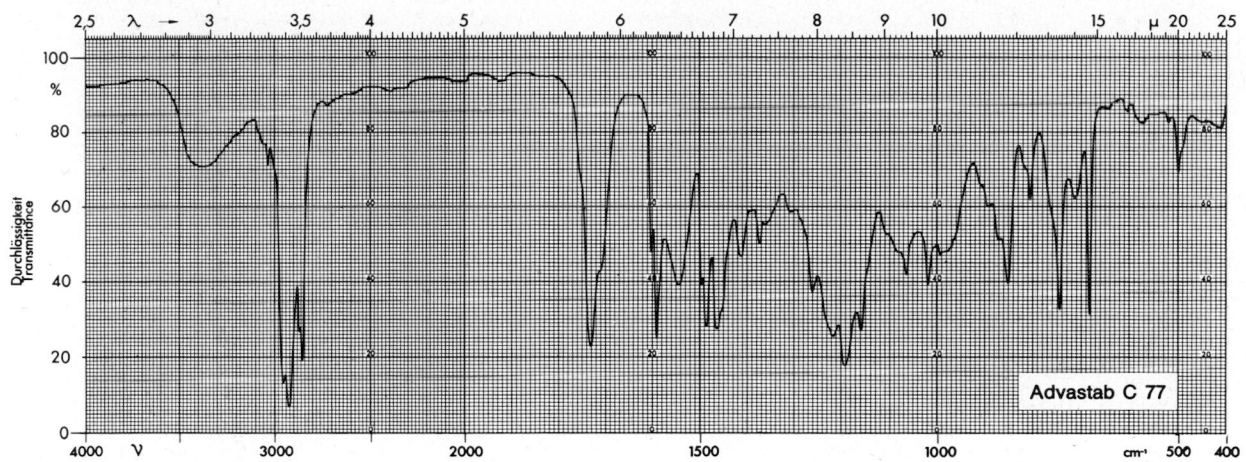

Zusammensetzung:	Ba-Cd-P-Stabilisator		Composition:	Ba-Cd-P-stabilizer		6104
Handelsname:	Advastab C 77	Herst.: Advance	Tradename:	Advastab C 77	Manuf.: Advance	
Präparation:	Kapill. Film	Dez. Nr.: 2.6.1	Preparation:	Capill. film	Dec. No.: 2.6.1	

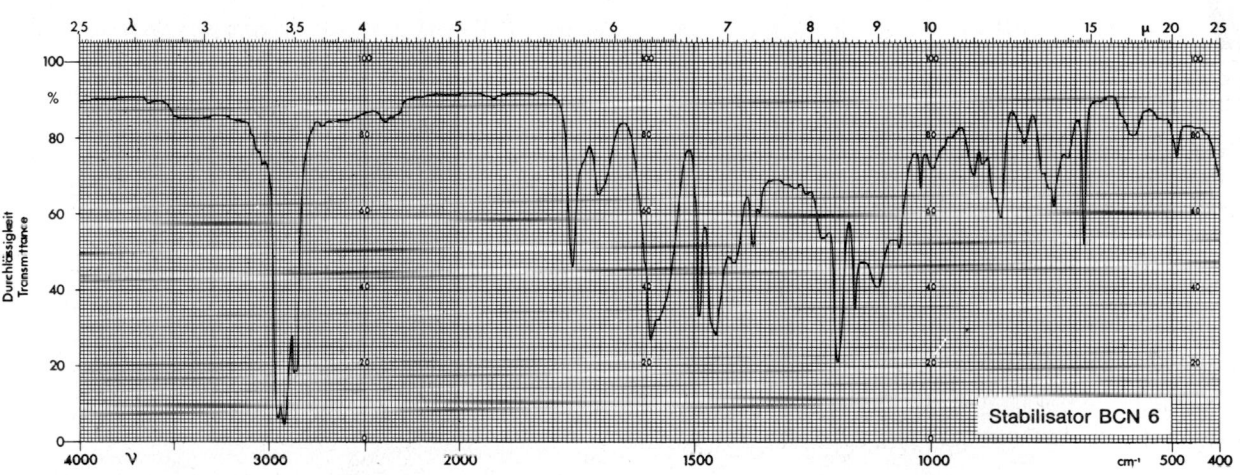

Zusammensetzung:	Ca-Zn-Cd-Mg-P-Stabilisator		Composition:	Ca-Zn-Cd-Mg-P-stabilizer		6105
Handelsname:	Stabilisator BCN 6	Herst.: Bärlocher	Tradename:	Stabilisator BCN 6	Manuf.: Bärlocher	
Präparation:	Kapill. Film	Dez. Nr.: 2.6.2	Preparation:	Capill. film	Dec. No.: 2.6.2	

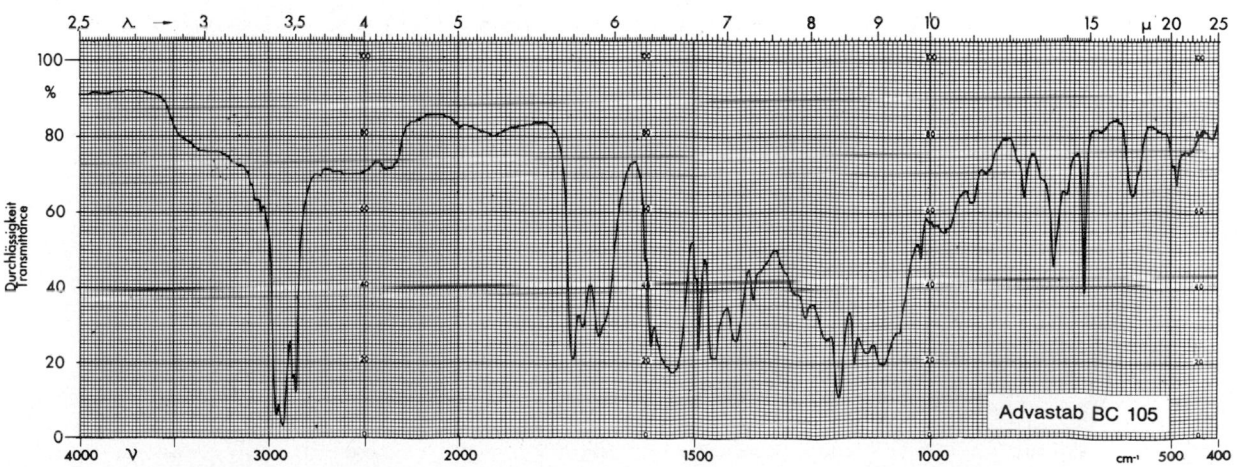

Zusammensetzung:	Ba-Cd-Na-Ca-P-Stabilisator		Composition:	Ba-Cd-Na-Ca-P-stabilizer		6106
Handelsname:	Advastab BC 105	Herst.: Advance	Tradename:	Advastab BC 105	Manuf.: Advance	
Präparation:	Kapill. Film	Dez. Nr.: 2.6.3	Preparation:	Capill. film	Dec. No.: 2.6.3	

Stabilisatoren
2. Metallcarboxylat-Stabilisatoren
2.6. Ester- und phosphorhaltige Metallsalz-Stabilisatoren

Stabilizers
2. Metal Carboxylate Stabilizers
2.6. Ester and Phosphorus containing Metal Salts Stabilizers

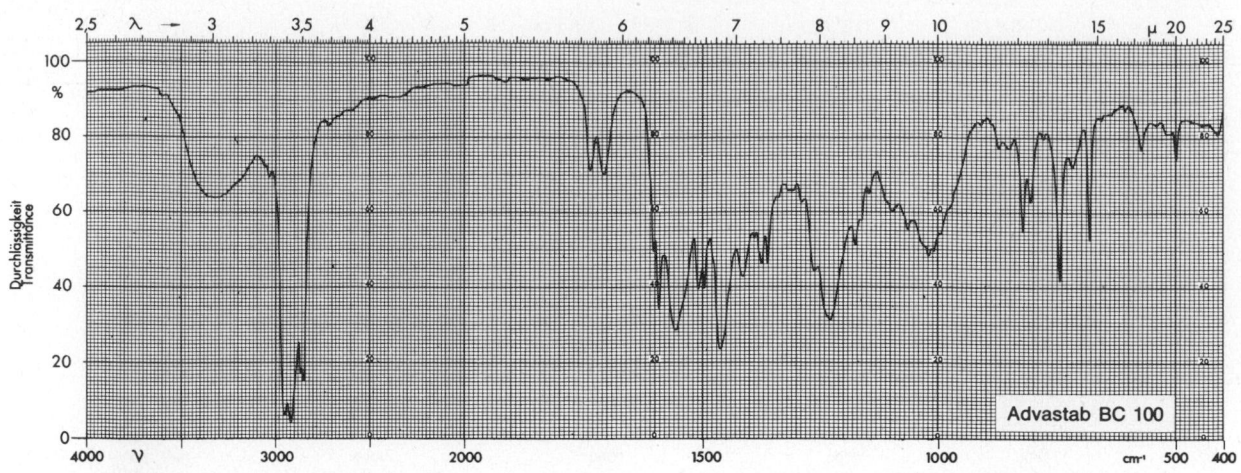

6107   Zusammen-setzung: **Ba-Cd-P-Stabilisator**   Composition: **Ba-Cd-P-stabilizer**

Handelsname: **Advastab BC 100**   Herst.: **Advance**   Tradename: **Advastab BC 100**   Manuf.: **Advance**
Präparation: **Kapill. Film**   Dez. Nr.: **2.6.4**   Preparation: **Capill. film**   Dec. No.: **2.6.4**

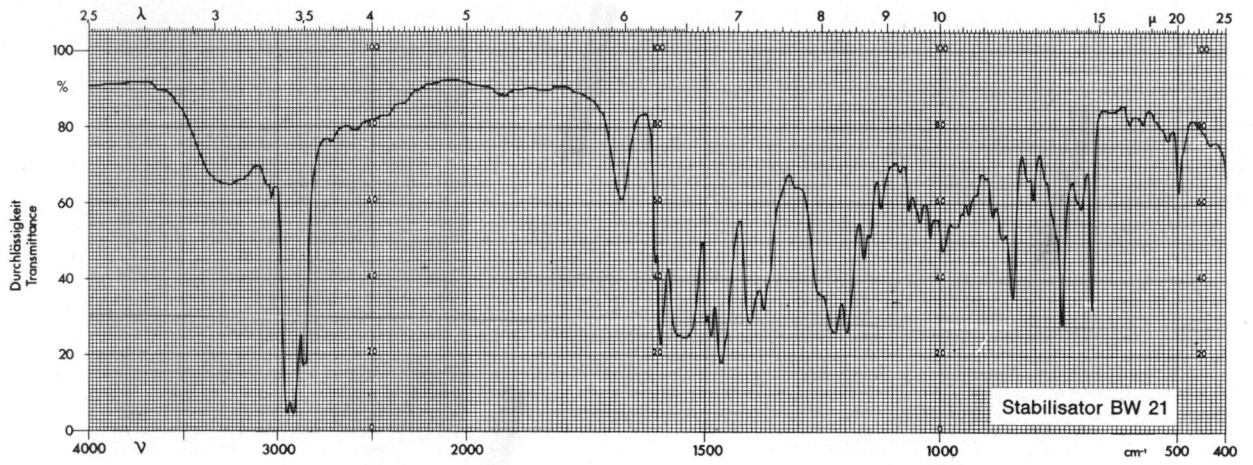

6108   Zusammen-setzung: **Ba-Cd-Ca-P-Stabilisator**   Composition: **Ba-Cd-Ca-P-stabilizer**

Handelsname: **Stabilisator BW 21**   Herst.: **Bärlocher**   Tradename: **Stabilisator BW 21**   Manuf.: **Bärlocher**
Präparation: **Kapill. Film**   Dez. Nr.: **2.6.5**   Preparation: **Capill. film**   Dec. No.: **2.6.5**

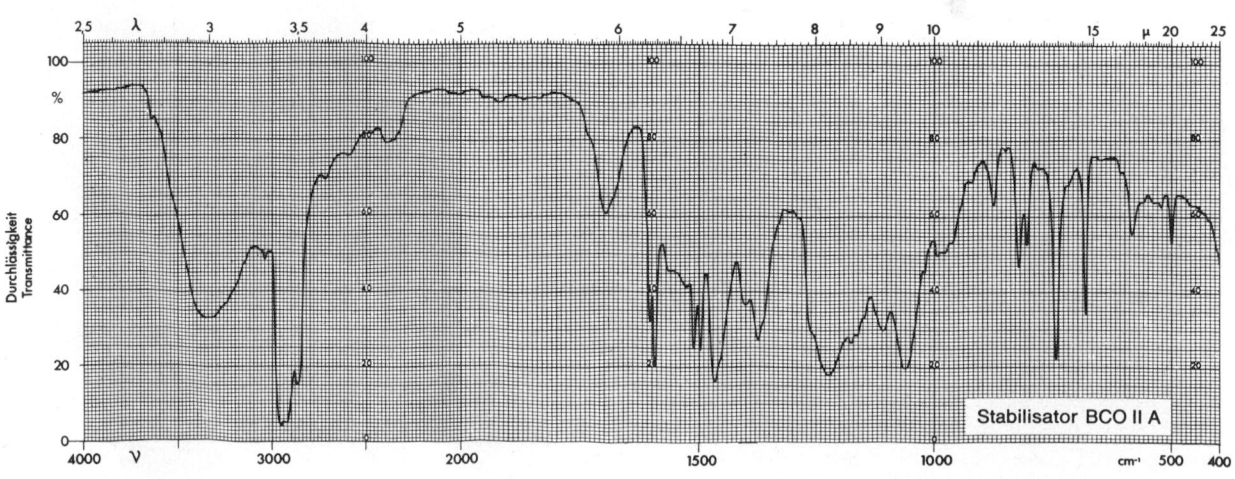

6109   Zusammen-setzung: **Ba-Cd-P-Stabilisator**   Composition: **Ba-Cd-P-stabilizer**

Handelsname: **Stabilisator BCO IIA** Herst.: **Bärlocher**   Tradename: **Stabilisator BCO IIA** Manuf.: **Bärlocher**
Präparation: **flüssig, ~ 20 μ**   Dez. Nr.: **2.6.6**   Preparation: **liquid, ~ 20 μ**   Dec. No.: **2.6.6**

Stabilisatoren
2. Metallcarboxylat-Stabilisatoren
2.6. Ester- und phosphorhaltige Metallsalz-Stabilisatoren

Stabilizers
2. Metal Carboxylate Stabilizers
2.6. Ester and Phosphorus containing Metal Salts Stabilizers

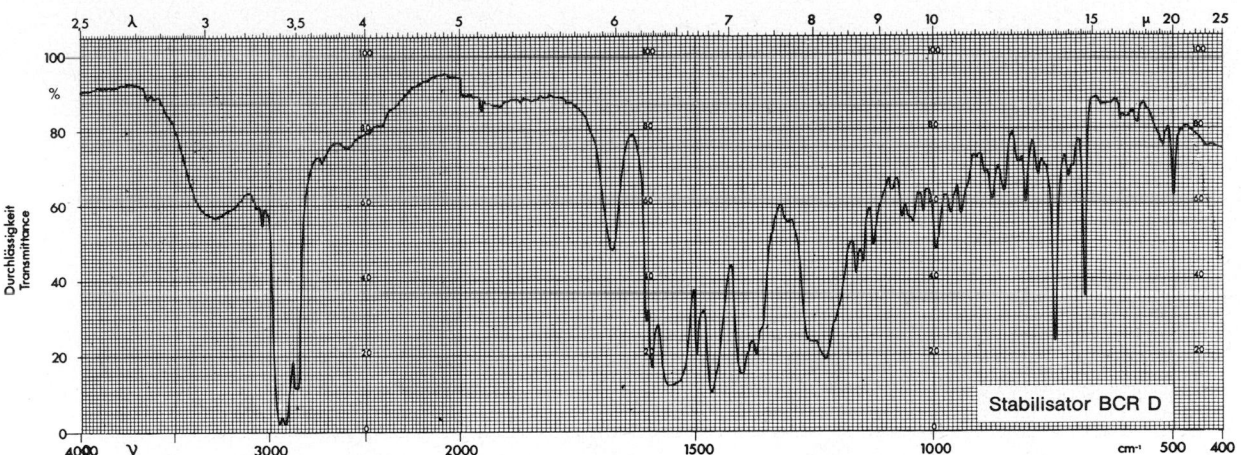

Zusammensetzung:	Ba-Ca-Cd-P-Stabilisator		Composition:	Ba-Ca-Cd-P-stabilizer		6110
Handelsname:	Stabilisator BCR D	Herst.: Bärlocher	Tradename:	Stabilisator BCR D	Manuf.: Bärlocher	
Präparation:	flüssig, ~ 20 μ	Dez. Nr.: 2.6.7	Preparation:	liquid, ~ 20 μ	Dec. No.: 2.6.7	

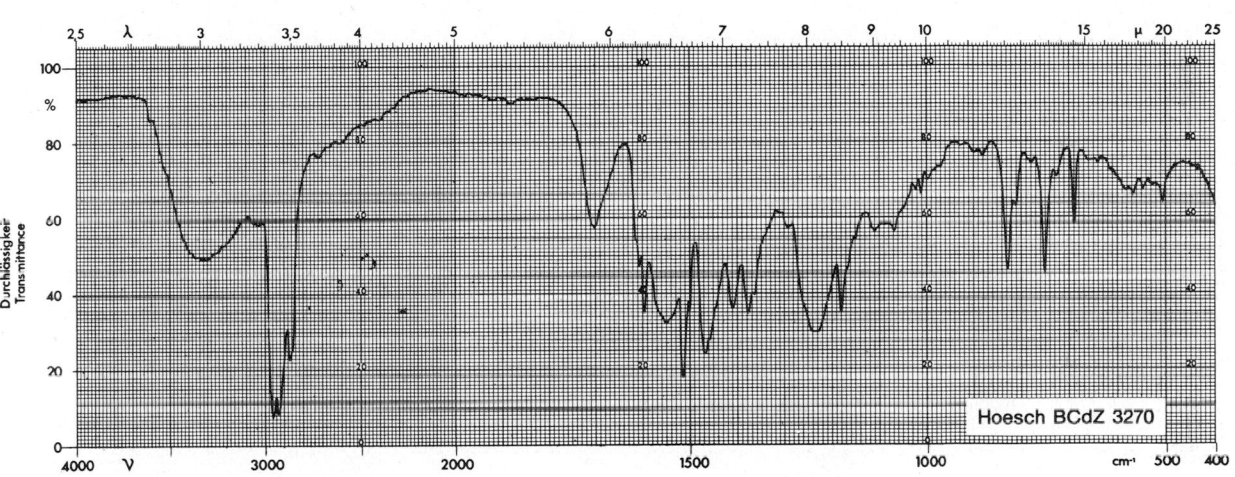

Zusammensetzung:	Ba-Cd-Zn-P-Stabilisator		Composition:	Ba-Cd-Zn-P-stabilizer		6111
Handelsname:	Hoesch BCdZ 3270	Herst.: Hoesch	Tradename:	Hoesch BCdZ 3270	Manuf.: Hoesch	
Präparation:	flüssig, ~ 13 μ	Dez. Nr.: 2.6.8	Preparation:	liquid, ~ 13 μ	Dec. No.: 2.6.8	

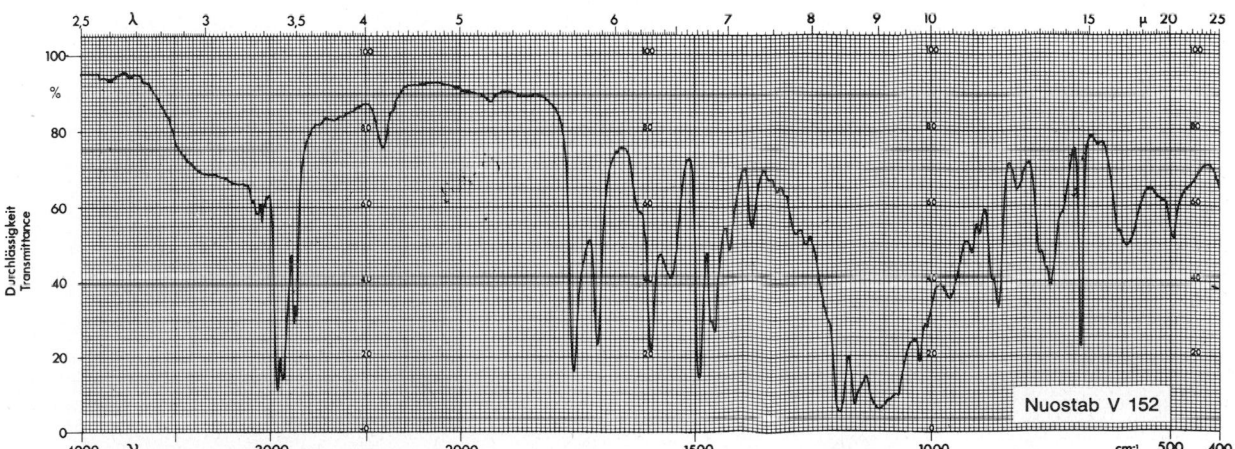

Zusammensetzung:	Zn-P-Stabilisator		Composition:	Zn-P-stabilizer		6112
Handelsname:	Nuostab V 152	Herst.: Siegle	Tradename:	Nuostab V 152	Manuf.: Siegle	
Präparation:	Kapill. Film 25 μ	Dez. Nr.: 2.6.9	Preparation:	Capill. film 25 μ	Dec. No.: 2.6.9	

Stabilisatoren
2. Metallcarboxylat-Stabilisatoren
2.6. Ester- und phosphorhaltige Metallsalz-Stabilisatoren

Stabilizers
2. Metal Carboxylate Stabilizers
2.6. Ester and Phosphorus containing Metal Salts Stabilizers

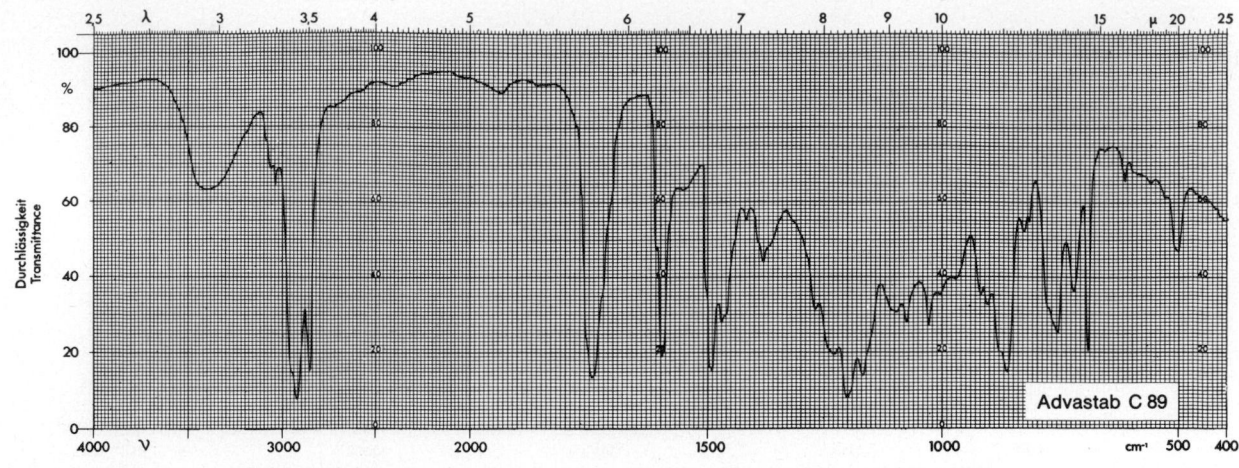

Advastab C 89

6113	Zusammen- setzung:	Cd-P-Stabilisator			Composition:	Cd-P-stabilizer	
	Handelsname:	Advastab C 89	Herst.:	Advance	Tradename:	Advastab C 89	Manuf.: Advance
	Präparation:	Kapill. Film	Dez. Nr.:	2.6.10	Preparation:	Capill. film	Dec. No.: 2.6.10

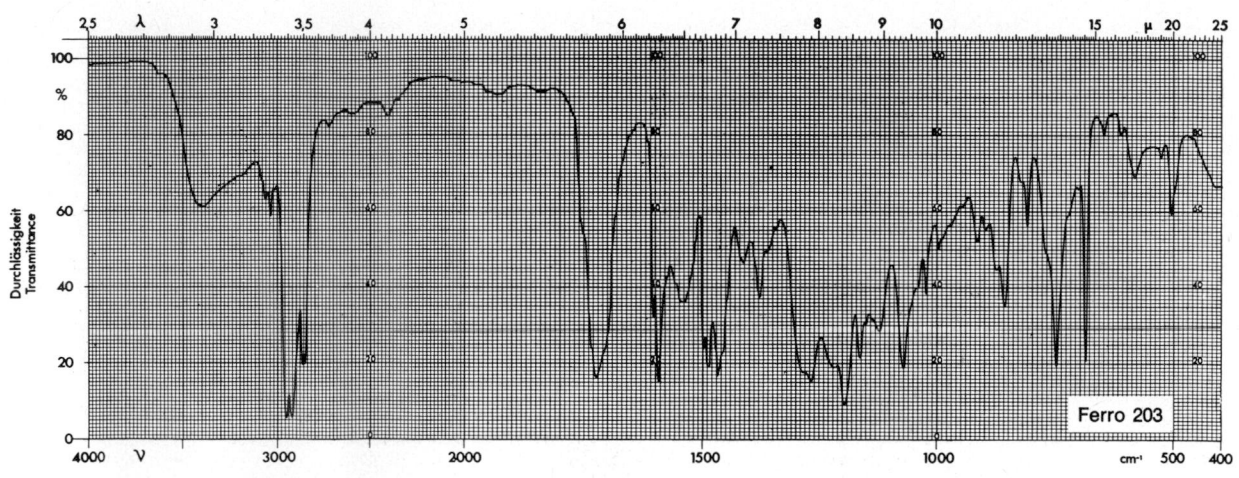

Ferro 203

6114	Zusammen- setzung:	Cd-P-Stabilisator			Composition:	Cd-P-stabilizer	
	Handelsname:	Ferro 203	Herst.:	Bärlocher	Tradename:	Ferro 203	Manuf.: Bärlocher
	Präparation:	Kapill. Film	Dez. Nr.:	2.6.11	Preparation:	Capill. film	Dec. No.: 2.6.11

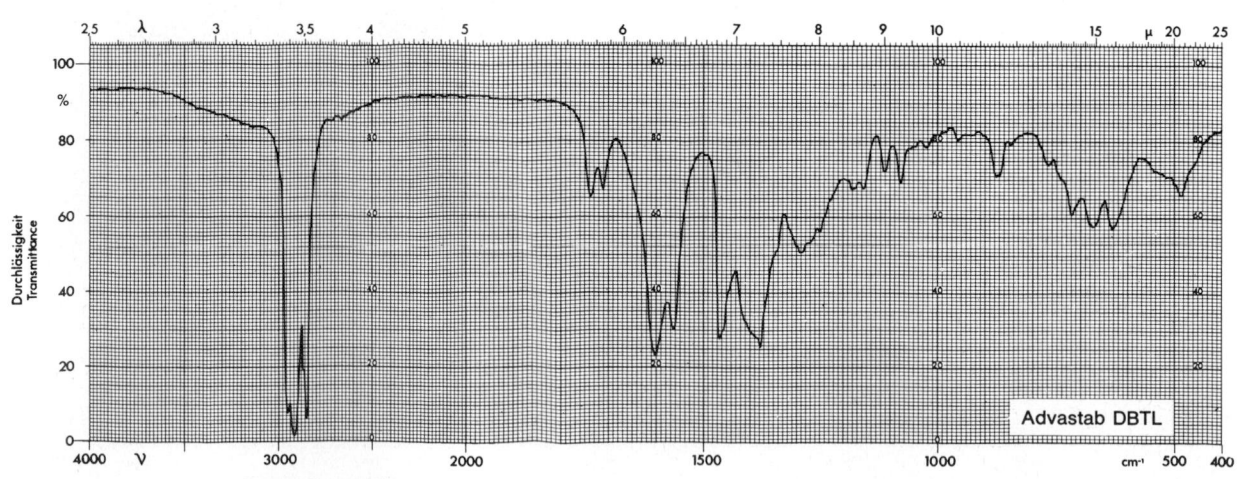

Advastab DBTL

6115	Zusammen- setzung:	Dibutylzinndilaurat			Composition:	Dibutyl tin dilaurate	
	Handelsname:	Advastab DBTL	Herst.:	Advance	Tradename:	Advastab DBTL	Manuf.: Advance
	Präparation:	Kapill. Film	Dez. Nr.:	2.7.1	Preparation:	Capill. film	Dec. No.: 2.7.1

Stabilisatoren
2. Metallcarboxylat-Stabilisatoren
2.7. Schwefelfreie Zinn-Stabilisatoren

Stabilizers
2. Metal Carboxylate Stabilizers
2.7. Sulfur free Tin Stabilizers

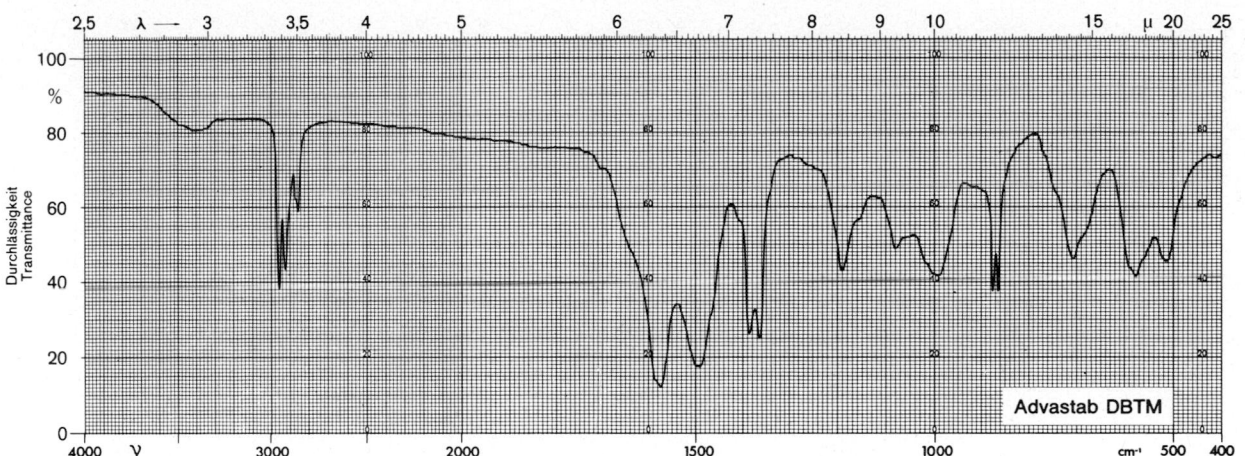

Zusammen-setzung:	**Dibutylzinnmaleat**		Composition:	**Dibutyl tin maleate**		6116
Handelsname:	**Advastab DBTM**	Herst.: **Advance**	Tradename:	**Advastab DBTM**	Manuf.: **Advance**	
Präparation:	**KBr (2/1000)**	Dez. Nr.: **2.7.2**	Preparation:	**KBr (2/1000)**	Dec. No.: **2.7.2**	

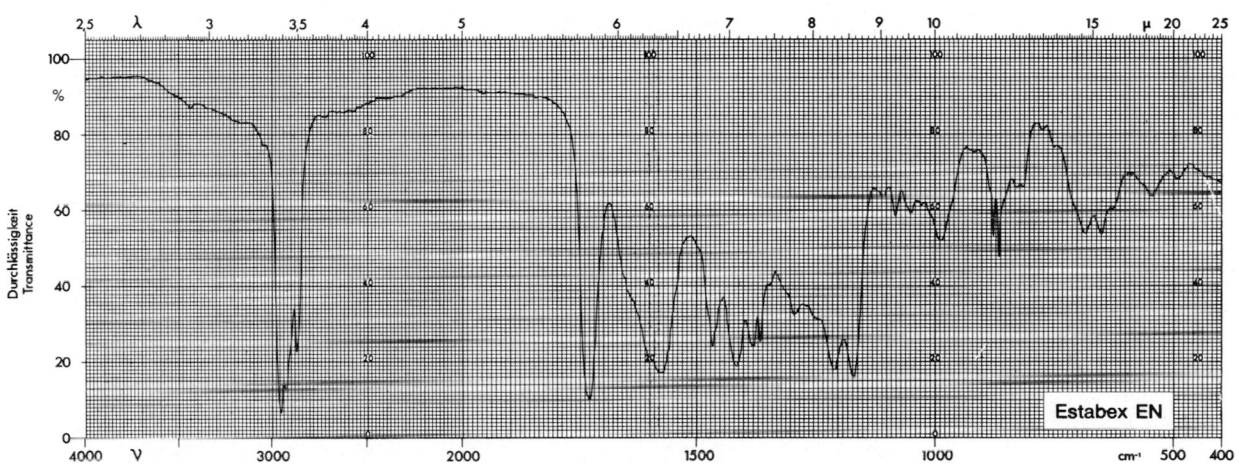

Zusammen-setzung:	**Modifiziertes Dibutylzinnmaleat**		Composition:	**Modified dibutyl tin maleate**		6117
Handelsname:	**Estabex EN**	Herst.: **Oxydo**	Tradename:	**Estabex EN**	Manuf.: **Oxydo**	
Präparation:	**Kapill. Film**	Dez. Nr.: **2.7.3**	Preparation:	**Capill. film**	Dec. No.: **2.7.3**	

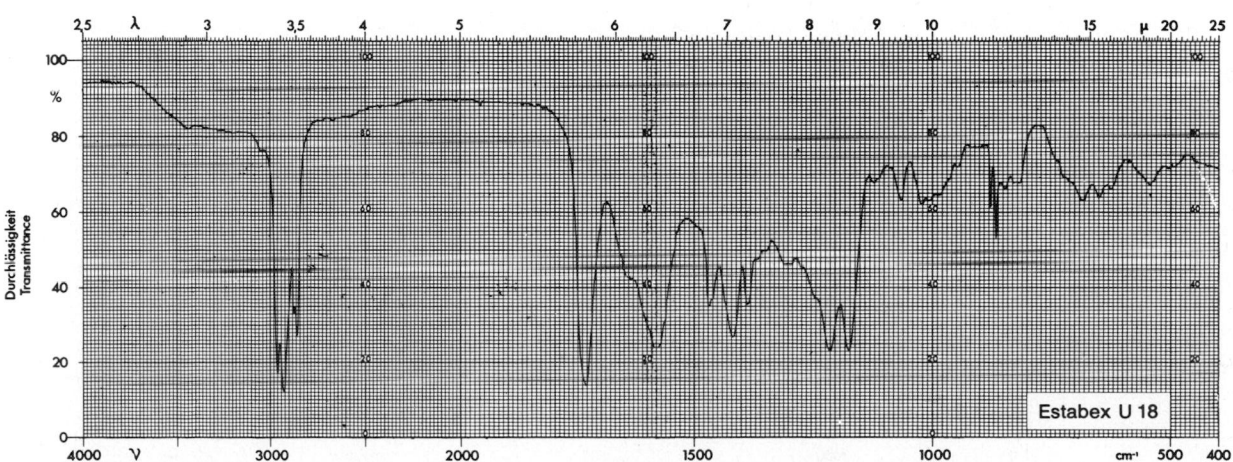

Zusammen-setzung:	**Dioctylzinnmaleat**		Composition:	**Dioctyl tin maleate**		6118
Handelsname:	**Estabex U 18**	Herst.: **Oxydo**	Tradename:	**Estabex U 18**	Manuf.: **Oxydo**	
Präparation:	**Kapill. Film**	Dez. Nr.: **2.7.4**	Preparation:	**Capill. film**	Dec. No.: **2.7.4**	

Stabilisatoren
2. Metallcarboxylat-Stabilisatoren
2.7. Schwefelfreie Zinn-Stabilisatoren

Stabilizers
2. Metal Carboxylate Stabilizers
2.7. Sulfur free Tin Stabilizers

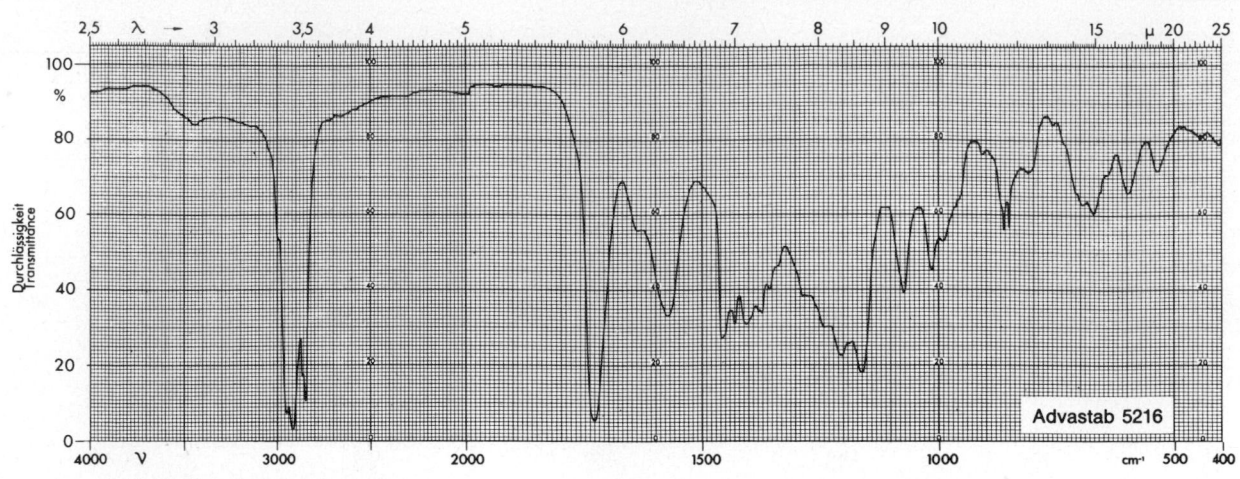

6119   Zusammen-setzung: **Dialkylzinnmaleat**   Composition: **Dialkyl tin maleate**

Handelsname: **Advastab 5216**   Herst.: **Advance**   Tradename: **Advastab 5216**   Manuf.: **Advance**

Präparation: **Kapill. Film**   Dez. Nr.: **2.7.5**   Preparation: **Capill. film**   Dec. No.: **2.7.5**

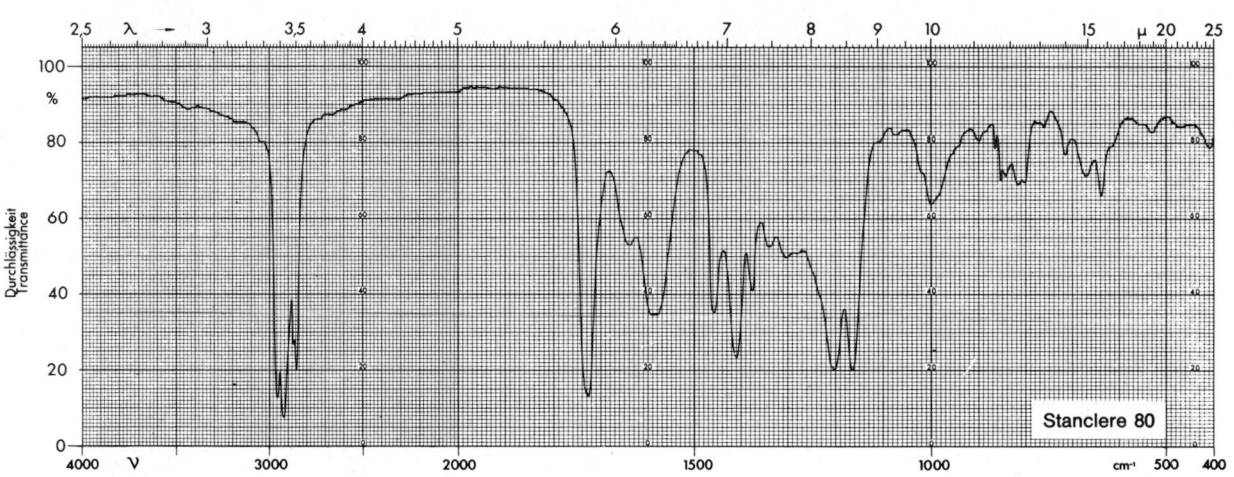

6120   Zusammen-setzung: **Di-n-octylzinn-Verbindung**   Composition: **Di-n-octyl tin compound**

Handelsname: **Stanclere 80**   Herst.: **Pure Lim.**   Tradename: **Stanclere 80**   Manuf.: **Pure Lim.**

Präparation: **Kapill. Film**   Dez. Nr.: **2.7.6**   Preparation: **Capill. film**   Dec. No.: **2.7.6**

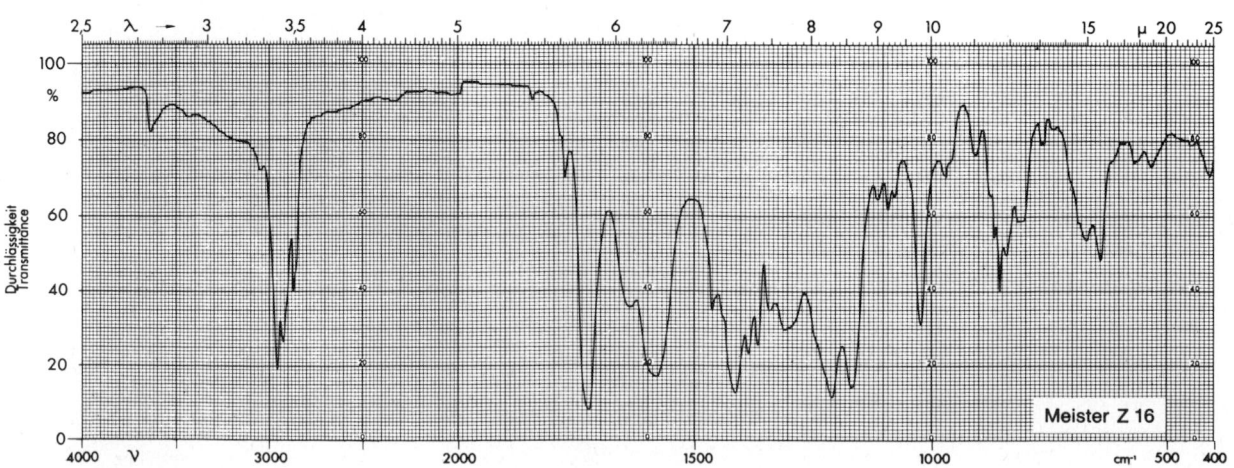

6121   Zusammen-setzung: **Modifiziertes Dialkylzinnmaleat**   Composition: **Modified dialkyl tin maleate**

Handelsname: **Meister Z 16**   Herst.: **Meister**   Tradename: **Meister Z 16**   Manuf.: **Meister**

Präparation: **Kapill. Film**   Dez. Nr.: **2.7.7**   Preparation: **Capill. film**   Dec. No.: **2.7.7**

Stabilisatoren
2. Metallcarboxylat-Stabilisatoren
2.7. Schwefelfreie Zinn-Stabilisatoren

Stabilizers
2. Metal Carboxylate Stabilizers
2.7. Sulfur free Tin Stabilizers

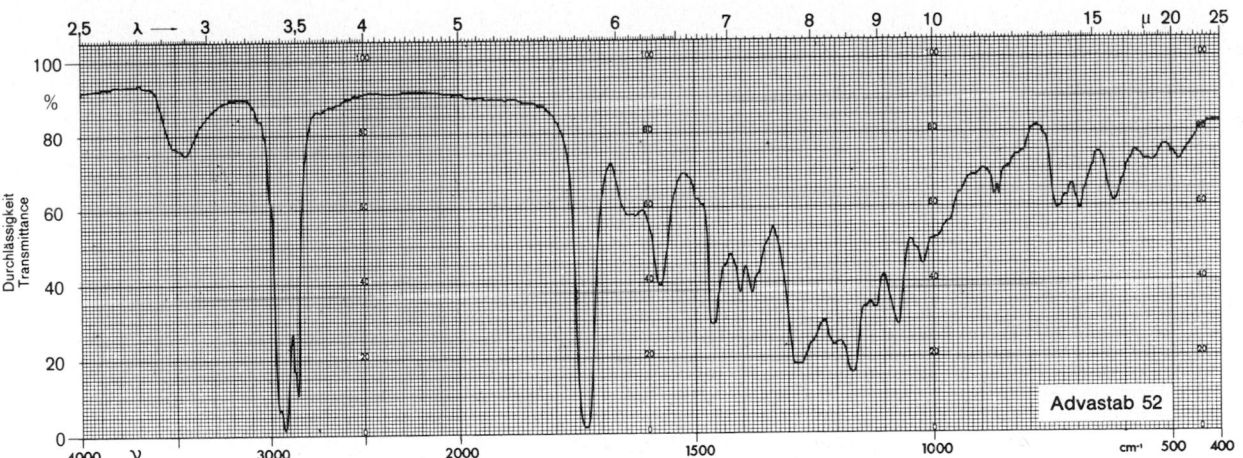

Zusammen-setzung:	**Modifiziertes Dialkylzinnmaleat**		Composition:	**Modified dialkyl tin maleate**		6122
Handelsname:	**Advastab 52**	Herst.: **Advance**	Tradename:	**Advastab 52**	Manuf.: **Advance**	
Präparation:	**Kapill. Film**	Dez. Nr.: **2.7.8**	Preparation:	**Capill. film**	Dec. No.: **2.7.8**	

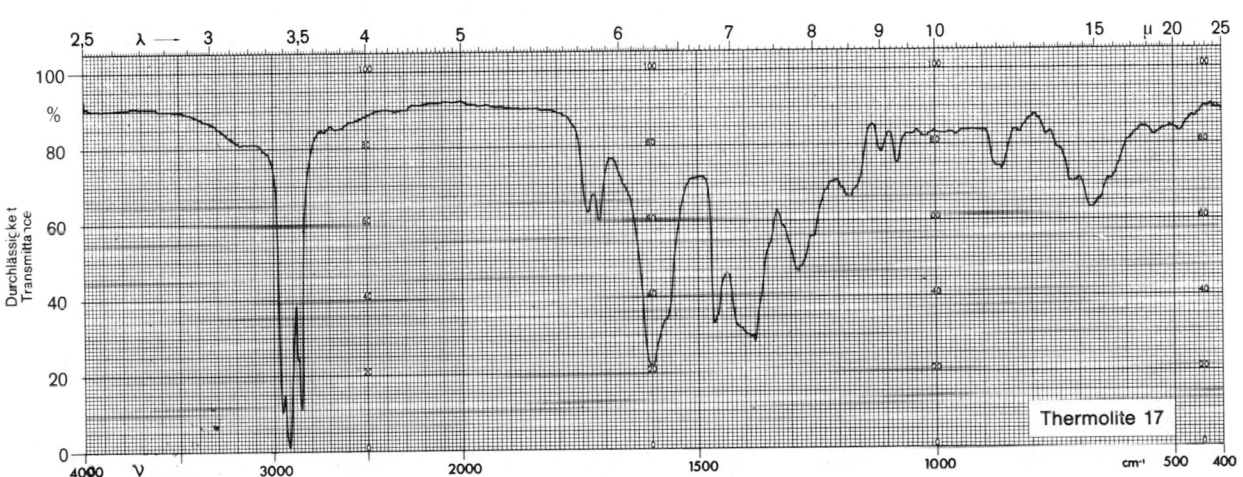

Zusammen-setzung:	**Bis-(dibutylzinnmonolaurat)maleat**		Composition:	**Bis-(dibutyl tin laurate) maleate**		6123
Handelsname:	**Thermolite 17**	Herst.: **M & T**	Tradename:	**Thermolite 17**	Manuf.: **M & T**	
Präparation:	**Kapill. Film**	Dez. Nr.: **2.7.9**	Preparation:	**Capill. film**	Dec. No.: **2.7.9**	

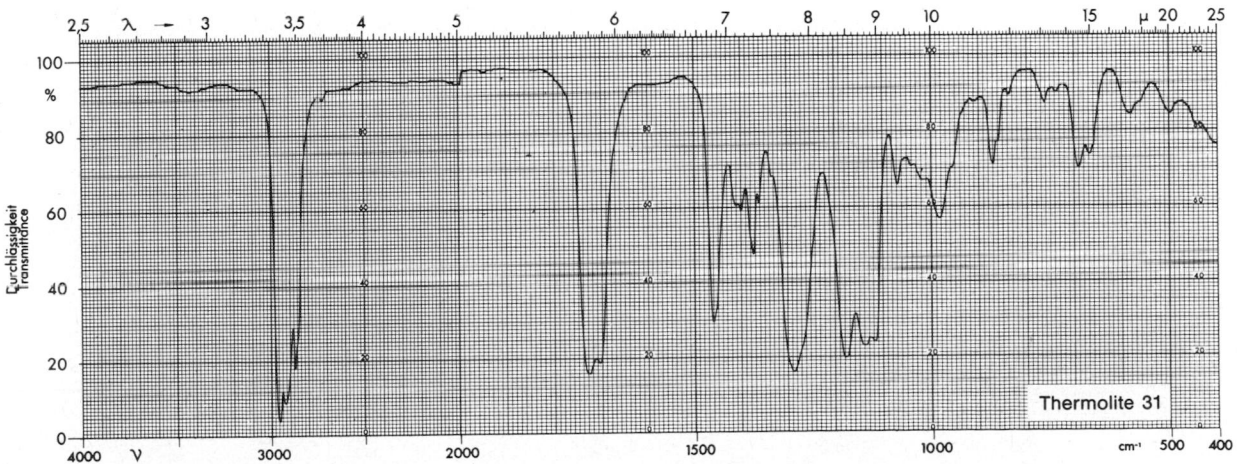

Zusammen-setzung:	**Dibutylzinnmercaptoester**		Composition:	**Dibutyl tin mercapto ester**		6124
Handelsname:	**Thermolite 31**	Herst.: **M & T**	Tradename:	**Thermolite 31**	Manuf.: **M & T**	
Präparation:	**Kapill. Film**	Dez. Nr.: **2.8.1**	Preparation:	**Capill. film**	Dec. No.: **2.8.1**	

Stabilisatoren
2. **Metallcarboxylat-Stabilisatoren**
2.8. **Schwefelhaltige Zinn-Stabilisatoren**

Stabilizers
2. **Metal Carboxylate Stabilizers**
2.8. **Sulfur containing Tin Stabilizers**

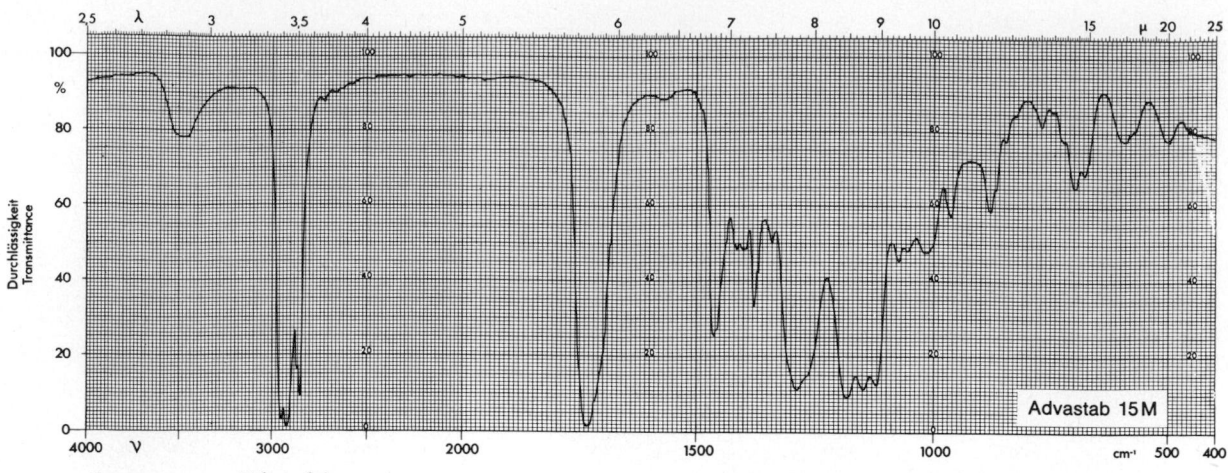

6125   Zusammen-setzung: **Dibutylzinnmercaptoester**   Composition: **Dibutyl tin mercapto ester**

Handelsname: **Advastab 15 M**	Herst.: **Advance**	Tradename: **Advastab 15 M**	Manuf.: **Advance**
Präparation: **Kapill. Film**	Dez. Nr.: **2.8.2**	Preparation: **Capill. film**	Dec. No.: **2.8.2**

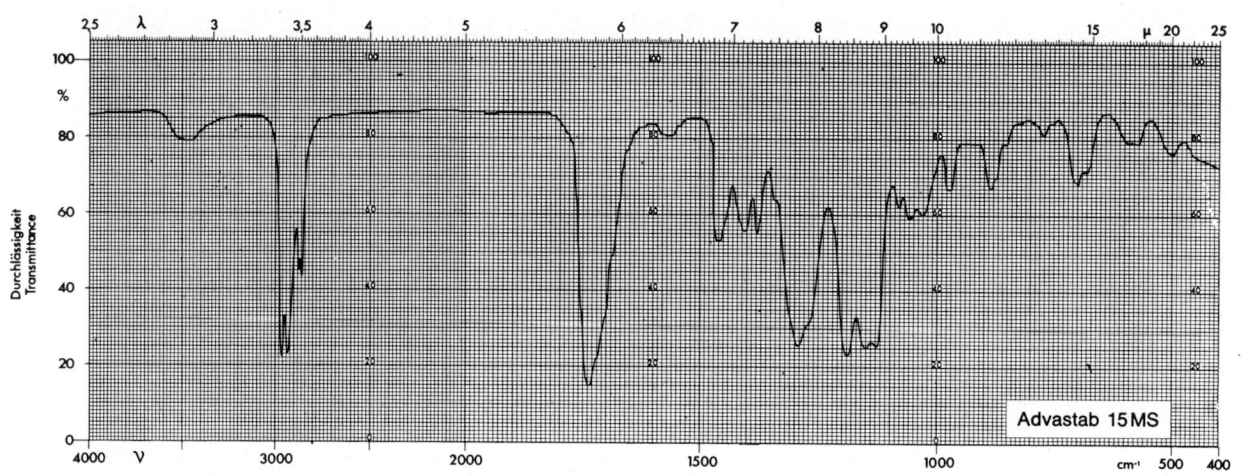

6126   Zusammen-setzung: **Dialkylzinnmercaptoester**   Composition: **Dialkyl tin mercapto ester**

Handelsname: **Advastab 15 MS**	Herst.: **Advance**	Tradename: **Advastab 15 MS**	Manuf.: **Advance**
Präparation: **Kapill. Film**	Dez. Nr.: **2.8.3**	Preparation: **Capill. film**	Dec. No.. **2.8.3**

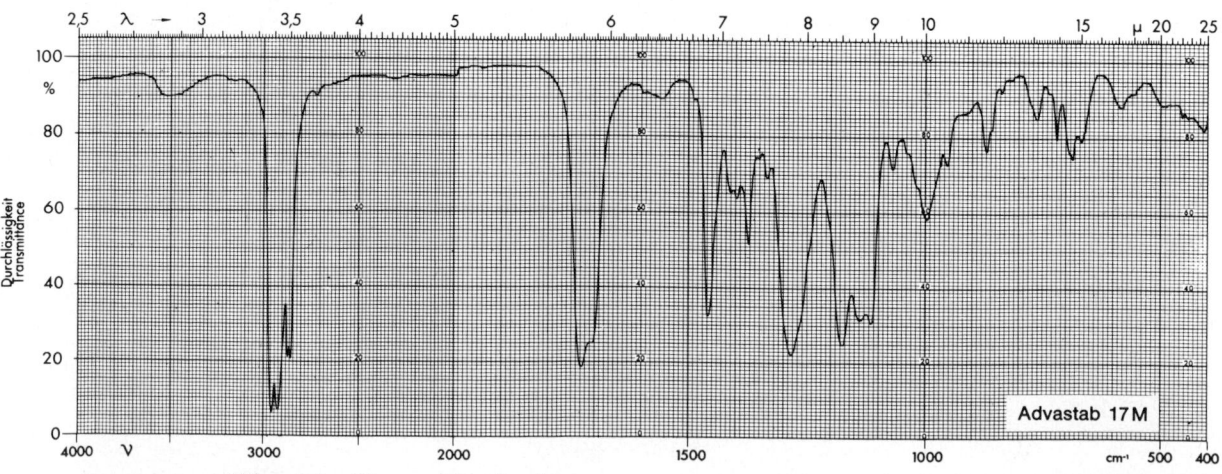

6127   Zusammen-setzung: **Dibutylzinndiisooctylthioglycolat**   Composition: **Dibutyl tin diisooctyl thioglycolate**

Handelsname: **Advastab 17 M**	Herst.: **Advance**	Tradename: **Advastab 17 M**	Manuf.: **Advance**
Präparation: **Kapill. Film**	Dez. Nr.: **2.8.4**	Preparation: **Capill. film**	Dec. No.: **2.8.4**

Stabilisatoren
2. Metallcarboxylat-Stabilisatoren
2.8. Schwefelhaltige Zinn-Stabilisatoren

Stabilizers
2. Metal Carboxylate Stabilizers
2.8. Sulfur containing Tin Stabilizers

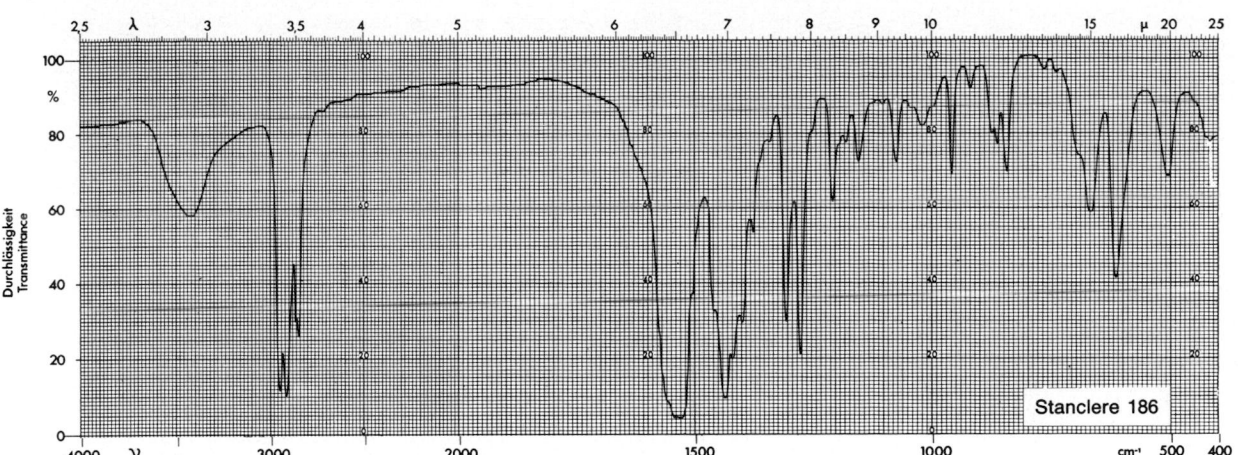

Zusammen-setzung:	**Dibutylzinnmercaptid**		Composition:	**Dibutyl tin mercaptide**		6128
Handelsname:	**Stanclere 186**	Herst.: **Pure Lim.**	Tradename:	Stanclere 186	Manuf.: Pure Lim.	
Präparation:	**KBr (6/1000)**	Dez. Nr.: **2.8.5**	Preparation:	KBr (6/1000)	Dec. No.: 2.8.5	

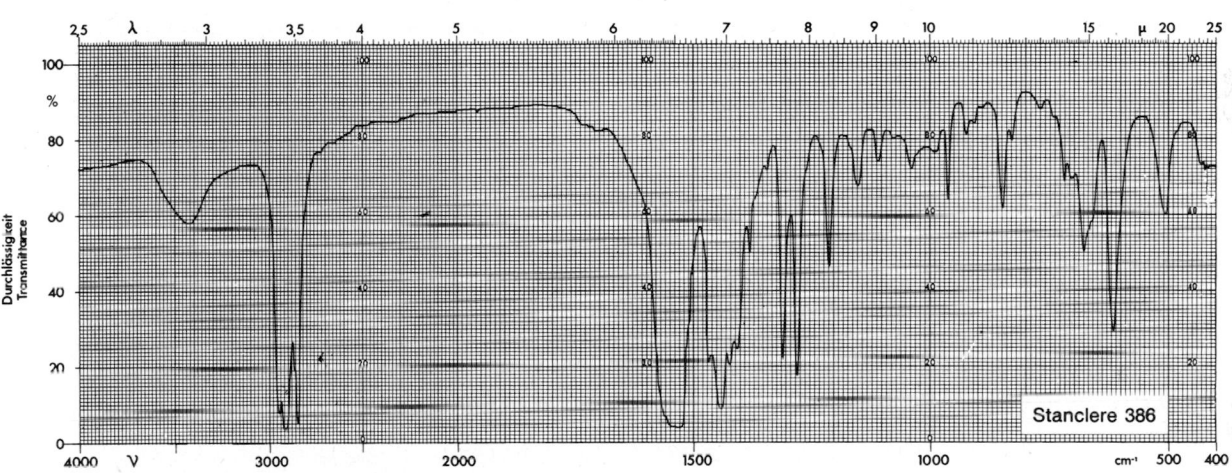

Zusammen-setzung:	**Di-n-octylzinnmercaptid**		Composition:	**Di-n-octyl tin mercaptide**		6129
Handelsname:	**Stanclere 386**	Herst.: **Pure Lim.**	Tradename:	Stanclere 386	Manuf.: Pure Lim.	
Präparation:	**KBr (6/1000)**	Dez. Nr.: **2.8.6**	Preparation:	KBr (6/1000)	Dec. No.: 2.8.6	

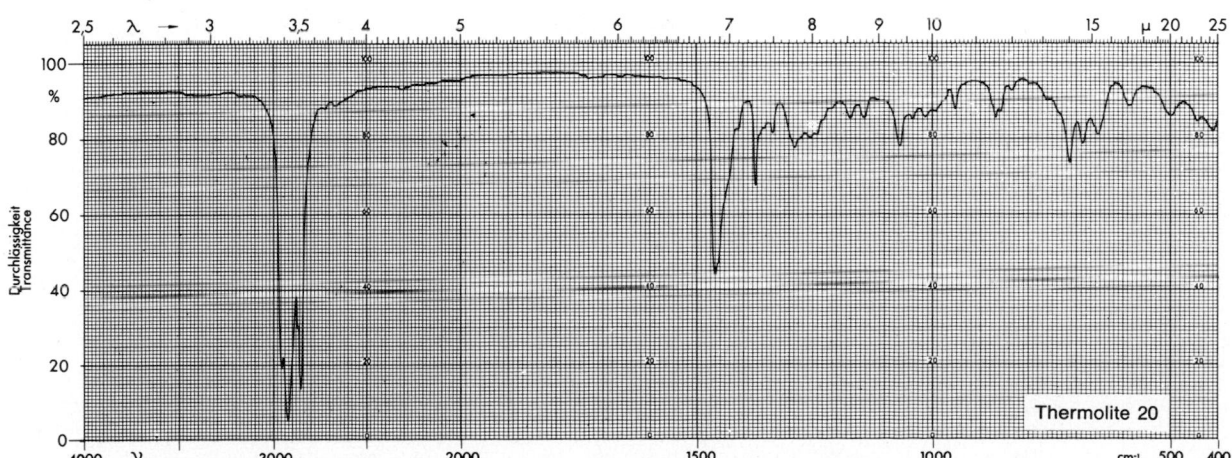

						6130
Zusammen-setzung:	**Dibutyl-Sn-dilauroylmercaptid**		Composition:	**Dibutyl tin dilauroylmercaptide**		
Handelsname:	**Thermolite 20**	Herst.: **M & T**	Tradename:	**Thermolite 20**	Manuf.: **M & T**	
Präparation:	**Kapill. Film**	Dez. Nr.: **2.8.7**	Preparation:	Capill. film	Dec. No.: 2.8.7	

Stabilisatoren
2. Metallcarboxylat-Stabilisatoren
2.9. Sonstige Metallsalz-Stabilisatoren

Stabilizers
2. Metal Carboxylate Stabilizers
2.9. Other Metal Stabilizers

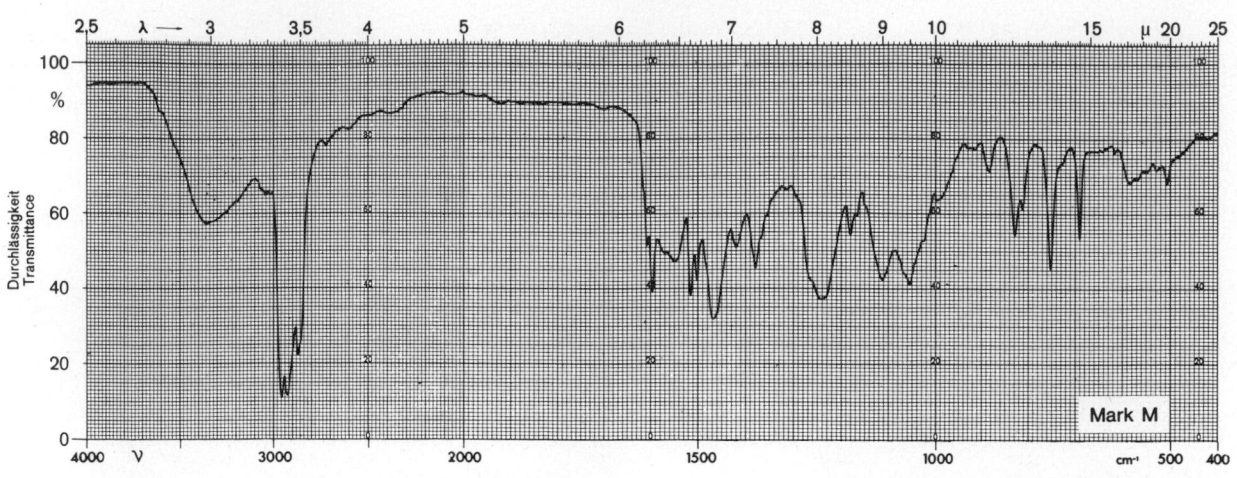

6131   Zusammen-   **Gem. v. Ba-octylphenolat, Cd-2-äthyl-**   Composition: **Mixture of barium octylphenolate, cadmium**
         setzung: **hexanoat und Triphenylphosphit**   **2-ethylhexanoate and triphenyl phosphite**

Handelsname: **Mark M**   Herst.:   **Argus**   Tradename: **Mark M**   Manuf.:   **Argus**

Präparation: **Kapill. Film**   Dez. Nr.: **2.9.1**   Preparation: **Capill. film**   Dec. No.: **2.9.1**

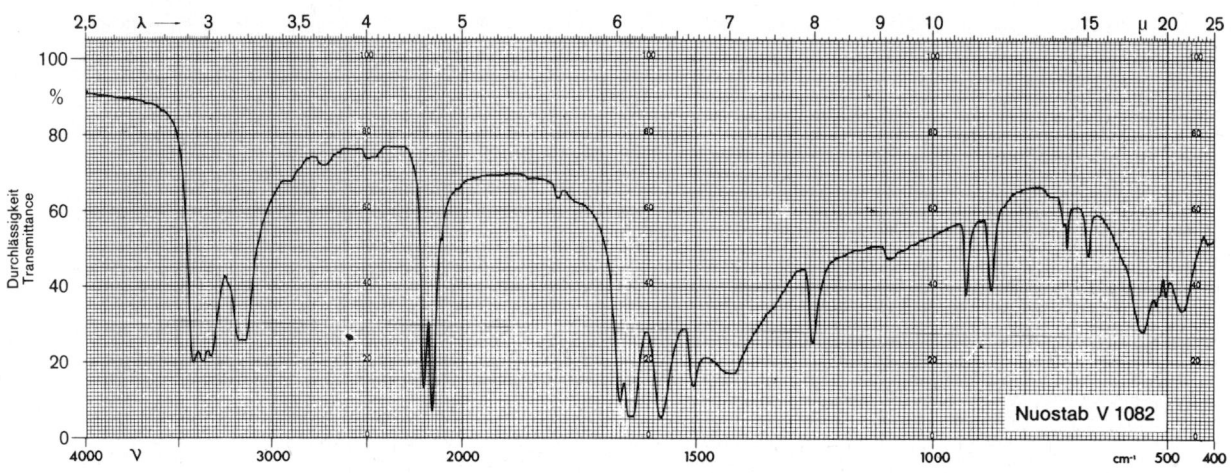

6132   Zusammen-   **Ca-Mg-Stabilisator**   Composition: **Ca-Mg-stabilizer**
         setzung:

Handelsname: **Nuostab V 1082**   Herst.:   **Siegle**   Tradename: **Nuostab V 1082**   Manuf.:   **Siegle**

Präparation: **KBr (5/1000)**   Dez. Nr.: **2.9.2**   Preparation: **KBr (5/1000)**   Dec. No.: **2.9.2**

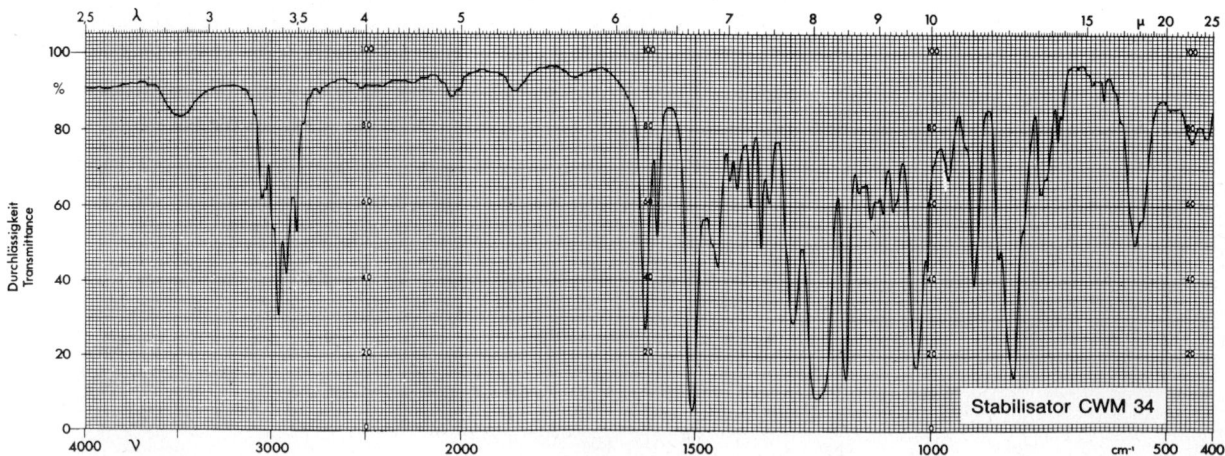

6133   Zusammen-   **Epoxidharz**   Composition: **Epoxy resin**
         setzung:

Handelsname: **Stabilisator CWM 34** Herst.:   **Bärlocher**   Tradename: **Stabilisator CWM 34** Manuf.:   **Bärlocher**

Präparation: **Kapill. Film**   Dez. Nr.: **3.1.1**   Preparation: **Capill. film**   Dec. No.: **3.1.1**

Stabilisatoren
3. Epoxyverbindungen
3.2. Epoxyfettsäureester

Stabilizers
3. Epoxy Derivatives
3.2. Epoxy Fatty Acid Esters

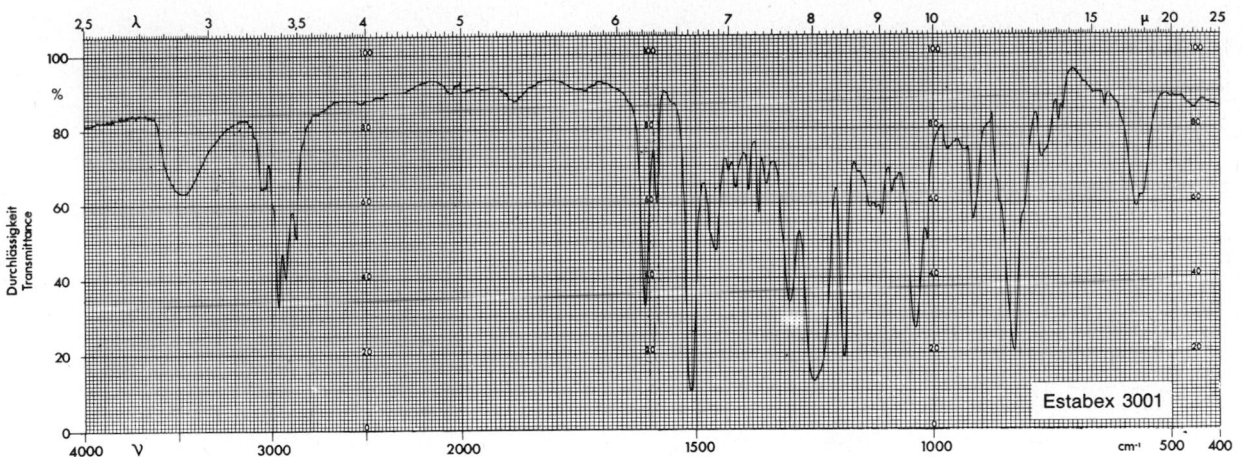

Zusammen-   Epoxidharz   Composition: Epoxy resin   6134
setzung:
Handelsname: Estabex 3001   Herst.: Oxydo   Tradename: Estabex 3001   Manuf.: Oxydo
Präparation: Kapill. Film   Dez. Nr.: 3.1.2   Preparation: Capill. film   Dec. No.: 3.1.2

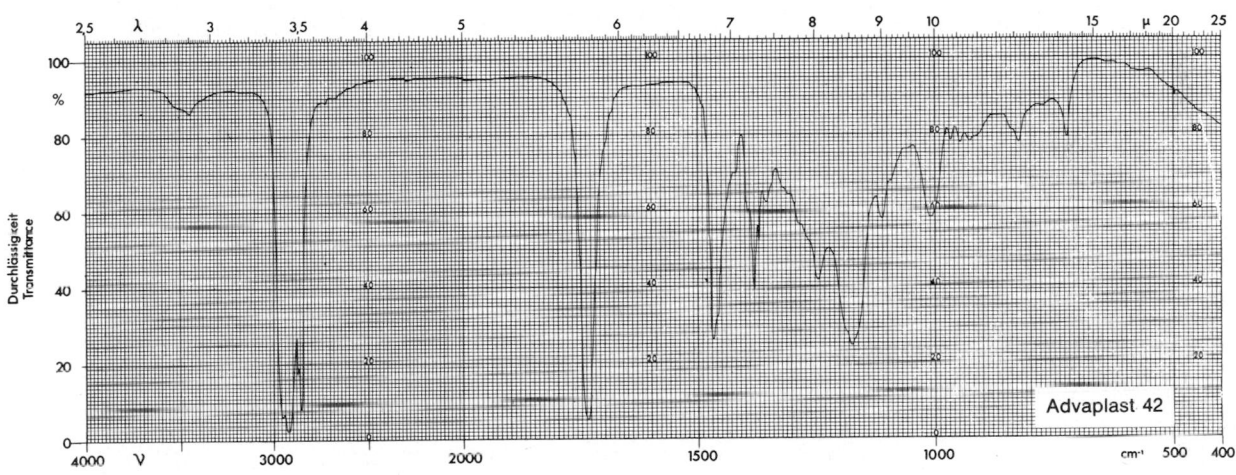

Zusammen-   Epoxidiertes Butyloleat   Composition: Epoxidized butyl oleate   6135
setzung:
Handelsname: Advaplast 42   Herst.: Advance   Tradename: Advaplast 42   Manuf.: Advance
Präparation: Kapill. Film   Dez. Nr.: 3.2.1   Preparation: Capill. film   Dec. No.: 3.2.1

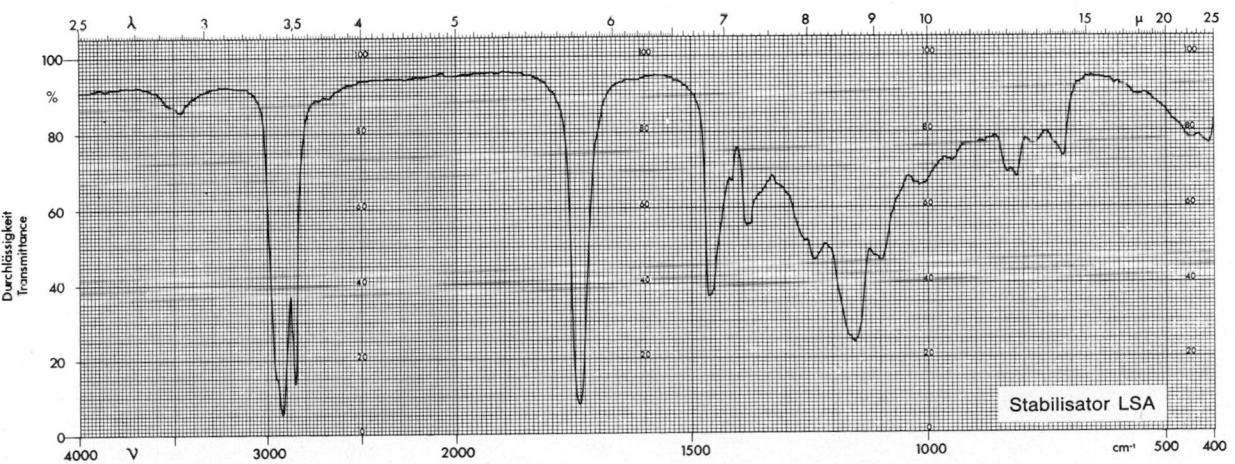

Zusammen-   Alkylepoxystearat   Composition: Alkyl epoxy stearate   6136
setzung:
Handelsname: Stabilisator LSA   Herst.: Bärlocher   Tradename: Stabilisator LSA   Manuf.: Bärlocher
Präparation: Kapill. Film   Dez. Nr.: 3.2.2   Preparation: Capill. film   Dec. No.: 3.2.2

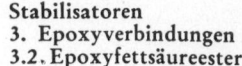

Stabilisatoren
3. Epoxyverbindungen
3.2. Epoxyfettsäureester

Stabilizers
3. Epoxy Derivatives
3.2. Epoxy Fatty Acid Esters

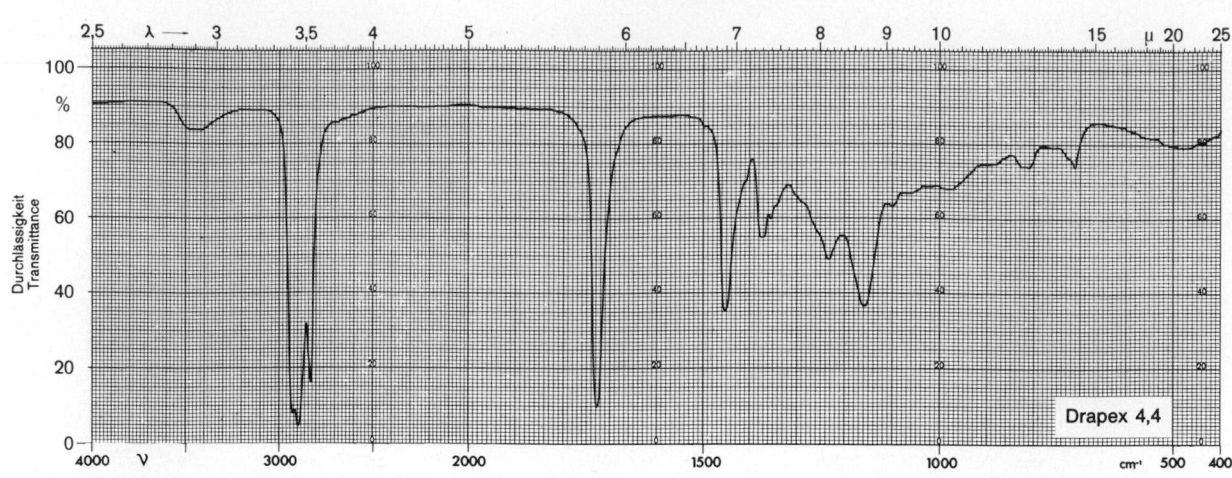

6137	Zusammensetzung:	Octylepoxystearat		Composition:	Octyl epoxy stearate	
	Handelsname:	**Drapex 4,4**	Herst.: **Argus**	Tradename:	**Drapex 4,4**	Manuf.: **Argus**
	Präparation:	**Kapill. Film**	Dez. Nr.: **3.2.3**	Preparation:	**Capill. film**	Dec. No.: **3.2.3**

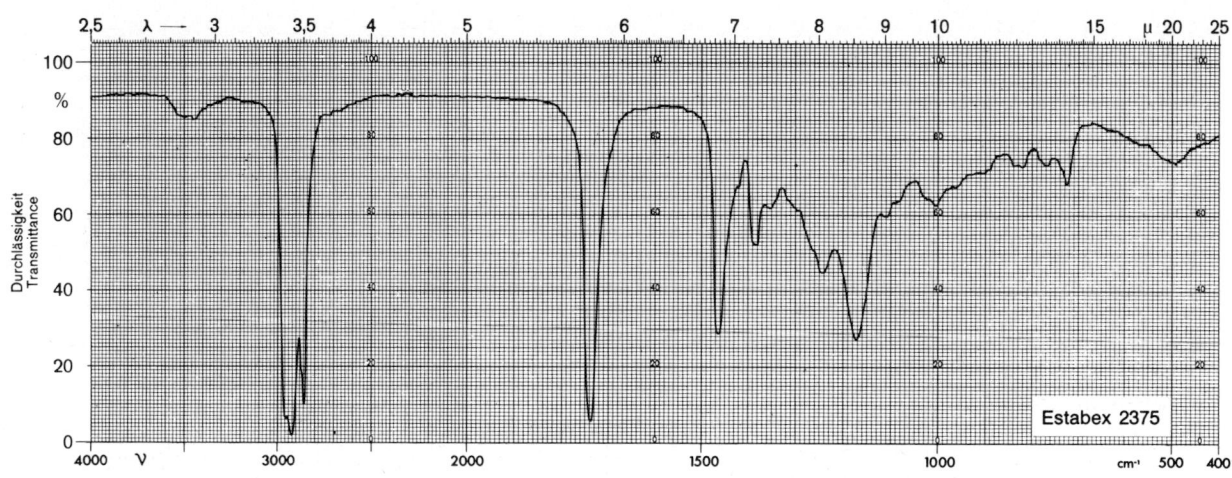

6138	Zusammensetzung:	Alkylepoxystearat		Composition:	Alkyl epoxy stearate	
	Handelsname:	**Estabex 2375**	Herst.: **Oxydo**	Tradename:	**Estabex 2375**	Manuf.: **Oxydo**
	Präparation:	**Kapill. Film**	Dez. Nr.: **3.2.4**	Preparation:	**Capill. film**	Dec. No.: **3.2.4**

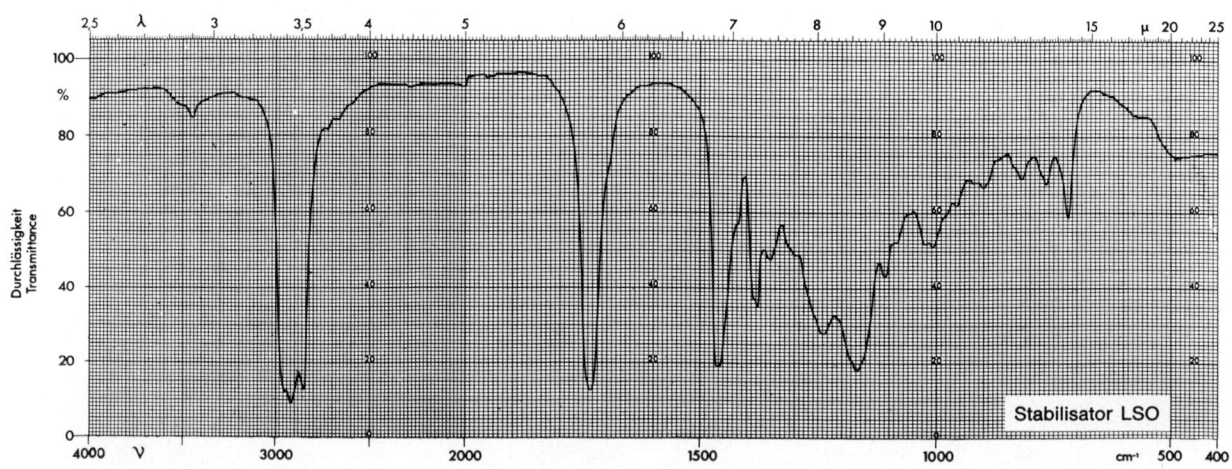

6139	Zusammensetzung:	Epoxidierter Alkylfettsäureester		Composition:	Alkyl epoxy fatty acid ester	
	Handelsname:	Stabilisator LSO	Herst.: **Bärlocher**	Tradename:	Stabilisator LSO	Manuf.: **Bärlocher**
	Präparation:	**Kapill. Film**	Dez. Nr.: **3.2.5**	Preparation:	**Capill. film**	Dec. No.: **3.2.5**

Stabilisatoren
3. Epoxyverbindungen
3.3. Epoxyverbindungen-Metallseifen-Stabilisatoren

Stabilizers
3. Epoxy Derivatives
3.3. Epoxy Metal Salts Stabilizers

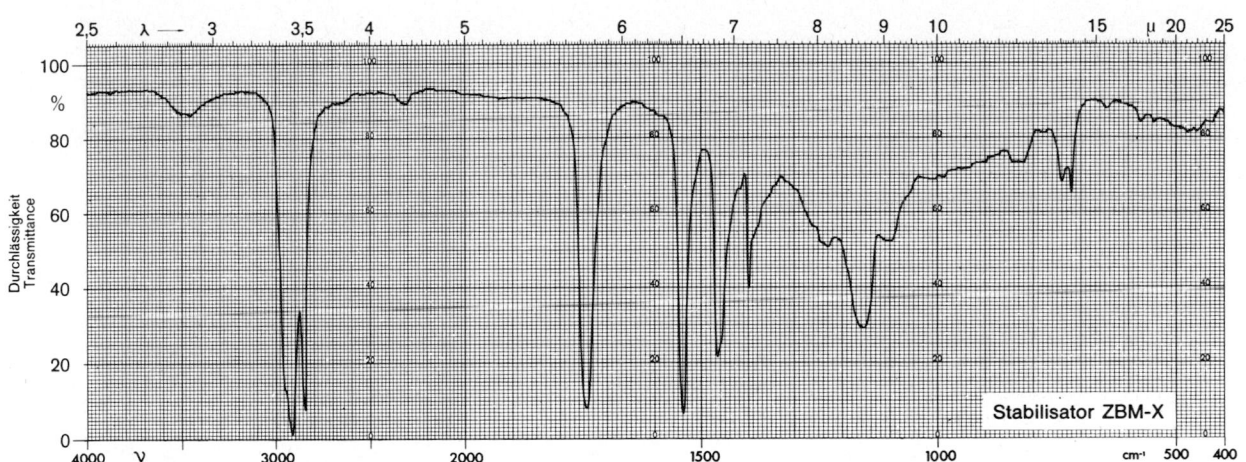

Stabilisator ZBM-X

| Zusammensetzung: | Epoxyfettsäureester, Zinkseife | Composition: | Epoxy fatty acid ester, zinc soap | 6140 |

| Handelsname: | Stabilisator ZBM-X | Herst.: | Bärlocher | Tradename: | Stabilisator ZBM-X | Manuf.: | Bärlocher |
| Präparation: | Kapill. Film | Dez. Nr.: | 3.3.1 | Preparation: | Capill. film | Dec. No.: | 3.3.1 |

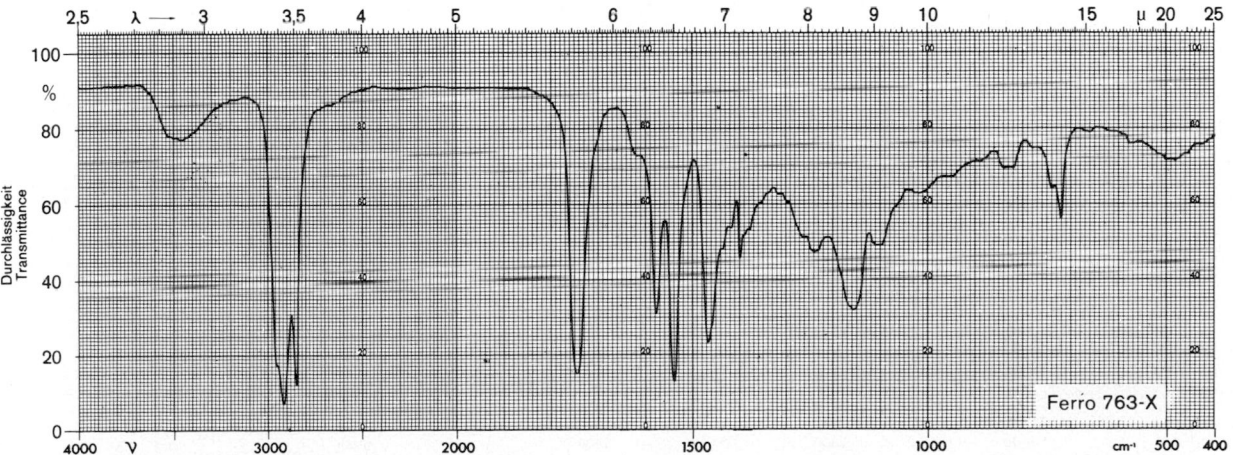

Stabilisator ZBM-O

| Zusammensetzung: | Epoxyfettsäureester, Zink-Calcium-Seifen | Composition: | Epoxy fatty acid ester, zinc calcium soaps | 6141 |

| Handelsname: | Stabilisator ZBM-O | Herst.: | Bärlocher | Tradename: | Stabilisator ZBM-O | Manuf.: | Bärlocher |
| Präparation: | Kapill. Film | Dez. Nr.: | 3.3.2 | Preparation: | Capill. film | Dec. No.: | 3.3.2 |

Ferro 763-X

| Zusammensetzung: | Epoxyfettsäureester, Zink-Calcium-Seifen | Composition: | Epoxy fatty acid ester, zinc calcium soaps | 6142 |

| Handelsname: | Ferro 763-X | Herst.: | Bärlocher | Tradename: | Ferro 763-X | Manuf.: | Bärlocher |
| Präparation: | Kapill. Film | Dez. Nr.: | 3.3.3 | Preparation: | Capill. film | Dec. No.: | 3.3.3 |

Stabilisatoren
3. Epoxyverbindungen
3.3. Epoxyverbindungen-Metallseifen-Stabilisatoren

Stabilizers
3. Epoxy Derivatives
3.3. Epoxy Metal Salts Stabilizers

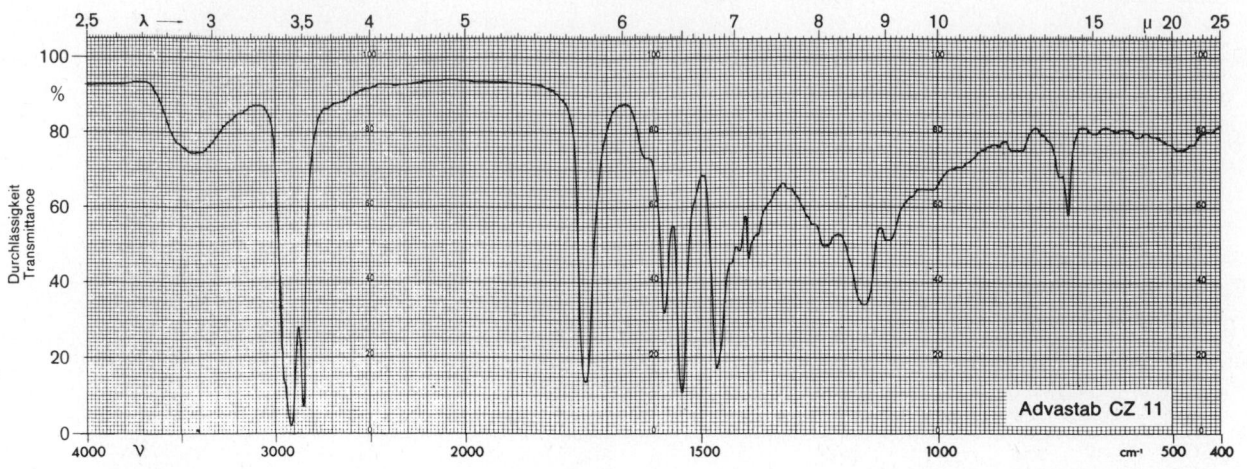

6143   Zusammen-   **Epoxyfettsäureester, Zink-Calcium-Seifen**   Composition: **Epoxy fatty acid ester, zinc calcium soaps**
setzung:

Handelsname: **Advastab CZ 11**   Herst.:   **Advance**   Tradename: **Advastab CZ 11**   Manuf.:   **Advance**
Präparation: **Kapill. Film**   Dez. Nr.: **3.3.4**   Preparation: **Capill. film**   Dec. No.: **3.3.4**

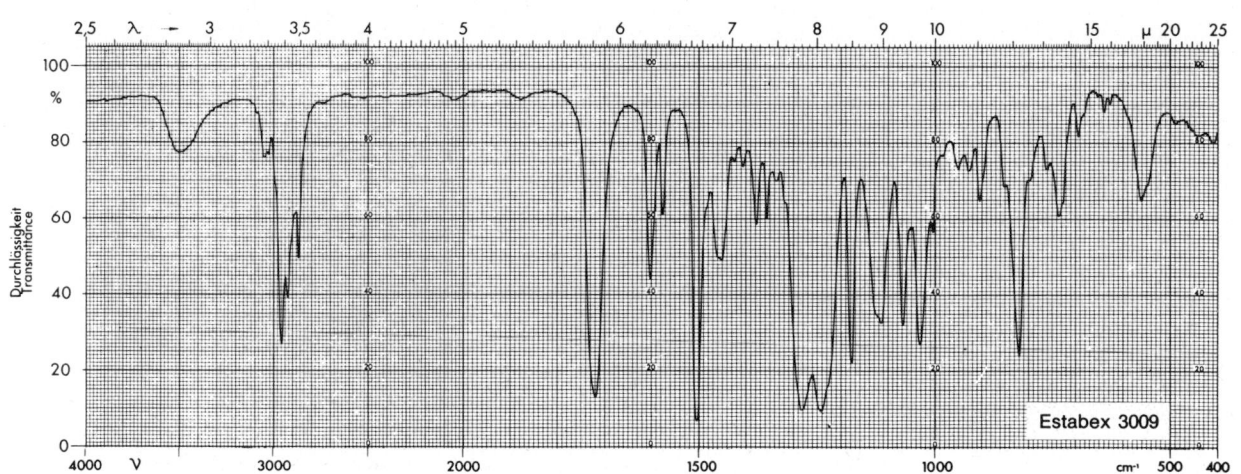

6144   Zusammen-   **Epoxidharz, Phthalester (2 + 1)**   Composition: **Epoxy resin, phthalic ester (2 + 1)**
setzung:

Handelsname: **Estabex 3009**   Herst.:   **Oxydo**   Tradename: **Estabex 3009**   Manuf.:   **Oxydo**
Präparation: **Kapill. Film**   Dez. Nr.: **3.3.5**   Preparation: **Capill. film**   Dec. No.: **3.3.5**

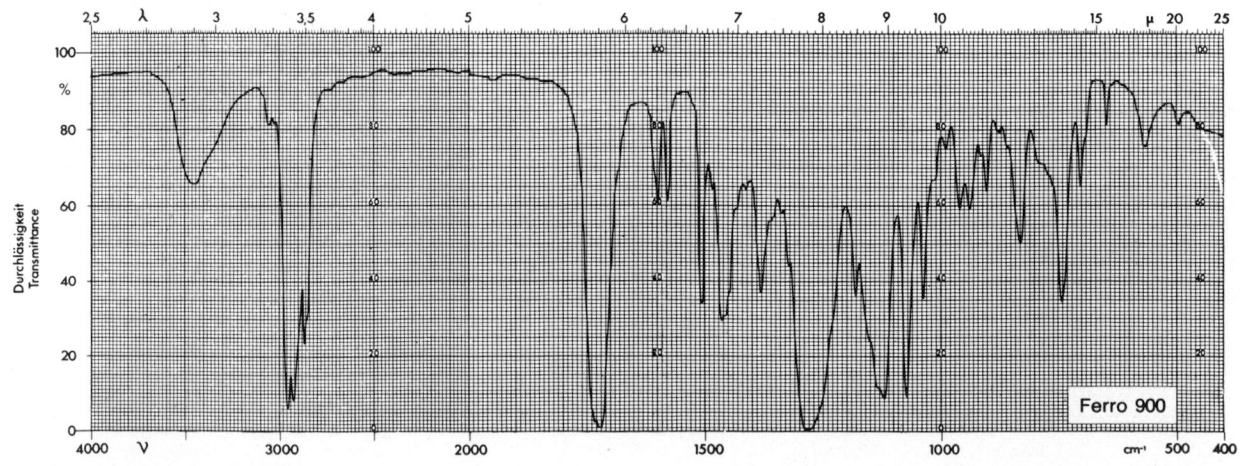

6145   Zusammen-   **Epoxidharz, Weichmacher**   Composition: **Epoxy resin, plasticizer**
setzung:

Handelsname: **Ferro 900**   Herst.:   **Bärlocher**   Tradename: **Ferro 900**   Manuf.:   **Bärlocher**
Präparation: **Kapill. Film**   Dez. Nr.: **3.3.6**   Preparation: **Capill. film**   Dec. No.: **3.3.6**

Stabilisatoren
4. Phosphorverbindungen
4.1. Aryl- und Alkylphosphite

Stabilizers
4. Phosphorus Compounds
4.1. Aryl- and Alkyl Phosphites

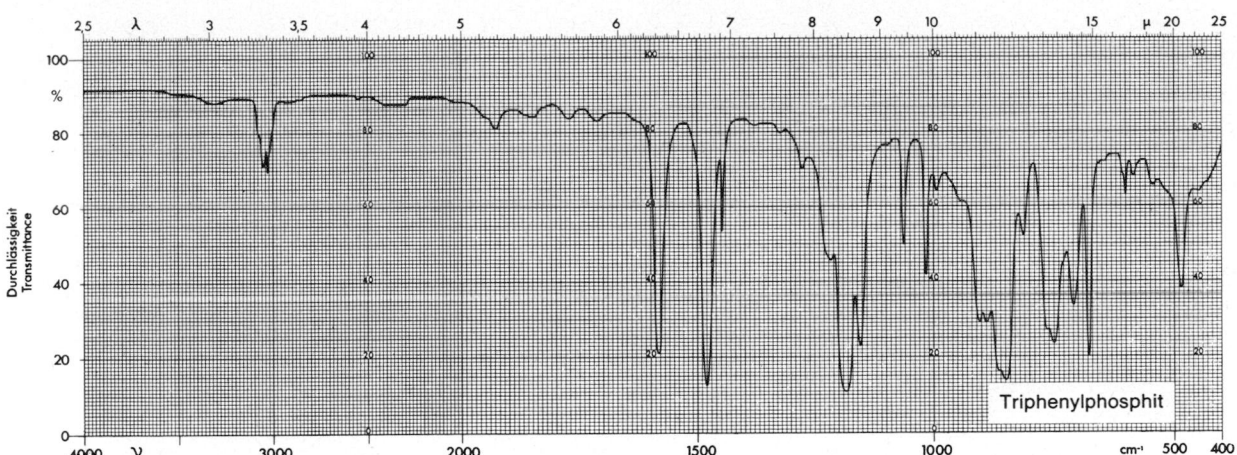

Zusammen- setzung:	Triphenylphosphit			Composition:	Triphenyl phosphite		6146
Handelsname: Triphenylphosphit	Herst.: Monsanto			Tradename: Triphenylphosphit	Manuf.: Monsanto		
Präparation: Kapill. Film	Dez. Nr.: 4.1.1			Preparation: Capill. film	Dec. No.: 4.1.1		

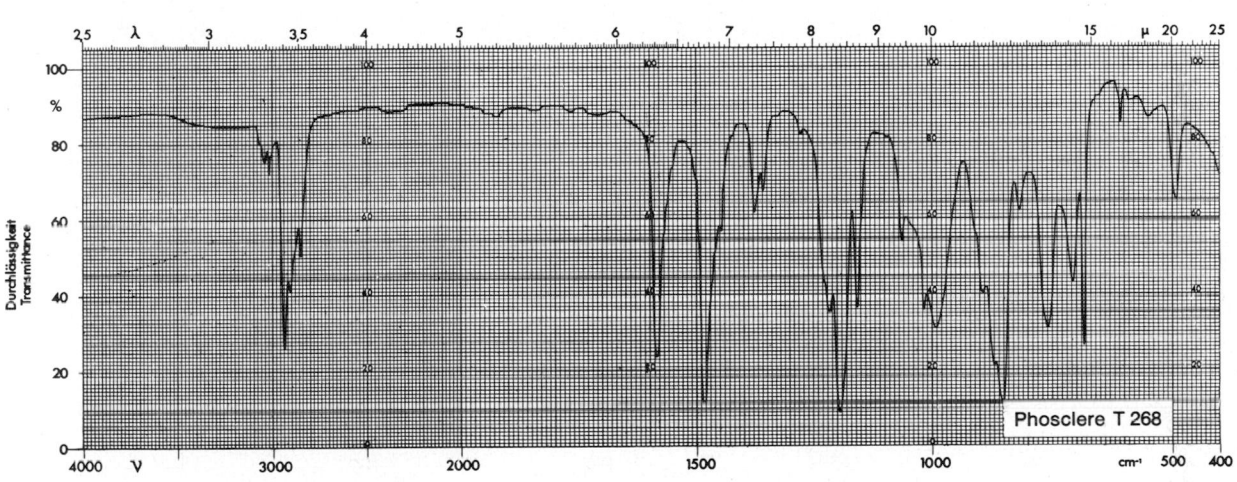

Zusammen- setzung:	Diphenylisooctylphosphit			Composition:	Diphenyl isooctyl phosphite		6147
Handelsname: Phosclere T 268	Herst.: Pure Chem.			Tradename: Phosclere T 268	Manuf.: Pure Chem.		
Präparation: Kapill. Film	Dez. Nr.: 4.1.2			Preparation: Capill. film	Dec. No.: 4.1.2		

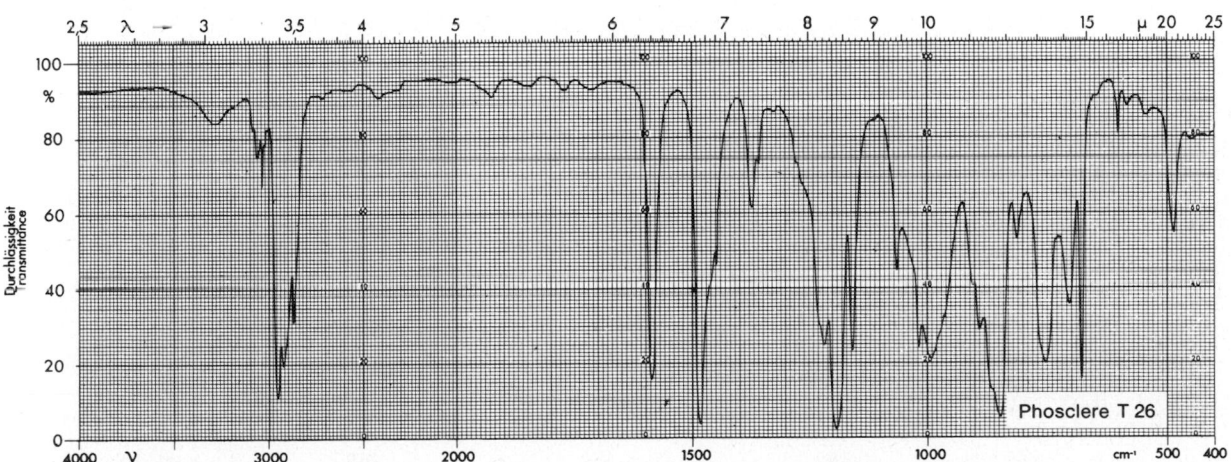

Zusammen- setzung:	Diphenylisodecylphosphit			Composition:	Diphenyl isodecyl phosphite		6148
Handelsname: Phosclere T 26	Herst.: Pure Chem.			Tradename: Phosclere T 26	Manuf.: Pure Chem.		
Präparation: Kapill. Film	Dez. Nr.: 4.1.3			Preparation: Capill. film	Dec. No.: 4.1.3		

Stabilisatoren
4. Phosphorverbindungen
4.1. Aryl- und Alkylphosphite

Stabilizers
4. Phosphorus Compounds
4.1. Aryl- and Alkyl Phosphites

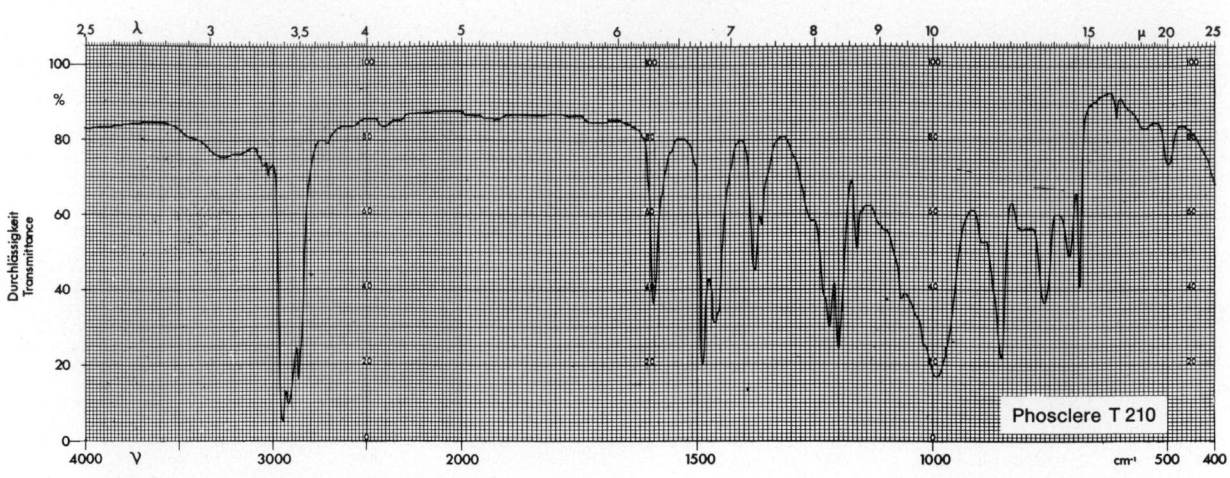

6149   Zusammen-   **Diisodecylphenylphosphit**   Composition: **Diisodecyl phenyl phosphite**
         setzung:

| Handelsname: | **Phosclere T 210** | Herst.: | **Pure Chem.** | Tradename: | **Phosclere T 210** | Manuf.: | **Pure Chem.** |
| Präparation: | **Kapill. Film** | Dez. Nr.: | **4.1.4** | Preparation: | **Capill. film** | Dec. No.: | **4.1.4** |

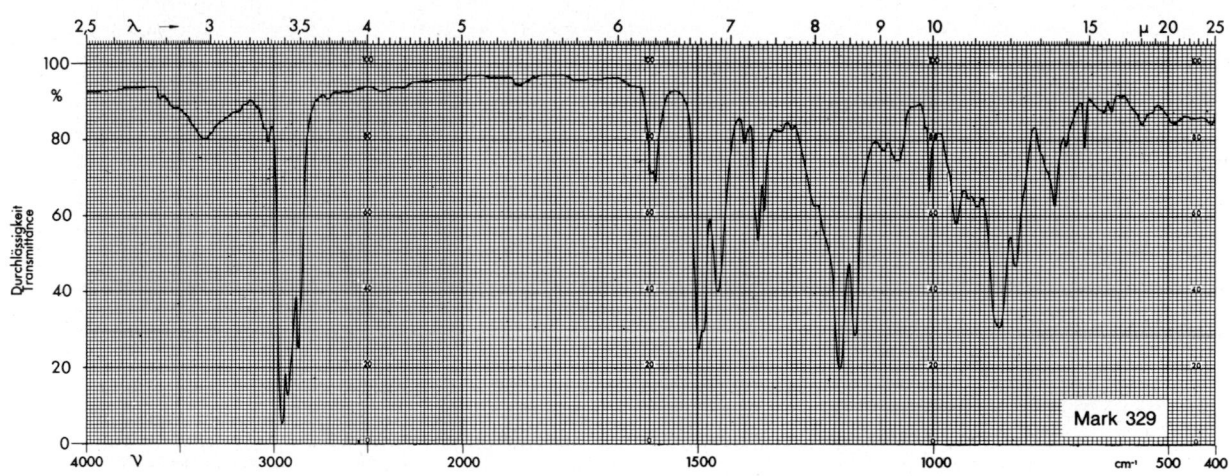

6150   Zusammen-   **Tri(nonylphenyl)phosphit**   Composition: **Tri(nonylphenyl) phosphite**
         setzung:

| Handelsname: | **Mark 329** | Herst.: | **Argus** | Tradename: | **Mark 329** | Manuf.: | **Argus** |
| Präparation: | **Kapill. Film** | Dez. Nr.: | **4.1.5** | Preparation: | **Capill. film** | Dec. No.: | **4.1.5** |

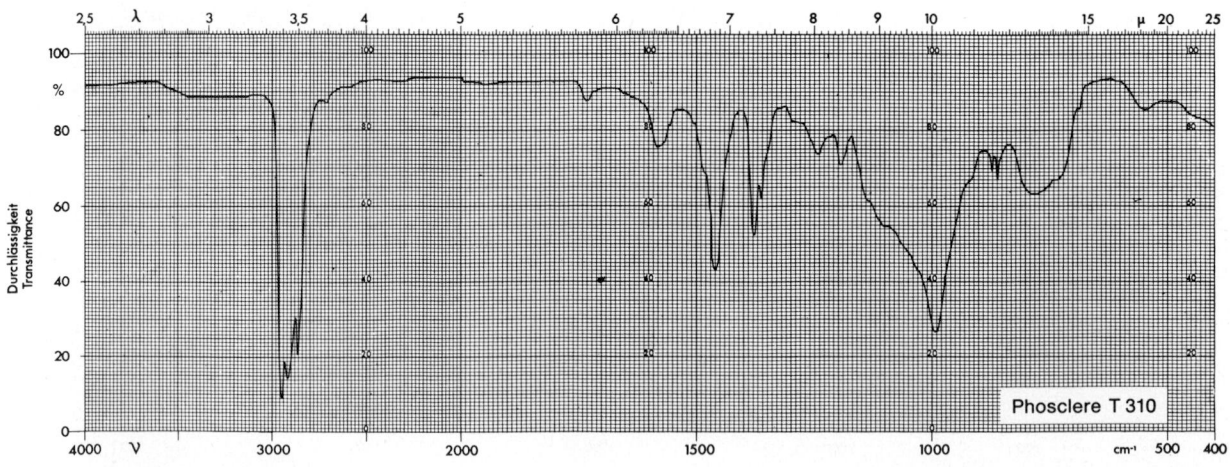

6151   Zusammen-   **Triisodecylphosphit**   Composition: **Triisodecyl phosphite**
         setzung:

| Handelsname: | Phosclere T 310 | Herst.: | **Pure Chem.** | Tradename: | Phosclere T 310 | Manuf.: | **Pure Chem.** |
| Präparation: | **Kapill. Film** | Dez. Nr.: | **4.1.6** | Preparation: | **Capill. film** | Dec. No.: | **4.1.6** |

Stabilisatoren
4. Phosphorverbindungen
4.2. Phosphithaltige Gemische

Stabilizers
4. Phosphorus Compounds
4.2. Phosphites containing Mixtures

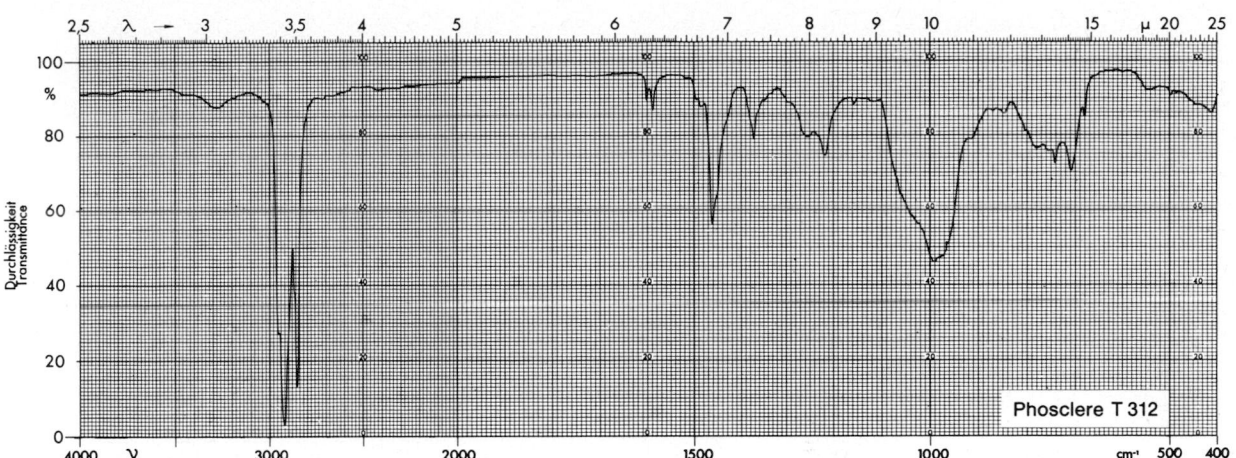

Zusammen-   **Tridodecylphosphit**   Composition: **Tridodecyl phosphite**   6152
setzung:

Handelsname: **Phosclere T 312**   Herst.:   **Pure Chem.**   Tradename: **Phosclere T 312**   Manuf.:   **Pure Chem.**
Präparation: **Kapill. Film**   Dez. Nr.: **4.1.7**   Preparation: **Capill. film**   Dec. No.: **4.1.7**

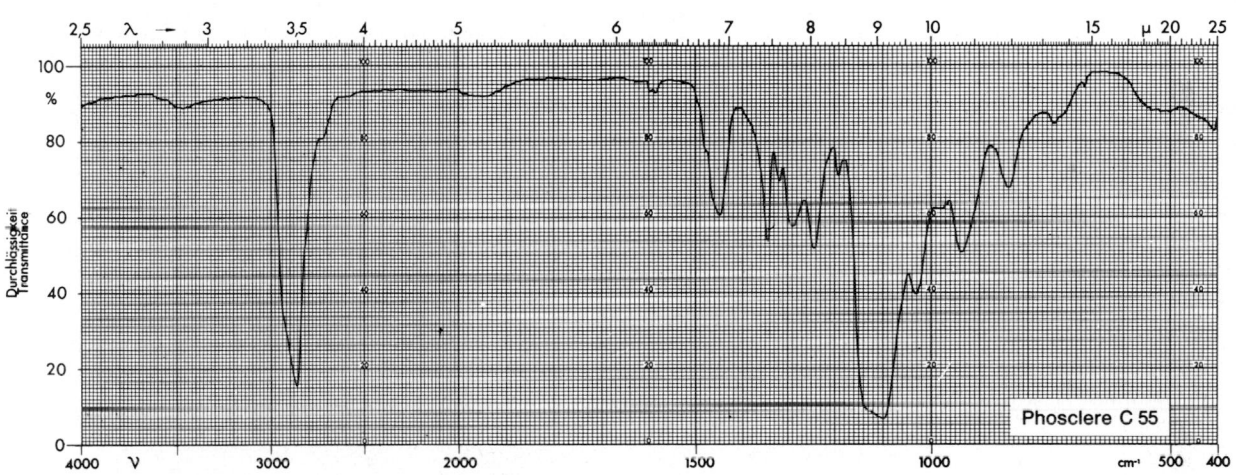

Zusammen-   **Trimethoxycarbowax 550, Phosphitester**   Composition: **Trimethoxy carbowax 550, phosphite ester**   6153
setzung:

Handelsname: **Phosclere C 55**   Herst.:   **Pure Chem.**   Tradename: **Phosclere C 55**   Manuf.:   **Pure Chem.**
Präparation: **Kapill. Film**   Dez. Nr.: **4.2.1**   Preparation: **Capill. film**   Dec. No.: **4.2.1**

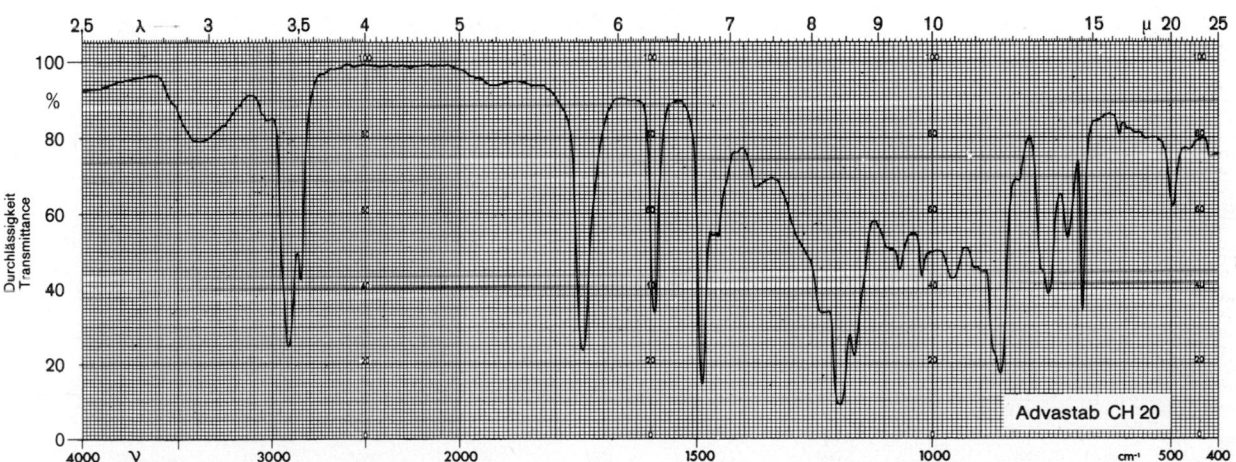

Zusammen-   **Triphenylphosphit, Epoxyfettsäureester**   Composition: **Triphenyl phosphite, epoxy fatty acid ester**   6154
setzung:

Handelsname: **Advastab CH 20**   Herst.:   **Advance**   Tradename: **Advastab CH 20**   Manuf.:   **Advance**
Präparation: **KBr (6/1000)**   Dez. Nr.: **4.2.2**   Preparation: **KBr (6/1000)**   Dec. No.: **4.2.2**

Stabilisatoren
4. Phosphorverbindungen
4.2. Phosphithaltige Gemische

Stabilizers
4. Phosphorus Compounds
4.2. Phosphites containing Mixtures

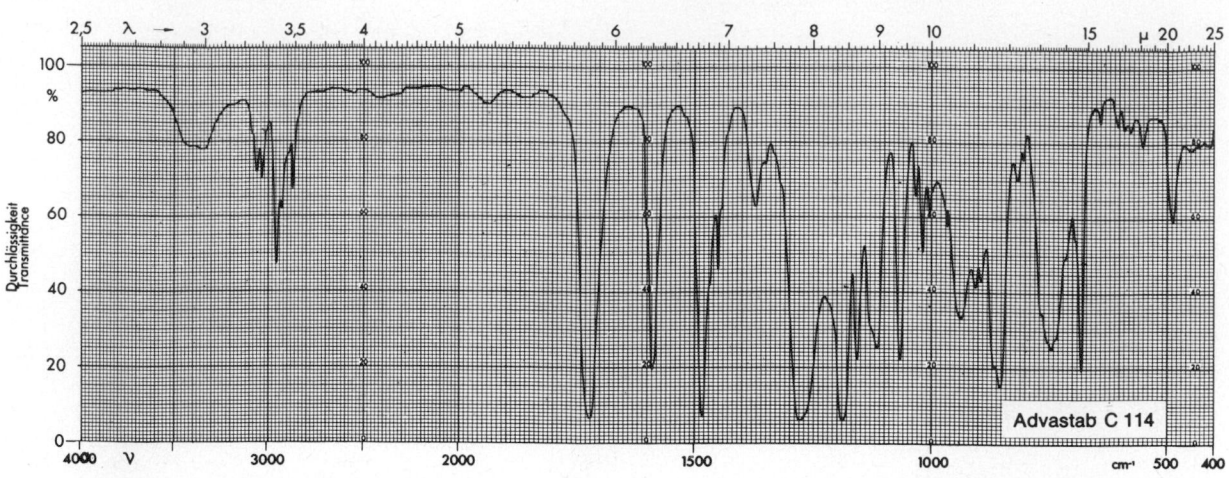

Advastab C 114

6155   Zusammen-setzung: **Arylphosphit, Phthalester**   Composition: **Aryl phosphite, phthalic ester**

Handelsname:	**Advastab C 114**	Herst.:	**Advance**	Tradename:	**Advastab C 114**	Manuf.:	**Advance**
Präparation:	**Kapill. Film**	Dez. Nr.:	**4.2.3**	Preparation:	**Capill. film**	Dec. No.:	**4.2.3**

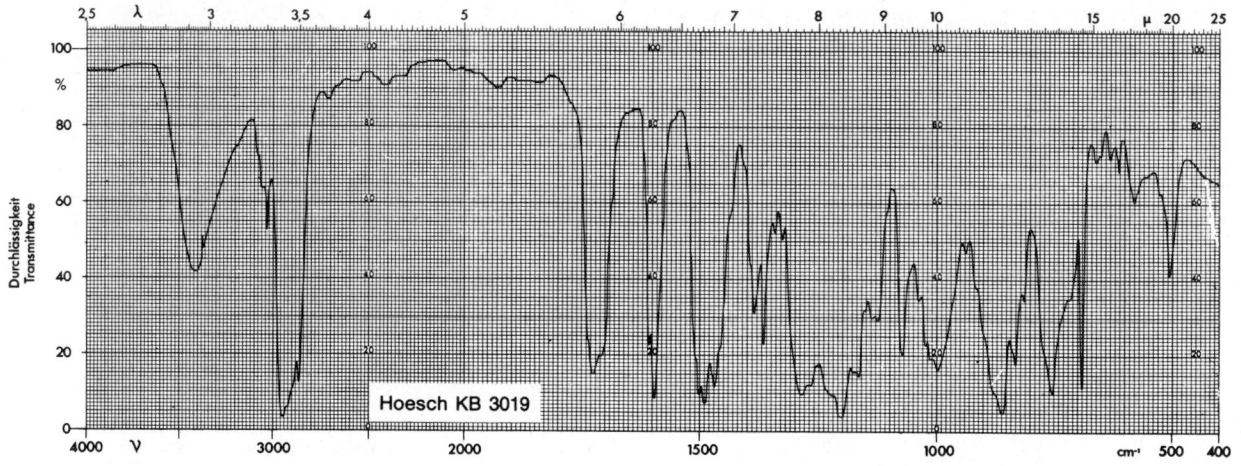

Hoesch KB 3019

6156   Zusammen-setzung: **Arylalkylphosphit + Ester + Zusätze**   Composition: **Aryl alkyl phosphite + ester + additives**

Handelsname:	**Hoesch KB 3019**	Herst.:	**Hoesch**	Tradename:	**Hoesch KB 3019**	Manuf.:	**Hoesch**
Präparation:	**Kapill. Film**	Dez. Nr.:	**4.2.4.**	Preparation:	**Capill. film**	Dec. No.:	**4.2.4**

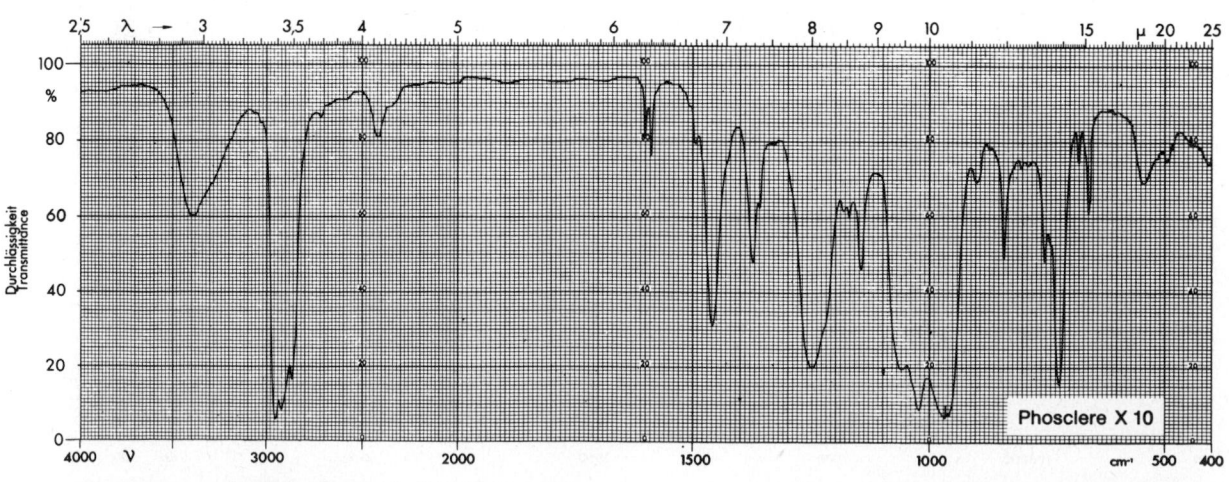

Phosclere X 10

6157   Zusammen-setzung: **3,9-Diisodecyloxy-2,4,8,10-tetraoxa-3,9-diphosphaspiro-(5,5)-undecan**   Composition: **3,9-diisodecyloxy-2,4,8,10-tetraoxa-3,9-diphosphaspiro-5,5-undecan**

Handelsname:	**Phosclere X 10**	Herst.:	**Pure Chem.**	Tradename:	**Phosclere X 10**	Manuf.:	**Pure Chem.**
Präparation:	**Kapill. Film**	Dez. Nr.:	**4.3.1**	Preparation:	**Capill. film**	Dec. No.:	**4.3.1**

Stabilisatoren
4. Phosphorverbindungen
4.3. Sonstige Phosphor-Stabilisatoren

Stabilizers
4. Phosphorus Compounds
4.3. Other Phosphorus Stabilizers

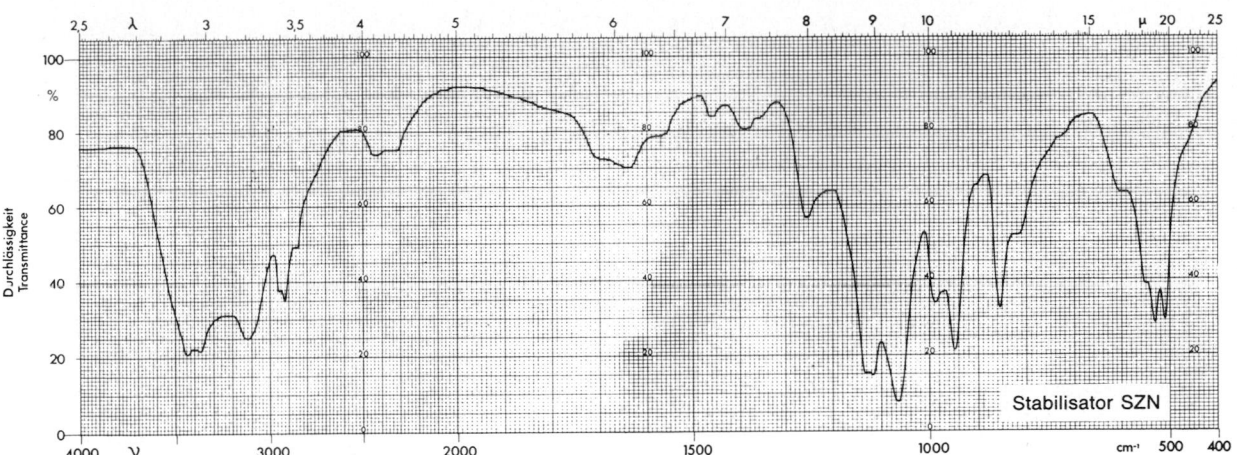

| Zusammensetzung: | Na-Ba-Ca-Polyalkyltriphosphat | | Composition: | Na-Ba-Ca-Polyalkyl triphosphate | | 6158 |

| Handelsname: | Stabilisator SZN | Herst.: | Bärlocher | Tradename: | Stabilisator SZN | Manuf.: | Bärlocher |
| Präparation: | KBr (3/1000) | Dez. Nr.: | 4.3.2 | Preparation: | KBr (3/1000) | Dec. No.: | 4.3.2 |

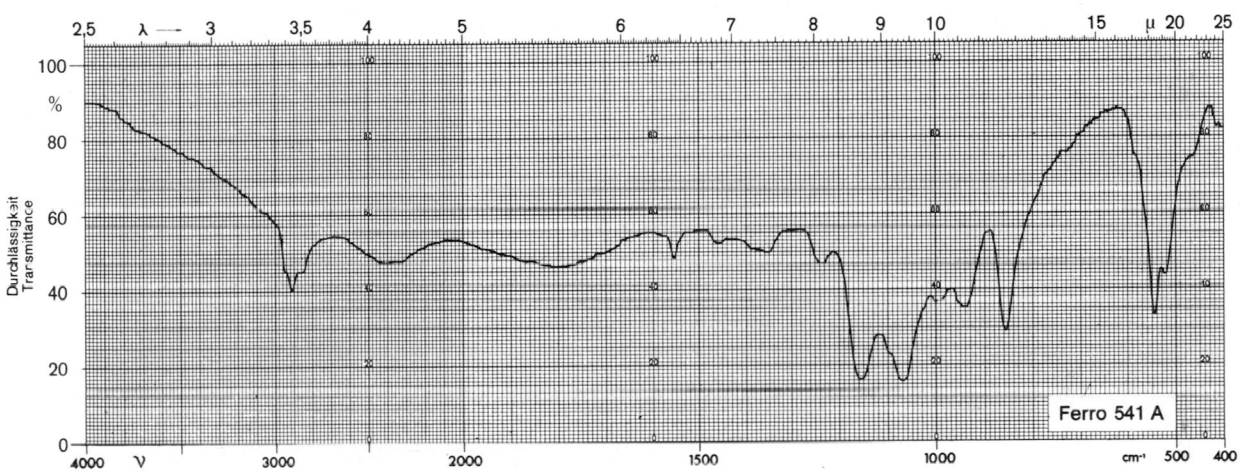

| Zusammensetzung: | Na-Ba-Polyalkylpolyphosphat | | Composition: | Na-Ba-poly alkyl polyphosphate | | 6159 |

| Handelsname: | Ferro 541 A | Herst.: | Bärlocher | Tradename: | Ferro 541 A | Manuf.: | Bärlocher |
| Präparation: | KBr (9/1000) | Dez. Nr..: | 4.3.3 | Preparation: | KBr (9/1000) | Dec. No.: | 4.3.3 |

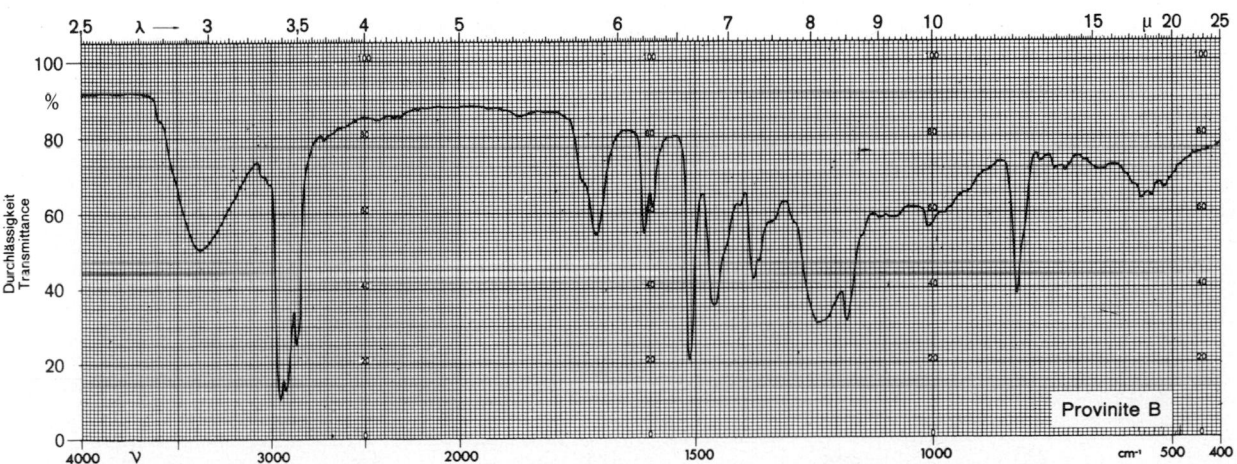

| Zusammensetzung: | Ba-Cd-P-B-Stabilisator | | Composition: | Ba-Cd-P-B-stabilizer | | 6160 |

| Handelsname: | Provinite B | Herst.: | National Lead | Tradename: | Provinite B | Manuf.: | National Lead |
| Präparation: | Kapill. Film | Dez. Nr.: | 4.3.4 | Preparation: | Capill. film | Dec. No.: | 4.3.4 |

Stabilisatoren
5. Sonstige Stabilisatoren
5.1.Thiofettsäureester

Stabilizers
5. Miscellaneous Stabilizers
5.1.Thio Fatty Acid Esters

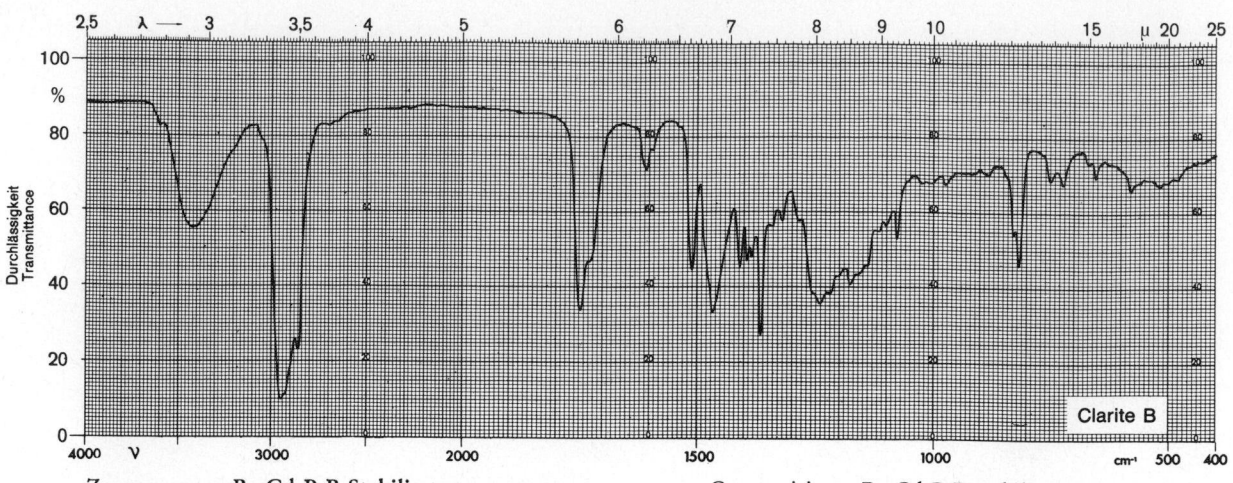

6161

Zusammen-setzung:	**Ba-Cd-P-B-Stabilisator**		Composition:	**Ba-Cd-P-B-stabilizer**	
Handelsname:	**Clarite B**	Herst.: **National Lead**	Tradename:	**Clarite B**	Manuf.: **National Lead**
Präparation:	**Kapill. Film**	Dez. Nr.: **4.3.5**	Preparation:	**Capill. film**	Dec. No.: **4.3.5**

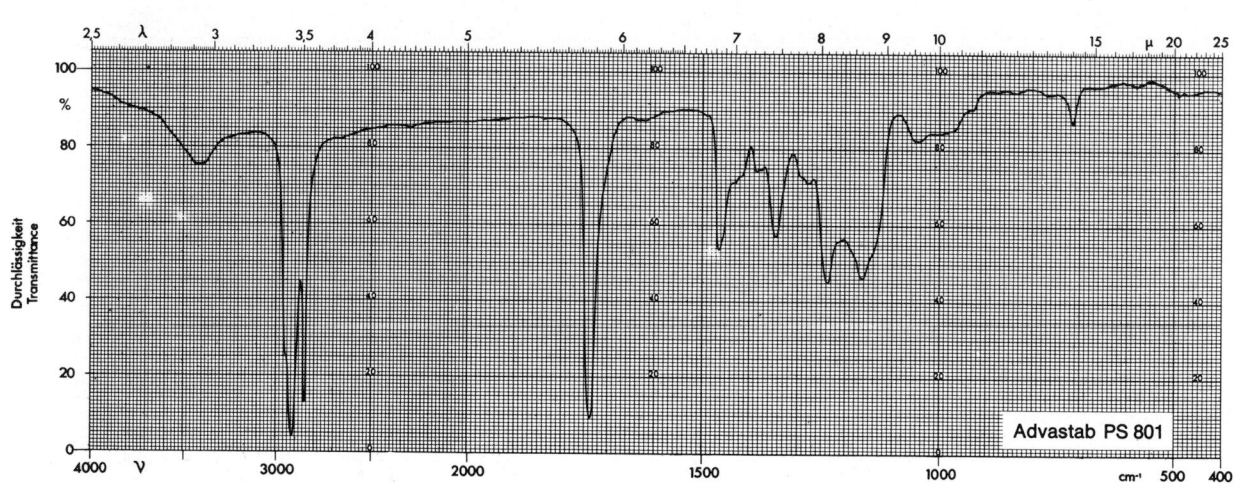

6162

Zusammen-setzung:	**Thiodipropionsäurelaurylester**		Composition:	**Thio dilauryl propionate**	
Handelsname:	**Advastab PS 801**	Herst.: **Advance**	Tradename:	**Advastab PS 801**	Manuf.: **Advance**
Präparation:	**KBr (2/1000)**	Dez. Nr.: **5.1.1**	Preparation:	**KBr (2/1000)**	Dec. No.: **5.1.1**

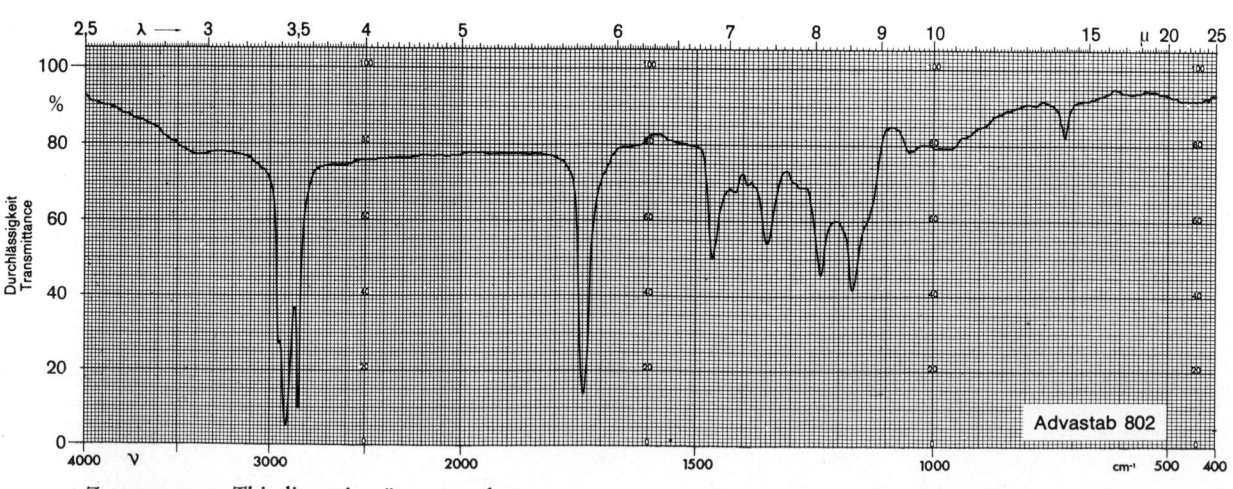

6163

Zusammen-setzung:	**Thiodipropionsäurestearylester**		Composition:	**Thio distearyl propionate**	
Handelsname:	**Advastab 802**	Herst.: **Advance**	Tradename:	**Advastab 802**	Manuf.: **Advance**
Präparation:	**Kapill. Film**	Dez. Nr.: **5.1.2**	Preparation:	**Capill. film**	Dec. No.: **5.1.2**

Stabilisatoren
5. Sonstige Stabilisatoren
5.2. Aminocrotonsäureester

Stabilizers
5. Miscellaneous Stabilizers
5.2. Amino Crotonic Acid Esters

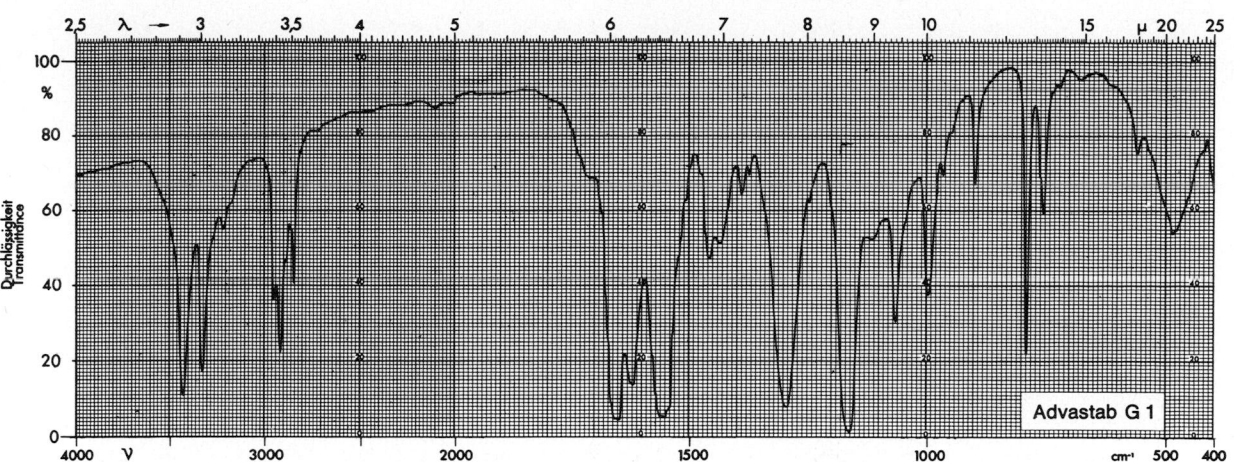

Zusammen-   Aminocrotonsäureester von 1,4-Butylen-
setzung: glykol und Fettalkoholen (C$_{16}$-C$_{18}$)
Handelsname: Advastab G 1   Herst.:   Advance
Präparation: KBr (4/1000)   Dez. Nr.: 5.2.1

Composition: Amino crotonic acid esters of 1,4-butylene –
               glycol and fatty alcohols (C$_{16}$-C$_{18}$)
Tradename: Advastab G 1   Manuf.:   Advance
Preparation: KBr (4/1000)   Dec. No.: 5.2.1

6164

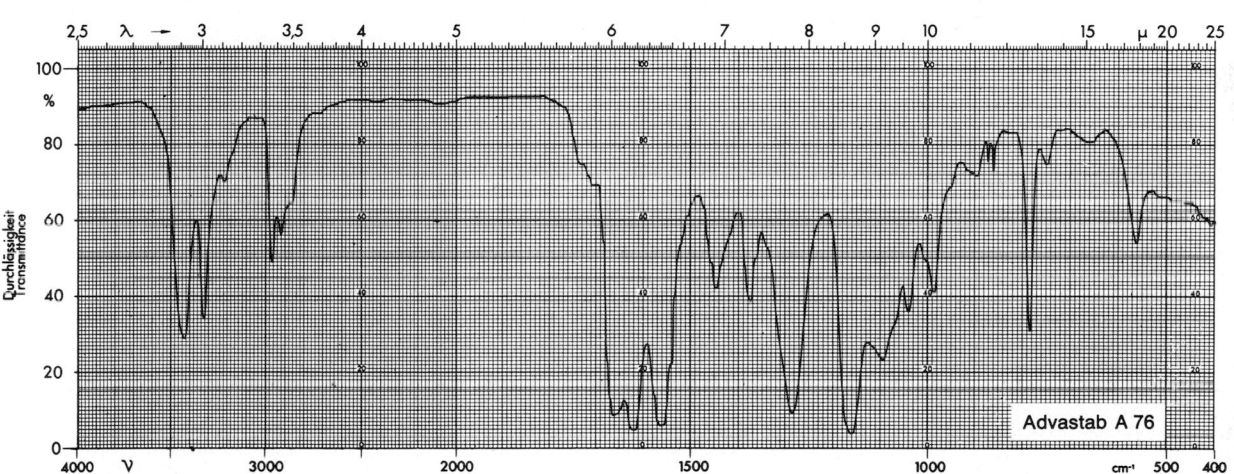

Zusammen-   Thioaminocrotonsäureester
setzung:
Handelsname: **Advastab A 76**   Herst.:   Advance
Präparation: **Kapill. Film**   Dez. Nr.: **5.2.2**

Composition: **Thio amino crotonic ester**
Tradename: **Advastab A 76**   Manuf.:   **Advance**
Preparation: **Capill. film**   Dec. No.: **5.2.2**

6165

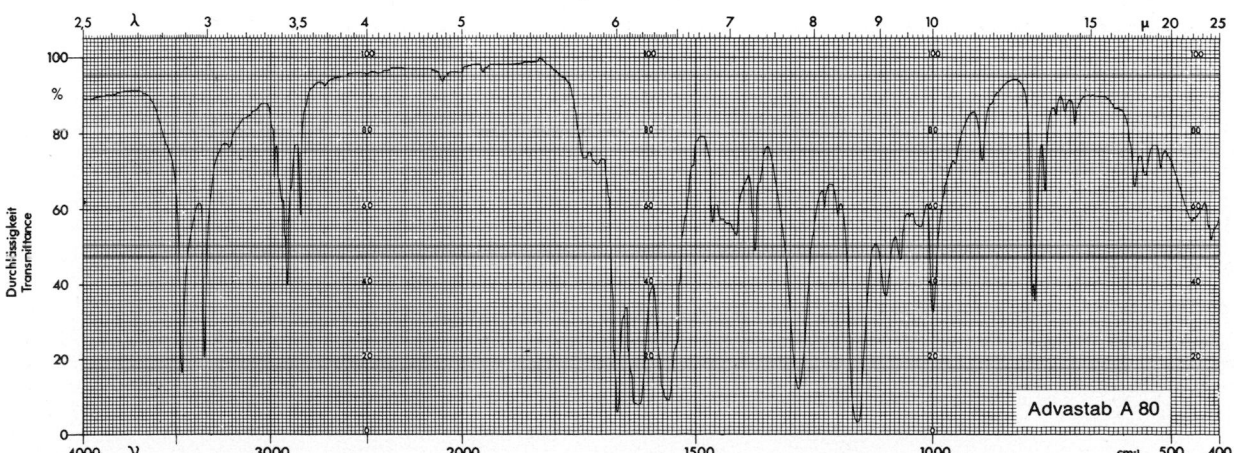

Zusammen-   Thiodiethylenglykol-bis-β-amino-
setzung: crotonat + Ca-Zn-Stearat
Handelsname: Advastab A 80   Herst.:   Advance
Präparation: KBr (4/1000)   Dez. Nr.: 5.2.3

Composition: Thio diethyleneglycol-bis-β-amino
               crotonate + Ca-Zn-stearate
Tradename: Advastab A 80   Manuf.:   **Advance**
Preparation: KBr (4/1000)   Dec. No.: 5.2.3

6166

Stabilisatoren
5. Sonstige Stabilisatoren
5.3. Andere Komplexbildner

Stabilizers
5. Miscellaneous Stabilizers
5.3. Other Chelating Agents

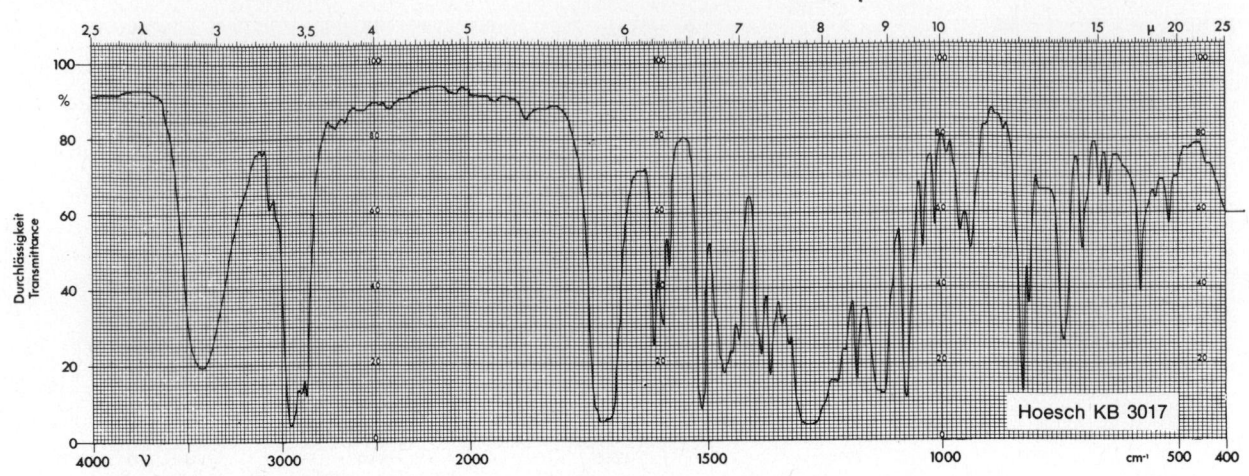

Hoesch KB 3017

6167

Zusammen-setzung:	Organischer Komplexbildner, Phthalester, Epoxyverbindung		
Handelsname:	Hoesch KB 3017	Herst.:	Hoesch
Präparation:	Kapill. Film	Dez. Nr.:	5.3.1

Composition:	Organic chelating agent, phthalic ester, epoxide		
Tradename:	Hoesch KB 3017	Manuf.:	Hoesch
Preparation:	Capill. film	Dec. No.:	5.3.1

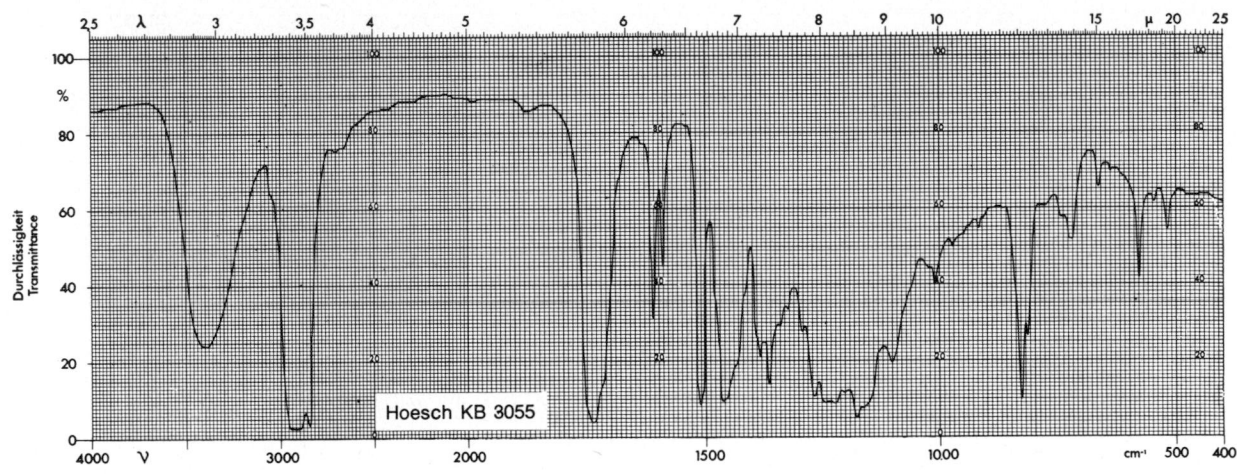

Hoesch KB 3055

6168

Zusammen-setzung:	Organischer Komplexbildner, Ester, Epoxyverbindung		
Handelsname:	Hoesch KB 3055	Herst.:	Hoesch
Präparation:	Kapill. Film	Dez. Nr.:	5.3.2

Composition:	Organic chelating agent, ester, epoxide		
Tradename:	Hoesch KB 3055	Manuf.:	Hoesch
Preparation:	Capill. film	Dec. No.:	5.3.2

Antistatica
Antistatic Agents

Antistatica
1. Stickstoff-Verbindungen
1.1. Quaternäre Ammoniumverbindungen

Antistatica
1. Nitrogen Compounds
1.1. Quaternary Ammonia Compounds

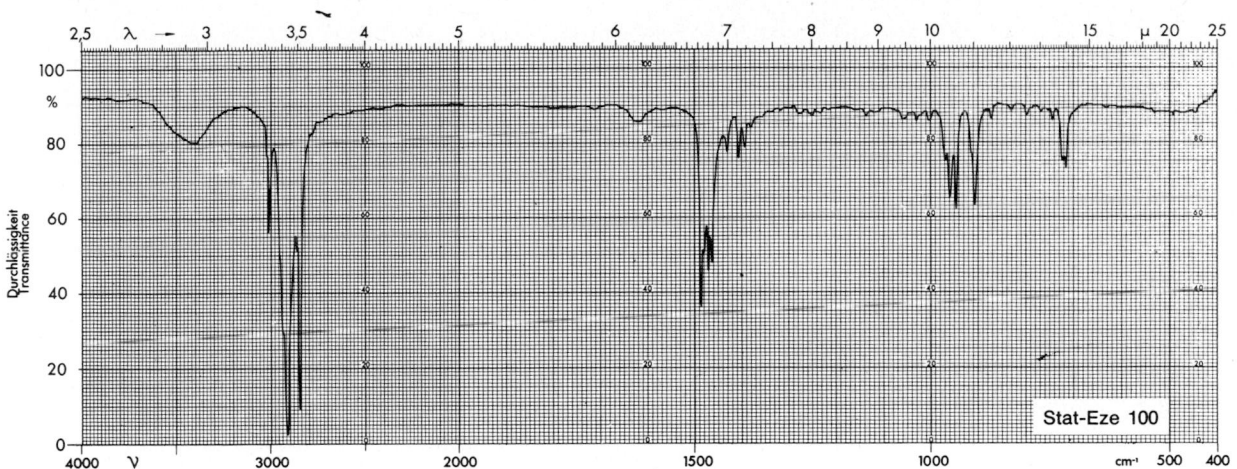

Haupt-bestandteil:	Alkyltrimethylammoniumchlorid		Main component:	Alkyl trimethyl ammonia chloride		6200
Handelsname:	Stat-Eze 100	Herst.: Fine Org.	Tradename:	Stat-Eze 100	Manuf.: Fine Org.	
Präparation:	KBr (3/1000)	Dez. Nr.: 1.1.1	Preparation:	KBr (3/1000)	Dec. No.: 1.1.1	

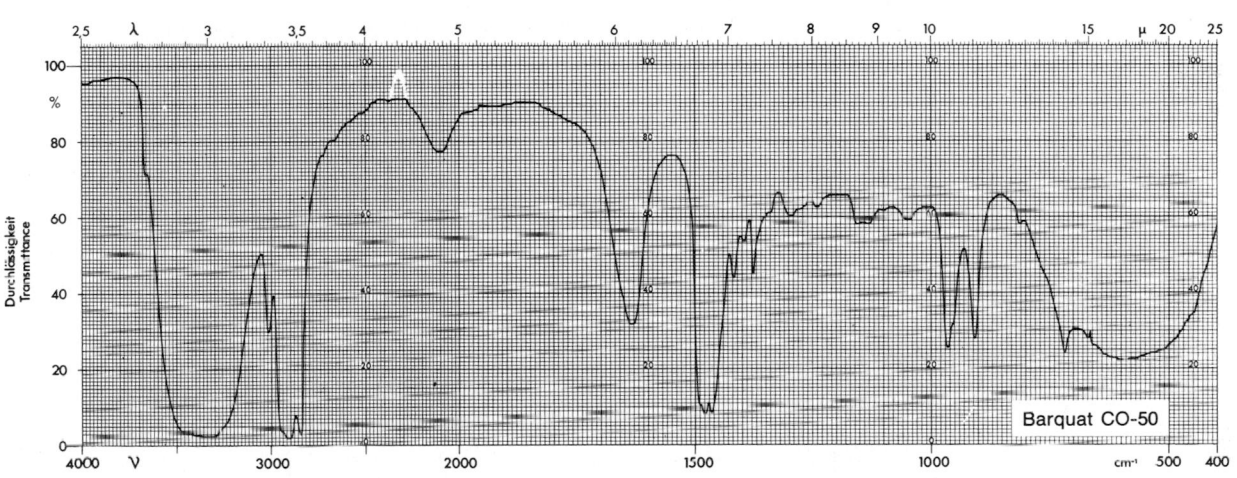

Haupt-bestandteil:	Alkyltrimethylammoniumchlorid		Main component:	Alkyl trimethyl ammonia chloride		6201
Handelsname:	Barquat CO-50	Herst.: Baird	Tradename:	Barquat CO-50	Manuf.: Baird	
Präparation:	Film, R	Dez. Nr.: 1.1.2	Preparation:	Film, R	Dec. No.: 1.1.2	

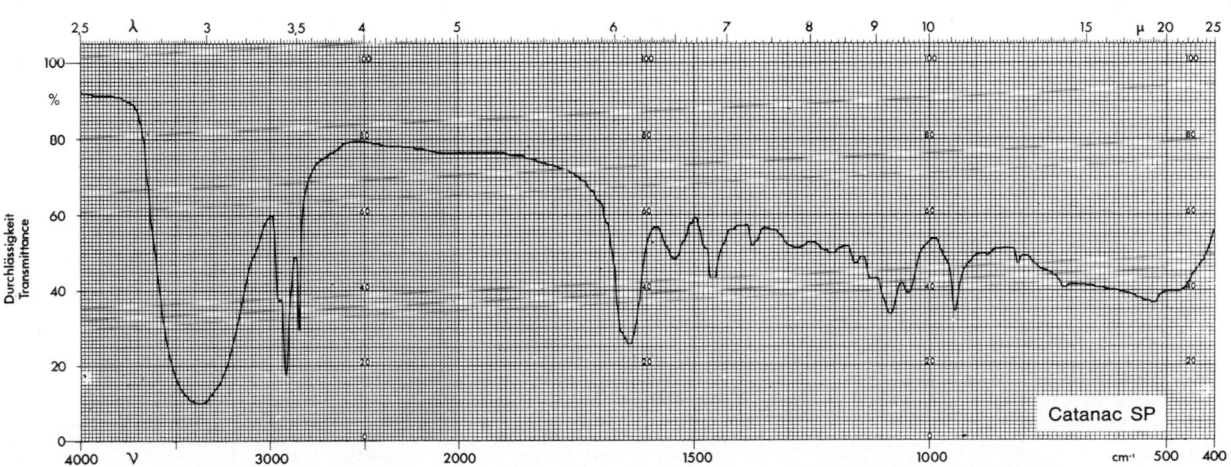

Haupt-bestandteil:	Stearamidopropyl-dimethyl-β-hydroxy-ethylammoniumphosphat		Main component:	Stearamidopropyl-dimethyl-β-hydroxy-ethyl ammonia phosphate		6202
Handelsname:	Catanac SP	Herst.: Cyanamid	Tradename:	Catanac SP	Manuf.: Cyanamid	
Präparation:	Film, flüssig, R	Dez. Nr.: 1.1.3	Preparation:	Film, liquid, R	Dec. No.: 1.1.3	

Antistatica
1. Stickstoff-Verbindungen
1.1. Quaternäre Ammoniumverbindungen

Antistatica
1. Nitrogen Compounds
1.1. Quaternary Ammonia Compounds

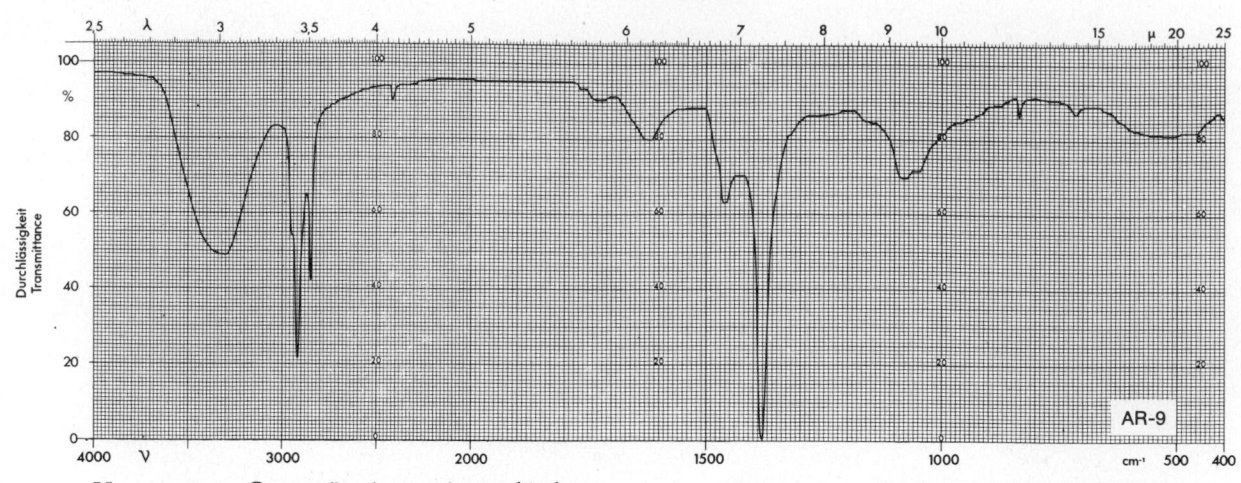

6203

Haupt-bestandteil:	Quaternäre Ammoniumverbindung		Main component:	Quaternary ammonia compound	
Handelsname:	**AR-9**	Herst.: **An. Chem. L.**	Tradename:	**AR-9**	Manuf.: **An. Chem. L.**
Präparation:	**KBr (3/1000), R**	Dez. Nr.: **1.1.4**	Preparation:	**KBr (3/1000), R**	Dec. No.: **1.1.4**

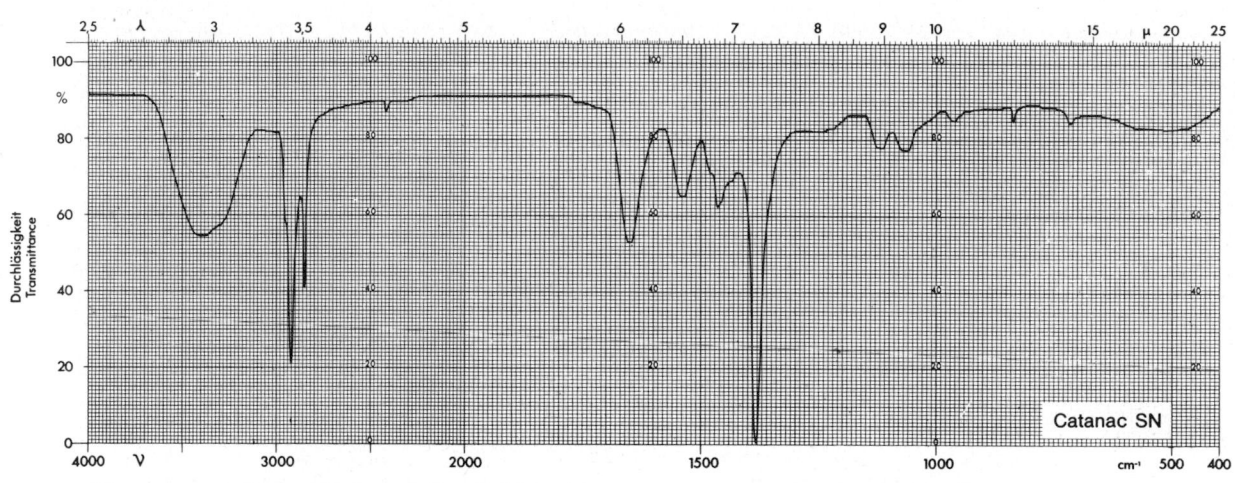

6204

Haupt-bestandteil:	Stearamidopropyl-dimethyl-β-hydroxy-ethylammoniumnitrat		Main component:	Stearamidopropyl-dimethyl-β-hydroxy-ethyl ammonia nitrate	
Handelsname:	**Catanac SN**	Herst.: **Cyanamid**	Tradename:	**Catanac SN**	Manuf.: **Cyanamid**
Präparation:	**KBr (3/1000), R**	Dez. Nr.: **1.1.5**	Preparation:	**KBr (3/1000), R**	Dec. No.: **1.1.5**

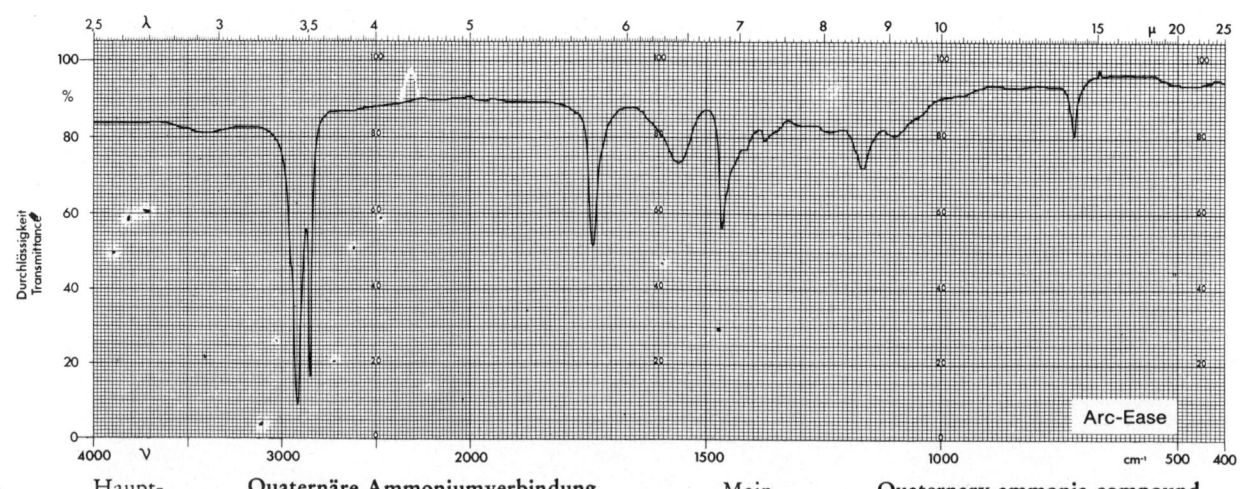

6205

Haupt-bestandteil:	Quaternäre Ammoniumverbindung		Main component:	Quaternary ammonia compound	
Handelsname:	**Arc-Ease**	Herst.: **Am. Resin**	Tradename:	**Arc-Ease**	Manuf.: **Am. Resin**
Präparation:	**KBr (3/1000), R**	Dez. Nr.: **1.1.6**	Preparation:	**KBr (3/1000), R**	Dec. No.: **1.1.6**

Antistatica
1. Stickstoff-Verbindungen
1.1. Quaternäre Ammoniumverbindungen

Antistatica
1. Nitrogen Compounds
1.1. Quaternary Ammonia Compounds

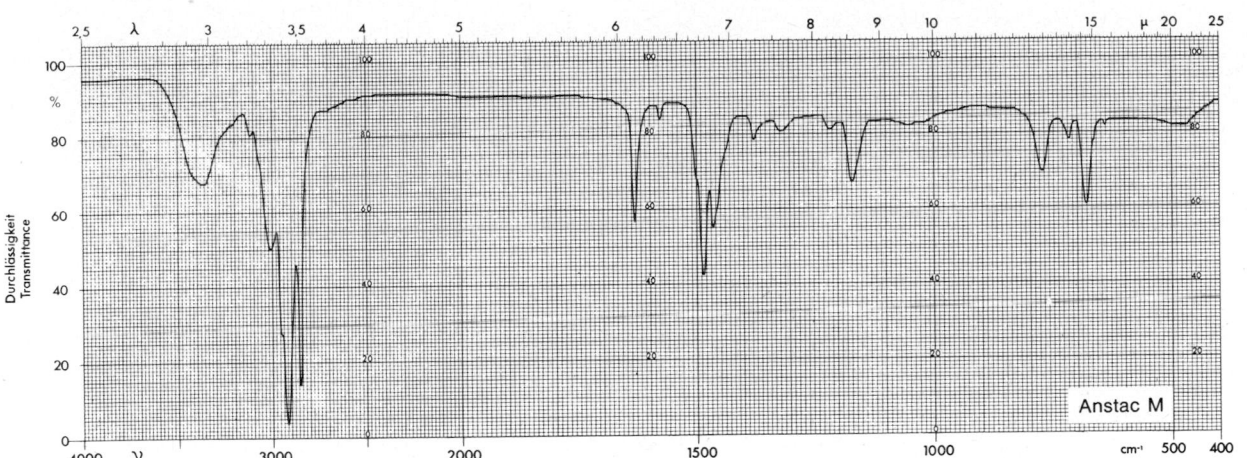

Haupt-bestandteil:	Quaternäre Ammoniumverbindung		Main component:	Quaternary ammonia compound		6206
Handelsname:	Anstac M	Herst.: Chem. Devel.	Tradename:	Anstac M	Manuf.: Chem. Devel.	
Präparation:	Film, fest	Dez. Nr.: 1.1.7	Preparation:	Film, solid	Dec. No.: 1.1.7	

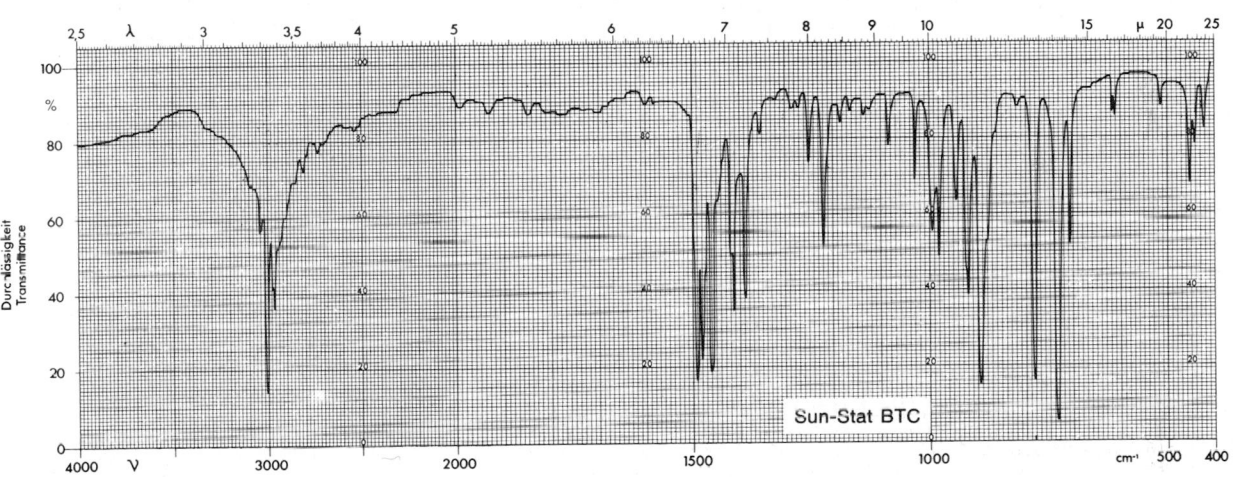

Haupt-bestandteil:	Benzyltrimethylammoniumchlorid		Main component:	Benzyl trimethyl ammonia chloride		6207
Handelsname:	Sun-Stat BTC	Herst.: Sun Chem.	Tradename:	Sun-Stat BTC	Manuf.: Sun Chem.	
Präparation:	KBr (3/1000), R	Dez. Nr.: 1.1.8	Preparation:	KBr (3/1000), R	Dec. No.: 1.1.8	

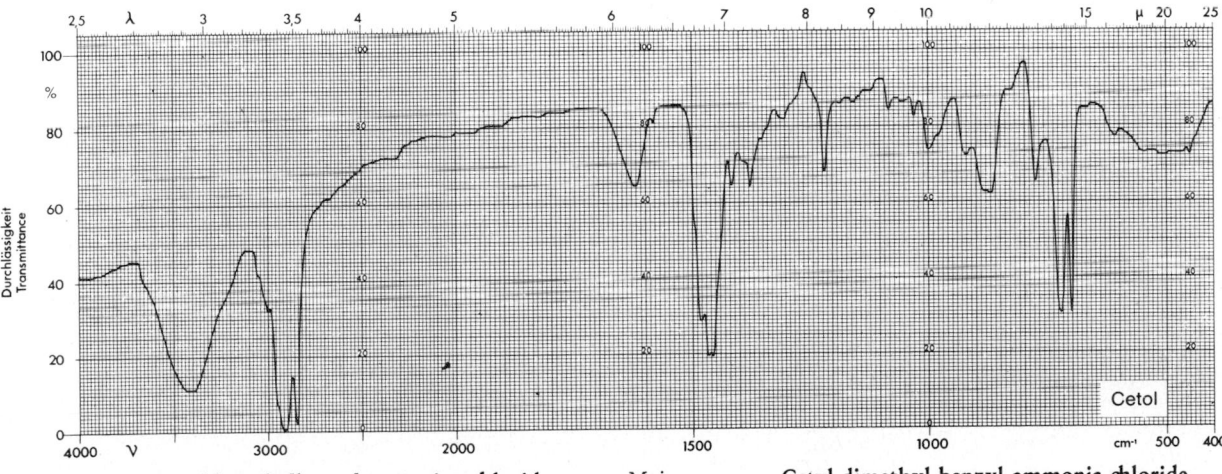

Haupt-bestandteil:	Cetyldimethylbenzylammoniumchlorid		Main component:	Cetyl dimethyl benzyl ammonia chloride		6208
Handelsname:	Cetol	Herst.: Fine Org.	Tradename:	Cetol	Manuf.: Fine Org.	
Präparation:	KBr (3/1000), R	Dez. Nr.: 1.1.9	Preparation:	KBr (3/1000), R	Dec. No.: 1.1.9	

Antistatica
1. Stickstoff-Verbindungen
1.2. Alkylolamine, Amide

Antistatica
1. Nitrogen Compounds
1.2. Alkylolamines, Amides

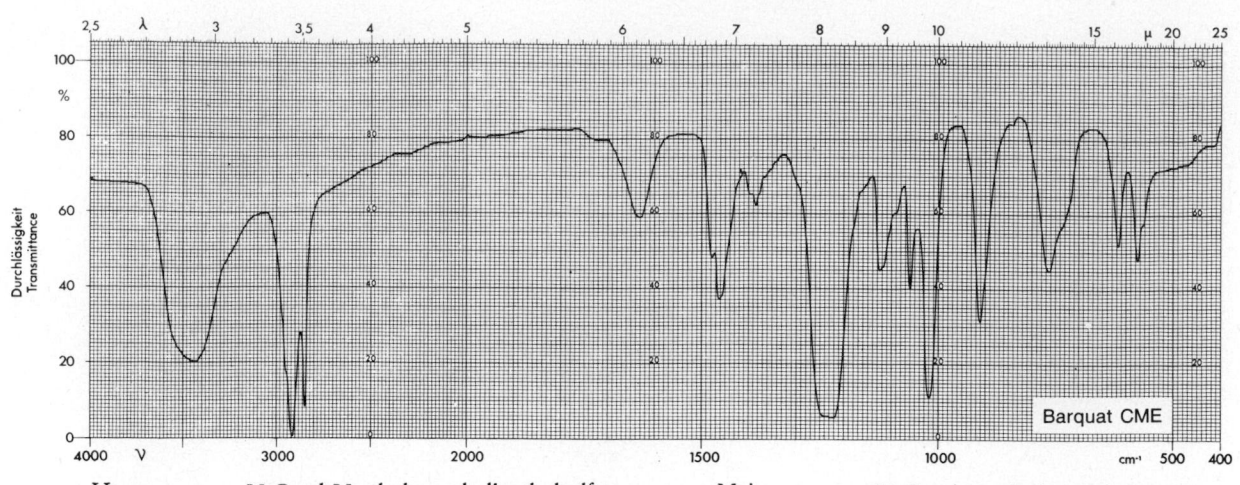

6209

Haupt-bestandteil:	N-Cetyl-N-ethylmorpholinethylsulfat		Main component:	N-Cetyl-N-ethyl morpholine ethyl sulfate	
Handelsname:	Barquat CME	Herst.: Baird	Tradename:	Barquat CME	Manuf.: Baird
Präparation:	KBr (3/1000)	Dez. Nr.: 1.1.10	Preparation:	KBr (3/1000)	Dec. No.: 1.1.10

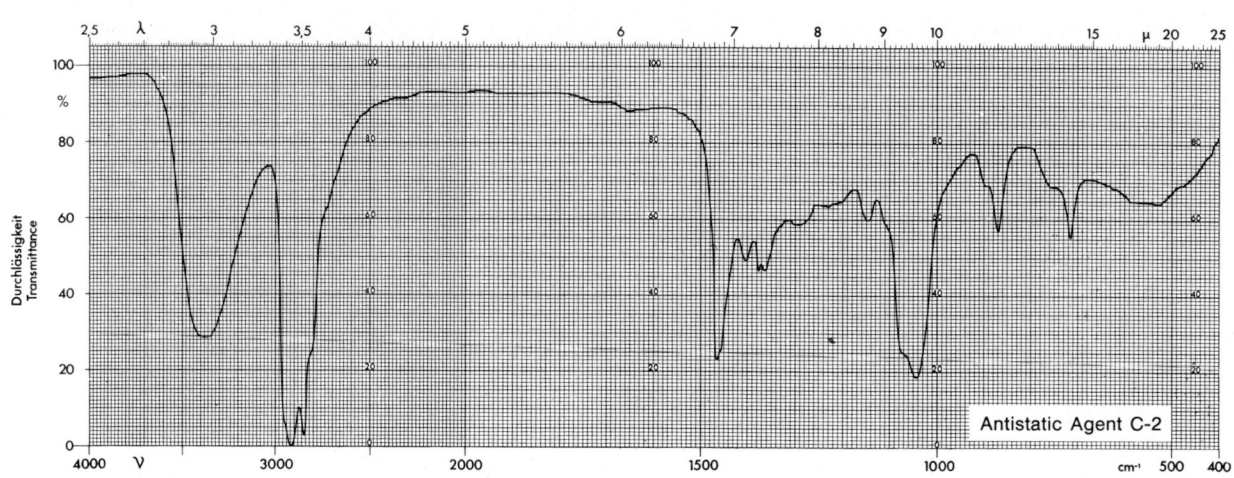

6210

Haupt-bestandteil:	N,N-Bis(2-hydroxyethyl)-alkylamin		Main component:	N,N-Bis(2-hydroxy ethyl)-alkyl amine	
Handelsname:	Antistat. Agent C-2	Herst.: Alcolac	Tradename:	Antistat. Agent C-2	Manuf.: Alcolac
Präparation:	Film, flüssig	Dez. Nr.: 1.2.1	Preparation:	Film, liquid	Dec. No.: 1.2.1

6211

Haupt-bestandteil:	Alkylolamin		Main component:	Alkylolamine	
Handelsname:	Antist. Agent 273-E	Herst.: Fine Org.	Tradename:	Antist. Agent 273-E	Manuf.: Fine Org.
Präparation:	KBr (3/1000)	Dez. Nr.: 1.2.2	Preparation:	KBr (3/1000)	Dec. No.: 1.2.2

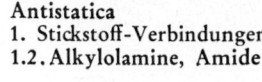

Antistatica
1. Stickstoff-Verbindungen
1.2. Alkylolamine, Amide

Antistatica
1. Nitrogen Compounds
1.2. Alkylolamines, Amides

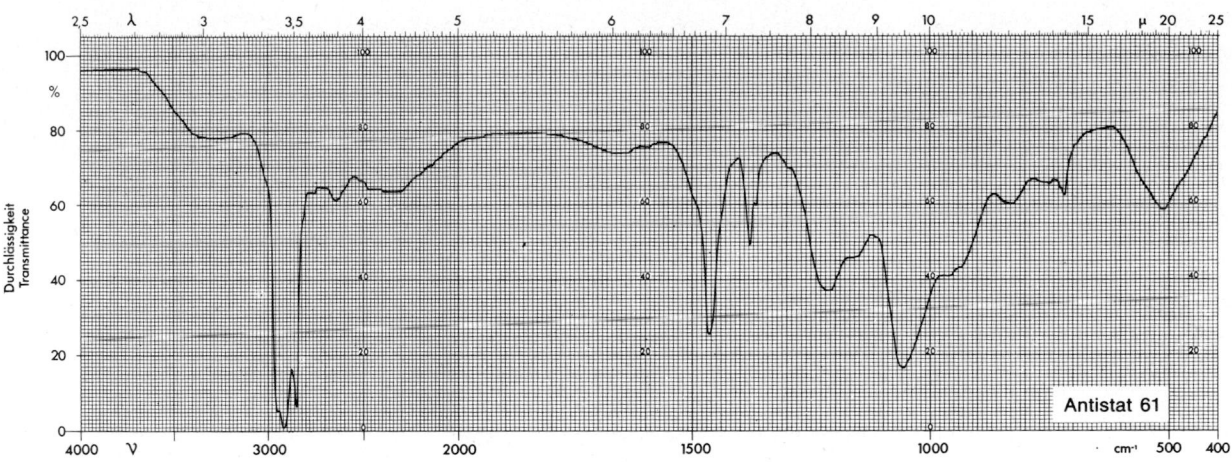

Haupt-bestandteil:	Alkylaminderivat			Main component:	Alkylamino compound			6212
Handelsname:	Antistat 61	Herst.:	Pfizer	Tradename:	Antistat 61	Manuf.:	Pfizer	
Präparation:	Film, flüssig	Dez. Nr.:	1.2.3	Preparation:	Film, liquid	Dec. No.:	1.2.3	

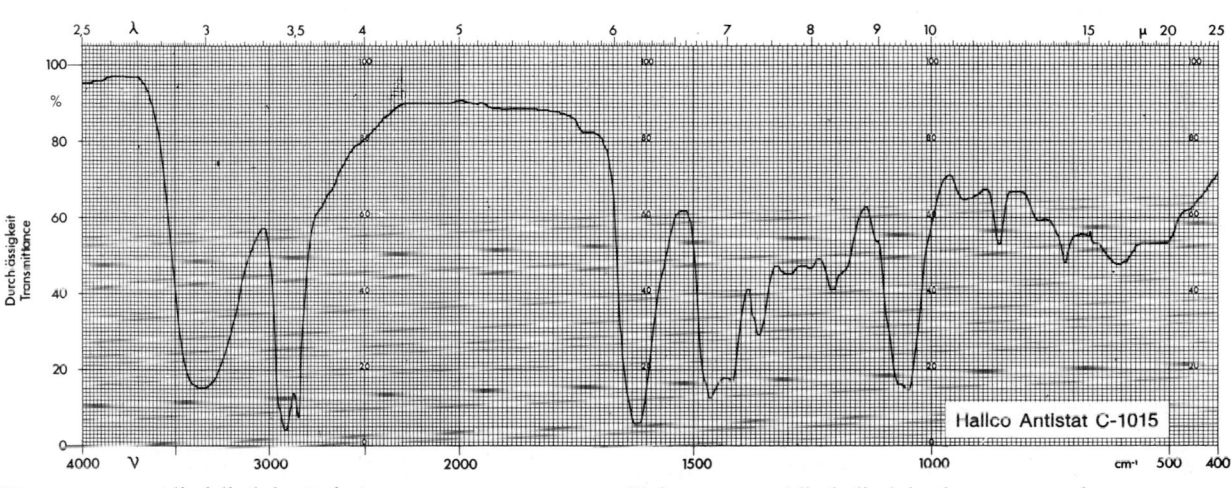

Haupt-bestandteil:	Alkylalkylolaminderivat			Main component:	Alkyl alkylolamino compound			6213
Handelsname:	Hallco Antistat C-1015	Herst.:	Hall	Tradename:	Hallco Antistat C-1015	Manuf.:	Hall	
Präparation:	Film, fest	Dez. Nr.:	1.2.4	Preparation:	Film, solid	Dec. No.:	1.2.4	

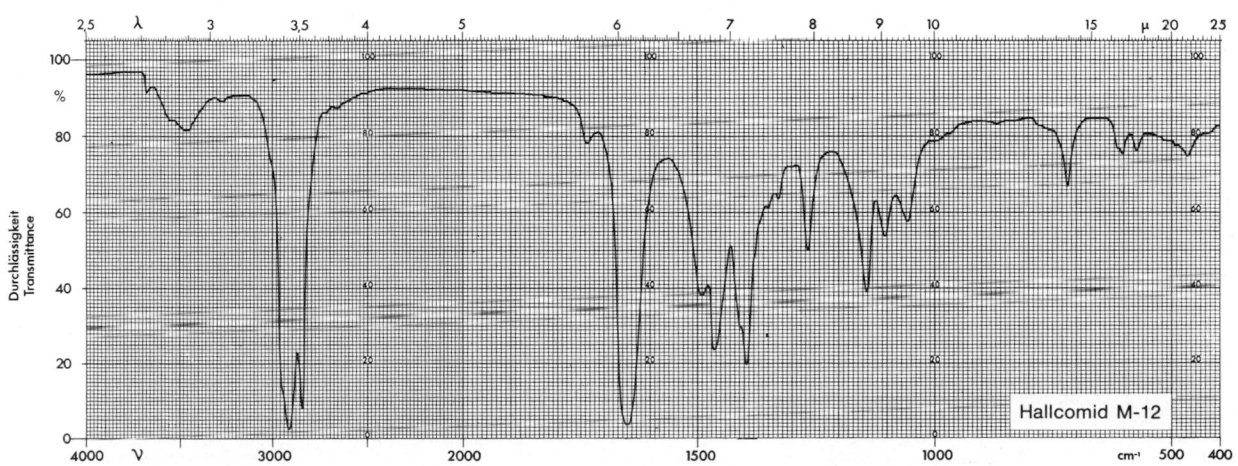

Haupt-bestandteil:	Alkylamid			Main component:	Alkylamide			6214
Handelsname:	Hallcomid M-12	Herst.:	Hall	Tradename:	Hallcomid M-12	Manuf.:	Hall	
Präparation:	Film, flüssig, R	Dez. Nr.:	1.2.5	Preparation:	Film, liquid, R	Dec. No.:	1.2.5	

Antistatica
2. Glykolderivate
2.1. Polyglykolether

Antistatica
2. Glycol Derivatives
2.1. Polyglycol Ethers

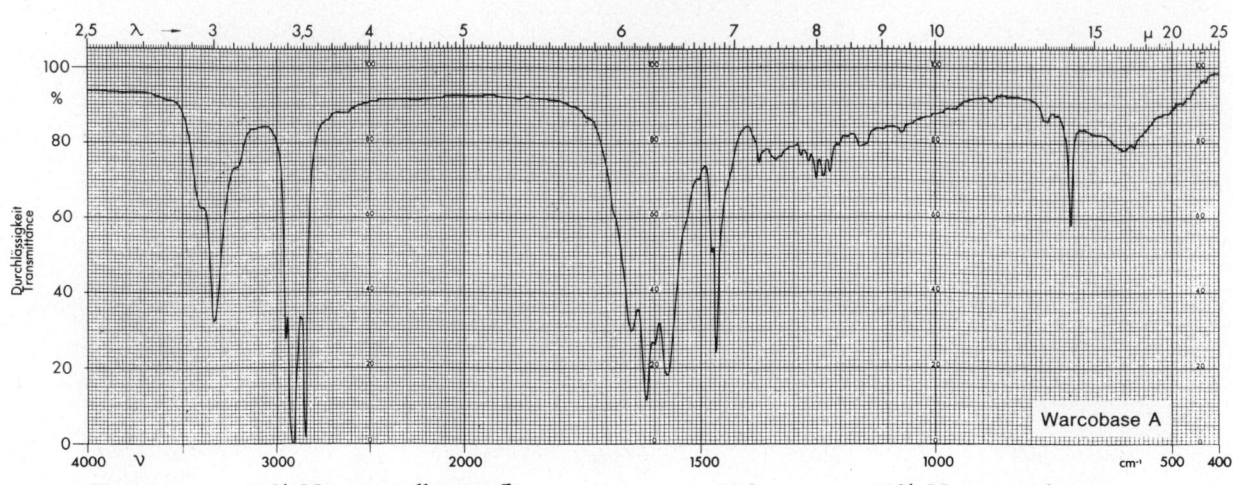

6215

Haupt-bestandteil:	60% Monostearylharnstoff 40% Distearylharnstoff			Main component:	60% Monostearyl urea 40% Distearyl urea		
Handelsname:	Warcobase A	Herst.:	Sun Chem.	Tradename:	Warcobase A	Manuf.:	Sun Chem.
Präparation:	KBr (3/1000)	Dez. Nr.:	1.2.6	Preparation:	KBr (3/1000)	Dec. No.:	1.2.6

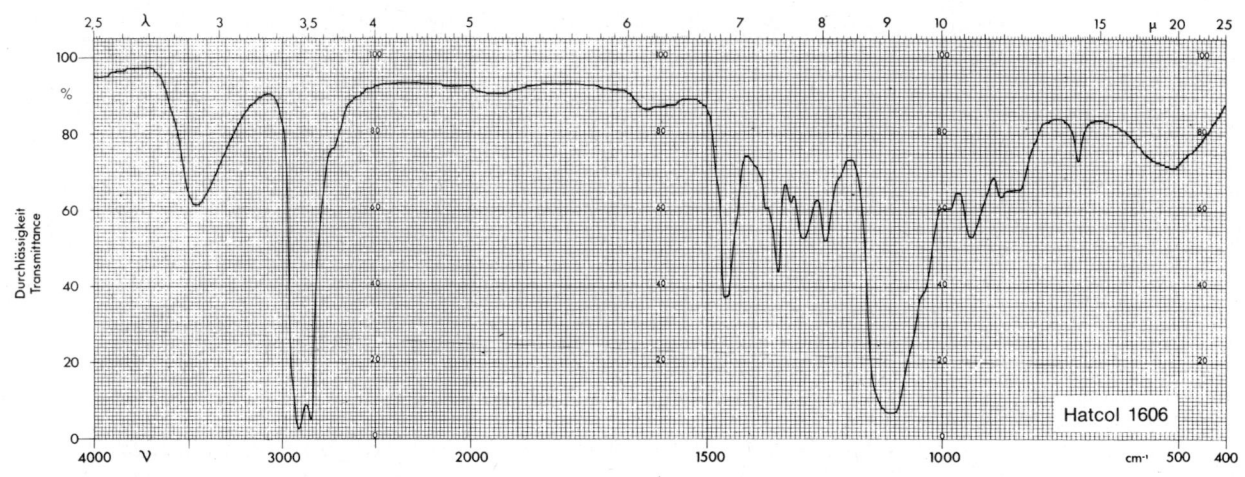

6216

Haupt-bestandteil:	Polyglykolether			Main component:	Polyglycol ether		
Handelsname:	Hatcol 1606	Herst.:	Hatco	Tradename:	Hatcol 1606	Manuf.:	Hatco
Präparation:	Film, flüssig	Dez. Nr.:	2.1.1	Preparation:	Film, liquid	Dec. No.:	2.1.1

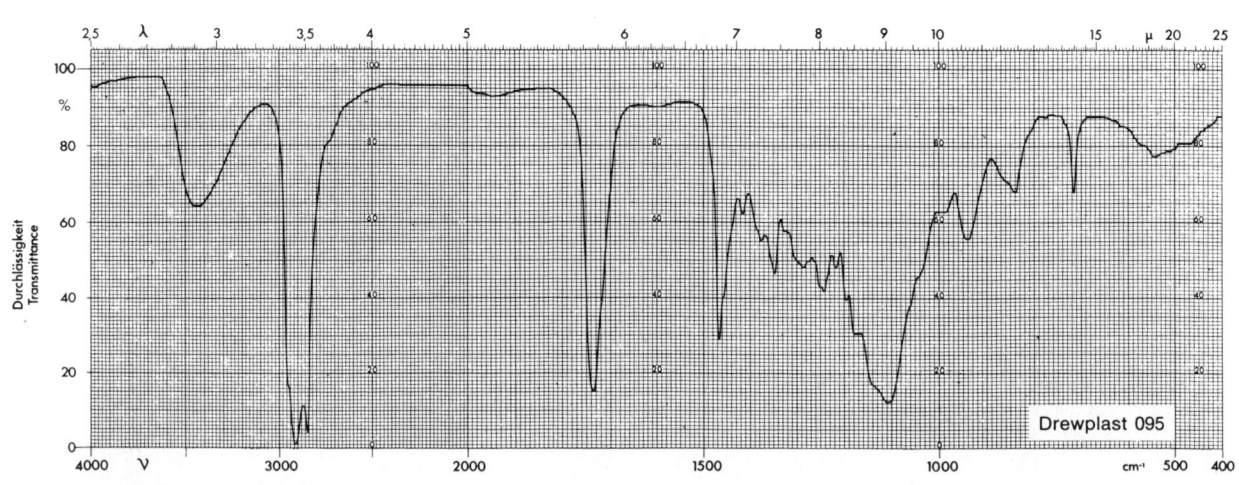

6217

Haupt-bestandteil:	Polyethylenglykol + Ester			Main component:	Polyethylene glycol + ester		
Handelsname:	Drewplast 095	Herst.:	Drew	Tradename:	Drewplast 095	Manuf.:	Drew
Präparation:	Film	Dez. Nr.:	2.2.2	Preparation:	Film	Dec. No.:	2.2.2

Antistatica
2. Glykolderivate
2.3. Polyglykolether und oxethylierte Alkylphenole
mit Zusätzen

Antistatica
2. Glycol Derivatives
2.3. Polyglycol Ethers and Oxethylated Alkylphenoles
with Additives

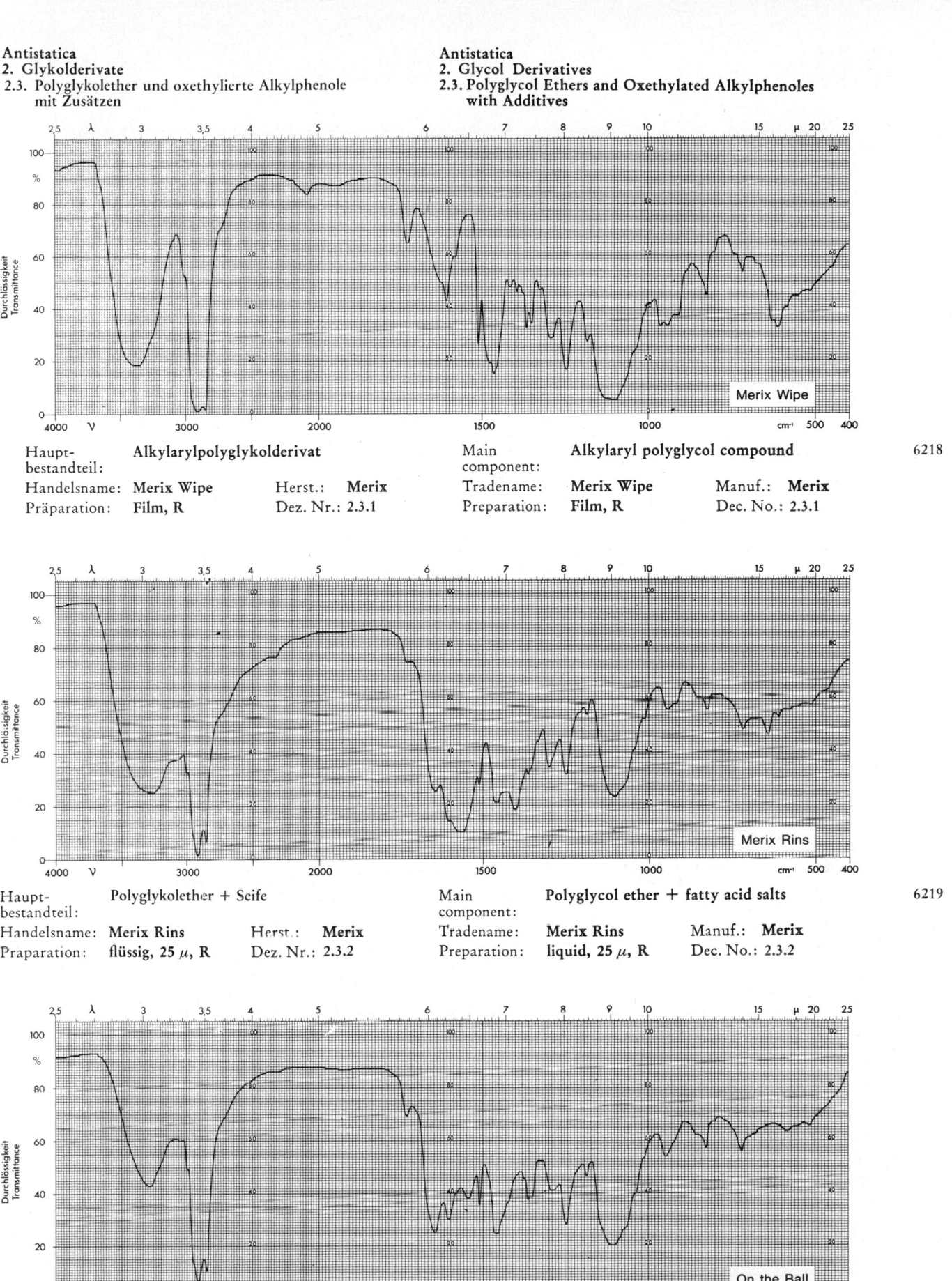

Haupt-bestandteil:	Alkylarylpolyglykolderivat			Main component:	Alkylaryl polyglycol compound			6218
Handelsname:	Merix Wipe	Herst.:	Merix	Tradename:	Merix Wipe	Manuf.:	Merix	
Präparation:	Film, R	Dez. Nr.:	2.3.1	Preparation:	Film, R	Dec. No.:	2.3.1	

Haupt-bestandteil:	Polyglykolether + Seife			Main component:	Polyglycol ether + fatty acid salts			6219
Handelsname:	Merix Rins	Herst.:	Merix	Tradename:	Merix Rins	Manuf.:	Merix	
Präparation:	flüssig, 25 μ, R	Dez. Nr.:	2.3.2	Preparation:	liquid, 25 μ, R	Dec. No.:	2.3.2	

Haupt-bestandteil:	Polyglykolether + Seife			Main component:	Polyglycol ether + fatty acid salts			6220
Handelsname:	On the Ball	Herst.:	Merix	Tradename:	On the Ball	Manuf.:	Merix	
Präparation:	Film, flüssig, R	Dez. Nr.:	2.3.3	Preparation:	Film, liquid, R	Dec. No.:	2.3.3	

Antistatica
3. Fettsäureesterhaltige Gemische

Antistatica
3. Mixtures with Fatty Acid Esters

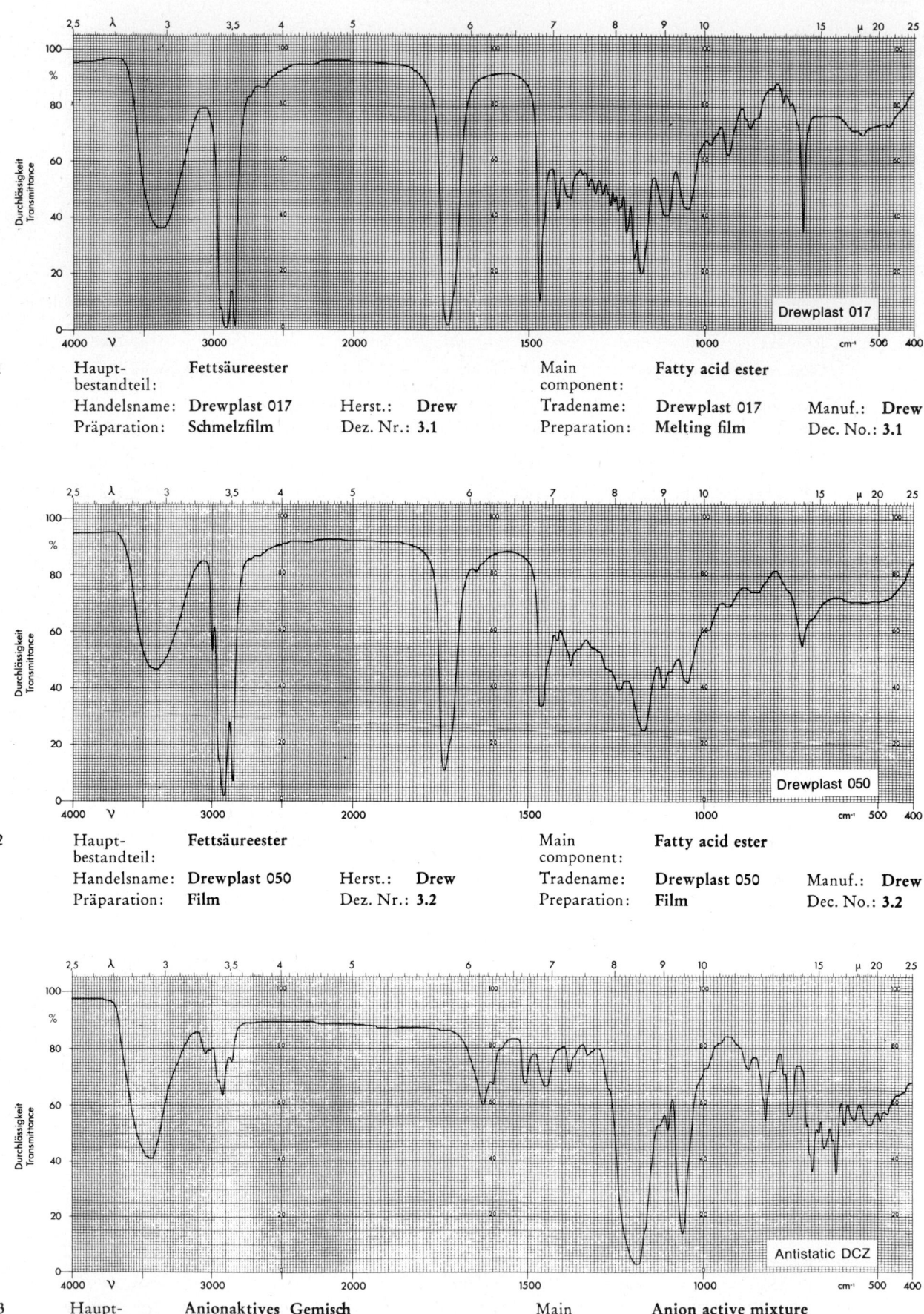

6221	Haupt-bestandteil:	**Fettsäureester**			Main component:	**Fatty acid ester**	
	Handelsname:	**Drewplast 017**	Herst.:	**Drew**	Tradename:	**Drewplast 017**	Manuf.: **Drew**
	Präparation:	**Schmelzfilm**	Dez. Nr.:	**3.1**	Preparation:	**Melting film**	Dec. No.: **3.1**

6222	Haupt-bestandteil:	**Fettsäureester**			Main component:	**Fatty acid ester**	
	Handelsname:	**Drewplast 050**	Herst.:	**Drew**	Tradename:	**Drewplast 050**	Manuf.: **Drew**
	Präparation:	**Film**	Dez. Nr.:	**3.2**	Preparation:	**Film**	Dec. No.: **3.2**

6223	Haupt-bestandteil:	**Anionaktives Gemisch**			Main component:	**Anion active mixture**	
	Handelsname:	**Antistatic DCZ**	Herst.:	**Axel**	Tradename:	**Antistatic DCZ**	Manuf.: **Axel**
	Präparation:	**KBr (3/1000)**	Dez. Nr.:	**4.1**	Preparation:	**KBr (3/1000)**	Dec. No.: **4.1**

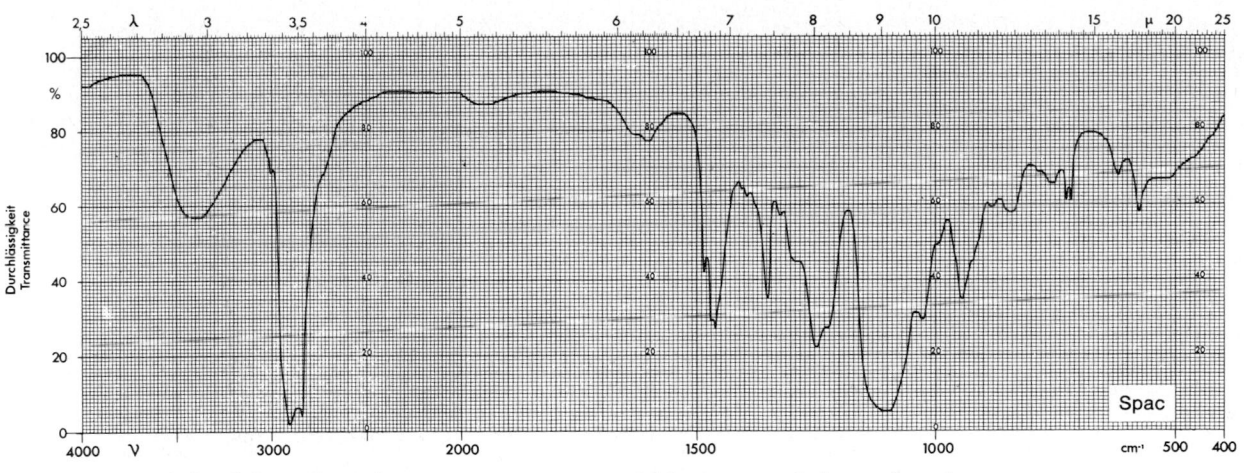

Haupt-bestandteil:	Anionaktives Gemisch		Main component:	Anion active mixture		6224
Handelsname:	Spac	Herst.: Kleen	Tradename:	Spac	Manuf.: Kleen	
Präparation:	Film, R	Dez. Nr.: 4.2	Preparation:	Film, R	Dec. No.: 4.2	

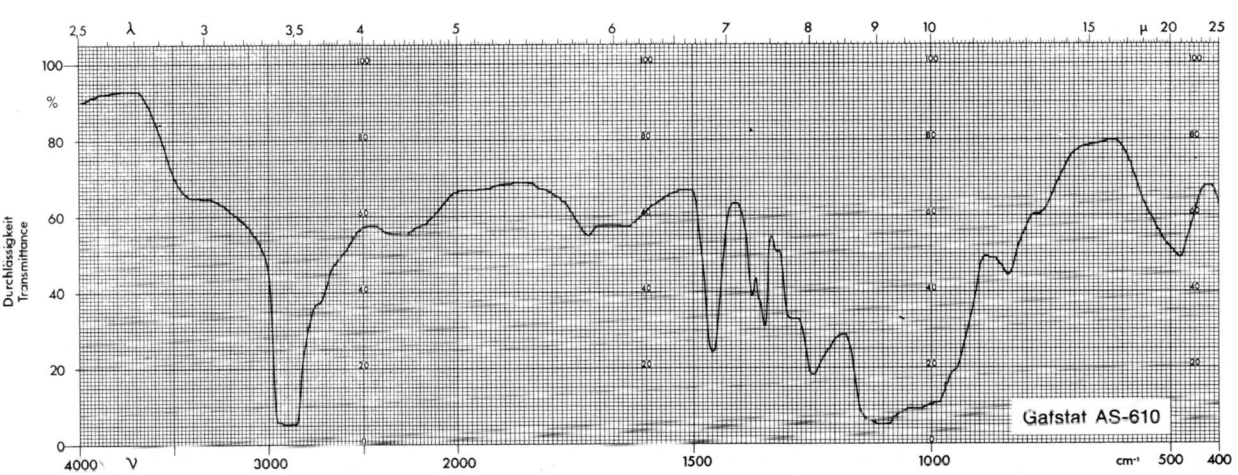

Haupt-bestandteil:	Anionaktives Gemisch		Main component:	Anion active mixture		6225
Handelsname:	Gafstat AS-610	Herst.: GAF	Tradename:	Gafstat AS-610	Manuf.: GAF	
Präparation:	Film, flüssig	Dez. Nr.: 4.3	Preparation:	Film, liquid	Dec. No.: 4.3	

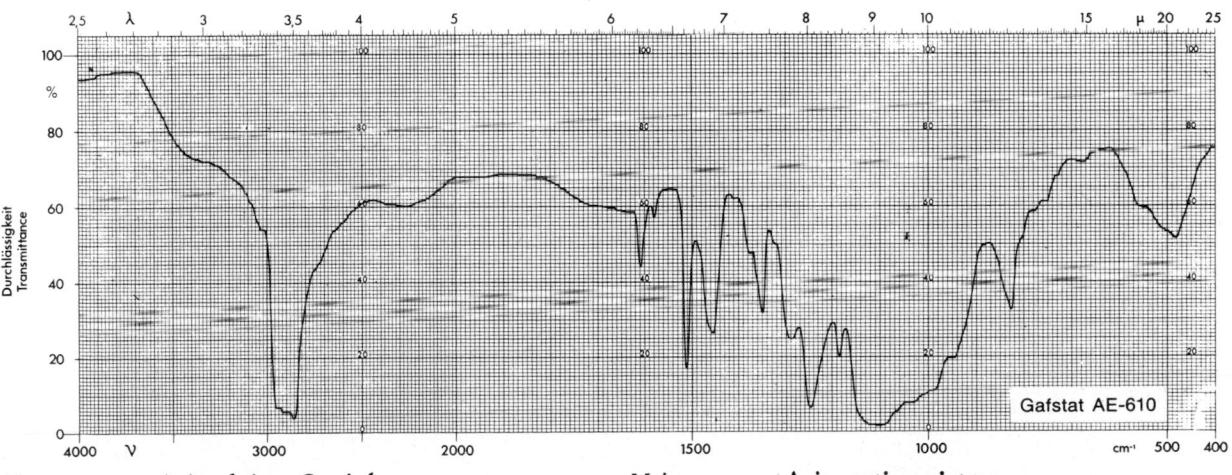

Haupt-bestandteil:	Anionaktives Gemisch		Main component:	Anion active mixture		6226
Handelsname:	Gafstat AE-610	Herst.: GAF	Tradename:	Gafstat AE-610	Manuf.: GAF	
Präparation:	Film, flüssig	Dez. Nr.: 4.4	Preparation:	Film, liquid	Dec. No.: 4.4	

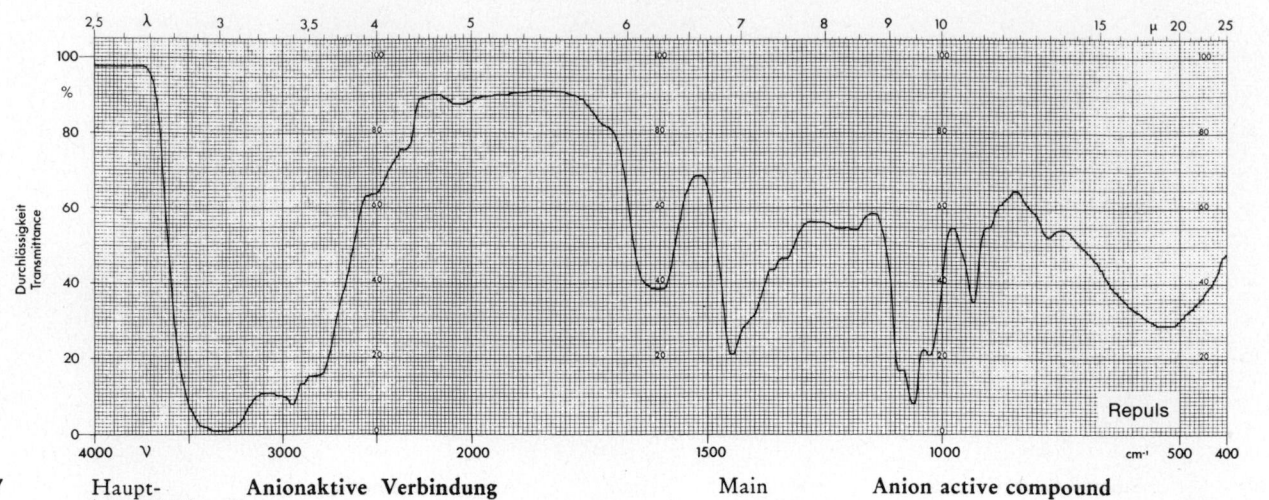

6227

Haupt- bestandteil:	**Anionaktive Verbindung**			Main component:	**Anion active compound**	
Handelsname:	**Repuls**	Herst.:	**Gen. Mills**	Tradename:	**Repuls**	Manuf.: **Gen. Mills**
Präparation:	**Film, R**	Dez. Nr.:	**4.5**	Preparation:	**Film, R**	Dec. No.: **4.5**

Biostabilisatoren

Biocides

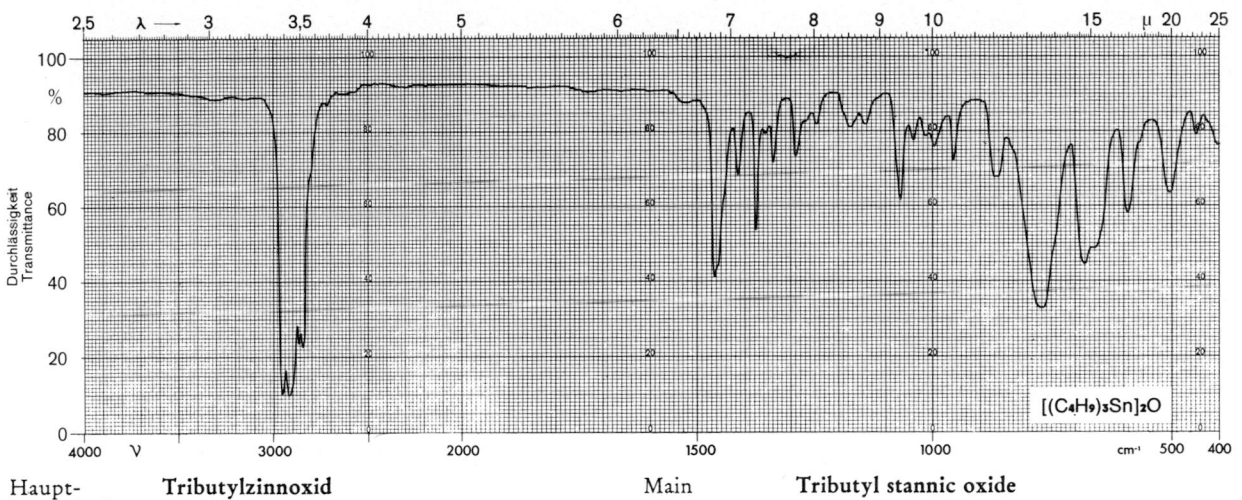

Haupt-bestandteil:	**Tributylzinnoxid**		Main component:	**Tributyl stannic oxide**		6250
Handelsname:	**Irgarol BI 540**	Herst.: **DAP**	Tradename:	**Irgarol BI 540**	Manuf.: **DAP**	
Präparation:	**Kapill. Film**	Dez. Nr.: **1**	Preparation:	**Capill. film**	Dec. No.: **1**	

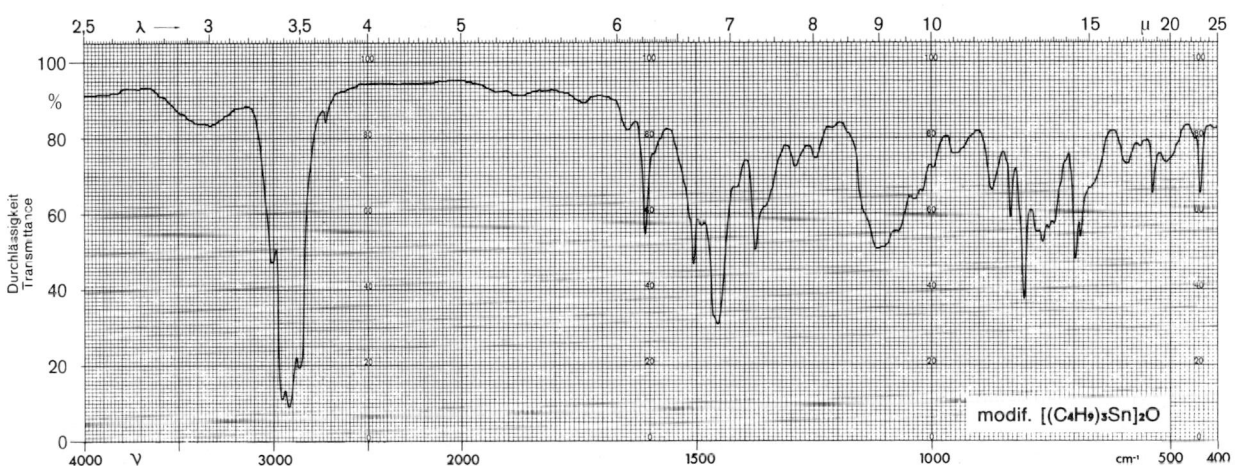

Haupt-bestandteil:	**Modifiz. Tri-n-butylzinnoxid**		Main component:	**Modif. tri-n-butyl stannic oxide**		6251
Handelsname:	**Irgarol BI 543**	Herst.: **DAP**	Tradename:	**Irgarol BI 543**	Manuf.: **DAP**	
Präparation:	**Kapill. Film**	Dez. Nr.: **2**	Preparation:	**Capill. film**	Dec. No.: **2**	

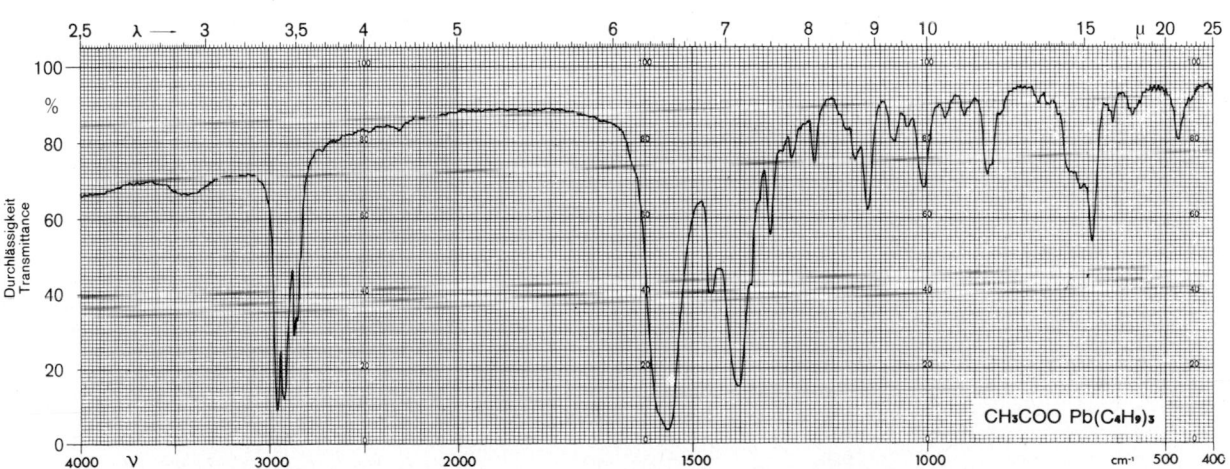

Haupt-bestandteil:	**Tributylbleiacetat**		Main component:	**Tributyl lead acetate**		6252
Handelsname:	**Tributylbleiacetat**	Herst.: **DAP**	Tradename:	**Tributylbleiacetat**	Manuf.: **DAP**	
Präparation:	**KBr (3/1000)**	Dez. Nr.: **3**	Preparation:	**KBr (3/1000)**	Dec. No.: **3**	

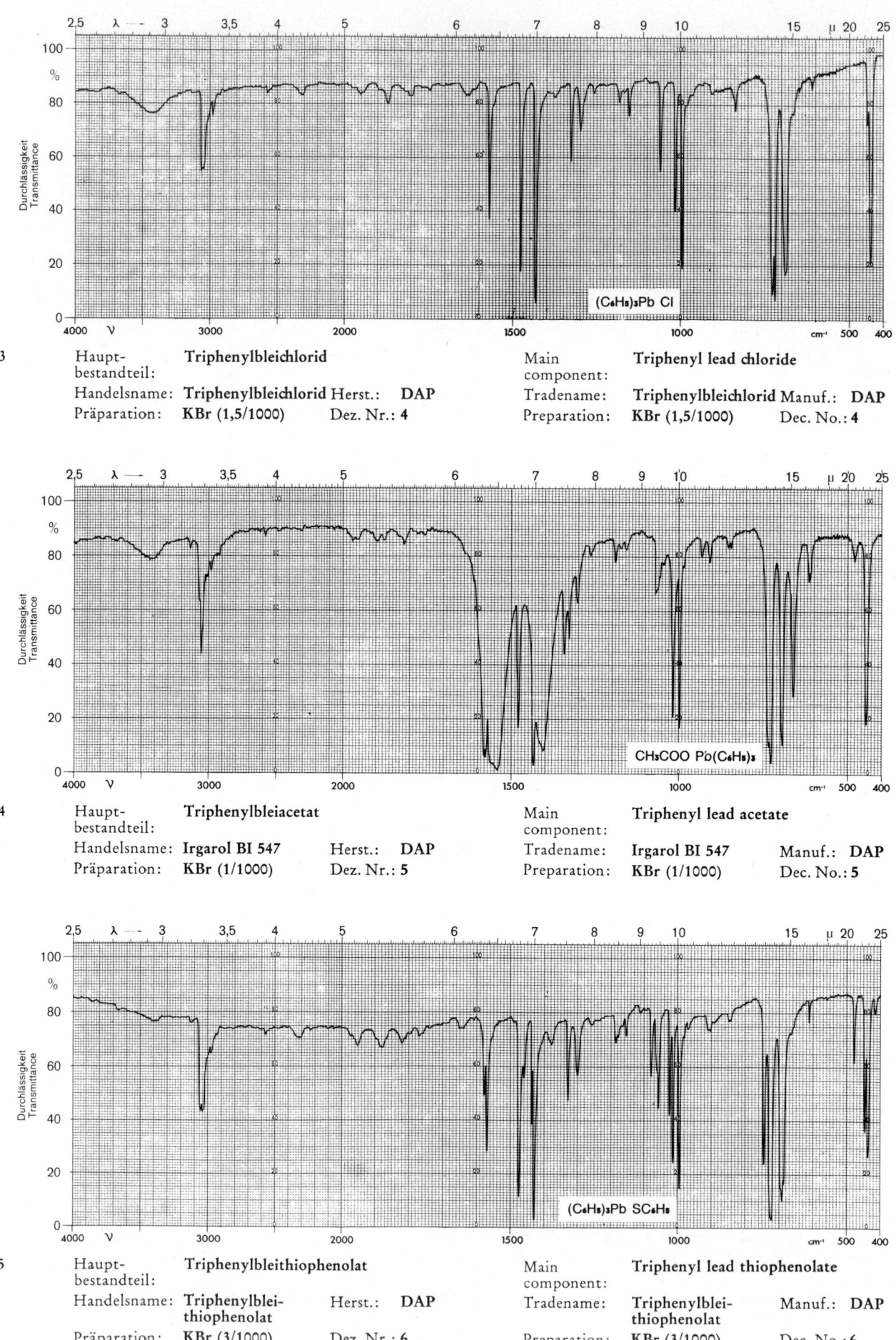

6253 Haupt-   **Triphenylbleichlorid**   Main   **Triphenyl lead chloride**
      bestandteil: component:

      Handelsname: **Triphenylbleichlorid** Herst.: **DAP**   Tradename: **Triphenylbleichlorid** Manuf.: **DAP**
      Präparation: **KBr (1,5/1000)**   Dez. Nr.: **4**   Preparation: **KBr (1,5/1000)**   Dec. No.: **4**

6254 Haupt-   **Triphenylbleiacetat**   Main   **Triphenyl lead acetate**
      bestandteil: component:

      Handelsname: **Irgarol BI 547**   Herst.: **DAP**   Tradename: **Irgarol BI 547**   Manuf.: **DAP**
      Präparation: **KBr (1/1000)**   Dez. Nr.: **5**   Preparation: **KBr (1/1000)**   Dec. No.: **5**

6255 Haupt-   **Triphenylbleithiophenolat**   Main   **Triphenyl lead thiophenolate**
      bestandteil: component:

      Handelsname: **Triphenylblei-**   Herst.: **DAP**   Tradename: **Triphenylblei-**   Manuf.: **DAP**
                   thiophenolat   **thiophenolat**
      Präparation: **KBr (3/1000)**   Dez. Nr.: **6**   Preparation: **KBr (3/1000)**   Dec. No.: **6**

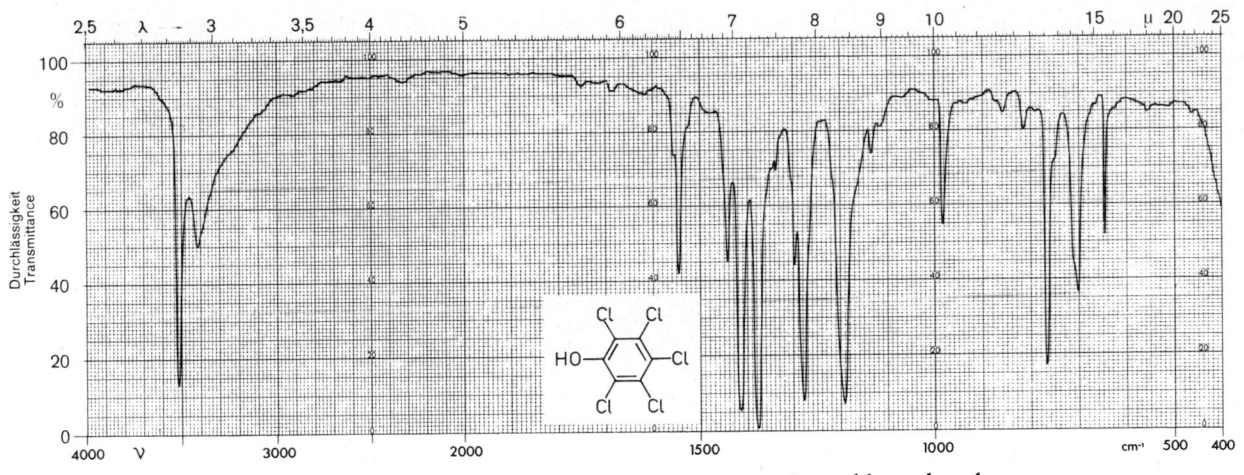

Haupt-bestandteil:	**Pentachlorphenol**		Main component:	**Pentachloro phenol**		6256
Handelsname:	**Pentachlorphenol**	Herst.: **Raschig**	Tradename:	**Pentachlorphenol**	Manuf.: **Raschig**	
Präparation:	**KBr (3/1000)**	Dez. Nr.: **7**	Preparation:	**KBr (3/1000)**	Dec. No.: **7**	

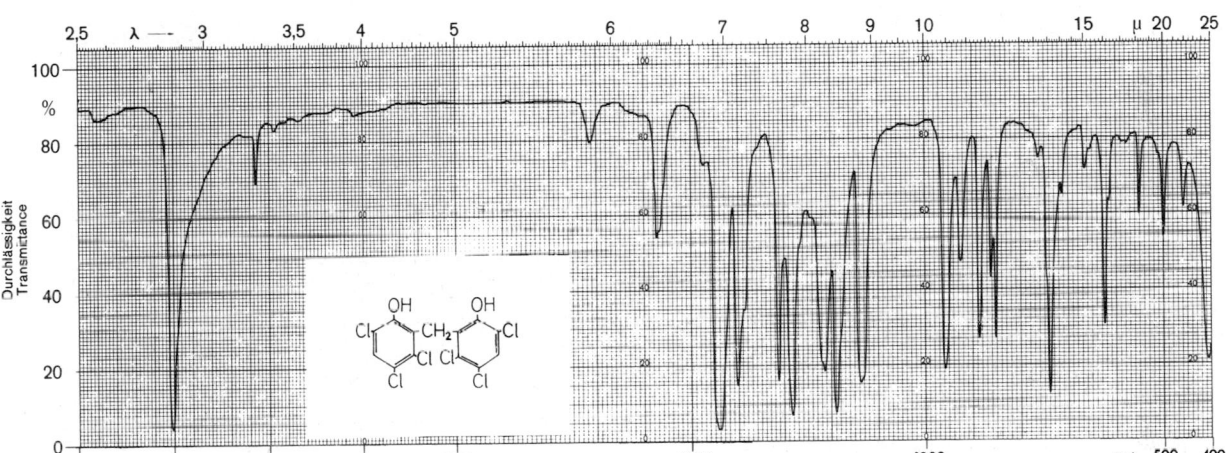

Haupt-bestandteil:	**2,2'-Methylen bis (3,4,6-tri-** chlorophenol)		Main component:	**2,2'-Methylene bis (3,4,6-tri-** chlorophenol)		6257
Handelsname:	**Hexachlorophen**	Herst.: **Schuchardt**	Tradename:	**Hexachlorophene**	Manuf.: **Schuchardt**	
Präparation:	**KBr (3/1000)**	Dez. Nr.: **8**	Preparation:	**KBr (3/1000)**	Dec. No.: **8**	

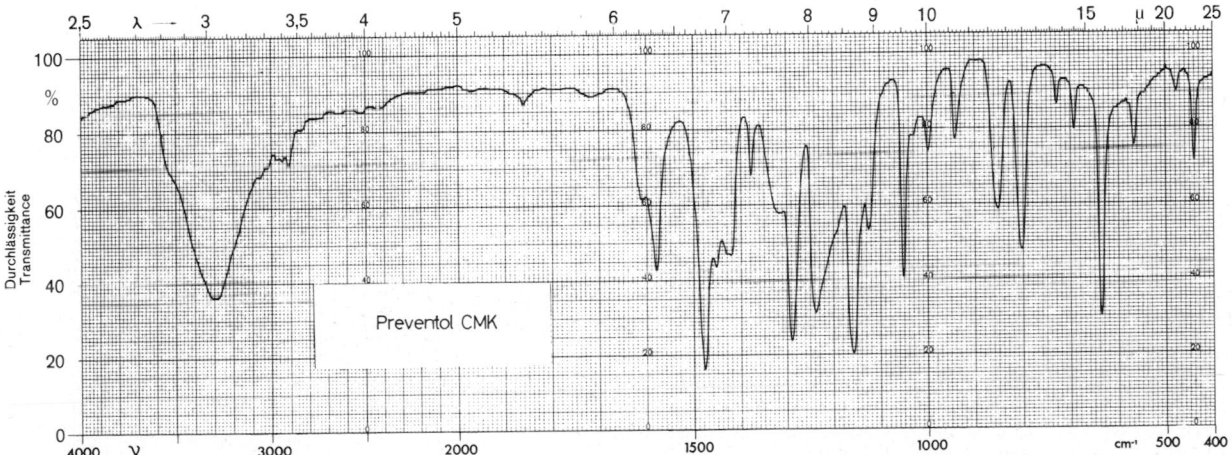

Haupt-bestandteil:	**2-Methyl-4-chlorphenol**		Main component:	**2-Methyl-4-chlorphenol**		6258
Handelsname:	Preventol CMK	Herst.: **Bayer**	Tradename:	Preventol CMK	Manuf.: **Bayer**	
Präparation:	**KBr (3/1000)**	Dez. Nr.: **9**	Preparation:	**KBr (3/1000)**	Dec. No.: **9**	

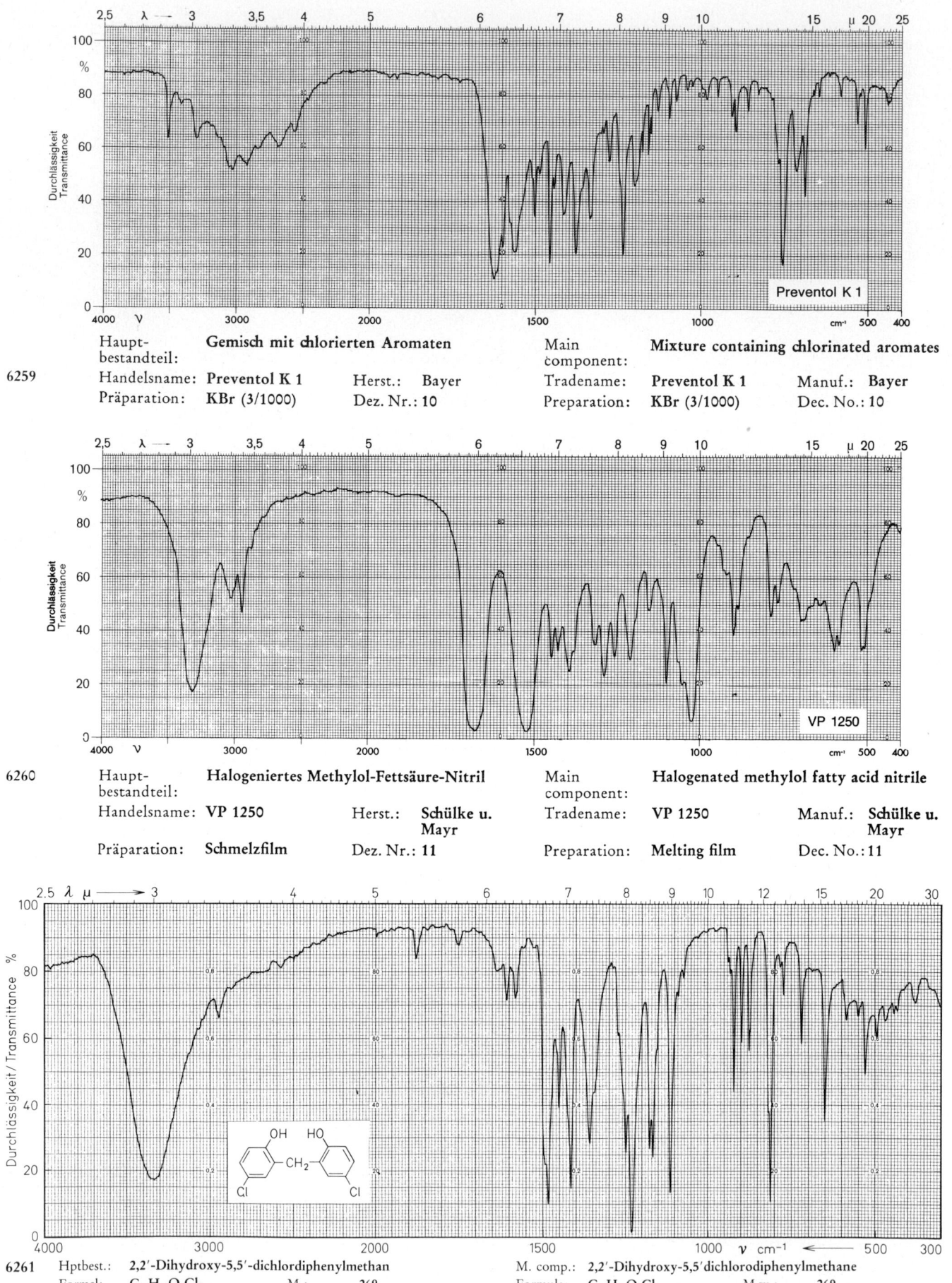

6259

Haupt-bestandteil:	**Gemisch mit chlorierten Aromaten**		Main component:	**Mixture containing chlorinated aromates**	
Handelsname:	**Preventol K 1**	Herst.: **Bayer**	Tradename:	**Preventol K 1**	Manuf.: **Bayer**
Präparation:	**KBr (3/1000)**	Dez. Nr.: **10**	Preparation:	**KBr (3/1000)**	Dec. No.: **10**

Preventol K 1

6260

Haupt-bestandteil:	**Halogeniertes Methylol-Fettsäure-Nitril**		Main component:	**Halogenated methylol fatty acid nitrile**	
Handelsname:	**VP 1250**	Herst.: **Schülke u. Mayr**	Tradename:	**VP 1250**	Manuf.: **Schülke u. Mayr**
Präparation:	**Schmelzfilm**	Dez. Nr.: **11**	Preparation:	**Melting film**	Dec. No.: **11**

VP 1250

6261

Hptbest.:	**2,2′-Dihydroxy-5,5′-dichlordiphenylmethan**		M. comp.:	**2,2′-Dihydroxy-5,5′dichlorodiphenylmethane**	
Formel:	$C_{13}H_{10}O_2Cl_2$	M.: **269**	Formula:	$C_{13}H_{10}O_2Cl_2$	M.w.: **269**
Name:	**Preventol GD**	Manuf.: **Bayer**	Prpt.: **KBr**	Dec. No.: **12**

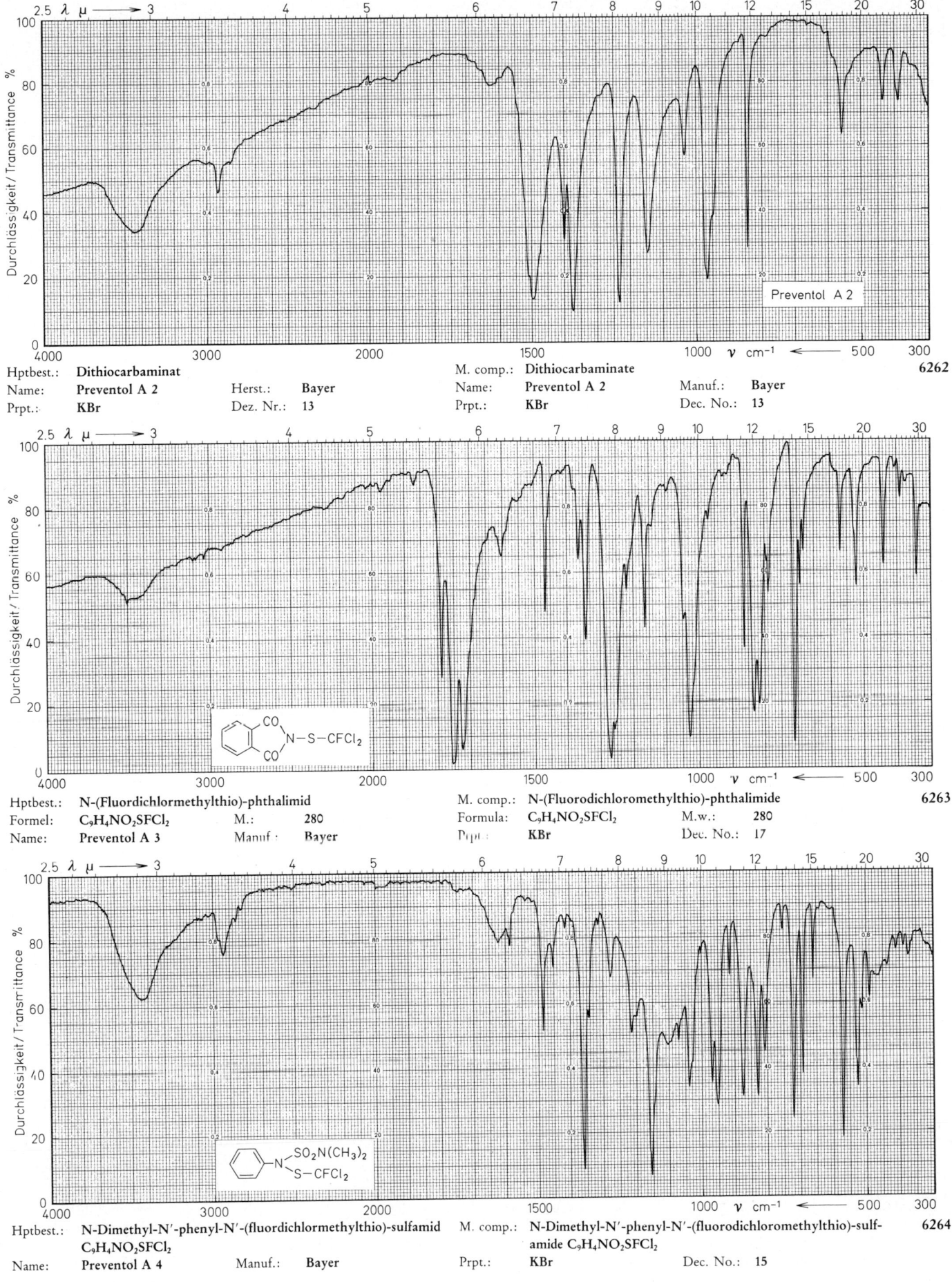

Hptbest.:   **Dithiocarbaminat**   M. comp.:   **Dithiocarbaminate**   6262
Name: **Preventol A 2**   Herst.:   **Bayer**   Name: **Preventol A 2**   Manuf.:   **Bayer**
Prpt.:   **KBr**   Dez. Nr.:   **13**   Prpt.: **KBr**   Dec. No.:   **13**

Hptbest.:   **N-(Fluordichlormethylthio)-phthalimid**   M. comp.:   **N-(Fluorodichloromethylthio)-phthalimide**   6263
Formel: **C₉H₄NO₂SFCl₂**   M.:   **280**   Formula: **C₉H₄NO₂SFCl₂**   M.w.:   **280**
Name: **Preventol A 3**   Manuf ·   **Bayer**   Prpt.   **KBr**   Dec. No.:   **17**

Hptbest.:   **N-Dimethyl-N′-phenyl-N′-(fluordichlormethylthio)-sulfamid**   M. comp.:   **N-Dimethyl-N′-phenyl-N′-(fluorodichloromethylthio)-sulf-**   6264
            C₉H₄NO₂SFCl₂   **amide C₉H₄NO₂SFCl₂**
Name: **Preventol A 4**   Manuf.:   **Bayer**   Prpt.:   **KBr**   Dec. No.:   **15**

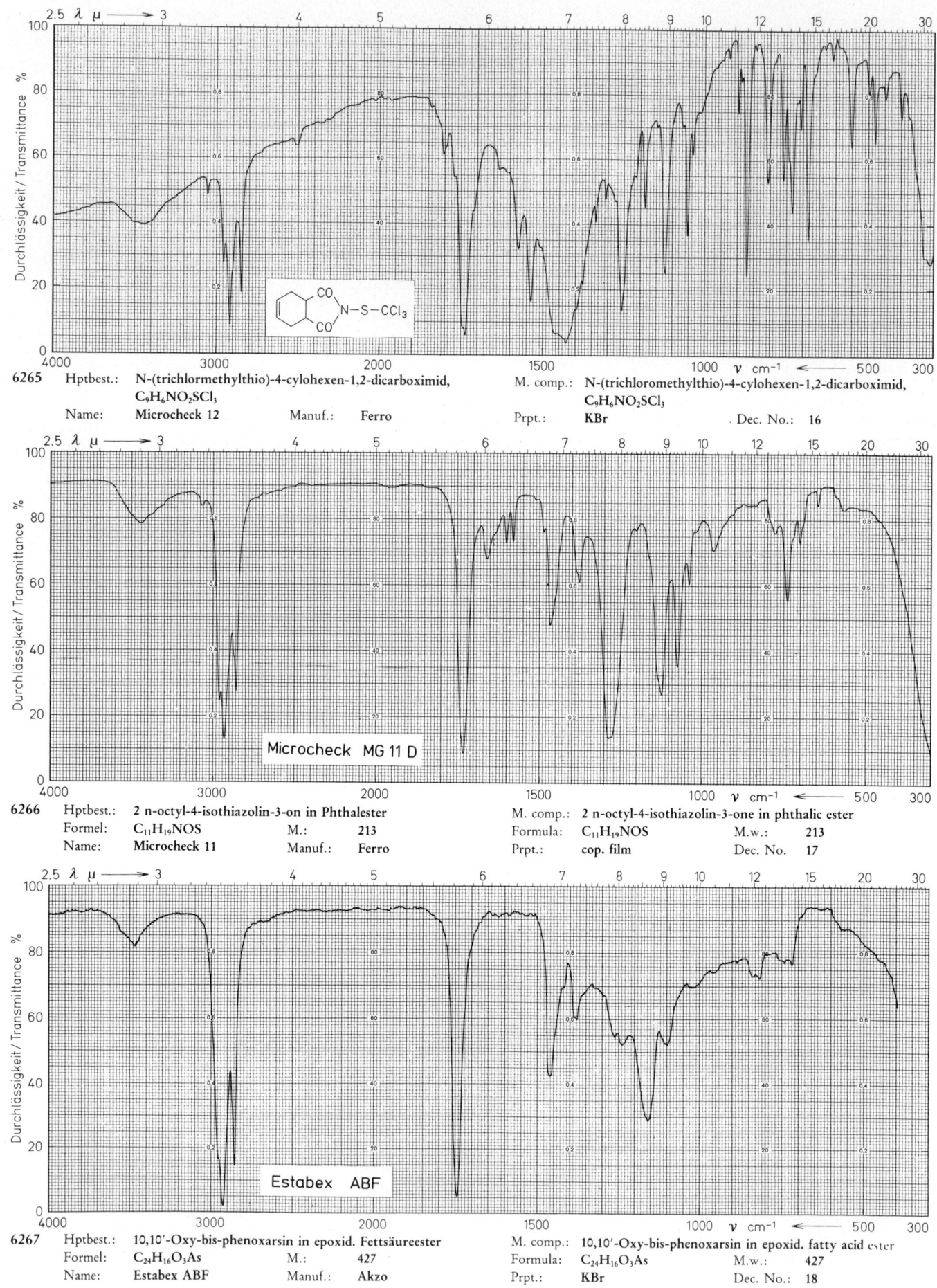

6265 Hptbest.: **N-(trichlormethylthio)-4-cylohexen-1,2-dicarboximid,**
                          C₉H₆NO₂SCl₃

$C_9H_6NO_2SCl_3$

M. comp.: **N-(trichloromethylthio)-4-cylohexen-1,2-dicarboximid,**
                C₉H₆NO₂SCl₃

Name: **Microcheck 12**   Manuf.: **Ferro**   Prpt.: **KBr**   Dec. No.: **16**

6266 Hptbest.: **2 n-octyl-4-isothiazolin-3-on in Phthalester**   M. comp.: **2 n-octyl-4-isothiazolin-3-one in phthalic ester**

Formel: **C₁₁H₁₉NOS**   M.: **213**   Formula: **C₁₁H₁₉NOS**   M.w.: **213**

$C_{11}H_{19}NOS$

Name: **Microcheck 11**   Manuf.: **Ferro**   Prpt.: **cop. film**   Dec. No. **17**

6267 Hptbest.: **10,10′-Oxy-bis-phenoxarsin in epoxid. Fettsäureester**   M. comp.: **10,10′-Oxy-bis-phenoxarsin in epoxid. fatty acid ester**

Formel: **C₂₄H₁₆O₃As**   M.: **427**   Formula: **C₂₄H₁₆O₃As**   M.w.: **427**

$C_{24}H_{16}O_3As$

Name: **Estabex ABF**   Manuf.: **Akzo**   Prpt.: **KBr**   Dec. No.: **18**

Flammschutzmittel

Flame Retardants

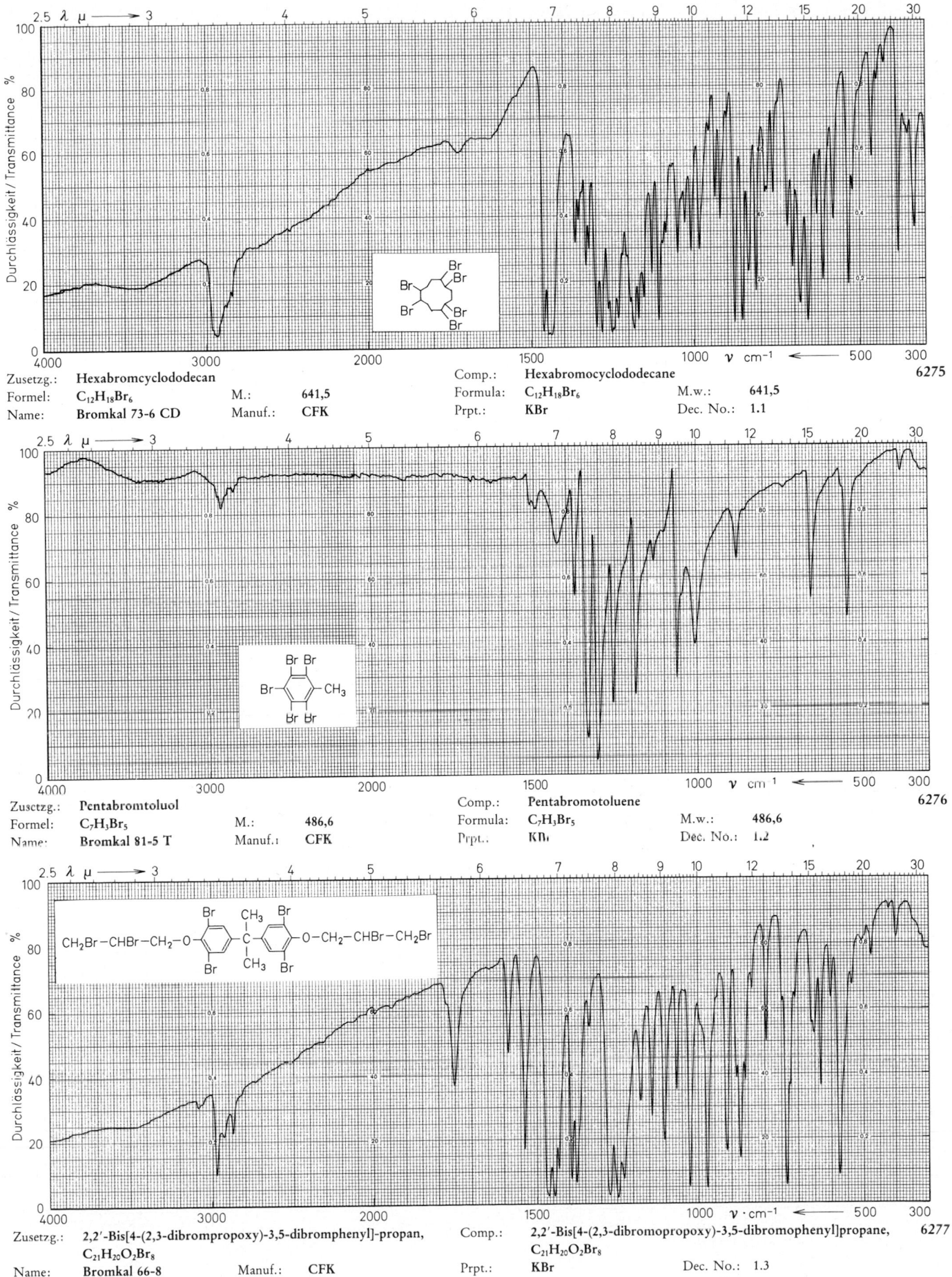

6275

Zusetzg.: Hexabromcyclododecan   Comp.:   Hexabromocyclododecane
Formel: C$_{12}$H$_{18}$Br$_6$ M.:   641,5   Formula: C$_{12}$H$_{18}$Br$_6$ M.w.:   641,5
Name: Bromkal 73-6 CD   Manuf.: CFK   Prpt.:   KBr   Dec. No.: 1.1

6276

Zusetzg.: Pentabromtoluol   Comp.:   Pentabromotoluene
Formel: C$_7$H$_3$Br$_5$ M.:   486,6   Formula: C$_7$H$_3$Br$_5$ M.w.:   486,6
Name: Bromkal 81-5 T   Manuf.: CFK   Prpt.:   KBr   Dec. No.: 1.2

6277

Zusetzg.: 2,2′-Bis[4-(2,3-dibrompropoxy)-3,5-dibromphenyl]-propan,   Comp.:   2,2′-Bis[4-(2,3-dibromopropoxy)-3,5-dibromophenyl]propane,
           C$_{21}$H$_{20}$O$_2$Br$_8$ C$_{21}$H$_{20}$O$_2$Br$_8$
Name: Bromkal 66-8   Manuf.: CFK   Prpt.:   KBr   Dec. No.: 1.3

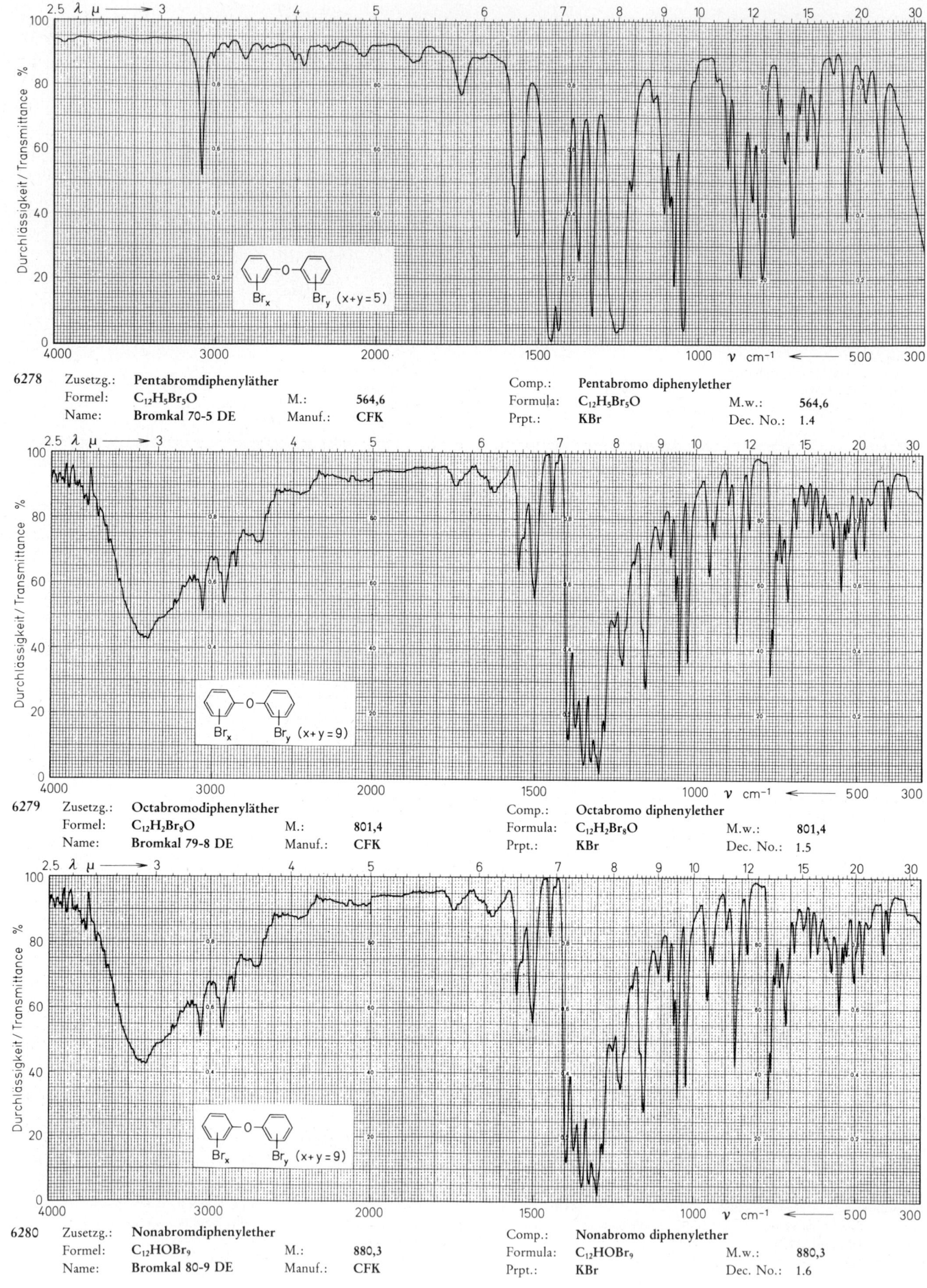

6278 Zusetzg.: **Pentabromdiphenyläther**   Comp.: **Pentabromo diphenylether**
Formel: $C_{12}H_5Br_5O$ M.: **564,6**   Formula: $C_{12}H_5Br_5O$ M.w.: **564,6**
Name: **Bromkal 70-5 DE**   Manuf.: **CFK**   Prpt.: **KBr**   Dec. No.: 1.4

6279 Zusetzg.: **Octabromodiphenyläther**   Comp.: **Octabromo diphenylether**
Formel: $C_{12}H_2Br_8O$ M.: **801,4**   Formula: $C_{12}H_2Br_8O$ M.w.: **801,4**
Name: **Bromkal 79-8 DE**   Manuf.: **CFK**   Prpt.: **KBr**   Dec. No.: 1.5

6280 Zusetzg.: **Nonabromdiphenylether**   Comp.: **Nonabromo diphenylether**
Formel: $C_{12}HOBr_9$ M.: **880,3**   Formula: $C_{12}HOBr_9$ M.w.: **880,3**
Name: **Bromkal 80-9 DE**   Manuf.: **CFK**   Prpt.: **KBr**   Dec. No.: 1.6

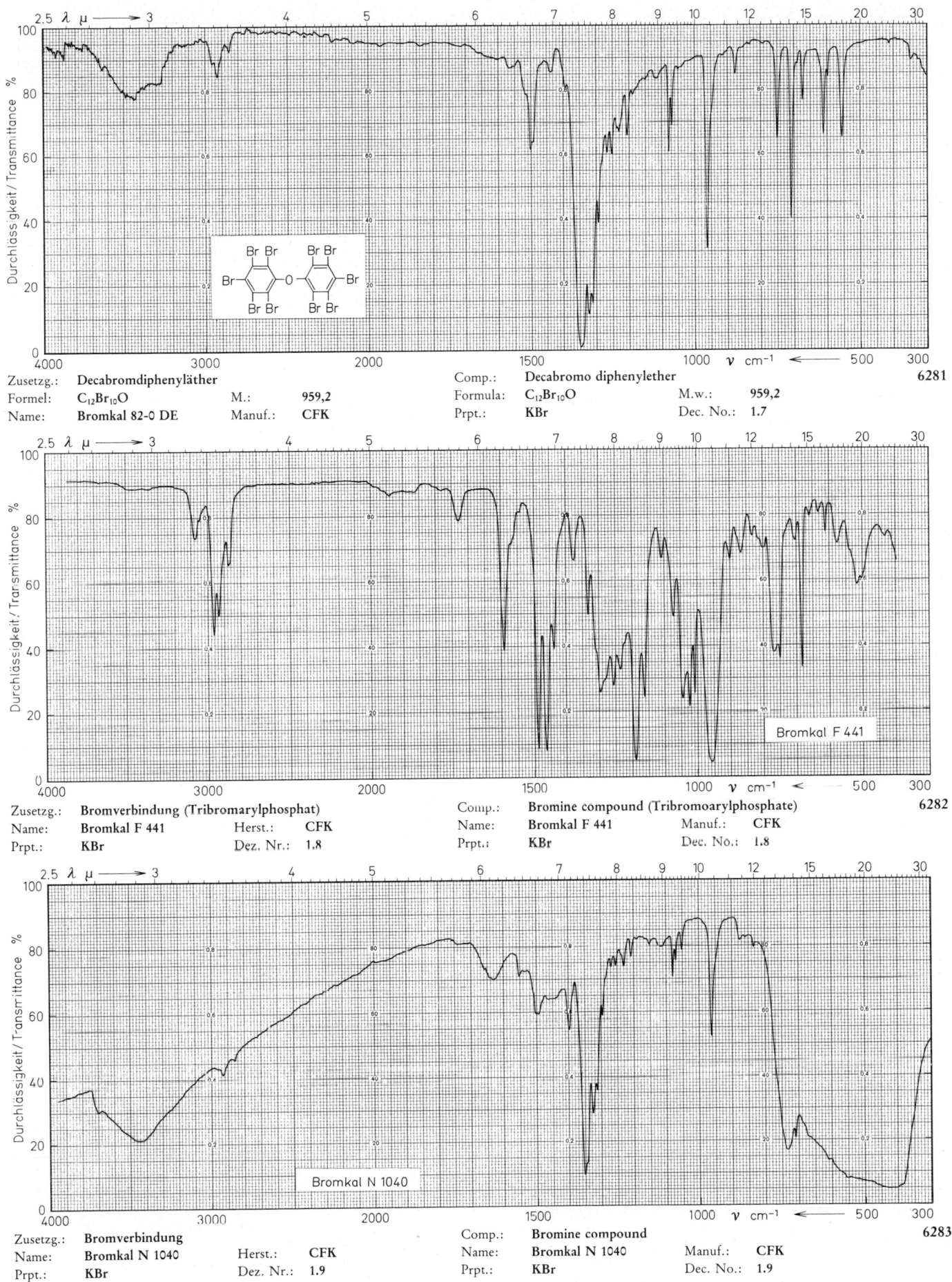

Zusetzg.:	Decabromdiphenyläther			Comp.:	Decabromo diphenylether		
Formel:	$C_{12}Br_{10}O$	M.:	959,2	Formula:	$C_{12}Br_{10}O$	M.w.:	959,2
Name:	Bromkal 82-0 DE	Manuf.:	CFK	Prpt.:	KBr	Dec. No.:	1.7

6281

Bromkal F 441

Zusetzg.:	Bromverbindung (Tribromarylphosphat)			Comp.:	Bromine compound (Tribromoarylphosphate)		
Name:	Bromkal F 441	Herst.:	CFK	Name:	Bromkal F 441	Manuf.:	CFK
Prpt.:	KBr	Dez. Nr.:	1.8	Prpt.:	KBr	Dec. No.:	1.8

6282

Bromkal N 1040

Zusetzg.:	Bromverbindung			Comp.:	Bromine compound		
Name:	Bromkal N 1040	Herst.:	CFK	Name:	Bromkal N 1040	Manuf.:	CFK
Prpt.:	KBr	Dez. Nr.:	1.9	Prpt.:	KBr	Dec. No.:	1.9

6283

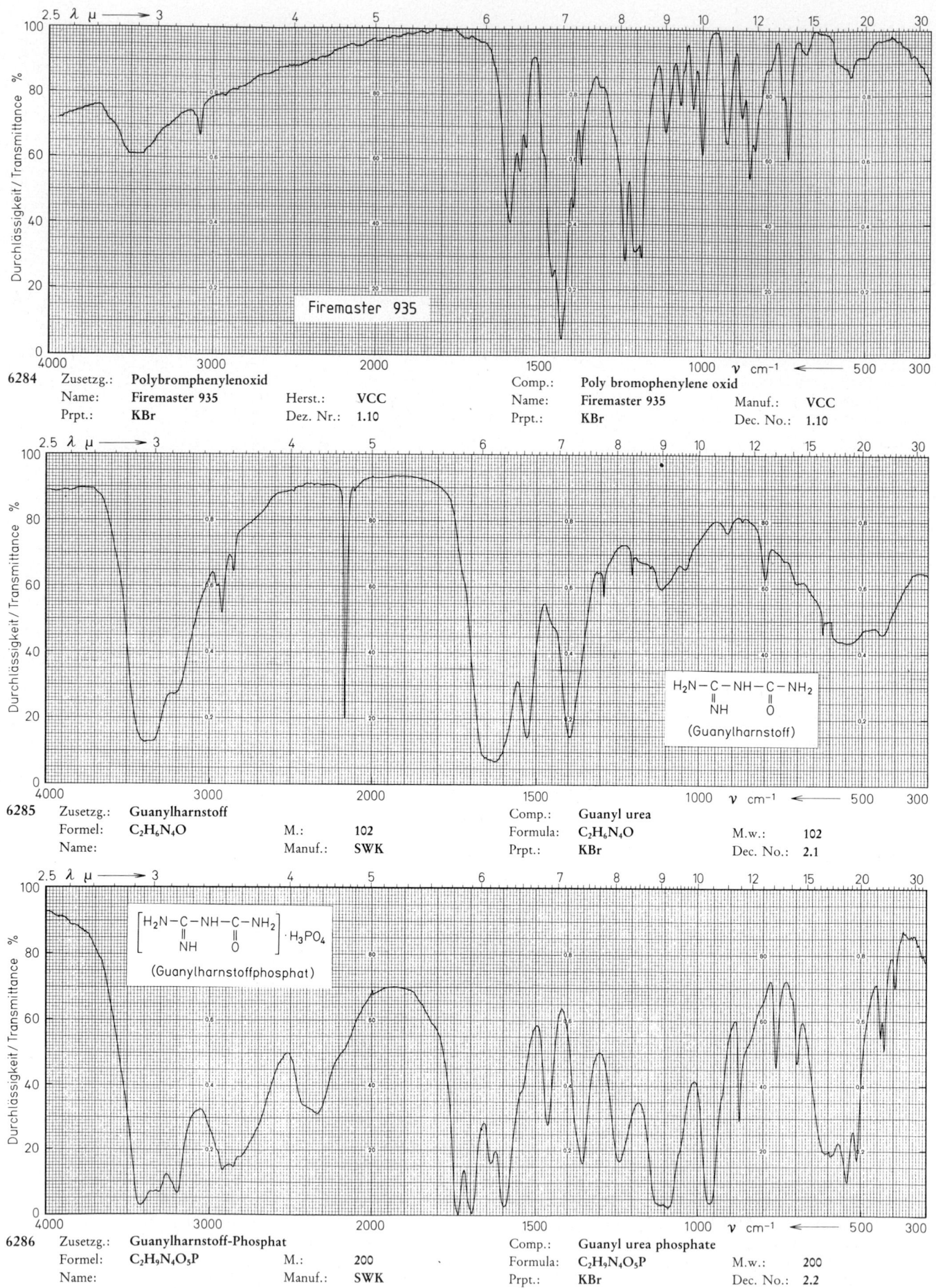

6284   Zusetzg.:   **Polybromphenylenoxid**   Comp.:   **Poly bromophenylene oxid**
        Name: **Firemaster 935**   Herst.:   **VCC**   Name: **Firemaster 935**   Manuf.:   **VCC**
        Prpt.:   **KBr**   Dez. Nr.: **1.10** Prpt.:   **KBr**   Dec. No.: **1.10**

6285   Zusetzg.:   **Guanylharnstoff**   Comp.:   **Guanyl urea**
        Formel: **C₂H₆N₄O**   M.:   **102**   Formula: **C₂H₆N₄O**   M.w.:   **102**
        Name: Manuf.:   **SWK**   Prpt.:   **KBr**   Dec. No.: **2.1**

6286   Zusetzg.:   **Guanylharnstoff-Phosphat**   Comp.:   **Guanyl urea phosphate**
        Formel: **C₂H₉N₄O₅P**   M.:   **200**   Formula: **C₂H₉N₄O₅P**   M.w.:   **200**
        Name: Manuf.:   **SWK**   Prpt.:   **KBr**   Dec. No.: **2.2**

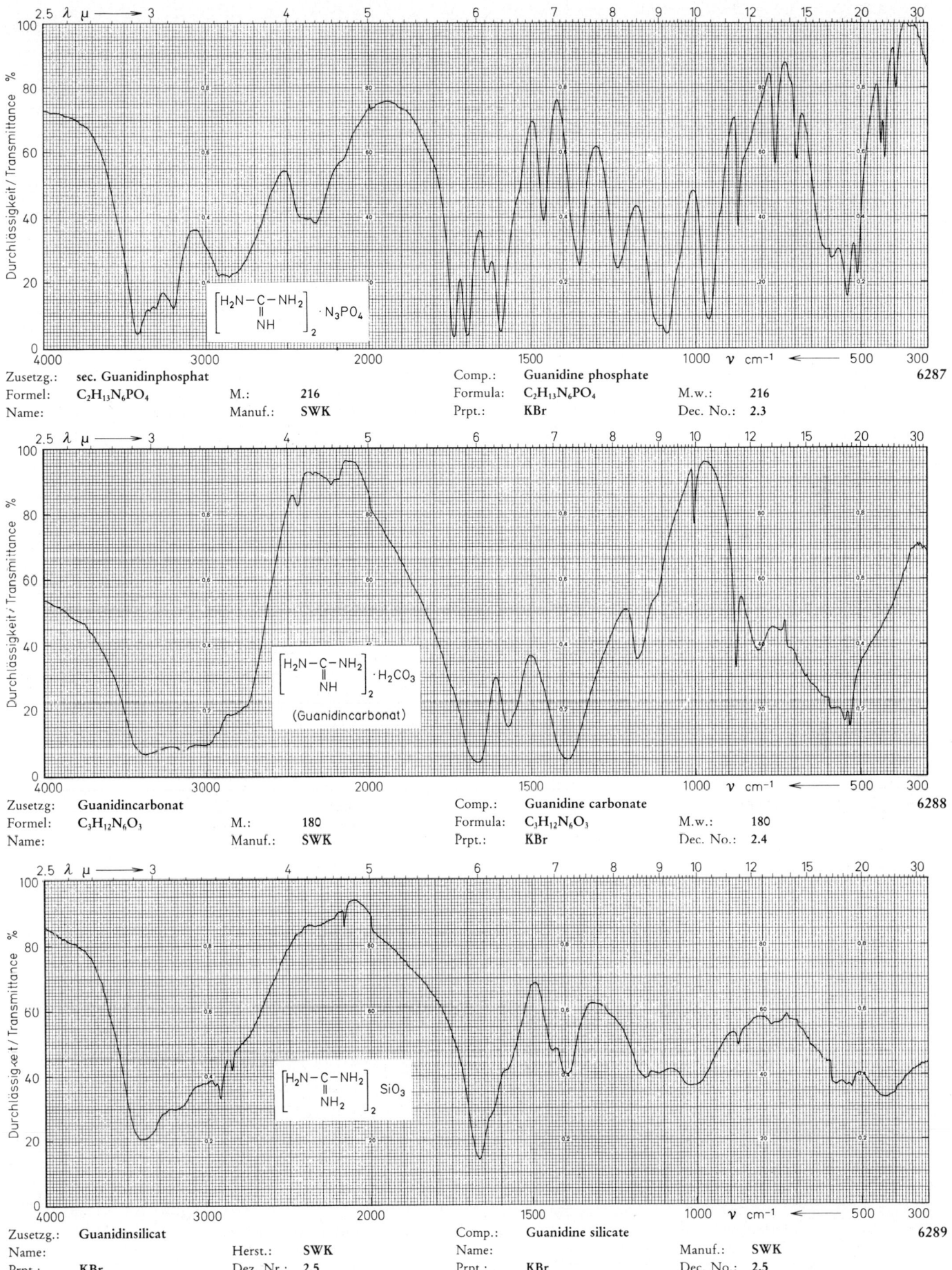

Zusetzg.:   sec. Guanidinphosphat   Comp.:   Guanidine phosphate   6287
Formel: C₂H₁₃N₆PO₄   M.:   216   Formula: C₂H₁₃N₆PO₄   M.w.:   216
Name: Manuf.:   SWK   Prpt.:   KBr   Dec. No.: 2.3

Zusetzg: Guanidincarbonat   Comp.:   Guanidine carbonate   6288
Formel: C₃H₁₂N₆O₃   M.:   180   Formula: C₃H₁₂N₆O₃   M.w.:   180
Name: Manuf.:   SWK   Prpt.:   KBr   Dec. No.: 2.4

Zusetzg.:   Guanidinsilicat   Comp.:   Guanidine silicate   6289
Name: Herst.:   SWK   Name: Manuf.: SWK
Prpt.:   KBr   Dez. Nr.: 2.5   Prpt.:   KBr   Dec. No.: 2.5

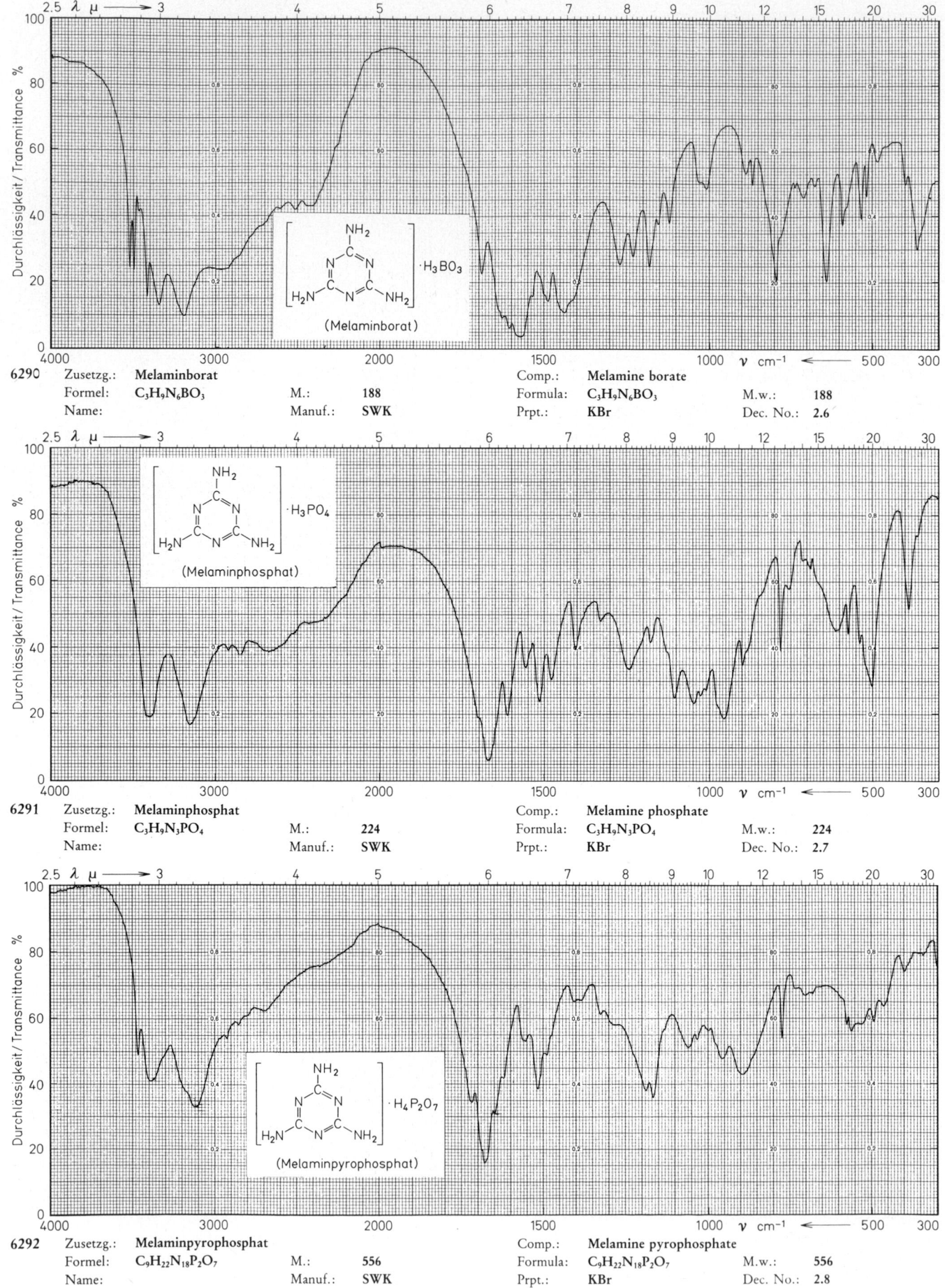

6290   Zusetzg.:   **Melaminborat**   Comp.:   **Melamine borate**
        Formel: **C₃H₉N₆BO₃**   M.:   **188**   Formula: **C₃H₉N₆BO₃**   M.w.:   **188**
        Name: Manuf.: **SWK**   Prpt.:   **KBr**   Dec. No.: **2.6**

6291   Zusetzg.:   **Melaminphosphat**   Comp.:   **Melamine phosphate**
        Formel: **C₃H₉N₃PO₄**   M.:   **224**   Formula: **C₃H₉N₃PO₄**   M.w.:   **224**
        Name: Manuf.: **SWK**   Prpt.:   **KBr**   Dec. No.: **2.7**

6292   Zusetzg.:   **Melaminpyrophosphat**   Comp.:   **Melamine pyrophosphate**
        Formel: **C₉H₂₂N₁₈P₂O₇**   M.:   **556**   Formula: **C₉H₂₂N₁₈P₂O₇**   M.w.:   **556**
        Name: Manuf.: **SWK**   Prpt.:   **KBr**   Dec. No.: **2.8**

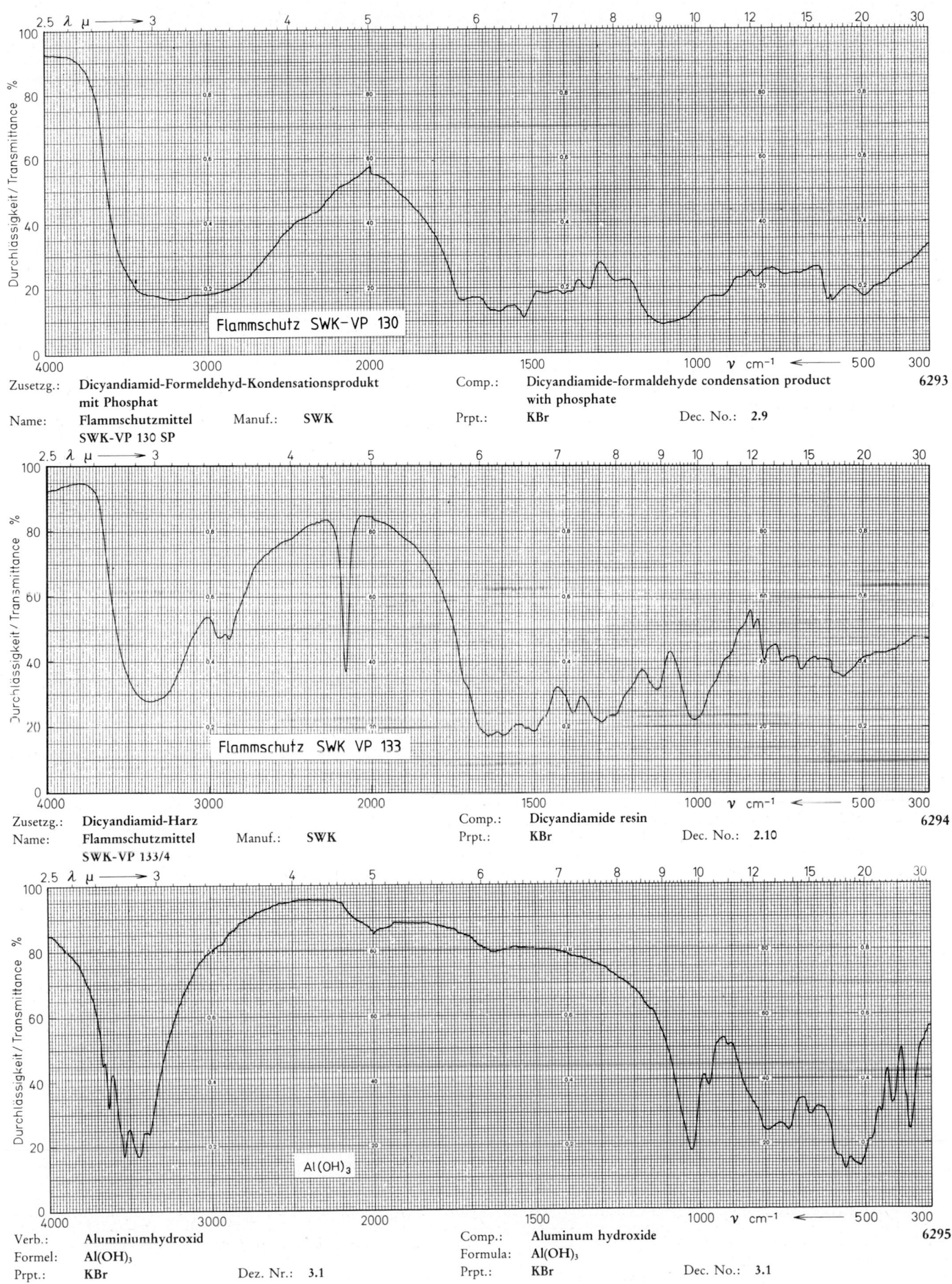

Zusetzg.:   Dicyandiamid-Formeldehyd-Kondensationsprodukt   Comp.:   Dicyandiamide-formaldehyde condensation product   **6293**
         mit Phosphat   with phosphate

Name: **Flammschutzmittel**   Manuf.:   **SWK**   Prpt.:   **KBr**   Dec. No.:   **2.9**
         SWK-VP 130 SP

Zusetzg.:   **Dicyandiamid-Harz**   Comp.:   **Dicyandiamide resin**   **6294**

Name: **Flammschutzmittel**   Manuf.:   **SWK**   Prpt.:   **KBr**   Dec. No.:   **2.10**
         SWK-VP 133/4

Verb.:   **Aluminiumhydroxid**   Comp.:   **Aluminum hydroxide**   **6295**

Formel: **Al(OH)$_3$**   Formula: **Al(OH)$_3$**

Prpt.:   **KBr**   Dez. Nr.:   **3.1**   Prpt.:   **KBr**   Dec. No.:   **3.1**

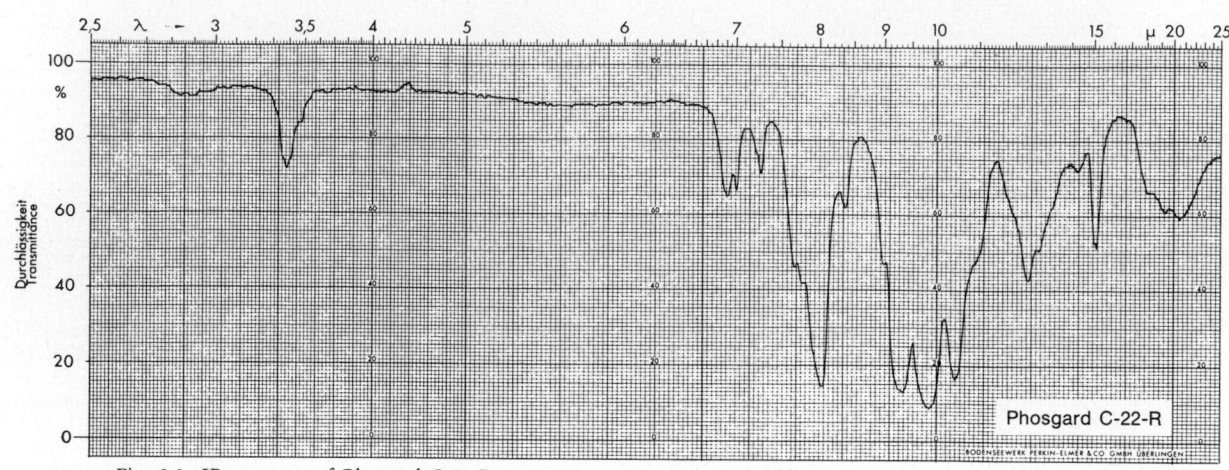

Fig. 8.2: IR spectrum of Phosgard C-22-R   Abb. 8.2: IR-Spektrum von Phosgard C-22-R

6296	Verb.:	**Poly-di(2-chlorethyl)ethylphosphonat**			Comp.:	**Poly-di(2-chlorethyl)ethylphosponate**		
	Name:	**Phosgard C-22-R**	Herst.:	**Monsanto**	Name:	**Phosgard C-22-R**	Manuf.:	**Monsanto**
	Prpt.:	**Cap. Film**	Dez. Nr.:	**3.2**	Prpt.:	**Cap. film**	Dec. No.:	**3.2**

Beschleuniger

Accelerators

Beschleuniger
1. Aminoverbindungen
1.1. Aldehyd-Ammoniak
    Kondensationsprodukte

Accelerators
1. Amino Compounds
1.1. Aldehyde-Ammonia
    Condensation Products

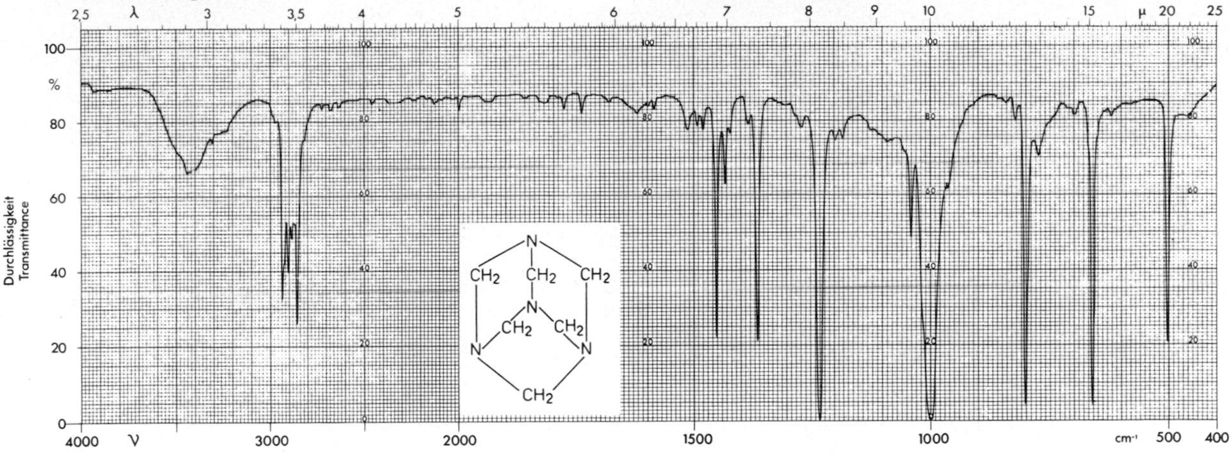

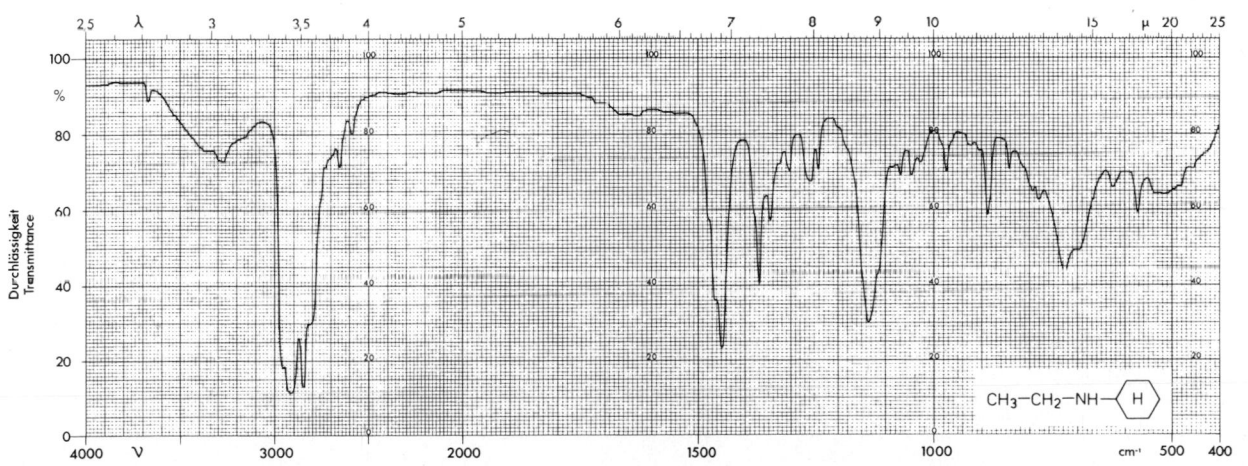

Verbindung:	Hexamethylentetramin			Compound:	Hexamethylene tetramine			6300
Formel:	$C_6H_{12}N_4$	M.:	140	Formula:	$C_6H_{12}N_4$	M. w.:	140	
Handelsname:	Vulkacit H 30	Herst.:	Bayer	Tradename:	Vulkacit H 30	Manuf.:	Bayer	
Präparation:	KBr (6/1000)	Dez. Nr.:	1.1.1	Preparation:	KBr (6/1000)	Dec. No.:	1.1.1	

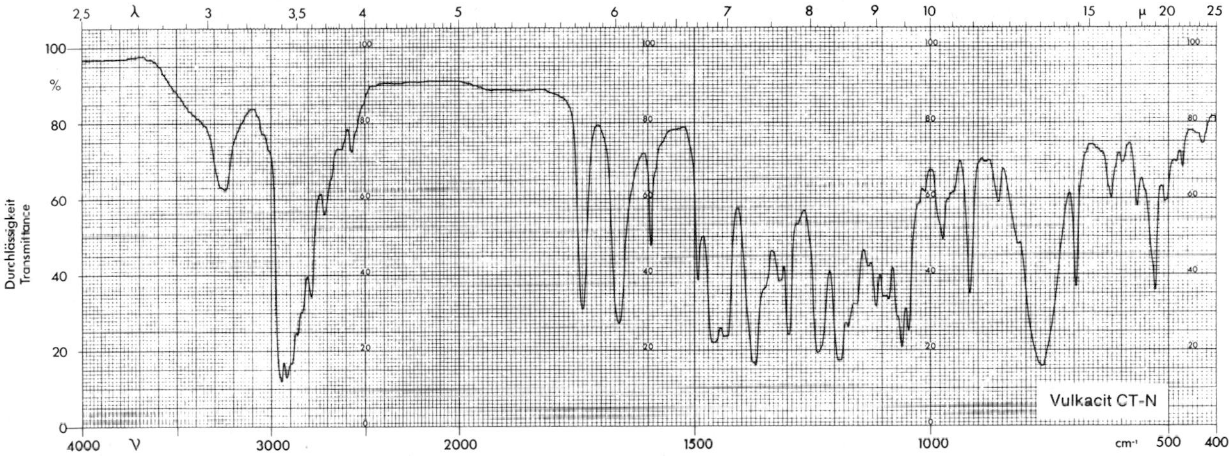

Verbindung:	Tricrotonylidentetramin			Compound:	Tricrotonylidene tetramine			6301
Formel:		M.:		Formula:		M. w.:		
Handelsname:	Vulkacit CT-N	Herst.:	Bayer	Tradename:	Vulkacit CT-N	Manuf.:	Bayer	
Präparation:	Kapill. Film	Dez. Nr.:	1.1.2	Preparation:	Capill. Film	Dec. No.:	1.1.2	

Verbindung:	Cyclohexylethylamin			Compound:	Cyclohexylethylamine			6302
Formel:	$C_8H_{17}N$	M.:	127,2	Formula:	$C_8H_{17}N$	M. w.:	127,2	
Handelsname:	Vulkacit HX	Herst.:	Bayer	Tradename:	Vulkacit HX	Manuf.:	Bayer	
Präparation:	Kapill. Film	Dez. Nr.:	1.2.1	Preparation:	Capill. Film	Dec. No.:	1.2.1	

Beschleuniger
1.2. Aliphatische Amine und ihre Kondensationsprodukte
1.3. Anilin- und Toluidin-Kondensationsprodukte

Accelerators
1.2. Aliphatic Amines and their Condensations Products
1.3. Aniline and Toluidine Condensations Products

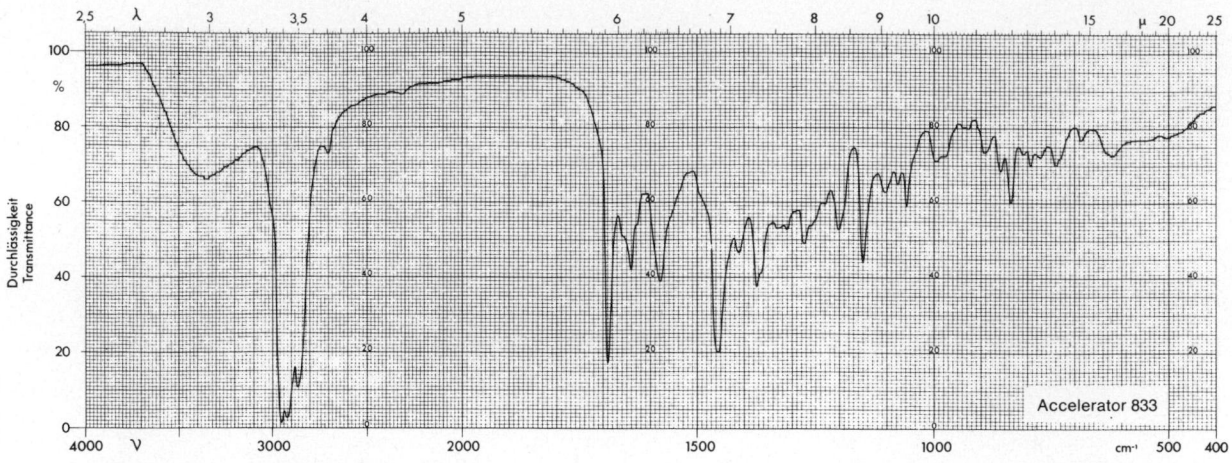

6303

Verbindung:	Kondens.produkt aus Butyraldehyd und Monobutylamin		Compound:	Condens.product of butyraldehyde a. monobutylamine
Formel:		M.:	Formula:	M. w.:
Handelsname:	**Accelerator 833**	Herst.: **Du Pont**	Tradename: **Accelerator 833**	Manuf.: **Du Pont**
Präparation:	**Kapill. Film**	Dez.Nr.: **1.2.2**	Preparation: **Capill. Film**	Dec.No.: **1.2.2**

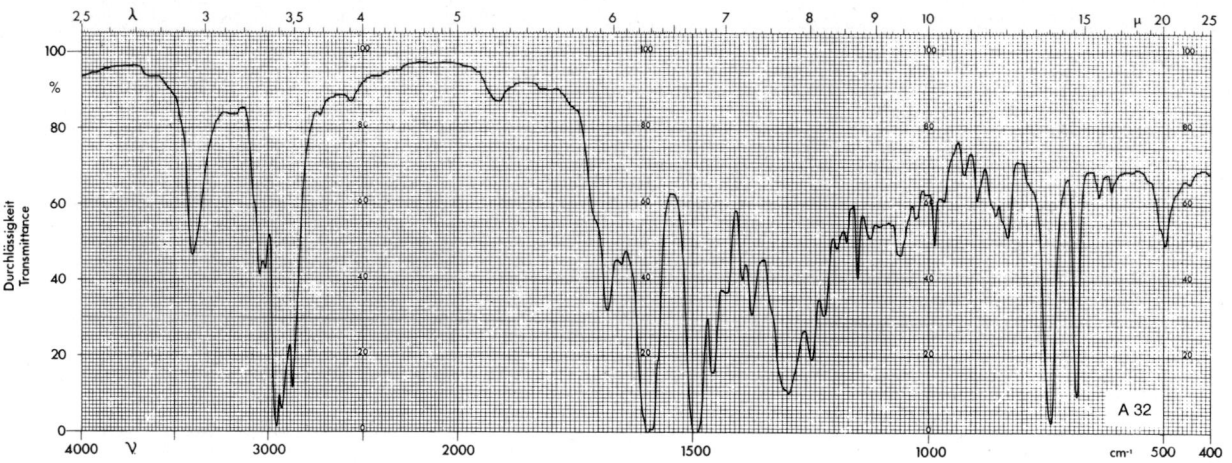

6304

Verbindung:	Kondens.produkt aus Butyraldehyd und Anilin		Compound:	Condens.product of butyraldehyde a. aniline
Formel:		M.:	Formula:	M. w.:
Handelsname:	**A 32**	Herst.: **Monsanto**	Tradename: **A 32**	Manuf.: **Monsanto**
Präparation:	**Kapill. Film**	Dez.Nr.: **1.3.1**	Preparation: **Capill. Film**	Dec.No.: **1.3.1**

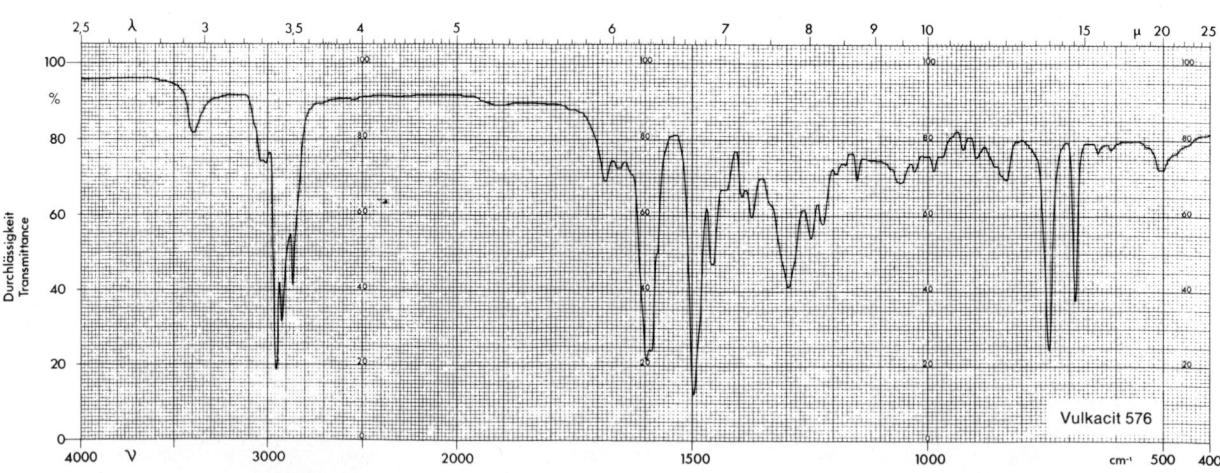

6305

Verbindung:	Kondens.produkt aus α-Ethyl-β-propylacrolein und Anilin		Compound:	Condens.product of α-ethyl-β-propylacrolein u. anilin
Formel:		M.:	Formula:	M. w.:
Handelsname:	**Vulkacit 576**	Herst.: **Bayer**	Tradename: **Vulkacit 576**	Manuf.: **Bayer**
Präparation:	**Kapill. Film**	Dez.Nr.: **1.3.2**	Preparation: **Capill. Film**	Dec.No.: **1.3.2**

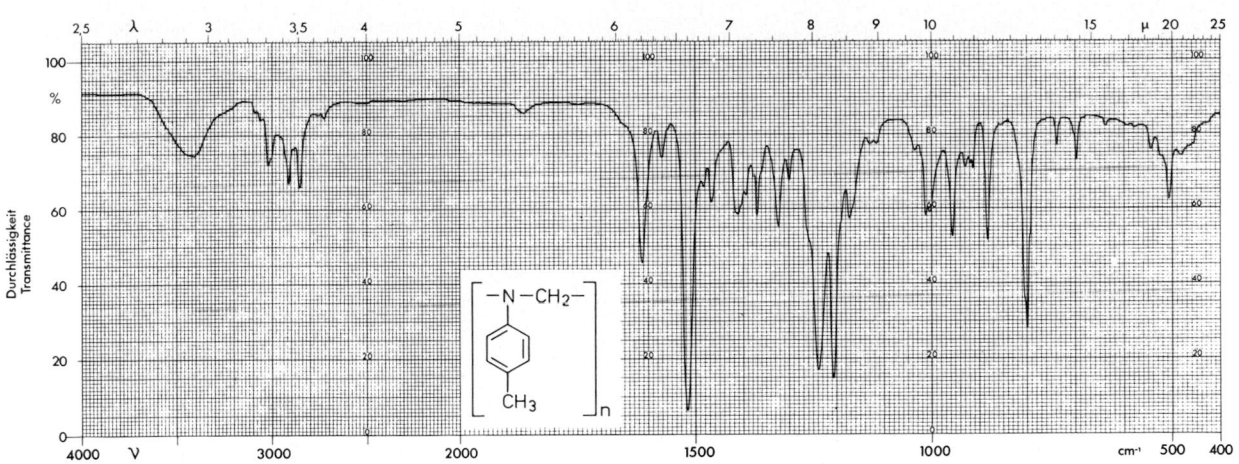

Verbindung:	Anhydroformaldehyd-p-toluidin		Compound:	Anhydroformaldehyde-p-toluidine		6306
Formel:		M.:	Formula:		M. w.:	
Handelsname:	Vulkacit FP	Herst.: Bayer	Tradename:	Vulkacit FP	Manuf.: Bayer	
Präparation:	KBr (5/1000)	Dez. Nr.: 1.3.3	Preparation:	KBr (5/1000)	Dec. No.: 1.3.3	

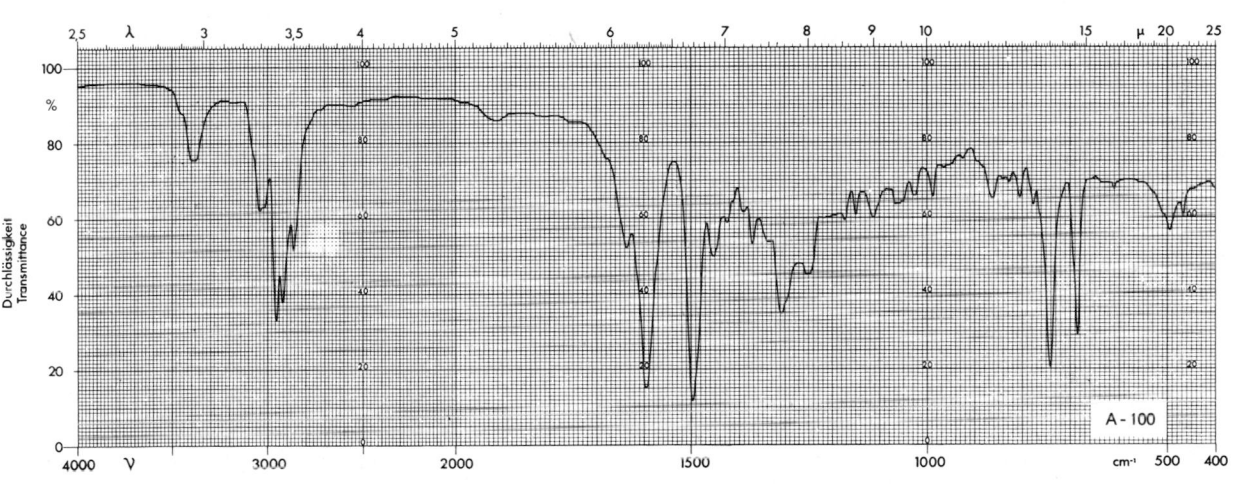

Verbindung:	Kondens.produkt aus Acetaldehyd, Butyraldehyd u. arom. Amin		Compound:	Condens.product of acetaldehyde, butyraldehyde a. arom. amine		6307
Formel:		M.:	Formula:		M. w.:	
Handelsname:	A-100	Herst.: Monsanto	Tradename:	A-100	Manuf.: Monsanto	
Präparation:	Kapill. Film	Dez. Nr.: 1.3.4	Preparation:	Capill. Film	Dec. No.: 1.3.4	

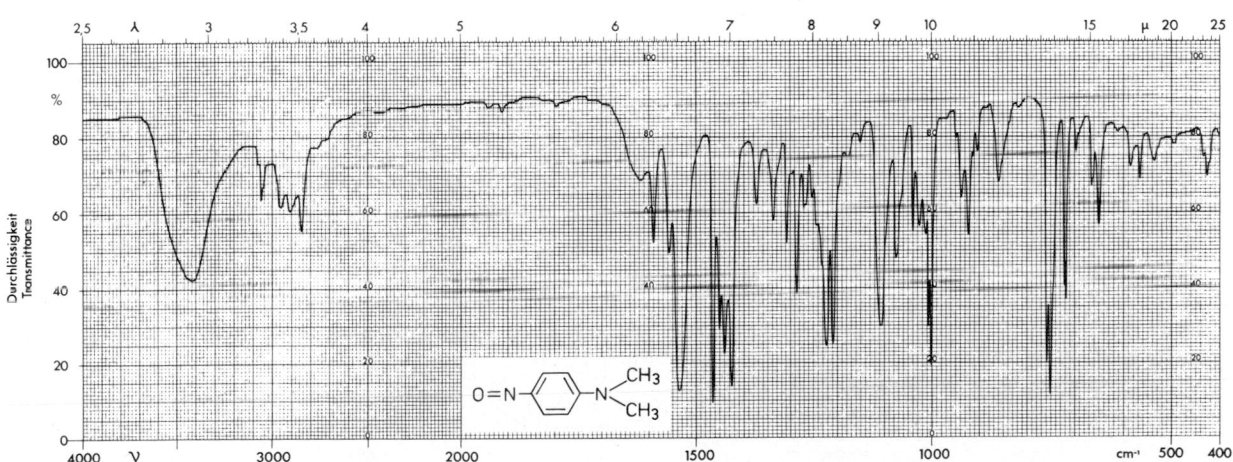

Verbindung:	p-Nitrosodimethylanilin		Compound:	p-Nitrosodimethylaniline		6308
Formel:	$C_8H_{10}N_2O$	M.: 150,6	Formula:	$C_nH_{10}N_2O$	M. w.: 150,6	
Handelsname:	Accelerator 1	Herst.: Du Pont	Tradename:	Accelerator 1	Manuf.: Du Pont	
Präparation:	KBr (3/1000)	Dez. Nr.: 2.1	Preparation:	KBr (3/1000)	Dec. No.: 2.1	

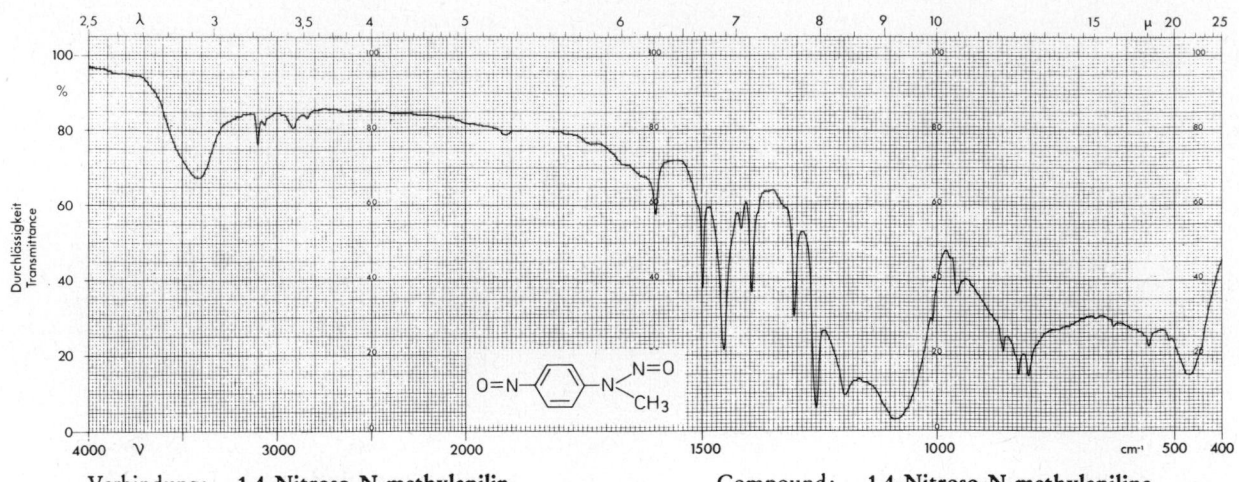

6309   Verbindung: **1,4-Nitroso-N-methylanilin**

Formel:	$C_7H_7N_3O_2$	M.:	**165,1**
Handelsname:	**Elastopar**	Herst.:	**Monsanto**
Präparation:	**KBr (4/1000)**	Dez. Nr.:	**2.2**

Compound: **1,4-Nitroso-N-methylaniline**

Formula:	$C_7H_7N_3O_2$	M. w.:	**165,1**
Tradename:	**Elastopar**	Manuf.:	**Monsanto**
Preparation:	**KBr (4/1000)**	Dec. No.:	**2.2**

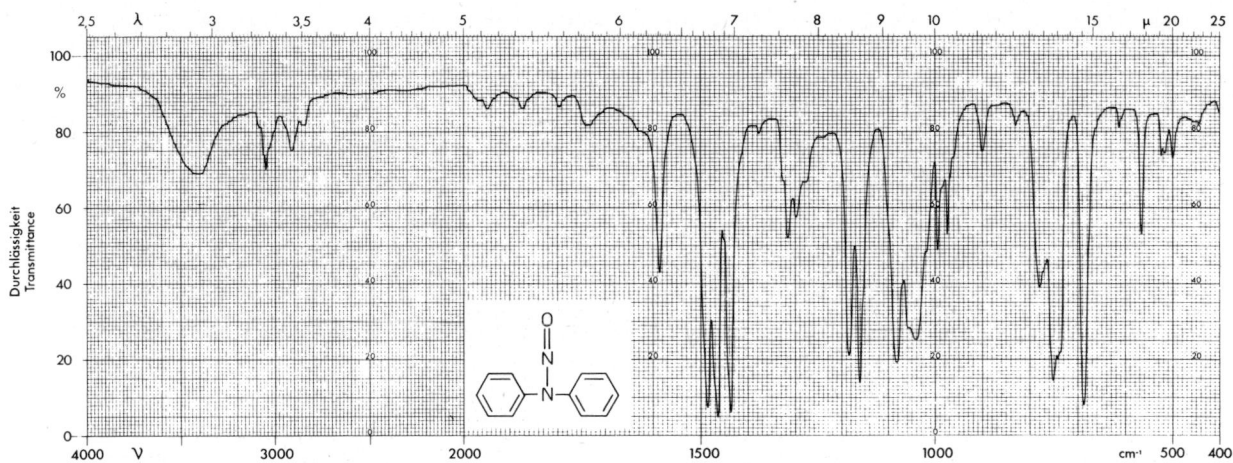

6310   Verbindung: **N-Nitrosodiphenylamin**

Formel:	$C_{12}H_{10}N_2O$	M.:	**198,2**
Handelsname:	**Vulkalent A**	Herst.:	**Bayer**
Präparation:	**KBr (4/1000)**	Dez. Nr.:	**2.3**

Compound: **N-Nitrosodiphenylamine**

Formula:	$C_{12}H_{10}N_2O$	M. w.:	**198,2**
Tradename:	**Vulkalent A**	Manuf.:	**Bayer**
Preparation:	**KBr (4/1000)**	Dec. No.:	**2.3**

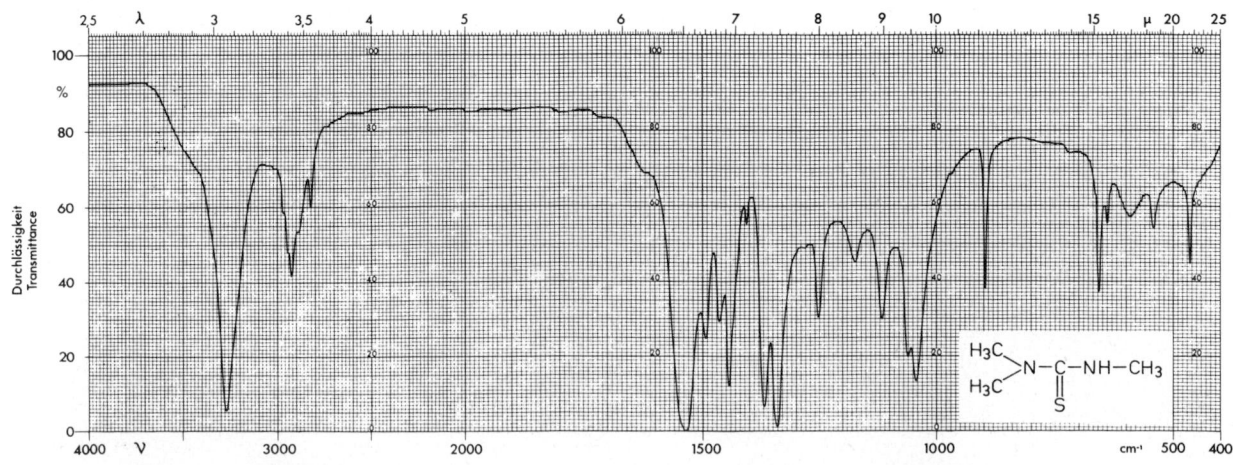

6311   Verbindung: **Trimethylthioharnstoff**

Formel:	$C_4H_{10}N_2S$	M.:	**118,2**
Handelsname:	**Thiate E**	Herst.:	**Vanderbilt**
Präparation:	**KBr (3/1000)**	Dez. Nr.:	**3.1**

Compound: **Trimethylthiourea**

Formula:	$C_4H_{10}N_2S$	M. w.:	**118,2**
Tradename:	**Thiate E**	Manuf.:	**Vanderbilt**
Preparation:	**KBr (3/1000)**	Dec. No.:	**3.1**

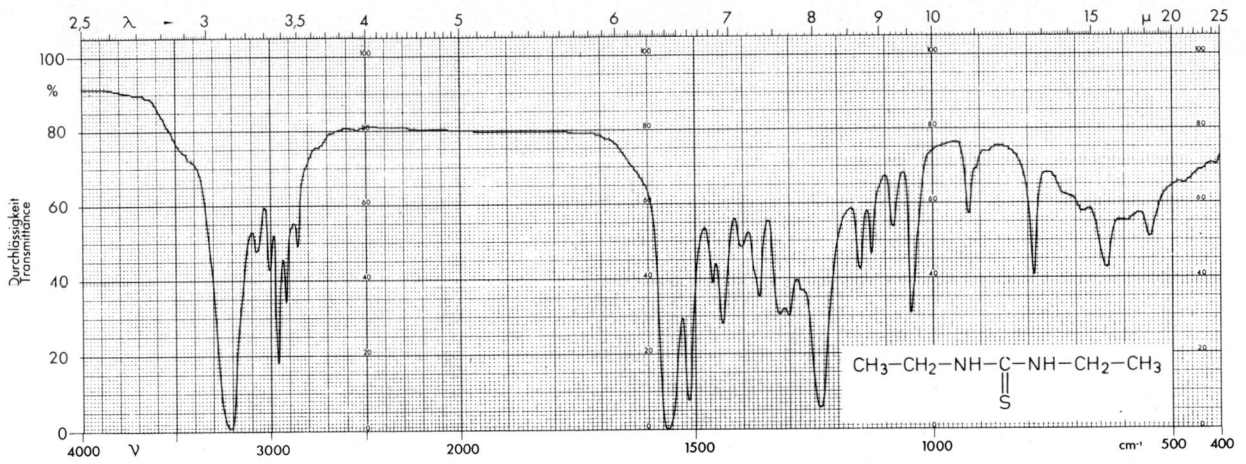

Verbindung:	N,N'-Diethylthioharnstoff			Compound:	**N,N'-Diethylthiourea**			6312
Formel:	$C_5H_{12}N_2S$	M.:	**132,2**	Formula:	$C_5H_{12}N_2S$	M. w.:	**132,2**	
Handelsname:	**Pennzone E**	Herst.:	**Pennsalt**	Tradename:	**Pennzone E**	Manuf.:	**Pennsalt**	
Präparation:	**KBr (2/1000)**	Dez. Nr.:	**3.2**	Preparation:	**KBr (2/1000)**	Dec. No.:	**3.2**	

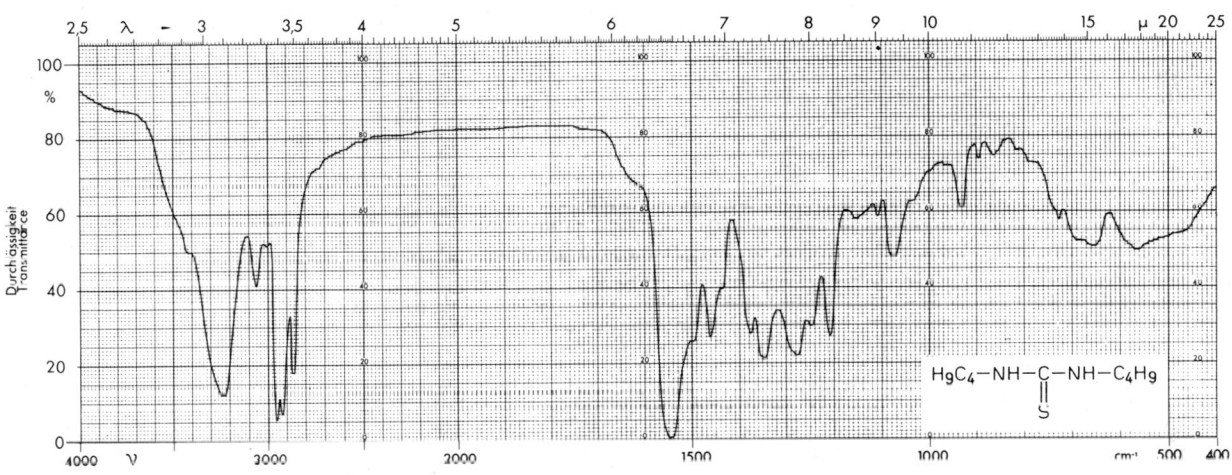

Verbindung:	N,N'-Dibutylthioharnstoff			Compound:	**N,N'-Dibutylthiourea**			6313
Formel:	$C_9H_{20}N_2S$	M.:	**188,3**	Formula:	$C_9H_{20}N_2S$	M. w.:	**188,3**	
Handelsname:	**Pennzone B**	Herst.:	**Pennsalt**	Tradename:	**Pennzone B**	Manuf.:	**Pennsalt**	
Präparation:	**KBr (3/1000)**	Dez. Nr.:	**3.3**	Preparation:	**KBr (3/1000)**	Dec. No.:	**3.3**	

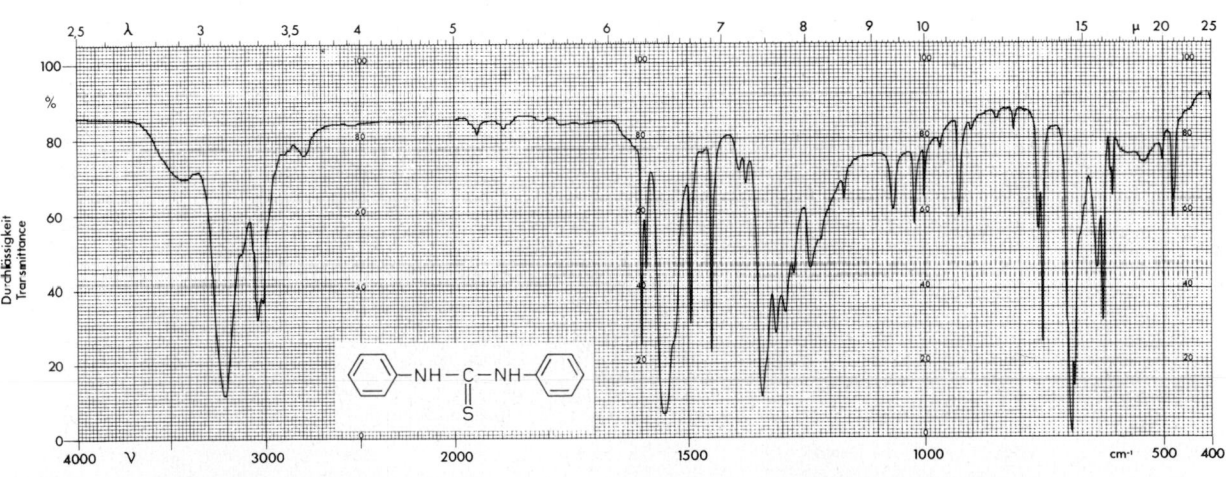

Verbindung:	N,N'-Diphenylthioharnstoff			Compound:	**N,N'-Diphenylthiourea**			6314
Formel:	$C_{13}H_{12}N_2S$	M.:	**228,3**	Formula:	$C_{13}H_{12}N_2S$	M. w.:	**228,3**	
Handelsname:	**A-1**	Herst.:	**Monsanto**	Tradename:	**A-1**	Manuf.:	**Monsanto**	
Präparation:	**KBr (5/1000)**	Dez. Nr.:	**3.4**	Preparation:	**KBr (5/1000)**	Dec. No.:	**3.4**	

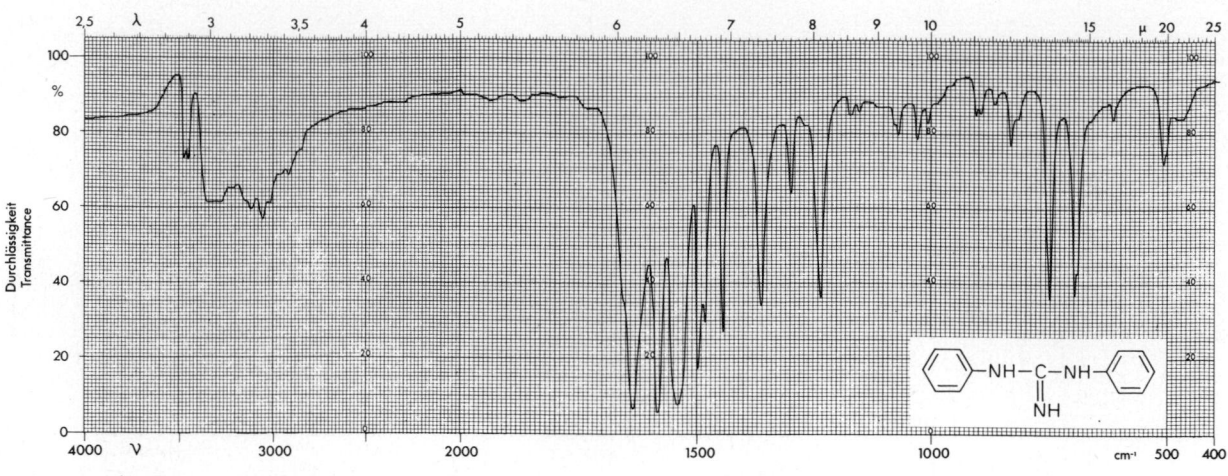

6315   Verbindung: N,N'-Diphenylguanidin   Compound: N,N'-Diphenylguanidine
        Formel: $C_{13}H_{13}N_3$ M.:   **211,2**   Formula: $C_{13}H_{13}N_3$ M. w.:   **211,2**
        Handelsname: **Vulkacit D**   Herst.:   **Bayer**   Tradename: **Vulkacit D**   Manuf.:   **Bayer**
        Präparation: **KBr (3/1000)**   Dez. Nr.:   **4.1**   Preparation: **KBr (3/1000)**   Dec. No.:   **4.1**

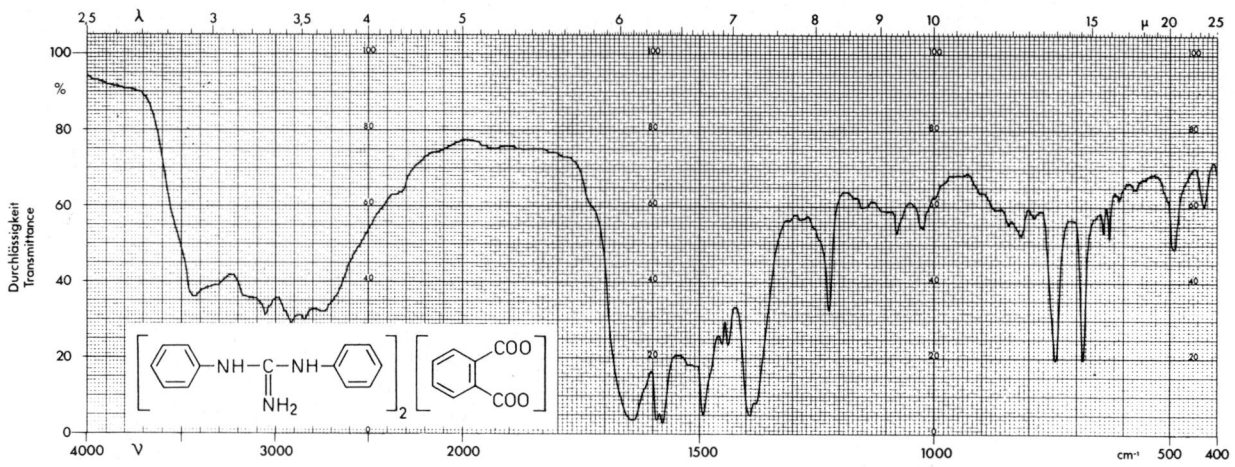

6316   Verbindung: **Diphenylguanidinphthalat**   Compound: **Diphenylguanidine phthalate**
        Formel: $C_{34}H_{32}N_6O_4$ M.:   **588,6**   Formula: $C_{34}H_{32}N_6O_4$ M. w.:   **588,6**
        Handelsname: **Guantal**   Herst.:   **Monsanto**   Tradename: **Guantal**   Manuf.:   **Monsanto**
        Präparation: **KBr (5/1000)**   Dez. Nr.:   **4.2**   Preparation: **KBr (5/1000)**   Dec. No.:   **4.2**

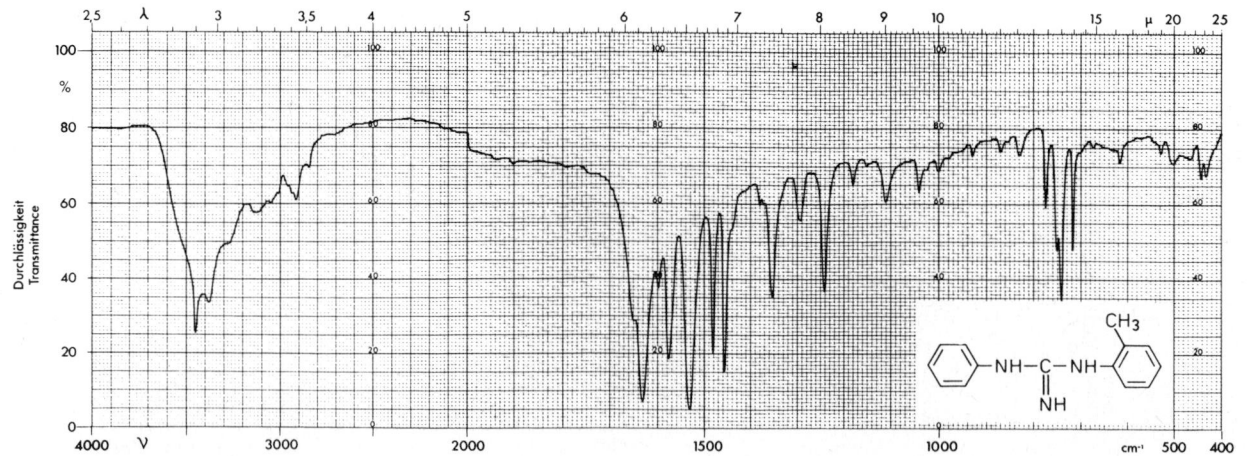

6317   Verbindung: **N-Phenyl-N'-o-tolylguanidin**   Compound: **N-Phenyl-N'-o-tolylouanidine**
        Formel: $C_{14}H_{15}N_3$ M.:   **225,3**   Formula: $C_{14}H_{15}N_3$ M. w.:   **225,3**
        Handelsname: **DOTG**   Herst.:   **Cyanamid**   Tradename: **DOTG**   Manuf.:   **Cyanamid**
        Präparation: **KBr (3/1000)**   Dez. Nr.:   **4.3**   Preparation: **KBr (3/1000)**   Dec. No.:   **4.3**

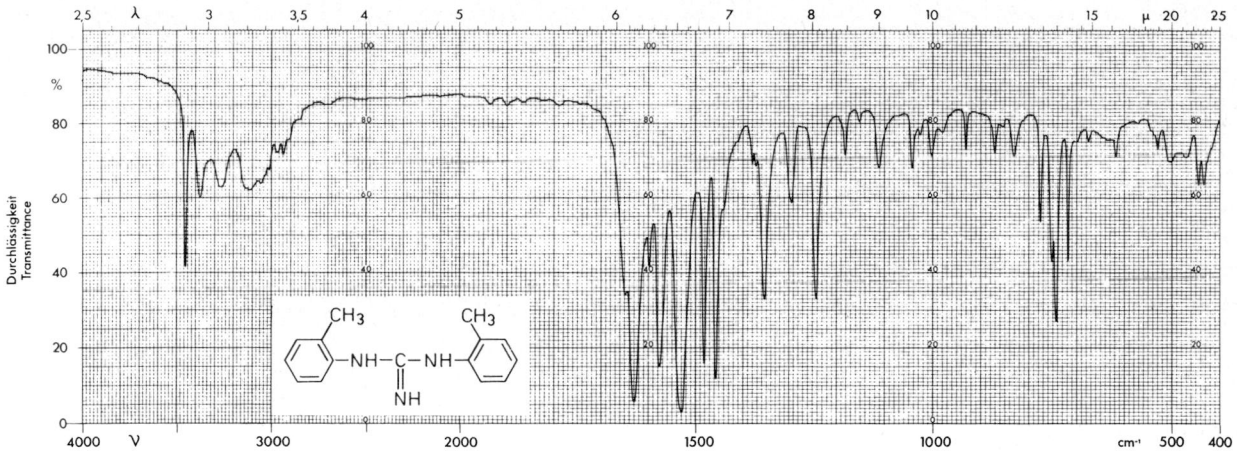

Verbindung:	N,N'-Di-o-tolylguanidin			Compound:	N,N'-Di-o-tolylguanidine			6318
Formel:	$C_{15}H_{17}N_3$	M.:	249,3	Formula:	$C_{15}H_{17}N_3$	M. w.:	249,3	
Handelsname:	Vulkacit DOTG	Herst.:	Bayer	Tradename:	Vulkacit DOTG	Manuf.:	Bayer	
Präparation:	KBr (6/1000)	Dez. Nr.:	4.4	Preparation:	KBr (6/1000)	Dec. No.:	4.4	

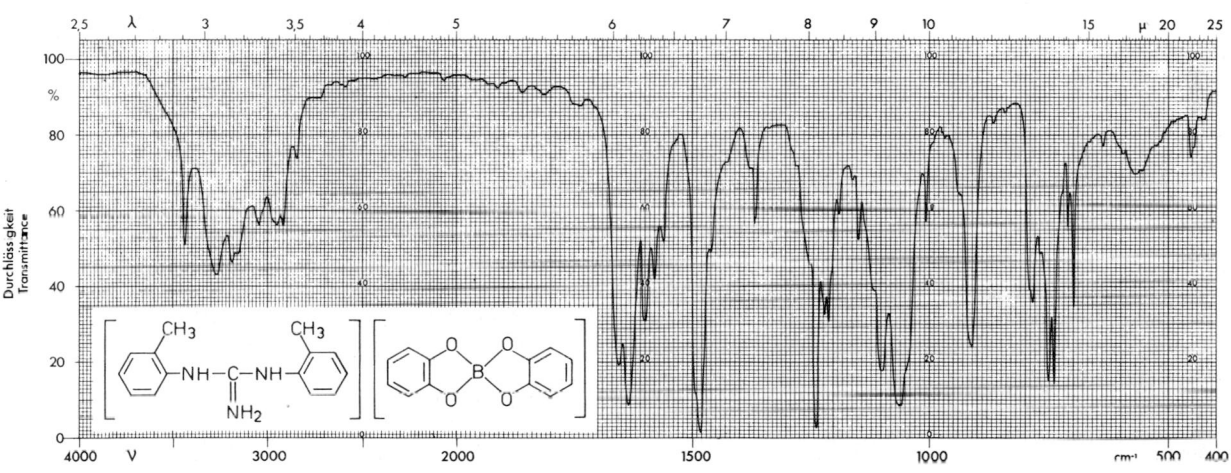

Verbindung:	Di-o-tolylguanidinsalz v. Di-brenzcatechinborat			Compound:	Di-o-tolylguanidine salt of dipyrocatechol borate			6319
Formel:	$C_{27}H_{26}N_3O_4B$	M.:	477,3	Formula:	$C_{27}H_{26}N_3O_4B$	M. w.:	477,3	
Handelsname:	Permalux	Herst.:	Du Pont	Tradename:	Permalux	Manuf.:	Du Pont	
Präparation:	KBr (5/1000)	Dez. Nr.:	4.5	Preparation:	KBr (5/1000)	Dec. No.:	4.5	

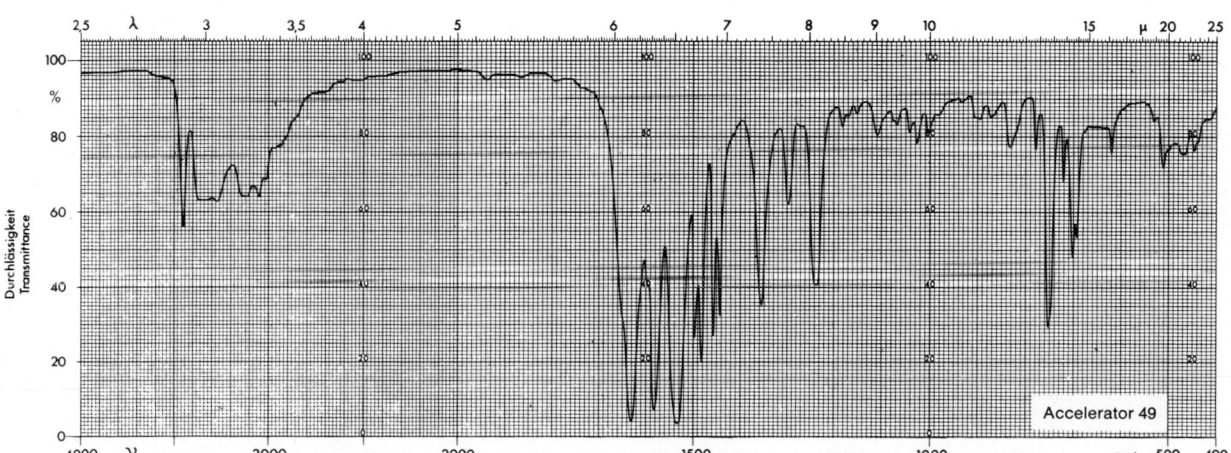

Verbindung:	Gemischtes Diarylguanidin			Compound:	Mixed diarylguanidine			6320
Formel:		M.:		Formula:		M. w.:		
Handelsname:	Accelerator 49	Herst.:	Cyanamid	Tradename:	Accelerator 49	Manuf.:	Cyanamid	
Präparation:	KBr (3/1000)	Dez. Nr.:	4.6	Preparation:	KBr (3/1000)	Dec. No.:	4.6	

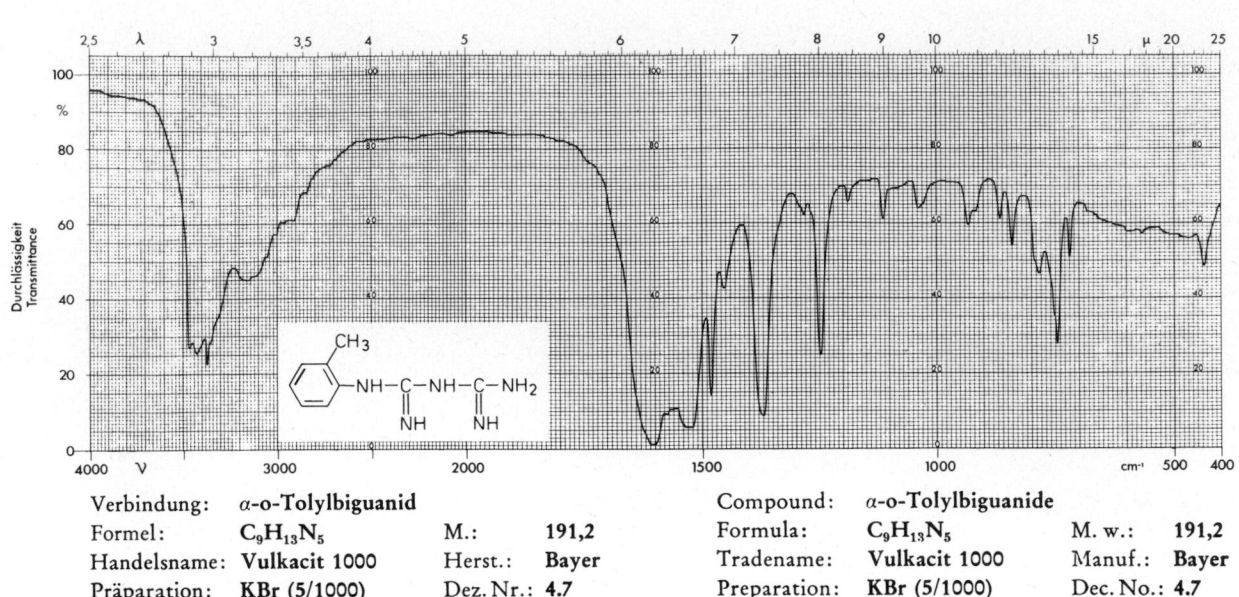

6321
Verbindung:	α-o-Tolylbiguanid		
Formel:	C₉H₁₃N₅	M.:	191,2
Handelsname:	Vulkacit 1000	Herst.:	Bayer
Präparation:	KBr (5/1000)	Dez. Nr.:	4.7

Compound:	α-o-Tolylbiguanide		
Formula:	C₉H₁₃N₅	M. w.:	191,2
Tradename:	Vulkacit 1000	Manuf.:	Bayer
Preparation:	KBr (5/1000)	Dec. No.:	4.7

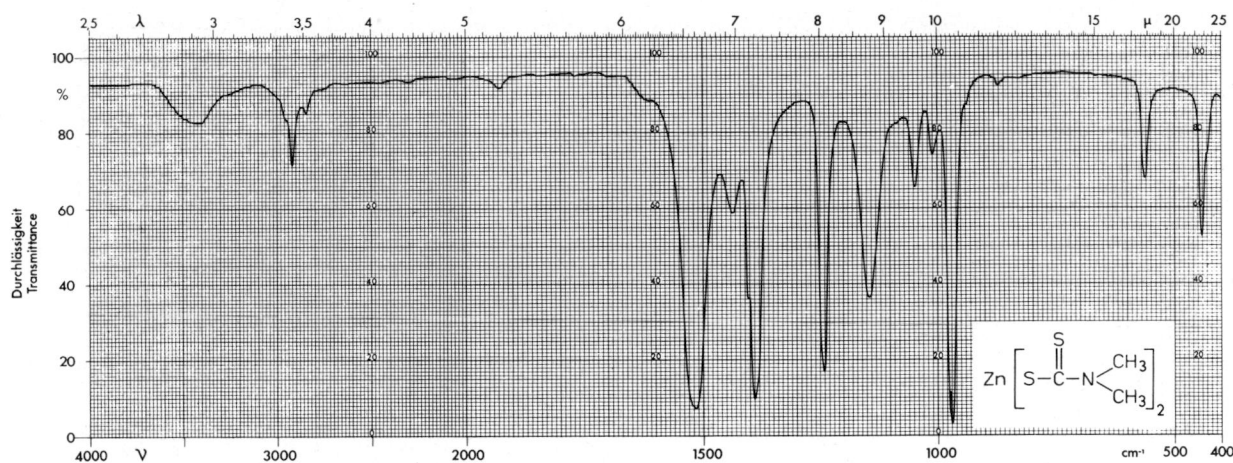

6322
Verbindung:	Zink-dimethyldithiocarbamat		
Formel:	C₆H₁₂N₂S₄Zn	M.:	305,8
Handelsname:	Vulkacit L	Herst.:	Bayer
Präparation:	KBr (3/1000)	Dez. Nr.:	5.1

Compound:	Zinc dimethyl dithiocarbamate		
Formula:	C₆H₁₂N₂S₄Zn	M. w.:	305,8
Tradename:	Vulkacit L	Manuf.:	Bayer
Preparation:	KBr (3/1000)	Dec. No.:	5.1

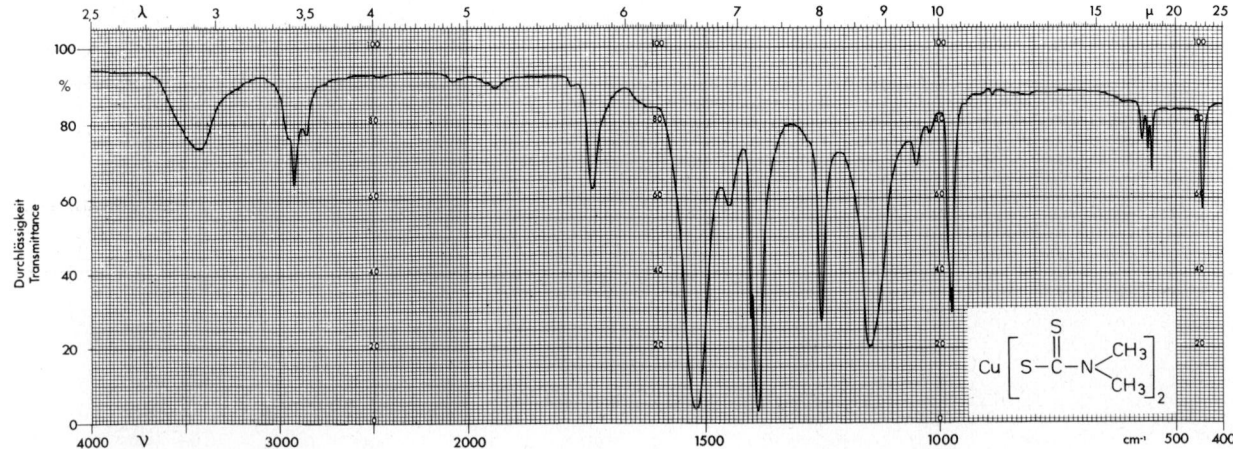

6323
Verbindung:	Cu-dimethyldithiocarbamat		
Formel:	C₆H₁₂N₂S₄Cu	M.:	304,0
Handelsname:	Cumate	Herst.:	Vanderbilt
Präparation:	KBr (5/1000)	Dez. Nr.:	5.2

Compound:	Cu dimethyl dithiocarbamate		
Formula:	C₆H₁₂N₂S₄Cu	M. w.:	304,0
Tradename:	Cumate	Manuf.:	Vanderbilt
Preparation:	KBr (5/1000)	Dec. No.:	5.2

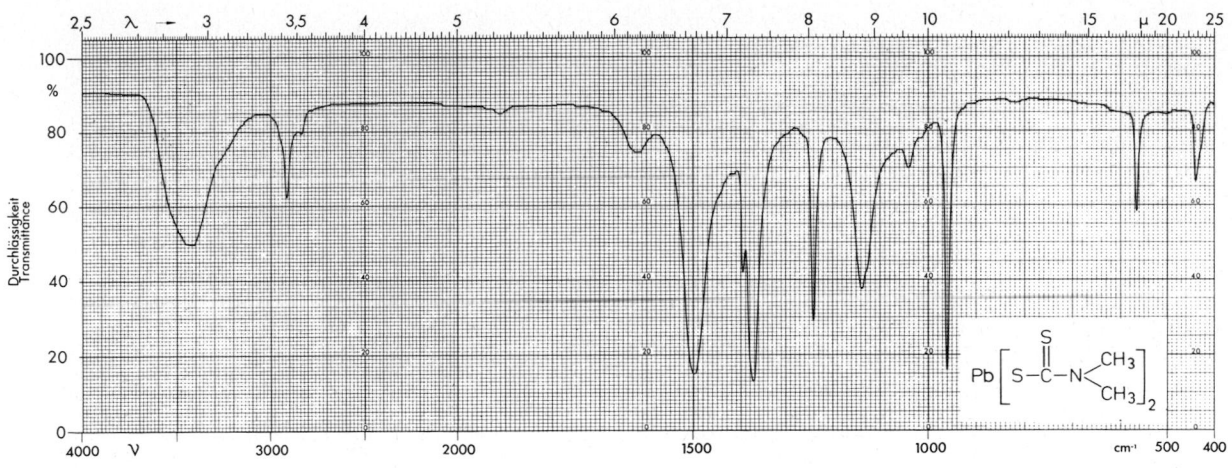

Verbindung: **Pb-dimethyldithiocarbamat**   Compound: **Pb dimethyl dithiocarbamate**   6324
Formel: **C₆H₁₂N₂S₄Pb**   M.: **447,6**   Formula: **C₆H₁₂N₂S₄Pb**   M. w.: **447,6**
Handelsname: **Ledate**   Herst.: **Vanderbilt**   Tradename: **Ledate**   Manuf.: **Vanderbilt**
Präparation: **KBr (3/1000)**   Dez. Nr.: **5.3**   Preparation: **KBr (3/1000)**   Dec. No.: **5.3**

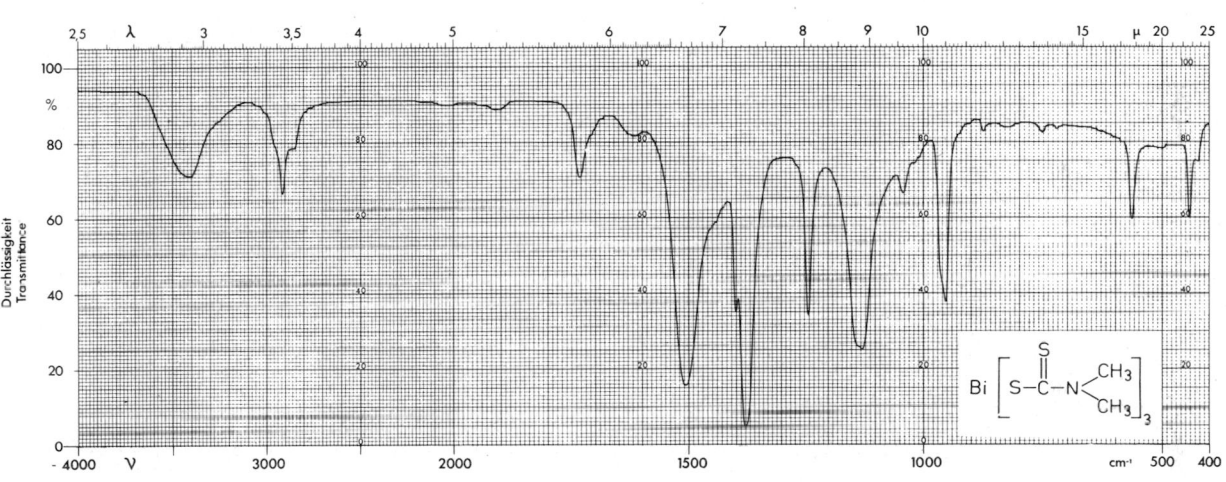

Verbindung: **Bi-dimethyldithiocarbamat**   Compound: **Bi-dimethyl dithiocarbamate**   6325
Formel: **C₉H₁₈N₃S₆Bi**   M.: **579,6**   Formula: **C₉H₁₈N₃S₆Bi**   M. w.: **579,6**
Handelsname: **Bismate**   Herst.: **Vanderbilt**   Tradename: **Bismate**   Manuf.: **Vanderbilt**
Präparation: **KBr (6/1000)**   Dez. Nr.: **5.4**   Preparation: **KBr (6/1000)**   Dec. No.: **5.4**

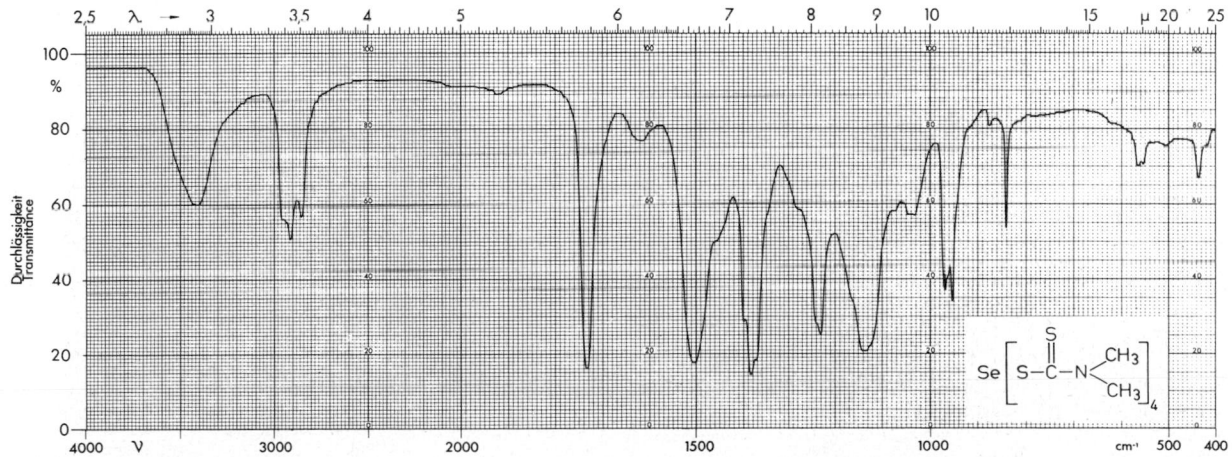

Verbindung: **Se-dimethyldithiocarbamat**   Compound: **Se dimethyl dithiocarbamate**   6326
Formel: **C₁₂H₂₄N₄S₈Se**   M.: **559,7**   Formula: **C₁₂H₂₄N₄S₈Se**   M. w.: **559,7**
Handelsname: **Methyl Selenac**   Herst.: **Vanderbilt**   Tradename: **Methyl Selenac**   Manuf.: **Vanderbilt**
Präparation: **KBr (4/1000)**   Dez. Nr.: **5.5**   Preparation: **KBr (4/1000)**   Dec. No.: **5.5**

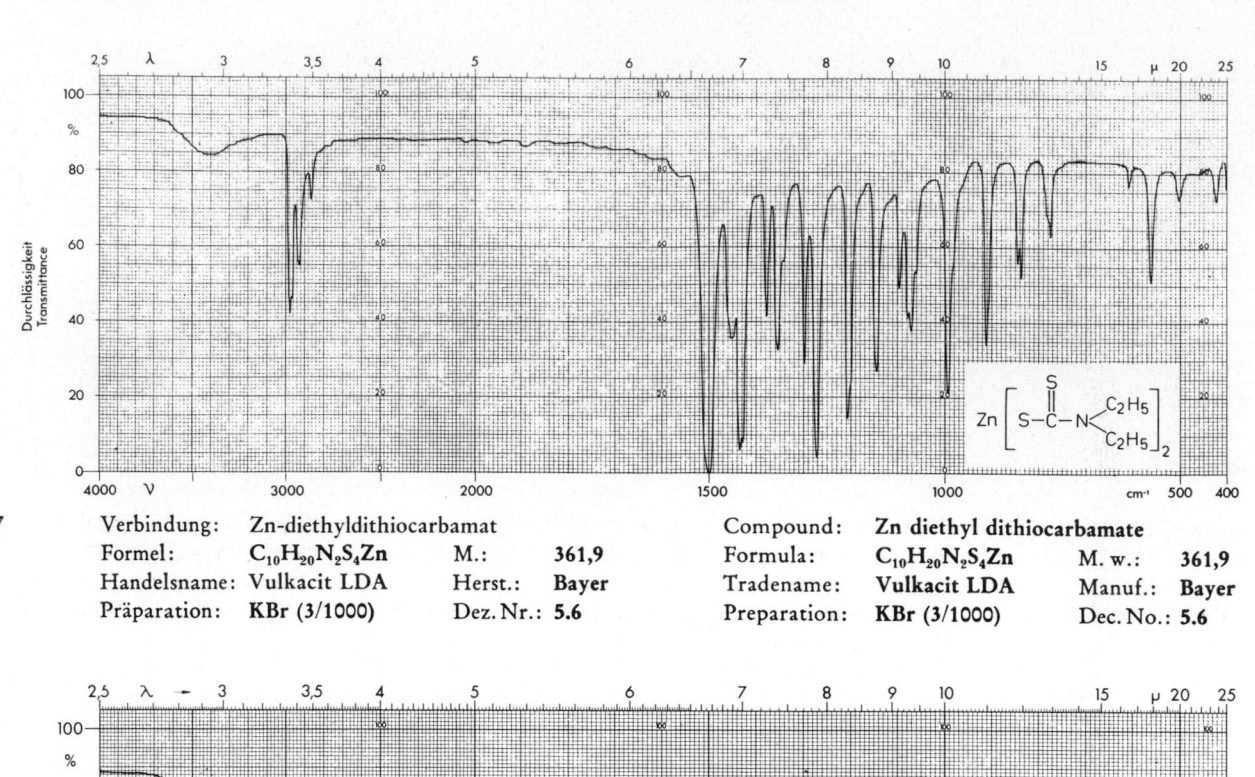

6327   Verbindung: Zn-diethyldithiocarbamat

Formel:	$C_{10}H_{20}N_2S_4Zn$	M.:	**361,9**
Handelsname:	**Vulkacit LDA**	Herst.:	**Bayer**
Präparation:	**KBr (3/1000)**	Dez. Nr.:	**5.6**

Compound: **Zn diethyl dithiocarbamate**

Formula:	$C_{10}H_{20}N_2S_4Zn$	M. w.:	**361,9**
Tradename:	**Vulkacit LDA**	Manuf.:	**Bayer**
Preparation:	**KBr (3/1000)**	Dec. No.:	**5.6**

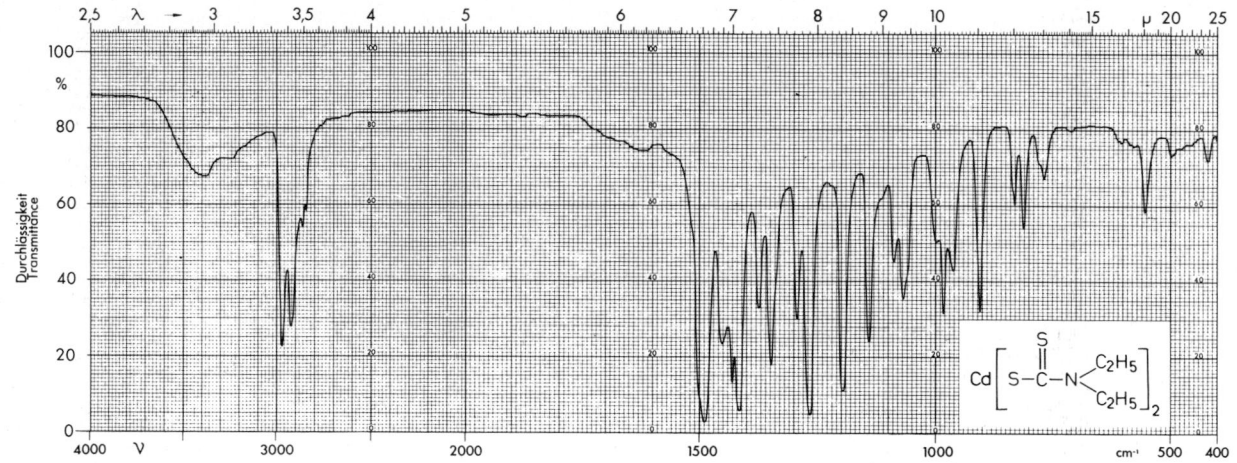

6328   Verbindung: Cd-diethyldithiocarbamat

Formel:	$C_{10}H_{20}N_2S_4Cd$	M.:	**408,9**
Handelsname:	**Ethyl Cadmate**	Herst.:	**Vanderbilt**
Präparation:	**KBr (3/1000)**	Dez. Nr.:	**5.7**

Compound: **Cd diethyl dithiocarbamate**

Formula:	$C_{10}H_{20}N_2S_4Cd$	M. w.:	**408,9**
Tradename:	**Ethyl Cadmate**	Manuf.:	**Vanderbilt**
Preparation:	**KBr (3/1000)**	Dec. No.:	**5.7**

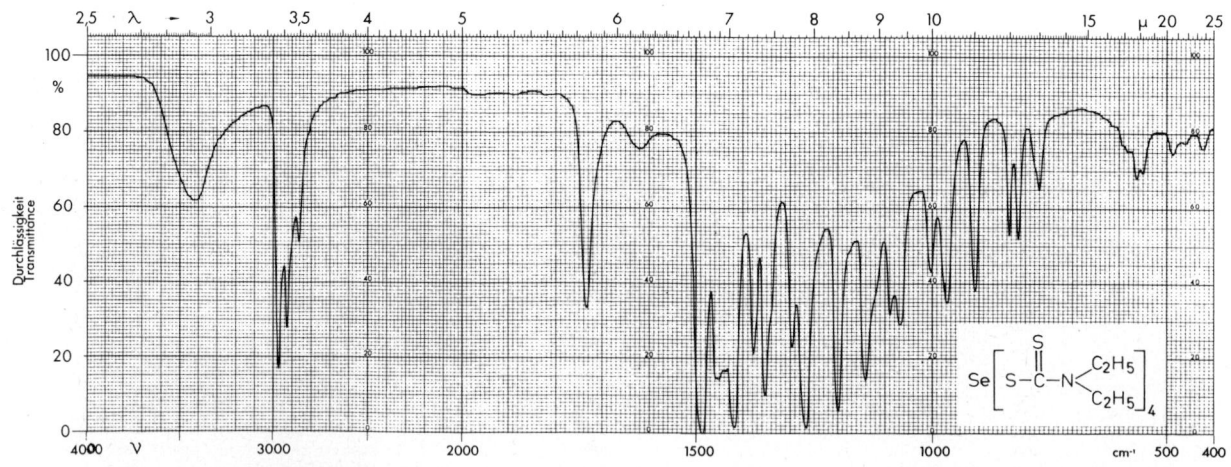

6329   Verbindung: Se-diethyldithiocarbamat

Formel:	$C_{20}H_{40}N_4S_8Se$	M.:	**671,9**
Handelsname:	**Ethyl Selenac**	Herst.:	**Vanderbilt**
Präparation:	**KBr (5/1000)**	Dez. Nr.:	**5.8**

Compound: **Se diethyl dithiocarbamate**

Formula:	$C_{20}H_{40}N_4S_8Se$	M. w.:	**671,9**
Tradename:	**Ethyl Selenac**	Manuf.:	**Vanderbilt**
Preparation:	**KBr (5/1000)**	Dec. No.:	**5.8**

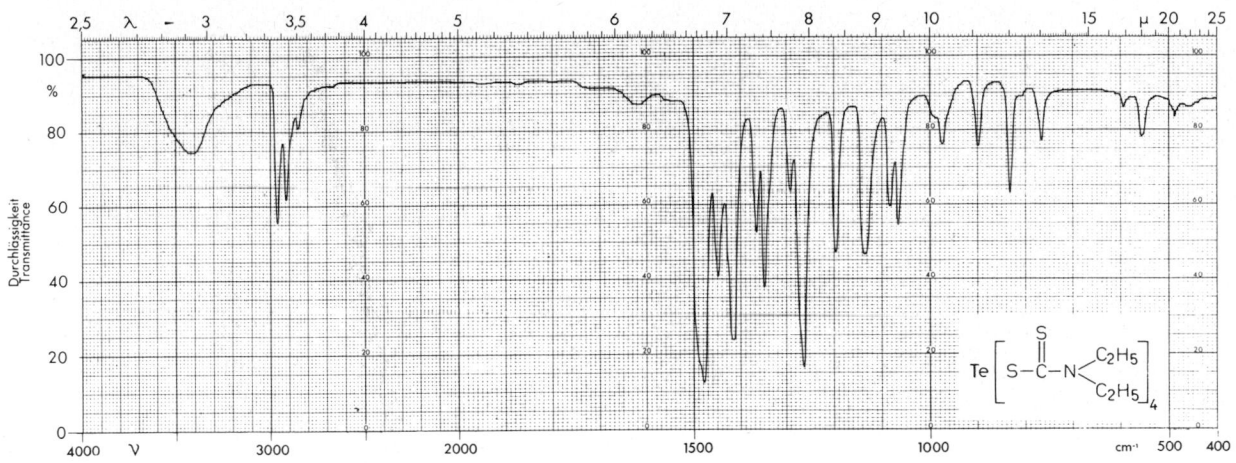

Verbindung:	Te-diethyldithiocarbamat		Compound:	Te diethyl dithiocarbamate		6330
Formel:	$C_{20}H_{40}N_4S_8Te$	M.: **720,6**	Formula:	$C_{20}H_{40}N_4S_8Te$	M. w.: **720,6**	
Handelsname:	**Ethyl Tellurac**	Herst.: **Vanderbilt**	Tradename:	**Ethyl Tellurac**	Manuf.: **Vanderbilt**	
Präparation:	**KBr (3/1000)**	Dez. Nr.: **5.9**	Preparation:	**KBr (3/1000)**	Dec. No.: **5.9**	

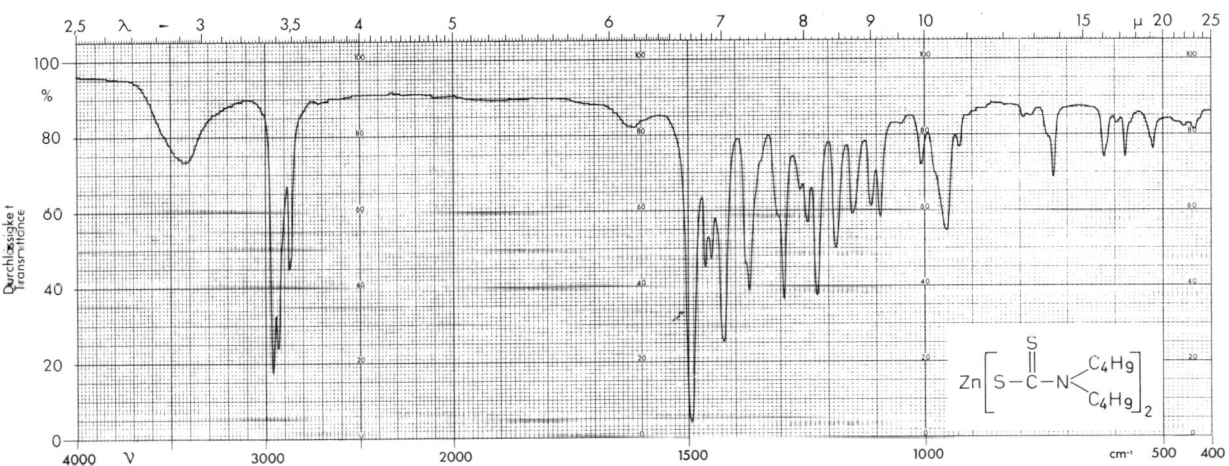

Verbindung:	**Zn-dibutyldithiocarbamat**		Compound:	**Zn dibutyl dithiocarbamate**		6331
Formel:	$C_{18}H_{36}N_2S_4Zn$	M.: **474,0**	Formula:	$C_{18}H_{36}N_2S_4Zn$	M. w.: **474,0**	
Handelsname:	**Vulkacit LDB**	Herst.: **Bayer**	Tradename:	**Vulkacit LDB**	Manuf.: **Bayer**	
Präparation:	**KBr (5/1000)**	Dez. Nr.: **5.10**	Preparation:	**KBr (5/1000)**	Dec. No.: **5.10**	

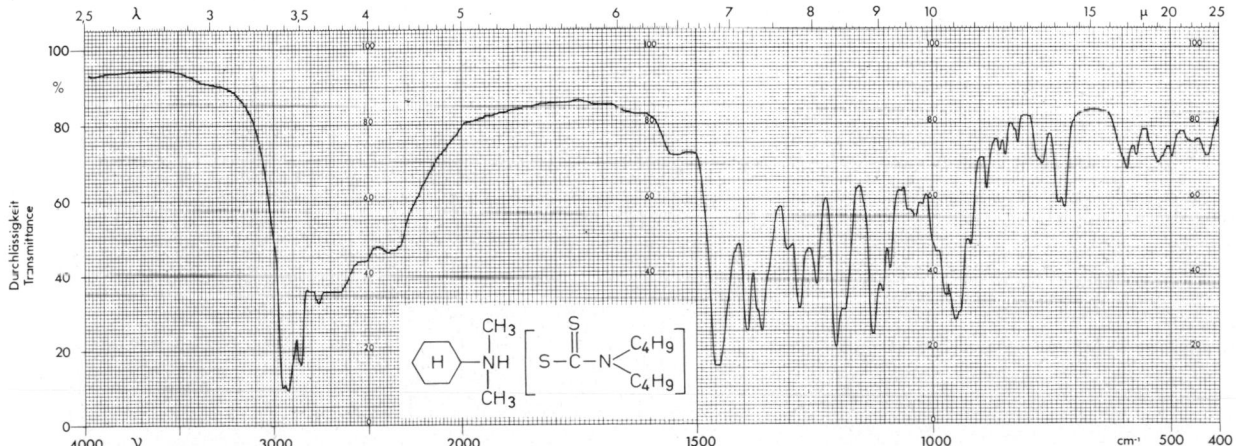

Verbindung:	**N,N-Dimethylcyclohexylammonium- dibutyldithiocarbamat**		Compound:	N,N-Dimethylcyclohexylammonia dibutyl dithiocarbamate		6332
Formel:	$C_{17}H_{36}N_2S_2$	M.: **332,5**	Formula:	$C_{17}H_{36}N_2S_2$	M. w.: **332,5**	
Handelsname:	**R. Z. 100**	Herst.: **Monsanto C**	Tradename:	**R. Z. 100**	Manuf.: **Monsanto C**	
Präparation:	**Kapill. Film**	Dez. Nr.: **5.11**	Preparation:	Capill. film	Dec. No.: **5.11**	

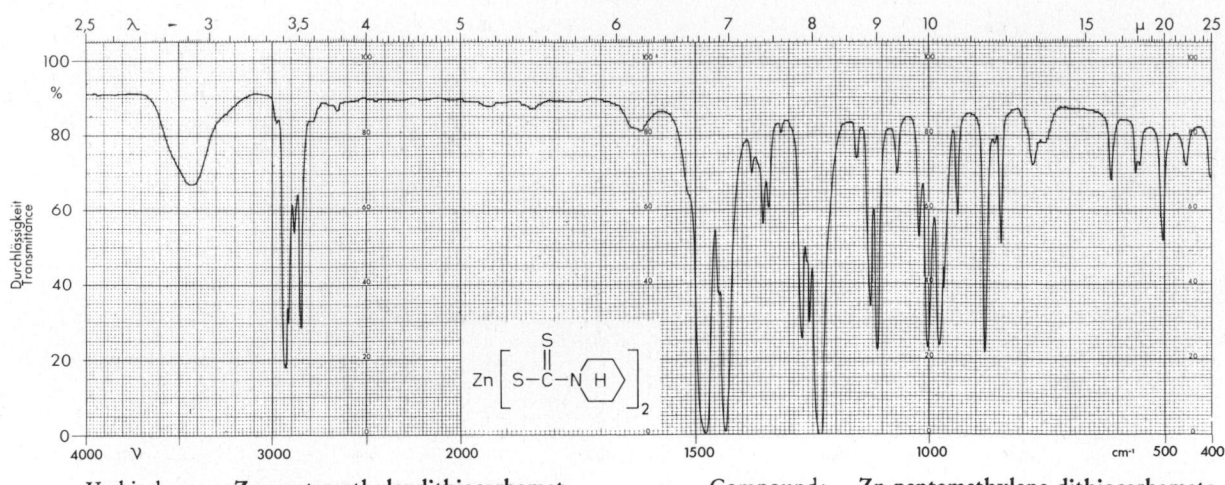

6333   Verbindung: **Zn-pentamethylendithiocarbamat**   Compound: **Zn pentamethylene dithiocarbamate**

Formel:	$C_{12}H_{20}N_2S_4Zn$	M.:	**385,9**		
Handelsname:	**Vulkacit ZP**	Herst.:	**Bayer**		
Präparation:	**KBr (6/1000)**	Dez. Nr.:	**5.12**		

Formula: $C_{12}H_{20}N_2S_4Zn$ M. w.: **385,9**
Tradename: **Vulkacit ZP**   Manuf.: **Bayer**
Preparation: **KBr (6/1000)**   Dec. No.: **5.12**

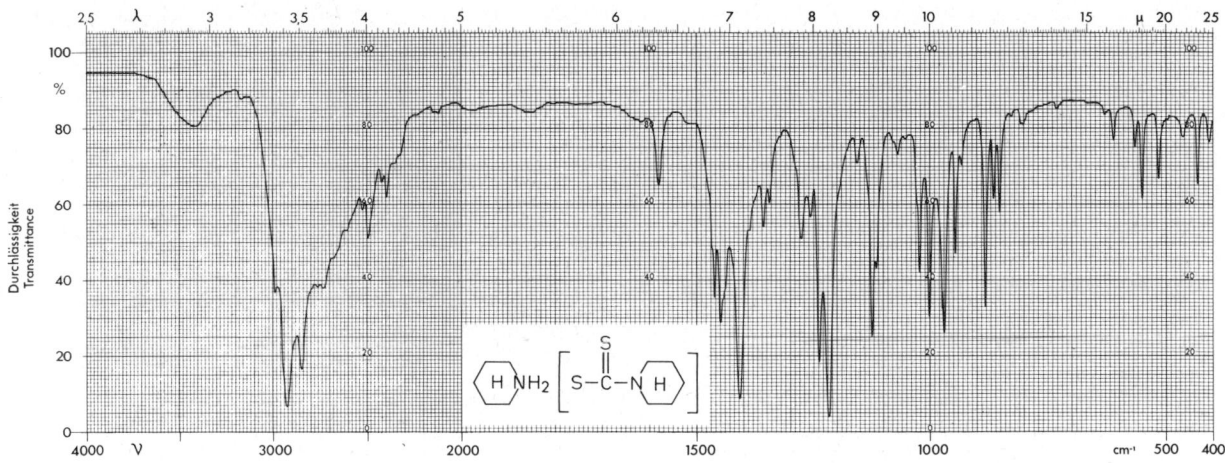

6334   Verbindung: **Piperidin-pentamethylendithiocarbamat**   Compound: **Piperidinium pentamethylene dithiocarbamate**

Formel: $C_{11}H_{22}N_2S_2$ M.: **246,4**
Handelsname: **Vulkacit P**   Herst.: **Bayer**
Präparation: **KBr (3/1000)**   Dez. Nr.: **5.13**

Formula: $C_{11}H_{22}N_2S_2$ M. w.: **246,4**
Tradename: **Vulkacit P**   Manuf.: **Bayer**
Preparation: **KBr (3/1000)**   Dec. No.: **5.13**

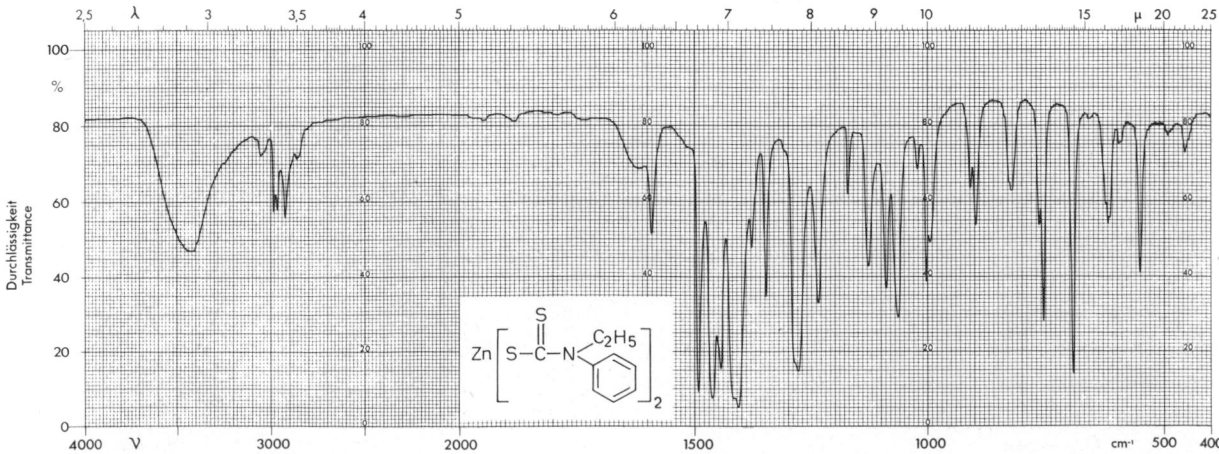

6335   Verbindung: **Zn-ethylphenyldithiocarbamat**   Compound: **Zn ethyl-phenyl dithiocarbamate**

Formel: $C_{18}H_{20}N_2S_4Zn$ M.: **457,9**
Handelsname: **Vulkacit P extra N**   Herst.: **Bayer**
Präparation: **KBr (3/1000)**

Formula: $C_{18}H_{20}N_2S_4Zn$ M. w.: **457,9**
Tradename: **Vulkacit P extra N**   Manuf.: **Bayer**
Preparation: **KBr (3/1000)**   Dec. No.: **5.14**

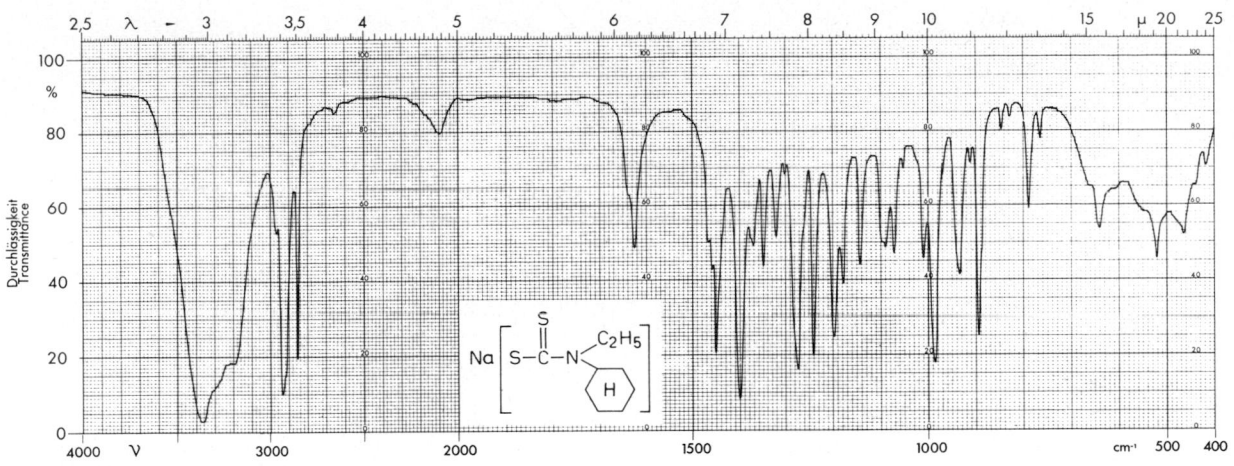

Verbindung: Na-cyclohexylethyldithiocarbamat

Compound: Na-cyclohexyl-ethyl dithiocarbamate   6336

Formel:	$C_9H_{16}NS_2Na$	M.:	225,3

Formula:	$C_9H_{16}NS_2Na$	M. w.:	225,3

Handelsname: Vulkacit WL   Herst.: **Bayer**

Tradename: Vulkacit WL   Manuf.: **Bayer**

Präparation: KBr (2/1000)   Dez. Nr.: **5.15**

Preparation: KBr (2/1000)   Dec. No.: **5.15**

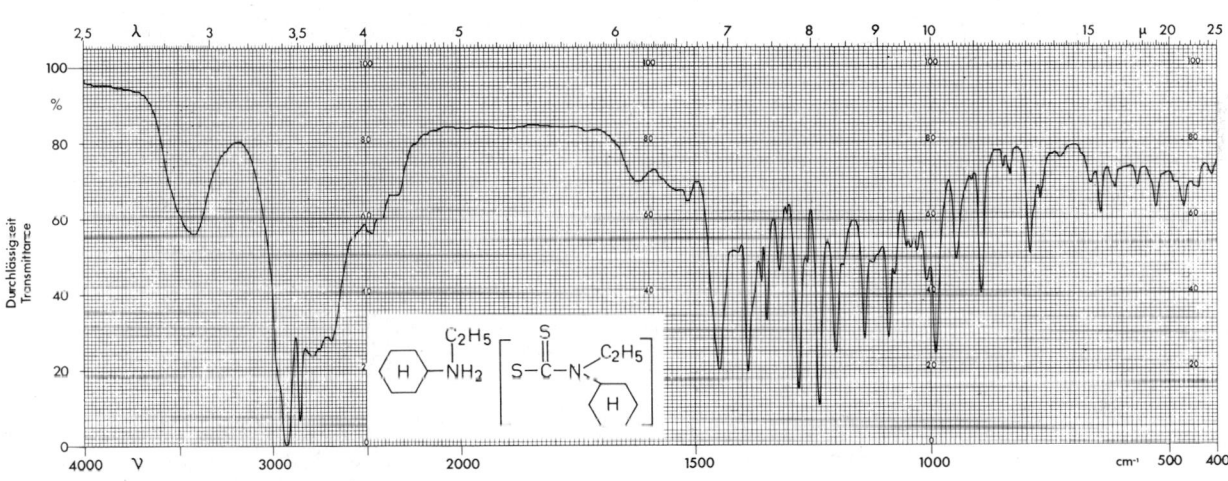

Verbindung: Cyclohexylethylammonium-cyclohexylethyldithiocarbamat

Compound: Cyclohexylethylammonia cyclohexylethyl dithiocarbamate   6337

Formel:	$C_{17}H_{34}N_2S_2$	M.:	330,5

Formula:	$C_{17}H_{34}N_2S_2$	M. w.:	330,5

Handelsname: Vulkacit 774   Herst.: **Bayer**

Tradename: Vulkacit 774   Manuf.: **Bayer**

Präparation: KBr (5/1000)   Dez. Nr.: **5.16**

Preparation: KBr (5/1000)   Dec. No.: **5.16**

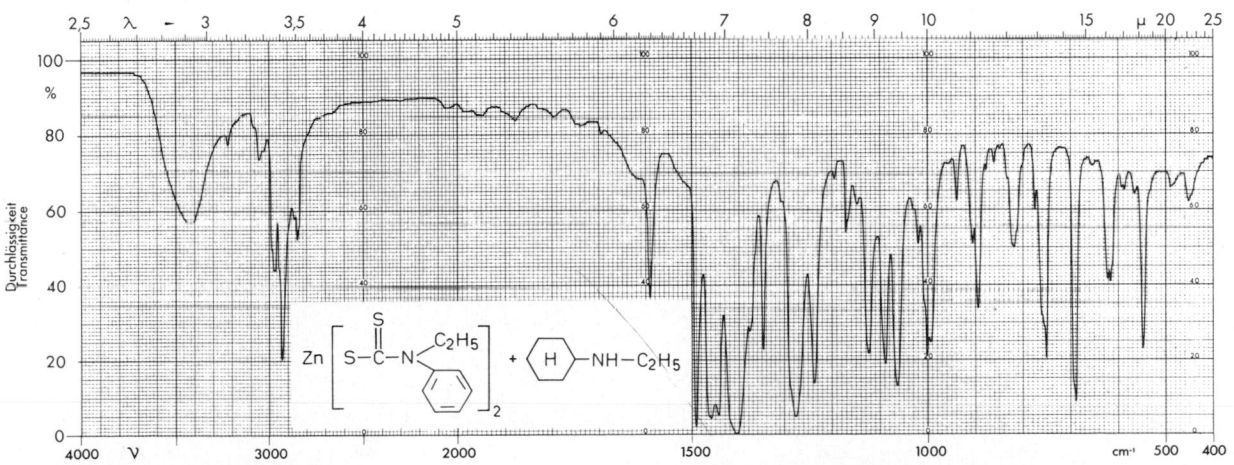

Verbindung: Zn-ethylphenyldithiocarbamat + Cyclohexyl-ethylamin

Compound: Zn ethyl-phenyl dithiocarbamate + Cyclohexylethylamine   6338

Formel:		M.:	

Formula:		M. w.:	

Handelsname: Vulkacit DB 1   Herst.: **Bayer**

Tradename: Vulkacit DB 1   Manuf.: **Bayer**

Präparation: KBr (4/1000)   Dez. Nr.: **5.17**

Preparation: KBr (4/1000)   Dec. No.: **5.17**

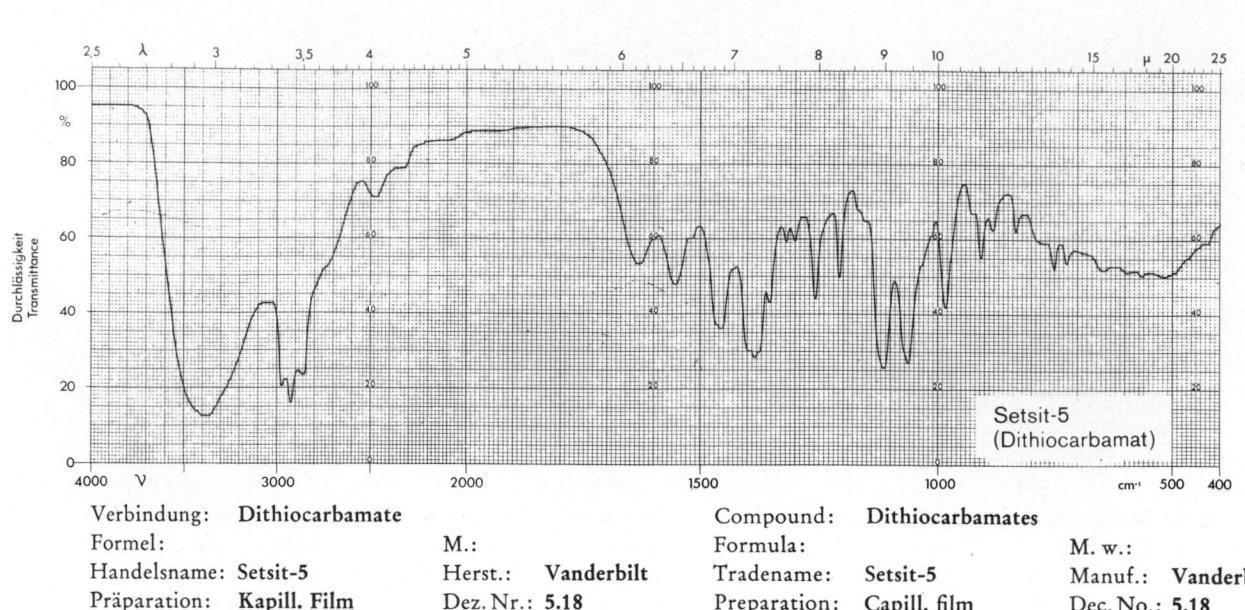

Setsit-5
(Dithiocarbamat)

6339

Verbindung:	**Dithiocarbamate**			Compound:	**Dithiocarbamates**		
Formel:		M.:		Formula:		M. w.:	
Handelsname:	Setsit-5	Herst.:	**Vanderbilt**	Tradename:	Setsit-5	Manuf.:	**Vanderbilt**
Präparation:	**Kapill. Film**	Dez. Nr.:	**5.18**	Preparation:	Capill. film	Dec. No.:	**5.18**

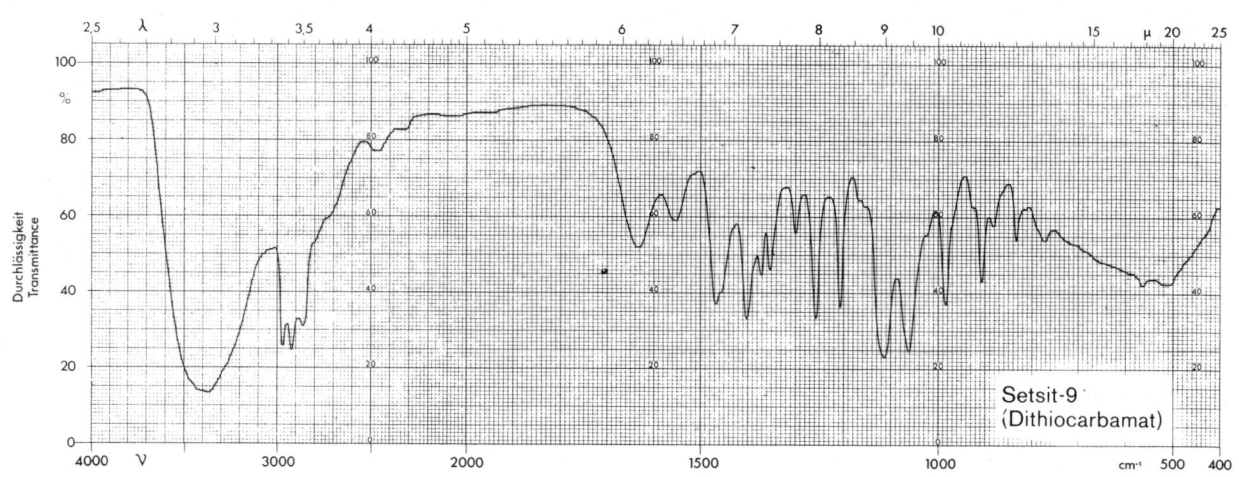

Setsit-9
(Dithiocarbamat)

6340

Verbindung:	**Dithiocarbamate**			Compound:	**Dithiocarbamates**		
Formel:		M.:		Formula:		M. w.:	
Handelsname:	**Setsit-9**	Herst.:	**Vanderbilt**	Tradename:	Setsit-9	Manuf.:	**Vanderbilt**
Präparation:	**Kapill. Film**	Dez. Nr.:	**5.19**	Preparation:	Capill. film	Dec. No.:	**5.19**

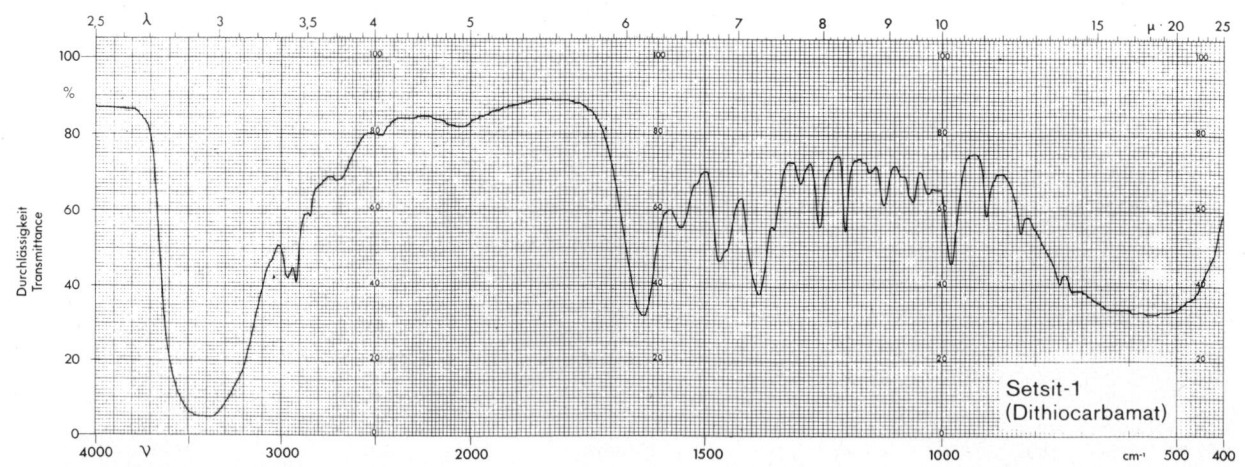

Setsit-1
(Dithiocarbamat)

6341

Verbindung:	**Dithiocarbamate**			Compound:	**Dithiocarbamates**		
Formel:		M.:		Formula:		M. w.:	
Handelsname:	Setsit-1	Herst.:	**Vanderbilt**	Tradename:	Setsit-1	Manuf.:	**Vanderbilt**
Präparation:	**Kapill. Film**	Dez. Nr.:	**5.20**	Preparation:	Capill. film	Dec. No.:	**5.20**

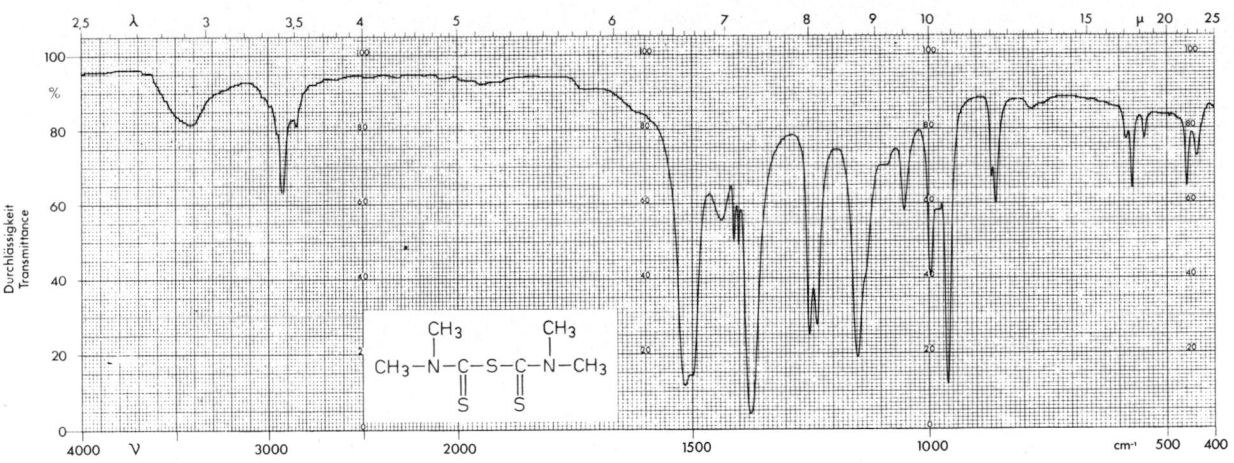

Verbindung: Tetramethylthiurammonosulfid
Formel: $C_6H_{12}N_2S_3$ M.: 208,3
Handelsname: Vulk. Thiuram MS   Herst.: Bayer
Präparation: KBr (4/1000)   Dez. Nr.: 6.1

Compound: Tetramethyl thiuram monosulfide   6342
Formula: $C_6H_{12}N_2S_3$ M. w.: 208,3
Tradename: Vulk. Thiuram MS   Manuf.: Bayer
Preparation: KBr (4/1000)   Dec. No.: 6.1

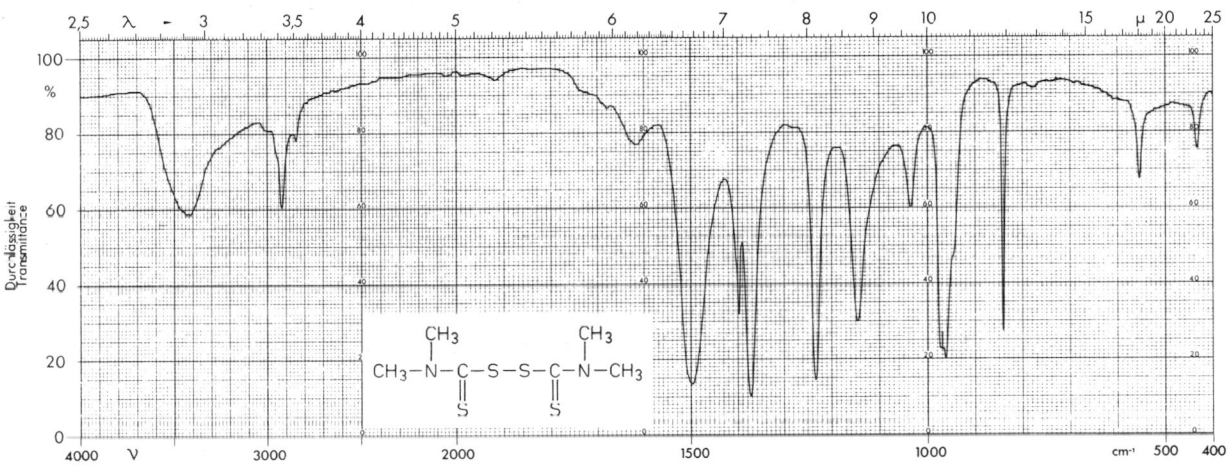

Verbindung: Tetramethylthiuramdisulfid
Formel: $C_6H_{12}N_2S_4$ M.: 240,4
Handelsname: Vulkacit Thiuram   Herst.: Bayer
Präparation: KBr (6/1000)   Dez. Nr.: 6.2

Compound: Tetramethyl thiuram disulfide   6343
Formula: $C_6H_{12}N_2S_4$ M. w.: 240,4
Tradename: Vulkacit Thiuram   Manuf.: Bayer
Preparation: KBr (6/1000)   Dec. No.: 6.2

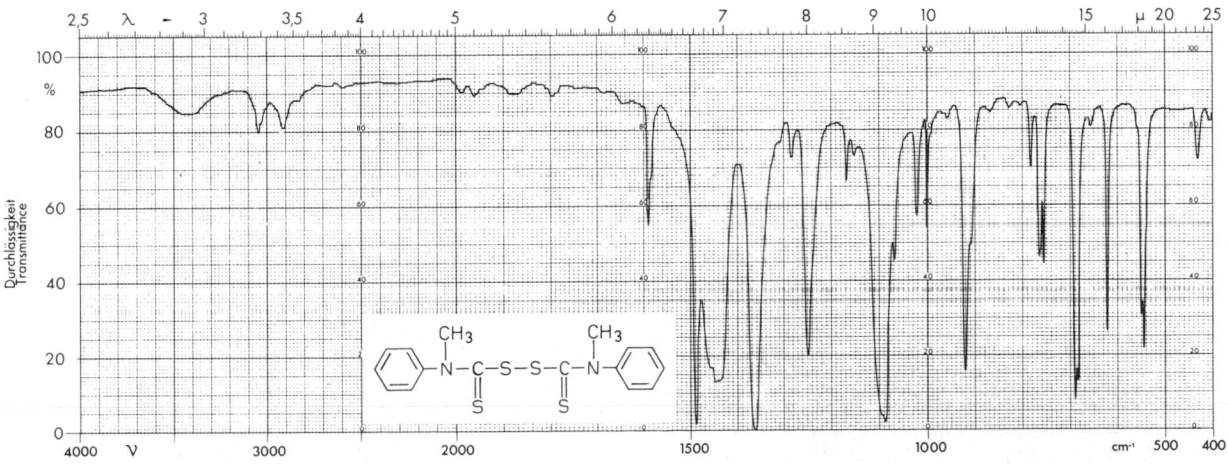

Verbindung: N,N'-Dimethyl-N,N'-diphenyl-
thiuramdisulfid
Formel: $C_{16}H_{16}N_2S_4$ M.: 364,5
Handelsname: Vulkacit J   Herst.: Bayer
Präparation: KBr (3/1000)   Dez. Nr.: 6.3

Compound: N,N'-Dimethyl-N,N'-diphenyl thiuram
disulfide   6344
Formula: $C_{16}H_{16}N_2S_4$ M. w.: 364,5
Tradename: Vulkacit J   Manuf.: Bayer
Preparation: KBr (3/1000)   Dec. No.: 6.3

Beschleuniger
7. Heterocyclische Verbindungen
7.1. Imidazoline und Piperidinderivate

Accelerators
7. Heterocyclic Compounds
7.1. Imidazolines and Piperidine Derivatives

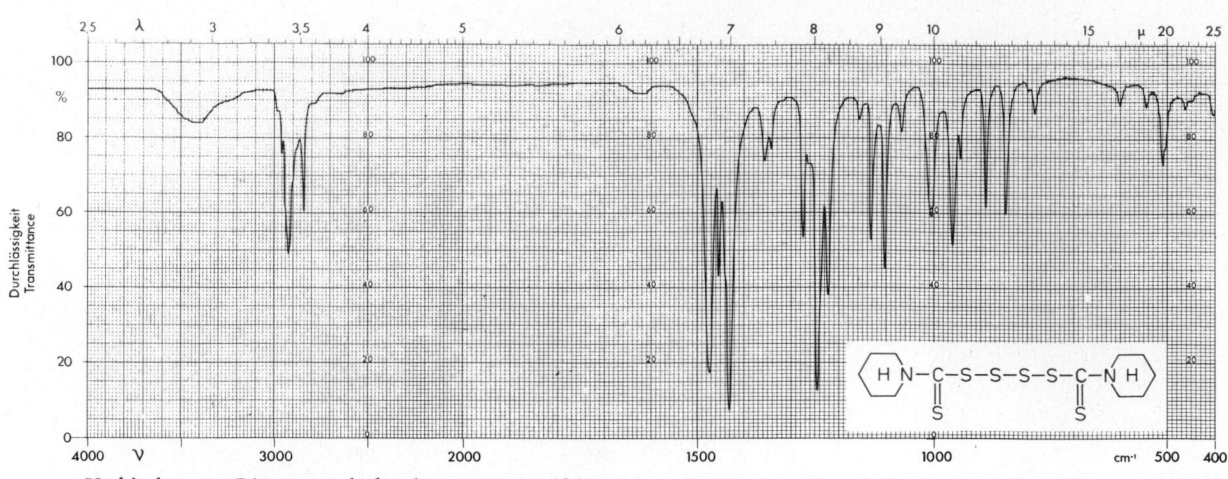

6345

Verbindung:	Dipentamethylenthiuramtetrasulfid			
Formel:	$C_{12}H_{20}N_2S_6$	M.:	384,6	
Handelsname:	Tetrone A	Herst.:	Du Pont	
Präparation:	KBr (3/1000)	Dez. Nr.:	6.4	

Compound:	Dipentamethylene thiuram tetrasulfide			
Formula:	$C_{12}H_{20}N_2S_6$	M. w.:	384,6	
Tradename:	Tetrone A	Manuf.:	Du Pont	
Preparation:	KBr (3/1000)	Dec. No.:	6.4	

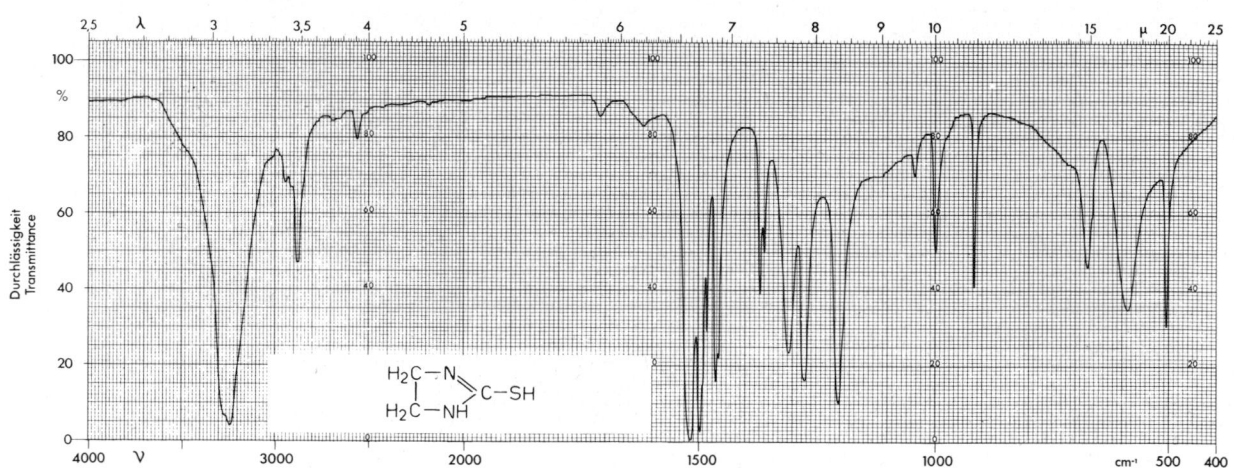

6346

Verbindung:	2-Merkaptoimidazolin			
Formel:	$C_3H_6N_2S$	M.:	102,1	
Handelsname:	NA-22	Herst.:	Du Pont	
Präparation:	KBr (2/1000)	Dez. Nr.:	7.1.1	

Compound:	2-Mercapto-imidazoline			
Formula:	$C_3H_6N_2S$	M. w.:	102,1	
Tradename:	NA-22	Manuf.:	Du Pont	
Preparation:	KBr (2/1000)	Dec. No.:	7.1.1	

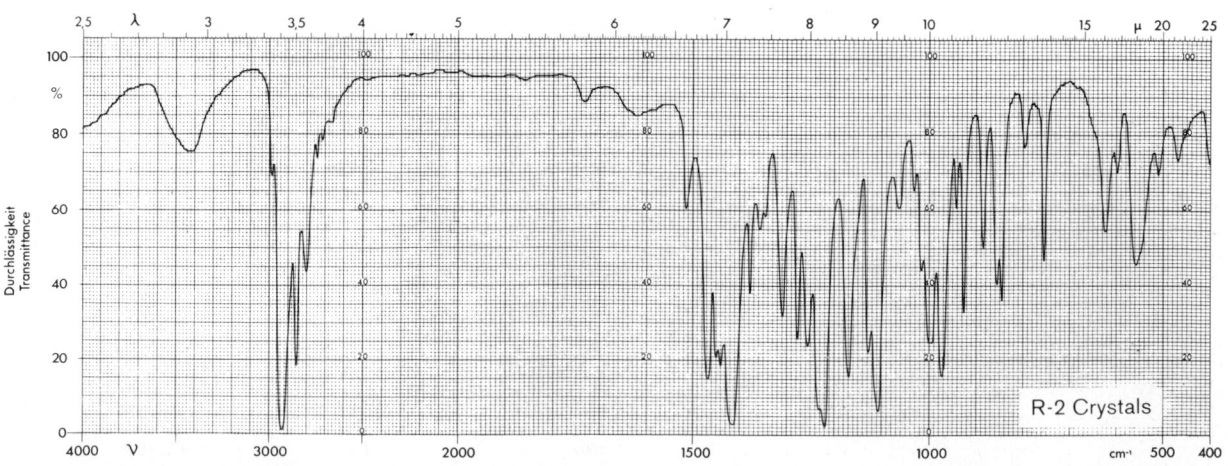

6347

Verbindung:	Reaktionsprodukt von Methylenpiperidin und Schwefelkohlenstoff			
Formel:		M.:		
Handelsname:	R-2 Crystals	Herst.:	Monsanto	
Präparation:	KBr (6/1000)	Dez. Nr.:	7.1.2	

Compound:	Reaction product of methylene piperidine and carbon disulfide			
Formula:		M. w.:		
Tradename:	R-2 Crystals	Manuf.:	Monsanto	
Preparation:	KBr (6/1000)	Dec. No.:	7.1.2	

Beschleuniger
7. Heterocyclische Verbindungen
7.2. Benzothiazolderivate

Accelerators
7. Heterocyclic Compounds
7.2. Benzothiazole Derivatives

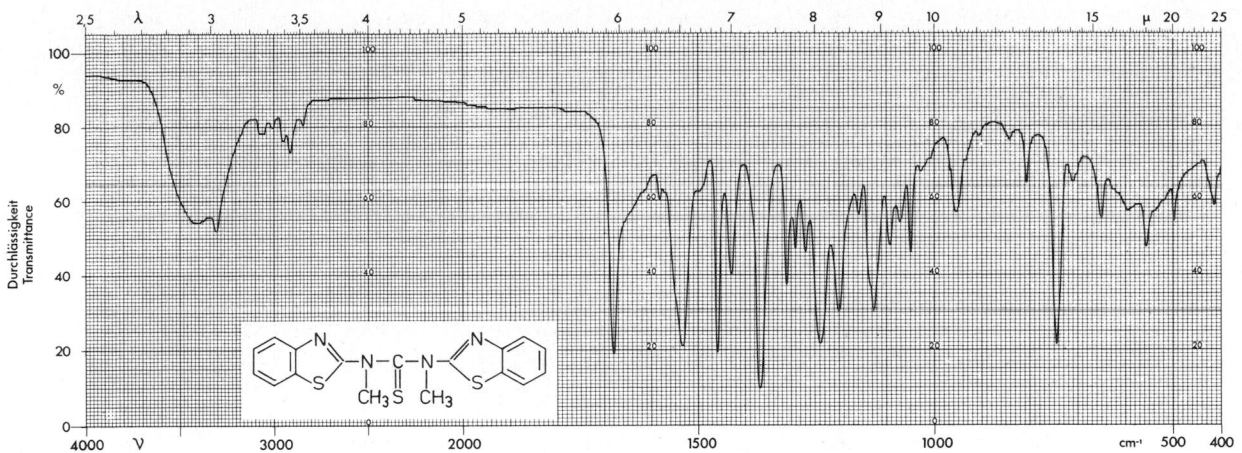

Verbindung:	**Di-benzothiazyl-dimethylthioharnstoff**	Compound:	**Di-benzothiazyl-dimethylthiourea**
Formel:	$C_{17}H_{14}N_4S_3$ M.: **370,5**	Formula:	$C_{17}H_{14}N_4S_3$ M. w.: **370,5**
Handelsname: **El-Sixty** Herst.: **Monsanto**		Tradename: **El-Sixty** Manuf.: **Monsanto**	
Präparation: **KBr (6/1000)** Dez. Nr.: **7.2.1**		Preparation: **KBr (6/1000)** Dec. No.: **7.2.1**	

6348

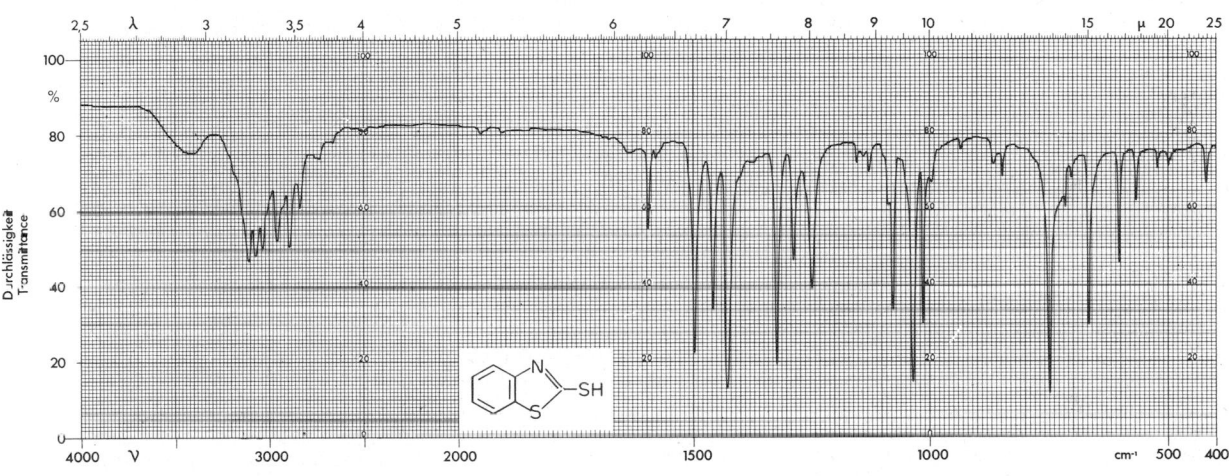

Verbindung:	**2-Merkaptobenzothiazol**	Compound:	**2-Mercaptobenzothiazole**
Formel:	$C_7H_5NS_2$ M.: **167,2**	Formula:	$C_7H_5NS_2$ M. w.: **167,2**
Handelsname: **Vulkacit Mercapto** Herst.: **Bayer**		Tradename: **Vulkacit Mercapto** Manuf.: **Bayer**	
Präparation: **KBr (5/1000)** Dez. Nr.: **7.2.2**		Preparation: **KBr (5/1000)** Dec. No.: **7.2.2**	

6349

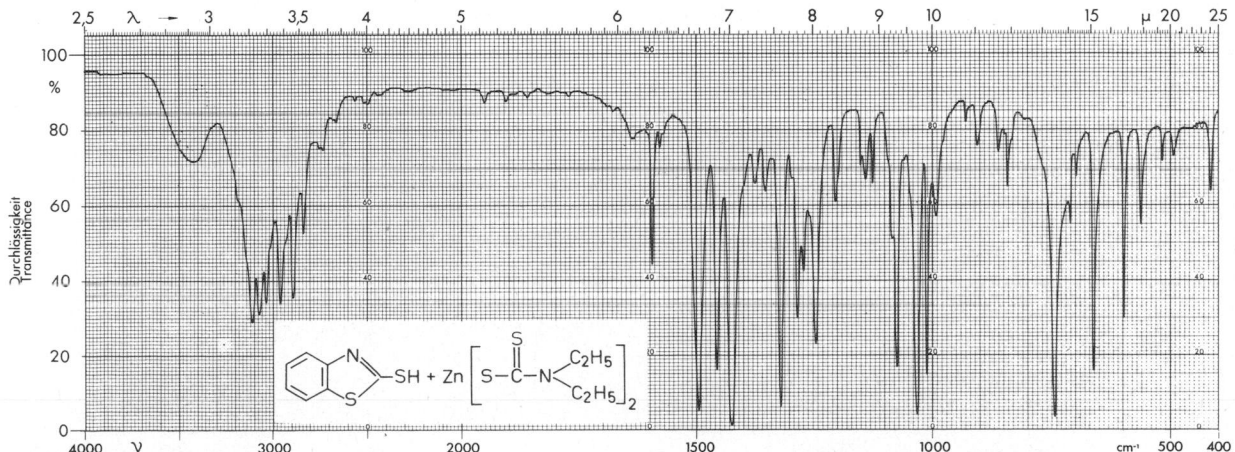

Verbindung:	**2-Merkaptobenzothiazol + Zn-**	Compound:	**2-Mercaptobenzothiazole + Zn-**
	N-diethyldithiocarbamat		**N-diethyl dithiocarbamate**
Formel:	M.:	Formula:	M. w.:
Handelsname: **Vulkacit MDA/C** Herst.: **Bayer**		Tradename: **Vulkacit MDA/C** Manuf.: **Bayer**	
Präparation: **KBr (4/1000)** Dez. Nr.: **7.2.3**		Preparation: **KBr (4/1000)** Dec. No.: **7.2.3**	

6350

Beschleuniger
7. Heterocyclische Verbindungen
7.2. Benzothiazolderivate

Accelerators
7. Heterocyclic Compounds
7.2. Benzothiazole Derivatives

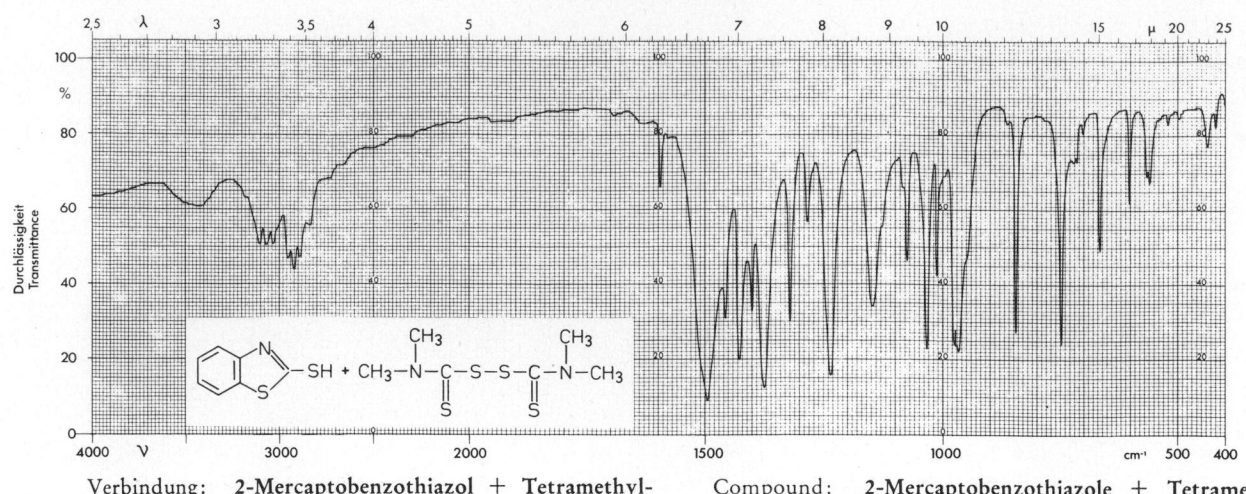

6351

Verbindung:	2-Mercaptobenzothiazol + Tetramethyl-thiuramdisulfid	Compound:	2-Mercaptobenzothiazole + Tetramethyl thiuram disulfide
Formel:	M.:	Formula:	M. w.:
Handelsname: Vulkacit MT/C	Herst.: Bayer	Tradename: Vulkacit MT/C	Manuf.: Bayer
Präparation: KBr (6/1000)	Dez. Nr.: 7.2.4	Preparation: KBr (6/1000)	Dec. No.: 7.2.4

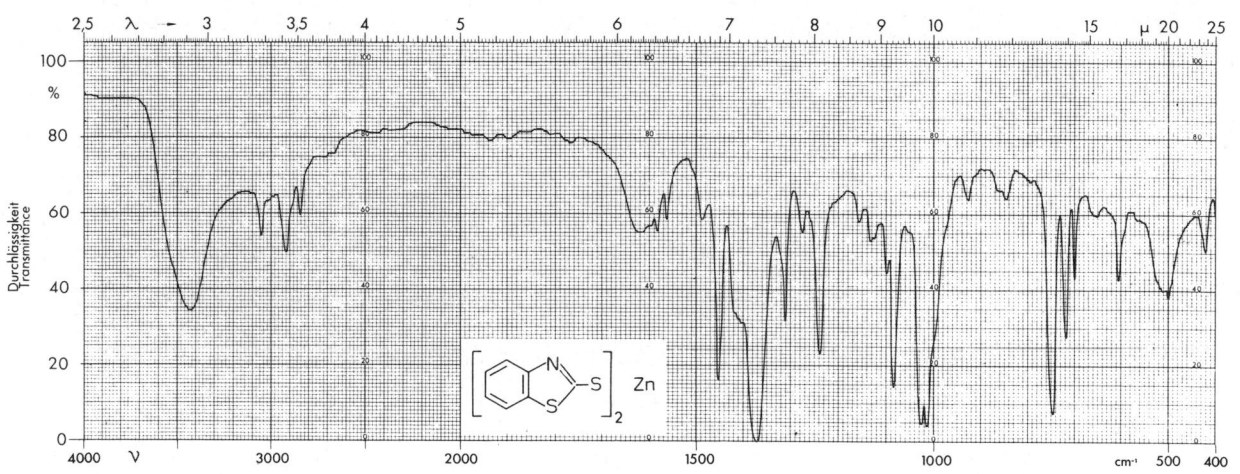

6352

Verbindung:	Zink-2-merkaptobenzothiazol	Compound:	Zinc-2-mercaptobenzothiazole
Formel: $C_{14}H_8N_2S_4Zn$	M.: 397,8	Formula: $C_{14}H_8N_2S_4Zn$	M. w.: 397,8
Handelsname: Vulkacit ZM	Herst.: Bayer	Tradename: Vulkacit ZM	Manuf.: Bayer
Präparation: KBr (10/1000)	Dez. Nr.: 7.2.5	Preparation: KBr (10/1000)	Dec. No.: 7.2.5

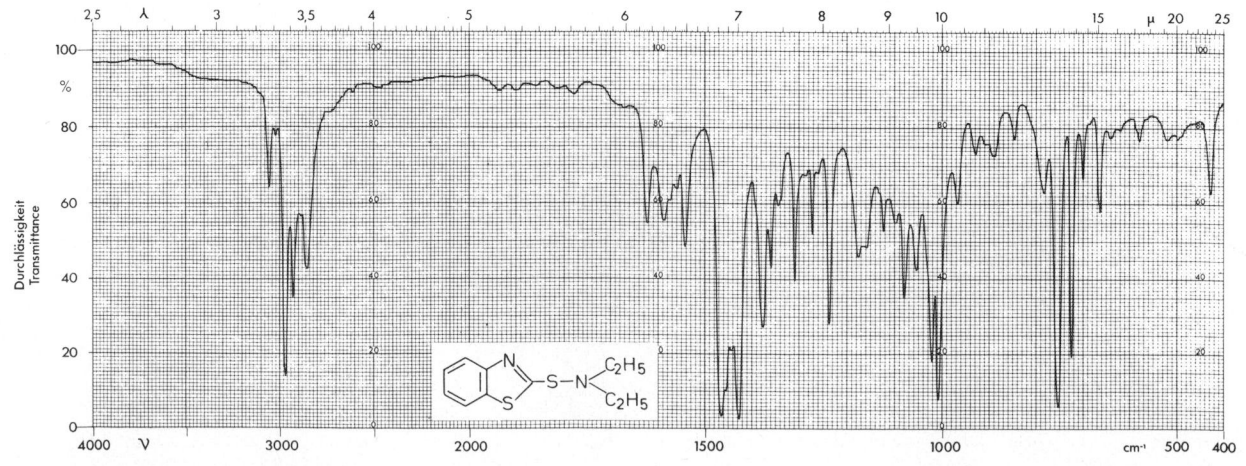

6353

Verbindung:	N,N-Diethyl-2-benzothiazolsulfenamid	Compound:	N,N-Diethyl-2-benzothiazole sulfenamide
Formel: $C_{11}H_{14}N_2S_2$	M.: 238,3	Formula: $C_{11}H_{14}N_2S_2$	M. w.: 238,3
Handelsname: Vulkacit AZ	Herst.: Bayer	Tradename: Vulkacit AZ	Manuf.: Bayer
Präparation: Kapill. Film	Dez. Nr.: 7.2.6	Preparation: Capill. film	Dec. No.: 7.2.6

Beschleuniger
7. Heterocyclische Verbindungen
7.2. Benzothiazolderivate

Accelerators
7. Heterocyclic Compounds
7.2. Benzothiazole Derivatives

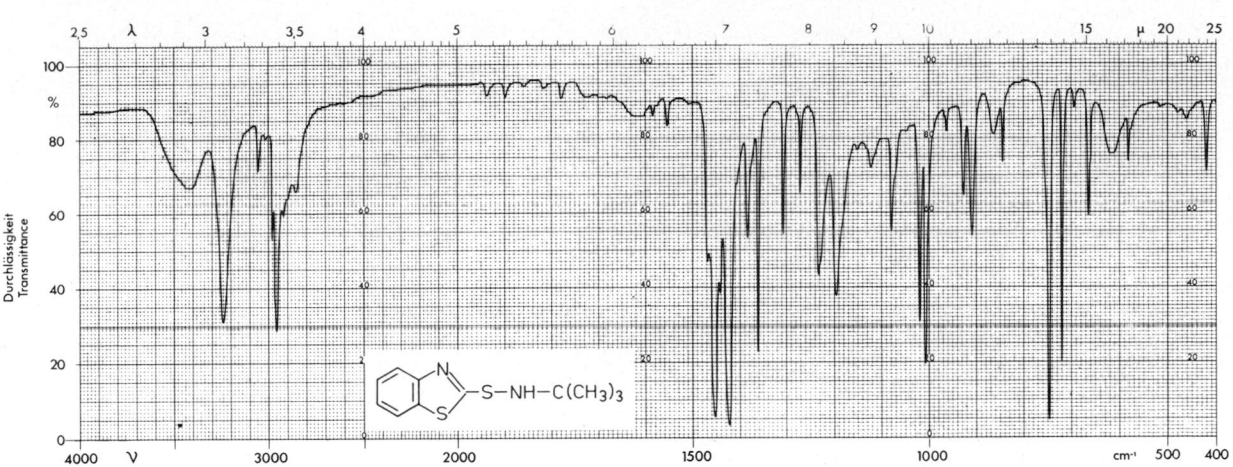

Verbindung:	N-Tert.butyl-2-benzothiazolsulfenamid			Compound:	N-Tert.butyl-2-benzothiazolesulfenamide		6354
Formel:	$C_{11}H_{14}N_2S_2$	M.:	238,3	Formula:	$C_{11}H_{14}N_2S_2$	M. w.: 238,3	
Handelsname:	Santocure NS	Herst.:	Monsanto	Tradename:	Santocure NS	Manuf.: Monsanto	
Präparation:	KBr (6/1000)	Dez. Nr.:	7.2.7	Preparation:	KBr (6/1000)	Dec. No.: 7.2.7	

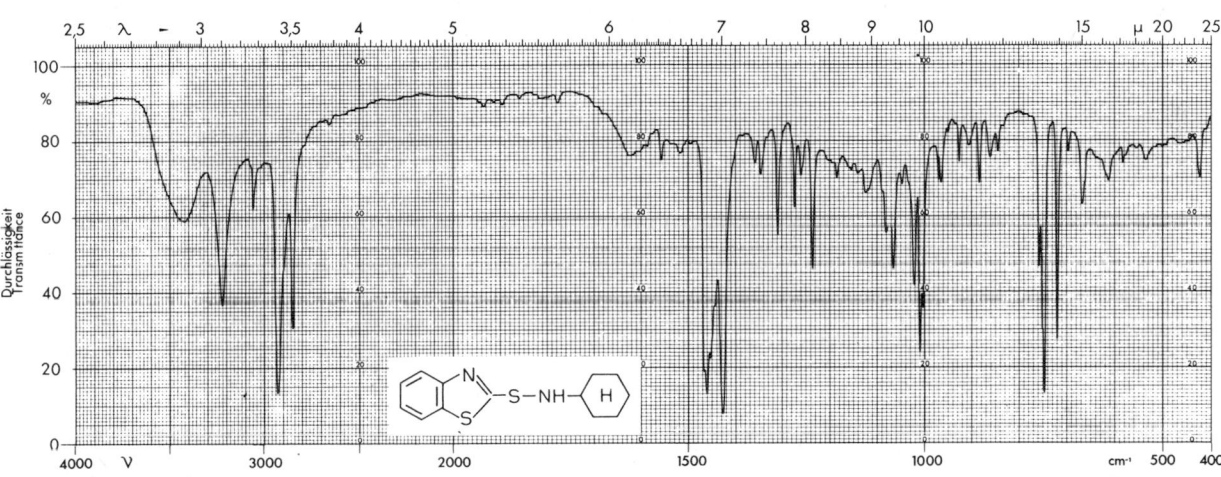

Verbindung:	N-Cyclohexyl-2-benzothiazolsulfenamid			Compound:	N-Cyclohexyl-2-benzothiazolesulfenamide		6355
Formel:	$C_{13}H_{16}N_2S_2$	M.:	264,4	Formula:	$C_{13}H_{16}N_2S_2$	M. w.: 264,4	
Handelsname:	Vulkacit CZ	Herst.:	Bayer	Tradename:	Vulkacit CZ	Manuf.: Bayer	
Präparation:	KBr (6/1000)	Dez. Nr.:	7.2.8	Preparation:	KBr (6/1000)	Dec. No.: 7.2.8	

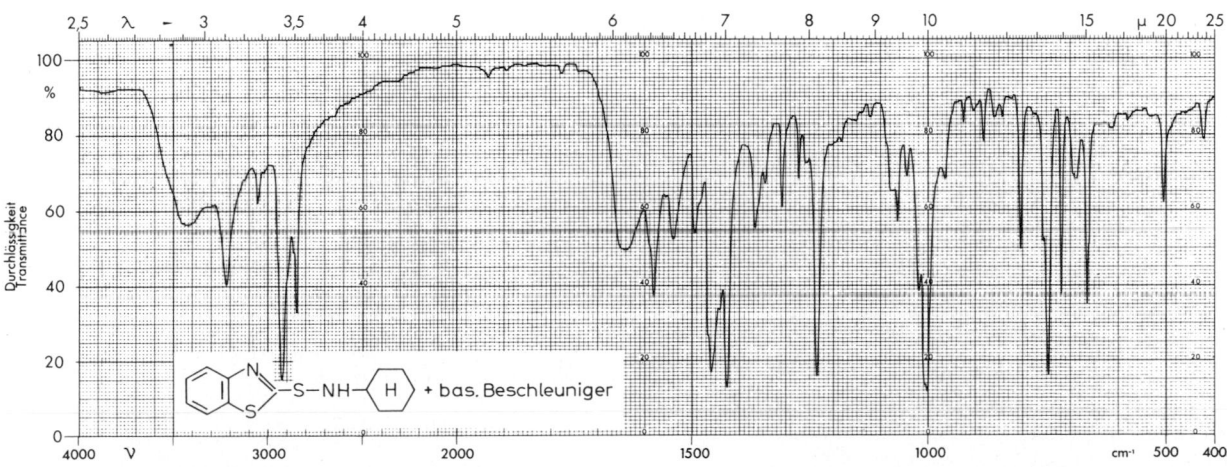

Verbindung:	Mischungen von N-Cyclohexyl-2-benzothiazolsulfenamid mit basischen Beschleunigern			Compound:	Mixture of N-cyclohexyl-2-benzothiazole-sulfenamide with basic accelerators		6356
Formel:		M.:		Formula:		M. w.:	
Handelsname:	Vulkacit FZ	Herst.:	Bayer	Tradename:	Vulkacit FZ	Manuf.: Bayer	
Präparation:	KBr (6/1000)	Dez. Nr.:	7.2.9	Preparation:	KBr (6/1000)	Dec. No.: 7.2.9	

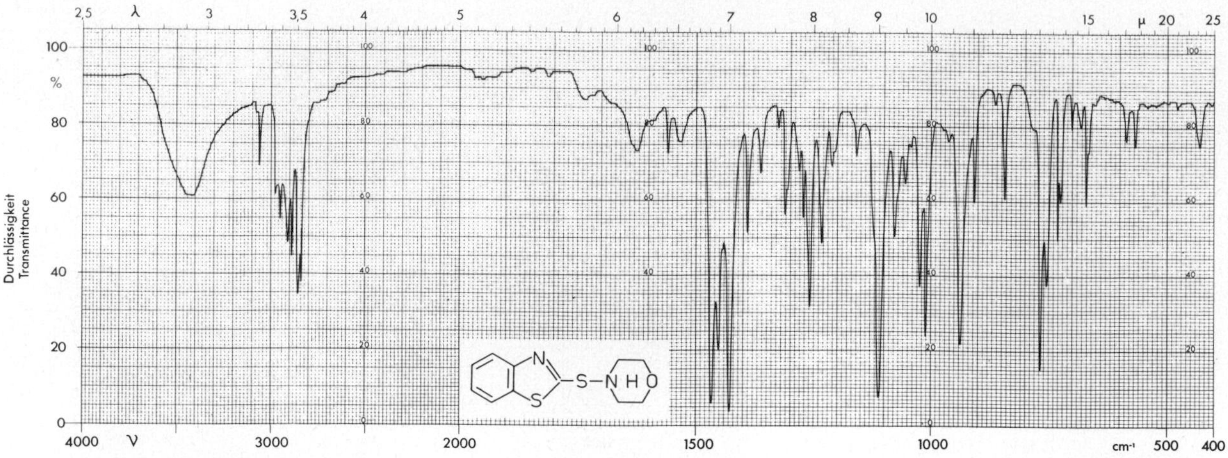

Beschleuniger
7. Heterocyclische Verbindungen
7.2. Benzothiazolderivate

Accelerators
7. Heterocyclic Compounds
7.2. Benzothiazole Derivatives

6357

Verbindung:	N-Oxydiethylen-2-benzothiazolsulfenamid		Compound:	N-Oxydiethylene-2-benzothiazole-sulfenamide
Formel:	$C_{11}H_{12}N_9OS_2$	M.: 252,3	Formula:	$C_{11}H_{12}N_2OS_2$	M. w.: 252,3
Handelsname:	Vulkacit MOZ	Herst.: Bayer	Tradename:	Vulkacit MOZ	Manuf.: Bayer
Präparation:	KBr (4/1000)	Dez. Nr.: 7.2.10	Preparation:	KBr (4/1000)	Dec. No.: 7.2.10

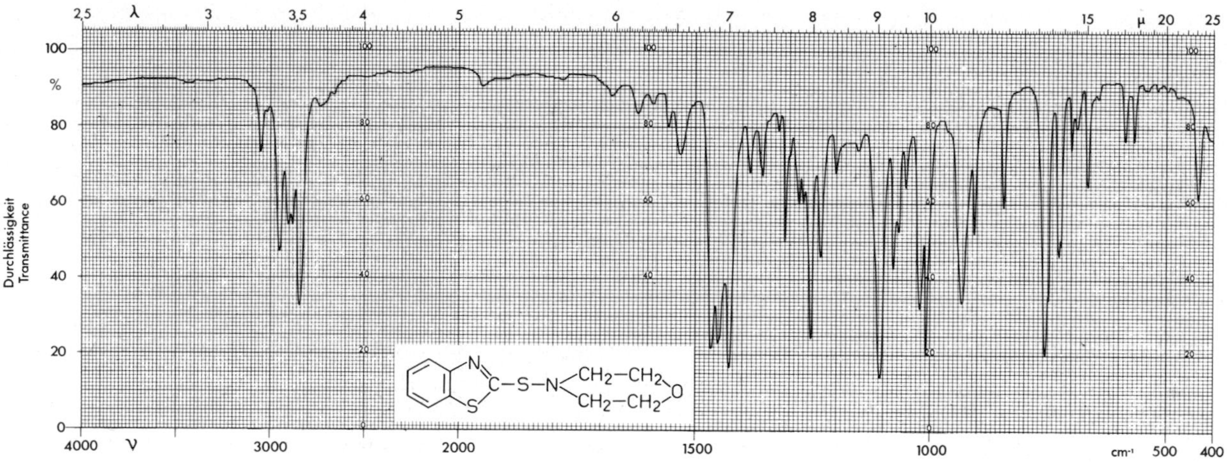

6358

Verbindung:	N-Oxydiethylen-2-benzothiazolsulfenamid		Compound:	N-Oxydiethylene-2-benzothiazole-sulfenamide
Formel:	$C_{11}H_{12}N_9OS_2$	M.: 252,3	Formula:	$C_{11}H_{12}N_2OS_2$	M. w.: 252,3
Handelsname:	Vulkacit MOZ	Herst.: Bayer	Tradename:	Vulkacit MOZ	Manuf.: Bayer
Präparation:	Capill. Film	Dez. Nr.: 7.2.10	Preparation:	Capill. film	Dec. No.: 7.2.10

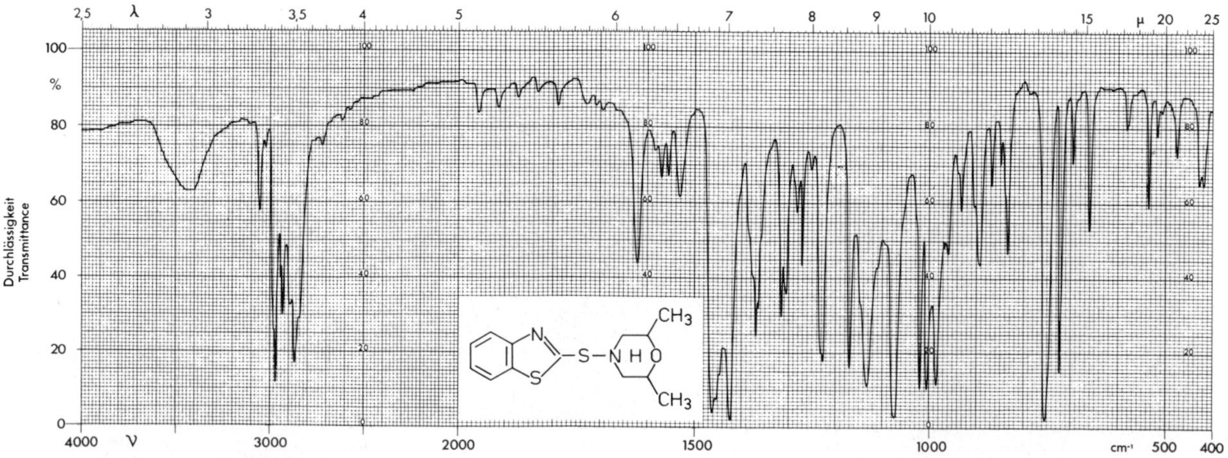

6359

Verbindung:	N-Oxydiisopropylen-2-benzothiazolsulfenamid		Compound:	N-Oxydiisopropylene-2-benzothiazole-sulfenamide
Formel:	$C_{13}H_{16}N_2OS_2$	M.: 280,3	Formula:	$C_{13}H_{16}N_2OS_2$	M. w.: 280,3
Handelsname:	Santocure 26	Herst.: Monsanto	Tradename:	Santocure 26	Manuf.: Monsanto
Präparation:	KBr (4/1000)	Dez. Nr.: 7.2.11	Preparation:	KBr (4/1000)	Dec. No.: 7.2.11

Beschleuniger
7. Heterocyclische Verbindungen
7.2. Benzothiazolderivate

Accelerators
7. Heterocyclic Compounds
7.2. Benzothiazole Derivatives

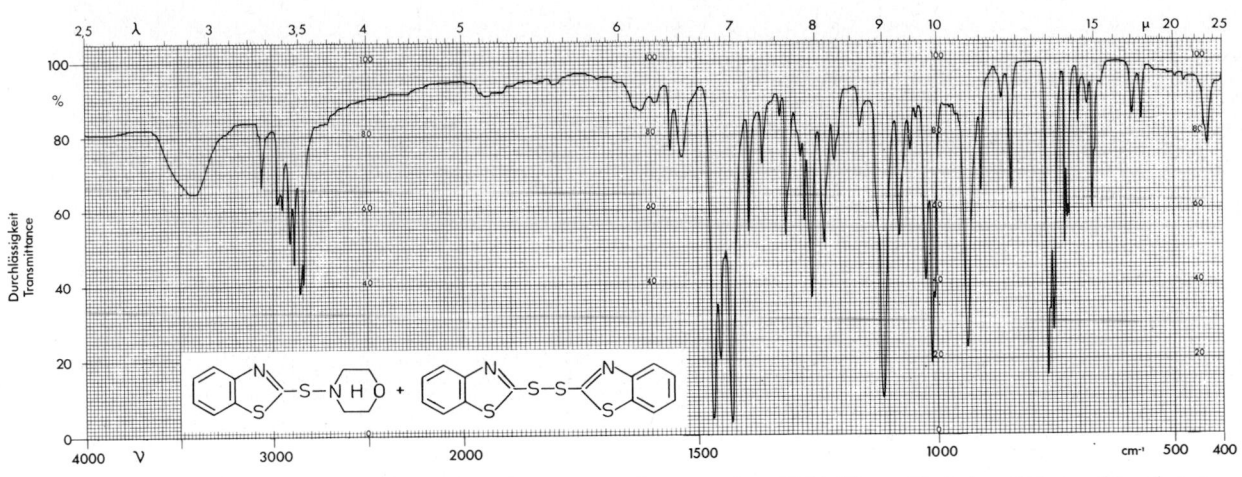

Verbindung: 90% N-Oxydiethylen-2-benzothiazol-sulfenamid u. 10% Di-2-benzothiazyl-disulfid

Compound: 90 % N-oxydiethylene-2-benzothiazole-sulfenamide a. 10 % di-2-benzothiazyl disulfide

6360

Formel: — M.: —
Handelsname: Nobs No. 1 — Herst.: Cyanamid
Präparation: KBr (3/1000) — Dez. Nr.: 7.2.12

Formula: — M. w.: —
Tradename: Nobs No. 1 — Manuf.: Cyanamid
Preparation: KBr (3/1000) — Dec. No.: 7.2.12

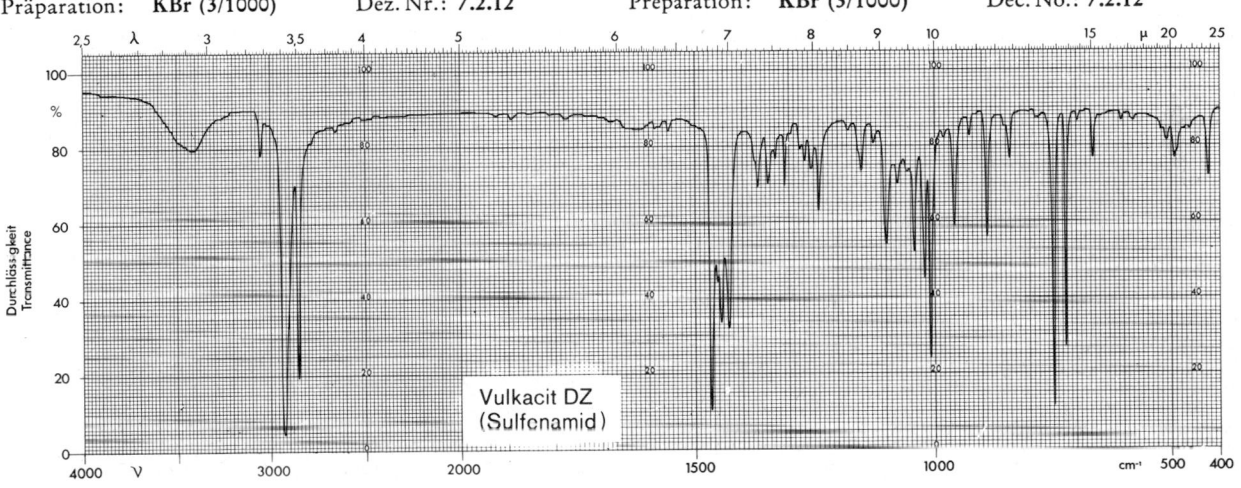

Vulkacit DZ (Sulfenamid)

Verbindung: Dicyclohexyl-2-benzothiazol-sulfenamid

Compound: Dicyclohexyl-2-benzothiazole-sulfenamide

6361

Formel: — M.: —
Handelsname: Vulkacit DZ — Herst.: Bayer
Präparation: KBr (5/1000) — Dez. Nr.: 7.2.13

Formula: — M. w.: —
Tradename: Vulkacit DZ — Manuf.: Bayer
Preparation: KBr (5/1000) — Dec. No.: 7.2.13

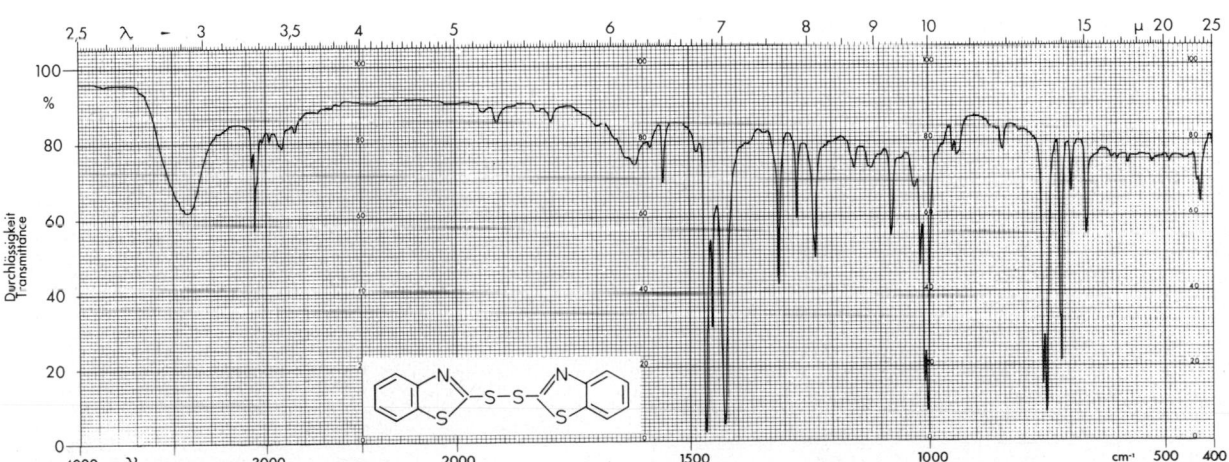

Verbindung: Di-2-benzothiazyldisulfid
Formel: $C_{14}H_8N_2S_4$ — M.: 332,4
Handelsname: Vulkacit DM — Herst.: Bayer
Präparation: KBr (5/1000) — Dez. Nr.: 7.2.14

Compound: Di-2-benzothiazyl disulfide
Formula: $C_{14}H_8N_2S_4$ — M. w.: 332,4
Tradename: Vulkacit DM — Manuf.: Bayer
Preparation: KBr (5/1000) — Dec. No.: 7.2.14

6362

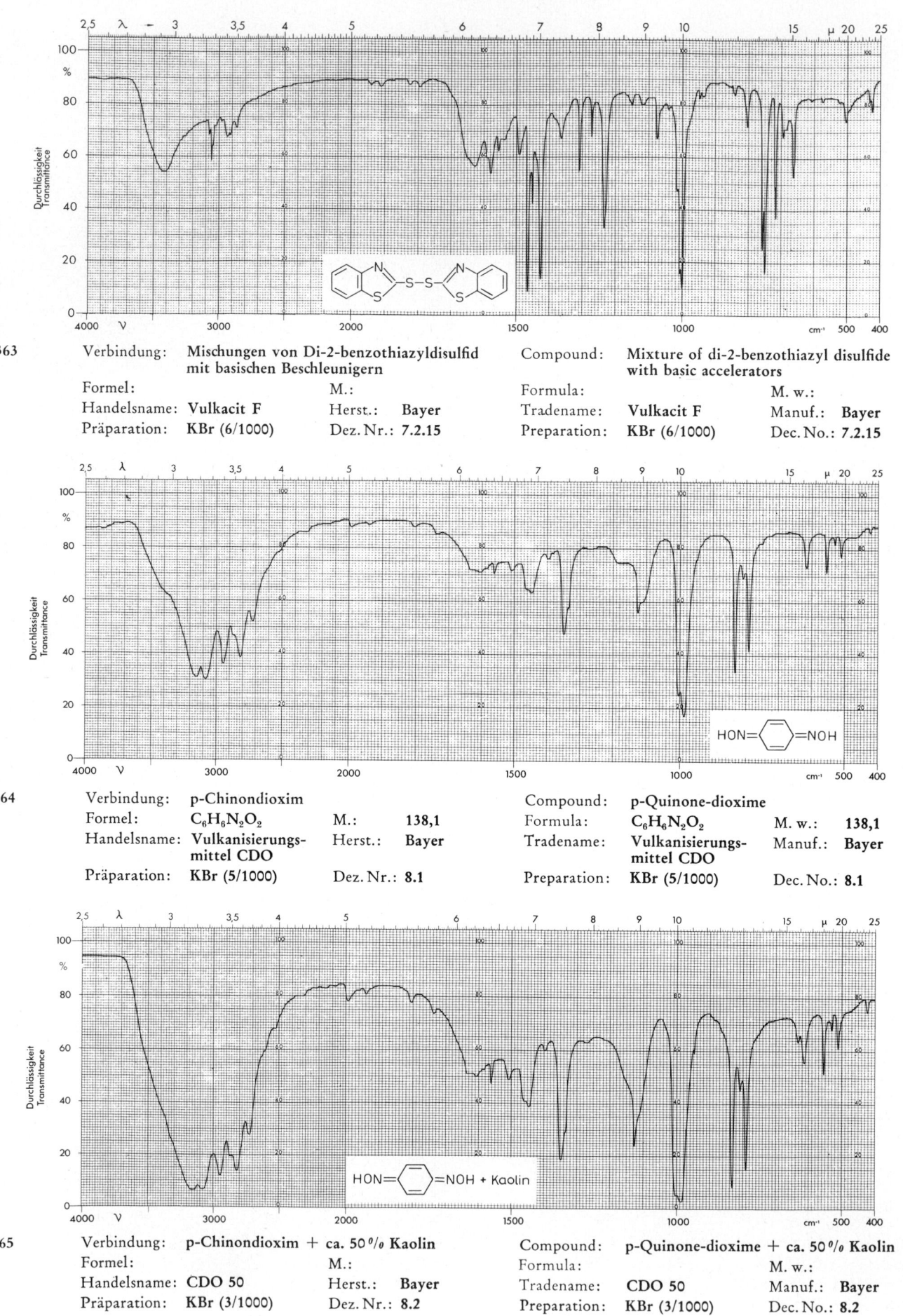

6363   Verbindung: Mischungen von Di-2-benzothiazyldisulfid   Compound: Mixture of di-2-benzothiazyl disulfide
            mit basischen Beschleunigern   with basic accelerators

Formel:		M.:	Formula:	M. w.:
Handelsname: **Vulkacit F**	Herst.: **Bayer**		Tradename: **Vulkacit F**	Manuf.: **Bayer**
Präparation: **KBr (6/1000)**	Dez. Nr.: **7.2.15**		Preparation: **KBr (6/1000)**	Dec. No.: **7.2.15**

6364   Verbindung: p-Chinondioxim   Compound: p-Quinone-dioxime

Formel: $C_6H_6N_2O_2$	M.: **138,1**		Formula: $C_6H_6N_2O_2$	M. w.: **138,1**
Handelsname: **Vulkanisierungs-**	Herst.: **Bayer**		Tradename: **Vulkanisierungs-**	Manuf.: **Bayer**
mittel CDO			**mittel CDO**	
Präparation: **KBr (5/1000)**	Dez. Nr.: **8.1**		Preparation: **KBr (5/1000)**	Dec. No.: **8.1**

6365   Verbindung: p-Chinondioxim + ca. **50 %** Kaolin   Compound: p-Quinone-dioxime + ca. **50 %** Kaolin

Formel:	M.:		Formula:	M. w.:
Handelsname: **CDO 50**	Herst.: **Bayer**		Tradename: **CDO 50**	Manuf.: **Bayer**
Präparation: **KBr (3/1000)**	Dez. Nr.: **8.2**		Preparation: **KBr (3/1000)**	Dec. No.: **8.2**

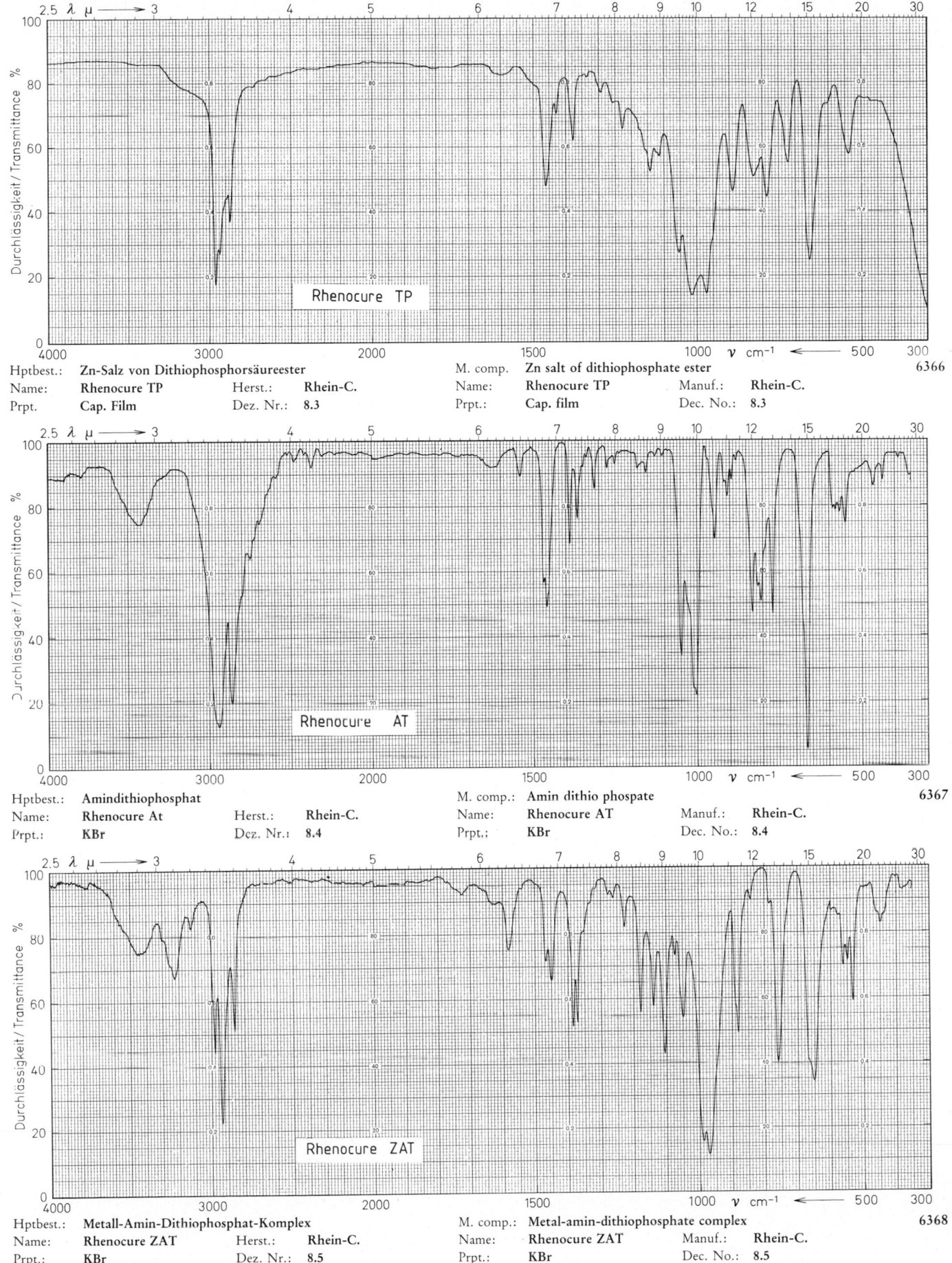

Rhenocure TP

Hptbest.: Zn-Salz von Dithiophosphorsäureester
Name: Rhenocure TP   Herst.: Rhein-C.
Prpt. Cap. Film   Dez. Nr.: 8.3

M. comp. Zn salt of dithiophosphate ester
Name: Rhenocure TP   Manuf.: Rhein-C.
Prpt.: Cap. film   Dec. No.: 8.3

6366

Rhenocure AT

Hptbest.: Amindithiophosphat
Name: Rhenocure At   Herst.: Rhein-C.
Prpt.: KBr   Dez. Nr.: 8.4

M. comp.: Amin dithio phospate
Name: Rhenocure AT   Manuf.: Rhein-C.
Prpt.; KBr   Dec. No.: 8.4

6367

Rhenocure ZAT

Hptbest.: Metall-Amin-Dithiophosphat-Komplex
Name: Rhenocure ZAT   Herst.: Rhein-C.
Prpt.: KBr   Dez. Nr.: 8.5

M. comp.: Metal-amin-dithiophosphate complex
Name: Rhenocure ZAT   Manuf.: Rhein-C.
Prpt.: KBr   Dec. No.: 8.5

6368

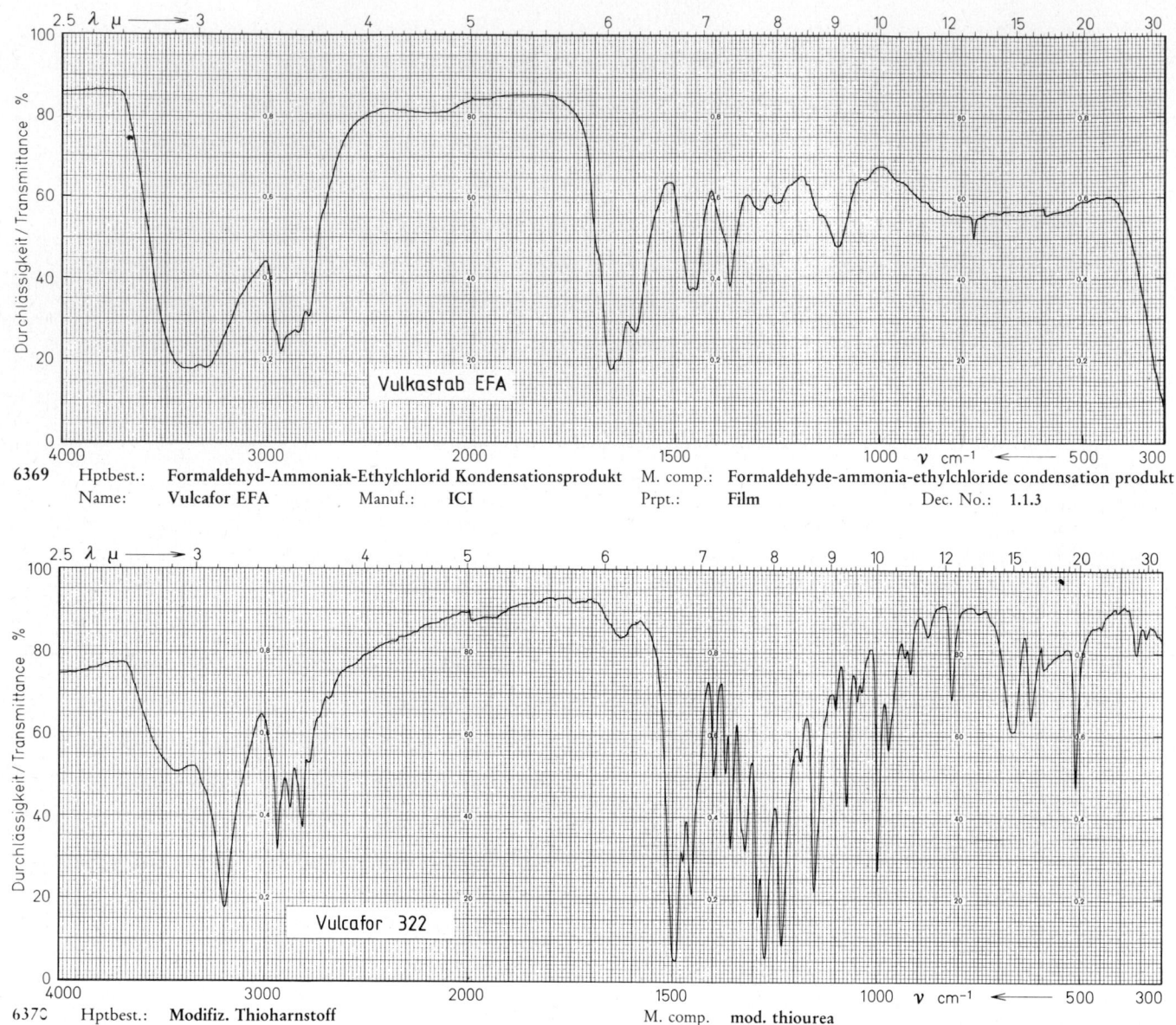

6369   Hptbest.:   **Formaldehyd-Ammoniak-Ethylchlorid Kondensationsprodukt**   M. comp.:   **Formaldehyde-ammonia-ethylchloride condensation produkt**
     Name: **Vulcafor EFA**   Manuf.:   **ICI**   Prpt.:   **Film**   Dec. No.:   **1.1.3**

6370   Hptbest.:   **Modifiz. Thioharnstoff**   M. comp.   **mod. thiourea**
     Name: **Vulcafor 322**   Herst.:   **ICI**   Name: **Vulcafor 322**   Manuf.:   **ICI**
     Prpt.:   **KBr**   Dez. Nr.   **3.5**   Prpt.:   Dec. No.:   **3.5**

Härter und Aktivatoren
für Epoxidharze und Polyurethane

Curing Agents and Activators
for Epoxide Resins and Polyurethanes

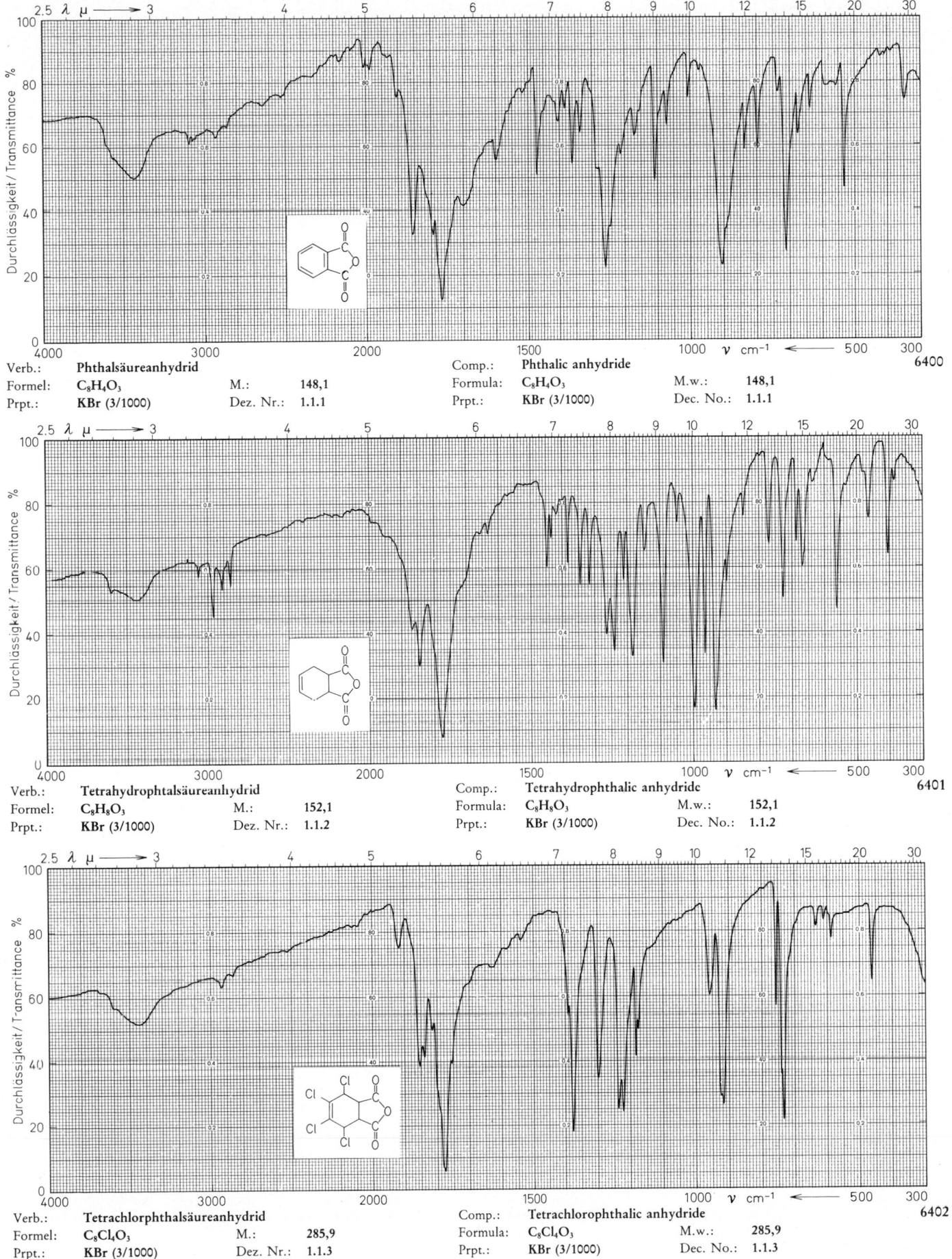

Verb.: **Phthalsäureanhydrid**

Formel: **C₈H₄O₃** M.: **148,1**

Prpt.: **KBr (3/1000)** Dez. Nr.: **1.1.1**

Comp.: **Phthalic anhydride**

Formula: **C₈H₄O₃** M.w.: **148,1**

Prpt.: **KBr (3/1000)** Dec. No.: **1.1.1**

6400

Verb.: **Tetrahydrophtalsäureanhydrid**

Formel: **C₈H₈O₃** M.: **152,1**

Prpt.: **KBr (3/1000)** Dez. Nr.: **1.1.2**

Comp.: **Tetrahydrophthalic anhydride**

Formula: **C₈H₈O₃** M.w.: **152,1**

Prpt.: **KBr (3/1000)** Dec. No.: **1.1.2**

6401

Verb.: **Tetrachlorphthalsäureanhydrid**

Formel: **C₈Cl₄O₃** M.: **285,9**

Prpt.: **KBr (3/1000)** Dez. Nr.: **1.1.3**

Comp.: **Tetrachlorophthalic anhydride**

Formula: **C₈Cl₄O₃** M.w.: **285,9**

Prpt.: **KBr (3/1000)** Dec. No.: **1.1.3**

6402

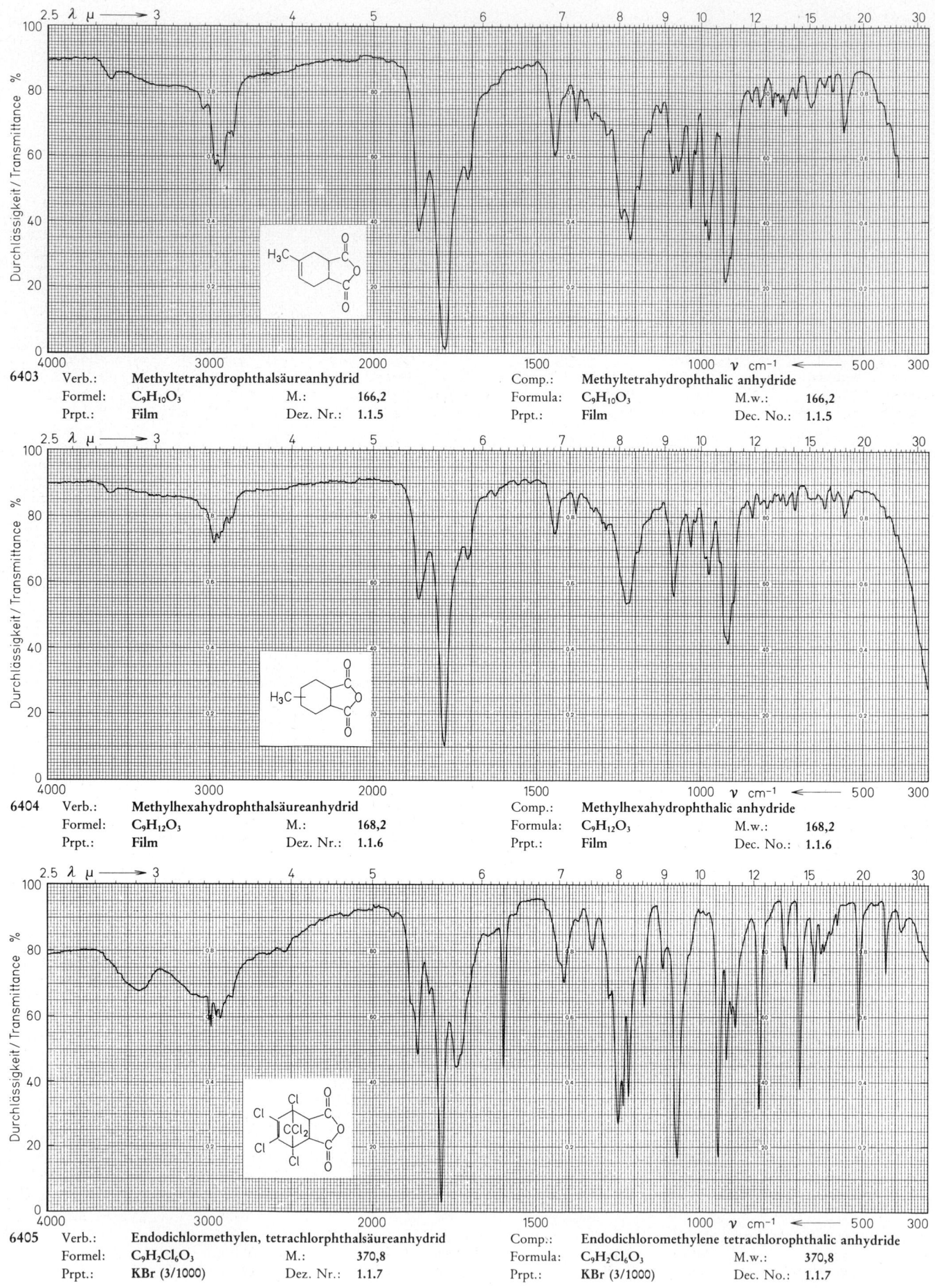

6403 Verb.: **Methyltetrahydrophthalsäureanhydrid** Comp.: **Methyltetrahydrophthalic anhydride**

Formel:	**C₉H₁₀O₃**	M.:	**166,2**	Formula: **C₉H₁₀O₃**	M.w.: **166,2**
Prpt.:	**Film**	Dez. Nr.:	**1.1.5**	Prpt.: **Film**	Dec. No.: **1.1.5**

6404 Verb.: **Methylhexahydrophthalsäureanhydrid** Comp.: **Methylhexahydrophthalic anhydride**

Formel:	**C₉H₁₂O₃**	M.:	**168,2**	Formula: **C₉H₁₂O₃**	M.w.: **168,2**
Prpt.:	**Film**	Dez. Nr.:	**1.1.6**	Prpt.: **Film**	Dec. No.: **1.1.6**

6405 Verb.: **Endodichlormethylen, tetrachlorphthalsäureanhydrid** Comp.: **Endodichloromethylene tetrachlorophthalic anhydride**

Formel:	**C₉H₂Cl₆O₃**	M.:	**370,8**	Formula: **C₉H₂Cl₆O₃**	M.w.: **370,8**
Prpt.:	**KBr (3/1000)**	Dez. Nr.:	**1.1.7**	Prpt.: **KBr (3/1000)**	Dec. No.: **1.1.7**

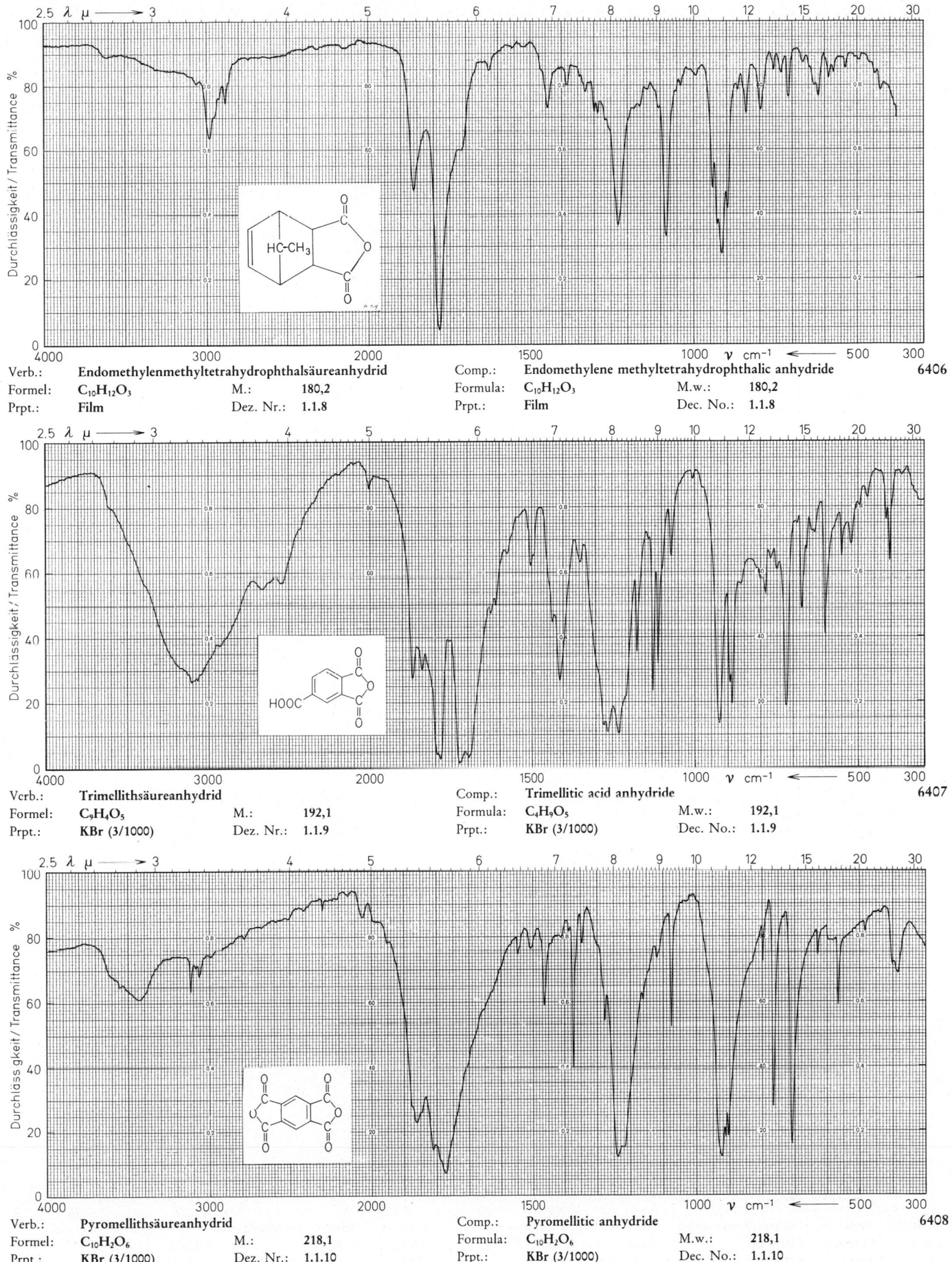

Verb.: **Endomethylenmethyltetrahydrophthalsäureanhydrid**
Formel: **C₁₀H₁₂O₃** M.: **180,2**
Prpt.: **Film** Dez. Nr.: **1.1.8**

Comp.: **Endomethylene methyltetrahydrophthalic anhydride** 6406
Formula: **C₁₀H₁₂O₃** M.w.: **180,2**
Prpt.: **Film** Dec. No.: **1.1.8**

Verb.: **Trimellithsäureanhydrid**
Formel: **C₉H₄O₅** M.: **192,1**
Prpt.: **KBr (3/1000)** Dez. Nr.: **1.1.9**

Comp.: **Trimellitic acid anhydride** 6407
Formula: **C₄H₉O₅** M.w.: **192,1**
Prpt.: **KBr (3/1000)** Dec. No.: **1.1.9**

Verb.: **Pyromellithsäureanhydrid**
Formel: **C₁₀H₂O₆** M.: **218,1**
Prpt.: **KBr (3/1000)** Dez. Nr.: **1.1.10**

Comp.: **Pyromellitic anhydride** 6408
Formula: **C₁₀H₂O₆** M.w.: **218,1**
Prpt.: **KBr (3/1000)** Dec. No.: **1.1.10**

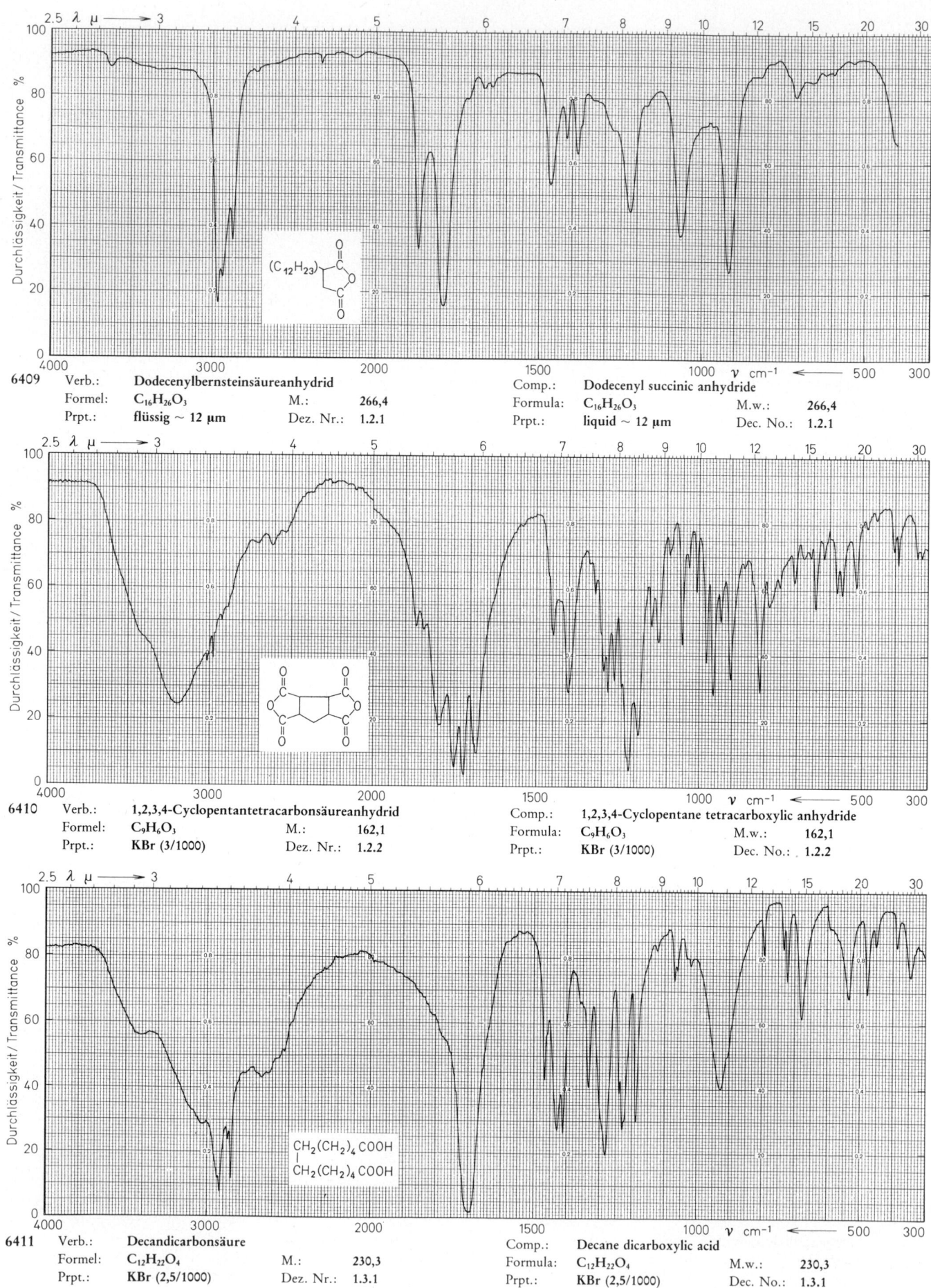

6409 Verb.:   Dodecenylbernsteinsäureanhydrid   Comp.:   Dodecenyl succinic anhydride
      Formel: C₁₆H₂₆O₃   M.:   266,4   Formula: C₁₆H₂₆O₃   M.w.:   266,4
      Prpt.:   flüssig ~ 12 μm   Dez. Nr.: 1.2.1   Prpt.:   liquid ~ 12 μm   Dec. No.: 1.2.1

6410 Verb.:   1,2,3,4-Cyclopentantetracarbonsäureanhydrid   Comp.:   1,2,3,4-Cyclopentane tetracarboxylic anhydride
      Formel: C₉H₆O₃   M.:   162,1   Formula: C₉H₆O₃   M.w.:   162,1
      Prpt.:   KBr (3/1000)   Dez. Nr.: 1.2.2   Prpt.:   KBr (3/1000)   Dec. No.: 1.2.2

6411 Verb.:   Decandicarbonsäure   Comp.:   Decane dicarboxylic acid
      Formel: C₁₂H₂₂O₄   M.:   230,3   Formula: C₁₂H₂₂O₄   M.w.:   230,3
      Prpt.:   KBr (2,5/1000)   Dez. Nr.: 1.3.1   Prpt.:   KBr (2,5/1000)   Dec. No.: 1.3.1

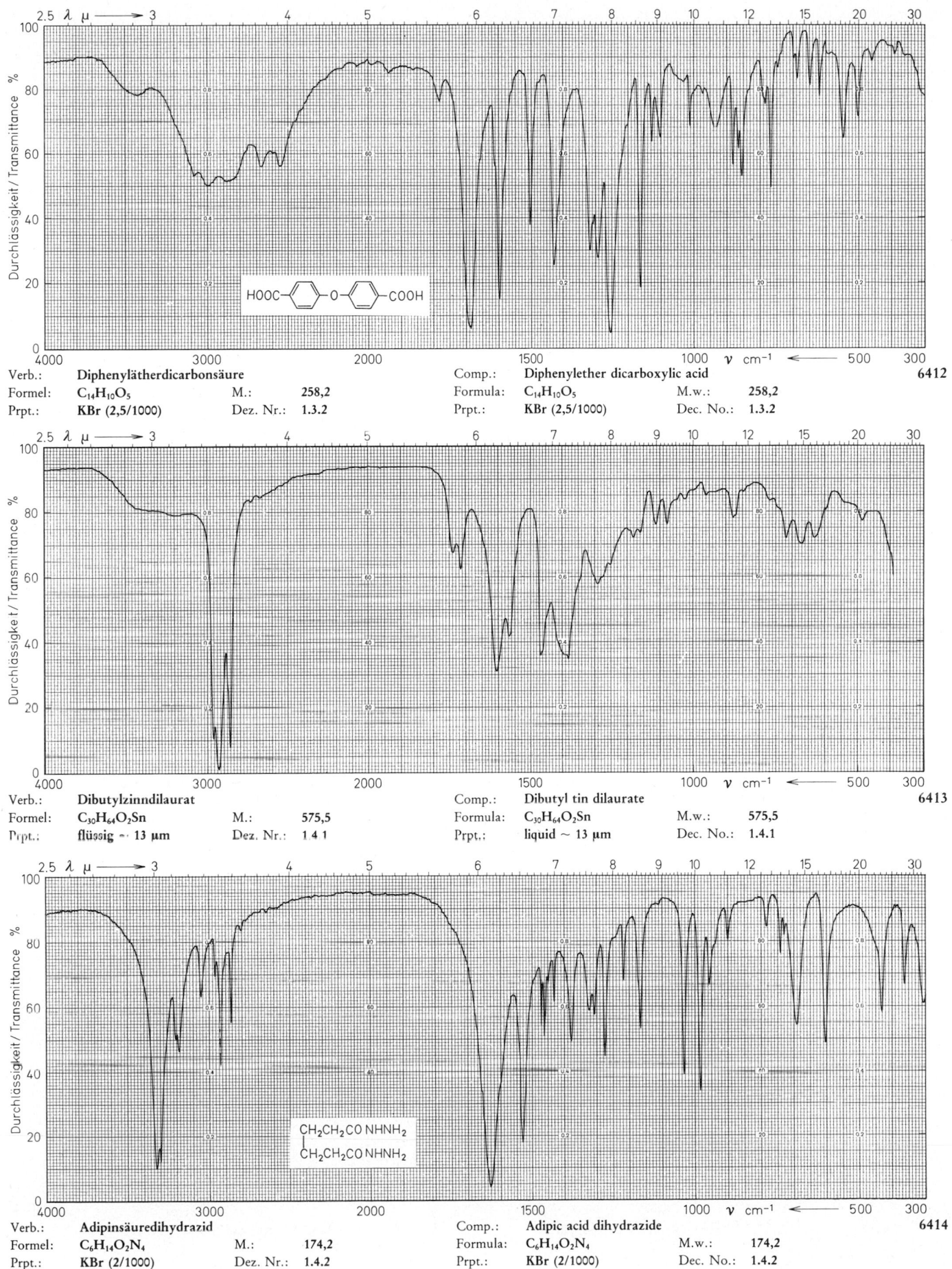

Verb.: **Diphenylätherdicarbonsäure**
Formel: **C₁₄H₁₀O₅** M.: **258,2**
Prpt.: **KBr (2,5/1000)** Dez. Nr.: **1.3.2**

Comp.: **Diphenylether dicarboxylic acid**
Formula: **C₁₄H₁₀O₅** M.w.: **258,2**
Prpt.: **KBr (2,5/1000)** Dec. No.: **1.3.2**

6412

Verb.: **Dibutylzinndilaurat**
Formel: **C₃₀H₆₄O₂Sn** M.: **575,5**
Prpt.: **flüssig ~ 13 µm** Dez. Nr.: **1.4.1**

Comp.: **Dibutyl tin dilaurate**
Formula: **C₃₀H₆₄O₂Sn** M.w.: **575,5**
Prpt.: **liquid ~ 13 µm** Dec. No.: **1.4.1**

6413

Verb.: **Adipinsäuredihydrazid**
Formel: **C₆H₁₄O₂N₄** M.: **174,2**
Prpt.: **KBr (2/1000)** Dez. Nr.: **1.4.2**

Comp.: **Adipic acid dihydrazide**
Formula: **C₆H₁₄O₂N₄** M.w.: **174,2**
Prpt.: **KBr (2/1000)** Dec. No.: **1.4.2**

6414

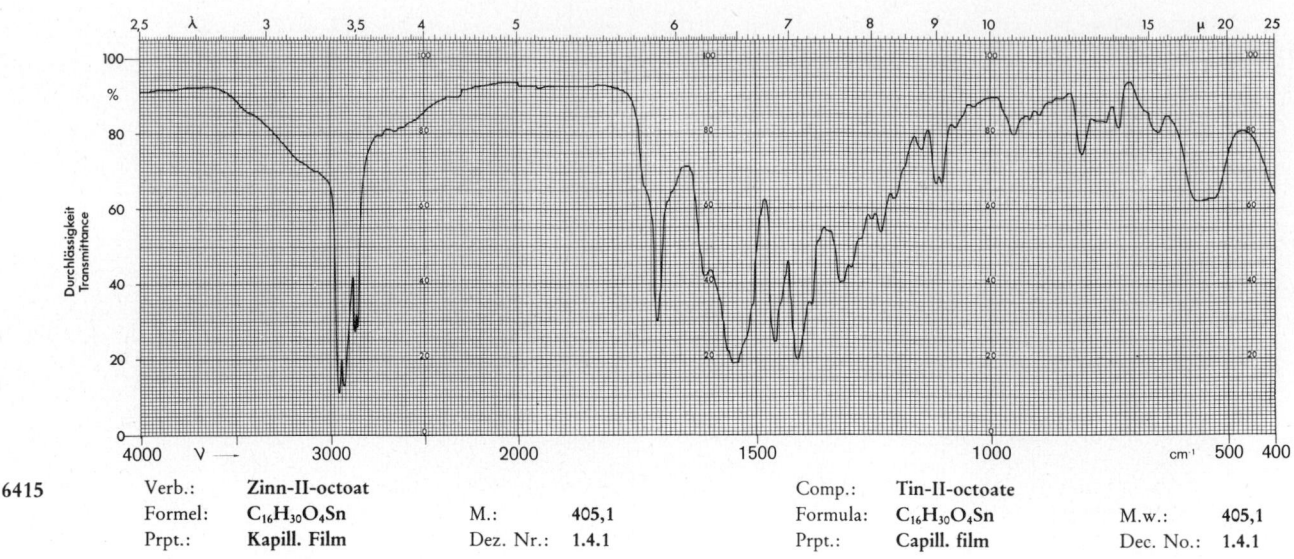

6415

Verb.:	**Zinn-II-octoat**		
Formel:	**C₁₆H₃₀O₄Sn**	M.:	**405,1**
Prpt.:	**Kapill. Film**	Dez. Nr.:	**1.4.1**

Comp.:	**Tin-II-octoate**		
Formula:	**C₁₆H₃₀O₄Sn**	M.w.:	**405,1**
Prpt.:	**Capill. film**	Dec. No.:	**1.4.1**

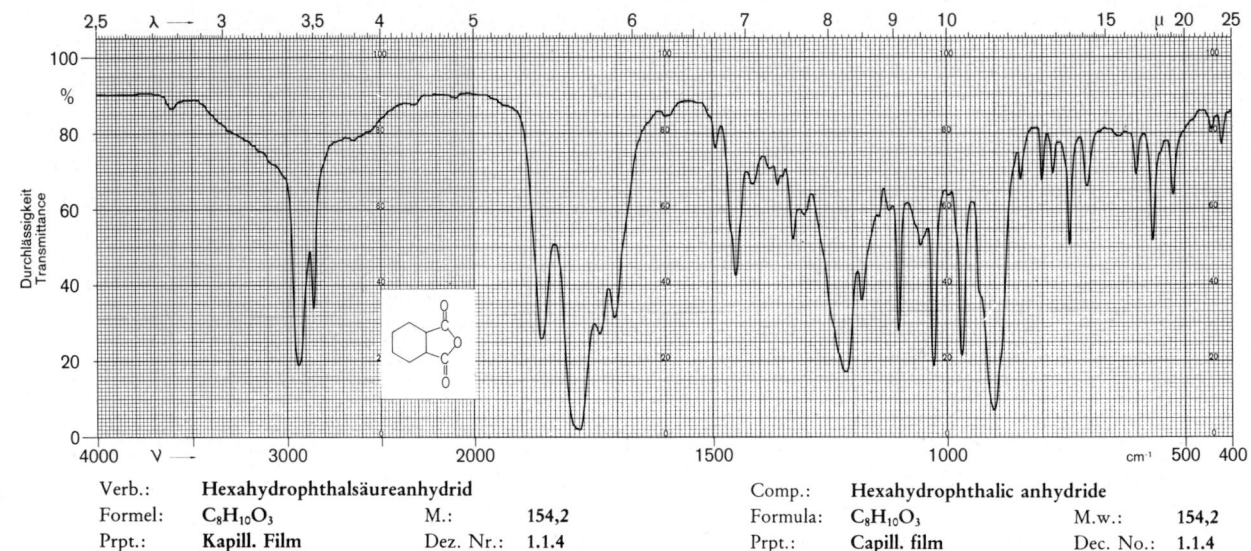

6416

Verb.:	**Hexahydrophthalsäureanhydrid**		
Formel:	**C₈H₁₀O₃**	M.:	**154,2**
Prpt.:	**Kapill. Film**	Dez. Nr.:	**1.1.4**

Comp.:	**Hexahydrophthalic anhydride**		
Formula:	**C₈H₁₀O₃**	M.w.:	**154,2**
Prpt.:	**Capill. film**	Dec. No.:	**1.1.4**

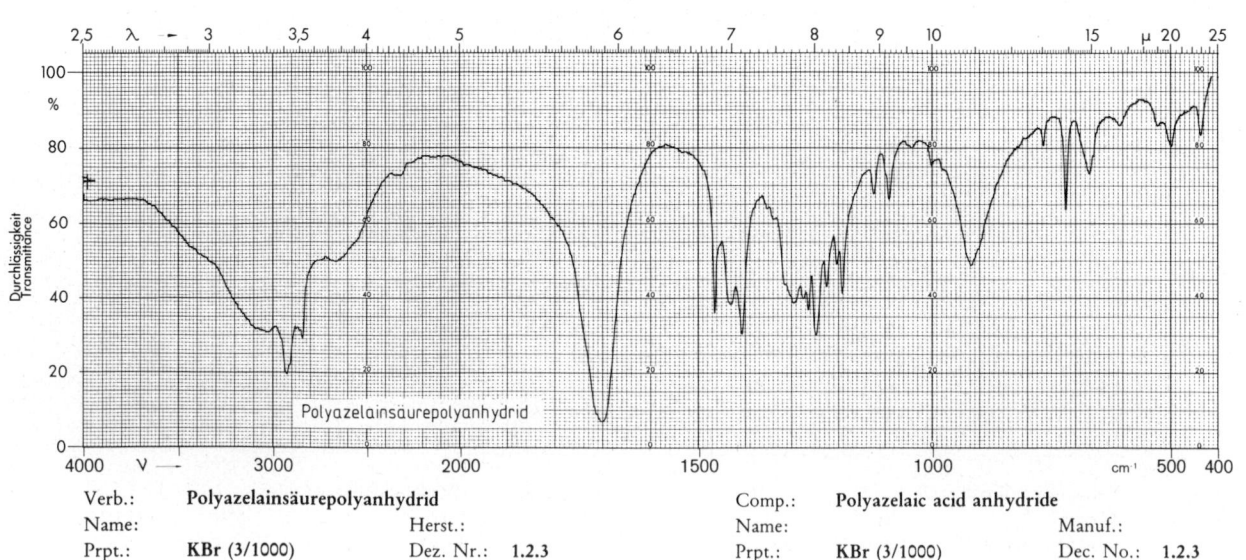

6417

Verb.:	**Polyazelainsäurepolyanhydrid**		
Name:		Herst.:	
Prpt.:	**KBr (3/1000)**	Dez. Nr.:	**1.2.3**

Comp.:	**Polyazelaic acid anhydride**		
Name:		Manuf.:	
Prpt.:	**KBr (3/1000)**	Dec. No.:	**1.2.3**

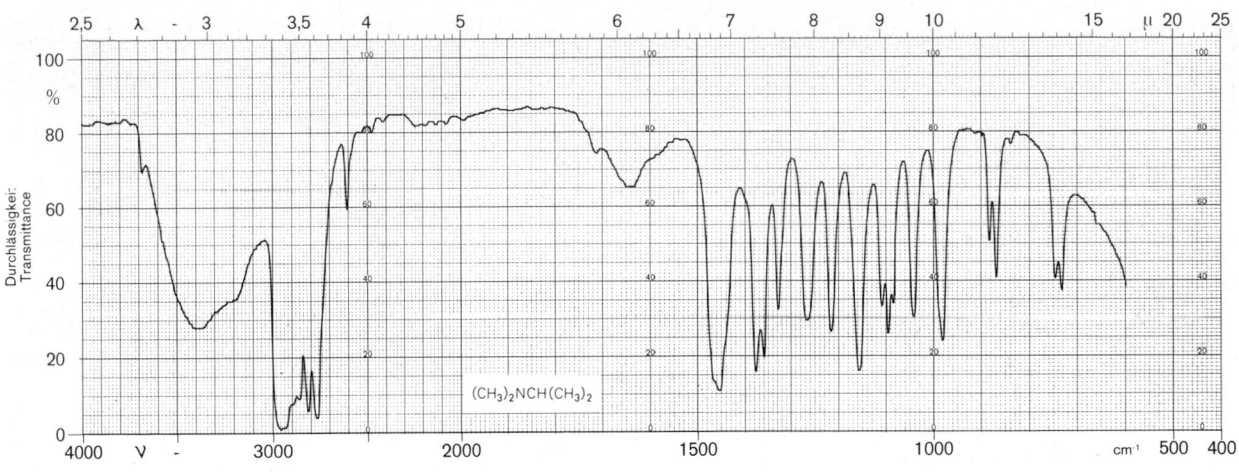

(CH₃)₂NCH(CH₃)₂

Verb.:	**N,N-Dimethylisopropylamin**		
Formel:	**C₅H₁₃N**	M.:	**87,2**
Prpt.:	**flüssig ~ 15 μm**	Dez. Nr.:	**2.1.3**

				6418
Comp.:	**N,N-Dimethylisopropyl amine**			
Formula:	**C₅H₁₃N**	M.w.:	**87,2**	
Prpt.:	**liquid ~ 15 μm**	Dec. No.:	**2.1.3**	

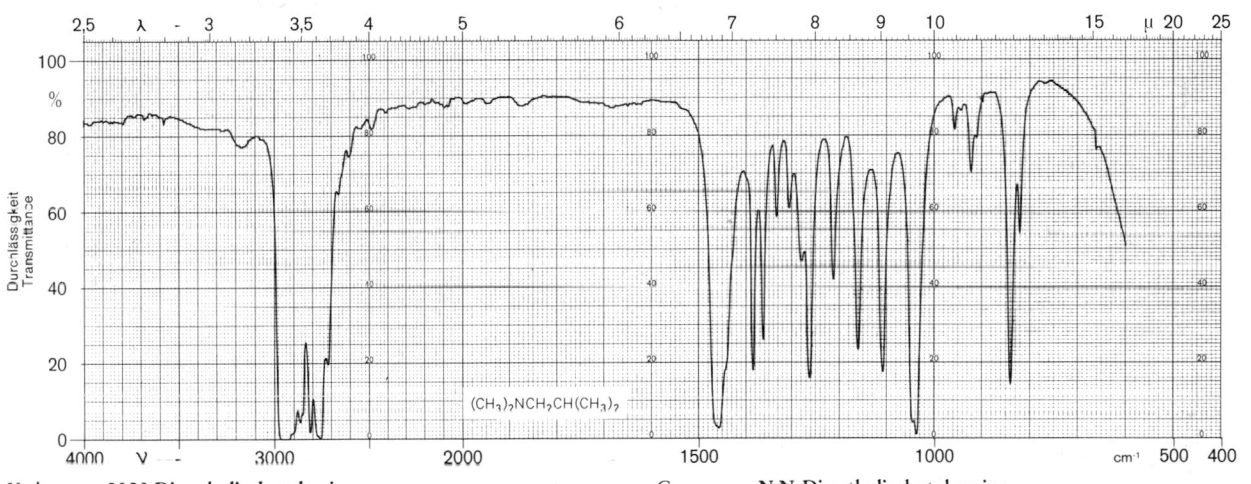

(CH₃)₂NCH₂CH(CH₃)₂

Verb.:	**N,N-Dimethylisobutylamin**		
Formel:	**C₆H₁₅N**	M.:	**101,2**
Prpt.:	**flüssig ~ 15 μm**	Dez. Nr.:	**2.1.4**

				6419
Comp.:	**N,N-Dimethylisobutyl amine**			
Formula:	**C₆H₁₅N**	M.w.:	**101,2**	
Prpt.:	**liquid ~ 15 μm**	Dec. No.:	**2.1.4**	

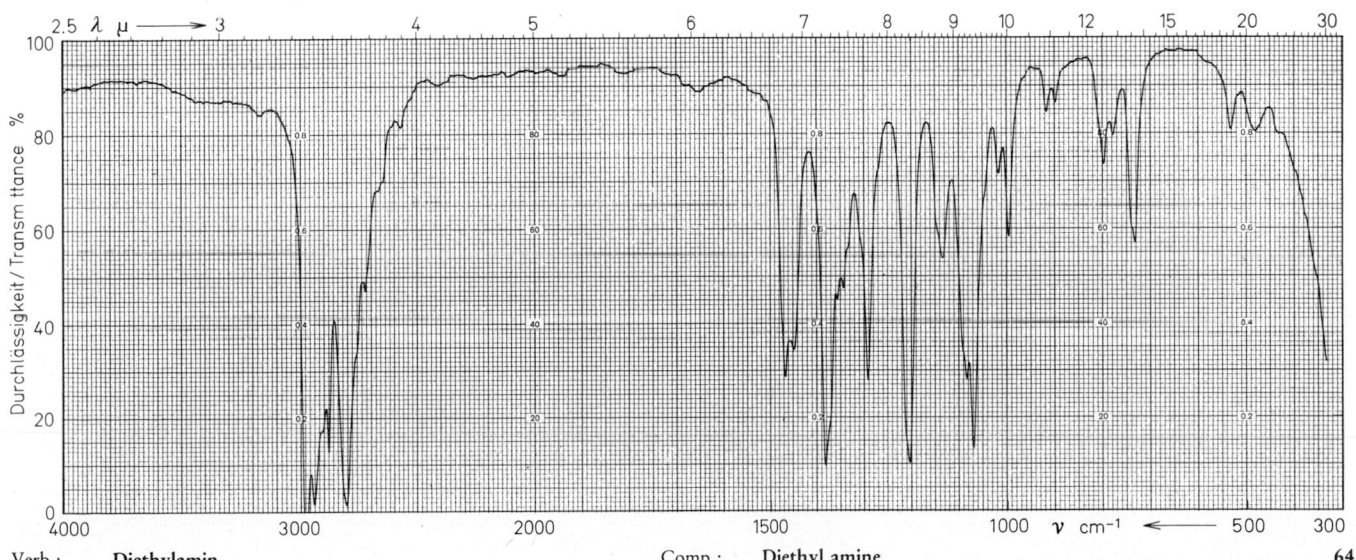

Verb.:	**Diethylamin**		
Formel:	**C₄H₁₁N**	M.:	**73,1**
Prpt.:	**flüssig ~ 13 μm**	Dez. Nr.:	**2.1.1**

				6420
Comp.:	**Diethyl amine**			
Formula:	**C₄H₁₁N**	M.w.:	**73,1**	
Prpt.:	**liquid ~ 13 μm**	Dec. No.:	**2.1.1**	

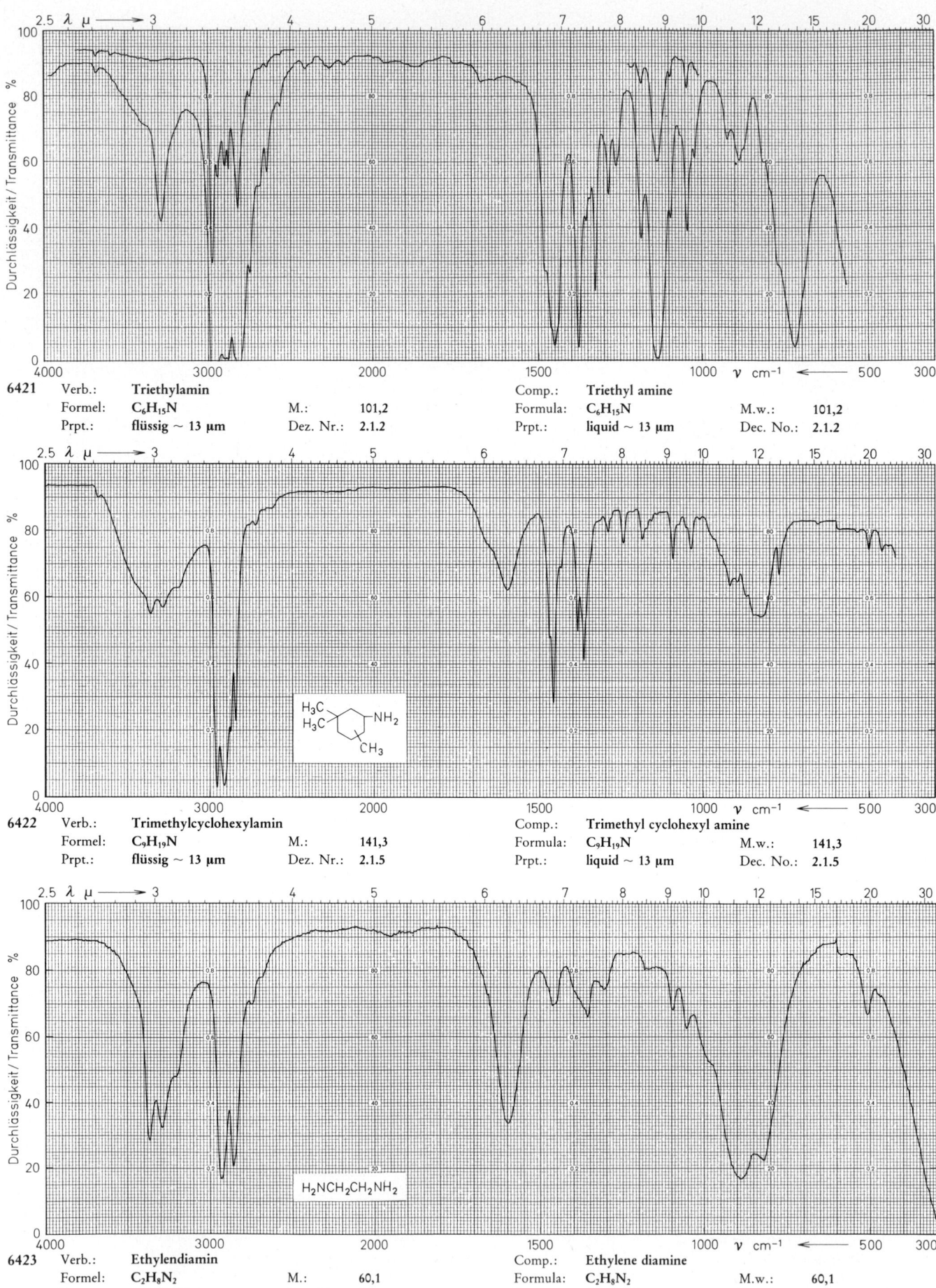

6421 Verb.: **Triethylamin**

| Formel: | $C_6H_{15}N$ | M.: | **101,2** |
| Prpt.: | flüssig ~ 13 μm | Dez. Nr.: | **2.1.2** |

Comp.: **Triethyl amine**

| Formula: | $C_6H_{15}N$ | M.w.: | **101,2** |
| Prpt.: | liquid ~ 13 μm | Dec. No.: | **2.1.2** |

6422 Verb.: **Trimethylcyclohexylamin**

| Formel: | $C_9H_{19}N$ | M.: | **141,3** |
| Prpt.: | flüssig ~ 13 μm | Dez. Nr.: | **2.1.5** |

Comp.: **Trimethyl cyclohexyl amine**

| Formula: | $C_9H_{19}N$ | M.w.: | **141,3** |
| Prpt.: | liquid ~ 13 μm | Dec. No.: | **2.1.5** |

6423 Verb.: **Ethylendiamin**

| Formel: | $C_2H_8N_2$ | M.: | **60,1** |
| Prpt.: | **Kapill. Film** | Dez. Nr.: | **2.1.6** |

Comp.: **Ethylene diamine**

| Formula: | $C_2H_8N_2$ | M.w.: | **60,1** |
| Prpt.: | **Capill. film** | Dec. No.: | **2.1.6** |

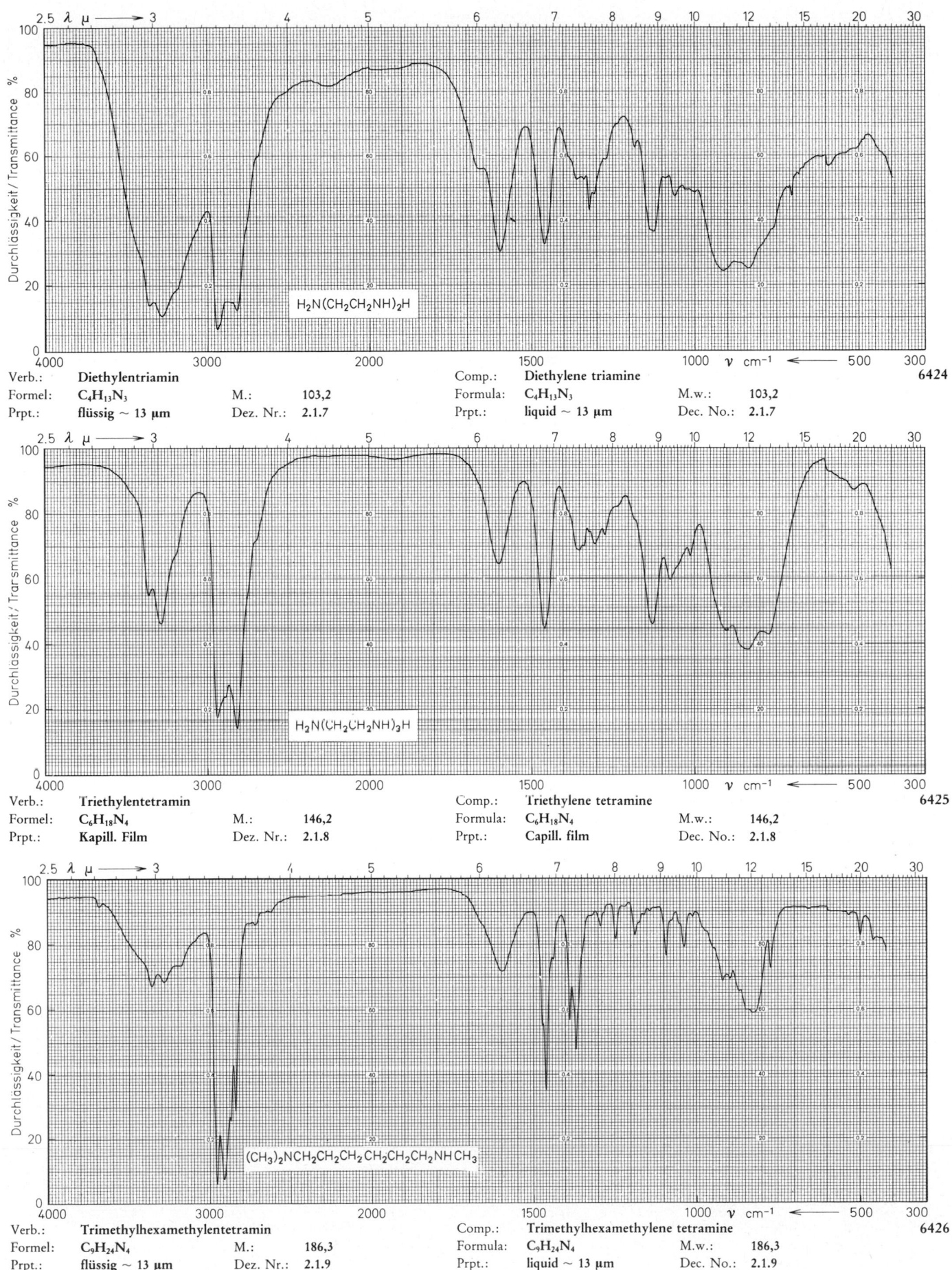

Verb.: **Diethylentriamin**   Comp.: **Diethylene triamine**   **6424**
Formel: **C₄H₁₃N₃**   M.: **103,2**   Formula: **C₄H₁₃N₃**   M.w.: **103,2**
Prpt.: **flüssig ~ 13 μm**   Dez. Nr.: **2.1.7**   Prpt.: **liquid ~ 13 μm**   Dec. No.: **2.1.7**

Verb.: **Triethylentetramin**   Comp.: **Triethylene tetramine**   **6425**
Formel: **C₆H₁₈N₄**   M.: **146,2**   Formula: **C₆H₁₈N₄**   M.w.: **146,2**
Prpt.: **Kapill. Film**   Dez. Nr.: **2.1.8**   Prpt.: **Capill. film**   Dec. No.: **2.1.8**

Verb.: **Trimethylhexamethylentetramin**   Comp.: **Trimethylhexamethylene tetramine**   **6426**
Formel: **C₉H₂₄N₄**   M.: **186,3**   Formula: **C₉H₂₄N₄**   M.w.: **186,3**
Prpt.: **flüssig ~ 13 μm**   Dez. Nr.: **2.1.9**   Prpt.: **liquid ~ 13 μm**   Dec. No.: **2.1.9**

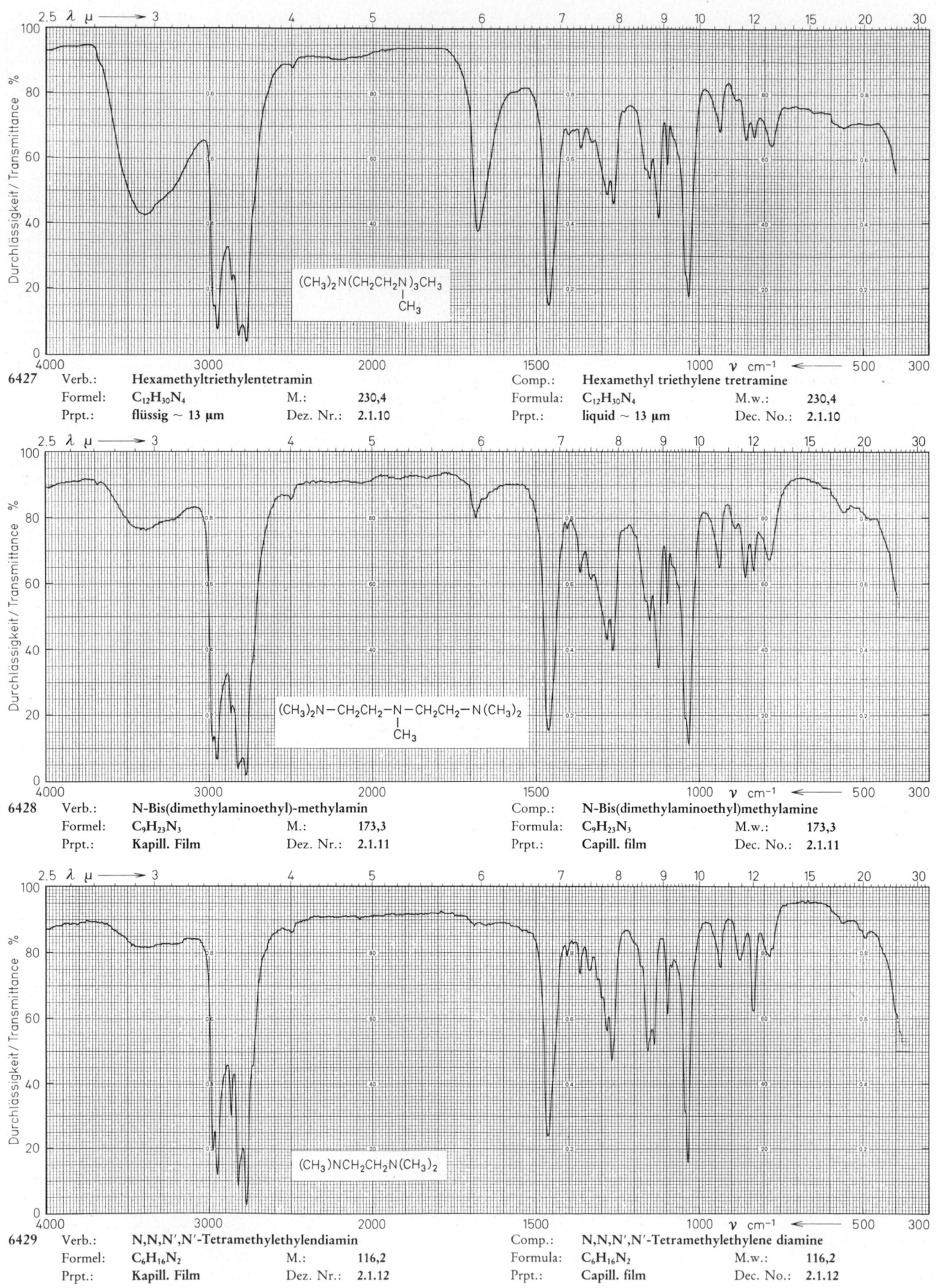

6427 Verb.: Hexamethyltriethylentetramin
Formel: C₁₂H₃₀N₄ M.: 230,4
Prpt.: flüssig ~ 13 µm Dez. Nr.: 2.1.10

Comp.: Hexamethyl triethylene tretramine
Formula: C₁₂H₃₀N₄ M.w.: 230,4
Prpt.: liquid ~ 13 µm Dec. No.: 2.1.10

6428 Verb.: N-Bis(dimethylaminoethyl)-methylamin
Formel: C₉H₂₃N₃ M.: 173,3
Prpt.: Kapill. Film Dez. Nr.: 2.1.11

Comp.: N-Bis(dimethylaminoethyl)methylamine
Formula: C₉H₂₃N₃ M.w.: 173,3
Prpt.: Capill. film Dec. No.: 2.1.11

6429 Verb.: N,N,N′,N′-Tetramethylethylendiamin
Formel: C₆H₁₆N₂ M.: 116,2
Prpt.: Kapill. Film Dez. Nr.: 2.1.12

Comp.: N,N,N′,N′-Tetramethylethylene diamine
Formula: C₆H₁₆N₂ M.w.: 116,2
Prpt.: Capill. film Dec. No.: 2.1.12

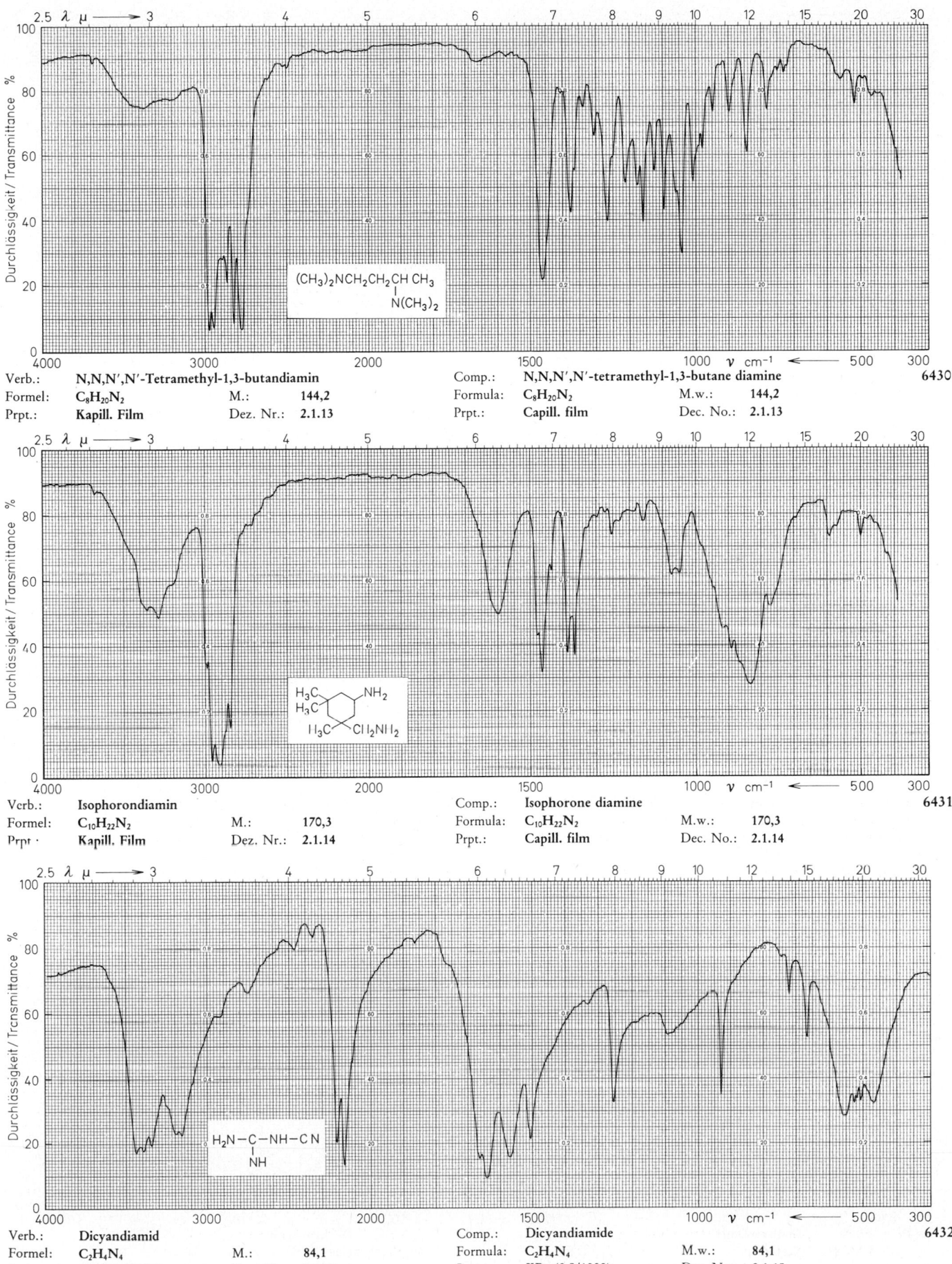

Verb.: **N,N,N',N'-Tetramethyl-1,3-butandiamin**

Formel: **C₈H₂₀N₂**   M.: **144,2**

Prpt.: **Kapill. Film**   Dez. Nr.: **2.1.13**

Comp.: **N,N,N',N'-tetramethyl-1,3-butane diamine**

Formula: **C₈H₂₀N₂**   M.w.: **144,2**

Prpt.: **Capill. film**   Dec. No.: **2.1.13**

6430

Verb.: **Isophorondiamin**

Formel: **C₁₀H₂₂N₂**   M.: **170,3**

Prpt.: **Kapill. Film**   Dez. Nr.: **2.1.14**

Comp.: **Isophorone diamine**

Formula: **C₁₀H₂₂N₂**   M.w.: **170,3**

Prpt.: **Capill. film**   Dec. No.: **2.1.14**

6431

Verb.: **Dicyandiamid**

Formel: **C₂H₄N₄**   M.: **84,1**

Prpt.: **KBr (2,5/1000)**   Dez. Nr.: **2.1.15**

Comp.: **Dicyandiamide**

Formula: **C₂H₄N₄**   M.w.: **84,1**

Prpt.: **KBr (2,5/1000)**   Dec. No.: **2.1.15**

6432

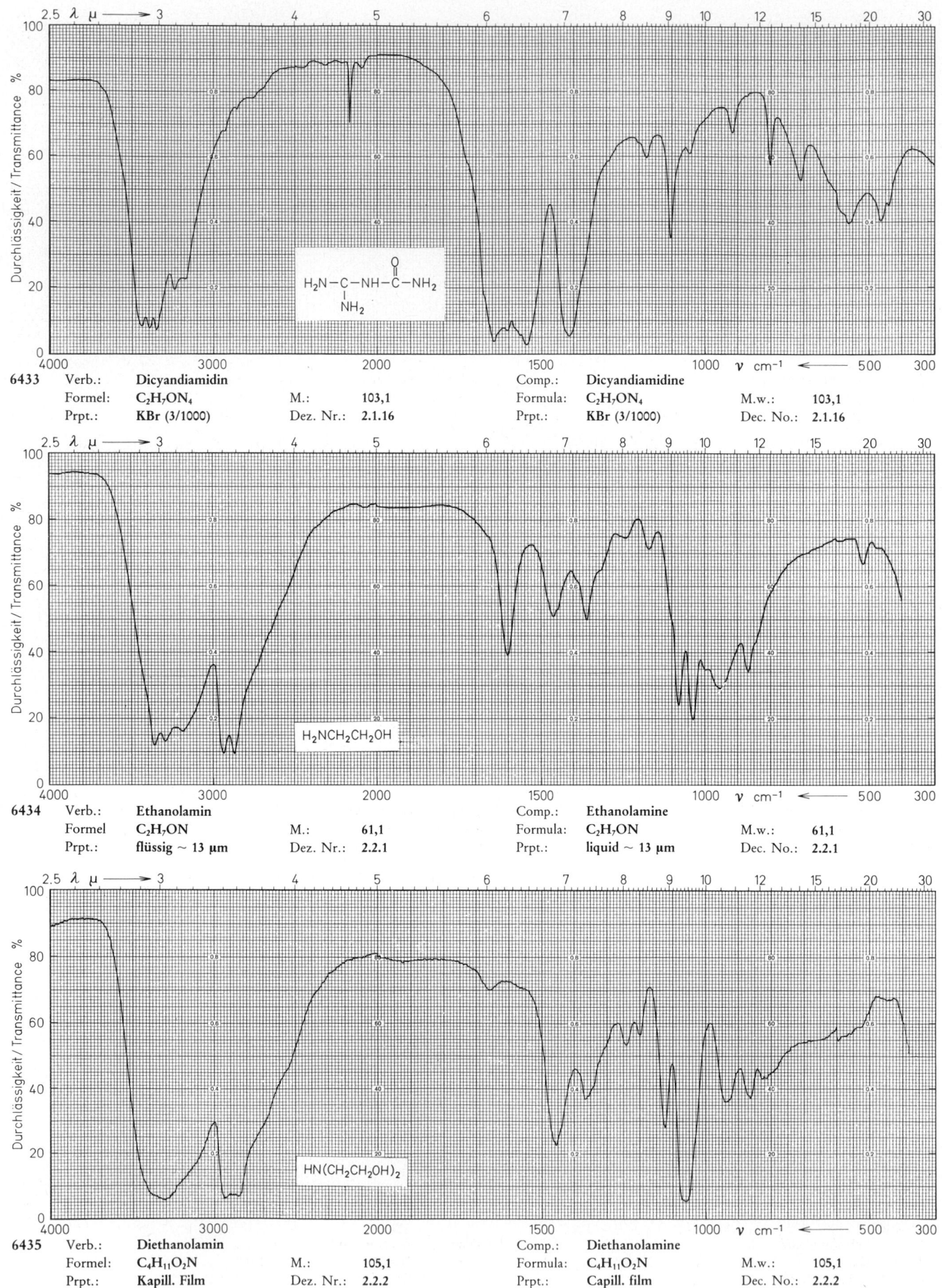

6433

Verb.:	**Dicyandiamidin**			
Formel:	**C₂H₇ON₄**	M.:	**103,1**	
Prpt.:	**KBr (3/1000)**	Dez. Nr.:	**2.1.16**	

Comp.:	**Dicyandiamidine**			
Formula:	**C₂H₇ON₄**	M.w.:	**103,1**	
Prpt.:	**KBr (3/1000)**	Dec. No.:	**2.1.16**	

6434

Verb.:	**Ethanolamin**			
Formel	**C₂H₇ON**	M.:	**61,1**	
Prpt.:	**flüssig ~ 13 μm**	Dez. Nr.:	**2.2.1**	

Comp.:	**Ethanolamine**			
Formula:	**C₂H₇ON**	M.w.:	**61,1**	
Prpt.:	**liquid ~ 13 μm**	Dec. No.:	**2.2.1**	

6435

Verb.:	**Diethanolamin**			
Formel	**C₄H₁₁O₂N**	M.:	**105,1**	
Prpt.:	**Kapill. Film**	Dez. Nr.:	**2.2.2**	

Comp.:	**Diethanolamine**			
Formula:	**C₄H₁₁O₂N**	M.w.:	**105,1**	
Prpt.:	**Capill. film**	Dec. No.:	**2.2.2**	

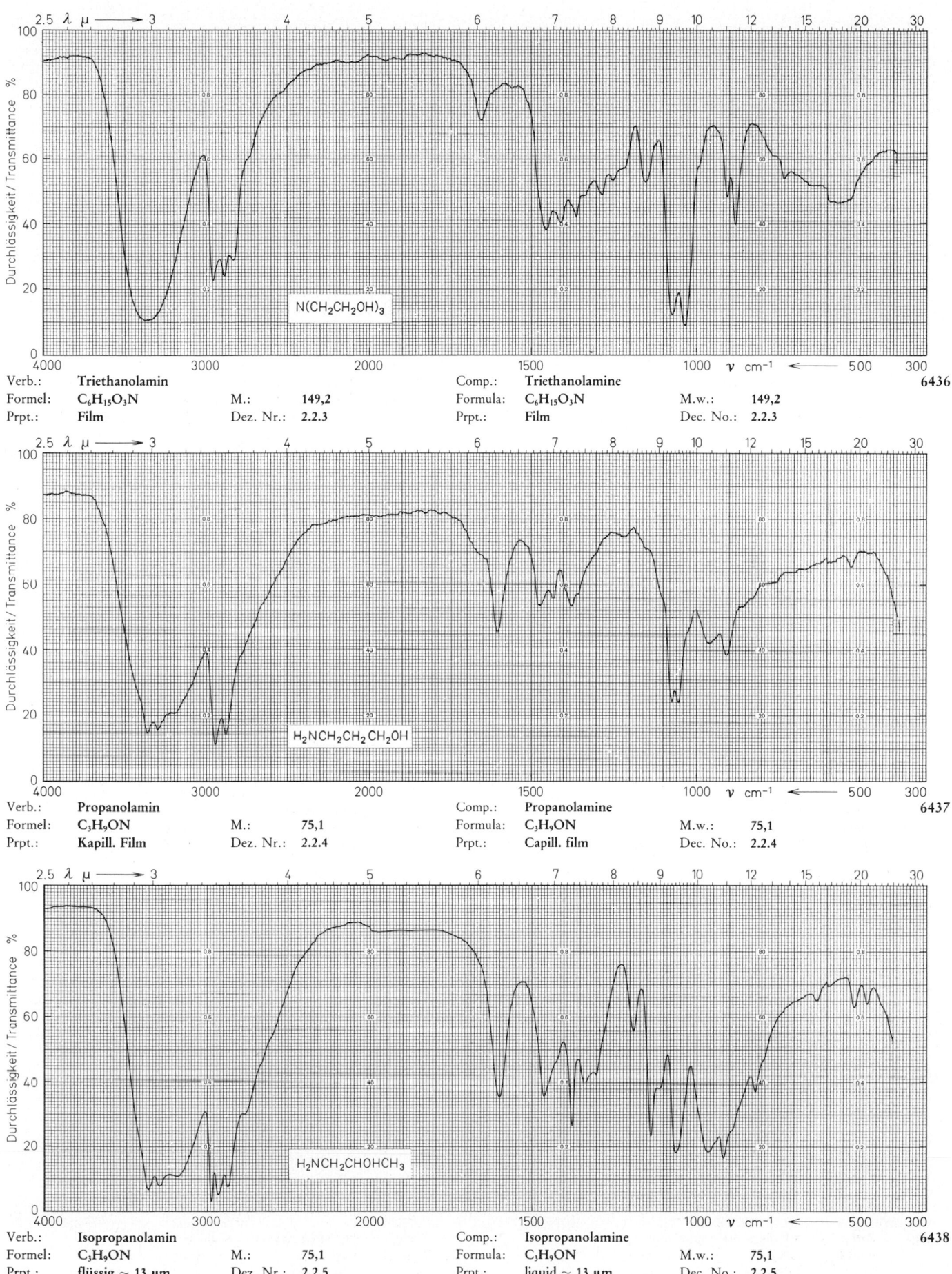

Verb.: **Triethanolamin**

Formel: **C₆H₁₅O₃N**   M.: **149,2**

Prpt.: **Film**   Dez. Nr.: **2.2.3**

Comp.: **Triethanolamine**

Formula: **C₆H₁₅O₃N**   M.w.: **149,2**

Prpt.: **Film**   Dec. No.: **2.2.3**

6436

Verb.: **Propanolamin**

Formel: **C₃H₉ON**   M.: **75,1**

Prpt.: **Kapill. Film**   Dez. Nr.: **2.2.4**

Comp.: **Propanolamine**

Formula: **C₃H₉ON**   M.w.: **75,1**

Prpt.: **Capill. film**   Dec. No.: **2.2.4**

6437

Verb.: **Isopropanolamin**

Formel: **C₃H₉ON**   M.: **75,1**

Prpt.: **flüssig ~ 13 μm**   Dez. Nr.: **2.2.5**

Comp.: **Isopropanolamine**

Formula: **C₃H₉ON**   M.w.: **75,1**

Prpt.: **liquid ~ 13 μm**   Dec. No.: **2.2.5**

6438

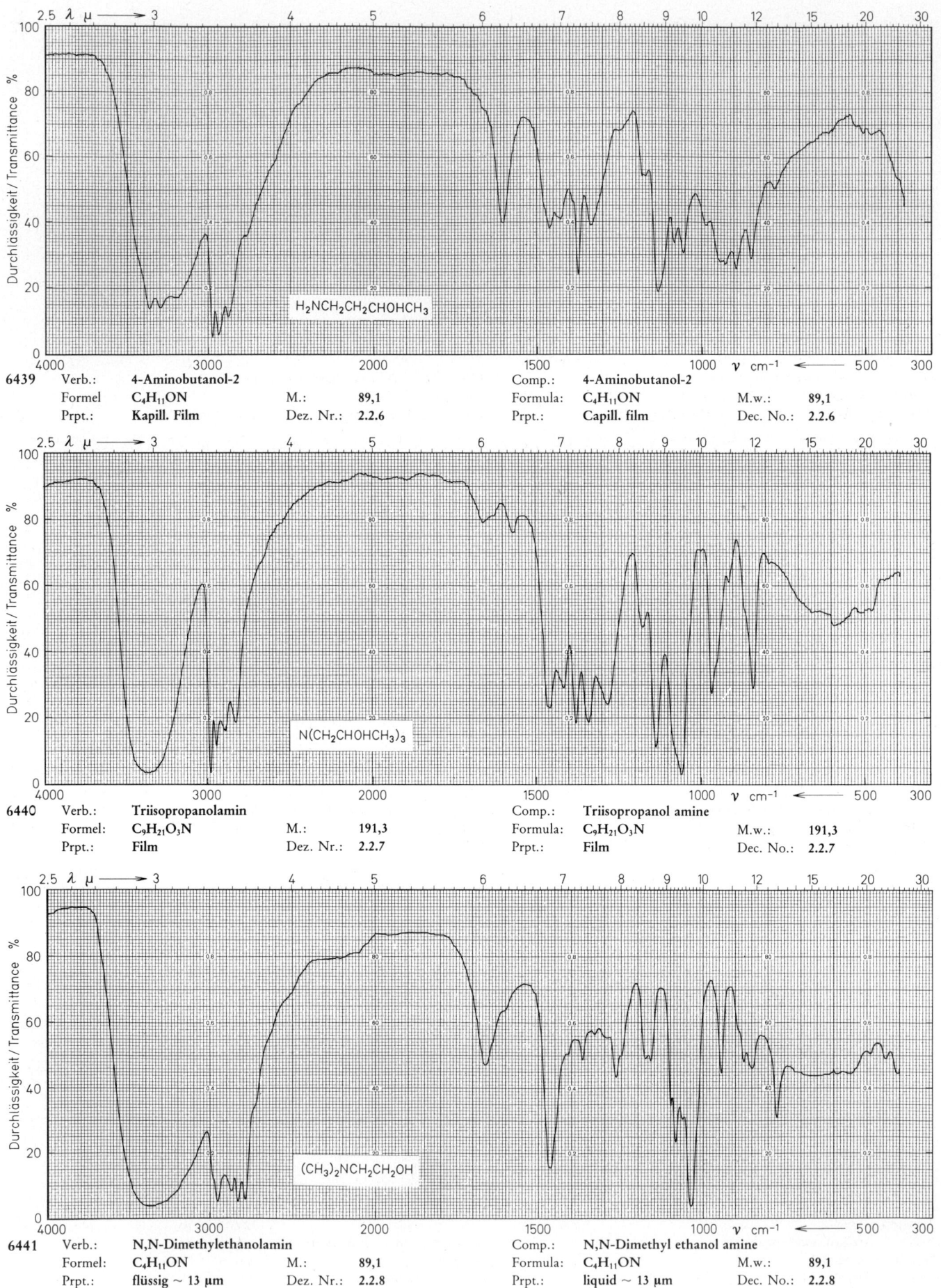

H₂NCH₂CH₂CHOHCH₃

6439   Verb.:   **4-Aminobutanol-2**   Comp.:   **4-Aminobutanol-2**
       Formel $C_4H_{11}ON$ M.:   **89,1**   Formula: $C_4H_{11}ON$ M.w.:   **89,1**
       Prpt.:   **Kapill. Film**   Dez. Nr.:   **2.2.6**   Prpt.:   **Capill. film**   Dec. No.:   **2.2.6**

N(CH₂CHOHCH₃)₃

6440   Verb.:   **Triisopropanolamin**   Comp.:   **Triisopropanol amine**
       Formel: $C_9H_{21}O_3N$ M.:   **191,3**   Formula: $C_9H_{21}O_3N$ M.w.:   **191,3**
       Prpt.:   **Film**   Dez. Nr.:   **2.2.7**   Prpt.:   **Film**   Dec. No.:   **2.2.7**

(CH₃)₂NCH₂CH₂OH

6441   Verb.:   **N,N-Dimethylethanolamin**   Comp.:   **N,N-Dimethyl ethanol amine**
       Formel: $C_4H_{11}ON$ M.:   **89,1**   Formula: $C_4H_{11}ON$ M.w.:   **89,1**
       Prpt.:   **flüssig ~ 13 μm**   Dez. Nr.:   **2.2.8**   Prpt.:   **liquid ~ 13 μm**   Dec. No.:   **2.2.8**

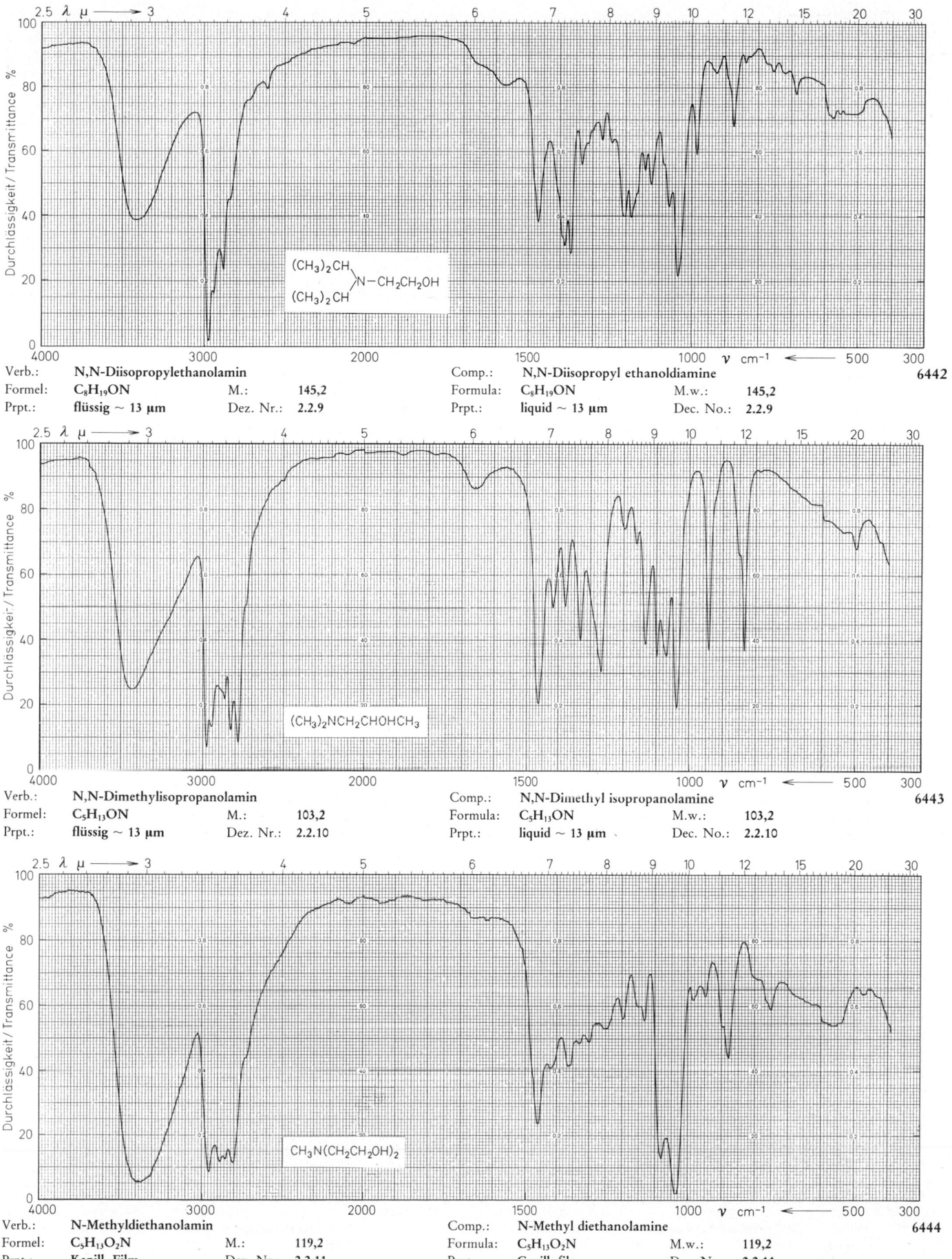

Verb.: **N,N-Diisopropylethanolamin** Comp.: **N,N-Diisopropyl ethanoldiamine** 6442
Formel: **C₈H₁₉ON** M.: **145,2** Formula: **C₈H₁₉ON** M.w.: **145,2**
Prpt.: **flüssig ~ 13 μm** Dez. Nr.: **2.2.9** Prpt.: **liquid ~ 13 μm** Dec. No.: **2.2.9**

Verb.: **N,N-Dimethylisopropanolamin** Comp.: **N,N-Dimethyl isopropanolamine** 6443
Formel: **C₅H₁₃ON** M.: **103,2** Formula: **C₅H₁₃ON** M.w.: **103,2**
Prpt.: **flüssig ~ 13 μm** Dez. Nr.: **2.2.10** Prpt.: **liquid ~ 13 μm** Dec. No.: **2.2.10**

Verb.: **N-Methyldiethanolamin** Comp.: **N-Methyl diethanolamine** 6444
Formel: **C₅H₁₃O₂N** M.: **119,2** Formula: **C₅H₁₃O₂N** M.w.: **119,2**
Prpt.: **Kapill. Film** Dez. Nr.: **2.2.11** Prpt.: **Capill. film** Dec. No.: **2.2.11**

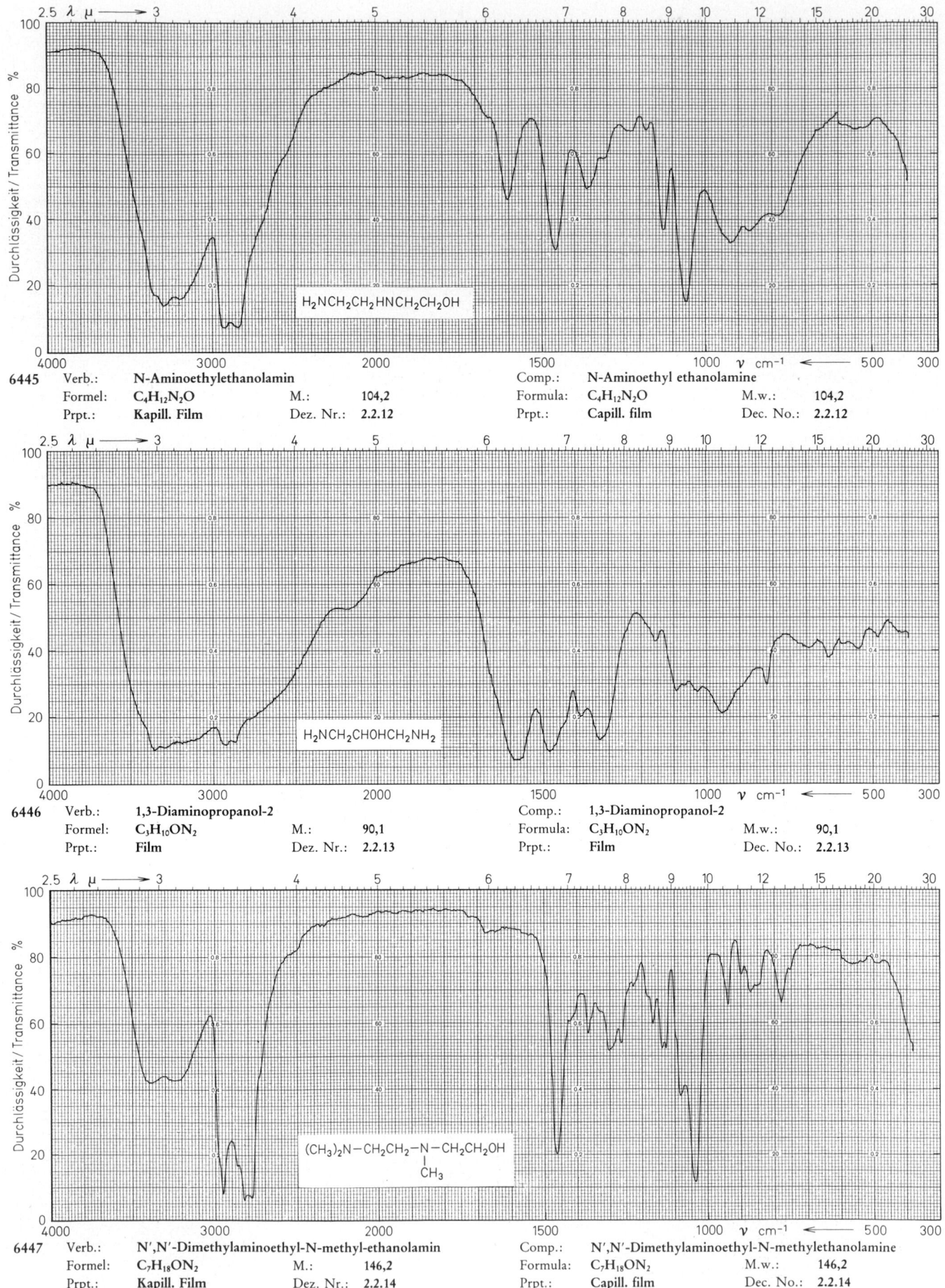

6445 Verb.: **N-Aminoethylethanolamin**

Formel: **C₄H₁₂N₂O**   M.: **104,2**

Prpt.: **Kapill. Film**   Dez. Nr.: **2.2.12**

Comp.: **N-Aminoethyl ethanolamine**

Formula: **C₄H₁₂N₂O**   M.w.: **104,2**

Prpt.: **Capill. film**   Dec. No.: **2.2.12**

6446 Verb.: **1,3-Diaminopropanol-2**

Formel: **C₃H₁₀ON₂**   M.: **90,1**

Prpt.: **Film**   Dez. Nr.: **2.2.13**

Comp.: **1,3-Diaminopropanol-2**

Formula: **C₃H₁₀ON₂**   M.w.: **90,1**

Prpt.: **Film**   Dec. No.: **2.2.13**

6447 Verb.: **N',N'-Dimethylaminoethyl-N-methyl-ethanolamin**

Formel: **C₇H₁₈ON₂**   M.: **146,2**

Prpt.: **Kapill. Film**   Dez. Nr.: **2.2.14**

Comp.: **N',N'-Dimethylaminoethyl-N-methylethanolamine**

Formula: **C₇H₁₈ON₂**   M.w.: **146,2**

Prpt.: **Capill. film**   Dec. No.: **2.2.14**

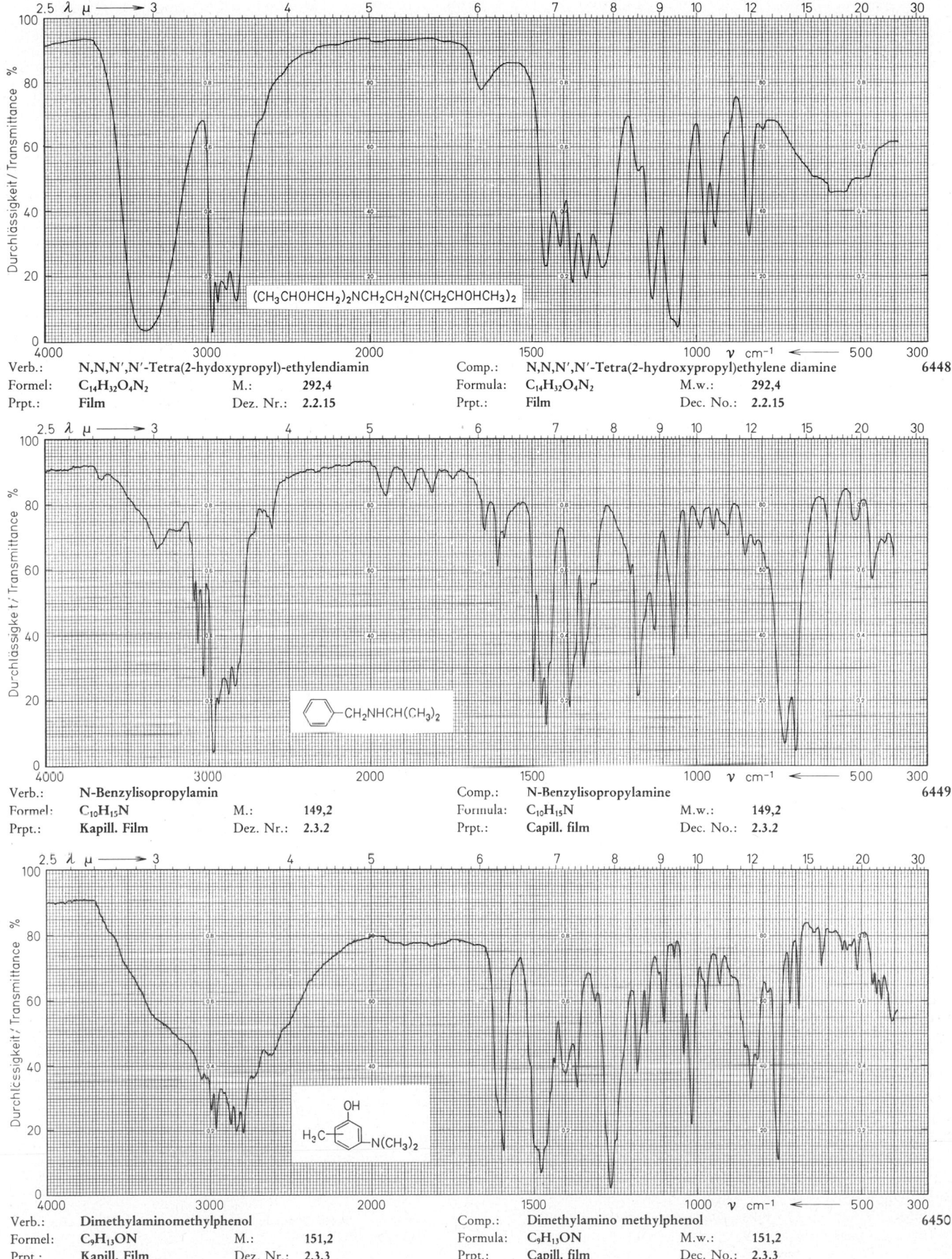

Verb.: **N,N,N′,N′-Tetra(2-hydoxypropyl)-ethylendiamin**   Comp.: **N,N,N′,N′-Tetra(2-hydroxypropyl)ethylene diamine**   **6448**
Formel: **C₁₄H₃₂O₄N₂**   M.: **292,4**   Formula: **C₁₄H₃₂O₄N₂**   M.w.: **292,4**
Prpt.: **Film**   Dez. Nr.: **2.2.15**   Prpt.: **Film**   Dec. No.: **2.2.15**

Verb.: **N-Benzylisopropylamin**   Comp.: **N-Benzylisopropylamine**   **6449**
Formel: **C₁₀H₁₅N**   M.: **149,2**   Formula: **C₁₀H₁₅N**   M.w.: **149,2**
Prpt.: **Kapill. Film**   Dez. Nr.: **2.3.2**   Prpt.: **Capill. film**   Dec. No.: **2.3.2**

Verb.: **Dimethylaminomethylphenol**   Comp.: **Dimethylamino methylphenol**   **6450**
Formel: **C₉H₁₃ON**   M.: **151,2**   Formula: **C₉H₁₃ON**   M.w.: **151,2**
Prpt.: **Kapill. Film**   Dez. Nr.: **2.3.3**   Prpt.: **Capill. film**   Dec. No.: **2.3.3**

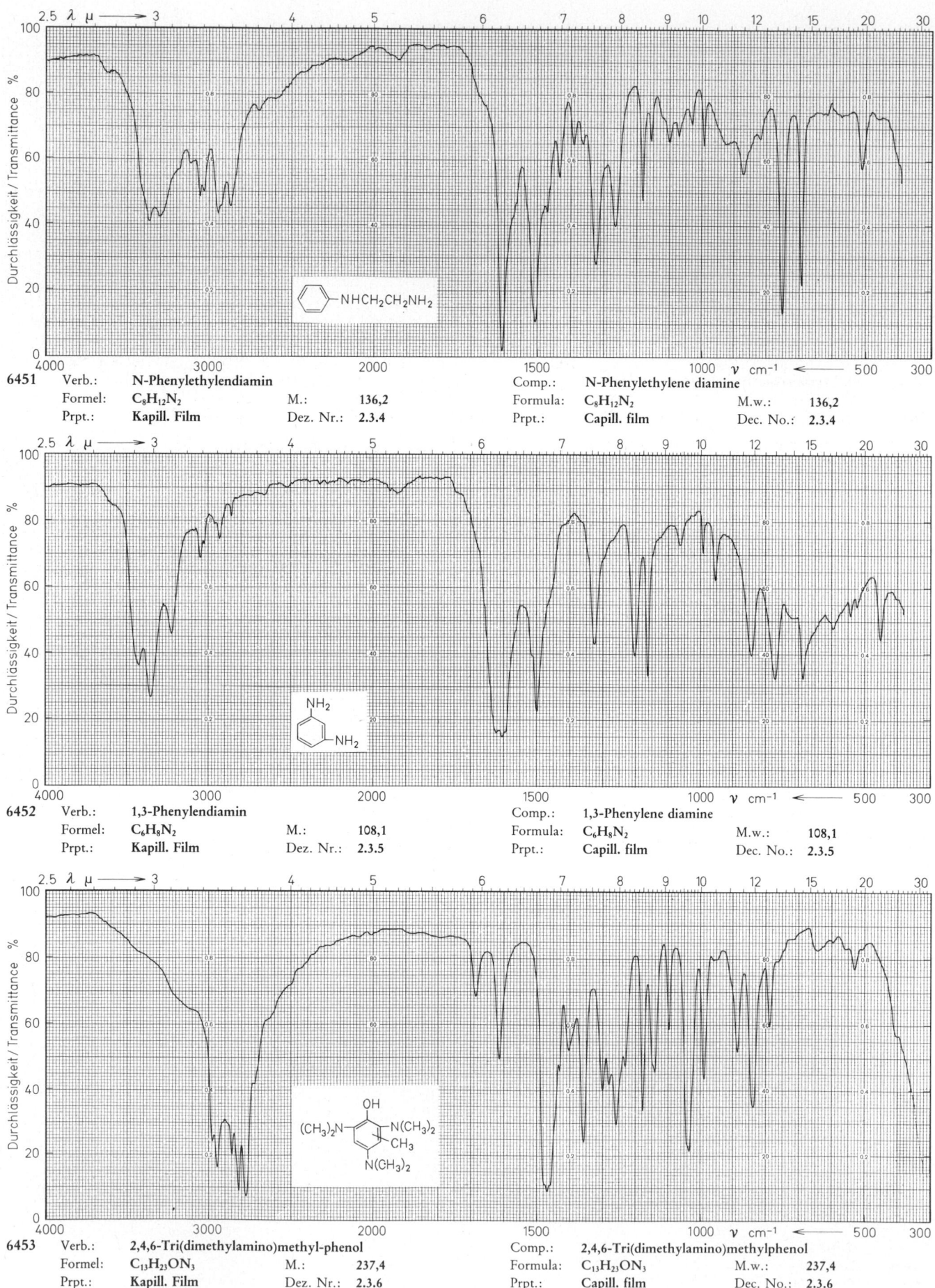

6451   Verb.:   **N-Phenylethylendiamin**   Comp.:   **N-Phenylethylene diamine**
         Formel: **C₈H₁₂N₂**   M.:   **136,2**   Formula: **C₈H₁₂N₂**   M.w.:   **136,2**
         Prpt.:   **Kapill. Film**   Dez. Nr.:   **2.3.4**   Prpt.:   **Capill. film**   Dec. No.:   **2.3.4**

6452   Verb.:   **1,3-Phenylendiamin**   Comp.:   **1,3-Phenylene diamine**
         Formel: **C₆H₈N₂**   M.:   **108,1**   Formula: **C₆H₈N₂**   M.w.:   **108,1**
         Prpt.:   **Kapill. Film**   Dez. Nr.:   **2.3.5**   Prpt.:   **Capill. film**   Dec. No.:   **2.3.5**

6453   Verb.:   **2,4,6-Tri(dimethylamino)methyl-phenol**   Comp.:   **2,4,6-Tri(dimethylamino)methylphenol**
         Formel: **C₁₃H₂₃ON₃**   M.:   **237,4**   Formula: **C₁₃H₂₃ON₃**   M.w.:   **237,4**
         Prpt.:   **Kapill. Film**   Dez. Nr.:   **2.3.6**   Prpt.:   **Capill. film**   Dec. No.:   **2.3.6**

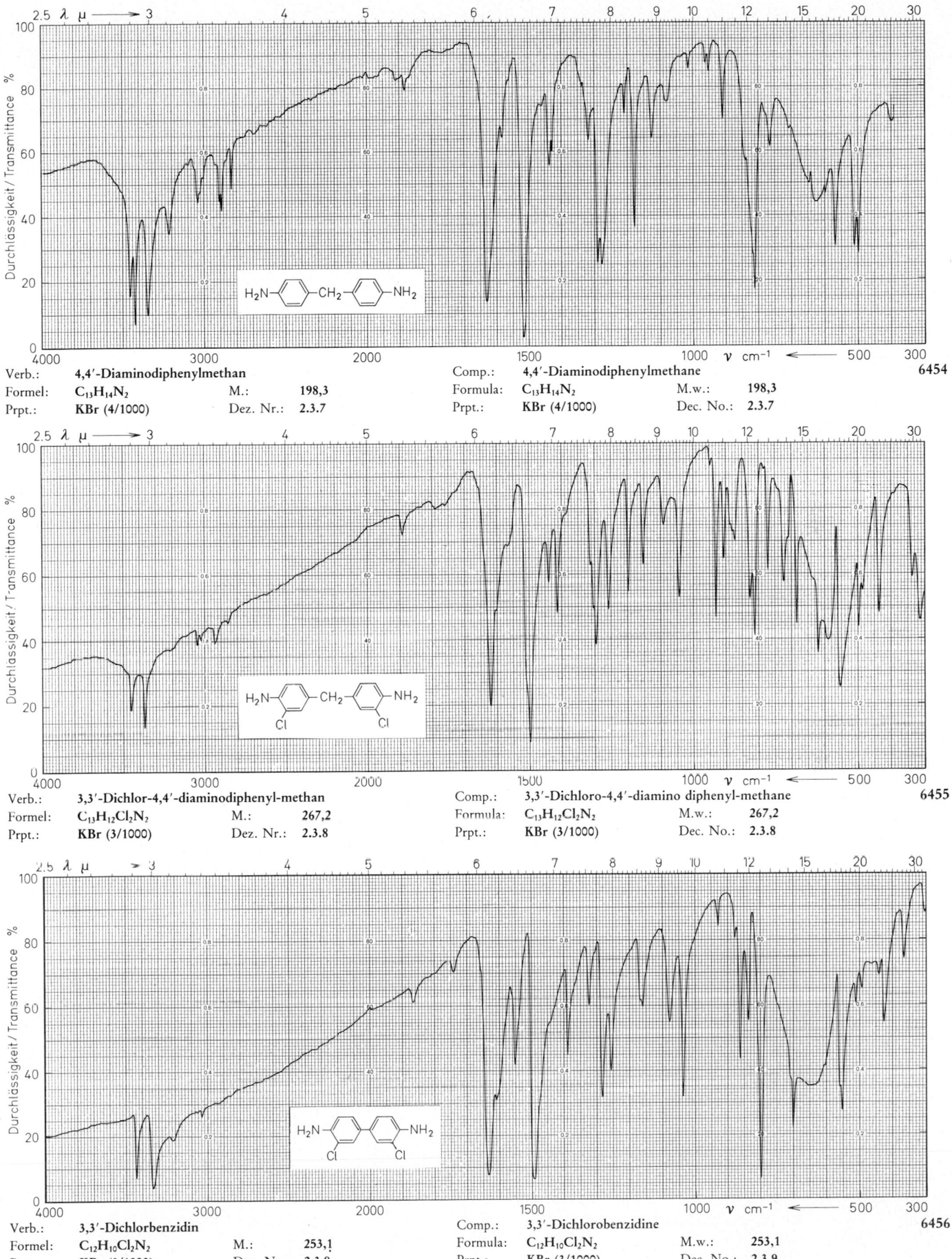

Verb.: **4,4'-Diaminodiphenylmethan**

Formel: **C₁₃H₁₄N₂**   M.: **198,3**

Prpt.: **KBr (4/1000)**   Dez. Nr.: **2.3.7**

Comp.: **4,4'-Diaminodiphenylmethane**

Formula: **C₁₃H₁₄N₂**   M.w.: **198,3**

Prpt.: **KBr (4/1000)**   Dec. No.: **2.3.7**

6454

Verb.: **3,3'-Dichlor-4,4'-diaminodiphenyl-methan**

Formel: **C₁₃H₁₂Cl₂N₂**   M.: **267,2**

Prpt.: **KBr (3/1000)**   Dez. Nr.: **2.3.8**

Comp.: **3,3'-Dichloro-4,4'-diamino diphenyl-methane**

Formula: **C₁₃H₁₂Cl₂N₂**   M.w.: **267,2**

Prpt.: **KBr (3/1000)**   Dec. No.: **2.3.8**

6455

Verb.: **3,3'-Dichlorbenzidin**

Formel: **C₁₂H₁₀Cl₂N₂**   M.: **253,1**

Prpt.: **KBr (3/1000)**   Dez. Nr.: **2.3.9**

Comp.: **3,3'-Dichlorobenzidine**

Formula: **C₁₂H₁₀Cl₂N₂**   M.w.: **253,1**

Prpt.: **KBr (3/1000)**   Dec. No.: **2.3.9**

6456

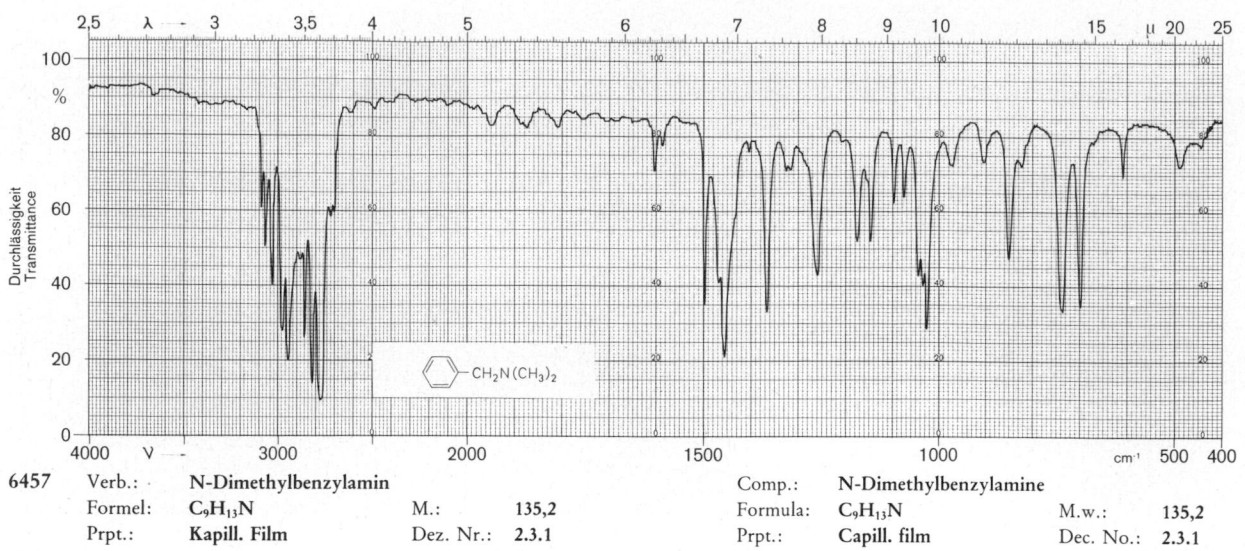

6457

Verb.:	N-Dimethylbenzylamin	Comp.:	N-Dimethylbenzylamine
Formel:	$C_9H_{13}N$	M.:	135,2
Prpt.:	Kapill. Film	Dez. Nr.:	2.3.1

Formula:	$C_9H_{13}N$	M.w.:	135,2
Prpt.:	Capill. film	Dec. No.:	2.3.1

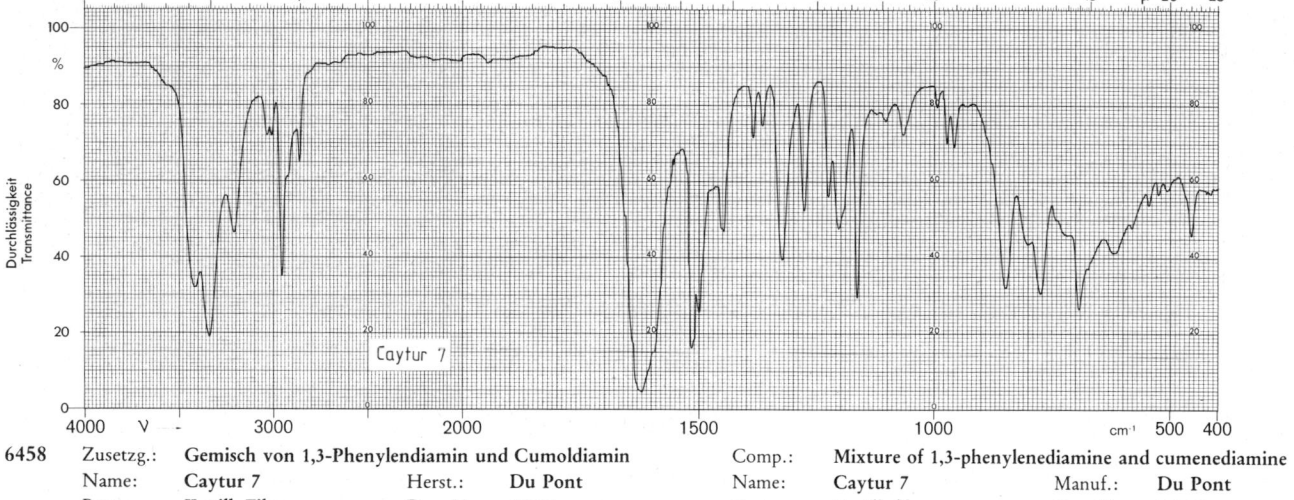

6458

Zusetzg.:	Gemisch von 1,3-Phenylendiamin und Cumoldiamin	Comp.:	Mixture of 1,3-phenylenediamine and cumenediamine
Name:	Caytur 7	Herst.:	Du Pont
Prpt.:	Kapill. Film	Dez. Nr.:	2.3.11

Name:	Caytur 7	Manuf.:	Du Pont
Prpt.:	Capill. film	Dec. No.:	2.3.11

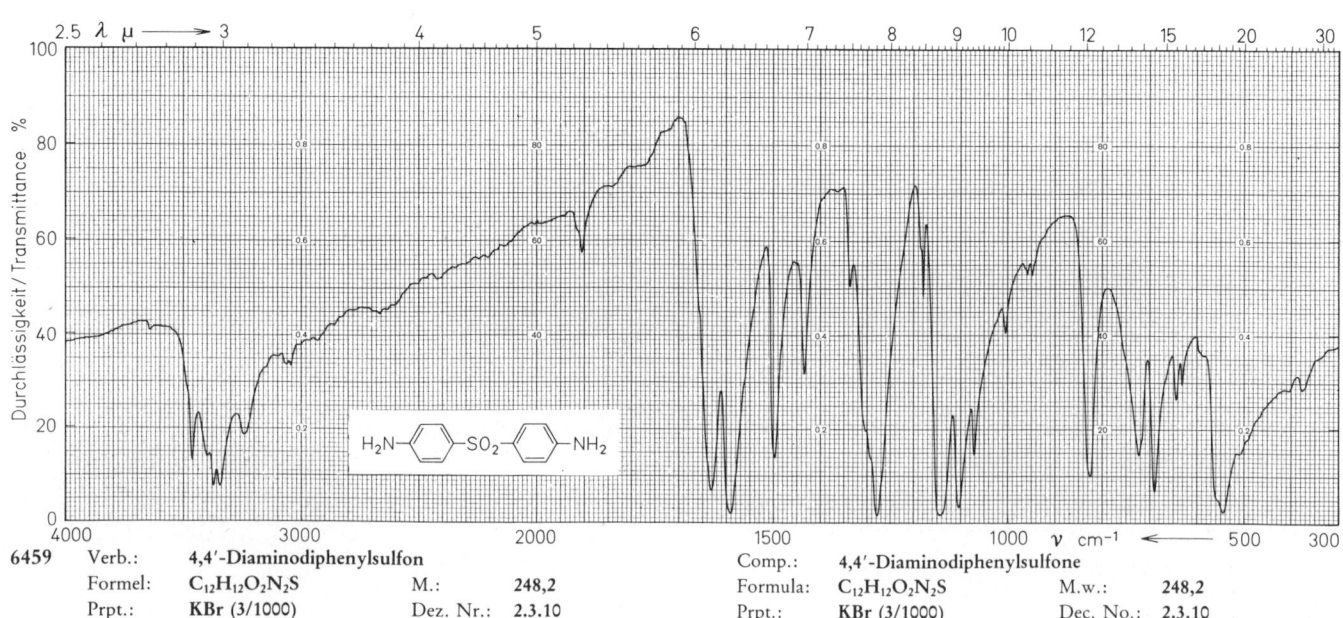

6459

Verb.:	4,4'-Diaminodiphenylsulfon	Comp.:	4,4'-Diaminodiphenylsulfone
Formel:	$C_{12}H_{12}O_2N_2S$	M.:	248,2
Prpt.:	KBr (3/1000)	Dez. Nr.:	2.3.10

Formula:	$C_{12}H_{12}O_2N_2S$	M.w.:	248,2
Prpt.:	KBr (3/1000)	Dec. No.:	2.3.10

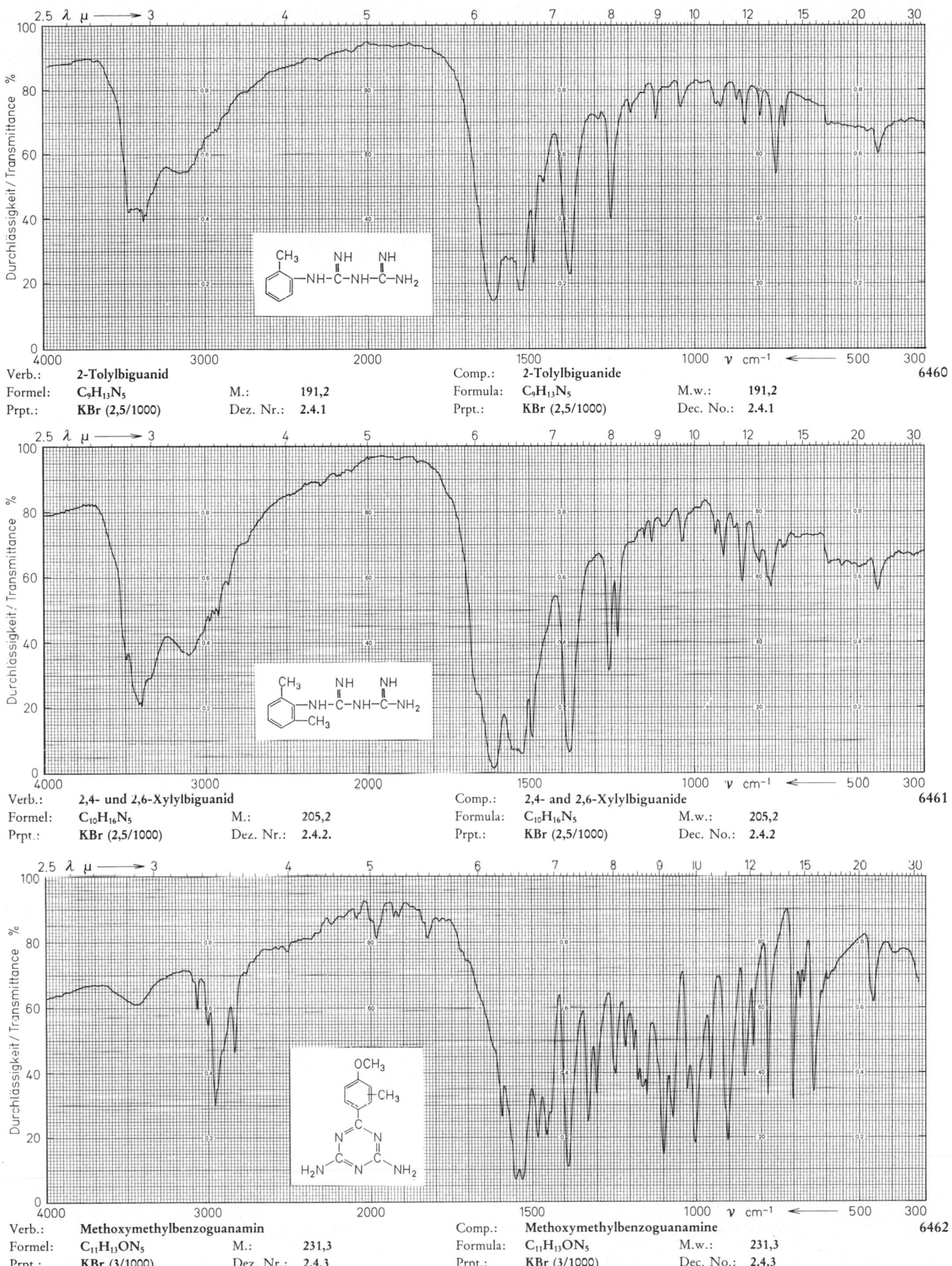

Verb.: **2-Tolylbiguanid**
Formel: **C₉H₁₃N₅**   M.: **191,2**
Prpt.: **KBr (2,5/1000)**   Dez. Nr.: **2.4.1**

Comp.: **2-Tolylbiguanide**
Formula: **C₉H₁₃N₅**   M.w.: **191,2**
Prpt.: **KBr (2,5/1000)**   Dec. No.: **2.4.1**

6460

Verb.: **2,4- und 2,6-Xylylbiguanid**
Formel: **C₁₀H₁₆N₅**   M.: **205,2**
Prpt.: **KBr (2,5/1000)**   Dez. Nr.: **2.4.2.**

Comp.: **2,4- and 2,6-Xylylbiguanide**
Formula: **C₁₀H₁₆N₅**   M.w.: **205,2**
Prpt.: **KBr (2,5/1000)**   Dec. No.: **2.4.2**

6461

Verb.: **Methoxymethylbenzoguanamin**
Formel: **C₁₁H₁₃ON₅**   M.: **231,3**
Prpt.: **KBr (3/1000)**   Dez. Nr.: **2.4.3**

Comp.: **Methoxymethylbenzoguanamine**
Formula: **C₁₁H₁₃ON₅**   M.w.: **231,3**
Prpt.: **KBr (3/1000)**   Dec. No.: **2.4.3**

6462

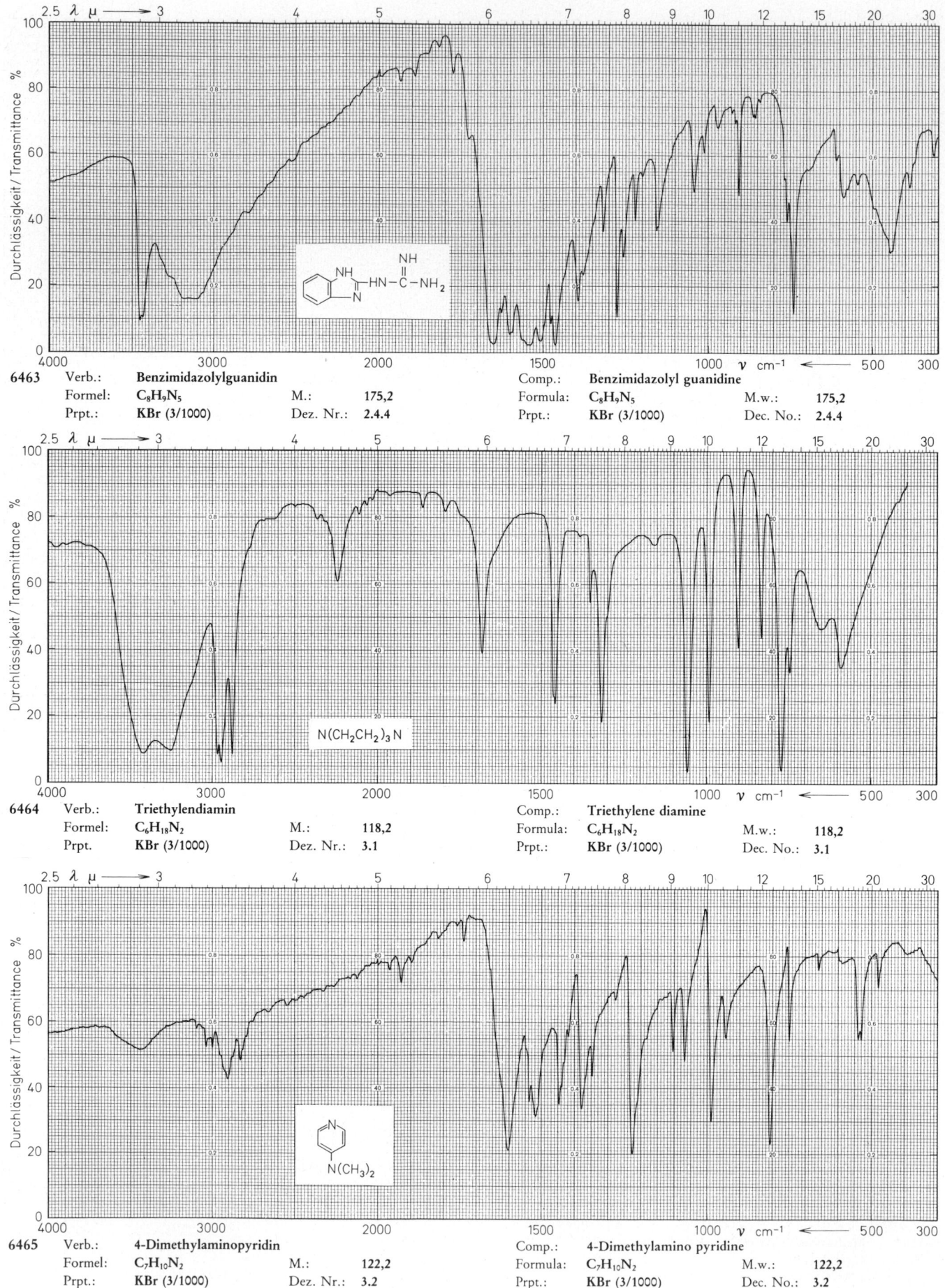

6463   Verb.:   **Benzimidazolylguanidin**

Formel: **C₈H₉N₅**   M.:   **175,2**

Prpt.:   **KBr (3/1000)**   Dez. Nr.:   **2.4.4**

Comp.:   **Benzimidazolyl guanidine**

Formula: **C₈H₉N₅**   M.w.:   **175,2**

Prpt.:   **KBr (3/1000)**   Dec. No.:   **2.4.4**

6464   Verb.:   **Triethylendiamin**

Formel: **C₆H₁₈N₂**   M.:   **118,2**

Prpt.   **KBr (3/1000)**   Dez. Nr.:   **3.1**

Comp.:   **Triethylene diamine**

Formula: **C₆H₁₈N₂**   M.w.:   **118,2**

Prpt.:   **KBr (3/1000)**   Dec. No.:   **3.1**

6465   Verb.:   **4-Dimethylaminopyridin**

Formel: **C₇H₁₀N₂**   M.:   **122,2**

Prpt.:   **KBr (3/1000)**

Comp.:   **4-Dimethylamino pyridine**

Formula: **C₇H₁₀N₂**   M.w.:   **122,2**

Prpt.:   **KBr (3/1000)**   Dec. No.:   **3.2**

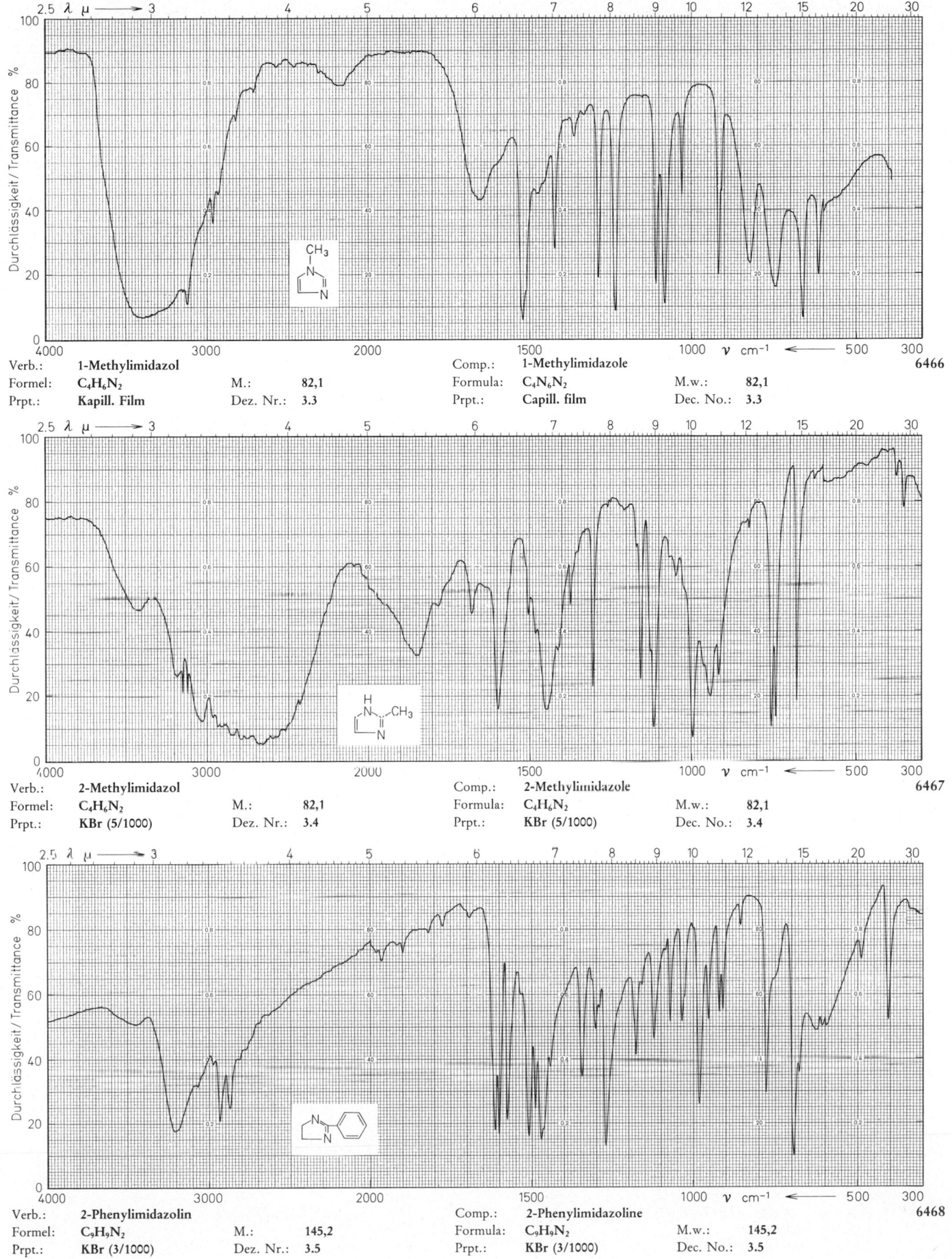

Verb.: **1-Methylimidazol**

Formel: **$C_4H_6N_2$** M.: **82,1**

Prpt.: **Kapill. Film** Dez. Nr.: **3.3**

Comp.: **1-Methylimidazole**

Formula: **$C_4N_6N_2$** M.w.: **82,1**

Prpt.: **Capill. film** Dec. No.: **3.3**

6466

Verb.: **2-Methylimidazol**

Formel: **$C_4H_6N_2$** M.: **82,1**

Prpt.: **KBr (5/1000)** Dez. Nr.: **3.4**

Comp.: **2-Methylimidazole**

Formula: **$C_4H_6N_2$** M.w.: **82,1**

Prpt.: **KBr (5/1000)** Dec. No.: **3.4**

6467

Verb.: **2-Phenylimidazolin**

Formel: **$C_9H_9N_2$** M.: **145,2**

Prpt.: **KBr (3/1000)** Dez. Nr.: **3.5**

Comp.: **2-Phenylimidazoline**

Formula: **$C_9H_9N_2$** M.w.: **145,2**

Prpt.: **KBr (3/1000)** Dec. No.: **3.5**

6468

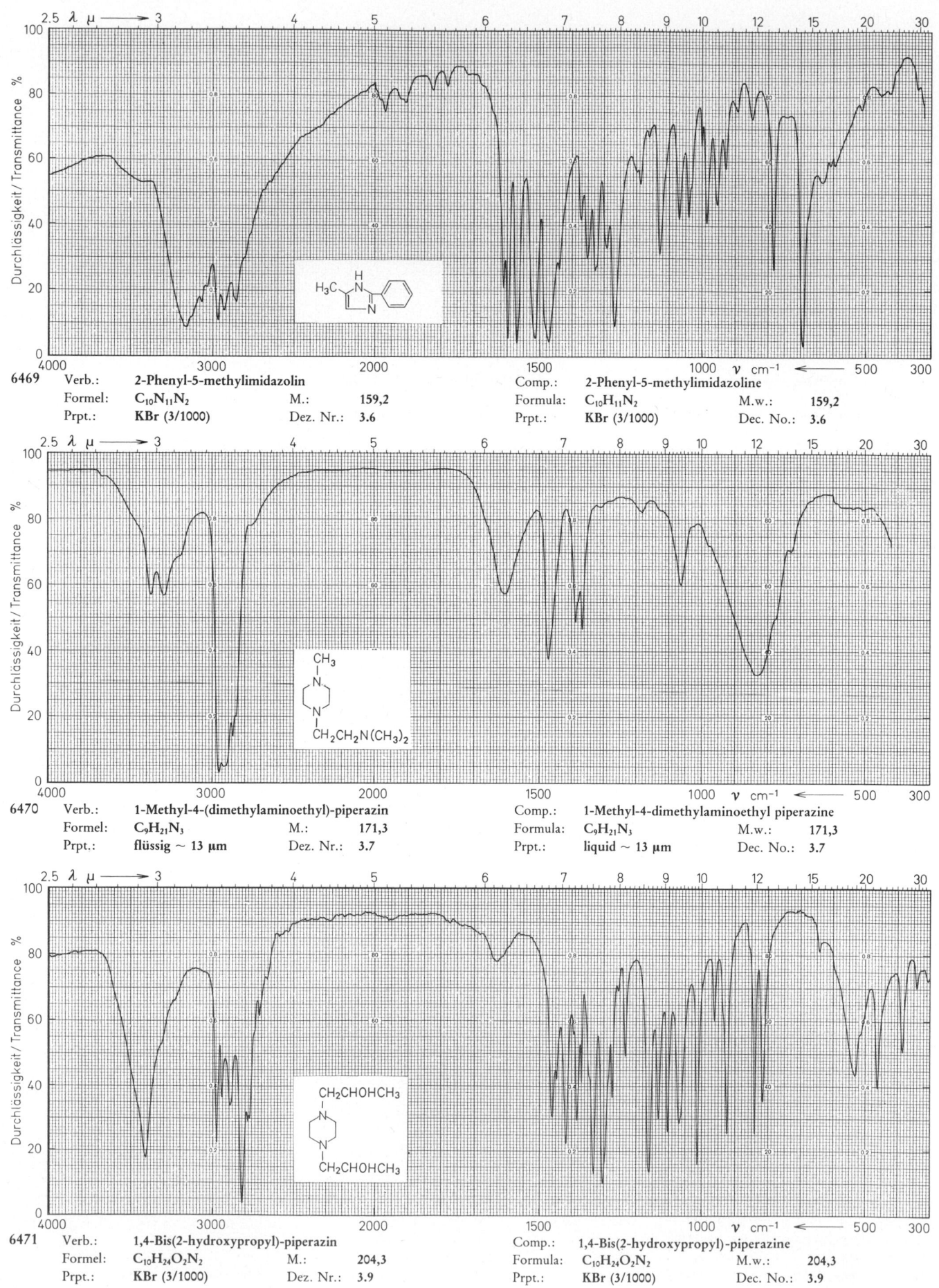

6469 Verb.: **2-Phenyl-5-methylimidazolin**
Formel: **C₁₀N₁₁N₂**
Prpt.: **KBr (3/1000)**
M.: **159,2**
Dez. Nr.: **3.6**

Comp.: **2-Phenyl-5-methylimidazoline**
Formula: **C₁₀H₁₁N₂**
Prpt.: **KBr (3/1000)**
M.w.: **159,2**
Dec. No.: **3.6**

6470 Verb.: **1-Methyl-4-(dimethylaminoethyl)-piperazin**
Formel: **C₉H₂₁N₃**
Prpt.: **flüssig ~ 13 µm**
M.: **171,3**
Dez. Nr.: **3.7**

Comp.: **1-Methyl-4-dimethylaminoethyl piperazine**
Formula: **C₉H₂₁N₃**
Prpt.: **liquid ~ 13 µm**
M.w.: **171,3**
Dec. No.: **3.7**

6471 Verb.: **1,4-Bis(2-hydroxypropyl)-piperazin**
Formel: **C₁₀H₂₄O₂N₂**
Prpt.: **KBr (3/1000)**
M.: **204,3**
Dez. Nr.: **3.9**

Comp.: **1,4-Bis(2-hydroxypropyl)-piperazine**
Formula: **C₁₀H₂₄O₂N₂**
Prpt.: **KBr (3/1000)**
M.w.: **204,3**
Dec. No.: **3.9**

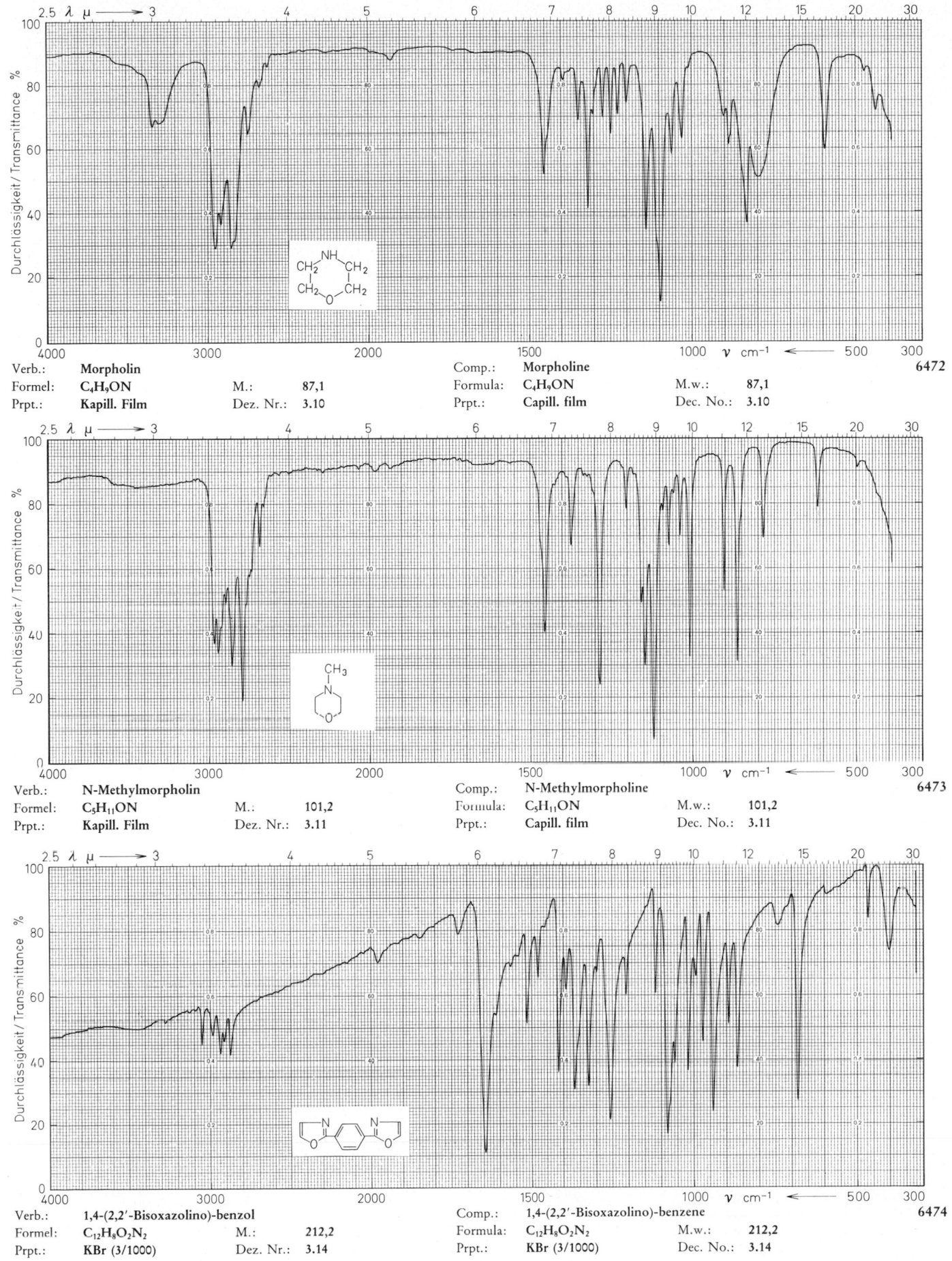

Verb.: **Morpholin**

Formel: **C₄H₉ON**   M.: **87,1**

Prpt.: **Kapill. Film**   Dez. Nr.: **3.10**

Comp.: **Morpholine**

Formula: **C₄H₉ON**   M.w.: **87,1**

Prpt.: **Capill. film**   Dec. No.: **3.10**

6472

Verb.: **N-Methylmorpholin**

Formel: **C₅H₁₁ON**   M.: **101,2**

Prpt.: **Kapill. Film**   Dez. Nr.: **3.11**

Comp.: **N-Methylmorpholine**

Formula: **C₅H₁₁ON**   M.w.: **101,2**

Prpt.: **Capill. film**   Dec. No.: **3.11**

6473

Verb.: **1,4-(2,2′-Bisoxazolino)-benzol**

Formel: **C₁₂H₈O₂N₂**   M.: **212,2**

Prpt.: **KBr (3/1000)**   Dez. Nr.: **3.14**

Comp.: **1,4-(2,2′-Bisoxazolino)-benzene**

Formula: **C₁₂H₈O₂N₂**   M.w.: **212,2**

Prpt.: **KBr (3/1000)**   Dec. No.: **3.14**

6474

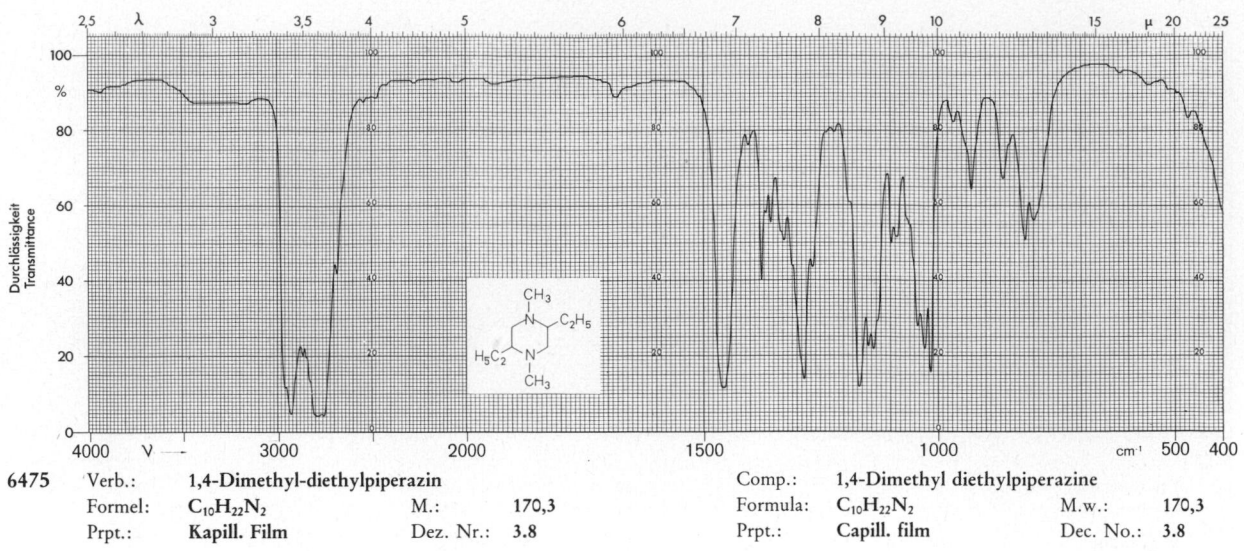

6475 Verb.: **1,4-Dimethyl-diethylpiperazin**
Formel: **C₁₀H₂₂N₂**   M.: **170,3**
Prpt.: **Kapill. Film**   Dez. Nr.: **3.8**

Comp.: **1,4-Dimethyl diethylpiperazine**
Formula: **C₁₀H₂₂N₂**   M.w.: **170,3**
Prpt.: **Capill. film**   Dec. No.: **3.8**

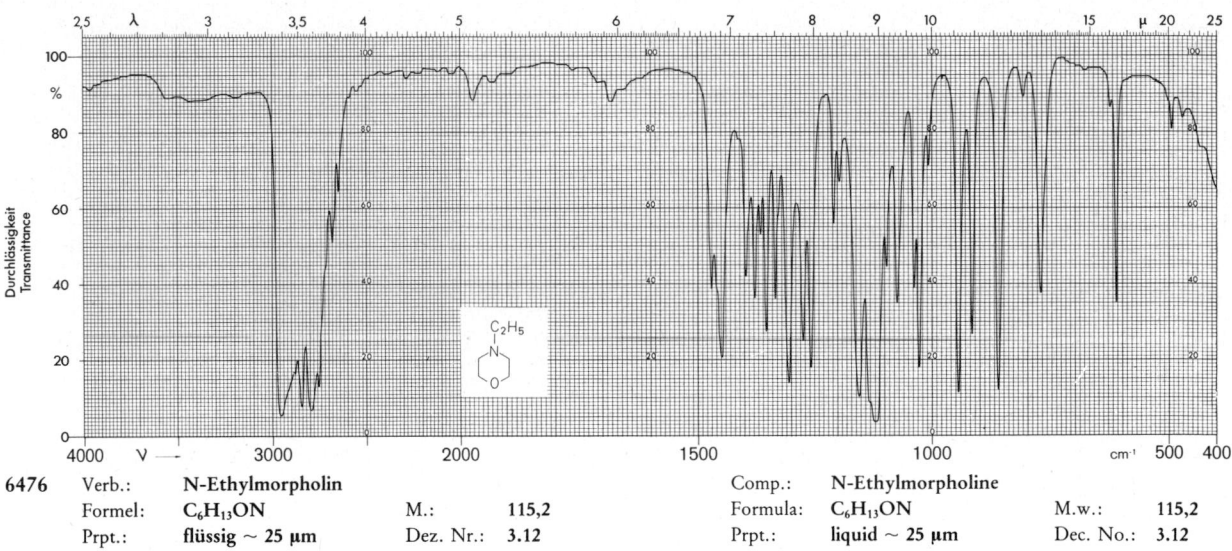

6476 Verb.: **N-Ethylmorpholin**
Formel: **C₆H₁₃ON**   M.: **115,2**
Prpt.: **flüssig ~ 25 μm**   Dez. Nr.: **3.12**

Comp.: **N-Ethylmorpholine**
Formula: **C₆H₁₃ON**   M.w.: **115,2**
Prpt.: **liquid ~ 25 μm**   Dec. No.: **3.12**

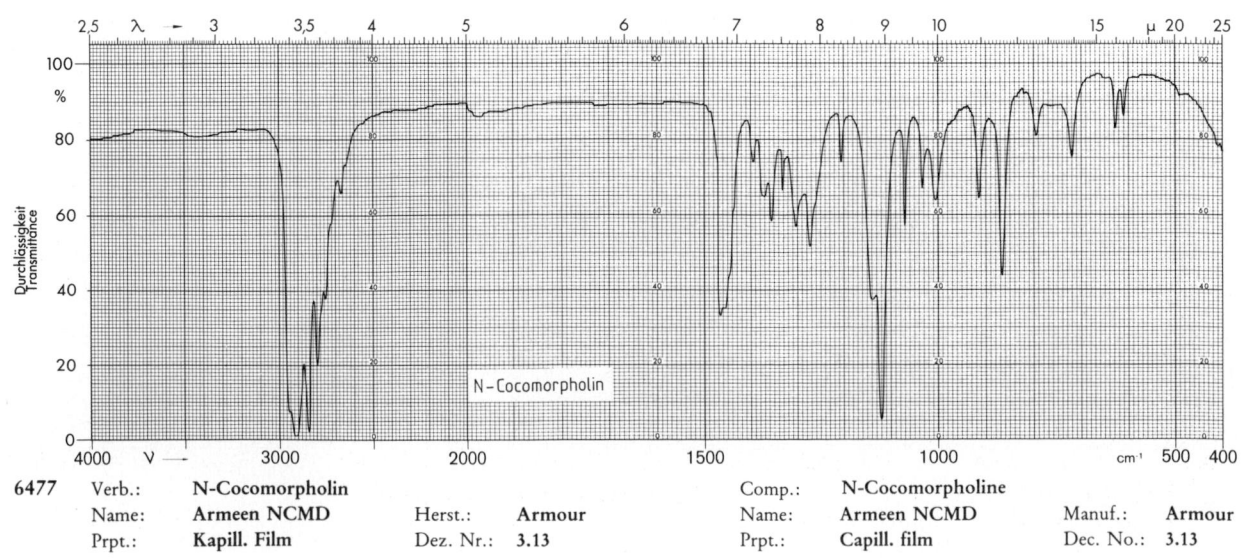

6477 Verb.: **N-Cocomorpholin**
Name: **Armeen NCMD**   Herst.: **Armour**
Prpt.: **Kapill. Film**   Dez. Nr.: **3.13**

Comp.: **N-Cocomorpholine**
Name: **Armeen NCMD**   Manuf.: **Armour**
Prpt.: **Capill. film**   Dec. No.: **3.13**

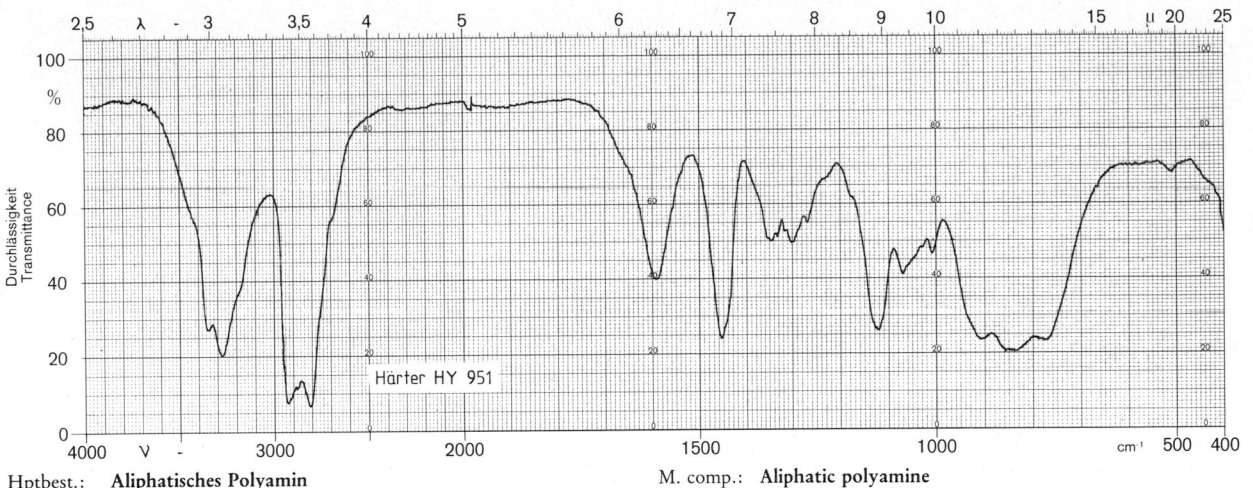

Hptbest.:	**Aliphatisches Polyamin**			M. comp.:	**Aliphatic polyamine**			6478
Name:	**Härter HY 951**	Herst.:	**CIBA**	Name:	**Härter HY 951**	Manuf.:	**CIBA**	
Prpt.:	**Kapill. Film**	Dez. Nr.:	**4.1**	Prpt.:	**Capill. film**	Dec. No.:	**4.1**	

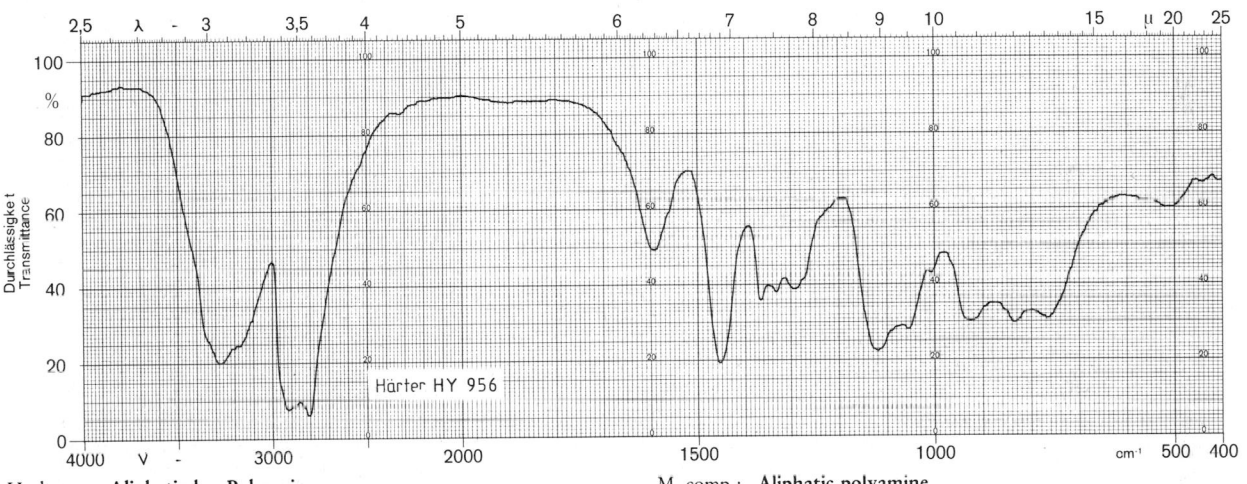

Hptbest.:	**Aliphatisches Polyamin**			M. comp.:	**Aliphatic polyamine**			6479
Name:	**Härter HY 956**	Herst.:	**CIBA**	Name:	**Härter HY 956**	Manuf.:	**CIBA**	
Prpt.:	**Kapill. Film**	Dez. Nr.:	**4.2**	Prpt.:	**Capill. film**	Dec. No.:	**4.2**	

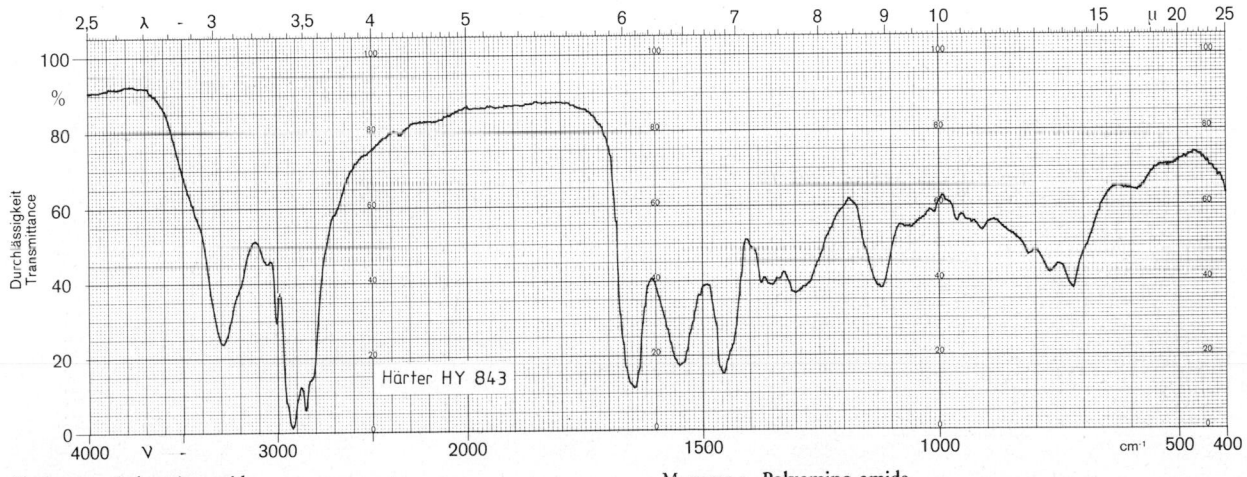

Hptbest.:	**Polyaminoamid**			M. comp.:	**Polyamino amide**			6480
Name:	**Härter HY 843**	Herst.:	**CIBA**	Name:	**Härter HY 843**	Manuf.:	**CIBA**	
Prpt.:	**Kapill. Film**	Dez. Nr.:	**4.3**	Prpt.:	**Capill. film**	Dec. No.:	**4.3**	

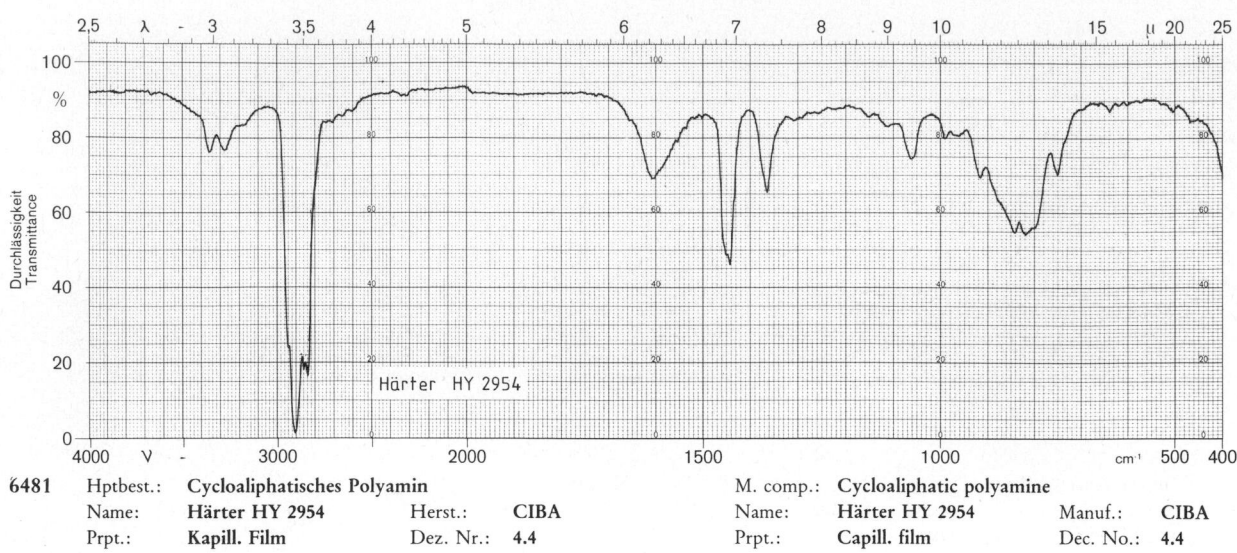

6481 Hptbest.: **Cycloaliphatisches Polyamin** M. comp.: **Cycloaliphatic polyamine**
Name: **Härter HY 2954** Herst.: **CIBA** Name: **Härter HY 2954** Manuf.: **CIBA**
Prpt.: **Kapill. Film** Dez. Nr.: **4.4** Prpt.: **Capill. film** Dec. No.: **4.4**

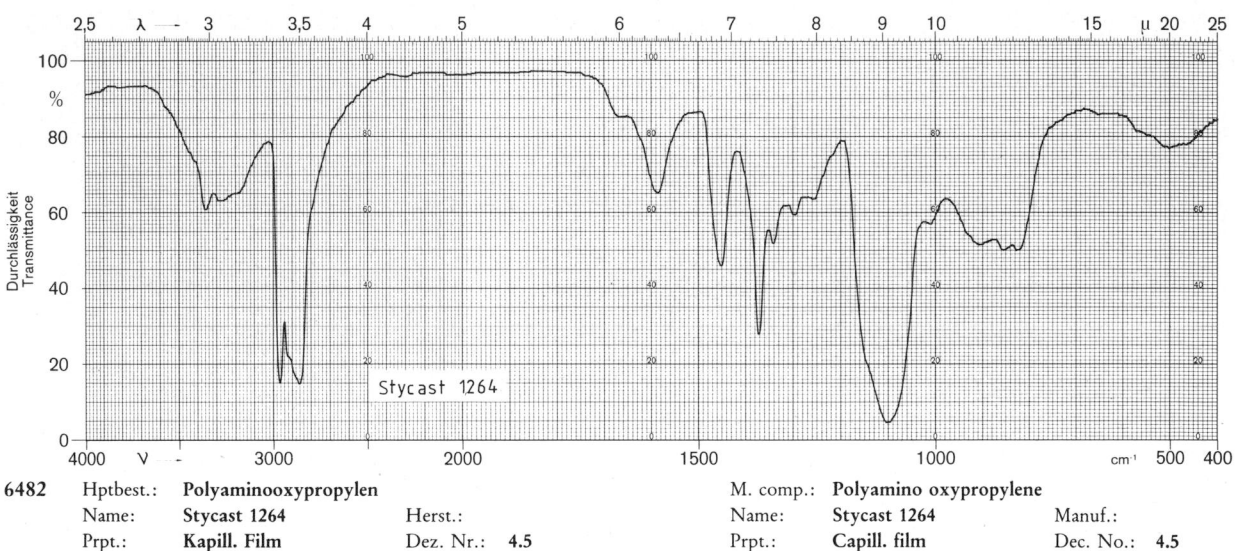

6482 Hptbest.: **Polyaminooxypropylen** M. comp.: **Polyamino oxypropylene**
Name: **Stycast 1264** Herst.: Name: **Stycast 1264** Manuf.:
Prpt.: **Kapill. Film** Dez. Nr.: **4.5** Prpt.: **Capill. film** Dec. No.: **4.5**

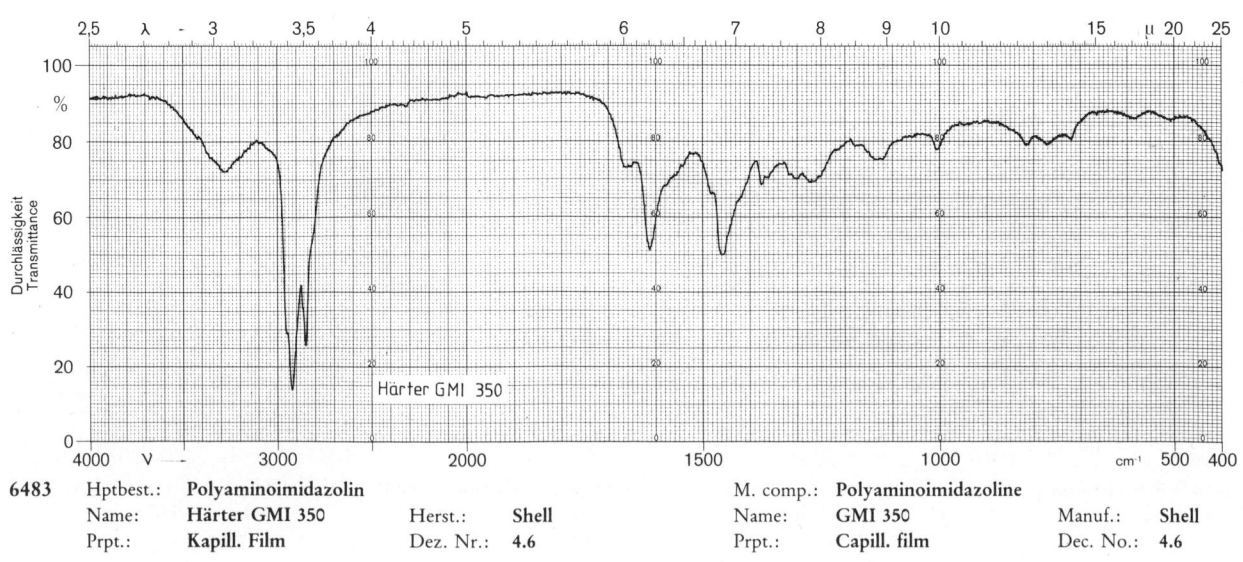

6483 Hptbest.: **Polyaminoimidazolin** M. comp.: **Polyaminoimidazoline**
Name: **Härter GMI 350** Herst.: **Shell** Name: **GMI 350** Manuf.: **Shell**
Prpt.: **Kapill. Film** Dez. Nr.: **4.6** Prpt.: **Capill. film** Dec. No.: **4.6**

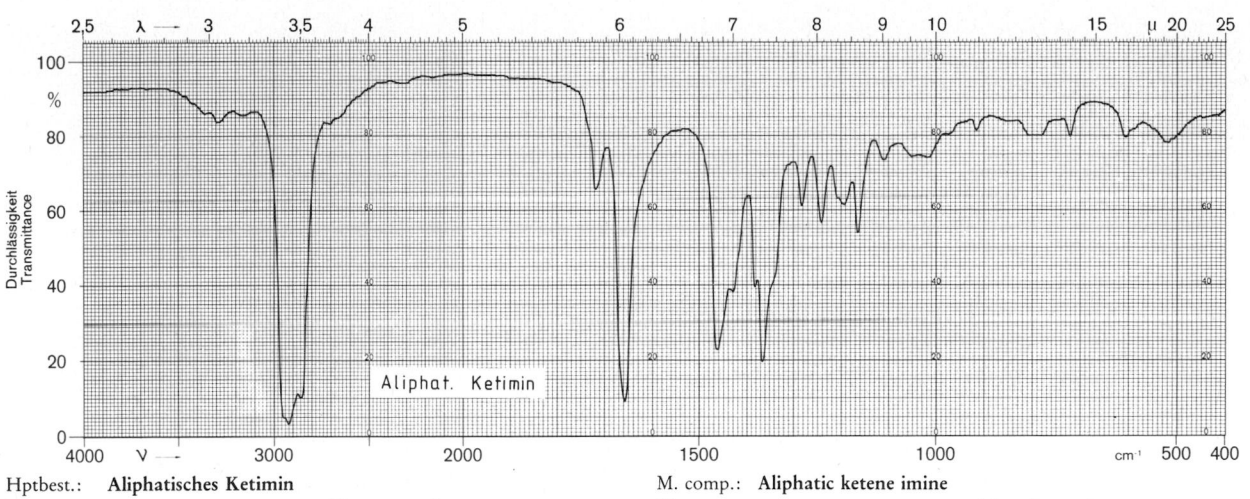

Hptbest.:	**Aliphatisches Ketimin**			M. comp.:	**Aliphatic ketene imine**			**6484**
Name:		Herst.:	**Bayer**	Name:		Manuf.:	**Bayer**	
Prpt.:	**Kapill. Film**	Dez. Nr.:	**5.1**	Prpt.:	**Capill. film**	Dec. No.:	**5.1**	

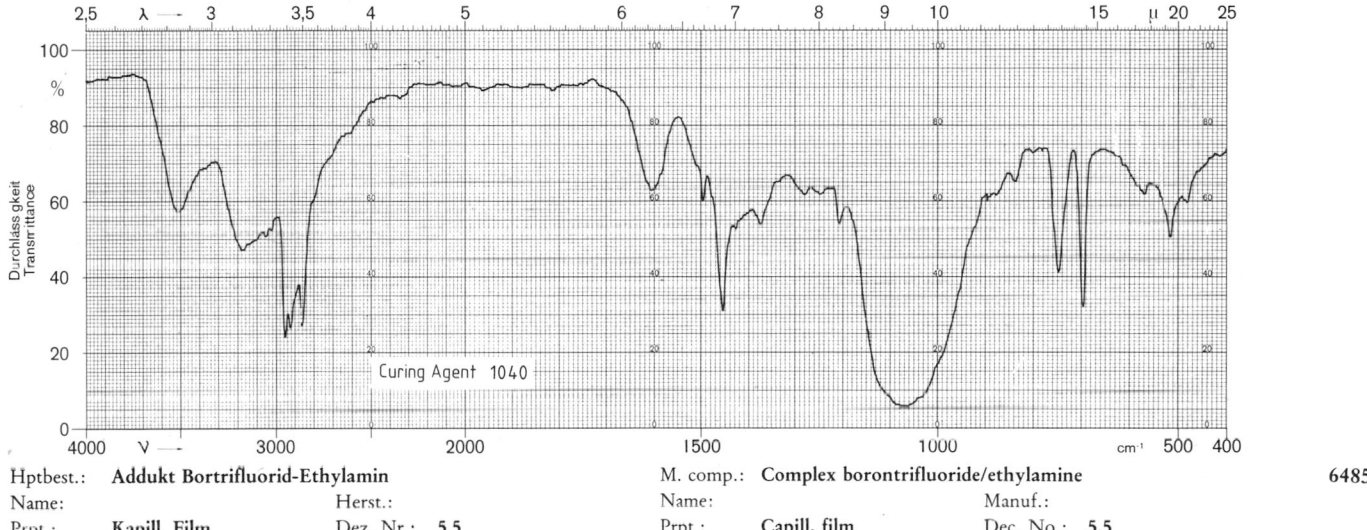

Hptbest.:	**Addukt Bortrifluorid-Ethylamin**			M. comp.:	**Complex borontrifluoride/ethylamine**			**6485**
Name:		Herst.:		Name:		Manuf.:		
Prpt.:	**Kapill. Film**	Dez. Nr.:	**5.5**	Prpt.:	**Capill. film**	Dec. No.:	**5.5**	

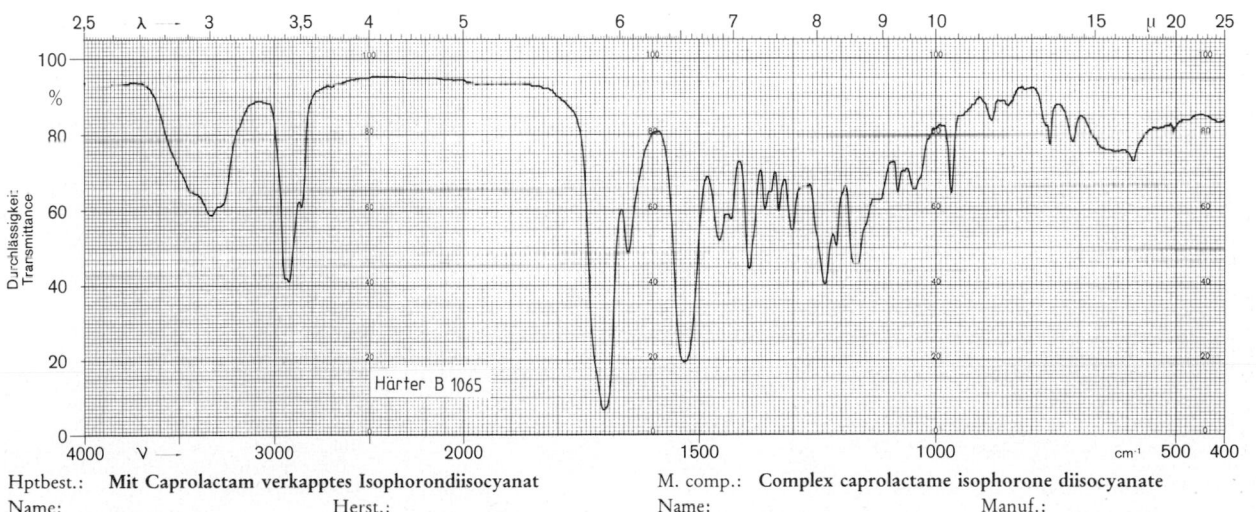

Hptbest.:	**Mit Caprolactam verkapptes Isophorondiisocyanat**			M. comp.:	**Complex caprolactame isophorone diisocyanate**			**6486**
Name:		Herst.:		Name:		Manuf.:		
Prpt.:	**KBr (3/1000)**	Dez. Nr.:	**5.6**	Prpt.:	**KBr (3/1000)**	Dec. No.:	**5.6**	

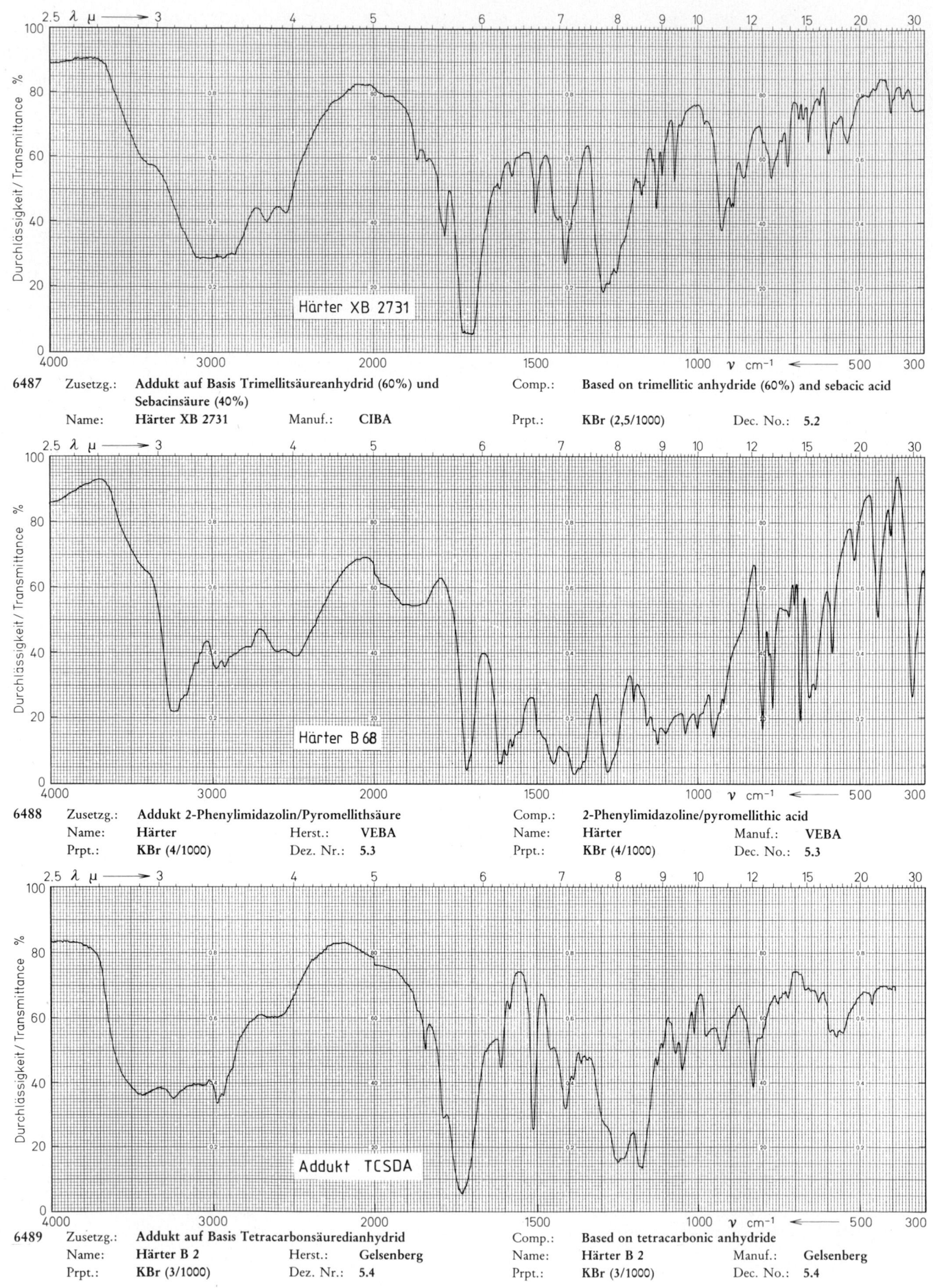

6487 Zusetzg.: **Addukt auf Basis Trimellitsäureanhydrid (60%) und Sebacinsäure (40%)**   Comp.: **Based on trimellitic anhydride (60%) and sebacic acid**

Name: **Härter XB 2731**   Manuf.: **CIBA**   Prpt.: **KBr (2,5/1000)**   Dec. No.: **5.2**

6488 Zusetzg.: **Addukt 2-Phenylimidazolin/Pyromellithsäure**   Comp.: **2-Phenylimidazoline/pyromellithic acid**

Name: **Härter**   Herst.: **VEBA**   Name: **Härter**   Manuf.: **VEBA**

Prpt.: **KBr (4/1000)**   Dez. Nr.: **5.3**   Prpt.: **KBr (4/1000)**   Dec. No.: **5.3**

6489 Zusetzg.: **Addukt auf Basis Tetracarbonsäuredianhydrid**   Comp.: **Based on tetracarbonic anhydride**

Name: **Härter B 2**   Herst.: **Gelsenberg**   Name: **Härter B 2**   Manuf.: **Gelsenberg**

Prpt.: **KBr (3/1000)**   Dez. Nr.: **5.4**   Prpt.: **KBr (3/1000)**   Dec. No.: **5.4**

Verarbeitungshilfsmittel

Processing Aids

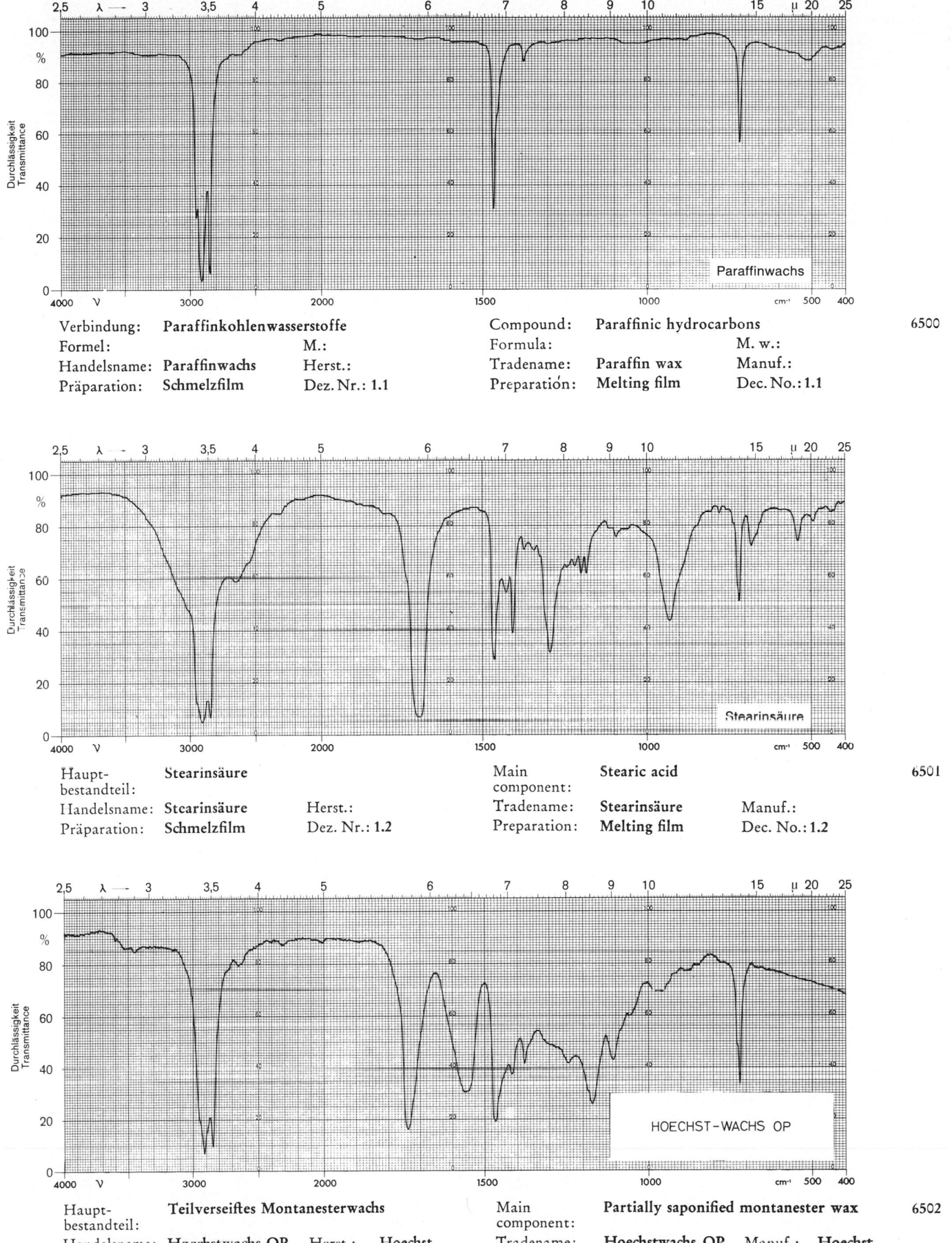

Verbindung:	Paraffinkohlenwasserstoffe		Compound:	Paraffinic hydrocarbons	6500
Formel:		M.:	Formula:		M. w.:
Handelsname:	Paraffinwachs	Herst.:	Tradename:	Paraffin wax	Manuf.:
Präparation:	Schmelzfilm	Dez. Nr.: 1.1	Preparation:	Melting film	Dec. No.: 1.1

Haupt-bestandteil:	Stearinsäure		Main component:	Stearic acid	6501
Handelsname:	Stearinsäure	Herst.:	Tradename:	Stearinsäure	Manuf.:
Präparation:	Schmelzfilm	Dez. Nr.: 1.2	Preparation:	Melting film	Dec. No.: 1.2

Haupt-bestandteil:	Teilverseiftes Montanesterwachs		Main component:	Partially saponified montanester wax	6502
Handelsname:	Hoechstwachs OP	Herst.: Hoechst	Tradename:	Hoechstwachs OP	Manuf.: Hoechst
Präparation:	Schmelzfilm	Dez. Nr.: 1.3	Preparation:	Melting film	Dec. No.: 1.3

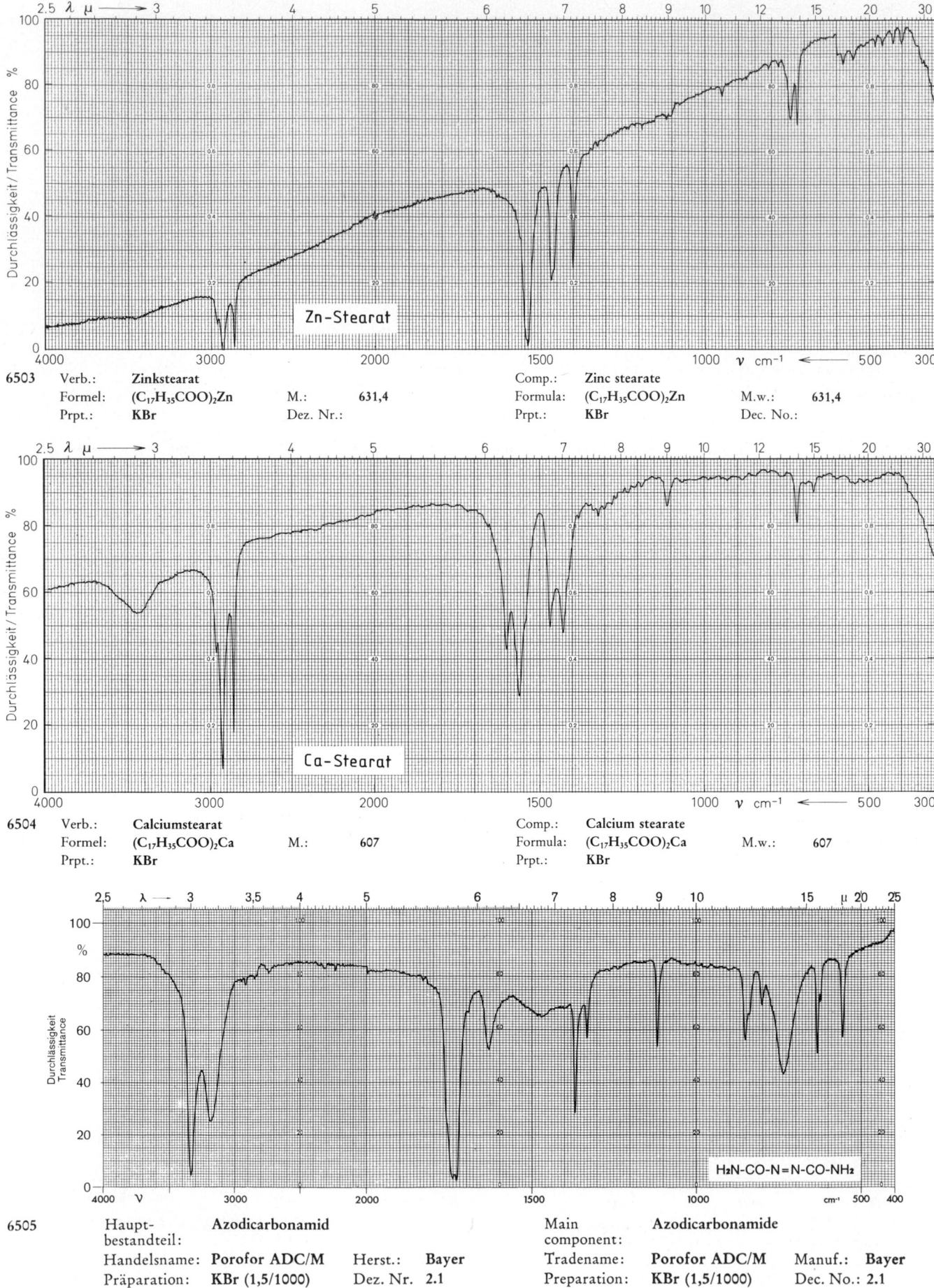

6503

Verb.:	**Zinkstearat**		
Formel:	**(C₁₇H₃₅COO)₂Zn**	M.:	**631,4**
Prpt.:	**KBr**	Dez. Nr.:	

Comp.: **Zinc stearate**
Formula: (C₁₇H₃₅COO)₂Zn   M.w.: 631,4
Prpt.: KBr   Dec. No.:

6504

Verb.:	**Calciumstearat**		
Formel:	**(C₁₇H₃₅COO)₂Ca**	M.:	**607**
Prpt.:	**KBr**		

Comp.: **Calcium stearate**
Formula: (C₁₇H₃₅COO)₂Ca   M.w.: 607
Prpt.: KBr

H₂N-CO-N=N-CO-NH₂

6505

Haupt-bestandteil:	**Azodicarbonamid**		
Handelsname:	**Porofor ADC/M**	Herst.:	**Bayer**
Präparation:	**KBr (1,5/1000)**	Dez. Nr.	**2.1**

Main component: **Azodicarbonamide**
Tradename: **Porofor ADC/M**   Manuf.: **Bayer**
Preparation: **KBr (1,5/1000)**   Dec. No.: **2.1**

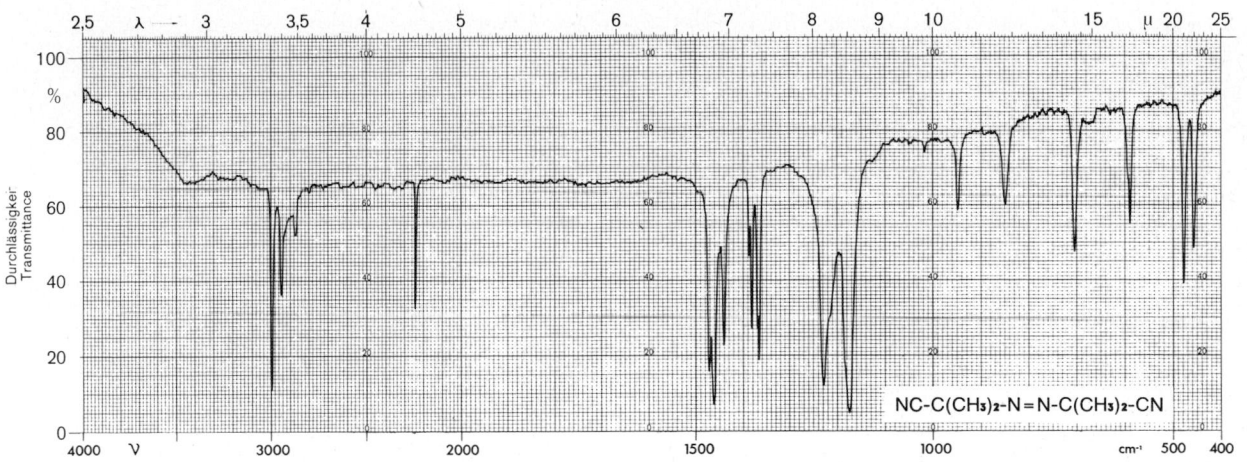

NC-C(CH₃)₂-N=N-C(CH₃)₂-CN

Haupt-bestandteil:	**Azobisisobutyronitril**		Main component:	**Azobisisobutyronitrile**		6506
Handelsname:	**Porofor N**	Herst.: **Bayer**	Tradename:	**Porofor N**	Manuf.: **Bayer**	
Präparation:	**KBr (1,5/1000)**	Dez. Nr. **2.2**	Preparation:	**KBr (1,5/1000)**	Dec. No.: **2.2**	

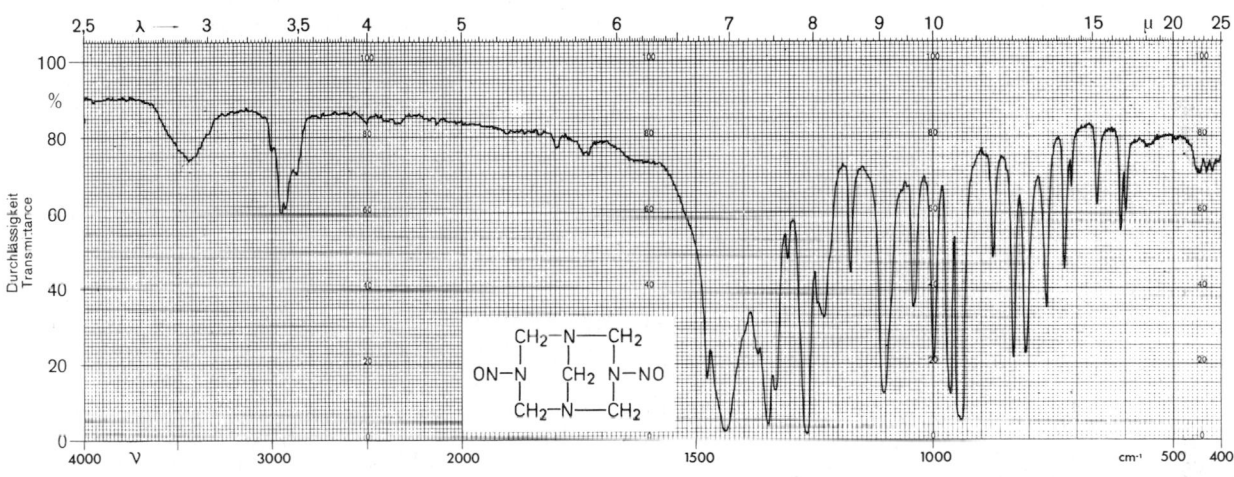

Haupt-bestandteil:	**N,N′-Dinitrosopentamethylentetramin**		Main component:	**N,N′-Dinitrosopentamethylene tetramine**		6507
Handelsname:	**Vulcacel BN 94**	Herst.: **ICI**	Tradename:	**Vulcacel BN 94**	Manuf.: **ICI**	
Präparation:	**KBr (1,5/1000)**	Dez. Nr.: **2.3**	Preparation:	**KBr (1,5/1000)**	Dec. No.: **2.3**	

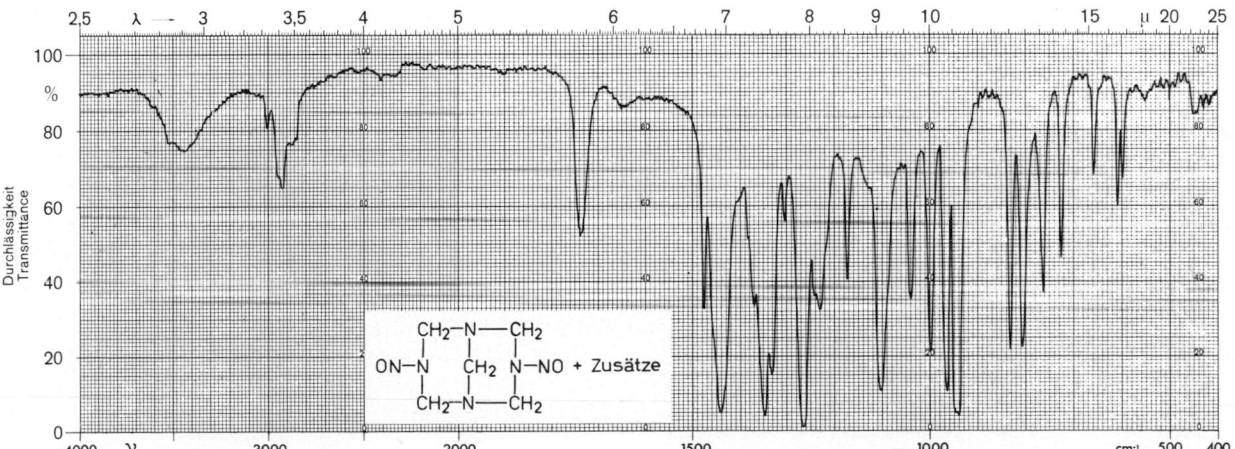

Haupt-bestandteil:	**80 % Dinitrosopentamethylentetramin + 20 % inaktive Zusatzstoffe**		Main component:	**80 % Dinitrosopentamethylene tetramine + 20 % inactive Additives**		6508
Handelsname:	**Porofor DNO/F**	Herst.: **Bayer**	Tradename:	**Porofor DNO/F**	Manuf.: **Bayer**	
Präparation:	**KBr (3/1000)**	Dez. Nr.: **2.4**	Preparation:	**KBr (3/1000)**	Dec. No.: **2.4**	

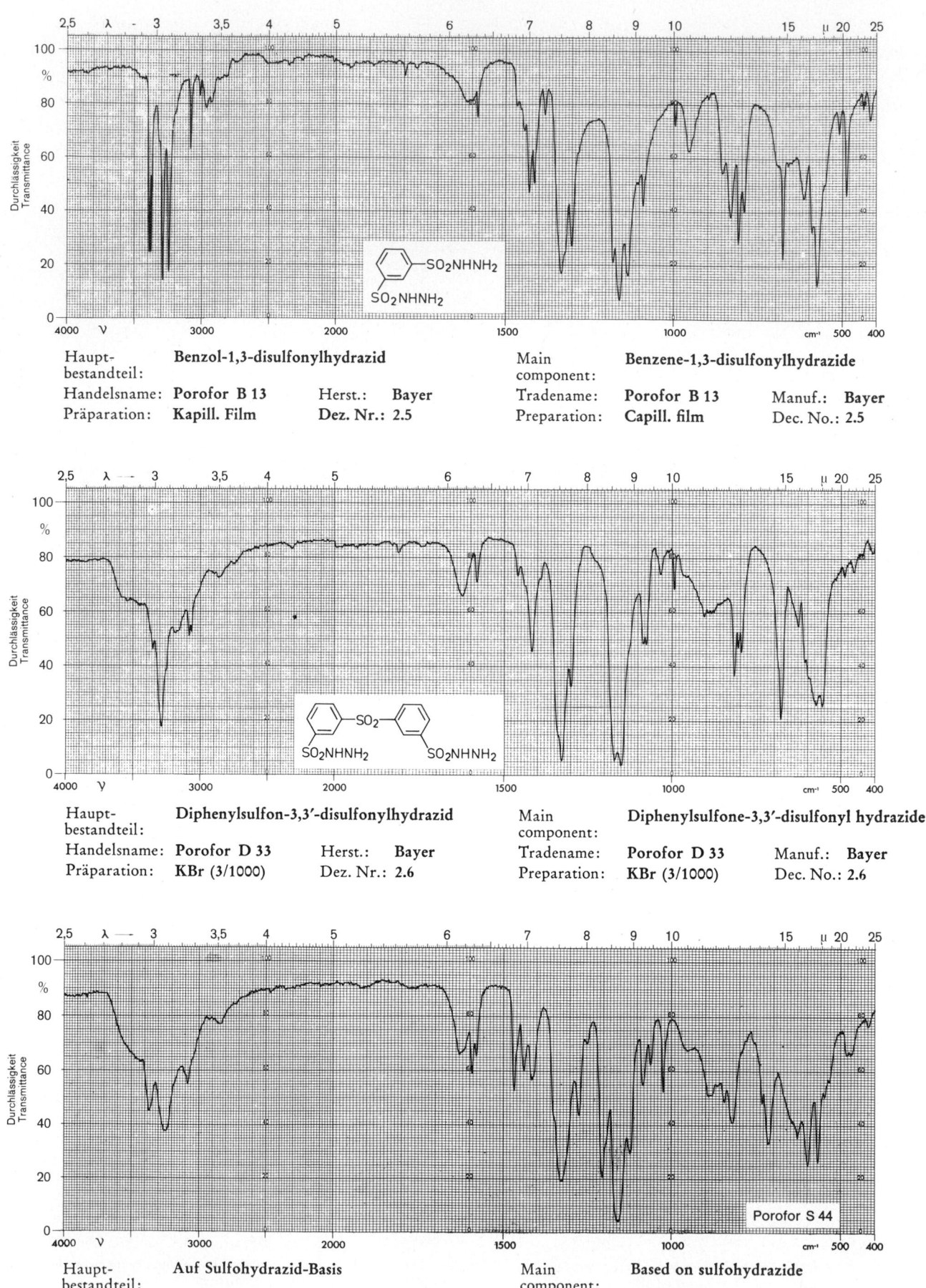

6509 Haupt-   **Benzol-1,3-disulfonylhydrazid**   Main   **Benzene-1,3-disulfonylhydrazide**
      bestandteil: component:

      Handelsname: **Porofor B 13**   Herst.: **Bayer**   Tradename: **Porofor B 13**   Manuf.: **Bayer**
      Präparation: **Kapill. Film**   Dez. Nr.: **2.5**   Preparation: **Capill. film**   Dec. No.: **2.5**

6510 Haupt-   **Diphenylsulfon-3,3′-disulfonylhydrazid**   Main   **Diphenylsulfone-3,3′-disulfonyl hydrazide**
      bestandteil: component:

      Handelsname: **Porofor D 33**   Herst.: **Bayer**   Tradename: **Porofor D 33**   Manuf.: **Bayer**
      Präparation: **KBr (3/1000)**   Dez. Nr.: **2.6**   Preparation: **KBr (3/1000)**   Dec. No.: **2.6**

6511 Haupt-   **Auf Sulfohydrazid-Basis**   Main   **Based on sulfohydrazide**
      bestandteil: component:

      Handelsname: **Porofor S 44**   Herst.: **Bayer**   Tradename: **Porofor S 44**   Manuf.: **Bayer**
      Präparation: **KBr (3/1000)**   Dez. Nr.: **2.7**   Preparation: **KBr (3/1000)**   Dec. No.: **2.7**

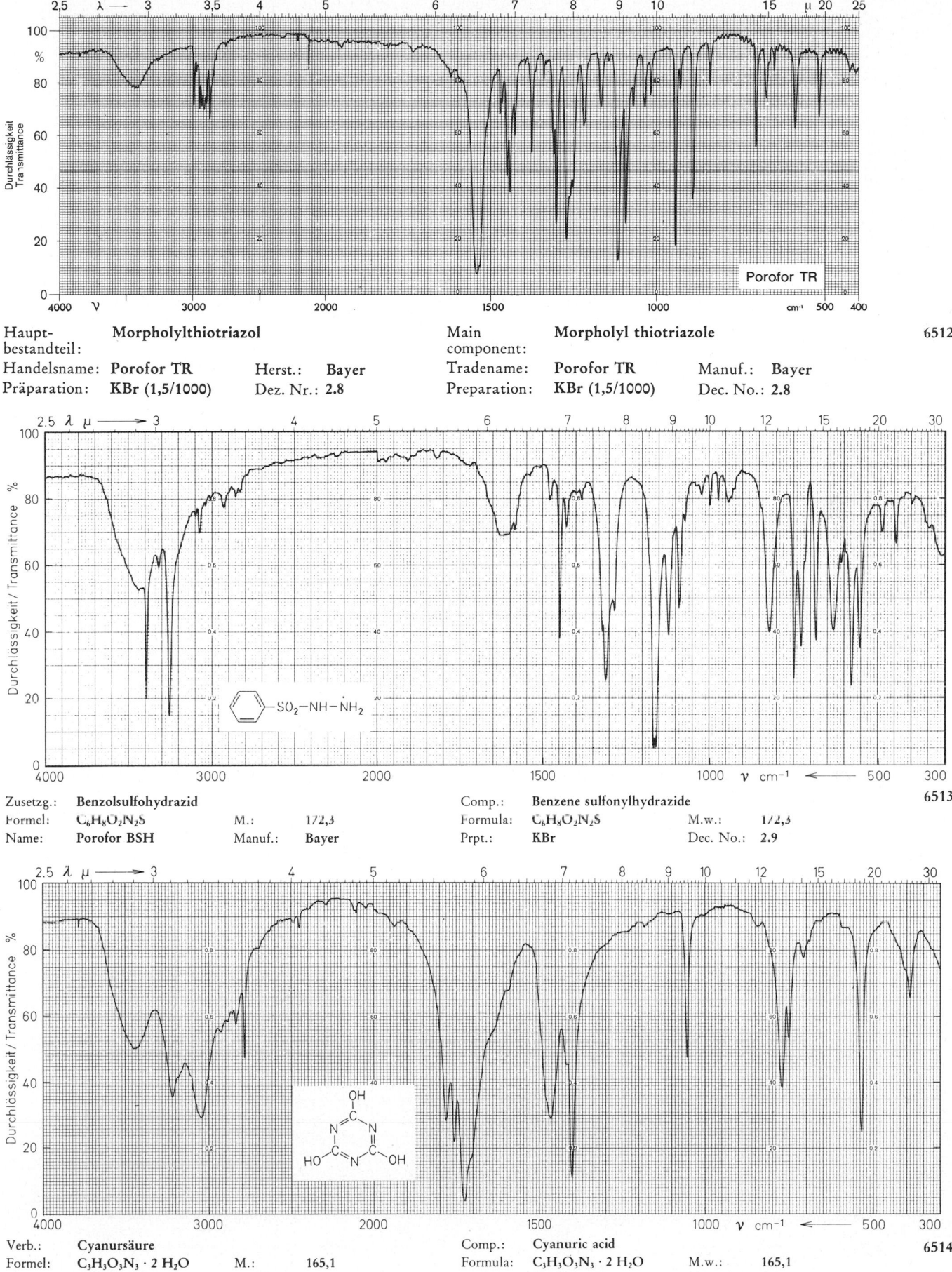

Porofor TR

Haupt-bestandteil:	**Morpholylthiotriazol**		Main component:	**Morpholyl thiotriazole**		6512
Handelsname:	**Porofor TR**	Herst.: **Bayer**	Tradename:	**Porofor TR**	Manuf.: **Bayer**	
Präparation:	**KBr (1,5/1000)**	Dez. Nr.: **2.8**	Preparation:	**KBr (1,5/1000)**	Dec. No.: **2.8**	

Zusetzg.:	**Benzolsulfohydrazid**		Comp.:	**Benzene sulfonylhydrazide**		6513
Formel:	**C₆H₈O₂N₂S**	M.: **172,3**	Formula:	**C₆H₈O₂N₂S**	M.w.: **172,3**	
Name:	**Porofor BSH**	Manuf.: **Bayer**	Prpt.: **KBr**	Dec. No.: **2.9**	

Verb.:	**Cyanursäure**		Comp.:	**Cyanuric acid**		6514
Formel:	**C₃H₃O₃N₃ · 2 H₂O**	M.: **165,1**	Formula:	**C₃H₃O₃N₃ · 2 H₂O**	M.w.: **165,1**	
Prpt.:	**KBr (1,5/1000)**	Dez. Nr.: **2.7**	Prpt.:	**KBr (3/1000)**	Dec. Nr. **2.7**	

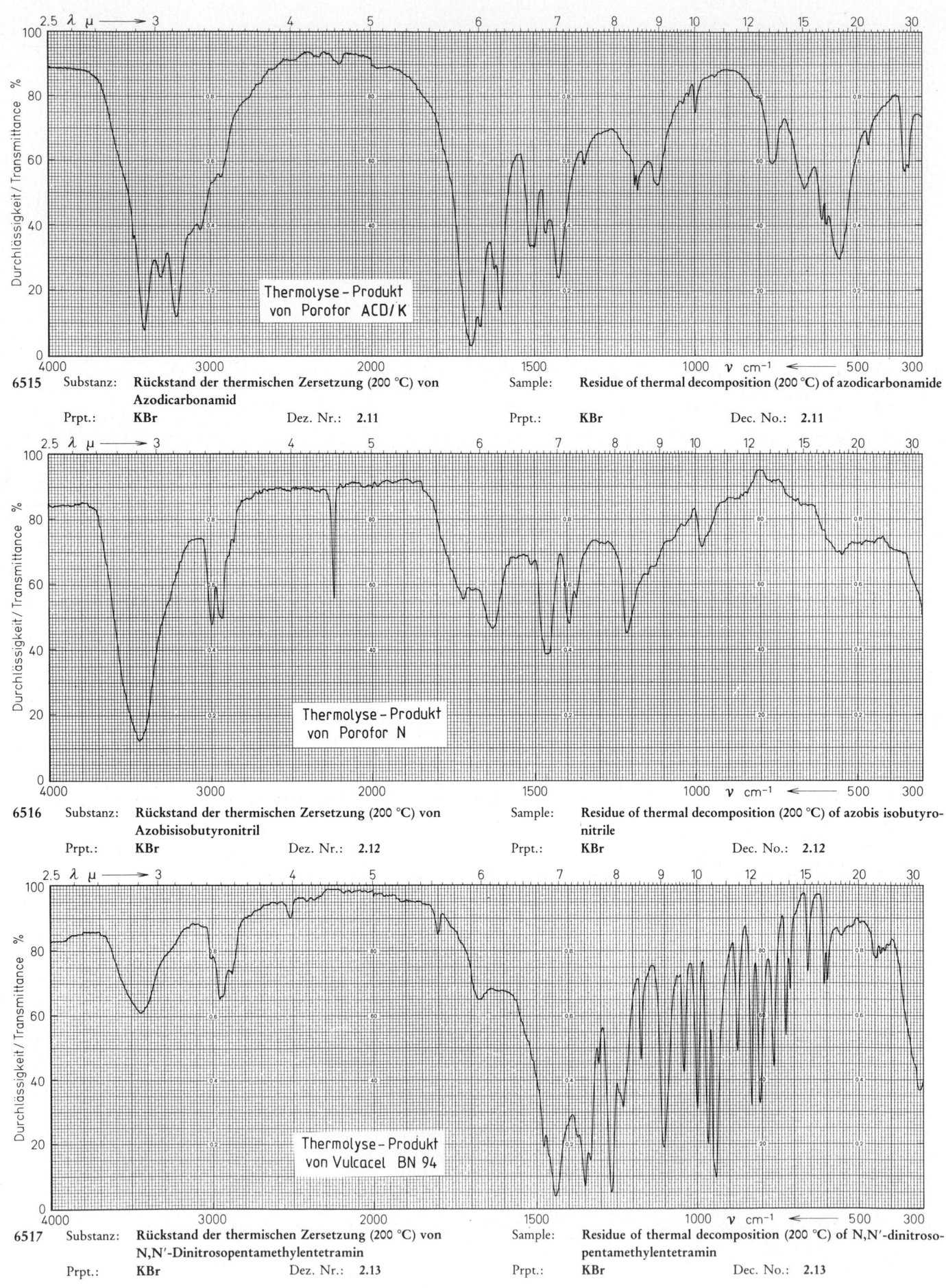

6515 Substanz: **Rückstand der thermischen Zersetzung (200 °C) von Azodicarbonamid**

Sample: **Residue of thermal decomposition (200 °C) of azodicarbonamide**

Prpt.: **KBr**   Dez. Nr.: **2.11**   Prpt.: **KBr**   Dec. No.: **2.11**

6516 Substanz: **Rückstand der thermischen Zersetzung (200 °C) von Azobisisobutyronitril**

Sample: **Residue of thermal decomposition (200 °C) of azobis isobutyronitrile**

Prpt.: **KBr**   Dez. Nr.: **2.12**   Prpt.: **KBr**   Dec. No.: **2.12**

6517 Substanz: **Rückstand der thermischen Zersetzung (200 °C) von N,N′-Dinitrosopentamethylentetramin**

Sample: **Residue of thermal decomposition (200 °C) of N,N′-dinitrosopentamethylentetramin**

Prpt.: **KBr**   Dez. Nr.: **2.13**   Prpt.: **KBr**   Dec. No.: **2.13**

Thermolyse – Produkt
von Porofor ACD/K

Thermolyse – Produkt
von Porofor N

Thermolyse – Produkt
von Vulcacel BN 94

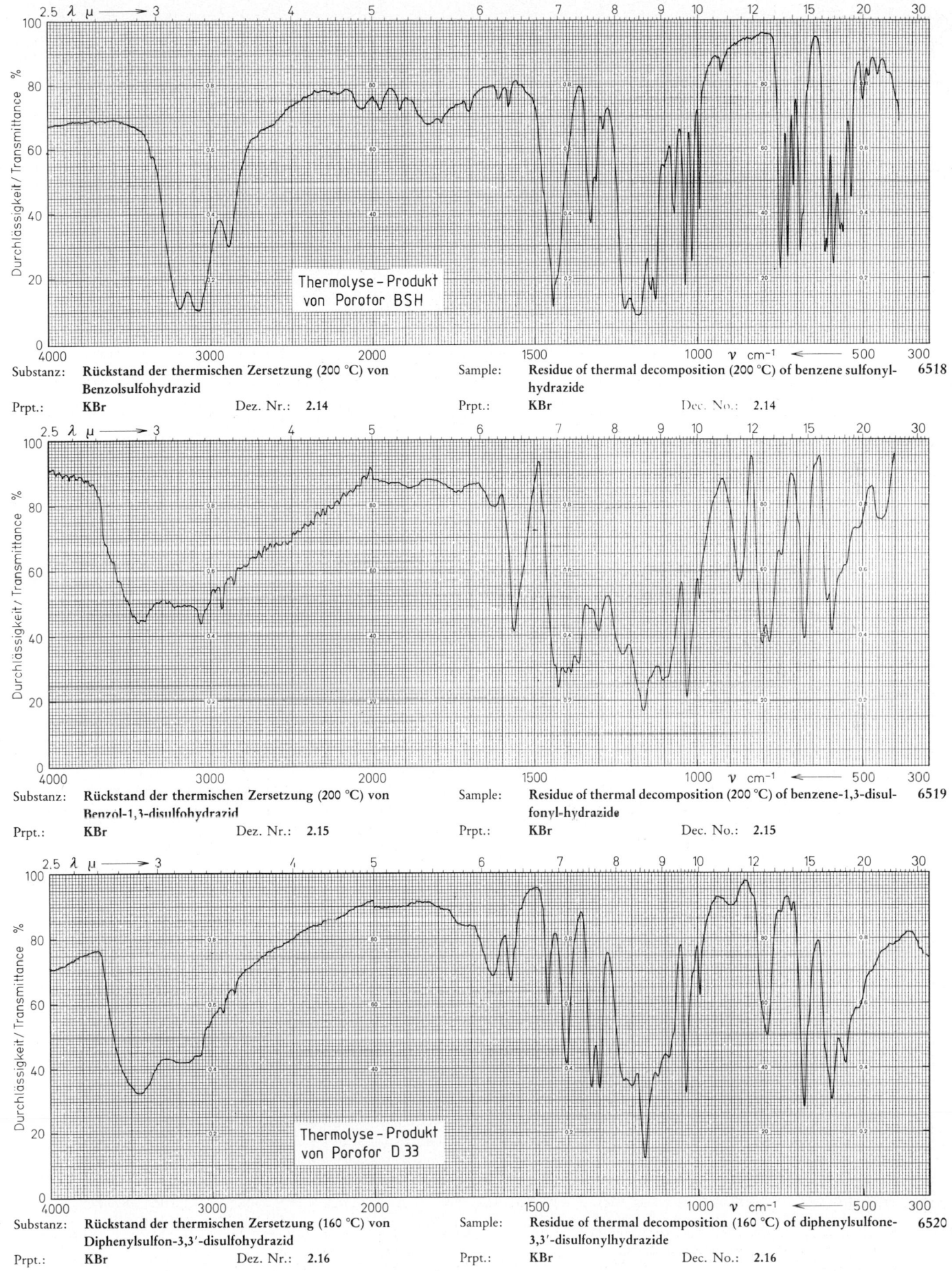

Thermolyse – Produkt von Porofor BSH

Substanz:	Rückstand der thermischen Zersetzung (200 °C) von Benzolsulfohydrazid
Prpt.: KBr	Dez. Nr.: **2.14**

Sample:	Residue of thermal decomposition (200 °C) of benzene sulfonyl-hydrazide
Prpt.: KBr	Dec. No.: **2.14**

6518

Thermolyse – Produkt von Porofor D 33

Substanz:	Rückstand der thermischen Zersetzung (200 °C) von Benzol-1,3-disulfohydrazid
Prpt.: KBr	Dez. Nr.: **2.15**

Sample:	Residue of thermal decomposition (200 °C) of benzene-1,3-disul-fonyl-hydrazide
Prpt.: KBr	Dec. No.: **2.15**

6519

Substanz:	Rückstand der thermischen Zersetzung (160 °C) von Diphenylsulfon-3,3'-disulfohydrazid
Prpt.: KBr	Dez. Nr.: **2.16**

Sample:	Residue of thermal decomposition (160 °C) of diphenylsulfone-3,3'-disulfonylhydrazide
Prpt.: KBr	Dec. No.: **2.16**

6520

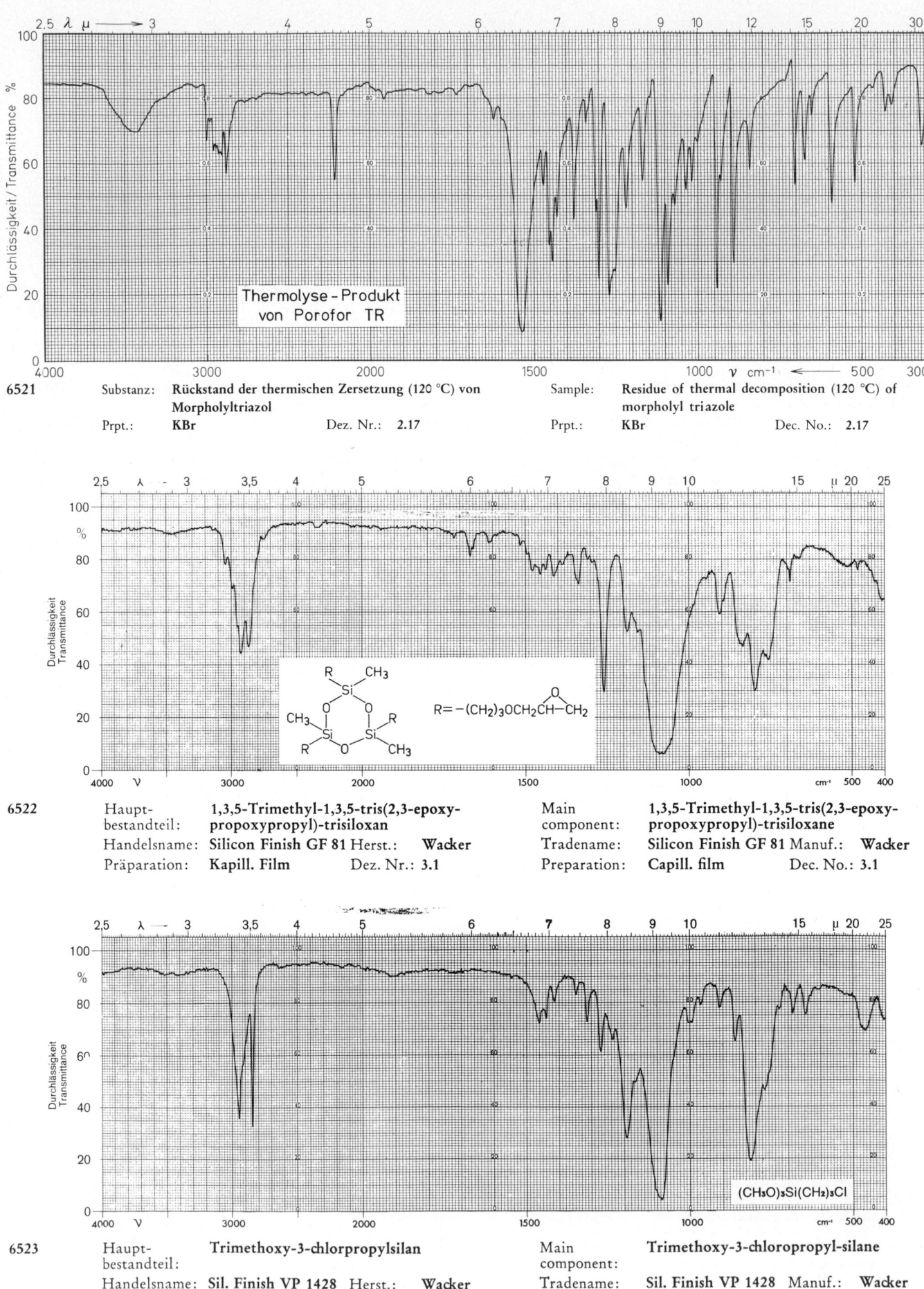

6521 Substanz: **Rückstand der thermischen Zersetzung (120 °C) von Morpholyltriazol** Sample: **Residue of thermal decomposition (120 °C) of morpholyl triazole**

Prpt.: **KBr**   Dez. Nr.: **2.17**   Prpt.: **KBr**   Dec. No.: **2.17**

6522 Haupt-bestandteil: **1,3,5-Trimethyl-1,3,5-tris(2,3-epoxy-propoxypropyl)-trisiloxan** Main component: **1,3,5-Trimethyl-1,3,5-tris(2,3-epoxy-propoxypropyl)-trisiloxane**

Handelsname: **Silicon Finish GF 81** Herst.: **Wacker**   Tradename: **Silicon Finish GF 81** Manuf.: **Wacker**

Präparation: **Kapill. Film**   Dez. Nr.: **3.1**   Preparation: **Capill. film**   Dec. No.: **3.1**

6523 Haupt-bestandteil: **Trimethoxy-3-chlorpropylsilan** Main component: **Trimethoxy-3-chloropropyl-silane**

Handelsname: **Sil. Finish VP 1428** Herst.: **Wacker**   Tradename: **Sil. Finish VP 1428** Manuf.: **Wacker**

Präparation: **Kapill. Film**   Dez. Nr.: **3.2**   Preparation: **Capill. film**   Dec. No.: **3.2**

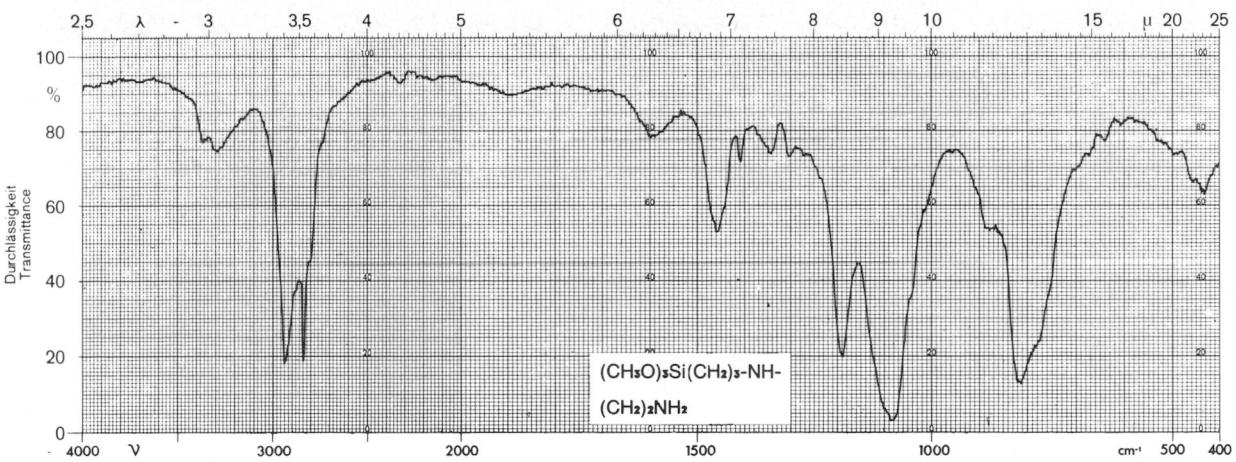

Haupt-bestandteil:	Trimethoxy-[3(2'-aminoethylamino)propyl]-silan	Main component:	Trimethoxy[3-(2'-aminoethylamino)-propyl]-silane	6524
Handelsname:	Silicon Finish GF 91 Herst.: **Wacker**	Tradename:	Silicon Finish GF 91 Manuf.: **Wacker**	
Präparation:	**Kapill. Film** Dez. Nr.: **3.3**	Preparation:	**Capill. film** Dec. No.: **3.3**	

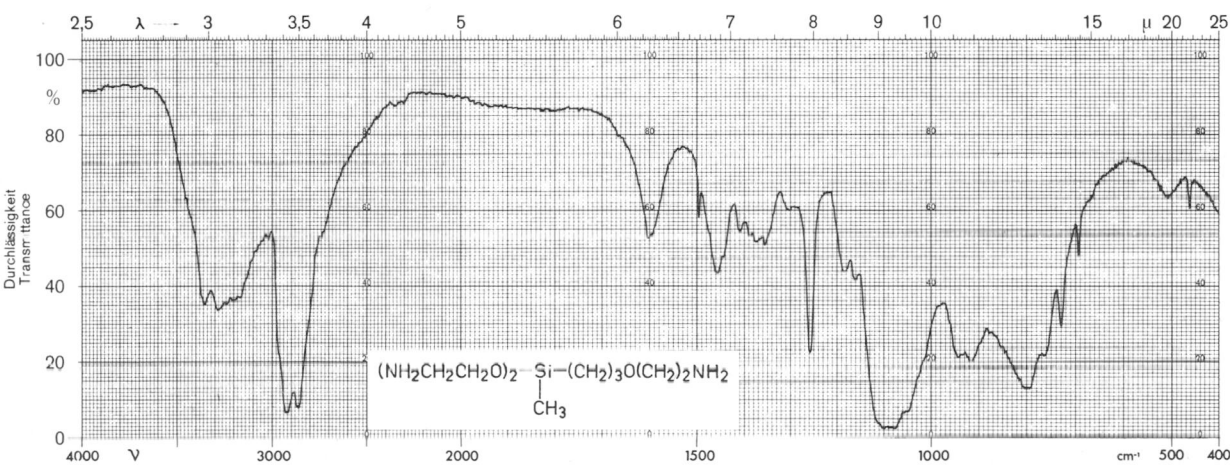

Haupt-bestandteil:	Methyl-di-(2'-aminoethoxy)-[3(2''-aminoethoxy)propyl]-silan	Main component:	Methyl-di-(2'-aminoethoxy)-[3-(2''-aminoethoxy)propyl]-silane	6525
Handelsname:	Silicon Finish GF 90 Herst.: **Wacker**	Tradename:	Silicon Finish GF 90 Manuf.: **Wacker**	
Präparation:	**Kapill. Film** Dez. Nr.: **3.4**	Preparation:	**Capill. film** Dec. No.: **3.4**	

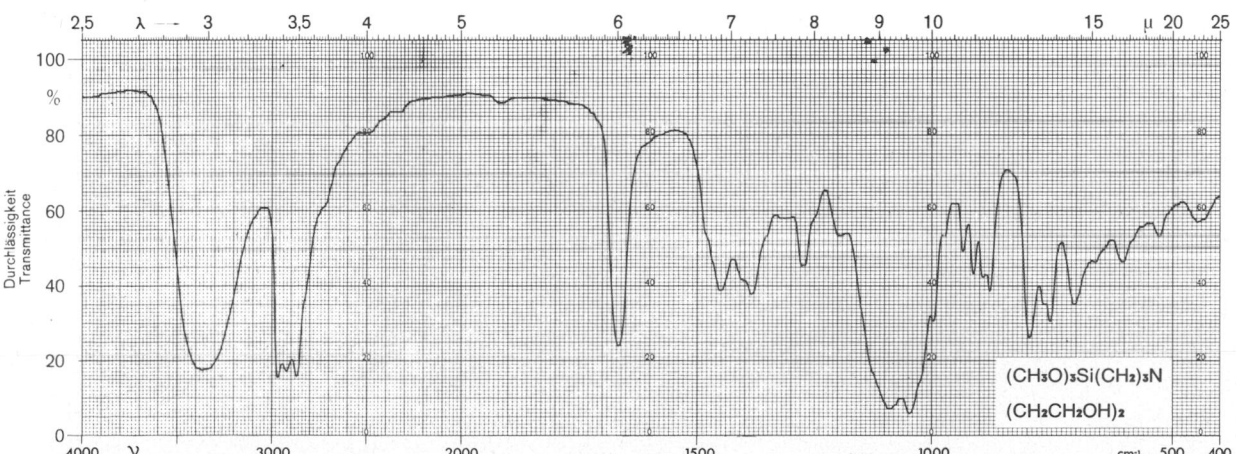

Haupt-bestandteil:	Trimethoxy-[3-(di-2'-hydroxyethyl-amino-)propyl]-silan	Main component:	Trimethoxy-[3-(di-2'-hydroxyethyl-amino-)propyl]-silane	6526
Handelsname:	Sil. Finish VP 1451 Herst.: **Wacker**	Tradename:	Sil. Finish VP 1451 Manuf.: **Wacker**	
Präparation:	**Kapill. Film** Dez. Nr.: **3.5**	Preparation:	**Capill. film** Dec. No.: **3.5**	

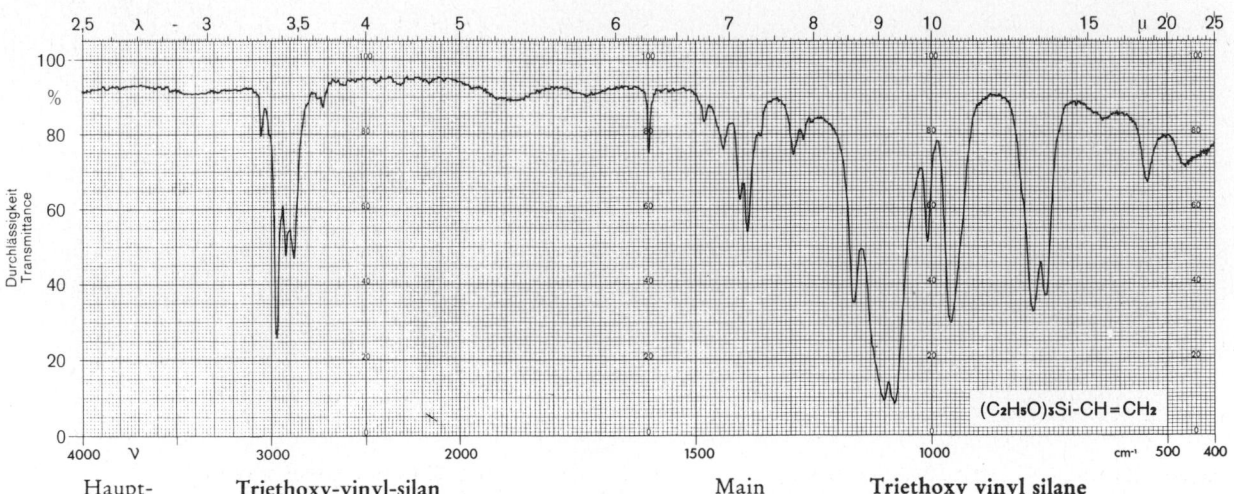

6527   Haupt-   **Triethoxy-vinyl-silan**   Main   **Triethoxy vinyl silane**
       bestandteil: component:
       Handelsname: **Silicon Finish GF 56** Herst.: **Wacker**   Tradename: **Silicon Finish GF 56** Manuf.: **Wacker**
       Präparation: **Kapill. Film**   Dez. Nr.: **3.6**   Preparation: **Capill. film**   Dec. No.: **3.6**

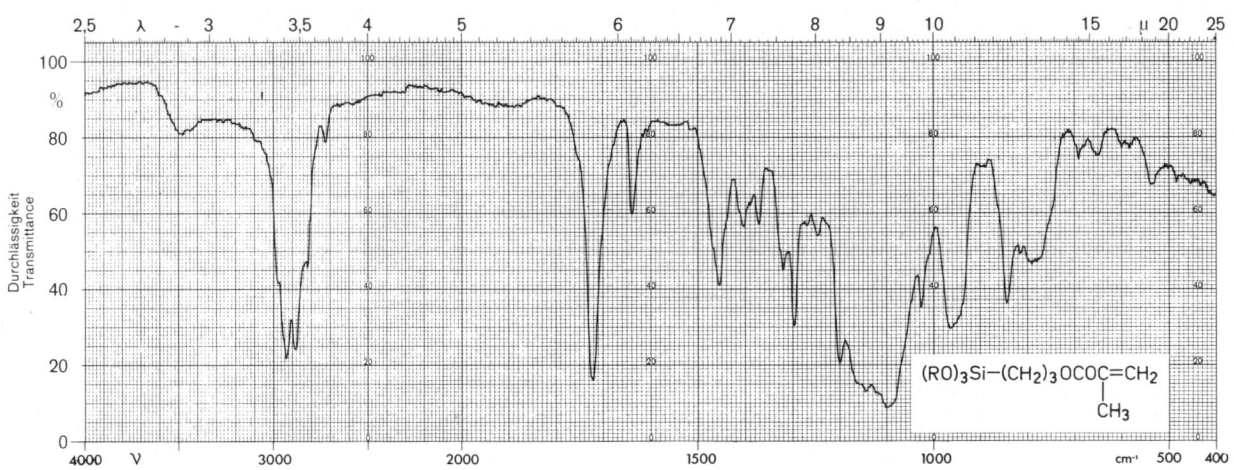

6528   Haupt-   **Trialkoxy-[3-(methacryloyloxy)propyl]-**   Main   **Trialkoxy-[3-(methacryloyloxy)-**
       bestandteil: **silan**   component: **propyl]-silane**
       Handelsname: **Silicon Finish GF 66** Herst.: **Wacker** Tradename: **Silicon Finish GF 66** Manuf.: **Wacker**
       Präparation: **Kapill. Film**   Dez. Nr.: **3.7**   Preparation: **Capill. film**   Dec. No.: **3.7**

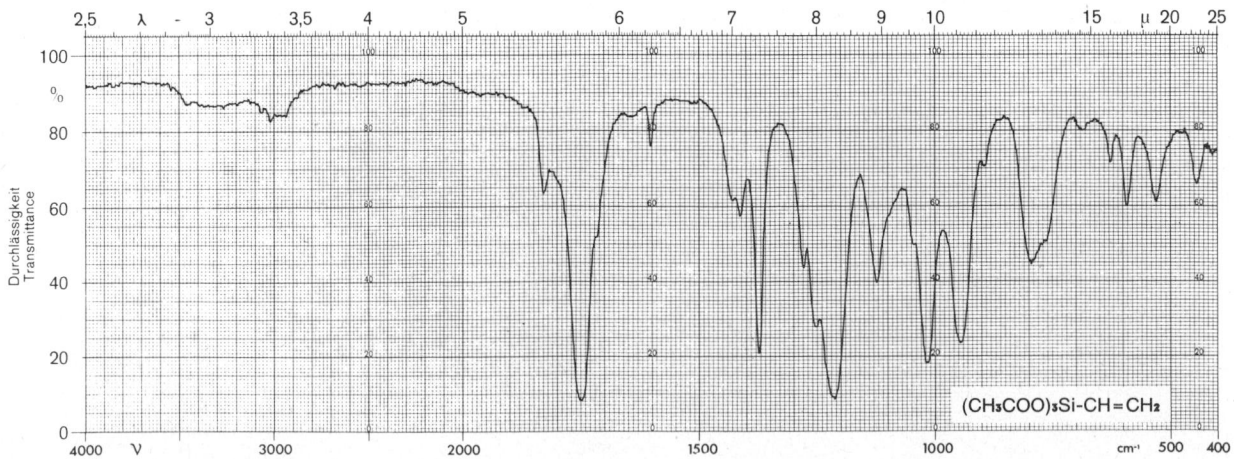

6529   Haupt-   **Vinyl-triacetoxysilan**   Main   **Vinyl-triacetoxy silane**
       bestandteil: component:
       Handelsname: **Silicon Finish GF 62** Herst.: **Wacker** Tradename: **Silicon Finish GF 62** Manuf.: **Wacker**
       Präparation: **Kapill. Film**   Dez. Nr.: **3.8**   Preparation: **Capill. film**   Dec. No.: **3.8**

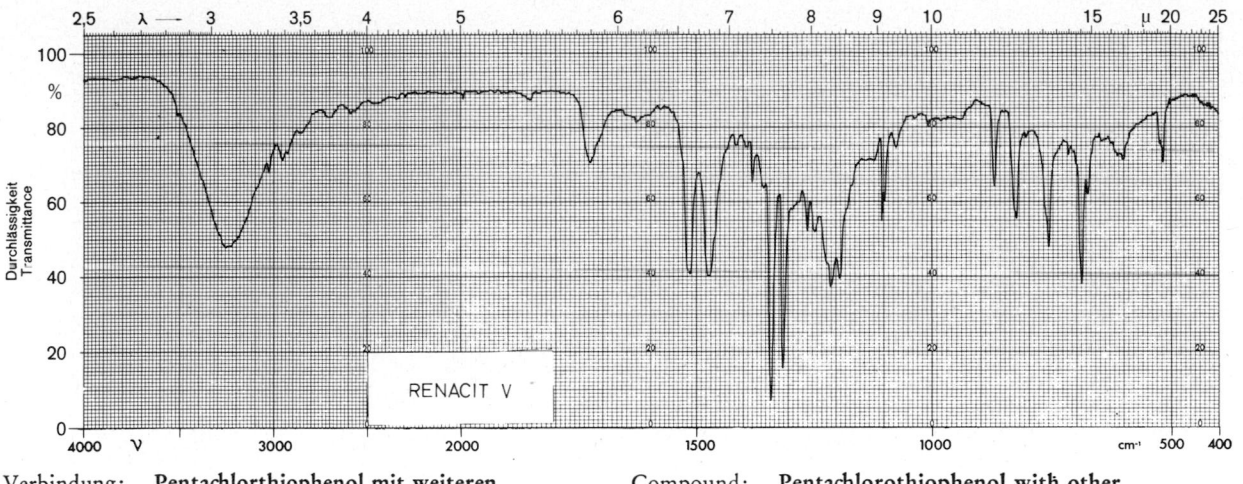

Verbindung:	Pentachlorthiophenol mit weiteren Bestandteilen		Compound:	Pentachlorothiophenol with other ingredients		6530
Formel:		M.:	Formula:		M. w.:	
Handelsname:	**Renacit V**	Herst.: **Bayer**	Tradename:	**Renacit V**	Manuf.: **Bayer**	
Präparation:	**KBr (5/1000)**	Dez. Nr.: **4.1**	Preparation:	**KBr (5/1000)**	Dec. No.: **4.1**	

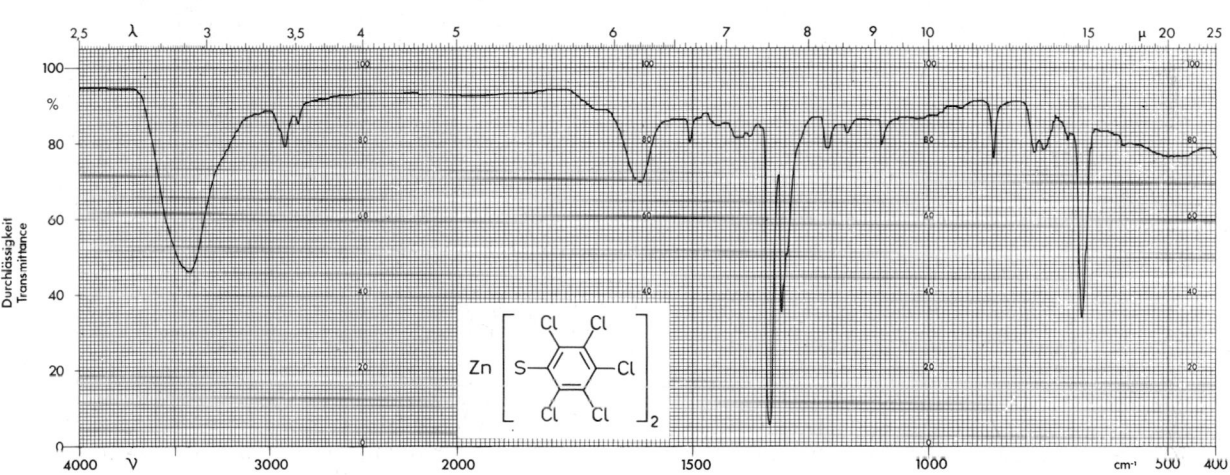

Verbindung:	**Zinksalz von Pentachlorthiophenol**		Compound:	**Zinc salt of pentachlorothiophenol**		6531
Formel:	$C_{12}Cl_{10}S_9Zn$	M.: **628,1**	Formula:	$C_{12}Cl_{10}S_9Zn$	M. w.: **628,1**	
Handelsname:	**Renacit IV**	Herst.: **Bayer**	Tradename:	**Renacit IV**	Manuf.: **Bayer**	
Präparation:	**KBr (6/1000)**	Dez. Nr.: **4.2**	Preparation:	**KBr (6/1000)**	Dec. No.: **4.2**	

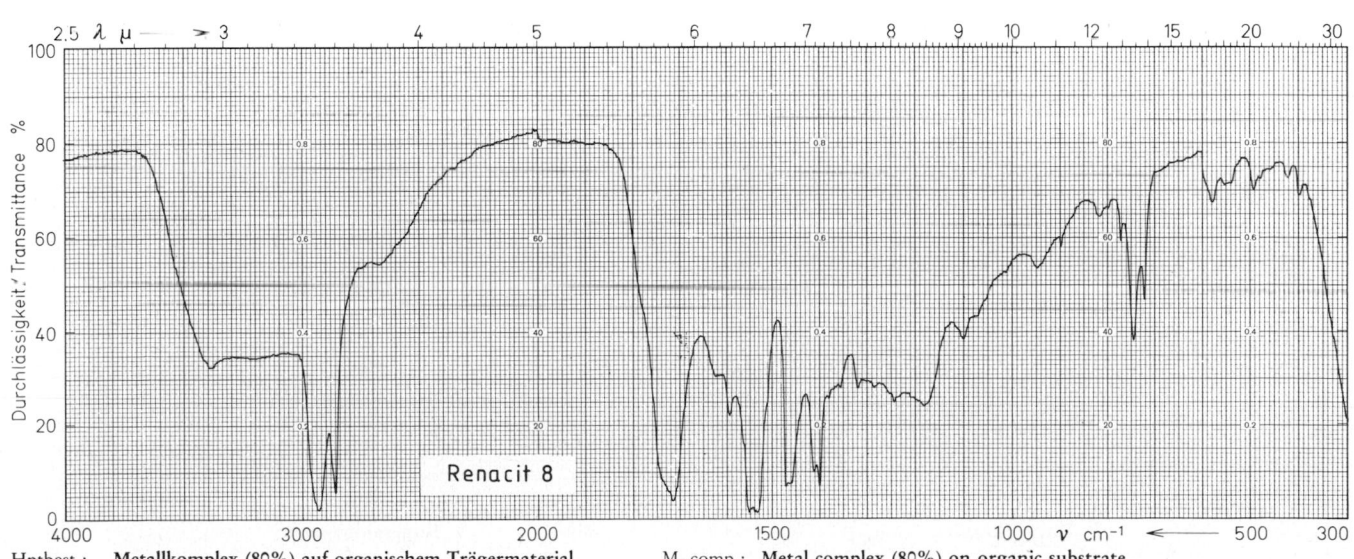

Hptbest.:	**Metallkomplex (80%) auf organischem Trägermaterial**		M. comp.:	**Metal complex (80%) on organic substrate**	
Name:	**Renacit 8**	Herst.: **Bayer**	Name:	**Renacit 8**	Manuf.: **Bayer**
Prpt.:	**KBr**	Dez. Nr.: **4.3**	Prpt.:	**KBr**	Dec. No.: **4.3**

6532

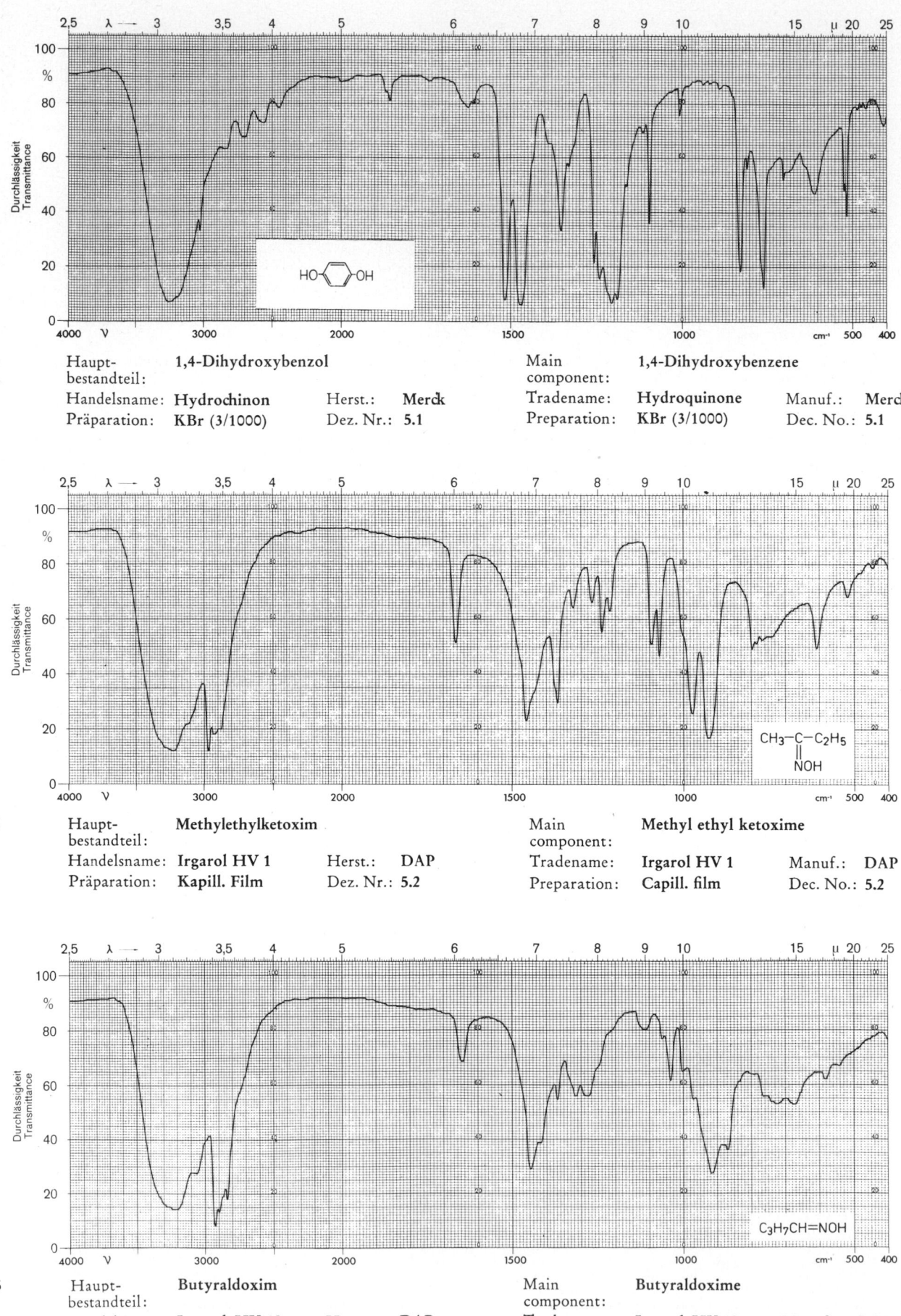

6533   Haupt-   **1,4-Dihydroxybenzol**   Main   **1,4-Dihydroxybenzene**
bestandteil: component:

Handelsname: **Hydrochinon**   Herst.: **Merck**   Tradename: **Hydroquinone**   Manuf.: **Merck**
Präparation: **KBr (3/1000)**   Dez. Nr.: **5.1**   Preparation: **KBr (3/1000)**   Dec. No.: **5.1**

6534   Haupt-   **Methylethylketoxim**   Main   **Methyl ethyl ketoxime**
bestandteil: component:

Handelsname: **Irgarol HV 1**   Herst.: **DAP**   Tradename: **Irgarol HV 1**   Manuf.: **DAP**
Präparation: **Kapill. Film**   Dez. Nr.: **5.2**   Preparation: **Capill. film**   Dec. No.: **5.2**

6535   Haupt-   **Butyraldoxim**   Main   **Butyraldoxime**
bestandteil: component:

Handelsname: **Irgarol HV 48**   Herst.: **DAP**   Tradename: **Irgarol HV 48**   Manuf.: **DAP**
Präparation: **Kapill. Film**   Dez. Nr.: **5.3**   Preparation: **Capill. film**   Dec. No.: **5.3**

Lösungsmittel

Solvents

Lösungsmittel
1. Kohlenwasserstoffe
1.1. Aliphatische Kohlenwasserstoffe

Solvents
1. Hydrocarbons
1.1. Aliphatic hydrocarbons

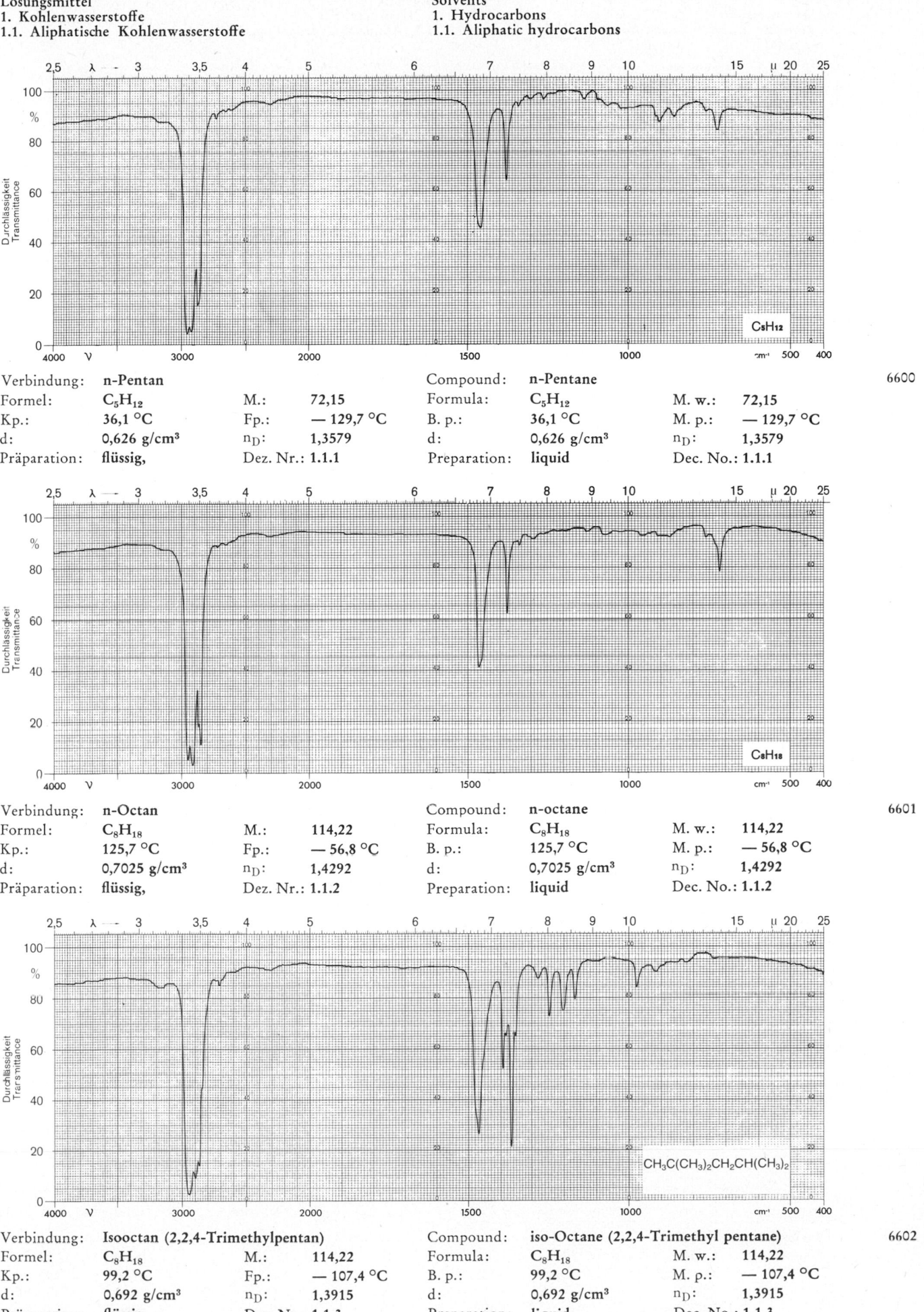

Verbindung:	n-Pentan			Compound:	n-Pentane			6600
Formel:	C_5H_{12}	M.:	72,15	Formula:	C_5H_{12}	M. w.:	72,15	
Kp.:	36,1 °C	Fp.:	— 129,7 °C	B. p.:	36,1 °C	M. p.:	— 129,7 °C	
d:	0,626 g/cm³	n_D:	1,3579	d:	0,626 g/cm³	n_D:	1,3579	
Präparation:	flüssig,	Dez. Nr.:	1.1.1	Preparation:	liquid	Dec. No.:	1.1.1	

Verbindung:	n-Octan			Compound:	n-octane			6601
Formel:	C_8H_{18}	M.:	114,22	Formula:	C_8H_{18}	M. w.:	114,22	
Kp.:	125,7 °C	Fp.:	— 56,8 °C	B. p.:	125,7 °C	M. p.:	— 56,8 °C	
d:	0,7025 g/cm³	n_D:	1,4292	d:	0,7025 g/cm³	n_D:	1,4292	
Präparation:	flüssig,	Dez. Nr.:	1.1.2	Preparation:	liquid	Dec. No.:	1.1.2	

Verbindung:	Isooctan (2,2,4-Trimethylpentan)			Compound:	iso-Octane (2,2,4-Trimethyl pentane)			6602
Formel:	C_8H_{18}	M.:	114,22	Formula:	C_8H_{18}	M. w.:	114,22	
Kp.:	99,2 °C	Fp.:	— 107,4 °C	B. p.:	99,2 °C	M. p.:	— 107,4 °C	
d:	0,692 g/cm³	n_D:	1,3915	d:	0,692 g/cm³	n_D:	1,3915	
Präparation:	flüssig,	Dez. Nr.:	1.1.3	Preparation:	liquid	Dec. No.:	1.1.3	

Lösungsmittel
1. Kohlenwasserstoffe
1.1. Aliphatische Kohlenwasserstoffe

Solvents
1. Hydrocarbons
1.1. Aliphatic hydrocarbons

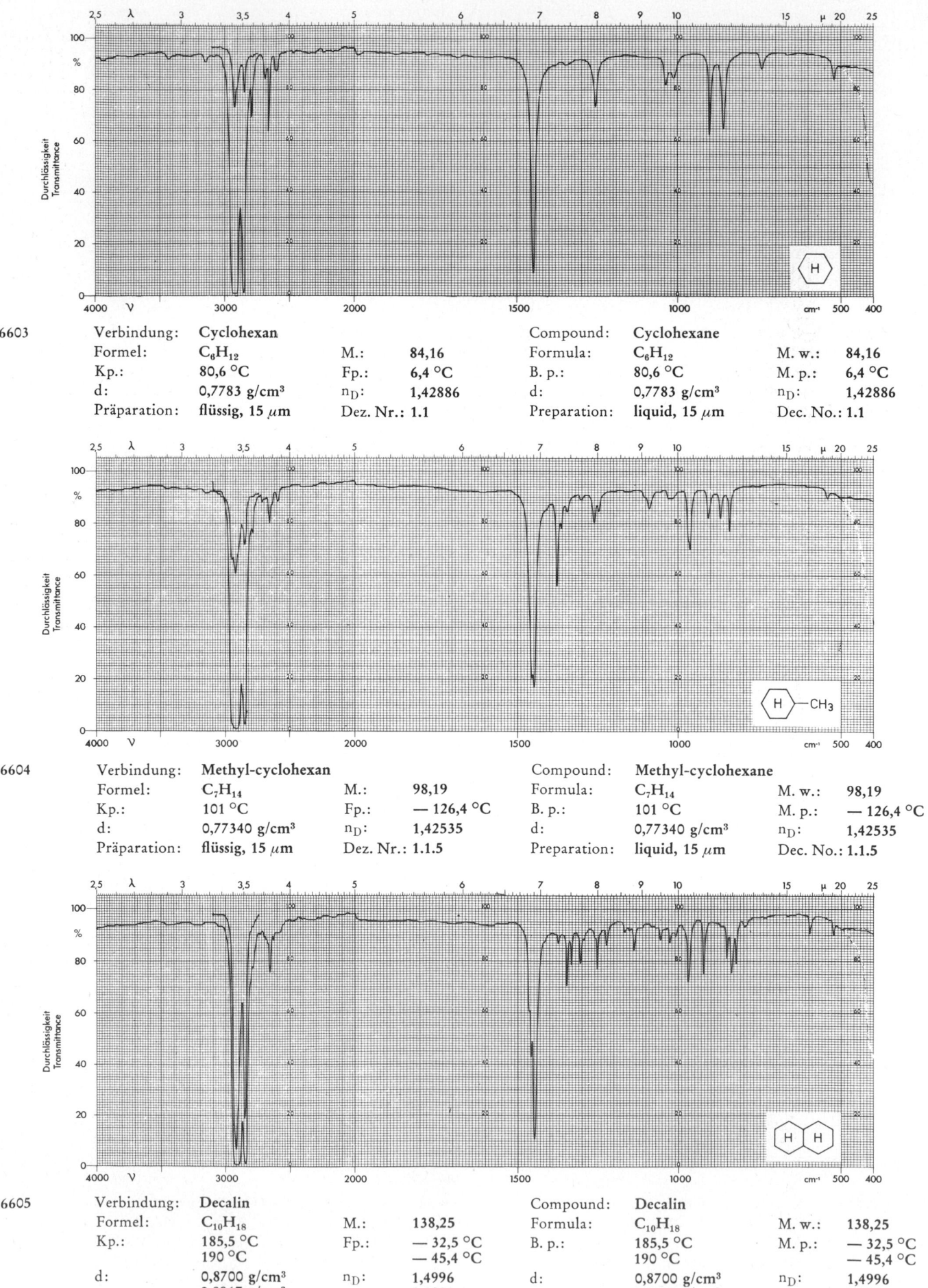

6603   Verbindung: **Cyclohexan**

Formel:	C_6H_{12}	M.:	**84,16**	Formula:	C_6H_{12}	M. w.: **84,16**
Kp.:	80,6 °C	Fp.:	**6,4 °C**	B. p.:	80,6 °C	M. p.: **6,4 °C**
d:	0,7783 g/cm³	n_D:	**1,42886**	d:	0,7783 g/cm³	n_D: **1,42886**
Präparation:	flüssig, 15 μm	Dez. Nr.:	**1.1**	Preparation:	liquid, 15 μm	Dec. No.: **1.1**

Compound: **Cyclohexane**

6604   Verbindung: **Methyl-cyclohexan**

Formel:	C_7H_{14}	M.:	**98,19**	Formula:	C_7H_{14}	M. w.: **98,19**
Kp.:	101 °C	Fp.:	**— 126,4 °C**	B. p.:	101 °C	M. p.: **— 126,4 °C**
d:	0,77340 g/cm³	n_D:	**1,42535**	d:	0,77340 g/cm³	n_D: **1,42535**
Präparation:	flüssig, 15 μm	Dez. Nr.:	**1.1.5**	Preparation:	liquid, 15 μm	Dec. No.: **1.1.5**

Compound: **Methyl-cyclohexane**

6605   Verbindung: **Decalin**

Formel:	$C_{10}H_{18}$	M.:	**138,25**	Formula:	$C_{10}H_{18}$	M. w.: **138,25**
Kp.:	185,5 °C	Fp.:	**— 32,5 °C**	B. p.:	185,5 °C	M. p.: **— 32,5 °C**
	190 °C		**— 45,4 °C**		190 °C	**— 45,4 °C**
d:	0,8700 g/cm³	n_D:	**1,4996**	d:	0,8700 g/cm³	n_D: **1,4996**
	0,8967 g/cm³		**1,4811**		0,8967 g/cm³	**1,4811**
Präparation:	flüssig, 15 μm	Dez. Nr.:	**1.1.6**	Preparation:	liquid, 15 μm	Dec. No.: **1.1.6**

Compound: **Decalin**

Lösungsmittel
1. Kohlenwasserstoffe
1.2. Aromatische Kohlenwasserstoffe

Solvents
1. Hydrocarbons
1.2. Aromatic hydrocarbons

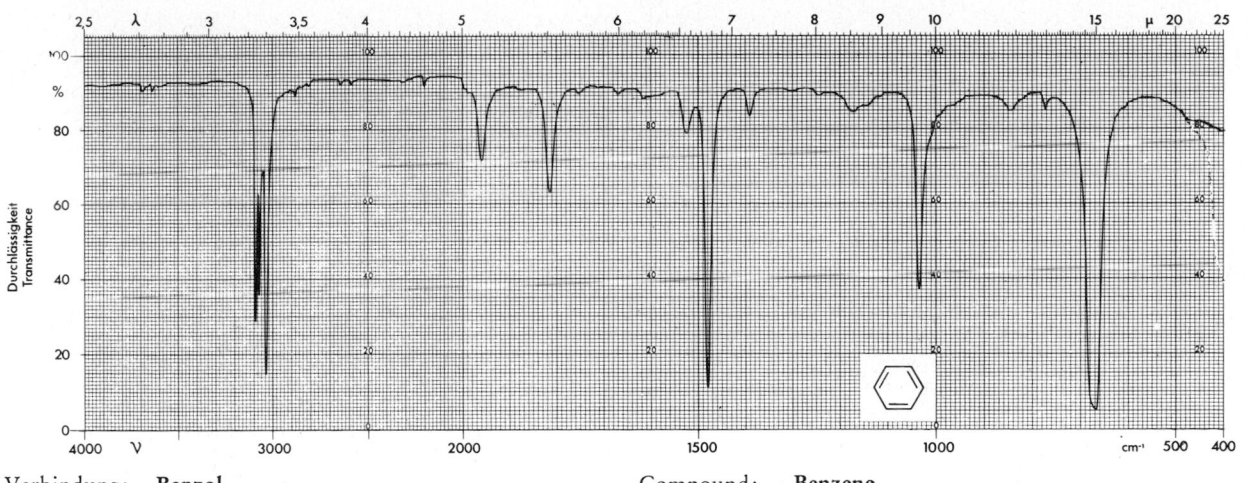

Verbindung:	**Benzol**			Compound:	**Benzene**			6606
Formel:	C_6H_6	M.:	**78,11**	Formula:	C_6H_6	M. w.:	**78,11**	
Kp.:	**80,2 °C**	Fp.:	**5,49 °C**	B. p.:	**80,2 °C**	M. p.:	**5,49 °C**	
d:	**0,8788 g/cm³**	n_D:	**1,5007**	d:	**0,8788 g/cm³**	n_D:	**1,5007**	
Präparation:	**flüssig, 15 μm**	Dez. Nr.:	**1.2.1**	Preparation:	**liquid, 15 μm**	Dec. No.:	**1.2.1**	

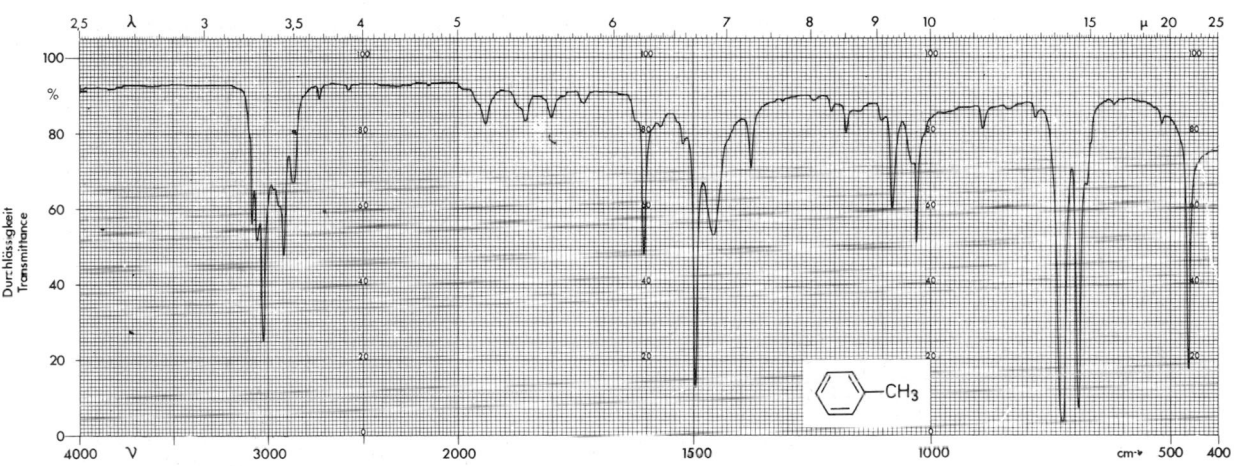

Verbindung:	**Toluol**			Compound:	**Toluene**			6607
Formel:	C_7H_8	M.:	**92,14**	Formula:	C_7H_8	M. w.:	**92,14**	
Kp.:	**110,8 °C**	Fp.:	**— 95 °C**	B. p.:	**110,8 °C**	M. p.:	**— 95 °C**	
d:	**0,8716 g/cm³**	n_D:	**1,49985**	d:	**0,8716 g/cm³**	n_D:	**1,49985**	
Präparation:	**flüssig, 15 μm**	Dez. Nr.:	**1.2.2**	Preparation:	**liquid, 15 μm**	Dec. No.:	**1.2.2**	

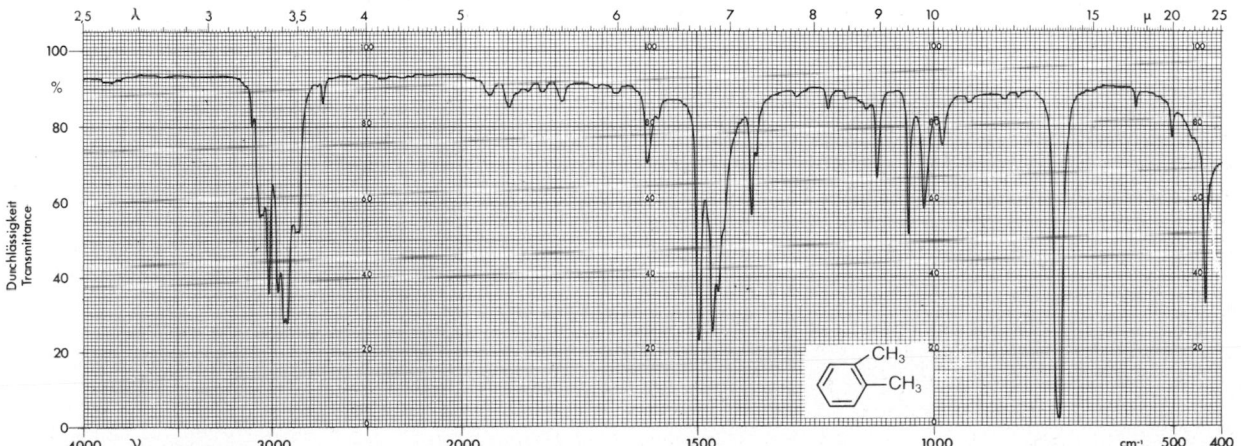

Verbindung:	**o-Xylol**			Compound:	**o-Xylene**			6608
Formel:	C_8H_{10}	M.:	**106,17**	Formula:	C_8H_{10}	M. w.:	**106,17**	
Kp.:	**143,6 °C**	Fp.:	**— 28 °C**	B. p.:	**143,6 °C**	M. p.:	**— 28 °C**	
d:	**0,860 g/cm³**	n_D:	**1,5050**	d:	**0,860 g/cm³**	n_D:	**1,5050**	
Präparation:	**flüssig, 15 μm**	Dez. Nr.:	**1.2.3**	Preparation:	**liquid, 15 μm**	Dec. No.:	**1.2.3**	

Lösungsmittel
1. Kohlenwasserstoffe
1.2. Aromatische Kohlenwasserstoffe

Solvents
1. Hydrocarbons
1.2. Aromatic hydrocarbons

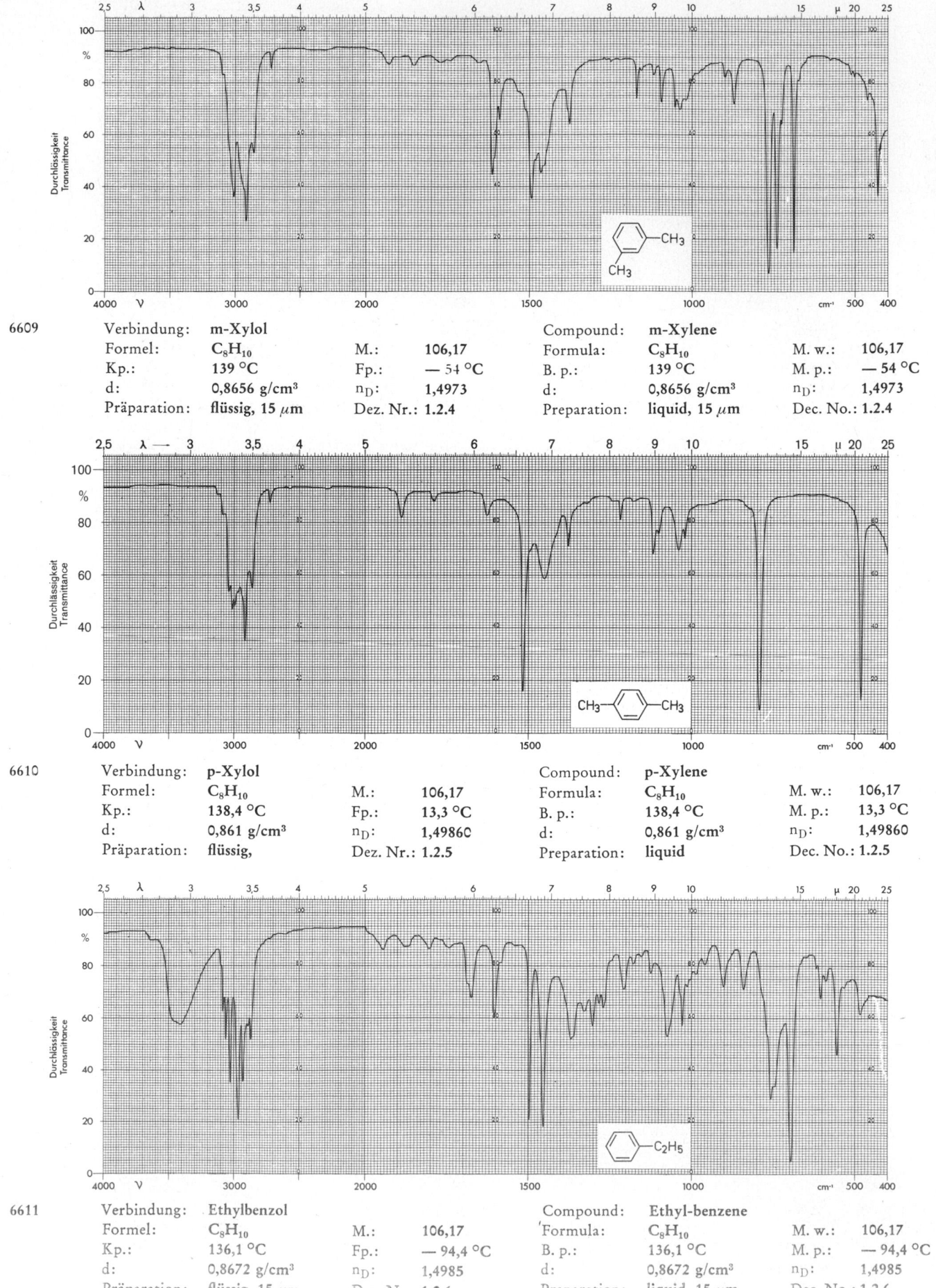

6609

Verbindung:	**m-Xylol**			Compound:	**m-Xylene**		
Formel:	**C₈H₁₀**	M.:	**106,17**	Formula:	**C₈H₁₀**	M. w.:	**106,17**
Kp.:	**139 °C**	Fp.:	**— 54 °C**	B. p.:	**139 °C**	M. p.:	**— 54 °C**
d:	**0,8656 g/cm³**	n_D:	**1,4973**	d:	**0,8656 g/cm³**	n_D:	**1,4973**
Präparation:	**flüssig, 15 μm**	Dez. Nr.:	**1.2.4**	Preparation:	**liquid, 15 μm**	Dec. No.:	**1.2.4**

6610

Verbindung:	**p-Xylol**			Compound:	**p-Xylene**		
Formel:	**C₈H₁₀**	M.:	**106,17**	Formula:	**C₈H₁₀**	M. w.:	**106,17**
Kp.:	**138,4 °C**	Fp.:	**13,3 °C**	B. p.:	**138,4 °C**	M. p.:	**13,3 °C**
d:	**0,861 g/cm³**	n_D:	**1,49860**	d:	**0,861 g/cm³**	n_D:	**1,49860**
Präparation:	**flüssig,**	Dez. Nr.:	**1.2.5**	Preparation:	**liquid**	Dec. No.:	**1.2.5**

6611

Verbindung:	Ethylbenzol			Compound:	Ethyl-benzene		
Formel:	C₈H₁₀	M.:	106,17	Formula:	C₈H₁₀	M. w.:	106,17
Kp.:	136,1 °C	Fp.:	— 94,4 °C	B. p.:	136,1 °C	M. p.:	— 94,4 °C
d:	0,8672 g/cm³	n_D:	1,4985	d:	0,8672 g/cm³	n_D:	1,4985
Präparation:	flüssig, 15 μm	Dez. Nr.:	1.2.6	Preparation:	liquid, 15 μm	Dec. No.:	1.2.6

Lösungsmittel
1. Kohlenwasserstoffe
1.2. Aromatische Kohlenwasserstoffe

Solvents
1. Hydrocarbons
1.2. Aromatic hydrocarbons

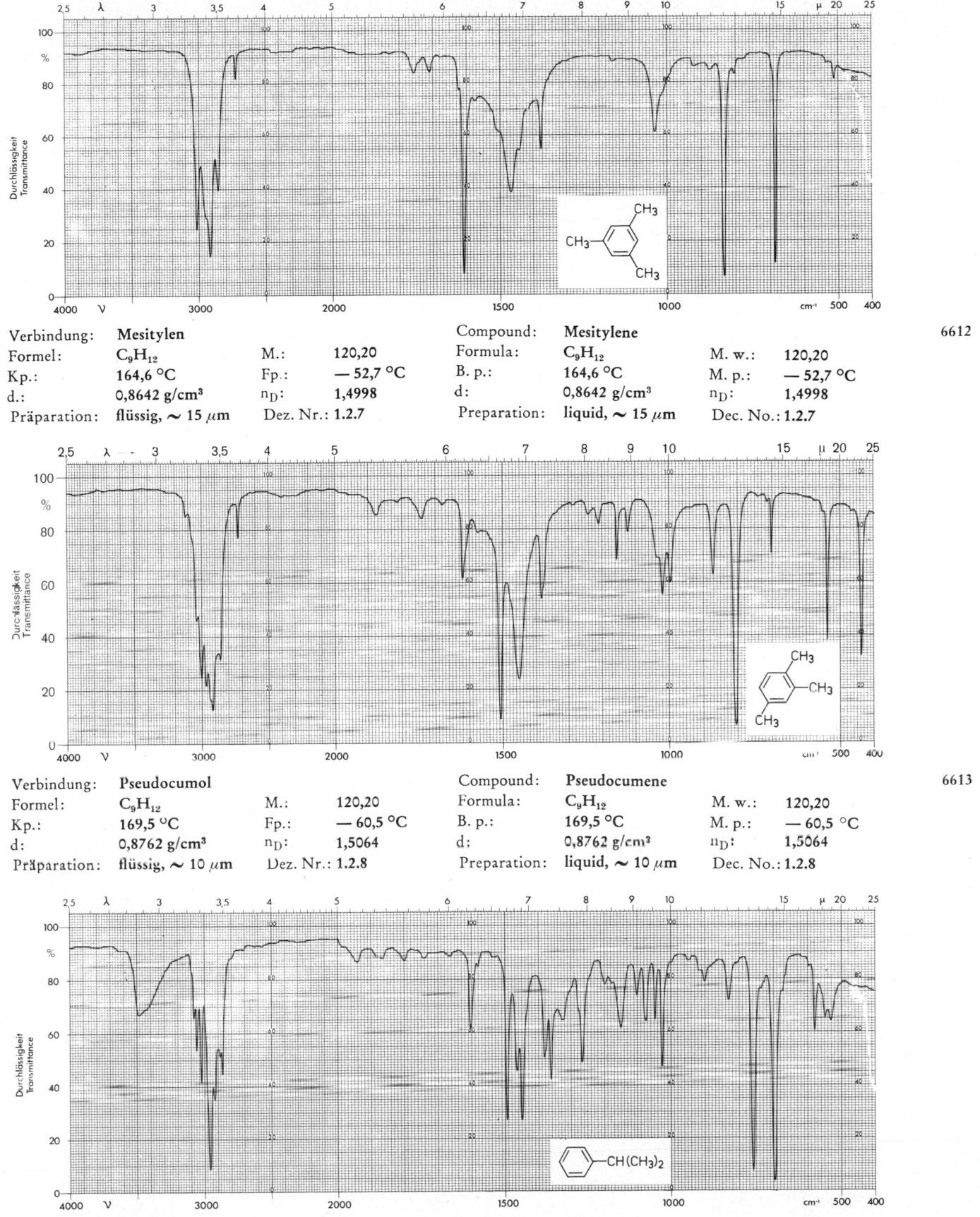

Verbindung:	**Mesitylen**			Compound:	**Mesitylene**			6612
Formel:	C_9H_{12}	M.:	**120,20**	Formula:	C_9H_{12}	M. w.:	**120,20**	
Kp.:	**164,6 °C**	Fp.:	**— 52,7 °C**	B. p.:	**164,6 °C**	M. p.:	**— 52,7 °C**	
d.:	**0,8642 g/cm³**	n_D:	**1,4998**	d:	**0,8642 g/cm³**	n_D:	**1,4998**	
Präparation:	flüssig, ∼ 15 μm	Dez. Nr.:	**1.2.7**	Preparation:	liquid, ∼ 15 μm	Dec. No.:	**1.2.7**	

Verbindung:	**Pseudocumol**			Compound:	**Pseudocumene**			6613
Formel:	C_9H_{12}	M.:	**120,20**	Formula:	C_9H_{12}	M. w.:	**120,20**	
Kp.:	**169,5 °C**	Fp.:	**— 60,5 °C**	B. p.:	**169,5 °C**	M. p.:	**— 60,5 °C**	
d:	**0,8762 g/cm³**	n_D:	**1,5064**	d:	**0,8762 g/cm³**	n_D:	**1,5064**	
Präparation:	flüssig, ∼ 10 μm	Dez. Nr.:	**1.2.8**	Preparation:	liquid, ∼ 10 μm	Dec. No.:	**1.2.8**	

Verbindung:	**Cumol**			Compound:	**Cumene**			6614
Formel:	C_9H_{12}	M.:	**120,20**	Formula:	C_9H_{12}	M. w.:	**120,20**	
Kp.:	**152,5 °C**	Fp.:	**— 96,9 °C**	B. p.:	**152,5 °C**	M. p.:	**— 96,9 °C**	
d:	**0,864 g/cm³**	n_D:	**1,4911**	d:	**0,864 g/cm³**	n_D:	**1,4911**	
Präparation:	flüssig, ∼ 15 μm	Dez. Nr.:	**1.2.9**	Preparation:	liquid, ∼ 15 μm	Dec. No.:	**1.2.9**	

Lösungsmittel
1. Kohlenwasserstoffe
1.2. Aromatische Kohlenwasserstoffe

Solvents
1. Hydrocarbons
1.2. Aromatic hydrocarbons

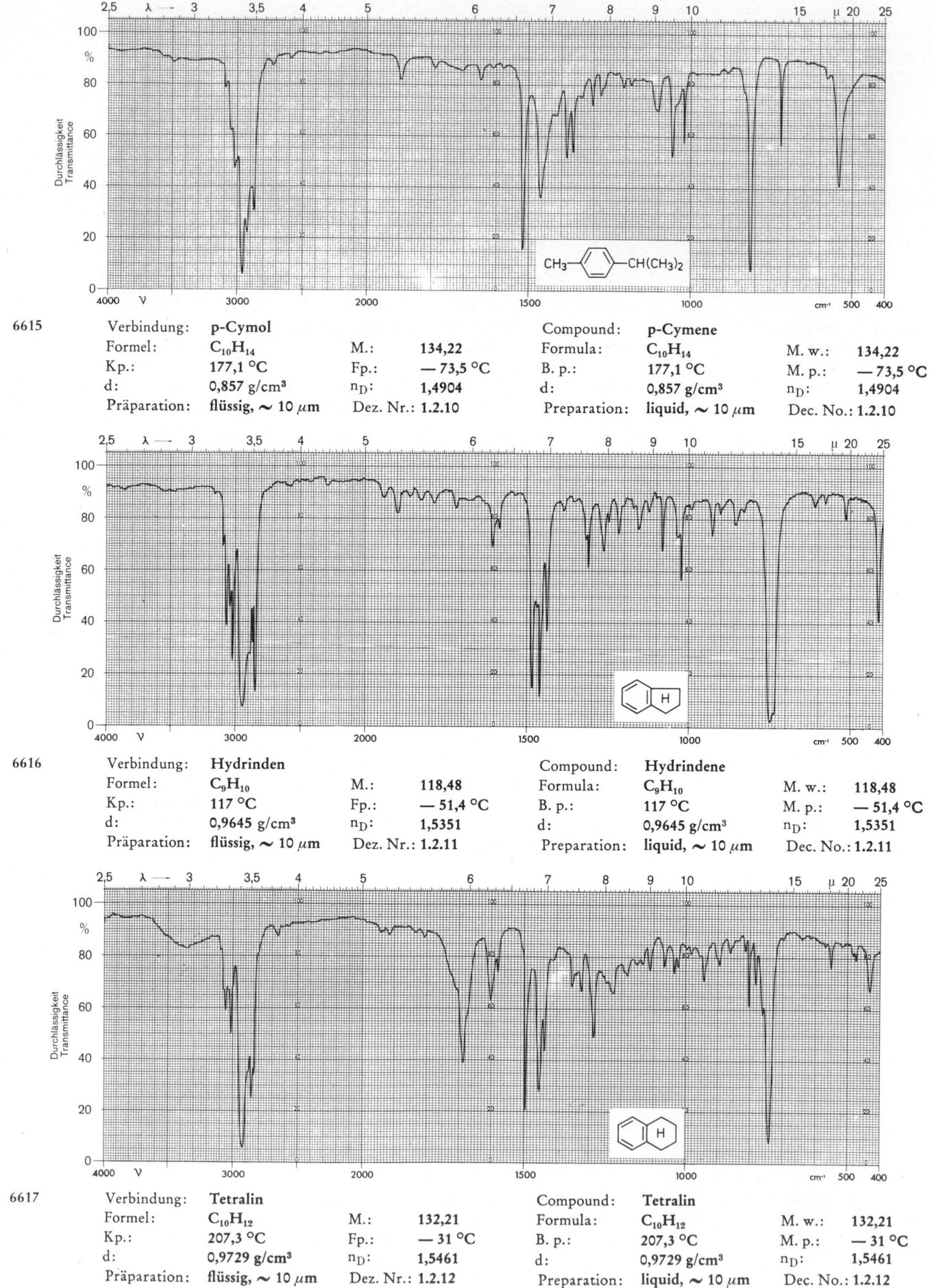

6615

Verbindung:	**p-Cymol**			Compound:	**p-Cymene**		
Formel:	$C_{10}H_{14}$	M.:	**134,22**	Formula:	$C_{10}H_{14}$	M. w.:	**134,22**
Kp.:	**177,1 °C**	Fp.:	**— 73,5 °C**	B. p.:	**177,1 °C**	M. p.:	**— 73,5 °C**
d:	**0,857 g/cm³**	n_D:	**1,4904**	d:	**0,857 g/cm³**	n_D:	**1,4904**
Präparation:	**flüssig, ~ 10 μm**	Dez. Nr.:	**1.2.10**	Preparation:	**liquid, ~ 10 μm**	Dec. No.:	**1.2.10**

6616

Verbindung:	**Hydrinden**			Compound:	**Hydrindene**		
Formel:	C_9H_{10}	M.:	**118,48**	Formula:	C_9H_{10}	M. w.:	**118,48**
Kp.:	**117 °C**	Fp.:	**— 51,4 °C**	B. p.:	**117 °C**	M. p.:	**— 51,4 °C**
d:	**0,9645 g/cm³**	n_D:	**1,5351**	d:	**0,9645 g/cm³**	n_D:	**1,5351**
Präparation:	**flüssig, ~ 10 μm**	Dez. Nr.:	**1.2.11**	Preparation:	**liquid, ~ 10 μm**	Dec. No.:	**1.2.11**

6617

Verbindung:	**Tetralin**			Compound:	**Tetralin**		
Formel:	$C_{10}H_{12}$	M.:	**132,21**	Formula:	$C_{10}H_{12}$	M. w.:	**132,21**
Kp.:	**207,3 °C**	Fp.:	**— 31 °C**	B. p.:	**207,3 °C**	M. p.:	**— 31 °C**
d:	**0,9729 g/cm³**	n_D:	**1,5461**	d:	**0,9729 g/cm³**	n_D:	**1,5461**
Präparation:	**flüssig, ~ 10 μm**	Dez. Nr.:	**1.2.12**	Preparation:	**liquid, ~ 10 μm**	Dec. No.:	**1.2.12**

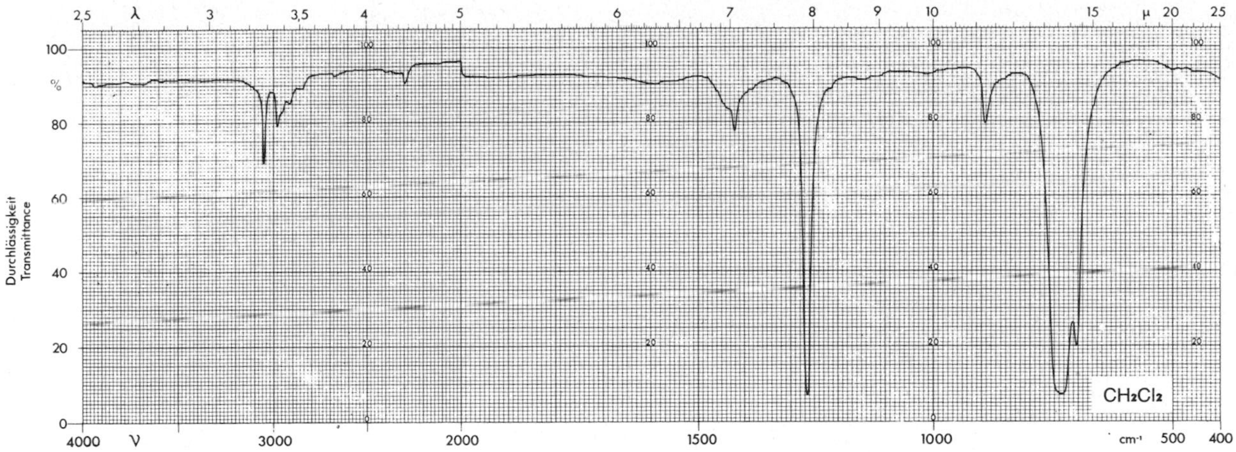

Lösungsmittel
1. Kohlenwasserstoffe
1.3. Halogenkohlenwasserstoffe

Solvents
1. Hydrocarbons
1.3. Halogenated hydrocarbons

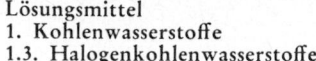

Verbindung:	**Methylenchlorid**			Compound:	**Methylenechloride**			6618
Formel:	CH_2Cl_2	M.:	**84,93**	Formula:	CH_2Cl_2	M. w.:	**84,93**	
Kp.:	40,67 °C	Fp.:		B. p.:	40,67 °C	M. p.:		
d.:	1,336 g/cm³	n_D:	**1,3348**	d:	1,336 g/cm³	n_D:	1,3348	
Präparation:	flüssig, ~ 15 µm	Dez. Nr.: 1.3.1		Preparation:	liquid, ~ 15 µm	Dec. No.: 1.3.1		

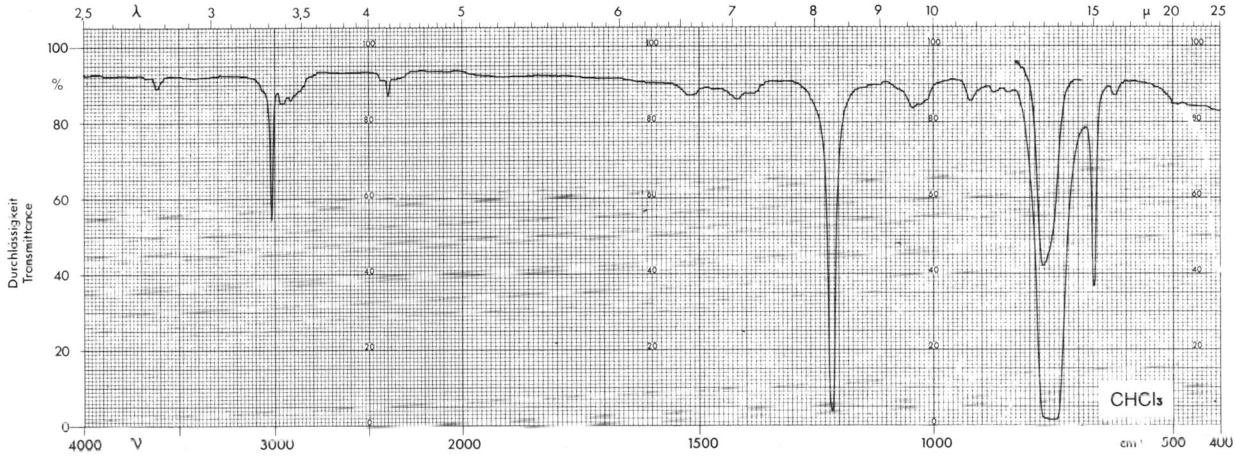

Verbindung:	**Chloroform**			Compound:	**Chloroform**			6619
Formel:	$CHCl_3$	M.:	**119,38**	Formula:	$CHCl_3$	M. w.:	**119,38**	
Kp.:	60,7 °C	Fp.:	— 63,5 °C	B. p.:	60,7 °C	M. p.:	— 63,5 °C	
d:	1,4817 g/cm³	n_D:	**1,4486**	d.:	1,4817 g/cm³	n_D:	**1,4486**	
Präparation:	flüssig, ~ 15 µm	Dez. Nr.: 1.3.2		Preparation:	liquid, ~ 15 µm	Dec. No.: 1.3.2		

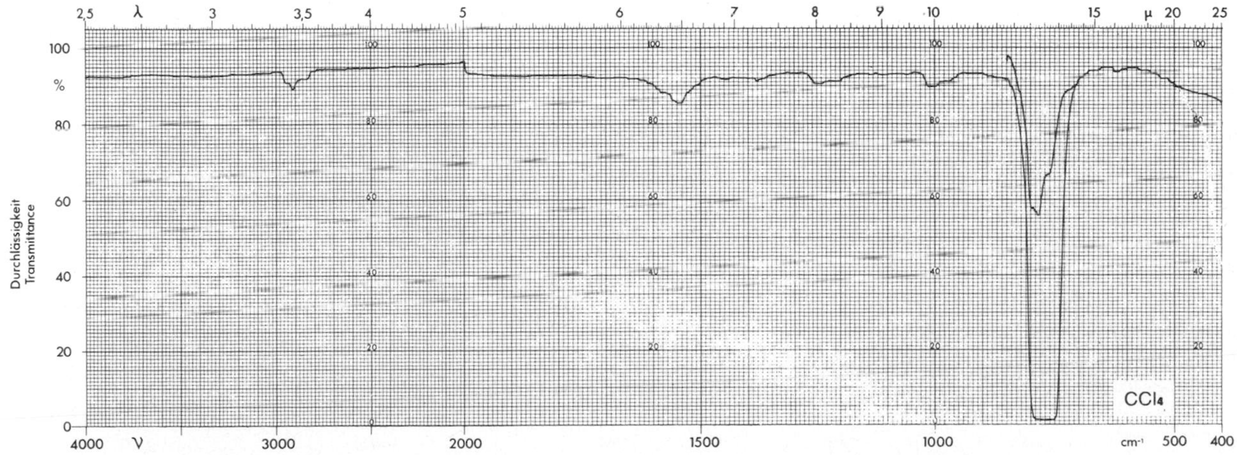

Verbindung:	**Tetrachlorkohlenstoff**			Compound:	**Tetrachloromethane**			6620
Formel:	CCl_4	M.:	**153,82**	Formula:	CCl_4	M. w.:	**153,82**	
Kp.:	76,7 °C	Fp.:	— 22,9 °C	B. p.:	76,7 °C	M. p.:	— 22,9 °C	
d:	1,5924 g/cm³	n_D:	**1,4631**	d.:	1,5924 g/cm³	n_D:	1,4631	
Präparation:	flüssig, ~ 15 µm	Dez. Nr.: 1.3.3		Preparation:	liquid, ~ 15 µm	Dec. No.: 1.3.3		

Lösungsmittel
1. Kohlenwasserstoffe
1.3. Halogenkohlenwasserstoffe

Solvents
1. Hydrocarbons
1.3. Halogenated hydrocarbons

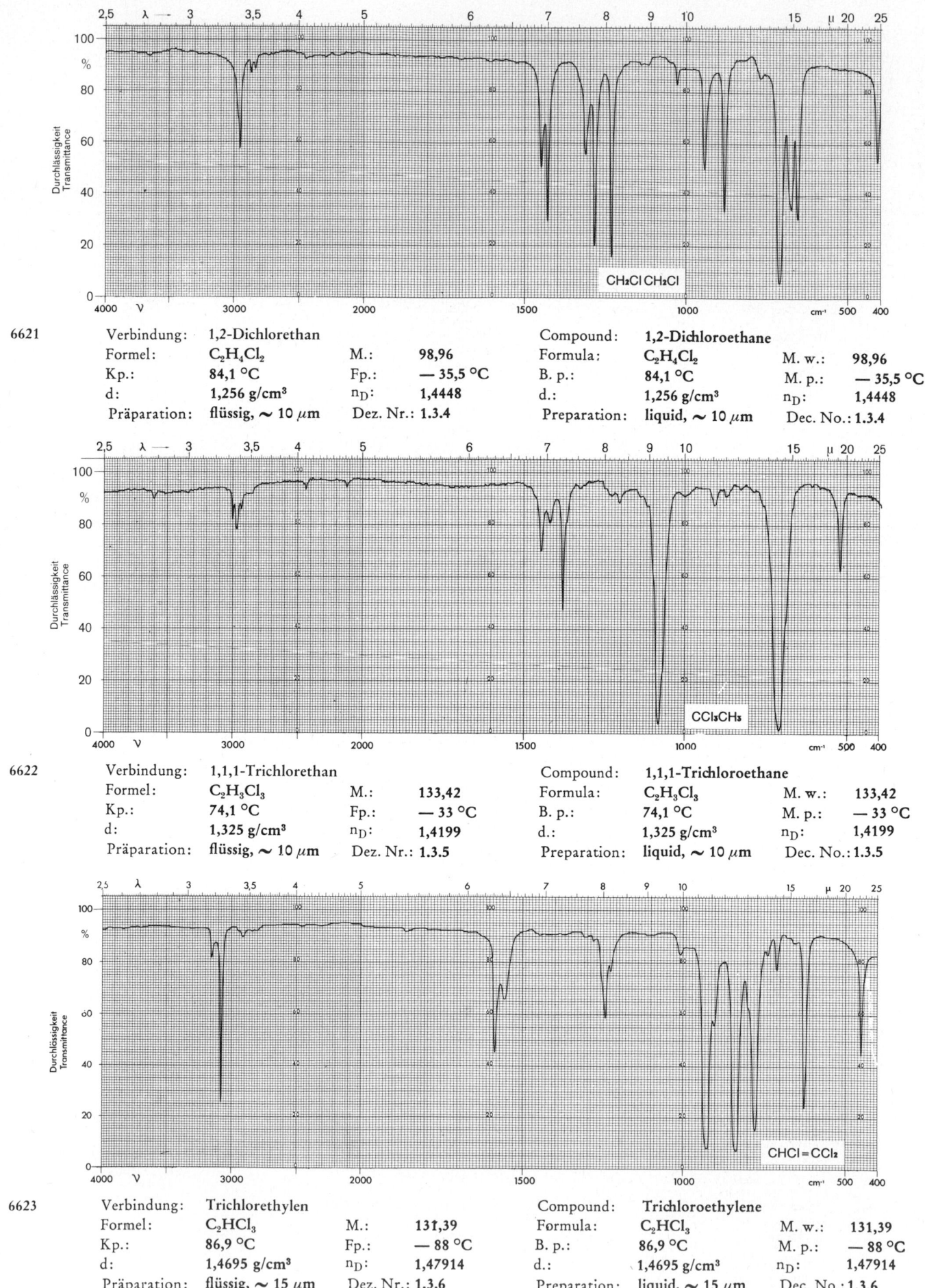

6621

Verbindung:	1,2-Dichlorethan			Compound:	1,2-Dichloroethane		
Formel:	C₂H₄Cl₂	M.:	98,96	Formula:	C₂H₄Cl₂	M. w.:	98,96
Kp.:	84,1 °C	Fp.:	— 35,5 °C	B. p.:	84,1 °C	M. p.:	— 35,5 °C
d:	1,256 g/cm³	n_D:	1,4448	d.:	1,256 g/cm³	n_D:	1,4448
Präparation:	flüssig, ∼ 10 μm	Dez. Nr.:	1.3.4	Preparation:	liquid, ∼ 10 μm	Dec. No.:	1.3.4

6622

Verbindung:	1,1,1-Trichlorethan			Compound:	1,1,1-Trichloroethane		
Formel:	C₂H₃Cl₃	M.:	133,42	Formula:	C₂H₃Cl₃	M. w.:	133,42
Kp.:	74,1 °C	Fp.:	— 33 °C	B. p.:	74,1 °C	M. p.:	— 33 °C
d:	1,325 g/cm³	n_D:	1,4199	d.:	1,325 g/cm³	n_D:	1,4199
Präparation:	flüssig, ∼ 10 μm	Dez. Nr.:	1.3.5	Preparation:	liquid, ∼ 10 μm	Dec. No.:	1.3.5

6623

Verbindung:	Trichlorethylen			Compound:	Trichloroethylene		
Formel:	C₂HCl₃	M.:	131,39	Formula:	C₂HCl₃	M. w.:	131,39
Kp.:	86,9 °C	Fp.:	— 88 °C	B. p.:	86,9 °C	M. p.:	— 88 °C
d:	1,4695 g/cm³	n_D:	1,47914	d.:	1,4695 g/cm³	n_D:	1,47914
Präparation:	flüssig, ∼ 15 μm	Dez. Nr.:	1.3.6	Preparation:	liquid, ∼ 15 μm	Dec. No.:	1.3.6

Lösungsmittel
1. Kohlenwasserstoffe
1.3. Halogenkohlenwasserstoffe

Solvents
1. Hydrocarbons
1.3. Halogenated hydrocarbons

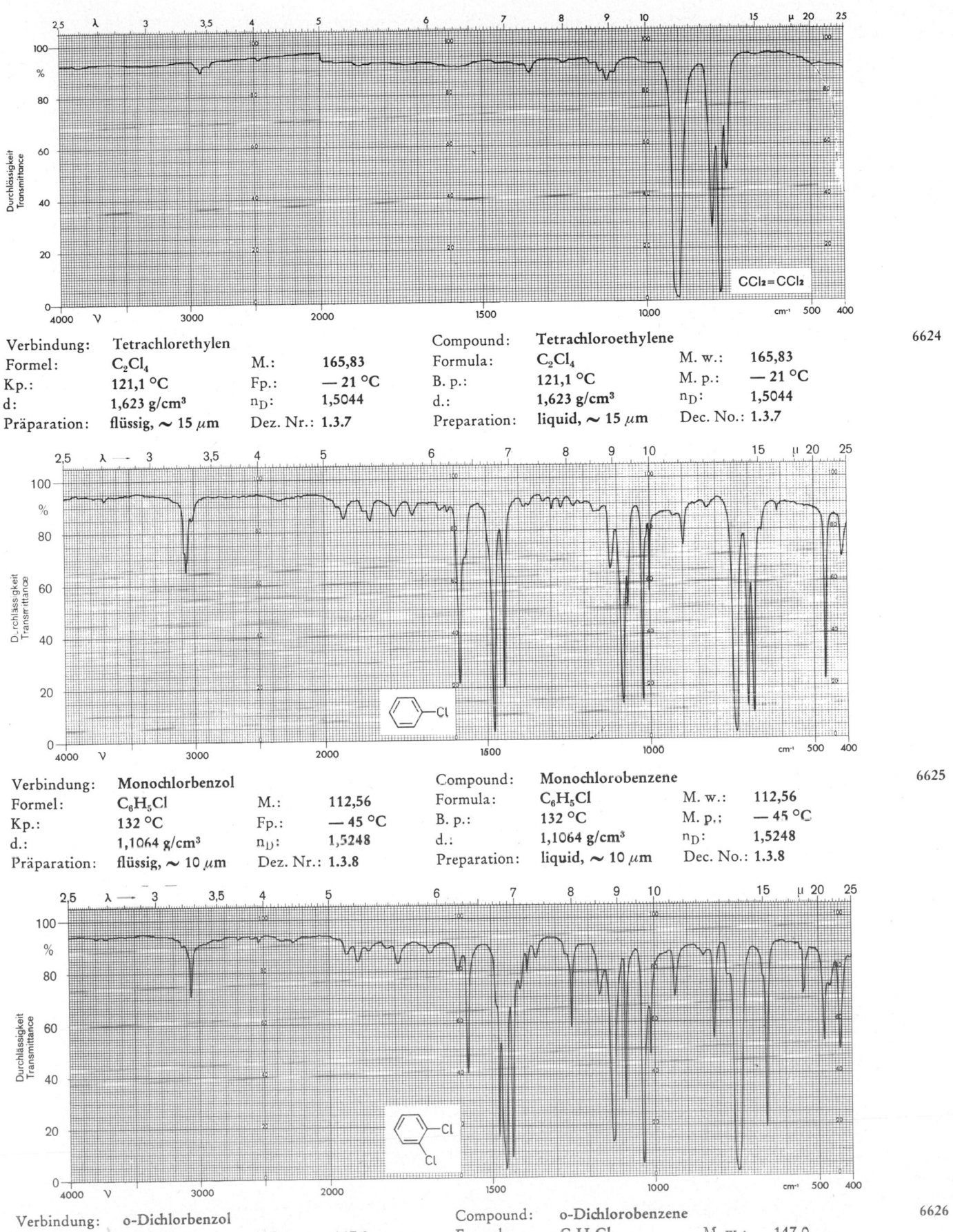

6624

Verbindung:	Tetrachlorethylen			Compound:	Tetrachloroethylene		
Formel:	C₂Cl₄	M.:	165,83	Formula:	C₂Cl₄	M. w.:	165,83
Kp.:	121,1 °C	Fp.:	— 21 °C	B. p.:	121,1 °C	M. p.:	— 21 °C
d:	1,623 g/cm³	n_D:	1,5044	d.:	1,623 g/cm³	n_D:	1,5044
Präparation:	flüssig, ∼ 15 μm	Dez. Nr.:	1.3.7	Preparation:	liquid, ∼ 15 μm	Dec. No.:	1.3.7

6625

Verbindung:	Monochlorbenzol			Compound:	Monochlorobenzene		
Formel:	C₆H₅Cl	M.:	112,56	Formula:	C₆H₅Cl	M. w.:	112,56
Kp.:	132 °C	Fp.:	— 45 °C	B. p.:	132 °C	M. p.:	— 45 °C
d.:	1,1064 g/cm³	n_D:	1,5248	d.:	1,1064 g/cm³	n_D:	1,5248
Präparation:	flüssig, ∼ 10 μm	Dez. Nr.:	1.3.8	Preparation:	liquid, ∼ 10 μm	Dec. No.:	1.3.8

6626

Verbindung:	o-Dichlorbenzol			Compound:	o-Dichlorobenzene		
Formel:	C₆H₄Cl₂	M.:	147,0	Formula:	C₆H₄Cl₂	M. w.:	147,0
Kp.:	179,2 °C	Fp.:	— 17 °C	B. p.:	179,2 °C	M. p.:	— 17 °C
d.:	1,3048 g/cm³	n_D:	1,5485	d.:	1,3048 g/cm³	n_D:	1,5485
Präparation:	flüssig, ∼ 10 μm	Dez. Nr.:	1.3.9	Preparation:	liquid, ∼ 10 μm	Dec. Nr.:	1.3.9

Lösungsmittel
1. Kohlenwasserstoffe
1.3. Halogenkohlenwasserstoffe

Solvents
1. Hydrocarbons
1.3. Halogenated hydrocarbons

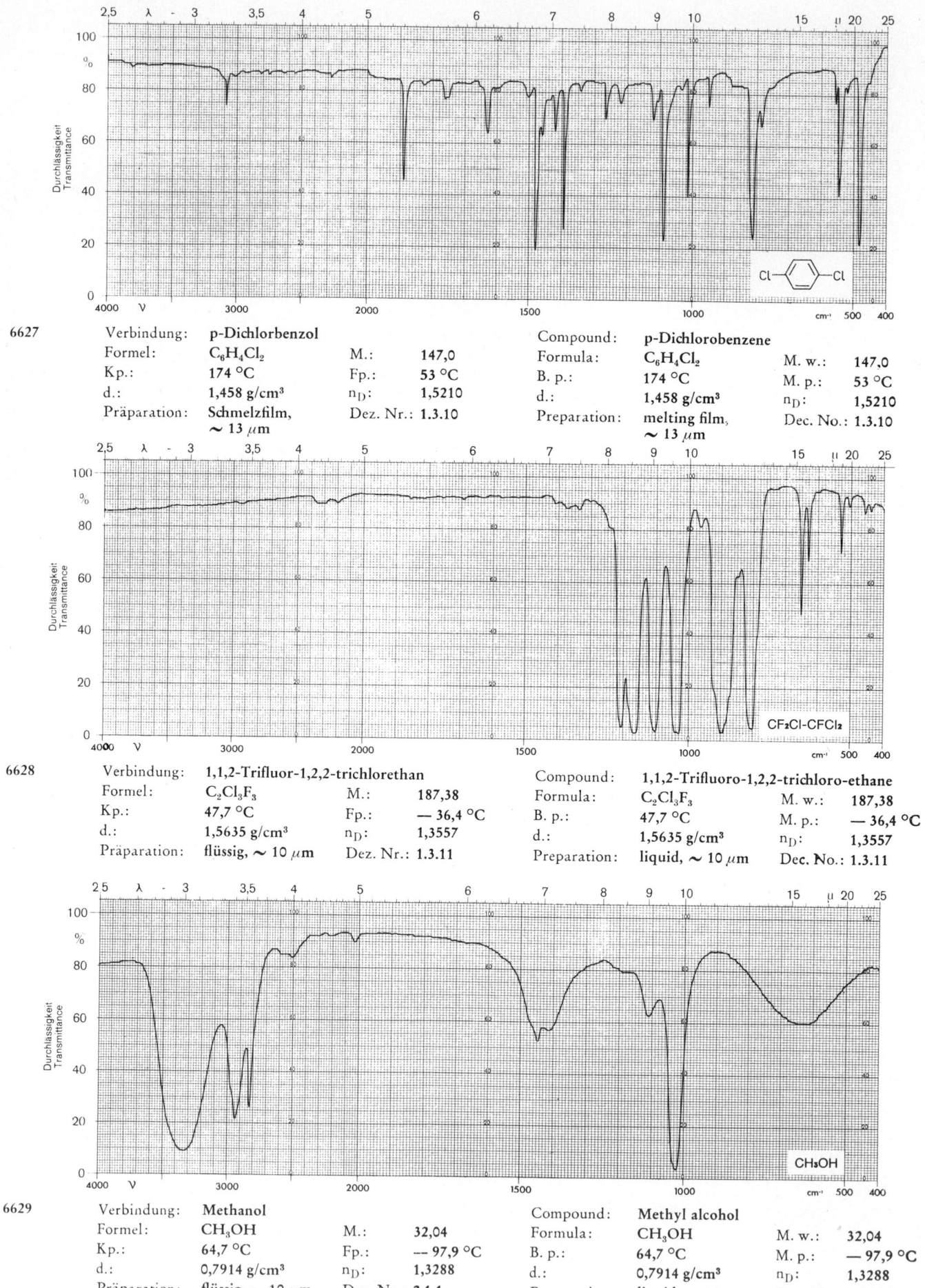

6627

Verbindung:	**p-Dichlorbenzol**			Compound:	**p-Dichlorobenzene**		
Formel:	$C_6H_4Cl_2$	M.:	**147,0**	Formula:	$C_6H_4Cl_2$	M. w.:	**147,0**
Kp.:	**174 °C**	Fp.:	**53 °C**	B. p.:	**174 °C**	M. p.:	**53 °C**
d.:	**1,458 g/cm³**	n_D:	**1,5210**	d.:	**1,458 g/cm³**	n_D:	**1,5210**
Präparation:	Schmelzfilm, ~ 13 μm	Dez. Nr.:	**1.3.10**	Preparation:	melting film, ~ 13 μm	Dec. No.:	**1.3.10**

6628

Verbindung:	**1,1,2-Trifluor-1,2,2-trichlorethan**			Compound:	**1,1,2-Trifluoro-1,2,2-trichloro-ethane**		
Formel:	$C_2Cl_3F_3$	M.:	**187,38**	Formula:	$C_2Cl_3F_3$	M. w.:	**187,38**
Kp.:	**47,7 °C**	Fp.:	**— 36,4 °C**	B. p.:	**47,7 °C**	M. p.:	**— 36,4 °C**
d.:	**1,5635 g/cm³**	n_D:	**1,3557**	d.:	**1,5635 g/cm³**	n_D:	**1,3557**
Präparation:	flüssig, ~ 10 μm	Dez. Nr.:	**1.3.11**	Preparation:	liquid, ~ 10 μm	Dec. No.:	**1.3.11**

6629

Verbindung:	**Methanol**			Compound:	**Methyl alcohol**		
Formel:	CH_3OH	M.:	**32,04**	Formula:	CH_3OH	M. w.:	**32,04**
Kp.:	**64,7 °C**	Fp.:	**— 97,9 °C**	B. p.:	**64,7 °C**	M. p.:	**— 97,9 °C**
d.:	**0,7914 g/cm³**	n_D:	**1,3288**	d.:	**0,7914 g/cm³**	n_D:	**1,3288**
Präparation:	flüssig, ~ 10 μm	Dez. Nr.:	**2.1.1**	Preparation:	liquid, ~ 10 μm	Dec. No.:	**2.1.1**

Lösungsmittel
2. Alkohole
2.1. Monoalkohole

Solvents
2. Alcohols
2.1. Monoalcohols

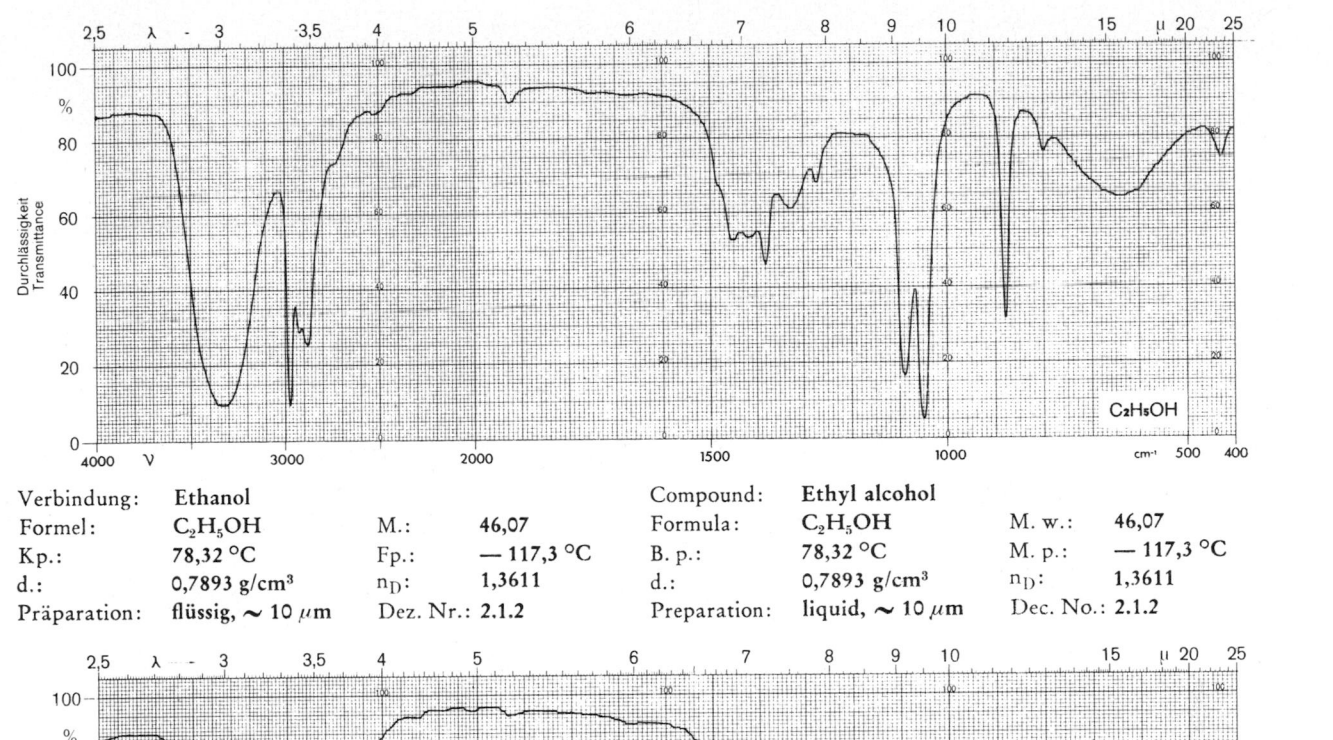

Verbindung:	Ethanol			Compound:	Ethyl alcohol			6630
Formel:	C_2H_5OH	M.:	46,07	Formula:	C_2H_5OH	M. w.:	46,07	
Kp.:	78,32 °C	Fp.:	— 117,3 °C	B. p.:	78,32 °C	M. p.:	— 117,3 °C	
d.:	0,7893 g/cm³	n_D:	1,3611	d.:	0,7893 g/cm³	n_D:	1,3611	
Präparation:	flüssig, ~ 10 µm	Dez. Nr.:	2.1.2	Preparation:	liquid, ~ 10 µm	Dec. No.:	2.1.2	

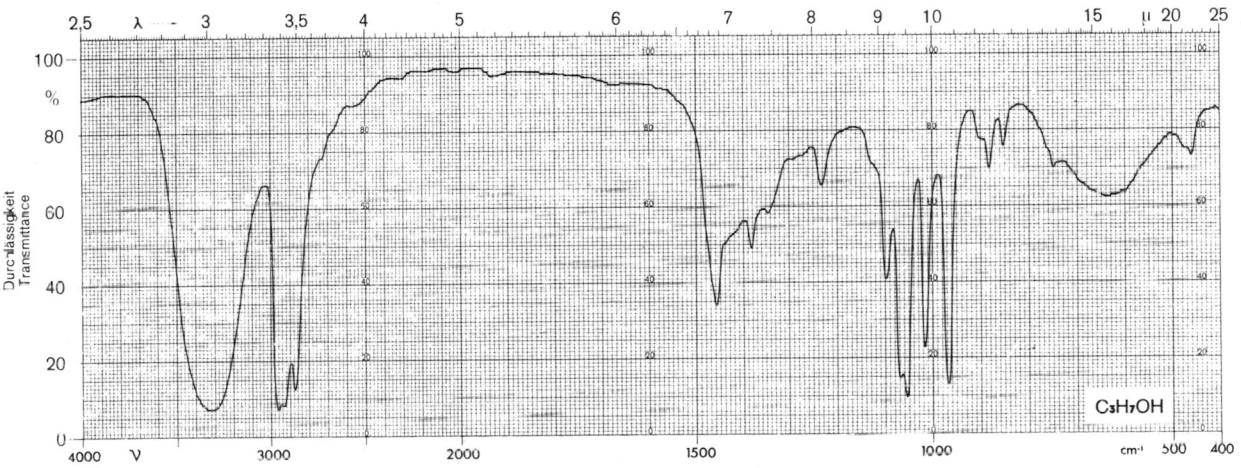

Verbindung:	n-Propanol			Compound:	n-Propyl alcohol			6631
Formel:	C_3H_7OH	M.:	60,10	Formula:	C_3H_7OH	M. p.:	60,10	
Kp.:	97,4 °C	Fp.:	— 126,2 °C	B. p.:	97,4 °C	M. w.:	— 126,2 °C	
d.:	0,7796 g/cm³	n_D:	1,3850	d.:	0,7796 g/cm³	n_D:	1,3850	
Präparation:	flüssig, ~ 10 µm	Dez. Nr.:	2.1.3	Preparation:	liquid, ~ 10 µm	Dec. No.:	2.1.3	

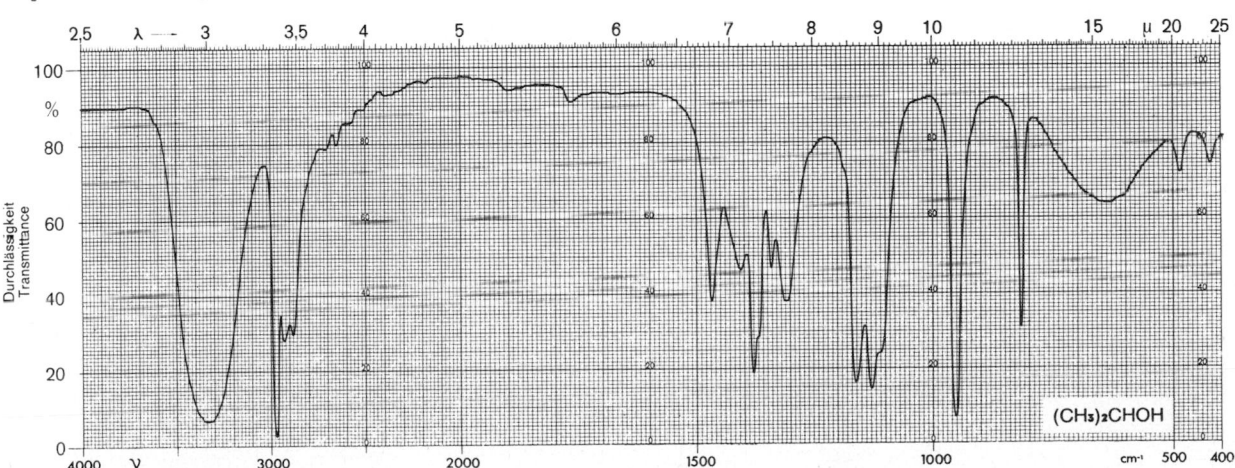

Verbindung:	iso-Propanol			Compound:	iso-Propyl alcohol			6632
Formel:	C_3H_7OH	M.:	60,10	Formula:	C_3H_7OH	M. w.:	60,10	
Kp.:	82,4 °C	Fp.:	— 89,5 °C	B. p.:	82,4 °C	M. p.:	— 89,5 °C	
d.:	0,7851 g/cm³	n_D:	1,3776	d.:	0,7851 g/cm³	n_D:	1,3776	
Präparation:	flüssig, ~ 10 µm	Dez. Nr.:	2.1.4	Preparation:	liquid, ~ 10 µm	Dec. No.:	2.1.4	

Lösungsmittel
2. Alkohole
2.1. Monoalkohole

Solvents
2. Alcohols
2.1 Monoalcohols

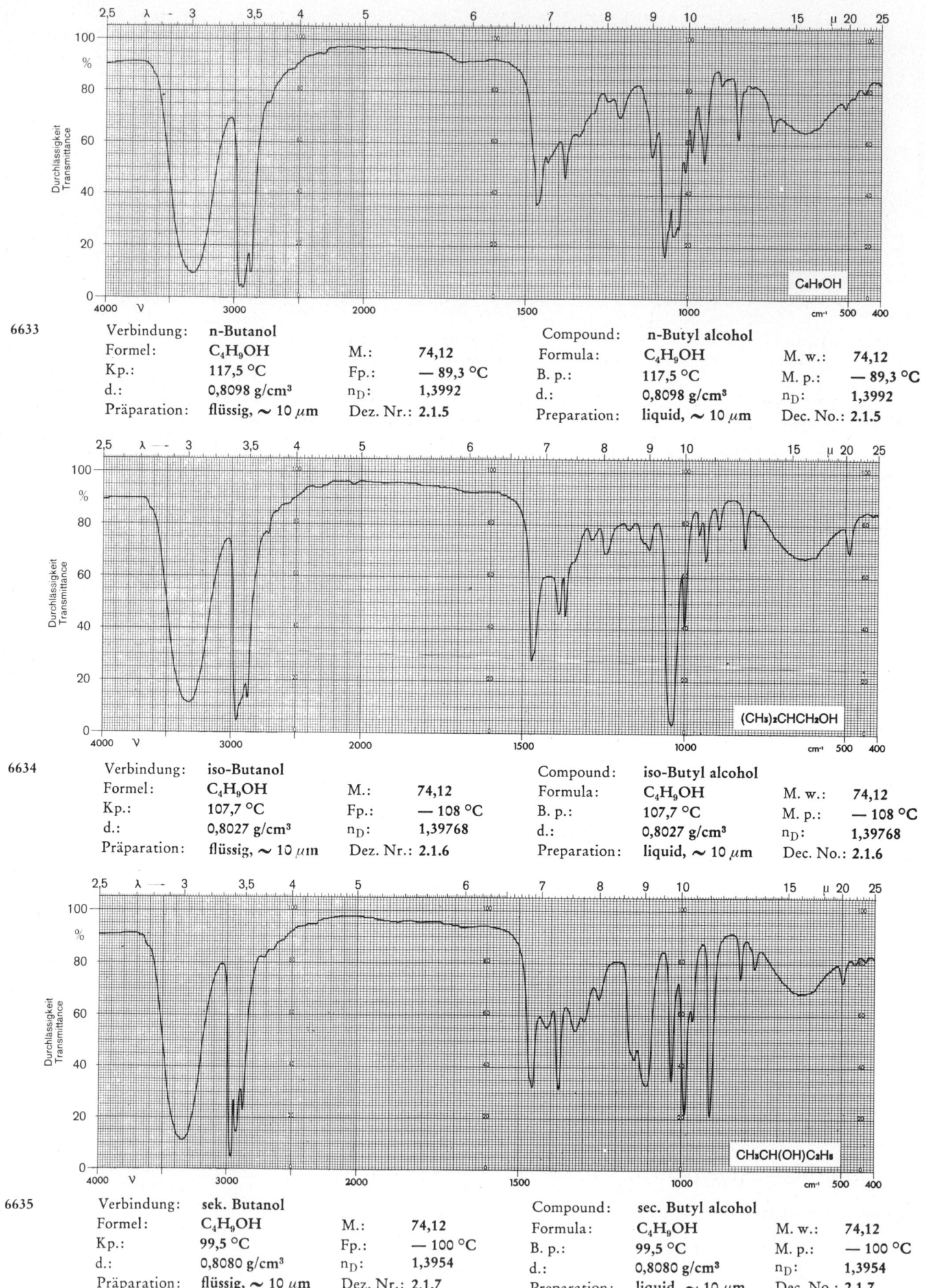

6633

Verbindung:	**n-Butanol**			Compound:	**n-Butyl alcohol**		
Formel:	C_4H_9OH	M.:	**74,12**	Formula:	C_4H_9OH	M. w.:	**74,12**
Kp.:	117,5 °C	Fp.:	— 89,3 °C	B. p.:	117,5 °C	M. p.:	— 89,3 °C
d.:	0,8098 g/cm³	n_D:	1,3992	d.:	0,8098 g/cm³	n_D:	1,3992
Präparation:	flüssig, ~ 10 μm	Dez. Nr.:	2.1.5	Preparation:	liquid, ~ 10 μm	Dec. No.:	2.1.5

6634

Verbindung:	**iso-Butanol**			Compound:	**iso-Butyl alcohol**		
Formel:	C_4H_9OH	M.:	**74,12**	Formula:	C_4H_9OH	M. w.:	**74,12**
Kp.:	107,7 °C	Fp.:	— 108 °C	B. p.:	107,7 °C	M. p.:	— 108 °C
d.:	0,8027 g/cm³	n_D:	1,39768	d.:	0,8027 g/cm³	n_D:	1,39768
Präparation:	flüssig, ~ 10 μm	Dez. Nr.:	2.1.6	Preparation:	liquid, ~ 10 μm	Dec. No.:	2.1.6

6635

Verbindung:	**sek. Butanol**			Compound:	**sec. Butyl alcohol**		
Formel:	C_4H_9OH	M.:	**74,12**	Formula:	C_4H_9OH	M. w.:	**74,12**
Kp.:	99,5 °C	Fp.:	— 100 °C	B. p.:	99,5 °C	M. p.:	— 100 °C
d.:	0,8080 g/cm³	n_D:	1,3954	d.:	0,8080 g/cm³	n_D:	1,3954
Präparation:	flüssig, ~ 10 μm	Dez. Nr.:	2.1.7	Preparation:	liquid, ~ 10 μm	Dec. No.:	2.1.7

Lösungsmittel
2. Alkohole
2.1. Monoalkohole

Solvents
2. Alcohols
2.1 Monoalcohols

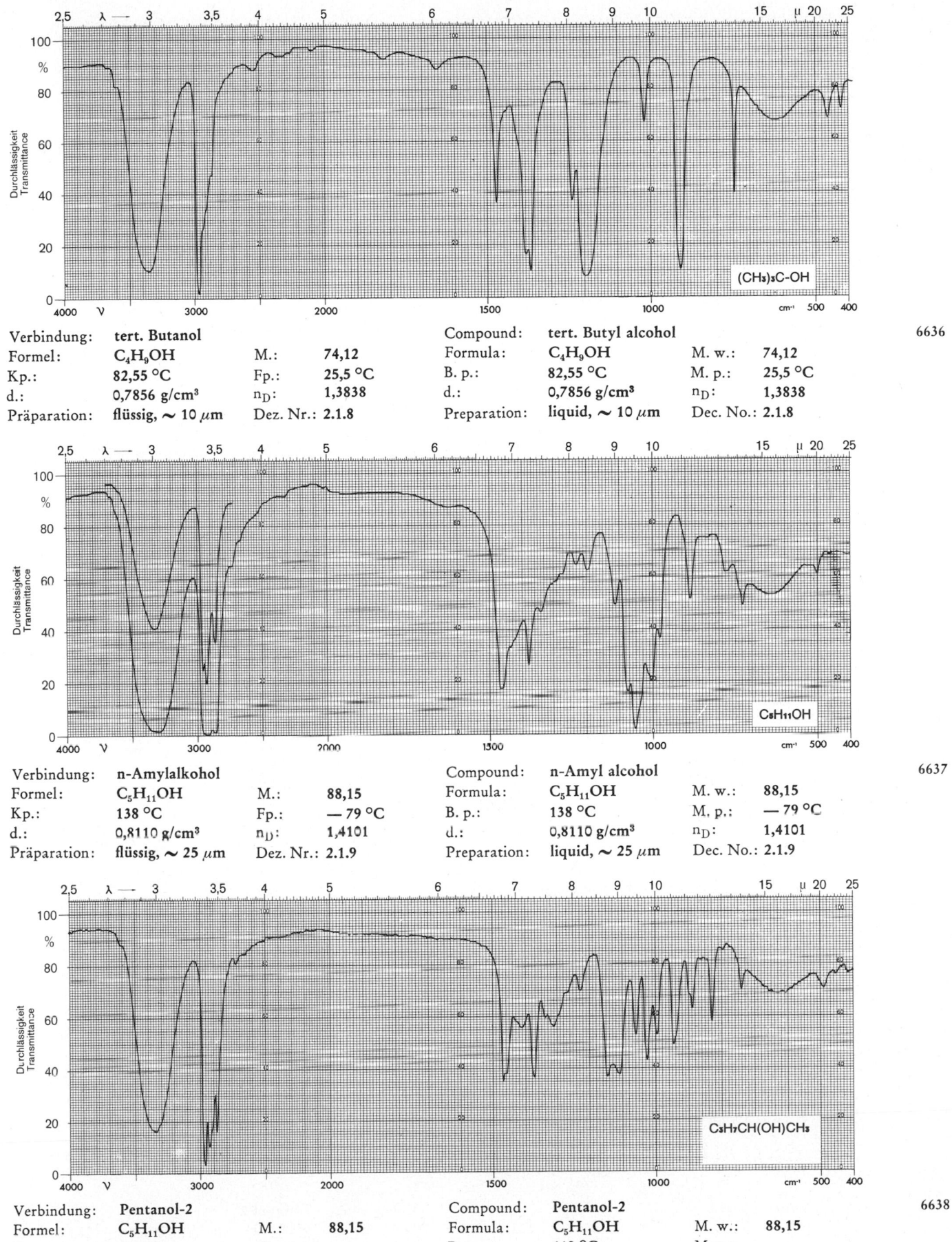

6636

Verbindung:	tert. Butanol			Compound:	tert. Butyl alcohol		
Formel:	C_4H_9OH	M.:	74,12	Formula:	C_4H_9OH	M. w.:	74,12
Kp.:	82,55 °C	Fp.:	25,5 °C	B. p.:	82,55 °C	M. p.:	25,5 °C
d.:	0,7856 g/cm³	n_D:	1,3838	d.:	0,7856 g/cm³	n_D:	1,3838
Präparation:	flüssig, ~ 10 µm	Dez. Nr.:	2.1.8	Preparation:	liquid, ~ 10 µm	Dec. No.:	2.1.8

6637

Verbindung:	n-Amylalkohol			Compound:	n-Amyl alcohol		
Formel:	$C_5H_{11}OH$	M.:	88,15	Formula:	$C_5H_{11}OH$	M. w.:	88,15
Kp.:	138 °C	Fp.:	— 79 °C	B. p.:	138 °C	M. p.:	— 79 °C
d.:	0,8110 g/cm³	n_D:	1,4101	d.:	0,8110 g/cm³	n_D:	1,4101
Präparation:	flüssig, ~ 25 µm	Dez. Nr.:	2.1.9	Preparation:	liquid, ~ 25 µm	Dec. No.:	2.1.9

6638

Verbindung:	Pentanol-2			Compound:	Pentanol-2		
Formel:	$C_5H_{11}OH$	M.:	88,15	Formula:	$C_5H_{11}OH$	M. w.:	88,15
Kp.:	119 °C	Fp.:		B. p.:	119 °C	M. p.:	
d.:	0,8103 g/cm³	n_D:	1,4053	d.:	0,8103 g/cm³	n_D:	1,4053
Präparation:	flüssig, ~ 10 µm	Dez. Nr.:	2.1.10	Preparation:	liquid, ~ 10 µm	Dec. No.:	2.1.10

Lösungsmittel
2. Alkohole
2.1. Monoalkohole

Solvents
2. Alcohols
2.1 Monoalcohols

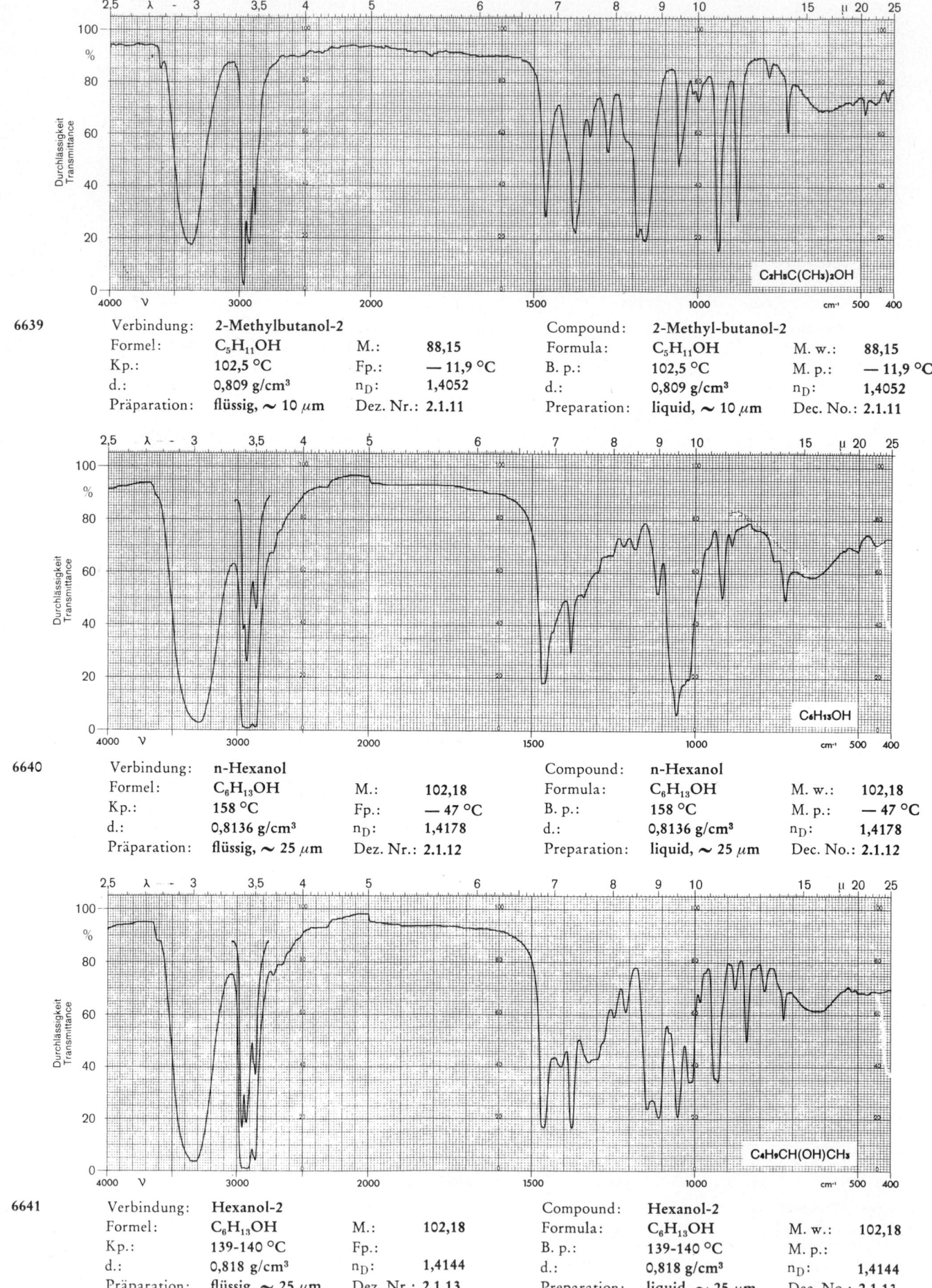

6639

Verbindung:	**2-Methylbutanol-2**			Compound:	**2-Methyl-butanol-2**		
Formel:	$C_5H_{11}OH$	M.:	**88,15**	Formula:	$C_5H_{11}OH$	M. w.:	**88,15**
Kp.:	102,5 °C	Fp.:	— 11,9 °C	B. p.:	102,5 °C	M. p.:	— 11,9 °C
d.:	0,809 g/cm³	n_D:	1,4052	d.:	0,809 g/cm³	n_D:	1,4052
Präparation:	flüssig, ~ 10 μm	Dez. Nr.:	**2.1.11**	Preparation:	liquid, ~ 10 μm	Dec. No.:	**2.1.11**

6640

Verbindung:	**n-Hexanol**			Compound:	**n-Hexanol**		
Formel:	$C_6H_{13}OH$	M.:	**102,18**	Formula:	$C_6H_{13}OH$	M. w.:	**102,18**
Kp.:	**158 °C**	Fp.:	— 47 °C	B. p.:	**158 °C**	M. p.:	— 47 °C
d.:	0,8136 g/cm³	n_D:	1,4178	d.:	0,8136 g/cm³	n_D:	1,4178
Präparation:	flüssig, ~ 25 μm	Dez. Nr.:	**2.1.12**	Preparation:	liquid, ~ 25 μm	Dec. No.:	**2.1.12**

6641

Verbindung:	**Hexanol-2**			Compound:	**Hexanol-2**		
Formel:	$C_6H_{13}OH$	M.:	**102,18**	Formula:	$C_6H_{13}OH$	M. w.:	**102,18**
Kp.:	**139-140 °C**	Fp.:		B. p.:	**139-140 °C**	M. p.:	
d.:	0,818 g/cm³	n_D:	1,4144	d.:	0,818 g/cm³	n_D:	1,4144
Präparation:	flüssig, ~ 25 μm	Dez. Nr.:	**2.1.13**	Preparation:	liquid, ~ 25 μm	Dec. No.:	**2.1.13**

Lösungsmittel
2. Alkohole
2.1. Monoalkohole

Solvents
2. Alcohols
2.1. Monoalcohols

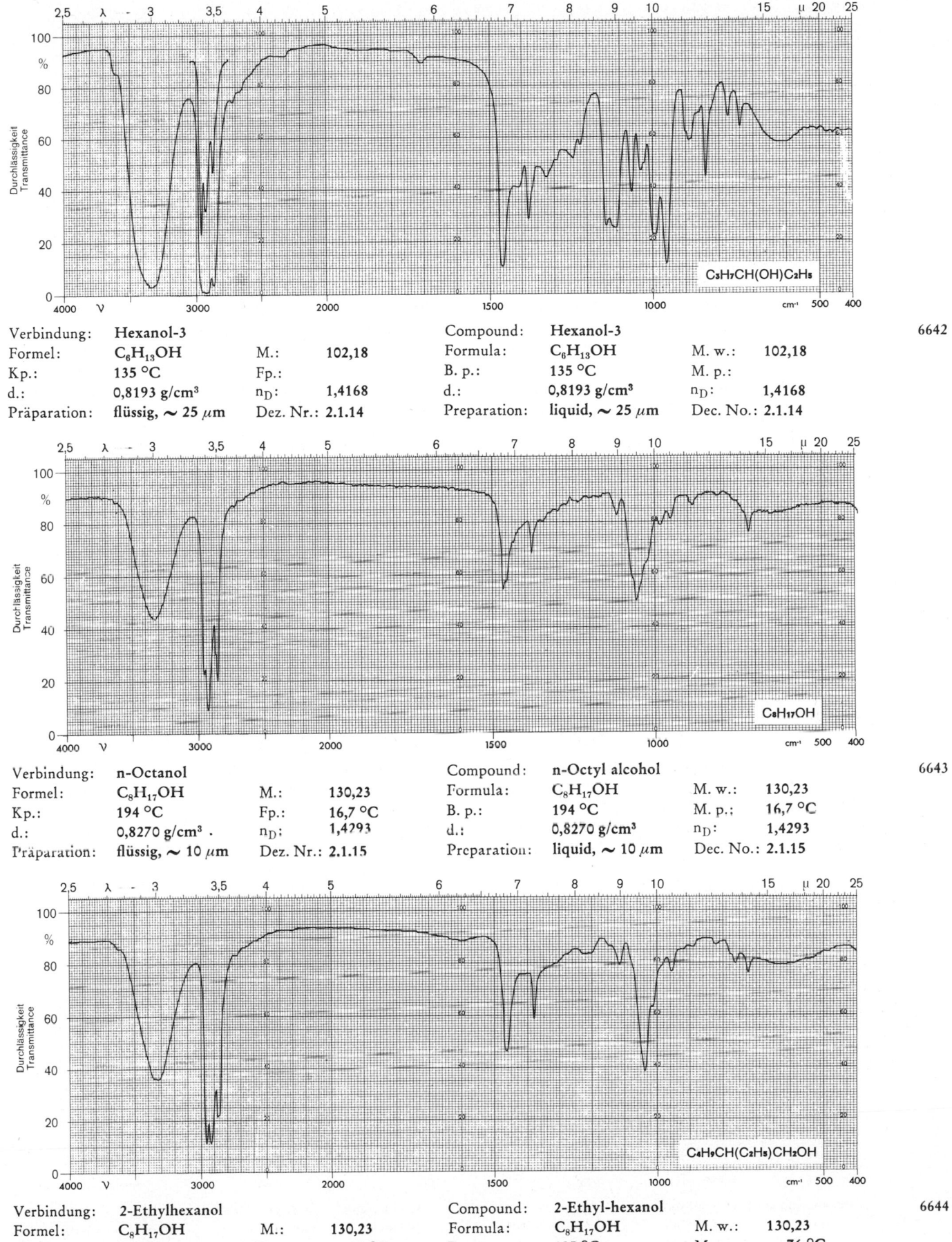

C₃H₇CH(OH)C₂H₅

Verbindung:	Hexanol-3			Compound:	Hexanol-3			6642
Formel:	C₆H₁₃OH	M.:	102,18	Formula:	C₆H₁₃OH	M. w.:	102,18	
Kp.:	135 °C	Fp.:		B. p.:	135 °C	M. p.:		
d.:	0,8193 g/cm³	n_D:	1,4168	d.:	0,8193 g/cm³	n_D:	1,4168	
Präparation:	flüssig, ~ 25 μm	Dez. Nr.:	2.1.14	Preparation:	liquid, ~ 25 μm	Dec. No.:	2.1.14	

C₈H₁₇OH

Verbindung:	n-Octanol			Compound:	n-Octyl alcohol			6643
Formel:	C₈H₁₇OH	M.:	130,23	Formula:	C₈H₁₇OH	M. w.:	130,23	
Kp.:	194 °C	Fp.:	16,7 °C	B. p.:	194 °C	M. p.:	16,7 °C	
d.:	0,8270 g/cm³ .	n_D:	1,4293	d.:	0,8270 g/cm³	n_D:	1,4293	
Präparation:	flüssig, ~ 10 μm	Dez. Nr.:	2.1.15	Preparation:	liquid, ~ 10 μm	Dec. No.:	2.1.15	

C₄H₉CH(C₂H₅)CH₂OH

Verbindung:	2-Ethylhexanol			Compound:	2-Ethyl-hexanol			6644
Formel:	C₈H₁₇OH	M.:	130,23	Formula:	C₈H₁₇OH	M. w.:	130,23	
Kp.:	185 °C	Fp.:	— 76 °C	B. p.:	185 °C	M. p.:	— 76 °C	
d.:	0,8328 g/cm³	n_D:	1,4318	d.:	0,8328 g/cm³	n_D:	1,4318	
Präparation:	flüssig, ~ 10 μm	Dez. Nr.:	2.1.16	Preparation:	liquid, ~ 10 μm	Dec. No.:	2.1.16	

Lösungsmittel
2. Alkohole
2.1. Monoalkohole

Solvents
2. Alcohols
2.1 Monoalcohols

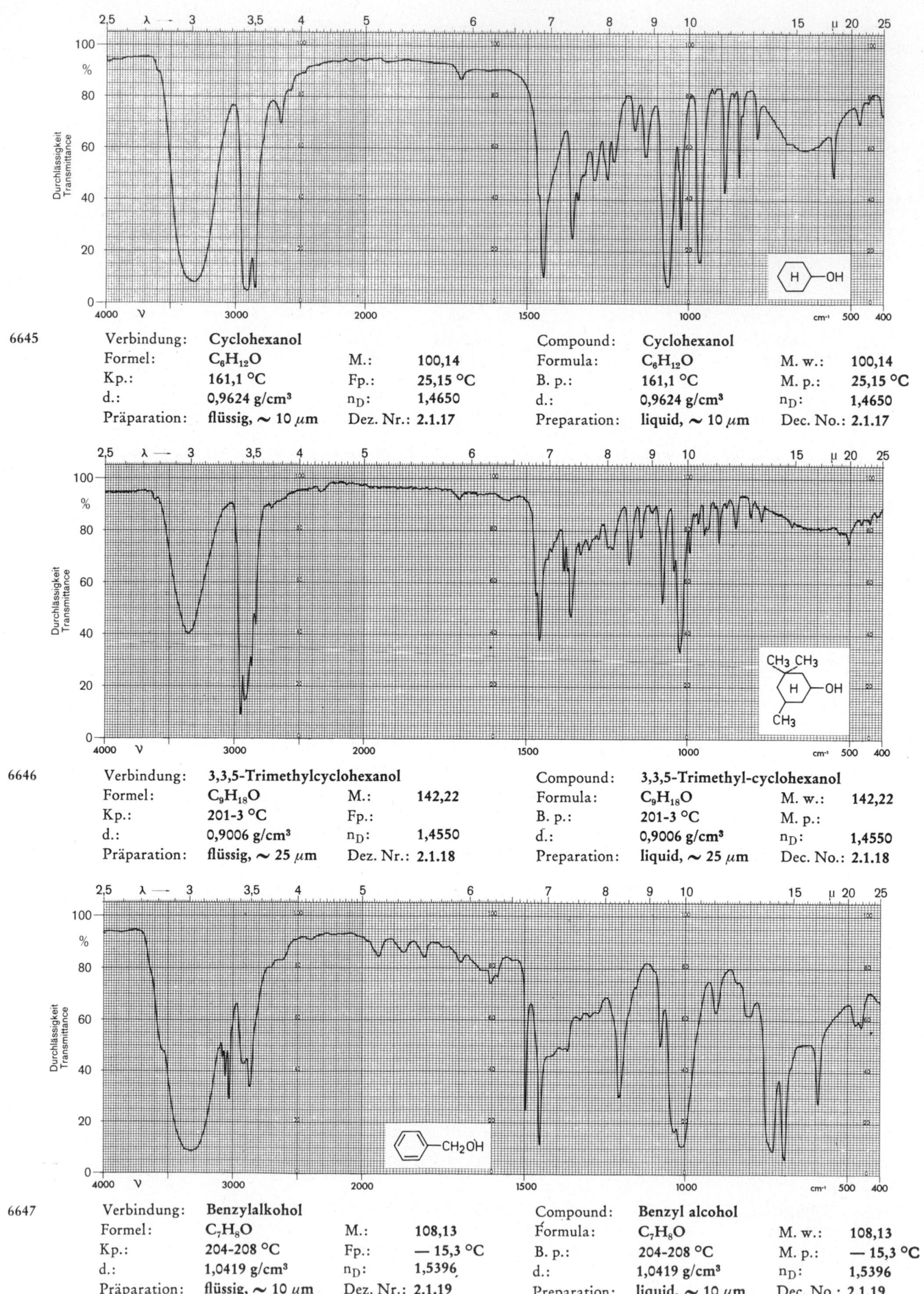

6645

Verbindung:	**Cyclohexanol**			Compound:	**Cyclohexanol**		
Formel:	$C_6H_{12}O$	M.:	**100,14**	Formula:	$C_6H_{12}O$	M. w.:	**100,14**
Kp.:	**161,1 °C**	Fp.:	**25,15 °C**	B. p.:	**161,1 °C**	M. p.:	**25,15 °C**
d.:	**0,9624 g/cm³**	n_D:	**1,4650**	d.:	**0,9624 g/cm³**	n_D:	**1,4650**
Präparation:	**flüssig, ~ 10 μm**	Dez. Nr.:	**2.1.17**	Preparation:	**liquid, ~ 10 μm**	Dec. No.:	**2.1.17**

6646

Verbindung:	**3,3,5-Trimethylcyclohexanol**			Compound:	**3,3,5-Trimethyl-cyclohexanol**		
Formel:	$C_9H_{18}O$	M.:	**142,22**	Formula:	$C_9H_{18}O$	M. w.:	**142,22**
Kp.:	**201-3 °C**	Fp.:		B. p.:	**201-3 °C**	M. p.:	
d.:	**0,9006 g/cm³**	n_D:	**1,4550**	d.:	**0,9006 g/cm³**	n_D:	**1,4550**
Präparation:	**flüssig, ~ 25 μm**	Dez. Nr.:	**2.1.18**	Preparation:	**liquid, ~ 25 μm**	Dec. No.:	**2.1.18**

6647

Verbindung:	**Benzylalkohol**			Compound:	**Benzyl alcohol**		
Formel:	C_7H_8O	M.:	**108,13**	Formula:	C_7H_8O	M. w.:	**108,13**
Kp.:	**204-208 °C**	Fp.:	**— 15,3 °C**	B. p.:	**204-208 °C**	M. p.:	**— 15,3 °C**
d.:	**1,0419 g/cm³**	n_D:	**1,5396**	d.:	**1,0419 g/cm³**	n_D:	**1,5396**
Präparation:	**flüssig, ~ 10 μm**	Dez. Nr.:	**2.1.19**	Preparation:	**liquid, ~ 10 μm**	Dec. No.:	**2.1.19**

Lösungsmittel
2. Alkohole
2.2. Di- und Trialkohole

Solvents
2. Alcohols
2.2 Di- and Trialcohols

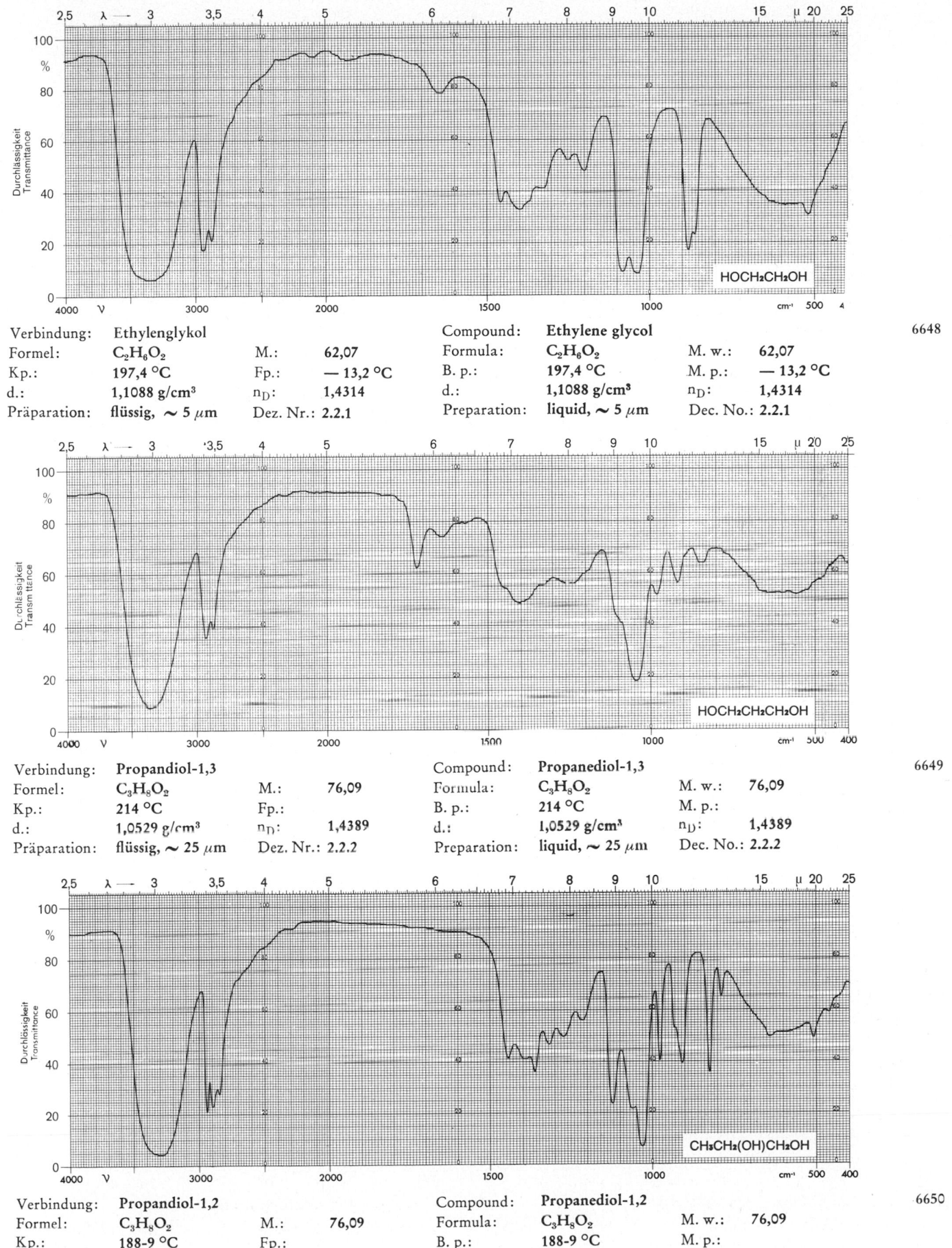

Verbindung: Ethylenglykol

Formel:	$C_2H_6O_2$	M.:	62,07
Kp.:	197,4 °C	Fp.:	— 13,2 °C
d.:	1,1088 g/cm³	n_D:	1,4314
Präparation:	flüssig, ~ 5 μm	Dez. Nr.:	2.2.1

Compound: Ethylene glycol

Formula:	$C_2H_6O_2$	M. w.:	62,07
B. p.:	197,4 °C	M. p.:	— 13,2 °C
d.:	1,1088 g/cm³	n_D:	1,4314
Preparation:	liquid, ~ 5 μm	Dec. No.:	2.2.1

6648

Verbindung: **Propandiol-1,3**

Formel:	$C_3H_8O_2$	M.:	76,09
Kp.:	214 °C	Fp.:	
d.:	1,0529 g/cm³	n_D:	1,4389
Präparation:	flüssig, ~ 25 μm	Dez. Nr.:	2.2.2

Compound: **Propanediol-1,3**

Formula:	$C_3H_8O_2$	M. w.:	76,09
B. p.:	214 °C	M. p.:	
d.:	1,0529 g/cm³	n_D:	1,4389
Preparation:	liquid, ~ 25 μm	Dec. No.:	2.2.2

6649

Verbindung: **Propandiol-1,2**

Formel:	$C_3H_8O_2$	M.:	76,09
Kp.:	188-9 °C	Fp.:	
d.:	1,0361 g/cm³	n_D:	1,4324
Präparation:	flüssig, ~ 25 μm	Dez. Nr.:	2.2.3

Compound: **Propanediol-1,2**

Formula:	$C_3H_8O_2$	M. w.:	76,09
B. p.:	188-9 °C	M. p.:	
d.:	1,0361 g/cm³	n_D:	1,4324
Preparation:	liquid, ~ 25 μm	Dec. No.:	2.2.3

6650

Lösungsmittel
2. Alkohole
2.2. Di- und Trialkohole

Solvents
2. Alcohols
2.2. Di- and trialcohols

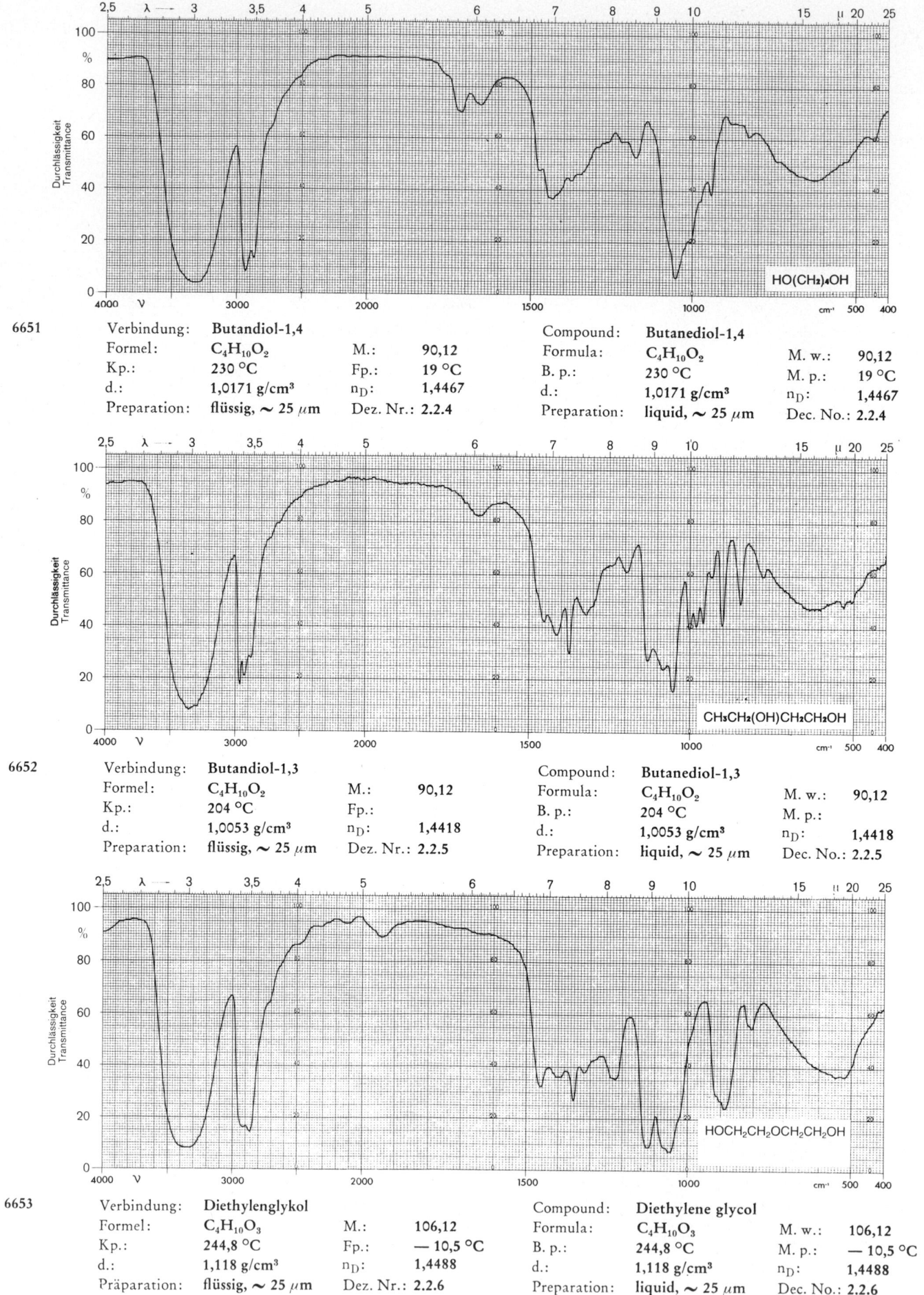

HO(CH₂)₄OH

6651

Verbindung:	**Butandiol-1,4**			Compound:	**Butanediol-1,4**		
Formel:	$C_4H_{10}O_2$	M.:	**90,12**	Formula:	$C_4H_{10}O_2$	M. w.:	**90,12**
Kp.:	230 °C	Fp.:	**19 °C**	B. p.:	230 °C	M. p.:	**19 °C**
d.:	1,0171 g/cm³	n$_D$:	**1,4467**	d.:	1,0171 g/cm³	n$_D$:	**1,4467**
Preparation:	flüssig, ~ 25 μm	Dez. Nr.:	**2.2.4**	Preparation:	liquid, ~ 25 μm	Dec. No.:	**2.2.4**

CH₃CH₂(OH)CH₂CH₂OH

6652

Verbindung:	**Butandiol-1,3**			Compound:	**Butanediol-1,3**		
Formel:	$C_4H_{10}O_2$	M.:	**90,12**	Formula:	$C_4H_{10}O_2$	M. w.:	**90,12**
Kp.:	204 °C	Fp.:		B. p.:	204 °C	M. p.:	
d.:	1,0053 g/cm³	n$_D$:	**1,4418**	d.:	1,0053 g/cm³	n$_D$:	**1,4418**
Preparation:	flüssig, ~ 25 μm	Dez. Nr.:	**2.2.5**	Preparation:	liquid, ~ 25 μm	Dec. No.:	**2.2.5**

HOCH₂CH₂OCH₂CH₂OH

6653

Verbindung:	**Diethylenglykol**			Compound:	**Diethylene glycol**		
Formel:	$C_4H_{10}O_3$	M.:	**106,12**	Formula:	$C_4H_{10}O_3$	M. w.:	**106,12**
Kp.:	244,8 °C	Fp.:	**— 10,5 °C**	B. p.:	244,8 °C	M. p.:	**— 10,5 °C**
d.:	1,118 g/cm³	n$_D$:	**1,4488**	d.:	1,118 g/cm³	n$_D$:	**1,4488**
Präparation:	flüssig, ~ 25 μm	Dez. Nr.:	**2.2.6**	Preparation:	liquid, ~ 25 μm	Dec. No.:	**2.2.6**

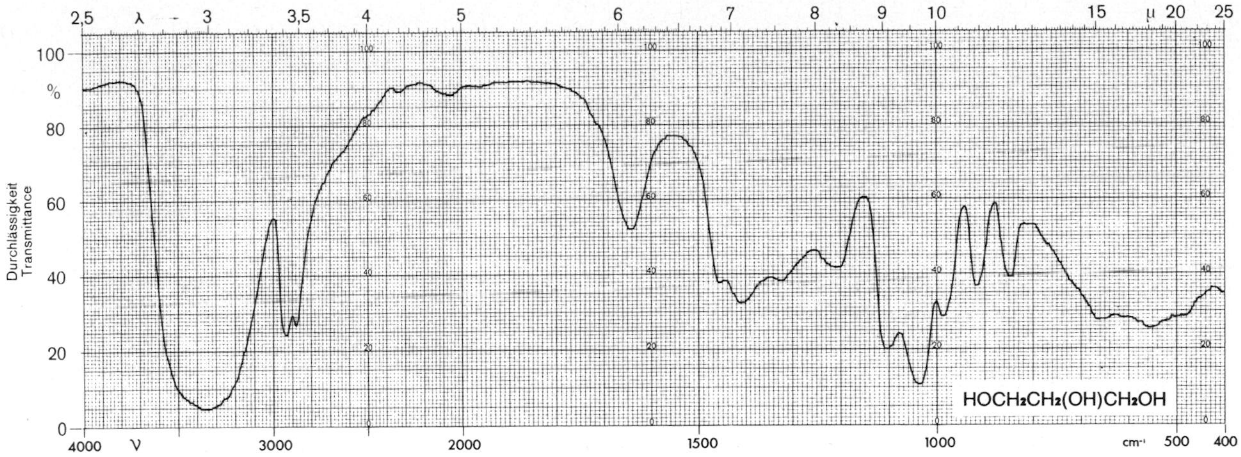

Lösungsmittel
2. Alkohole
2.2. Di- und Trialkohole

Solvents
2. Alcohols
2.2. Di- and trialcohols

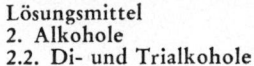

HOCH₂CH₂(OH)CH₂OH

Verbindung:	**Glycerin**			Compound:	**Glycerol**			6654
Formel:	C₃H₈O₃	M.:	92,09	Formula:	C₃H₈O₃	M. w.:	92,09	
Kp.:	290 °C	Fp.:	17,9 °C	B. p.:	290 °C	M. p.:	17,9 °C	
d.:	1,2613 g/cm³	n_D:	1,4746	d.:	1,2613 g/cm³	n_D:	1,4746	
Präparation:	flüssig, ∼ 25 μm	Dez. Nr.:	2.2.7	Preparation:	liquid, ∼ 25 μm	Dec. No.:	2.2.7	

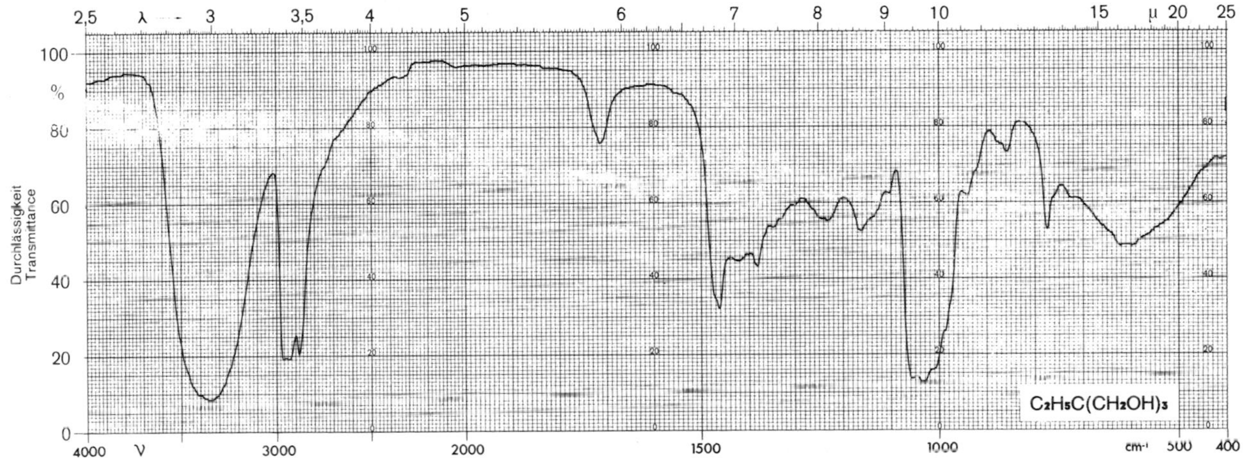

C₂H₅C(CH₂OH)₃

Verbindung:	**Trimethylolpropan**			Compound:	**Trimethylolpropane**			6655
Formel:	C₆H₁₄O₃	M.:	134,17	Formula:	C₆H₁₄O₃	M. w.:	134,17	
Kp.:	160 °C	Fp.:	58 °C	B. p.:	160 °C	M. p.:	58 °C	
d.:		n_D:		d.:		n_D:		
Präparation:	Schmelzfilm	Dez. Nr.:	2.2.8	Preparation:	melting film	Dec. No.:	2.2.8	

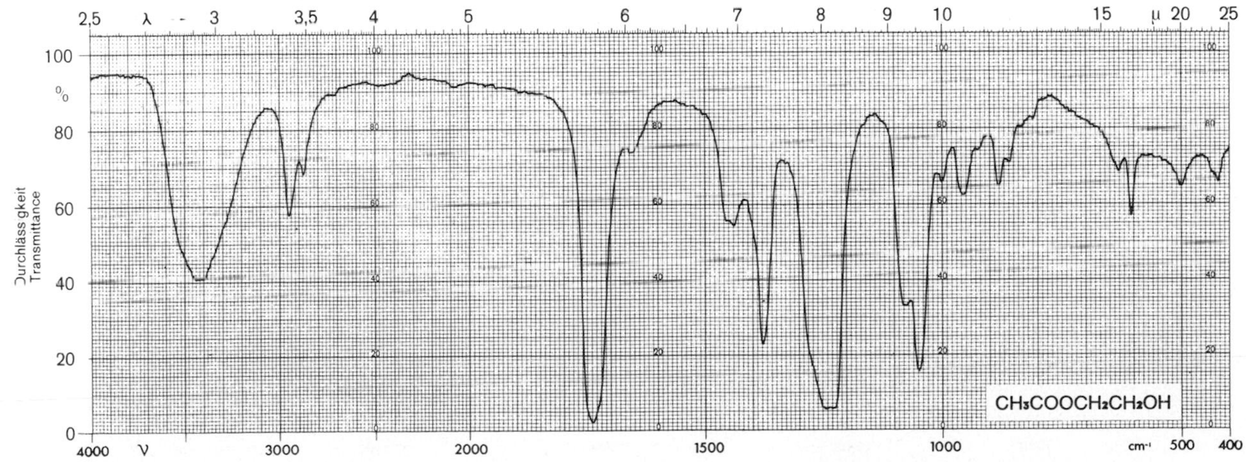

CH₃COOCH₂CH₂OH

Verbindung:	Ethylenglykolmonoacetat			Compound:	**Ethylene glycol monoacetate**			6656
Formel:	C₄H₈O₃	M.:	104,11	Formula:	C₄H₈O₃	M. w.:	104,11	
Kp.:	187-9 °C	Fp.:		B. p.:	187-9 °C	M. p.:		
d.:	1,107-11 g/cm³	n_D:		d.:	1,107-11 g/cm³	n_D:		
Präparation:	flüssig, ∼ 10 μm	Dez. Nr.:	2.3.1	Preparation:	liquid, ∼ 10 μm	Dec. No.:	2.3.1	

Lösungsmittel
2. Alkohole
2.3. Ester-, Keto-, Halogenalkohole

Solvents
2. Alcohols
2.3. Ester-, keto-, halogenated alcohols

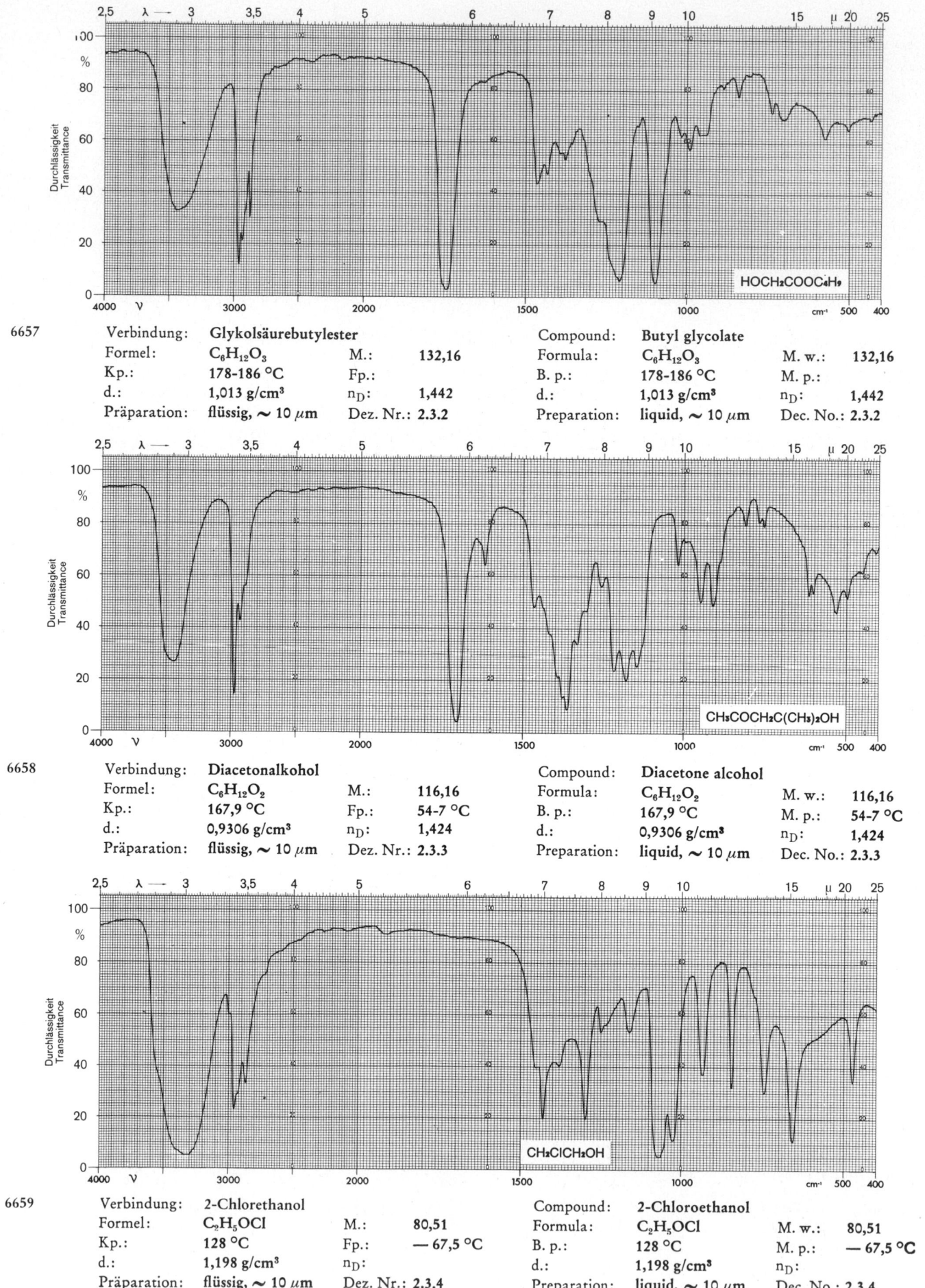

6657   Verbindung: **Glykolsäurebutylester**   Compound: **Butyl glycolate**

Formel:	$C_6H_{12}O_3$	M.:	**132,16**	Formula:	$C_6H_{12}O_3$	M. w.: **132,16**
Kp.:	**178-186 °C**	Fp.:		B. p.:	**178-186 °C**	M. p.:
d.:	**1,013 g/cm³**	n_D:	**1,442**	d.:	**1,013 g/cm³**	n_D: **1,442**
Präparation:	**flüssig, ~ 10 μm**	Dez. Nr.:	**2.3.2**	Preparation:	**liquid, ~ 10 μm**	Dec. No.: **2.3.2**

6658   Verbindung: **Diacetonalkohol**   Compound: **Diacetone alcohol**

Formel:	$C_6H_{12}O_2$	M.:	**116,16**	Formula:	$C_6H_{12}O_2$	M. w.: **116,16**
Kp.:	**167,9 °C**	Fp.:	**54-7 °C**	B. p.:	**167,9 °C**	M. p.: **54-7 °C**
d.:	**0,9306 g/cm³**	n_D:	**1,424**	d.:	**0,9306 g/cm³**	n_D: **1,424**
Präparation:	**flüssig, ~ 10 μm**	Dez. Nr.:	**2.3.3**	Preparation:	**liquid, ~ 10 μm**	Dec. No.: **2.3.3**

6659   Verbindung: **2-Chlorethanol**   Compound: **2-Chloroethanol**

Formel:	C_2H_5OCl	M.:	**80,51**	Formula:	C_2H_5OCl	M. w.: **80,51**
Kp.:	**128 °C**	Fp.:	**— 67,5 °C**	B. p.:	**128 °C**	M. p.: **— 67,5 °C**
d.:	**1,198 g/cm³**	n_D:		d.:	**1,198 g/cm³**	n_D:
Präparation:	**flüssig, ~ 10 μm**	Dez. Nr.:	**2.3.4**	Preparation:	**liquid, ~ 10 μm**	Dec. No.: **2.3.4**

Lösungsmittel
2. Alkohole
2.4. Etheralkohole

Solvents
2. Alcohols
2.4. Ether alcohols

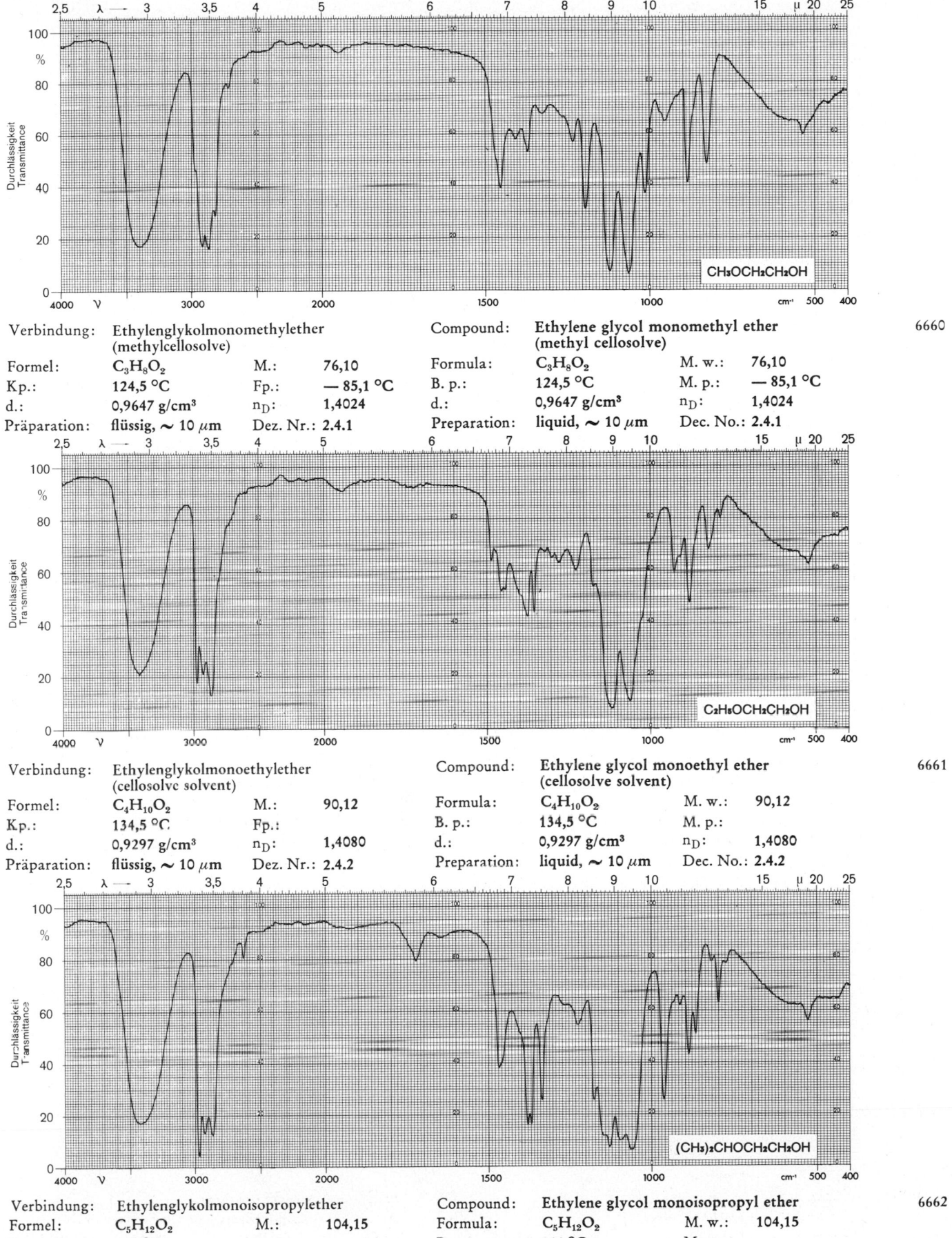

CH₃OCH₂CH₂OH

Verbindung:	Ethylenglykolmonomethylether (methylcellosolve)			Compound:	Ethylene glycol monomethyl ether (methyl cellosolve)			6660
Formel:	$C_3H_8O_2$	M.:	76,10	Formula:	$C_3H_8O_2$	M. w.:	76,10	
Kp.:	124,5 °C	Fp.:	— 85,1 °C	B. p.:	124,5 °C	M. p.:	— 85,1 °C	
d.:	0,9647 g/cm³	n_D:	1,4024	d.:	0,9647 g/cm³	n_D:	1,4024	
Präparation:	flüssig, ~ 10 μm	Dez. Nr.:	2.4.1	Preparation:	liquid, ~ 10 μm	Dec. No.:	2.4.1	

C₂H₅OCH₂CH₂OH

Verbindung:	Ethylenglykolmonoethylether (cellosolve solvent)			Compound:	Ethylene glycol monoethyl ether (cellosolve solvent)			6661
Formel:	$C_4H_{10}O_2$	M.:	90,12	Formula:	$C_4H_{10}O_2$	M. w.:	90,12	
Kp.:	134,5 °C	Fp.:		B. p.:	134,5 °C	M. p.:		
d.:	0,9297 g/cm³	n_D:	1,4080	d.:	0,9297 g/cm³	n_D:	1,4080	
Präparation:	flüssig, ~ 10 μm	Dez. Nr.:	2.4.2	Preparation:	liquid, ~ 10 μm	Dec. No.:	2.4.2	

(CH₃)₂CHOCH₂CH₂OH

Verbindung:	Ethylenglykolmonoisopropylether			Compound:	Ethylene glycol monoisopropyl ether			6662
Formel:	$C_5H_{12}O_2$	M.:	104,15	Formula:	$C_5H_{12}O_2$	M. w.:	104,15	
Kp.:	144 °C	Fp.:		B. p.:	144 °C	M. p.:		
d.:	0,9030 g/cm³	n_D:	1,4095	d.:	0,9030 g/cm³	n_D:	1,4095	
Präparation:	flüssig, ~ 10 μm	Dez. Nr.:	2.4.3	Preparation:	liquid, ~ 10 μm	Dec. No.:	2.4.3	

Lösungsmittel
2. Alkohole
2.4. Etheralkohole

Solvents
2. Alcohols
2.4. Ether alcohols

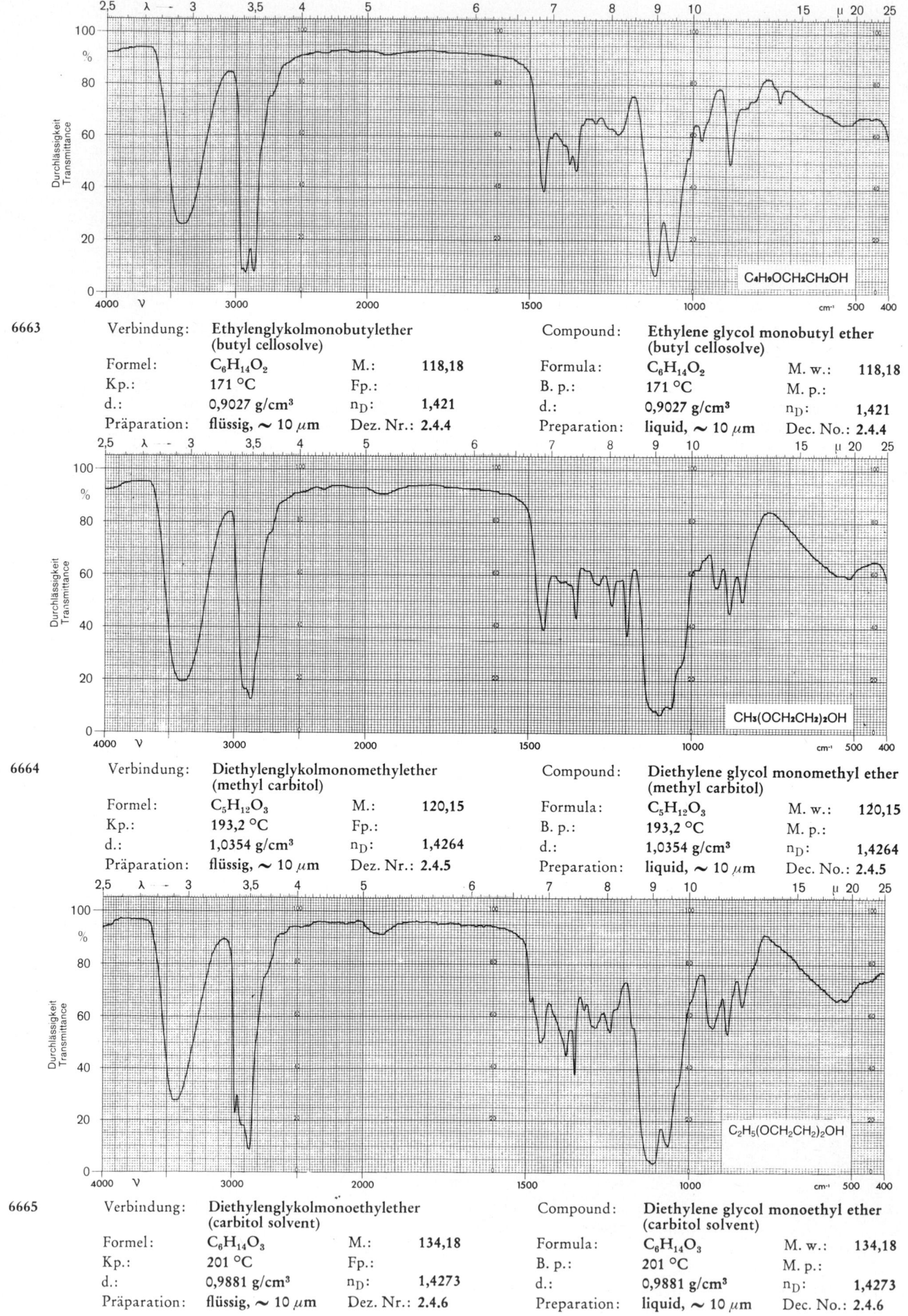

6663

Verbindung:	Ethylenglykolmonobutylether (butyl cellosolve)			Compound:	Ethylene glycol monobutyl ether (butyl cellosolve)	
Formel:	$C_6H_{14}O_2$	M.:	**118,18**	Formula:	$C_6H_{14}O_2$	M. w.: **118,18**
Kp.:	171 °C	Fp.:		B. p.:	171 °C	M. p.:
d.:	0,9027 g/cm³	n_D:	**1,421**	d.:	0,9027 g/cm³	n_D: **1,421**
Präparation:	flüssig, ∼ 10 μm	Dez. Nr.:	**2.4.4**	Preparation:	liquid, ∼ 10 μm	Dec. No.: **2.4.4**

C₄H₉OCH₂CH₂OH

6664

Verbindung:	Diethylenglykolmonomethylether (methyl carbitol)			Compound:	Diethylene glycol monomethyl ether (methyl carbitol)	
Formel:	$C_5H_{12}O_3$	M.:	**120,15**	Formula:	$C_5H_{12}O_3$	M. w.: **120,15**
Kp.:	193,2 °C	Fp.:		B. p.:	193,2 °C	M. p.:
d.:	1,0354 g/cm³	n_D:	**1,4264**	d.:	1,0354 g/cm³	n_D: **1,4264**
Präparation:	flüssig, ∼ 10 μm	Dez. Nr.:	**2.4.5**	Preparation:	liquid, ∼ 10 μm	Dec. No.: **2.4.5**

CH₃(OCH₂CH₂)₂OH

6665

Verbindung:	Diethylenglykolmonoethylether (carbitol solvent)			Compound:	Diethylene glycol monoethyl ether (carbitol solvent)	
Formel:	$C_6H_{14}O_3$	M.:	**134,18**	Formula:	$C_6H_{14}O_3$	M. w.: **134,18**
Kp.:	201 °C	Fp.:		B. p.:	201 °C	M. p.:
d.:	0,9881 g/cm³	n_D:	**1,4273**	d.:	0,9881 g/cm³	n_D: **1,4273**
Präparation:	flüssig, ∼ 10 μm	Dez. Nr.:	**2.4.6**	Preparation:	liquid, ∼ 10 μm	Dec. No.: **2.4.6**

C₂H₅(OCH₂CH₂)₂OH

Lösungsmittel
2. Alkohole
2.4. Etheralkohole

Solvents
2. Alcohols
2.4. Ether alcohols

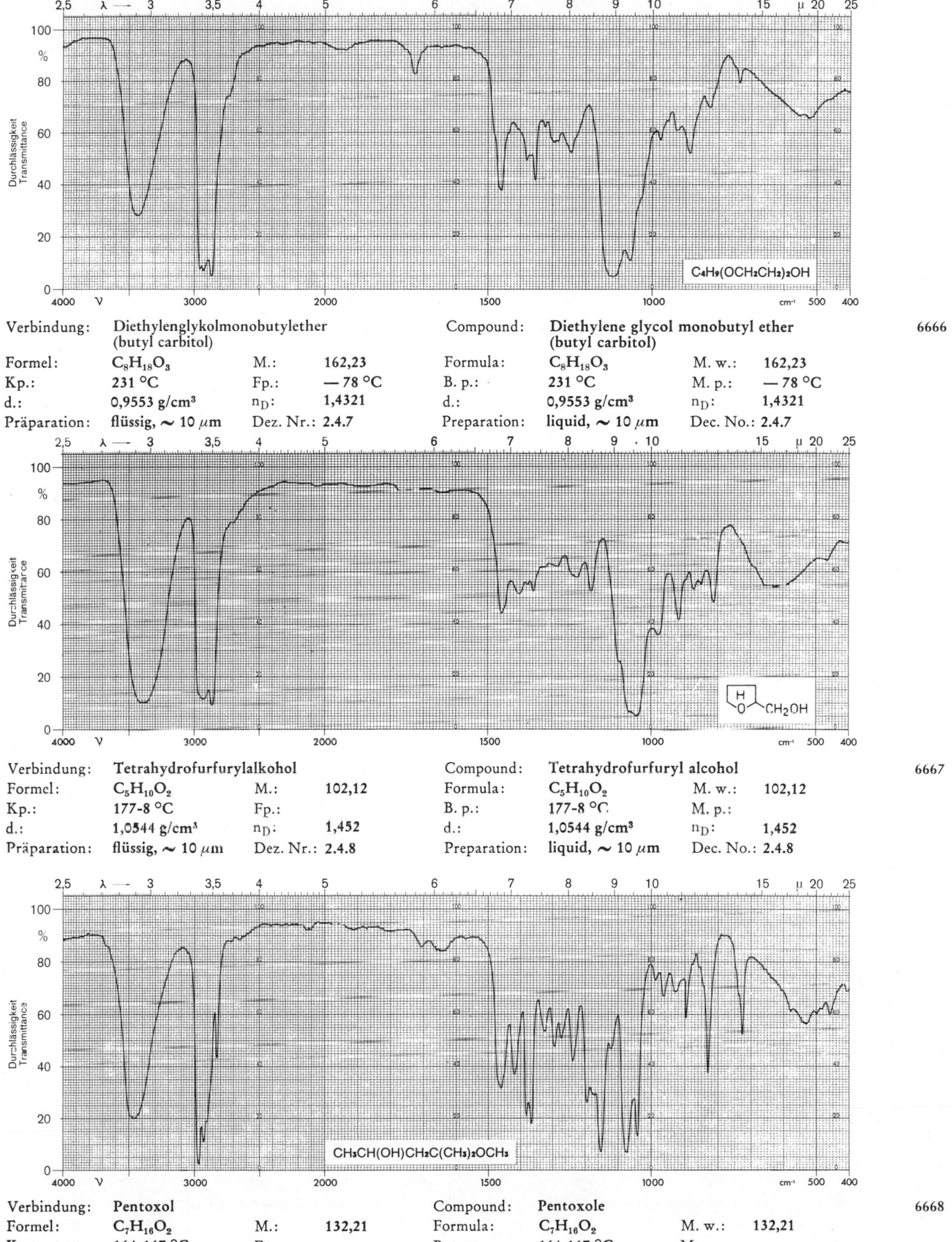

Verbindung: Diethylenglykolmonobutylether (butyl carbitol)

Compound: Diethylene glycol monobutyl ether (butyl carbitol)

6666

Formel:	$C_8H_{18}O_3$	**M.:**	162,23
Kp.:	231 °C	**Fp.:**	— 78 °C
d.:	0,9553 g/cm³	**n_D:**	1,4321
Präparation:	flüssig, ~ 10 μm	**Dez. Nr.:**	2.4.7

Formula:	$C_8H_{18}O_3$	**M. w.:**	162,23
B. p.:	231 °C	**M. p.:**	— 78 °C
d.:	0,9553 g/cm³	**n_D:**	1,4321
Preparation:	liquid, ~ 10 μm	**Dec. No.:**	2.4.7

Verbindung: Tetrahydrofurfurylalkohol

Compound: Tetrahydrofurfuryl alcohol

6667

Formel:	$C_5H_{10}O_2$	**M.:**	102,12
Kp.:	177-8 °C	**Fp.:**	
d.:	1,0544 g/cm³	**n_D:**	1,452
Präparation:	flüssig, ~ 10 μm	**Dez. Nr.:**	2.4.8

Formula:	$C_5H_{10}O_2$	**M. w.:**	102,12
B. p.:	177-8 °C	**M. p.:**	
d.:	1,0544 g/cm³	**n_D:**	1,452
Preparation:	liquid, ~ 10 μm	**Dec. No.:**	2.4.8

Verbindung: Pentoxol

Compound: Pentoxole

6668

Formel:	$C_7H_{16}O_2$	**M.:**	132,21
Kp.:	164-167 °C	**Fp.:**	
d.:		**n_D:**	
Präparation:	flüssig, ~ 10 μm	**Dez. Nr.:**	2.4.9

Formula:	$C_7H_{16}O_2$	**M. w.:**	132,21
B. p.:	164-167 °C	**M. p.:**	
d.:		**n_D:**	
Preparation:	liquid, ~ 10 μm	**Dec. No.:**	2.4.9

Lösungsmittel
3. Ester
3.1. Einfache Ester

Solvents
3. Esters
3.1. Simple esters

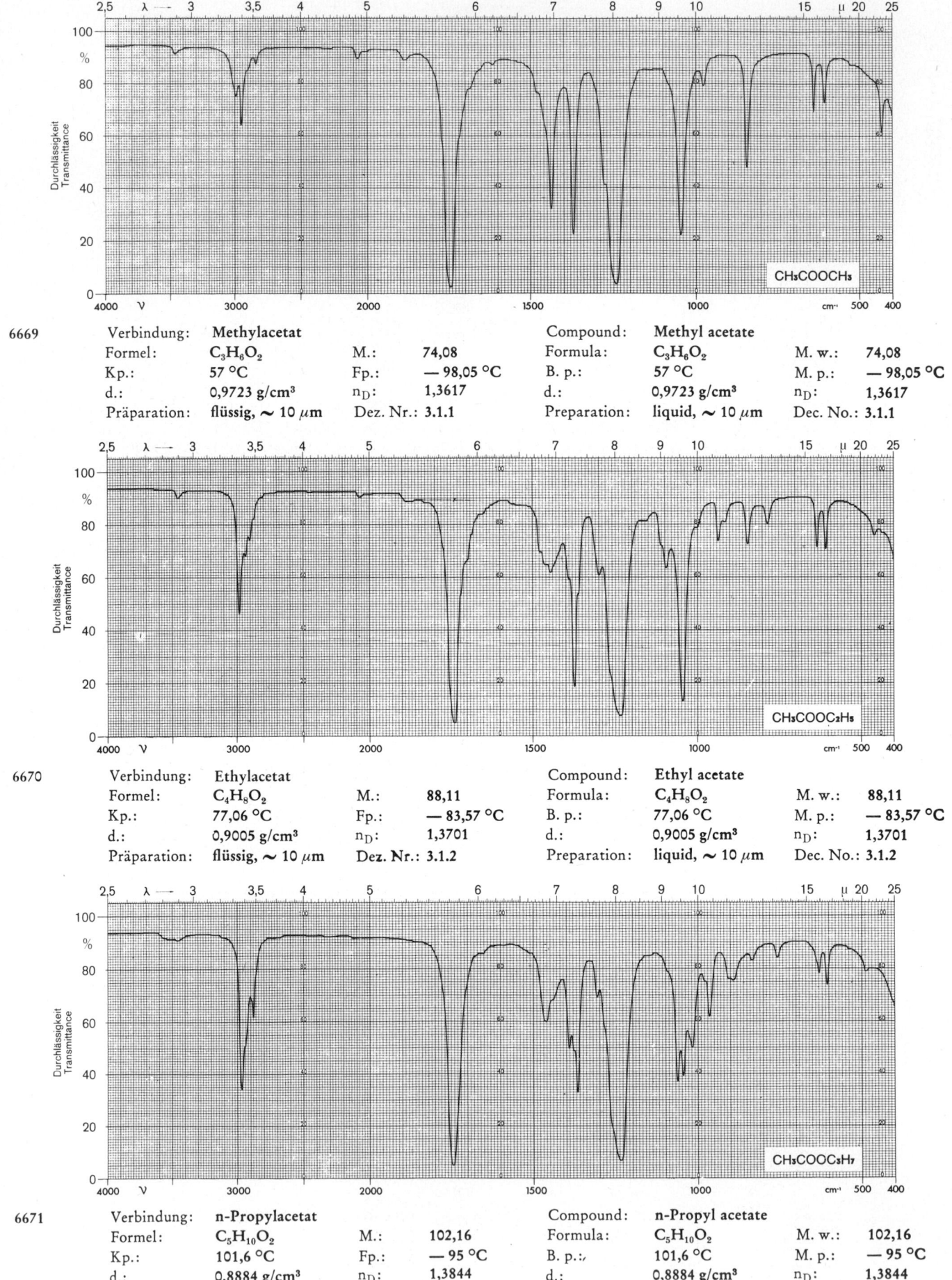

6669

Verbindung:	**Methylacetat**			Compound:	**Methyl acetate**	
Formel:	$C_3H_6O_2$	M.:	**74,08**	Formula:	$C_3H_6O_2$	M. w.: **74,08**
Kp.:	57 °C	Fp.:	**— 98,05 °C**	B. p.:	57 °C	M. p.: **— 98,05 °C**
d.:	0,9723 g/cm³	n_D:	**1,3617**	d.:	0,9723 g/cm³	n_D: **1,3617**
Präparation:	flüssig, ~ 10 μm	Dez. Nr.:	**3.1.1**	Preparation:	liquid, ~ 10 μm	Dec. No.: **3.1.1**

6670

Verbindung:	**Ethylacetat**			Compound:	**Ethyl acetate**	
Formel:	$C_4H_8O_2$	M.:	**88,11**	Formula:	$C_4H_8O_2$	M. w.: **88,11**
Kp.:	77,06 °C	Fp.:	**— 83,57 °C**	B. p.:	77,06 °C	M. p.: **— 83,57 °C**
d.:	0,9005 g/cm³	n_D:	**1,3701**	d.:	0,9005 g/cm³	n_D: **1,3701**
Präparation:	flüssig, ~ 10 μm	Dez. Nr.:	**3.1.2**	Preparation:	liquid, ~ 10 μm	Dec. No.: **3.1.2**

6671

Verbindung:	**n-Propylacetat**			Compound:	**n-Propyl acetate**	
Formel:	$C_5H_{10}O_2$	M.:	**102,16**	Formula:	$C_5H_{10}O_2$	M. w.: **102,16**
Kp.:	101,6 °C	Fp.:	**— 95 °C**	B. p.:	101,6 °C	M. p.: **— 95 °C**
d.:	0,8884 g/cm³	n_D:	**1,3844**	d.:	0,8884 g/cm³	n_D: **1,3844**
Präparation:	flüssig, ~ 10 μm	Dez. Nr.:	**3.1.3**	Preparation:	liquid, ~ 10 μm	Dec. No.: **3.1.3**

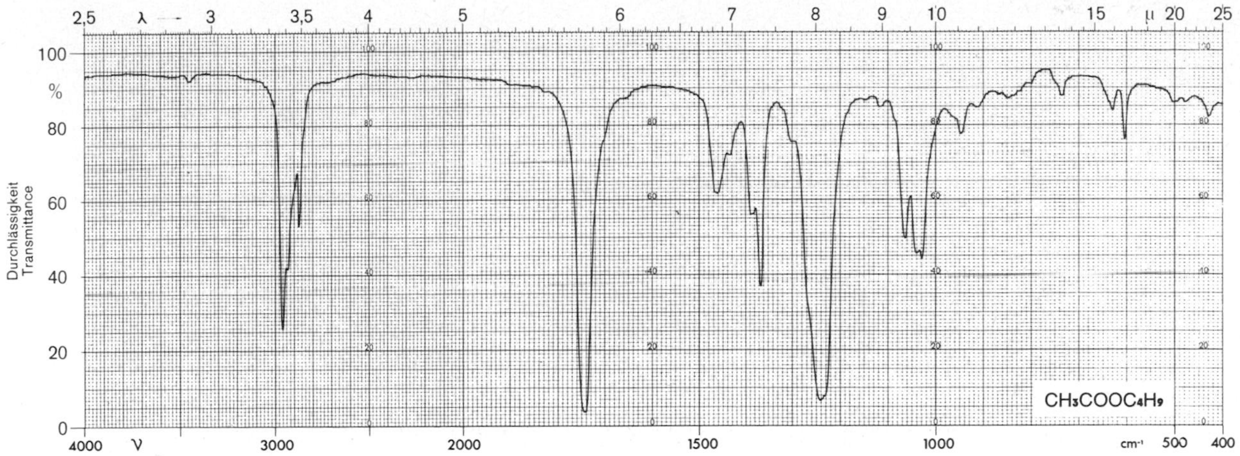

Lösungsmittel
3. Ester
3.1. Einfache Ester

Solvents
3. Esters
3.1. Simple esters

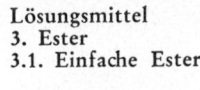

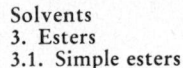

Verbindung:	**n-Butylacetat**			Compound:	**n-Butyl acetate**			6672
Formel:	$C_6H_{12}O_2$	M.:	**116,16**	Formula:	$C_6H_{12}O_2$	M. w.:	**116,16**	
Kp.:	**126,5 °C**	Fp.:	**— 77,9 °C**	B. p.:	**126,5 °C**	M. p.:	**— 77,9 °C**	
d.:	**0,8824 g/cm³**	n_D:	**1,39614**	d.:	**0,8824 g/cm³**	n_D:	**1,39614**	
Präparation:	**flüssig, ~ 10 μm**	Dez. Nr.:	**3.1.4**	Preparation:	**liquid, ~ 10 μm**	Dec. No.:	**3.1.4**	

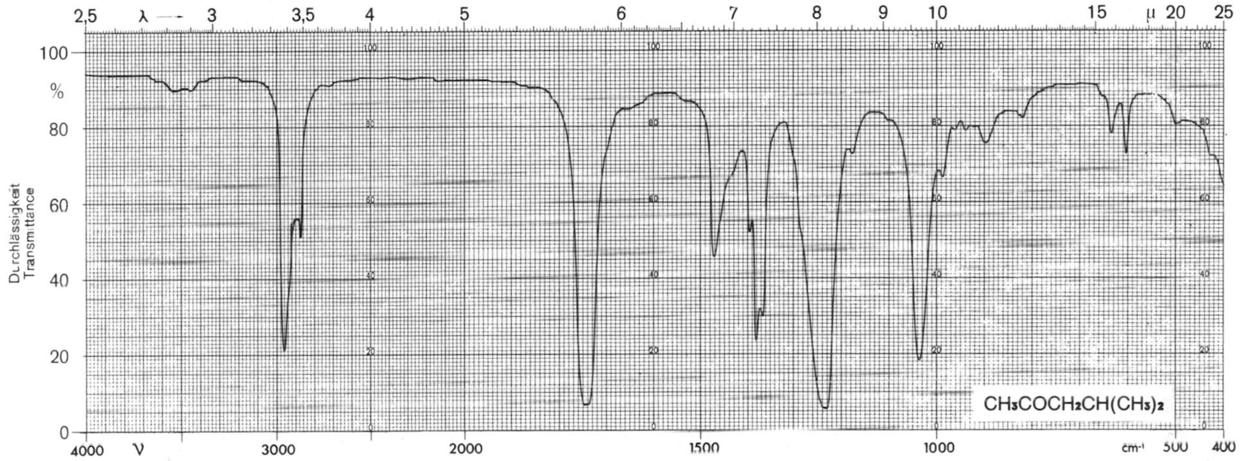

Verbindung:	**iso-Butylacetat**			Compound:	**iso-Butyl acetate**			6673
Formel:	$C_6H_{12}O_2$	M.:	**116,16**	Formula:	$C_6H_{12}O_2$	M. w.:	**116,16**	
Kp.:	**117,2 °C**	Fp.:	**— 98,85 °C**	B. p.:	**117,2 °C**	M. p.:	**— 98,85 °C**	
d.:	**0,8747 g/cm³**	n_D:	**1,3901**	d.:	**0,8747 g/cm³**	n_D:	**1,3901**	
Präparation:	**flüssig, ~ 10 μm**	Dez. Nr.:	**3.1.5**	Preparation:	**liquid, ~ 10 μm**	Dec. No.:	**3.1.5**	

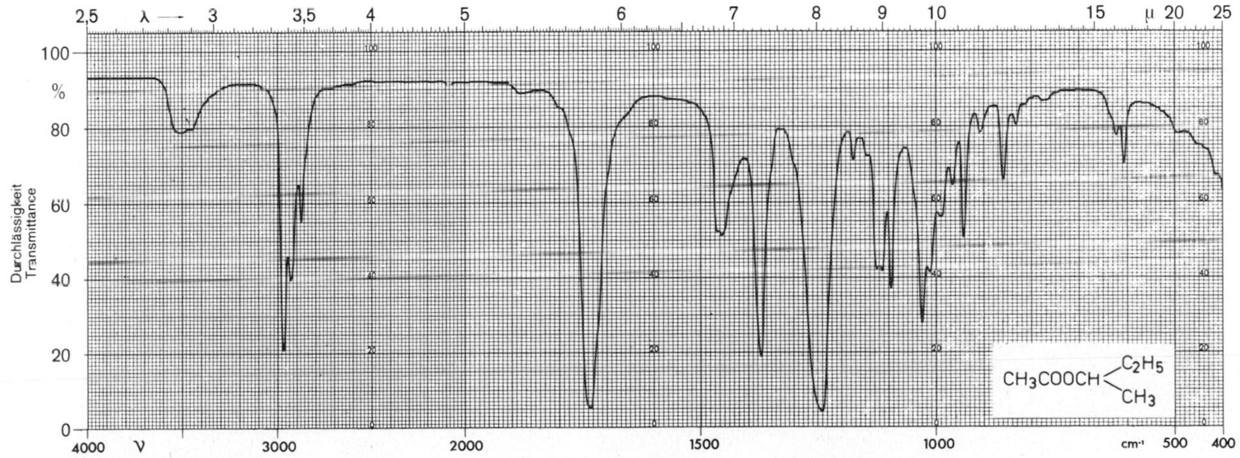

Verbindung:	**sec. Butylacetat**			Compound:	**sec. Butyl acetate**			6674
Formel:	$C_6H_{12}O_2$	M.:	**116,16**	Formula:	$C_6H_{12}O_2$	M. w.:	**116,16**	
Kp.:	**112,4 °C**	Fp.:			B. p.:	**112,4 °C**	M. p.:		
d.:	**0,864 g/cm³**	n_D:	**1,3887**	d.:	**0,864 g/cm³**	n_D:	**1,3887**	
Präparation:	**flüssig, ~ 10 μm**	Dez. Nr.:	**3.1.6**	Preparation:	**liquid, ~ 10 μm**	Dec. No.:	**3.1.6**	

Lösungsmittel
3. Ester
3.1. Einfache Ester

Solvents
3. Esters
3.1. Simple esters

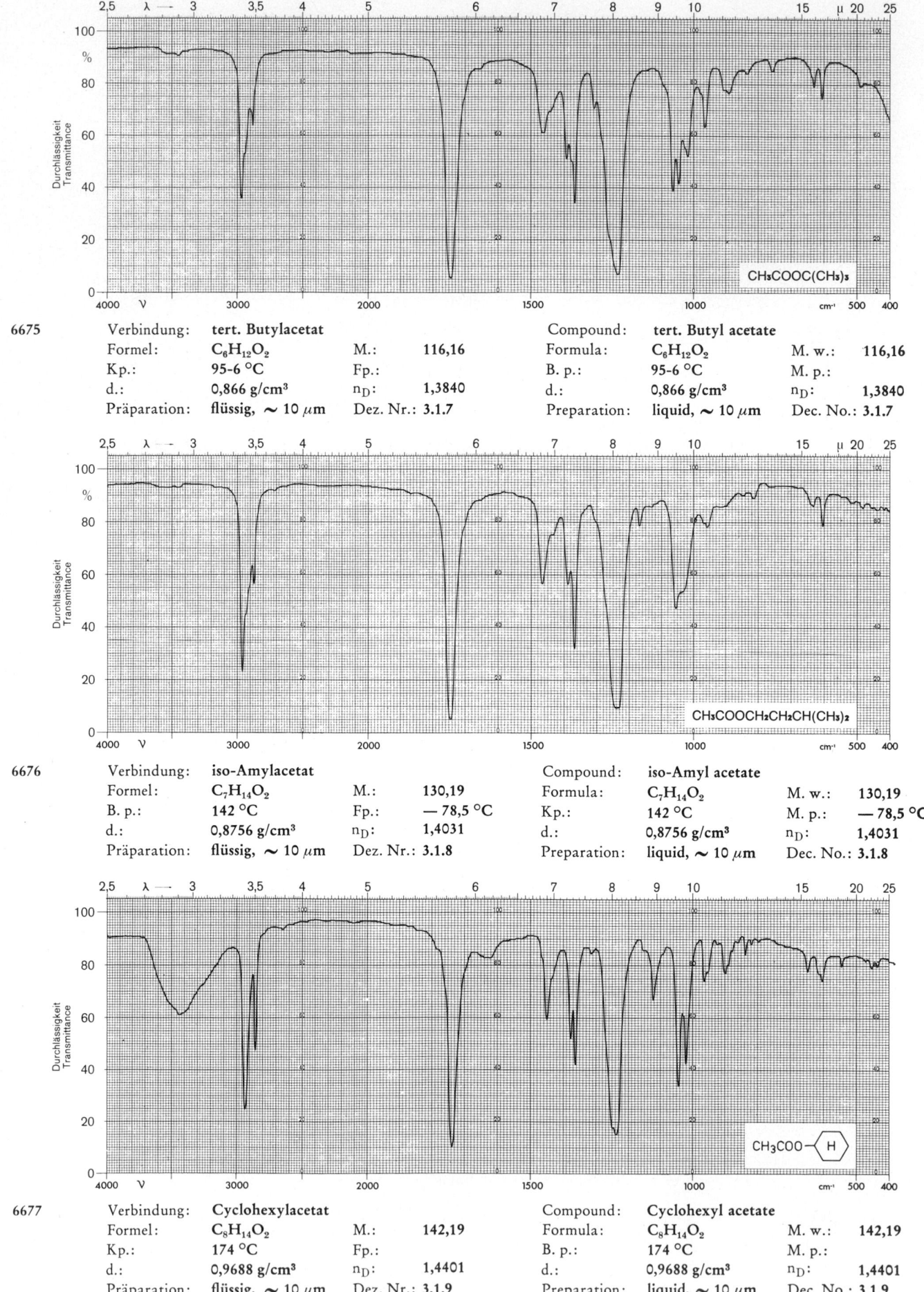

CH₃COOC(CH₃)₃

6675

	Verbindung:	**tert. Butylacetat**			Compound:	**tert. Butyl acetate**		
	Formel:	$C_6H_{12}O_2$	M.:	**116,16**	Formula:	$C_6H_{12}O_2$	M. w.:	**116,16**
	Kp.:	**95-6 °C**	Fp.:		B. p.:	**95-6 °C**	M. p.:	
	d.:	**0,866 g/cm³**	n_D:	**1,3840**	d.:	**0,866 g/cm³**	n_D:	**1,3840**
	Präparation:	**flüssig, ~ 10 μm**	Dez. Nr.:	**3.1.7**	Preparation:	**liquid, ~ 10 μm**	Dec. No.:	**3.1.7**

CH₃COOCH₂CH₂CH(CH₃)₂

6676

	Verbindung:	**iso-Amylacetat**			Compound:	**iso-Amyl acetate**		
	Formel:	$C_7H_{14}O_2$	M.:	**130,19**	Formula:	$C_7H_{14}O_2$	M. w.:	**130,19**
	B. p.:	**142 °C**	Fp.:	**— 78,5 °C**	Kp.:	**142 °C**	M. p.:	**— 78,5 °C**
	d.:	**0,8756 g/cm³**	n_D:	**1,4031**	d.:	**0,8756 g/cm³**	n_D:	**1,4031**
	Präparation:	**flüssig, ~ 10 μm**	Dez. Nr.:	**3.1.8**	Preparation:	**liquid, ~ 10 μm**	Dec. No.:	**3.1.8**

CH₃COO—⬡—H

6677

	Verbindung:	**Cyclohexylacetat**			Compound:	**Cyclohexyl acetate**		
	Formel:	$C_8H_{14}O_2$	M.:	**142,19**	Formula:	$C_8H_{14}O_2$	M. w.:	**142,19**
	Kp.:	**174 °C**	Fp.:		B. p.:	**174 °C**	M. p.:	
	d.:	**0,9688 g/cm³**	n_D:	**1,4401**	d.:	**0,9688 g/cm³**	n_D:	**1,4401**
	Präparation:	**flüssig, ~ 10 μm**	Dez. Nr.:	**3.1.9**	Preparation:	**liquid, ~ 10 μm**	Dec. No.:	**3.1.9**

Lösungsmittel
3. Ester
3.1. Einfache Ester

Solvents
3. Esters
3.1. Simple esters

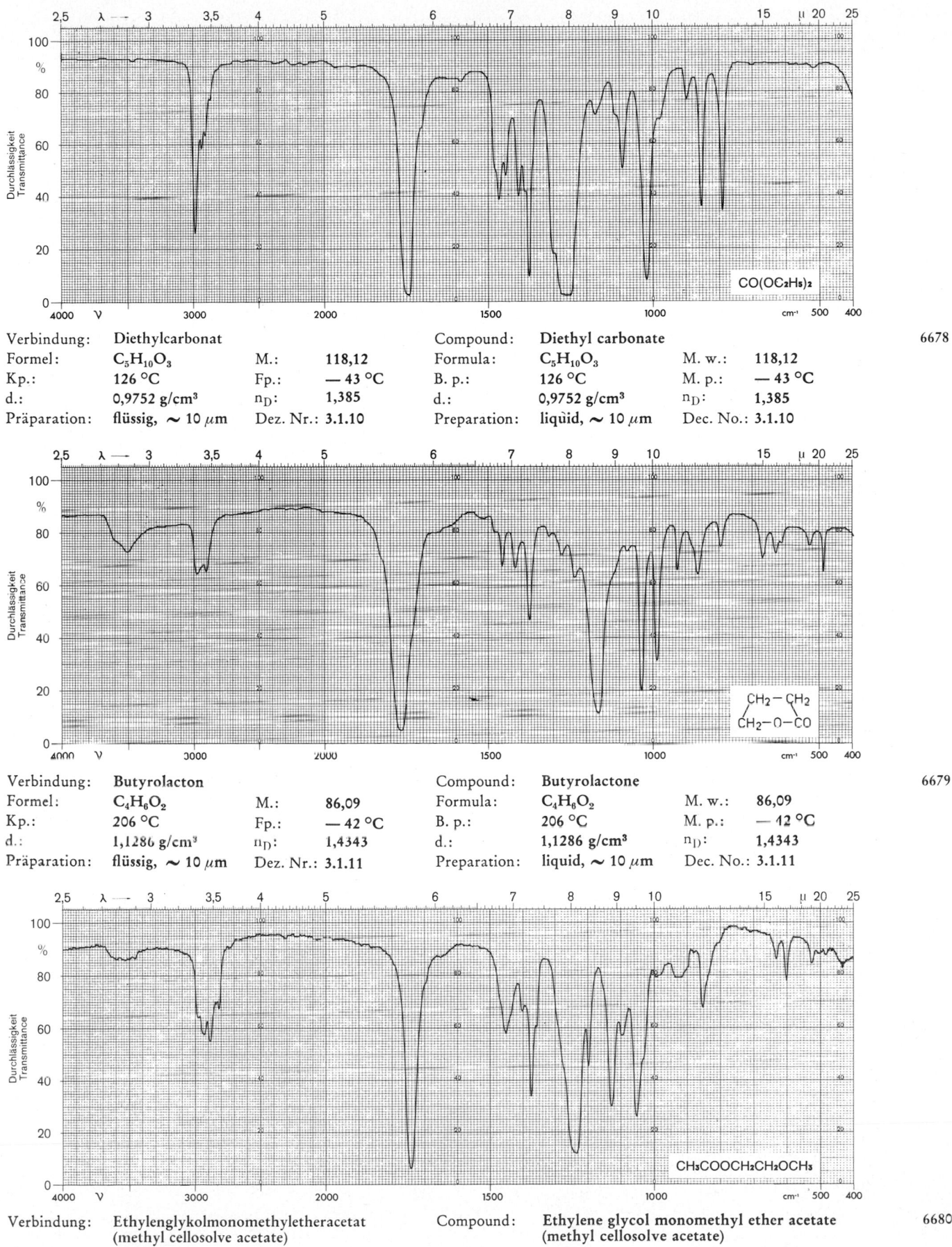

Verbindung:	Diethylcarbonat			Compound:	Diethyl carbonate			6678
Formel:	$C_5H_{10}O_3$	M.:	118,12	Formula:	$C_5H_{10}O_3$	M. w.:	118,12	
Kp.:	126 °C	Fp.:	— 43 °C	B. p.:	126 °C	M. p.:	— 43 °C	
d.:	0,9752 g/cm³	n_D:	1,385	d.:	0,9752 g/cm³	n_D:	1,385	
Präparation:	flüssig, ～ 10 μm	Dez. Nr.:	3.1.10	Preparation:	liquïd, ～ 10 μm	Dec. No.:	3.1.10	

Verbindung:	Butyrolacton			Compound:	Butyrolactone			6679
Formel:	$C_4H_6O_2$	M.:	86,09	Formula:	$C_4H_6O_2$	M. w.:	86,09	
Kp.:	206 °C	Fp.:	— 42 °C	B. p.:	206 °C	M. p.:	— 42 °C	
d.:	1,1286 g/cm³	n_D:	1,4343	d.:	1,1286 g/cm³	n_D:	1,4343	
Präparation:	flüssig, ～ 10 μm	Dez. Nr.:	3.1.11	Preparation:	liquid, ～ 10 μm	Dec. No.:	3.1.11	

Verbindung:	Ethylenglykolmonomethyletheracetat (methyl cellosolve acetate)			Compound:	Ethylene glycol monomethyl ether acetate (methyl cellosolve acetate)			6680
Formel:	$C_5H_{10}O_3$	M.:	118,36	Formula:	$C_5H_{10}O_3$	M. w.:	118,36	
Kp.:	144,5 °C	Fp.:	— 70 °C	B. p.:	144,5 °C	M. p.:	— 70 °C	
d.:	1,007 g/cm³	n_D:		d.:	1,007 g/cm³	n_D:		
Präparation:	flüssig, ～ 10 μm	Dez. Nr.:	3.2.1	Preparation:	liquid, ～ 10 μm	Dec. No.:	3.2.1	

Lösungsmittel
3. Ester
3.2. Etherester

Solvents
3. Esters
3.2. Ether esters

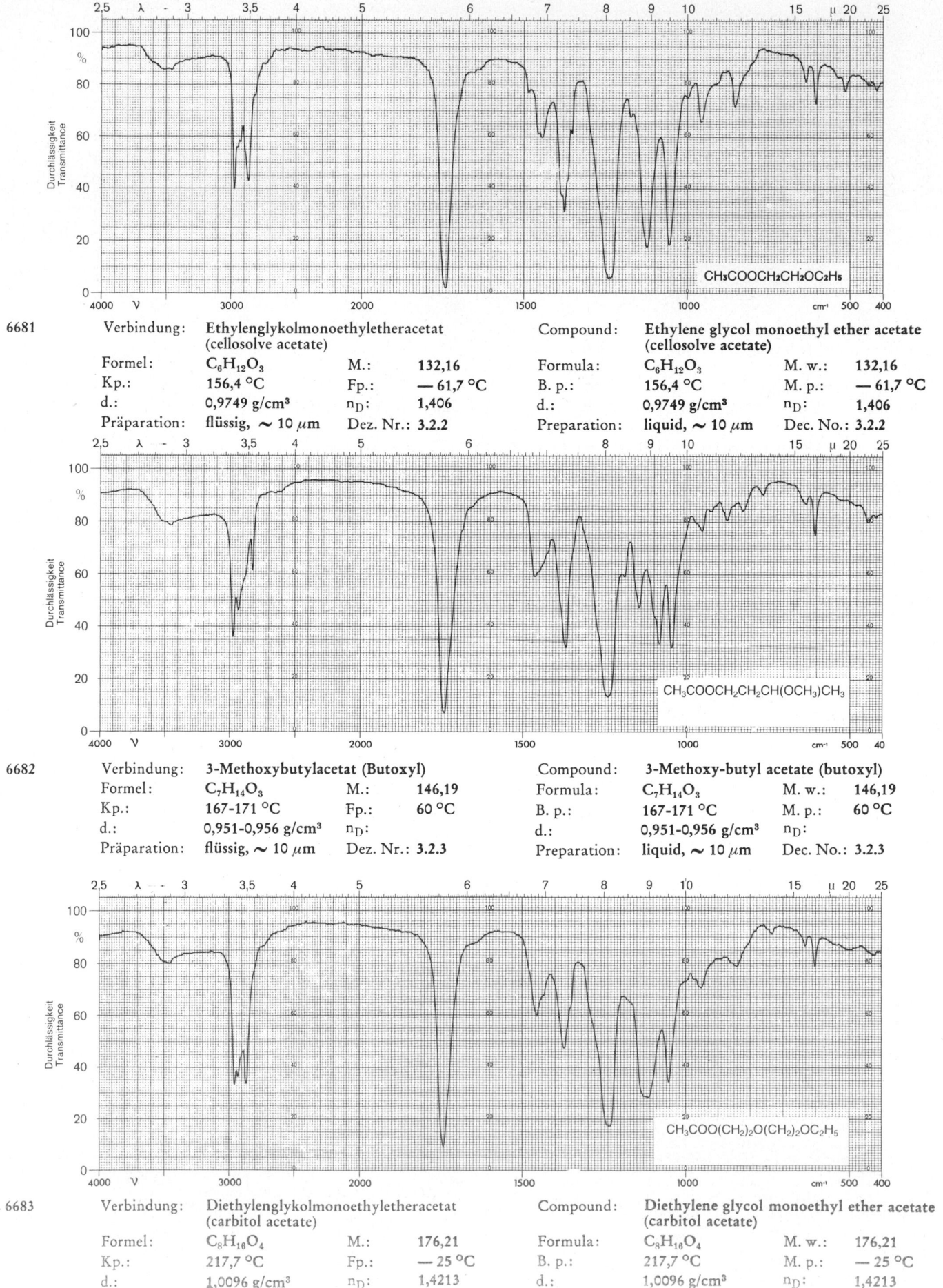

CH₃COOCH₂CH₂OC₂H₅

6681   Verbindung: **Ethylenglykolmonoethyletheracetat (cellosolve acetate)**   Compound: **Ethylene glycol monoethyl ether acetate (cellosolve acetate)**

Formel:	C₆H₁₂O₃	M.:	132,16	Formula:	C₆H₁₂O₃	M. w.:	132,16
Kp.:	156,4 °C	Fp.:	— 61,7 °C	B. p.:	156,4 °C	M. p.:	— 61,7 °C
d.:	0,9749 g/cm³	n_D:	1,406	d.:	0,9749 g/cm³	n_D:	1,406
Präparation:	flüssig, ~ 10 μm	Dez. Nr.:	3.2.2	Preparation:	liquid, ~ 10 μm	Dec. No.:	3.2.2

CH₃COOCH₂CH₂CH(OCH₃)CH₃

6682   Verbindung: **3-Methoxybutylacetat (Butoxyl)**   Compound: **3-Methoxy-butyl acetate (butoxyl)**

Formel:	C₇H₁₄O₃	M.:	146,19	Formula:	C₇H₁₄O₃	M. w.:	146,19
Kp.:	167-171 °C	Fp.:	60 °C	B. p.:	167-171 °C	M. p.:	60 °C
d.:	0,951-0,956 g/cm³	n_D:		d.:	0,951-0,956 g/cm³	n_D:	
Präparation:	flüssig, ~ 10 μm	Dez. Nr.:	3.2.3	Preparation:	liquid, ~ 10 μm	Dec. No.:	3.2.3

CH₃COO(CH₂)₂O(CH₂)₂OC₂H₅

6683   Verbindung: **Diethylenglykolmonoethyletheracetat (carbitol acetate)**   Compound: **Diethylene glycol monoethyl ether acetate (carbitol acetate)**

Formel:	C₈H₁₆O₄	M.:	176,21	Formula:	C₈H₁₆O₄	M. w.:	176,21
Kp.:	217,7 °C	Fp.:	— 25 °C	B. p.:	217,7 °C	M. p.:	— 25 °C
d.:	1,0096 g/cm³	n_D:	1,4213	d.:	1,0096 g/cm³	n_D:	1,4213
Präparation:	flüssig, ~ 10 μm	Dez. Nr.:	3.2.4	Preparation:	liquid, ~ 10 μm	Dec. No.:	3.2.4

Lösungsmittel
4. Ketone
4.1. Einfache Ketone

Solvents
4. Ketones
4.1. Simple ketones

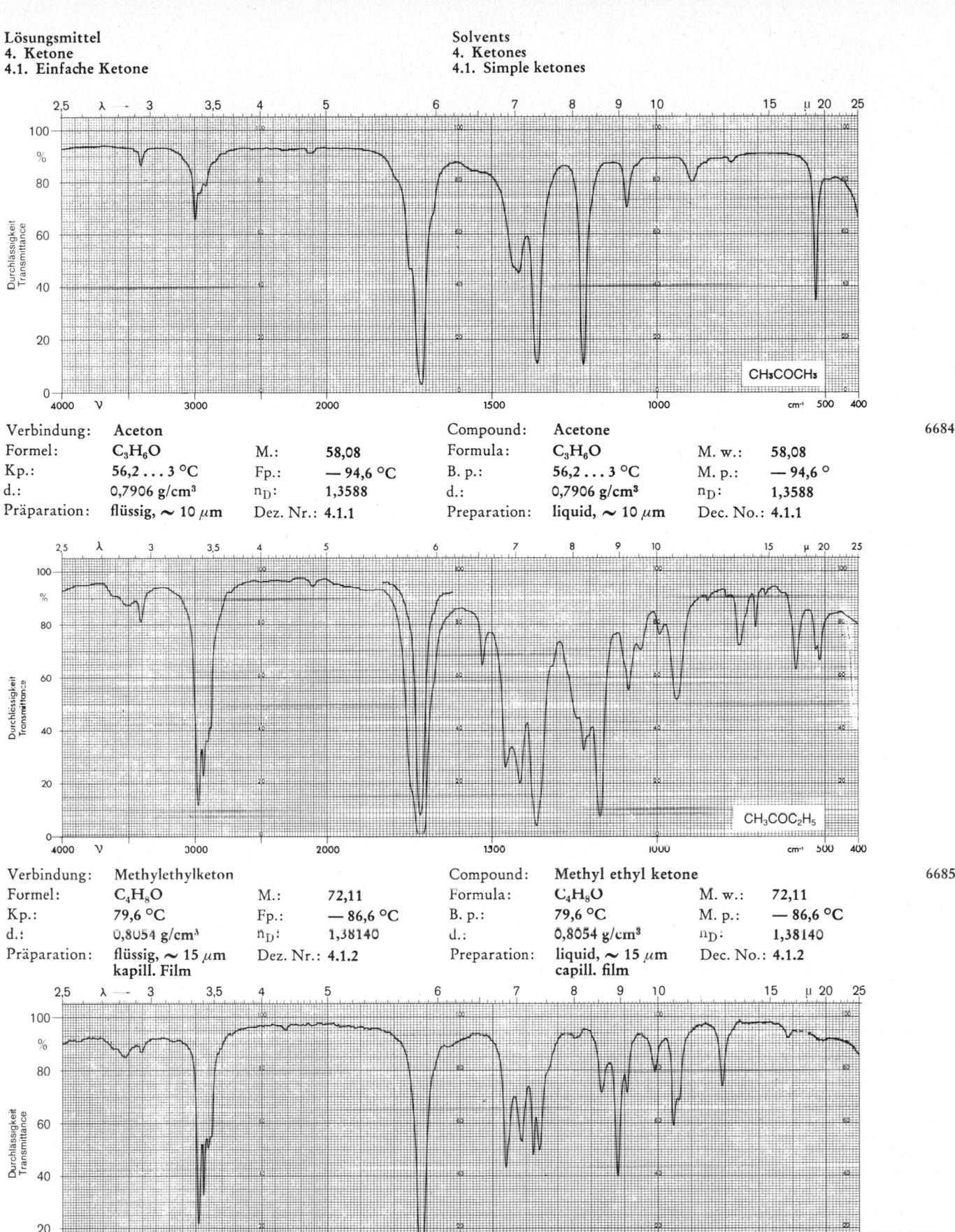

Verbindung:	Aceton			Compound:	Acetone			6684
Formel:	C_3H_6O	M.:	58,08	Formula:	C_3H_6O	M. w.:	58,08	
Kp.:	56,2 ... 3 °C	Fp.:	— 94,6 °C	B. p.:	56,2 ... 3 °C	M. p.:	— 94,6 °	
d.:	0,7906 g/cm³	n_D:	1,3588	d.:	0,7906 g/cm³	n_D:	1,3588	
Präparation:	flüssig, ~ 10 μm	Dez. Nr.:	4.1.1	Preparation:	liquid, ~ 10 μm	Dec. No.:	4.1.1	

Verbindung:	Methylethylketon			Compound:	Methyl ethyl ketone			6685
Formel:	C_4H_8O	M.:	72,11	Formula:	C_4H_8O	M. w.:	72,11	
Kp.:	79,6 °C	Fp.:	— 86,6 °C	B. p.:	79,6 °C	M. p.:	— 86,6 °C	
d.:	0,8054 g/cm³	n_D:	1,38140	d.:	0,8054 g/cm³	n_D:	1,38140	
Präparation:	flüssig, ~ 15 μm kapill. Film	Dez. Nr.:	4.1.2	Preparation:	liquid, ~ 15 μm capill. film	Dec. No.:	4.1.2	

Verbindung:	Diethylketon			Compound:	Diethyl ketone			6686
Formel:	$C_5H_{10}O$	M.:	86,13	Formula:	$C_5H_{10}O$	M. w.:	86,13	
Kp.:	101,7 °C	Fp.:	— 41,5 °C	B. p.:	101,7 °C	M. p.:	— 41,5 °C	
d:	0,8156 g/cm³	n_D:	1,39385	d:	0,8156 g/cm³	n_D:	1,39385	
Präparation:	flüssig, ~ 10 μm	Dez. Nr.:	4.1.3	Preparation:	liquid, ~ 10 μm	Dec. No.:	4.1.3	

Lösungsmittel
4. Ketone
4.1. Einfache Ketone

Solvents
4. Ketones
4.1. Simple ketones

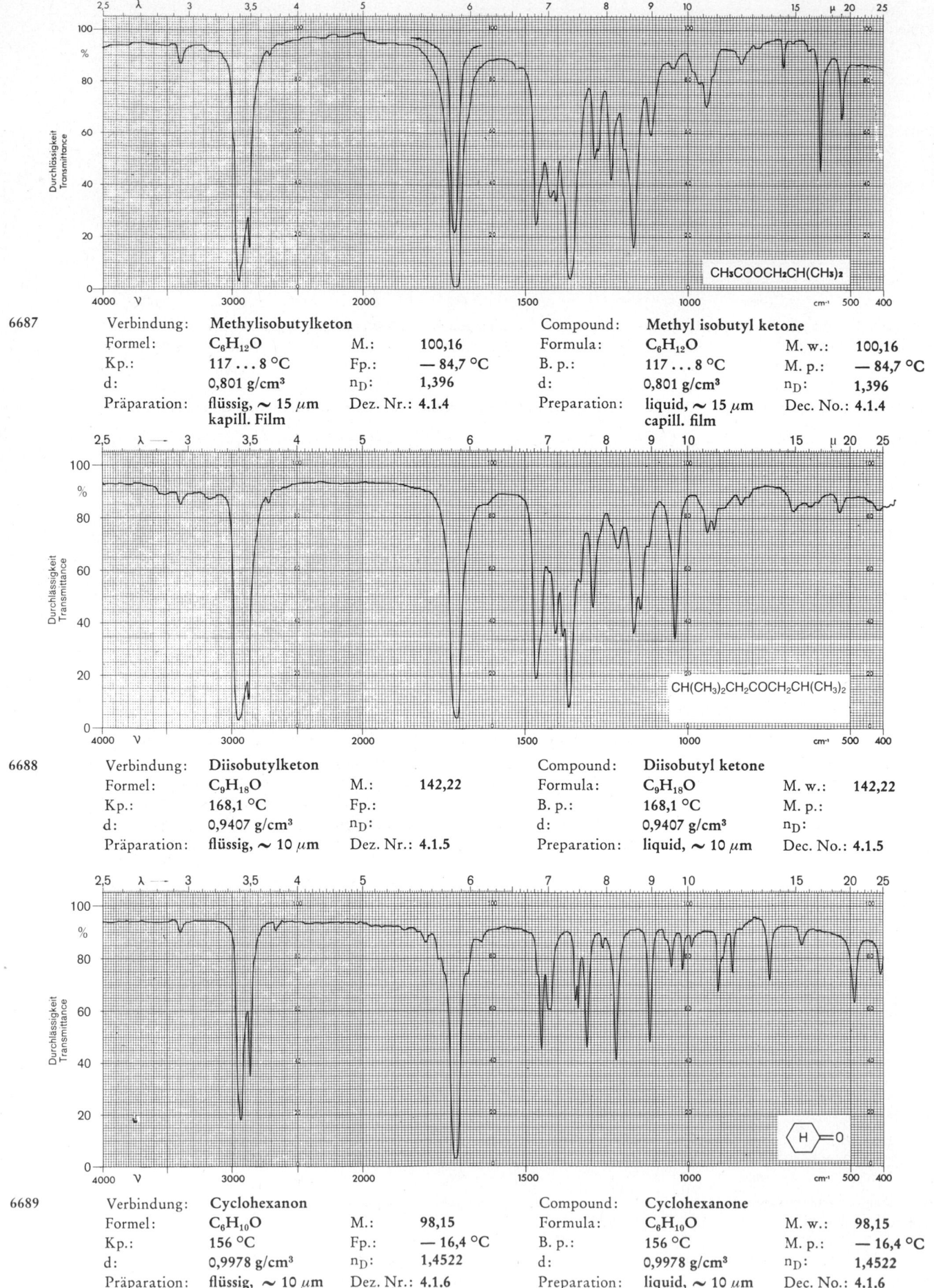

CH₃COOCH₂CH(CH₃)₂

6687	Verbindung:	**Methylisobutylketon**			Compound:	**Methyl isobutyl ketone**		
	Formel:	$C_6H_{12}O$	M.:	**100,16**	Formula:	$C_6H_{12}O$	M. w.:	**100,16**
	Kp.:	**117 ... 8 °C**	Fp.:	**— 84,7 °C**	B. p.:	**117 ... 8 °C**	M. p.:	**— 84,7 °C**
	d:	**0,801 g/cm³**	nD:	**1,396**	d:	**0,801 g/cm³**	nD:	**1,396**
	Präparation:	**flüssig, ~ 15 μm kapill. Film**	Dez. Nr.:	**4.1.4**	Preparation:	**liquid, ~ 15 μm capill. film**	Dec. No.:	**4.1.4**

CH(CH₃)₂CH₂COCH₂CH(CH₃)₂

6688	Verbindung:	**Diisobutylketon**			Compound:	**Diisobutyl ketone**		
	Formel:	$C_9H_{18}O$	M.:	**142,22**	Formula:	$C_9H_{18}O$	M. w.:	**142,22**
	Kp.:	**168,1 °C**	Fp.:		B. p.:	**168,1 °C**	M. p.:	
	d:	**0,9407 g/cm³**	nD:		d:	**0,9407 g/cm³**	nD:	
	Präparation:	**flüssig, ~ 10 μm**	Dez. Nr.:	**4.1.5**	Preparation:	**liquid, ~ 10 μm**	Dec. No.:	**4.1.5**

6689	Verbindung:	**Cyclohexanon**			Compound:	**Cyclohexanone**		
	Formel:	$C_6H_{10}O$	M.:	**98,15**	Formula:	$C_6H_{10}O$	M. w.:	**98,15**
	Kp.:	**156 °C**	Fp.:	**— 16,4 °C**	B. p.:	**156 °C**	M. p.:	**— 16,4 °C**
	d:	**0,9978 g/cm³**	nD:	**1,4522**	d:	**0,9978 g/cm³**	nD:	**1,4522**
	Präparation:	**flüssig, ~ 10 μm**	Dez. Nr.:	**4.1.6**	Preparation:	**liquid, ~ 10 μm**	Dec. No.:	**4.1.6**

Lösungsmittel
4. Ketone
4.1. Einfache Ketone

Solvents
4. Ketones
4.1. Simple ketones

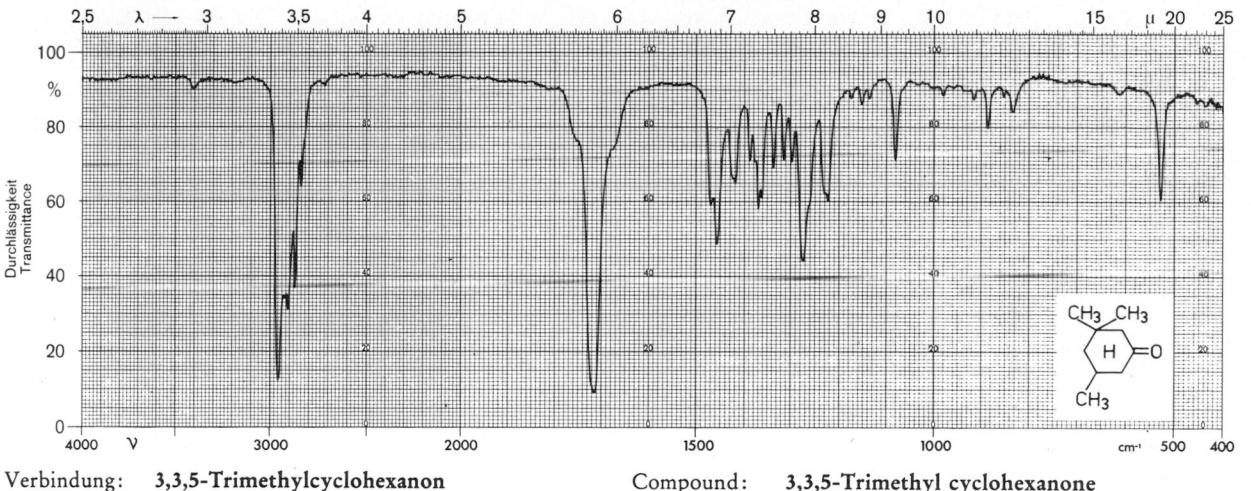

Verbindung:	**3,3,5-Trimethylcyclohexanon**			Compound:	**3,3,5-Trimethyl cyclohexanone**		6690
Formel:	$C_9H_{16}O$	M.:	140,22	Formula:	$C_9H_{16}O$	M. w.: 140,22
Kp.:		Fp.:		B. p.:		M. p.:
d:		n_D:		d:		n_D:
Präparation:	flüssig, $\sim 10\ \mu m$	Dez. Nr.: **4.1.7**		Preparation:	liquid, $\sim 10\ \mu m$	Dec. No.: **4.1.7**

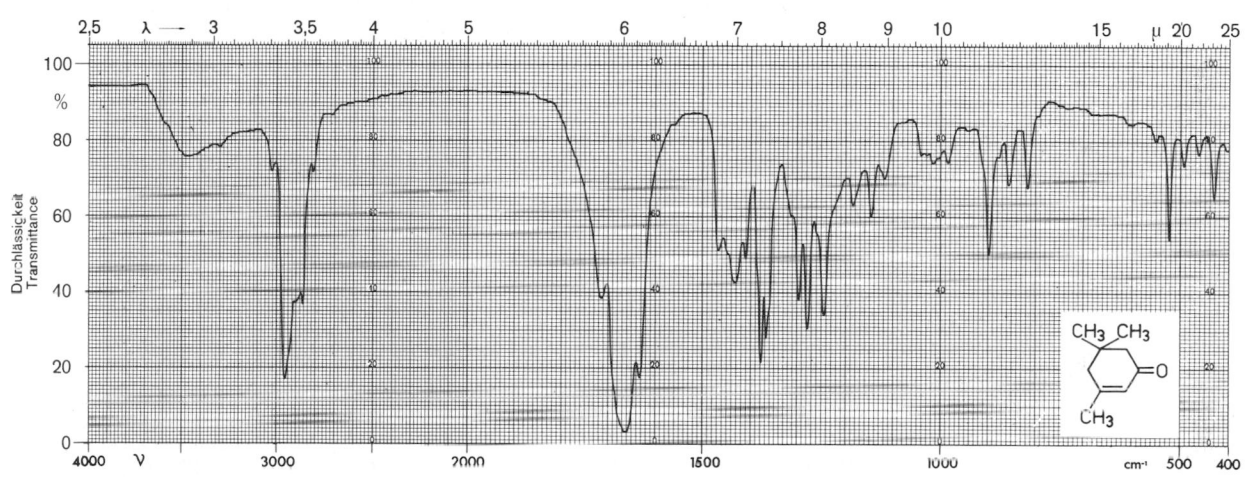

Verbindung:	**Isophoron**			Compound:	**iso-Phorone**		6691
Formel:	$C_9H_{14}O$	M.:	128,19	Formula:	$C_9H_{14}O$	M. w.: 128,19
Kp.:	205-220 °C	Fp.:		B. p.:	205-220 °C	M. p.:
d.:	0,920- 0,925 g/cm³	n_D:	1,4775	d:	0,920-0,925 g/cm³	n_D: 1,4775
Präparation:	flüssig, $\sim 10\ \mu m$	Dez. Nr.: **4.1.8**		Preparation:	liquid, $\sim 10\ \mu m$	Dec. No.: **4.1.8**

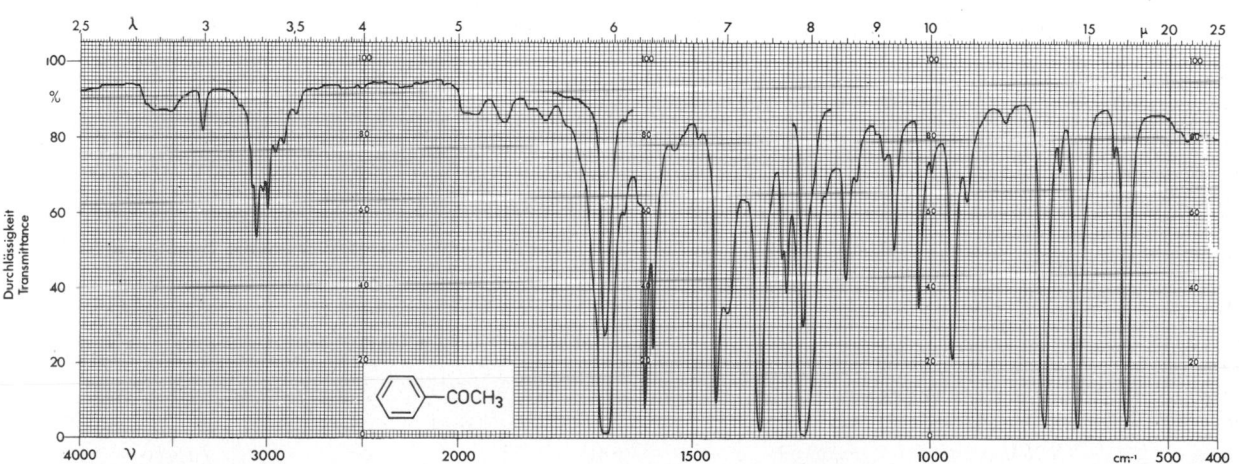

Verbindung:	**Acetophenon**			Compound:	**Acetophenone**		6692
Formel:	C_8H_8O	M.:	120,15	Formula:	C_8H_8O	M. w.: 120,15
Kp.:	202 °C	Fp.:	19,65 °C	B. p.:	202 °C	M. p.: 19,65 °C
d.:	1,0281 g/cm³	n_D:	1,5363	d:	1,0281 g/cm³	n_D: 1,5363
Präparation:	flüssig, $\sim 15\ \mu m$ kapill. Film	Dez. Nr.: **4.1.9**		Preparation:	liquid, $\sim 15\ \mu m$ capill. film	Dec. No.: **4.1.9**

Lösungsmittel
4. Ketone
4.2. Etherketone

Solvents
4. Ketones
4.2. Ether ketones

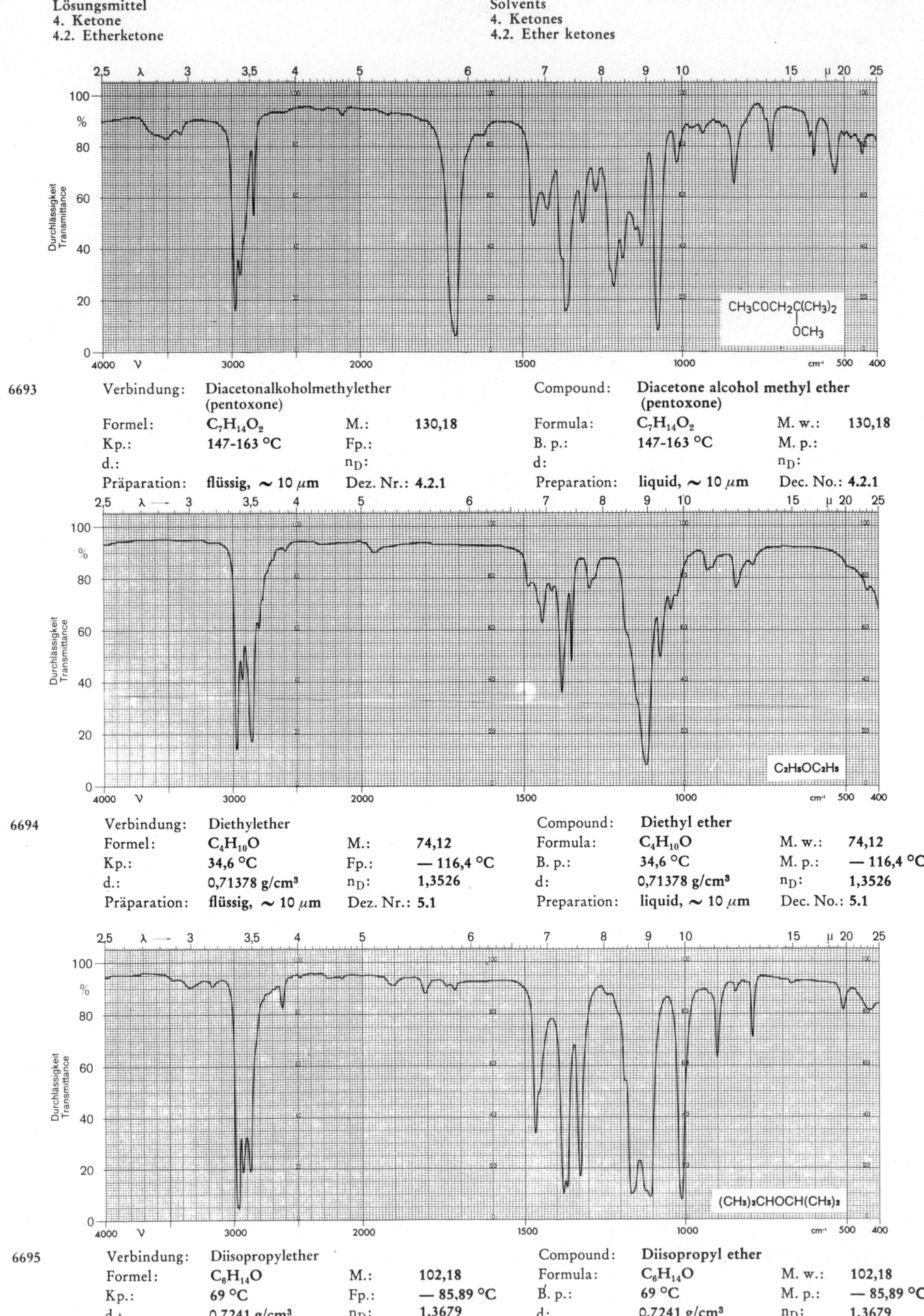

$CH_3COCH_2C(CH_3)_2$
OCH_3

6693

Verbindung:	Diacetonalkoholmethylether (pentoxone)			Compound:	Diacetone alcohol methyl ether (pentoxone)		
Formel:	$C_7H_{14}O_2$	M.:	130,18	Formula:	$C_7H_{14}O_2$	M. w.:	130,18
Kp.:	147-163 °C	Fp.:		B. p.:	147-163 °C	M. p.:	
d.:		n_D:		d:		n_D:	
Präparation:	flüssig, ~ 10 μm	Dez. Nr.:	4.2.1	Preparation:	liquid, ~ 10 μm	Dec. No.:	4.2.1

$C_2H_5OC_2H_5$

6694

Verbindung:	Diethylether			Compound:	Diethyl ether		
Formel:	$C_4H_{10}O$	M.:	74,12	Formula:	$C_4H_{10}O$	M. w.:	74,12
Kp.:	34,6 °C	Fp.:	— 116,4 °C	B. p.:	34,6 °C	M. p.:	— 116,4 °C
d.:	0,71378 g/cm³	n_D:	1,3526	d:	0,71378 g/cm³	n_D:	1,3526
Präparation:	flüssig, ~ 10 μm	Dez. Nr.:	5.1	Preparation:	liquid, ~ 10 μm	Dec. No.:	5.1

$(CH_3)_2CHOCH(CH_3)_2$

6695

Verbindung:	Diisopropylether			Compound:	Diisopropyl ether		
Formel:	$C_6H_{14}O$	M.:	102,18	Formula:	$C_6H_{14}O$	M. w.:	102,18
Kp.:	69 °C	Fp.:	— 85,89 °C	B. p.:	69 °C	M. p.:	— 85,89 °C
d.:	0,7241 g/cm³	n_D:	1,3679	d:	0,7241 g/cm³	n_D:	1,3679
Präparation:	flüssig, ~ 10 μm	Dez. Nr.:	5.2	Preparation:	liquid, ~ 10 μm	Dec. No.:	5.2

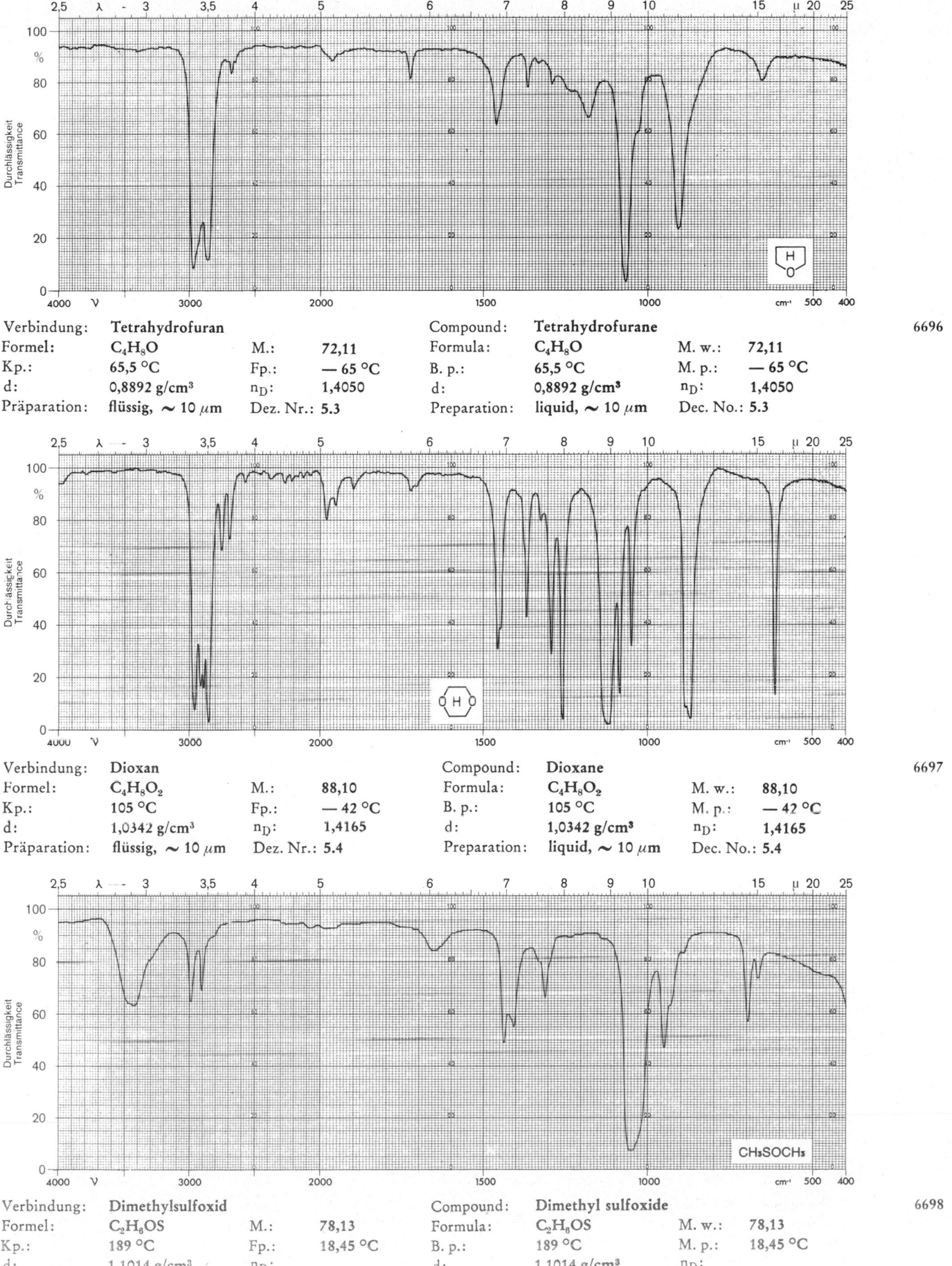

Verbindung:	**Tetrahydrofuran**			Compound:	**Tetrahydrofurane**			6696
Formel:	C_4H_8O	M.:	**72,11**	Formula:	C_4H_8O	M. w.:	**72,11**	
Kp.:	65,5 °C	Fp.:	— 65 °C	B. p.:	65,5 °C	M. p.:	— 65 °C	
d:	0,8892 g/cm³	n_D:	1,4050	d:	0,8892 g/cm³	n_D:	1,4050	
Präparation:	flüssig, ~ 10 μm	Dez. Nr.:	**5.3**	Preparation:	liquid, ~ 10 μm	Dec. No.:	**5.3**	

Verbindung:	**Dioxan**			Compound:	**Dioxane**			6697
Formel:	$C_4H_8O_2$	M.:	**88,10**	Formula:	$C_4H_8O_2$	M. w.:	**88,10**	
Kp.:	105 °C	Fp.:	— 42 °C	B. p.:	105 °C	M. p.:	— 42 °C	
d:	1,0342 g/cm³	n_D:	1,4165	d:	1,0342 g/cm³	n_D:	1,4165	
Präparation:	flüssig, ~ 10 μm	Dez. Nr.:	**5.4**	Preparation:	liquid, ~ 10 μm	Dec. No.:	**5.4**	

Verbindung:	**Dimethylsulfoxid**			Compound:	**Dimethyl sulfoxide**			6698
Formel:	C_2H_6OS	M.:	**78,13**	Formula:	C_2H_6OS	M. w.:	**78,13**	
Kp.:	189 °C	Fp.:	18,45 °C	B. p.:	189 °C	M. p.:	18,45 °C	
d:	1,1014 g/cm³	n_D:		d:	1,1014 g/cm³	n_D:		
Präparation:	flüssig, ~ 10 μm	Dez. Nr.:	6.1.1	Preparation:	liquid, ~ 10 μm	Dec. No.:	6.1.1	

Lösungsmittel
6. S- und N-haltige Lösungsmittel
6.1. Schwefelhaltige Lösungsmittel

Solvents
6. Solvents containing S and N
6.1. Solvents containing S

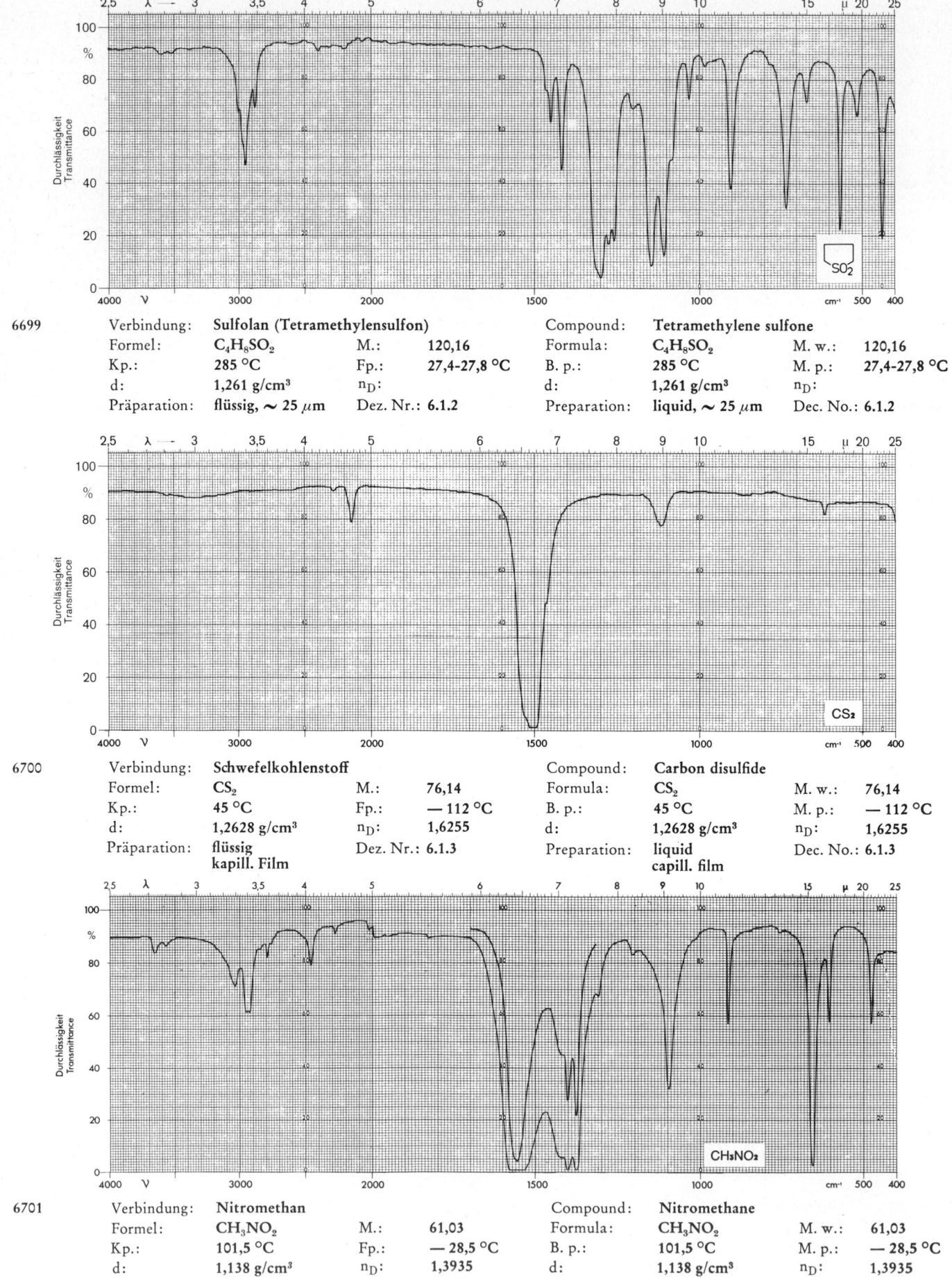

6699   Verbindung: **Sulfolan (Tetramethylensulfon)**   Compound: **Tetramethylene sulfone**

Formel:	$C_4H_8SO_2$	M.:	**120,16**	Formula:	$C_4H_8SO_2$	M. w.:	**120,16**
Kp.:	**285 °C**	Fp.:	**27,4-27,8 °C**	B. p.:	**285 °C**	M. p.:	**27,4-27,8 °C**
d:	**1,261 g/cm³**	n_D:		d:	**1,261 g/cm³**	n_D:	
Präparation:	**flüssig, ~ 25 μm**	Dez. Nr.:	**6.1.2**	Preparation:	**liquid, ~ 25 μm**	Dec. No.:	**6.1.2**

6700   Verbindung: **Schwefelkohlenstoff**   Compound: **Carbon disulfide**

Formel:	CS_2	M.:	**76,14**	Formula:	CS_2	M. w.:	**76,14**
Kp.:	**45 °C**	Fp.:	**— 112 °C**	B. p.:	**45 °C**	M. p.:	**— 112 °C**
d:	**1,2628 g/cm³**	n_D:	**1,6255**	d:	**1,2628 g/cm³**	n_D:	**1,6255**
Präparation:	**flüssig kapill. Film**	Dez. Nr.:	**6.1.3**	Preparation:	**liquid capill. film**	Dec. No.:	**6.1.3**

6701   Verbindung: **Nitromethan**   Compound: **Nitromethane**

Formel:	CH_3NO_2	M.:	**61,03**	Formula:	CH_3NO_2	M. w.:	**61,03**
Kp.:	**101,5 °C**	Fp.:	**— 28,5 °C**	B. p.:	**101,5 °C**	M. p.:	**— 28,5 °C**
d:	**1,138 g/cm³**	n_D:	**1,3935**	d:	**1,138 g/cm³**	n_D:	**1,3935**
Präparation:	**flüssig, ~ 15 μm**	Dez. Nr.:	**6.2.1**	Preparation:	**liquid, ~ 15 μm**	Dec. No.:	**6.2.1**

Lösungsmittel
6. S- und N-haltige Lösungsmittel
6.2. Stickstoffhaltige Lösungsmittel

Solvents
6. Solvents containing S and N
6.2. Solvents containing N

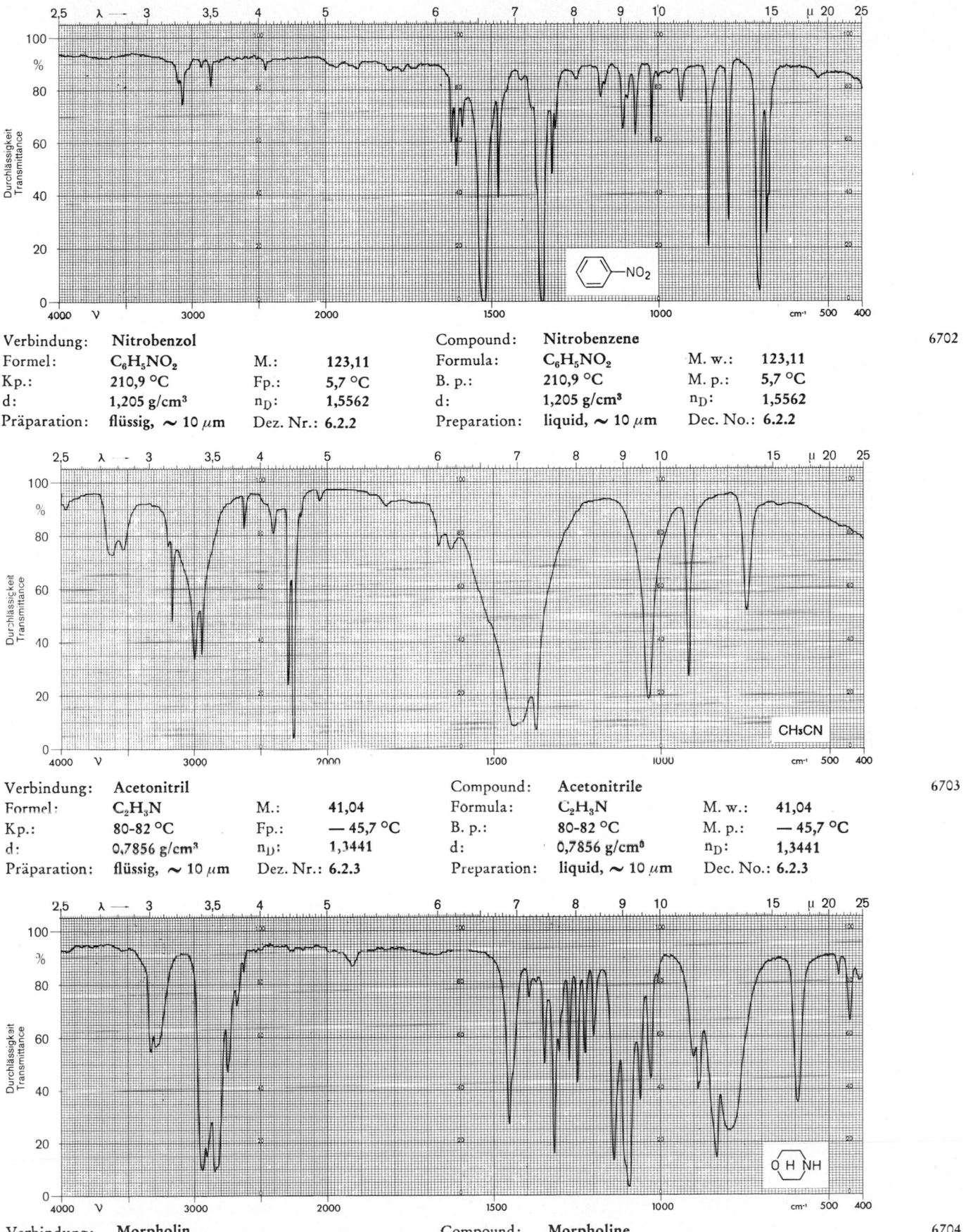

Verbindung:	**Nitrobenzol**			Compound:	**Nitrobenzene**			6702
Formel:	$C_6H_5NO_2$	M.:	**123,11**	Formula:	$C_6H_5NO_2$	M. w.:	**123,11**	
Kp.:	210,9 °C	Fp.:	5,7 °C	B. p.:	210,9 °C	M. p.:	5,7 °C	
d:	1,205 g/cm³	n_D:	1,5562	d:	1,205 g/cm³	n_D:	1,5562	
Präparation:	flüssig, ~ 10 µm	Dez. Nr.:	**6.2.2**	Preparation:	liquid, ~ 10 µm	Dec. No.:	**6.2.2**	

Verbindung:	**Acetonitril**			Compound:	**Acetonitrile**			6703
Formel:	C_2H_3N	M.:	**41,04**	Formula:	C_2H_3N	M. w.:	**41,04**	
Kp.:	80-82 °C	Fp.:	— 45,7 °C	B. p.:	80-82 °C	M. p.:	— 45,7 °C	
d:	0,7856 g/cm³	n_D:	1,3441	d:	0,7856 g/cm⁰	n_D:	1,3441	
Präparation:	flüssig, ~ 10 µm	Dez. Nr.:	**6.2.3**	Preparation:	liquid, ~ 10 µm	Dec. No.:	**6.2.3**	

Verbindung:	**Morpholin**			Compound:	**Morpholine**			6704
Formel:	C_4H_9ON	M.:	**87,10**	Formula:	C_4H_9ON	M. w.:	**87,10**	
Kp.:	125-132 °C	Fp.:		B. p.:	125-132 °C	M. p.:		
d:	0,999- 1,004 g/cm³	n_D:		d:	0,999-1,004 g/cm³	n_D:		
Präparation:	flüssig, ~ 10 µm	Dez. Nr.:	**6.2.4**	Preparation:	liquid, ~ 10 µm	Dec. No.:	**6.2.4**	

Lösungsmittel
6. S- und N-haltige Lösungsmittel
6.2. Stickstoffhaltige Lösungsmittel

Solvents
6. Solvents containing S and N
6.2. Solvents containing N

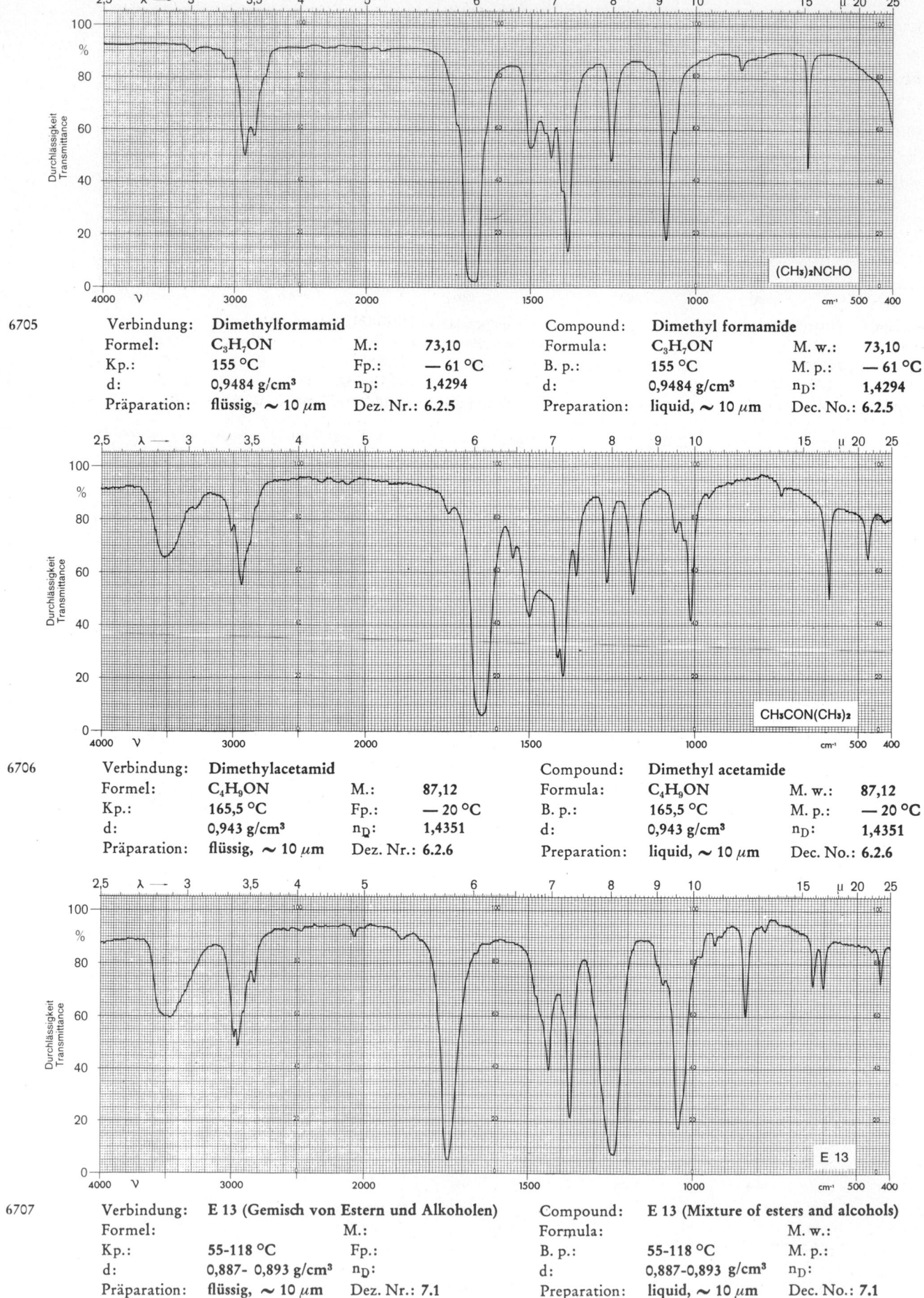

6705

Verbindung:	Dimethylformamid			Compound:	Dimethyl formamide		
Formel:	C_3H_7ON	M.:	73,10	Formula:	C_3H_7ON	M. w.:	73,10
Kp.:	155 °C	Fp.:	− 61 °C	B. p.:	155 °C	M. p.:	− 61 °C
d:	0,9484 g/cm³	n_D:	1,4294	d:	0,9484 g/cm³	n_D:	1,4294
Präparation:	flüssig, ~ 10 μm	Dez. Nr.:	6.2.5	Preparation:	liquid, ~ 10 μm	Dec. No.:	6.2.5

6706

Verbindung:	Dimethylacetamid			Compound:	Dimethyl acetamide		
Formel:	C_4H_9ON	M.:	87,12	Formula:	C_4H_9ON	M. w.:	87,12
Kp.:	165,5 °C	Fp.:	− 20 °C	B. p.:	165,5 °C	M. p.:	− 20 °C
d:	0,943 g/cm³	n_D:	1,4351	d:	0,943 g/cm³	n_D:	1,4351
Präparation:	flüssig, ~ 10 μm	Dez. Nr.:	6.2.6	Preparation:	liquid, ~ 10 μm	Dec. No.:	6.2.6

6707

Verbindung:	E 13 (Gemisch von Estern und Alkoholen)			Compound:	E 13 (Mixture of esters and alcohols)		
Formel:		M.:		Formula:		M. w.:	
Kp.:	55-118 °C	Fp.:		B. p.:	55-118 °C	M. p.:	
d:	0,887- 0,893 g/cm³	n_D:		d:	0,887-0,893 g/cm³	n_D:	
Präparation:	flüssig, ~ 10 μm	Dez. Nr.:	7.1	Preparation:	liquid, ~ 10 μm	Dec. No.:	7.1

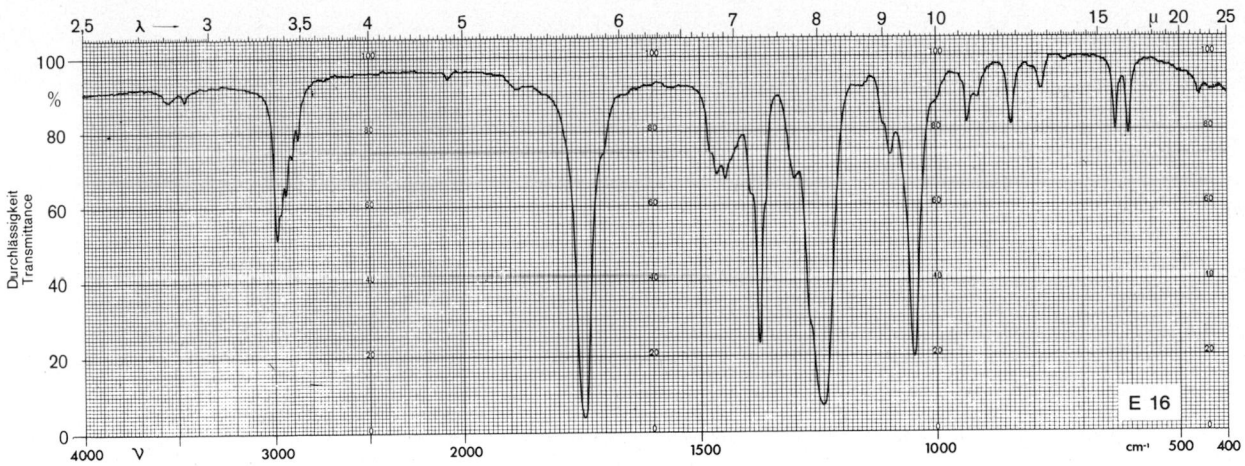

6708

Verbindung:	E 16 (Gemisch von Estern)		Compound:	E 16 (Mixture of esters)	
Formel:		M.	Formula:		M. w.:
Kp.:	77-130 °C	Fp.:	B. p.:	77-130 °C	M. p.:
d:	0,892- 0,897 g/cm³	n_D.	d:	0,892-0,897 g/cm³	n_D:
Präparation:	flüssig, ~ 10 μm	Dez. Nr.: 7.2	Preparation:	liquid, ~ 10 μm	Dec. No.: 7.2

UV-Spectren

UV-Spectra

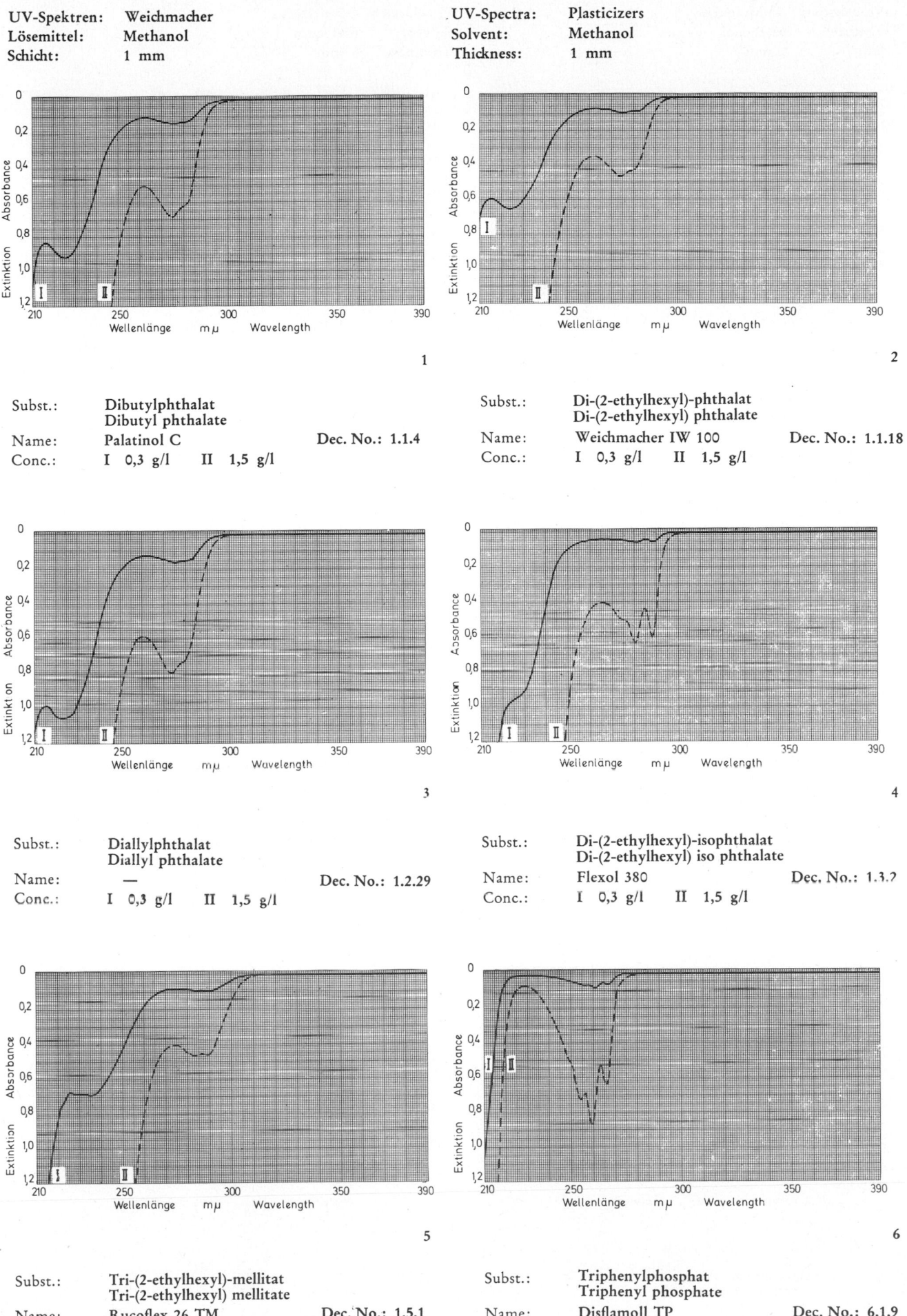

1

Subst.: Dibutylphthalat
Dibutyl phthalate
Name: Palatinol C   Dec. No.: 1.1.4
Conc.: I 0,3 g/l   II 1,5 g/l

2

Subst.: Di-(2-ethylhexyl)-phthalat
Di-(2-ethylhexyl) phthalate
Name: Weichmacher IW 100   Dec. No.: 1.1.18
Conc.: I 0,3 g/l   II 1,5 g/l

3

Subst.: Diallylphthalat
Diallyl phthalate
Name: —   Dec. No.: 1.2.29
Conc.: I 0,3 g/l   II 1,5 g/l

4

Subst.: Di-(2-ethylhexyl)-isophthalat
Di-(2-ethylhexyl) iso phthalate
Name: Flexol 380   Dec. No.: 1.3.2
Conc.: I 0,3 g/l   II 1,5 g/l

5

Subst.: Tri-(2-ethylhexyl)-mellitat
Tri-(2-ethylhexyl) mellitate
Name: Rucoflex 26 TM   Dec. No.: 1.5.1
Conc.: I 0,3 g/l   II 1,5 g/l

6

Subst.: Triphenylphosphat
Triphenyl phosphate
Name: Disflamoll TP   Dec. No.: 6.1.9
Conc.: I 0,3 g/l   II 1,5 g/l

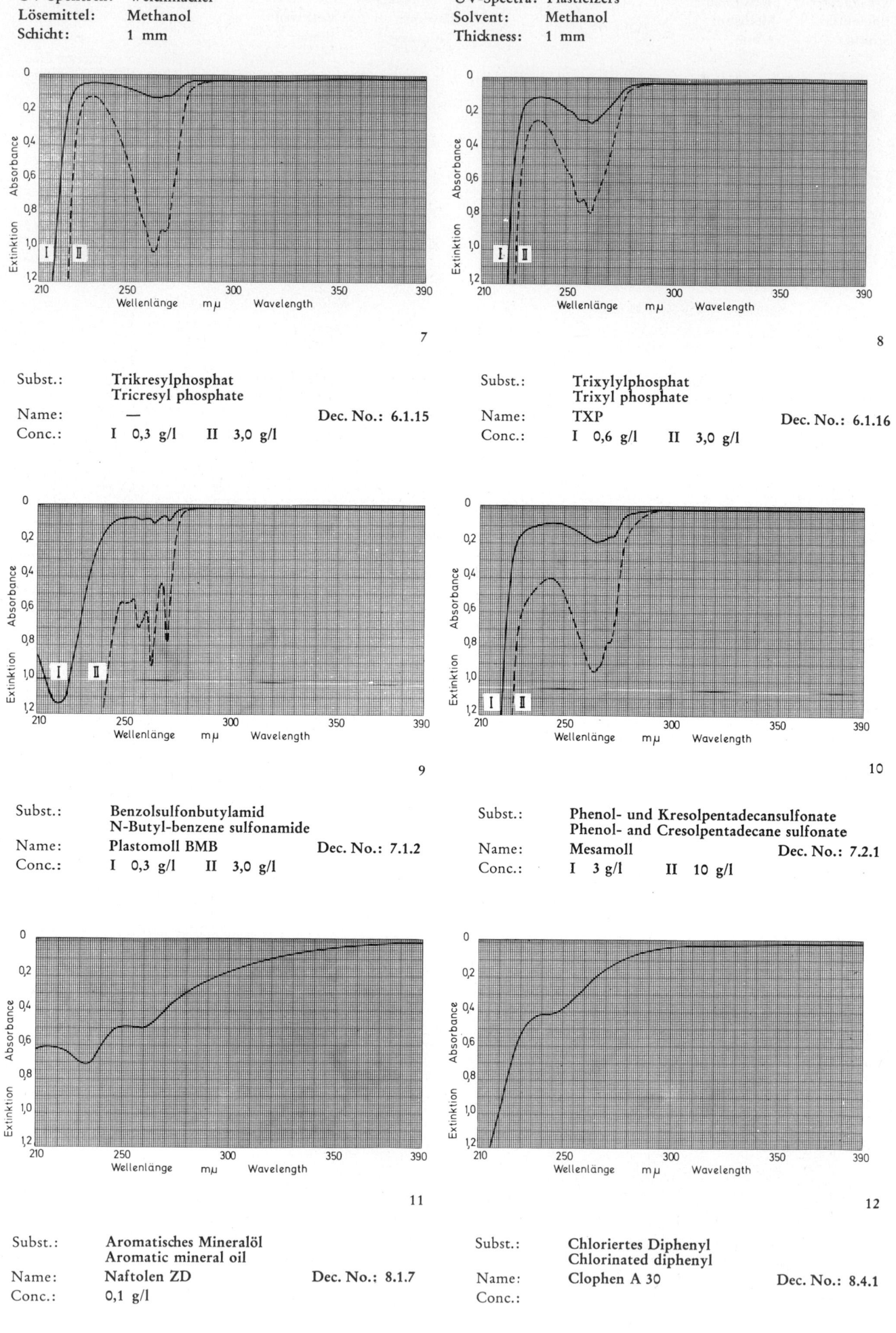

UV-Spektren: Weichmacher
Lösemittel: Methanol
Schicht: 1 mm

UV-Spectra: Plasticizers
Solvent: Methanol
Thickness: 1 mm

7

Subst.: Trikresylphosphat
Tricresyl phosphate
Name: —   Dec. No.: 6.1.15
Conc.: I 0,3 g/l   II 3,0 g/l

8

Subst.: Trixylylphosphat
Trixyl phosphate
Name: TXP   Dec. No.: 6.1.16
Conc.: I 0,6 g/l   II 3,0 g/l

9

Subst.: Benzolsulfonbutylamid
N-Butyl-benzene sulfonamide
Name: Plastomoll BMB   Dec. No.: 7.1.2
Conc.: I 0,3 g/l   II 3,0 g/l

10

Subst.: Phenol- und Kresolpentadecansulfonate
Phenol- and Cresolpentadecane sulfonate
Name: Mesamoll   Dec. No.: 7.2.1
Conc.: I 3 g/l   II 10 g/l

11

Subst.: Aromatisches Mineralöl
Aromatic mineral oil
Name: Naftolen ZD   Dec. No.: 8.1.7
Conc.: 0,1 g/l

12

Subst.: Chloriertes Diphenyl
Chlorinated diphenyl
Name: Clophen A 30   Dec. No.: 8.4.1
Conc.:

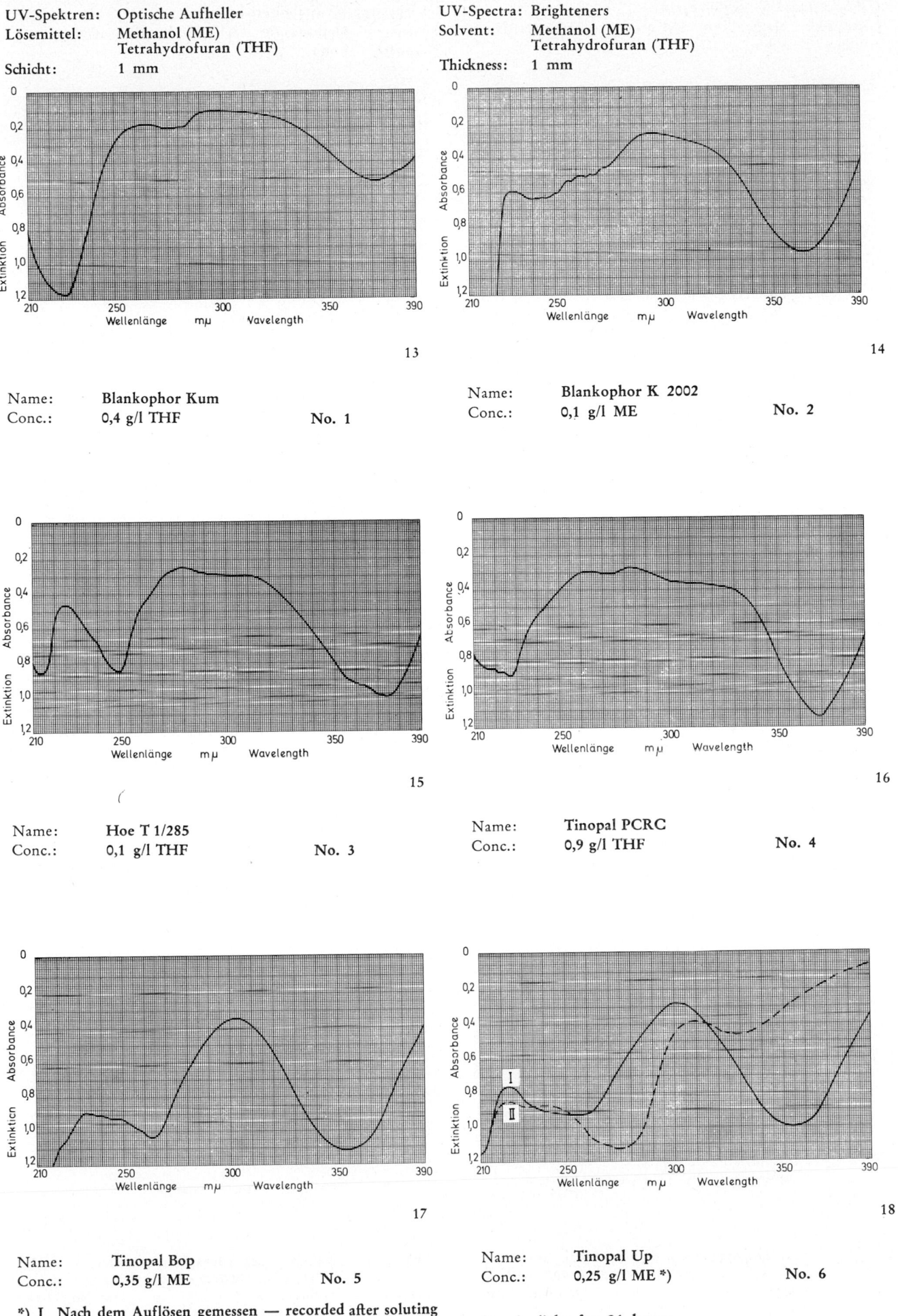

UV-Spektren: Optische Aufheller
Lösemittel: Methanol (ME)
Tetrahydrofuran (THF)
Schicht: 1 mm

UV-Spectra: Brighteners
Solvent: Methanol (ME)
Tetrahydrofuran (THF)
Thickness: 1 mm

13

14

Name: Blankophor Kum
Conc.: 0,4 g/l THF   No. 1

Name: Blankophor K 2002
Conc.: 0,1 g/l ME   No. 2

15

16

Name: Hoe T 1/285
Conc.: 0,1 g/l THF   No. 3

Name: Tinopal PCRC
Conc.: 0,9 g/l THF   No. 4

17

18

Name: Tinopal Bop
Conc.: 0,35 g/l ME   No. 5

Name: Tinopal Up
Conc.: 0,25 g/l ME *)   No. 6

*) I Nach dem Auflösen gemessen — recorded after soluting
   II Nach 96stündigem Belichten gemessen — recorded after standing in light for 96 hours

UV-Spektren: UV-Stabilisatoren
Lösemittel: Methanol (n)   0,1 n methanolische NaOH (a)
Schicht: 1 mm

UV-Spectra: UV-Stabilizers
Solvent: Methanol (n)   0,1 n methanolic NaOH (a)
Thickness: 1 mm

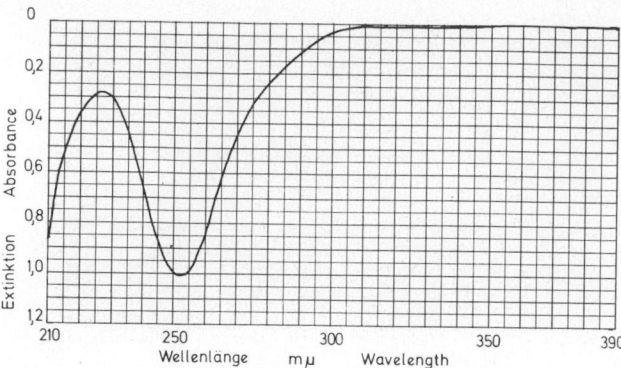

19

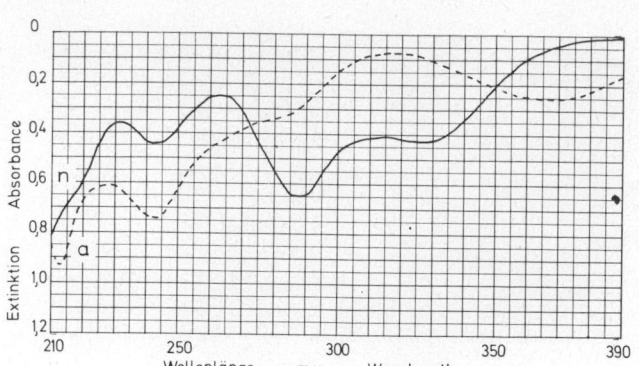

20

Subst.: Benzophenon
         Benzophenone
Name: Benzophenone   Dec. No.: 1.1
Conc.:   0,1 g/l

Subst.: 2-Hydroxy-4-methoxy-benzophenon
         2-Hydroxy-4-methoxy-benzophenone
Name: Advastab 45   Dec. No.: 1.2
Conc.:   0,1 g/l

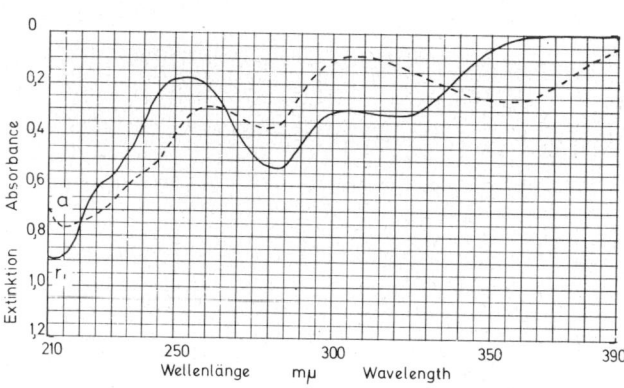

21

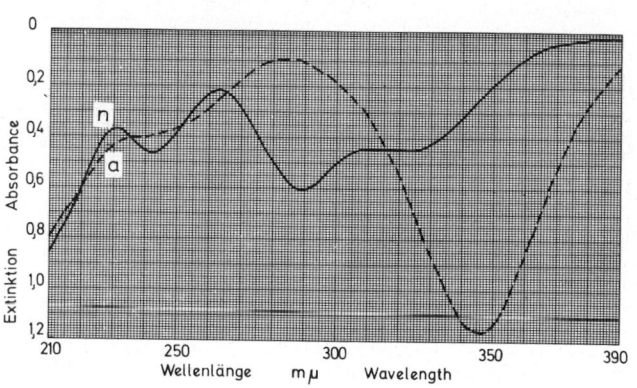

22

Subst.: 2-Hydroxy-4-methoxy-2-carboxybenzophenon
         2-Hydroxy-4-methoxy-2-carboxybenzophenone
Name: Cyasorb UV 207   Dec. No.: 1.7
Conc.:   0,1 g/l

Subst.: 2,4-Dihydroxybenzophenon
         2,4-Dihydroxy-benzophenone
Name: Inhibitor DHBP   Dec. No.: 1.9
Conc.:   0,1 g/l

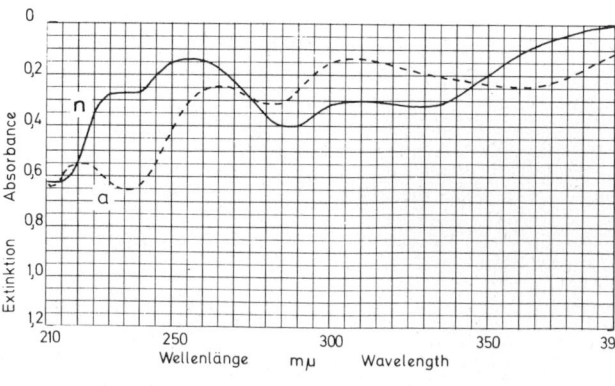

23

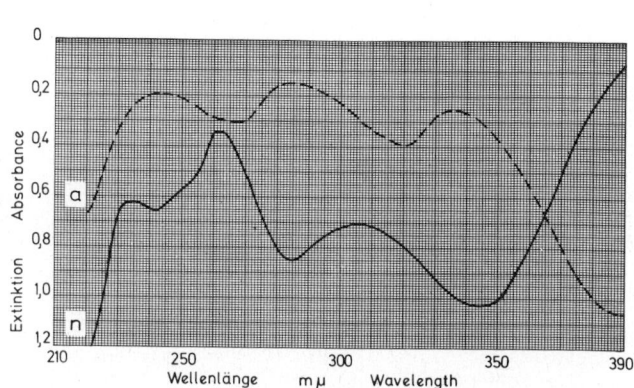

24

Subst.: 2,2'-Dihydroxy-4-n-octyloxybenzophenon
         2,2'-Dihydroxy-4-n-octyloxybenzophenone
Name: Cyasorb UV 314   Dec. No.: 1.11
Conc.:   0,1 g/l

Subst.: 2,2',4,4'-Tetrahydroxybenzophenon
         2,2',4,4'-Tetrahydroxy-benzophenone
Name: Uvinol D 50   Dec. No.: 1.14
Conc.:   n: 0,18 g/l   a: 0,08 g/l

UV-Spektren: UV-Stabilisatoren
Lösemittel: Methanol (n)   0,1 n methanolische NaOH (a)
Schicht: 1 mm

UV-Spectra: UV-Stabilizers
Solvent: Methanol (n)   0,1 n methanolic NaOH (a)
Thickness: 1 mm

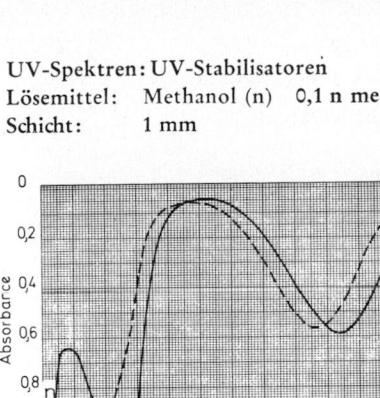

25

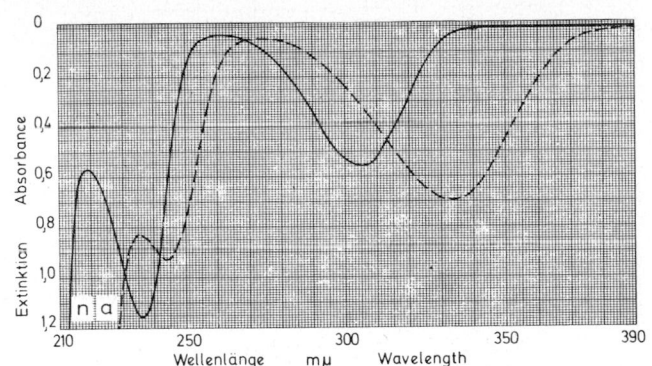

26

Subst.:	Salicylsäure p. a. Salicylic acid G. R.	
Name:	—	Dec. No.: 2.1
Conc.:	0,2 g/l	

Subst.:	Methylsalicylat Methyl salicylate	
Name:	Sunkem MS	Dec. No. 2.3
Conc.:	0,2 g/l	

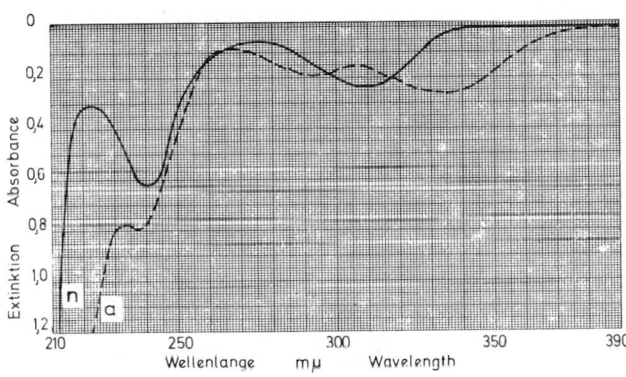

27

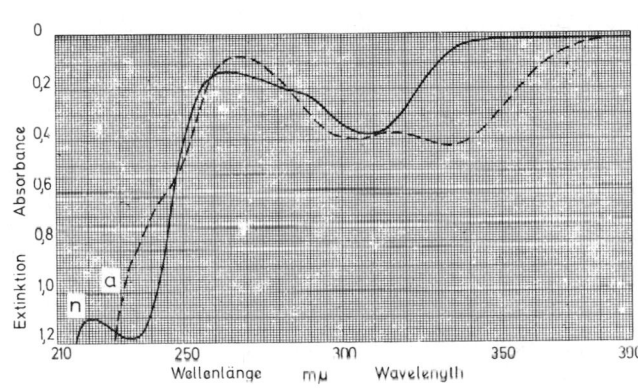

28

Subst.:	Phenylsalicylat Phenyl salicylate	
Name:	—	Dec. No.: 2.1
Conc.:	0,1 g/l	

Subst.:	Carboxyphenylsalicylat Carboxyphenyl salicylate	
Name:	Sunkem CPS	Dec. No.: 2.8
Conc.:	0,2 g/l	

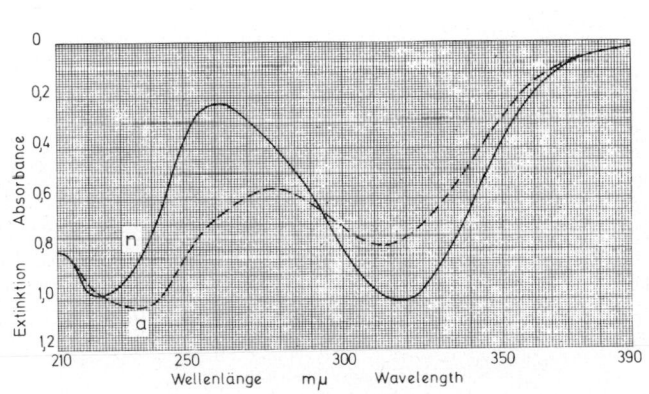

29

30

Subst.:	Resorcinmonobenzoat Resorcinol monobenzoate	
Name:	Eastman RMB	Dec. No.: 2.9
Conc.:	I 0,1 g/l II 0,5 g/l	

Subst.:	α-Cyano-β-methyl-4-methoxy-zimtsäure- methylester Methyl-(α-cyano-β-methyl-4-methoxy- cinnamate)	
Name:	UV-Absorber 318	Dec. No.: 3.1
Conc.:	0,1 g/l	

UV-Spektren: UV-Stabilisatoren
Lösemittel: Methanol (n)
0,1 n methanolische KOH (a)
Schicht: 1 mm

UV-Spectra: UV-Stabilizers
Solvent: Methanol (n)
0,1 n methanolic KOH (a)
Thickness: 1 mm

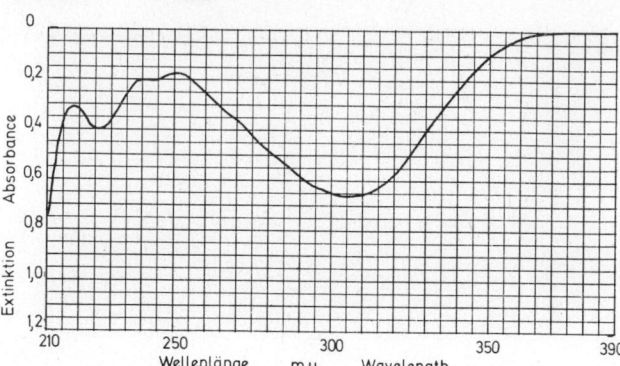

31

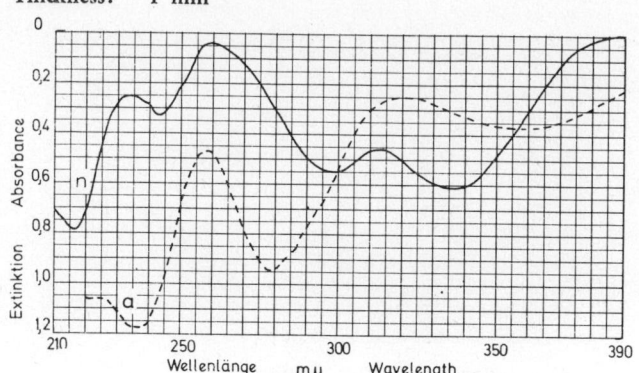

32

Subst.: 2-Ethylhexyl-(α-cyano-β,β-diphenylacrylat)
2-Ethylhexyl-(α-cyano-β,β-diphenyl acrylate)
Name: Uvinol N 539   Dec. No.: 3.3
Conc.: 0,2 g/l

Subst.: 2-(2'-Hydroxy-5'-methylphenyl)-benzotriazol
2-(2'-Hydroxy-5'-methylphenyl) benzotriazole
Name: Tinuvin P   Dec. No.: 4.1
Conc.: 0,1 g/l

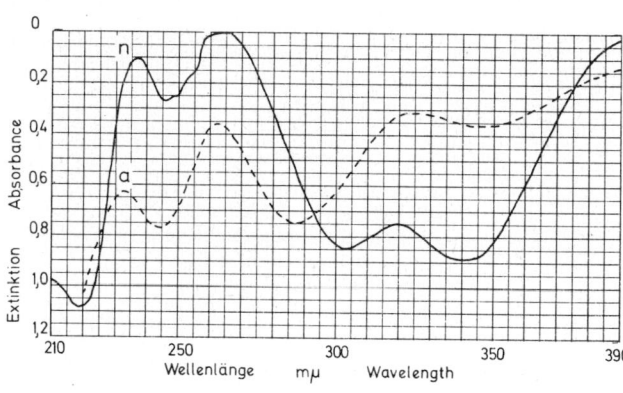

33

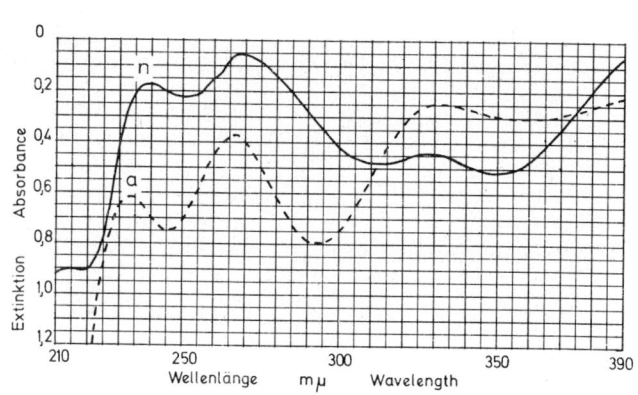

34

Subst.: 2-(2'-Hydroxy-3',5'-di-tert-butyl-phenyl)-
benzotriazol
2-(2'-Hydroxy-3',5'-di-tert-butyl-phenyl)
benzotriazole
Name: Tinuvin 320   Dec. No.: 4.2
Conc.: 0,2 g/l

Subst.: 2-(2'-Hydroxy-3'-tert-butyl-5'-methylphenyl)-
5-chlorbenzotriazol
2-(2'-Hydroxy-3'-tert-butyl-5'-methylphenyl
5-chloro benzotriazole
Name: Tinuvin 326   Dec. No.: 4.4
Conc.: 0,1 g/l

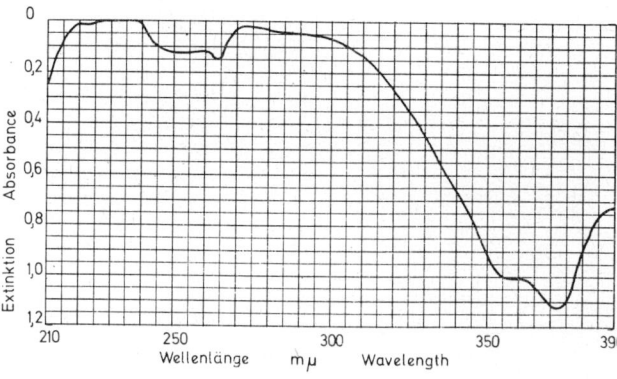

35

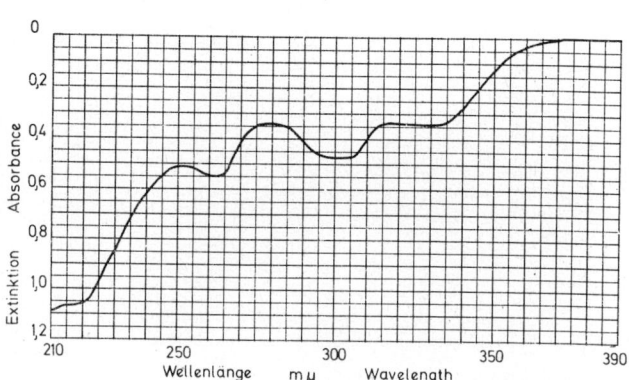

36

Subst.: Benzotriazolderivat
Benzotriazole derivate
Name: Uvitex OB   Dec. No.: 4.5
Conc.: 0,1 g/l

Subst.: 2,5-Diphenyl1p-benzochinon
2,5-Diphenyl-p-benzoquinone
Name: Eastman DPQ   Dec. No.: 5.1
Conc.: 0,05 g/l

UV-Spektren: Antioxydantien
Lösemittel: Methanol (n)
0,1 n methanolische KOH (a)
Schicht: 1 mm

UV-Spectra: Antioxidants
Solvent: Methanol (n)
0,1 n methanolic (KOH (a)
Thickness: 1 mm

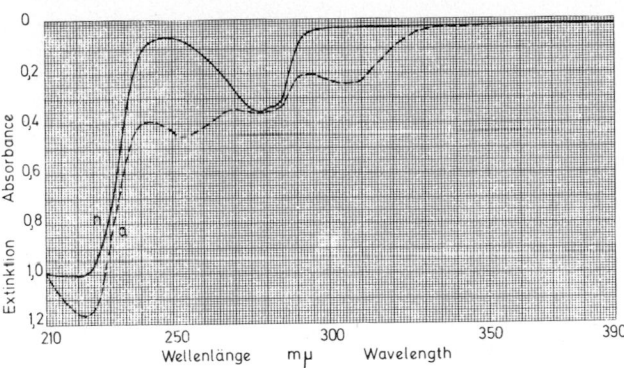

37

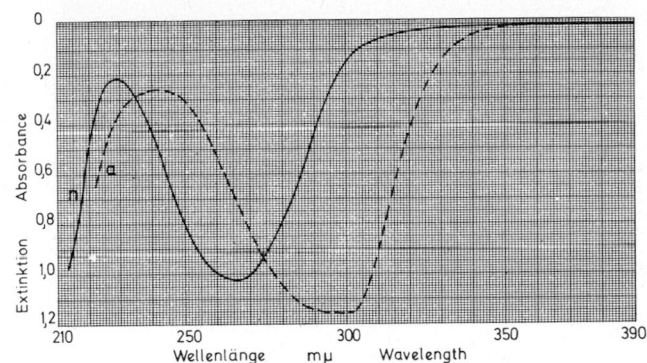

38

Subst.:	2,6-Di-tert-butyl-p-kresol	
	2,6-Di-tert-butyl-p-cresol	
Name:	ASM KB	Dec. No.: 1.1.5
Conc.:	0,4 g/l	

Subst.:	4,4'-Dihydroxydiphenyl	
	4,4'-Dihydroxydiphenyl	
Name:	ASM DOD	Dec. No.: 1.3.1
Conc.:	1,0 g/l	

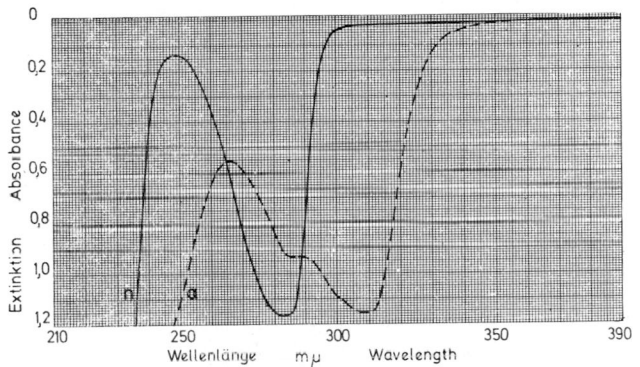

39

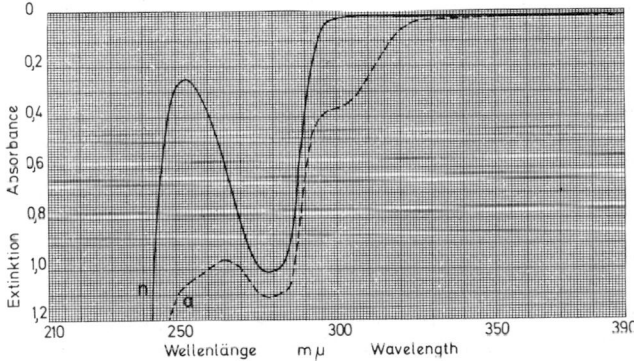

40

Subst.:	4,4'-Methylenbis-(2-methyl-6-tert-butylphenol)	
	4,4'-Methylene bis-(2-methyl-6-tert-butyl phenol)	
Name:	Antioxidant 720	Dec. No.: 1.3.4
Conc.:	1,0 g/l	

Subst.:	2,2'-Methylenbis-(4-methyl-6-tert-butylphenol)	
	2,2'-Methylene bis-(4-methyl-6-tert-butyl phenol)	
Name:	CAO 5	Dec. No.: 1.3.6
Conc.:	n: 1,0 g/l a: 0,75 g/l	

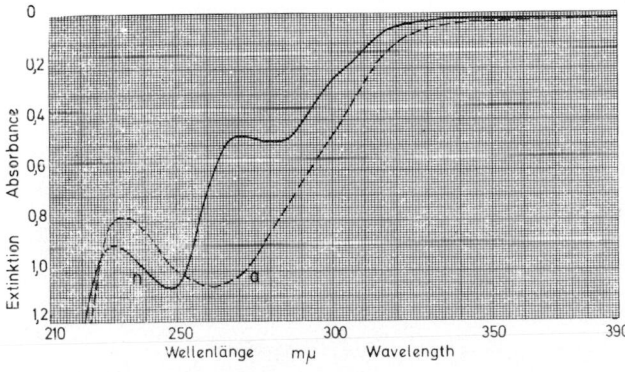

41

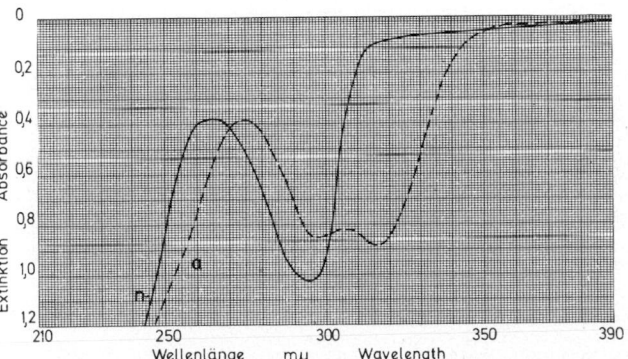

42

Subst.:	4,4'-Thiobis-(3-methyl-6-tert-butylphenol)	
	4,4'-Thiobis-(3-methyl-6-tertbutyl phenol)	
Name:	Santowhite Crystals	Dec. No.: 1.4.2
Conc.:	0,25 g/l	

Subst.:	2,2'-Thiobis-(4-methyl-6-tert-butylphenol)	
	2,2'-Thiobis-(4-methyl-6-tert-butyl phenol)	
Name:	CAO 4	Dec. No.: 1.4.3
Conc.:	0,5 g/l	

UV-Spektren: Antioxydantien
Lösemittel: Methanol (n)
            0,1 n methanolische KOH (a)
Schicht: 1 mm

UV-Spectra: Antioxidants
Solvent: Methanol (n)
             0,1 n methanolic (KOH (a)
Thickness: 1 mm

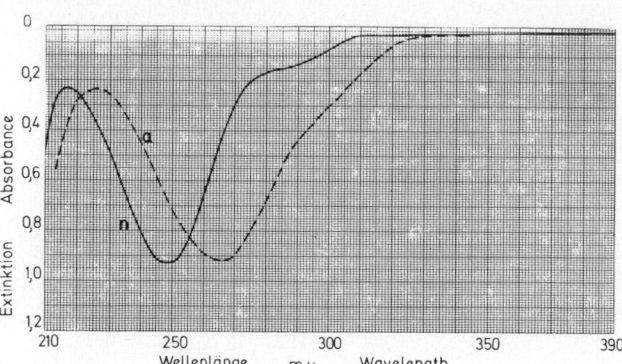

43

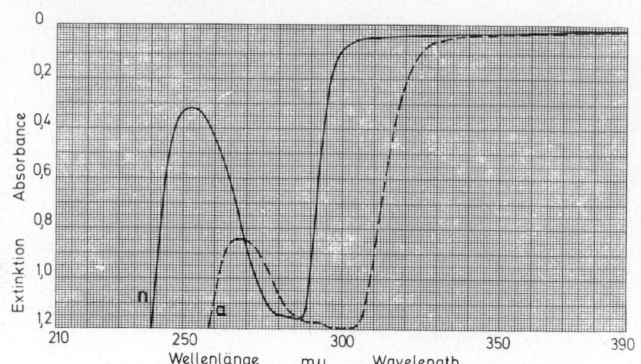

44

Subst.: N-Lauroyl-4-aminophenol
         N-Lauroyl-4-aminophenol
Name: Suconox 12   Dec. No.: 1.6.2
Conc.:   0,2 g/l

Subst.: Phenolkondensationsprodukte
         Phenol kondensation products
Name: Nonox EX   Dec. No.: 1.7.1
Conc.:   1,0 g/l

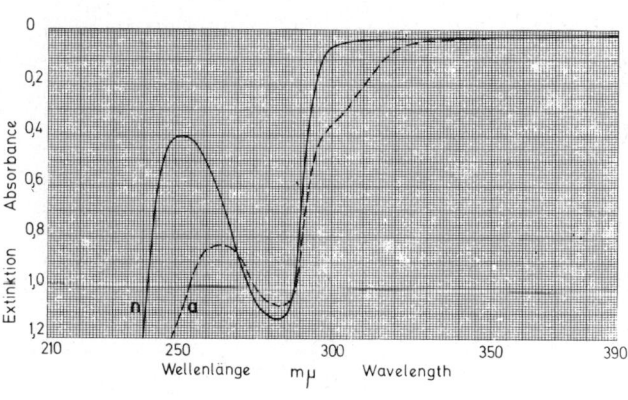

45

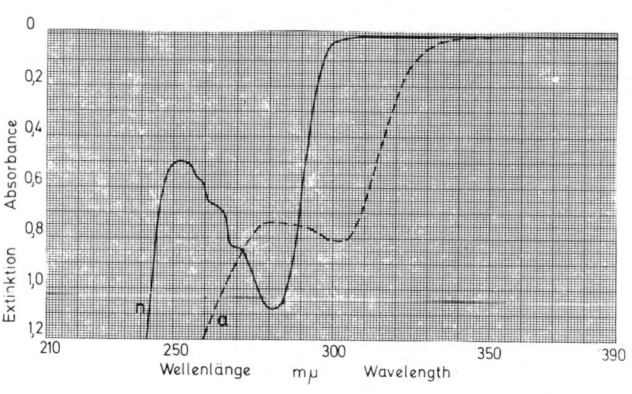

46

Subst.: Alkyliertes Polyphenol
         Alkylated polyphenol
Name: Agerite Superlite   Dec. No.: 1.8.5
Conc.:   1,25 g/l

Subst.: Styrolisiertes Phenol
         Styrenated phenol
Name: Dec. No.: 1.8.9
Conc.:   n: 1,5 g/l   a: 0,9 g/l

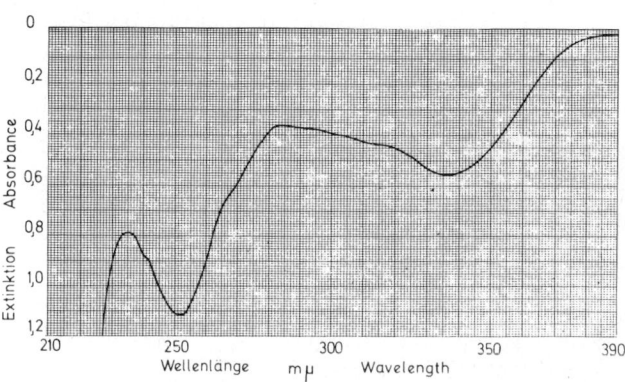

47

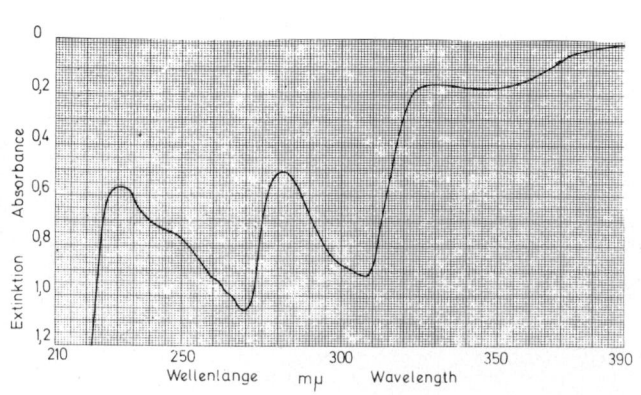

48

Subst.: N-Phenyl-1-naphthylamin
         N-Phenyl-1-naphthyl amine
Name: ASM PAN   Dec. No.: 2.1.1
Conc.:   0,16 g/l

Subst.: N-Phenyl-2-naphthylamin
         N-Phenyl-2-naphthyl amine
Name: Nonox D   Dec. No.: 2.1.2
Conc.:   0,1 g/l

UV-Spektren: Antioxydantien
Lösemittel: Methanol (ME)
              Tetrahydrofuran (THF)
Schicht: 1 mm

UV-Spectra: Antioxidants
Solvent: Methanol (ME)
              Tetrahydrofuran (THF)
Thickness: 1 mm

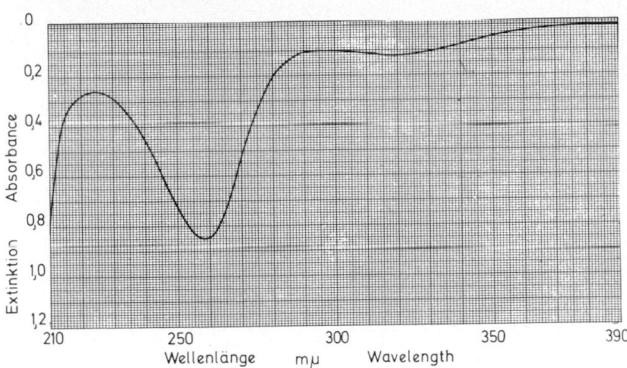

49

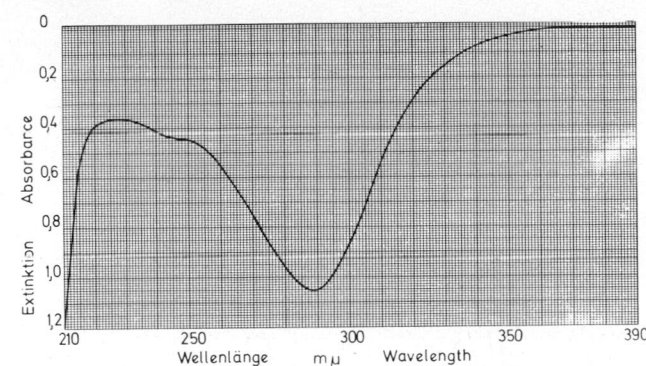

50

Subst.:   N,N′-Bis-2-octyl-p-phenyldiamin
          N,N′-Bis-2-octyl-p-phenyldiamin
Name: UOP 288   Dec. No.: 2.3.3
Conc.:   0,15 g/l ME

Subst.:   N-Cyclohexyl-N′-phenyl-p-phenylendiamin
          N-Cyclohexyl-N′-phenyl-p-phenylene diamine
Name: ASM 4010   Dec. No.: 2.3.8
Conc.:   0,15 g/l ME

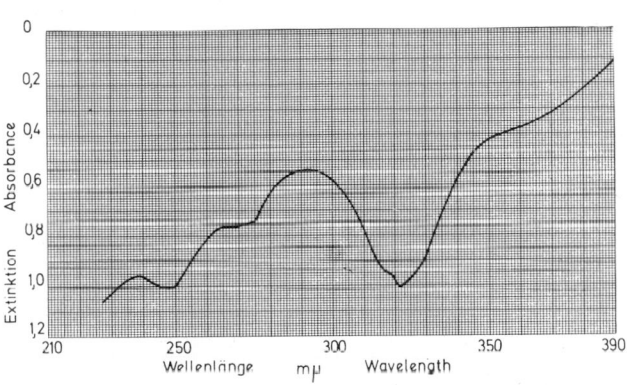

51

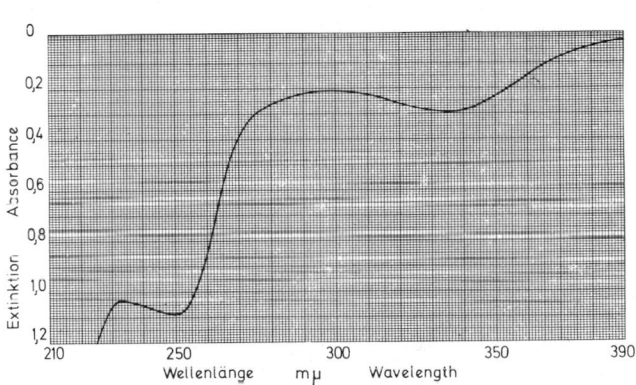

52

Subst.:   N,N′-Bis-2-naphthyl-p-phenylen-diamin
          N,N′-Bis-2-naphthyl-p-phenylene diamine
Name: ASM DNP   Dec. No. 2.3.10
Conc.:   0,1 g/l THF

Subst.:   Polymeres 2,2,4-Trimethyl-1,2-dihydrochinolin
          Polymer 2,2,4-Trimethyl-1,2-dihydroquinoline
Name: Agerite Resin D   Dec. No.: 3.1.4
Conc.:   0,15 g/l ME

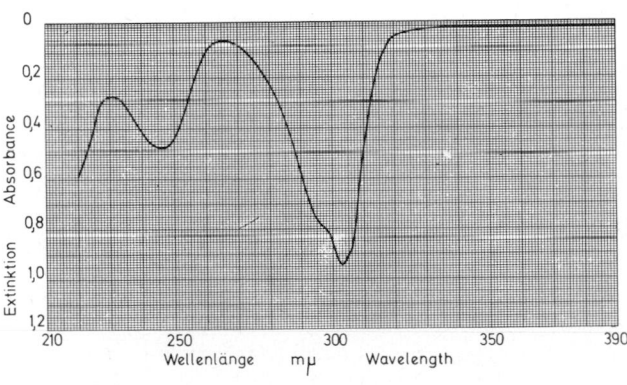

53

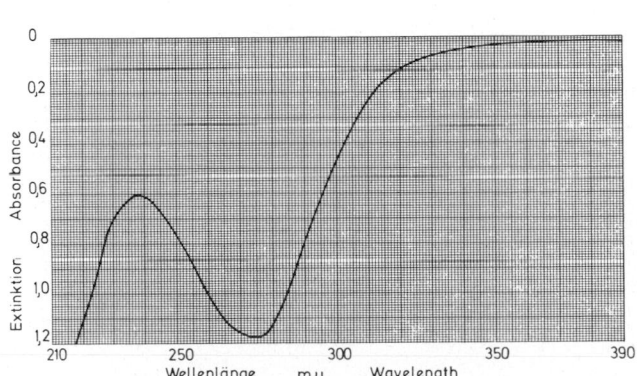

54

Subst.:   2-Mercaptobenzimidazol
          2-Mercaptobenzimidazole
Name: ASM MB   Dec. No.: 3.2.1
Conc.:   0,05 g/l ME

Subst.:   N,N′-Diphenylthioharnstoff
          N,N′-Diphenylthiourea
Name: Stabilisator C   Dec. No.: 3.3.2
Conc.:   0,15 g/l ME

55

55 a

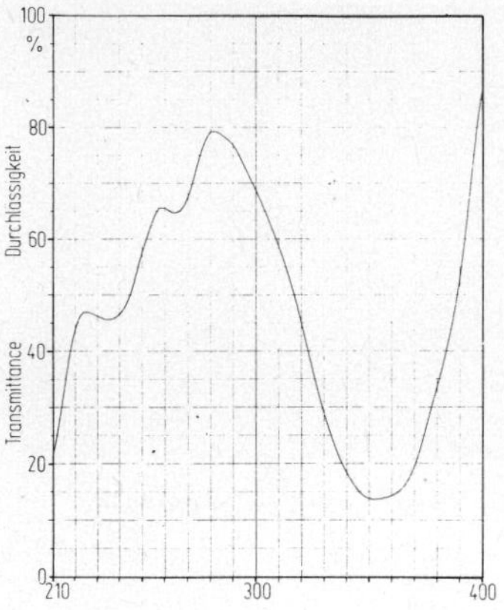

| Subst.: | 4,4'-Bis(4-phenyl-1,2,3-triazol-2-yl)stilben-2,2'-disulfonsäure, Na-Salz | Subst.: | Wie 55/as 55
a: Nach 1 h/after 1 h
b: Nach 24 h/after 24 h |
| Conc.: | 0,1 g/l ME | Conc.: | 0,1 g/l ME |

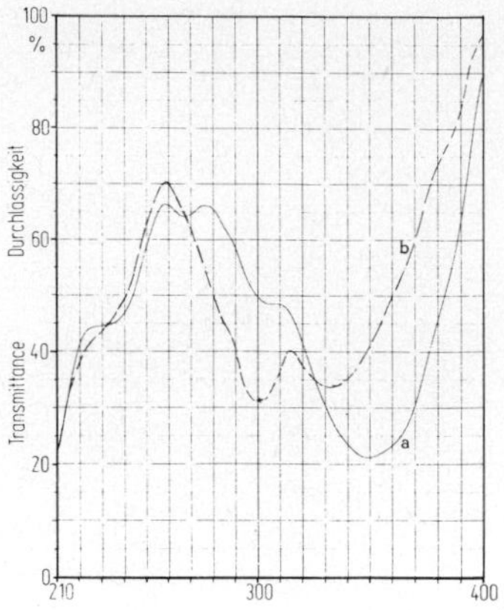

56

57

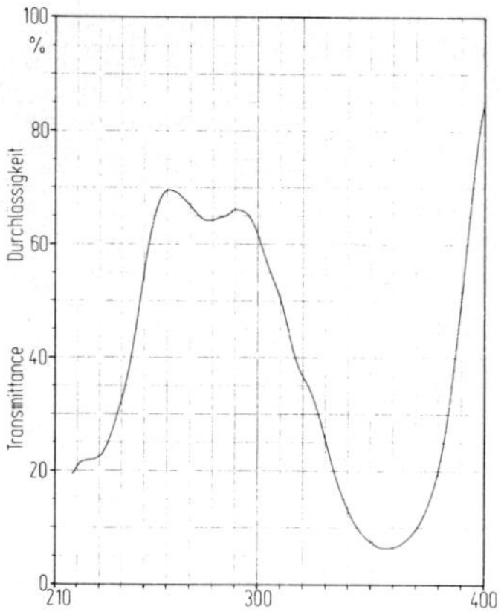

| Subst.: | 3-Phenyl-7-(4-methyl-5-phenyl-1,2,3-triazol-2-yl)-cumarin | Subst.: | 1-(4-Amidosulfonylphenyl)-3-(4-chlorphenyl)-2-pyrazolin |
| Conc.: | 0,1 g/l THF | Conc.: | 0,1 g/l THF |

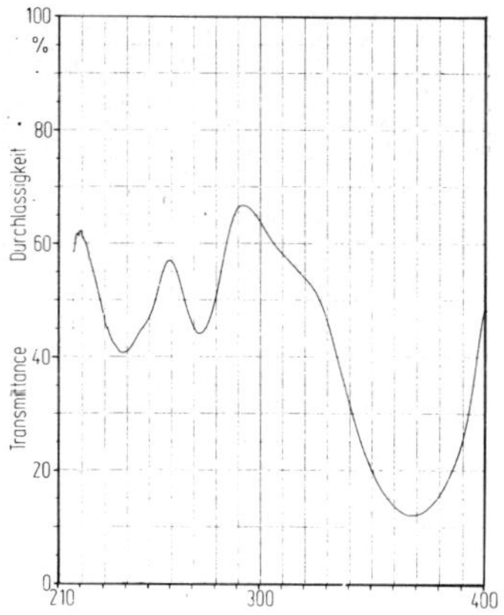

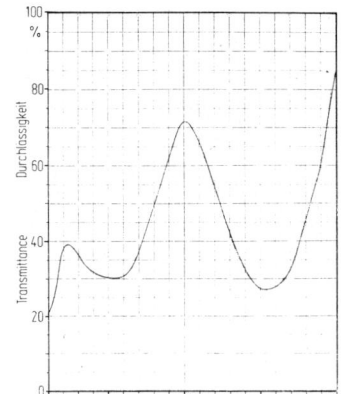

58

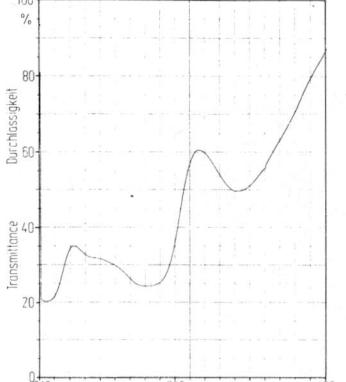

58 a

| Subst.: | 4,4'-Bis[(4-anilino-6-bis(2-hydroxyethyl)amino-1,3,5-triazin-2-yl)amino]stilben-2,2'-disulfonsäure, Na-Salz | Subst.: | Wie 58/as 58
nach 24 h/after 24 h |
| Conc.: | 0,1 g/l ME | Conc.: | 0,1 g/l ME |

Index

Index of Spectra

Index of Spectra

Subject Index